GW00399922

ENCYCLOPEDIA

OF

IMMUNOLOGY

SECOND EDITION

ENCYCLOPEDIA
OF
IMMUNOLOGY

SECOND EDITION

Editor-in-Chief

PETER J. DELVES

Consultant Editor

IVAN M. ROITT

ACADEMIC PRESS

Harcourt Brace & Company Publishers

San Diego   London   Boston   New York
Sydney   Tokyo   Toronto

ACADEMIC PRESS LIMITED
24-28 Oval Road
London NW1 7DX

United States Edition published by
ACADEMIC PRESS INC.
San Diego, CA 92101

British Library Cataloging in Publication Data is available

ISBN 0-12-226765-6

Access for a limited period to an on-line version of the Encyclopedia of Immunology Second Edition is
included in the purchase price of the print edition.
This on-line version has been uniquely and persistently identified by the Digital Object Identifier (DOI)

10.1006/0127995102

By following the link

http://dx.doi.org/10.1006/0127995102

from any Web Browser, buyers of the Encyclopedia of Immunology Second Edition will find instructions
on how to register for access.

Photo·graphics, Honiton, Devon, UK.
Printed and bound in Great Britain by The Bath Press, Bath, Avon, UK.

PREFACE

This encyclopedia provides the largest integrated reference source of immunological knowledge that is available. In the six years since the first edition of the Encyclopedia of Immunology was published, there have been astounding advances in many areas of the subject. The second edition of the encyclopedia seeks to encompass these advances and to provide a more up-to-date coverage of the subject as a whole than is now provided by the original text. The large number of the topics covered will be of direct interest not only to experimental and clinical immunologists but also to scientists from many other disciplines, including microbiologists, veterinary surgeons, protein chemists, physiologists, hematologists, and so forth. In addition to being a primary reference source, the encyclopedic format readily lends itself to casual reading with most entries being only two or three pages long.

The encyclopedia has been expanded to four volumes, with entries given in alphabetic order; Volume 1 covers ABO Blood Group System to Cooperation, Mechanisms of Cellular; Volume 2 covers Copper and the Immune System to Idiotype Network; Volume 3 covers Igα/Igβ (CD79a/CD79b) to Nude (Athymic) Mice; Volume 4 covers Nutrition and the Immune System to Zinc and the Immune System. A complete list of entries is given at the beginning of each volume. Any topic that does not have its own separate entry will be quickly located by reference to the index.

The vast majority of the articles have been totally rewritten from those that appeared in the first edition and the overall production time of the Encyclopedia has been speeded up in an attempt to make the work as current as possible. To reflect important advances there are 64 completely new entries. These cover fields such as second signals for lymphocyte activation, apoptosis, anergy, dendritic cells, nucleic acid immunization, MHC-peptide binding specificity, bacteriophage display of antibody fragments and humanization of antibodies. All areas that were in their infancy when the first edition was produced, but are now central to immunology. Other entries reflect the fact that many cytokines and cell surface molecules have been discovered in the intervening six years. Individual entries are contributed by researchers widely acknowledged as experts in their field. There are a total of 630 entries, and 1200 authors have contributed to this work. Because each entry has been written to be self-contained it would be impossible for there not to be some repetition between entries. Whilst this has in most cases been kept to a minimum, we make no apologies for such overlap as it is felt that the alternative would require the irritating practice of having to flick back and forth between several different entries for the uninitiated reader to fully interpret a particular entry. Inevitably, size limitations have not permitted each entry to be exhaustive; entire books could (and have!) been written with titles similar to individual entry headings. Rather, the aim has been to provide the most pertinent information for each topic. The space allocation imposed upon each contributor has also meant that contributors have not been able to cite by name the work of every individual who has made a significant contribution to their field, but rather they have tried to provide the essential core of the available data.

Readers should note that whilst convention dictates that genes are identified using italicized characters and their protein products referred to using plain text, we have generally only adopted this procedure in entries dealing with nomenclature. Otherwise we have stayed with the approach used by the majority of the contributors, namely using plain text also for the genes whilst making it clear that it is the gene that is being referred to.

The reader will find a list of further reading at the end of each entry, comprising a selection of review articles and perhaps some key papers in each area. Furthermore, at the end of each article there is a cross-referencing 'See also' section where the reader is directed to other entries within the encyclopedia which contain additional and/or related information.

We have introduced color plate sections into the second edition, not only to add to the attractiveness of these volumes but also to present information, such as computer generated images derived from X-ray crystallographic data, that is otherwise difficult to visualize. Also new for the Second Edition is a glossary providing concise definitions of commonly encountered immunological terms.

An electronic version of the Encyclopedia is available online to purchasers of the print edition (see page iii) which will add to the value of this edition. The user of the electronic version will enjoy extensive hypertext linking and advanced search tools.

We have ourselves, as the first individuals able to consult the completed work, again found it extremely useful as a reference source, a teaching aid, and a text for general interest. We trust others will find this Second Edition of the Encyclopedia of Immunology equally valuable.

April 1998   PJD
                                                                                                             IMR

ACKNOWLEDGEMENTS

The major credit for these volumes clearly rests with the authors of each entry. They are all recognized as being amongst those pre-eminent in their field. We wish to thank each of these authors for their excellent contribution and for their willingness to produce entries to tight deadlines. An additional 'thank you' is also due to the many contributors who provided suggestions and constructive criticism regarding the encyclopedia.

Our task as editors was helped immeasurably by the participation of our outstanding Editorial Advisory Board. Their ability to 'name names', their comments regarding additions or modifications to the list of entries and their expert reviewing of manuscripts established a solid foundation upon which the encyclopedia could be built. We would particularly like to welcome Ian McConnell, Fritz Melchers, Fred Rosen, Emil Unanue and Harald von Boehmer to the Editorial Advisory Board for the second edition of the Encyclopedia.

We greatly thank the following members of Academic Press for the publishing services of editorial development support and production of both print and electronic versions:
Carey Chapman, Lorraine Parry, Sara Gorman, Heather Burroughs, Manjula Kariyawasam, Ed Pentz, Emma Parkinson, Helen Knapp, Debi Kruse, Peter Lord, and also to picture researcher Emma Krikler and indexer Jan Ross.

Finally, thanks to Jane, Joe, Tom and Jess for the inevitable sacrifices that they had to make during the preparation of this second edition of the encyclopedia.

CONTRIBUTORS

Jacobo Abadi
Department of Pediatrics
Division of Pediatric Infectious Diseases
New York
USA

SB Abramson
Department of Rheumatology
Hospital for Joint Diseases
301 East 17th Street
New York NY 10003
USA

David WK Acheson
Division of Geographic Medicine and Infectious
Diseases
Tupper Research Institute
750 Washington Street
Boston
Massachusetts MA 02111
USA

John P Ackers
Department of Medical Parasitology
London School of Hygiene and Tropical Medicine
Keppel Street (Gower Street)
London WC1E 7HT
UK

Gordon Ada
Division of Cell Biology
John Curtin School of Medical Research
The Australian National University
Canberra ACT
Australia

Margaret A Adelsman
Department of Laboratory Medicine and Pathology
Center for Immunology
University of Minnesota Medical School
Box 609
UMHC
420 Delaware Street SE
Minneapolis, MN 55455 USA

Robert Ader
Center for Psychoneuroimmunology Research and the
Departments of Microbiology and Immunology and of
Psychiatry
University of Rochester Medical Center
New York
USA

Matteo Adinolfi
The Galton Laboratory
Department of Genetics
University College London
4 Stephenson Way
London NW1 2HE
UK

Luciano Adorini
Roche Milano Ricerche
Via Olgettina 58
Milan 20132
Italy

Ann Ager
Division of Cellular Immunology
MRC National Institute for Medical Research
The Ridgeway
Mill Hill
London NW7 1AA
UK

Begona Aguado
Department of Biochemistry
MRC Immunochemistry Unit
University of Oxford
Oxford
UK

Balbino Alarcon
Centro de Biologa Molecular Severo Ochoa
CSIC-Universidad Autonoma de Madrid
Cantoblanco
Madrid
Spain

Salvatore Albani
Department of Pediatrics
University of California San Diego
9500 Gilman Drive
La Jolla
California CA 92093-0663
USA

Mark R Alderson
Department of Immunology
Corixa Corporation
1124 Columbia Street
Suite 464
Seattle
Washington WA 98104
USA

Maria-Luisa Alegre
Howard Hughes Medical Institute
University of Chicago
924 East 57th Street
Chicago
Illinois IL 60637-5420
USA

Michael Alkan
Department of Medicine 'B' and the Research Unit of
Autoimmune Diseases
Sheba Medical Center
Tel-hashomer 52621
Tel-Aviv
Israel

Todd M Allen
Wisconsin Regional Primate Research Center and
Department of Pathology and Laboratory Medicine
University of Wisconsin
1220 Capital Court
Madison
Wisconsin WI 53719-1299
USA

Pedro M Alzari
Departement d'Immunologie
Institut Pasteur
25 Rue du Dr Roux
75724 Paris Cedex 15
France

Kim N Andersen
Oklahoma Medical Research Foundation
825 NE 13th Street
Oklahoma City
Oklahoma OK 73104
USA

Colin C Anderson
Laboratory for Cellular and Molecular Immunology
National Institute of Allergy and Infectious Disease
National Institutes of Health
Bethesda
Maryland MD 20892
USA

Per Antonsson
Pharmacia & Upjohn
Lund Research Center
Box 724
S-2207
Lund
Sweden

Michael A Apicella
Department of Microbiology
The University of Iowa College of Medicine
Bowen Science Building
3-403
51 Newton Road
Iowa City IA 52242
USA

Raymond Apple
Department of Human Genetics
Roche Molecular Systems
1145 Atlantic Avenue
Alameda
California CA 94501
USA

Ken-ichi Arai
Department of Molecular and Developmental Biology
Institute of Medical Science
University of Tokyo
4-6-1 Shirokanedai
Tokyo 108
Japan

Barry GW Arnason
Department of Neurology
University of Chicago
5841 South Maryland Avenue
Chicago
Illinois IL 60637
USA

Robert B Ashman
Department of Pathology
University of Western Australia
The Queen Elizabeth II Medical Centre
Nedlands 6009
Australia

John P Atkinson
Department of Internal Medicine
Washington University School of Medicine
Department of Medicine
660 S Euclid
Box 8 121
St Louis
Missouri MO 63110-1031
USA

Karen J Auborn
Department of Otolaryngology and Communications Disorders
Section of Otolaryngologic Research
Long Island Jewish Medical Centre
New Hyde Park
New York NY 11042
USA

Hugh Auchincloss
Department of Surgery
Harvard Medical School
Massachusetts General Hospital
White 51013
Boston
Massachusetts MA 02114-2696
USA

Jonathan M Austyn
Nuffield Department of Surgery
University of Oxford
The John Radcliffe Hospital
Headington
Oxford OX3 9DU
UK

Greojorio Aversa
Human Immunology Department
DNAX Research Institute
901 California Avenue
Palo Alto
California CA 94304-1104
USA

Stratis Avrameas
Department of Immunology
Pasteur Institute
25 Rue du Dr Roux
75725 Paris Cedex
France

Claude Bagnis
Department of Gene Transfer
Institute for Paoli-Calmettes
232 Boulevard de Ste Marguerite
BP 156
13272 Marseille Cedex 9
France

Jurgen Bajorath
Bristol-Myers Squibb Pharmaceutical Research Institute
11804 North Creek Parkway South
Washington
USA

Jacques Banchereau
Baylor Institute of Immunology Research
Dallas
Texas
USA

Gregory J Bancroft
Infectious and Tropical Diseases
London School of Hygiene and Tropical Medicine
Keppel Street
London WC1E 7HT
UK

Antonio Bandeira
Unite d'Immunobiologie
Institut Pasteur
24 Rue du Dr Roux
75724 Paris Cedex
France

J Paul Banga
Department of Medicine
King's College School of Medicine
Denmark Hill
London SE5 8RX
UK

Adrian Barbul
Department of Surgery
Sinai Hospital and The Johns Hopkins Medical Institutions
Baltimore
Maryland MD 21215-5271
USA

Amelia Bartholomew
Department of Surgery
University of Illinois
Chicago
Illinois
USA

Götz Baumann
Transplantation Research
Novartis Pharma Inc.
Basel
Switzerland

Christopher J Bayne
Department of Zoology
Oregon State University
Corvallis
Oregon OR 97331-2914
USA

Blaine L Beaman
Department of Medical Microbiology and Immunology
University of California School of Medicine
Davis
California CA 95616
USA

Rebecca L Beavil
The Randall Institute
King's College London
26–29 Drury Lane
London WC2B 5RL
UK

Henry Beekhuizen
Department of Infectious Diseases
University Hospital
Building 1
PO Box 9600
2300 RC Leiden
The Netherlands

Jerzy M Behnke
Department of Life Science
University of Nottingham
University Park
Nottingham NG7 2RD
UK

William R Beisel
Department of Molecular Microbiology and Immunology
The Johns Hopkins School of Hygiene and Public
Health Maryland MD 211205
USA

Adrianne Bendich
Human Nutrition Research Department
Roche Vitamins and Fine Chemicals
340 Kingsland Street
Nutley
New Jersey NJ 07110-1199
USA

Stephen J Benkovic
Department of Chemistry
The Pennsylvania State University
4141 Wartik Laboratory
Pennsylvania PA 16802
USA

Claudia Berek
Deutsches Rheuma Forschungs Zentrum
Berlin
Germany

Rodney D Berg
Department of Microbiology and Immunology
Louisiana State University Medical School-Shreveport
1501 King's Hwy
Shreveport
Louisiana LA 1130-3932
USA

Thomas Beveridge
Transplantation Research
Novartis Pharma Inc.
Basel
Switzerland

F Bex
Molecular Biology and Animal Physiology
Department
Bembloux University
13 Avenue Marechial Juin
B-3050 Gembloux
Belgium

Russell Bey
Department of Veterinary Pathobiology
College of Veterinary Medicine
University of Minnesota
1971 Commonwealth Avenue
St Paul
Minnesota
USA

Kishor Bhatia
Lymphoma Biology Section
Pediatric Brnach
NCI, NIH
Bethesda
Maryland MD 20892
USA

Pierluigi E Bigazzi
Department of Pathology
University of Connecticut Health Center
Farmington
Connecticut CT 06032
USA

Elizabeth K Bikoff
Department of Molecular and Cellular Biology
The Biological Laboratories
Harvard University
16 Divinity Avenue
Cambridge
Massachusetts MA 02138
USA

Richard M Binns
Department of Immunology
Babraham Institute
Babraham
Cambridge CB2 4AT
UK

Gail A Bishop
Department of Microbiology and Internal Medicine
The University of Iowa
3-570 BSB
Iowa City IA 52242-0001
USA

Barbara A Blacklaws
Department of Clinical Veterinary Medicine
University of Cambridge
Madingley Road
Cambridge CB3 0ES
UK

J Edwin Blalock
Department of Physiology and Biophysics
University of Alabama at Birmingham
896 Basic Health Sciences Building
1918 University Boulevard
Birmingham
Alabama AL 35294-0005
USA

Andrew Blauvelt
Dermatology Branch
National Cancer Institute
Bethesda
Maryland MD 20892
USA

Bruce R Blazar
Department of Pediatrics
University of Minnesota
420 Delaware St WE
Box 109
UMHC
Minneapolis MN 55455-0362
USA

Jeffrey A Bluestone
Department of Pathology
The Ben May Institute
University of Chicago
5841 South Maryland Avenue
Box 424
Chicago
Illinois IL 60637
USA

Janice S Blum
Department of Microbiology and Immunology
Indiana University School of Medicine
Indianapolis IN 46202
USA

Hans AR Bluyssen
Department of Cell Biology and Genetics
Erasmus University
Rotterdam
The Netherlands

Constantin A Bona
Department of Microbiology
Mount Sinai Medical School
1 Gustave Levy Place
New York NY 10029-6574
USA

Carl-Henrik von Bonsdorff
Department of Virology
Haartman Institute
Helsinki
Finland

Roger J Booth
Department of Molecular Medicine
Faculty of Medicine and Health Science
University of Auckland
Auckland
New Zealand

Jean F Borel
Preclinical Research
Sandoz Pharma Ltd
CH-4002
Basel
Switzerland

Jan D Bos
Laboratory of Cell Biology and Histology
University of Amsterdam
Academisch Medisch Centrum
Meibergdreef 9
1105 AZ Amsterdam
The Netherlands

Lilly W Bourguignon
Department of Cell Biology and Anatomy
School of Medicine
University of Miami
Miami
Florida FL 33101
USA

Vassiliki A Boussiotis
Division of Hematologic Malignancies
Dana-Farber Cancer Institute
44 Binney Street
Boston
Massachusetts MA 02115
USA

Richard L Boyd
Department of Pathology and Immunology
Monash Medical School
Melbourne
Victoria
Australia

Michael DP Boyle
Department of Microbiology and Immunology
Medical College of Ohio
PO Box 10008
3000 Arlington Avenue
Toledo
Ohio OH 43614-5802
USA

Arthur W Boylston
Department of Pathology
University of Leeds
Leeds LS2 9JT
UK

M Viviana Bozon
Division of Immunogenetics
Harvard Medical School
Massachusetts MA 02114-2696
USA

Anthony Todd Braciak
Central Laboratory of Haematology
Inselspital/University Hospital
Berne
Switzerland

Vivian Lam Braciale
Department of Microbiology
University of Virginia
The Beirne Carter Center for Immunology Research
HSC Box MR4 Box 4012
Charlottesville
Virginia VA 22908
USA

Bradford C Braden
Center for Advanced Research in Technology
Rockville
Maryland
USA

Per Brandtzaeg
Laboratory of Immunohistochemistry
Immunopathology (LIIPAT) and Institute of Pathology
The National Hospital
Rickshospitalet
N-0027 Oslo
Norway

Maryvonne DR Brasher
Division of Immunobiology
National Institute for Biological Standards and Control
Hertfordshire
UK

Pierre G Braquet
Biol-Ionova DNA Tech Corp
48-52 Rue de la Gare
Plaisir
F-78380
France

Arthur S Brecher
Department of Chemistry
Bowling Green State University
Bowling Green
Ohio OH 43403-0001
USA

Fionula M Brennan
Charing Cross Sunley Research Centre
1 Lurgan Avenue
Hammersmith
London W6 8LW
UK

Joan K Brieland
Unit for Laboratory Animal Medicine
University of Michigan Medical School
Ann Arbor
Michigan MI 48109-0614
USA

Francine Briere
Laboratory for Immunological Research
Schering-Plough
27 ch des Peupliers
BP11
Dardilly 69571
France

Bernard Brochier
Department of Virology-Immunology
Faculty of Veterinary Medicine
University of Liege
B43 Sart Tilman
400 Liege
Belgium

A van den Broeke
University of Brussels
B-1640 Rhode-St-Genèse
Belgium

Itzhak Brook
Department of Pediatrics
Georgetown University
Washington DC 20016
USA

Peter Brouckaert
Department of Molecular Biology
Molecular Pathophysiology and Experimental Therapy Unit
B-9000 Gent
Belgium

Christopher Bunch
Nuffield Department of Medicine
John Radcliffe Hospital
Headley Way
Headington
Oxford OX3 9DU
UK

Chantanee P Buranathai
Department of Microbiology
University of Iowa College of Medicine
Iowa
USA

C Lynne Burek
Department of Pathology
The Johns Hopkins University School of Medicine
Ross Research Building
720 Rutland Avenue
Baltimore
Maryland MD 21205-2196
USA

Julian F Burke
Biological Sciences
University of Sussex
Brighton BN1 9QG
UK

James P Burnie
Department of Pathological Sciences
University of Manchester
Oxford Road
Manchester M13 9WL
UK

A Burny
Molecular Biology and Animal Physiology Department
Bembloux University
13 Avenue Marechal Juin
B-5030 Gembloux
Belgium

Gregory F Burton
Department of Anatomy
Division of Immunobiology
Medical College of Virginia
Virginia Commonwealth University
PO Box 709
Richmond
Virginia VI 233298-0709
USA

Dennis R Burton
Departments of Immunology and Molecular Biology
The Scripps Research Institute
Room MB204
10550 North Torrey Pines Road
La Jolla
California CA 92037
USA

Anthony E Butterworth
School of Biological Sciences
University of Wales
Gwynedd
UK

Raul DeLa Cadena
Sol Sherry Thrombosis Research Center
Temple University School of Medicine
Pennsylvania
USA

Federico Caligaris-Cappio
Department of Biomedical Science and Oncology
Cattedra di Immunologia Clinica
University of Torino
Turin
Italy

Michael A Caligiuri
Department of Hematology/Oncology
Arthur G. James Comprehensive Cancer Center
Ohio State University Medical Centre
Columbus
Ohio
USA

Michael V Callahan
Department of Medicine
Tufts University School of Medicine
136 Harrison Avenue
Boston
Massachusetts MA 02111
USA

Steven M Callister
Microbiology Research Laboratory
Gundersen Medical Foundation
1836 South Avenue
La Crosse
Wisconsin WI 54601
USA

Dario Campana
Department of Hematology-Oncology
St. Jude Children's Research Hospital
332 North Lauderdale
Memphis
Tennessee TN 38101
USA

Ailsa M Campbell
Division of Biochemistry and Molecular Biology
Institute of Biomedical and Life Sciences
University of Glasgow
Davidson Building
Glasgow G12 8QQ
UK

R Duncan Campbell
Department of Biochemistry
MRC Immunochemistry Unit
University of Oxford
South Parks Road
Oxford OX1 3QU
UK

Harvey Cantor
Harvard Medical School and Laboratory of Immunopathology
Dana-Farber Cancer Institute
44 Biney Street
Boston
Massachusetts MA 02115
USA

J Donald Capra
Department of Microbiology
University of Texas Southwestern Medical Centre
5323 Harry Hines Boulevard
Dallas
Texas TX 75235-9048
USA

Jose M Carballido
Human Immunology Department
DNAX Research Institute
901 California Avenue
Palo Alto
California CA 94304-1104
USA

Andrew Carmichael
Department of Medicine
University of Cambridge Clinical School
Level 5,
Adenbrooke's Hospital, (Box 157)
Hills Road
Cambridge CB2 2QQ
UK

Michael J Carter
School of Biological Sciences
University of Surrey
Guildford
UK

Paolo Casali
Department of Pathology
Division of Molecular Immunology
Cornell University Medical College
1300 York Avenue
New York NY 10021
USA

Rachel R Caspi
Laboratory of Immunology
National Eye Institute
National Institutes of Health Building 10
Room 10 N 222
Bethesda
Maryland MD 20892-1858
USA

Gian Luigi Castoldi
Hematology Section
Department of Biomedical Sciences
University of Ferrara
44100 Ferrara
Italy

David Catty
Departments of Immunology and Infection
University of Birmingham Medical School
Edgbaston
Birmingham BI5 2TT
UK

Antonio La Cava
Department of Medicine
University of California San Diego
California
USA

Alessandra Cesano
The Wistar Institute
3601 Spruce Street
Philadelphia
Pennsylvania PA 19104
USA

Bulbul Chakravarti
Department of Medicine
Clinical Immunology/Allergy and Rheumatology Unit
Box 695
601 Elmwood Avenue
Rochester
New York NY 14642
USA

Deb N Chakravarti
Department of Protein and Analytical Chemistry
Wyeth-Lederle Vaccines and Pediatrics
211 Bailey Road
West Henrietta
New York NY 14586
USA

Thomas J Chambers
Department of Molecular Microbiology and Immunology
St Louis University Health Sciences Center
Room 410
14025 Grand Boulevard
St Louis
Missouri MO 63104
USA

Ranjit K Chandra
Janeway Child Health Centre
St John's
Newfoundland A1A 1RS
Canada

Martin D Chapman
Department of Medicine
Asthma and Allergic Diseases Center
University of Virginia
Charlottesville
Virginia VI 22908
USA

Jacques Charlemagne
Groupe of Comparative Immunology
University of Pierre and Marie Curie
Box 29
9 Quai Saint-Bernard
75252 Paris Cedex 05
France

Christina Cheers
Department of Microbiology
University of Melbourne
Parkville
Victoria
Australia

Carlo Chizzolini
Division of Immunology and Allergy
University Hospital
Geneva
Switzerland

Konstantin M Chumakov
Center for Biologics Evaluation and Research
Food and Drug Administration
1401 Rockville Pike
Rockville
Maryland MD 20852-1448
USA

Bernhard Cinader
Department of Clinical Biochemistry
University of Toronto
1 King's College Circle
Toronto
Ontario M5S 1A8
Canada

Edward A Clark
Departments of Microbiology and Immunology
University of Washington
Medical Centre
1959 NE Pacific
Box 357342
Seattle
Washington WA 98195-0001
USA

Cyril A Clarke
Formerly at Department of Genetics and Microbiology
University of Liverpool
Liverpool
UK

Janice E Clements
Department of Comparative Medicine and Molecular
Biology and Genetics
Johns Hopkins University School of Medicine
Traylor Building
Room G-60
720 Rutland Avenue
Baltimore
Maryland MD 2120
USA

Alan Cockayne
Department of Microbiology
Division of Clinical Laboratory Sciences
University of Nottingham
Queen's Medical Centre
Nottingham NG7 2UH
UK

Alan S Cohen
Amyloid Program
Boston University School of Medicine
80 E. Concord Street, F113
Boston
Maryland MD 02118
USA

Nicholas Cohen
Center for Psychoneuroimmunology Research and the
Departments of Microbiology, Immunology and
Psychiatry
University of Rochester Medical Centre
601 Elmwood Avenue
Box 672
New York NY 14642
USA

Irun R Cohen
Department of Immunology
The Weizmann Institute of Science
76100 Rehovot
Israel

Trevor Collen
Institute for Animal Health
Compton Laboratory
Compton
Berkshire RG20 7NN
UK

Edward J Collins
Department of Microbiology and Immunology
University of North Carolina
North Carolina
USA

Robert W Colman
Sol Sherry Thrombosis Research Center
Temple University School of Medicine
Pennsylvania
USA

Robert E Cone
Department of Pathology
University of Connecticut Health Center
Farmington
Connecticut CT 06030-3105
USA

Mary Ellen Conley
Department of Pediatrics
University of Tennessee College of Medicine
St Jude Children's Research Hospital
332 North Lauderdale
Memphis
Tennessee TN 38105
USA

Marcela Contreras
North London Blood Transfusion Centre
Colindale Avenue
London NW9 5BG
UK

Edwin L Cooper
Laboratory of Comparative Immunology
Department of Neurobiology
UCLA
California
USA

Morris D Cooper
Department of Medical Microbiology and Immunology
Southern Illinois University
Illinois
USA

Y Corda
Laboratory of Engineering and System Dynamics
Membranaires
Institute of Biological Structures and Microbiology
CNRS
Marseille
France

Oscar J Cordero
Department of Biochemistry and Molecular Biology
Faculty of Biology
University of Santiago of Compostela
Galicia
Spain

Frank EG Cox
Immunology Section
Division of Life Sciences
King's College London
London
UK

James B Crawley
Kennedy Institute of Rheumatology
Sunley Division
Lurgan Avenue
Hammersmith
London W6 8LW
UK

Sue Cresswell
Pharmacia Biosystems Limited
Davy Avenue
Knowhirll
Milton Keynes MK5 8PH
UK

Derrick WM Crook
Nuffield Department of Medicine
John Radcliffe Hospital
Headley Way
Headington
Oxford OX3 9DU
UK

Kathryn E Crosier
Department of Molecular Medicine
School of Medicine
University of Auckland
Private Bag 92019
Auckland
New Zealand

Philip S Crosier
Department of Molecular Medicine
School of Medicine
University of Auckland
Private Bag 92019
Auckland
New Zealand

David A Crouse
Department of Cell Biology and Anatomy
University of Nebraska Medical Center
Omaha
Nebraska NB 68198-6395
USA

W David Cubitt
Institute of Child Health
Great Ormond Street
London
UK

Carolyn A Cuff
Department of Epidemiology and Public Health
School of Medicine
Yale University
60 College Street
PO Box 3333
New Haven
Connecticut CT 06510
USA

Charlotte Cunningham-Rundles
Department of Medicine and Pediatrics
Mount Sinai Medical Center
1 Gustave Levy Place
New York NY 10029-6574
USA

Anthony J Cutler
Rheumatology Unit
Royal Postgraduate Medical School
Hammersmith Hospital
Du Cane Road
London W12 ONN
UK

C J Czuprynski
Department of Pathobiological Sciences
School of Veterinary Medicine
University of Wisconsin
2015 Linden Drive West
Madison
Wisconsin WI 53706
USA

Mohamed R Daha
Department of Pulmonology
Leiden University Hospital
2300 RC Leiden
The Netherlands

Clemens A Dahinden
Institute of Immunology and Allergology
Inselspital
CH-3010 Bern
Switzerland

Angus Dalgleish
Department of Cellular and Molecular Sciences
Communicable Diseases
St George's Hospital Medical School
Cranmer Terrace
London SW17 0RE
UK

Raymond Dalgleish
Department of Genetics
University of Leicester
Leicester LE1 7RH
UK

Margaret J Dallman
Department of Biology
Imperial College of Science, Technology and Medicine
Prince Consort Road
London SW7 2BB
UK

Agustin P Dalmasso
Department of Laboratory Medicine and Pathology
University of Minnesota
DVA Medical Center
1 Veterans Drive
Minneapolis 55417
USA

Pritam Das
Department of Immunology
Mayo Clinic and Medical School
Rochester
Minnesota MN 55905
USA

Gregory A Dasch
Rickettsial Diseases Program
Department of the Navy Naval Medical Research
Institute
National Naval Medical Center
Maryland MD 20889-5055
USA

Chella S David
Department of Immunology
Mayo Clinic and Medical School
Rochester
Minnesota MN 55905
USA

Anne Davidson
Department of Medicine and Microbiology and
Immunology
Albert Einstein College of Medicine
1300 Morris Park 4505
Bronx
New York NY 10461
USA

Alexandra Davies
Department of Medicine
University of Cambridge
MIP Unit
MRC Center
Hills Road
Cambridge CB2 2QH
UK

Huw Davies
Division of Life Sciences
King's College London
Campden Hill Road
London W8 7AH
UK

Kevin A Davies
Rheumatology Unit
Royal Postgraduate Medical School
Hammersmith Hospital
Du Cane Road
London W12 0NN
UK

Malcolm Davis
Bristol-Myers Squibb Research Institute
Princeton
New Jersey
USA

Jean-Michel Dayer
Department of Medicine
Division of Immunology and Allergy
University Hospital Contonal
24 Rue Micheli-du-Crest
1211 Geneva 4
Switzerland

George S Deepe Jr
Department of Medicine
Division of Infectious Diseases
University of Cincinnati College of Medicine
Cincinnati
Ohio OH 45267-0560
USA

Elisabetta Dejana
Department of Biomedical Science and Biotechnology
University of Degli Studi Di Brescia
Brescia
Italy

Peter J Delves
Department of Immunology
University College London Medical School
Windeyer Building
46 Cleveland Street
London W1P 6DB
UK

Jon W Denning
Department of Medicine
Division of Infectious Diseases
Santa Clara Valley Medical Center
San Jose
California
USA

Michael S Denyer
AFRC Institute for Animal Health
Pirbright Laboratory
Ash Road
Pirbright
Woking
Surrey GU24 0NF
UK

F Dequiedt
Molecular Biology and Animal Physiology
Department
Bembloux University
13 Avenue Marechal Juin
B-5030 Gembloux
Belgium

Bruce H Devens
Targeted Genetics Corporation
Seattle
Washington
USA

Jan E de Vries
Immunology Department
DNAX Research Institute
901 California Avenue
Palo Alto
California CA 94304-1104
USA

T Michael Dexter
Department of Experimental Haematology
Paterson Institute
Christie Hospital NHS Trust
Wilmslow Road
Manchester M20 9BX
UK

Bertrand Lisa Djavadi-Ohaniance
Unit for Cellular Biology
Pasteur's Institute
28 Rue du Dr Roux
75724 Paris Cedex 15
France

Michael J Doenhoff
School of Biological Sciences
University of Wales
Bangor
Gwynedd LL57 2UW
UK

Peter C Doherty
Department of Immunology
St Jude Children's Research Hospital
332 North Lauderdale
PO Box 318
Memphis
Tennessee TN 38181-0318
USA

Mikael Dohlsten
Pharmacia and Upjohn
Lund Research Center
Box 724
S-2207 Lund
Sweden

John J Donnelly
Department of Virus and Cell Biology
Merck Research Laboratories
WP 16-101
West Point
Pennsylvania PA 19486
USA

Gino Doria
Laboratory of Immunology
AMB-BIO-MED
ENEA Casaccia
Via Anguillarese
30100060 S Maria di Galeria
Rome
Italy

Hans-Michael Dosch
Department of Pediatrics and Immunology
University of Toronto
The Hospital for Sick Children
555 University Avenue
Toronto
Ontario M5G 1X8
Canada

Alan Ebringer
Infection and Immunity Group
Division of Life Sciences
King's College
Campden Hill Road
London W8 7AH
UK

Allen B Edmundson
Department of Crystallography
Oklahoma Medical Research Foundation
825 NE 13th Street
Okalhoma City
Oklahoma OK 73104
USA

Mark Egerton
Transplantation Biology Unit
Queensland Institute of Medical Research
Queensland 4029
Australia

RP Ekins
Department of Molecular Endocrinology
University College London Medical School
Mortimer Street
London W1N 8AA
UK

Tim Elliott
Nuffield Department of Clinical Medicine
University of Oxford
Oxford OX3 9DU
UK

A E Ellis
SOAEFD Marine Laboratory
Department of Agriculture and Fisheries for Scotland
PO Box 101
Victoria Road
Aberdeen AB9 8DB
UK

C J Elson
Department of Pathology and Microbiology
University of Bristol
The Medical School
University Walk
Bristol BS8 1TD
UK

C Paul Engelfriet
Central Laboratory of the Netherlands Red Cross Blood
Transfusion Service
Plesmanlaan 125
PO Box 9190
106 AD Amsterdam
The Netherlands

N Cary Engleberg
Department of Internal Medicine and Microbiology and
Immunology
Division of Infectious Diseases
University of Michigan
Ann Arbor
Michigan MI 48109-0614
USA

Jahan T Eppig
The Jackson Laboratory
600 Main Street
Bar Harbor
Maine ME 04609
USA

Henry Erlich
Department of Human Genetics
Roche Molecular Systems
1145 Atlantic Avenue
Alameda
California CA 94501
USA

David M Essayan
Department of Medicine
Division of Clinical Immunology
John Hopkins University
Asthma and Allergy Center
5501 Hopkins Bayview Circle
Baltimore
Maryland MD 21224-6801
USA

Amos Etzioni
Department of Pediatrics and Clinical Immunology
Rambam Medical Center
Bruce Rappaport Faculty of Medicine
Technion-Israel Institute of Technology
Haifa 3010
Israel

Gerald A Evans
Intramural Research Support Program
Scientific Applications International Corporation
Frederick
National Cancer Institute
Frederick Cancer Research and Development Center
Frederick
Maryland MD 21702
USA

Benoît den Eynde
Ludwig Institute for Cancer Research and Cellular
Genetics Unit
Universite Catholique de Louvain
Brussels
Belgium

John W Fabre
The Institute of Child Health
Division of Cell and Molecular Biology
University College London Medical School
20 Guildford Street
London WC1N 1EH
UK

Michael W Fanger
Department of Microbiology and Medicine
Dartmouth Medical School
Hanover
New Hampshire NH 03756
USA

Neil A Fanger
Department of Physiology
Dartmouth Medical School
Hanover
New Hampshire NH 03756
USA

CF Farquhar
Institute for Animal Health
AFRC & MRC Neuropathogenesis Unit
Ogston Building
West Mains Road
Edinburgh EH9 3JF
UK

William L Farrar
Laboratory of Molecular Immunoregulation
Cytokine Molecular Mechanisms Section
Biological Response Modifiers Program
National Cancer Institute
Frederick
Maryland MD 21701
USA

George Feinberg
Formerly of The Rayne Institute
The United Medical Dental School
London
UK

Ten Feizi
The Glycosciences Laboratory
Imperial College School of Medicine
Watford Road
Harrow
Middlesex HA1 3UJ
UK

Heinz Feldmann
Institute for Virologie
Philipps University of Marburg
Marburg 35011
Germany

Marc Feldmann
Kennedy Institute of Rheumatology
1 Aspenlea Road
Hammersmith
London W6 8LH
UK

TEW Feltkamp
Research Center for Rheumatic Diseases
1056 AB Amsterdam
The Netherlands

Silvano Ferrini
Istituto Nazionale per la Ricerca sul Cancro
Genoa
Italy

Michael FW Festing
MRC Toxicology Unit
Hodgkin Building
University of Leicester
PO Box 138
Lancaster Road
Leicester LE1 9HN
UK

Frank W Fitch
The Ben May Institute
Division of Biological Sciences
The University of Chicago
5841 South Maryland Avenue
Box 424
Chicago
Illinois IL 60637
USA

David R Fitzpatrick
The Queensland Institute of Medical Research
Post Office
Royal Brisbane Hospital
Queensland 4029
Australia

Willy A Flegel
Abteilung Transfusionsmedizin
University of Ulm
DRK-Blutspendezentrake ULM
Helmholtstrasse 10
D-89081 ULM
Germany

Gert Jan Fleuren
Department of Pathology
Leiden University Hospital
PO Box 9600
Gebouwi
Leiden
The Netherlands

Patrick M Flood
La Jolla Institute for Allergy and Immunology
11149 North Torrey Pines Road
La Jolla
California CA 92037
USA

Andrew W Fogarty
Nottingham City Hospital
Department of Respiratory Medicine
Hucknall Road
Nottingham NG5 1PB
UK

Howard S Fox
Department of Neuropharmacology
The Scripps Research Institute
10550 N Torrey Pines Road
La Jolla
California CA 92037-1092
USA

Brian MJ Foxwell
Kennedy Institute of Rhematology
Lurgan Avenue
Hammersmith
London W6 9LW
UK

AW Frankland
Department of Allergy and Respiratory Medicine
Guy's Hospital
4th Floor
Hunts House
London SE1 9RT
UK

Gordon J Freeman
Division of Hematologic Malignancies
Dana-Farber Cancer Institute
44 Binney Streeet
Boston
Massachusetts MA 02115
USA

Jeffrey A Frelinger
Department of Microbiology and Immunology
University of North Carolina
Chapel Hill
North Carolina NC 27599-7290
USA

Manuel Fresno
Centro de Biologa Molecular Severo Ochoa
CSIC-Universidad Autonoma de Madrid
Madrid
Spain

N Frickhofen
Department of Hematology/Oncology
Clinical Center Wiesbaden (HSK)
Ludwig-Erhard-Strasse 100
65199 Wiesbaden
Germany

Herman Friedman
Department of Medical Microbiology and Immunology
University of South Florida College of Medicine
72901 Bruce B Downs Boulevard
Tampa
Florida FL 33612-4799
USA

PS Friedmann
Department of Dermatology
Royal Liverpool University Hospital
PO Box 147
Liverpool L69 3BX
UK

Richard L Friedman
Department of Microbiology and Immunology
University of Arizona Health Science Center
1501 North Campbell
Tucson
Arizona AZ 85724
USA

Bertrand Friguet
Unit for Cellular Biochemistry
Institut Pasteur
28 rue du Dr Roux
75724 Paris Cedex 15
France

Ramsay L Fuleihan
Section of Immunology
Department of Pediatrics
Yale University School of Medicine
New Haven
Connecticut CT 06250
USA

Ralph van Furth
Laan van Oued Palgeest 44
2341 ML Oegstgeest
The Netherlands

Robert D Fusunyan
Combined Program in Pediatric Gastroenterology and Nutrition
Department of Pediatric Gastroenterology
Massachusetts General Hospital
149 13th Street (149-3404)
Charlestown
Massachusetts MA 02129-2060
USA

Thomas F Gajewski
Department of Medicine
Section of Hematology-Oncology
University of Chicago
924 E 57th Street
R413A
Chicago
Illinois IL 60637-5420
USA

Chris Galanos
Max-Planck Institute for Immunology
Stuebeweg 51
D-79108
Freiburg
Germany

Laurent Gapin
Laboratory of Molecular Biology of the Gene
Pasteur Institute
25 Rue du Dr Roux
75724 Paris Cedex
France

David L Gasser
Department of Genetics
University of Pennsylvania School of Medicine
415 Curie Boulevard
Philadelphia
USA

Paul Gatenby
Department of Health and Community Care
Canberra Clinical School
University of Sydney
Canberra Clinical School
Garran ACT 2605
PO Box 11
Wooden ACT 2605
Australia

JS Gatot
Molecular Biology and Animal Physiology
Department
Bembloux University
13 Avenue Marechal Juin
B-5030 Gembloux
Belgium

Richard A Gatti
Department of Pathology
UCLA School of Medicine
Los Angeles
California CA 90024-1732
USA

Susan L Gdovin
Department of Comparative Medicine and Molecular
Biology and Genetics
Johns Hopkins University School of Medicine
720 Rutland Avenue/Traylor G-60
Baltimore
Maryland MD 21205
USA

Bryan M Gebhardt
LSU Eye Center
Louisiana State University Medical Center School of
Medicine
2020 Gravier School
Louisiana LA 70112-2234
USA

Jorge Raúl Geffner
Institute for Investigations in Hematology
National Academy of Medicine
Pacheco de Melo 3081
1425 Buenos Aires
Argentina

Erwin W Gelfand
Department of Pediatrics
National Jewish Medical Center for Immunology and
Respiratory Medicine
1400 Jackson Street
Denver
Colorado CO 80206
USA

Jeffrey A Gelfand
Department of Medicine
Tufts University School of Medicine
136 Harrison Avenue
Boston
Massachusetts MA 02111
USA

Vincent Geli
CNRS-CBBM
31 Chemin Joseph Aiguier
BP 71
13402 Marseille Cedex 9
France

Robert M Genta
Department of Pathology
Baylor College of Medicine
2002 Holcombe Boulevard
Houston
Texas TX 77030
USA

Jacob George
Department of Medicine 'B' and the Research Unit of
Autoimmune Diseases
Sheba Medical Center
Tel-hashomer 52621
Tel-Aviv
Israel

Tom Geppert
Department of Internal Medicine
The University of Texas
South Western Medical School
5323 Harry Hines Boulevard
Dallas
Texas TX 75235-8884
USA

J Bruce German
Department of Food Science and Technology
University of California
Davis
California CA 95616
USA

Dori R Germolec
Environmental Immunology Section
National Institute of Environmental Health Sciences
111 Alexander Drive
NIEHS South Campus Research Triangle Park
North Carolina NC 27709
USA

M Eric Gershwin
Division of Rheumatology
Allergy and Clinical Immunology
University of California
Davis
California CA 95616
USA

Allan Gibofsky
The Hospital for Special Surgery
535 East 70th Street
New York NY 10021
USA

Thomas Gill III
Department of Pathology
University of Pittsburgh
716A Scaife Hall
Pittsburgh
Pennsylvania PA 15261
USA

Jean-Pierre Girard
Institute of Immunology and Allergy
Hospital de la Tour
CH-1217 Meyrin
Geneva

David Givol
Department of Molecular Cell Biology
Weizmann Institute of Science
76100 Rehovot
Israel

Cornelis PJ Glaudemans
Section on Carbohydrates
National Institute of Diabetes/Digestive/Kidney Diseases
Building 8
Room B1A-23
Bethesda
Maryland MD 20892-0815
USA

Michel E Goldberg
Unit of Cellular Biochemistry
Institut Pasteur
25 Rue du Dr Roux
75724 Paris Cedex
France

Pierre Golstein
Centre for Immunology of Marseille-Luminy
Case 906-13288
Marseille Cedex 9
France

Edward S Golub
Pacific Center of Ethics and Applied Biology
450 Lirio Street
Solana Beach
California CA 92075
USA

Matthew A Gonda
Laboratory of Cell and Molecular Structure
Frederick National Cancer Institute/Cancer Research
and Development Center
Frederick
Maryland MD 21701
USA

Shiaoching Gong
Laboratory of Molecular Immunology
The Howard Hughes Medical Institute
University of Chicago
924 East 57th Street
Chicago
New York NY 60637-5420
USA

Siamon Gordon
Sir William Dunn School of Pathology
University of Oxford
South Parks Road
Oxford OX1 3RE
UK

Arko Gorter
Department of Surgery
Leiden University Hospital
Building 1
LI-Q
POB 9600
Leiden
The Netherlands

Hannah J Gould
The Randall Institute
King's College London
26–29 Drury Lane
London WC2B 5RL
UK

David Gray
Department of Immunology
Royal Postgraduate Medical School
Hammersmith Hospital
Du Cane Road
London W12 0NN
UK

Douglas R Green
La Jolla Institute for Allergy and Immunology
11149 North Torrey Pines Road
La Jolla
California CA 92037
USA

Nancy S Green
Department of Pediatrics and Cell Biology
Albert Einstein College of Medicine of Yeshiva
University
1300 Morris Park Avenue
Bronx
New York NY 10461
USA

Philip D Greenberg
Department of Immunology and Medicine
Fred Hutchinson Cancer Research Center
University of Washington
Health Science Building
Box 356527
Seattle
Washington 98195-6527
USA

Philip R Greipp
Divisions of Hematology and Hematopathology
Mayo Clinic
Rochester
Minnesota
USA

G Gribben
Division of Hematologic Malignancies
Dana-Farber Cancer Institute
44 Binney Street
Boston
Massachusetts MA 0215
USA

Diane E Griffin
Department of Molecular Microbiology and Immunology
The Johns Hopkins University School of Hygiene and Public Health and School of Medicine
Baltimore
Maryland MD 211205
USA

PD Griffiths
Department of Virology
Royal Free Hospital School of Medicine
Pond Street
London NW3 2QG
UK

Luigi ME Grimaldi
Department of Neurology
University of Milan
Via Olgettina 58
20132 Milan
Italy

Charles F Grose
Department of Pediatrics and Microbiology
University of Iowa College of Medicine
200 Hawkins Drive
Iowa City IA 52242
USA

CE Grossi
National Institute for Cancer Research
University of Genoa
Via De Toni 14
16132 Genoa
Italy

Michael J Grusby
Department of Cancer Biology
Harvard School of Public Health
665 Huntigton Avenue
Boston
Massachusetts MA 02115
USA

Ian D Gust
CSL Ltd
45 Poplar Road
Parkville
Victoria 3052
Australia

Marina Gutierrez
Lymphoma Biology Section
Pediatric Branch
NCI, NIH
Bethesda
Maryland MD 20892
USA

Paul M Guyre
Department of Physiology
Dartmouth Medical School
Hanover
New Hampshire NH 03756
USA

BF Hague
Laboratory of Immunogenetics
National Institute of Allergy and Infectious Diseases
Bethesda
Maryland
USA

Geoff Hale
Sir William Dunn School of Pathology
University of Oxford
Headington
Oxford OX3 7JT
UK

Joseph G Hall
Formerly of The Royal Marsden Hospital
University of London
London
UK

Terry Hamblin
Department of Hematology
Royal Bournemouth Hospital
Castle Lane Ast
Bournemouth BH7 7DW
UK

Richard J Hamillton
Department of Veterans Affairs Medical Center
Infectious Disease Section
Room 4B-370
2002 Holcoombe Boulevard
Houston
Texas TX 77030
USA

Thomas A Hamilton
Department of Immunology
The Cleveland Clinic Foundation
9500 Euclid Avenue
Cleveland
Ohio OH 44195
USA

Juergen Hammer
Roche Milano Ricerche
Via Olgettina 58
1-20132 Milan
Italy

Jef M Hammond
CSIRO
Australian Animal Health Laboratory
Private Mail Bag 24
Geelong
Victoria 3220
Australia

Robert EW Hancock
Department of Microbiology and Immunology
University of British Columbia
300-6174 University Boulevard
Vancouver V6T 123
Canada

Richard R Hardy
Fox Chase Cancer Center
7701 Burholme Avenue
Philadelphia 19111
USA

William J Harris
Department of Molecular and Cell Biology
University of Aberdeen
Marichal College
Aberdeen AB9 1AS
UK

Thomas S Harrison
The Evans Memorial Department of Clinical Research
and the Department of Medicine
Boston University School of Medicine
Boston
Massachusetts MA 02118-2393
USA

Liana Harvath
Laboratory of Cellular Hematology
Division of Hematology
CBER
Building 29
Room 331
8800 Rockville Pike
Maryland MD 20892
USA

PJ Hastings
Department of Molecular and Human Genetics
Baylor College of Medicine
1 Baylor Plaza
Houston
Texas TX 77030
USA

Catherine Haworth
Department of Haematology
Leicester Royal Infirmary
Leicester
UK

Kent T HayGlass
Department of Immunology
University of Manitoba
770 Bannatyne Avenue
Winnipeg R3T OW3
Canada

Anthony R Hayward
Department of Pediatrics
University of Colorado School of Medicine
Box A 040
4200 East Ninth Avenue
Denver
Colorado CO 80262
USA

Adrian Hayday
Department of Biology
Yale University
PO Box 6666
New Haven
Connecticut CT 06520
USA

William R Heath
The Walter and Eliza Hall Institute of Medical Research
Post Office
Royal Melbourne Hospital
Victoria 3050
Australia

Susan R Heimer
Department of Microbiology and Immunology
Division of Infectious Diseases
University of Maryland School of Medicine
655 West Baltimore Street
BRB 13-009
Baltimore
Maryland MD 21201
USA

Paul G Hellewell
Department of Applied Pharmacology
Imperial College School of Medicine at the National
Heart and Lung Institute
London SW3 6LY
UK

Ingegerd Hellström
Pacific Northwest Research Foundation
720 Broadway
Washington WA 98121
USA

Karl Erik Hellström
Pacific Northwest Research Foundation
720 Broadway
Washington WA 98121
USA

Peter M Henson
National Jewish Center for Immunology and Respiratory
Medicine
1400 Jackson Street
Denver
Colorado CO 80206
USA

Juliane Hentschel
Department of Neonatology
Virchow-Klinikum
Humboldt-Universitat Berlin
D-13353 Berlin
Germany

Beate M Henz
Department of Dermatology and Allergology
Charite and Virchow Klinikum
Augustenburger Platz 1
13353 Berlin
Germany

Ronald B Herberman
Department of Medicine and Pathology
University of Pittsburgh Cancer Institute
3471 Fifth Avenue
Suite 201
Pennsylvania
Pittsburgh 5213-2592
USA

Steve Herrmann
Genetics Institute
87 Cambridge Park Lane
Cambridge
Massachusetts MA 02140
USA

Leonard A Herzenberg
Department of Genetics
Stanford University
Beckman Center B009
Stanford
California CA 94305-5125
USA

Leonore A Herzenberg
Department of Genetics
Stanford University
Beckman Center B009
Stanford
California CA 94305-5125
USA

Pieter S Hiemstra
Department of Pulmonology
Leiden University Hospital
Building I C3-P
Rijnsburgerweg 10
PO Box 9600
2300 RC Leiden
The Netherlands

Toshri Hirano
Division of Molecular Oncology
Biomedical Research Center
Osaka University
2-2 Yamadaoke
Suita City
Osaka 565
Japan

Fusao Hirata
Department of Pharmaceutical Science and
Pharmacology
Institute of Chemical Toxicology
Wayne State University
528 Shapero Hall
Detroit
Michigan MI 48202
USA

Tage Hjort
Department of Medical Microbiology and Immunology
University of Aarhus
DK-8000 Aarhus
Denmark

Gertrud M Hocke
Department of Genetics
University of Erlangen
Schlosplatz 4
91054 Erlangen
Germany

Amy Hodson
Department of Microbiology and Immunology
University of South Carolina
171 Ashley Avenue
Charleston
South Carolina
SC 29425-2230
USA

Donald R Hoffman
Department of Pathology and Laboratory Medicine
East Carolina University School of Medicine
Greenville
North Carolina NC 27858-4354
USA

Laurie Hoffman-Goetz
Department of Health Studies and Gerontology
Faculty of Applied Health Sciences
University of Waterloo
Ontario N2L 3G1
Canada

Nancy Hogg
Leukocyte Adhesion Laboratory
Imperial Cancer Research Fund
Lincoln's Inn Fields
London WC2A 3PX
UK

Anthony A Holder
Division of Parasitology
National Institute for Medical Research
The Ridgeway
Mill Hill
London NW7 1AA
UK

Kevin J Horgan
UCLA Division of Digestive Diseases
UCLA School of Medicine
CHS 44-138
Box 951604
Los Angeles
California CA 90095-1604
USA

Carlos E Hormaeche
Department of Microbiology
University of Newcastle Upon Tyne
Framlington Place
Newcastle Upon Tyne NE2 4HH
UK

Amelia Dale Horne
Division of Biostatistics and Epidemiology
Center for Biologics Evaluation and Research
Rockville
Maryland MD 20852
USA

Francis J Hornicek
Department of Orthopaedics and Rehabilitation (R-12)
University of Miami School of Medicine
PO Box 016960
Miami
Florida FL 33101
USA

Yasuhiro Horii
Division of Molecular Oncology
Biomedical Research Center
Osaka University
2-2 Yamadaoke
Suita City
Osaka 565
Japan

Marshall S Horwitz
Department of Medicine
Microbiology and Immunology
University of California
37-121 Los Angeles
California CA 90024
USA

David Hosford
Biol-Ionova DNA Tech Group
48–52 Rue de la Gare
Plaisir
F-78380
France

Nobumichi Hozumi
Department of Immunology and Molecular Genetics
Samuel Lunenfeld Research Institute
Mount Sinai Hospital
600 University Avenue
Toronto
Ontario M5G 1X5
Canada

Yun Hu
Laboratory of Molecular Immunology
The Howard Hughes Medical Institute
1230 York Avenue
Box 220
New York NY 10021-6399
USA

Nevin Hughes-Jones
Molecular Immunopathology Unit
Medical Research Council
Long Road
Cambridge CB2 2PT
UK

Alan J Husband
Department of Veterinary Anatomy and Pathology
University of Sydney
Sydney 2006
Australia

David N Irani
Department of Molecular Microbiology and Immunology
The Johns Hopkins University School of Hygiene and
Public Health and School of Medicine
Baltimore
Maryland MD 211205
USA

William L Irving
Department of Microbiology
University of Nottingham
Queen's Medical Centre
Nottingham NG7 2UH
UK

David A Isenberg
Bloombury Rheumatology Unit
University College London Medical School
40–50 Tottenham Street
London W1P 9PG
UK

Catherine Ison
Department of Medical Microbiology
Imperial College School of Medicine at St Mary's
Norfolk Place
Paddington
London W2 1PG
UK

Peter D Issitt
Transfusion Service
Duke University Medical Center
PO Box 2928
Durham
North Carolina NC 27710
USA

Helmut Jacobsen
F. Hoffmann-La Roche AG
PRP/Gene Technology
CH-4002 Basel
Switzerland

Nicholas D James
University of Birmingham
CRC Institute for Cancer Studies
Edgbaston
Birmingham B15 2TJ
UK

Stephen P James
Department of Medicine
Division of Gastroenterology
University of Maryland at Baltimore
Room N3W62
22 South Green Street
Baltimore
Maryland MD 21201
USA

C Jamin
Laboratory of Immunology
Brest University Medical School
Brest
France

Mila Jankovic
Laboratory of Molecular Immunology
Rockefeller University
1230 York Avenue
Box 220
New York
NY 10021-6399
USA

Royston Jefferis
Department of Immunology
The Medical School
University of Birmingham
Vincent Drive
Edgbaston
Birmingham B15 2TT
UK

David J Jenkins
The Australian Hydatid Control and Epidemiology
Program
12 Mildura Street
Fyshwick
Canberra ACT 2609
Australia

Finn-Erik Johansen
Laboratory of Immunohistochemistry
Immunopathology (LIIPAT) and Institute of Pathology
The National Hospital
Rickshospitalet
N-0027 Oslo
Norway

Peter M Johnson
Department of Immunology
University of Liverpool
PO Box 147
Liverpool L69 3BX
UK

Joan Judge
Department of Pathology
Norwalk Hospital
Norwalk
Connecticut CT 06856
USA

Hee-Sook Jun
Department of Microbiology and Infectious Diseases
Julia McFarlane Diabetes Research Centre
Suwon
Korea

Carl H June
Immune Cell Biology Program
Naval Medical Research Institute
Bethesda
Maryland MD 20889-5055
USA

Elvin A Kabat
Department of Microbiology
College of Physicians and Surgeons
Columbia University
701 West 168th Street
New York NY 10032
USA

Teresa Kakauer
Department of Immunology and Molecular Biology
US Army Medical Research Institute of Infectious
Diseases
Building 560
Frederick
Maryland MD 21702-1201
USA

Terje Kalland
Pharmacia & Upjohn
Lund Research Center
Lund
Sweden

James Kalmakoff
Department of Microbiology
University of Otago
Dunedin
New Zealand

M Ilyas Kamboh
Department of Human Genetics
Graduate School of Public Health
University of Pittsburgh
Pittsburgh
Pennsylvania 15261
USA

Jerry Kaplan
Department of Pathology
Division of Cell Biology and Immunology
University of Utah School of Medicine
Room 5C239
Salt Lake City
Utah UT 84132-1001
USA

Martien L Kapsenberg
Laboratory of Cell Biology and Histology
University of Amsterdam
Academish Medisch Centrum
Meibergdreef 15
1105 AZ Amsterdam
The Netherlands

Hajime Karasuyama
Department of Immunology
Tokyo Metropolitan Institute of Medical Science
4-6-1 Shirokonedai Minato-Ku
Tokyo 108
Japan

David R Katz
Department of Immunology
University College London Medical School
Windeyer Building
46 Cleveland Street
London W1P 6DB
UK

John F Kearney
Department of Microbiology and The Comprehensive
Cancer Center
Division of Developmental and Clinical Immunology
378 Wallace Tumor Institute
University of Alabama
Birmingham AL 352904-3300
USA

Achsah D Keegan
Department of Immunology
Jerome H Holland Laboratory
American Red Cross
15601 Crabbs Branch Way
Rockville
Maryland MD 20750
USA

John H Kehrl
Laboratory of Immunoregulation
National Institute of Allergy and Infectious Diseases
Building 10
Bethesda
Maryland MD 20892-1876
USA

E. Keinan
Department of Molecular Biology
Scripps Research Institute
10666 N Torrey Pines Road
La Jolla
California CA 92037-1092
USA

Anne Kelso
Transplantation Biology Unit
Queensland Institute of Medical Research
Post Office
Royal Brisbane Hospital
Queensland
QLD 4029
Australia

Malcolm W Kennedy
Division of Infection and Immunity
Institute of Biomedical and Life Sciences
Joseph Black Building
University of Glasgow
Glasgow G12 8QQ
UK

Mary K Kennedy
Immunex Corporation
51 University Street
Seattle
Washington WA 98101-2936
USA

P Kerkhofs
National Institute of Veterinary
Research
B1120 Uccle
Belgium

Michael A Kerr
Department of Molecular and Cellular Pathology
University of Dundee
Ninewells Hospital Medical School
Dundee DD1 9SY
Scotland
UK

Gerald T Keusch
Department of Medicine
Division of Geographic Medicine and Infectious
Diseases
Tupper Research Institute
Tufts University School of Medicine
750 Washington Street
Boston
Massachusetts MA 02111
USA

Nancy M Khardori
Department of Internal Medicine
Southern Illinois University
Illinois
USA

Vijay P Khatri
Division of Surgical Oncology
Roswell Park Cancer Institute
Buffalo
New York
USA

TJ Kindt
Division of Intramural Research
Laboratory of Immunogenetics
National Institute of Allergy and Infectious Diseases
Building 10, Rm 4A31B
9000 Rockville Pike
Bethesda
Maryland MD 20892
USA

Taroh Kinoshita
Department of Immunoregulation
Research Institute for Microbioal Diseases
Osaka University
3-1 Yamada-oka, Suita
Osaka 565
Japan

Stephen J Kirk
Department of Surgery
Sinai Hospital and The Johns Hopkins Medical
Institutions
Baltimore
Maryland
USA

Charles H Kirkpatrick
University of Colorado Health Sciences Center
Cytokine Sciences Inc
1899 Gaylord Street
Denver
Colorado CO 80206-1210
USA

Tadamitsu Kishimoto
Department of Medicine III
Osaka University Medical School
1-1-50 Fukushima-ku
Osaka 53
Japan

Pawel Kisielow
Basel Institute for Immunology
Grenzacherstrasse 487
CH-4005 Basel
Switzerland

R Paul Kitching
Institute for Animal Health
Pirbright Laboratory
Ash Road
Pirbright
Woking
Surrey GU24 0NF
UK

Seymour J Klebanoff
Department of Medicine
Division of Allergy and Infectious Diseases
University of Washington
Box 357185
Seattle
Washington WA 98195-7185
USA

Jan Klein
Department of Immunogenetics
Max-Planck-Institute for Biology
Corrensstrasse 42
Tubingen
Germany 74001

Hans-Dieter Klenk
Institut fur Virologie
Philipps-Universitat Marburg
Robert Koch Strasse 17
D 35037 Marburg
Germany

Norman R Klinman
The Scripps Research Institute
1066 North Torrey Pines Road
La Jolla
California CA 92037
USA

Walter Knapp
Institute of Immunology
University of Vienna
Borschkegasse BA
Vienna
Austria A-1090

Nicholas J Knowles
Institute for Animal Health
Pirbright Laboratory
Ash Road
Pirbright
Woking
Surrey SU24 ONF
UK

George A Kollias
Department of Molecular Genetics
Hellenic Pasteur Institute
127 Vas Sofias Avenue
115 21 Athens
Greece

Fris Koning
Department of Immunohematology and Blood Bank
Building 1
E3-Q
Academisch Ziekenhuis Leiden
PO Box 9600
2300 RC Leiden
The Netherlands

Joop P Koopman
Central Animal Laboratory
Catholic University of Nijmegen
PO Box 9101
6500 HB Nijmegen
The Netherlands

Robert Korngold
Department of Pediatrics
University of Minnesota Hospital and Clinics
Minnesota
USA

Philippe Kourilsky
Department of Immunology
Laboratory of Molecular Biology of the Gene
Pasteur Institute
25 rue du Dr Roux
75724 Paris Cedex 15
France

Georg Kraal
Department of Cell Biology
Medical Faculty of Vrije University
vd Bocchhozstraat 7
1001 BT Amsterdam
The Netherlands

Peter Krajei
Laboratory of Immunohistochemistry and
Immunopathology (LIIPAT) and Institute of Pathology
University of Oslo
The National Hospital
Rickshospitalet
N-0027 Oslo
Norway

Margaret L Kripke
Department of Immunology
University of Texas
M.D. Anderson Cancer Center
1515 Holcombe Blvd
Houston
Texas TX 77030
USA

Guido Kroemer
Centre National de la Recherche Scientifique – UPR
420
Villejuif
France

Sabine Krüger-Krasagakes
Department of Dermatology
Medizinische Fakultat
Charite and Virchow Klinikum
der Humbold-Universitat Berlin
Augustenburger Platz 1, 13353
Germany

John de Kruif
Department of Immunology
University Hospital Utrecht
Utrecht
The Netherlands

Ada M Kruisbeek
Division of Immunology
The Netherlands Cancer Institute
Plesmanlaan 121
1066 CX Amsterdam
The Netherlands

Heinz W Kunz
Department of Pathology
School of Medicine
University of Pittsburgh
710A Scaife Hall
Pittsburgh PA 15261
USA

Peter JK Kuppen
Department of Surgery
Leiden University Hospital
Building 1, K6-R50
POB 9600
2300 RC Leiden
The Netherlands

Peter J Lachmann
SmithKline Beecham Microbial Immunology Laboratory
Department of Clinical and Veterinary Medicine
Coombs Building
Madingley Road
Cambridge CB3 0ES
UK

Joseph S Lam
Department of Microbiology
University of Guelph
Guelph
Ontario N1G 2W1
Canada

David W Lancki
Frank W Fitch Monoclonal Antibody Facility
The Gwen Knapp Center
Jules F Knapp Research Center
924 E 57th Street
Chicago
Illinois IL 60637
USA

Jerome A Langer
Department of Molecular Genetics and Microbiology
University of Medicine and Dentistry of New Jersey
Robert Wood Johnson Medical School
675 Hoes Lane
Piscataway
New Jersey NJ 08854-5635
USA

Jean Langhorne
Department of Biology
Imperial College of Science
Techology and Medicine
Mill Hill
London NW1 1AA
UK

Christian Larsen
Department of Haematology
Herlev Hospital
University of Copenhagen
Denmark

Anna-Brita Laurell
Department of Medical Microbiology
Section of Clinical Immunology
University of Lund
Solvegatan 23
S-223 62 Lund
Sweden

J E Layton
Ludwig Institute for Cancer Research
Melbourne Tumour Biology Branch
Post Office
Royal Melbourne Hospital
Victoria 3050
Australia

Junming Le
Department of Microbiology
New York University Medical Center
550 First Avenue
New York NY 10016
USA

Claude Leclerc
Biologie des Regulations Immunitaires
Institut Pasteur
25 rue du Docteur Roux
75724 Paris Cedex 15
France

Jeffrey A Ledbetter
Bristol-Myers Squibb Pharmaceutical Research Institute
Seattle
Department of Microbiology
University of Washington
3005 First Avenue
Seattle
Washington WA 98121
USA

Irene Lee
Department of Chemistry
The Pennsylvania State University
414 Wartik Laboratory
University Park
Pennsylvania PA 16802
USA

Ann Kari Lefvert
Department of Medicine and Immunological Research
Laboratory
Karolinska Hospital
S-10401 Stockholm
Sweden

Robert I Lehrer
Section of Molecular Host Defense
Department of Medicine
Center for the Health Sciences
UCLA School of Medicine
10833 Le Conte Avenue
Los Angeles
California CA 90024-1678
USA

Moyha Lennon-Pierce
The Jackson Laboratory
600 Main Street
Bar Harbor
Maine ME 04609
USA

Bruce L Levine
Immune Cell Biology Program
Naval Medical Research Institute
Tissue Bank
Bldg 1, Room 163
8901 Wisconsin Avenue
Bethesda
Maryland MD 20889-56
USA

Stuart M Levitz
The Evans Memorial Department of Clinical Research
and the Department of Medicine
Boston University School of Medicine
Medical Center Hospital
Boston
Massachusetts MA 02118-2393
USA

T Chyau Liang
Department of Biochemistry and Molecular Biology
University of Texas Medical School
PO Box 20708
Houston
Texas TX 7725-0708
USA

Lawrence M Lichtenstein
Division of Clinical Immunology
Department of Medicine
Johns Hopkins University
Asthma and Allergy Center
5501 Hopkins Bay View Cir
Baltimore
Maryland MD 21224-6801
USA

Foo Y Liew
Department of Bacteriology and Immunology
Western Infirmary
Glasgow G11 6NT
UK

David C Linch
Department of Haematology
University College London Medical School
98 Chenies Mews
London WC1E 6HX
UK

Hans Link
Division of Neurology
Karolinska Institute
Huddinge Hospital
S141-86 Huddinge
Stockholm
Sweden

Peter S Linsley
Bristol-Myers Squibb Pharmaceutical Research Institute
Department of Microbiology
University of Washington
3005 First Avenue
Seattle
Washington WA 98121
USA

Phyllis-Jean Linton
Department of Immunology
The Scripps Research Institute
10666 North Torrey Pines Road
La Jolla
California CA 92037
USA

Halina Lis
The Weizmann Institute of Science
Department of Membrane Research and Biophysics
76100 Rehovot
Israel

M Kathryn Liszewski
Department of Internal Medicine
Washington University School of Medicine
660 S Euclid
Box 8121
St Louis
Missouri MO 63110-1031
USA

Chau-Ching Liu
Department of Medicine
University of Pittsburgh School of Medicine
Pennsylvania
USA

Margaret A Liu
Chiron Corporation
Emeryville
California
USA

Åsa Ljungh
Department of Medical Microbiology
Lund University
Solvegatan 23
Lund
Sweden

Lucille London
Department of Microbiology and Immunology
University of South Carolina
171 Ashley Avenue
Charleston
South Carolina SC 29425-2230
USA

Steve D London
Department of Microbiology and Immunology
University of South Carolina
171 Ashley Avenue
Charleston
South Carolina SC 29425-2230
USA

Ton Logtenberg
Department of Immunology
University Hospital Utrecht
Utrecht
The Netherlands

Eric O Long
Laboratory of Immunogenetics
NIAID National Institutes of Health
Twinbrook 11
12441 Parklawn Drive
Rockville
Maryland MD 20852
USA

Francis Loor
Pharmacological and Biotechnological Research Center
University of Strasbourg
Laboratoire d'Immunologie
BP24
67401 Illkirch Cedex
France

Henk Van Loveren
Laboratory of Pathology and Immunobiology
National Institute of Public Health and the Environment
Bilthoven
The Netherlands

Anatole Lubenko
North London Blood Transfusion Centre
Colindale Avenue
London
UK

Omelan A Lukasewycz
Medical Microbiology and Immunology
Office of Curricular Affairs
III Medical School Building
School of Medicine
University of Minnesota
Duluth
Minnesota MN 55812-2487
USA

Igor S Lukashevich
Belarussian Research Institute for Epidemiology and
Microbiology
Minsk
Belarus

Torben Lund
Department of Immunology
University College London Medical School
Windeyer Building
46 Cleveland Street
London W1P 6DB

Michael I Luster
Toxicology and Molecular Biology Branch
Health Effects Laboratory Division
1095 Willowdale Road
Mailstop L3014
Morgantown
West Virginia WV 26505
USA

Jon E Lutz
Department of Medicine
Division of Infectious Diseases
Santa Clara Valley Medical Center
San Jose
California
USA

PM Lydyard
Department of Immunology
University College London Medical School
Windeyer Building
46 Cleveland Street
London W1P 6DB

David H Lynch
Department of Immunobiology
Immunex Corporation
51 University Street
Seattle
Washington WA 98101
USA

John T Macfarlane
Thoracic Medicine
City Hospital
Hucknall Road
Nottingham NG5 1PB
UK

Malcolm R MacKenzie
University of California School of Medicine
Section of Hematology and Oncology
4501X St
Sacramento
California CA 95817-2214
USA

Ian R Mackay
Centre for Molecular Biology and Medicine
Monash University
Clayton
Victoria 3168
Australia

CD Mackenzie
Department of Pathology
A620 East Fee Hall
Michigan State University
East Lansing
Michigan MI 48824-1314
USA

Noel Maclaren
Department of Pathology and Laboratory Medicine
University of Florida College of Medicine
Florida
Gainesville
USA

Ravinder N Maini
The Mathilda and Terence Kennedy Institute of
Rheumatology
Kennedy Building
6 Bute Gardens
London W6 7DW
UK

Fabrizio Mainiero
Department of Experimental Medicine
University of Rome School of Medicine
Viale Regina Elena 324
Rome 00161
Italy

Otto Majdic
Institute of Immunology
University of Vienna
A-1235 Vienna
Brunner Strasse 59
Austria

Tak W Mak
The Ontario Cancer Institute
500 Sherbourne Street
Toronto
Ontario M4X 1K9
Canada

Olli Makelä
Department of Bacteriology and Immunology
University of Helsinki
Haartmaninkatu 3
00290 Helsinki
Finland

George I Malinin
Department of Orthopaedics and Rehabilitation (R-12)
University of Miami School of Medicine
Miami
Florida
USA

David Manchester
University of Colorado School of Medicine
Department of Pediatrics
Box A040
4200 East Ninth Avenue
Denver
Colorado CO 80262
USA

Paul A Manning
Microbial Pathogenesis Unit
Department of Microbiology and Immunology
The University of Adelaide
PO Box 498
Adelaide
South Adelaide SA 5001
Australia

Patrice Mannoni
Department of Gene Transfer
Institute for Paoli-Calmettes
232 Boulevard de Ste Marguerite
BP 156
13273 Marseille Cedex 9
France

Alberto Mantovani
Department of Biomedical Science and Biotechnology
University of Degli Studi Di Brescia
Brescia
Italy

John J Marchalonis
Department of Microbiology and Immunology
College of Medicine
University of Arizona
101 N Campbell Avenue
Tucson
Arizona AZ 85724
USA

Steven D Marlin
Imperial Cancer Research Fund
Lincoln's Inn Fields
London
UK

Seamus J Martin
Molecular Cell Biology Laboratory
Department of Biology
Maynooth University College
Maynooth
Co Kildare
Ireland

Gianvito Martino
Department of Neurology
University of Milan
Milan
Italy

Eric Martz
Department of Microbiology and Program in Molecular
and Cell Biology
University of Massachusetts
Amherst
Massachusetts MA 01003
USA

Don Mason
Medical Research Council Cellular Immunology Unit
Sir William Dunn School of Pathology
5 Parks Road
Oxford OX1 3RE
UK

Andrei Matsaev
Department of Membrane Research
The Weizmann Institute of Science
76100 Rehovot
Israel

Tadashi Matsuda
Department of Biochemistry
St Jude Children's Research Hospital
Memphis
Tennessee
USA

Koui Matsushima
Department of Haematology
Herlev Hospital
University of Copenhagen
Denmark

Kouji Matsushima
Department of Pharmacology
Cancer Research Institute
Kanozawa University
13-1 Takara-Machi Kanazawa
Ishikawa 920
Tokyo
Japan

George L Mayers
Department of Molecular Immunology
Roswell Park Memorial Institute
Buffalo
New York NY 14263
USA

WP McArthur
College of Dentistry
University of Florida
Periodontal Disease Research Center
Box 100-424
Gainesville
Florida FL 32610-0402
USA

Brian W McBride
Centre for Applied Microbiology and Research
Porton Down
Salisbury
Wiltshire SP4 0JG
UK

Myra McClure
Department of GU
Communicable Diseases
Imperial College School of Medicine
Jefferiss Research Trust
Norfolk Place
London W12 1PG
UK

Ian McConnell
Department of Clinical and Veterinary Medicine
University of Cambridge
Madingley Road
Cambridge CB3 0ES
UK

Kenneth C McCullough
Institute of Virology and Immunoprophylaxis
Sensemattsstrasse 293
CH 3147 Mittelhausern
Switzerland

Jerry R McGhee
The Immunobiology Vaccine Center
University of Alabama at Birmingham
845 19th Street South
761 Bevill Biomedical Research Building
Birmingham
Alabama AL 35294-2170
USA

Alan M McGregor
Department of Medicine
King's College School of Medicine and Dentistry
Denmark Hill
London SE5 3RX
UK

Donald P McManus
Molecular Parasitology Unit
Tropical Health Program
Queensland Institute of Medical Research
The Bancroft Center
300 Herston Road
Brisbane
Queensland 4029
Australia

Robert McMillan
Scripps Clinic
10666 N Torrey Pines Road
La Jolla
California CA 92037
USA

Stephen J McSorley
Institut de Pharmacologie Moleculaire et Cellulaire
UPR411 CNRS
06560 Valbonne
France

Peter A McSweeney
University of Washington School of Medicine and
Clinical Research Division
Fred Hutchinson Cancer Research Center
1124 Columbia Street
Seattle
Washington WA 98104
USA

Fritz Melchers
Basel Institute for Immunology
Grenzacherstrasse 487
Basel
CH-4005
Switzerland

Roger W Melvold
Department of Microbiology–Immunology
Northwestern University Medical School
303 East Chicago Avenue
Chicago
Illinois IL 60611
USA

Seppo Meri
Department of Bacteriology and Immunology
Haartman Institute
PO Box 21
(Haartmaninkatu 3)
FIN-00014
University of Helsinki
Helsinki
Finland

Jiri Mestecky
Department of Microbiology
University of Alabama at Birmingham
University Station
Birmingham
Alabama AL 35294
USA

Stefan C Meuer
Ruprechts-Karls-Universitat
Heidelberg
Germany

Felix Milgrom
Department of Microbiology
State University of New York at Buffalo
333 Sherman Hall
Buffalo
New York NY 14214
USA

Lorraine T Miller
Department of Nutrition and Food Management
Oregon State University
117A Milam Hall
Corvallis
Oregon OR 97331-5103
USA

Richard G Miller
Ontario Cancer Institute
Princess Margaret Hospital
610 University Avenue
Toronto
Ontario M5G 2M9
Canada

Caroline Milner
Department of Biochemistry
MRC Immunochemistry Unit
University of Oxford
South Parks Road
Oxford OX1 3QU
UK

Rita Mirakian
Department of Immunology
St Bartholomew's and the Royal London School of
Medicine and Dentistry
56–76 Ashfield Street
London E1 2AD
UK

Gyan C Mishra
Institute of Microbial Technology
Chandigrah
Pune 411007
India

Dhirendra N Misra
Department of Pathology
School of Medicine
University of Pittsburgh
710A Scaife Hall
Pittsburgh PA 15261
USA

Masayuki Miyasaka
Department of Bioregulation
Biomedical Research Center
Osaka University Medical School
2-2 Yamadaoka
Suita-shi
Osaka 565
Japan

Masaaki Miyazawa
Department of Immunology
Kinki University School of Medicine
Osaka
Japan

Joel Lawrence Moake
Medical Hematology Section
Baylor College of Medicine and the Methodist Hospital
6565 Fannin
Mail Station 902 Main Building
Houston
Texas TX 77030
USA

Harry LT Mobley
Division of Infectious Diseases
University of Maryland School of Medicine
Baltimore
Maryland MD 21201
USA

David R Moller
Department of Medicine
The Johns Hopkins University School of Medicine
720 Rutland Avenue
Room 850
Baltimore
Maryland MD 21205
USA

Marjorie Anne Monnickendam
PHLS Communicable Disease Surveillance Centre
Public Health Laboratory Service
61 Collindale Avenue
London NW9 5EQ
UK

John G Monroe
Department of Pathology and Laboratory Medicine
University of Pennsylvania School of Medicine
Hospital of the University of Pennsylvania
538A Clinical Research Building
415 Curie Boulevard
Philadelphia
Pennsylvania PA 19104-6142
USA

B Morein
Department of Veterinary Microbiology
Section of Virology
Biomedicum
Box 585, S-751
23 Uppsala
Sweden

Lorenzo Moretta
Istituto Nazionale per la Ricerca sul Cancro
Viale Benedetto XV
n10, 16132 Genoa
Italy

Richard A Morgan
Gene Transfer Technology Section
Clinical Gene Therapy Branch
National Center for Human Genome Research
NIH 9000
Rockville Pike
Bethesda
Maryland MD 20892
USA

Itaru Moro
Department of Pathology
Nihon University School of Dentistry
1-8-13 Kanda Surugadai
Chioda-ku
Tokyo
Japan

Peter J Morris
Nuffield Department of Surgery
University of Oxford
John Radcliffe Hospital
Headington
Oxford OX3 9DU
UK

Trudy G Morrison
Department of Molecular Genetics and Microbiology
University of Massachusetts Medical School
Worcester
Maryland MA 01655
USA

Subhash P Morzaria
International Livestock Research Institute
PO Box 30709
Nairobi
Kenya

Kamal D Moudgil
UCLA, Department of Microbiology and Molecular
Genetics
1602 Molecular Sciences Building
609 Circle Drive East
Los Angeles
California CA 90095-1489
USA

Nicholas A Moynihan
Center for Psychoneuroimmunology Research and the
Departments of Microbiology and Immunology and of
Psychiatry
University of Rochester Medical Center
601 Elmwood Avenue
Box 672
New York NY 14642
USA

Daniel L Mueller
University of Minnesota Medical School
Section of Rheumatology
Box 108
420 Delaware Street SE
Minnesota MN 55455
USA

R Allan Mufson
Department of Immunology
American Red Cross
Holland Laboratory
15601 Crabbs Branch Way
Rockville
Maryland MD 20855
USA

Reto Muggli
Department of Immunochemistry
Faculty of Pharmaceutical Sciences
Okayama
Japan

Peter F Mühlradt
Immunobiology Research Group
Gesellschaft fur Biotechnologische Forschung
Braunschweig
Germany

Andrew Muir
Department of Pathology and Laboratory Medicine
University of Florida College of Medicine
Gainesville
Florida
USA

Naofumi Mukaida
Department of Pharmacology
Cancer Research Institute
Kanazawa University
13-1 Tokara-Machi Kanazawa
Ishikawa 920
Japan

Allan Munck
Department of Physiology
Dartmouth Medical School
Lebanon NH 03756-0001
USA

Brendan F Murphy
Department of Nephrology
St Vincent's Hospital
41 Victoria Parade
Fitzroy 3065
Victoria
Australia

Timothy F Murphy
Department of Medicine
Division of Infectious Diseases
SUNY
Buffalo NY 14215
USA

Daniel M Musher
Department of Veterans Affairs Medical Center
Infectious Disease Section
Baylor College of Medicine
Houston
Texas TX 77030
USA

Lee M Nadler
Division of Hematologic Malignancies
Dana-Faber Cancer Institute
44 Binney Street
Boston
Massachusetts MA 02115
USA

Stanley Naguwa
Division of Rheumatology
Allergy and Clinical Immunology
School of Medicine
University of California
Davis
California CA 95616
USA

David Naor
The Lautenberg Center for General and Tumor
Immunology
The Hebrew University Hadassah Medical School
Jerusalem 91120
Israel

Anthony A Nash
Department of Veterinary Pathology
University of Edinburgh
Summerhall
Edinburgh EH9 1QH
UK

Inger B Natvig
Laboratory of Immunohistochemistry and
Immunopathology (LIIPAT)
University of Oslo
N-0027 Oslo
Norway

Guy Neild
Institute of Urology and Nephrology
UCL Hospitals
The Middlesex Hospital
Mortimer Street
London W1N 8AA
UK

Brad H Nelson
Virginia Mason Research Center
Department of Immunology
1124 Columbia Street
Seattle
Washington WA 98104
USA

David M Nelson
Gene Transfer Technology Section
Clinical Gene Therapy Branch
Maryland
USA

Ruth Neta
Office of International Health Programs
Department of Energy
EH-63, 270CC
19901 Germantown Road
Germantown
Maryland MD 20874-1290
USA

Diane G Newell
Central Veterinary Laboratory
New Haw
Addlestone
Surrey KT15 3NB
UK

John Newsom-Davis
Neurosciences Group
Institute of Molecular Medicine
John Radcliffe Hospital
Oxford OX3 9DU
UK

Lars-Åke Nilsson
Department of Medical Microbiology and Immunology
University of Goteborg
Guldhedsgatan 10
S-413 46 Goteburg
Sweden

Shin-Ichi Nishikawa
Department of Molecular Genetics
Faculty of Medicine
Kyoto University
Sakyo-ku, 606 Kyoto
Japan

WC Noble
Department of Microbial Diseases
The Institute of Dermatology
United Medical and Dental Schools of Guy's and St
Thomas' Hospitals
St Thomas Hospital
London SE1 7EH
UK

Shigeaki Nonoyama
Department of Pediatrics
School of Medicine
Tokyo Medical and Dental University
5-45 Yushima 1-Chome
Bunkyo-ku
Tokyo 113
Japan

David A Norris
Department of Dermatology
University of Colorado School of Medicine and Denver
Department of Veterans Affairs Hospital
4200 East 9th Avenue
Denver
Colorado CO 80262
USA

Hinnak Northoff
Abteilung Transfusionsmedizin
Eberhard-Karls-Universitat
Hoppe-Seyer-Strasse 3
D-72076 Tubingen
Germany

Jiri Novotny
Bristol-Myers Squibb Research Institute
PO Box 4000
Princeton
New Jersey NJ 08543-4000
USA

Michel C Nussenzweig
Laboratory of Molecular Immunology
The Howard Hughes Medical Institute
Rockefeller University
1230 York Avenue
Box 220
New York NY 10021-6399
USA

Thomas B Nutman
Laboratory of Parasitic Diseases
NIAID, NIH
Building 4
Bethesda
Maryland MD 20892-0425
USA

Urs E Nydegger
Central Laboratory of Haematology
Inselspital/University Hospital
CH3010 Berne
Switzerland

Hirohiko Onoyama
The First Department of Surgery
Kobe University School of Medicine
7-5-2 Kusunoki-cho
Kobe 650
Japan

Joost J Oppenheim
Laboratory of Molecular Immunoregulation
National Cancer Institute
Building 560
Room 21-89A
Frederick
Maryland MD 21702-1201
USA

Anders Örn
Microbiology and Tumor Biology Center
Karolinska Institute
Stockholm 60
S-10401
Sweden

Harry T Orr
Institute of Human Genetics
Box 198 UMHC
Harvard Street at East River Road
Minnesota MN 55455
USA

Catherine H Orteu
Department of Dermatology
The Royal Free Hospital
Pond Street
London NW3 2QG
UK

Carel van Oss
Department of Microbiology
School of Medicine
SUNY
Buffalo
New York
USA

Richard Ostlund Jr
Department of Internal Medicine
Metabolism Division
Washington University School of Medicine
Box 8127
660 South Euclid Avenue
St Louis
Missouri MO 63110
USA

Ørjan TG Ouchterlony
Department of Medical Microbiology and Immunology
University of Gotenborg
Guldhedsgatan 10
S413 46 Gotenborg
Sweden

Karen S Ovington
Division of Biochemistry and Microbiology
Faculty of Science
Australian National University
PO Box 4
Canberra ACT
Australia 2601

Shoichi Ozaki
Department of Medicine and Clinical Science
Kyoto University Graduate School of Medicine
54 Kawahara-cho
Shogoin
Sakyo-ku
Kyoto 606
Japan

Reinhard Pabst
Centre of Anatomy
Medical School of Hannover
D 30623 Hannover
Germany

Jacques Padawer
Department of Anatomy and Structural Biology
Albert Einstein College of Medicine
Yeshiva University, 1300 Morris Park Avenue
Bronx
New York NY 10461
USA

Theresa H Page
Kennedy Institute of Rheumatology
Sunley Division
Lurgan Avenue
Hammersmith
London W6 8LW
UK

Robert H Painter
Department of Biochemistry
University of Toronto
6 Hoskin Avenue
Toronto
Ontario M5S 1HB
Canada

Ekaterini Paizis
Department of Nephrology
St Vincent's Hospital
41 Victoria Parade
Fitzroy 3065
Victoria
Melbourne
Australia

George Panayotou
Ludwig Institute for Cancer Research
91 Riding House Street
London W1P 8BT
UK

William Pao
Department of Biology
Yale University
PO Box 6666
New Haven
Connecticut CT 06520
USA

Fotini Papavasiliou
Laboratory of Molecular Immunology
Rockefeller University
1230 York Avenue
Box 220
New York NY 10021-6399
USA

Raj B Parekh
Oxford Glycosystems
Blacklands Way
Abingdon OX14 1RG
UK

Linda S Park
Department of Biology
Immunex Corporation
5 University Street
Seattle
Washington WA 98101
USA

Robertson Parkman
Division of Research Immunology and Bone Marrow
Transplantation
Childrens Hospital of Los Angeles; University of
Southern California School of Medicine
4650 Sunset Boulevard
Mailstop #62
Los Angeles
California CA 90027
USA

David R Parks
Department of Genetics
Stanford University School of Medicine
Beckman Center B009
Stanford
California CA 94305-5125
USA

Jane R Parnes
Division of Immunology and Rheumatology
Department of Medicine
Stanford University Medical Center
S-021
Stanford
California CA 94306
USA

Paul-Pierre Pastoret
Department of Virology-Immunology
Faculty of Veterinary Medicine
University of Liege
B34, Sart Tilman
400 Liege
Belgium

Frederick L Pearce
Department of Chemistry
University College London
20 Gordon Street
London WC1H 0AJ
UK

Bente K Pedersen
Department of Infectious Diseases
Rigshospitalet
20 Tagensvej
2200 Copenhagen N
Denmark

W J Penhale
Institute of Molecular Genetics and Animal Disease
School of Veterinary Studies
Murdoch University
South Street
Murdoch
Western Australia 6150
Australia

Mark B Pepys
Immunological Medicine Unit
Department of Medicine
Royal Postgraduate Medical School
Hammersmith Hospital
Du Cane Road
London W12 0NN
UK

Benvenuto Pernis
Department of Microbiology
College of Microbiology
College of Physicians and Surgeons of Columbia
University
701 West 168th Street
New York NY 10032
USA

Charles M Perou
Division of Cell Biology and Immunology
Department of Pathology
Utah
USA

E Roy Pettipher
Central Research Division
Pfizer Inc.
Groton
Connecticut CT 06340
USA

Tom R Phillips
Department of Neuropharmacology
The Scripps Research Institute
10666 North Torrey Pines Road
La Jolla
California CA 92037
USA

Anthony J Pinching
Department of Immunology
St Bartholomew's and the Royal London School of
Medicine and Dentistry
London EC1A 7BE
UK

J L Pink
Pharma Research PRPN
F Hoffmann-La Roche Ltd
CH4002 Basel
Switzerland

Liise-Anne Pirofski
Department of Cell Biology
Albert Einstein College of Medicine
1300 Morris Park Avenue
Bronx
New York NY 10461
USA

Roberto J Poljak
Center for Advanced Research in Technology
9600 Gudelsky Drive
Rockville
Maryland MD 20850
USA

James S Porterfield
Formerly of the Sir William Dunn School of Pathology
University of Oxford
Oxford
UK

D Portetelle
Molecular Biology and Animal Physiology
Department
Bembloux University
13 Avenue Marechal Juin
B-5030 Gembloux
Belgium

Charalabos Pothoulakis
Beth Israel Deaconess Medical Center
Division of Gastroenterology
330 Brookline Avenue
Boston
Massachusetts MA 02215
USA

Kathleen N Potter
Southampton University Hospitals
Tenovus Laboratory
Tremona Road
Southampon
Hampshire SO16 6YD
UK

Jean-Louis Preud'homme
Laboratory of Immunology and Immunopathology
URA 1172 du CNRS
Central University Hospital
BP 577
86021 Poitiers Cedex
France

Joseph R Prohaska
Biochemistry and Molecular Biology
Office of Curricular Affairs
111 Medical School Building
School of Medicine
University of Minnesota
Duluth
Minnesota MN 55812-2487
USA

Juha Punnonen
Human Immunology Department
DNAX Research Institute
901 California Avenue
Palo Alto
California CA 94304-1104
USA

Michael A Purdy
Hepatitis Branch
Division of National Center for Infectious Diseases Viral
and Rickettsial Diseases
Atlanta
Georgia
USA

Anthony Quinn
UCLA, Department of Microbiology and Molecular
Genetics
1602 Molecular Sciences Building
609 Circle Drive East
Los Angeles
California CA 90095-1489
USA

Andreas Radbruch
Deutsches Rheuma-Forschengszentrum Berlin
Berlin
Germany

Claudia Raja-Gabaglia
UCLA, Department of Microbiology and Molecular
Genetics
1602 Molecular Sciences Building
609 Circle Drive East
Los Angeles
California CA 90095-1489
USA

Manoj Raje
Immunology Laboratory
Institute of Microbial Technology
Sector 39A
Chanigarh 160 014
India

Klaus Rajewsky
Institute for Genetics
University of Cologne
Weyertal 121
D-50931 Koln
Germany

Venkatesh Ramakrishna
Department of Membrane Research
The Weizmann Institute of Science
76100 Rehovot
Israel

Roger G Rank
Department of Microbiology and Immunology
University of Arkansas for Medical Sciences
4301 West Markham Street
Little Rock
Arkansas AR 72205
USA

Padmini Rao
Division of Hematologic Products
Center for Biologics Evaluation and Research/FDA
Building 29A, Room 3
8800 Rockville Pike
HFM-547
Bethesda
Maryland MD 208
USA

Norman A Ratcliffe
Biomedical and Physiological Research Group
School of Biological Sciences
University of Wales
Swansea
Singleton Park, Swansea SA2 8PP
UK

Jef CM Raus
Multiple Sclerosis Research and Immunology
Dr Wilems Institute
University Campus
D-3590 Diepenbeek
Belgium

Frank A Redegeld
Department of Pharmacology and Pathophysiology
Utrecht Institute of Pharmaceutical Sciences
Utrecht University
Utrecht
PO Box 80.082
The Netherlands

Yair Reisner
Department of Immunology
Weizmann Institute of Science
76100 Rehovot
Israel

Jack S Remington
Research Institute
Palo Alto Medical Foundation
860 Bryant Street
Palo Alto
California CA 94301
USA

Michael Reth
Max Planck Institute for Immunobiology
Stuebeweg 51
D79108 Freiburg
Germany

Wolfgang J Rettig
Department of Chemical Immunology
The Weizmann Institute of Science
76100 Rehovot
Israel

Janice Riberdy
Department of Immunology
St Jude Children's Research Hospital
332 North Lauderdale
PO Box 318
Memphis
Tennessee TN 38181-0318
USA

Rashika El Ridi
Zoology Department
Faculty of Science
University of Cairo
Cairo
Egypt

Richard L Riley
Department of Microbiology and Immunology
PO Box 016960 (R138)
University of Miami School of Medicine
Miami
Florida FL 33101
USA

Richard B Rimler
Avian and Swine Respiratory Diseases Research Unit
USDA/Agricultural Research Service/National Animal
Disease Center
2300 Dayton Road
Ames
Iowa IA 50010
USA

Lothar Rink
Institute of Immunology and Transfusion Medicine
University of Lubeck School of Medicine
Ratzeber Allee 160
D-23538 Lubeck
Germany

C Rittner
Institute for Legal Medicine of Johannes Gutenberg
Universitaet Mainz
Am Pulverturm 3
6500 Mainz
Germany

Dick L Robbins
Division of Rheumatology
Allergy and Clinical Immunology
Department of Internal Medicine
School of Medicine
University of California
Davis
California CA 95616
USA

Brian Robertson
Department of Medical Microbiology
Imperial College School of Medicine at St Mary's
Norfolk Place
Paddington
London W1 1PG
UK

Mary Ann Robinson
Laboratory of Immunogenetics
National Institutes of Health
Twinbrook 11 Room 217
12441 Parklawn Drive
Maryland MD 20852
USA

Eyvind Rødahl
Department of Ophthalmology
Haukeland Hospital
Bergen
Norway

Mario Roederer
Stanford University School of Medicine
Department of Genetics
Beckman Center B009
Stanford
California CA 94305-5125
USA

Thomas J Rogers
Department of Microbiology and Immunology
Temple University Medical School
3400 N Broad Street
Philadelphia PA 19140
USA

Marek Rola-Pleszczynski
Faculty of Medicine
Immunity Division
Universite de Sherbrooke
3001 12th Avenue North
Sherbrooke
Quebec J1H 5N4
Canada

N van Rooijen
Cell Biology and Immunology
Medical Faculty of Urije University
Amsterdam
The Netherlands

Graham W Rook
Department of Bacteriology
UCL Medical School
Windeyer Building
48 Cleveland Street
London W1P 6DB
UK

Ronald Rooke
Montreal Institute of Clinical Research
Immunology Laboratory
110 Ave des Pins ouest
Montreal
Quebec
Canada

Dirk Roos
Central Laboratory of the Netherlands Red Cross Blood
Transfusion Service and Laboratory for Experimental
and Clinical Immunology
Plesmanlaan 125
1066 CX Amsterdam
The Netherlands

Noel R Rose
Department of Molecular Microbiology and Immunology
Johns Hopkins University
615 North Wolfe Street
Baltimore
Maryland MD 21205
USA

Susan M Rosenberg
Department of Molecular and Human Genetics
Baylor College of Medicine
Houston
Texas
USA

Sanna Rosengren
Department of Immunology
Gensia Inc.
9360 Towne Center Drive
San Diego
California
USA

Gordon D Ross
Department of Pathology
Division of Experimental Immunology and
Immunopathology
University of Louiseville
Louiseville
Kentucky KY 40292-0001
USA

Adriano G Rossi
Respiratory Medicine Unit
Department of Medicine
University of Edinburgh
Edinburgh
UK

Ursula A Rother
Institute of Immunology
University of Heidelberg
Im Neuenheimer Feld 305
6900 Heidelberg
Germany

Klaus O Rother
Institute of Immunology
University of Heidelberg
Im Heuenheimer Feld 305
6900 Heidelberg
Germany

Robert Rothlein
Imperial Cancer Research Fund
Lincoln's Inn Fields
London
UK

Martn E Rottenberg
Microbiology and Tumor Biology Center
Karolinska Institute
Stockholm
Sweden

Martin Rowe
Department of Medicine
University of Wales
Tenovus Building
Heath Park
Cardiff CF4 4XX
UK

Lee Rowen
Department of Molecular Biotechnology
University of Washington
Seattle
Washington WA 98195-7730
USA

Nancy H Ruddle
Department of Epidemiology and Public Health
Yale University School of Medicine
60 College Street, PO Box 3333
New Haven
Connecticut CT 06510
USA

John H Russell
Department of Molecular Biology and Pharmacology
Washington University School of Medicine
St Louis
Missouri MO 63110
USA

Malcolm HA Rustin
Department of Dermatology
The Royal Free Hospital
Pond Street
London NW3 2QG
UK

Edward T Ryan
Harvard Medical School
Massachusetts General Hospital
Fruit Street
Boston
Massachussetts MA 02114
USA

Yoichi Saitoh
The First Department of Surgery
Kobe University School of Medicine
7-5-2 Kusunoki-cho
Kobe 650
Japan

Maria S Salvato
Pathology Department
University of Wisconsin Medical School
505 SMI, 1300 University Avenue
Madison
Wisconsin WI 53706
USA

Göran Sandberg
Lymphocyte Unit
Department of Neuroscience
Karolinska Institute
Doktorsringen 12
S-17177 Stockholm
Sweden

Colin J Sanderson
TVW Telethon Institute for Child Health Research
PO Box 855
West Perth 6872
Western Australia

Ian R Sanderson
Combined Program in Pediatric Gastroenterology and Nutrition
Massachusetts General Hospital
19-3404 13th Street
Charlestown
Massachussetts MA 02129-2060
USA

Daniela Santoli
The Wistar Institute
3601 Spruce Street
Philadelphia
Pennsylvania PA 19104
USA

Angela Santoni
Department of Experimental Medicine
University of Rome
School of Medicine
Vaile Regina Elena 324
Rome 00161
Italy

Juan Saus
Instituto de Investigaciones Citologicas de la Fundacion Valenciana de Investigaciones Biomedicas and Departamento de Bioqumica y Biologa Molecular de la Universitat de Valencia
ci Tologicas
c/Amadeo de Saboya 4
46010 Valencia
Spain

Glenis Scadding
Royal National Throat, Nose and Ear Hospital
Gray's Inn Road
London WC1X 8DA
UK

Andreas Schaffner
Clinical Mycology
Department of Medicine
University of Zurich
Rammistrasse 100
8091 Zurich
Switzerland

Konrad Schauenstein
Institute for Functional Pathology
Karl-Franzens University
Mozartgasse 14
8010 Graz
Austria

Ronald F Schell
Department of Medical Microbiology and Immunology
University of Wisconsin Medical School and Department of Bacteriology
Wisconsin State Laboratory of Hygiene
University of Wisconsin
465 Henry Mall, Madison
Wisconsin WA 53706
USA

Michael Schlesinger
The Hubert H Humphrey Center for Experimental Medicine and Cancer Research
The Hebrew University-Hadassah Medical School
PO Box 1172
Jerusalem
Israel

Jürgen Schmitz
Miltenyi Biotec GmbH
Friedrich-Ebert-Strasse 68
51429 Bergisch Gladbach
Germany

PM Schneider
Institute for Rhematology
Johannes Gutenberg University of Mainz
Am Pulverturm 3
D-55131 Mainz
Germany

Sussane C Schneider
UCLA, Department of Microbiology and Molecular Genetics
1602 Molecular Sciences Building
609 Circle Drive East
Los Angeles
California CA 90095-1489
USA

John W Schrader
The Biomedical Research Centre
2222 Health Sciences Mall, UBC
Vancouver
British Columbia V6T 1Z3
Canada

Alan D Schreiber
Department of Medicine
7 Silvester Building
Hospital of the University of Pennsylvania
Philadelphia PA 19119
USA

Thomas F Schulz
Department of Medical Microbiology and Genito-urinary
Medicine
The University of Liverpool
Duncan Building
Daulby Street
Liverpool L69 36A
UK

Ronald H Schwartz
Laboratory of Cellular and Molecular Immunology
NIAID, National Institutes of Health
Building 4, Room 11
Bethesda
Maryland MD 20892-0001
USA

Andrew M Scott
Ludwig Institute for Cancer Research and Austin and
Repatriation Medical Centre
University of Melbourne
Victoria
Australia

David W Scott
Department of Immunology
Holland Laboratory of the American Red Cross
15601 Crabbs Branch Way
Rockville
Maryland MD 20855
USA

John Seavitt
Howard Hughes Medical Institute
Box 8118
Center for Immunology and Department of Pathology
Washington University School of Medicine
660 S Euclid Avenue
St Louis
Missouri MO 63110-1093
USA

Jonathon D Sedgwick
Centenary Institute of Cancer Medicine and Cell Biology
Building 93
Royal Prince Alfred Hospital
Missenden Road
Camperdown
Sydney NSW 2050
Australia

Anthony W Segal
Department of Medicine
University College London
Rayne Institute
University Street
London WC1E 6JJ
UK

Rafick Pierre Sekaly
Montreal Institute of Clinical Research
Immunology Laboratory
110 Avenue des Pins Ouest
Montreal
Quebec H2W 1R
Canada

Michael Sela
Department of Chemical Immunology
The Weizmann Institute of Science
76100 Rehovot
Israel

Thomas A Selvaggi
Mucosal Immunity Section
National Institute of Allergy and Infectious Diseases
National Institutes of Health
Building 10, Room 11N238
Bethesda
Maryland MD 20892
USA

Richard D Semba
Department of Ophthalmology
Johns Hopkins University School of Medicine
615 North Wolfe Street
Baltimore
Maryland MD 21205
USA

Laura del Senno
Department of Biochemistry and Molecular Biology
University of Ferrera
Ferrera
Italy

Rho H Seong
Department of Molecular Biology
Institute for Molecular Biology and Genetics
Seoul National University
Seoul 151-742
Korea

Ilkka JT Seppälä
Department of Bacteriology and Immunology
University of Helsinki
Haartmaninkatu 3
00290 Helsinki
Finland

Eli E Sercarz
Department of Microbiology and Molecular Genetics
University of California
1602 Molecular Sciences Building
609 Circle Drive East
Los Angeles
California CA 90095-1489
USA

Roswitha Sgonc
Centre National de la Recherche Scientifique – UPR
420
Villejuif
France

Dennis Sgroi
Department of Pathology
Harvard Medical School
Massachusetts General Hospital
MGH East 7th Floor 149 13th Street
Charlestown
Massachussetts MA 02129
USA

Keerti V Shah
Department of Molecular Immunology
School of Hygiene and Public Health
The Johns Hopkins University
615 North Wolfe Street
Baltimore
Maryland MD 21205
USA

Uzma Shah
Combined Program in Pediatric Gastroenterology and
Nutrition
Massachusetts General Hospital
Massachusetts
USA

Michael E Shapiro
Harvard Medical School
Beth Israel Hospital
330 Brookline Avenue
Boston
Maryland MA 022115
USA

Nathan Sharon
The Weizmann Institute of Science
Department of Membrane Research and Biophysics
76100 Rehovot
Israel

Arlene H Sharpe
Department of Pathology
Division of Hematologic Malignancies
Dana-Farber Cancer Institute
Brigham and Women's Hospital
44 Binney Street
Boston
Maryland MA 02115
USA

Said M Shawar
R and D Department
SA Scientific
Baylor College of Medicine
De Bakey Building
One Baylor Plaza
Houston
Texas TX 77030
USA

C-R Shen
Department of Pathology and Microbiology
University of Bristol
The Medical School
University Walk
Bristol BS13 1TD
UK

Steven Sheriff
Macromolecular Crystallography
Bristol-Myers Squibb Pharmaceutical Research Institute
PO Box 4000
Princeton
New Jersey NJ 08543-4000
USA

AR Sherman
Department of Nutritional Sciences
Cook College
Rutgers, The State University of New Jersey
PO Box 231
New Brunswick
New Jersey NJ 08903-0231
USA

Ethan M Shevach
Laboratory of Immunology
National Institute of Allergy and Infectious Diseases
National Institutes of Health
Building 10, Room 11N315
Bethesda
Maryland MD 20892-1892
USA

Yogi Shimizu
Department of Laboratory Medicine and Pathology
Centre for Immunology
University of Minnesota Medical School
7-132 PWB
Box 609 UMHC
420 Delaware Street
Minneapolis 55455
USA

Meir Shinitzky
Department of Membrane Research
The Weizmann Institute of Science
76100 Rehovot
Israel

Nobukata Shinohara
Mitsubishi-Kasei Institute of Life Science
11 Minamioya Machida-shi
Tokyo
Japan 194

Yehuda Shoenfeld
Department of Medicine 'B' and the Research Unit of
Autoimmune Diseases
Sheba Medical Center
Tel-hasomer 52621
Tel-Aviv
Israel

Adrian Shuttleworth
School of Biological Sciences
University of Manchester
Wellcome Trust Centre for Cell/Matrix Research
2.205 Stopford Building
Oxford Road
Manchester M13 9PT
UK

Karol Sikora
Department of Clinical Oncology
Royal Postgraduate Medical School
Hammersmith Hospital
Du Cane Road
London W12 0NN
UK

David S Silberstein
Zeneca Pharmaceuticals
1800 concord Pike
PO Box 15437
Wilmington
Delaware 19850-5437
USA

Robert B Sim
MRC Immunochemistry Unit and Department of
Biochemistry
University of Oxford
South Parks Road
Oxford OX1 3QU
UK

Petia P Simeonova
Toxicology and Molecular Biology Branch
Health Effects Laboratory
1095 Willowdale Road
Mailstop L3014
Morgantown
West Virginia WV 26505
USA

Elizabeth Simpson
Transplantation Biology Group
MRC Clinical Sciences Centre
RPMS
Hammersmith Hospital
Du Cane Road
London W12 0NN
UK

Nicholas StC Sinclair
Department of Microbiology and Immunology
The University of Western Ontario
London
Ontario N6A 5C1
Canada

Francesco Sinigaglia
Roche Milano Ricerche Pharma Research Technology
via Olgettina 58
1-20132 Milano
Italy

Reuben P Siraganian
Receptors and Signal Transduction Section
Laboratory of Immunology
National Institutes of Health
Building 10
Bethesda
Maryland MD 20892
USA

Stitaya Sirisinha
Department of Microbiology
Faculty of Science
Mahidol University
Roma VI Road
Bangkok 10400
Thailand

JG Patrick Sissons
Department of Medicine
University of Cambridge Clinical School
Level 5, Addenbrooke's Hospital (Box 157)
Hills Road
Cambridge BB2 2QQ
UK

Roberto Sitia
DIBIT HSR – San Raffaele Scientific Institute
via Olgettina 58
20132 Milan
Italy

RJT Smeenk
Central Laboratory of the Netherlands Red Cross
Blood Transfusion Service
Diagnostics Department
Plesmaniaan 125
1066 CX Amsterdam
The Netherlands

Stephen T Smiley
Department of Cancer Biology
Harvard School of Public Health
665 Huntingdon Avenue
Boston
Maryland MA 02115
USA

Taede Sminia
Department of Cell Biology
Medical Faculty of Vrije University
vd Bocchhozstraat 7
1011 BT Amsterdam
The Netherlands

Ian KM Smith
Department of Veterinary Pathology and Infectious
Diseases
The Royal Veterinary College
356 Knights Field
Welwyn Garden City
London AL8 7NG
UK

J Cecil Smith
Phytonutrients Laboratory
Beltsville Human Nutrition Research Center
Agricultural Research Service
US Department of Agriculture
Beltsville
Maryland MD 20705
USA

KGC Smith
Department of Medicine
University of Cambridge
Cambridge
UK

Michael C Sneller
Immunologic Diseases Section
National Institute of Allergy and Infectious Diseases
National Institute of Health
Building 10, Room 11B13
Bethesda
Maryland MD 20892-0001
USA

Edward L Snyder
Yale University School of Medicine
Blood Bank/Apheresis Service
Yale-New Haven Hospital20 York Street
New Haven
Connecticut CT 06504
USA

Morten Sögaard
Pharmacia & Upjohn
Lund Research Center
Box 724
S-22007 Lund
Sweden

Peter G Sohnie
Research Service/151
VA Medical Center
Milwaukee
Wisconsin WI 53295
USA

Anne Sperling
Committee on Immunology
The Ben May Institute
University of Chicago
5841 S, Maryland
Chicago
Illinois IL 60637
USA

Jonathan Sprent
Department of Immunology
The Scripps Research Institute
10666 North Torrey Pines Road
La Jolla
California CA 92037
USA

Ivan Stamenkovic
Department of Pathology
Harvard Medical School
Massachusetts General Hospital
MGH East 7th Floor
149 13th Street
Charlestown
Massachusetts MA 02129
USA

E Richard Stanley
Department of Developmental and Molecular Biology
Albert Einstein College of Medicine
1300 Morris Park Avenue
Bronx
New York NY 10461
USA

Abram B Stavitsky
Department of Molecular Biology and Microbiology
Case Western Reserve University School of Medicine
10900 Euclid Avenue
Cleveland
Ohio OH 44106-4960
USA

John Stephen
Microbial Molecular Genetics and Cell Biology Group
School of Biological Sciences
The University of Birmingham
PO Box 363
Birmingham B15 2TT
UK

David B Stevens
Santa Clara Valley Medical Center
751 South Boscom Avenue
San Jose
California CA 95128-2699
USA

David B Stevens
UCLA Department of Microbiology and Molecular
Genetics
University of California
1602 Molecular Sciences Building
609 Circle Drive East
California CA 90095-1489
USA

George T Stevenson
Lymphoma Research Unit
Tenovus Research Laboratory
Southampton University Hospital
Tremona Road
Southampton SO9 4XY
UK

Patrick J Stiff
Bone Marrow Transplant Program
Loyola University Medical Center
2160 South First Avenue
Maywood
Illinois IL 60153
USA

Hannes Stockinger
Institute of Immunology
University of Vienna
A-1235 Vienne
Brunner Strasse 59
Brunner
Austria

B David Stollar
Department of Biochemistry
Tufts University School of Medicine
136 Harrison Avenue
Boston
Massachusetts MA 02111-1800
USA

Rainer Storb
University of Washington School of Medicine and
Clinical Research Division
Fred Hutchinson Cancer Research Center
1124 Columbia Street, Seattle
Washington WA 98104
USA

David C Straus
Department of Microbiology and Immunology
School of Medicine
Texas Tech University Health Sciences Center
Lubbock
Texas TX 79430
USA

J Wayne Streilein
President and Director of Research
The Schepens Eye Research Institute
Department of Ophthalmology
20 Staniford Street
Boston
Massachusetts MA 02114-2500
USA

Timothy J Sullivan
Department of Medicine
Emory University School of Medicine
1365 Clifton Road NE,
Atlanta
Georgia GA 30322
USA

Charles D Surh
Department of Immunology IMM4
The Scripps Research Institute
10666 North Torrey Pines Road
La Jolla
California CA 92037
USA

Richard H Sutton
Department of Veterinary Pathology
University of Queensland
Queensland 4072
Australia

Yasuhiro Suzuki
Research Institute
Palo Alto Medical Foundation
860 Bryant Street
Palo Alto
California CA 94301
USA

Catharina Svanborg
Department of Medical Microbiology
Lund University
Section of Clinical Immunology
Solvegatan 23
S-223 62 Lund
Sweden

Robert H Swanborg
Department of Immunology and Microbiology
Wayne State University School of Medicine
Detroit
Michigan MI 48201
USA

Andras K Szakal
Department of Anatomy, Division of Immunobiology
Medical College of Virginia
Virginia Commonwealth University
MCV Station
PO Box 709
Richmond
Virginia VA 233298-0709
USA

Kiyoshi Takatsu
Department of Immunology
Tokyo Metropolitan Institute of Medical Science
University of Tokyo
4-6-1 Shirokanedai
Minato-ku
Tokyo 108
Japan

GP Talwar
International Centre for Genetic Engineering and
Biotechnology
Aruna Asaf Ali Marg
New Delhi 110 067
India

David M Tarlinton
The Walter and Eliza Hall Institute of Medical Research
Post Office Royal Melbourne Hospital
Victoria 3050
Australia

Arne Tärnvik
Department of Infectious Diseases
University of Umeå
S-901 85 Umeå
Umeå
Sweden

Dennis D Taub
Clinical Services Program
National Cancer Institute – Frederick Cancer Research
and Development Center
Box 21, 4940 Eastern Avenue
Baltimore
Maryland MD 21224-2780
USA

David G Telander
University of Minnesota Medical School
Section of Rheumatology
Box 108, 420 Delaware Street SE
Minnesota MN 55455
USA

Paul I Terasaki
UCLA Tissue Typing Laboratory
Department of Surgery
UCLA School of Medicine
950 Veteran Avenue
Los Angeles
California CA 90024-1652
USA

Therese Ternynck
Department of Immunology
Pasteur Institute
28 rue du Dr Roux
75724 Paris Cedex 15
France

Risto Tertti
Department of Medicine
Helsinki University Central Hospital
Helsinki
Finland

John G Tew
Department of Anatomy
Division of Immunobiology
Medical College of Virginia
Virginia Commonwealth University
MCV Station
PO Box 609
Richmond
Virginia VA 233298-0709
USA

Yasmin Thanavala
Department of Molecular Immunology
Roswell Park Cancer Institute
666 Elm Street
Buffalo
New York NY 14263
USA

Argyrios N Theofilopoulos
Immunology Department
Research Institute of Scripps Clinic
10666 North Torrey Pines Road
La Jolla
California CA 92037
USA

S Theus
Department of Veterans Affairs
Medical Center
3200 Vine Street
Cincinnati
Ohio OH 45220
USA

Jacques Théze
Pasteur Institute
Unite d'Immunogenetique Cellulaire
28 rue du Dr Roux
75724 Paris Cedex 15
France

Howard C Thomas
Department of Medicine
Imperial College of Medicine
University of London
South Kensington
London SW7 2AZ
UK

Matthew L Thomas
Howard Hughes Medical Institute
Center for Immunology and Department of Pathology
Washington University
St Louis
Missouri
USA

Amy H Thompson
Department of Microbiology and Immunology
University of South Carolina
171 Ashley Avenue
Charleston
South Carolina SC 29425-2230
USA

Craig B Thompson
Department of Medicine
Section of Hematology-Oncology
University of Chicago
924 E 57th Street
R413 A
Chicago
Illinois IL 60637-5420
USA

Glenys Thomson
Department of Integrative Biology
University of California
Berkeley
California CA 94720
USA

Robin Thorpe
Division of Immunobiology
National Institute for Biological Standards and Control
Blanche Lane
South Mimms
Potters Barr
Hertfordshire EN6 3QG
UK

Ian R Tizard
Department of Veterinary Pathobiology
The Texas Veterinary Medical Center
Texas A and M University
College Station
Texas TX 77843-4467
USA

Auli Toivanen
Department of Medicine
Turku University
Turku
Finland

Paavo Toivanen
Department of Medical Microbiology
Turku University
Kiinamyllynkatu 13
SF-20520 Turku
Finland

Ian M Tomlinson
Medical Research Council Centre for Protein
Engineering
Hills Road
Cambridge CB2 2QH
UK

Annick Tournefier
Laboratoire d'Immunologie Comparee
Universite de Bourgogne
6 Boulevard Gabriel
21000 Dijon
France

Harry Towbin
Novartis Pharma Inc.
Pharmaceuticals Research Laboratory
Building K-681.546
4002 Basel
Switzerland

Joseph A Trapani
The Austin Research Institute
Studley Road
Heidelberg
Victoria 3084
Australia

Ilja Trebichavsky
Section of Immunology and Gnotobiology
Institute of Microbiology
Czech Academy of Sciences
Videnska 1083
Novy Hradek
14220 Praha 4
Czech Republic

Ralph A Tripp
St Jude's Children's Research Hospital
Memphis
Tennessee
USA

Jurg Tschopp
Institute of Biochemistry
University of Lausanne
Chemin des Boveresses 155
1066 Epalinges
Switzerland

Alan Tunnacliffe
Anglia Research Foundation
School of Applies Sciences
Anglia Polytechnic
University East Road
Cambridge CB2 1PT
UK

John L Turk
Department of Pathology
The Royal College of Surgeons of England
35–43 Lincoln's Inn Fields
London WC2A 3PN
UK

Peter CB Turnbull
Centre for Applied Microbiology and Research
Division of Biologics
Porton Down
Salisbury
Wiltshire SP4 0JG
UK

C Michael R Turner
Division of Infection and Immunity
Institute of Biomedical and Life Science
Joseph Black Building
University of Glasgow
Glasgow G12 8QQ
UK

Saul Tzipori
Department of Comparative Medicine
Division of Infectious Diseases
Tufts University School of Veterinary Medicine
North Grafton
Massachusetts MA 0153
USA

Stephen E Ullrich
Department of Immunology
University of Texas
M.D. Anderson Cancer Center
Houston
Texas TX 77030
USA

Emil R Unanue
Department of Pathology and Center for Immunology
Washington University School of Medicine
Box 8118
660 South Euclid Avenue
St Louis
Missouri MO 63110
USA

Brian J Underdown
Pasteur Merieux Connaught Canada Research Centre
Department of Pathology
Faculty of Health Sciences
McMaster University
1200 Main Street
Hamilton
Ontario L8N 3Z5
Canada

Olli Vainio
Department of Medical Microbiology
University of Turku
Turku
Finland

Daniel Vallera
Department of Pediatrics
University of Minnesota Hospital and Clinics
Minnesota
Minneapolis
USA

Gerardo R Vasta
Center of Marine Biotechnology
Suite 236
Columbus Center
701 E Pratt Street
Baltimore
Maryland MD 21202
USA

PJW Venables
The Mathilda and Terence Kennedy Institute of
Rheumatology
Kennedy Building
London
UK

Jan Verhoef
Eijkman-Winkler Institute for Microbiology
Infectious Diseases & Inflammation
University Hospital
Room G04 515
Heidelbergiaan 100
3584 CX Utrecht
The Netherlands

Morton N Verreck
Department of Immunohematology and Blood Bank
Building 1, E3-Q
Academisch Ziekennhuis Leiden
PO Box 9600
2300 RC Leiden
The Netherlands

Keith Vickerman
Division of Environmental and Evolutionary Biology
Institute of Biomedical and Life Science
University of Glasgow
Glasgow G12 8QQ
UK

Jan Vilček
Department of Microbiology
New York University Medical Center
550 First Avenue
New York NY 10016
USA

Angela Vincent
Neurosciences Group
Institute of Molecular Medicine
John Radcliffe Hospital
Oxford OX3 9DU
UK

Carl-Wilhelm Vogel
Department of Biochemistry and Molecular Biology
Institute of Biochemistry and Food Chemistry
University of Hamburg
Martin Luther King Pl 6
D-20146 Hamburg
Germany

Edward W Voss
Department of Microbiology
Chemical and Life Sciences Laboratory
University of Illinois at Urbana-Champaign
131 Burrill Hall
407 South Goodwin Avenue
Urbana
Illinois IL 61801
USA

Frank AW Wagner
Research SErvice/151
VA Medical Center
Milwaukee
Wisconsin WI 53295
USA

Derek Wakelin
Department of Life Science
University of Nottingham
University Park
Nottingham NG7 2RD
UK

Herman Waldmann
Immunology Division
Sir William Dunn School of Pathology
South Parks Road
Oxford OX1 3RE
UK

John L Wallace
Department of Pharmacology and Therapeutics
Faculty of Medicine
University of Calgory
3330 Hospital Drive NW
Calgary
Alberta
Canada

David Wallach
Department of Membrane Research and Biophysics
The Weizmann Institute of Science
Rehovot 76100
Israel

Peter D Walzer
Department of Veterans Affairs
Medical Center
3200 Vine Street
Cincinnati
Ohio OH 45220
USA

Denong Wang
Department of Microbiology
College of Physicians and Surgeons of Columbia
University
701 West 168th St
Room 1412
New York NY 10032
USA

Stephen G Ward
Department of Pharmacology
School of Pharmacy and Pharmacology
University of Bath
Claverton Down
Bath
Avon
UK

H Shaw Warren
Infectious Diseases Unit
Massachusetts General Hospital East
5th Floor, 149 13th Street
Charlestown
Massachusetts MA 12129
USA

Aan H Waters
Department of Haematology
St Bartholomew's Hospital
London EC1A 7BE
UK

Jennifer A Waters
Department of Medicine
Imperial College of Medicine
St Mary's Hospital
South Kensington
London SW7 2AZ
UK

David I Watkins
Wisconsin Regional Primate Research Center and
Department of Pathology and Laboratory Medicine
University of Wisconsin
1220 Capital CT
Madison
Wisconsin WI 53719-1299
USA

David K Watson
Genentech Inc
460 Point
San Bruno Boulevard
South San Francisco
California CA 94080
USA

Ronald R Watson
Department of Family and Community Medicine
University of Arizona College of Medicine
Health Science Center
1501 N Campbell AvenueTucson
Arizona AZ 85724-001
USA

David R Webb
Institute of Immunology and Biological Sciences
Cadus Pharmaceutical Corporation
777 Old Saw Mill River Road
Tarrytown
New York NY 10591-6705
USA

Georg F Weber
Harvard Medical School and Laboratory of
Immunopathology
Dana-Farber Cancer Institute
44 Binney Street
Boston
Massachusetts MA 02115
USA

A David B Webster
Department of Clinical Immunology
MRC Immunodeficiency Research Group
Royal Free Hospital School of Medicine
Pond Street
London NW3 2QG
UK

Stephanie K Webster
MRC Immunodeficiency Research Group
Department of Clinical Immunology
Royal Free Hospital School of Medicine
Pond Street
London NW3 2QG
UK

Alain de Weck
Gerimmun Foundation
Allergy Research Laboratory
Fribourg
Switzerland

Anthony P Weetman
Department of Medicine
University of Sheffield Clinical Services Centre
Northern General Hospital
Sheffield S5 7AU
UK

Helmut Wege
Institut fur Virusdiagnostik
Federal Research Centre for Virus Diseases of Animals
Friedrich-Loeffler-Institute
17498 Insel Riems
Germany

Xiaohua Wei
Institute of Human Genetics
Minneapolis
Minnesota
USA

William O Weigle
Department of Immunology
The Scripps Research Institute
10666 North Torrey Pines Road
La Jolla
California CA 92037
USA

Howard L Weiner
Center for Neurologic Diseases
Brigham and Women's Hospital and Harvard Medical
School
221 Longwood Avenue
Boston
Massachusetts MA 02115-5817
USA

Raymond M Welsh
Department of Pathology
University of Massachusetts Medical Center
55 Lake Avenue North
Worcester
Massachusetts MA 01655-0125
USA

Jurgen Westermann
Babraham Institute
Babraham
Cambridge
UK

John T Whicher
School of Medicine
University of Leeds
Leeds LS2 9LN
UK

Theresa L Whiteside
Department of Pathology
University of Pittsburgh Cancer Institute
211 Lothrop Street, W1041 BST
Pittsburgh PA 15213-2582
USA

Senga Whittingham
Centre for Molecular Biology and Medicine
Monash University
Clayton
Victoria 3168
Australia

Konrad Wicher
New York State Department of Health
Wadsworth Center for Laboratories and Research
120 New Scotland Avenue
Albany
New York NY 12208
USA

Victoria Wicher
New York State Department of Health
Wadsworth Center for Laboratories and Research
120 New Scotland Avenue
Albany
New York NY 12208
USA

Georg Wick
Institute for General and Experimental Pathology
University of Innsbruck
Fritz-Pregl-Strasse 3/IV
A-6020 Innsbruck
Austria

Meir Wilchek
AFRC Institute for Animal Health
Pirbright Laboratory
Ash Road
Pirbright
Woking
Surrey GU24 0NF
UK

Peter C Wilkinson
Department of Immunology
University of Glasgow (Western Infirmary)
Glasgow G11 6NT
UK

Philip J Wilkinson
Institute for Animal Health
AFRC
Pirbright Laboratory
Ash Road
Pirbright
Working
Surrey GU24 0NF
UK

L Willems
Department of Molecular Biology and Animal
Physiology
Gembloux Faculte University
Belgium

Ifor R Williams
Department of Dermatology
Brigham and Women's Hospital
Harvard Medical School
75 Francis Street
Massachusetts MA 02115
USA

Thomas E Willnow
Max-Delbruck Center for Molecular Medicine
Berlin
Germany

Graeme Wistow
Section on Molecular Structure and Function
LMDB, National Eye Institute
Building 6, Room 222
National Institutes of Health
Bethesda
Maryland MD 20892-2730
USA

Gayle E Woloschak
Center for Mechanistic Biology and Biotechnology
Argonne National Laboratory
Illinois
USA

Robert G Wood
Department of Microbiology and Immunology
The University of Arizona
Health Sciences Center
Tuscon
Arizona AZ 94724
USA

Robert T Woodland
Department of Molecular Genetics and Microbiology
University of Massachusetts Medical Center
55 Lake Avenue North
Worcester
Massachusetts MA 01655-0125
USA

Jerold G Woodward
Department of Microbiology and Immunology
University of Kentucky Medical Center
MS 415 UKMC
Lexington
Kentucky KY 40536-0084
USA

Bao-Guo Xiao
Division of Neurology
Karolinska Institutet
Huddinge Hospital
S-141 86 Huddinge
Stockholm
Sweden

Nobuto Yamamoto
Laboratory of Cancer Immunology and Molecular
Biology
Albert Einstein Cancer Center
Korman Pavilion B-31
5501 Old York Road
Pennsylvania PA 19141
USA

Yu-Chung Yang
Departments of Medicine (Hematology/Oncology) and
Biochemistry/Molecular Biology and Walther Oncology
Center
Indiana University School of Medicine
975 W Walnut Street
Indiana IN 46202-5121
USA

Jun-ichi Yata
Department of Pediatrics
School of Medicine
Tokyo Medical and Dental University
5-45 Yushima 1-Chome
Bunkyo-ku
Tokyo 113
Japan

Ji-Won Yoon
Department of Microbiology and Infectious Diseases
Julia McFarlane Diabetes Research Centre
Suwon
Korea

Yasunobu Yoshikai
Laboratory of Host Defense
Research Institute for Disease Mechanism and Control
Nagoya University School of Medicine
65 Tsuramai, Showa-ku
Nagoya 466
Japan

P Y Youinou
Department of Immunology
Brest University Medical School
Brest
France

John Ding-E Young
Laboratory of Cellular Physiology and Immunology
The Rockefeller University
New York
USA

NS Young
Clinical Hematology Branch
National Heart Lung and Blood Institute
900 Rockville Pike
Bethesda
Maryland MD 20892
USA

Theodore J Yun
Department of Microbiology
University of Washington Medical Center
1059 NE Pacific
Box 357342
Seattle
Washington WA 98195-0001
USA

Edmond J Yunis
Division of Immunogenetics
Harvard Medical School
Dana-Farber Cancer Institute
44 Binney Street
Boston
Massachusetts MA 02115
USA

John B Zabriskie
The Rockefeller University
1230 York Avenue
New York NY 10021-6399
USA

Claus OC Zachariae
Department of Haematology
Herlev Hospital
University of Copenhagen
Denmark

John Zagorski
Oral Infection and Immunity Research
National Institute of Dental Research
Maryland
USA

Maurice Zauderer
Immunology Division, Cancer Center
University of Rochester Medical Center
601 Elmwood Avenue
Box 704
Rochester
New York NY 14642
USA

Rainer Zawatzky
German Cancer Research Centre
Institute for Virus Research/ATV
Heidelberg
Germany

Rudolf H Zubler
Department of Medicine
Division of Hematology
Hospital Cantonal University
CH-1211 Geneva 4
Switzerland

CONTENTS

VOLUME 1

A

ABO BLOOD GROUP SYSTEM   *Anatole Lubenko, Marcela Contreras*   1

ACQUIRED IMMUNE DEFICIENCY SYNDROME (AIDS)   *Anthony J Pinching*   6

ACQUIRED IMMUNE RESPONSE   *Anne Sperling, Jeffrey A Bluestone*   13

ACUTE INFLAMMATORY REACTION   *Sanna Rosengren*   15

ACUTE PHASE PROTEINS   *Mark B Pepys*   18

ADENOVIRUS, INFECTION AND IMMUNITY   *Liise-Anne Pirofski, Marshall S Horwitz*   21

ADHESION MOLECULES   *Margaret A Adelsman, Yoji Shimizu*   26

ADJUVANT ARTHRITIS   *Irun R Cohen*   33

ADJUVANTS   *H Shaw Warren, Claude Leclerc*   36

ADRENAL AUTOIMMUNITY   *Pierluigi E Bigazzi*   39

AFFINITY   *Bertrand Friguet, Lisa Djavadi-Ohaniance, Michel E Goldberg*   43

AFFINITY CHROMATOGRAPHY   *George L Mayers, Carel van Oss*   47

AFFINITY LABELING   *David Givol, Meir Wilchek*   50

AFFINITY MATURATION   *Klaus Rajewsky*   52

AFRICAN SWINE FEVER   *Michael S Denyer, Philip J Wilkinson*   54

AGGLUTINATION   *Abram B Stavitsky*   56

AGING AND THE IMMUNE SYSTEM   *Bernhard Cinader*   59

ALLELIC EXCLUSION   *Michael Reth*   62

ALLERGENS   *Martin D Chapman*   64

ALLOANTIGENS   *Dhirendra N Misra, Heinz W Kunz, Thomas Gill III*   70

ALLOTYPES, IMMUNOGLOBULIN   *Royston Jefferis*   74

AMEBIASIS   *John P Ackers*   77

AMPHIBIAN IMMUNE SYSTEM   *Jacques Charlemagne, Annick Tournefier*   79

AMYLOID   *Alan S Cohen*   84

ANAPHYLATOXINS   *Clemens A Dahinden*   86

ANEMIA, AUTOIMMUNE HEMOLYTIC IN ANIMAL MODELS   *C J Elson, C-R Shen*   91

ANEMIA, AUTOIMMUNE HEMOLYTIC IN HUMAN   *Alan D Schreiber*   94

ANEMIA, DRUG-INDUCED IMMUNE HEMOLYTIC   *Alan H Waters*   99

ANEMIA, PERNICIOUS   *Senga Whittingham*   101

ANERGY, B CELL   *David M Tarlinton*   105

ANERGY, T CELL   *Ronald H Schwartz*   109

ANNEXINS (LIPOCORTINS)   *Fusao Hirata*   111

ANTI-GLOBULIN (COOMBS') TEST   *Nevin Hughes-Jones*   115

ANTI-INFLAMMATORY (NONSTEROIDAL) DRUGS   *John L Wallace*   117

ANTI-LYMPHOCYTE SERUM   *Göran Sandberg*   121

ANTI-NUCLEAR ANTIBODIES   *RJT Smeenk, TEW Feltkamp*   125

ANTI-OXIDANT MICRONUTRIENTS AND THE IMMUNE SYSTEM   *Adrianne Bendich*   133

ANTIBODIES: ANTIGENICITY OF   *Felix Milgrom*   136

ANTIBODIES, BISPECIFIC   *Constantin A Bona*   138

ANTIBODIES, DETECTION OF   *Michael A Kerr*   141

ANTIBODIES, SECRETION   *Roberto Sitia*   144

ANTIBODIES, SPECIFICITY   *Denong Wang, Elvin Kabat*   148

ANTIBODIES, SYNTHESIS   *Fritz Melchers*   154

ANTIBODY–ANTIGEN COMPLEXES, THREE-DIMENSIONAL STRUCTURES   *Steven Sheriff*   159

ANTIBODY–ANTIGEN INTERMOLECULAR FORCES   *Carel van Oss*   163

ANTIBODY-DEPENDENT CELLULAR CYTOTOXICITY   *Jorge Raúl Geffner*   168

ANTIGEN-BINDING SITE   *Bradford C Braden, Roberto J Poljak*   171

ANTIGEN-PRESENTING CELLS   *Emil R Unanue*   174

ANTIGEN-SPECIFIC CELLS: ENRICHMENT AND ISOLATION   *KGC Smith, JE Layton, DM Tarlinton*   178

ANTIGEN CLEARANCE   *Anthony Cutler, Kevin A Davies*   182

ANTIGEN, ENTRY INTO THE BODY   *Taede Sminia, Georg Kraal*   188

ANTIGEN PRESENTATION VIA MHC CLASS I MOLECULES   *Emil R Unanue*   191

ANTIGEN PRESENTATION VIA MHC CLASS II MOLECULES   *Emil R Unanue*   194

ANTIGENIC VARIATION   *Janice E Clements, Susan L Gdovin*   199

ANTIGENS   *Michael Sela*   201

ANTIGENS, CELL SURFACE   *Wolfgang J Rettig*   207

ANTIGENS, T DEPENDENT AND INDEPENDENT   *Rudolf H Zubler*   214

ANTISERUM   *Yasmin Thanavala*   218

APOPTOSIS   *Seamus J Martin*   220

ARACHIDONIC ACID AND THE LEUKOTRIENES   *Marek Rola-Pleszczynski*   228

ARENAVIRUS, INFECTION AND IMMUNITY   *Maria S Salvato, Igor S Lukashevich*   232

ARGININE AND IMMUNITY   *Stephen J Kirk, Adrian Barbul*   235

ARTHUS REACTION   *Paul G Hellewell, Adriano G Rossi*   237

ASCARIASIS   *Malcolm W Kennedy*   241

ASTHMA   *David M Essayan*   243

ATAXIA TELANGIECTASIA   *Richard A Gatti*   247

ATOPIC ALLERGY   *Glenis Scadding*   251

ATTENUATED ORGANISMS AS VACCINES   *Konstantin M Chumakov*   255

AUTOANTIBODIES, TESTS FOR   *C Lynne Burek*   260

AUTOANTIGENS   *Ian R Mackay*   266

AUTOIMMUNE DISEASE, INDUCED ANIMAL MODELS   *W J Penhale*   270

AUTOIMMUNE DISEASE, PATHOGENESIS   *Konrad Schauenstein*   275

AUTOIMMUNE DISEASE, SPONTANEOUS ANIMAL MODELS   *Georg Wick, Roswitha Sgonc, Guido
   Kroemer*   280

AUTOIMMUNE DISEASES   *Ian R Mackay*   287

AUTOIMMUNITY   *Peter J Delves*   292

AUTORADIOGRAPHY   *Manoj Raje, Gyan C Mishra*   296

AVIAN IMMUNE SYSTEM   *J L Pink, Olli Vainio*   300

B

B7 (CD80 AND CD86)   *Gordon J Freeman, Vassiliki A Boussiotis, John G Gribben, Arlene H Sharpe, Lee M Nadler*   304

BABESIOSIS   *Jeffrey A Gelfand, Michael V Callahan*   308

BACILLUS, INFECTION AND IMMUNITY   *Brian W McBride, Peter CB Turnbull*   311

BACTERIA, IMMUNITY TO   *Graham AW Rook*   315

BACTERIAL CELL WALLS   *Alan Cockayne*   320

BACTERIAL IMMUNOGLOBULIN-BINDING PROTEINS   *Michael DP Boyle*   323

BACTEROIDES, INFECTION AND IMMUNITY   *Michael E Shapiro*   327

BARE LYMPHOCYTE SYNDROME   *Janice S Blum*   329

BASOPHILS   *Reuben P Siraganian*   332

BCG   *Jacob George, Michael Alkan, Yehuda Shoenfeld*   335

BEHAVIORAL REGULATION OF IMMUNITY   *Nicholas Cohen, Jan A Moynihan, Robert Ader*   336

BENCE JONES PROTEINS   *Jean-Louis Preud'homme*   341

BIOZZI MICE   *Gino Doria*   342

BLOOD TRANSFUSION REACTIONS   *C Paul Engelfriet*   346

B LYMPHOCYTE ACTIVATION   *Hajime Karasuyama, Kiyoshi Takatsu*   349

B LYMPHOCYTE ANTIGEN PROCESSING AND PRESENTATION   *Nobumichi Hozumi*   352

B LYMPHOCYTE DIFFERENTIATION   *John H Kehrl*   355

B LYMPHOCYTE REPERTOIRE   *Phyllis-Jean Linton*   359

B LYMPHOCYTES   *B David Stollar*   363

β_2-MICROGLOBULIN   *Rho H Seong, Jane R Parnes*   367

bm MUTANTS   *Roger W Melvold*   371

BONE MARROW AND HEMATOPOIESIS   *David C Linch*   374

BORDETELLA, INFECTION AND IMMUNITY   *Gwendolyn E Wood, Richard L Friedman*   377

BORRELIA, INFECTION AND IMMUNITY   *Ronald F Schell, Steven M Callister*   379

BRUCELLA, INFECTION AND IMMUNITY   *Christina Cheers*   383

BRUTON'S AGAMMAGLOBULINEMIA   *Mary Ellen Conley*   386

BUNYAVIRIDAE, INFECTION AND IMMUNITY   *James S Porterfield*   390

BURSA OF FABRICIUS   *Paavo Toivanen*   393

BYSTANDER EFFECTS   *Jacques Theze*   396

C

CALICIVIRUS, INFECTION AND IMMUNITY   *Michael J Carter, W David Cubitt*   399

CAMPATH-1 ANTIGEN (CD52)   *Geoff Hale*   402

CAMPYLOBACTER, INFECTION AND IMMUNITY   *Diane G Newell*   407

CANDIDA, INFECTION AND IMMUNITY   *David K Wagner, Peter G Sohnle*   409

CANINE IMMUNE SYSTEM   *Tom R Phillips*   411

CAPPING, CLUSTERING, MEMBRANE MICRODOMAINS AND CELL SURFACE DYNAMICS   *Francis Loor*   414

CARBOHYDRATE ANTIGENS   *Cornelis PJ Glaudemans*   422

CARDIAC DISEASE, AUTOIMMUNE   *John B Zabriskie, Allan Gibofsky*   431

CARRIER   *Huw Davies*   436

CATALYTIC ANTIBODIES   *Irene Lee, Stephen J Benkovic*   438

CD ANTIGENS   *Hannes Stockinger, Otto Majdic, Walter Knapp*   444

CD1   *Said M Shawar*   458

CD2   *Stefan C Meuer*   463

CD3   *Alan Tunnacliffe*   465

CD4   *Rafick Pierre Sekaly, Ronald Rooke*   468

CD5   *PM Lydyard, C Jamin, P Y Youinou*   472

CD8   *Georg F Weber, Harvey Cantor*   475

CD22   *Dennis Sgroi, Ivan Stamenkovic*   479

CD28   *Jeffrey A Ledbetter, Peter S Linsley*   482

CD40 AND ITS LIGAND   *Jacques Banchereau, Francine Briere*   484

CD44   *David Naor*   488

CD45   *John Seavitt, Matthew L Thomas*   491

CD46 (MEMBRANE COFACTOR PROTEIN, MCP)   *M Kathryn Liszewski, John P Atkinson*   495

CD59   *Alexandra Davies, Peter Lachmann*   497

CELL-MEDIATED IMMUNITY   *Frank W Fitch*   501

CELL-MEDIATED LYSIS   *David W Lancki*   504

CELL SEPARATION TECHNIQUES   *Silvano Ferrini, Lorenzo Moretta*   507

CELL SURFACE MOLECULES, IMMUNOPRECIPITATION OF   *Frank AW Verreck, Frits Koning*   513

CELL SURFACE RECEPTORS AND ADHESION MOLECULES, THREE-DIMENSIONAL
  STRUCTURES   *Jurgen Bajorath*   515

CHAGAS' DISEASE   *Martin E Rottenberg, Anders Örn*   521

CHÉDIAK–HIGASHI SYNDROME   *Charles M Perou, Jerry Kaplan*   526

CHEMOKINES   *Dennis D Taub*   529

CHEMOTAXIS   *Peter C Wilkinson*   533

CHEMOTAXIS OF LYMPHOCYTES   *Peter C Wilkinson*   538

CHEMOTAXIS OF MACROPHAGES AND MONOCYTES   *Peter C Wilkinson*   540

CHEMOTAXIS OF NEUTROPHILS   *Peter C Wilkinson*   541

CHIMERISM, HEMATOPOIETIC   *Yair Reisner*   544

CHLAMYDIA, INFECTION AND IMMUNITY   *Roger G Rank*   549

CHROMOSOME TRANSLOCATIONS OF IMMUNE GENES   *Kishor Bhatia, Marina Gutiérrez*   522

CHRONIC ACTIVE AND AUTOIMMUNE HEPATITIS   *Ian R Mackay*   561

CHRONIC GRANULOMATOUS DISEASE   *Anthony W Segal*   565

CIRCULATORY SYSTEM INFECTIONS   *James P Burnie*   567

CLONAL DELETION   *Jon H Russell*   569

CLONAL SELECTION   *Norman R Klinman*   573

CLOSTRIDIUM, INFECTION AND IMMUNITY   *Charalabos Pothoulakis*   576

CLOTTING SYSTEM   *Arthur S Brecher*   578

COBRA VENOM FACTOR   *Carl-Wilhelm Vogel*   586

COCCIDIOIDES, INFECTION AND IMMUNITY   *Jon Elutz, Jon W Denning, David A Stevens*   589

COCCIDIOSIS   *David A Stevens*   591

COLD AGGLUTININS   *Ten Feizi*   593

COLONY-STIMULATING FACTORS   *John W Schrader*   596

COMMON VARIABLE IMMUNODEFICIENCY   *Thomas A Selvaggi, Michael C Sneller*   599

COMPLEMENT, ALTERNATIVE PATHWAY   *Peter J Lachmann*   602

COMPLEMENT, CLASSICAL PATHWAY   *Robert B Sim*   604

COMPLEMENT DEFICIENCIES   *Klaus O Rother, Ursula A Rother*   612

COMPLEMENT FIXATION TEST   *Seppo Meri, Carl-Henrik von Bonsdorff*   617

COMPLEMENT, GENETICS   *C Rittner, PM Schneider*   619

COMPLEMENT, MEMBRANE ATTACK PATHWAY   *Agustin P Dalmasso*   624

COMPLEMENT RECEPTORS   *Gordon D Ross*   629
CONGENIC MICE   *M Viviana Bozon, Edmond J Yunis*   634
CONTACT HYPERSENSITIVITY   *PS Friedmann*   637
CONTRACEPTION, IMMUNOLOGICAL   *GP Talwar*   640
CONTRASUPPRESSION   *Douglas R Green, Patrick M Flood*   648
COOPERATION, MECHANISMS OF CELLULAR   *Theodore J Yun, Edward A Clark*   651

VOLUME 2

COPPER AND THE IMMUNE SYSTEM   *Omelan A Lukasewycz, Joseph R Prohaska*   657
CORONAVIRUS, INFECTION AND IMMUNITY   *Helmut Wege*   658
CORYNEFORM BACTERIA, INFECTION AND IMMUNITY   *WC Noble*   661
C-REACTIVE PROTEIN   *Mark B Pepys*   663
CRYOGLOBULIN   *John T Whicher*   665
CRYOPRESERVATION OF IMMUNE CELLS   *Patrick J Stiff*   668
CRYPTOCOCCOSIS, INFECTION AND IMMUNITY   *Andreas Schaffner*   671
CRYPTOSPORIDIOSIS   *Saul Tzipori*   674
CUTANEOUS ANAPHYLAXIS   *Malcolm HA Rustin, Catherine H Orteu*   678
CYCLOSPORINE   *Jean F Borel, Götz Baumann, Thomas Beveridge*   686
CYSTICERCOSIS   *Donald P McManus*   690
CYTOKINE ASSAYS   *Fionula M Brennan, Catherine Haworth*   694
CYTOKINE GENES, REGULATION OF   *David R Fitzpatrick, Mark Egerton, Anne Kelso*   699
CYTOKINE INHIBITORS   *Carlo Chizzolini, Jean-Michel Dayer*   702
CYTOKINE RECEPTORS   *Brian MJ Foxwell, James B Crawley, Theresa H Page*   708
CYTOKINE RECEPTORS, SOLUBLE   *David Wallach*   712
CYTOKINES   *Marc Feldmann*   719
CYTOMEGALOVIRUS, INFECTION AND IMMUNITY   *PD Griffiths*   722
CYTOTOXIC T LYMPHOCYTES   *Vivian Lam Braciale*   725
CYTOTOXICITY, ASSAYS FOR   *Nobukata Shinohara*   730
CYTOTOXICITY, MECHANISMS OF   *Pierre Golstein*   732

D

DECAY-ACCELERATING FACTOR (CD55)   *Taroh Kinoshita*   735
DEGRANULATION   *Peter M Henson*   736
DELAYED-TYPE HYPERSENSITIVITY   *Alain de Weck*   738
DENDRITIC CELLS   *Jonathan M Austyn*   742
DEOXYGUANOSINE   *Erwin W Gelfand*   748
DERMATOLOGICAL INFECTIONS   *Edward T Ryan, Morton N Swartz*   750
DETERMINANT SPREADING   *Kamal D Moudgil, David B Stevens, Eli E Sercarz*   754
DIAPEDESIS   *Henry Beekhuizen, Ralph van Furth*   757
DiGEORGE SYNDROME   *Anthony R Hayward, David Manchester*   761
DIVERSITY, GENERATION OF   *Kathleen N Potter, J Donald Capra*   764
DNA VACCINES   *John J Donnelly, Margaret A Liu*   771
DOMAINS, IMMUNOGLOBULIN-TYPE   *Pedro M Alzari*   775
DRUGS, ALLERGY TO   *Timothy J Sullivan*   778

E

ECHINOCOCCUS, INFECTION AND IMMUNITY   *David J Jenkins*   783

ECZEMA   *Jan D Bos*   786

EFFECTOR LYMPHOCYTES   *Dennis D Taub*   789

ELECTRON MICROSCOPY, IMMUNOLOGICAL APPLICATIONS   *Matthew A Gonda*   790

ELISPOT ASSAY   *Jonathon D Sedgwick*   796

EMBRYONIC ANTIGENS   *Matteo Adinolfi*   798

ENDOTHELIUM   *Alberto Mantovani, Elisabetta Dejana*   802

ENDOTOXIN (LIPOPOLYSACCHARIDE (LPS))   *Chris Galanos*   806

ENHANCEMENT, IMMUNOLOGICAL   *John W Fabre*   809

ENZYME LABELING OF ANTIBODIES AND ANTIGENS   *Stratis Avrameas, Thérèse Ternynck*   813

ENZYME-LINKED IMMUNOSORBENT ASSAY (ELISA)   *Stratis Avrameas, Thérèse Ternynck*   816

EOSINOPHIL CHEMOTACTIC FACTORS   *Sabine Krüger-Krasagakes, Beate M Henz*   819

EOSINOPHILS   *David S Silberstein*   822

EPITOPES   *T Chyau Liang*   825

EPSTEIN–BARR VIRUS, INFECTION AND IMMUNITY   *Martin Rowe*   828

ERYTHROCYTES   *Gian Luigi Castoldi, Laura del Senno*   833

ESCHERICHIA COLI, INFECTION AND IMMUNITY   *Rodney D Berg*   842

EXERCISE AND THE IMMUNE RESPONSE   *Laurie Hoffman-Goetz, Bente K Pedersen*   845

EXOCYTOSIS   *Jacques Padawer*   849

EXPERIMENTAL AUTOIMMUNE ENCEPHALOMYELITIS   *Robert H Swanborg*   856

EXTRACELLULAR MATRIX   *Adrian Shuttleworth*   861

EYE, AUTOIMMUNE DISEASE   *Rachel R Caspi*   867

EYE INFECTIONS   *Marjorie Anne Monnickendam*   871

F

FAS (CD95) AND FAS LIGAND   *Mark R Alderson, David H Lynch*   874

FASCIOLIASIS   *Karen S Ovington*   880

FATTY ACIDS (DIETARY) AND THE IMMUNE SYSTEM   *J Bruce German*   884

Fc RECEPTORS   *Neil A Fanger, Michael W Fanger, Paul M Guyre*   886

FELINE IMMUNE SYSTEM   *Ian R Tizard*   892

FETAL CALF SERUM   *Hinnak Northoff, Willy A Flegel*   896

FETUS AS ALLOGRAFT   *Peter M Johnson*   898

FEVER   *Robert B Ashman*   901

FIBROBLASTS   *Ifor R Williams*   905

FIBRONECTIN   *Fabrizio Mainiero, Angela Santoni*   909

FILARIASIS, LYMPHATIC   *Thomas B Nutman*   913

FILOVIRUSES (MARBURG VIRUS AND EBOLA VIRUS), INFECTION AND IMMUNITY   *Hans-Dieter Klenk, Heinz Feldmann*   916

FISH IMMUNE SYSTEM   *A E Ellis*   920

FLAVIVIRUS, INFECTION AND IMMUNITY   *Thomas J Chambers*   926

FLOW CYTOMETRY   *Mario Roederer, David R Parks, Leonore A Herzenberg, Leonard A Herzenberg*   932

FLUOROCHROME LABELING   *Richard R Hardy*   943

FOOD ALLERGY   *Jean-Pierre Girard*   947

FORSSMAN ANTIGEN   *Peter F Mühlradt*   953

FRANCISELLA, INFECTION AND IMMUNITY   *Arne Tärnvik*   956

FUNGI, IMMUNITY TO   *Thomas S Harrison, Stuart M Levitz*   957

FUSOBACTERIUM, INFECTION AND IMMUNITY   *Itzhak Brook*   962

G

GAMMAGLOBULIN   *Charlotte Cunningham-Rundles*   964

GASTROINTESTINAL TRACT INFECTIONS   *Herman Friedman*   967

GENE CONVERSION   *PJ Hastings, Susan M Rosenberg*   969

GENE THERAPY   *Claude Bagnis, Patrice Mannoni*   974

GENETIC ANALYSIS AT THE MOLECULAR LEVEL   *Philippe Kourilsky, Laurent Gapin*   981

GENETIC ANALYSIS AT THE PHENOTYPIC LEVEL   *M Ilyas Kamboh*   986

GERM-FREE ANIMALS   *Joop P Koopman*   990

GERMINAL CENTER   *Federico Caligaris-Cappio*   992

GLUCOCORTICOIDS   *Paul M Guyre, Allan Munck*   996

GLYCOSYLATION OF IMMUNE SYSTEM MOLECULES   *Raj B Parekh*   1001

GOODPASTURE'S SYNDROME   *Juan Saus*   1005

GRAFT REJECTION   *Margaret J Dallman*   1011

GRAFT-VERSUS-HOST REACTION   *Robertson Parkman*   1015

GRANULOCYTE COLONY-STIMULATING FACTOR (G-CSF)   *T Michael Dexter*   1018

GRANULOCYTE-MACROPHAGE COLONY-STIMULATING FACTOR (GM-CSF)   *Philip S Crosier,*
   Kathryn E Crosier   1020

GRANULOMA   *John L Turk*   1023

GRANZYMES   *Joseph A Trapani*   1026

GRAVITY, EFFECT OF SPACE FLIGHT ON IMMUNITY   *William R Beisel*   1030

GUINEA PIG, INBRED STRAINS OF   *Ethan M Shevach*   1033

H

H2 CLASS I   *Jeffrey A Frelinger, Edward J Collins*   1035

H2 CLASS II   *Gail A Bishop*   1040

H2 CLASS III REGION   *Torben Lund*   1045

HAEMOPHILUS, INFECTION AND IMMUNITY   *Michael A Apicella, Timothy F Murphy*   1048

HAPTEN   *Ilkka JT Seppälä, Olli Mäkkelä*   1050

HEAVY CHAIN DISEASES   *Jean-Louis Preud'homme*   1053

HELICOBACTER PYLORI, INFECTION AND IMMUNITY   *Diane G Newell*   1056

HELPER T LYMPHOCYTES   *Frank W Fitch*   1058

HEMATOPOIETIC STEM CELL TRANSPLANTATION   *Peter A McSweeney, Rainer Storb*   1062

HEMOLYTIC DISEASE OF THE NEWBORN   *Cyril A Clarke*   1070

HEPATITIS A VIRUS, INFECTION AND IMMUNITY   *Ian D Gust*   1073

HEPATITIS B VIRUS, INFECTION AND IMMUNITY   *Howard C Thomas, Jennifer A Waters*   1075

HEPATITIS C VIRUS, INFECTION AND IMMUNITY   *William L Irving*   1079

HEPATITIS E, F AND G VIRUSES, INFECTION AND IMMUNITY   *Michael A Purdy*   1082

HERPES SIMPLEX VIRUS, INFECTION AND IMMUNITY   *Barbara A Blacklaws, Anthony A Nash*   1084

HERPESVIRUS-6, INFECTION AND IMMUNITY   *William L Irving*   1089

HERPESVIRUS-8, INFECTION AND IMMUNITY   *Thomas F Schulz*   1090

HETEROPHILE ANTIBODIES   *Felix Milgrom*   1092

HIGH ENDOTHELIAL VENULES   *Ann Ager*   1093

HISTAMINE   *Frederick L Pearce*   1101

HISTOPLASMA, INFECTION AND IMMUNITY   *Georges S Deepe Jr*   1105

HLA CLASS I   *Xiaohua Wei, Harry T Orr*   1108

HLA CLASS II   *Eric O Long*   1111

HLA CLASS III REGION   *Caroline M Milner, Begona Aguado, R Duncan Campbell*   1114

HOOKWORM DISEASE   *Jerzy M Behnke*   1121

hu-SCID MICE   *Gianvito Martino, Luigi ME Grimaldi*   1125

HUMAN IMMUNODEFICIENCY VIRUSES   *Myra McClure, Angus Dalgleish*   1130

HUMANIZED ANTIBODIES   *William J Harris*   1139

HUMORAL IMMUNITY   *Claudia Berek*   1144

HYBRIDOMAS, B CELL   *John F Kearney*   1148

HYBRIDOMAS, T CELL   *Shoichi Ozaki*   1152

HYDROSTATIC PRESSURE, EFFECT ON IMMUNE SYSTEM   *Meir Shinitzky, Venkatesh Ramakrishna, Andrei Matsaeu*   1155

H-Y, THE MALE-SPECIFIC TRANSPLANTATION ANTIGEN   *Elizabeth Simpson*   1158

HYPERGAMMAGLOBULINEMIA   *Philip R Greipp*   1161

HYPER-IgM SYNDROME   *Ramsay L Fuleihan*   1166

HYPERSENSITIVITY REACTIONS   *Rita Mirakian*   1169

I

IDIOPATHIC THROMBOCYTOPENIC PURPURA   *Robert McMillan*   1180

IDIOTYPE   *Constantin A Bona*   1182

IDIOTYPE, INTERNAL IMAGE   *Constantin A Bona*   1186

IDIOTYPE NETWORK   *Constantin A Bona*   1190

VOLUME 3

Igα/Igβ (CD79a/CD79b)   *Shiaoching Gong, Fotini Papavasiliou, Mila Jankovic, Yun Hu, Michel C Nussenzweig*   1194

IgA   *Brian J Underdown*   1196

IgD   *Benvenuto Pernis*   1199

IgE   *Hannah J Gould, Rebecca L Beavil*   1202

IgG   *Robert H Painter*   1208

IgM   *Paolo Casali*   1212

I-J   *Thomas J Rogers*   1217

IMMUNE ADHERENCE   *John L Turk*   1219

IMMUNE COMPLEXES   *Urs E Nydegger*   1220

IMMUNE RESPONSE   *Anthony Quinn, Claudia Raja-Gabaglia, Sussane L Schneider, Anthony Todd Braciak, Eli E Sercarz*   1226

IMMUNE RESPONSE (Ir) GENES   *Jerold G Woodward*   1229

IMMUNE RESPONSE *IN VITRO*   *Kenneth C McCullough*   1233

IMMUNE SURVEILLANCE   *Gert Jan Fleuren, Arko Gorter, Peter JK Kuppen*   1243

IMMUNE SYSTEM, ANATOMY OF   *CE Grossi, PM Lydyard*   1247

IMMUNOADSORBENTS   *Richard Ostlund Jr*   1250

IMMUNOASSAYS   *RP Ekins*   1252

IMMUNOCONGLUTININS   *Peter J Lachmann*   1257

IMMUNOCYTOCHEMISTRY AND ENZYME MARKERS   *CD Mackenzie*   1258

IMMUNODEFICIENCY, ANIMAL MODELS OF   *Gregory J Bancroft*   1267

IMMUNODEFICIENCY, PRIMARY   *A David B Webster*   1276

IMMUNODEFICIENCY, SECONDARY   *A David B Webster*   1283

IMMUNODIFFUSION, SINGLE RADIAL   *George Feinberg*   1287

IMMUNODOMINANCE   *Luciano Adorini*   1290

IMMUNOELECTROPHORESIS   *Anna-Brita Laurell*   1292

IMMUNOGEN   *Michael Sela*   1297

IMMUNOGLOBULIN, CELL SURFACE   *John G Monroe*   1298

IMMUNOGLOBULIN CLASS SWITCHING   *Jürgen Schmitz, Andreas Radbruch*   1302

IMMUNOGLOBULIN, EVOLUTION OF   *John J Marchalonis*   1307

IMMUNOGLOBULIN, FUNCTIONS   *Dennis R Burton*   1315

IMMUNOGLOBULIN GENE SUPERFAMILY   *Peter J Delves*   1319

IMMUNOGLOBULIN GENES   *Ian M Tomlinson*   1323

IMMUNOGLOBULIN STRUCTURE   *Allen B Edmundson, Kim N Andersen*   1329

IMMUNOLOGY, A BRIEF HISTORICAL PERSPECTIVE   *Edward S Golub*   1334

IMMUNOPATHOLOGY   *David R Katz*   1339

IMMUNOPOTENTIATION   *Paul Gatenby*   1342

IMMUNOSUPPRESSION   *Jean F Borel*   1349

IMMUNOTHERAPY OF ALLERGIC DISEASES   *Kent T HayGlass*   1353

IMMUNOTHERAPY OF AUTOIMMUNE DISEASES   *Marc Feldmann, Ravinder N Maini*   1356

IMMUNOTHERAPY OF TUMORS   *Nicholas D James, Karol Sikora*   1359

IMMUNOTOXICOLOGY   *Michael I Luster, Petia P Simeonova, Dori R Germolec*   1365

INBRED STRAINS   *Michael FW Festing*   1369

INFERTILITY, IMMUNOLOGICAL CAUSES OF   *Tage Hjort*   1373

INFLAMMATORY BOWEL DISEASE   *Robert D Fusunyan, Ian R Sanderson*   1375

INFLAMMATORY BOWEL DISEASE, ANIMAL MODELS   *Uzma Shah, Ian R Sanderson*   1381

INFLUENZA VIRUS (ORTHOMYXOVIRUS), INFECTION AND IMMUNITY   *Robert G Webster, Peter C
Doherty, Ralph A Tripp*   1385

INNATE IMMUNITY   *Edwin L Cooper*   1387

INSULIN-DEPENDENT DIABETES MELLITUS, EXPERIMENTAL MODELS   *Ji-Won Yoon, Hee-Sook
Jun*   1390

INSULIN-DEPENDENT DIABETES MELLITUS, HUMAN   *Andrew Muir, Noel Maclaren*   1399

INTEGRINS   *Nancy Hogg*   1404

INTERCELLULAR ADHESION MOLECULES: ICAM-1, ICAM-2 AND ICAM-3   *Steven D Marlin, Robert
Rothlein*   1409

INTERFERON α   *Hans AR Bluyssen*   1413

INTERFERON β   *Rainer Zawatzky, Helmut Jacobsen*   1417

INTERFERON γ   *Jan Vilček, Junming Le*   1421

INTERFERON γ RECEPTOR   *Jerome A Langer*   1426

INTERLEUKIN 1 AND ITS RECEPTOR   *Teresa Krakauer, Joost J Oppenheim*   1429

INTERLEUKIN 2   *Jacques Théze*   1436

INTERLEUKIN 2 RECEPTOR   *Philip D Greenberg, Brad H Nelson*   1439

INTERLEUKIN 3   *John W Schrader*   1442

INTERLEUKIN 3 RECEPTOR   *Padmini Rao, R Allan Mufson*   1446

INTERLEUKIN 4   *Stephen T Smiley, Michael J Grusby*   1451

INTERLEUKIN 4 RECEPTOR   *Achsah D Keegan*   1453

INTERLEUKIN 5 AND ITS RECEPTOR   *Colin J Sanderson*   1456

INTERLEUKIN 6   *Tadashi Matsuda, Tadamitsu Kishimoto*   1458

INTERLEUKIN 6 RECEPTOR   *Tadamitsu Kishimoto*   1461

INTERLEUKIN 7 AND ITS RECEPTOR   *Shin-Ichi Nishikawa*   1462

INTERLEUKIN 8 AND ITS RECEPTOR   *Naofumi Mukaida, Kouji Matsushima*   1466

INTERLEUKIN 9 AND ITS RECEPTOR   *Yu-Chung Yang*   1471

INTERLEUKIN 10 AND ITS RECEPTOR   *Vijay P Khatri, Michael A Caligiuri*   1475

INTERLEUKIN 11 AND ITS RECEPTOR   *Yu-Chung Yang*   1478

INTERLEUKIN 12 AND ITS RECEPTOR   *Erwin Rüde, Edgar Schmitt, Tieno Germann*   1483

INTERLEUKIN 13 AND ITS RECEPTOR   *Juha Punnonen, José M Carballido, Gregorio Aversa, Jan E de Vries*   1489

INTERLEUKIN 15 AND ITS RECEPTOR   *Mary K Kennedy, Linda S Park*   1492

INVARIANT CHAIN (Ii)   *Elizabeth K Bikoff*   1495

INVERTEBRATE IMMUNE SYSTEMS   *Christopher J Bayne, Gerardo R Vasta*   1498

IRIDOVIRUS, INFECTION AND IMMUNITY   *Stephanie K Watson, James Kalmakoff*   1502

IRON AND THE IMMUNE SYSTEM   *AR Sherman*   1505

ISCOM (IMMUNO-STIMULATING COMPLEX)   *B Morein*   1507

ISOELECTRIC FOCUSING   *Maryvonne DR Brasher, Robin Thorpe*   1510

ISOTYPE   *Jacobo Abadi, Liise-Anne Pirofski*   1514

J

JOINING (J) CHAIN   *Jiri Mestecky, Itaru Moro*   1516

K

KALLIKREIN–KININ SYSTEM   *Raul DeLa Cadena, Robert W Colman*   1518

KLEBSIELLA, INFECTION AND IMMUNITY   *David C Straus*   1522

KNOCKOUT, GENETIC   *Thomas E Willnow*   1524

L

LANGERHANS CELLS   *Andrew Blauvelt*   1528

LARGE GRANULAR LYMPHOCYTES   *Chau-Ching Liu, John Ding-E Young*   1532

LECTINS   *Halina Lis, Nathan Sharon*   1535

LEGIONELLA, INFECTION AND IMMUNITY   *N Cary Engleberg, Joan K Brieland*   1542

LEISHMANIASIS   *Stephen J McSorley, Foo Y Liew*   1546

LEPTOSPIRA, INFECTION AND IMMUNITY   *Russell Bey*   1551

LEUKEMIA   *Dario Campana*   1554

LEUKEMIA INHIBITORY FACTOR   *Gertrud M Hocke*   1560

LEUKEMIA VIRUSES   *A Burny, F Dequiedt, E Devos-Adam, J-S Gatot, P Kerhhofs, R Kettman, D Portetelle, L Willems*   1562

LEUKOCYTE ADHESION DEFICIENCY   *Amos Etzioni*   1566

LEUKOCYTE CULTURE   *Alessandra Cesano, Daniela Santoli*   1569

LEWIS ^{X}/SIALYL-LEWIS^X (CD15/CD15S)   *Ten Feizi*   1576

LIFESPAN OF IMMUNE CELLS AND MOLECULES   *David Gray*   1579

LIMITING DILUTION ANALYSIS   *Herman Waldmann*   1584

LINKAGE DISEQUILIBRIUM   *Mary Ann Robinson*   1586

LIPOSOMES   *N van Rooijen*   1588

LISTERIA, INFECTION AND IMMUNITY   *C J Czuprynski*   1592

LYMPHATIC SYSTEM   *Joseph G Hall*   1596

LYMPH NODES   *CE Grossi, PM Lydyard*   1603

LYMPHOCYTE FUNCTION-ASSOCIATED ANTIGEN 1 (LFA-1)   *Eric Martz*   1607

LYMPHOCYTE FUNCTION-ASSOCIATED ANTIGEN 3 (LFA-3)   *Steve Herrmann*   1612

LYMPHOCYTE TRAFFICKING   *Reinhard Pabst, Jurgen Westermann, Richard M Binns*   1616

LYMPHOCYTE TRANSFORMATION TEST   *Charles H Kirkpatrick*   1621

LYMPHOCYTES   *Don Mason*   1625

LYMPHOKINE-ACTIVATED KILLER (LAK) CELLS   *Ronald B Herberman*   1627

LYMPHOMA   *George T Stevenson*   1631

LYMPHOTOXIN   *Carolyn A Cuff, Nancy Ruddle*   1637

M

MACROPHAGE ACTIVATION   *Siamon Gordon*   1642

MACROPHAGE COLONY-STIMULATING FACTOR (CSF-1)   *E Richard Stanley*   1650

MACROPHAGE MIGRATION INHIBITORY FACTOR (MIF)   *Graeme Wistow*   1655

MALARIA   *Jean Langhorne, Anthony A Holder*   1658

MARSUPIAL IMMUNE SYSTEM   *Richard H Sutton*   1663

MAST CELLS   *Reuben P Siraganian*   1667

MATERNAL ANTIBODIES   *Ann Kari Lefvert*   1671

MATURATION OF IMMUNE RESPONSES   *Edward W Voss*   1677

MEMBRANE-ASSOCIATED CYTOSKELETON: ROLE IN REGULATING IMMUNE CELL FUNCTION
   Lilly W Bourguignon   1679

MEMORY, IMMUNOLOGICAL   *Kevin J Horgan*   1681

MERCURY AND THE IMMUNE SYSTEM   *Göran Sandberg*   1686

MHC DISEASE ASSOCIATIONS   *Henry Erlich, Raymond Apple*   1690

MHC, EVOLUTION OF   *Jan Klein*   1700

MHC, FUNCTIONS OF   *Janice Riberdy, Peter Doherty*   1703

MHC PEPTIDE-BINDING SPECIFICITY   *Juergen Hammer, Francesco Sinigaglia*   1706

MHC RESTRICTION   *Ethan M Shevach*   1709

MICROBICIDAL MECHANISMS, OXYGEN-DEPENDENT   *Seymour J Klebanoff*   1713

MICROBICIDAL MECHANISMS, OXYGEN-INDEPENDENT   *Robert I Lehrer*   1719

MICROENVIRONMENT   *Andras K Szakal, Gregory F Burton, John G Tew*   1725

MINOR TRANSPLANTATION (HISTOCOMPATIBILITY) ANTIGENS   *Elizabeth Simpson*   1729

MIXED LYMPHOCYTE REACTION   *Jonathan Sprent*   1733

MOLECULAR MIMICRY   *Alan Ebringer*   1736

MONOCLONAL ANTIBODIES (mAbs)   *Ailsa M Campbell*   1742

MONOCYTE CHEMOATTRACTANT PROTEIN (CMCP-1)   *Claus O C Zachariae, Christian G Larsen,*
   Kouji Matsushima   1748

MONOCYTES   *Ralph van Furth, Henry Beekhuizen*   1750

MONONUCLEAR PHAGOCYTE SYSTEM   *Ralph van Furth*   1755

MOTILITY OF IMMUNE CELLS   *Liana Harvath*   1759

MOUSE INBRED STRAINS   *Mohya Lennon-Pierce, Janan T Eppig*   1762

MOUSE INBRED STRAINS, ORIGINS OF   *François Bonhomme, Jean-Louis Guénet*   1771

MUCOSA-ASSOCIATED LYMPHOID TISSUE (MALT)   *Jerry R McGhee*   1774

MUCOSAL IMMUNITY   *Stephen P James*   1780

MULTIPLE SCLEROSIS   *Jef CM Raus*   1786

MYCOBACTERIA, INFECTION AND IMMUNITY   *Graham W Rook*   1793

MYCOPLASMA, INFECTION AND IMMUNITY   *Juliane Hentschel, Peter F Muhlradt*   1798

MYELOID ANTIGENS   *David C Linch*   1803

N

NATURAL ANTIBODIES   *Stratis Avrameas, Therese Ternynck*   1806

NATURAL KILLER (NK) CELLS   *Theresa L Whiteside*   1809

NEISSERIA, INFECTION AND IMMUNITY   *Catherine Ison, Brian Robertson*   1816

NEONATAL IMMUNE RESPONSE   *Richard L Riley*   1818

NEPHELOMETRY   *Lars Åke Nilsson*   1822

NEUROENDOCRINE REGULATION OF IMMUNITY   *Bryan M Gebhardt, J Edwin Blalock*   1824

NEUROLOGICAL AUTOIMMUNE DISEASES   *Barry GW Arnason*   1834

NEUROLOGICAL INFECTIONS   *David N Irani, Diane E Griffin*   1844

NEUROMUSCULAR JUNCTION AUTOIMMUNITY   *John Newsom-Davis, Angela Vincent*   1847

NEUTRALIZATION OF BIOLOGICAL REACTIONS BY ANTIBODIES   *John P Hearn, Georgina E
   Webley*   1851

NEUTROPHILS   *Dirk Roos*   1854

NITRIC OXIDE   *Stephen J McSorley, Foo Y Liew*   1859

NOCARDIA, INFECTION AND IMMUNITY   *Blaine L Beaman*   1861

NORTHERN BLOTTING   *Akihiko Muto, Ken-ichi Arai*   1864

NUDE (ATHYMIC) MICE   *Yasunobu Yoshikai*   1866

VOLUME 4

NUTRITION AND THE IMMUNE SYSTEM   *Ranjit K Chandra*   1869

O

ONCHOCERCIASIS   *Bulbul Chakravarti, Deb N Chakravarti*   1872

ONTOGENY OF THE IMMUNE RESPONSE   *Constantin A Bona*   1875

OPISTHORCHIASIS–CLONORCHIASIS   *Stitaya Sirisinha*   1879

OPPORTUNISTIC INFECTIONS   *Christopher Bunch, Derrick WM Crook*   1881

OPSONIZATION   *Pieter S Hiemstra, Mohamed R Daha*   1885

ORAL IMMUNOLOGY   *WP McArthur*   1888

ORAL TOLERANCE   *Howard L Weiner*   1893

ORGAN CULTURE OF LYMPHOID CELLS   *David A Crouse*   1899

OVINE IMMUNE SYSTEM   *Ian McConnell, John Hopkins*   1902

P

PAPILLOMAVIRUS, INFECTION AND IMMUNITY   *Karen J Auborn*   1907

PARAMYXOVIRUSES, INFECTION AND IMMUNITY   *Trudy G Morrison*   1909

PARASITES, IMMUNITY TO   *Frank EG Cox*   1916

PARVOVIRUS, INFECTION AND IMMUNITY   *N Frickhofen, NS Young*   1922

PASTEURELLA, INFECTION AND IMMUNITY   *Richard B Rimler*   1927

PERFORIN   *Jurg Tschopp*   1929

PHAGE DISPLAY OF ANTIBODIES   *John de Kruif, Ton Logtenberg*   1931

PHAGOCYTOSIS   *Jan Verhoef*   1935

PHORBOL ESTERS   *Gerald A Evans, William L Farrar*   1940

PHOTOIMMUNOLOGY   *Stephen E Ullrich, Margaret L Kripke*   1942

PHYLOGENY OF IMMUNE RESPONSE   *Norman A Ratcliffe*   1946

PHYTOHEMAGGLUTININ (PHA)   *Tom Geppert*   1952

PICORNAVIRUS, INFECTION AND IMMUNITY   *Nicholas J Knowles, Trevor Collen*   1953

PLAQUE-FORMING CELL (PFC) ASSAYS   *Hans-Michael Dosch*   1960

PLASMA   *Edward L Snyder, Joan Judge*   1964

PLASMAPHERESIS   *Terry Hamblin*   1969

PLATELET-ACTIVATING FACTOR (PAF)   *David Hosford, Pierre Braquet*   1971

PLATELETS   *Joel Lawrence Moake*   1973

PNEUMOCYSTIS CARINI, INFECTION AND IMMUNITY   *Sue A Theus, Peter D Walzer*   1977

POKEWEED MITOGEN (PWM)   *Yasuhiro Horii, Toshio Hirano*   1978

POLYCLONAL ACTIVATORS   *Nicholas StC Sinclair, Colin C Anderson*   1979

POLYENDOCRINE AUTOIMMUNITY   *Anthony P Weetman*   1984

POLYMERASE CHAIN REACTION (PCR) AMPLIFICATION   *Julian F Burke*   1987

POLYOMAVIRUS, INFECTION AND IMMUNITY   *Keerti V Shah*   1988

PORCINE IMMUNE SYSTEM   *Ilja Trebicharský*   1991

POXVIRUS, INFECTION AND IMMUNITY   *R Paul Kitching, Jef M Hammond*   1995

PRECIPITATION REACTION   *Örjan TG Ouchterlony*   1999

PRIMARY BILIARY CIRRHOSIS   *M Eric Gershwin, Ian R Mackay*   2002

PRIMATE (NONHUMAN) IMMUNE SYSTEM   *Todd M Allen, David I Watkins*   2004

PRIVILEGED SITES   *J Wayne Streilein*   2012

PROKARYOTES, IMMUNITY IN   *Vincent Geli, Yves Corda*   2013

PROLIFERATION, LYMPHOCYTE   *Bruce L Levine, James H Mond, Carl H June*   2017

PROSTAGLANDINS   *E Roy Pettipher*   2024

PROTEIN KINASES   *Thomas A Hamilton*   2028

PROTEIN SEPARATION TECHNIQUES   *Sue Cresswell*   2034

PROTEUS, INFECTION AND IMMUNITY   *Susan R Heimer, Harry LT Mobley*   2039

PSEUDOMONAS AERUGINOSA: INFECTION AND IMMUNITY   *Robert EW Hancock, Joseph S Lam*   2042

R

RABBIT IMMUNE SYSTEM   *BF Hague, TJ Kindt*   2046

RADIATION, EFFECTS ON IMMUNE SYSTEM   *Ruth Neta, Gayle E Woloschak*   2050

RADIOLABELING   *Robert E Cone*   2053

RAT, INBRED STRAINS OF   *David L Gasser*   2055

RECRUITMENT   *Sharon M Wahl, John Zagorski*   2059

RELATIVE RISK   *Glenys Thomson*   2064

RENAL INFECTIONS   *Guy Neild*   2065

REOVIRUS, INFECTION AND IMMUNITY   *Amy Hodson Thompson, Lucille London, Steven D London*   2067

REPRODUCTIVE TRACT INFECTIONS   *Morris D Cooper, Nancy M Khardori*   2071

REPTILIAN IMMUNE SYSTEM   *Rashika El Ridi*   2076

RESPIRATORY AND CARDIAC INFECTIONS   *Andrew Fogarty, John Macfarlane*   2081

RETROVIRAL VECTORS   *David M Nelson, Richard A Morgan*   2084

RETROVIRUS, INFECTION AND IMMUNITY   *Thomas F Schulz*   2092

RHABDOVIRUS, INFECTION AND IMMUNITY   *Paul-Pierre Pastoret, Bernard Brochier*   2098

Rh ANTIGENS   *Peter D Issitt*   2102

RHEUMATOID ARTHRITIS, ANIMAL MODELS   *Pritam Das, Chella S David*   2106

RHEUMATOID ARTHRITIS, HUMAN   *Antonio La Cava, Salvatore Albani*   2111

RHEUMATOLOGICAL DISORDERS   *Stanley Naguwa, Dick L Robbins*   2117

RHINITIS, ALLERGIC   *AW Frankland*   2121

RICKETTSIA, INFECTION AND IMMUNITY   *Gregory A Dasch*   2126

ROSETTING TECHNIQUES   *Malcolm R MacKenzie*   2128

S

SALMONELLA, INFECTION AND IMMUNITY   *Carlos E Hormaeche*   2131

SARCOIDOSIS   *David R Moller*   2133

SCHISTOSOMIASIS   *Michael J Doenhoff, Anthony E Butterworth*   2137

SDS-POLYACRYLAMIDE GEL ELECTROPHORESIS (SDS-PAGE)   *J Paul Banga*   2143

SECOND SIGNALS FOR LYMPHOCYTE ACTIVATION   *Maria-Luisa Alegre, Craig B Thompson, Thomas F Gajewski*   2145

SECRETORY COMPONENT (THE POLYMERIC Ig RECEPTOR)   *Per Brandtzaeg, Finn-Erik Johansen, Peter Krajĉi, Inger B Natvig*   2152

SELECTINS (CD62-E/L/P)   *Masayuki Miyasaka*   2158

SEPTIC SHOCK   *Peter Brouckaert*   2161

SEROTONIN   *Frank A Redegeld, Henk Van Loveren*   2164

SERUM SICKNESS   *Ekaterini Paizis, Brendan F Murphy*   2168

SEVERE COMBINED IMMUNODEFICIENCY   *Shigeaki Nonoyama, Jun-ichi Yata*   2170

SEX HORMONES AND IMMUNITY   *Howard S Fox*   2175

SHIGELLA, INFECTION AND IMMUNITY   *David WK Acheson, Gerald T Keusch*   2178

SJÖGREN'S SYNDROME   *PJW Venables, RN Maini*   2181

SKIN, AUTOIMMUNE DISEASES   *Jan D Bos*   2185

SKIN, CONTRIBUTION TO IMMUNITY   *Martien L Kapsenberg, Jan D Bos*   2190

SOMATIC MUTATION   *Nancy S Green, Anne Davidson*   2192

SOUTHERN BLOTTING   *Raymond Dalgleish*   2194

SPECIFICITY   *Jiri Novotny, Malcolm Davis*   2198

SPLEEN   *CE Grossi, PM Lydyard*   2205

STAPHYLOCOCCUS, INFECTION AND IMMUNITY   *Åsa Ljungh*   2208

STATISTICS, USE IN IMMUNOLOGY   *Amelia Dale Horne*   2211

STREPTOBACILLUS, INFECTION AND IMMUNITY   *Ian KM Smith*   2215

STREPTOCOCCUS, INFECTION AND IMMUNITY   *Richard J Hamill, Daniel M Musher*   2217

STRESS AND THE IMMUNE SYSTEM   *Roger J Booth*   2220

STRESS PROTEINS   *Tim Elliott*   2228

STROMAL CELLS   *Richard L Boyd*   2233

STRONGYLOIDIASIS   *Robert M Genta*   2238

SUPERANTIGENS   *Terje Kalland, Mikael Dohlsten, Per Antonsson, Morten Sögaard*   2239

SUPPRESSOR T LYMPHOCYTES   *David R Webb, Bruce H Devens*   2243

SURFACE PLASMON RESONANCE   *George Panayotou*   2247

SYSTEMIC LUPUS ERYTHEMATOSUS, ANIMAL MODELS   *Argyrios N Theofilopoulos*   2251

SYSTEMIC LUPUS ERYTHEMATOSUS (SLE), HUMAN   *David A Isenberg*   2255

T

TARGETING OF IMMUNOLOGICAL AGENTS   *Bruce R Blazar, Daniel Vallera, Robert Korngold*   2261

T CELL RECEPTOR, αβ   *Tak W Mak*   2264

T CELL RECEPTOR, γδ   *Adrian Hayday, William Pao*   2268

T CELL RECEPTOR, EVOLUTION OF   *Lee Rowen*   2278

T CELL RECEPTOR, RECOGNITION BY   *Arthur W Boylston*   2282

T CELL VACCINATION   *Irun R Cohen*   2284

THEILERIOSIS   *Subhash P Morzaria*   2286

THY-1   *Michael Schlesinger*   2290

THYMIC EPITHELIUM: POTENTIAL ROLE IN REGULATORY T CELL TOLERANCE   *Antonio Bandeira*   2292

THYMIC HORMONES AND PEPTIDES   *Oscar J Cordero, Montserrat Nogueira*   2300

THYMUS   *Jonathan Sprent, Charles D Surh*   2304

THYROID AUTOIMMUNITY, ANIMAL MODELS   *Noel R Rose*   2309

THYROID AUTOIMMUNITY, HUMAN   *Alan M McGregor*   2313

TISSUE TYPING   *Paul I Terasaki*   2318

T LYMPHOCYTE ACTIVATION   *Stephen G Ward, Carl H June*   2323

T LYMPHOCYTE CLONAL EXPANSION   *David G Telander, Daniel L Mueller*   2330

T LYMPHOCYTE DIFFERENTIATION   *Ada M Kruisbeek*   2334

T LYMPHOCYTES   *William R Heath*   2341

T LYMPHOCYTES, AUTOREACTIVE   *Maurice Zauderer*   2343

TNF RECEPTORS   *David Wallach*   2345

TOGAVIRUS, INFECTION AND IMMUNITY   *Ian McConnell*   2350

TOLERANCE, CENTRAL   *Pawel Kisielow*   2352

TOLERANCE, MODELS   *William O Weigle*   2359

TOLERANCE, PERIPHERAL   *David W Scott*   2362

TOXINS   *John Stephen*   2367

TOXOCARIASIS   *Malcolm W Kennedy*   2379

TOXOPLASMOSIS   *Yasuhiro Suzuki, Jack S Remington*   2382

TRANSFER FACTORS   *Charles H Kirkpatrick*   2385

TRANSFERRIN RECEPTOR (CD71)   *Balbino Alarcon, Manuel Fresno*   2389

TRANSFORMING GROWTH FACTOR β (TGFβ)   *Hans Link, Bao-Guo Xiao*   2392

TRANSFUSION   *Willy A Flegel*   2399

TRANSGENIC ANIMALS   *George A Kollias*   2404

TRANSMISSIBLE SPONGIFORM ENCEPHALOPATHIES, INFECTION AND IMMUNITY   *CF Farquhar*   2409

TRANSPLANTATION   *Peter J Morris*   2411

TREPONEMA, INFECTION AND IMMUNITY   *Konrad Wicher, Victoria Wicher*   2415

TRICHURIASIS   *Derek Wakelin*   2418

TRYPANOSOMIASIS, AFRICAN   *C Michael R Turner, Keith Vickerman*   2420

TUMOR ANTIGENS   *Benoît den Eynde, Andrew M Scott*   2424

TUMOR IMAGING   *Hirohiko Onoyama, Yoichi Saitoh, Masaaki Miyazawa*   2431

TUMOR NECROSIS FACTOR α   *Lothar Rink*   2435

TUMORS, IMMUNE RESPONSE TO   *Karl Erik Hellström, Ingegerd Hellström*   2440

TUMORS, IMMUNOLOGICAL ESCAPE OF   *Karl Erik Hellström, Ingegerd Hellström*   2443

U

ULTRACENTRIFUGATION   *Eyvind Rødahl*   2446

UNGULATE IMMUNE SYSTEMS   *Alan J Husband*   2449

URINARY TRACT INFECTIONS   *Catharina Svanborg*   2452

V

VACCINATION, METHODS OF ADMINISTRATION   *Gordon Ada*   2454

VACCINES   *Gordon Ada*   2456

VACCINES, ADVERSE REACTIONS TO   *Gordon Ada*   2462

VALENCY OF ANTIGENS AND ANTIBODIES   *David Catty*   2465

VARICELLA-ZOSTER VIRUS, INFECTION AND IMMUNITY   *Charles F Grose, Chantanee P Buranathai*   2468

VENOMS   *Donald R Hoffman*   2470

VETO CELLS   *Richard G Miller*   2473

VIABILITY, METHODS OF ASSESSING LEUKOCYTE   *Francis J Hornicek, George I Malinin*   2474

VIBRIO CHOLERAE, INFECTION AND IMMUNITY   *Paul A Manning*   2476

VIRUSES, IMMUNITY TO   *Andrew Carmichael, JG Patrick Sissons*   2479

VIRUSES, INFECTION OF IMMUNE CELLS BY   *Raymond M Welsh, Robert T Woodland*   2484

VITAMIN A AND THE IMMUNE SYSTEM   *Richard D Semba, J Cecil Smith*   2488

VITAMIN B GROUP AND THE IMMUNE SYSTEM   *Lorraine T Miller*   2490

VITAMIN C AND THE IMMUNE SYSTEM   *Reto Muggli*   2491

VITAMIN D AND THE IMMUNE SYSTEM   *Nobuto Yamamoto*   2494

VITAMIN E AND THE IMMUNE SYSTEM   *Ronald R Watson*   2500

VITILIGO   *David A Norris*   2501

W

WESTERN BLOTTING   *Harry Towbin*   2503

X

XENOTRANSPLANTATION   *Amelia Bartholomew, Hugh Auchincloss*   2508

Y

YERSINIA, INFECTION AND IMMUNITY   *Risto Tertti, Auli Toivanen*   2512

Z

ZINC AND THE IMMUNE SYSTEM   *William R Beisel*   2515

COLOR PLATE SECTION   between 336 –337

GLOSSARY   G i

INDEX   I i

ABO BLOOD GROUP SYSTEM

Anatole Lubenko and **Marcela Contreras**, North London Blood Transfusion Centre, Colindale Avenue, London, UK

The ABO blood group system was discoverred by Landsteiner in 1901. By mixing separated sera with suspensions of red cells obtained from the blood of different individuals, four patterns of agglutination could be obtained. The frequency of the four ABO groups varies in different populations: Amerindians are almost exclusively group O while Asians have a higher incidence of group B. In the UK the proportions of the four main blood groups are as follows: O (46.5%), A (42%), B (8.5%) and AB (3%). Agglutination of red cells arises because one individual's serum contains naturally occurring antibodies against ABO antigens that are missing from that individual's own red cells, but which are present on the cells of another; e.g. group A individuals have anti-B that agglutinates group B cells (see **Table 1**). Testing of red cells with selected potent anti-A, -B and -A,B reagents, while simultaneously testing the sera of the same subjects with reagent red cells (group A_1, A_2, B and O), provides the basis for ABO grouping (see **Table 1**).

The major subgroups of A are A_1 and A_2; the difference between them is partly quantitative and partly qualitative. These subgroups can be distinguished using specific anti-A_1 reagents, and are only significant clinically if the serum of an A_2 individual reacts at 37°C, which may hence cause destruction of transfused group A_1 red cells. Quantitative variants of A (A_{int}, A_x, A_{end}, A_3, A_m, A_y, A_{el}, etc.) and B (B_3, B_x, B_m, B_i, B_{ii}, B_{el}, etc.) are also known, which are characterized by the absence of the appropriate ABO antibodies from their plasma; e.g. the cells of A_x individuals fail to react with anti-A from B subjects although they react with strong anti-A in group O subjects; such individuals do not have anti-A. A and B variants are rare and usually of little clinical significance.

Genetics

The genes controlling the expression of A or B antigens are autosomal codominant alleles (A and B respectively) that map to the 9q34 region of chromosome 9. Because the A and B antigens are sugars, the genes coding for ABO are glycosyltransferases. Group O individuals possess alleles at the ABO locus

Table 1 ABO grouping

ABO group	Agglutination of test cells with reagent				Agglutination by subject's plasma of control cells of group			
	Anti-A	Anti-A_1[a]	Anti-B	Anti-A,B	A_1	A_2	B	O
A_1	+	+	0	+	0	0	+	0
A_2	+	0	0	+	+/0[b]	0	+	0
B	0	0	+	+	+	+	0	0
A_1B	+	+	+	+	0	0	0	0
A_2B	+	0	+	+	+/0[b]	0	0	0
O	0	0	0	0	+	+	+	0

[a]Anti-A_1 reagents can be: a lectin prepared from *Dolichos biflorus* seeds; sera of group B subjects absorbed with group A_2 red cells; or mouse monoclonal antibodies.
[b]The plasma of 1–8% of group A_2 and 22–35% of group A_2B individuals have weak naturally occurring anti-A_1.

on both homologous chromosomes that code for functionally inert proteins (see below), while A and B code for an *N*-acetylgalactosaminyl- and galactosyltransferase respectively. The appropriate alleles that encode the A^1, A^2 and B-transferases have been cloned and sequenced. The A and B genes code for 41 kDa proteins composed of 353 amino acids, which contain a 21 amino acid long leader peptide that is cleaved off to form the mature transferase. The two genes differ at seven nucleotide positions, which generate only four amino acid differences, found at positions 176, 235, 266 and 268 of the A- or B-transferase polypeptide. These correspond to Arg, Gly, Leu and Gly in the A-transferase, and to Gly, Ser, Met and Ala, respectively, in the B-transferase. The most critical differences are at positions 266 and 268 but the four are collectively responsible for the immunochemical differences between A and B and their associated transferases; substitution of one or more of these four key amino acids can critically affect ABO expression (see O^2 below).

Three types of O alleles have been described to date; the commonest has a nucleotide sequence similar to that of the A allele, but with a single base deletion that generates a change in reading frame (hence scrambling the amino acid sequence) at amino acid position 87. This deletion also produces a new in-frame stop codon that generates a truncated O allele polypeptide that is only 116 amino acids long, and which is enzymically inactive. An analogous O allele, with an incidence one-quarter of that of the former and representing an equivalent single base deletion in a B gene, has also been reported. The third type of O (sometimes called O^2) arises from Arg→Gly and Gly→Arg substitutions at amino acids 176 and 268, respectively, of an A allele which abolishes the enzymatic activity of the resulting protein, thereby emphasizing the metabolic importance of these amino acids at the transferase active site.

The differences between the A^1 and A^2 alleles arise from a Pro→Leu mutation at amino acid position 156 coupled to a single base deletion near the C-terminus of an equivalent A^1-allele. This in turn results in a frame shift so that the original stop codon is no longer recognized, and a new stop codon is generated downstream, giving rise to a polypeptide for the A^2 enzyme that is 21 amino acids longer than the A^1 enzyme. The extra sequence thus generated, together with the Pro-Leu substitution in the A^2-transferase, should account for the differences in kinetics and specificity between the two enzymes (see below). In addition to A^1 and A^2, the alleles encoding several examples of various other ABO subgroups have also been cloned: A_3, A_x, B_3, B(A) and *cis*-AB. All have so far proven to be heterogeneous at the

nucleotide level despite having been considered to characterize a single phenotypic subtype.

The A- and B-transferases synthesize A and B carbohydrate antigens by transfer of *N*-acetylgalactosamine (GalNAc) or galactose (Gal) moieties from UDP-GalNAc or UDP-Gal respectively to the C-3 carbon atom of a fucosylated terminal galactose residue present in a variety of oligosaccharide precursors with blood group H activity (see **Figure 1**). These precursors are the sugar component of glycolipids and glycoproteins. The transferases of the A_1 and A_2 alleles are known to have different pH optima, isoelectric points, thermal stabilities and metal ion cofactor requirements, which result in differences in their substrate transfer kinetics.

It is rarely possible to deduce a genotype from an ABO phenotype unless the groups of the family are available. For example, a group B individual could be B/B or B/O; an A_1 subject could be A^1/A^1, A^1/A^2 or even A^1/O. In contrast, group AB and group O individuals are A/B and O/O respectively, unless they are of the extremely rare *cis*-AB (with A and B antigens both derived from a rare allele at a single locus) or O 'Bombay' (see below) phenotypes.

Knowledge of the nucleotide sequences that distinguish the ABO alleles has enabled primers to be designed that can be used to determine ABO genotypes through the application of PCR. These include sequence specific primers that uniquely amplify A, B or O, as well as generic primers that amplify all ABO alleles; the products of the latter are distinguished by their sensitivity to restriction endonucleases that recognize the DNA sequences of specific ABO alleles.

ABO epitopes

ABO antigens are synthesized by glycosylation of oligosaccharides with H antigen activity. The H antigen is synthesized by a fucosyltransferase that is the product of the H gene on the long arm of chromosome 19. Carbohydrate chains carrying the A, B, and H antigens are present on 1) the short-chain oligosaccharides of simple glycolipids in plasma; 2) the heavily branched polysaccharides that form the polyglycosyl moieties of either soluble glycoproteins present in secretions or of polyglycosyl ceramides in the red cell membrane, and 3) the short O-linked and highly branched N-linked polysaccharides of integral membrane proteins. The immunodominant sugars of the A and B antigens are at the terminal (nonreducing end) of the various polysaccharide chains expressing A or B, and are invariably attached by an α1-3 linkage to a fucosylated galactose residue with H antigen activity (see **Figure 1**) such that the simplest A epitope is a trisaccharide with the structure:

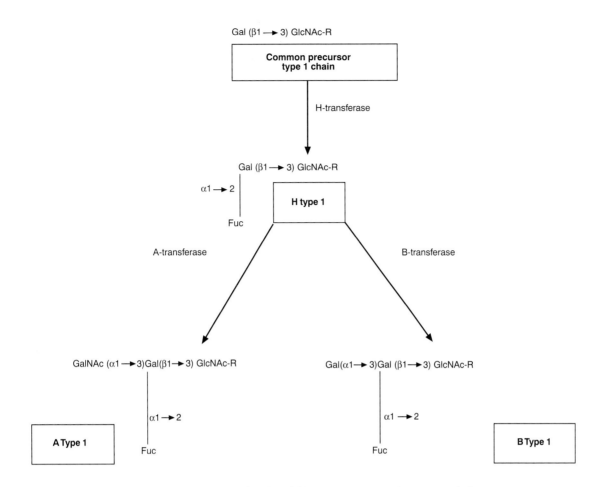

Gal (β1 ⟶ 3) GlcNAc-R

**Common precursor
type 1 chain**

H-transferase

Gal (β1 ⟶ 3) GlcNAc-R

α1 ⟶ 2

H type 1

Fuc

A-transferase   B-transferase

GalNAc (α1 ⟶ 3)Gal(β1 ⟶ 3) GlcNAc-R   Gal(α1 ⟶ 3)Gal (β1 ⟶ 3) GlcNAc-R

α1 ⟶ 2   α1 ⟶ 2

A Type 1   **B Type 1**

Fuc   Fuc

Figure 1   Biosynthetic pathways for the synthesis of A, B and H structures on type 1 precursor chains.

$$GalNAc(\alpha 1\text{–}3)Gal\text{——}R$$
$$|\alpha 1 \rightarrow 2$$
$$Fuc$$

where R represents the rest of the polysaccharide chain. The B epitopes have Gal instead of GalNAc as the immunodominant sugar. The presence of the fucosyl residue, i.e. the H antigen, is essential for A and B expression: its absence, as in the rare 'Bombay' phenotype, leads to an inability of the A- and B-transferases to add their respective sugars to the Gal part of Gal—R, and hence A and B antigens are not expressed, even though the relevant transferases can be detected in cells and plasma and are functionally active in *in vitro* assays using fucosylated substrates from normal subjects as acceptors. Such 'Bombay' individuals lack an H gene, being homozygous for the silent allele h.

The terminal trisaccharides can be attached to R in at least six different ways: e.g. by either a 1–3 or 1–4 linkage to βGlcNAc (type 1 and type 2 A or B structures respectively), by a 1–3 link to αGalNAc (type 3), βGalNAc (type 4) or βGal (type 5) or even a 1–4 link to βGlc (type 6). Of these, types 1 and 2 are the more abundant in the red cell membrane and the most important in red cell serology: integral red cell membrane proteins and glycolipids have almost exclusively type 2 linked sugars. Red cells may also contain glycolipids, passively adsorbed from plasma, that have exclusively type 1 chains. Secretions have a mixture of type 1 and type 2 epitopes. The existence of these various epitopes probably explains the heterogeneity in reactivity of different ABO antibodies with group A or B variants; seven reaction patterns for monoclonal anti-A and anti-B have been described.

In secretory tissues and other epithelia, ABH antigen expression is modulated by the genes of the 'secretor' (Se) locus which is not linked to the ABO locus; nonsecretor (se/se) individuals fail to produce type 1 and type 2 H in their secretions whereas red cell (type 2) H expression is unaffected.

Expression of ABO on red cells may be deliberately modified by treatment with glycosidases: an α-galactosidase extractable from green coffee beans can remove galactose from group B red cells and hence enzymically convert them to group O. Such 'ECO' (enzymically converted group O) red cells may survive normally when transfused to group O subjects. However, the clinical potential of such techniques is limited.

Biosynthesis and ontogeny

The A- and B-transferases and their respective antigens in adults are most abundant in intestinal and gastric mucosa, lungs and salivary glands. Significant levels are found in kidneys, bladder, urothelial cells, bone marrow and hematopoietic cells. The enzymes exist in the cytoplasm and bound to the membranes of the cells of the above tissues and in the membranes of red cells and platelets. The transferases are in free solution in the transtubular network and their relevant secretions, e.g. mucin droplets, plasma, ovarian cyst fluid, milk, saliva. Molecules glycosylated by the transferases include membrane enzymes, membrane structural proteins and receptors, as well as secreted proteins, e.g. IgA. The ABO transferases, but not others, can be lost in various cancers, e.g. carcinoma of the bladder and of the colon. Both N-linked and O-linked oligosaccharide moieties of glycoproteins with A or B activity are synthesized in the Golgi.

During ontogeny, ABH (and Lewis) activity is at its highest in the early embryo from the 5th week postfertilization; ABH antigens are found in large amounts on endothelial cells and most epithelial primordia, and in practically all early organs e.g. blood islands of the yolk sac, erythropoietic foci of the liver, digestive tube epithelia, pharyngeal pouches, the thymus, the pituitary, thyroid glands, trachea and bronchi, hepatic and pancreatic diverticula, the cloaca, urachos and allantois, mesonephros and the ducts of the metanephros. The CNS, liver, adrenal glands and secretory tubules show no ABH activity at this stage.

From the end of the 12–14th week of gestation, there is regression of ABH expression from epithelial cell walls, thyroid pituitary, and other glands and organs, to the adult vestigial pattern described above. The biological significance of this regression is unknown. The number of A and B sites on the red cell is increased approximately fourfold in adults as compared with newborn infants, such that there are $0.25–0.37 \times 10^6$ A sites per red cell in the newborn and $0.81–1.2 \times 10^6$ in the adult, as compared with $0.2–0.32 \times 10^6$ B sites per red cell in the newborn and 0.75×10^6 for adults.

A- and B-like antigens have been detected in a variety of microorganisms and animal tissues. During phylogeny, ABH antigens are confined to the endodermal tissues of amphibia and reptiles, and are present on the epidermis of all mammals studied to date. While ABH is found on baboon vascular endothelium, only humans and the great apes have red cells expressing ABH. ABO are 'histocompatibility' antigens; it is simply the peculiarity of their original description that has led to ABH antigens being thought of as 'blood groups'.

ABO antibodies

The clinical importance of the ABO blood group system derives from the universality of its antibodies and their *in vivo* potency. The 'naturally occurring' antibodies of the majority of group A or B individuals are mainly IgM and produced in response to environmental ABO antigens, e.g. from microbes in the gut and respiratory tract. Such IgM antibodies, although displaying optimal activity in the cold, are reactive at 37°C and can activate the complement cascade up to the C9 stage, leading to the immediate intravascular lysis of transfused incompatible red cells *in vivo*. In the UK, roughly one in every three randomly selected, ungrouped blood donations would be incompatible with a given recipient; such incompatible transfusions can lead to renal failure, disseminated intravascular coagulation and even death. The majority of the signs and symptoms of severe ABO hemolytic transfusion reactions can be attributed to the generation of C3a and C5a fragments as a result of complement fixation, with the consequent release of vasoactive amines from mast cells and of cytokines such as interleukin-1 (IL-1), IL-6, IL-8 and tumor necrosis factor α (TNFα) from mononuclear cells.

Most, if not all, group O adults, and a small proportion of group A and B subjects, have naturally occurring, usually weak, IgG in addition to stronger IgM ABO antibodies. The IgG component can cross the placenta and bind to fetal red cells; however, lysis of fetal red cells is generally minimal and hemolytic disease of the newborn (HDN) caused by ABO antibodies is usually mild or inapparent in Western Europe and North America. The occurrence of HDN due to ABO antibodies cannot be predicted, but it only affects the offspring of group O mothers. The lack of severity of most cases of ABO HDN is thought to be due to: 1) IgG ABO antibodies being predominantly IgG2, which is incapable of initiating complement-mediated hemolysis or destruction of antibody-coated red cells by the mononuclear phagocytic system (many sera have IgG1 ABO antibodies as well as an IgG2 component; a few sera have trace amounts of IgG3 and IgG4 antibodies); 2) substantial amounts of maternal IgG ABO antibodies binding to ABO sites on tissues other than red cells in the fetus; 3) soluble ABH antigens in plasma and body fluids of the fetus which neutralize IgG anti-A and anti-B and inhibit their binding; 4) the ABO epitopes of fetal red cells being present on unbranched oligosaccharides, which are thought to be unable to support the divalent IgG binding needed for complement activation by IgG1 or IgG3 antibodies; 5) fetal complement levels being too low to support efficient lysis of cord (or even adult) target red cells. However, in some parts of the world, ABO HDN is often more severe and this is attributed to environmental factors such as the stimulation of ABO antibodies by microbes and parasites.

Some individuals possess plasma IgA ABO antibodies irrespective of immunization; ABO antibodies of colostrum are often wholly IgA, although sometimes IgM antibodies can also be found.

Cord blood usually does not contain ABO antibodies although maternally derived IgG anti-A or -B can sometimes be detected. Newborn infants do not produce ABO antibodies until the 3rd–6th month of age (median titer = 4), reaching a maximal titer (approx. = 128) between the ages of 5 and 10 years. Anti-A seems to attain higher titers more rapidly than anti-B. Adult titers of anti-A range from 32 to 2048 (median = 256) and anti-B from 8 to 512 (median = 64). The vast majority of healthy adults

have readily detected ABO antibodies. Weakening of ABO antibodies can occur naturally in individuals aged over 50; a third of patients over 65 have ABO antibody titers of 4 or less. Occasional subjects may lack the appropriate ABO agglutinins, especially if hypogammaglobulinemic, or if their plasma IgM levels are low. Antibodies can be lost by exhaustive plasma exchange (used therapeutically in ABO incompatible bone marrow and organ transplantation) or by immunosuppression caused by therapy or by disease. IgM anti-A or -B are completely absent in individuals with the very rare Wiskott–Aldrich syndrome.

See also: **Alloantigens; Blood transfusion reactions; Cold agglutinins; Complement, classical pathway; Embryonic antigens; Erythrocytes; Forssman antigen; Hemolytic disease of the newborn; Maternal antibodies; Natural antibodies; Rh antigens.**

Further reading

Clausen H, Bennett EP and Grunnet N (1994) Molecular genetics of ABO histo-blood groups. *Transfusion Clinique Biologique* 2: 79–89.
Daniels G (1995) *Human Blood Groups*, Chapter 2, pp 8–120. Oxford: Blackwell.
Mollison PL, Engelfriet CP and Contreras M (1993) *Blood Transfusion in Clinical Medicine*, 9th edn, pp 148–203. Oxford: Blackwell.
Oriol R, Samuelsson BE and Messetov L (1990) ABO antibodies – serological behaviour and immunochemical characterisation. *Journal of Immunogenetics* 17: 279–299.
Schenkel-Brunner H (1995) *Human Blood Groups, Chemical and Biochemical Basis of Antigen Specificity*, pp 47–147. New York: Springer-Verlag.
Yamamoto F-I (1995) Molecular genetics of the ABO histo-blood group system. *Vox Sanguinis* 69: 1–7.

ACQUIRED IMMUNE DEFICIENCY SYNDROME (AIDS)

Anthony J Pinching, Department of Immunology, St Bartholomew's and the Royal
London School of Medicine and Dentistry, Queen Mary and Westfield College,
University of London, London, UK

In the early 1980s, reports appeared of a new immunodeficiency disease, which was later called the acquired immune deficiency syndrome or AIDS. Over the following decade and a half, the scale of AIDS has risen from a mere handful of cases in the USA to hundreds of thousands of cases affecting most countries worldwide. The human imunodeficiency viruses (HIV-1 and HIV-2), the causative retroviruses of AIDS, have already spread to 15–20 million individuals in less than three decades, and continue to spread rapidly in many communities, especially in the developing world. This epidemic of profound immunodeficiency, predominantly affecting cell-mediated immunity, has had a devastating and pervasive impact on many individuals and societies and has presented many challenges to immunology and to other clinical and scientific disciplines. Although an inadequate counterweight to its tragic personal and social impact, AIDS has served to focus and increase our knowledge of the immune system in health and disease as well as our understanding of individuals and of human society.

Epidemiology

Although the first cases of AIDS were seen in homosexual men in the USA, it soon became apparent that the epidemic of HIV and AIDS was occurring more widely in North America, Europe and Australasia, not only among homosexual men but also among intravenous drug users, recipients of blood and blood products, notably hemophiliacs, and to a lesser extent among heterosexual men and women, and among children of HIV-infected women. It also gradually emerged that a substantial epidemic was affecting several regions in the developing world, such as sub-Saharan Africa and the Caribbean, with a somewhat different pattern of infection, predominantly affecting heterosexual men and women and their children, as well as recipients of blood transfusions. South America showed a mixture of the two patterns, while other regions such as the Middle East and Asia initially showed a lower incidence of a type more similar to that seen in Africa. In the late 1980s, there was a rapid expansion of the epidemics in India and South-East Asia, predominantly through heterosexual spread and among injecting drug users.

These epidemics are almost entirely due to HIV-1, although there is regional variation in serotypes. Type B virus is found mainly in the USA and Europe, while other serotypes are seen in Africa and Asia; it has recently been suggested that type E, found in parts of Thailand, may have a greater capacity for heterosexual transmission. HIV-2, a related virus, has been seen in West Africa and remains largely restricted to that region. It appears to be less readily transmissible (though by the same routes) and is also less pathogenic, but causes the same spectrum of disease as HIV-1.

Such overall patterns of spread, together with detailed case and cluster studies, indicated that HIV was spread by three routes: sexual transmission, transmission by blood and from an infected mother to the fetus. Sexual transmission could occur through penetrative intercourse between homosexual men or between men and women. Regional differences in the type of sexual spread mainly reflect differences in prevalent sexual behavioural patterns and frequency of sexual partner change. Intercurrent sexually transmitted infections, especially those associated with genital ulceration, in either partner increase the risk of transmission but are clearly not essential. Blood-borne transmission occurred through transfusion of blood or blood products, but also, on a larger scale, between intravenous drug users who shared needles and syringes and other equipment; there is a small but definite risk of infection through inoculation injury. Vertical transmission occurs in part transplacentally, in part during delivery and in part through breastfeeding, although the proportions remain uncertain. Casual transmission has not been documented.

There has been considerable interest in the possibility that individuals exposed to HIV may develop protective immunity that prevents or clears initial infection or have features that prevent or reduce the risk of subsequent infection. For example, cohorts of female prostitutes in Africa and of homosexual men include individuals who appear to have been multiply exposed but remain uninfected. These show some HLA association and evidence of HIV-specific cytotoxic immune responses. The mechanism remains obscure. Recent observations on second receptors for

HIV, which are variably expressed among some populations, raise the possibility that lack of such receptors could be protective. Some infants appear to show evidence of transient infection as evidenced by polymerase chain reaction (PCR) or viral culture in the weeks after delivery but do not seroconvert or show any other signs of infection later. It has been proposed that they have cleared the infection, although the possibility of prolonged circulation of latently infected maternal cells has not been excluded.

Spectrum of HIV infection

A person infected by HIV will, within 3 weeks to 3 months, develop a detectable antibody response and will remain HIV antibody positive thereafter. Given that HIV establishes persistent infection, antibody positivity can be taken as evidence of current infection and has been widely used clinically and epidemiologically as a marker.

At the time of seroconversion, a significant minority of patients develop an acute transient glandular fever-like illness, with fever, malaise, rash, sore throat, lymphadenopathy, arthralgia and headaches (HIV seroconversion illness). In a few cases there is frank encephalopathy or aseptic meningitis. It is also now recognized that some patients develop acute, transient cellular immunodeficiency, manifested, for example, by oral and esophageal candidiasis. The symptoms and signs of acute HIV infection typically resolve after a few weeks. Patients with a severe and prolonged acute illness appear to progress to AIDS more rapidly, and those who develop any symptomatic seroconversion are more likely to progress than those who do not. After the resolution of the acute illness, patients will pass into a phase of chronic symptomless HIV infection.

Chronic symptomless HIV infection may take one of two forms – patients without any abnormal physical signs and those with persistent generalized lymphadenopathy. The lymph nodes are in most instances moderately enlarged in cervical, axillary and inguinal regions (although inguinal nodes may be enlarged to a similar degree in people without HIV infection) and some other peripheral sites, such as the epitrochlear nodes. They are sometimes slightly tender and may fluctuate in size with intercurrent illness, but are otherwise unremarkable. Patients may remain symptomless, with or without enlarged lymph nodes, for many years but over time a substantial proportion go on to develop disease. The risk for developing symptomatic disease is similar for patients with and without lymphadenopathy.

A few patients with otherwise symptomless chronic infection and without immunodeficiency develop thrombocytopenic purpura. The pathogenesis of this is somewhat unclear, with evidence for platelet-specific antibodies and for immune complexes in different studies. The disorder is rarely associated with severe bleeding and seems to remit spontaneously after a few years in most cases. It does not presage progression.

With increasing years of infection, an increasing proportion of patients with chronic HIV infection will progress to develop evidence of immunodeficiency and other disease. This may initially be seen as constitutional illness (malaise, weight loss, diarrhea) or evidence of moderately severe immunodeficiency (oral candidiasis, oral hairy leukoplakia, multidermatomal shingles, salmonellosis). Patients may first develop such symptoms and later progress to AIDS, while others develop AIDS without any intervening symptomatic stage.

AIDS itself comprises two main categories: patients with major opportunist infections of cell-mediated type (e.g. *Pneumocystis carinii* pneumonia, cryptococcal meningitis, disseminated mycobacterial infection, cytomegalovirus retinitis), and those with opportunist tumors, Kaposi's sarcoma and B cell lymphoma. These will be considered in more detail below. It is worth noting that patients with Kaposi's sarcoma alone and some patients with lymphoma have less severe immunodeficiency than those with major opportunist infections.

In addition to the problems with cell-mediated opportunists, some patients, especially children, show significantly increased susceptibility to infections with capsulated bacteria of a type more typically associated with humoral immunodeficiency. This results from the dysglobulinemia seen in HIV infection, in which there is immunoglobulin G2 (IgG2) subclass deficiency and impairment of specific antibody development against antigens not previously encountered. These infections can occur with increased incidence in people with otherwise symptomless infection.

As well as its immunopathogenic effects, HIV can also cause chronic progressive disease of the nervous system, including HIV encephalopathy (or AIDS dementia complex), vacuolar myelopathy, peripheral and autonomic neuropathy, and occasionally an inflammatory myopathy. The central nervous system disorders typically occur after the onset of immunodeficiency disease, but go on to affect a high proportion to varying degrees.

A variety of other clinical disorders are seen, including: lymphocytic interstitial pneumonitis and an associated chronic lymphocytic parotitis, which are commonly seen in children but rarely in adults;

the appearance or increased severity of psoriasis and Reiter's syndrome and other seronegative arthropathies; HIV enteropathy with partial villous atrophy; and recrudescence of atopic disease in predisposed subjects.

Clinical features of AIDS

The profound and progressive immunodeficiency seen in AIDS is broadly characterized by infections with facultative intracellular and related pathogens and herpesviruses, and by opportunist tumors. While some of these pathogens only cause disease in immunodeficient subjects, others show altered and enhanced pathogenicity, causing different clinical disorders or more disseminated disease. The profile of these infections shows regional variation determined by locally prevalent pathogens and risk behaviour, which also affect the likelihood of infection by the relevant organisms, many of which are latent in the immunocompetent host.

Common and early infections in AIDS include *Pneumocystis carinii* pneumonia, disseminated tuberculosis, esophageal candidiasis, cryptococcal meningitis and ulcerative mucocutaneous herpes simplex infection. Other common infections seen, typically later in the course of the progressive decline in cell-mediated immunity, include cerebral toxoplasmosis, cytomegalovirus disease (presenting as retinitis, colitis, esophagitis and adrenalitis and, less often, pneumonitis, encephalitis and radiculitis), disseminated *Mycobacterium avium intracellulare* infection, histoplasmosis, gastrointestinal cryptosporidiosis, progressive multifocal leukoencephalopathy, visceral leishmaniasis, disseminated penicilliosis, nocardiosis and disseminated strongyloidiasis. Some of these organisms present predominantly in one organ system – lungs, gut, central nervous system, lymph nodes – but may also show varying degrees of dissemination.

Kaposi's sarcoma, which is most common among homosexual men and among heterosexually acquired cases of HIV in the developing world, is thought to result from infection with a newly recognized human herpesvirus, HHV-8. It often presents as cutaneous disease, later progressing in some patients to affect lymph nodes, lungs and gastrointestinal tract. Severe visceral disease more commonly presents early in patients in Africa. B cell lymphoma, of a variety of histological types, may present as isolated cerebral lymphoma or as systemic disease, with frequent extranodal involvement. Hodgkin's lymphoma, seminoma, squamous carcinoma of the anorectal region, cervical carcinoma and acute myeloid leukemia have also been observed somewhat more frequently in HIV-infected subjects, although the association is less clear.

Natural history of HIV infection

The risk of development of disease in HIV-infected subjects has been assessed in large cohort studies. These have shown that in time the majority will develop AIDS (50% in 10 years; 65% in 14), with others progressing to less severe symptomatic HIV disease. It is now recognized that a small proportion of patients remain well and without evidence of immunodeficiency for 10 or more years. It is not clear whether they represent a discrete group or simply those with much slower progression rates. They are the subject of many studies attempting to define whether there are immune or other protective mechanisms.

Several factors affecting the likelihood of progression in HIV-infected subjects have been identified. Increased risk of disease and of immunological decline has been shown in patients with the HLA-A1, -B8, -DR3 haplotype in cohorts of hemophiliacs and homosexual men and HLA-B35 may also increase the risk of progression. In some ethnic groups HLA-DR5 is associated with increased risk of Kaposi's sarcoma. Patients with HLA-B27 appear to have a lower risk of progression.

Intercurrent infections may also affect progression: evidence of such an effect has been shown for sexually transmitted infections among homosexual men and for cytomegalovirus infection among hemophiliacs. It is plausible that other infections may have a similar effect, including systemic bacterial infections in injecting drug users using unsterile equipment, and possibly some of the infections that result from immunodeficiency, such as tuberculosis, listeriosis and pneumocystosis.

Age may also have some effect. This is most clearly seen in children infected in the neonatal period who show a much higher proportion of rapid progressions than adults. This is unlikely to reflect immunological immaturity and may result from immunological activation during the acquisition of an immunological repertoire. Children over 4 years of age show similar progression rates to adults. Adults over 50 years of age may also have slightly increased risk of progression.

The effect of pregnancy is controversial. Early studies that were carried out on women who had already given birth to a child with AIDS showed that subsequent pregnancies were associated with increased risk of progressive disease in the mother. More recent studies on women having their first HIV-positive pregnancy indicate no increased risk. It is possible to reconcile these findings by concluding that having more than one HIV-positive pregnancy increases the risk to the mother.

Although formal epidemiological data are lacking, it is plausible that malnutrition, which itself induces cell-mediated immunodeficiency, may enhance the risk of progression to HIV disease. A higher rate of progression has been reported in a prospectively studied cohort in Uganda; several factors could have contributed to this, including different viral strains, different human genotypes, intercurrent parasitic and other infections and nutritional state. The use of immunosuppressive drugs such as prolonged high doses of corticosteroids may enhance risk.

The overall picture is one where increased risk of progression is associated with events that may activate the immune system, and thus active CD4 lymphocytes and macrophages which are latently infected with HIV, hence increasing virus replication, cell-to-cell spread and progressive immunological decline, as well as with events that suppress cell-mediated immune responses, thus compounding the factors leading to immunological deterioration.

Some strains of virus, whether the initially infecting virus or one that emerges through mutation within the infected host, may have greater pathogenic potential. One transfusion-associated cluster of HIV infections has been reported in which long-term nonprogression was a feature and where the HIV strain had a defective nef gene; this does not appear to be a generalizable feature but indicates the role of viral genotype, as do the lower rates of progression with HIV-2.

The role of protective immunity, whether humoral or cell mediated, is far from clear. Neither neutralizing antibody titer nor HIV-specific cytotoxicity, whether of antibody-dependent type or major histocompatibility complex (MHC)-restricted type, have any consistent relationship with progression. These responses are present throughout the spectrum of HIV infection and disease. It remains to be established whether or not innate resistance or susceptibility to HIV infection or disease play any part, or whether genetic factors serve rather to influence the ease with which, for example, immunological activation by intercurrent events is achieved, as is implied by the association with the HLA-A1, -B8, -DR3 phenotype. The study of long-term nonprogressors has attempted to elicit evidence of special features associated with nonprogression but has not yet shown any unique or general characteristic of host or virus. One problem with such studies is that of finding an appropriate comparator group, as their rapidly progressing peers may already have died and

current rapid progressors may have different initial host and viral characteristics.

Predictive markers for progression

Another objective of cohort analysis has been the identification of markers that can predict risk of future progression in HIV-infected subjects. The numbers of CD4 cells in blood have been widely used in this way, not least because they can reflect a significant component of the pathogenesis of disease. In grouped data over long-term follow-up, falling CD4 counts are strongly associated with progression. However, there is considerable variability in individual trends and, as many other factors can affect CD4 count, CD4 counts must be used with caution in individual patients. Serum markers of immunological activation such as β_2-microglobulin, neopterin and interleukin 2 (IL-2) receptor are also associated with an increased risk of progression, as are raised IgA levels. The CD8 count may rise during the early years of HIV infection and then fall in the 2 years before progression, but the predictive value is unclear. CD8 derived cytokines may inhibit virus spread.

Virological markers are also of value. In early studies, HIV p24 antigenemia was strongly associated with progression in patients in temperate climates, although a significant proportion of AIDS patients do not develop antigenemia. Prior to the appearance of HIV p24 antigen, antibody levels against p24 fall, perhaps reflecting the complexing of p24 antigen and antibody following increased virus replication. Reduced levels of antibodies to p17 and to reverse transcriptase may show similar trends. These changes are not seen in patients in tropical environments, perhaps due to increased polyclonal B cell activation due to parasitic and other infections. It is evident that p24 antigen is an imperfect and crude index of virus replication.

Recently, it has become possible to measure viral load by quantitative PCR. Studies on a large prospective cohort of HIV-infected individuals have shown that viral load measures on initial samples provide a powerful predictive marker for subsequent progression. Such tests appear to be more discriminatory than CD4 count alone. Such findings are likely to provide a valuable means of assessing prognosis and suitability for antiretroviral therapy. They may help to identify those subjects with a high CD4 count who do poorly and those with a low CD4 counts who do well. Although the use of the two markers in conjunction has yet to be analyzed, this is likely to be a particularly useful combination for assessing future progression. Longitudinal analysis of both markers may add further value. Earlier data showed that combining CD4 counts with serum neopterin, IgA, IL-2 receptor and p24 antigen could provide a better prediction of outcome than CD4 alone, although these are likely to be superseded by viral load measures, which probably correlate with activation markers.

Immunopathogenesis

HIV is a retrovirus, having an RNA gene that encodes for reverse transcriptase, which allows a DNA copy of the virus to be made. This DNA copy is then spliced into the gene of the infected cell, through the action of virally encoded endonuclease, leading to persistent and typically productive infection.

A major HIV gene product is the outer envelope glycoprotein gp120, which is expressed on the surface of the virus and of infected cells, and contains a region which binds with high affinity to the CD4 molecule on host cells. CD4 thus acts as the main virus receptor, enabling HIV gp120 to target cells of the immune system for infection and subsequent damage. Second receptors (CXCR4 and CCR5) for HIV on CD4 T lymphocytes and on antigen-presenting cells are a family of transmembrane proteins which are physiological receptors for chemokines. They appear to be critical to fusion events and cellular infectivity, and may also explain data showing that combinations of chemokines (RANTES, MIP-1α and MIP-1β) can inhibit cell-to-cell infection *in vitro*.

After the attachment of gp120 to CD4 and the second receptor on lymphocytes or macrophages, the virus membrane fuses with the membrane of the CD4-bearing cell, internalizing the virus genome and leading to cellular infection. This occurs both in initial infection and in the gradual process of cell-to-cell spread within the body that leads ultimately to disease. Infection of CD4 lymphocytes is central to the immunopathogenetic effects of HIV. Macrophages and related cells can also be infected by routes other than CD4 binding, e.g. Fc or C3b receptor binding. Such cells serve as an important reservoir of HIV infection and are implicated in the neuropathogenesis of HIV encephalopathy. Recent data have emphasized that most cell-to-cell infection occurs in lymphoid tissue, where extensive viral replication has been documented. As disease progresses, this results in significant structural damage to these key microenvironments.

The viral replication cycle proceeds at a rapid rate in infected patients, with durations of as little as 2.6 days, giving some 140 generations each year. This, combined with the error-prone transcription of retroviral genes, gives the opportunity for enormous diversity of viruses within any individual. It is against this background that pathogenetically diverse strains, such as syncytium-inducing strains, and drug-resistant strains may emerge. In turn these affect the rate of immunological decline and responsiveness to therapy.

The most striking and most consistent effects of HIV in progressive disease are a reduction both in the number and in the function of CD4 lymphocytes. Infection of CD4 lymphocytes by HIV leads to their premature death or rapid elimination, so that few viable circulating CD4 cells show evidence of infection at any time, yet their numbers are progressively depleted. This may be due to virus cytopathic effects or to host-mediated cytotoxicity, or both. Virus-induced damage includes cell lysis and, more importantly, apoptosis and the formation of syncytia by fusion of infected as well as uninfected CD4 lymphocytes.

In addition to the progressive attrition of CD4 lymphocytes, various defects in the function of the CD4 cells that remain have been shown, even though most of them are uninfected at the time. These include failure of T cell responses to antigen, to T cell mitogens (phytohemagglutinin, concanavalin A) and to T cell-dependent B cell mitogen (pokeweed), whether measured by proliferation or cytokine/antibody production. Impaired cytokine release is seen for IL-2 and macrophage-activating cytokines such as interferon γ, as well as cytokines involved in regulating B cell responses. It seems that the failure of these mechanisms is largely responsible for the defects in killing of facultative intracellular pathogens, failure to control virally-induced tumors and herpesvirus infection and for some of the B cell defects seen in patients.

One common means whereby these effects on CD4 cell function could be mediated by HIV has been shown. HIV infection of lymphocytes *in vitro* or exposure of uninfected lymphocytes to gp120 causes activation of the inositol polyphosphate (InsP) signal transduction pathway; this causes a rise in resting levels of $InsP_3$ and $InsP_4$, and hence of intracellular calcium. This leads to a state of chronic cellular activation, rendering the cells less responsive to new signals. Similar changes are seen in lymphocytes taken from patients. These effects may be mediated by binding to CD4 and subsequent alterations in the intracellular signaling pathways involving tyrosine phosphorylation, starting with p56[lck]. Similar changes in activation are seen in macrophages and it is possible that similar effects underlie the effect of HIV proteins on B cell function.

Depletion of CD4 lymphocytes and their functional impairment has knock-on effects on many other cells, in addition to any direct effects that HIV has on them. Patients' macrophages show impaired microbicidal activity for intracellular pathogens in the presence of cytokines produced by autologous lymphocytes, although they retain responsiveness to exogenous interferon γ. Other macrophage functions, including antigen-presenting function and receptor expression, show changes that may result from loss of CD4 lymphocyte signals or from HIV infection. Dendritic cells, which may be infected by HIV, may be depleted and show marked dysfunction in antigen-presenting activity from an early stage of HIV infection. Natural killer (NK) cells and other cytotoxic cells show reduced recruitment and activity, in part due to reduced IL-2 and interferon γ production.

CD8 T lymphocytes are clearly altered in number with disease progression (see above) and show increased activation markers. Previously thought not to be infected, a recent report suggests that they may indeed be infected especially in patients with advanced disease, possibly as a result of infection of thymic precursors which coexpress CD4. This may contribute to the decline in their number in late disease and to their functional abnormalities. Furthermore, CD8 cells produce factors, which may include chemokines acting on the second receptor and/or other factors, that inhibit viral infection of CD4 cells. If these *in vitro* effects are operative *in vivo*, they may act to control or contain viral replication earlier in HIV infection. This is in addition to any role of CD8 cell-mediated specific cellular cytotoxicity, discussed above.

B cells show polyclonal activation in HIV-infected subjects, notably those with persistent generalized lymphadenopathy and Kaposi's sarcoma, with raised IgG1, IgG3, IgA, IgE and IgM levels. IgG2 and IgG4 levels may be low. Spontaneous immunoglobulin production is increased and responses to T cell-independent antigens are reduced. Enhanced B cell IgD production and raised serum IgD levels imply increased immaturity of B cells, which is also suggested by phenotypic alterations. In addition, responses to B cell mitogens and T cell-dependent mitogens and antigens are impaired, whether at a T cell level, antigen-presenting cell level, B cell level or a combination of any of these. Follicular dendritic cells in lymph nodes, which show evidence of HIV infection, show progressive destruction in patients with symptomatic HIV infection and AIDS. As a result of these various defects, patients show increased levels of antibodies to previously encountered antigens but are unable to develop new antibody responses.

The neuropathogenesis of HIV encephalopathy and other nervous system disorders is more obscure. However, HIV encephalopathy also appears to result from both loss of cells and defective function of those that remain. The main cell type in the nervous system that harbours HIV is the macrophage, including perivascular macrophages and microglia, with little indication of infection of neuronal or glial elements. It is likely that HIV infection of such cells causes release of virus proteins or macrophage products, which in turn damage or alter the function of neighbouring nerve cells. gp120 can interfere with neuronal function in a similar way to that seen in lymphocytes, with activation of signal transduction pathways and raised intracellular calcium.

Treatment strategies in HIV disease

The AIDS pandemic has meant that large numbers of patients with severe immunodeficiency now require health care provision. Such patients need substantial specialist input from a wide variety of medical disciplines as well as a wider multidisciplinary team. Accessible and appropriate health care systems are being developed to cater for the various stages of HIV disease. Patients are increasingly involved in aspects of their care, notably in health maintenance (avoiding undernutrition, smoking, alcohol excess, and other cofactors). Specific therapies are of three types: treatment/prophylaxis of opportunist diseases, antiretroviral therapies and immunorestorative approaches.

Many of the opportunist infections are readily manageable, especially in the earlier stages of AIDS, with the use of specific antimicrobials and antitumor therapies. For many of the infections, maintenance therapy is required to avoid relapse. For some common infections, the use of antimicrobial prophylaxis offers considerable benefit, although there is often a trade-off of toxicity or drug hypersensitivity. Indeed drug hypersensitivity (type I and/or type III) to sulfonamides, antifungals and other drugs is notably more common in these immunodeficient patients. The increasingly effective use of antimicrobial treatment and prophylaxis has changed the clinical profile of disease, with deferral or elimination of some opportunistic events and decreased morbidity. However, it presents further challenges as more patients have more prolonged periods of severe immunodeficiency, leading to a greater proportion being affected by the less treatable infections and tumors, and new and more complex clinical events.

Antiretroviral therapy has developed rapidly in recent years. Zidovudine (AZT), a reverse transcriptase inhibitor and the first agent to show clinical efficacy, has had a significant impact when given as monotherapy in AIDS and symptomatic HIV infection, reducing viral replication and hence reducing the rate at which disease progresses. This led to valuable increases in length and quality of life; improvement in HIV encephalopathy and reduction in its incidence are other notable benefits. Myelosuppression, gastrointestinal symptoms and a mitochondrial myopathy are seen, particularly at high doses, in patients with more advanced disease or where other drugs add to these problems. The benefit of zidovudine monotherapy seems on average to wane after some 2 years, whether due to its intrinsic limitations or the emergence of viral resistance. A logical approach to antiviral therapy would be to start treatment earlier, while the virus is active but when immune destruction is not so far advanced. With zidovudine alone, despite early encouragement, there is no general benefit in terms of clinical outcome. Zidovudine has, however, been shown to decrease vertical transmission if given to mothers during pregnancy and to the neonate.

Given the nature of the viral challenge, the use of combination therapies seems highly appropriate, with the objective of increasing efficacy and inhibiting the emergence of viral resistance, and possibly reducing toxicity. Initially this approach was focused on other nucleoside analogues, such as didanosine, zalcitabine, lamivudine and stavudine. Recent studies have shown the greater and more prolonged clinical efficacy of dual therapy with pairs of nucleoside analogs, confirming earlier studies showing their greater impact on CD4 count and on viral load. These therapies appear to offer some efficacy in earlier stages of infection, but the optimal timing is uncertain.

Two other major classes of antiretroviral agents have emerged – non-nucleoside reverse transcriptase inhibitors (NNRTI) (e.g. nevirapine, delavirdine, loviride) and protease inhibitors (e.g. saquinavir, ritonavir and indinavir). Triple combinations (e.g. two nucleosides and an NNRTI, or two nucleosides and a protease inhibitor) have an even more potent and durable impact on markers and, at least on early evidence, on clinical outcomes than two-drug regimens. Viral resistance appears to be more profoundly inhibited, which offers encouraging prospects for long-term efficacy. These more substantial effects raise the possibility of much earlier treatment, and some studies are exploring the effect of treating at or around the time of seroconversion.

Many issues still need to be resolved regarding antiretroviral therapy: optimal timing; optimal initial combinations; suitable means of monitoring patients on treatment; how these can inform decisions about if and when to change and, if so, what to change to;

and appropriate sequences of therapy. While some further approaches to antiviral treatment are being studied, the current portfolio of three classes seems likely to remain the core of treatment for some time, and there is a need to ensure that the armamentarium is deployed most effectively.

Among antiretroviral approaches that have been tried was the use of soluble CD4 or CD4 linked to an Fc molecule as a decoy for viral gp120. This looked promising *in vitro* and appeared not to interfere with cell function, but *in vivo* results were disappointing. This may be for a number of reasons, including the need to achieve very high levels to inhibit viral spread, the short plasma half-life of CD4 and the probability that much cell-to-cell transmission occurs directly, without a fluid phase.

Immunological approaches to therapy have been disappointing to date, although most were tried before effective antiretrovirals were available. Some are being re-explored in combination with antiretroviral therapy. Bone marrow transplantation has been generally disappointing, even when combined with antivirals. Several cytokines have been tried, including IL-2 and interferon γ, with some encouraging *in vitro* changes, and these are being tried with antiretrovirals. Immunostimulation has always been hard to achieve in reality and no clear agent of this type has been shown to be effective. One trial has shown that inosine pranobex (isoprinosine) may delay disease progression when given to asymptomatic patients, but other trials have not confirmed this; the mechanism of action is not clear.

Immunoglobulin therapy has proved helpful in patients, especially children, with antibody deficiency, by reducing problems with pyogenic infections. HIV antibody from asymptomatic subjects has been used as passive specific antibody therapy in a few studies but the results are not impressive and do not suggest that any effect is necessarily due to an antiretroviral mechanism; it is doubtful that passively acquired antibody will be any better than that produced actively in stemming viral replication and cell-to-cell transmission. Some have suggested that immunization with certain HIV antigens may be effective but such approaches may be subject to similar provisos; recent reports of therapeutic vaccines show no benefit with envelope glycoprotein or p24.

Vaccines

Extensive work is being done to develop vaccines against primary HIV infection. This work has utilised gp120 or other viral proteins and has employed a variety of viral and other vectors. Antibody and cytotoxic responses can be readily obtained, but most work in animals shows that infection is not prevented or is restricted to a few strains. It remains unclear whether these problems reflect limitations of the immune responses obtained with such approaches or whether they reflect the fact that in most cases primary infection of target cells occurs at the mucosal level, where contact between virus and macrophage or lymphocyte is unlikely to be impeded by such antibody as reaches that site. Some studies have examined ways of producing more substantial mucosal immunity and this would seem a critical element in any vaccine approach. The prospect of an effective vaccine in the imminent future seems remote.

See also: **Chemokines; Chimerism, hematopoietic; Dendritic cells; Human immunodeficiency viruses; Opportunistic infections; Retrovirus, infection and immunity.**

Further reading

Barré-Simoussi F (1996) HIV as the cause of AIDS. *Lancet* 348: 31–35.
Bloom BR (1996) A perspective on AIDS vaccines. *Science* 272: 1888–1890.
Carpenter CCJ, Fischl MA, Hammer SM et al for the International AIDS Society – USA (1997) Antiretroviral therapy for HIV infection in 1997. *Journal of the American Medical Association* 277: 1962–1969.
Corey L and Holmes KK (1996) Therapy for human immunodeficiency virus infection – what have we learned? *New England Journal of Medicine* 335: 1142–1144.
de Boer RJ and Boerlijst MC (1994) Diversity and virulence thresholds in AIDS. *Proceedings of the National Academy of Sciences of the USA* 91: 544–548.
de Vita VT Jr, Hellman S and Rosenberg SA (eds) (1997) *AIDS: Etiology, Diagnosis, Treatment and Prevention*, 4th edn. Philadelphia: Lippincott-Raven.
Feinberg MB and McLean AR (1997) AIDS: decline and fall of immune surveillance. *Current Biology* 7: R136–140.
Fowke KR, Nagelkerke NJD, Kimani J, Simonsen JN et al. (1996) Resistance to HIV-1 infection among persistently seronegative prostitutes in Nairobi, Kenya. *Lancet* 348: 1347–1351.
Haynes BF, Pantaleo G and Fauci AS (1996) Toward an understanding of the correlates of protective immunity to HIV infection. *Science* 271: 324–328.
Ho DD, Neumann AU, Perelson AS, Chen W, Leonard JM, Markowitz M (1995) Rapid turnover of plasma virions and CD4 lymphocytes in HIV-1 infection. *Nature* 373: 123–126.
Kaslow RA, Carrington M, Apple R, Park L, Munoz A, Saah AJ et al (1996) Influence of combinations of human major histocompatibility complex genes on the course of HIV-1 infection *Nature Medicine* 4: 405–411.
Levy JA (1996) Infection by Human Immunodeficiency Virus – CD4 is not enough. *New England Journal of Medicine* 335: 1528–1530.
Mellors JW, Rinaldo CR, Gupta P, White RM, Todd JA, Kingsley LA (1996) Prognosis in HIV-1 infection predicted by the quantity of virus in plasma. *Science* 272: 1167–1170.
Saag MS, Holodniy M, Kuritzkes DR et al (1996) HIV viral load markers in clinical practice *Nature Medicine* 2: 625–629.
Ng TTC, Pinching AJ, Guntermann C and Morrow WJW (1996) Molecular immunopathogenesis of HIV infection. *Genitourinary Medicine* 72: 408–418.
Quinn TC (1996) Global burden of the HIV pandemic. *Lancet* 348: 99–106.
Rosenberg PS (1995) Scope of the AIDS epidemic in the United States. *Science* 270: 1372–1375.
Weiss RA (1996) HIV receptors and the pathogenesis of AIDS. *Science* 272: 1885–1886.

ACQUIRED IMMUNE RESPONSE

Anne Sperling, Committee on Immunology, the Ben May Institute, University of Chicago, Chicago, Illinois, USA

Jeffrey A Bluestone, Department of Pathology, University of Chicago, Chicago, Illinois, USA

The development of immunity to a particular pathogen occurs after initial exposure to the antigen. The immunity is due to the development of an acquired immune response to the pathogen. A baby is born virtually immunologically naive. Maternal antibodies that have crossed the placenta provide transient protection from infection until the newborn's own immune system has developed sufficiently to mount an immune response strong enough and fast enough to protect against initial infection. After a primary immune response to a pathogen, an acquired immunity is developed such that any further infection by that pathogen is immediately controlled. The secondary or acquired immune response to the pathogen is more rapid and of greater magnitude and thus provides elevated protection against infection. From birth throughout a person's life, the immune system is continually responding to new environmental challenges (e.g. bacteria and viruses), and developing immunity to those challenges. The study of the acquired immune response is the basis of the science of immunology.

Historical background

The phenomenon of acquired immunity was observed as early as 430 BC when the historian Thucydides in his description of the plague of Athens wrote: 'Yet it was with those who had recovered from the disease that the sick and the dying found most compassion. These knew what it was from experience, and had now no fear for themselves; for the same man was never attacked twice – never, at least, fatally.' Thus even the early Greeks understood that individuals who had been exposed to a disease were provided protection from later susceptibility.

In the eighteenth century, the practice of active immunizations by inoculation with diseased material from smallpox victims (or later the inoculation of related or attenuated virus discovered by Jenner) was the impetus for modern studies of the acquired immune response. Today the acquired immune response is still being investigated on both the cellular and the molecular level.

Characteristics of the acquired immune response

The first time an antigen enters the body a wide spectrum of events occurs. The antigen is usually contained at the site of entry and in nearby lymph nodes by various phagocytic cells such as macrophages and dendritic cells. These cells process the antigen and present pathogen-derived peptides to $CD4^+$ and $CD8^+$ T cells in association with major histocompatibility complex (MHC)-encoded molecules. Antigen binding by surface immunoglobulin and cognate help by $CD4^+$ T cells induce B cells to differentiate to antibody-secreting plasma cells. During a primary immune response there is a lag time of approximately 3–4 days before antigen-specific antibody is evident in serum, and the levels do not peak until approximately day 7. The antibodies produced are primarily immunoglobulin M (IgM), which are characteristically very heterogeneous in their affinity for the antigen. IgG antibodies do not appear in the serum until approximately day 7 and do not peak until day 14. Thus the primary humoral immune response is very slow and weak.

The acquired or secondary immune response occurs when the antigen is encountered by the immune system any time after the primary response. This may occur several days or many years after the initial encounter. The acquired response is characterized by a more rapid and intense attack by the immune system. Increased levels of IgG antibodies appear in the serum within 24 h after infection. In the case of cell-mediated immunity, greater numbers of antigen-specific T cells rapidly respond. The ability of the immune system to 'remember' past exposure to antigens is called immunological memory and is one of the hallmarks of the immune system.

Mechanisms of acquired immunity

Development of high-affinity memory B cells

Towards the end of a primary response, higher affinity antibodies are found than were apparent early on. This phenomenon is called affinity maturation, and is found primarily with antibodies derived from B cells that have undergone isotype switching to IgG or IgA classes. During the primary response, many of the B cells differentiate to memory B cells. These memory B cells have been found to be extremely long-lived and, when activated, characteristically produce immunoglobulin that is similar to that found during the later stages of the primary response. Thus, when antigen is encountered by memory B cells, the cells are easily activated and able to produce a strong and rapid humoral immune response.

Memory B cells are highly effective antigen-presenting cells

The clonal expansion of antigen-specific memory B cells provides a large population of highly specific antigen-presenting cells. It has been shown by several groups that antigen-specific B cells are much more effective presenting cells than other known accessory cells such as macrophages and dendritic cells. Memory B cells take up antigen through their high-affinity surface immunoglobulin, and present high concentrations of antigen in association with MHC on their surface. Thus, antigen presentation to T cells, a critical early event in generating an immune response, is also more effective during a secondary immune response.

Clonal expansion of antigen-specific T cells

During the primary immune response, antigen-specific T cells are clonally expanded. It is believed that this expansion provides a further level of protection from reinfection. The mechanisms involved in the development and maintenance of T cell memory are still unclear. After the initial T cell expansion, the antigen-specific T cells are downregulated through induction of programmed cell death and anergy. This stage is followed by the development of an antigen-specific memory T cell population. This population of T cells can remain with the individual for a lifetime, and can provide protection from further infections by the organism that expresses the antigen. There are two proposed mechanisms for how the body maintains these antigen-specific memory T cells. The first is that once these memory cells develop, they are extremely long-lived and can survive indefinitely to provide protection for the individual. The second hypothesis is that a small but significant amount of antigen persists in the individual. This antigen-persistence provides a continual level of stimulation for these memory T cells and is able to stimulate the production of new memory T cells.

Antigens that do not induce acquired immunity

Interestingly, not all antigens induce immunological memory. The best studied of these are T-independent (TI) antigens. TI antigens are capable of stimulating B cell proliferation and differentiation in the absence of cognate T cell help. Common TI antigens are polysaccharides and polymers, both of which are composed of highly repetitive subunits. The reason that these antigens are unable to effect an acquired immune response is still unclear. However, it is known that TI antigens tend to stimulate a subset of B cells, $CD5^+$ cells, that may not be capable of differentiating into memory cells.

Medical indications of the acquired immune response

Clearly the most impressive medical indication of the acquired immune response is vaccination. The simple and elegant theory of vaccination is that induction of a primary immune response by a nonpathogenic form of an antigen leads to immunity of the infectious form. Common types of vaccines are attenuated pathogen, related noninfectious antigen, and purified proteins from the pathogen. Examples of all of these vaccines have been used to induce a primary immune response that confers acquired immunity.

See also: **Affinity maturation; Antigen-presenting cells; Antigens, T dependent and independent; Immune response; Immunoglobulin class switching; Maternal antibodies; Memory, immunological; Vaccines.**

Further reading

Croft M (1994) Activation of naive, memory and effector T cells. *Current Opinion in Immunology* 6: 431–437.

Doherty PC, Hou S and Tripp RA (1994) $CD8^+$ T-cell memory to viruses. *Current Opinion in Immunology* 6: 545–552.

Gray D (1993) Immunological memory. *Annual Review of Immunology* 11: 49–77.

Gray D (1994) Regulation of immunological memory. *Current Opinion in Immunology* 6: 425–430.

Knight SC and Stagg AJ (1993) Antigen-presenting cell types. *Current Opinion in Immunology* 5: 374–382.

Mackay CR. Homing of naive, memory and effector lymphocytes. *Current Opinion in Immunology* 5: 423–427.

Paul W (ed) (1993) *Fundamental Immunology*, 3rd edn. New York: Raven Press.

Sprent J (1993) Lifespans of naive, memory and effector lymphocytes. *Current Opinion in Immunology* 5: 433–438.

ACUTE INFLAMMATORY REACTION

Sanna Rosengren, Department of Immunology, Gensia Inc., San Diego, California, USA

The acute inflammatory reaction constitutes the first line of defense against infection as well as the initial stage in restoring injured tissue to normalcy. Acute inflammation is recognized by redness, swelling, heat and pain in the affected area. These symptoms stem from a multitude of events taking place within the inflamed site. The humoral arm of the immune response, including circulating antibodies and the complement system, is activated. Leukocytes which normally travel within the bloodstream recognize signs of tissue in distress, adhere to and traverse the blood vessel wall and migrate toward the source of irritation. The permeability of small venules increases, leading to edema formation, and furthermore the blood flow through inflamed tissue is altered as a result of modification of arteriolar tone. Additionally, a multitude of cell types are activated to liberate various inflammatory mediators, including cytokines and arachidonic acid metabolites, which in turn can affect every aspect of inflammation mentioned above. The intricacy and complexity of the inflammatory reaction cannot be underestimated and the detrimental impact of these events on normal function is often massive.

Cause of inflammation

While a classical immune response can elicit acute inflammation, both through antibody–antigen complex formation and through activation by cytokines secreted by T cell activated macrophages, the focus of this entry will be on effector cells such as neutrophils and endothelial cells. Signs of acute inflammation are seen in connection with infection by various pathogens, but tissue injury induced by physical, chemical or thermal means, without infection of foreign bodies *per se*, will also induce an inflammatory response. Additionally, a host of mediators, some of them listed in **Table 1**, will induce inflammation upon injection.

A particularly important clinical problem is the inflammatory response followed by tissue injury which is associated with ischemia/reperfusion situations such as myocardial infarction, stroke or transplantation of organs. Another example of an inflammatory response gone awry is the systemic inflammatory response syndrome (SIRS) sometimes seen in connection with systemic infection, extensive burns, ischemia, trauma or hemorrhagic shock. These conditions highlight the importance of understanding the inflammatory reaction for the purpose of adequate clinical intervention.

Table 1 Some inflammatory mediators and their actions *in vivo*

Mediator	Neutrophil accumulation	Edema formation[a]
Histamine		x
Bradykinin		x
Serotonin		x
Complement factor C3a		x
Complement factor C5a	x	x
PGD$_2$, PGE$_2$, PGI$_2$		x[b]
LTC$_4$, LTD$_4$, LTE$_4$		x
LTB$_4$	x	
PAF	x	x
TNFα	x	
IL-1	x	
IL-8	x	
Substance P	x[b]	x

PG, prostaglandin; LT, leukotriene; PAF, platelet activating factor; TNFα, tumor necrosis factor α; IL, interleukin.
[a]Includes mediators that induce edema through direct action on endothelium only.
[b]In some models only.

The neutrophil granulocyte

Mechanisms of neutrophil infiltration

The first leukocytes to infiltrate a site of inflammation are neutrophil granulocytes, which sometimes begin to accumulate within minutes of induction of inflammation. A host of adhesion molecules essential for neutrophil recruitment have been identified. During its journey through the vasculature, the neutrophil makes transient contact with the vascular wall of postcapillary venules, which gives the cell a rolling motion across the endothelium. This phenomenon is dependent on L-selectin (CD62L), present on the neutrophil surface, which recognizes and binds carbohydrates on the luminal surface of the vascular endothelium. Near an inflammatory site, however, the neutrophil becomes activated, the L-selectin is shed from the surface, and now the CD11b/CD18 adhesion complex, part of the integrin family, comes into play as the neutrophil adheres firmly to the vascular wall. Next, the neutrophil migrates out of the vessel through the junction between adjacent endothelial cells, and continues to move through the tissue toward the inflamed area, guided by inflammatory mediators which form a chemotactic gradient.

Other selectins, P- and E-selectin (CD62P and CD62E, respectively), can be found on the endothelial surface after stimulation with certain inflammatory mediators. P-selectin appears within minutes, whereas E-selectin is first found some hours after stimulation. Both P- and E-selectin can support neutrophil rolling along the endothelium together with neutrophil L-selectin.

An interesting exception to this scenario is seen in the lung. The low pressure in the pulmonary circulation combined with the narrow dimensions of lung capillaries leads to occasional trapping of neutrophils in these vessels, a phenomenon referred to as 'plugging'. When activated, neutrophils become stiffer as a result of intracellular actin polymerization, facilitating capillary trapping which may take place independently of the above-mentioned adhesion proteins. The cells may then migrate from the capillaries, which appear to be the main site for neutrophil extravasation in the lung. Plugging is also seen in some ischemia/reperfusion models, and has been suggested to account for the no-reflow phenomenon after severe ischemia, although this remains controversial.

Tissue injury by neutrophils

The neutrophil contains a formidable arsenal of proteinases, lysozyme and oxygen radical-forming enzymes in its granules, usually employed to kill microorganisms ingested by the neutrophil. Occasionally, however, these injurious products may be released to the extracellular space and cause tissue damage, for example if the perceived foreign body is too large for ingestion. In addition, antiproteinases normally present in the interstitial fluids can be inactivated by neutrophil-derived oxygen radicals, thereby enhancing the damage inflicted by neutrophil proteinases such as elastase, gelatinase and collagenase. Experimental proof for neutrophil-inflicted tissue injury is found in models of immune complex-induced dysfunction of various organs such as the Arthus reaction and nephrotoxic nephritis, among others.

Vascular leakage

Tissue swelling is one of the most obvious signs of inflammation. It is generated by an increase in vascular permeability to plasma proteins and fluid. Under normal conditions the endothelial layer lining blood vessel walls is relatively nonpermeable to proteins and other molecules above 30 Å, and the small exchange between the intravascular and extravascular compartments occurs by transport through the endothelial cell bodies as well as through junctions between adjacent endothelial cells. During inflammation the endothelial cells in small venules retract from each other after cell junctions, in the form of cadherins, break apart. This results in large pore formation and massive exudation of plasma proteins. Many inflammatory mediators, including histamine, bradykinin, certain complement factors and serotonin, can act directly on the endothelial cells to cause retraction, although the exact underlying mechanism is yet to be described. This is partly due to the difficulty in studying these events in *in vitro* cell culture.

In some experimental models of inflammation the observed edema is dependent entirely on neutrophil infiltration. Many of the products liberated from activated neutrophils increase the permeability of vascular walls by causing endothelial damage. In some cases, however, neutrophils cause edema without apparent dependency on its proteases or oxygen radicals and in the absence of evidence of injury to the vessel wall. The migration through endothelial junctions by neutrophils could theoretically be enough to open a gap between endothelial cells. An alternative explanation is found in the multiple

polycationic proteins present in neutrophil granules, which can cause endothelial retraction through a poorly understood charge interaction with the endothelial surface. In a fulminant multifactorial inflammatory response, however, all of these mechanisms are likely to contribute to the observed edema.

Concluding remarks

The acute inflammatory reaction stems from a complex and interdependent set of events at the microvascular level which lead to the easily recognizable symptoms of inflammation: redness, swelling, heat and pain. Depending on the situation, it can constitute a necessary defense against a potentially threatening invasion of pathogens, or it can itself be a threat to the organism because of the destruction of tissue taking place in the process. A better understanding of the relative importance of the various mediators and cell types involved is crucial for successful therapeutic intervention in inflammatory disease.

See also: **Anaphylatoxins; Arachidonic acid and the leukotrienes; Chemotaxis; Histamine; Mast cells; Neutrophils; Phagocytosis; Platelet-activating factor (PAF); Prostaglandins.**

Further reading

Albelda SM, Smith CW and Ward PA (1994) Adhesion molecules and inflammatory injury. *FASEB Journal* 8: 504–512.

Henson PM and Murphy RC (1989) Mediators of the inflammatory process. In: Glynn LE, Houck JC and Weissman G (eds) *Handbook of Inflammation*, vol 6, pp 1–404. Amsterdam: Elsevier.

Kishimoto TK and Rothlein R (1994) Integrins, ICAMs, and selectins: role and regulation of adhesion molecules in neutrophil recruitment to inflammatory sites. *Advances in Pharmacology* 25: 118–169.

Walker BML and Fantone JC (1994) The inflammatory response. In: Sigal LH and Ron Y (eds) *Immunology and Inflammation: Basic Mechanisms and Clinical Consequences*, pp 359–385. New York: McGraw-Hill.

Wang X and Anderson R (1995) The role of endothelial cells in the systemic inflammatory response syndrome and multiple organ failure. *European Journal of Surgery* 161: 703–713.

Weiss SJ (1989) Tissue destruction by neutrophils. *New England Journal of Medicine* 320: 365–376.

ACUTE PHASE PROTEINS

Mark B Pepys, Immunological Medicine Unit, Royal Postgraduate Medical School, Hammersmith Hospital, London, UK

Acute phase proteins are plasma proteins, the synthesis and the circulating concentrations of which are adaptively regulated in response to most forms of inflammation, infection and tissue injury. The name arises from the fact that the first such protein, C-reactive protein (CRP), was originally discovered in serum of patients in the acute phase of pneumococcal pneumonia. However, it soon became apparent that increased levels of CRP and certain other plasma proteins occurred during active, tissue-damaging disease processes, whether acute or chronic. Nevertheless the term 'acute phase' has persisted and is in general use to describe a large group of disparate plasma proteins (**Table 1**) which share the property of increased production after injury and in disease states. A small number of proteins, including albumin, the single most abundant plasma protein, show the reverse pattern and are called 'negative acute phase proteins' because their levels fall during the acute phase response (**Table 1**).

Table 1 Plasma protein concentrations in the acute phase response

	Increased	Decreased
Proteinase inhibitors	α_1-Antitrypsin α_1-Antichymotrypsin	Inter α-antitrypsin
Coagulation proteins	Fibrinogen Prothrombin Factor VIII Plasminogen	
Complement proteins	C1s C2, B C3, C4, C5, C6 C9 C1 INH	Properdin (P)
Transport proteins	Haptoglobin hemopexin (Ceruloplasmin)	
Lipoproteins		High density lipoprotein Low-density lipoprotein
Miscellaneous	C-reactive protein Serum amyloid A protein α_1-Acid glycoprotein Gc globulin Ceruloplasmin (Fibronectin)	Albumin Prealbumin (Transthyretin)

The acute phase proteins include members of the coagulation and complement systems, proteinase inhibitors and transport proteins, as well as several proteins of unknown function. The response as a whole, and many of the individual proteins, are conserved among endothermic animals and it therefore seems likely that it has an overall beneficial effect, possibly related to minimizing tissue injury, enhancing host resistance and promoting resolution of inflammation and repair. However, the whole, essentially nonspecific, phenomenon of the acute phase response is very complex and forms part of an even wider response to viable or nonviable noxious stimuli, involving fever, the immune system, the hematopoietic system, the stress-related endocrine system and protein, lipid and carbohydrate metabolism both locally and generally.

Synthesis of acute phase proteins

Most acute phase proteins are synthesized in the liver, although the genes for some are also expressed in cells and tissues elsewhere. Transcriptional control is the main mechanism for regulation of production but mRNA stability contributes in some cases. A large number of cytokines, including interleukin 1 (IL-1), IL-6, tumor necrosis factor α and various interferons, are capable of inducing increased, or in some cases decreased, production of various acute phase proteins *in vivo* and in cultured hepatocytes and liver cell lines *in vitro*. Glucocorticoids and steroid sex hormones can play an important permissive role and neural and neuroendocrine influences may be significant *in vivo*. Results obtained in different laboratories with different acute phase proteins, different cytokines and different cell lines or experimental systems have shown much variation. It has been difficult to reconcile all the findings and to identify the critical participation of particular mediators in control of particular reactants, especially because of the cascade effects by which some cytokines promote the production of others. Nevertheless it is striking that IL-6 knockout mice mount absolutely no acute phase response of serum amyloid A protein (SAA), serum amyloid P component (SAP) or complement component C3 following induction of sterile inflammation by casein or silver nitrate injection, whereas lipopolysaccharide (LPS) induces a definite, although subnormal, response.

Studies with transgenic mice bearing the human CRP gene, with transfected cells containing human SAA genes, and with hepatoma cell lines, have identified regulatory flanking regions of DNA which are targets for the action of nuclear factors responsive to IL-6 and IL-1.

Diversity of acute phase proteins

There is considerable diversity among acute phase proteins with respect to the concentrations attained, their structures, their behavior in different species and in different diseases. The concentration of a plasma protein depends on the balance between its secretion rate and its clearance rate. The availability of the protein for a particular function is the important factor in physiological and pathophysiological situations, rather than simply its serum concentration measured *ex vivo*. Increased availability can exist by virtue of increased production and yet be disguised by increased utilization or clearance so that plasma levels are normal or even decreased. Definition of acute phase proteins solely on the behavior of their plasma levels, while easy and convenient, is thus superficial and clearly misses important patterns of metabolic regulation of plasma proteins.

Among the acute phase proteins the increases vary between one- and twofold, for example, for some complement components, through up to five- to tenfold, for example for some clotting factors and proteinase inhibitors, and up to 1000-fold or more for CRP and SAA. CRP and SAA are trace constituents of normal plasma and are the most dramatic acute phase reactants increasing very rapidly to peak levels which may be up to 3000 times normal at about 48 h after an acute event. Persistently high levels may occur in chronic active disease processes, but with effective therapy or spontaneous resolution they fall to normal with a half-time as fast as 24–30 h. In contrast, all other acute phase proteins respond more slowly, taking days to reach their peak values, and also falling much more slowly, reflecting clearance and catabolic half-lives of days rather than hours. Furthermore, unlike most other acute phase proteins, there seems to be little effect of disease processes on the clearance or catabolism of CRP and SAA. The synthesis rate, which reflects the intensity of the pathology which induced their production, is thus the most important or even sole determinant of their plasma levels. For all these reasons these two acute phase proteins are the most useful for clinical purposes in humans.

Acute phase proteins are structurally extremely diverse. Most are glycoproteins produced predominantly, though not exclusively, by hepatocytes. The extent and heterogeneity of glycosylation is often significantly increased during the acute phase response, apparently under the influence of the stimulatory cytokines. However, CRP and SAA are not glycosylated. SAA, unlike all the other acute phase proteins, is an apolipoprotein associated with high density lipoprotein, and unlike CRP, which shows no polymorphism, SAA is highly polymorphic. There are several sets of genes for SAA, including some which are predominantly expressed in tissues other than liver and and the products of which are not significantly present in the plasma. There are also differences in the responses of different SAA genes to different acute phase stimuli. The importance of this diversity is not clear since the normal function of SAA, and its role in acute phase situations, are not known. However, SAA is the precursor of AA protein which forms the fibrils in reactive systemic, AA-type amyloidosis, a serious and usually fatal complication of chronic persistent infections and inflammatory disorders.

While the profile of acute phase plasma proteins is broadly similar across species there are nonetheless important differences. For example, SAP is a major acute phase reactant only in the mouse, and there are many other differences in normal levels and acute phase behavior of other members of the pentraxin family of proteins to which it belongs. While these differences may be important for the usefulness of particular proteins as markers in clinical or experimental situations, they may not reflect, as has been pointed out above, the underlying metabolic regulation. On the other hand, some species differences are clearly of physiological and pathophysiological importance. Thus, although rats have a gene for a homolog of SAA, the expression of which is regulated as an acute phase protein, the product does not appear as a plasma lipoprotein and rats never get AA amyloidosis. This contrasts with the behavior of SAA in all other mammals and birds which have been studied.

Finally, even within a species there is diversity in the acute phase response to different stimuli, to different disease processes and between different individuals. This has been most extensively studied in the case of CRP and SAA responses in humans, in whom there is a small number of serious inflammatory or tissue-damaging disorders characterized by absent or minimal acute phase production of these proteins. These exceptional disorders include systemic lupus erythematosus, dermatomyositis, Sjögren's disease, scleroderma, ulcerative colitis and leukemia, in all of which only a minority of patients have more than modest elevations of CRP or SAA concentration, even in the face of extensive and active disease. Other acute phase proteins are produced, apparently normally, and if these patients acquire a significant intercurrent infection they then mount major acute phase responses of CRP and SAA. These phenomena are of considerable clinical value but the underlying mechanisms, whether of macrophage response, cytokine production or hepatocyte response are not known. In the great majority of other diseases in which CRP and SAA levels are greatly increased, the levels attained closely reflect the extent and activity of the pathological process in each individual, and serial monitoring provides valuable objective and quantitative information about the natural history of the disorder or its response to treatment. However, while there is usually a good general correlation between disease activity and CRP/SAA concentration there may nonetheless be considerable variation between the acute phase protein levels seen in different individuals with apparently comparable degrees of clinical activity. These variations are due partly to difficulties in clinical assessment of disease activity but mostly to genuine interindividual differences in the acute phase response.

Biological and clinical importance of acute phase proteins

Acute phase proteins and the response in general are stably conserved in evolution and are universal within each species. They are thus presumably of benefit to the organism undergoing infection, inflammation and/or tissue damage, although much remains to be learned of the properties and functions of many acute phase reactants. On the other hand, sustained, increased production of SAA is a necessary though not sufficient condition for the development of reactive, systemic AA amyloidosis, a grave complication of chronic infection or inflammation. Monitoring of the acute phase response, particularly by measurement of CRP in man, CRP or SAA in other species, and SAP in the mouse, is a powerful and sensitive test for organic disease or the toxicity of an administered agent. It also provides the most accessible means for objective, quantitative assessment of disease extent and activity, and is valuable in the differential diagnosis of intercurrent infection especially in the immunocompromised host.

The application of new high sensitivity immunoassays for CRP in studies of atherosclerosis has lately revealed very important prognostic associations between previously undetected low grade acute phase responses and the progression and complications, especially of coronary heart disease. These findings open up a new area of considerable fundamental interest and clinical significance, relating mild chronic inflammation to the most common cause of death in the developed world.

See also: **Acute inflammatory reaction; Amyloid; Clotting system; C-reactive protein; Cytokines; Plasma; Rheumatoid arthritis, human.**

Further reading

Kushner I, Volanakis JE and Gewurz H (eds) (1982) C-reactive protein and the plasma protein response to tissue injury. *Annals of the New York Academy of Sciences* 389.

Liuzzo G, Biasucci LM, Gallimore JR *et al.* (1996) The prognostic value of C-reactive protein and serum amyloid A protein in severe unstable angina. *New England Journal of Medicine* 331: 417–424.

Pepys MB (ed) (1989) *Acute Phase Proteins in the Acute Phase Response.* London: Springer.

Pepys MB (1994) Amyloidosis. In: Frank MM, Austen KF, Claman HN and Unanue ER (eds) *Samter's Immunologic Diseases*, pp 637–655. Boston: Little, Brown.

Pepys MB and Baltz ML (1983) Acute phase proteins with particular reference to C-reactive protein and related proteins (pentaxins) and serum amyloid A protein. *Advances in Immunology* 34: 141–212.

Steel D and Whitehead AS (1994) The major acute phase reactants: C-reactive protein, serum amyloid P component and serum amyloid A protein. *Immunology Today* 15: 81–88.

ADENOVIRUS, INFECTION AND IMMUNITY

Liise-anne Pirofski and **Marshall S Horwitz**, Departments of Medicine, Microbiology and Immunology, Albert Einstein College of Medicine, New York, USA

Adenoviruses (Ad) are highly species-specific icosahedral DNA viruses. Multiple Ad serotypes cause a variety of clinical syndromes in humans including respiratory, genitourinary, gastrointestinal and conjunctival infections. Ads are relatively resistant to conventional antiviral chemotherapy, though a highly effective oral Ad vaccine has been used to prevent acute respiratory disease (ARD) in the military population. The human immune response to Ad infection is characterized by the development of serotype-specific neutralizing antibodies to Ad structural proteins which prevent reinfection with the same serotype. In addition, Ad genomes are characterized by four transcription groups that lead to the production of early (E) nonstructural proteins which exert important immunologic effects. The E3 region is not essential for viral replication and can be replaced with foreign DNA. Ad vectors for the delivery of foreign genes have been developed for immunization against non-Ad infections and for gene therapy. Achieving the long-term expression of foreign Ad-inserted genes and abrogating host immune responses that lead to rejection of delivered genes are active areas of research.

Adenoviruses were first isolated by Rowe and Hartley in 1953 when cytopathology was noted serendipitously in cultures of human tissue removed during tonsillectomies and adenoidectomies. Although the first Ad isolates were from patients without acute infectious symptoms, it was recognized subsequently that Ads were associated with a group of respiratory and ocular syndromes. Some of these diseases, such as conjunctivitis, had been known as distinct clinical entities for almost a century before the first isolation of Ads. The number of unique Ad serotypes proliferated and now there are at least 49 distinct types that are currently recognized by neutralization reactions. The Ads are classified into six subgroups (A–F) based on criteria which include the patterns of hemagglutination (HA) of a variety of species of red blood cells. Cross-hybridization of the Ad DNA genomes is greater than 50% for agents within a single sub-group. The discovery by Trentin in 1962, that Ad 12 was highly oncogenic in hamsters, began an era of excitement and uncertainty as attempts were made to link Ads and other DNA viruses with human tumors. All these efforts failed to reveal any reproducible association between Ads and human malignancy. However, molecular biologic studies of the mechanism of Ad transformation have provided a paradigm for understanding virus-mediated transformation in general.

As a parallel development to the studies of Ad oncogenesis in model systems, investigators were exploring the use of Ad vaccines to prevent acute respiratory disease (ARD) in military recruits as they entered a new epidemiologic environment (see below). The first batches of inactivated Ad vaccine were contaminated with live simian virus-40 (SV40), an unknown virus at the time. The helper effect of SV40 on Ad growth in monkey cells was discovered during these studies.

Ads cause upper respiratory tract infections (URI) and pneumonia. Serotypes 8, 19 and 37 are associated with severe conjunctivitis. Ad infections of the urinary tract due to types 11 and 21 may produce hemorrhagic cystitis, especially in males. Ads 40 and 41, which induce gastroenteritis, are more difficult to grow in conventional tissue culture systems such as human embryonic kidney (HEK) and require special cells such as HEK 293 transformed by the Ad5 early region E1 for propagation. Other Ad serotypes cultivatable from enteric sources have not been reproducibly associated with diarrhea even though they may be persistently shed.

Characteristics of the organism and its antigens

The Ads of different serotypes have an icosahedral architecture, a double-stranded linear DNA, and more than 12 structural proteins, three of which are major components of the capsid (**Figure 1**). There is no virus envelope; 240 hexons, each a trimer of identical polypeptides, are the major subunits of the 252 capsomere shell with 12 different structures called pentons at each of the vertices. The penton is composed of five penton base and three fiber polypeptides which project out from the base in an antenna-like structure. These polypeptides are antigens for host immunologic responses to natural and vaccine-associated infection. The internal structural proteins are divided into those associated with the DNA in a core-like structure and others that bind to the inner surfaces of the hexon or penton capsomeres. None of the internal proteins appear to be involved in humoral or cell-mediated immunity.

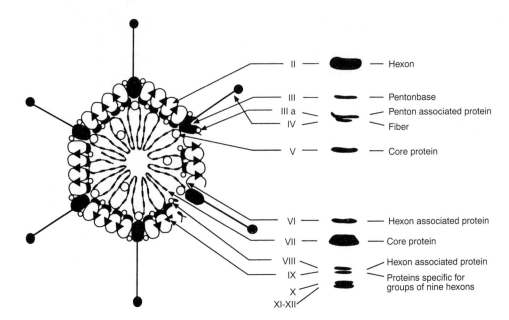

II	— Hexon	
III	— Pentonbase	
III a	— Penton associated protein	
IV	— Fiber	
V	— Core protein	
VI	— Hexon associated protein	
VII	— Core protein	
VIII	— Hexon associated protein	
IX	— Proteins specific for groups of nine hexons	
X		
XI-XII		

Figure 1 Schematic representation of an adenovirus. The mobilities and relative amounts of each protein after electrophoresis of the dissociated virus on a sodium dodecyl sulfate-containing polyacrylamide gel are shown on the right. The position of each polypeptide in the virion is designated (modified from Horwitz, M.S. (1990) *Adenoviruses and their Replication in Fields' Virology*, 2nd edition, pp. 1679–1721, Raven Press, edited by Fields, *et al*.

Several nonstructural proteins that are made early after infection have immunologic significance. These early proteins are the products of four transcription groups: the E1A, E1B, E3 and E4 genes have all been postulated to exert important immunologic effects. Both the E1A and E3 regions affect the expression of class I major histocompatibility complex (MHC)-encoded proteins on the cell surface. In model systems *in vivo* and *in vitro*, the E1A gene of Ad12 (which together with the E1B gene is responsible for transformation by the oncogenic Ads), has been shown to inhibit transcription of the class I MHC. This mechanism appears to be limited to the highly oncogenic Ads. In most of the other Ad serotypes that have been studied, a 19 kDa glycoprotein (E3-19 kDa) product of the E3 region has been demonstrated to bind tightly to the class I MHC heavy chain in the endoplasmic reticulum and prevent transport of this complex to the cell surface. Thus, the Ads have evolved two mechanisms to regulate cell surface MHC. The E3 region, which contains 10% of the Ad-coding sequence, includes other genes whose products may have immunologic significance. There is a 14.7 kDa protein and a heterodimer of 10.4/14.5 kDa that inhibit tumor necrosis factor (TNF) lysis of Ad-infected cells. The 14.7 kDa protein does not inhibit TNF by interacting with the ligand or its receptor: it exerts its effect intracellularly by inhibiting the cell death pathway. The details of this process are unknown, though 14.7 kDa inhibits TNF-induced release of arachidonic acid.

Four 14.7 kDa interacting intracellular proteins have been isolated recently; one of them, FIP-1, is a small GTPase with homology to members of the ras family. The 10.4 kDa protein also promotes the internalization of both the epidermal growth factor (EGF) and insulin receptors by a mechanism that is currently unknown. The biological importance of these proteins *in vivo* is under active investigation. For example, the entire cassette of E3 proteins has been expressed as a transgene in mice behind the rat insulin promoter. The E3-transgenic islets can evade the immune system in both allogeneic transplantation and autoimmune diabetes models. Recently, it has been shown that the Ad E3 that is overexpressed in rats by replication-defective Ad vectors used for gene therapy can suppress the humoral immune response to the virus. The E3 genes responsible for this effect and their mechanism of immunomodulation are under investigation.

Another nonstructural gene, VA-1, produces a transcript using RNA polymerase III. This transcript is not known to code for any protein, but the VA-1 can inhibit the action of interferon-induced phosphorylation and allow protein synthesis to continue in Ad-infected cells.

The Ad structural proteins – hexon, fiber and penton – are the antigenic determinants for both group- and type-specific antibodies. The fiber is the major attachment protein but entry is facilitated by the penton base protein. Adenovirus types 2 and 5 fibers bind through the terminal knob to a common receptor shared with the coxsackie B viruses, but have also been reported to bind to class I MHC molecules. The penton base binds to both the $\alpha_v\beta_3$ and $\alpha_v\beta_5$ integrins. The α determinant demonstrable on hexon is a cross-reacting group antigen found on most of the known human and animal Ads. The ϵ determinant of hexon and the γ determinant of fiber both give rise to type-specific neutralization (Nt) antibodies. Some of these determinants have now been mapped to specific nucleic acid sequences. Classically, type-specific antibodies have been detectable by hemagglutination inhibition (HAI), and Nt assays. Ad neutralization is serotype specific and generally demonstrable only with homologous antisera. However, some heterologous sera are capable of neutralizing virion at low pH (pH 5.5). Neutralizing antibodies recognizing the Ad hexon of serotypes 1–5 and the Ad fiber of types 1, 2 and 5 have been extensively studied in animal models. Antibodies against fiber can induce virion aggregation though virus attachment to host cells is facilitated by this mechanism. However, such aggregated Ads do not uncoat or enter the cytoplasm for eventual transport along microtubules to the nucleus. Although neutralization parallels aggregation, another mechanism for virus neutralization apparently occurs by antibody-mediated inhibition of viral entry from acidic vesicles into the cytoplasmic compartment. A similar mechanism has also been described for antibodies to penton base which also appear to inhibit by a mechanism independent of virus aggregation. Complement fixation or fluorescent antibody (FA) tests generally detect the presence of group-specific antibody, whereas HAI and Nt assays determine the serotype and the existence of serotype-specific immunity. In addition, type-specific monoclonal antibodies against Ads 40 and 41 can be used with FA, latex agglutination or ELISA assays to distinguish these enteric serotypes from others that are shed in the gastrointestinal tract as a component of Ad infection of the respiratory tract. Immunologic assays and other techniques such as nucleic acid hybridization, quantitative electron microscopy, direct Ad genomic DNA restriction endonuclease profiles of nucleic acid in stool specimens, and polymerase chain reaction (PCR) with selected serotype-specific primers are facilitating the diagnosis of Ad-related gastrointestinal and other clinical syndromes.

Immune responses of the host

Adenovirus infections are followed by serotype-specific immunity which is most likely mediated by serum-neutralizing antibodies. These antibodies protect against reinfection with the same serotype, though asymptomatic viral shedding from tonsillar epithelium, lymphocytes and enteric epithelium may occur for many months in the presence of neutralizing antibodies. The role of cell-mediated immunity in recovery from acute infection and prevention of reinfection is not understood. Proteins encoded in the E1A or E1B regions are major targets for both cytotoxic T lymphocytes (CTLs) and for natural killer (NK) cell responses. CTLs have been induced in mice inoculated with human Ads.

Animal models of human Ad infection are imperfect because these viruses are highly species specific. In most species, human Ad infections result in abortive infections in which early viral genes are expressed. However, adenovirus infection of the cotton rat produces progeny virus and causes an inflammatory response in the lungs after intranasal infection. The effect of the E3 genes has been studied after intranasal infection of both cotton rats and mice with adenovirus E3-deletion mutants. Deletion of three anti-TNF genes (E3 14.7 kDa, 10.4 kDa and 14.5 kDa) resulted in worsening of pulmonary pathology as evidenced by the conversion of a mononuclear to a polymorphonuclear response in the peribronchial area of the cotton rat lung and the increase of alveolar inflammation in the mouse lung. The pulmonary response to deletion of gp19kDa was discrepant in that the inflammatory response increased in the cotton rat but was unchanged in the mouse.

Adenovirus infections are not as common as infections with members of the herpesvirus group in immunocompromised hosts. However, patients with various malignancies or following cytotoxic therapy have had more severe and more frequent episodes of Ad disease. Liver transplant patients in the pediatric age group have had fatal infection due to the ubiquitous Ad5 serotype. Patients with the acquired immune deficiency syndrome (AIDS) have had persistent infections with various Ad serotypes. Group B Ads 34 and 35 have been isolated chronically from the urine of many AIDS patients. Group D agents have been persistent in the stools of other AIDS patients studied. Both of these patient groups appear to be asymptomatic from their genitourinary or gastrointestinal tract Ad infections. Adult AIDS patients infected with Ads 34 and 35 do not make serum antibodies against these viruses though most of these patients had antibodies against Ad2, a serotype that they most likely acquired before HIV infection. The target of the major neutralizing antibodies against Ad35, the fiber gene, manifested changes from the prototype in many Ad35 isolates from AIDS patients. There appeared to be intermolecular recombination between genomes that were primarily Ad34 or 35 by restriction endonuclease analysis, but that had the fibers characteristic of other group B Ads such as Ad 3, 7, 11, 16 and 21. Recombination between serotypes within the Ad subgroups is known to occur both in tissue culture and *in vivo*, though there was no evidence that the intermolecular changes, thought to occur by recombination, had arisen during chronic carriage of these Ads in any of the patients studied. This conclusion was reached by examining serial isolates over many months and finding that the serologic reactivity as well as the restriction endonuclease patterns of each Ad isolate had not changed during this period of observation. Thus, the frequency of these important antigenic changes is uncommon in each chronically infected individual.

Vaccines

Historically, the development of Ad vaccines provided new insights into important issues regarding the determination of the safety and efficacy of live viruses for disease prophylaxis. The development of an Ad vaccine became a major priority in the early 1960s after the realization that Ads were responsible for most of the ARDs in up to 80% of American military recruits (who often required hospitalization). Types 3, 4, 7, 14, and 21 Ads caused most of the disease in military recruits and trials of the first vaccines took place between 1958 and 1962. The initial vaccines consisted of inactivated whole-virus strains. However, besides not being completely effective, it was discovered that the seed stocks of vaccine virus were contaminated with fully viable SV40 as noted above. SV40 actually functioned as a helper virus that was essential for the replication of both Ad4 and Ad7. It was realized then that Ad grew in monkey kidney tissue culture only because many of these cells were contaminated *in vivo* by SV40 which produced a T antigen that complemented the Ad replication defect in cells of simian origin. Attempts to rid the Ad seed stocks of SV40 by the use of antibodies against the latter virus were responsible for promoting the intermolecular recombination of portions of the SV40 T antigen gene with the Ad genome. The resulting Ad–SV40 hybrid viruses were shown to be more oncogenic than Ad alone in various rodent species, though extensive studies have failed to show any oncogenic effect of these hybrid viruses in humans inadvertently inoculated with them during the early field trials of Ad vaccines. With increased knowledge of the biology of Ads, a live vaccine free of SV40 genes was formulated against Ads 4 and 7 for use in the military. Despite the anticipation that other respiratory

Ad strains would need to be included as vaccination programs proceeded, this has not been the case.

The adenovirus vaccine currently in use is an enteric coated tablet that protects the host from respiratory infection. It contains Ad 4 and 7 strains adapted for growth in human embryonic fibroblast (W1-38) tissue culture. Vaccine amounts of greater than 10^4 tissue culture infection dose$_{50}$ (TCID$_{50}$) in a single administration protect at least 95% of vaccinated recruits. Some individuals develop neutralizing antibodies without evidence of infection, although the vaccine infection rate is greater than 90% as measured by fecal excretion of vaccine Ad strains. In contrast to natural infection, Ad vaccine-induced neutralizing antibodies are not secretory IgA. Nonetheless, the vaccine is highly protective. It must be given within 2 h of the recruit's arrival at the training base because vaccine-mediated protection does not occur during the incubation period of wild-type Ad infection. The adenovirus vaccine strains are safe and are not oncogenic: since the introduction of the vaccine in 1965 it has been administered to over 10 million people.

Ad infections in children cause 5–10% of all pediatric respiratory infections. Since children are infected with other serotypes such as Ads 1, 2 and 5, it was anticipated that the adult vaccines would be reformulated to include these serotypes. However, Ad vaccines for civilians and children are not presently available. Ad vaccination of children has lagged behind the successful efforts to protect the military population because of some uncertainties about the initial safety of the vaccines, and the present enteric formulation which requires swallowing the vaccine tablet intact.

Adenoviruses as vectors for the delivery of foreign genes

Ads have been developed as vectors for the delivery of foreign antigens for immunization against other (non-Ad) infectious agents and for gene therapy. Ads are good vectors for the delivery of foreign DNA in that viral replication is not dependent upon host cell replication, they can be molecularly engineered to enter host cells and express foreign proteins without infectious viral progeny, and they are extremely safe immunogens that have already been administered to many people. For gene delivery, the E3 region, described above as a cluster of viral genes potentially controlling pathogenesis, has been physically or functionally deleted. Experience with Ad/SV40, described above, paved the way for these constructs by demonstrating that the Ad E3 region is not essential for viral replication. The E3 region can be replaced with foreign DNA: insertion of the hepatitis B surface antigen (HBsAg) gene in place of the partially deleted Ad E3 results in the expression of HBsAg which elicited an antibody response in hamsters. Recently, many additional foreign genes have been cloned into Ad vectors. Foreign genes have also been placed and expressed in other Ad sites including positions downstream from the Ad major late promoter (MLP). The Ad MLP is a very active transcriptional start site which results in the expression of large amounts of foreign proteins. To elicit higher titers against a given antigen, duplicate cloning of the gene into several serotypes is performed, permitting booster immunizations without augmentation of a serotype-specific anti-Ad-neutralizing antibody response. Since there has been extensive use of the Ad4 and 7 serotypes in young adults in the military, these types are obvious choices for such recombinant vaccines. The efficacy of Ad constructs designed for immunization is largely dependent upon viral replication and expression of foreign proteins.

Ad constructs designed for gene therapy are replication defective. Foreign genes are inserted into deleted E1A and E1B regions. Growth of these vectors is dependent upon a cell line that is stably transfected with the E1A and E1B sequences. The viruses are infection competent and enter host cells where they efficiently transcribe inserted sequences without the production of significant progeny virus. Human trials have been attempted to test Ad constructs containing the cystic fibrosis gene, one of the numerous inserts placed into Ad vectors to date. Genes that can replace congenitally absent gene products and genes that can control cell growth or promote cell death of malignant cells have been engineered into Ads for therapeutic purposes. The p53 gene and the herpes simplex thymidine kinase gene (used with ganciclovir) are examples of this approach. Adenoviruses that have cell death genes such as Fas are also being used to control the overgrowth of vascular wall myocytes and endothelium after angioplasty. In many of these situations, there is a need for prolonged expression of the transgene or the requirement to re-administer the vector. However, the immune response to the initial injection of Ad, or even preexisting immunity from natural Ad infection, may preclude this possibility. A number of approaches to solve this problem have been undertaken in model systems, including short-term immunosuppression with FK506 or cyclosporine at the time of vector administration; oral or intrathymic tolerance with viral proteins; or using the immunosuppressive properties of overexpressed Ad E3. Inhibition of the antibody response to replication-deficient Ads containing overexpressed E3 genes has allowed readministration of an Ad vector containing a functional bilirubin conjugating enzyme for correction of an enzymatic defect in rat liver. Though the expression of Ad-inserted genes is prolonged in some tissues, many problems remain to be solved to ensure the success of Ad vectors as delivery systems for gene therapy; achieving long-term expression of foreign Ad-inserted genes in the desired tissue(s) and circumventing host immune responses that ultimately lead to rejection of delivered genes are significant issues that must be resolved. This very active area of research is likely to lead to significant advances in the near future.

Therapy

Ads have remained rather resistant to antiviral chemotherapy. Although Ads code for their own viral DNA polymerase, this enzyme has not been hitherto exploited as a target for chemotherapy. The nucleoside analogs effective in the treatment of herpes simplex virus have not been effective in controlling Ad disease.

See also: **Acquired immune deficiency syndrome (AIDS); Adjuvants; Eye infections; Vaccines; Viruses, immunity to.**

Further reading

Bramson JLL, Graham F and Gauldie J (1995) The use of adenoviral vectors for gene therapy and gene transfer *in vivo. Current Opinion in Biotechnology* **6**: 590–595.

Bergelson JM, Cunningham JA, Kurt-Jones E, Hong JS, Droguett G, Horwitz MS, Crowell RL and Finberg RW (1997) Isolation of a common receptor for coxsackie B viruses and adenoviruses 2 and 5. *Science* **275**: 1320–1323.

Efrat S, Fejer G, Brownlee M and Horwitz MS (1995) Prolonged survival of pancreatic islet allografts mediated by adenovirus immunoregulatory transgenes. *Proceedings of the National Academy of Sciences of the USA* **92**: 6947–6951.

Flomemberg P, Babbitt J, Drobyski WR *et al* (1994) Increasing evidence of adenovirus disease in bone marrow transplant recipients. *Journal of Infectious Diseases* **169**: 775–781.

Grunhaus A and Horwitz MS (1992) Adenoviruses as cloning vectors. In: Rice C (ed) *Seminars in Virology*, pp 237–252. London: Saunders Scientific.

Hong SS, Karayan L, Tournier J, Curiel DT and Boulanger PA (1997) Adenovirus type 5 fiber knob binds to MHC class I α2 domain at the surface of human epithelial and B lymphoblastoid cells *EMBO Journal* **16**: 2294–2306.

Horwitz MS (1996) Adenoviral diseases. In: Fields, Knipe Chanock *et al* (eds) *Fields' Virology*, 3rd edn, pp 2149–2171. New York: Raven Press.

Ilan Y, Atavar P, Takahashi M *et al.* (1996) Induction of central tolerance by intrathymic inoculation of adenoviral antigens into the host thymus permits long-term gene therapy in Gunn rats. *Journal of Clinical Investigation* **98**: 2640–2647.

Ilan Y, Droguett G, Roy Chowdhury N *et al.* (1997) Insertion of the adenoviral E3 region into a recombinant viral vector prevents antiviral humoral and cellular immune responses and permits long-term gene expression. *Proceedings of the National Academy of Sciences of the USA* **94**: 2587–2592.

Ilan Y, Prakash R, Davidson A *et al.* (1997) Oral tolerization to adenoviral antigens permits long-term gene expression using recombinant adenoviral vectors. *Journal of Clinical Investigation* **99**: 1098–1106.

Li Y, Kang J and Horwitz MS (1997) Interaction of an adenovirus 14.7kDa protein inhibitor of TNF-α cytolysis with a new member of the GTPase superfamily of signal transducers. *Journal of Virology* **71**: 1576–1582.

Rubin B and Rorke LB (1988) In: Plotkin SA and Mortimer EA (eds) *Adenovirus Vaccines.* Philadephia: WB Saunders.

Sparer T, Tripp RA, Dilleha DL, Hermiston TW, Wold WS, Gooding LR (1996) The role of human adenovirus early region 3 proteins (gp19K, 10.4K, 14.5K and 14.7K) in a murine pneumonia model. *Journal of Virology* **70**: 2431–2439.

Wold WSM, Hermiston TW and Tollefson AE (1994) Adenovirus proteins that subvert host defenses. In: *Trends in Microbiology.* Cambridge: Elsevier Trends Journals.

Yang L, Li Q, Ertl HC and Wilson JM (1995) Cellular and humoral immune responses to viral antigens create barriers to lung-directed gene therapy with recombinant adenoviruses. *Journal of Virology* **69**: 2004–2014.

ADHESION MOLECULES

Margaret A Adelsman and **Yoji Shimizu**, Department of Laboratory Medicine and Pathology, Center for Immunology, University of Minnesota Medical School, Minneapolis, Minnesota, USA

In 1922, biologist Warren Lewis wrote, if 'cells (were) to lose their stickiness for one another and for the supporting extracellular white fibers, reticuli, etc., our bodies would at once disintegrate and flow off onto the ground. ... The so-called cement, so commonly described as existing between various types of cells, may possibly be an adhesive substance'. Over 75 years later, we now know that this necessity for cells to adhere to their surroundings or to their cellular neighbors is reflected in the vast array of molecules identified that mediate cell adhesion. In the immune system, adhesion molecules are essential to many, if not all, aspects of leukocyte function, including normal recirculation of lymphocytes through lymphoid organs, recruitment of leukocytes into inflammatory sites, antigen-specific recognition, and wound healing. Defects in adhesion molecule expression can result in immunodeficiency, and the central role of adhesion molecules in the immune system suggests that adhesion can be used as a therapeutic strategy for intentional modulation of the immune response.

Five main structural families of adhesion molecules have been identified: integrins, immunoglobulin superfamily (IgSF) proteins, selectins, mucins and cadherins (**Table 1**). This discussion will focus on an introduction to the structure and function of these adhesion molecules, followed by emerging concepts of how the distinct functions of these many adhesive proteins are integrated to mediate key immunological processes.

Integrins

The integrin family of adhesion molecules is composed of structurally related proteins that combine to form noncovalent αβ heterodimers. Currently 16 α subunits and eight β subunits have been cloned, resulting in a minimum of 22 different combinations. The VLA (very late antigen) integrins, leukocyte integrins, and cytoadhesins represent integrin subfamilies based on the pairing of α subunits with the β_1, β_2 or β_3 subunits, respectively. However, the identification of five other β subunits, together with the ability of certain α subunits to associate with more than one β subunit, blurs the distinctions between these integrin subfamilies. Integrin ligands include extracellular matrix (ECM) proteins, as well as cell surface proteins. Many of the integrin cell surface counter-receptors are members of the immunoglobulin (Ig) superfamily (see below). In addition, some bacteria and viruses use integrins to bind to host tissue. Ligand binding specificity is contributed by both α and β subunits. The ligand binding regions of integrins are invariably located at cation-binding sites, and consequently integrin-mediated adhesion is divalent cation dependent.

Table 1 Adhesion molecules in immunology

Receptor	Alternate name	Cell type	Extracellular matrix ligands	Cell surface/ other ligands
1. Integrins				
$\alpha_1\beta_1$	VLA-1	T_a, Mono, NK	COLL, LAM	
$\alpha_2\beta_1$	VLA-2	B, T, Pl, Endo	COLL, LAM	Echovirus
$\alpha_3\beta_1$	VLA-3	B	COLL, LAM, FN, Epiligrin, Entactin/Nidogen	Invasin
$\alpha_4\beta_1$	VLA-4; LPAM-2	Thym, Mono, B, T, NK Eosin, $Eryth_{imm}$	FN, Thrombospondin	VCAM-1, Invasin
$\alpha_5\beta_1$	VLA-5; FnR	Mono, Leuko, T, Pl, NK	FN, Thrombospondin	Invasin, L1
$\alpha_6\beta_1$	VLA-6	Pl, Mono, T, Thym, NK	LAM	Invasin
$\alpha_4\beta_7$	LPAM-1, $\alpha_4\beta_p$	Some T, NK, Eosin, B	FN	VCAM-1, MAdCAM-1
$\alpha_E\beta_7$	HML-1	Intraepithelial lympho		E-Cadherin
$\alpha_L\beta_2$	LFA-1, CD11a/CD18	Lympho, Neutro, Mono, Macro, NK		ICAM-1, ICAM-2, ICAM-3
$\alpha_M\beta_2$	Mac-1, CD11b/CD18	Mono, Macro, Granulo, NK	FG	ICAM-1, ICAM-2, C3bi, Heparin, *B. pertussis* hemagglutinin, Haptoglobulin
$\alpha_x\beta_2$	p150/95, CD11c/CD18	Macro, Mono, Granulo, T_a, B_a, NK, Dendr	FG	C3bi, Endothelial ligand?, ICAM-1 (rabbit)
$\alpha_D\beta_2$		Some Macro and CD8$^+$ T, Large granular lympho		ICAM-3, ICAM-1
$\alpha_V\beta_3$	VN-R	Endo, some B, Macro, Mono, Pl	VN, FN, FG, COLL, VWF, Thrombospondin, Osteopontin	CD31, L1
$\alpha_{IIb}\beta_3$	gpIIb/IIIa	Pl, Megakar	VN, FG, VWF, FN, Thrombospondin	
2. Ig superfamily				
ICAM-1	CD54	Mono, Endo, *(B, T, Thym, Dendr, Endo, Keratino, epithel)		$\alpha_L\beta_2$, $\alpha_M\beta_2$, $\alpha_x\beta_2$, $\alpha_D\beta_2$
ICAM-2	CD102	Endo, Mono, Dendr		$\alpha_L\beta_2$, $\alpha_M\beta_2$
ICAM-3	CD50	Leuko, Dendr		$\alpha_L\beta_2$, $\alpha_D\beta_2$
MAdCAM-1		Peyer's patch HEV, Mesenteric LN HEV, Mucosal lamina propria venules		$\alpha_4\beta_7$, L-selectin
VCAM-1	CD106	$Endo_a$, tissue Macro, Dendr		$\alpha_4\beta_1$, $\alpha_4\beta_7$
CD31	PECAM-1	Pl, Endo, Mono, Granulo, some T		$\alpha_V\beta_3$, CD31
CD2	LFA-2, Leu-5	Thym, T, NK		LFA-3 (CD58), CD48, CD59
3. Selectins				
L-Selectin	CD62L, LECAM1 Leu-8, LAM-1	Most B and T, Granulo, NK $Thym_{imm}$, some mature Thym, Mono, bone marrow myeloid progen, eryth precursors, Eosin		GlyCAM-1, MAdCAM-1, CD34, Sgp200
E-Selectin	CD62E, ELAM-1, LECAM-2	$endo_a$		PSGL-1, CLA, ESL-1
P-Selectin	CD62P, GMP-140, PADGEM, LECAM-3	$Endo_a$, Pl, Megakar		PSGL-1

Table 1 Continued

Receptor	Alternate name	Cell type	Extracellular matrix ligands	Cell surface/ other ligands
4. *Mucins*				
GlyCAM-1		PLN HEV, hemato progen		L-selectin
CD34		Wide intravascular expression		L-selectin
MAdCAM-1		See above (Ig superfamily)		$\alpha_4\beta_7$, L-selectin
5. *Cadherins*				
E-cadherin	Arc-1, L-CAM, Cell CAM 120/80, uvumorulin	Epithel		E-cadherin, $\alpha_E\beta_7$, internalin
6. *Other adhesion molecules*				
CD44	Hermes, Pgp-1, H-CAM, ECMR III	Wide expression	COLL, osteopontin	HA
VAP-1		HEV, PLN HEV, Synovium, tonsils		?
LVAP-2	CD73	HUVEC, B, CD8+ T, Lymphoid and nonlymphoid venules		?
uPAR		Mono, Neutro, T_a, Endo	VN	uPA

Ligands: FN, fibronectin; VN, vitronectin; COLL, collagen; HA, hyaluronic acid; LAM, laminin; FG, fibrinogen; VWF, von Willibrand factor.
Cell types: Pl, platelet; T_a, activated T cell; Endo, endothelial cell; Mono, monocyte; Thym, thymocyte; PBL, peripheral blood leukocytes; NK, natural killer cells; Eosin, eosinophils; Eryth$_{imm}$, immature erythroid cells; Leuko, leukocytes; T_m, memory T cells; Epithel, epithelial cells; Lympho, lymphocytes; Neutro, neutrophils; Macro, macrophages; Granulo, granulocytes; Dendr, dendritic cells; Megakar, megakaryocytes; endo$_a$, activated endothelial cells; HEV, high endothelial venules; LN, lymph nodes; HUVEC, human umbilical vein endothelial cells; *, inducible expression.

The cytoplasmic domains of both the α and β subunits are critical to regulating the ability of integrins to mediate cell adhesion, as well as for transmitting information into the cell interior. Furthermore, recent studies have identified a number of intracellular proteins that associate with or are functionally coupled to integrins via these cytoplasmic tails. Additional complexity in the integrin subfamily is likely, given recent findings that variant forms of the β_1 and β_3 subunits exist that have different cytoplasmic tails as a result of alternative splicing.

Immunoglobulin (Ig) superfamily

Cell surface proteins of the Ig superfamily are characterized by the presence of a variable number of related 70–110 amino acid Ig-like domains originally described in the Ig variable and constant regions. Several IgSF members have been implicated in cell adhesion. CD2 has been shown to bind several distinct ligands, including the IgSF members CD58, CD48 and CD59. CD31, which can mediate homophilic adhesion, has also been implicated in binding to the $\alpha_v\beta_3$-integrin. The integrin counter-receptors ICAM-1, ICAM-2, ICAM-3, VCAM-1 and MAdCAM-1 (**Table 1**) round out the list of IgSF adhesion molecules described to date. MAdCAM-1 is a unique IgSF member in that it contains mucin-like properties in addition to Ig domains (see below).

Selectins

Selectins represent a family of three structurally and functionally related adhesion molecules: E-selectin, P-selectin and L-selectin. Each selectin consists of an extracellular lectin-like domain, an EGF-like domain, and variable numbers of a consensus repeat bearing homology to complement proteins, followed by transmembrane and short intracellular sequences. The lectin-like domains are primarily responsible for Ca^{2+}-dependent interactions with fucosylated, mucin-like ligands. Functionally, the rapid association and dissociation rate constants that characterize selectin-mediated adhesion allow selectins to function as important initiators of leukocyte adhesion to endothelium under conditions of shear flow. A role for selectins as signal transducing receptors is also now becoming evident.

Mucins

Mucins are characterized by their extensive and dense array of carbohydrates. The carbohydrate linkages are primarily O-linked with sulfated core groups, termed sialyl Lewis x (sLe^x). The mucins characterized to date are primarily selectin counter-receptors. L-Selectin binds to at least four distinct mucins: GlyCAM-1, MAdCAM-1, CD34, and a poorly characterized protein called Sgp200. As mentioned previously, MAdCAM-1 has both Ig domains and a mucin domain, allowing it to bind to both an integrin ($\alpha_4\beta_7$) and a selectin (L-selectin). GlyCAM-1 is somewhat unique in that it lacks a transmembrane domain. PSGL-1 binds both E- and P-selectin, although additional ligands have been described for each of these selectins. The E-selectin ligand ESL-1 appears to require N-linked carbohydrate structures rather than the typical O-linked sialomucin structures. The CLA antigen also binds to E-selectin and is expressed on a subset of memory T cells that preferentially migrate to the skin. The protein backbones of mucins are also postulated to play a role in binding specificity.

Cadherins

Cadherins have been implicated in Ca^{2+}-dependent homotypic aggregation of nonlymphoid cells and play an important structural role in cell–cell junctions. Although there are several different cadherins, to date only E-cadherin has been implicated in regulating immunological function. Intraepithelial lymphocytes express the $\alpha_E\beta_7$-integrin, which binds to E-cadherin expressed on epithelial cells. This adhesive interaction has been proposed to play a role in retaining $\alpha_E\beta_7$-expressing T cells at specific tissue sites *in vivo*. E-Cadherin is also the cell surface receptor for the *Listeria monocytogenes* protein internalin.

Other adhesion molecules

Several molecules that are not easily categorized into these adhesion molecule families are listed in **Table 1** and deserve mention here. VAP-1 is an adhesion molecule that is expressed on endothelium derived from peripheral lymph nodes, synovium and tonsils, and may play a role in tissue-specific migration of lymphocytes to synovial tissue. LVAP-2 is a putative endothelial adhesion molecule for lymphocytes and has been found on human umbilical vein endothelium (HUVEC), lymphoid and nonlymphoid venules, B cells, and CD8$^+$ T cells. The urokinase plasminogen activator receptor (uPAR) has been shown to bind vitronectin, as well as regulate the binding activity of β_1- and β_2-integrins (see below). CD44 is a widely distributed molecule that is related to cartilage link proteins and proteoglycan core protein. The CD44 transcript can undergo extensive alternative splicing, generating many different protein isoforms. Several CD44 ligands have been reported, the most notable being hyaluronic acid. Antibodies to CD44 can inhibit lymphocyte recirculation, and, like selectins, CD44 binding to hyaluronic acid can support lymphocyte rolling under shear flow. However, the precise function of CD44 in the immune system remains elusive.

Roles of adhesion molecules in regulating immune function

As mentioned previously, the wide array of adhesion molecules and ligand possibilities provides for exquisite specificity as well as diversity in the tasks adhesion molecules perform in the immune system. Some salient points regarding the importance of these molecules in both normal immune regulation and with respect to the disease state are addressed below.

Adhesion molecules and lymphocyte recognition

The process by which an antigen-specific cytotoxic T lymphocyte (CTL) recognizes and kills a target cell has provided a valuable system for elucidating the function of adhesion molecules in the immune response. In the early 1980s, several monoclonal antibodies were identified that inhibited CTL killing. Subsequent analysis revealed that these antibodies recognize the adhesion molecules LFA-1, a β_2-integrin, CD2 (LFA-2), and its cellular counter-receptor LFA-3 (CD58). Further analysis of CTL killing identified the first LFA-1 counter-receptor, ICAM-1. Antibodies against these molcules are effective in inhibiting CTL function, because they impair the physical contact between the CTL and the target cell that is required for T cell activation to occur. Thus, one function of adhesion molecules during T cell activation is to provide the adhesive force necessary to allow for effective binding of the antigen-specific T cell receptor with major histocompatibility complex (MHC)-peptide complexes on the antigen-presenting cell. In addition, adhesion molecules also provide intracellular signals during T cell activation that further facilitate T cell activation (see below).

Adhesion molecules and leukocyte recruitment and recirculation

Interaction of circulating blood cells with endothelial cells is essential for the recruitment of lymphocytes to sites of injury and inflammation and for normal recirculation of lymphocytes. The successful movement of leukocytes out of the bloodstream through the endothelium and into the underlying tissue requires the coordinated and sequential interaction of adhesion molecules on the leukocyte and the endothelium, as well as the correct temporal expression of activating signals provided by cytokines and chemokines. This process has been defined generally as the multistep paradigm of leukocyte adhesion to endothelium. The process of adhesion under shear flow is typically initiated by low-affinity binding of leukocytes to activated endothelium, which results in a characteristic rolling or tumbling of leukocytes along the endothelial surface. Although selectins typically mediate rolling, α_4-integrins can also mediate rolling in the absence of a contribution from selectins. Upon encounter with an appropriate stimulus, rolling can be converted rapidly into stable, shear-resistant attachment of leukocytes to the endothelial surface. This is accomplished by rapid agonist-induced activation of integrins such as $\alpha_4\beta_1$ (VLA-4), $\alpha_4\beta_7$, LFA-1, and Mac-1. A number of stimuli have been proposed to serve as the 'trigger' that activates integrins in this process, including chemokines immobilized on the endothelial surface by proteoglycans and, perhaps, intracellular signals generated by the selectins during rolling. Following tight adhesion to the endothelium, leukocytes migrate through the endothelium into the underlying tissue. Current evidence suggests a role for chemotactic factors, integrins and CD31 in this process. Thus, the successful extravasation of a leukocyte from the bloodstream into tissue requires the coordinated and sequential interaction of different adhesion molecules, each of which serves to carry out distinct phases of the process. Underlying this orchestrated utilization of adhesion molecules is the role of soluble factors, which serve to dictate the spectrum of adhesion molecules expressed on the endothelial surface, as well as to provide the appropriate signals and chemotactic gradients that initiate key steps in this cascade of adhesive events.

Regulation of adhesion molecule expression and function

The adhesive nature of cells is regulated at many levels. The level of expression of adhesion molecules on the cell surface is dependent in large part on the activation status of the cell. Activation of endothelial cells with inflammatory cytokines, such as interleukin 1 (IL-1) and tumor necrosis factor α (TNFα), results within hours in an increase in expression of E-selectin, ICAM-1 and VCAM-1. This cytokine-induced expression of these adhesion molecules is due to transcriptional upregulation of the genes encoding these molecules. P-selectin is also expressed on activated endothelium, as well as on platelets. However, P-selectin is stored in granules, ready to be upregulated within minutes in response to stimulation. Stimulation of neutrophils with agonists such as formyl-Met-Leu-Phe (fMLP) also results in the rapid upregulation of the Mac-1 integrin due to

fusion of intracellular granules containing Mac-1 molecules with the plasma membrane.

Adhesion molecules can also be rapidly lost from the cell surface. The most notable example is L-selectin, which is constitutively expressed on most peripheral blood leukocytes. However, leukocyte activation can result in rapid proteolytic cleavage (shedding) of L-selectin from the cell surface. Although the protease responsible for L-selectin shedding has not been identified, the cleavage of L-selectin from the cell surface has been demonstrated to be important for leukocyte interactions with endothelium. Other adhesion molecules, including CD44, E-selectin, ICAM-1 and VCAM-1, can also be found in soluble form. The functional significance of soluble adhesion molecules is not entirely clear, but changes in the level of expression of soluble adhesion molecules in various disease states have been noted.

Stable changes in the expression of adhesion molecules can also be observed during the process of lymphocyte differentiation. For example, when naive T cells are activated, some of the activated T cells differentiate into memory T cells. These memory T cells can be distinguished from naive T cells by differential expression of several adhesion molecules. Some adhesion molecules, such as the LFA-1 integrin, β_1-integrins and CD44, show increased expression on memory T cells, while others, such as L-selectin, show reduced expression. These differences in adhesion molecule expression on naive and memory T cells are believed to be responsible in part for the differences in naive and memory T cell recirculation *in vivo*. For example, uniform expression of L-selectin on naive T cells is believed to be critical for the preferential migration of naive T cells into peripheral lymph nodes via adhesion and transmigration through peripheral lymph node high endothelial venules (HEV). Differentiation of thymocytes is also characterized by discrete changes in the expression of various adhesion molecules.

The functional activity of adhesion molecules can also be regulated by cellular activation. Stimulation of leukocytes and platelets results within seconds to minutes in rapid increases in integrin-mediated adhesion that do not require changes in levels of integrins on the cell surface. Such activation of integrins from a latent cell surface form is an essential element of the multistep paradigm of leukocyte interactions with endothelium. Furthermore, the ability of T cell receptor stimulation to activate integrins in such a manner implicates this mode of regulation in enhancing T cell contact with antigen presenting cells. T Cell receptor stimulation has also been reported to increase the adhesiveness of the CD2 molecule. The intracellular mechanisms by which activation rapidly upregulates the adhesive nature of these molecules remain poorly defined.

Adhesion molecules may also be regulated by other molecules that physically associate with adhesion receptors and consequently alter adhesive activity. Integrin-mediated cell adhesion to fibronectin has been shown to be inhibited by expression of the uPAR, which physically associates with β_1-integrins as well as the Mac-1 integrin. Studies of four transmembrane-containing (TM-4) proteins (CD9, CD63 and CD81/TAPA-1) have also demonstrated an association of these proteins on the cell surface with integrins, although the functional significance of this association for integrin function remains unclear. These observations suggest that additional membrane localized proteins may be identified in the future with similar roles of enhancing or inhibiting adhesion molecule function through physical association in the plasma membrane.

Signal transduction through adhesion molecules

While the term 'adhesion molecules' highlights the ability of these receptors to serve as the 'glue' that binds cells to each other and to ECM, it is now clear that engagement of adhesion molecules also results in the generation of intracellular signals that alter cell function. Evidence for adhesion molecule-mediated signal transduction is now plentiful. Analysis of integrin-mediated signaling, in particular, has been extensive and highlights the broad array of intracellular signals that adhesion molecules can transduce when appropriately stimulated. In the immune system, initial evidence for integrin-mediated signaling has been obtained by findings that interactions between integrin counter-receptors and ECM ligands can enhance T cell receptor-mediated activation of T cells. More direct evidence for integrin-mediated signaling has developed from biochemical studies of various signal transduction pathways using a large number of cell types. Integrin engagement by ligand or monoclonal antibodies has been shown to result in the activation of early signaling events, such as calcium influx, a rise in intracellular pH, and the activation of a number of intracellular kinases. These include tyrosine kinases, mitogen-activated protein kinases (MAPKs) and lipid kinases. Integrin stimulation also results in the tyrosine phosphorylation of a number of proteins, most notably an intracellular tyrosine kinase, focal adhesion kinase (pp125[FAK]), the p130[Cas] adapter protein, and several cytoskeletal proteins. In adherent cells, such as fibroblasts, many of these tyrosine phosphorylated proteins are associated functionally with integrins at focal adhesions,

the point of cell contact with the underlying ECM. A link between integrin-mediated tyrosine phosphorylation of pp125[FAK] and activation of the Ras signaling pathway has been suggested. Certain transcriptional effects of integrin activation have been noted, including the induced expression of metalloproteinase and transcription factor genes. A critical role for integrins in cell survival has also been documented. However, the functional relationship between early integrin-mediated activation events, such as tyrosine phosphorylation, and later events, such as induction of gene transcription, remains poorly characterized.

Integrins are not the only adhesion molecules that transduce signals upon engagement. Stimulation of certain selectins (L- and E-selectin) and IgSF members (CD2, CD31) can upregulate β_1- and β_2-integrin activity. Thus, signals generated by one type of adhesion molecule can alter the functional activity of another. In the case of CD2, a role for CD2 as a signaling molecule was appreciated before any role for the molecule in adhesion was uncovered. Although not as extensively studied, it is now becoming clear that selectins, like integrins, also initiate intracellular signals upon ligand engagement. While typical markers of intracellular cascades, such as Ca^{2+} influx and tyrosine phosphorylation, have been noted following activation of many of these adhesion molecules, notable distinctions also appear to be emerging. Thus, there is likely to be considerable complexity and specificity in adhesion molecule signaling, reflecting the complex but specific nature of receptor–ligand interactions discussed previously and shown in **Table 1**.

Adhesion molecules and disease

The physiological relevance of adhesion molecule function is elegantly demonstrated by naturally occurring defects in the expression and/or function of adhesion molecules, which consequently leads to disease. The inherited bleeding disorder, Glanzmann's thrombasthenia, is caused by loss of expression and/or function of the $\alpha_{IIb}\beta_3$-integrin on platelets. Consequently, platelet aggregation, which is necessary to prevent excessive loss of blood during injury, fails to occur. The importance of adhesive functions of the β_2-integrins has been demonstrated by a syndrome termed leukocyte adhesion deficiency (LAD-1). Patients afflicted with this disease lack expression of the β_2-integrin subunit, and the adherent function of their macrophages and granulocytes is essentially absent. As a result, affected individuals have severely reduced life expectancies and suffer from recurrent bacterial and fungal infections.

Recently, a syndrome, termed LAD-2, with a similar phenotype to that of LAD-1 has been characterized. LAD-2 results from a defect in fucose metabolism, which impairs the expression of the carbohydrate ligands recognized by selectins. The neutrophils of afflicted individuals fail to bind endothelial cells, further demonstrating the importance of adhesion molecules in normal physiological cell functions.

The *in vivo* relevance of adhesion molecules in the immune response has also been demonstrated experimentally in a variety of ways. Altered expression and/or function of adhesion molecules has been noted in various disease states. The functional relevance of these findings has been demonstrated by *in vivo* blocking studies using antibodies specific for adhesion molecules, soluble adhesion receptors, blocking peptides or carbohydrates, and antisense oligonucleotides. Thus, targeting of adhesion molecules with these reagents has been shown to be effective in many different animal models of human disease, including models of ischemia/reperfusion injury, acute inflammation, allograft rejection during organ transplantation and various chronic inflammatory disorders such as rheumatoid arthritis. In most of these studies, the primary focus has been on blocking or modulating leukocyte or lymphocyte attachment to endothelial cells. Modulation of adhesion molecule expression has also been shown to be effective in inhibiting tumor cell growth and metastasis.

The use of homologous recombination in embryonic stem cells to generate mice deficient in expression of various adhesion molecules has also been utilized to uncover the function of these molecules *in vivo*. Mice lacking expression of several individual integrin α and β subunits have been produced. For the most part, these integrin mutations have been either embryonic or neonatal lethal in phenotype, emphasizing the global importance of integrins in embryonic development. Mice lacking expression of signaling components linked to integrins, such as pp125[FAK], also fail to develop normally. Mice lacking expression of the β_7-integrin subunit are viable, but exhibit defects in development of gut-associated lymphoid tissue, presumably due to the inability of T cells to migrate into this tissue site. L-selectin, E-selectin and P-selectin knockout mice have also been individually generated, confirming the importance of these molecules in leukocyte–endothelial interactions. E-selectin-deficient mice present with little change in phenotype from wild-type. However, mice genetically deficient for both E- and P-selectin show a synergistic reduction in neutrophil and lymphocyte adhesion to endothelium, confirming roles for both P- and E-selectin in this process.

Conclusions

Clearly, the variety of adhesion molecules described to date lends itself well to diverse mechanisms of immune regulation. New adhesion molecules are likely to be discovered, and the mechanisms of adhesion molecule function will continue to be further delineated. Given the breadth of this diversity, it will be crucial to begin a closer scrutiny of the structural and signaling requirements of these molecules. A more precise knowledge of these roles may lead to valuable tools that target adhesion molecules for therapeutic intervention in diseases whose etiology includes aberrations of the immune response.

See also: **Carbohydrate antigens; CD2; CD44; Chemokines; Chemotaxis; Chemotaxis of lymphocytes; Chemotaxis of macrophages and monocytes; Chemotaxis of neutrophils; Diapedesis; Endothelium; Extracellular matrix; Fibronectin; High endothelial venules; Immune adherence; Immunodeficiency, animal models; Immunoglobulin gene superfamily; Integrins; Intercellular adhesion molecules: ICAM-1, ICAM-2 and ICAM-3; Knockout, genetic; Lectins; Leukocyte adhesion deficiency; Lewis^x/sialyl-Lewis^x (CD15/CD15s); Lymphocyte function-associated antigen 1 (LFA-1); Lymphocyte function-associated antigen 3 (LFA-3); Lymphocyte trafficking; Proliferation, lymphocyte; Second signals for lymphocyte activation; Selectins (CD62-E/L/P); T lymphocyte activation; Yersinia, infection and immunity.**

Further reading

Bruinsma R (1997) Les liaisons dangereuses: adhesion molecules do it statistically. *Proceedings of the National Academy of Sciences of the USA* 94: 375–376.

Butcher EC and Picker LJ (1996) Lymphocyte homing and homeostasis. *Science* 272: 60–66.

Carlos TM and Harlan JM (1994) Leukocyte-endothelial adhesion molecules. *Blood* 84: 2068–2101.

Ebnet K, Kaldjian EP, Anderson AO and Shaw S (1996) Orchestrated information transfer underlying leukocyte endothelial interactions. *Annual Review of Immunology* 14: 155–177.

Gearing AJH and Newman W (1993) Circulating adhesion molecules in disease. *Immunology Today* 14: 506–512.

Gilat D, Cahalon L, Hershkoviz R and Lider O (1996) Interplay of T cells and cytokines in the context of enzymatically modified extracellular matrix. *Immunology Today* 17: 16–20.

Gumbiner BM (1996) Cell adhesion: the molecular basis of tissue architecture and morphogenesis. *Cell* 84: 345–357.

Hunt SW, III, Harris ES, Kellerman S-A and Shimizu Y

(1996) T-lymphocyte interactions with endothelium and extracellular matrix. *Critical Review in Oral Biology and Medicine* 7: 59–86.

Lasky LA (1995) Selectin-carbohydrate interactions and the initiation of the inflammatory response. *Annual Review of Biochemistry* 64: 113–139.

Marra A and Isberg RR (1996) Bacterial pathogenesis: common entry mechanisms. *Current Biology* 6: 1084–1086.

Rainger GE, Buckley C, Simmons DL *et al.* (1997) Cross-talk between cell adhesion molecules regulates the migration velocity of neutrophils. *Current Biology* 7: 316–325.

Schwartz MA, Schaller MD and Ginsberg MH (1995) Inte-grins: emerging paradigms of signal transduction. *Annual Review of Cell Biology* 11: 549–600.

Shimizu Y and Hunt SW, III (1996) Regulating integrin-mediated adhesion: one more function for PI 3-kinase? *Immunology Today* 17: 565–573.

Springer TA (1994) Traffic signals for lymphocyte recirculation and leukocyte emigration: the multistep paradigm. *Cell* 76: 301–314.

Stewart M and Hogg N (1996) Regulation of leukocyte integrin function: affinity vs. avidity. *Journal of Cell Biochemistry* 61: 554–561.

Vestweber D (1996) Ligand-specificity of the selectins. *Journal of Cell Biochemistry* 61: 585–591.

ADJUVANT ARTHRITIS

Irun R Cohen, Department of Immunology, The Weizmann Institute of Science, Rehovot, Israel

Adjuvant arthritis (AA) is a disease induced in rats by immunization with killed *Mycobacterium tuberculosis* (MT) organisms in oil, a substance known as complete Freund's adjuvant. The work of C.M. Pearson and his colleagues in the 1950s and 1960s helped establish AA as a standard model of chronic inflammation produced by immunological processes. Two opposing theories were put forth to explain the pathogenesis of AA: the first proposed that the joints were damaged as bystanders to an immune response directed to MT antigens disseminated to the sites of inflammation; the second proposed that AA was caused by an autoimmune attack against a cross-reactive self antigen. Despite the uncertainty of its pathogenesis, AA has served for many years as a reliable and convenient model for testing treatments for inflammation.

Induction of AA

AA appears about 2 weeks after immunization of rats to MT. The severity, duration and consequences of the arthritis seem to be influenced by various factors:

1. Genes; major histocompatibility complex (MHC) and other genes contribute to susceptibility. AA is most readily induced in rats and has been studied almost exclusively in this species. Mice, however, were reported to develop AA 2 months after administration of MT.
2. Gender; male rats are more susceptible than are female rats.
3. Microbial environment; germ-free rats and rats maintained in very clean surroundings are much more susceptible to severe AA than are rats raised in contaminated quarters.
4. Amount of MT; the maximum clinical score of the arthritis is directly related to the amount of MT administered to the rats. About 0.2 mg of MT produces mild AA. Increasing the dose of MT causes more severe arthritis; a maximum clinical score is usually elicited by 1 mg of MT.
5. State of MT inoculum; finely pulverized MT is much more arthritogenic than is whole MT. Merely mixing the MT in oil is more arthritogenic than is emulsifying the MT in oil.
6. Site of immunization; intradermal inoculation is most arthritogenic, intramuscular is least and intraperitoneal is intermediate.

The severity of acute AA in rats peaks about 2 weeks after the disease first appears. The arthritis then slowly regresses and may disappear totally (for example in dirty female rats); but it may also persist for a year or more (for example in clean male rats). Protracted AA can lead to irreversible damage (ankylosis) to the joints of the extremities.

The rats that recover from AA acquire resistance to further attempts to induce AA. Resistance to AA can also be obtained by first administering MT under conditions that are not arthritogenic; for example, MT administered intramuscularly or without oil. Thus, the clinical expression of arthritis appears to result from many seemingly trivial factors impinging on the process of immunization to MT; the particulars of the immunization determine the nature of the response, which in turn determines the pathogenic consequences. Such complexity implies regulation.

The hsp65 connection

In 1984 it became possible to study the complexities of AA using an etiologic agent of disease, a clone of T cells capable of adoptively transferring AA, called A2b. It was demonstrated that A2b recognized an MT antigen and an antigen in the proteoglycan moiety of joint cartilage. This supported the autoimmune theory: AA was caused by antigen mimicry between MT and a joint antigen.

The MT epitope recognized by clone A2b was later identified as the nine amino acids at positions 180–188 in the sequence of the 65 kDa heat shock protein (hsp65) molecule of MT. This molecule belongs to the hsp60 family and is closely homologous to the mammalian hsp60 molecules. The general importance of hsp65 to arthritis was suggested by the observation that T cells responsive to hsp65 could be detected in the synovial fluids of patients suffering from rheumatoid arthritis. Moreover, some patients with juvenile arthritis showed immunity to the human hsp60 molecule. Thus, immunity to hsp65/hsp60 could be associated with spontaneous forms of immunological arthritis in humans as well as with AA of rats.

Is T cell immunity to hsp65 the cause or only the result of AA? The answer awaits the resolution of four issues.

1. *Identity of the joint antigen.* The 180–188 peptide recognized by clone A2b is in a variable region of the hsp65 molecule of MT; despite an overall homology of 50%, the 180–186 amino acid sequence is not present in the known mammalian hsp60 molecules. Thus the epitope recognized by A2b in the joints is probably not on the endogenous hsp60 molecule but is likely to be present on another molecule. A very weak homology between the 180–188 peptide and a sequence in the link protein of cartilage proteoglycan exists. This is compatible with the earlier observation that clone A2b recognizes an element in cartilage proteoglycan. However, clone A2b does not proliferate in response to the link protein peptide, so some other cross-reactivity is probably responsible for AA. Cross-reactivity has been sought between hsp65 and chondrocyte and proteoglycan antigens, and between hsp65 and lactoferrin, but these studies have failed to shed any light on pathogenesis. AA seems to be distinct immunologically from the arthritis inducible by immunization to collagen type II, yet spleen cells from rats immunized to collagen type II could partially inhibit AA. Thus, the immunological connection between MT and AA, and between hsp65 and the joints, remains circumstantial.

2. *Induction of AA.* The fact that clone A2b caused arthritis led to the hypothesis that the target epitope of AA must be present in the hsp65 molecule of MT. This idea would be more tenable if active immunization to hsp65 were to actually induce AA. However, immunization with hsp65 has as yet failed to induce arthritis. Nevertheless, hsp65 must be involved in the process responsible for arthritis because administration of whole hsp65 or the 180–188 nonapeptide to rats induces resistance to AA.

   There is yet another problem: not only can hsp65 prevent AA, it can also prevent arthritis induced by streptococcal cell walls or arthritis induced by the oil pristane. These forms of arthritis are not related, at least superficially, to MT. Why then should administration of the hsp65 of MT influence them?

3. *Specificity of hsp65 immunity.* The immune response to hsp65 is not exclusive to arthritis. It appears that inflammatory exudates outside of the joints, pleural effusions for example, are also rich in T cells responsive to hsp65. Moreover, immunization of some strains of mice with hsp65 or hsp60 has been found to induce diabetes mellitus. The epitope of hsp60 associated with diabetes differs from the 180–188 epitope associated with arthritis. Nevertheless, it is clear that hsp65 immunity is not limited to the inflammation of immunological arthritis. In fact, immunity to hsp65 is not necessarily associated with immunopathology; the T cells of healthy humans respond very well to hsp65 and even to self hsp 60. Moreover, hsp65 is a dominant antigen in the immune response to infection or vaccination with *Mycobacteria* or other bacteria.

4. *Regulation of AA.* AA is a manifestation of the inflammatory reaction, so it is not surprising that AA can be suppressed by various anti-inflammatory treatments, particularly treatments that inhibit proinflammatory cytokines, such as tumor necrosis factor α (TNFα), or that block the T-cell receptor. Interestingly, AA can be inhibited by T cells that recognize specific epitopes from the T-cell receptor of an anti-hsp65 T cell. In addition to regulatory T cells, it appears that antibodies may be important in the regulation of AA. AA can be inhibited by normal immunoglobulin (IVIg) and by immunoglobulins from strains of rats resistant to AA. Furthermore, AA is marked by changes in the glyco-

sylation of antibodies of the IgG1 and IgG2b isotypes.

The future

Although AA has been a familiar laboratory model for decades, we are only now appreciating the charm of its complexity and the value of the secrets it can reveal about health, autoimmunity and the immunology of the host–parasite interaction. As we might have guessed from the constellation of elements affecting its induction, the development of AA is an outward expression of the subleties of immune regulation. Health or disease is not the mere outcome of response or nonresponse. The immune system can respond to MT and to the hsp65/hsp60 molecules in many ways and it is the nature of this response that determines health or disease. 'The nature of this response' is a conceptual handle of the black box of immunological regulation. Present research is attempting to open the box to reveal the clockwork of the system.

See also: **Adjuvants; Autoimmune disease, induced experimental models; Molecular mimicry; Rheumatoid arthritis, animal models; Stress proteins; T cell vaccination.**

Further reading

Achiron A, Margalit R, Hershkoviz R *et al* (1994) Intravenous immunoglobulin treatment of experimental T cell-mediated autoimmune disease. Upregulationof T cell proliferation and down-regulation of tumor necrosis factor alpha secretion. *Journal of Clinical Investigation* 93: 600–605.

Anderton SM, van der Zee R, Noordzij A and van Eden W (1994) Differential mycobacterial 65-kDa heat shock T cell epitope recognition after adjuvant arthritis-inducing or protective immunization protocols. *Journal of Immunology* 152: 3656–3664.

Anderton SM, van der Zee R, Prakken B, Noordzij A and van Eden W (1995) Activation of T cells recognizing self 60-KD heat shock protein can protect against experimental arthritis. *Journal of Experimental Medicine* 181: 943–952.

Broeren CP, Lucassen MA, van der Zee R, Boog CJ, Kusters JG and van Eden W (1995) Anti-T-cell receptor peptide specific T-cells and adjuvant arthritis. *Annals of the New York Academy of Sciences* 756: 227–278.

Cohen IR (1991) Autoimmunity to chaperonins in the pathogenesis of arthritis and diabetes. *Annual Review of Immunology* 9: 567–589.

Cohen IR (1992) The cognitive paradigm and the immunological homunculus. *Immunology Today* 13: 490–494.

Cohen IR (1992) The cognitive principle challenges clonal selection. *Immunology Today* 13: 441–444.

Halloran MM, Szekanecz Z, Barquin N *et al* (1996) Cellular adhesion molecules in rat adjuvant arthritis. *Arthritis and Rheumatism* 39: 810–909.

Holoshitz J, Matitau A and Cohen IR (1984) Arthritis induced in rats by cloned T lymphocytes responsive to mycobacteria but not to collagen type II. *Journal of Clinical Investigation* 73: 211–215.

Hunt DW, Corson L, Barker HD, Levy JG and Petty RE (1993) Relationship between collagen-induced and adjuvant arthritis in the Lewis rat. *Journal of Autoimmunity* 6: 691–700.

Knight B, Katz DR, Isenberg DA *et al* (1992) Induction of adjuvant arthritis in mice. *Clinical and Experimental Immunology* 90: 459–465.

Pelegri C, Kuhnlein P, Buchner E *et al* (1996) Depletion of γ/δ T cells does not prevent or ameliorate, but rather aggravates, rat adjuvant arthritis. *Arthritis and Rheumatism* 39: 204–215.

Prakken BJ, van der Zee R, Anderton SM *et al* (1997) Peptide-induced nasal tolerance for a mycobacterial heat shock protein 60 T cell epitope in rats suppresses both adjuvant arthritis and nonmicrobially induced experimental arthritis. *Proceedings of the National Academy of the Sciences USA* 94(7): 3284–3289.

Ragno S, Colston MJ, Lowrie DB *et al* (1997) Protection of rats from adjuvant arthritis by immunization with naked DNA encoding for mycobacterial heat shock protein 65. *Arthritis and Rheumatism* 40: 277–283.

Roubenoff R, Freeman LM, Smith DE *et al* (1997) Adjuvant arthritis as a model of inflammatory cachexia. *Arthritis and Rheumatism* 40: 534–539.

Ulmansky R and Naparstek Y (1995) Immunoglobulins from rats that are resistant to adjuvant arthritis suppress the disease in arthritis-susceptible rats. *European Journal of Immunology* 25: 952–957.

van Eden W (1991) Heat-shock proteins as immunogenic bacterial antigens with the potential to induce and regulate autoimmune arthritis. *Immunological Reviews* 121: 5–28.

van Eden W, Thole H, Van der Zee R *et al* (1988) Synovial fluid T cell reactivity against 65 kD heat shock protein of *Mycobacteria* in early chronic arthritis. *Lancet* ii: 478–480.

Walter UM and Issekutz AC (1997) The role of E- and P-selectin in neutrophil and monocyte migration in adjuvant-induced arthritis in the rat. *European Journal of Immunology,* 27: 1498–1505.

Yagev H, Frenkel A, Cohen IR and Friedman A (1993) Adjuvant arthritis is associated with changes in the glycosylation of serum IgG1 and IgG2b. *Clinical and Experimental Immunology* 94: 452–458.

ADJUVANTS

H Shaw Warren, Infectious Disease Unit, Massachusetts General Hospital East, Charlestown, Massachusetts, USA

Claude Leclerc, Biologie des Régulations Immunitaires, Institut Pasteur, Paris, France

The word 'adjuvant' is used in many ways in biology and medicine. Most commonly, it is used to refer to compounds that act in a nonspecific manner to augment specific immunity to an antigen. A series of experiments in 1925 by Ramon first indicated that compounds of a vaccine formulation other than antigen itself are important for a successful biological response. Ramon found that the addition of substances as diverse as metal salts, oil, tapioca and pyogenic bacteria to his vaccine preparations increased the antitoxic response to diphtheria and tetanus toxins. These simple but elegant experiments started a search, which is still ongoing, for vaccine adjuvants that are suitable for a wide range of uses.

Older vaccines contained antigen preparations that were frequently impure and poorly characterized. Retained contaminants resulted in toxicity and antigenic competition. In some cases, such as with killed bacterial vaccines, the contaminants themselves were adjuvants. Technical advances in biochemistry and molecular biology have led to the production of increasingly pure antigens in order to induce a specific immune response. Modern antigen preparations are usually very well characterized and are now often synthetic or recombinant constructs. These new preparations have reduced side-effects but in many cases are less immunogenic than older killed or subunit vaccines; therefore, in most cases, adjuvants are needed to increase their potency. Adjuvants are substances capable of stimulating an earlier, stronger or more prolonged response to an antigen. In some systems the antibody or the cell-mediated (CMI) immune response, as well as the antibody class or subclass and/or T helper subset (T_H1 and T_H2), can be selected for by manipulating the adjuvant and vaccine formulations.

There are several properties that an adjuvant should ideally possess to be effective, safe and practical for use in human vaccines. Foremost, it should accomplish its desired goal without toxicity. Additionally, however, it should be well characterized and stable even in the absence of refrigeration. Although there are numerous compounds presently utilized as adjuvants in animals, no compound fits all of these desired criteria for clinical use.

The development of vaccine adjuvants has been largely empirical. Antigen preparations have tra-ditionally been administered with and without an adjuvant and the specific immune responses directed towards the antigen have been compared by assessing antibody and/or CMI utilizing assays current for the epoch of the experiment. Improved immunologic and biochemical techniques are permitting the construction of new, better characterized adjuvants and vaccine formulations. Nonetheless, a fundamental understanding of the mechanisms by which adjuvants stimulate immune responses is incomplete, slowing progress in the field and making classification of the numerous and diverse adjuvants that are currently known somewhat arbitrary.

Compounds with adjuvant activity (Table 1)

Aluminum compounds

Aluminum was used as an adjuvant as early as 1926 by Glenny. The positive results of these studies led to its use worldwide in animal and human vaccines in the following decades. Aluminum continues to be

Table 1 Commonly studied adjuvants, based on mechanism[a]

Depot based
Aluminum
Degradable polymer microspheres
Emulsions

Hydrophobic and surfactant
Emulsions
Liposomes
ISCOMs
Saponin (QS21)
Nonionic block copolymers

Bacterial derivatives
Lipopolysaccharide and derivatives
Muramyl dipeptide and derivatives
Trehalose dimycolate
Corynebacterium parvum
Pertussis toxin
Cholera toxin
Heat-labile enterotoxin and derivatives

Cytokines
IL-1 and derived synthetic peptide
IL-2, IL-4, IL-6, IL-12, etc
IFNγ

[a]This list is not inclusive. Adjuvants may be listed in more than one category.

utilized today, primarily because it is generally regarded as safe.

Vaccines are prepared by adsorbing the antigen on to aluminum compounds such as aluminum hydroxide or phosphate, or by precipitating the antigen with alum [Al(SO$_4$)$_2$ 12 H$_2$O]. Several hypotheses have been proposed for its mechanism of action. However, most investigators believe that the primary mechanism by which aluminum acts is by the creation of a depot so that the antigen is relatively slowly released, prolonging the time in which it can interact with antigen-presenting cells and lymphocytes. Despite its wide acceptance for clinical use, there are some disadvantages in the use of aluminum as an adjuvant for human vaccines. Although clinical trials have confirmed that aluminum is safe, it augments antibody responses much more effectively than CMI. Furthermore, its adjuvanticity varies depending upon the antigen. Other problems are that vaccines containing aluminum cannot be frozen for storage or lyophilized, and therefore require refrigerated transport. Overall, aluminum compounds are adequate adjuvants if antibody is sufficient for protection and the antigen is a strong immunogen.

Hydrophobic compounds and surfactants

The empirical knowledge that hydrophobic substances tend to augment antibody production and CMI has been a framework for the development of several classes of adjuvants. Examples include emulsions containing water and oil, lipopolysaccharide (LPS), liposomes and saponin.

The use of emulsions began in the 1930s with the experiments of Freund, who mixed paraffin oil with solutions of killed mycobacteria. This compound, called Freund's complete adjuvant, is one of the most potent adjuvants known. It is, however, too toxic for use in humans. An oil emulsion without the mycobacteria, called Freund's incomplete adjuvant, is less toxic and was clinically utilized in the past for influenza and poliomyelitis vaccines. It is no longer used because of a low incidence of induced sterile abscesses, the question of carcinogenicity in mice, lot-to-lot variation, lack of long-term stability, and the fact that CMI is not substantially boosted.

The use of liposomes as adjuvants has been studied experimentally for 20 years. Adjuvant activity depends upon the charge, the number of multilamellar phospholipid layers, the composition and the method of preparation. Both antibody and CMI are augmented. Some liposome preparations induce a potent cytotoxic T lymphocyte (CTL) response. A physical association between antigen and liposome is necessary, suggesting that a depot effect and/or altered antigen presentation are important mechanisms.

Stability, long-term toxicity and lot-to-lot variation are potential problems.

Saponin is a compound that was initially purified from the bark of the tree, *Quillaja saponaria*. It has been studied for decades, but is too toxic for use in humans. Chemical extraction procedures led to the less toxic derivative, Quil A, which is utilized widely for veterinary vaccines, and subsequently to QS21. Complexes of cholesterol, Quil A and amphipathic antigen (called ISCOMs) provide an efficient means of inducing a potent antibody and CMI response, and may provide a formulation in which the toxicity of Quil A is diminished, while its efficacy, including its ability to induce CTL, is maintained. QS21 is less toxic than both parent compounds, and can stimulate a T$_H$1 response and antigen-specific CTL in addition to antibody responses. Its safety and efficacy are being evaluated in several clinical trials.

Adjuvants of bacterial origin

It is not surprising that animals have evolved an elegant immune response to bacterial products. Although many adjuvants of bacterial origin are too toxic in their natural form for use in humans, analogs of LPS and muramyl dipeptide have been developed for reduced toxicity.

Experiments in the 1960s and 1970s revealed that the adjuvant active moiety of LPS is a unique bacterial lipid called lipid A. Chemical manipulations such as phthalylination or succinylation of the LPS or removal of a phosphate group from lipid A to create monophosphoryl lipid A results in diminished toxicity of the compound, while retaining adjuvanticity.

Freund's complete adjuvant consists of an oil emulsion containing killed mycobacteria. Successive biochemical studies revealed that one of the most active components is *N*-acetylmuramyl-L-alanyl-D-isoglutamine (muramyl dipeptide, MDP). Over the last decade, numerous analogs of MDP have been synthesized and studied. Hydrophilic MDP analogs administered in saline induce mainly antibody responses, whereas CMI is induced if MDP is given together with antigen in oil emulsions or in liposomes. Similarly, if the MDP analog itself is made lipophilic by the addition of glycerol mycolate, CMI is induced. Nontoxic candidate MDP analogs for clinical use are murametide (NAcMur-L-Ala-D-Gln-OCH$_3$), murabutide (NAcMur-L-Ala-D-Gln-alpha-*n*-butyl ester) and muramyl tripeptide (MTP-PE). A combination of threonyl-MDP with a squalane and pluronic copolymer emulsion (Syntex adjuvant formulation, SAF) is a potent adjuvant in experimental models. MTP-PE and SAF are currently being assessed as adjuvants for some human immunodeficiency virus (HIV) vaccine candidates.

The mucosal immune response is important for protection against many infections. Cholera toxin and *Escherichia coli* heat-labile enterotoxin (LT) are the most potent adjuvants described for the induction of mucosal immunity. Unfortunately, neither can be used in humans because of associated toxicity. Recently, however, a nontoxic derivative of LT has been developed which retains its adjuvanticity for mucosal immunization.

Cytokines

Interleukin 1 (IL-1), IL-2, IL-4, IL-6 and interferon γ (IFNγ) stimulate immune responses when injected together with antigens. A synthetic nonapeptide of IL-1β has been identified that possesses immunostimulatory but not inflammatory activity. Other cytokines are attractive candidates for the development of vaccines that specifically stimulate certain arms of the immune system. For example, IL-12 is a potent stimulator of T_H1 responses and therefore may be helpful as a component of vaccines for some parasitic diseases, such as leishmaniasis, or for viral infections for which these T cell responses play an essential role.

Adjuvant and antigen combinations

Several strategies have been utilized to increase the immunogenicity of small or weak antigens. To increase its apparent molecular weight, an antigen can be coupled on to an inert support, coupled chemically or genetically to a larger 'carrier' molecule (such as tetanus toxoid), or coupled to itself or other antigens to create a univalent or polyvalent polymer. Peptides can be also directly synthesized on to a branching core structure to create defined branching molecules with multiple antigenic peptides (called MAPs). Polysaccharides that are T cell independent can be coupled to protein carriers to create protein–polysaccharide conjugates that confer T cell-dependent characteristics to the polysaccharide. Similarly, conjugation of the antigen directly to the adjuvant can increase its immunogenicity. Another approach to further augment the immune response is to utilize combinations of adjuvants, such as the use of LPS, MDP, saponin, or cytokines in liposomes or oil emulsions together with the antigen. Biodegradable delivery systems have also been developed that can be utilized for the controlled release of antigen and to target antigen to antigen-presenting cells. In particular, microspheres based on poly(lactic acid) and poly(lactic/glycolic acid) are being actively developed.

Living organisms as vector/adjuvants

An exciting recent approach is to engineer genetically a nonpathogenic but infectious living organism to deliver foreign protective antigen(s) to the immune system. The vaccine recipient is infected with the organism, which is utilized as a vector in order to induce an immune response to the antigen. The first live vector to be utilized was vaccinia virus; however, many other viral or bacterial vectors are now being developed to deliver protective antigens to the immune system. One excellent candidate for the construction of such an attenuated vaccine is BCG, which has already been extensively utilized worldwide in humans as a vaccine that has a very low incidence of serious side-effects. Attenuated *Salmonella* or *Shigella* strains that stimulate local immune responses after oral immunization are also being developed. Viruses, including adenovirus or poliovirus, have considerable potential for the ability to deliver foreign antigens to the immune system. Recombinant poxvirus vectors that are unable to replicate in mammalian species, such as fowlpoxvirus or canarypox, have also been used to elicit antibody and CTL responses against diverse pathogens in animals. A canarypox coding for the HIV-1 envelope proved to be safe and immunogenic in humans. Such live recombinant vaccines may be easier to prepare and administer than existing vaccines. Disadvantages include the risks inherent with all live vaccines and the fact that repeated use of the same vector for different antigens may decrease its efficacy.

Future prospects

Despite the large number of currently known substances that are capable of increasing specific immunity, only aluminum hydroxide is currently utilized routinely as an adjuvant in humans. The major obstacle to the use of the remaining agents is that the toxic:therapeutic ratio is too narrow. The documented dissociation of efficacy from severe toxicity with many adjuvants suggests that acceptable compounds can be developed in the future. With the growing use of sophisticated small antigenic fragments containing defined B and T cell epitopes, such adjuvants will become increasingly necessary. Since different subsets of the immune system may be needed in different settings, it is to be anticipated that multiple distinct adjuvants and vaccine preparations will be desirable. It is therefore appropriate that the adjuvants currently being utilized or studied are highly diverse, including minerals such as aluminum, bacterial products such as LPS and MDP, and living viral and bacterial vectors. Nevertheless, although progress is being made through modifications of known adjuvants, a fundamental unifying hypothesis as to the necessary mechanisms needed for adjuvanticity is still lacking. As our understanding of the underlying physiology of the immune system broadens, the parameters that are important for the development of newer generations of adjuvants will hopefully become more evident.

See also: **Bacterial cell walls; Carrier; Immunogen; Liposomes; Muramyl dipeptide;** *Mycobacteria,* **infection and immunity; Vaccination, methods of administration; Vaccines.**

Further reading

Cox JC and Coulter AR (1997) Adjuvants: a classification and review of their modes of action. *Vaccine* 15: 248–256.

Gupta RK and Siber GR (1995) Adjuvants for human vaccines: current status, problems, and future prospects. *Vaccine* 13: 1263–1276.

Leclerc C and Vogel F (1986) Synthetic immunomodulators and synthetic vaccines. *Critical Reviews in Therapeutic Drug Carrier Systems* 2: 353–406.

Leclerc C (Ed) (1995) Live DNA vaccines. *Biologicals* 23: 111–178.

Roman M, Martin-Orozco E, Goodman JS *et al* (1997) Immunostimulatory DNA sequences function as T helper-1-promoting adjuvants. *Nature Medicine* 3: 849–854.

Stewart-Tull DES (Ed) (1995) *The Theory and Practical Application of Adjuvants.* John Wiley and Sons, Chichester, UK.

Vogel FR. Immunologic adjuvants for modern vaccine formulations. *Annals of the New York Academy of Sciences* 754: 153–160.

Warren HS and Chedid LA (1988) Future prospects for vaccine adjuvants. *Critical Reviews in Immunology* 8: 83–101.

ADRENAL AUTOIMMUNITY

Pierluigi E Bigazzi, Department of Pathology, University of Connecticut Health Center, Farmington, Connecticut, USA

Adrenal autoimmunity is currently the most common cause of Addisons disease, a chronic disorder of the adrenal cortex characterized by atrophy of the adrenals. This results in deficient production of adrenocortical hormones together with increased secretion of anterior pituitary adrenocorticotropic hormone (ACTH). The clinical picture of Addisons disease may comprise weakness, anorexia, nausea, vomiting and weight loss. Hypotension and mucocutaneous hyperpigmentation are usually present. Levels of serum potassium and urea nitrogen are elevated, whereas serum sodium may be decreased. Significant laboratory findings are low plasma levels of cortisol and elevations of ACTH. Stimulation with synthetic ACTH does not result in cortisol increases.

Idiopathic adrenal atrophy is probably an autoimmune disease, as suggested by the facts that the histopathology of the affected adrenals resembles that observed in tissues which are targets of other organ-specific autoimmune diseases, and that autoimmune responses to various adrenocortical antigens have been detected in patients with idiopathic Addisons disease.

Addisons disease can occur as an isolated (sporadic) disorder or in association with other conditions (autoimmune polyendocrinopathy syndrome type 1 or type 2) (see **Table 1**). Sporadic autoimmune Addisons disease usually affects young females, who may outnumber male patients by a factor of 4. Contrary to the reported increased incidence of insulin-dependent diabetes mellitus (IDDM) and Hashimoto's thyroiditis, Addisons disease continues to be an extremely rare occurrence. In the United States, its incidence approximates 1 per 4500–6250 patients hospitalized for various disorders. In the London area the prevalence of Addisons disease has been estimated at 30 per million inhabitants and in Denmark it was reported to be 60 per million. In New Zealand there are approximately 4.5 new cases per million population per year.

Pathology and immunopathology

At autopsy, the adrenal glands of most patients with idiopathic Addisons disease are small, very thin and often are very difficult to recognize or may be missing altogether (substituted by adipose and fibrotic tissue). The most characteristic findings by light microscopy are: loss of adrenocortical cells, localized hypertrophy and hyperplasia of adrenocortical cells as well as chronic inflammatory infiltrates (**Figure 1**). A severe loss of adrenocortical cells is the most characteristic feature of adrenals from patients with autoimmune Addisons disease. Where cortical epi-

Table 1 Human diseases with adrenal autoimmunity

Characteristics	Adult Addisons disease	Autoimmune polyendocrinopathy type 1	Autoimmune polyendocrinopathy type 2
Clinical features	Idiopathic adrenal insufficiency	Idiopathic adrenal insufficiency + hypoparathyroidism + chronic mucocutaneous candidiasis + gonadal failure	Idioopathic adrenal insufficiency + insulin-dependent diabetes mellitus + autoimmune thyroiditis
Age of onset	All ages, but more commonly in adults	Most commonly in childhood	All ages, but more commonly in adults
Gender	Mostly females	Males and females	Mostly females
Prevalence	3–6 per 100 000	Unknown (very rare)	Possibly 50% of adult Addisons patients
Immunogenetics	HLA-DR3	No HLA-DR association	HLA-DR3 and/or DR4
Autoantibodies against	Steroid 21-hydroxylase P450	P450 side-chain cleavage enzyme Steroid 17α-hydroxylase (?)	Steroid 21-hydroxylase P450
T cell responses to	Adrenal antigens (?)	?	?

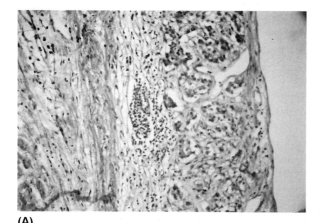

(A)

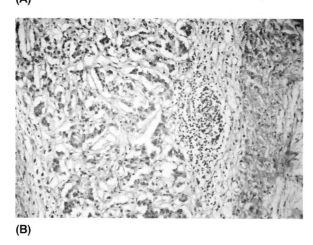

(B)

Figure 1 (A) Adrenal gland from patient with Addisons disease, showing atrophy of the cortex and infiltration with mononuclear cells. (B) Another area from same adrenal gland, photographed at higher magnification. (See also color **Plate 6**.)

thelium is present, it is not arranged in three different zones, but in strands or rows of irregular size, contour and direction. There is loss of cellular outline, swelling and vacuolar appearance. Some cells are extremely large, with granular or vacuolated cytoplasm, others are small. In addition, both hyperplasia and hypertrophy can be observed in adrenals from patients with idiopathic Addisons disease. Scattered islands of cells may be seen in the cortex as well as large well-circumscribed adenoma-like nodules, without typical zonal division of the parenchyma. These cells resemble those of the zona fasciculata, less often those of the zona glomerulosa. They may have a bizarre appearance and sometimes are huge, with deeply pigmented cytoplasm and large hyperchromatic nuclei. A chronic inflammatory infiltrate is usually present, with a prevalence of small lymphocytes. Plasma cells and macrophages are also present, but in lesser numbers. The adrenal medulla is usually intact or infiltrated by a few lymphoid cells. The lymphocytic infiltrate is usually diffuse, but in some areas lymphocytes may form aggregates of various dimensions. Germinal centers are seldom present.

Studies of adrenal immunopathology in patients with Addisons disease have been rather scarce. Direct immunofluorescence of the adrenals has shown dense deposits of immunoglobulin G (IgG) in some areas of the adrenal cortex, with specific fluorescence localized more intensely at the level of the cell membranes. To date, there are no reports on the composition of the adrenocortical lymphocytic infiltrates. However, immunohistopathology studies of micronodules of Cushing's disease have shown that the lymphocytic infiltrates, present around vessel walls but also inside the nodules themselves, were composed mostly of T cells, usually CD4$^+$ with a minority of CD8$^+$. In addition, B cells were also present in the infiltrates. It is possible that a similar situation also occurs in the adrenals of patients with autoimmune Addisons disease. Class II major histocompatibility complex (MHC) expression by human adrenal cortical cells appears to be a physiological phenomenon. Approximately 10% of normal adrenocortical cells express MHC class II antigenic determinants. These antigens are mostly localized in the zona reticularis and occasionally may extend to the zona glomerulosa or fasciculata. In adrenal glands from Addisons disease patients, the majority of residual cortical cells show MHC class II antigens, with variation in extent from 50 to 100%. Staining is most intense at the periphery of residual nodules. Adrenal glands from patients with tuberculous Addisons disease have a similar pattern to normal glands, but show class II positivity in cortical cells immediately adjacent to foci of caseous necrosis.

Humoral and cellular autoimmune responses

Newly diagnosed patients with Addisons disease have a variety of circulating autoantibodies to adrenal antigens. Autoantibodies directed against organ-specific antigens localized in the cytoplasm of the adrenocortical cells are present in the circulation of approximately 70% of Addisons disease patients. These antibodies can be detected by indirect immunofluorescence, radioimmunoassay and ELISA, are usually of low titer, belong to the IgG class and react with one or more organ-specific antigens localized in the adrenal cortex. In most cases, immunofluorescence shows that all three layers of the cortex react with adrenal autoantibodies (**Figure 2**). However, different patterns of staining can be observed: sera from some patients stain all three zones of the cortex, whereas others react with the zona fasciculata and zona reticularis alone. A few sera react with the zona glomerulosa alone. The clinical significance of these findings is unknown, but suggests an immunologic heterogeneity of Addisons disease, with preferential involvement of different adrenal antigens. Complement fixing adrenal autoantibodies have also been observed by immunofluorescence. Autoantibodies to organ-specific surface antigens of adrenal cells are present in the sera of 86% of patients with Addisons disease who have circulating antibodies to adrenal cytoplasmic autoantigens. The adrenal-specific surface antigens appear by immunofluorescence as a continuous rim, but separate granules are visible on focusing over the plasma

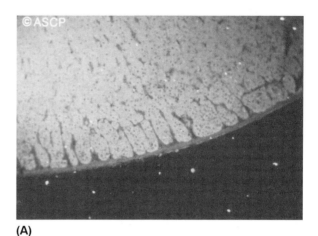

(A)

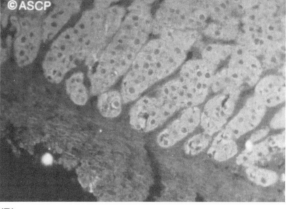

(B)

Figure 2 (A) Antibodies to adrenocortical antigens (indirect immunofluorescence with serum from a patient with Addison's disease on cryostat section of monkey adrenal). (B) Higher magnification of similar field. (With permission from American Society of Clinical Pathologists, Chicago, USA.)

membrane. Antibodies to steroid-producing cells of other tissues have also been detected in the circulation of patients with Addisons disease. These autoantibodies react with theca interna cells, interstitial cells and corpus luteum cells of the ovary as well as interstitial cells of the testis and placental trophoblasts.

Recent studies using molecular cloning and western blotting have shown that different steroidogenic enzymes of the cytochrome P450 family may be the target autoantigens of autoimmune Addisons disease. Purification of native human adrenal proteins, comparative western blotting using patients' sera and rabbit antibodies against recombinant 21-hydroxylase as well as antibody absorption studies, have demonstrated that steroid 21-hydroxylase P450, an enzyme involved in both the glucocorticoid-synthesizing pathway and the mineralocorticoid pathway, is the major target of adrenal autoantibodies found in patients with isolated Addisons disease or polyendocrine autoimmune syndrome type 2 (**Table 1**). On the other hand, patients with polyendocrine autoimmune syndrome type 1 (characterized by adrenal insufficiency, hypoparathyroidism and hypogonadism) have antibodies that react with P450 SCC (cholesterol side-chain cleavage) or, as reported by other authors, another enzyme, the microsomal steroid 17α-hydroxylase (**Table 1**). It is still uncertain whether these autoantigens are expressed on the surface of adrenal cells or are otherwise accessible to adrenal antibodies *in vivo*. Finally, IgG preparations from patients with Addisons disease have been reported to cause a dose-dependent decrease of *in vitro* cortisol production and/or DNA synthesis induced by ACTH in guinea pig adrenal segments maintained in organ culture. The blocking effects occurred irrespective of the presence or absence of adrenal cytoplasmic autoantibodies and were attributed to the production of antibodies against the receptor for ACTH. This hypothesis has not been confirmed by recent studies that suggest an inhibitory effect of non-IgG components.

Studies of cellular immunity to adrenal antigens have been based on classical (but now rather outdated) methods to detect delayed hypersensitivity reactions and lymphokine production. In these procedures, peripheral blood lymphocytes from patients were incubated *in vitro* with the putative antigens, often used as a rather crude suspension. Thus, it has been shown that most patients with Addisons disease have cell-mediated immune reactions to adrenal antigens as determined by the leukocyte migration test. There was no correlation with onset of disease, its duration and the presence of adrenal antibodies. The antigen preparations that have been utilized in leukocyte migration studies were organ-specific, but not species-specific, since monkey and porcine adrenals were used with the same success as human adrenals. In some studies the antigenic activity was localized in the mitochondrial but not the microsomal fraction, whereas in other experiments leukocyte migration inhibition was observed after incubation with both components. More modern investigations of cellular immunity (e.g. with steroid 21-hydroxylase P450) are still lacking.

Immunogenetics and disease association

Adrenal autoimmunity may be a heterogeneous condition, as suggested by reports that Addisons disease is inherited in at least three different fashions: autosomal recessive, autosomal dominant with decreased penetrance and X-linked recessive. Inherited susceptibility to autoimmune Addisons disease is linked to HLA-DR3 and/or DR4, except when the disease occurs as part of type 1 autoimmune polyglandular syndrome. A high prevalence of other autoimmune diseases (ovarian failure, Graves disease, Hashimoto's disease, hypothyroidism and insulin-dependent diabetes mellitus) is associated with Addisons disease (see **Table 1**).

Animal models of Addisons disease

Idiopathic Addisons disease occurs spontaneously in dogs and more rarely in cats. In the few cases that have undergone autopsy, atrophy, regeneration of adrenocortical cells and chronic inflammation of the adrenal cortex have been observed. The cause of adrenal insufficiency in dogs is probably of autoimmune, not tubercular, origin. A preferential occurrence in Chow-Chow dogs suggests a genetic predisposition. Adrenal autoimmunity with lesions of the chronic inflammatory type has been experimentally induced by immunization of monkeys, rabbits, guinea pigs, rats and mice with suspensions of adrenal cortex in complete Freund's adjuvant. Circulating autoantibodies to the adrenal cortex have been demonstrated in these models, whereas there is a paucity of reports on cellular autoimmunity. As for other experimental models, adrenalitis was induced in histocompatible recipients by adoptive transfer of lymph node cells from animals with adrenal autoimmunity. Modern immunogenetic studies are lacking, but there was a suggestion that some inbred strains may be more susceptible than others to the induction of experimental adrenalitis. More recently, adrenalitis and adrenal antibodies have been detected in BALB/c nu/nu mice reconstituted with thymic rudiments from young rats. The same mice also had thyroiditis, oophoritis or orchitis, i.e. were good models of autoimmune polyendocrinopathies.

Pathogenesis

Immunologically mediated lesions of the adrenal cortex may occur in a variety of ways. Adrenal parenchyma may be affected by a slow destructive process and is gradually replaced by connective tissue, with eventual loss of physiological function. The mechanisms involved may be cellular or humoral (autoantibody- and/or cytokine-mediated). The role of T lymphocyte-mediated cytotoxicity in Addisons disease is still unclear. Antibody-dependent cytotoxic destruction of adrenal cells might occur in several ways (phagocytosis or lysis of antibody-coated adrenal cells, antibody-dependent cellular cytotoxicity, immune complex-mediated reactions, inhibitory effects on steroid-producing enzymes). However, babies born to mothers with autoimmune Addisons disease and circulating IgG antibodies to adrenal antigens develop none of the manifestations of the maternal disease during the neonatal period, despite the transplacental passage of adrenocortical antibodies. The role of cytokines and oxygen radicals in adrenal cortex damage is still relatively unexplored. Finally, the suggestion that antireceptor immunity may play a role in Addisons disease has not yet been confirmed.

Etiology

The cause(s) of autoimmune Addisons disease is(are) still unknown. Expression of MHC class II antigens, suggested as a key event in the initiation and/or maintenance of organ-specific autoimmunity, occurs in normal adrenals and, therefore, is unlikely to be the primary etiologic event of Addisons disease. Defects in HLA-DQβ chain, found in IDDM, have not been reported in patients with Addisons disease. On the other hand, a deficiency of T suppressor cell activity was noted by some authors. To date, restricted T cell receptor (TCR) usage, alterations of the idiotype–anti-idiotype network and changes in the balance of the cytokine network have not been demonstrated in autoimmune Addisons disease.

Environmental agents (e.g. microorganisms and/or xenobiotics) might cause adrenal autoimmunity by modifying autoantigens (so that they are no longer recognized as self), releasing tissue components normally absent from the circulation, or sharing antigens with tissues (molecular mimicry). In addition, they could inhibit T suppressor cells, stimulate T helper cells, B cells or macrophages, interfere with the idiotype–anti-idiotype network, alter tissue MHC expression and finally cause changes in the production of cytokines and lymphokines. However, none of these possibilities have yet been demonstrated in autoimmune Addisons disease.

See also: **Autoantigens; Autoimmune diseases; Autoimmunity; Polyendocrine autoimmunity.**

Further reading

Beaune P, Pessayre D, Dansette P, Mansuy D and Manns M (1994) Autoantibodies against cytochromes P450: role in human diseases. *Advances in Pharmacology* 30: 199–245.
Bigazzi PE (1990) Autoimmune Addison's disease. In: Volpé R (ed) *Autoimmune Diseases of the Endocrine System.* Boca Raton, FL: CRC Press.
Brosnan CM and Gowing NF (1996) Addison's disease. *British Medical Journal* 312: 1085–1087.
Weetman AP (1995) Autoimmunity to steroid-producing cells and familial polyendocrine autoimmunity. *Baillière's Clinical Endocrinology and Metabolism* 9: 157–174.

AFFINITY

Bertrand Friguet, Lisa Djavadi-Ohaniance and **Michel E Goldberg**, Unité de Biochimie Cellulaire, Institut Pasteur, Paris, France

The affinity (K_A) is a thermodynamic parameter that quantifies the strength of the association between two molecules in solution. For antibody–antigen complexes, K_A can be interpreted rigorously only for an equilibrium in solution involving a single species of antibody-combining sites and a single species of antigenic sites. Consequently, for polyclonal antibodies which contain a mixture of antibodies, no true affinity can be defined. The affinity of an antibody for an antigen depends on the structural complementarity of the binding site on the antibody (paratope) and the binding site on the antigen (epitope). Antibodies have a wide range of affinities that are generally between 10^5 (low affinity) and 10^{12} M^{-1} (high affinity). The overall stability of the complex between an antibody and an antigen is expressed by the term 'avidity' and is governed by the affinity, the valency of the antibody and the antigen and the steric hindrance of the interacting components. Small changes in antigen structure can affect the strength of the antibody–antigen interaction. Similarly, changing the structure of the binding site of the antibody may alter the affinity of the antibody for the antigen. For instance, the progressive increase in affinity that occurs with time upon immunization (affinity maturation) arises from mutations in the complementarity-determining regions that build the paratope. Thus, antibodies that are different in their binding site structure are expressed and cells producing antibodies with higher affinities are stimulated preferentially to divide.

Definition and theoretical aspects

The antibody site to antigenic site association reaction at equilibrium can be written as:

$$\text{antibody} + \text{antigen} \leftrightarrow \text{complex}$$

with the concentrations of free antibody sites, free antigen sites and complex (saturated antibody or antigen sites) at equilibrium given as [Ab], [Ag] and [x] respectively.

The affinity, K_A, is defined by the Law of Mass Action as:

$$K_A = [x]/[Ag].[Ab]$$

The concentration of antibody sites [Ab] and the antigen sites [Ag] at equilibrium are related to the total antibody sites [Ab_t] and the total antigen sites [Ag_t] by:

$$[Ab] = [Ab_t] - [x]$$

$$[Ag] = [Ag_t] - [x]$$

If [Ag_t] is varied while [Ab_t] is kept constant:

$$1/K_A = K_D = [Ag] ([Ab_t] - [x])/[x]$$

with K_D defined as the equilibrium dissociation constant.

Consequently

$$[x]/[Ab_t] = [Ag]/([Ag] + K_D)$$

Several linear plots have been proposed for the determination of K_D, the most commonly used of which are the Scatchard equation:

$$[x]/[Ab_t][Ag] = (1 - x/[Ab_t])/K_D$$

and the Klotz equation:

$$[Ab_t]/[x] = K_D/[Ag] + 1$$

If Ab_t and Ag_t are known, the experimental determination of K_D (or $K_A = 1/K_D$) requires precise measurement of only one of the three concentrations [Ab], [Ag] or [x] (**Figure 1**).

K_A depicts an equilibrium property and therefore does not reflect the speed at which equilibrium is reached. Yet, K_A does depend on the association and dissociation rate constants. When binding is a simple one-step reaction, K_A is equal to k_{on}/k_{off}, where k_{on} and k_{off} are the association and dissociation rate con-

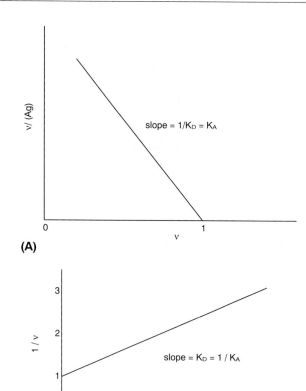

(A)

(B)

Figure 1   (x)/(Ab_t) is usually referred to as v and corresponds to the fraction of bound antibody sites at equilibrium. (Ag) corresponds to the concentration of free antigenic site at equilibrium. (A) Scatchard plot; (B) Klotz plot.

stants. However, when a significant conformational change of either the monoclonal antibody or the antigen occurs upon binding, important deviations from that simple equation can be observed. For such cases, measuring only k_{on} and k_{off} would provide an erroneous estimate of the affinity.

The true affinity cannot be determined for antibody–antigen interaction in heterogeneous phase systems. No straightforward thermodynamic theory describes the equilibrium in heterogeneous phase systems, such as the binding of a monoclonal antibody to an antigen present on a cell surface or immobilized on an ELISA plate or a biosensor chip. K_A is defined in solution, with both the monoclonal antibody and the antigen diffusing and rotating freely in solution, while in the solid phase assay one partner is immobile. This can result in estimates of K_A by solid-phase assay being orders of magnitude away from the real affinity in solution. In such cases, the strength of monoclonal antibody–antigen interaction is best described by an appropriate operational parameter that is dependent of defined experimental conditions. Moreover it is now well established that immobilization of either antibody or antigen often results in a partial denaturation of the protein, thus modifying its binding properties.

Methods for affinity measurement

As already pointed out, affinity is measured when the equilibrium between the two molecules has been achieved in solution. Hence, measuring K_A for monoclonal antibody and its antigen consists in mixing the monoclonal antibody (mAb) and the antigen at various initial concentrations, letting the equilibrium be established, measuring the concentrations of free and saturated sites at equilibrium and analyzing the binding curve. The experimental difficulty resides in distinguishing the free and bound state of either the monoclonal antibody or the antigen. Several methods can be used, such as equilibrium dialysis, radioimmunoassay (RIA) using precipitation with salts and other agents, filtration, fluorescence measurements and RIA- or ELISA-based methods. Equilibrium dialysis is the method of choice for hapten and dialyzable antigen but is not applicable for macromolecular antigens. Radioimmunoassays require radiolabeling of the antigen which may alter the binding properties of the antigen. Precipitation or filtration methods need the complex to be stable enough during the time required to achieve its separation so that the equilibrium is not disrupted. The use of fluorescence to determine K_A requires that either the monoclonal antibody or the antigen be fluorescent, and that a change in fluorescence should occur upon formation of the monoclonal antibody/antigen complex. The fluorescence signal used can be either intrinsic (e.g. tryptophan residues from the antibody and, possibly, from the protein antigens; some prosthetic groups such as pyridoxal-phosphate, NADH, NADPH, flavins, etc.) or result from prior fluorescent labeling of the antigen or the antibody with a fluorochrome. The fluorescent change observed upon association may be one of the following: excitation or emission wavelength shift, fluorescence quenching, fluorescence transfer, change in fluorescence polarization. As already underlined for radiochemical labeling, adding an extrinsic fluorescent label may affect the binding characteristics of the antigen or the antibody, either by steric hindrance or through a change in conformation, thus modifying the K_A. The sensitivity of current fluorimeters sets a higher limit of 10^8–10^9 M^{-1} on the K_A that can be determined. Some mAbs have much higher affinities for their Ag. Several methods such as indirect ELISA or surface plasmon resonance using immobilized antigen or monoclonal antibody have been developed to determine values of the affinity.

Such measurements yield real values of K_A only rarely. Friguet and colleagues have defined a procedure to measure by a competition ELISA method the real association equilibrium constant in solution. This method requires no labeling of either the antigen or the antibody, which ensures that the affinity is characteristic of native antibody and antigen. This method gives access to affinity constants as high as 10^{10}–10^{11} M^{-1} and can be used for studies on protein–protein interactions that do not involve antibodies. Since this method has been frequently used for affinity determination, its principle is described in the next paragraph.

Affinity measurement in solution by competition ELISA

In the competition ELISA the monoclonal antibody at a fixed concentration and the antigen at varying concentrations are first incubated in solution until the equilibrium is reached. Then, the concentration of the free (i.e. not associated with antigen) monoclonal antibody at equilibrium is determined by a classical indirect ELISA using antigen-coated plates.

For correct determination of the free antibody concentration at equilibrium, several requirements must be fulfilled: 1) The absorbance obtained in the last step of the indirect ELISA, which reflects the free antibody concentration, must be proportional to the antibody concentration tested. 2) Only a small percentage of the free antibody molecules (i.e. less than 10%) must bind to the coated antigen, to prevent any significant disruption of the equilibrium in the liquid phase. This ensures that, during the ELISA, the equilibrium in solution is not significantly modified. By this means, the observed equilibrium constant corresponds to the real affinity. 3) Since the association constant K_A is generally dependent on the temperature, the temperature must be kept constant throughout.

To satisfy requirements (1) and (2), it is necessary in previous ELISA experiments to determine the total (i.e. initial) antibody concentration range that must be used, the concentration of the coated antigen and the optimal incubation time of the antibody solutions in the coated wells. The state (native or partially denatured upon coating) of the coated antigen and whether or not it is recognized by the mAb differently from the soluble antigen is not important as long as the coated antigen can specifically and quantitatively trap the free antibody.

An example of affinity determination by the competition ELISA method described above is given in **Figure 2** using a computerized fitting program.

The multivalency of antibodies and antigens

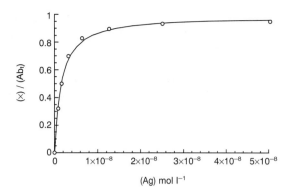

Figure 2 Saturation curve in solution of a monoclonal antibody by its antigen: $[x]/[Ab_t] = [Ag]/([Ag] + K_D)$. The value of K_D (1.5×10^{-9} M) was directly extracted with a computerized non-linear regression method.

sometimes complicates the determination of affinity. The distortion of the saturation curves (as compared with simple binding) caused by the multivalence of immunoglobulins in indirect competition ELISA was first analyzed by Stevens and has become the object of much attention. However, the simple data analysis initially proposed by Friguet and colleagues provides satisfactory results when divalent immunoglobulins are used, provided one extracts the affinity only from the part of the saturation curve obtained at high saturation of the monoclonal antibody by the antigen.

Why is affinity important?

The affinity is of considerable importance in understanding the biological activity of antibodies. For instance, when the immune system is challenged with antigen, the immune response and host defense is evaluated by the affinity of the antibodies. However, immune sera contain a mixture of antibodies with different affinities and the experimental conditions can considerably influence the apparent affinity. It is now well established that in the commonly used competition ELISA, the conditions must be carefully selected to minimize disruption of the liquid-phase equilibrium by the solid-phase antigen. In the case of a polyclonal serum-containing antibodies with widely different affinities, it is practically impossible to simultaneously fulfil this requirement for all the antibodies under a unique set of experimental conditions. Schematically, low-density coating of the antigen will trap essentially high-affinity antibodies, resulting in the determination of the apparent affinity of only these molecules, which will not be representa-

tive of the average affinity of the serum. In contrast, high-density coating of the antigen will trap low-affinity antibodies too, but the trapped fraction of high-affinity molecules will be large and their contribution to the average affinity will be seriously biased by the disruption of the equilibrium. The knowledge of antibody affinity and specificity for its antigen determines its reliability and usefulness as a reagent in a variety of immunochemical techniques such as histoimmunochemistry, immunochemical labeling of cells or cellular components, immunodetection by ELISA, RIA or western blotting. Most often, strict specificity and high affinity are a prerequisite for the accuracy of these techniques. However, it is sometimes useful to have antibodies of moderate affinity available as in the case of purification by immunoadsorption which needs, as a final step, the immunocomplex to be dissociated.

Since the affinity of a monoclonal antibody for a protein depends on the structural complementarity of the binding sites on the two molecules, changes in affinity can reflect changes in protein structure occurring at the site recognized by the antibody. Thus, thoroughly characterized monoclonal antibodies have been used as probes to detect and analyze conformational changes within proteins.

See also: **Affinity chromatography; Affinity maturation; Antibody-antigen intermolecular forces; Antigen-binding site; Clonal selection; Immunoassays; Somatic mutation; Surface plasmon resonance; Valency of antigens and antibodies.**

Further reading

Butler JE (1991) The behavior of antigens and antibodies immobilized on a solid phase. In: Van Regenmortel MHV (ed) *Structure of Antigens*, pp 209–259. Boca Raton, FL: CRC Press.

Djavadi-Ohaniance L and Friguet B (1991) The specificity of monoclonal antibodies for enzymes in solution versus immobilized on solid phases. In: Butler JE (ed) *The Immunochemistry of Solid-phase Immunoassay*, pp 201–206. Boca Raton, FL: CRC Press.

Friguet B, Chaffotte AF, Djavadi-Ohaniance L and Goldberg ME (1985) Measurements of the true affinity constant in solution of antigen-antibody complexes by enzyme-linked immunosorbent assay. *Journal of Immunological Methods* 77: 305–319.

Friguet B, Djavadi-Ohaniance L and Goldberg ME (1997) Immunochemical analysis of protein conformation. In: Creighton TE (ed) *Protein Structure: A Practical Approach*, 2nd edn, pp 323–348. Oxford: IRL Press.

Goldberg ME and Djavadi-Ohaniance L (1993) Methods for measurement of antibody-antigen affinity based on ELISA and RIA. *Current Opinion in Immunology* 5: 278–281.

Karlsson R, Altschuh D and Van Regenmortel MHV (1991) Measurement of antibody affinity. In: Van Regenmortel MHV (ed) *Structure of Antigens*, pp 127–148. Boca Raton, FL: CRC Press.

Stevens FJ (1987) Modification of an ELISA-based procedure for affinity determination: Correction necessary for use with bivalent antibody. *Molecular Immunology* 24: 1055–1060.

Steward MW and Lew AM (1985) The importance of antibody affinity in the performance of immunoassays for antibody. *Journal of Immunological Methods* 78: 173–190.

Steward MW and Steensgaard J (1983) *Antibody Affinity: Thermodynamic Aspects and Biological Significance*. Boca Raton, FL: CRC Press.

AFFINITY CHROMATOGRAPHY

George L Mayers, Department of Molecular Immunology, Roswell Park Memorial Institute, Buffalo, New York, USA

Carel J van Oss, Department of Microbiology, School of Medicine, State University of New York at Buffalo, Buffalo, New York, USA

Affinity chromatography is the process by which the reversible biospecific interactions between a molecular species and its ligand are used in the isolation of that molecular species from a biological milieu. Conceptually the process is extremely simple. The ligand is attached to a solid support to form a specific adsorbent to which the biological system, usually in the form of a homogenate or extract containing the molecular species of interest, is exposed. Only the molecular species that shows appreciable affinity for the ligand will be retained or retarded; other materials which have no specificity for the insolubilized ligand will pass through the column. The molecular species that has become attached to the adsorbent must then be eluted without destroying its biological properties.

Unlike many of the other isolation techiques that depend upon differences in physical properties of the biological materials to effect a separation, the use of affinity chromatography takes advantage of functional properties of the system. Since almost all biological processes depend on specificity between different molecules, affinity chromatography has found a wide range of applications and new ones are always being developed. These include the use of antibiotics, antibodies, antigens, chromophores and dyes, coenzymes, drugs, hormones, enzymes, inhibitors, lectins, nucleic acids, nucleotides, polynucleotides, substrates and substrate analogs, sugars and polysaccharides, tRNA, and vitamins to isolate macromolecules, organelles, viruses and cells.

Successful application requires that the interactions between the biological molecules and their ligands have an affinity that is at least 10^5, but not so strong that the binding cannot be reversed without detriment to the biological materials of interest. Thus the preparation of appropriate ligand conjugates often requires a considerable amount of extra work, but, when successful, the results can be dramatic. The exquisite sensitivity of this system has allowed application to the separation of large protein assemblies involved in signal transduction, transcription complexes and cytoskeletal structure. The technique of affinity chromatography is one of the few procedures that will usually achieve a major purification in one or two steps, often producing an homogeneous sample for study. In addition the process is effective for extremely dilute solutions and allows extensive concentration of the biological sample. Such a dramatic example of the use of affinity chromatography is the successful isolation of 6.26 mg, a 12% yield of transcobalamin II from 1400 liters of human plasma.

Historical perspective

The earliest forms of affinity chromatography were actually developed by immunochemists. In 1951 Campbell, Luescher and Lerman developed antigen–cellulose columns for use in isolating specific antibodies, a separation that could not be achieved unless one could take advantage of the affinity of the antibody for its specific antigen. The conjugation of an antigen to a solid matrix was called an immunoadsorbent and will be further described in the section on immunoadsorbents. In 1968, Cuatrecasas, Wilchek and Anfinsen applied this concept to the isolation of enzymes and introduced the term affinity chromatography. Application of the technique exploded not only because the generality of the approach became clear, but also because a new solid support based on agarose with appropriate chemistry for coupling many types of ligands was introduced. Since then this technique has had extensive application in all aspects of the biological sciences.

Recently, the use of affinity chromatography has been integrated with high-pressure liquid chromatography (HPLC) systems to combine the specificity of affinity chromatography with the speed and sensitivity of HPLC. This has been extended to include high-pressure immunoaffinity chromatography. One area that has been under-exploited is the use of specific antibodies to isolate biological materials such as growth factors that are produced at low concentrations in cell culture.

The procedure of affinity chromatography

Unlike the use of physical separation procedures, the use of affinity chromatography requires more extensive knowledge of the biological material and its binding to the ligand that will be used for isolation. The use of agarose has been the overwhelming choice for a solid support for attachment of ligands because of its hydrophilicity and thus low non-specific binding for most macromolecules, its good porosity and uniform spherical beads for preparing columns with suitable flow rates and good resolution, and its ability to be modified readily using cyanogen bromide to allow coupling of most important ligands either directly or via a linking molecule.

Ligand or ligand analogs must be selected that permit conjugation without significantly affecting the ligand's complementarity structure and thus detrimentally reducing its ability to bind the biological material. The attachment of the ligand may decrease or increase its affinity for the biological molecule depending on the nature of the linkage molecules and the conformational constraints induced by the coupling chemistry and the solid support, and these factors must be evaluated experimentally. For most isolations of macromolecules, the ligand–conjugated matrix is packed in a standard chromatography column, and the sample containing the biological molecules of interest is applied to the column. Biological materials that do not recognize determinants on the solid phase pass through, and the column is thoroughly washed with neutral buffers to remove all nonspecifically attached materials. Since the commonly used cyanogen bromide coupling chemistry introduces an isourea group at the linkage point which has a $pK_a = 10.4$, there are positive charges in the matrix, and these columns tend to have some weak ion exchange properties. Some of the commercially available supports have attached suitable functional groups for coupling while avoiding the introduction of a charged moiety. However, if a protein such as albumin is used for linking the ligand, there is often increased weak binding between some of the impurities and the column. The amount of these weaker binding contaminants can be reduced by washing the column with higher ionic strength buffers, 1 or 2 M NaCl in borate or phosphate at pH 7–8, or 0.5 M carbonate buffer at pH 9.0 as long as they do not also elute any of the specific material.

Following removal of impurities and nonspecifically attached materials, conditions are changed to effect an elution of the desired biological molecules in their native state. Since the binding results from noncovalent interactions that include electrostatic, hydrophobic, and van der Waals forces, solvent changes must be made to reduce these interactions or compete with the ligand on the matrix to release the sample from the column without denaturing the macromolecule. The most commonly used method of elution is to reduce the pH to 2.8 with glycine–HCl buffer or 1 M propionic acid. If that fails to elute the sample or those conditions denature the protein, the use of alkaline conditions often yields better results. Probably the best alkaline buffer is 0.1 M diethylamine which has a pH of approximately 11. Many anti-idiotypic antibodies and some antibodies to protein determinants seem to prefer these elution conditions to the use of acid. In a number of cases, when a secondary antigen–antibody interaction (which usually is of the 'hydrophobic' variety) has set in, in addition to an increase in pH, a lowering of the surface tension of the medium should be effected at the same time by means of the admixture of a water-miscible organic solvent with strong hydrogen-acceptor properties, such as ethylene glycol, dimethylsulfoxide (DMSO, approximately 30–50%), or propanol (approximately 3–10%). Elution of various blood group antibodies from red cells can be effected at pH 9.5–10.0, in the presence of $\approx 47\%$ DMSO. Elution of DNA-specific antibodies from immobilized DNA (which is a preponderantly electrostatic system) can usually be effected by just a pH increase to 11 (for low-affinity antibodies), or 12 (for high-affinity antibodies), using glycine buffers. In the relatively rare cases where Ca^{2+} bridging is the main mechanism of antigen–antibody binding, elution is best done with Na_2EDTA, or other complexing agents. The protein should be maintained in the unfavorable conditions for as short a time as possible and should be kept cold during such procedures. The use of ligands can be very effective, but it is sometimes difficult to remove the ligand completely from the sample. The use of strong denaturants such as guanidine–HCl, urea and SDS should usually be avoided since it is often difficult to recover the biological sample in a native state, although these reagents can be effective in regenerating the column for reuse. In those cases where the antigen and/or antibody do not become irreversibly denatured by some of the more robust dissociating agents, and those cases where an affinity column or surface has to be regenerated regardless of the fate of the eluate, the most efficient eluants are: 10 mM HCl (no salt or other additive), pH approximately 2; 50 mM NaOH (pH 10); or 50 mM NaOH together with 15–30% acetonitrile. These eluants have been found effective in regenerating antigen- or antibody-coated surfaces in the bioaffinity sensor apparatus.

Besides the use of affinity chromatography for specific interactions, there are many examples of using ligands to isolate a restricted family of biological molecules. Protein A and, more recently, Protein G can be used to isolate a large number of immunoglobulin subclasses from a variety of species and have found extensive use in the isolation of monoclonal antibodies. Hydrophobic columns have found application for membrane proteins; Cibacron Blue 3GA and related dyes have found restricted applications such as removal of albumin from serum. With more readily available molecular models of protein-binding sites, efforts have been made to design analogs of these textile dyes that would have higher specificity for the protein of interest. The use of metal chelate columns has permitted separations based on very subtle differences in amino acid residues, and sequence-specific DNA affinity chromatography allows the isolation of DNA-binding proteins important in regulating transcription and replication. Thus, affinity chromatography has made a major impact on the procedures used to isolate specific substances in all areas of biology and medicine.

See also: **Antibody-antigen intermolecular forces; Immunoadsorbents; Bacterial immunoglobulin-binding proteins; Protein separation techniques.**

Further reading

Anon. (1993) *Guidelines for Regeneration in BIAcore*^{TM}. Uppsala: Pharmacia Biosensor.

Cuatrecasas P (1970) Protein purification by affinity chromatography: derivatizations of agarose and polyacrylamide beads. *Journal of Biological Chemistry* **245**: 3059–3065.

Dean PDG, Johnson WS and Middle FA (eds) (1985) *Affinity Chromatography – A Practical Approach*. IRL Press.

de Groot ER, Lamers MC, Aarden LA, Smeenk RJT and van Oss CJ (1980) Dissociation of DNA/anti-DNA complexes at high pH. *Immunology Communications* **9**: 515–528.

Fassina G and Chaiken IM (1987) Analytical high-performance affinity chromatography. *Advances in Chromatography* **27**: 247–297.

Formosa T, Barry J, Alberts BM and Greenblatt J (1991) Using protein affinity chromatography to probe structure of protein machines. *Methods in Enzymology* **208**: 24–45.

Hermanson GT, Mallia AK and Smith PK (1992) *Immobilized Affinity Ligand Techniques*, New York: Academic Press.

Kline T (ed) (1993) *Handbook of Affinity Chromatography*. New York: Marcel Dekker.

Lowe CR, Burton SJ, Burton NP, Aldertron WK, Pitts JM and Thomas JA (1992) Designer dyes: 'biomimetric' ligands for the purification of pharmaceutical proteins by affinity chromatography. *Trends in Biotechnology* **10**: 442–448.

Phillips TM (1989) High-performance immunoaffinity chromatography. *Advances in Chromatography* **29**: 133–173.

Prickett KS, Amberg DC and Hopp TP (1989) A calcium-dependent antibody for identification and purification of recombinant proteins. *Biotechniques* **7**: 580–589.

van Oss CJ, Beckers D, Engelfriet CP, Absolom DR and Neumann AW (1981) Elution of blood group antibodies from red cells. *Vox Sanguinis* **40**: 367–371.

AFFINITY LABELING

David Givol, Department of Molecular Cell Biology, Weizmann Institute of Science, Rehovot, Israel

Meir Wilchek, AFRC Institute for Animal Health, Pirbright Laboratory, Pirbright, Woking, Surrey, UK

Biological processes are catalyzed and regulated by the specific interactions between corresponding molecular species. The strength of interactions reflects the affinity between the molecules. The affinity is determined by the sum of the reciprocal interactions between the components in a given biological system. In biology, the proteins are the most prominent ligand-binding molecules. Whether we consider enzymes, immune proteins, receptors or transport proteins, the key step in their biological function is the specific recognition and binding of a ligand (substrate, antigen, hapten, hormone, etc.). A small, and in many cases well-defined, part of the total surface of the protein is presumed to be involved in this selective, high-affinity interaction with the specific ligand, and this part of the molecule is referred to as the binding site. Affinity labeling is one of the effective means of studying the binding site.

Affinity labeling and photoaffinity labeling

Affinity labeling is a technique for labeling the binding (or active) site of proteins by virtue of a ligand analog to which a chemically reactive or photoreactive group has been attached. The latter can form a covalent bond with a suitably oriented amino acid in the binding (active) site. Such a labeling reagent (R–L) would consist of 1) a biologically active substance (R) capable of forming a reversible complex with a given protein (P), and 2) a properly positioned, chemically or photochemically reactive leaving group (L) (**Figure 1**). Upon incubation, the affinity label interacts with its protein counterpart, resulting in the formation of an irreversible protein–ligand complex. This process is illustrated in **Figure 1** and described in the following formula:

$$P + R\text{--}L \underset{K_2}{\overset{K_1}{\rightleftharpoons}} P\cdots R\text{--}L \overset{K_3}{\rightarrow} P\text{--}R + L$$

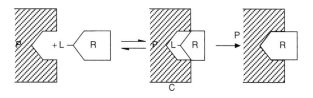

Figure 1 Affinity labeling.

The formation of the initial reversible complex ($P\cdots R$–L) increases the local concentration of the reagent at the active site relative to its concentration in solution. This ensures that the labeling reaction will take place at the binding site and not elsewhere. Following the formation of the reversible complex ($P\cdots R$–L), a functional group(s) on the protein adjacent to the active site reacts chemically with the affinity label, resulting in a covalent bond to form P–R. The affinity-labeled protein is either totally or partially inactivated by virtue of covalent bond formation.

The experimental criteria for a good affinity label are stipulated as follows: 1) its reaction with a given protein should result in a concomitant inactivation of the reversible binding activity; 2) it should not significantly label unrelated proteins; 3) specific ligands should protect against the affinity labeling; 4) it should facilitate the localization of the covalently bound ligand at the active site of the protein.

In planning an affinity labeling reagent, one should ensure that the reactive group (L) is relatively small and does not interfere significantly with the protein–ligand interaction. One should also consider the availability of radioactively labeled precursors and the facility of synthesis and stability. Finally, the labeled residue should remain stable to degradative techniques in order to permit its identification.

The first demonstration of affinity labeling by deliberate design was accomplished in 1961. Although affinity labeling was originally developed for investigations of purified enzymes, it has also added significantly to the study of the structure of active sites in other systems – for example, antibodies, ribosomes and membrane receptors. Affinity labeling of active transport carriers and hormone receptors has been used to identify and isolate these systems.

Affinity labeling of the antibody combining site

Antibodies and myeloma proteins against haptens comprise the most commonly used experimental system in which the determination of the antibody structure–function relationship has been attempted. Affinity labeling studies of antibodies were initiated by Singer, Wofsy and Metzger using diazonium labeling reagents attached to a benzene arsonate hapten. Converse and Richards used diazoketones attached to dinitrophenyl (DNP) haptens as affinity labels, while Givol, Wilchek and coworkers used bromoacetyl derivatives attached to DNP haptens to label DNP-specific antibodies and MOPC 315 (a myeloma protein that binds DNP). A homologous series of reagents was prepared in which the bromoacetyl group was attached to the DNP hapten at progressively increasing distances from the haptenic moiety, thus allowing the labeling of residues in the combining site at various distances from the DNP ring. A photoaffinity label using aromatic azides was introduced by Porter's group. The photoaffinity reagent was introduced to overcome the limitations of the other reagents which can interact only with electrophilic reagents; the azide reacts with any amino acid residue. In addition, the design of this reagent made the chemical reactive group (L) part of the hapten.

Major results obtained

The results derived from affinity labeling studies of antibodies and myeloma proteins from different species that have different ligand specificities were surprising in their consistency.

1. Both light and heavy chains of the antibodies were labeled using affinity labeling reagents. With homogeneous myeloma proteins, it was possible to design reagents such that either the light or heavy chain could be labeled. Particularly interesting information was obtained with the homologous bromoacetyl derivatives of DNP ligands and the MOPC 315 protein. For example, it was shown that N-bromoacetyl-N'-DNP-ethylenediamine exclusively labeled tyrosine 34 on the light chain, whereas N^α bromoacetyl-N^ϵ-DNP-L-lysine labeled lysine 54 on the heavy chain. These experiments demonstrated that both chains contribute contact residues to the antibody-combining site.

2. Affinity labeling studies on antibodies derived from different species using five different reagents showed that the labeled residues were confined to three major stretches of the NH_2-terminal variable region, i.e. around positions 30, 55, 90 in either the light or heavy chain. These results clearly indicated that three restricted segments of both chains actually constitute the specific combining site. This was fully supported by independent evidence, e.g. the identification by statistical analysis of hypervariable segments (CDR) in the V region and by the isolation of the Fv fragment which provided final direct

proof that the combining site is entirely formed by the variable regions. X-ray crystallography of Fab–hapten complexes supported and extended this picture.

Affinity cross-linking

One outcome of affinity labeling using the homologous series of bromoacetyl derivatives, which labeled different residues of the light and heavy chains, was that it enabled the first demonstration of affinity cross-linking by a reagent which contained two bromoacetyl groups and a DNP moiety. This reagent cross-linked the heavy and light chains at the correct positions. Affinity cross-linking is today a major tool in biology and immunology for the identification, localization and isolation of receptors. This is usually accomplished by using a radioactive ligand that is allowed to bind to its receptor, after which a general cross-linking reagent is applied. Alternatively, a ligand to which a photoreactive group has been attached can be used; after binding to the target membrane, light is applied which establishes a covalent bond at the site of binding. Affinity cross-linking allows the identification of the labeled receptor and determination of its size by gel electrophoresis. Because it makes use of a cross-linker which is separate from the ligand, it can be applied to large complex ligands such as growth factors and other proteins. Examples of the use of affinity cross-linking in the immune system are interleukin-2 and its receptor, Fc and receptor, major histocompatibility complex (MHC) class II molecules and nominal antigen peptides on antigen-presenting cells, and photoreactive vinblastine and the 170 kDa protein from multidrug-resistant human cancer cells. Affinity cross-linking is mainly used to identify the molecular size and cellular localization of receptors. Its use, however, can be extended to study the ligand-binding site of the receptor, as has been shown for the epidermal growth factor receptor.

Immunoaffinity chromatography

Another outcome of the affinity labeling studies was the development of immunoaffinity chromatography. The localization of the modified residues in the antibody sequence requires the isolation of the labeled peptides. Givol and Wilchek introduced the immobilized antibody, with the same specificity as the labeled antibody, to 'fish out' the labeled peptides. Thus, peptides that were labeled with the DNP group could be isolated on a DNP-specific antibody column and peptides labeled with diazoarsonate were similarly isolated on an anti-phenylarsonate column. Immunoaffinity chromatography on immobilized monoclonal and polyclonal antibody columns is the most useful approach today to isolate biologically active proteins prepared by recombinant technology and for purification of other proteins which have no known ligands. For example, a commercial preparation of human factor VIII utilizes an insoluble antibody column.

Conclusion

The most significant contributions of affinity labeling have been in the elucidation of structure–function relationships of the active site of a given biological system. For antibodies, affinity labeling provided structural information regarding the binding site before the X-ray structure was known. The techniques that have evolved from these studies are very important tools in modern biology and will continue to be so in the future. It is hoped that refined information regarding binding sites in various complex biological systems will revive the initial impetus which led to the development of affinity labeling as a method: namely, the potential for designing better and more effective drugs. Such drugs may inactivate receptors or intracellular enzymes via affinity labeling.

See also: **Affinity chromatography; Antigen-binding site; Hapten.**

Further reading

Bayley H (1983) *Photogenerated Reagents in Biochemistry and Molecular Biology.* Laboratory Techniques in Biochemistry and Molecular Biology Series (Work TS and Burdon RH, eds). Amsterdam: Elsevier.

Belshaw PJ, Schoepfer JG, Liu K-Q, Morrison L and Schreiber SL (1995) Rational design of orthogonal receptor–ligand combinations. *Angewandte Chemie* (English edition) **34**: 2129.

Brunner J (1993) New photolabeling and crosslinking methods. *Annual Review of Biochemistry* **62**: 483–514.

Felschow DM, MacDiarmid J, Bardos T, Wu R, Woster PM and Porter CW (1995) Photoaffinity labeling of a cell surface polyamine binding protein. *Journal of Biological Chemistry* **270**: 28705–28711.

Givol D (1979) The antibody combining site. In: Lennox ES (ed) Defence and Recognition, vol IIB: Structural Aspects, pp 71–127. *International Reviews of Biochemistry* **23**.

Jakoby WB and Wilchek M (eds) (1977) Affinity Labelling. *Methods in Enzymology* **46**.

Rechtin TM, Black ME and Drake RR (1996) Proteolytic mapping of the thymidine/thymidylate binding site of herpes simplex virus type 1 thymidine kinase: a general photoaffinity labeling method for identifying active site peptides. *Analytical Biochemistry* **237**: 135–140.

Tran CM and Farley RA (1996) Photoaffinity labeling of the active site of the Na$^+$/K$^+$-ATPase with 4-azido-2-nitrophenyl phosphate. *Biochemistry* **35**: 47–55.

Yan X, Corbin JD, Francis SH and Lawrence DS (1996) Precision targeting of protein kinases: an affinity label that inactivates the cGMP but not the cAMP-dependent protein kinase. *Journal of Biological Chemistry* **271**: 1845–1848.

Yu Z, Caldera P, McPhee F *et al* (1996) Irreversible inhibition of the HIV-1 protease: targeting alkylating agents to the catalytic aspartate groups. *Journal of the American Chemical Society* **118**: 5846–5856.

AFFINITY MATURATION

Klaus Rajewsky, Institute for Genetics, University of Cologne, Weyertal 121, Koln, Germany

The changes of antibody quality in the course of the antibody response is a classical immunological phenomenon. One such change is the gradual increase of antibody affinity for the immunizing antigen with time, called affinity maturation. Affinity maturation is typical of, and regularly observed in, T cell-dependent responses and is a key feature of immunological memory in B cells. Upon secondary immunization with a T cell-dependent antigen an anamnestic antibody response is produced, consisting of antibodies with a higher affinity than that of primary response antibodies.

Burnet's clonal selection theory provided a theoretical framework for affinity maturation, as shown in **Figure 1**. The B cells in the peripheral B cell pool express a clonally distributed, diverse antibody repertoire. This repertoire includes antibody specificities against any given antigen or antigenic determinant, but, in general, high-affinity antibodies should be less frequent than antibodies of average or low affinity. The clonal selection theory postulates that antigen selectively expands B cells expressing antibodies on their surface to which it can bind. With decreasing antigen concentration in the course of the response this mechanism results in the preferential expansion of B cells expressing high-affinity antibodies, as depicted in the upper part of **Figure 1**. We have

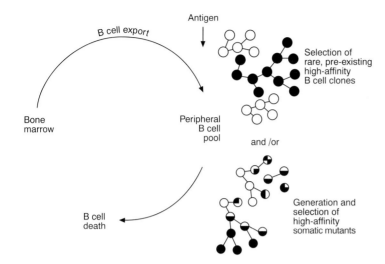

Figure 1 Models of affinity maturation. (Taken, with modification, from Rajewsky K (1989) *Progress in Immunology* **7**: 400.)

learned in the meantime that the process of B cell triggering is more complex: the B cell captures antigen by its receptor antibody from antigen-presenting (follicular dendritic) cells, processes it intracellularly and exposes fragments of the antigen on its surface, in the groove of major histocompatibility complex (MHC) antigens of class II. Subsequently, T helper cells recognize the antigen-loaded MHC molecules and signal the B cell into its pathway of proliferation and differentiation. This multistage process, together with the variability of antigenic valency, makes the relation of antibody affinity to cellular selection complicated (indeed selection seems sometimes driven by the on-rate of antigen binding rather than affinity), but does not change the picture in principle.

The model depicted in the upper part of **Figure 1** is in line with experimental evidence that the B cell clones dominating secondary and hyperimmune responses to a given antigen often differ strikingly from those dominating the primary response in terms of antibody variable (V) region gene usage. However, it has become clear that the central mechanism of affinity maturation is not the selection of rare, pre-existing high-affinity antibodies, but a process of somatic evolution, in which somatic antibody mutants are generated at high rate as a consequence of antigenic contact and high-affinity mutants subsequently selected by antigen (**Figure 1**, lower part). It is often forgotten that Burnet considered this possibility already in his clonal selection theory: 'The . . . postulate, that active sites on cell surface or globulin molecules can be modified to a wider reactivity by somatic mutation, provides the chief agent to allow change in antibody character as immunization proceeds. If the primary postulates of the clonal selection theory are accepted, such a result of somatic mutation is as much in order as any other'. The tools

of molecular biology allowed this possibility to be studied directly, by isolating and sequencing antibody V genes expressed by B cells participating in model immune responses. Initially, the V genes were identified in hybridoma cells selected from various stages of the immune response. They can now be isolated from the overall B cell population or even single B cells by specific gene amplification, using the polymerase chain reaction. These experiments demonstrated that, within a short time after priming with a T cell-dependent antigen, the initial repertoire of germ line-encoded antibodies is completely changed into a repertoire of somatic antibody mutants as they are exclusively seen in secondary and hyperimmune responses. This is achieved by a mechanism introducing somatic point mutations into rearranged antibody genes at an exceedingly high rate, estimated to be in the range of 1×10^{-3} per base pair per generation. The mutations are introduced in a stepwise manner in the course of cellular proliferation and mutants expressing high affinity for the antigen are selected out in a highly efficient manner, preventing the accumulation of mutants expressing useless, potentially harmful (autoaggressive) specificities. Genetic engineering experiments have directly demonstrated that certain key mutations, often repeatedly seen in the repertoire of antibody mutants as it arises after immunization with a given antigen, are directly responsible for an increase of affinity for the antigen. However, because of the high rate of somatic mutation the antibodies also harbor a multitude of mutations which are not affinity selected (e.g. 'silent' exchanges). Affinity maturation through somatic hypermutation occurs in a particular B cell differentiation pathway, namely the proliferation of B cells and their maturation into memory or plasma cells in germinal centers. In this pathway the hypermutation mechanism (whose molecular basis remains to be elucidated) is turned on through an unknown (T cell-derived?) signal and is later turned off to allow the stable expression of the affinity-matured secondary antibody repertoire.

Taken together, affinity maturation of antibodies is mainly based on a process of somatic evolution in which somatic antibody mutants are generated at high rate upon T cell-dependent immunization, and high-affinity mutants selected by antigen. This allows the antibody system to rapidly adapt to any given immune stimulus – the key requirement of acquired immunity. Only in this way will the system be able to deal efficiently with microbial infection, in the course of which mutants of the infecting agent often accumulate rapidly, threatening to circumvent immune protection.

See also: **Affinity; Antigen presentation via MHC class I molecules; Antigen presentation via MHC class II molecules; B lymphocyte repertoire; Clonal selection; Diversity, generation of; Germinal center; Immunoglobulin genes; Maturation of immune responses; Memory, immunological; Somatic mutation.**

Further reading

Berek C and Milstein C (1988) The dynamic nature of the antibody repertoire. *Immunological Reviews* 105: 5–26.

Burnet FM (1959) *The Clonal Selection Theory of Acquired Immunity*. Cambridge: The University Press.

Jerne NK (1951) A study of avidity based on rabbit skin responses to diphtheria toxin–antitoxin mixtures. *Acta Patholgica et Microbiologica Scandinavica* 87 (suppl): 1–183.

Knocks C and Rajewsky K (1993) Overview: somatic hypermutation and affinity mutation. *Immunology Today* 14: 400–410.

Rajewsky K (1996) Clonal selection and learning in the antibody system. *Nature* 381: 751–758.

Siskind GW and Benacerraf B (1969) Cell selection by antigen in the immune response. *Advances in Immunology* 10: 1–50.

Steiner LA and Eisen HN (1967) Sequential changes in the relative affinity of antibodies synthesized during the immune response. *Journal of Experimental Medicine* 126: 1161–1183.

Wagner SD and Neuberger MS (1996) Somatic hypermutation of immunoglobulin genes. *Annual Review of Immunology* 14: 441–457.

AFRICAN SWINE FEVER

Michael S Denyer and **Philip J Wilkinson**, Institute for Animal Health, Pirbright Laboratory, Pirbright, UK

African swine fever (ASF) is a highly contagious acute hemorrhagic disease of domestic pigs caused by a large icosahedral DNA virus which produces a wide range of clinical signs. Protective immunity can be stimulated *in vivo* but classical neutralizing antibodies have not been demonstrated. The complete genome has been sequenced and some proteins that could enable the virus to evade the host immune response have been identified. There is no vaccine.

Characteristics of the organism and its antigens

The virus persists in the southern half of Africa, either in wildlife reservoirs – wart hogs and soft ticks (*Ornithodoros moubata*) – or as an enzootic disease of domestic pigs. After more than 30 years as an enzootic disease in domestic pigs in southern Europe it has been eradicated from Portugal (1993) and Spain (1995). Because it has icosahedral symmetry and replicates in the cytoplasm of infected cells, ASF virus was originally classified as an iridovirus but the genome structure and replication strategy differ substantially from the Iridoviridae and are more like the Poxviridae. The virus is currently classified as the only member of a family called African swine fever-like viruses. The entire genome of a tissue culture-adapted Spanish isolate has been sequenced; it is 170 101 nucleotides long and contains 151 open reading frames which include five multigene families of unknown function.

The only cells in the pig in which ASF virus is known to replicate are those of the mononuclear phagocytic system in which virus produces hemadsorption (HAD) of pig erythrocytes to a CD2 homolog expressed on the cell surface (**Figure 1**).

Infection occurs by receptor-mediated endocytosis via saturable binding sites; it has been shown that

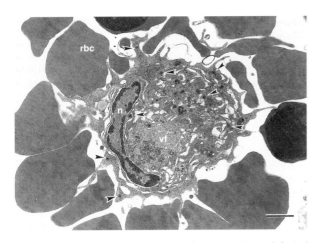

Figure 1 Hemadsorption to an alveolar macrophage infected with the Malawi isolate of African swine fever virus. The red blood cells (rbc) adhere to the surface of the infected cells producing a classical rosette. The viral structures include the perinuclear virus factory (vf) containing virus particles at various stages of assembly and cytoplasmic virus (arrow heads) prior to leaving the cell by budding. Cell nucleus (n). The bar represents 5 μm. (Provided by S.M. Brookes).

one receptor-binding protein of the virus is a low molecular weight protein (12 kDa) expressed as a homodimer (17 kDa).

Virus is released from infected cells by budding and acquires an external lipoprotein envelope containing glycosylated components; extracellular virus does not contain glycoproteins. The virus contains over 50 structural proteins, the most highly conserved of which are good immunogens and are used as antigens for serological tests to detect virus. There is no clear identification of virus strains by traditional serological methods but some differentiation is possible by monoclonal antibodies and antibodies that inhibit HAD. There is evidence that field isolates contain viruses with variable polypeptides, that these may also vary on passage in pig macrophages and that there is a complex variety of virus serotypes. Different and distinct genotypes have been identified by restriction enzyme analysis.

Immune response of the host

Circulating antibodies in infected pigs can be detected by radioimmunoassay or ELISA 3–4 days after infection and they persist for life. Neutralizing antibodies have never been demonstrated. After recovery from infection with less virulent isolates, pigs are persistently infected for at least 6 months and are resistant to challenge with homologous virus, although the challenge virus may undergo limited replication without producing clinical disease; they are usually fully susceptible to infection with different virus genotypes.

Pigs given passive antibody or piglets given colostral antibody have reduced levels of virus in the blood and tissues when challenged with virulent virus and show little or no clinical signs of disease. Studies *in vitro* have also shown that antibodies can reduce virus yield from infected pig macrophages in the absence of complement but the transfer of immune lymphocytes has no effect on the course of disease.

Antibodies which mediate lysis of ASF virus infected pig kidney cells (IBRS2) *in vitro*, by either antibody-dependent cell-mediated cytotoxicity (ADCC) or complement-mediated lysis, are present in serum 12–14 days after infection but are not able to lyse infected pig macrophages.

Because the humoral immune response does not appear to mediate the immunity of pigs which recover from infection, the cell-mediated immune responses have been investigated to determine what immune mechanisms may be important, and the following observations have been made.

Natural cytotoxic cells are also unable to lyse infected macrophages but may be important as producers of interferon γ (IFNγ). Some isolates of ASF virus can induce IFNγ production, and recombinant bovine IFNα and porcine IFNγ reduce infectious virus production by pig alveolar macrophages and monocytes *in vitro*.

Stimulation of peripheral blood lymphocytes from uninfected pigs with recombinant porcine interleukin 2 (IL-2) will induce a lymphokine-activated killer (LAK) cell which will lyse infected pig macrophages. Lymphocytes from recovered animals stimulated with ASF virus *in vitro* will produce IL-2, which indicates that a lymphokine-activated cytotoxic lymphocyte may be involved. ASF virus-specific cytotoxic T lymphocytes obtained from infected inbred pigs with defined SLA haplotypes are major histocompatibility complex (MHC) class I restricted.

Evasive strategies by the organism

The interaction of ASF virus with the host cells and its immune system and the processes involved in producing disease are still poorly understood; however, the complete genome sequence has indicated that some novel strategies may be employed to avoid the immune response, by direct and indirect effects of the virus on the cells of the immune system, in the absence of neutralizing antibody.

ASF virus replication in pig macrophages, and the release of immune mediators, may be important in aiding the virus to evade the immune system, in addition to being possible factors in the pathogenesis of the disease. Infection of pig macrophages does not alter the expression of Fc receptors nor their ability to mediate ADCC of antibody-coated bovine erythrocytes but does modulate antibody-mediated phagocytosis and chemotaxis. A protein isolated from infected cells has been shown to have a strong immunosuppressive effect *in vitro*. Infection of these cells will cause the downregulation of the pro-inflammatory cytokines IL-8, IFNα and tumor necrosis factor α (TNFα) but not of TGFβ.

The ASF virus genome also encodes for a Bcl-2 homolog which may aid the survival of infected cells and maintain persistence. In contrast, lymphocytes in infected tissues have been found to be apoptotic. Thus ASF virus may downregulate inflammation, increase the survival of infected cells and cause apoptosis of surrounding effector cells.

Although virus-specific delayed-type hypersensitivity, antibody production and lymphoproliferation are readily demonstrable, there are reports that the more virulent isolates can interfere with the immune response to foot-and-mouth disease virus in pigs inoculated with this virus 3 days after infection with ASF virus.

Vaccines

There are no commercial vaccines available for ASF. All attempts to produce suitable vaccines from either inactivated virus or viruses attenuated by passage in culture have been unsuccessful. There are reports in which a limited number of pigs were protected from death, but not clinical disease, after inoculation with infected spleen treated with a nonionic detergent in Freund's complete adjuvant.

See also: **Iridovirus, infection and immunity; Porcine immune system; Poxvirus, infection and immunity; Viruses, immunity to.**

Further reading

Becker Y (ed) (1987) *African Swine Fever*. Developments in Veterinary Virology Series. Dordrecht: Martinus Nijhoff.

Dixon LK, Twigg SRF, Baylis SA *et al* (1994) Nucleotide sequence of a 55 kbp region from the right end of the genome of a pathogenic African swine fever virus isolate (Malawi LIL 20/1). *Journal of General Virology* 75: 1655–1684.

Gómez-Villamandos JC, Hervás J, Méndez A *et al* (1995) Experimental African swine fever: apoptosis of lymphocytes and virus replication in other cells. *Journal of General Virology* 76: 2399–2405.

Martins CLV and Leitão AC (1994) Porcine immune responses to African swine fever virus (ASFV) infection. *Veterinary Immunology and Immunopathology* 43: 99–106.

Wilkinson PJ (1985) Iridoviridae and African swine fever virus. In: Porterfield JS (ed) *Andrewes' Viruses of Vertebrates*, 5th edn, pp 333–345. London: Baillière Tindall.

Wilkinson PJ (1990) African swine fever. In: Collier LH and Timbury MC (eds) *Topley and Wilson's Principles of Bacteriology, Virology and Immunity*, 8th edn, pp 623–629. London: Edward Arnold.

Yáñez RJ, Rodríguez JM, Nogal ML *et al* (1995) Analysis of the complete nucleotide sequence of African swine fever virus. *Virology* 208: 249–278.

AGGLUTINATION

Abram B Stavitsky, Department of Molecular Biology and Microbiology, Case Western Reserve University School of Medicine, Cleveland, Ohio, USA

A variety of particles bearing either natural or conjugated epitopes on their surfaces are specifically agglutinated by polyclonal or monoclonal antibodies to these epitopes. These particles can be inert but bearing these epitopes on their surfaces. They can also be large viruses, eukaryotic cells, or a variety of other cells, including bacteria, yeasts, fungi, protozoa and parasites. Inasmuch as very low concentrations of these antibodies can specifically agglutinate these cells, this reaction has served as a very sensitive and specific assay for the presence of specific antibodies in the serum or body fluids, e.g. antibodies to the bacillus of typhoid fever. The reaction can also be employed for the detection and measurement of antigen in the serum or body fluids. Agglutination is rarely used in research and for diagnosis because it has not been possible to easily and precisely quantitate this reaction. Therefore, it has been replaced by more quantifiable assays for antibodies, including the ELISA (enzyme-linked immunosorbent assay), various radioimmunoassays and other types of immunoassays. More recently, however, methods which facilitate, speed up and make more precise the reading of agglutination reactions may eventually result in the more frequent use of this very sensitive reaction for both research and diagnosis.

History

Specific bacterial agglutination was first observed about 100 years ago by Charrin and Roger. *Pseudomonas pyocyanea* grown in the serum of an immunized animal yielded a clear supernate with clumps of microbes at the bottom of the culture tube, whereas organisms cultured in normal serum were uniformly distributed throughout the tube. Bordet was the first to suggest that specific agglutination could be used for the diagnosis of infectious diseases. Widal and Grunbaum in 1896 applied this reaction to the diagnosis of typhoid fever. Bordet and Gay made the first fundamental analysis of the mechanisms of this reaction.

Landsteiner and Ehrlich, and Morgenroth in 1890 independently observed that normal human sera agglutinated the erythrocytes of other individuals. They also found that the injection of human red cells induced the formation of antibodies which by agglutination could distinguish the blood cells of different individuals within the species. These observations formed the basis of blood typing for transfusion.

In 1951 Boyden reported that proteins are observed on tannic acid-treated erythrocytes and that these cells are specifically agglutinated by antiprotein sera. Battisto and Chase, in 1963, extended this passive hemagglutination method to the detection of antibodies to haptens by the absorption of soluble hapten–protein conjugates to tanned erythrocytes.

Coombs and colleagues detected 'incomplete' Rh antibodies by the use of a second antiglobulin reaction. Pickles showed in 1946, that these 'incomplete' antibodies specifically agglutinated enzyme-treated erythrocytes. Bozicevich and coworkers in 1951 adsorbed various antigens to bentonite particles and observed that these particles were then flocculated by specific antisera. In 1956 Singer and Plots demonstrated that human gammaglobulin-coated polystyrene latex particles could be used for the detection of rheumatoid factors in human sera.

Boyd and Renkonen independently reported in 1946 and 1947, respectively, that different seed extracts contained substances which selectively agglutinated the erythrocytes of various species through binding to particular polysaccharides on the cell surface. These plant proteins are called lectins.

Definitions and classification of agglutination reactions

Agglutination is defined as the formation of clumps of cells or inert particles by specific antibodies to surface antigenic components (direct agglutination) or to antigenic components adsorbed or chemically coupled to red cells or inert particles (passive hemagglutination and passive agglutination, respectively). Erythrocytes are also agglutinated by nonantibody substances such as plant proteins, viruses, salts of heavy metals, inorganic colloidal acids and bases, and basic proteins (protamines, histones). Agglutination inhibition or hemagglutination inhibition refers to the inhibition of these reactions by soluble antigen which reacts with the combining sites of the antibodies and thereby prevents their binding to and agglutination of the particles.

Mechanisms of specific agglutination

Agglutination occurs in two stages: first, specific combination of antibody with antigen on the cell surface; second, formation of visible aggregates of the particles. According to Bordet, the antibody sensitized the cells to subsequent nonspecific agglutination by electrolytes but the alternative 'lattice' theory suggested that the cells were agglutinated through their specific linkage by bivalent or multivalent antibodies. The bulk of the evidence favors the 'lattice' theory, but under some conditions the second stage may be nonspecific so that cells of different antigenic specificities are coagglutinated in the presence of antibody to only one of the specificities. Usually, however, the second stage is also specific.

Agglutination may be influenced by many factors, including ionic strength (0.15 M sodium chloride is optimal), temperature (from 0 to 30°C agglutination is increased), and viscosity of the medium. Hemagglutination cannot be achieved with certain immunoglobulin G (IgG) class anti-protein or anti-blood group antibodies. Erythrocytes suspended in isotonic saline on account of mutual repulsion by negative zeta potential and intercellular attraction induced by van der Waals forces cannot approach each other more closely than 5–10 nm. The two valences of single IgG class antibodies are at most about 12 nm apart; therefore, they cannot bring the erythrocytes close enough together to agglutinate them. On the other hand the two diametrically opposed valences of the potentially decavalent IgM antibodies can easily bridge a distance of about 300 nm. Hemagglutination by IgG antibodies can be achieved by extending the IgG antibodies with anti-IgG antibodies or through the treatment of erythrocytes with enzymes which permits a much closer approach of the erythrocytes.

It seems paradoxical that agglutination often does not occur in the presence of the highest antibody concentrations. This is called the prezone or prozone phenomenon. This phenomenon may be due to the coating of the antigenic particles with such large numbers of antibody molecules that the number of cross-particle linked antigen–antibody complexes is decreased. The presence of nonagglutinating or blocking antibodies or other nonspecific factors which inhibit agglutination has not been excluded.

Applications of agglutination and agglutination inhibition reactions

Because of the ease of their performance and high sensitivity, specific agglutination reactions have been employed for: 1) the serological diagnosis of infectious diseases through the detection of a rising titer (concentration) of serum antibody; 2) screening for specific tissue-directed antibodies in connective tissue and autoimmune diseases; 3) detection of the presence of antigenic determinants on cells (mixed agglutination reaction); 4) blood typing and cross-matching procedures for blood transfusion, including the use of antiglobulin as a second antibody to directly cross-link incomplete agglutinins bound to Rh and ABO blood cell antigens; 5) diagnosis of viral infection: influenza, rubella and other viruses that directly agglutinate erythrocytes. The inhibition of viral hemagglutination by specific antibody to the virus is a particularly useful and sensitive test for titers of antiviral antibody.

A number of lectins are employed in blood banks for the hemagglutination of erythrocytes through binding to A, B and H blood group substances, thus providing an alternative method of identification of blood group substances.

Quantitation

The agglutination method has fallen somewhat into disuse for research and, to some extent, even for diagnosis because it is not possible to precisely quantitate the reaction. Concentrations of agglutinating antibody are assayed by preparing a series of doubling dilutions of the test serum, adding cells to each dilution, incubating the cell suspension, and then observing the highest dilution of the serum which produces a visual agglutination pattern at the bottom of the tube. Thus, failure to observe the presence or absence of agglutination in one tube or one doubling dilution represents a 100% error in determining the quantity of antibody. Therefore, agglutination has been replaced by more quantifiable assays, including the ELISA, various radioimmunoassays and other types of immunoassays. However, agglutination can be quantitated. The actual amount of antibody nitrogen or protein bound by cells can be determined, but is too complicated and time-consuming to be a routine assay. Modern technology has provided a number of methods for the quantitation of agglutination through measurements of turbidity, light scattering or the mean diffusion constants of the particulate suspension.

Automated reading and processing of agglutination results

Microplate agglutination techniques are commonly used for the quantitative or qualitative isotypic analysis of specific antibodies, but require optical reading by the researcher and, therefore, can be quite subjective. Aubert and colleagues have used an automatic reader scanning each of the wells of a standard microtiter plate. The advantages of the automatic reader were additionally maximized by coupling it to a dedicated computer running customized software designed to process data coming on-line from the spectrophotometer. This approach was applied to the diagnosis of human toxoplasmosis and candidiasis. Suspensions of *Toxoplasma gondii* tachyzoites or of sensitized erythrocytes were used for the determination of IgG antibodies or the quantitation of IgM-, IgA- or IgE-specific isotypes.

Rapid agglutination testing in an ultrasonic standing wave

The time required to perform diagnostic agglutination tests can be significantly reduced by applying an ultrasonic standing wave field to a droplet of reagents in a capillary tube. Avian erythrocytes, bacteria and latex particles were agglutinated in 15 s, 5 min and 1 min, respectively with no loss in sensitivity or specificity. Moreover, a series of five droplets in a single capillary can be tested in less than 4 min by drawing the capillary along the axis of the ultrasonic field of a ring transducer.

Agglutination as a protective mechanism in infections

Specific agglutination of bacteria by antibody *in vivo* is observed only with rather enormous numbers of bacteria. Therefore, this serologic reaction is presumably not very important in natural infections of the bloodstream where enormous numbers of bacteria are unusual. In a local lesion, however, where the number of bacteria may be high, it is possible that agglutination of bacteria by antibody may aid in localizing the infection as well as keeping the growing bacteria in a clump rather than disseminating.

See also: **Alloantigens; Antigens; Antiglobulin**

(Coombs') test; Autoantibodies, tests for; Bacterial cell walls; Erythrocytes; Lectins; Phytohemagglutinin (PHA); Valency of antigens and antibodies; Viruses, immunity to.

Further reading

Aubert D, Foudrinier F, Kaltenbach ML *et al* (1995) Automated reading and processing of quantitative IgG, IgM, IgA and IgE isotypic agglutination results in microplates. Development and application in parasitology-mycology. *Journal of Immunological Methods* 186: 323–328.

Casadevall A (1995) Antibody immunity and invasive fungal infections. *Infection and Immunity* 63: 4211–4218.

Grundy MA, Bolek WE, Coakley WT and Benes EJ (1993) Rapid agglutination testing in an ultrasonic standing wave. *Journal of Methods* 165: 47–57.

Howanitz JH and Howanitz PJ (1991) *Test Selection and Interpretation. Laboratory Medicine*, pp 805 and 809. Edinburgh: Churchill Livingstone.

Isenberg HD (ed) (1992) *Clinical Microbiology Procedures Handbook*, vol 11, chap 9. Washington DC, American Society for Microbiology.

Koneman EW, Allen SD, Janda WM, Schreckenberger PC and Winn WC Jr (1992) *Color Atlas and Textbook of Diagnostic Microbiology*, 4th edn, pp 774; 948–949; 1085–1086; 1023–1025; 1029. Philadelphia: JB Lippincott.

Lachmann PJ and Peters DK (eds) (1982) *Clinical Aspects of Immunology*. vol 2, pp 55; 320; 350; 497; 748; 1106; 1165–1166; 1180; 1448–1450; 1450–1451. Oxford: Blackwell Scientific.

Parker MT and Collier LH (eds) (1990) *Topley and Wilson's Principles of Bacteriology, Virology and Immunity*, 8th edn, vol 1, pp 404–406. St. Louis, BC Decker.

Roitt IM (1997) *Essential Immunology*, 9th edn, pp 111–113. Oxford: Blackwell Science.

Rose NR and Friedman H (eds) (1992) *Manual of Clinical Immunology*, 4th edn, pp 40; 91–92; 103; 196. Washington DC, American Society for Microbiology.

van Oss CJ (1989) Energetics of cell–cell and cell–biopolymer interactions. *Cell Biophysics* 14: 1–14.

AGING AND THE IMMUNE SYSTEM

Bernhard Cinader, Department of Clinical Biochemistry, University of Toronto, Toronto, Canada

Lifespan and hence the rate of aging is a component of the evolution of different species. The magnitude of lifespan affects programs for sexual maturation and subsequent decline of reproductive activity. Body size and metabolic activity are in turn correlated with capacity for repair; this has been demonstrated for excision repair after DNA damage induced by ultraviolet light. Since the capacity for repair is limited, damage will ultimately result in age-related decline of synthetic capacity. While the quantity of products and the propensity for cell division generally diminish as a function of advancing age, amino acid sequences of proteins and nucleotide sequences of DNA do not change with age.

Having referred to factors which may determine differences in age-related progression of different species, we shall turn to differences in aging which occur in different individuals of the same species. It is reasonable to assume that some or many of these result from the presence of multiallelic genes with products which differ in their capacity to overcome wear and tear. This is certainly the case for individual differences in onset of diseases caused by inborn errors of metabolism. The age of the onset of several genetic diseases is related to the functional competence of the molecule which is defective in a

given disease. The absence of a particular molecule crucial for a given function, or the synthesis of an incompetent molecule, results in an early onset of the disease; the disease onset may be delayed if the molecule retains some functional capacity (e.g. Duchenne Becker muscular dystrophy, Sandhoff disease).

Aging of the immune system involves changes in the capacity for self-renewal, in the relative preponderance of cell populations and in the quantity of immunoglobulin molecules of different isotypes and of different interleukins. We have relatively little definitive information on the exact nature of changes in the capacity for self-renewal of stem cells and of precursor cells. There appears to be an age-related decrease in the number of cells which synthesize terminal deoxynucleotidyl transferase (TdT) and are precursors of both T and B cells. However, it remains possible that the observed decrease does not depend on changes in the precursor cells themselves but is due to regulator cells: feeder cells from old mice cannot support the *in vitro* growth of TdT$^+$ cells, while feeder layers from young animals can do so. In short it is possible that self-renewal decreases with age as a function of regulator cells rather than of precursor cells themselves.

Age-related changes in the quantity of molecules

may be controlled by feedback mechanisms. There is considerable polymorphism in the quantity of molecules produced in young individuals of different genetic backgrounds. The quantity produced by the youthful organism is in many cases directly correlated to the extent of subsequent decrease; this correlation has been referred to as 'economic correction'.

In the immune system the most striking age-related change occurs in the thymus, in which some cell populations decrease and others show a compensating increase up to late middle age when the total number of self-renewing thymus cells becomes drastically reduced. These central cellular changes cause marked age-related changes in various subpopulations of T cells, and particularly in different classes of suppressor and of helper cells.

Individual differences, i.e. the polymorphism of age-related changes, will be exemplified in terms of two classes of suppressor capacity, one affecting the humoral, the other cell-mediated immunity.

Suppressor capacity in the thymus, affecting humoral response, can be measured by reconstitution experiments, in which lethally irradiated mice are given lymphocytes of young donors, mixed with thymus cells from donors of different ages; the reconstituted mice are then immunized, and antibody is measured. In some strains of mice, thymus cells from young donors reduce the humoral response of the lymphocytes, while thymus cells from old donors increase it.

Changes in suppressor capacity for cell-mediated immunity can be measured by the ability of thymus cells to prevent lymphocytes to be sensitized by targets and to kill them.

Within the same strain the potency of the two classes of suppressor capacity, i.e. suppressor capacity for humoral immunity and suppressor capacity for cell-mediated immunity can change in opposite directions. The independence of aging of the two classes can also be seen when progression of age-related changes are modified by nutritional, hormonal or pharmacological interventions; these can affect aging of one class without affecting aging of the other. In general, it seems that age-related changes of the two classes vary as if they were controlled by two different genes.

We shall now turn to changes in T helper cells, in terms of interleukins. In mice of different strains, interleukin 1 (IL-1) and IL-2 decrease with age, though to different extents. In striking contrast, IL-3, IL-4, IL-6 and IL-10 increase up to a fairly advanced age. These contrasting changes in the direction of age-related alterations of different interleukins may be attributable to relative changes in the proportion of two sets of T helper cells, T_H1 and

T_H2 cells, the latter include memory cells. Thus, changes of interleukins may result from a lifelong accumulation of encounters with foreign macromolecules, and so reflect immunological experiences.

In summary, considerable age-related changes in suppressor cells occur to an extent which shows individual variation; different types of suppressor cells can change in opposite directions in the same individuals. Changes in helper cells are attributable to changes in the relative proportion of subpopulations and manifest themselves in age-related changes in the quantity of different interleukins. In some strains of inbred mice these changes can result in a decrease in humoral response. In other strains of mice a marked decrease in suppressor cells for the humoral response can result in autoimmune disease.

In the heterogeneous human population, there is an age-related increase in the proportion of individuals who show a decrease in the capacity to make a potent immune response and a greater tendency to make autoimmune responses. From the foregoing discussions on age-related changes in different strains of inbred mice, it is clear that both changes observed in human populations can be interpreted as resulting from the heterogeneity of the population i.e. from individual differences in genetic background; some individuals have a tendency to the changes which we have observed in the age-related patterns of certain inbred strains of mice. In this context, it is intriguing that certain interleukins seem to increase in each of the five inbred strains examined; the question arises whether these changes might be advantageous.

In fact, this is not necessarily the case. Immunity to leishmania can be reduced via IL-3 and IL-4, which impair the capacity of macrophages to kill intracellular organisms. IL-4 can directly inhibit the induction of cytotoxic T lymphocytes (CTL) and lymphokine activated killer (LAK) cells against virus-infected cells and tumors. It is possible, therefore, that increases in interleukins may reduce the ability of the immune system to deal effectively with some infections. However, this is not necessarily applicable to all infections, indeed some changes of old age can have adaptive advantages. This appears to be the case in age-related decreases of factors which affect growth of certain tumors. In one situation, age-related decrease in the growth of some tumors is attributed to age-related decrease in the production of angiogenic factors by T cells of aged animals.

In several strains of mice, NK cells have been found to increase to middle age and then to decrease. Similar observations have been made with respect to LAK cells, which show polymorphism in the quantity of these cells in young individuals and subsequent decreases that are proportional to the magnitude of the youthful level, i.e. 'economic correction'. There is a diversity of findings concerning the aging of human NK cells. One group reports an age-related decrease; others find no change; yet others find an increase of NK function with aging, most often correlated with an increased number of NK cells. Thus it might appear as if NK cells of humans and mice age in a different manner. In fact, this difference may be due to the difficulty of analyzing the relation between a given parameter in old, middle-aged and young human populations, since individuals with certain genetic traits are eliminated before old and middle age, but are present in the young population.

Some age-related changes of B cells are a manifestation of change in T cells and the accumulation of memory. However, there is some evidence that B cells from old mice are specifically defective in their ability to progress from the G_0 phase into the S phase of the cell cycle.

Having examined aging in T, NK and B cells, it remains to summarize the reason for the increase in autoimmunity in aging human populations. In part this may be attributable to the loss of suppressor capacity as has been found in some strains of inbred mice. In part it may be due to accumulation of denatured proteins which is the consequence of the age-related decrease in proteolytic enzymes. These denatured proteins may cause a breakdown of the tolerance which exists for intact autologous molecules.

Age-related changes are clearly compartmentalized in terms of different types of T suppressor cells and in terms of different subsets of helper cells. There is also a difference in age-related changes in the mucosal system and in the peripheral immune system; the former appears to be much less subject to age-related changes than the latter. The quantity of NK cells in mice goes through a peak in middle age and then declines moderately. In humans, this decline has not been observed and selected groups of aged individuals appear to have high levels of NK activity. There may be a decline in the self-renewal capacity of some stem cells but it is not clearly established whether or not this is in fact the outcome of the effect of controlling cells which prevent proliferation.

See also: **Effector lymphocytes; Sex hormones and immunity; Suppressor T lymphocytes; Thymus.**

Further reading

Abe Y, Yuasa M, Kajiwara Y and Hosono M (1994) Defects of immune cells in the senescence-accelerated mouse: a model for learning and memory deficits in the aged. *Cellular Immunology* 157: 59–69.

Bergener M, Ermini M and Stahelin HB (eds) (1988) *Crossroads in Aging. 1988 Sandoz Lecture in Gerontology.* London: Academic Press.

Chandra RK (ed) (1985) *Nutrition, Immunity and Illness in the Elderly.* New York: Pergamon Press.

Cinader B (ed) (1989) Symposium 2.4: *Genetics of Aging.* XVIth International Congress of Genetics. Ottawa: National Research Council.

Courtois Y, Faucheux B, Forette B, Knook DL and Treton JA (eds) (1986) *Modern Trends in Aging Research.* London: John Libby.

de Weck A (ed) (1984) Lymphoid cell functions in aging. In: *Topics in Aging Research in Europe.* Rijswijk: Eurage, 320pp.

Fleming AL, Field EH, Tolaymat N and Cowdery JS (1993) Age influences recovery of systemic and mucosal immune responses following acute depletion of CD4 T cells. *Clinical Immunology and Immunopathology* 69: 285–291.

Goidl EA (ed) (1986) *Aging and the Immune Response.* New York: Marcel Dekker.

Gonzalez-Quintial R, Baccala R, Balderas RS and Theofilopoulos AN (1995) V beta gene repertoire in the aging mouse: a developmental perspective. *International Reviews of Immunology* 12: 27–40.

Hodes RJ (1995) Molecular alterations in the aging immune system. *Journal of Experimental Medicine* 182: 1–3.

Kubo M and Cinader B (1990) The distinction between age- and disease-related change. *Immunology Letters* 24: 133–136.

Kubo M and Cinader B (1990) Polymorphism of age-related changes in interleukin (IL) production: differential changes of T helper subpopulations, synthesizing IL 2, IL 3 and IL 4. *European Journal of Immunology* 20: 1289–1296.

Miller RA (1996) The aging immune system: primer and prospectus. *Science* 273: 70–74.

Parham P (Ed) (1997) Aging and the immune system. *Immunological Reviews* 160.

Pawelec G, Adibzadeh M, Pohla H and Schaudt K (1995) Immunosenescence: ageing of the immune system. *Immunology Today* 16: 420–422.

Steeber DA, Green NE, Sato S *et al* (1996) Lymphocyte migration in L-selectin-deficient mice. Altered subset migration and aging of the immune system. *Journal of Immunology* 157: 1096–1106.

ALLELIC EXCLUSION

Michael Reth, Max Planck Institute for Immunobiology, Freiburg, Germany

In agreement with the proposal of the 'clonal selection theory' by Burnet in 1959, Nossal and Mäkelä could show in 1961 that indeed each B cell produced many copies of only one type of antibody. Thus each B cell is restricted to one specific antibody. With the discovery of allotypes another restriction of B cells was shown. Allotypes are serological markers on heavy or light chain of immunoglobulin (Ig) which differ among genetically different strains of one species. Anti-allotypic antisera can be produced by immunizing strain A_1 with strain A_2 Ig. Using anti-allotypic sera, Pernis, Chiappino, Kelus and Gell, as well as Cebra, Colberg and Dray, showed in 1965 that in an $(A_1 \times A_2)$ F_1 animal B cells express either A_1 or A_2 but not both allotypes on their cell surface. Hence, B cells are restricted to express Ig chain of only one of their two alleles, a phenomenon which is called 'allelic exclusion'.

The allelic exclusion control ensures that each B cell expresses only one type of binding site because an antibody binding site is determined by the combination of a particular heavy and light chain. **Figure 1A** shows that a B cell with a defined binding specificity can be efficiently selected and activated by the corresponding antigen. If expression of the Ig alleles was not regulated each B cell would express several combinations of the two different heavy and light chains and thus express a variety of antigen specificities (**Figure 1B**). Such unregulated B cells would not be able to mediate a specific immune response.

Allelic exclusion in the context of V gene assembly

Most cells of the vertebrate species have a diploid chromosomal organization and express both alleles of an active gene. The Ig genes are an exception to this rule because only one of their alleles is expressed as a functional product. This phenomenon is connected with another special feature of the Ig genes; namely, that the gene for the variable part of an Ig chain (V gene) is not encoded in the germ line but assembled from different gene segments during B cell development. The genes for the variable region of the heavy (H) and light (L) chain are assembled out of three (V_H, D and J_H) or two (V_L, J_L) germ-line gene segments, respectively. This assembly is mediated by two recombinase proteins, RAG-1 and RAG-2 which are only expressed in cells of the lymphoid lineage. The V gene segments are found in multiple different copies at the IgH and the two IgL gene loci (Igκ and Igλ). V Gene rearrangements occur in the developing B cell in an ordered fashion first at the IgH locus and only later at the Igκ locus. Before the segments are assembled into either a V_HDJ_H or a V_LJ_L complex

(A)

(B)

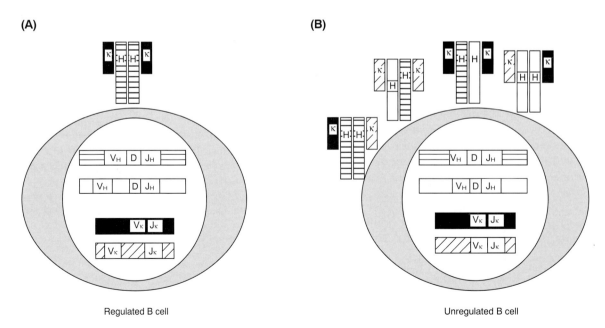

Regulated B cell

Unregulated B cell

Figure 1   Allelic exclusion ensures expression of a single specificity of antigen-binding site on the surface of the B cell.

their ends are frequently modified by the removal and/or addition of nucleotides. These modifications increase the variability of the expressed V genes. However, they may also result into a nonfunctional V gene in which the V_H or V_L segments are not joined in the correct reading frame to the DJ_H complexes or to the J_L segments (out of frame join). When the first sequences of both IgH and Igκ alleles of B cells became available it was noticed that in most cases only one allele carried a functional (in frame) $V_H DJ_H^+$ or $V_\kappa J_\kappa^+$ complex. At the Igκ locus the second allele either did not carry any V gene rearrangements (germ-line configuration) or had assembled a nonfunctional $V_\kappa J_\kappa$ complex. At the IgH locus the second allele carried either a DJH or a nonfunctional $V_H DJ_H$ complex. In a first attempt to explain these data it was proposed that allelic exclusion was simply due to a high frequency of nonfunctional V gene rearrangements (stochastic model). This model assumed that a V gene rearrangement occurs only once per allele and that due to the low frequency of a productive V gene rearrangement most developing B cells have either no or only one functional V gene. The latter population would then

be selected by the immune system. However, in studies of Abelson murine leukemia virus-transformed pre-B cell lines it became clear that the V gene assembly is a very dynamic process which can occur repeatedly on one allele. This is due to the fact that V gene segments are present in multiple different copies at each Ig locus. Thus a nonfunctional $V_\kappa J_\kappa$ complex can be deleted and replaced by a functional $V_\kappa J_\kappa$ complex on the same allele simply by joining an upstream V_κ to a downstream J_κ segment. Similarly a nonfunctional $V_H DJ_H$ allele can become productive by performing a V_H to $V_H DJ_H$ join. Further studies with pre-B cell lines also showed that the frequency of a functional V gene rearrangement was not very low. In a developing pre-B cell line roughly 30% of the analyzed V gene rearrangements are productive. However, in this analysis no cell line was found with a productive V gene on both alleles.

These data support the regulated model of allelic exclusion as proposed by Alt and Baltimore in 1982. According to this model the products of a functional V gene rearrangement exercise a feedback control preventing any further V gene assembly at a particular Ig locus. Thus in pre-B cells V_H gene rearrange-

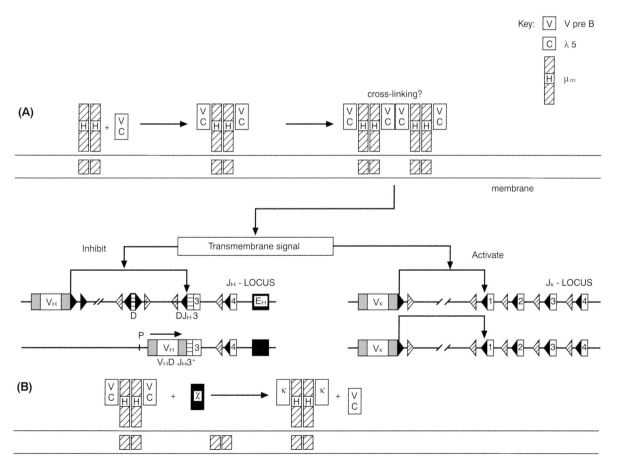

Figure 2   Transmembrane signals regulate antigen-receptor gene rearrangement.

ment occurs on one or both IgH alleles until a productive $V_H DJ_H$ complex is formed and a μ chain is produced. The μ chain then generates a signal preventing any further V_H gene assembly on both IgH alleles. Specifically it is the membrane-bound form of the μ heavy chain which exerts this feed back control, preventing any further V_H gene assembly on the two IgH alleles. In the endoplasmic reticulum of the pre-B cell the μ heavy chain binds to the surrogate light chain proteins VpreB and λ5 as well as to the Igα/Igβ heterodimer, the signaling component of the B cell antigen receptor. Together these molecules compose the pre-B cell receptor which at the cell surface initiates the signal for the expansion of the pre B cell clone and the inhibition of further V_H to DJ_H rearrangement (**Figure 2A**). Pre-B and pro-B cells in mutant mice lacking μ heavy chain, λ5 or Igβ expression do not show allelic exclusion of the IgH alleles, thus demonstrating the importance of the pre-B cell receptor in this control. How signals from the pre-B cell receptor stops further V_H gene rearrangement is not known at present; presumably the V_H segments are the target of this control as the J_H–C_H locus is already transcriptional active during pre-B cell development. During the expansion of the pre-B cell clone the RAG genes are switched off, but are re-expressed later on so that V_L to J_L rearrangements can occur. These rearrangements continue until a light chain is produced which can bind to the pre-existing μ heavy chain (**Figure 2B**). The subsequent expression of a B cell antigen receptor on the cell surface results in termination of further V_L to J_L rearrangements, thus establishing allelic exclusion of the IgL loci. Allelic exclusion occurs not only at the IgH and IgL loci but also at the TCR β chain locus. Similar to that which has been described above for the pre-B cells, the control of the TCR β chain locus is mediated via a pre-T cell receptor consisting of the CD3 complex, the TCR β chain, and the surrogate TCR α chain pre-Tα. In contrast to the IgL loci the TCR α chain locus does not show a tight allelic exclusion control; why this is so remains to be established.

See also: **B lymphocyte differentiation; Clonal selection; Immunoglobulin, cell surface; Immunoglobulin genes.**

Further reading

Alt FW (1984) Exclusive immunoglobulin genes. *Nature* **312**: 502–503.

Alt FW, Blackwell K and Yancopoulos GD (1985) Immunoglobulin genes in transgenic mice. *Trends in Genetics* **1**: 231–236.

Levelt CN, Wang B, Ehrfeld A, Terhorst C and Eichmann K (1995) Regulation of T cell receptor (TCR)-beta locus allelic exclusion and initiation of TCR-alpha locus rearrangement in immature thymocytes by signaling through the CD3 complex. *European Journal of Immunology* **25**: 1257–1261.

Li Z, Dordai DI, Lee J and Desiderio S (1996) A conserved degradation signal regulates RAG-2 accumulation during cell division and links V(D)J recombination to the cell cycle. *Immunity* **5**: 575–589.

Loffert D, Ehlich A, Muller W and Rajewsky K (1996) Surrogate light chain expression is required to establish immunoglobulin heavy chain allelic exclusion during early B cell development. *Immunity* **4**: 133–144.

Papavasiliou F, Misulovin Z, Suh H and Nussenzweig MC (1995) The role of Ig beta in precursor B cell transition and allelic exclusion. *Science* **268**: 408–411.

Pernis B, Chiappino G, Kelus AS and Gell PGH (1965) Cellular localization of immunoglobulins with different allotypic specificities in rabbit lymphoid tissues. *Journal of Experimental Medicine* **122**: 853–876.

Xu Y, Davidson L, Alt FW and Baltimore D (1996) Function of the pre-T-cell receptor alpha chain in T-cell development and allelic exclusion at the T-cell receptor beta locus. *Proceedings of the National Academy of Sciences of the USA* **93**: 2169–2173.

ALLERGENS

Martin D Chapman, Asthma and Allergic Diseases Center, University of Virginia, Charlottesville, Virginia, USA

The modern history of 'allergens' dates back to 1873, when Charles Blackley showed that wind-borne pollen grains caused the symptoms of June hayfever and that aqueous pollen extracts caused immediate wheal and flare reactions when scratched into the skin of a hayfever sufferer (himself). At the turn of the century, the causative agents of this 'supersensitivity' reaction were defined as allergens (Von Pirquet) and this form of immunity was shown to be mediated by homocytotropic (or 'reaginic') antibody (Prausnitz and Kustner). These historic developments are summarized in **Table 1**. By the 1920s, it was known that inhalation of allergens derived from pollens, house dust and animals, or

Table 1 A brief synopsis of the history of allergens

1873	Blackley	Showed that windborne pollen grains caused hayfever and that pollen extracts caused wheal and flare reactions when 'scratched' into the skin
1906	Von Pirquet	Defined 'allergy' as supersensitivity to foreign antigens or 'allergens'
1911	Noon	Used desensitizing injections of pollen extracts ('pollen toxin') to treat hayfever
1916	Cooke	Demonstrated familial inheritance of hayfever/asthma, i.e. a genetic trait
1921	Prausnitz and Kustner	Passive transfer of immediate skin test reactivity using serum from an allergic patient (the P-K test)
1940	Loveless	Production of 'blocking antibodies' during immunotherapy
1960s	Osler and Lichtenstein	Development of histamine release assay (1963)
	Voorhorst and Spieksma	Discovery of house dust mites (1964)
	King, Norman and Marsh	First allergens purified from ragweed (antigen E) and rye (Rye 1) (1964–1965)
	Ishizaka and Ishizaka	Discovery of IgE (1967)
	Norman and Lichtenstein	Controlled trials of ragweed immunotherapy (1966–1970)
1980	Chapman and Platts-Mills	Purification of dust mite allergen, Der p 1
1988	Chua and Thomas	First allergen to be cloned – Der p 1

ingestion of foods, was associated with the clinical symptoms of hayfever, asthma, atopic dermatitis or food allergy, and that these conditions affected 10–20% of the population. This was a 'golden era' of research on allergic disease and, indeed, the first edition of the *Journal of Immunology* contained an article by Robert Cooke, some 100 pages long, on the genetics of asthma, showing that the disease had strong hereditary links. The second golden era was in the 1960s, when the first allergens were purified from ragweed and rye grass pollen, histamine release assays were developed, and the landmark studies of the Ishizakas established that immediate hypersensitivity reactions were mediated by a new class of antibody, termed immunoglobulin E (IgE).

Inhalation of environmental allergens is the most common cause of IgE responses in humans and this feature distinguishes this class of antigens from other macromolecules or infectious agents which, with the exception of helminth parasites, do not usually cause IgE responses. There has been tremendous recent progress in research on allergens. Most important allergens from pollens, dust mite, animal danders, insects and foods (e.g. peanut, shrimp) have now been cloned and expressed as recombinant proteins. Amino acid sequence data derived from these studies have been used to establish the structure and biologic function of allergens, to identify the antigenic sites that are involved in IgE responses, and to investigate cellular mechanisms of inflammatory responses in asthma and atopic dermatitis. Recombinant allergens are being introduced for the diagnosis of allergic diseases and for developing therapeutic products. Allergens are one of the most well-defined groups of biomedically important proteins and we are now entering a new era in which the molecular basis of the immune response to these proteins is becoming established.

Nomenclature and general properties

Atopic individuals become sensitized to allergens through exposure by inhalation (e.g. pollen grains, mite feces, animal danders, cockroach secretions, and fungal spores), by ingestion (e.g. milk, egg, peanut, fish), and by injection (e.g. insect venoms and parenterally administered drugs, such as penicillin). In general use, the term allergen can refer to these sources, to aqueous extracts prepared from the source materials, or to highly purified or cloned allergen proteins. The systematic nomenclature for purified allergens developed by the World Health Organization and International Union of Immunological Societies was revised in 1994. The nomenclature uses the taxonomic name of the source material and an Arabic numeral to describe the allergen, in the chronologic order of identification and purification. In the abbreviated form, the first three letters are used for the genus, followed by a single letter for the species. For example, ragweed antigen E (the first pollen to be purified) is *Ambrosia artemisifolia* allergen 1, or Amb a 1. To be included in this nomenclature, newly described allergens have to have clearly defined molecular properties and to have demonstrable allergenic importance according to criteria established by the IUIS subcommittee on allergen nomenclature (**Table 2**). This committee reviews all proposals for inclusion of allergens in the nomenclature. The aim is to avoid redundancy and to ensure consistent use of allergen names in scientific and medical journals.

In most cases, multiple allergic proteins have been

purified from a given source. Thus more than ten different allergens have now been isolated or cloned from house dust mites or grass pollens. Usually, 80–90% of patients make IgE antibody responses to one or two proteins, e.g. mite allergens from *Dermatophagoides pteronyssinus*, Der p 1 and Der p 2, and these 'major' allergens are often used for immunologic and clinical studies. The prevalence of IgE antibodies to other 'minor' allergens is lower (<40%) and there is also evidence that a greater proportion of IgE is directed against the major allergens.

Allergens possess several characteristic features that appear to be important for immediate hypersensitivity reactions. They are usually low molecular weight proteins or glycoproteins (5–50 kDa) that are readily soluble and elute rapidly (within 1 min) from the allergen source, e.g. pollen grains or mite feces. These properties facilitate rapid penetration at mucosal surfaces, cross-linking of IgE antibodies on the mast cell surface, and mediator release to give immediate symptoms. Some allergens, such as penicillin and low molecular weight chemicals, act as haptens and require binding to a protein carrier (usually albumin) in order to elicit IgE responses. Other characteristic features of inhaled allergens are that allergic individuals become sensitized following exposure to extremely low doses of inhaled allergen, typically <1 μg of a single mite or pollen allergen per year, with no apparent adjuvant, on airborne particles of ~5–40 μm diameter. This form of immunization appears to prime preferentially for IgE antibody production and may be important in generating T cell (T_H2) responses with cytokine profiles that are required for IgE production.

Molecular biology

Cloning and sequencing

By the mid-1980s a large number of allergens had been purified using biochemical techniques, but in general the yields were poor and, apart from physicochemical properties, the molecular structures of these proteins were poorly defined. With the advent of molecular cloning techniques, the primary structures of many allergens were rapidly established and, by screening cDNA expression libraries with IgE antibodies, new allergens were identified and sequenced. More than 100 allergen sequences are now listed in protein databanks (GENBANK) and a partial listing of major allergens is shown in **Table 3**.

The aim of cloning and sequencing is to obtain the primary structure of the allergen and to express the allergen in recombinant form. For many major allergens, N-terminal or internal amino acid sequences, and monospecific antibodies, were available to confirm the identity of cDNA clones. In some cases, e.g. cat allergen, Fel d 1 or Aspergillus allergen, Asp f 1, the nucleotide sequences were obtained by polymerase chain reaction (PCR) using primers derived from amino acid sequence. However, the usual approach has been to isolate mRNA from allergen source material (e.g. pollen grains, mite or cockroach bodies, fungal spores) and to use reverse transcriptase to generate double-stranded cDNA, which is then packaged into λgt11 or similar expression vectors. The cDNA libraries are screened with pooled IgE antibodies from 6–8 allergic patients, or with high titer monospecific polyclonal antibodies, to identify cDNA clones expressing allergen. Increasingly, allergens are being identified solely based on screening cDNA libraries and this approach has been very successful for allergens which were previously ill defined, e.g. fungi (*Alternaria, Aspergillus, Trichophyton*); foods (peanut, shrimp); and insects (cockroaches, fire ants, hornets).

Protein families and biologic function

Phylogenetically related species usually produce allergens that share significant amino acid sequence homology. For example, the group 1 allergens from *D. pteronyssinus* (Der p 1) and *D. farinae* (Der f 1) show 80% homology and the group 2 allergens from these mites show 88% homology. Allergens showing

Table 2 Allergens: criteria for inclusion in the WHO/IUIS nomenclature

1. The molecular and structural properties should be clearly and unambiguously defined, including:
   - Purification of the allergen protein to homogeneity
   - Determination of molecular weight, pI and carbohydrate composition
   - Determination of nucleotide and/or amino acid sequence
   - Production of monospecific or monoclonal antibodies to the allergen
2. The importance of the allergen in causing IgE responses should be defined by:
   - Comparing the prevalence of serum IgE antibodies in large population(s) of allergic patients. Ideally, at least 50 or more patients should be tested
   - Demonstrating biologic activity, e.g. by skin testing or histamine release assay
   - Investigating whether depletion of the allergen from an allergic extract (e.g. by immunoabsorption) reduces IgE binding activity
   - Demonstrating, where possible, that recombinant allergens have comparable IgE antibody-binding activity to the natural allergen

Table 3 Molecular properties of common allergens

Source	Allergen	Mol. wt (kDa)	Homology/function
Inhalants			
Indoor			
House dust mite (*Dermatophagoides pteronyssinus*)	Der p 1	25	Cysteine protease[b]
	Der p 2	14	Epididymal protein
	Der p 3	30	Serine protease
	Der p 5	14	Unknown
Cat (*Felis domesticus*)	Fel d 1	36	(Uteroglobin)
Dog (*Canis familiaris*)	Can f 1	25	Calycin
Mouse (*Mus muscularis*)	Mus m 1	21	Pheromone binding protein (calycin)[b]
Rat (*Rattus norvegicus*)	Rat n 1	21	Pheromone binding protein (calycin)[b]
Cockroach (*Blattella germanica*)	Bla g 2	36	Aspartic protease
	Bla g 4	21	Calycin
Outdoor			
Pollens – grasses:			
Rye (*Lolium perenne*)	Lol p 1	28	Unknown
Timothy (*Phleum pratense*)	Phl p 5	32	Unknown
Bermuda (*Cynodon dactylon*)	Cyn d 1	32	Unknown
Weeds			
Ragweed (*Artemisia artemisifolia*)	Amb a 1	38[a]	Pectate lyase
	Amb a 5	5	Neurophysins[b]
Trees			
Birch (*Betula verucosa*)	Bet v 1	17	Pathogenesis-related protein
	Bet v 2	14	Profilin
Foods			
Milk	β-Lactoglobulin	36[a]	Retinol-binding protein (calycin)[b]
Egg	Ovomucoid	29	Trypsin inhibitor
Codfish (*Gadus callarias*)	Gad c 1	12	Ca^{2+}-binding protein (muscle parvalbumin)
Peanut (*Arachis hypogea*)	Ara h 1	63	Vicilin (seed-storage protein)
Venoms			
Bee (*Apis mellifera*)	Api m 1	19.5	Phospholipase A_2
Wasp (*Polestes annularis*)	Pol a 5	23	Mammalian testis proteins
Hornet (*Vespa crabro*)	Ves c 5	23	Mammalian testis proteins
Fire ant (*Solenopsis invicta*)	Sol i 2	13	Unknown
Fungi			
Aspergillus fumigatus	Asp f 1	18	Cytotoxin (mitogillin)
Alternaria alternata	Alt a 1	29[a]	Unknown
Latex			
Hevea brasiliensis	Hev b 1	58	Elongation factor
	Hev b 5	16	Unknown – homologous to kiwi fruit Protein of unknown function

[a]Most allergens have a single polypeptide chain; dimers are indicated.
[b]Allergens of known three-dimensional structure are also indicated.

a high degree of structural homology are also found in grasses and trees (group 1, group 5, etc.). It is quite common for a single allergen to show sequence polymorphisms, and variants with limited amino acid substitutions are termed *isoforms*. In some cases, e.g. birch pollen allergen, Bet v 1, the isoforms may have altered IgE antibody-binding properties.

Sequence similarity searches have enabled the protein families to which allergens belong to be ascertained and their biologic function to be identified. The major tree pollen allergens (e.g. Bet v 1) are related to pathogenesis resistance proteins; many mite allergens are proteolytic enzymes (cysteine and serine proteases, trypsin and chymotrypsin); and muscle proteins such as tropomyosin and troponin have been identified as allergens in mites, insects and shellfish (**Table 3**).

Recently, a new family of proteins has been identified that causes IgE antibody responses – ligand-binding proteins or calycins. These proteins bind small hydrophobic molecules such as pigments and pheromones. Calycins were first identified as a result of cloning cockroach allergens and the family also includes the major rodent urinary proteins, milk allergen β-lactoglobulin, and dog, bovine and equine allergens. It has been postulated that because many allergens, particularly from dust mites, are proteolytic enzymes, that this facilitates penetration through mucosal surfaces and induction of IgE antibody responses. There is also evidence that Der p 1 may upregulate IgE synthesis through its ability to cleave CD23, the low affinity receptor for IgE. However, several clinically important allergens have no enzymatic activity and there are other allergens which show no sequence homology to known proteins and whose function is as yet unknown (e.g. mite group 5 allergens) (Table 3).

Expression and biologic activity of recombinant allergens

Traditional methods of allergy diagnosis and treatment have relied on the use of heterogeneous allergen extracts. The problems with these extracts are that the absolute potency is difficult to define and some patients give adverse reactions when the extracts are injected (during immunotherapy), which can be life threatening. While there has been significant progress in the standardization of allergen extracts; the use of purified recombinant allergens expressed in bacteria, yeast or insect cells offers the prospect of using defined proteins for both diagnosis and treatment. An increasing number of recombinant allergens have been produced and it is possible to investigate whether cocktails of 3–4 allergens would be suitable for clinical purposes. Typical vectors in which allergens have been expressed include pGEX and pET (in *Escherichia coli*); pSAY-1 and *Pichia pastoris* (yeast), and the baculovirus system, giving yields of 1–10 mg l^{-1}. The allergens can be obtained with a high degree of purity and, in many cases, have excellent immunoreactivity on skin testing and in serum IgE antibody assays. Several recombinant allergens from mite (Der p 2, Blo t 5, Der p 5), aspergillus (Asp f 1), cockroach (Bla g 4, Bla g 5) and grasses (Phl p 1, Phl p 5) have been shown to have good biologic activity on skin testing, and elicit positive wheal and flare reactions using picogram doses of protein.

Molecular modeling and tertiary structure

Recombinant allergens are essential for providing sufficient quantities of highly purified protein for structural studies. It is also possible to manipulate allergen sequences and to produce partial constructs for investigation of functional or immunologic activity. Using site-directed mutagenesis, it has been possible to generate site-specific variants of Der p 2 that have reduced binding for IgE antibodies. These experiments allow B cell epitopes to be localized and can also be applied to investigate functional domains of the allergen, for example, the active sites of enzyme activity or the ligand-binding regions.

The homology between allergens and other protein families can be used to generate molecular models of the tertiary allergen structure. Two recent examples involve mite allergen Der p 1, whose structure has been modeled on the cysteine protease, papain, and cockroach allergen, Bla g 4, which has been modeled on other calycin structures for which X-ray crystal coordinates were known (**Figure 1**). The X-ray crystal structures of several allergens have been determined, including mouse and rat urinary proteins (Mus m 1 and Rat n 1), ragweed Amb a 5, and chironomid hemoglobin.

Immune response

Allergic individuals make IgG, IgA and IgE antibodies to allergens in both serum and nasal secretions. It is not uncommon to find asymptomatic individuals with positive skin tests and allergen-specific serum IgE antibody; however, most 'nonallergic' individuals do not make IgE antibody responses. The levels of IgG antibody in nonallergic individuals are usually lower than in allergic

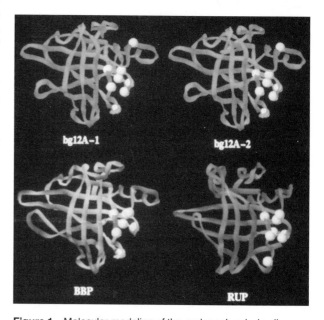

Figure 1   Molecular modeling of the cockroach calycin allergen, Bla g 4. The Cα backbone structures for two models of Bla g 4 (designated bg12A-1 and bg12A-2) were modeled on the X-ray crystal coordinates for butterfly bilin-binding protein (BBP) and are compared with rat urinary protein allergen (RUP), for which the X-ray crystal structure has also been determined. The conserved amino acid residue spheres form motifs which define the ligand-binding proteins, or calycins. (See also color **Plate 7**.)

patients and there is also evidence to suggest that the affinity for these IgG antibodies is lower. In hayfever patients, IgE antibodies to pollen allergens can account for a significant proportion (>20%) of the total IgE. IgE antibody responses to food allergens develop within the first few months of life, whereas antibody responses to inhaled allergens develop over the first 2–3 years of infancy. IgG antibody levels rise (up to 50-fold) in patients being treated by immunotherapy using aqueous allergen extracts. A rise in IgG antibody correlates with clinical efficacy in patients with insect venom allergy, but is not significantly associated with clinical improvement with inhaled allergens.

Recent work has focused on the role of T cells in regulating allergen-specific IgE responses. Proliferative T cell responses can be demonstrated *in vitro* using peripheral blood from allergic patients, and T cell clones specific for mite, pollen and cat allergens have been obtained. Assessing T cell responses to allergens is difficult because many patients, even with high antibody levels, make weak or inconsistent T cell responses. For these reasons, studies have often focused on small numbers of highly selected patients and there are few large population studies. T cell clones derived from allergic individuals have a predominantly T_H2 phenotype and secrete interleukin 2 (IL-2), IL-4 and IL-5. T cell clones have also been obtained from nonallergic individuals and these are T_H1 cells secreting interferon γ (IFNγ). Epitope mapping studies with Der p 1, Der p 2, Fel d 1 and Bet v 1, and other allergens, suggest that most allergens have multiple T cell epitopes, which are not HLA restricted, i.e. 'promiscuous' epitopes. In some cases immunodominant T cell sites have been identified, e.g. two 27 amino acid peptides on Fel d 1, chain 1.

There is also good evidence that allergen-specific T cells have inflammatory effects *in vivo*. Patch tests with purified mite allergens result in the recruitment of basophils, eosinophils and mononuclear cells into the skin of atopic dermatitis and the production of eczematous lesions at 48 h. The frequency of allergen-reactive T cells in the skin of these lesions is higher than in the peripheral blood. Allergen challenge in the lung also results in recruitment of inflammatory cells and is thought to be in part T cell mediated.

Now that the amino acid sequences of many allergens are known, strategies are being developed for new forms of allergen immunotherapy involving T cell epitopes and specifically designed molecules which no longer bind IgE. The key advan-

tage of these approaches is that the peptides can be synthesized, and any alterations in allergen structure can be clearly defined. One approach has been to immunize cat allergic patients with two immunodominant T cell epitopes of Fel d 1, with the aim of occupying the T cell receptor binding site without delivering the costimulatory signals that are necessary for IgE production. The cat vaccine is now undergoing clinical trials and early results show clinical improvements in treated patients, particularly at high peptide doses. Another approach is to design allergen vaccines containing a cocktail of recombinant allergens or variants which have been modified by mutagenesis so that they have markedly reduced binding to IgE. The rationale here is to deliver a broad spectrum of T cell epitopes and to reduce the possibility for IgE mediated side-effects.

Clinical significance

Allergic diseases such as hayfever, asthma and atopic dermatitis affect 10–20% of the population. Asthma is the most common chronic disease of children in Western countries and the prevalence of the disease has been increasing. Over the past 5–10 years, the clinical significance of allergens in causing asthma has become firmly established and there is now overwhelming evidence that sensitization to allergens is the single most important risk factor for the development of asthma. Asthma management has relied heavily on the use of bronchodilator and anti-inflammatory drugs (inhaled or oral steroids). In addition, greater emphasis on the role of indoor allergens in causing the disease has focused attention on the need to reduce allergen exposure in houses. Measuring allergen exposure in houses using monoclonal antibody based ELISA tests has established levels at which patients become sensitized (typically exposures of 1–2 μg allergen per gram dust) and at which they are likely to develop asthma exacerbations (>10 μg g⁻¹). Allergen avoidance studies carried out at high altitude or in hospital rooms have shown that reducing allergen exposure to <1 μg g⁻¹ can reduce bronchial hyperreactivity and improve asthma symptoms. Studies are now being designed to assess whether allergen avoidance protocols can be developed for routine use and whether early allergen avoidance procedures (in the first 3 years of life) will reduce the prevalence of asthma.

See also: **Antigens; Asthma; Atopic allergy; Enzyme-linked immunosorbent assay (ELISA); Epitopes; Food allergy; Hypersensitivity reactions; Immunoas-**

says; Monoclonal antibodies (mAbs); T cell vaccination.

Further reading

Arruda LK, Vailes LD, Hayden ML, Benjamin DC and Chapman MD (1995) Cloning of cockroach allergen, Bla g 4, identifies ligand binding proteins (or calycins) as a cause of IgE antibody responses. *Journal of Biological Chemistry* 270: 31196–31201.

Kapsenberg ML, Wierenga EA, Bos JD and Jensen HM (1991) Functional subsets of allergen-reactive human CD4+ T cells. *Immunology Today* 12: 392–395.

King TP, Hoffman D, Lowenstein H, Marsh DG, Platts-Mills TAE and Thomas WR (1994) Allergen nomenclature. *International Archives of Allergy and Applied Immunology* 105: 224–233.

Kraft D and Sehon A (1993) *Molecular Biology and Immunology of Allergens*. Boca Raton: CRC Press.

Marsh DG (1975) Allergens and the genetics of allergy. In: Sela M (ed) *The Antigens*, vol III, p 217. New York: Academic Press.

O'Hehir RE, Garman RD, Greenstein JL and Lamb JR (1991) The specificity and regulation of T-cell responsiveness to allergens. *Annual Review of Immunology* 9: 67–95.

Platts-Mills TAE (1982) Type I or immediate hypersensitivity: hayfever and asthma. In: Lachmann PJ and Peters DK (eds) *Clinical Aspects of Immunology*, 4th edn, vol. 1, pp 579–686. Oxford: Blackwell Scientific.

Scheiner O and Kraft D (1995) Basic and practical aspects of recombinant allergens. *Allergy* 50: 384–391.

Sporik RB, Chapman MD and Platts-Mills TAE (1992) House dust mites as a cause of asthma. *Clinical Experimental Allergy* 22: 897–906.

Thomas WR (1997) Molecular analysis of house dust mite allergens. In: Roberts AM and Walker MR (eds) *Molecular Analysis of IgE Mediated Hypersensitivity and Strategies for Immunologic Intervention*, pp 77–98. Chichester: John Wiley.

ALLOANTIGENS

Dhirendra N Misra, Heinz W Kunz and **Thomas J Gill III**, Department of Pathology, University of Pittsburgh, Pittsburgh, Pennsylvania, USA

Molecules expressed on biologically active cells include structural components, enzymes, receptors, transport system molecules, viral proteins and accessory molecules. Many of them carry unique determinants that can elicit xenogeneic and/or allogeneic immune responses. Alloantigens play crucial roles in the body's defense mechanisms and are of importance in the clinic with respect to blood transfusion and tissue or organ transplantation. Recent advances in serological and molecular biological techniques and in X-ray crystallographic structural analysis have increased our ability to identify and characterize new cell surface antigens and to understand their structure and function.

Alloantigenic polymorphism can arise in several ways: first, sequence variation in structural genes (e.g. major histocompatibility complex (MHC) antigens, Rh blood group antigens); second, variation in the activity of enzymes involved in the synthesis of antigenic epitopes (e.g. ABH or Lewis blood group carbohydrate determinants); third, sequence variation in regulatory elements controlling the expression of structural genes (e.g. expressed versus null alleles as for H2-T antigens in the mouse).

Alloantigenic responses also can occur in several ways: 1) alloimmunization; 2) natural immunization (e.g. naturally occurring antibodies against ABH antigens); and 3) the maternal immune response against fetal antigens during pregnancy (e.g. antibodies against human MHC antigens). Some major alloantigenic systems are described in the following section and summarized in **Table 1**.

Major alloantigenic systems

Blood group antigens

Hundreds of blood group antigens have been identified by red blood cell serology. The well-known major blood group alloantigenic systems (ABO(H), Rh) are very important from a clinical standpoint. The minor blood group systems (e.g. Lewis, MNS, Lutheran, Kell, Duffy, Kidd, P, I) also are clinically significant, but less so. The Rh system is one of the most polymorphic antigen systems known, as it comprises at least 50 antigens, all of which are encoded by alleles at either of two loci, D or CcEe; the D antigens are the most immunogenic of all the red blood cell antigens. The MNS system is also highly

Table 1 Major alloantigenic systems with their basic functions and clinical significance

1. *Blood group antigens*
   Major systems: ABO(H), Rh
   Minor systems: Lewis, MNS, Lutheran, Kell, Duffy, Kidd
   Functional and clinical significance: blood transfusion, tissue or organ transplantation, hemolytic diseases and inflammatory responses

2. *Histocompatibility antigens*
   A. Major Histocompatibility antigens (MHC)
      (a) Classical
         Class I: Human HLA-A, B, C
                     Mouse H2-K, D, L
                     Rat RT1.A, F, E
         Class II: Human HLA-DP, DQ, DR
                     Mouse H2-A, E
                     Rat RT1.H, B, D
      Functional and clinical significance: presentation of antigenic peptides to T cells; association with susceptibility to a number of diseases; tissue and organ transplantation

      (b) Nonclassical:
         Class I: Human HLA-E, F, G, H, J, K, L; MIC (MHC class I chain related)
                     Mouse H2-Q, T, M
                     Rat RT1.C, K, G, O, N, M
         Class II: Human HLA-DMA, DMB
                     Mouse Ma, Mb_1, Mb_2
      Functional and clinical significance: presentation of specific antigenic peptides to T cells; DMA/DMB act as accessory molecules in antigen presentation by class II antigens.

      (c) MHC class III antigens
         Human: C2, factor B (Bf), C4A and C4B (complement proteins); TNFα, TNFβ (tumor necrosis factors); steroid 21-hydroxylase (CYP21); major 70 kDa stress protein Hsp70; and TAP (transporter of antigenic peptides)
         Mouse   C2, C4, Bf, Slp (sex-limited protein), 21-hydroxylase (21-OH), Hsp70 and TNFα, TNFβ
         Rat   C2, C4, Bf, Hsp70, Cyp21, TAP, TNFα
      Functional and clinical significance: complement functions; transport of antigenic peptides; chaperones in antigen processing and presentation

      (d) MHC-like antigens encoded by genes residing outside the MHC
         Class I-like
            Human, mouse, rat: FcRn
            Human, mouse, rat: CD1
            Human: Zinc $α_2$-glycoprotein (ZAG)
      Functional and clinical significance: FcRn binds IgG from ingested milk from mother and transfers it across intestinal cells to the bloodstream; CD1 predominantly presents nonpeptide lipid and glycolipid antigens to T cells: and ZAG has no known physiological function

   B. Minor histocompatibility antigens
      (a) Sex-specific: H-Y (mouse, rat, human)
      (b) Many tissue-specific antigens in all species
      (c) Mls endogenous superantigens
         Mouse: Mls-1[a], Mls-2[a], Mls-3[a]
      Functional and clinical significance: slow tissue rejection, mixed lymphocyte stimulation

3. *Differentiation antigens (CD)*
   In excess of 100 clusters have been identified in humans
   Functional and clinical significance: Involved in cellular interactions.

complex, comprising two closely linked homologous genes GYPA and GYPB, that encode for at least 38 antigens. Recent studies at the molecular level indicate that a variety of genetic mechanisms gives rise to this complexity. So far, Rh antigens have been detected only on red blood cells, but the ABO(H), Lewis, P and I antigens are widely distributed throughout the body. Recent data suggest functional roles for blood group antigens unrelated to erythrocytes: cell adhesion, association with diseases, tumor markers and receptors for parasites, bacteria and viruses.

Major histocompatibility complex antigens

There is extensive allelism of genes within the MHC: their numbers vary from a few in the miniature swine to hundreds in the African pigmy mouse. The MHC-encoded classical class I (class Ia) and class II molecules bind peptides derived from endogenous or exogenous self proteins as well as nonself proteins from viruses, bacteria, multicellular parasite and many types of tumors. They present these peptides to mature CD8[+] and CD4[+] subsets of αβ T cells, respectively, for subsequent generation of specific cytotoxic/suppressor or helper/inducer T cells. Within a population, the classical MHC molecules are highly polymorphic: for example, in the human, at least 20 HLA-A, 45 HLA-B and 14 HLA-C class I antigens are known to date. A similar degree of polymorphism exists for class II antigens.

Besides the classical MHC genes, there are a large number of MHC genes with limited polymorphism and restricted tissue distribution of their products. The nonclassical antigens (class Ib) RT1.K and HLA-G are the only MHC antigens expressed, respectively, in rat and human placental trophoblasts. In the mouse, the Qa-2 molecules are restriction elements for a wide variety of nonameric peptides with restrictive binding motif. For example, Qa-1 binds peptides derived from heat shock proteins. Some H2-T antigens present peptides to γδ T cells, and the H2-M3 antigen presents peptides from intracellular pathogens such as *Listeria monocytogenes* and from allelic variants of a mitochondrial enzyme specifically containing *N*-formylated methionine, a unique structural component of prokaryotic mitochondrial proteins.

Recently, a second MHC class I-related oligomorphic gene family, MIC, has been detected in the human (near HLA-B), goat, pig, dog and hamster. This family appears to have evolved independently from other class I genes, since its gene sequences are quite divergent. No functions are known but their structure suggests antigen presenting capability.

There are also class I-like molecules encoded by genes residing outside the MHC and on different chromosomes. 1) Neonatal Fc receptor (FcRn) first detected in rats and more recently in mice and humans, is involved in the acquisition of passive humoral immunity in young mammals during the first few weeks after birth. FcRn binds immunoglobulin G (IgG) from ingested mother's milk and transports it through gut epithelial cells into the bloodstream by transcytosis. 2) CD1 is a small multigene family, so far detected in several mammals including the mouse, rat and human. These antigens do not show significant polymorphism. CD1 proteins present nonpeptide lipid (mycolic acid) or glycolipid antigens from intracellular mycobacteria such as *Mycobacterium leprae* and *M. tuberculosis* to CD8[+] αβ T, CD4[-]CD8[-] αβ T or γδ T cells or T cells within epithelial sheets. 3) Zinc α2-glycoprotein, a zinc-precipitable protein of human plasma, is another oligomorphic MHC-unlinked

class I protein. No physiological role for this protein is known.

Unlike the nonclassical class I MHC genes, only a few nonclassical class II MHC genes have been reported. Human HLA-DMA and HLA-DMB and the murine homologs Ma, Mb1 and Mb2 are examples. The human genes encode a heterodimer, DMA/DMB, which is not a cell surface molecule but is associated with class II antigens in the endosomal compartment. There is evidence that it helps peptide presentation by conventional class II molecules.

Minor histocompatibility antigens

A large number of minor histocompatibility antigens which contribute to the slow rejection of grafts has been detected. For example, the sex-specific antigen H-Y in males may cause rejection of male organs or bone marrow grafts by MHC-identical female recipients. The epitope of the H-Y antigen has been mapped to an 11-residue peptide located near one end of the protein encoded by the conserved Y-chromosome gene SMCY, which is homologous to the SMCX gene on the X chromosome. Identical results have been reported for the mouse H-Y antigen.

Mls and superantigens

Mls, or minor lymphocyte-stimulating, antigens represent another class of alloantigens that are recognized by T cells *in vitro*. They are encoded by endogenous mouse mammary tumor virus genes (Mls-1[a], Mls-2[a] and Mls-3[a]) and they elicit a strong primary mixed lymphocyte reaction (MLR) between cells derived from mice sharing the same MHC haplotype. Subsequently, similar antigens, known as superantigens (SAgs), have been found which include exogenous products of gram-positive bacteria (toxins), retroviruses and mycoplasma. These antigens are presented to CD4[+] T cells by class II molecules in association not with the peptide-binding groove but with an external face.

Immunoglobulin allotypes

Allotypic variants of immunoglobulin light chains and heavy chains exist in different species, and they arise due to allelic variation in the constant region genes. In humans, for example, the IgE isotype has two alleles, and the IgG3 isotype has as many as 14 alleles. Allotypes are useful in population studies, paternity testing and forensic science. Variation in the expression of certain allotypes may be related to disease susceptibilities. For example, the IgG2 isotype is associated with immune responses to certain bacteria, and lack of the Km1 or G2m(n) allotypes increases the risk of *Haemophilus influenzae* and *Meningococcus C* infections. Disease susceptibility due to interactive effects between Gm allotypes and HLA antigens has also been reported

Differentiation antigens

Leukocyte differentiation antigens provide markers for different lymphoid cell types, define cell lineages and mediate crucial leukocyte-specific functions. From serological, biochemical, structural and functional homologies, many of the antigens have been grouped into clusters of differentiation (CD), and some CD genes are polymorphic or oligomorphic, while others are monomorphic.

The CD antigen clusters are involved in numerous functions. Some examples are given below.

Accessory functions:

1. Interaction with MHC antigens leading to T cell activation: CD3 associates with $\alpha\beta$ TCR on CD4$^+$ and CD8$^+$ T cells, and the complex binds to MHC antigens along with antigenic peptides.
2. Activation of T cells requires a second signal that is delivered by the interaction of CD80(B-7)/CD28 and B cells via CD40/CD40-ligand molecules.
3. Signal transduction: Thy 1 (CDw90) is a signal transduction molecule that plays a role in T cell activation through the TCR/CD3 complex. CD19 and CD21 are involved in signal transduction in B cell activation.
4. Cell adhesion (integrins and their ligands): involves cell–cell or cell–tissue interactions during microbial infections, inflammation, tumor formation, metastasis and neural development. For example, the antigen-presenting cells (APC) and CD4$^+$ T cells are brought into close contact by interaction between LFA-1(CD11a/CD18) antigen on the T cells with its ligands ICAM-1 and ICAM-2 on the APC and also by interaction between LFA-3 (CD58) and its counterpart CD2 on the T cells.

Markers for different cell types: T cells (CD3), MHC class II-restricted T cells (CD4), MHC class I-restricted T cells (CD8), activated T and B cells (CD95), B cell lineage (CD19, CD20) and granulocytes (CD66).

Receptors for soluble molecules: Interleukins (CD25, CD121 through CDw130); Fc portion of IgG (CD16: Fcγ RIII; CD32: Fcγ RII; CD64: Fcγ RI) or IgE (CD23) and complement C3d (CD21).

Viral receptors: Human immunodeficiency virus (CD4); and Epstein–Barr virus (CD21 on B cells).

Enzymatic activity: CD10, CD13, CD26 (dipeptidylpeptidase IV); CD45 (phosphotyrosine phosphatase) and CD73 (ecto-5'nucleotidase).

Ion channels: CD20 forms ion channels and functions during receptor-mediated events.

Disease associations and clinical use: A few examples: defective CD43 expression on T cells with X-chromosome-linked Wiskott–Aldrich syndrome; some minor GPI (glycosyl-phosphatidylinositol)-anchored antigens (e.g. CD55, CD58, CD59) are deficient on the red blood cells from patients with paroxysmal nocturnal hemoglobinuria (PNH). Anti-CD19 antibodies are used to treat leukemias and lymphoma and anti-CD3 antibodies to treat renal, hepatic and cardiac allograft rejection.

Biochemistry and molecular biology of alloantigens

The majority of alloantigens are glycoproteins (e.g. MHC, MNS antigens), and the others are sialoglycoproteins (e.g. CD43), oligosaccharides (ABO(H), Secretor, Lewis, Li and P), sialo-oligosaccharides (sialyl-Lewis^x or sialyl-Lewis^a) or proteins (Rh). Most cell surface protein antigens are anchored through transmembrane hydrophobic interactions, but there is an increasing number of structurally diverse cell surface antigens that are anchored by a covalent linkage through GPI: Thy-1 (CDw90), Ly-6, Qa-2, RT6, CD14, CD55, CD59, CD73. Some antigens (CD58 (LFA-3) and probably CD55) occur in two forms: one has a GPI anchor, and the other has a transmembrane anchor. The GPI-anchored proteins are active in transmembrane signaling; for example, the GPI anchor of Qa-2 is essential for T cell activation via this molecule. In addition, a large number of alloantigens belong to the immunoglobulin supergene family: for example, membrane-proximal domains of MHC polypeptides, CD1, CD2, CD3, CD4, CD7, CD8, Ly-6, Qa-2, RT6, CD19, CD22, CD56, CD58(LFA-3), CD59 and CDw90 (Thy 1).

Molecular cloning and sequencing of many alloantigen genes have revealed the basis of their polymorphism and provided some insight into their function, either directly or by analogy with sequences of previously known genes. Many of the blood group antigens have been expressed by transfection of cDNA into nonerythroid or nonhuman mammalian cells in order to study their functions. Also, recent

X-ray crystallography of a number of peptide–MHC antigen complexes and protein modeling have yielded detailed information about the structure–function relationships of the MHC antigens.

See also: **ABO blood group system; Allotypes, immunoglobin; Antigens, cell surface; H2 class I; H2 class II; H2 class III; HLA class I; HLA class II; HLA class III region; Antibodies, detection of; Minor transplantation (histocompatibility) antigens; Rh antigens; Superantigens; Thy-1.**

Further reading

Albelda SM, Smith CW and Ward PA (1994) Adhesion molecules and inflammatory injury. *FASEB Journal* 8: 504–512.

Beckman EM and Brenner MB (1995) MHC class I-like, class II-like and CD1 molecules: distinct roles in immunity. *Immunology Today* 16: 349–352.

Carlos TM and Harlan JM (1994) Leukocyte-endothelial adhesion molecules. *Blood* 84: 2068–2101.

Garratty G (1995) Blood group antigens as tumor markers, parasite/bacteria/viral receptors, and their association with immunologically important proteins. *Immunological Investigations* 24: 213–232.

Porcelli SA and Modlin RL (1995) CD1 and the expanding universe of T cell antigens. *Journal of Immunology* 155: 3709–3710.

Schanberg LE, Fleenor DE, Kurtzberg J, Haynes BF and Kaufman RE (1995) Isolation and characterization of the genomic human *CD7* gene: structural similarity with the murine *Thy-1* gene. *Proceedings of the National Academy of Sciences of the USA* 88: 603–607.

Schlossman SF, Boumsell L, Gilks W *et al* (eds) (1994) *Leukocyte Typing*, vol V. Oxford: Oxford University Press.

Shawar SM, Vyas JM, Rodgers JR and Rich RR (1994) Antigen presentation by major histocompatibility complex class I-B molecules. *Annual Review of Immunology* 12: 839–880.

Shevach EM (1993) Accessory molecules. In: Paul WE (ed) *Fundamental Immunology*, pp 531–575. New York: Raven Press.

Stroynowski I and Forman J (1995) Novel molecules related to MHC antigens. *Current Opinion in Immunology* 7: 97–102.

Tanner MJA and Anstee DJ (eds) (1993) Red cell membrane and red cell antigens. *Baillière's Clinical Haematology* 6(2).

Telan M (1995) Erythrocyte blood group antigens: not so simple after all. *Blood* 85: 299–306.

Wang W, Meadows LR, den Hann JMM *et al* (1995) Human H-Y: A male-specific histocompatibility antigen derived from SMCY protein. *Science* 269: 1588–1590.

ALLOTYPES, IMMUNOGLOBULIN

Royston Jefferis, Department of Immunology, The Medical School, University of Birmingham, Birmingham, UK

Allelism is the existence of two or more variants of a given gene in an outbred population. Allelism within the immune system was first recognized for genes encoding immunoglobulin (Ig) molecules, through the antigenic properties of their protein products, i.e. antibody molecules. The extent of allelism at the Ig loci has resulted in the application of Ig phenotyping to paternity testing, forensic science, bone marrow transplantation, etc. Allelism and allotypy may be evident in its most diverse form within the major histocompatibility loci, where the phenotype of an individual may constitute immunological self-identity.

Nomenclature

In 1976 the World Health Organization (WHO) sponsored an expert committee meeting at which the nomenclature for human immunoglobulin allotypes was systematized and a logical numerical system was proposed to replace the apparently illogical alphameric system that had evolved. However, many expert laboratories continue to use the alphameric system since reference can be made to original publications in which the allotypes were defined. Both systems may therefore be encountered in current literature. The allotype of an Ig molecule is recognized by the expression of a unique epitope (allotope) and is designated by a capital letter representing the heavy-chain isotype or light-chain type with a small m standing for marker, viz: Gm, Am, Em, Km. Further, where appropriate the subclass of the protein is shown by the inclusion of the appropriate numeral. Thus, G1m(f) refers to genetic marker or allotope f expressed on molecules of the IgG1 subclass; G2m(n) to allotope n expressed on molecules of subclass IgG2, etc. The human Ig allotypes currently recognized are summarized in **Table 1** and those of mouse

Table 1 Human immunoglobulin allotypes

	Heavy chains						Light chain
Isotype/type	IgG1	IgG2	IgG3	IgG4	IgA	IgE	κ
Allotypes	G1m	G2m	G3m	G4m	A2m	Em	Km(Inv)
	a(1)	n(23)	g1(21),g5(28)	4a(1)	1	1	1
	x(2)		b0(11),b1(5)	4b(1)	2		2
	f(3)		b3(13),b4(14)				3
	z(17)		b5(10),s(15)				
			t(16),c3(6)				
			c5(24),u(26)				
			v(27)				

NB: Numeric notation given within brackets.

and rabbit in **Table 2**. The genes encoding the allotypic products are identified using the italicized form of the epitope nomenclature and the alphameric or numeric identity as a superscript, e.g. $G1m^a$, Km^1, etc.

Serological reagents that identify the products of some allelic genes may not be available, presumably because the resultant protein structure is not immunogenic, in humans. An example is IgG2 proteins for which reagents are available that identify a G2m(n) allotype and allow IgG2 paraproteins to be

Table 2 Mouse and rabbit immunoglobulin allotypes

Isotype/type	Allotypes
Mouse	
κ	None identified
λ	None identified
Heavy	
G1	4[a,c,d,e,f,g,h]; 4[b].
G2a	1[a], 1[b], 1[c], 1[d], 1[e], 1[f],1[g], 1[h]
G2b	3[a,c,h], 3[b], 3[d], 3[e], 3[f], 3[g]
G3	None identified
A	2[a,h], 2[b], 2[c,g], 2[d,e], 2[f]
D	5[a], 5[b]
M	6[a], 6[b]
Rabbit	
κ	b4, b5, b6, b9
λ	c7, c21
Heavy	
V_H	a1, a2, a3
	x32, x-
	y33, y-
C_μ	n81, n82
C_α	f71, f72, f73
	g74, g75
C_γ	d11, d12
	e14, e15

designated G2m(n$^+$) or G2m(n$^-$); a reagent is not available that specifically recognizes G2m(n$^-$) molecules.

Some reagents define isoallotypic epitopes; these epitopes are expressed on the product of a gene that is allelic for a given Ig subclass but are also expressed on the products of the other subclass genes. An example is a reagent recognizing the nG1m(a) epitope; IgG1 proteins that are the product of the $G1m^a$ gene express the G1m(a) allotope whilst proteins that are products of the allelic gene express the non-G1m(a) or nG1m(a) epitope. However, proteins of the IgG2 and IgG3 isotype also express the nG1m(a) epitope. Such reagents allow the typing of homogeneous proteins, but cannot be applied to polyclonal IgG or whole serum analysis.

Haplotypes

All the allotypes presented in **Table 1** are expressed on immunoglobulin constant regions. Since the genes encoding the constant region of the heavy chains are closely linked within the IgG gene locus they are inherited together as haplotypes with a very low frequency of cross-overs. However, cross-over events have occurred during evolution, resulting in present populations expressing characteristic haplotypes, hence the usefulness of the allotype system in population studies. Thus in northern Europe (The Netherlands) the haplotype $G1m^f$; $G2m^n$; $G3m^b$ is present with a frequency of 0.45 and virtually all individuals are homozygous for the $A2m^1$ allele, however, amongst Nigerian Africans the $G1m^z$; $G2m^n$; $G3m^b$ haplotype occurs with a frequency of 0.678 (the $G1m^f$; $G2m^n$; $G3m^b$ haplotype not being encountered) and the $A2m^2$ allele with a frequency of 0.826.

The structural difference between alleles is frequently restricted to a single base change within a codon resulting in a conservative amino acid interchange; examples are lysine or arginine at residue 214 in IgG1 proteins correlating with the expression of G1m(z) and G1m(f) allotypes respectively and leucine or valine within κ light chains with the expression of the Km1,2 or Km3 allotopes. Similar minor structural differences are observed between allotypic variants of Ig constant region in the mouse, rat and rabbit.

Applications

The value of allotypes in population studies, paternity testing and forensic science will be apparent from the heterogeneity of haplotypes present within and between population groups (Table 3). The value in forensic science is emphasized by the sensitivity of assay systems and the stable expression of allotypes by immunoglobulin present in aged, dried blood samples. A more recent application is in bone marrow transplantation where allotype disparities between the donor and recipient allow monitoring of the success of the transplantation protocol. Postoperative expression of donor allotypes, not expressed by the recipient B cells, is indicative of successful grafting. Allotype matching of human (humanized) monoclonal antibodies to recipients of *in vivo* immunotherapy may be important in minimizing immunogenicity and anti-idiotypic responses.

Disease associations

Immunoglobulin levels may also be associated with allotype and several studies have established that individuals homozygous for G2m(n) have higher IgG2 subclass levels than those homozygous for G2m(n⁻), heterozygotes having intermediate levels. Since protective immune responses to certain bacterial species are restricted to the IgG2 isotype, these findings may have implications for disease susceptibility. Such an effect has been reported for post-immunization levels of antibody to *Haemophilus influenzae* and *Meningococcus C* polysaccharides with individuals lacking the Km1 and G2m(n) allotype having an increased risk of infection. A more established finding is an interactive effect between Gm allotypes and HLA antigens on disease susceptibility. There is some evidence that antibody molecules of the same isotype but differing allotype may differ in their potential to activate effector mechanisms.

Detection

Although allotypes may be detected by a relatively simple hemagglutination system, it does employ a range of reagents that are only available from specialist hematology institutions such as national blood banking centers. Anti-allotype reagents are generally alloantibodies produced by apparently healthy blood donors and are induced to paternal allotype in multiparous women or to nonself allotypes in individuals receiving transfusions or undergoing deliberate immunization. The sample under review is assayed for inhibition of agglutination of human red blood cells coated with anti-Rh antibody of the appropriate allotype. Limited availability of these reagents has resulted in the development of some polyclonal reagents in heterologous species, but this is a generally difficult and unsatisfactory procedure.

The development of monoclonal antibodies has made assay systems widely available and allow new studies to confirm and extend the influence of Ig allotypy on immune responsiveness. Generally, these reagents show preferential reactivity with the target allotope, rather than exclusive specificity. They must be used with care in assay protocols defined by the originating laboratory.

See also: **Allelic exclusion; Antibodies, antigenicity of; Idiotype; Immunoglobulin genes; Immunoglobulin structure; Isotype.**

Further reading

Grubb R (1995) Advances in human immunoglobulin allotypes. *Experimental and Clinical Immunogenetics* 12: 191–197.

Grubb R (1995) Allotypes: perspectives and future directions. *Experimental and Clinical Immunogenetics* 12: 217–221.

Gutman GA (1996) Rat immunoglobulins. In: Herzenberg LA, Weir DM, Herzenberg LA and Blackwell C (eds) *Handbook of Experimental Immunology.* 23.1–23.11, 5th edn, Oxford: Blackwell Science.

Table 3 Gm haplotypes characteristic for a Race

G1m;G2m;G3m			Whites	Blacks	Orientals
f	; n	; b	+	−	−
f	; ..	; b	+	−	−
za	; ..	; g	+	−	+
zax	; ..	; g	+	−	+
za	; ..	; b	−	+	−
za	; ..	;c3c5	−	+	−
za	; ..	; c3	−	+	−
za	; ..	; s	−	+	−
za	; ..	; st	−	−	+
af	; n	; b	−	−	+

With permission of GG de Lange, personal communication.

Lange GG de (1989) Polymorphism of human immuno-globulins: Gm, Am, Em and Km. *Experimental and Clinical Immunogenetics* 6: 7–17.

Roux KH and Mage RG (1996) Rabbit immunoglobulin allotypes. In: Herzeberg LA, Weir DM, Herzenberg LA and Blackwell C (eds) *Handbook of Experimental Immunology*. 26.1–26.17, 5th edn, Oxford: Blackwell Science.

Stall AM (1996) Mouse immunoglobulin allotypes. In: Herzenberg LA, Weir DM, Herzenberg LA and Blackwell C (eds) *Handbook of Experimental Immunology*. 27.1–27.16, 5th edn, Oxford: Blackwell Science.

WHO (1976) Review of the notation for allotypic and related markers of human immunoglobulins. *European Journal of Immunology* 6: 599.

AMEBIASIS

John P Ackers, Department of Medical Parasitology, London School of Hygiene and Tropical Medicine, London, UK

The World Health Organization definition of amebiasis describes it as 'infection with *Entamoeba histolytica*, with or without clinical symptoms'. It has long been known that at least 90% of patients with amebiasis will be asymptomatic cyst passers but only recently appreciated that these cases are caused by a separate species of ameba, now usually referred to as *Entamoeba dispar*; it is generally felt that about 450 million people carry this organism without either pathology or an immune response. At least 50 million new cases of infection with *E. histolytica sensu stricto* are thought to occur each year; the proportion of those infected who show clinical symptoms at any one time is hotly debated but everyone agrees that all are at risk. The remainder of this entry will deal exclusively with *E. histolytica* in its new sense – previously described as the 'pathogenic zymodeme'. Methods of distinguishing it from *E. dispar* (they are morphologically identical) are only slowly coming into use and this must be borne in mind when reading any but the most recent literature.

Characteristics of the organism and its antigens

E. histolytica is a protozoan parasite that lives in the large bowel (probably mostly adhering to the mucosa) as an ameboid and phagocytic trophozoite dividing by binary fission. Responding to unknown stimuli, trophozoites may develop into resistant cysts which are shed in the feces and, by being ingested orally, are responsible for parasite transmission. Pathology occurs when trophozoites penetrate the mucosa causing ulceration and bloody diarrhea (amebic dysentery, AD); less frequently dissemination to the liver takes place with, ultimately, extensive tissue destruction (hepatic amebiasis or amebic liver abscess, ALA). ALA is about seven times less common than AD, and dissemination to other sites (brain, skin, etc.) is rarer still, but together these conditions cause much morbidity and 40–100 000 deaths a year, mainly in developing countries. Dissemination is aided by a formidable array of cytotoxic and cytolytic activities, most of which seem to have homologs in *E. dispar*; the specific factors which account for the invasive potential of *E. histolytica* have not yet been identified.

Western blots probed with patients' sera reveal a large number of immunogenic molecules, of which the best characterized are: the galactose/N-acetyl-D-galactosamine inhibitable lectin (GIL), a 260 kDa heterodimeric molecule involved in binding to and killing enterocytes; SREHP, a phosphorylated and glycosylated serine-rich membrane protein; a 29 kDa cysteine-rich protein (CRP) which may be involved in protection against oxygen toxicity; a 125 kDa variable surface antigen; additional 112 and 220 kDa molecules also capable of mediating adhesion; and a number of proteases.

Immune responses of the host

Antibody

Using sensitive tests, specific serum antibody may be detected in virtually all persons infected with *E. histolytica*, whether they have symptoms or not, although levels are significantly higher in those with ALA. Principally immunoglobulin G (IgG), and to a lesser extent IgA, are represented; IgM declines fairly rapidly while specific IgG remains elevated for months or years, reducing the diagnostic value of serology in endemic areas. In one study levels of specific IgG4 >> IgG2 > IgG3 > IgG1 were found. Coproantibodies have been detected in the feces of AD patients, and specific secretory IgA in the saliva and colostrum of those with ALA. Autoantibodies (directed against liver, colon, neutrophils and IgG) and circulating immune complexes have been described in patients but there is no real evidence for immunopathology in human amebiasis.

Cell-mediated responses

On histological examination neither the ulcers of AD nor the hepatic abscesses of ALA show much evidence of cellular infiltration and granuloma formation; one exception to this is the ameboma, a rarely found mass of granulation tissue in the colonic lumen. In small animal models intense inflammatory changes occur early in the development of lesions but whether this occurs in human amebiasis is not known. After recovery, most ALA patients are skin-test positive but appear to be specifically unresponsive to E. histolytica antigens earlier on.

Most studies have shown that normal human leukocytes of all sorts are harmless to and are killed by E. histolytica trophozoites. ALA patients' CD8+ cells became cytotoxic after incubation with soluble amebic antigen, phytohemagglutinin or GIL. More importantly, antigenic stimulation results in the production of cytokines (interferon γ (IFNγ) seems to be the most important) which activate macrophages to kill trophozoites. E. histolytica is powerfully chemotactic for neutrophils, which are rapidly killed by a contact-mediated, GIL-dependent process; lytic enzymes liberated from these dead cells may be responsible for much of the tissue destruction seen in amebiasis. IFNγ and tumor necrosis factor α (TNFα)-activated neutrophils can kill trophozoites and N-formylmethionine leucyl phenylalanine (fMLP)-activated eosinophils can do so even more effectively, although, again, normal cells are killed by contact with E. histolytica.

Role of complement

It seems inevitable that E. histolytica must reach the liver via the portal circulation and therefore obvious that it must survive the journey. Reed and her colleagues showed that while all E. dispar isolates (and old, laboratory-adapted E. histolytica isolates in axenic culture) were lysed, freshly isolated strains of E. histolytica in xenic culture were apparently largely resistant to complement activated by the alternative pathway. This fact alone could have been enough to explain the noninvasiveness of E. dispar. At least two resistance mechanisms have been postulated – cleavage of C3 by the parasite's own cysteine protease and one involving yet another function for GIL – the molecule shares sequence similarities and antigenic cross-

reactivity with the complement regulatory protein CD59 and inhibits E. histolytica lysis mediated by C5b–9. However, Hamelmann and coworkers have obtained quite different results – non-pathogenic isolates (i.e. E. dispar) were nearly unaffected; freshly isolated pathogenic strains (i.e. E. histolytica) were susceptible to lysis and became more so on long-term cultivation, with or without bacteria. Complement resistance could only be acquired by hamster liver passage or by growth in media containing increasing concentrations of normal human serum. The results of the two groups are incompatible and the differences need to be resolved before the role of complement in amebiasis can be assessed.

Animal models

There are currently no realistic small animal models of human amebiasis; in all cases trophozoites must be injected directly into cecum or liver. Mice, with the exception of SCID animals, are almost completely resistant and the large literature is concerned with the in vitro effects of murine macrophages. These cells (like their human counterparts) can be activated for killing by IFNγ and TNFα; the process appears to be nitric oxide mediated and TNFα increases the expression of nitric oxide synthase. The preferred model of ALA involves intrahepatic challenge of gerbils or hamsters (see below, Vaccines) where treatments which suppress cell-mediated immunity seem to enhance abscess formation.

Evasion strategies by the organism

These obviously exist, since amebic liver abscesses can enlarge relentlessly in the presence of high levels of circulating antibody, but their nature is not fully understood. Surrounded by necrotic tissue the parasite may not be exposed to the full concentration of serum antibody, and that which does bind is capped and shed very rapidly. Host cell-mediated responses are probably delayed and blunted by a number of mechanisms: antigen processing cells and effector cells are often killed on contact with the parasite; a monocyte (but not polymorph) locomotion inhibitory factor is produced which will minimize infiltration; and patient serum contains a factor that suppresses the production of activating cytokines by T cells – this may be the same as the parasite T cell mitogen which has recently been identified with GIL. Animal experiments have shown that macrophages from gerbil liver abscesses are deficient in the generation of reactive oxygen species, unresponsive to lymphokines and not cytotoxic (cells treated with E. histolytica extract in vitro showed much the same defects) while parasite proteins suppress the IFNγ-induced expression of major histocompatibility complex (MHC) class II molecules by murine macrophages. All this suggests that host immune responses need to be suppressed to permit long-term parasite survival and so it is surprising that, while the severity of amebiasis is markedly increased in pregnancy or by corticosteroid treatment, there is virtually no evidence for such a phenomenon in patients with the acquired immune deficiency syndrome.

Vaccines

Vaccine developers always like to see solid immunity following the natural infection, but only one study has produced evidence of this for ALA and there is none from AD patients. Considerable success has been achieved in protecting small animals against challenge, but the artificiality of the models (see above) should be remembered when assessing how close we are to a human vaccine. Gerbils have been protected against intrahepatic challenge by CRP, by GIL (as have rats) and a recombinant fragment thereof, and by recombinant SREHP; and SCID mice by passively transferred anti-SREHP. The same antigen administered orally with cholera toxin has produced high levels of sIgA in mice and primates (but these animals cannot be realistically challenged) and the SREHP gene has been expressed in a *Salmonella typhimurium* vaccine strain. Progress is being made but there is still a long way to go.

See also: **Cell-mediated immunity; Gastrointestinal tract infections; Parasites, immunity to.**

Further reading

Denis M and Chadee K (1988) Immunopathology of *Entamoeba histolytica* infections. *Parasitology Today* 4: 247–252.

Hamelmann C, Urban B, Foerster B and Horstmann RD (1993) Complement resistance of pathogenic *Entamoeba histolytica* mediated by trypsin-sensitive surface component(s). *Infection and Immunity* 61: 1636–1640.

Kretschmer RR and López-Osuna M (1990) Effector mechanisms and immunity to amebas. In: Kretschmer RR (ed) *Amebiasis: Infection and Disease by* Entamoeba histolytica, pp 105–122. Boca Raton: CRC Press.

Lotter H, Zhang TH, Seydel KB *et al* (1997) Identification of an epitope on the Entamoeba histolytica 170-kD lectin conferring antibody-mediated protection against invasive amebiasis. *Journal of Experimental Medicine* 185: 1793–1801.

Mann BJ and Petri WA Jr (1991) Cell surface proteins of *Entamoeba histolytica. Parasitology Today* 7: 173–176.

McCoy JJ, Mann BJ and Petri WA Jr (1994) Adherence and cytotoxicity of *Entamoeba histolytica* or how lectins let parasites stick around. *Infection and Immunity* 62: 3045–3050.

Ravdin JI (1995) Amebiasis. *Clinical Infectious Diseases* 20: 1453–1466.

Reed SL (1995) New concepts regarding the pathogenesis of amebiasis. *Clinical Infectious Diseases* 21: S182–S185.

Salata RA and Ravdin JI (1986) Review of human immune mechanisms directed against *Entamoeba histolytica. Reviews of Infectious Diseases* 8: 261–272.

Stanley SL (1997) Progress towards development of a vaccine for amebiasis. *Clinical Microbiology Reviews,* 10: 637.

AMPHIBIAN IMMUNE SYSTEM

Jacques Charlemagne, Groupe d'Immunologie Comparée, Université Pierre et Marie Curie, Paris, France

Annick Tournefier, Laboratoire d'Immunologie Comparée, Université de Bourgogne, Dijon, France

Living amphibians are the descendants of the first tetrapod vertebrates that diverged from their lungfish-like ancestors in the Devonian period, about 450 million years ago. Urodela (newts, salamanders), Anura (toads, frogs) and Gymnophiona (limbless coecilians) are the three orders of the Lissamphibia infraclass and they actually represent about 4000 species. From their key position in vertebrate evolution, amphibians are important models for the developmental and comparative analysis of the immune system. Two species are currently studied: the New World urodele *Ambystoma mexicanum* (axolotl, a neotenic species) and the African anuran *Xenopus laevis* (South African toad, or clawed toad).

Lymphoid organs and lymphocytes

The amphibian thymus anlagen arise from the dorsal epithelium of the second (anuran), or third, fourth and fifth (urodeles) pharyngeal pouches. In *Xenopus*, the thymus buds are rapidly colonized by hematopoietic precursors, and by day 6–8 the cortex–medulla architecture becomes visible. The larval thymus involutes during metamorphosis, but efficient regeneration occurs in the metamorphosed froglet. The thymus then regresses at the time of sexual maturity. In axolotl the thymic anlagen appear at the time of hatching, 3 weeks after fertilization. The thymus buds are invaded by hematopoietic precursors 12 days after hatching, and the thymus develops slowly up to sexual maturity (about 12 months), and then regresses. The urodele thymus shows no cortex–medulla differentiation. The axolotl and *Xenopus* thymus contains most of the cell types that constitute the stroma of mammalian thymus, such as macrophages, nurse-like cells, cortical large dendritic cells and different types of epithelial cells.

The spleen appears about 12–14 days following fertilization in *Xenopus* and the mature spleen has a clear-cut red and white pulp, but no structures reminiscent of the avian and mammalian germinal centers. The axolotl spleen anlagen appear at the time of hatching (about 3 weeks after fertilization). Although some red/white pulp-like organization can be seen macroscopically, there is no follicular-like structure and no germinal centers. In urodeles and anurans, the hematopoietic peripheral layer of the liver supports B cell lymphopoiesis and granulocytopoiesis.

Immunoglobulin M (IgM)-producing cells can be observed along the digestive tract in axolotl, and IgM-, IgX- but no IgY-producing cells are present in the digestive tract of *Xenopus*. The anuran kidneys contain B lymphocytes, and can retain antigens in the intertubular tissue. Amphibians possess B cells and T-like cells in the blood and in *Xenopus* these cells can collaborate *in vitro* in a major histocompatibility complex (MHC)-restricted manner for the production of antibodies to T cell dependent antigens.

B Cells can be recognized in axolotl and *Xenopus* by monoclonal antibodies (mAbs) specific for the different heavy (H) and light (L) Ig chain isotypes. More difficult was the production of mAbs specific for T cells. In the axolotl, mAb 34.38.6 labels all thymocytes, 60–63% of sIg⁻ splenic lymphocytes, hematopoietic stem cells, granulocytes and macrophages of normal animals, but only 9% of splenic lymphocytes from thymectomized animals. A polyclonal antibody (L12) coprecipitates several (38, 43 and 22 kDa)

covalently linked molecules that form a multimeric complex on the axolotl T cell surface.

A membrane glycoprotein (120 kDa), which may be a CD8 equivalent, has been identified on *Xenopus* J strain T cells using mAbs XT-1 and AM22 which recognize *Xenopus* cortical thymocytes and a subpopulation of peripheral T cells. mAb AM15 recognizes a 18 kDa protein on a subpopulation of *Xenopus* T cells. Two mAbs (anti-CTX: 1S9-2 and X71) stain a subpopulation (65–80%) of *Xenopus* cortical thymocytes which are also labeled by mAb AM22 (anti-CD8-like), and thus could be the *Xenopus* equivalent of the avian and mammalian cortical DP thymocytes.

In tadpoles and adult *Xenopus*, the use of classical mitogenic agents, such as lipopolysaccharide (LPS), phytohemagglutinin (PHA), concanavalin A (Con A) and purified protein derivative (PPD), stimulate *in vitro* proliferation of B cells and T cells with the same responses that are seen in mammals. The PHA and mixed leukocyte responses are sensitive to thymectomy. Furthermore, a T cell growth factor similar to interleukin 2 (IL-2) is produced by stimulated T lymphocytes.

The axolotl has a population of B lymphocytes that proliferate in the presence of LPS at all steps of ontogenesis. The splenic T cells from adult, but not from young axolotls, proliferate significantly in response to PHA and Con A. Axolotl lymphocytes are also stimulated *in vitro* by the enterotoxins A and B from *Staphylococcus aureus*.

Lymphocyte antigen-specific receptors

T cell receptors (TCRs)

No antibodies have yet been produced against TCR-equivalent molecules in amphibians and the present knowledge regarding these molecules comes from recombinant DNA studies. Genes encoding the α and β chains of the axolotl TCR have been cloned. Five Vα and 14 Jα segments have been identified, and the structure of the CDRα3 loops is in good agreement with that of mammals. The Cα domain has the typical structure of mammalian and avian Cαs, including the charged residues in the transmembrane segment that are thought to interact with other proteins in the membrane.

Fourteen Vβ families have been identified in the axolotl and several Vβ are sequence-related to the human Vβ13 and Vβ20 segments and to their murine Vβ8 and Vβ14 homologs. Four Cβ isotypes have been detected, Cβ1, Cβ2 and Cβ3 show a high degree of identity, but the Cβ4 is divergent (43–48% identity with Cβ1-3). The transmembrane axolotl Cβ domain maintains the lysine residue which is thought to be involved in the charged interaction between the TCRαβ heterodimer and the CD3 complex. Specific Jβ segments are associated with each Cβ isotype and 4 Dβ-like sequences have been identified, suggesting that the axolotl TCRβ locus may be organized into at least four independent (Dβ–Jβ–Cβ) clusters that use the same collection of Vβ segments.

The Vβ segments in *Xenopus* are organized into nine independent families, each containing one, or a few, members. Eight Jβ segments and two Dβ core segments have been detected, with probably a single Cβ.

B cell receptors (BCRs)

Two high molecular weight (IgM and IgX) and one low molecular weight (IgY) Ig classes have been characterized in *Xenopus*. The three heavy (H) chain isotypes can associate with 25, 27 and 29 kDa light (L) chains but almost no Cν (IgY) chain is associated with the 27 kDa L chains.

The genes encoding *Xenopus* Hμ, Hν and Hχ chains and the three L chain (ρ, σ and type III-λ-like) isotypes have been recently cloned. The Cμ region is well related to other vertebrate Cμ, and the Cν region of the IgY molecule is structurally related to avian Cν and mammalian Cε. The Cχ region is not clearly phylogenetically related to any other vertebrate isotype. Switch regions are found 5′ to the Cν and Cχ genes and a DNA switch recombination event leads to the expression of Cχ. Eleven V_H families, about 15 D_H segments and 9 J_H segments have been detected in the *Xenopus* IgH locus. The V, D and J elements can rearrange randomly, and junctional diversity arises at the V–D and D–J junctions, with the possible occurrence of random nucleotide deletion (nibbling) and template (P) or non-template (N) nucleotide addition.

The *Xenopus* Lρ chains are homologous to the mammalian Lκ chains. One Cρ and five Jρ elements that rearrange randomly with several members of a single Vρ family have been detected. The Lλ (also called type III) chains are built from at least six Vλ families, two Jλ and two Cλ segments; this is the most diverse *Xenopus* L chain isotype. The Lσ chains consist of two (Cσ1 and Cσ2) isotypes and two (Vσ1 and Vσ2) families that rearrange with their own set of Jσ1 and Jσ2 elements.

High molecular weight (IgM) and low molecular weight (IgY) Ig classes are present in the axolotl. No B cells double stain with anti-μ and anti-ν mAbs, suggesting that Bμ and Bν cells might represent independent B cell lineages. The axolotl Cμ and Cν are closely related to their *Xenopus* counterparts and additional cysteines in Cν1 and Cν2 domains are consistent with an additional intradomain S—S

bond similar to the avian Cν and the human Cε. Eleven V_H families, six J_H and two D_H segments have been identified and the same collection of V_H segments is used by IgM and IgY molecules. However, it is not known whether, as found in *Xenopus*, an IgM to IgY switch occurs in individual B cells.

Major histocompatibility complex (MHC)

The *Xenopus* MHC is a single genetic region encoding classical class Ia and class II molecules. A distinct chromosome harbors nine subfamilies of nonclassical class Ib genes. *Xenopus* has a single classical class Ia locus, and a single polymorphic class Ia molecule per MHC haplotype is expressed in all *Xenopus* species, regardless of the ploidy. They display three class II β genes, with a pattern of nucleotide substitutions in the β1 distal domain essentially similar to that found in functional mammalian class II genes.

Classical class Ia genes have also been characterized in the axolotl and show a strong structural homology with *Xenopus* class Ia genes. However, axolotls display 10–12 class Ia genes detected by Southern blot. Class II genes are not yet characterized.

The tissue distribution of MHC class I and class II molecules in the adult amphibian is somewhat similar to that seen in mammals: class Ia are ubiquitously expressed in all tissues except brain and gonads and class II are expressed by B lymphocytes and T lymphocytes. Class I molecules are not expressed in *Xenopus* before metamorphosis, but can be detected as soon as hatching in the axolotl.

The *Xenopus* MHC genetic region encoding class I and class II molecules directs rapid graft rejection, mixed lymphocyte reaction (MLR) and T–B collaboration. T cells interact with antigen-presenting cells similarly to mammals, and the *in vitro* secondary proliferative response is MHC restricted.

Immunobiology of T and B cells

Thymectomy in *Xenopus* either decreases or abolishes allograft rejection, MLR, PHA responsiveness, IgY antibody synthesis and antibody responses to thymus-dependent antigens. It does not abolish *in vivo* or *in vitro* responses to thymus-independent antigens or B cell polyclonal activation (LPS). *In vitro* assays using purified T and B cells from carrier- or hapten-primed *Xenopus* of various MHC types indicate that T cell help is involved in the differentiation of thymus-dependent antigen-primed B cells and that T–B collaboration is MHC restricted. IgM is produced first following antigenic stimulation, and then is produced in conjunction with IgY. A second injection generates a significantly stronger (×10–100), mainly IgY, secondary response. Although somatic mutation occurs in *Xenopus* V_H segments at almost the same frequency found in mammals, these mutations may not be properly selected, perhaps because of the absence of germinal centers in the lymphoid organs.

Larval thymectomy suppresses allograft rejection in urodeles, but does not abolish *in vivo* responses to certain thymus-dependent antigens, such as sheep or horse erythrocytes. Larval and adult thymectomy, low dose (50–150 rads; 0.5–1.5 Gy) irradiation and hydrocortisone treatment enhance specific antibody synthesis against erythrocyte antigens. These observations suggest that T cell help is impaired in urodeles, but that some kind of T cell-dependent suppression acts on antibody production. Urodeles can be immunized against particulate but not against soluble antigens, and in normal and thymectomized axolotls IgM is the single antigen-sensitive Ig class, specific IgY is not produced. The kinetics of the antibody response is slow and there is no occurrence of a typical secondary response following hyperimmunization. Thus, although the *Xenopus* and axolotl IgY molecules are clearly homologous at the molecular level, their respective physiological functions are different: IgY are IgG-like (thymus dependent, sensitive to thymectomy) in anurans, but IgA-like in axolotl, at least in the first 7–8 months of development; most IgY are found associated with the digestive epithelium and are secreted into the gut lumen following transepithelial transport in association with secretory component-like molecules.

Ontogeny of the immune response

Xenopus tadpoles develop allorecognition (graft rejection, MLR) from about 12 days after fertilization, but the capacity to reject or to tolerate grafts depends on genetic background (minor non-MHC, or MHC differences) and on the balance of several parameters, such as the size of the grafts, age of tadpoles and breeding conditions. Metamorphosis is a crucial period when a high frequency of allogeneic grafts can be tolerated and this seems to be an active phenomenon, as thymectomy before metamorphosis decreases the level of tolerance. MLR and the splenic response to T cell mitogens are depressed at metamorphosis, but recover in the young froglet. This might be correlated to the transient decline in the number of lymphocytes at the time of metamorphosis, and could be a means by which the metamorphosing tadpole is able to remain unreactive to the numerous new self antigens that appear during

the metamorphosis climax, and an opportunity for the young froglet to build a new repertoire of self tolerant T cells.

The anti-DNP antibody spectrotypes are different and less heterogeneous in *Xenopus* tadpoles compared with adults, suggesting that pre- and postmetamorphosed *Xenopus* express different antibody repertoires. B cells can first be detected in the liver at 3–4 days; a second wave of B cell production possibly arises after metamorphosis, accounting for the detection of two successive antibody repertoires. Sequential rearrangement of V_H genes occurs from day 5 in developing tadpoles, all the J_H and D_H elements are randomly expressed at early larval stages, and the production of specific antibodies arises at about 10 days. Most antibodies are IgM; switching to IgY seems not to be efficient before metamorphosis, although Igs of the three classes are present in tadpole serum.

Urodele development is much slower than anuran, and lymphoid organs begin to develop at the time of hatching, 2–3 weeks after fertilization. *Ambystoma tigrinum* (tiger salamander) larvae begin to reject allografts at about 40 days following fertilization and seem to be fully competent for rejection at 100 days. Thymectomy efficiently suppresses allograft rejection when performed at 50–60 days. Clusters of IgM- and IgY-producing B cells are first seen in the spleen of 70-day-old axolotls, 30 days after differentiation of the spleen anlagen. IgM is first detected in the serum at 90 days (4% of the adult value) and its concentration linearly increases until 13 months. IgY is first detected at 7 months (5% of the adult value) and its concentration increases rapidly until 11 months. However, abundant secretory IgY molecules are present in the stomach and intestinal mucosa of young axolotls from day 50, and until the 7th month. IgY then progressively disappears from the gut but becomes detectable in the serum.

Tumors of the immune system

Several spontaneous thymus lymphoid tumors have been detected in the *Xenopus* colony by Louis Du Pasquier at the Basel Institute for Immunology. The first one (MAR1) was from a 4-year-old *Xenopus* of the ff strain and was transplantable in isogenic ff tadpoles and froglets, but not in fully adult animals. *In vitro* cell lines were derived from MAR1 (e.g. B3B7). Three other tumors were found, one from the ff strain (ff-2), and two from the LG15 strain (LG15/0 and LG15/40). All these tumors are sIg⁻, and MHC class I molecules are not expressed on the surface of B3B7, 15/0 and 15/40, but are present (with β_2-microglobulin) on the surface of ff-2 cells. All the lines are labeled by mAbs X21.2 (thymocytes), AM22 (CD8 equivalent), and B3B7, ff-2 and 15/40 express large quantities of the CTX antigen which is thought to be a marker of the cortical DP lymphocytes. In the B3B7 line, the two alleles of the IgH locus are rearranged in frame (but are not transcribed), the two alleles of the IgLρ locus seem to be deleted, and the two alleles of the IgLσ locus are rearranged – one is out of frame and the second uses a Vσ pseudogene. These *Xenopus* lymphoid cell lines resemble some rare types of mammalian leukaemia and represent very useful tools for the analysis of lymphoid cell differentiation and Ig and TCR gene expression.

See also: **Immunoglobulin, evolution of; MHC, evolution of; Phylogeny of the immune response; T cell receptor, evolution of.**

Further reading

Blomberg B, Bernard CCA and Du Pasquier L (1980) *In vitro* evidence for T–B lymphocyte collaboration in the clawed toad, *Xenopus*. *European Journal of Immunology* 10: 869–876.

Charlemagne J (1981) Suppressor T cells and antibody synthesis in the X-irradiated Mexican axolotl. *European Journal of Immunology* 11: 717–721.

Charlemagne J and Tournefier A (1997) Immunology of amphibians. In: Pastoret PP, Bazin H, Griebel P and Govaerts H (eds) *Handbook of Vertebrate Immunology*. London: Academic Press (in press).

Du Pasquier L, Schwager J and Flajnik MF (1989) The immune system of *Xenopus*. *Annual Review of Immunology* 7: 251–275.

Du Pasquier L, Courtet M and Robert J (1995) A *Xenopus* lymphoid tumor cell line with complete Ig genes rearrangements and T-cell characteristics. *Molecular Immunology* 32: 523–593.

Fellah JS, Iscaki S, Vaerman JP and Charlemagne J (1992) Transient developmental expression of IgY and secretory component-like protein in the gut of the axolotl (*Ambystoma mexicanum*). *Developmental Immunology* 2: 181–190.

Fellah JS, Kerfourn F, Guillet F and Charlemagne J (1993) Conserved structure of amphibian T-cell antigen receptor β chain. *Proceedings of the National Academy of Sciences of the USA* 90: 6811–6814.

Flajnik MF and Du Pasquier L (1990) The major histocompatibility complex of frogs. *Immunological Reviews* 113: 47–63.

Flajnik MF, Hsu E, Kaufman JF and Du Pasquier L (1987) Changes in the immune system during metamorphosis of *Xenopus*. *Immunology Today* 8: 58–64.

Flajnik MF, Camel C, Kramer J and Kasahara M (1990) Evolution of the major histocompatibility complex: molecular cloning of MHC class I from the amphibian *Xenopus*. *Proceedings of the National Academy of Sciences of the USA*. 78: 537–541.

Salvadori F and Tournefier A (1996) Activation by mitogens and superantigens of axolotl lymphocytes; functional characteristics and ontogenic study. *Immunology* 88: 586–592.

Sammut B, Laurens V and Tournefier A (1997) Isolation of classical class I cDNAs from the axolotl, *Ambystoma mexicanum*. *Immunogenetics* 45: 285–294.

Sato K, Flajnik MF, Du Pasquier L, Katagiri M and Kasahara M (1993) Evolution of the MHC: isolation of class II β-chain cDNA clones from the amphibian *Xenopus laevis*. *Journal of Immunology* 150: 2831–2843.

Shum BP, Avila D, Du Pasquier L, Kasahara M and Flajnik MF (1993) Isolation of a classical MHC class I cDNA from an amphibian. Evidence for only one class I locus in the *Xenopus* MHC. *Journal of Immunology* 151: 5376–5386.

Tournefier A, Fellah JS and Charlemagne J (1988) Monoclonal antibodies to axolotl immunoglobulins specific for different heavy chains isotypes expressed by independent lymphocyte subpopulations. *Immunology Letters* 18: 145–148.

Tournefier A, Guillet F, Ardavin C and Charlemagne J (1988) Surface markers of axolotl lymphocytes as defined by monoclonal antibodies. *Immunology* 63: 269–276.

AMYLOID

Alan S Cohen, Amyloid Program, Boston University School of Medicine, Boston, USA

Although a waxy tissue deposit was observed in pathologic laboratories in the early eighteenth century, it was Rudolph Virchow in 1854 who called these 'lardaceous deposits' of the liver and spleen amyloid, when he found them to stain with iodine and sulfuric acid. This belief that the material was made up of carbohydrates (i.e. cellulose) was challenged, and the proteinaceous nature of the substance was generally accepted by the turn of the century. Most amyloid was thought to be related to chronic infections (tuberculosis, osteomyelitis) and subsequently to chronic inflammation (rheumatoid arthritis) and the term secondary or reactive amyloid has persisted in the clinical literature. In 1886, it was noted that amyloid could appear *de novo* and the then unusual clinical form named primary or idiopathic amyloid was discovered. The association of amyloid with aging, especially in the brain and heart, was long known, but regarded as incidental epiphenomena until recent years. Finally in 1952, in Portugal, a hereditary amyloid polyneuropathy was described, and has led to a growing literature of multiple kinships of hereditary amyloid.

Definition

Amyloidosis is now regarded as a generalized deposit of the protein amyloid extracellularly throughout parenchymal tissue (liver, spleen, kidney, adrenal), blood vessels, and heart. Virtually any tissue or organ may be involved, and in some cases the deposition is localized to a single area. The amyloid itself is an eosinophilic hyalin material, which after Congo red staining demonstrates green birefringence on polarization microscopy. Electron microscopy has shown amyloid to have a fibrillar ultrastructure and by X-ray diffraction it has a classical cross-β (β pleated sheet) appearance. It has generally been classified clinically as 1) Secondary (reactive) amyloidosis; 2) primary (idiopathic) amyloidosis; 3) amyloid associated with multiple myeloma (now known to have the same chemical characteristics as primary amyloid); 4) hereditary or familial amyloidosis; 5) amyloid associated with endocrine organs; 6) amyloid associated with aging (brain or heart); 7) amyloid associated with chronic hemodialysis; and finally 8) localized amyloid (**Table 1**). In the past few years,

Table 1 Simplified classification of amyloid

Clinical aspects	Protein or variant or precursor	Amyloid nomenclature
1. Secondary (reactive) Familial Mediterranean fever	apoSAA (precursor)	AA
2. Primary (idiopathic) Multiple myeloma associated	κ or λ chains	AL
3. Familial amyloid polyneuropathy	Transthyretin variant prototype Met 30 (multiple mutations)	ATTR
	Apolipoprotein A variant Arg 26 (multiple mutations)	AApoAI
	Gelsolin Asn 15	AGel
Familial amyloid cardiopathy	Transthyretin Met 111	ATTR
Senile cardiomyopathy	Transthyretin Ile 122	ATTR

4.   Alzheimer disease
      Down syndrome
      Dutch hereditary cerebral hemorrhage with
         amyloid
	β protein from amyloid β protein precursor	Aβ

5. Chronic hemodialysis	β2 microglobulin	AB$_2$M
6. Adult onset (type II) diabetes mellitus	Islet amyloid polypeptide (IAPP) (amylin)	AIAPP
7. Medullary carcinoma of thyroid	Procalcitonin	ACalc
8. Icelandic hereditary cerebral hemorrhage with amyloid	Cystatin C (trace γ) Gln 68	ACyst
9. Isolated amyloid of the heart (atrium)	Atrial natiuretic factor	AANF
10. Creutzfeldt-Jacob disease	Prion protein (scrapie protein)	APγP

it has been demonstrated that while all amyloid has common physical characteristics, biochemically there are multiple proteins, unique for each clinical form of amyloid listed above, and that a variety of proteins with specific point mutations are found in the hereditary dominant forms of the disorder.

Pathogenesis

AA

Secondary amyloid consists of the protein AA (amyloid A) an 8.5 kDa protein that is heterogeneous (at the amino terminal end). It is putatively derived by proteolysis from the normal circulating protein apoSAA (serum amyloid A related protein) which has a molecular weight of 12 kDa. apoSAA is an apolipoprotein associated with high density lipoprotein (HDL) especially HDL_3 and acts as a very sensitive acute phase protein. SAA is polymorphic in mice (four genes and two pseudogenes have been identified) and in man (three genes have been identified). In man SAA_1 isotype appears to be the major contributor to AA while in mice SAA_2 isotype is the sole contributor.

AL

Idiopathic (primary amyloid) and that associated with multiple myeloma consists of whole or partially degraded immunoglobulin light chains (i.e. whole or part of the V_L domain, with a molecular weight of 8–23 kDa). These fragments derived from the amino terminal region are more predominantly λ than κ chains. It has been deduced that some λ structures make the light chain fragments more likely to polymerize as amyloid. Indeed, λ VI was first discovered as an amyloid protein. The identical fragment that constitutes the amyloid deposit may be found in the serum or urine as a monoclonal spike. Cases of heavy chain amyloid have been described.

ATTR

In the prototypic Portuguese (autosomal dominant) familial amyloid polyneuropathy, transthyretin (prealbumin) variants have been found to constitute the amyloid. This molecule circulates as a 55 kDa tetramer composed of 4 identical 127 amino acid monomers. This molecule is a carrier of thyroxine and of retinol binding protein. It also acts as a negative acute phase reactant. It is determined by one gene located on chromosome 18. The most common abnormality is the substitution of methionine for valine at position 30 in families of Portuguese, Swedish,

Japanese, Italian, and Greek origin. Substitutions in the families with other phenotypic expression occur at over 50 other positions. Several different mutations may be present at one position (i.e. 30, 33, 35, 45, 47, 50, 58, 84). Hereditary amyloid composed of variant apolipoprotein A1, of the proteins gelsolin, fibrinogen Aα, lysozyme and of β protein have also been described, each in a different clinical syndrome.

AP

Other substances are associated with amyloid. Amyloid P component (AP) has been identified in all forms of amyloid as a molecule independent of the amyloid fibril but nonetheless intimately bound to it. AP is a glycoprotein of molecular weight 22 kDa in its monomeric form. It circulates as SAP (serum amyloid P component), a pentraxin composed of two pentameric units. SAP acts as an acute phase reactant in mice, but is clearly a constitutive protein in humans. Its role in amyloidogenesis is unclear. Do its ligand binding properties make it a focus for fibril deposition or is it an epiphenomenon? Glycosaminoglycans are also intimately associated with amyloid deposits.

AEF

Amyloid enhancing factor (AEF) has been extensively studied in animals and dramatically shortens the induction time for experimental AA deposition in mice. It appears to be a monokine produced by macrophages when stimulated by inflammation. Whether it plays a more pervasive role is yet to be determined.

AB2M

Other forms of amyloid exist. In chronic long-term hemodialysis, patients often develop a carpal tunnel syndrome, arthritis and cystic bone lesions, all due to amyloid. The protein isolated has been β2 microglobulin, a single chain low molecular weight (11.8 kDa) polypeptide that is continually shed from all membranes. It does not pass through most dialysis membranes and in chronic hemodialysis its concentration may rise 50-fold. The specific local factors influencing its precipitation as amyloid are not yet known.

Aβ

It has long been known that the senile plaques of Alzheimer disease stain positively for amyloid. The amyloid fibrils of the senile plaque and cerebral amyloid angiopathy from both Alzheimer disease and Down syndrome have been isolated and identified as β protein (also known as A4 protein), a 4.2 kDa protein (39 amino acid segment isolated from vessels; 43 amino acid segment from plaques). The 28 N-terminal amino acids are almost identical in the senile plaques and vessel. Beta protein is derived from a 695 amino acid glycoprotein of 79 kDa (β amyloid protein precursor AβPP) that crosses and constitutes part of the cell membrane. The precise cause of the cleavage of the AβPP is not known, but aberrant degradation involving serine protease inhibitors such as α1 antichymotrypsin (ACT) which is regularly found in plaques has been suggested.

See also: **Acute phase proteins; Bence Jones proteins; β₂-microglobulin; Lymphoma.**

Further reading

Benson MD (1995) Amyloidosis. In: Scriver CR, Beaudet AL, Sly WS, Valle, D (eds), *The Metabolic Basis of Inherited Disease*, 7th edn, pp 4159–4191. New York: McGraw-Hill.

Cohen AS (1967) Amyloidosis. *New England Journal Medicine* 277: 522–530; 574–583; 628–638.

Cohen AS (1986) General introduction and a brief history of amyloidosis. In: Marrink J, van Rijswijk M (eds), *Amyloidosis*, pp 3–19. Dordrecht, Netherlands: Martinus Nijhoff.

Cohen AS (1995) Amyloidosis. In: Beutler E, Lichtman MA, Coller BS and Kipps, T-J (eds), *Hematology*, 5th edn, pp 1137–1146. New York: McGraw-Hill.

Kyle RA, Baird ED (1975) Amyloidosis: review of 236 cases. *Medicine* 54: 271–298.

ANAPHYLATOXINS

Clemens A Dahinden, Institute of Immunology and Allergology Inselspital, Bern, Switzerland

The term anaphylatoxin stems from the observation, originally made by Friedberger in 1910, that injection of complement-activated serum in small experimental animals, such as guinea pigs, results in an anaphylactoid reaction similar to the symptoms of an acute hypersensitivity shock which occurs after exposure of sensitized animals to the antigen. This acute, potentially lethal, reaction was found to be due to small bioactive fragments, termed anaphylatoxins to describe the functional behavior of these humoral factors. Some of the effects of systemic administration of anaphylatoxins are due to the release of bioactive cell-derived mediators as in hypersensitivity reactions, but the lethal effect is rather related to the potent spasmogenic activity of the anaphylatoxins causing respiratory failure due to acute bronchiolar constriction. It is unlikely that in humans anaphylatoxins have such dramatic effects, although they certainly contribute to the pathogenesis of, for example, septic shock and the acute respiratory distress syndrome (ARDS) in synergy with other proinflammatory factors, such as lipopolysaccharide (LPS) and tumor necrosis factor (TNF). Indeed, high levels of C3a can be detected *in vivo* under these clinical conditions.

Mainly based on their activity on the isolated guinea pig ileum, the anaphylatoxins C3a, C4a and C5a have been isolated from complement-activated serum and their amino acid sequence was determined many years ago. A large number of more recent functional studies, and the characterization of anaphylatoxin receptors, however, clearly established that the anaphylatoxins are typical chemotactic cell agonists. They act in a very similar fashion to other chemotactic agonists, such as the bacterial leader sequence analogue *N*-formyl-met-leu-phe, the cell-derived lipid mediators leukotriene B₄ and platelet-activating factor, and the very large group of cell-derived chemotactic cytokines, the chemokines. All these agonists act on cells mainly of hematopoietic origin, by interaction with specific, pertussis toxin-sensitive, Gᵢ-coupled seven-transmembrane (serpentine) receptors, and they activate the cells by utilizing very similar signal transduction pathways leading to similar cellular functions. Based on sequence homologies and the similarity in function, the receptors for all chemotactic agonists, including the receptors for anaphylatoxins, constitute a subfamily of the rhodopsin receptor superfamily. It is important to note that, despite this redundancy, the anaphylatoxins are the only well-characterized endogenous humoral inflammatory mediators among this large group of chemotactic leukocyte agonists.

Generation of anaphylatoxins

The anaphylatoxins C3a, C4a and C5a are formed by specific cleavage of a single Arg–X bond in the α chains of C3, C4 and C5, respectively, through the corresponding convertase. The C3, C4 and C5 convertases are formed during complement activation by the classical pathway, the lectin pathway and (C3 and C5 convertases only) the alternative pathway. Thus, by the generation of bioactive activation products, the complement cascade connects recognition systems of the innate and adaptive immune system with effector systems for host defense. A major consequence of the anaphylatoxins generated locally due to tissue injury, infection or immunoglobulin–antigen complexes is to promote an inflammatory reaction. This inflammatory response is primarily due to the capacity of the anaphylatoxins to induce the release of cell-derived vasoactive mediators and to directly attract and activate inflammatory effector cells. C3a and C5a may also be generated without complement activation by certain proteases of the host or from pathogens (e.g. mast cell tryptase and a cysteine proteinase from *Bacteroides gingivalis*, cleaving C3 and C5, respectively).

The C-terminal arginine of the anaphylatoxins is rapidly cleaved by serum carboxypeptidase N, resulting in peptides with negligible (C3a$_{desarg}$, C4a$_{desarg}$) or altered (C5a$_{desarg}$) bioactivity. Thus, the radius and duration of action of C3a is rather short, while the major stable soluble bioactive product of complement activation is C5a$_{desarg}$. C5a$_{desarg}$ retains sufficient affinity for the C5a receptor to be cleared from the circulation or from inflammatory exudates by receptor-mediated endocytosis. C3a$_{desarg}$ and C4a$_{desarg}$, however, can be detected in bodily fluids, and assay systems to monitor the levels of these anaphylatoxins have been developed as an efficient and sensitive way to assess complement activation *in vivo*. Because of the central role of C3 in all the complement pathways, C3a is a general parameter of complement activation, while C4a has been regarded as a specific marker for the activation of the classical pathway by immune complexes. The recent discovery of the lectin pathway, which is initiated by recognition of certain carbohydrates on pathogens and which is homologous to the classical pathway, makes this assumption and the clinical utility of C4a measuresments less certain. The highest levels of anaphylatoxins are found in acute states such as ARDS, multisystem organ failure and sepsis, where anaphylatoxins may actually contribute to a potentially lethal outcome. However, more subtle changes in anaphylatoxins (C3a or C4a) have been described in a number of clinical patient studies in a variety of (primarily inflammatory) disorders. Complement is also activated by contact of plasma with artificial surfaces *in vivo* and well as *in vitro*. Thus, complement activation *ex vivo* must be carefully monitored when collecting blood samples. Furthermore, significant complement activation occurs during extracorporeal blood treatment by cardiopulmonary bypass surgery and dialysis, probably contributing to side-effects and complications of these procedures. Progress in decreasing complement activation by artificial surfaces has allowed an increase in the biocompatibility of such membranes.

Structure of anaphylatoxins

The complement fragments C3a, C4a and C5a released during complement activation are, in humans, 77–74 amino acid residues in length, and share, as their parent proteins C3, C4 and C5, significant homology in their primary sequence. They all have a core with three disulfide bridges. More importantly, crystallographic data of C3a and nuclear magnetic resonance (NMR) studies of C3a and C5a in solution showed that C3a and C5a have very similar secondary and tertiary structures. The first 63 residues of C5a in solution form an antiparallel bundle of four helices similar to the coiled-coil arrangement of helices in many other four-helix proteins, while the C-terminus is disordered. The helices I, II, and IV are quite regular and are compatible with an α-helical pitch. The N-terminal helix is amphiphilic and its hydrophobic residues are interdigitated with hydrophobic residues on helices II and IV. The structure of C5a seems to differ somewhat from the crystal structure of C3a, which shows a disordered N-terminus and a helical C-terminus, but NMR investigations of C3a in solution indicate that the terminal regions of both anaphylatoxins are similar.

Thus, based on similarities of bioactivity, of their receptors as well as of their structure, the anaphylatoxins must be regarded as a family of closely related molecules. Anaphylatoxins of other species are most likely very similar in structure as well. Furthermore, the bioactivity of C3a and C5a is not species restricted, as is the case for many cytokines. Human C5a has, however, some notable peculiarities. First, there is a N-terminal odd cysteine at position 27 in the loop connecting helix II with helix III, facing towards the solvent. It can be attached to molecules such as glutathione without effect on bioactivity, and it may covalently link to other proteins with a free accessible -SH group under an oxidative environment. Indeed, yet poorly defined high molecular weight chemotactic factors have been described in serum. Second, a bulky sugar moiety is attached in human C5a near the C-terminus which is of major importance in receptor activation. This glycosylation may be responsible in part for the fact that natural human C5a$_{desarg}$ is a potent chemoattractant but a very ineffective cell activator and spasmogen.

C3a and C4a receptors

It is still unclear whether C3a and C4a mediate their effects by common or separate receptors. Based on their activity and cross-desensitization on the guinea pig ileum contraction assay, C4a has been regarded as a weak C3a receptor agonist. This assumption requires confirmation on cells transfected with the C3a receptor. Other less conclusive data on guinea pig macrophages indicate that there may be separate receptors.

The C3a receptor could not be identified until recently, although C3a was isolated decades ago. Despite this lack of a defined cellular model, extensive investigations, mainly by T Hugli and coworkers in the heterologous guinea pig system, established the structure–function relationships of C3a analog peptides and identified the C-terminal pentapeptide as a full C3a receptor agonist. Further studies revealed that the C-terminal 21-residue fragment is nearly as potent as the complete anaphylatoxin, and, by attaching several hydrophobic residues to the N-terminus of a synthetic peptide based on the 12–13 residue C-terminal fragment of C3a, superagonists of even greater potency than the natural factor were obtained (**Figure 1**). Thus, the interaction of C3a with its receptor is clearly less complex than that of C5a and probably most other protein ligands of seven-transmembrane receptors.

The human C3a receptor has recently been cloned by two independent groups. It is a typical seven-transmembrane receptor of the chemotactic factor subfamily. As for other chemotaxin receptors, activation of the C3a receptor in transfected cells promotes a transient elevation of cytosolic calcium concentration by a pertussis sensitive G_i-coupled activation of phospholipase C. In contrast to other G protein-coupled receptors, the C3a receptor carries an unusually large second extracellular loop of over 160 amino acids of unknown function. Neglecting this loop, the C3a receptor is most closely related to the C5a and fMLP receptor, with 37% and 34% homology, respectively. The C3a receptor mRNA is widely expressed in peripheral blood lymphocytes, different lymphoid tissues as well as in different solid organs. The identification of the receptor for C3a will now permit better characterization of the role of this anaphylatoxin in homeostasis and host defense, and will aid in the development of specific antagonists.

C5a receptors

The C5a receptor was cloned independently by two groups several years ago, and was shown to be a G

Model C3a peptide

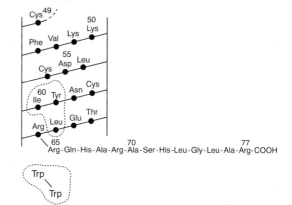

C3a/C3a 57-77 – Receptor interactions

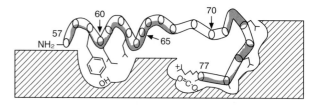

Model C3a peptide – receptor interactions

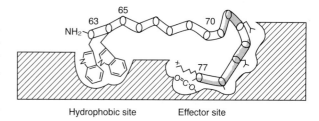

Hydrophobic site   Effector site

Figure 1 (Upper) The helical region of the C-terminal end of C3a is shown with the hydrophobic patch outlined (dashed line) including residues Tyr59, Ile60 and Leu63. This patch is believed to interact with a hydrophobic sub-binding site of the C3a receptor. The superpotent synthetic analog of C3a has two tryptophanyl residues substituted for the hydrophobic patch on the natural factor. The residues that are underlined are nonessential replacements that improve solubility of the analog. (Lower) The schematic model illustrates how the natural factor C3a and the synthetic analog C3a 57–77 interacts with the receptor. The hyopthesis is that the model Trp-containing superpotent peptide mimics C3a by interacting with the receptor in a similar manner. Interaction at the hydrophobic sub-binding site cooperatively enhances binding of the essential Leu-Gly-Leu-Ala-Arg effector site. If binding of Trp-Trp at the hydrophobic site is greater than the Tyr-Ile-Leu patch, it could explain the superpotency of the analog peptide.

protein coupled seven-transmembrane receptor of 350 residues in length with high (34%) homology to the fMLP receptor. This has allowed a detailed molecular characterization of ligand–receptor interaction using monoclonal antibodies and mutants of both C5a and its receptor. Furthermore, based on weak binding of the C-terminal octapeptide of C5a to the C5a receptor, several peptide analogs with reasonable affinity and agonistic, partial agonistic or antagonistic properties were developed. These studies led to a two-binding model of ligand–receptor interaction, as first proposed by MS Springer (**Figure 2**). One involves the core of C5a (with participation of Lys19 and Lys20) interacting with the extracellular N-terminus (in particular with several aspartic acid residues in this region), presumably resulting in a conformational change of C5a, which allows its C-terminus to interact with a second, ill-defined, binding site in a transmembrane segment. Using synthetic C5a hexapeptide analogs and mutant receptors, an interaction of the peptide C-terminal arginine with Arg206 in the fifth transmembrane helix of the receptor has been proposed as a mechanism to activate this second binding site. It should be noted, however, that $C5a_{desarg}$, which has no C-terminal arginine, is a potent chemoattractant, but is rather ineffective in activating many other cell functions, indicating that different types of ligand–receptor interactions exist which lead to distinct signaling events.

Bioactivity of anaphylatoxins

C3a

While most of the earlier investigations on C3a bioactivity dealt with its spasmogenic and vasoactive properties *in vivo* and in tissues of experimental animals, more recent studies revealed that the effect of C3a is not so much different from that of other chemotactic agonists. However, the target cell profile of C3a is more restricted than that of C5a. C3a induces calcium transients in all myeloid cells indicating wide expression of C3a receptors on leukocytes, although C3a has negligible effects on the function of monocytes and neutrophils. C3a is a chemoattractant and potent inducer of exocytosis for eosinophils. The efficacy of C3a in inducing the release of cytotoxic products is similar to that of C5a and clearly higher than that of chemokines, such as eotaxin. C3a also induces mediator release in cytokine-primed basophils and in mast cells from the skin but not from the lung, while the effects on mast cells from other sites (e.g. intestine, heart, uterus) are largely unknown. These data indicate that C3a may be important in allergic inflammation and other conditions involving mast cells, eosinophils and basophils. $C3a_{desarg}$ cannot activate the C3a receptor. High levels (around 10 μM) of $C3a_{desarg}$ seem to directly activate G proteins similar to other cationic peptides, such as mastoparan. The biological meaning of this effect is uncertain, although such high levels can theoretically be achieved *in vivo*.

C5a

C5a is a classical and most potent and effective chemoattractant and activator of effector functions of different leukocyte types, and, among the different chemotaxins, the effects are most similar to that of fMLP. Unlike chemokines, which have a more restricted target cell profile, C5a is rather pleiotropic and acts efficiently on neutrophils, monocytes, macrophages, eosinophils, basophils, dendritic cells

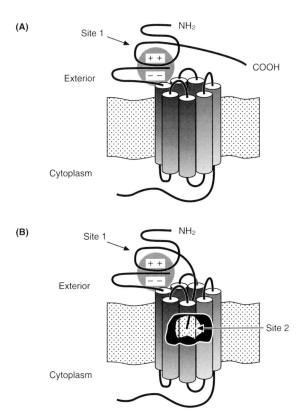

Figure 2 Model for the binding of C5a to its receptor. As shown in (B), the interaction takes place at distinct sites. The first, designated site 1, is between the N-terminus, and possibly the second extracellular loop of the receptor, and the core of C5a. Specifically, primary interaction is thought to be between several of the aspartic acid residues in the N-terminus and Arg40 and possibly Arg37 and His15 of C5a. The second interaction site, designated site 2, is between the C-terminus of C5a and the interhelical region of the receptor. The primary interaction involves Arg74 and Lys68 of C5a. The initial site of productive contact is believed to take place at site 1, as depicted in (A). The contact at site 1 effectively raises the local concentration of C5a and thereby promotes the more difficult interaction at site 2. (Reproduced from Siciliano *et al* (1994).)

and possibly some lymphocyte subpopulations. Neutrophil responses to C5a have been most extensively studied and shown to include the induction of calcium transients, shape change, cell polarization and chemotaxis, upregulation of receptors, integrin activation and, at higher concentrations, exocytosis, oxygen radical production, induction of a hyperadhesive state and enhancement of phagocytic and cytotoxic functions. Furthermore, after priming with the appropriate cytokine – granulocyte-macrophage colony-stimulating factor (GM-CSF) for neutrophils and monocytes, interleukin 3 (IL-3), IL-5 and GM-CSF for basophils and eosinophils – C5a promotes the synthesis of large amounts of the lipid mediators leukotriene B_4 (LTB_4), platelet-activating factor (PAF), and LTC_4. Together with fMLP, C5a induces the broadest range of biological responses in effector cells, in contrast to most other chemotactic agonists which more preferentially activate either chemotaxis or cell activation, indicating important, yet ill-defined, differences in receptor signaling. Interestingly, $C5a_{desarg}$ is a poor activator of most leukocytes, but retains potent chemotactic activity, thus becoming more similar to other chemotaxins such as IL-8 and LTB_4. The bioactivity of $C5a_{desarg}$ also depends on the cell type: it is still chemotactic for a broad range of leukocytes, yet stimulates efficient exocytosis only in basophils, but not in mast cells or mast cell lines. The reason for this complexity is unknown.

Cytokine expression and immunoregulation

More recent studies have shown that C5a in synergy with LPS promotes expression of IL-1 and IL-6 in monocytes. Combined stimulation of basophils with IL-3 and C5a induces the selective expression of IL-4 and IL-13, which are key immunoregulatory cytokines for the induction of a T_H2-type immune response and for the synthesis of immunoglobulin E (IgE). C5a is unique in this respect, as other chemotactic agonists, such as chemokines which are also effective triggers of chemotaxis and/or exocytosis, are unable to induce cytokine expression. Thus, C5a is not just an inflammatory mediator but may also have indirect immunoregulatory properties, and promote humoral and T_H2 type immune responses. These observations also emphasize the importance of studying the effects of anaphylatoxins within the network of other factors.

Activities outside the immune system

C5a also acts on liver cells and induces the expression of acute phase proteins. Furthermore, the mRNA for the receptors for C5a and C3a are widely expressed in a large number of tissues and organs, indicating that anaphylatoxins may have other, largely unexplored, functions outside the immune system. Particularly abundant transcripts for the C5a receptor are found in lung, spleen, heart, placenta, spinal cord and throughout the brain, and for the C3a receptor in lung, spleen, ovary, placenta, small intestine and less ubiquitously in the brain.

See also: **Acute inflammatory reaction; Arachidonic acid and the leukotrienes; Complement, alternative pathway; Chemokines; Chemotaxis; Complement, classical pathway; Complement, membrane attack pathway; Complement receptors; Cutaneous anaphylaxis; Platelet-activating factor (PAF).**

Further reading

Ames RS, Li Y, Sarau HM *et al* (1996) Molecular cloning and characterization of the human anaphylatoxin C3a receptor. *Journal of Biological Chemistry* **271**: 20231–20234.

Bischoff SC, Brunner T, de Weck AL and Dahinden CA (1990) Interleukin 5 modifies histamine release and leukotriene generation by human basophils in response to diverse agonists. *Journal of Experimental Medicine* **172**: 1577–1582.

Bischoff SC, de Weck AL and Dahinden CA (1990) Interleukin-3 and granulocyte/macrophage-colony-stimulating factor render human basophils responsive to low concentrations of complement component C3a. *Proceedings of the National Academy of Sciences of the USA* **87**: 6813–6817.

De Martino JA, Monteats ZD, Siciliano SJ *et al* (1995) Arginine 206 of the C5a receptor is critical for ligand recognition and receptor activation by C-terminal hexapeptide analogs. *Journal of Biological Chemistry* **270**: 15966–15969.

Ember JA, Johansen NL and Hugli TE (1991) Designing synthetic superagonists of C3a anaphylatoxin. *Biochemistry* **30**: 3603–3612.

Gerard C and Gerard NP (1994) C5a anaphylatoxin and its seven transmembrane-segment receptor. *Annual Review of Immunology* **12**: 775–808.

Hopken UE, Lu B, Gerard NP and Gerard C (1996) The C5a chemoattractant receptor mediates mucosal defence to infection. *Nature* **383**: 86–89.

Hugli TE (1986) Biochemistry and biology of anaphylatoxins. *Complement* **3**: 111–127.

McCoy R, Haviland DL, Molmenti EP, Ziambaras T, Wetsel RA and Perlmutter DH (1995) *N*-formylpeptide and complement C5a receptors are expressed in liver cells and mediate hepatic acute phase gene regulation. *Journal of Experimental Medicine* 182: 207–217.

Murphy PM (1994) The molecular biology of leukocyte chemoattractant receptors. *Annual Review of Immunology* 12: 593–633.

Ochensberger B, Rihs S, Brunner T and Dahinden CA (1995) IgE-independent interleukin-4 expression and induction of a late phase of leukotriene C4 formation in human blood basophils. *Blood* 86: 4039–4049.

Siciliano SJ, Rollins TE, De Martino J *et al* (1994) Two-site binding of C5a by its receptor: an alternative binding paradigm for G protein-coupled receptors. *Proceedings of the National Academy of Sciences of the USA* 91: 1214–1218.

ANEMIA, AUTOIMMUNE HEMOLYTIC IN ANIMAL MODELS

C J Elson and **C-R Shen**, Department of Pathology and Microbiology, University of Bristol, Bristol, UK

Autoimmune hemolytic anemia (AIHA) is a classic example of an antibody-mediated autoimmune disease. It is well documented how autoantibody-coated red blood cells (RBCs) can be destroyed by splenic macrophages, but by contrast, the mechanisms that initiate the production of RBC autoantibodies remain unclear. The New Zealand Black (NZB) strain of mice spontaneously develops AIHA. RBC-bound immunoglobulin G (IgG) autoantibodies can be detected by Coombs' test from 3 months of age and the mice develop signs of anemia 2–3 months later. For two decades after these mice were first bred in 1959, a flood of papers appeared documenting the specificity of the autoantibodies and attempting to pinpoint lesions in particular cells which could result in the generation of RBC autoantibodies. Many of these results are now open to re-evaluation in the light of recent studies.

Antigen specificity of RBC autoantibodies from NZB mice

Historically, four distinct RBC autoantigens were described in NZB mice, namely X, HB, I and HOL. The IgG response to the antigen designated X appears to be of primary pathogenic importance, since only antibodies of this specificity are exclusive to the NZB mouse and are capable of binding untreated murine RBCs, i.e. to determinants normally exposed on the RBC surface. By contrast, IgM autoantibodies reactive with the antigens HB and I, and IgG antibodies specific for HOL are also found in strains of healthy mice, and recognize cryptic epitopes on the RBC membrane. Recent work has confirmed that antibodies eluted from the RBCs of old, anemic NZB mice are pathogenic when injected into younger animals with prepatent disease. Moreover, as judged by immunoprecipitation, the target of these antibodies is band 3, the RBC anion channel protein. These results would suggest therefore that X is band 3.

One approach to understanding the pathogenesis of AIHA in NZB mice is to prepare and characterize hybridoma antibodies derived from spleen cells of anemic animals. A number of such monoclonal antibodies that react with intact murine RBCs have been generated and their properties examined in detail. For example, analysis of the variable region gene usage of NZB-derived RBC-specific monoclonal antibodies reveals evidence of somatic mutation, consistent with an antigen-driven response. Some of the monoclonal antibodies are pathogenic *in vivo*. Injection of pathogenic IgG monoclonal antibodies into mice induces hemolysis by Fc-dependent erythrophagocytosis, whereas massive accumulations of hemagglutinated RBCs are found in the recipients of pathogenic IgM monoclonals. It should be noted that hemagglutinated RBCs are not prominent on histological examination of spleens from anemic NZB mice.

The erythrocyte autoantigens recognized by a panel of eight hybridoma RBC autoantibodies were recently characterized. Two of the three pathogenic IgG monoclonal antibodies immunoprecipitated band 3. A third nonpathogenic IgG monoclonal also precipitated band 3 but only at high concentrations. This monoclonal was the only one to react with band 3 by immunoblotting and it alone of the IgG monoclonals reacts with RBCs from other species. None of the four IgM monoclonal antibodies precipitated any labeled RBC components. However, by immunoblotting, the two pathogenic IgM monoclonals bound to a doublet which corresponds in electrophoretic mobility with band 4.1 from the internal RBC membrane skeleton. An explanation of how these antibodies bound intact RBCs may come from the finding that they also bound to histones, suggesting that they are polyreactive and recognize surface autoantigens such as phospholipids. Thus, the demonstration that two pathogenic monoclonal autoantibodies recognize band 3 confirms that this protein bears important autoantigenic epitopes but also reveals that some pathogenic monoclonal antibodies do not share this characteristic. It could be argued that the latter monoclonal antibodies represent minor components of the total RBC autoantibody population or that antibodies to multiple RBC antigens, in addition to Band 3, contribute to hemolysis in NZB mice.

Transgenic mice

Honjo and his colleagues generated transgenic mice expressing one of the pathogenic IgM monoclonal antibodies derived from NZB mice. In these mice conventional (B-2) B cells were deleted, presumably after contact with RBCs, but normal numbers of CD5 B-1 cells were present in the peritoneal cavity and lamina propria. About 50% of these mice developed AIHA in a conventional environment but not if maintained in isolators. Oral administration of LPS induced AIHA in asymptomatic anti-RBC transgenic mice but not in transgenic mice bearing the xid (B-1 cell deficient) mutation. Since intraperitoneal injection of RBC into the transgenic mice induced apototic death of peritoneal B-1 cells and prevented AIHA developing, it appears that RBC-reactive B-1 cells survive in the RBC-free regions of the peritoneal cavity and gut and are stimulated by microorganisms to produce RBC autoantibodies. Are these findings relevant to NZB disease? It has been known for some years that the introduction of the xid mutation into NZB mice reduces the production of RBC autoantibodies and the development of anemia. The therapeutic effect of the xid gene could result not only from the lack of B-1 cells but also from defects introduced into conventional B cells. However, NZB mice injected intraperitoneally with distilled water weekly from birth to 12 months of age have markedly reduced splenic B-1 cells, increased hematocrit values and reduced levels of RBC-bound IgG and IgM. These results suggest that B-1 cells contribute directly to the development of NZB disease by secreting IgM RBC autoantibodies and that some IgG RBC autoantibody-secreting cells are derived, directly or indirectly, from B-1 cells.

Ontogenesis of RBC autoantibody response

Early work showed that neonatal thymectomy of NZB mice failed to prevent the generation of RBC autoantibody, although thymectomy immediately after birth appeared to delay the onset of autoantibody production. It was also established that RBC autoantibody production can be transferred to irradiated non-NZB H-2^d recipients with bone marrow cells. Since the anti-RBC plaque-forming response still occurred in chronically T-depleted recipients, it was argued that an intrinsic defect was present in NZB B cells and implied that the RBC autoantibody response was T-independent. Recent work calls these interpretations into question. First, SCID mice repopulated with NZB pre-B cells fail to develop RBC autoantibodies despite that fact that high levels of IgM anti-DNA and low levels of IgG anti-DNA are generated. Secondly, chronic treatment of NZB mice with monoclonal anti-CD4 prevents or considerably delays the generation of RBC autoantibodies. Interestingly, anemia still occurs in anti-CD4-treated NZB mice, possibly because they developed an ulcerative colitis. Finally, Gershwin and his colleagues have generated CD4 and CD8 gene-deleted NZB mice. Again the incidence and titers of RBC autoantibodies (particularly of the IgM isotype) were significantly reduced in NZB.CD4$^{-/-}$ mice as compared with wild-type NZBs. By contrast, no significant change in RBC autoantibody responses was observed in NZB.CD8$^{-/-}$ mice. Thus CD4$^+$ T cells clearly contribute to the development of NZB AIHA.

Specificity and characterization of T cells

Since the generation of pathogenic anti-RBC autoantibodies is CD4 T lymphocyte dependent, it would be predicted that NZB mice harbor helper T cells responsive to RBC autoantigens. Splenic T cells from NZB mice, but not other H-2^d strains such as BALB/c or DBA2 mice, do indeed proliferate in vitro in response to band 3. The majority of the responding cells express CD4 and the response is major histocompatibility complex class II restricted. Thus the T cells which help the production of the band 3 reactive autoantibodies may also be band 3 specific. The epitopes which stimulate band 3-reactive T cells have been mapped. Splenic T cells from old NZB mice respond to some 20 15mer peptides corresponding to the sequence of band 3. However, the response to one peptide is dominant in terms of magnitude and the appearance of the response with age. Splenic T cells from NZB mice as young as 3 weeks old respond to this peptide but generally not to others, suggesting that the response is initially focused on the dominant peptide and later spreads to other band 3 epitopes. So far attempts to demonstrate that band 3-reactive T cells are present and primed in the thymus have failed. Thus band 3-reactive T cells may be primed in the periphery. Nevertheless, the observation of abnormalities in the structure of the NZB thymus suggests that events in the thymus should not be neglected.

CD4$^+$ T cells can be classified into two types, T_H1 and T_H2, depending on the cytokines they produce. For example, T_H1 cells typically secrete interferon γ (IFNγ) and T_H2 cells interleukin 4 (IL-4). The type of cytokine secreted by helper T cells affects the isotype of antibody produced, and in mice T_H1-dominated responses are associated with IgG2a antibodies and T_H2 with IgG1. Whilst there is now a consensus that pathology of cell-mediated autoimmune diseases is linked to the stimulation of T_H1 autoreactive cells, it might be expected and indeed it has been suggested that T_H2 responses may be important in initiating and driving antibody-mediated autoimmune disorders such as AIHA. However, NZB T cells stimulated with band 3 produced high levels of IFNγ, but little or no IL-4, IL-5 or IL-10. Similar patterns were produced by NZB T cells responding to a spectrin preparation from the RBC membrane skeleton, or to mycobacterial heat shock protein (hsp) 65 following immunization of mice with hsp65 in incomplete adjuvant. By contrast, T cells from CBA mice similarly immunized with hsp65 produced high levels of IL-4 and IL-5 in response to hsp65.

Examination of the isotype of the RBC-bound immunoglobulins in NZB mice revealed that IgG2a autoantibodies were the first to be detected in most mice and that later in the disease, IgG3 autoantibodies were often prominent. Consequently, contrary to expectation, the development of RBC autoantibodies in NZB mice is associated with T_H1 cytokine-dominated responses. How T_H1 cytokines effect NZB disease remains to be determined, although it has been suggested that T_H1 cytokines can alter antigen processing so that previously cryptic epitopes become presented and are thus responsible for epitope spreading.

See also: **Anemia, autoimmune hemolytic in human; Antiglobulin (Coombs') test; Autoantigens; Autoimmune diseases; Suppressor T lymphocytes; Tolerance, peripheral.**

Further reading

Barker RN, De Sa Oliveira GG, Elson CJ and Lydyard PM (1993) Pathogenic autoantibodies in the NZB mouse are specific for Band 3 protein. *European Journal of Immunology* 23: 1723–1726.

Chen S-Y, Takeoka Y, Ansari AA et al (1996) The natural history of disease expression in CD4 and CD8 gene-deleted New Zealand Black (NZB) mice. *Journal of Immunology* 177: 2676–2684.

Deheer DH and Edgington TS (1976) Cellular events associated with the immunogenesis of anti-erythrocyte autoantibody responses of NZB mice. *Transplantation Reviews* 31: 116–155.

Elson CJ, Barker RN, Thompson SJ and Williams NA (1995) Immunologically ignorant autoreactive T-cells, epitope spreading and repertoire limitation. *Immunology Today* 16: 71–76.

Murakami M and Honjo T (1995) Involvement of B-1 cells in mucosal immunity and autoimmunity. *Immunology Today* 16: 534–539.

Murakami M, Tsubata T, Okamoto M et al (1992) Antigen-induced apoptotic death of Ly-1 B cells responsible for autoimmune disease in trangenic mice. *Nature* 35: 77–80.

Murakami M, Yoshioka Y, Shirai T et al (1995) Prevention of autoimmune symptoms in autoimmune-prone mice by elimination of B-1 cells. *International Immunology* 7: 877–882.

Nisitani S, Murakami M and Honjo T (1997) Anti-red blood cell immunoglobulin transgenic mice: an experimental model of autoimmune hemolytic anemia. *Annals of the New York Academy of Sciences* 815: 246–252.

Okamoto M, Murakami M, Shimizu A et al (1992) A transgenic model of autoimmune hemolytic anemia. *Journal of Experimental Medicine* 175: 71–79.

Oliveira GGS, Hutchings PR, Roitt IM and Lydyard PM (1994) Production of erythrocyte autoantibodies in NZB mice is inhibited by CD4 antibodies. *Clinical and Experimental Immunology* 96: 297–302.

Oliveira GGS, Izui S, Ravirajan CT et al (1996) Diverse antigen specificity of erythrocyte-reactive monoclonal autoantibodies from NZB mice. *Clinical and Experimental Immunology* 105: 313–320.

Perry FE, Barker RN, Mazza G et al (1996) Autoreactive T-cell specificity in autoimmune hemolytic anaemia of the NZB mouse. *European Journal of Immunology* 26: 136–141.

Reininger L, Shibata T and Ozaki S (1990) Variable region sequences of pathogenic anti-mouse red blood cell autoantibodies from autoimmune NZB mice. *European Journal of Immunology* 20: 771–777.

Reininger L, Winkler TH, Kalberer CP et al (1996) Intrinsic B cell defects in NZB and NZW mice contribute to systemic lupus erythematosus in (NZB × NZW)F1 mice. *Journal of Experimental Medicine* 184: 853–861.

Shen C-R, Mazza G, Perry FE et al (1996) T-helper 1 dominated responses to erythrocyte Band 3 in NZB mice. *Immunology* 89: 195–199.

Shibata T, Berney T, Reininger L et al (1990) Monoclonal anti-erythrocyte autoantibodies derived from NZB mice cause autoimmune hemolytic anaemia by two distinct pathogenic mechanisms. *International Immunology* 2: 1133–1141.

ANEMIA, AUTOIMMUNE HEMOLYTIC IN HUMAN

Alan D Schreiber, Department of Medicine, Hospital of the University of Pennsylvania, Philadelphia, USA

The autoimmune hemolytic anemias represent a group of disorders in which individuals produce antibodies directed toward one or more of their own erythrocyte membrane antigens. This in turn leads to destruction of the erythrocytes. An effective manner in which to approach autoimmune hemolytic anemia is to analyze which class of antibody is responsible for the hemolysis. In general, there are two major classes of antierythrocyte antibodies which produce hemolysis in humans: immunoglobulin G (IgG) and IgM. The pattern of red blood cell clearance, the site of organ sequestration, the response to therapy, and the prognosis all relate to the class of antierythrocyte antibody involved.

IgM-induced immune hemolytic anemia

Autoimmune hemolytic anemia caused by IgM antibody in humans is generally restricted to the clinical entity of cold hemagglutinin disease, in which the antibodies only bind significantly to the erythrocytes at temperatures below 37°C. The most common form of chronic cold hemagglutinin disease is the primary or idiopathic form caused by an IgM antibody. This is a clonal disorder and is associated with the presence of a monoclonal IgM antibody which usually has a high cold agglutinin titer. The IgM antibody is usually directed against the I antigen or related antigens on the human erythrocyte membrane. As with all IgM antibodies agglutinating activity is particularly efficient because of the multiple antigen combining sites on the IgM molecule. The cold agglutinin titer represents the least dilution of patient plasma or serum capable of agglutinating human red blood cells in the cold. In most patients with hemolysis the cold agglutinin titer is greater than 1:1000.

Secondary cold hemagglutinin disease is most commonly associated with an underlying mycoplasma infection, particularly *Mycoplasma pneumonia*. It may also occur with other infections, such as infectious mononucleosis or cytomegalovirus. Cold hemagglutinin disease (IgM-induced immune hemolytic anemia) can also be seen with an underlying immunoproliferative disorder, such as chronic lymphocytic leukemia, non-Hodgkin's lymphoma, or systemic lupus erythematosus. The disease may be chronic and the IgM protein may be of restricted heterogeneity (oligoclonal) or even be monoclonal. When this is the case, one should suspect an underlying malignant immunoproliferative disorder and the prognosis is adversely affected.

As in all patients with autoimmune hemolytic anemia, erythrocyte survival is generally proportional to the amount of antibody on the erythrocyte surface. In cold hemagglutinin disease the extent of hemolysis is a function of the titer of the antibody (cold agglutinin titer), the thermal amplitude of the IgM antibody (the highest temperature at which the antibody is active), and the level of the circulating control proteins of the C3b inactivator system. Hemolysis is complement-dependent and the IgM-coated erythrocytes become coated with C3b by classical complement pathway activation. These C3b-coated erythrocytes are cleared primarily by the macrophage C3b receptors in the liver. Two uncommon variants of cold hemagglutinin disease, low IgM titer cold hemagglutinin disease and cold hemagglutinin disease mediated by IgG antibody are more responsive to therapy.

IgG-induced immune hemolytic anemia

In IgG-induced immune hemolytic anemia, the antibodies are of the IgG class and the antigen to which the antibody is directed is usually an Rh erythrocyte antigen. The antibody has its maximal activity at 37°C, and, thus, this entity has been termed warm antibody-induced hemolytic anemia. IgG-induced immune hemolytic anemia may occur without an apparent underlying disease (idiopathic type); however, it may also occur with an underlying immunoproliferative disorder, such as chronic lymphocytic leukemia, non-Hodgkins lymphoma or systemic lupus erythematosus. The signs and symptoms are those of anemia in general. The diagnosis is established by directly examining the erythrocyte surface for the presence of IgG and C3b.

In addition to C3b receptors, macrophages within the reticuloendothelial system have receptors for the Fc fragment of IgG, called Fcγ receptors. The macrophage Fcγ receptors can detect IgG-coated erythrocytes, bind them, make them spherical, or phagocytose them in the absence of C3b. However, once C3b is placed on the erythrocyte surface, through complement activation, erythrocyte clearance is further accelerated. Thus, IgG-coated erythrocytes are progressively cleared from the circulation by macrophages possessing Fcγ receptors. Hemolysis is almost always extravascular and these IgG-coated cells are cleared predominantly in the spleen. Complement activation accelerates the clearance of IgG-coated cells.

Drug-induced immune hemolytic anemia

Drug-induced immune hemolytic anemia can be divided into four major pathophysiologic groups. Clinical signs and symptoms are identical to those of the other autoimmune hemolytic anemias. The diagnosis is established primarily by history.

Hapten type

This type of drug-induced immune hemolysis classically develops in patients exposed to high doses of penicillin. A portion of the penicillin molecule or its active metabolites combines with the erythrocyte surface, acting as a hapten. This induces an antibody response directed against the penicillin-coated erythrocyte membrane. This is usually an IgG response, and complement activation is common. The patient's erythrocytes become coated with IgG and often with C3. Patients rarely develop this syndrome unless they have received 10–20 million units of penicillin a day. Diagnosis can be established by incubating the patient's serum with donor erythrocytes preincubated with penicillin. The deposition of IgG antibody will occur only in the presence of penicillin and can be detected with the Coombs test.

Quinidine type

This type of autoimmune hemolytic anemia most commonly occurs with the use of quinidine or its derivatives. Commonly called an innocent bystander reaction, it is believed to be due to an antibody directed against quinidine bound to a plasma protein or the red blood cell membrane acting as a hapten. This interaction results in activation of the classic complement pathway and deposition of C3 on the erythrocyte surface. With quinidine it is commonly caused by IgM antiquinidine antibody. The diagnosis can be established *in vitro* by examining for complement deposition on donor erythrocytes by patient serum which occurs only in the presence of the drug, e.g. quinidine.

α-Methyldopa type

α-Methyldopa and its derivatives produce a clinical syndrome virtually identical to IgG-induced immune hemolytic anemia. The mechanism of the IgG antibody formation is poorly understood. Many patients, up to 25%, exposed to α-methyldopa, develop a positive Coombs' test for IgG. These IgG antibodies have specificity for Rh antigens. Most patients do not develop sufficient IgG coating for hemolysis; however, hemolysis is observed in approximately 0.8% of patients exposed to α-methyldopa. Diagnosis can be made by examining the patient's red blood cells and plasma. *In vitro* it is not necessary to have the drug present for the patient's plasma to deposit IgG antibody on donor erythrocytes. A similar syndrome has been reported with mefenamic acid.

Nonspecific coating

Nonspecific coating of the erythrocyte surface has been observed with the antibiotic cephalothin, in which cephalothin becomes bound to the erythrocyte membrane and causes the red blood cells to be coated by many plasma proteins. The Coombs test is positive, but hemolytic anemia is rare. Cephalosporins, however, can cause hemolytic anemia by acting as a hapten by a mechanism similar to that of penicillin.

In all these situations, the patients respond to withdrawal of the offending drug. If necessary, a brief course of glucocorticoid therapy can be effectively administered.

Therapeutic measures

In many patients with IgG- or IgM-induced immune hemolytic anemia, no therapeutic intervention is necessary, since the hemolysis may be mild. If an underlying disease is present, control of this disease often brings the hemolytic anemia also under control. However, if the patient is having significant anemia secondary to hemolysis, therapeutic intervention is in order.

Glucocorticoids

Patients with IgG-induced immune hemolytic anemia usually respond to glucocorticoid therapy in dosages equivalent to 40–120 mg of prednisone a day. Glucocorticoids work in IgG-induced hemolytic anemia by three primary mechanisms. First, they decrease the production of the abnormal IgG antibody. This is the most common effect and produces a gradual increase in hemoglobin within 2–6 weeks. Second, glucocorticoids have in several cases been demonstrated to cause the elution of IgG antibody from the erythrocyte surface, improving the red blood cell survival. This is probably an uncommon effect of therapy.

Third, glucocorticoids have been shown *in vitro* and *in vivo* to interfere with the macrophage Fcγ and to a lesser extent C3b receptors responsible for the erythrocyte destruction in this disease. This effect may be rapid and is probably responsible for the rise in hemoglobin which occurs in some patients within 1–4 days of therapy. This action of glucocorticoids causes an improvement in erythrocyte survival despite the continued presence of IgG and C3b on the erythrocyte surface.

Once a therapeutic response is achieved, tapering of glucocorticoids should be initiated. This may take several months. Alternate-day glucocorticoid therapy may be utilized during this time, or until the patient's hematologic picture stabilizes.

Since glucocorticoids may improve erythrocyte survival by interfering with macrophage detection of IgG-coated erythrocytes, the patient's Coombs test may remain positive in the face of an improved erythrocyte survival. Thus, some patients may continue to improve hematologically despite a persistently positive Coombs' test.

Approximately 80% of patients have an initial response to high-dose glucocorticoids. Nevertheless, only 20–30% have a sustained response following discontinuation of therapy. Several patients maintain control of their hemolytic process on low- or medium-dose glucocorticoid therapy. For the patients who are steroid dependent, the initial and long-term side-effects of steroids must be considered. These include gastritis, peptic ulcer disease, emotional lability, exacerbation of diabetes and hypertension, electrolyte imbalance, increased appetite and weight gain, moon-like faces, osteoporosis, myopathy and increased susceptibility to infection. The severity of these side-effects relates to both dosage and duration of therapy. Splenectomy is usually recommended for patients who are unresponsive to steroids or who require more than 10–20 mg per day or 20–25 mg every other day for maintenance. Each patient requires individual evaluation of underlying disease, surgical risk, extent of anemia and steroid intolerance. In some patients the presence of a mild hemolytic anemia may be preferable to splenectomy or other treatment options. The initial goal of therapy is to return the patient to normal hematologic values with nontoxic levels of glucocorticoid therapy. However, in some patients, a secondary goal of achieving improvement in hemolysis to a clinically asymptomatic state with minimum glucocorticoid side-effects is more realistic. Alternate-day glucocorticoids are worthy of consideration in many patients. Their efficacy is not generally appreciated.

Glucocorticoids are not usually effective in cold hemagglutinin disease. This is probably due to the fact that these patients generally have large amounts of IgM antierythrocyte antibody and large amounts of C3b on the erythrocyte surface. In addition, some of the hemolysis may be intravascular. A few patients with a low titer cold hemagglutinin disease syndrome, in which the IgM antierythrocyte antibody is active at temperatures approaching 37°C, and patients with cold hemagglutinin disease mediated by IgG antibodies, do respond to glucocorticoid therapy. Patients with cold hemagglutinin disease respond best to the avoidance of cold and control of their underlying disease. Fortunately, in many patients hemolytic anemia is mild.

Splenectomy

The reticuloendothelial system of the spleen with its resident macrophages is the major site for sequestration of IgG-coated blood cells. This appears to be due to the unique circulatory pathways in the spleen whereby hemoconcentration occurs in the splenic cords. This results in intimate contact between macrophages (with their membrane Fcγ receptors) and IgG-coated blood cells in the presence of a minimal amount of plasma IgG; plasma IgG competitively inhibits the macrophage Fcγ receptor binding of IgG-coated cells. Thus, the spleen is usually the major site of red cell sequestration in autoimmune hemolytic anemia, with the liver accounting for a variable degree of sequestration.

Removal of the major site of red cell destruction is an effective therapeutic strategy in IgG-induced immune hemolytic anemia. The response rate to splenectomy is approximately 50–70%; however, the vast majority of the responses are partial remissions. The partial remissions are often quite helpful in that they result in a lessening of the hemolytic rate, with a rise in the hemoglobin value, and/or allow for a reduction in the amount of glucocorticoid needed to control the hemolytic anemia. Patients who are unresponsive to glucocorticoids, require moderate to high maintenance doses of glucocorticoids, or have developed glucocorticoid intolerance are generally candidates for splenectomy. ^{51}Cr-labeled red cell kinetic studies are probably not beneficial, since the procedure is time consuming, expensive and not a reliable indicator of response to splenectomy.

Splenectomy is effective in IgG-induced hemolytic anemia because the cells are cleared primarily in the spleen. In addition, it has been shown that splenectomy can decrease the production of the IgG-antierythrocyte antibody, as the spleen contains a large B cell pool. Those patients in whom splenectomy fails are probably those with very high concentrations of IgG on the erythrocyte surface; in such patients the liver plays a more prominent role in clearance.

Splenectomy is not effective in patients with traditional cold hemagglutinin disease because IgM-coated erythrocytes are cleared predominantly in the liver, not in the spleen. An occasional case in which a patient with an apparent IgM-induced hemolytic anemia responded to splenectomy has been reported. This may be due to decreased production of IgM antibody by the spleen in these patients. Patients with the uncommon IgG-induced cold hemagglutinin disease syndrome do, however, respond to splenectomy.

The side-effects of splenectomy vary greatly from institution to institution. We have generally attempted to identify one or two surgical colleagues who carry out most of the splenectomies on our patient population. This experience enhances both the surgical procedures (speed and safety) and the postoperative follow-up. Postoperative thromboses and infection both above and below the diaphragm can occur. The risk of morbidity and mortality is greater in older patients, in those with unrelated underlying disease (benign or malignant immunoproliferative disorder), in those with unrelated medical problems, and, to some extent, is influenced by the degree of glucocorticoid side-effects. Thus, a thoughtful analysis of the benefit-versus-risk factors needs to be undertaken for each patient. A final consideration is that adults who undergo splenectomy may, in rare instances, have a propensity to life-threatening infection, particularly with Pneumococcus. For this reason it is generally recommended to immunize patients with Pneumovax some weeks prior to elective splenectomy in an effort to reduce this long-term complication.

Immunosuppressive agents

Several chemotherapeutic agents with known immunosuppressive effects have been used to treat immune hemolytic anemia. The drugs most commonly used include the thiopurines (6-mercaptopurine, azathioprine and thioguanine) and alkylating agents (cyclophosphamide and chlorambucil). Immunosuppressive therapy may be effective for treating patients with IgG-induced immune hemolytic anemia when patients are refractory to steroids or splenectomy. Immunosuppressive agents work by decreasing the production of antibody, and therefore it generally takes at least 2 weeks before any therapeutic result is observed.

Patients are selected for immunosuppressive therapy because they have a clinically unacceptable degree of hemolytic anemia resistant to glucocorticoid and splenectomy treatment. Alternatively, they may be intolerant of, or resistant to, glucocorticoids and poor surgical risks for splenectomy. Clinical benefit has been noted in about 50% of patients. A reasonable trial of this type of agent is about 3–4 months, and if no beneficial effect is noted, therapy is discontinued. If clinical benefit occurs, one can maintain the dosage level for a total of 6 months and then taper over several months. During therapy, patients are instructed to maintain a high fluid intake to reduce the incidence of chemical cystitis seen with cyclophosphamide and the need to have weekly blood counts to monitor bone marrow suppression, which can be seen with any of these immunosuppressive drugs. Dosage should be adjusted to maintain the leukocyte count >2000, granulocyte count >1000 and platelet count $>50\,000–100\,000\ \text{mm}^{-3}$.

Cyclophosphamide in this dosage range is usually well tolerated but a variety of side-effects may occur, including bone marrow suppression (primarily leukopenia), hemorrhagic cystitis, nausea, partial alopecia, amenorrhea and impaired spermatogenesis. The use of alkylating agents may also have long-term potential for increasing the incidence of malignancy, particularly acute leukemia. These side-effects require that the clinical indications for immunosuppressive therapy be strong and that patient exposure to the drug be limited.

Aside from supportive measures, immunosuppressive therapy has been the major therapy in traditional high titer IgM induced cold hemagglutinin disease. Alkylating agents (cyclophosphamide or chlorambucil) have been the primary drugs used and appear to have a beneficial effect in up to 50–60% of cases. Unresponsiveness is probably due to the fact that very little antibody is required for significant hemolysis to occur.

Miscellaneous therapy

Plasmapheresis has been used in patients with severe IgG-induced immune hemolytic anemia but has met with limited success, possibly because more than half of the IgG is extravascular and the plasma contains only small amounts of the specific antibody (most of the antibody being on the red blood cell surface). However, plasmapheresis has been effective in IgM-induced hemolytic anemia. This is only of short-term benefit, but has reduced the level of cold agglutinins by virtue of the fact that IgM is a high molecular weight molecule that remains predominantly within the intravascular space.

Other measures that have been used effectively are vincristine and vinblastine infusions, gamma globulin infusion and hormonal therapy. Gamma globulin infusion is effective in IgG-induced immune hemolytic anemia, probably by primarily inhibiting the clearance of the IgG-coated cells. In hormonal therapy the synthetic androgen danazol has been effective in several patients. Because of the limited side-effects (limited masculinizing effects, mild weight gain), danazol or a similar agent may become an attractive alternative to glucocorticoid therapy in some patients with IgG-induced immune hemolytic anemia. However, danazol does not appear effective in IgM-induced hemolytic anemia. The data suggest that one mechanism of danazol's effect is through modulation (inhibition) of macrophage Fcγ receptor expression. Hormonal influence of macrophage Fcγ receptor expression probably explains, at least in part, the increased clinical activity of IgG-induced immune hemolytic anemia during pregnancy. During pregnancy, blood estrogen levels increase to an extent where they enhance splenic macrophage Fcγ receptor expression and thereby accelerate the clearance of IgG-coated cells.

Supportive transfusion therapy

The majority of patients with autoimmune hemolytic anemia do not require transfusion therapy because the anemia has occurred gradually and there has been physiologic compensation. However, occasionally patients experience acute and/or severe anemia and require transfusions for support until other treatment modalities reduce the hemolysis. Transfusion therapy is complicated by the fact that the blood bank may be unable to find any 'compatible' blood. This is because the autoantibody is directed to a product of the Rh locus which is present on the erythrocytes of essentially all potential donors, regardless of Rh subtype. The usual recommendation is for the blood bank to identify the most compatible units of blood of the patient's own major blood group and Rh types. Using this approach, it is unlikely that the donor blood will have a dramatically shortened red blood cell survival.

The indication for transfusion therapy is prevention of any serious complications due to the anemia. These include angina, congestive heart failure and central nervous system symptoms of hypoxia (for example, syncope, lightheadedness, impairment of mental acuity). In addition, if the patient is experiencing blood loss, transfusion is required. The slow infusion of 1–2 units of packed red cells usually improves the clinical status of the patient. Elderly patients especially need to be monitored for circulatory overload and for transfusion reactions. The latter are unlikely to be serious since hemolysis is usually

extravascular. In the rare patient with little or no response to steroids and a continuing need for transfusions because of serious side-effects of anemia over the first 4–6 days of therapy, an early decision for splenectomy may be necessary.

In cold agglutinin disease it is important to prewarm all intravenous infusions, including whole blood, to 37°C because a decrease in temperature locally in a vein can enhance the binding of the IgM antibody to red cells and accelerate the hemolytic process. In addition, erythrocyte agglutination in a small blood vessel can result in vascular compromise and ischemia to an extremity.

See also: **Anemia, autoimmune hemolytic in animal models; Anemia, drug induced immune hemolytic; Autoimmune diseases; Autoimmunity; Erythrocytes; Glucocorticoids; Immunosuppression;** *Mycoplasma,* **infection and immunity; Plasmapheresis; Rh antigens; Spleen.**

Further reading

Barker RN, Hall AM, Standen GR *et al* (1997) Identification of T-cell epitopes on the rhesus polypeptides in autoimmune hemolytic anemia. *Blood* 90: 2701–2715.

Efremov DG, Ivanovski M, Siljanovski N *et al* (1996) Restricted immunoglobulin VH region repertoire in chronic lymphocytic leukemia patients with autoimmune hemolytic anemia. *Blood* 87: 3869–3876.

Flores G, Cunningham-Rundles C, Newland AC and Bussel JB (1993) Efficacy of intravenous immunoglobulin in the treatment of autoimmune hemolytic anemia: results in 73 patients. *American Journal of Hematology* 44: 237–242.

Friedman D, Nettl F and Schreiber AD (1985) Effect of estradiol and steroid analogues on the clearance of IgG coated erythrocytes. *Journal of Clinical Investigation* 75: 162–167.

Izui S (1994) Autoimmune hemolytic anemia. *Current Opinion in Immunology* 6: 926–930.

Liberato NL, Bollati P, Chiofalo F, Filipponi M and Poli M (1996) Autoimmune hemolytic anemia in multicentric Castleman's disease. *Haematologica* 81: 40–43.

LoBuglio AF, Cotran RS and Jandl JH (1967) Red cells coated with immunoglobulin G: binding and sphering by mononuclear cells in man. *Science* 158: 1582–1585.

Petz LD (1993) Drug-induced autoimmune hemolytic anemia. *Transfusion Medicine Review* 7: 242–254.

Schreiber AD and Frank MM (1972) Role of antibody and complement in the immune clearance and destruction of erythrocytes. I. *In vivo* effects of the IgG and IgM complement-fixing sites. *Journal of Clinical Investigation* 51: 575–582.

Schreiber AD, Rosse WF and Frank MM (1995) Autoimmune hemolytic anemia. In: Frank MM, Austen KF, Claman HN and Unanue ER (eds) *Samter's Immunologic Diseases*, 5th edn, pp 903–918. Boston: Little, Brown.

Silbertstein LE, Berkman EM and Schreiber AD (1987) Cold hemagglutinin disease associated with IgG cold-reactive antibody. *Annals of Internal Medicine* **106**: 238–242.

ANEMIA, DRUG-INDUCED IMMUNE HEMOLYTIC

A H Waters, Department of Haematology, St Bartholomew's Hospital, London, UK

Acquired hemolytic anemias may develop as the result of immunological reactions consequent to the administration of certain drugs. Clinically, they often closely mimic autoimmune hemolytic anemia of 'idiopathic' origin and for this reason a careful enquiry into the taking of drugs is a necessary part of the investigation of any patient suspected of having an immune hemolytic anemia.

It is common experience that a particular drug may cause hemolysis in one patient, thrombocytopenia in another, neutropenia in yet another, and sometimes combinations of these in the one patient. The drug-induced antibodies responsible for these immune cytopenias are cell specific. We are still at a loss to know why a particular drug binds to a particular cell in a particular patient.

Mechanisms of drug-induced immune cell destruction

The basic mechanisms are widely accepted, although some essential details remain hypothetical.

In a unifying concept, the primary immune response is initiated by an interaction between the drug or its metabolites and a component of the blood cell membrane to create a neoantigen (**Figure 1**). The target orientation of the antibodies covers a spectrum from drug-dependent antibodies, which bind to both the drug and the cell membrane, but not to either separately, to drug-independent autoantibodies for which the greater part of the neoantigen is sufficiently similar to the normal cell membrane to allow binding without the drug being present. Both types of antibody may be present at the same time in some patients.

Drug-dependent immune hemolytic anemias

In these cases the drug is required in the *in vitro* sys-tem for the antibodies to be detected. The red cells may be damaged in two ways.

1. *Complement-mediated lysis.* A typical history is for hemolysis, which may be severe and intravascular, to follow the readministration of a drug with which the patient has previously been treated, and for the hemolysis to subside when the offending drug has been identified and with-

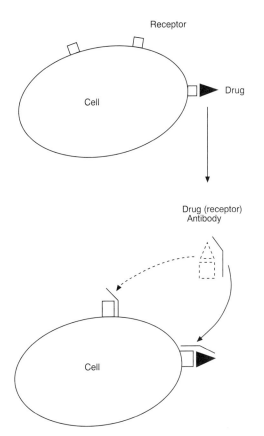

Figure 1 Mechanisms of drug-induced immune cytopenia. Drug-induced antibodies may react with the drug–receptor complex (drug-dependent antibody) or with the drug receptor alone (drug-independent autoantibody). Both types of antibody may be present at the same time.

drawn. The direct antiglobulin test (DAT) is likely to become strongly positive during the hemolytic phase, the patient's red cells being agglutinated by antibodies to complement and sometimes by anti-immunoglobulin G (IgG).

Drugs that have been shown to cause hemolysis by this mechanism include quinine, quinidine and rifampicin, as well as chlorpropamide, hydrochlorothiazide, nomifensine, phenacetin, salicylazosulfapyridine, the sodium salt of *p*-aminosalicylic acid and stibophen.

2. *Extravascular hemolysis*. This is brought about by IgG antibodies that usually do not activate complement, or if they do, not beyond C3. The direct antiglobulin test will be positive with anti-IgG, and sometimes also with antibodies to complement.

The hemolytic anemia associated with prolonged high-dose penicillin therapy is caused by this mechanism, and other penicillin derivatives, as well as cephalosporins and tetracycline, may cause hemolysis in a similar fashion. Hemolysis ceases when the offending drug has been identified and withdrawn.

Drug-independent autoimmune hemolytic anemias

In these cases the antibody reacts with the red cell in the absence of the drug. The anti-red cell autoantibodies seem to be serologically identical to those of 'idiopathic' warm-type autoimmune hemolytic anemia. The great majority of cases have followed the use of the anti-hypertension drug α-methyldopa (Aldomet). The red cells are coated with IgG and the serum contains autoantibodies which characteristically have Rh specificity.

In patients receiving α-methyldopa the autoantibody is often present (15–20%), but hemolysis is not common (<1%). Studies of reticuloendothelial clearance in patients receiving α-methyldopa suggest that the drug itself may blockade the reticuloendothelial

system in most patients, effectively blocking cell destruction by the autoantibody.

Other drugs that have been reported to act in a similar fashion to α-methyldopa include chlordiazepoxide (Librium), mefenamic acid (Ponstan), flufenamic acid and indomethacin.

Serological investigation

Typical serological features of the different types of drug-induced hemolytic anemia of immunological origin are summarized in **Table 1**. The drug may be added directly to the assay system (and included in the wash solution) or the cells may be pretreated with the drug (e.g. penicillin). For some drugs a metabolite and not the native drug is the appropriate antigen for testing; in these cases an *ex vivo* drug antigen may be used, from plasma or urine collected from volunteers or other patients after ingestion of therapeutic doses of the drug.

Review of the table reminds us that drug-induced antibodies may react as autoantibodies, so that positive reactions of serum and eluate with normal red cells do not exclude a drug as an etiologic agent.

Idiosyncrasy of drug-induced cytopenias

As already indicated, the antibody may recognize not only the drug but also a specific cell membrane component. Antibodies from patients with drug-induced thrombocytopenia or neutropenia show restriction, in that they react with variable proportions of normal donor cells exposed to the drug (10–80% in one study). This is not related to HLA or known cell-specific antigens, and family studies suggest that an unidentified polymorphic membrane determinant may be involved as a cell receptor/carrier. Another feature of drug-induced antibodies is their extreme heterogeneity from patient to patient and their individual specificity, reflecting a unique immune response.

See also: **Anemia, autoimmune hemolytic in human;**

Table 1   Serological features of the different types of drug-induced hemolytic anemia of immunological origin

Mechanism	Prototype drug	DAT	IAT No drug	IAT	
				Serum + drug	Eluate + drug
Drug-dependent antibody					
C activation	Quin(id)ine	C[a]	Negative	C[a]	Negative
No C activation	Penicillin	IgG	Negative	IgG	IgG
Autoantibody	α-Methyldopa	IgG	Positive (IgG)		

C, complement; [a] Occasionally also IgG. DAT, direct antiglobulin test; IAT, indirect antiglobulin test.
Reproduced from Waters (1995) with permission of Churchill Livingstone.

Carrier; Drugs, allergy to; Erythrocytes; Hapten; Idiopathic thrombocytopenic purpura.

Further reading

Ackroyd JF (1983) Drug-induced thrombocytopenia. An immunological phenomenon. *Vox Sanguinis* **45**: 257–259.

Claas FHJ, Langerak J and van Rood JJ (1981) Drug-induced antibodies with restricted specificity. *Immunology Letters* **2**: 323–326.

Engelfriet CP and von dem Borne AEGKr (eds) (1987) Alloimmune and autoimmune cytopenias. *Clinical Immunology and Allergy*, vol 1, no 2. London: Baillière Tindall.

Mueller-Eckhardt C and Salama A (1990) Drug induced cytopenias: a unifying pathogenetic concept with special emphasis on the role of drug metabolites. *Transfusion Medicine Reviews* **4**: 69–77.

Petz LD and Mueller-Eckhardt C (1992) Drug-induced immune hemolytic anemia. *Transfusion* **32**: 202–204.

Shulman NR (1964) A mechanism of cell destruction in individuals sensitized to foreign antigens and its implications in autoimmunity. *Annals of Internal Medicine* **60**: 506–521.

Waters AH (1995) Serological investigation of the autoimmune and drug-induced immune haemolytic anaemias. In: Dacie JV and Lewis SM (eds) *Practical Haematology*, 8th edn, pp 499–528. Edinburgh: Churchill Livingstone.

Worlledge SM (1973) Immune drug-induced hemolytic anemias. *Seminars in Hematology* **10**: 327–344.

ANEMIA, PERNICIOUS

Senga Whittingham, Centre for Molecular Biology and Medicine, Monash University, Clayton, Victoria, Australia

Pernicious anemia is an anemia which occurs in the terminal stages of the chronic destructive autoimmune disease, autoimmune gastritis. The anemia results from the death of parietal cells in the body of the stomach due to an immunologic reaction and in the absence of gastric parietal cells, a blood-sustaining vitamin B_{12} is no longer transported to its site of absorption.

Thomas Addison is acknowledged as the physician who, in 1849, described the clinical features of the anemia. The term 'pernicious' emphasized the inevitable progress and fatal outcome of the anemia and this description given by Biermer in 1972 has endured despite the knowledge that it is appropriate only to the terminal phase of the disease. The disease is, in fact, autoimmune gastritis for which histologic evidence was documented by Fenwick in 1870. However the importance of the link between the anemia and gastritis was not recognized until many years later.

Treatment played a major role in the eventual understanding of the development of pernicious anemia. The earliest studies were directed towards halting the progress of the anemia, and the prevention of death from the disease. Meals of crude extracts of hog stomach or cooked liver produced a reticulocyte response, indicating that new erythrocytes were made in response to ingestion of such meals. The reason for this became clear when Castle, in the 1950s, showed that the response was dependent on the presence in food of an extrinsic factor which reacted with intrinsic factor secreted into gastric juice. However, despite intensive treatment, relapses occurred and, in some instances, the anemia became refractory to treatment. The refractory state appeared to be due to the development of an inhibitory factor in the serum because serum mixed with gastric juice inhibited the effectiveness of the gastric juice. Rabbits injected with gastric juice produced antibodies which showed the same inhibitory effect. The essential factor, extrinsic factor, in food was shown to be vitamin B_{12} and the inhibitory factor in gastric juice (and serum) was autoantibody which reacted with the receptor for vitamin B_{12} on intrinsic factor. Binding of vitamin B_{12} to intrinsic factor was inhibited and the inhibition of this normal physiologic process prevented the transportation of vitamin B_{12} to its site of absorption. Blood cells deprived of their essential building block, vitamin B_{12}, failed to mature and the outcome was the development of a pernicious and progressively fatal anemia.

Clinical and hematologic features of pernicious anemia

The autoimmune processes that finally result in vitamin B_{12} deficiency may be operative for many years, perhaps 20 years or more, before the gastric parietal cells are functionally exhausted. The patient is usually a middle to older-aged woman of Northern

European origin. She is pale, mentally depressed, physically tired, has abdominal discomfort and may show signs of neurologic degeneration if vitamin B_{12} deficiency has been prolonged and severe. A film of blood or aspirate of bone marrow will show features of megaloblastic anemia. Her gastric juice is greatly reduced in volume and lacks acid. Her levels of vitamin B_{12} and pepsinogen 1 are low and there is an abnormally high level of serum gastrin.

These diagnostic criteria for anemia are 'insensitive' as disease markers for autoimmune gastritis because they are not evident until late in disease and therefore identify only a small proportion of patients. The earliest marker indicating the presence of chronic autoimmune gastritis is the gastric parietal cell autoantibody (GPCA), and since it is detectable early in the disease and persists throughout the evolution of the disease, it assumes considerable importance as a marker of the autoimmune process that may terminate in pernicious anemia. GPCA (**Figure 1**) is detected by immunofluorescence using frozen sections of parietal cell-rich areas of human or rodent stomach, preferable murine rather than rat because human serum may react nonspecifically with rat parietal cells. Over 90% of patients with autoimmune gastritis have GPCA.

Immunology

The gastric autoantigens

The two autoantigens targeted by autoantibodies are components unique to the gastric parietal cell in the body of the stomach. The autoantigen with which GPCA reacts is the enzyme H^+,K^+-adenosine triphosphatase (H^+,K^+-ATPase) which is cell-specific but not species-specific, indicating the importance of the physiologic role of the molecule in the gastric parietal cell. The second autoantigen is a secreted product of the gastric parietal cell, gastric intrinsic factor.

H^+,K^+-ATPase Gastric H^+,K^+-ATPase is the enzyme responsible for the acidification of gastric juice and is otherwise known as the proton pump. It belongs to a family of ion-motive-P-type ATPases which include Na^+,K^+-ATPase and Ca^{2+}-ATPase which have highly conserved catalytic α subunits that are phosphorylated during their reaction cycles. Only H^+,K^+-ATPase and Na^+,K^+-ATPase have a β subunit which includes a heavily glycosylated 35 kDa core protein. The gastric enzyme, which is heterodimeric, is located on intracellular and apical membranes of the gastric parietal cells. Autoantigenic determinants of H^+,K^+-ATPase are located on both the catalytic 100 kDa (α) and the glycosylated 60–90 kDa (β) subunits.

Gastric intrinsic factor Gastric intrinsic factor, the other major autoantigen in autoimmune gastritis, is a glycoprotein with a molecular weight of 44 kDa. Each molecule has the capacity to bind to one molecule of vitamin B_{12} and of its two autoantigenic determinants, one is at the binding site for vitamin B_{12} and the other is on a part of the molecule remote from this site.

The gastric autoantibodies

The major autoantibodies implicated in autoimmune gastritis are GPCA and the two antibodies that react with gastric intrinsic factor. Since H^+,K^+-ATPase is unique to the gastric parietal cell and is responsible for acid production, the inhibitory effect of the immune response on anti-H^+,K^+-ATPase accounts for hypochlorhydria. The scenario for the effect of autoantibodies is as follows.

Upon reaching the stomach after ingestion, vitamin B_{12} in the acid medium of gastric juice is freed from protein to bind to intrinsic factor. When acid secretion is inhibited by anti-H^+,K^+-ATPase the amount of vitamin B_{12} free to bind to intrinsic factor is greatly reduced and if the vitamin B_{12} site on intrinsic factor is blocked by antibody little, if any, will bind to intrinsic factor. The result is malabsorption of vitamin B_{12} and as the autoimmune gastritis progresses the stores of vitamin B_{12} dwindle to levels that can no longer sustain blood and nervous system metabolism. The patient becomes anemic and neurologic complications follow (**Figure 2**).

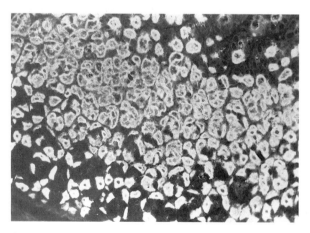

Figure 1 The gastric parietal cell antibody detected by immunofluorescence and illustrated here on murine gastric mucosa reacts with the cytoplasm of gastric parietal cells. Characteristic of the immunofluorescence reaction is the denser staining of the newly formed cells at the base of the mucosa (bottom left) and lighter staining of the mature cells towards the top of the mucosa. Experimental evidence suggests that the autoantigen in the parietal cell is the enzyme H^+,K^+-ATPase which is involved in production of acid secreted into the gastric juice.

Histologic features		Clinical features
Normal gastric mucosa	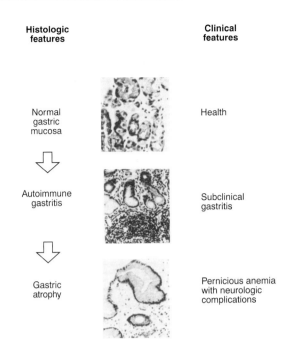	Health
Autoimmune gastritis		Subclinical gastritis
Gastric atrophy		Pernicious anemia with neurologic complications

Figure 2 The end-stage of autoimmune gastritis is gastric atrophy. This results in malabsorption of vitamin B_{12} and pernicious anemia with neurologic complications when vitamin B_{12} deficiency is severe. The histologic appearance of autoimmune gastritis is that of chronic inflammation.

In addition to autoantibodies to gastric antigens, patients with pernicious anemia have a substantially higher than normal frequency of antibodies to components of cells which are targets in diseases associated with autoimmune gastritis (**Table 1**). These autoantibodies include those reactive with thyroid peroxidase, thyroglobulin, pancreatic islet cells, adrenal cortical cells and ovarian cells and indicate the patient either has or is predisposed to the associated disease in which these antibodies occur.

Cell-mediated immunity to gastric antigens

The contribution of cell-mediated immunity to the gastric lesion in the body of the stomach is poorly understood. Increased numbers of T lymphocytes of the CD4 and CD8 lineages as well as a greatly increased number of B cells have been observed in the gastric lesion. It is presumed that T cells provide help required for the production of the gastric autoantibodies because these antibodies are predominantly of the immunoglobulin G (IgG) isotype, and that they also participate in the destruction of the gastric cells. One elegant study by electron microscopy showed T lymphocytes lined up against the membranes of gastric parietal cells and chief cells as if poised to destroy these cells.

Both gastric parietal cells and chief cells become greatly reduced in numbers as the inflammation progresses. Why there is accompanying loss of chief cells is, as yet, an enigma because the autoimmune attack is not thought to be directed at chief cells. Levels of serum gastrin are high probably because gastrin production by antral cells is under the control of gastric acidity and when acid is insufficient due to the absence of the parietal cells an essential feedback mechanism fails and levels of gastrin rise.

Gastritis

The autoimmune reaction is confined to the body of the stomach. The end-result is gastric atrophy but the rate at which the lesion progresses to this stage cannot be predicted in any individual patient. Some patients may maintain adequate vitamin B_{12} absorption for 20 years or more while others progress rapidly to atrophy.

The recognition of the 'pernicious anemia type' of gastritis was first made by Strickland and Mackay in 1973 who proposed a classification based on differences in the histologic findings in the body and antrum of the stomach. Type A gastritis was the 'pernicious anemia type' in which the immune reaction progressed until the glandular destruction was total and the mucosa atrophic. It was confined to the body of the stomach, and was associated with GPCA and high levels of serum gastrin. Type B gastritis was the 'simple' gastritis now mainly attributed to infection with *Helicobacter pylori* in which glandular destruction did not progress to total atrophy of the glands of both body and antrum, and was not associated

Table 1 Autoantibodies to nongastric components in pernicious anemia

Autoantibodies to:	Frequency	Disease association
Thyroid cells	30%	Hashimoto's thyroiditis
Thyroid peroxidase		Graves' disease
Thyroid hormone receptor		Atrophic hypothyroidism
Thyroglobulin		
Pancreatic islet cells	5%	Insulin-dependent diabetes mellitus
Adrenal cortical cells	5%	Primary Addison disease of the adrenal gland
Ovarian cells	Rare	Primary ovarian failure associated with Addison's disease
Neuromuscular junction	Rare	Lambert–Eaton syndrome

with GPCA or abnormally high levels of gastrin. Regeneration of gastric parietal cells, improved gastric function, and hematologic remission occurred after treatment with immunomodulating drugs such as the corticosteroid drugs and azathioprine, further suggesting that type A gastritis was immunologically mediated.

Animal models of autoimmune gastritis

Spontaneously occurring autoimmune gastritis

There is no animal model in which the primary disease is autoimmune gastritis although atypical forms of autoimmune gastritis are present in a proportion of animals whose primary autoimmune disease is one of the diseases associated with autoimmune gastritis. For example BB/W rats whose primary disease is insulin-dependent diabetes mellitus may have gastric parietal cell antibodies and histologic evidence of mild to moderate gastritis. However they have no reduction in acid secretion or fall in level of vitamin B_{12}. Another example, the obese strain chicken model of Hashimoto's thyroiditis may also have gastric parietal cell antibodies but the chicken provides a poor model of the human gastritis.

Experimentally induced autoimmune gastritis

Attempts to develop models of autoimmune gastritis in rhesus monkeys, dogs and rats by injecting gastric mucosa with immunologic adjuvants have met with only partial success and when inflammatory gastritis is induced it does not persist and progress like the human disease. The model that best mirrors the human disease is that which develops in BALB/c mice following four injections of murine H^+,K^+-ATPase emulsified in Freund's complete adjuvant. Although the lesion is reversible after cessation of immunization, the response to immunization is a florid gastritis with destruction of the parietal and chief cells and development of GPCA. An alternative model in the BALB/c mouse is the gastritis which follows thymectomy performed within 2–4 days of birth of the BALB/c mouse or thymectomy and a single dose of cyclophosphamide in the adult mouse. Two criteria are important in the development of these thymectomized models. One is the timing of thymectomy in the neonate which must be performed within 2–4 days of birth and the second is the need for combined treatment in the adult because neither thymectomy alone nor cyclophosphamide alone will result in gastritis.

Analysis of the cells in the early gastric lesion in the BALB/c models shows B cells, CD4 T cells and macrophages predominate. Transfer of splenic lymphocytes from affected animals to immunocompromised murine hosts results in autoimmune gastritis in the hosts, the cell responsible for the transfer being the CD4 T cell and its target the β subunit of gastric H^+,K^+-ATPase.

Inheritance

Three pieces of evidence converge to suggest that there is a genetic predisposition to pernicious anemia: the high prevalence of pernicious anemia in some racial groups, the high frequency of pernicious anemia in families within those racial groups, and the association of particular genetic markers among patients with pernicious anemia.

Pernicious anemia is predominantly a disease of people of Northern European origin. It is rare among Southern Europeans, Asians, Latin-Americans, and African and American Blacks and when it occurs in African and American Blacks it does so at an earlier age than it does in White Europeans and there is a higher frequency of antibodies to gastric intrinsic factor.

Multiple cases of pernicious anemia have been reported in families, often for several generations, and this frequency may be as much as 20 times greater than in the normal population. There is a raised but not absolute concordance of pernicious anemia in monozygotic twins and there are intrafamilial aggregations of the autoimmune diseases associated with pernicious anemia, namely the thyroid antoimmune diseases, insulin-dependent diabetes mellitus and primary Addison's disease of the adrenal gland which may be expressed as frank or subclinical disease marked by the presence of autoantibodies specific to these diseases. The prevalence of gastric parietal cell antibodies in first-degree relatives of patients with pernicious anemia is 20% which is three times higher than that found in normal controls and the frequency of autoantibodies to thyroid, pancreatic islet cells and adrenal cortical cells is also higher among relatives.

The higher frequency of gastric autoantibodies among relatives of patients with pernicious anemia is also in keeping with the high frequency of type A gastritis among relatives. Studies by Varis and colleagues on a large population of patients with pernicious anemia and their relatives in Finland showed that the prevalence of autoimmune gastritis was 13% higher in relatives than in controls. This familial aggregation of autoimmune gastritis was attributed to a genetic effect rather than an environmental factor. A delay in the onset of gastritis in males suggested that 'maleness' may have a protective effect.

Blood group A and blue eyes are phenotypes

which are common among Northern Europeans with pernicious anemia. Female gender on this phenotypic background potentiates predisposition to the autoimmune gastritis. Various HLA antigens have been associated with pernicious anemia although these associations are generally weak and have not been corroborated in all studies. Evidence for genetic polymorphism has been observed: HLA-B7, -B12, DR2 and DR2/4 heterozygosity has been shown to be increased in frequency in patients with pernicious anemia alone, and HLA-B8, -B18, -Bw15, DR3 and DR3/4 heterozygosity has been demonstrated in patients with pernicious anemia with an associated autoimmune endocrine disease. HLA-B12 has associated with severe vitamin B_{12} malabsorption and neuromyelopathy, and an increased frequency of Dw2 has been reported in patients with antibodies to gastric intrinsic factor.

Treatment

The standard treatment is administration of vitamin B_{12} by regular injection to replace that no longer absorbed from food. Being an immune-mediated disease, autoimmune gastritis is also ameliorated by immunomodulating drugs. However serious side-effects may result from treatment with such drugs and this is not the treatment of choice. If untreated, the outcome of the gastritis and vitamin B_{12} malabsorption is a fatal anemia with neurologic complications.

Conclusion

Pernicious anemia is the result of functional failure of the gastric parietal cell, and the gastritis associated with it fulfils the criteria for an autoimmune disease. Like most human autoimmune diseases, autoimmune gastritis predominates in women. It is associated with autoantibodies which react with the highly conserved and functionally important molecules, gastric H^+,K^+-ATPase and gastric intrinsic factor. There is a genetic predisposition to its development and this is potentiated in the female. It is associated with other well-defined organ-specific autoimmune diseases affecting endocrine glands. How these data are related to the cause, potentiation and maintenance of the gastritis remains unresolved.

See also: **Autoantibodies, tests for; Autoantigens; Autoimmune diseases; Autoimmunity.**

Further reading

Gleeson PA and Toh B-H (1991) Molecular targets in pernicious anaemia. *Immunology Today* 12: 233–238.

Gleeson PA, Toh B-H and van Driel IR (1996) Organ-specific autoimmunity induced by lymphopenia. *Immunological Reviews* 149: 97–125.

Kekki M, Siurala M, Varis K, Sipponen P and Nevanlinna HR (1987) Classification, principles and genetics of chronic gastritis. *Scandinavian Journal of Gastroenterology* 22 (suppl 141): 1–28.

Strickland RG (1990) Gastritis. *Springer Seminars in Immunopathology* 12: 203–217.

Toh B-H, Gleeson PA, van Driel IR and Whittingham S (1996) Autoimmune gastritis and pernicious anemia. In: Rose NR and Mackay IR (eds) *The Autoimmune Diseases*, 2nd edn. Orlando: Academic Press.

ANERGY, B CELL

David M Tarlinton, The Walter and Eliza Hall Institute of Medical Research, Royal Melbourne Hospital, Victoria, Australia

Generation of immunological diversity and the need for tolerance

The adaptive immune system, comprising B and T lymphocytes, functions by the clonal response of those lymphocytes to foreign antigen. Each lymphocyte recognizes a single antigen, and the existence of a particular specificity among a population of lymphocytes does not depend on the prior exposure of the animal to that antigen. That is, the introduction of an antigen does not induce the appearance of lymphocytes specific for that antigen; the cells already exist. What antigen does is to expand selectively those lymphocyte clones which recognize the antigen. This is the basis of the clonal selection theory formulated by Burnet. Defense against a potentially infinite number of foreign antigens requires the immune system to be able to generate an infinite number of specificities, each borne on a unique lymphocyte clone. The immune system can achieve a spectacular level of diversity among the antigen receptors of B and T lymphocytes by using the random association of gene segments to create the final receptor gene products during lymphocyte development. Because the selection of individual gene segments is random, the range of specificities embodied in the final receptor molecules is also random. Some lymphocytes will develop expressing receptors which recognize self antigens, while others will be specific for as yet unencountered foreign antigens. The problem for the immune system is how to prevent the self reactive lymphocytes from responding if and when they encounter their cognate self antigen, while allowing the remainder to survive. The means by which the body silences self reactive lymphocytes is called tolerance. Once the requirement for immunological tolerance had been recognized, it was proposed that its imposition was restricted to the early or neonatal stage of life. This model was subsequently modified by Lederberg to one in which each lymphocyte went through a tolerance-sensitive stage during its development. Encountering antigen during this phase resulted in the lymphocyte being permanently disabled. If, however, an antigen was encountered after this developmental stage, then the lymphocyte would be activated and initiate an immune response. Thus while some lymphocytes specific for a foreign antigen may be in a tolerance-sensitive state when they first encounter antigen, other lymphocytes with the same specificity which developed prior to the introduction of the antigen and which are therefore not tolerant, would respond. Self antigens, on the other hand, would always be present and thus able to tolerize each developing lymphocyte.

Early models of tolerance induction invariably invoked clonal deletion as the means by which self reactive cells were rendered tolerant. That is, self reactive lymphocytes were killed by interaction with self antigen. Numerous experiments dating from the 1970s, however, suggested that not all self reactive B cells were deleted. After Naor and Sulitzeanu described the enumeration of antigen-specific lymphocytes by their ability to bind radioactively labeled antigen, others used the same technique to determine whether antigen-specific B cells persisted in tolerant animals. In some instances a reduction in the number of such B cells was observed, while in others no change was seen, suggesting that B cell tolerance was not obligatorily associated with deletion. Using this technique it was possible to demonstrate in apparently healthy animals the presence of lymphocytes which could bind self antigens such as thyroglobulin. Yet other groups showed that polyclonal B cell activators such as lipopolysaccharide could induce the production of autoantibodies from animals with no overt signs of autoimmunity. The overall effect of these and other experiments was to call into question the exclusive role of clonal deletion in establishing and maintaining immunological tolerance.

Clonal anergy

Experiments pioneered by Nossal and Pike in the 1980s led to the enunciation of clonal anergy as an alternative mode of B cell tolerance induction. In the original experiments these workers reported that while both high and low doses of antigen could induce tolerance, only the high doses resulted in deletion. Low doses of antigen tolerized the animals such that they were subsequently unable to respond to immunogenic forms of the same antigen, despite the persistence of antigen-specific B cells. Data supporting clonal anergy as a means of tolerizing T cells subsequently emerged. Progress in resolving the relative importance of clonal deletion and anergy in maintaining immunological tolerance was hindered by the difficulty in detecting and enumerating antigen-specific lymphocytes in normal animals and in quantifying changes to this population upon the induction of tolerance. Subsequent advances in this field have depended on the use of immunoglobulin transgenic animals.

Transgenic models of B cell tolerance

Immunoglobulin transgenic mice are derived by the introduction of genes encoding functional immunoglobulin heavy and light chains into a zygote. Although every cell in the resultant transgenic mouse carries the introduced genes, expression will only occur in those cells containing the appropriate transcription elements. In the case of immunoglobulin genes, this means B cells and occasionally T cells. Expression of the transgenic immunoglobulin chains in early B cell precursors inhibits the rearrangement of the endogenous immunoglobulin genes and therefore results in an animal in which essentially every B cell develops with the same antigen specificity. If the antigen for which the immunoglobulin transgenes are specific is present in the same animal, then all the B cells will be autoreactive. A number of model systems have been developed employing this approach. In various forms the transgenic B cells are specific for DNA, for major histocompatibility complex (MHC) class I antigens, for mouse red blood cells and, in a particularly flexible model, the B cells are specific for hen-egg lysozyme (HEL). While HEL is obviously not a mouse self antigen, mice transgenic for HEL have been made and, when crossed with the immunoglobulin transgenic mice, create a situation of self reactivity. An advantage of this system has been that the form in which the HEL is expressed can be altered by changing aspects of the transgene, thereby allowing different forms of B cell tolerance to be studied. Using these transgenic models, it was quickly revealed that if the self antigen was a membrane-bound protein expressed on cells present in the bone marrow, blood or peripheral lymphoid organs, then self reactive B cells were deleted. This deletion was rapid, efficient and required a surprisingly low affinity for the antigen. In situations in which the self antigen was not membrane bound, but rather existed as a serum protein to which the B cells were chronically exposed, then the self reactive B cells were not rapidly deleted, but rather rendered anergic. Analysis of transgenic self reactive systems that promote B cell anergy rather than deletion has revealed some of the cellular and molecular changes that characterize this state of immunological unresponsiveness.

Anergic B cells

The biology of anergic B cells differs from that of nonself reactive B cells in several respects, including the level of expression and functional capability of surface immunoglobulin, activation of helper T cells, lifespan and migration within the lymphoid system. Mature B cells ordinarily express both immunoglobulin M (IgM) and IgD on the cell surface at relatively uniform levels. Anergic B cells express IgD at levels equal to that of nonself reactive (or normal) B cells, but they downregulate IgM by between 5- and 50-fold. The downregulation of IgM is associated with an inhibition in signaling such that phosphorylation of critical signal transduction molecules associated with surface immunoglobulin is diminished. Molecules such as the syk tyrosine kinase and the immunoglobulin coreceptors Igα and Igβ are underphosphorylated in anergic B cells following receptor stimulation. A further consequence of this inhibition in signaling is the fact that receptor stimulation of anergic B cells does not result in the release of intracellular calcium, a critical component in the pathway of B cell activation.

While the changes which are intrinsic to the B cell clearly inhibit the ability of the anergic B cell to respond to subsequent exposure to its cognate antigen, such a state of unresponsiveness can be reversed by signaling through CD40. In certain situations in which anergic B cells are exposed to either CD40 ligand or antibodies specific for CD40 in the presence of the cytokine interleukin 4 (IL-4), the B cells proliferate and differentiate into antibody-secreting plasma cells. This experimental result, however, does not extend to the anergic B cell being able to solicit help from antigen-specific T cells. B cells encountering their cognate antigen in a form which cross-links surface immunoglobulin will not only process and present the antigen to T cells on MHC class II, but will also upregulate the costimulatory B7 molecules. These molecules are critical for the activation of helper T cells which induces expression of CD40 ligand on T cells, which in turn is critical for the final differentiation of the B cell into an antibody secreting cell. Anergic B cells fail to significantly upregulate B7-2 in response to receptor cross-linking, meaning that they are unable to activate T cell help. This further diminishes the possibility of anergic B cells responding to self antigen.

Self reactive B cells, however, never constitute the entire output of the lymphoid system – they exist among cells which show no self reactivity. In this respect the transgenic models described above, while useful, are somewhat less than ideal. More realistic situations have been developed in which only a fraction of the B cells are specific for a self antigen and their behaviour in relation to their nonself reactive peers can be assessed. Such studies have been conducted by two groups, one being that of Cyster and Goodnow and the second Fulcher and Basten. These experiments have revealed that anergic B cells show a distinct pattern of recirculation in the lymphoid organs relative to nonself reactive B cells. Normally, mature B cells leave the blood, migrate through the T cell areas of the lymphoid organs and enter the B cell follicles. From here they enter the lymphatic circulation which eventually returns them to the blood. Self reactive B cells in the presence of their cognate self antigen enter the secondary lymphoid organs but are unable to enter the B cell follicles. Instead they accumulate at the border of the B and T cell areas of the spleen where they die within a few days in the absence of T cell help. If T cell help is available then the B cells become activated and give rise to structures characteristic of an immune response, namely antibody-forming cells and germinal centers. Thus tolerance of the immune system is a cooperative event, requiring both tolerance in the T and B cell compartments. The failure of self reactive B cells to enter the follicles has been the subject of two interpretations. In one case, Cyster and coworkers suggest that self reactive B cells are unable to compete effectively for a homing signal emanating from the follicle and therefore are excluded. In order for B cells to have a long life they need to have access to survival factors in the follicle, and thus excluded self reactive B cells die quite rapidly. Fulcher and Basten, on the other hand, suggest that localization of the cells in the T cell area of the spleen is a consequence of receptor stimulation and is indicative of the B cells searching for T cell help. If that help is not forthcoming, as would normally be the case for a self antigen, then the B cells rapidly die. Furthermore, this group argues that the critical factor determining whether an individual B cell is able to enter the follicles or not is the level of receptor engagement. If the concentration of self antigen is low, then the B cell is able to ignore the signal and behave like a nonself reactive cell. Once the concentration is above some threshold level, however, then the lymphocyte changes its trafficking pattern and has a reduced lifespan in the absence of T cell help.

Breaking anergy

B cells made anergic by chronic exposure to a self antigen are able to be activated in some instances. As indicated above, stimulation of anergic B cells through the CD40 molecule in the presence of IL-4 is able to induce proliferation and differentiation of the B cell. Similarly, extensive cross-linking of surface immunoglobulin on the B cell is able to activate the cell. This can be achieved, for example, when a B cell chronically exposed to soluble monomeric self antigen encounters the same antigen in a highly multimerized form such as a cell protein. In this case, the B cell will proliferate and differentiate into an antibody-forming cell in the presence of the appropriate cofactors. This reversal of anergy is dependent on the strength of the receptor signal. In the presence of soluble self antigen, anergic B cells are killed by antigen specific nontolerant helper T cells. This death is dependent on anergic B cells expressing the apoptosis-inducing molecule Fas and the helper T cells expressing its ligand. This lethal embrace can be transformed into a stimulatory one if the antigen receptor stimulation given to the B cell is sufficiently strong.

Why is anergy reversible?

Clonal anergy, defined as the presence of antigen-specific B cells in an unresponsive state, can be achieved by a number of mechanisms. Some involve modulation of the signaling of the B cell itself, while others alter the ability of these B cells to solicit and respond to T cell help. Still other mechanisms alter the location of anergic B cells in the lymphoid system and their lifespan. Why are so many tolerance mechanisms employed when it would be simpler to delete any lymphocyte which showed traces of self reactivity? Several explanations have been put forward to answer this question, most cogently by Goodnow. First, not all self antigens will be present in bone marrow when the B cells are developing and sensitive to tolerance induction. Second, if all B cells which show any degree of binding to self antigens were to be deleted, it is questionable that the lymphoid system could generate a sufficient number of cells to counter the infectious agents animals are exposed to. That is, anergy may be a means by which the immune system is able to silence potentially harmful B cell clones and yet have B cells survive long enough to be exported to the peripheral lymphoid organs. In these locations it is possible that the anergic B cells may encounter a foreign antigen to which they have a higher affinity than that with which they recognize the self antigen. If this were the case, then the anergic B cell could be activated and participate in a protective immune response. The anergic B cells would quickly die, however, if no such foreign antigen existed at the time it reached the periphery. This may also account for the reversibility of B cell anergy.

See also: **Anergy, T cell; Antigen presentation via MHC class II molecules; B lymphocyte activation; B lymphocyte repertoire; CD40 and its ligand; B7 (CD80 & CD86); Helper T lymphocytes; Clonal deletion; Clonal selection; Diversity, generation of; Effector lymphocytes; Fas (CD95) and fas ligand; Interleukin 4; Second signals for lymphocyte activation; Tolerance, peripheral.**

Further reading

Cornall RJ, Goodnow CC and Cyster JG (1995) The regulation of self-reactive B cells. *Current Opinion in Immunology* 7: 804–811.

Goodnow CC (1996) Balancing immunity and tolerance: deleting and tuning lymphocyte repertoires. *Proceedings of the National Academy of Sciences of the USA* 93: 2264–2271.

Hodgkin PD and Basten A (1995) B cell activation, tolerance and antigen-presenting function. *Current Opinion in Immunology* 7: 121–129.

Nossal GJV (1996) Clonal anergy of B cells: a flexible, reversible and quantitative concept. *Journal of Experimental Medicine* **183**: 1953–1956.

ANERGY, T CELL

Ronald H Schwartz, Laboratory of Cellular and Molecular Immunology, National Institutes of Health, Bethesda, Maryland, USA

In 1908 C. Von Pirquet first used the term anergy (from the Greek meaning without work or not working) to describe the loss of response to a tuberculin skin test in patients infected with the measles virus. Since then this type of phenomenon has been described for delayed-type hypersensitivity responses to a variety of antigens during the course of a number of different infectious diseases. It appears to be a nonspecific suppression of the T cell response which reverses when the infectious agent is cleared. In 1980 Nossal and Pike borrowed the term and used it to describe the state of antigen-binding B cells isolated from an adult mouse that had been made unresponsive by injection of a tolerogenic dose of antigen. The B cells failed to differentiate into immunoglobulin secreting cells when restimulated *in vitro* with either antigen or the mitogen lipopolysaccharide. They called this form of unresponsiveness 'clonal anergy', to denote that the unresponsiveness was antigen specific. The tolerogenic regimen used in these experiments was derived from the earlier work of Dresser, who demonstrated that intravenous injection of deaggregated proteins in the absence of an adjuvant would induce a subsequent state of unresponsiveness to that antigen. In contrast, if the same preparation of antigen was given with Freund's complete adjuvant as a costimulator, it was immunogenic. This work eventually gave rise to the concept that antigen stimulation of a lymphocyte in the absence of costimulation was tolerogenic. When a similar phenomenon was discovered for cloned T cells in tissue culture, the term clonal anergy was extended to this population as well. In this case the unresponsiveness was a failure of the T cells to proliferate on rechallenge with antigen presented by professional antigen-presenting cells (APCs). It is this last category of the use of the term clonal anergy to which this entry is confined.

The induction of T cell clonal anergy in the mouse was first achieved by stimulating cultured lymphocyte clones with peptide antigens and chemically fixed APCs. Induction of this same state with purified major histocompatibility complex (MHC) class II molecules in planar membranes made it clear that T cell receptor (TCR) occupancy by peptide – MHC complexes was all that was necessary for anergy to occur. Other forms of pure TCR engagement, such as concanavalin A crosslinking in the absence of

APCs or plate-bound anti-CD3 monoclonal antibody, also induced clonal anergy, although significant amounts of cell death were observed as well. Anergy induction was prevented by addition of APCs, giving support to the paradigm that signal 1 (the antigen-specific signal) alone was inhibitory, whereas signal 1 plus signal 2 (costimulation) was stimulatory. The nature of the costimulatory signal was subsequently shown to be engagement of the T cell CD28 molecule by its ligands CD80 and CD86 on the APC. The requirement for APC activation in order to express CD80/86 explains why the original chemical fixation experiments prevented costimulation.

Anergic T cell clones have a very distinct pattern of partial inactivation. Proliferation is prevented on restimulation by a number of mechanisms. First and foremost, interleukin 2 (IL-2) production is inhibited by 20–50 fold. This block is at the level of transcription and appears to involve interference with signal transduction through the $p21^{ras}$/MAP kinase pathway. The latter prevents activation of the transcription factor AP-1 which is required for IL-2 gene transcription. Overinduction of the IL-2 transcriptional repressor, Nil-2a, has also been reported in anergic T cells. Production of other cytokines is inhibited, but to varying degrees. IL-3 and tumor necrosis factor α production are inhibited about tenfold. In contrast, IL-4 and interferon γ production are only reduced slightly. Interestingly, in those clones capable of using IL-4 as a growth factor, anergy induction blocks only the ability of the cells to respond to IL-4. Similarly the augmentation of TCR-induced proliferation by IL-12 is inhibited. Finally, expression of CD40 ligand, which is required for T cell mediated, B cell proliferation, is inhibited. The overall pattern suggests that anergy is a growth arrest state designed to reduce proliferation in the T cell immune response.

Costimulation given within 2 hours of TCR occupancy blocks the induction of anergy. This is due to an increase in IL-2 production mediated by a CD28-induced augmentation of IL-2 mRNA stability and an increase in the activity of Jun N-terminal kinase (JNK), which enhances IL-2 gene transcription. The IL-2 produced inhibits anergy by two mechanisms. One is by activation of Janus kinase (JAK)3 via stimulation through the common γ chain of the IL-2 receptor. The other is by driving the cell into cycle. The division process antagonizes and even reverses the block in the Ras/MAP kinase pathway by an as yet unknown mechanism.

Anergy can also be induced in murine T cell clones by stimulating them with altered peptide ligands. In this case costimulation is normal, but signal transduction through the TCR is suboptimal. This partial signaling possibly results in the production of the inhibitor of the Ras/MAP kinase pathway, but is not sufficient to produce IL-2. As a consequence, the small production of inhibitor is unopposed and the cell becomes anergic. Human T cell clones can also be induced into an unresponsive state by exposure to high concentrations of normal peptide ligands. In this case too, the presence or absence of costimulation makes no difference. A biochemical analysis, however, suggests that the unresponsiveness is mediated by a different mechanism. Here signaling through the calcium/calcineurin pathway is impaired, while the MAP kinase pathway is normal. A similar biochemical block can be observed in mouse cells, but only after they are stimulated through the IL-2 receptor. The murine block, however, is transient, and the cells return to their normal responsiveness in 5–7 days. In order to distinguish the state of unresponsiveness in human clones stimulated with high concentrations of peptide from anergy induced in human and mouse clones in the absence of costimulation, it has been proposed that the latter be called Ras-blocked anergy and the former calcium-blocked anergy.

The in vitro demonstration of T cell anergy led to a major effort to identify this state in vivo. Two systems have been described which look as though they represent this phenomenon. The first is induced with superantigens such as staphylococcal enterotoxin B (SEB) and minor lymphocyte stimulating (Mls) antigen. In this case subsets of T cells expressing particular V_β receptors expand in response to the superantigen stimulus. Several days later many of these cells die, but a small cohort remains and these residual cells are often unresponsive to restimulation with either the superantigen or an antibody against the V_β receptor. An analysis of the biochemical events taking place in this population during restimulation revealed a profile similar to that seen in anergic T cell clones. Interestingly the cells in vivo showed a block in IL-2 receptor signaling as well as one in IL-2 production. Furthermore, multiple injections of the superantigen seemed to produce a more profound state of anergy in which signaling through the Ras/MAP kinase pathway was blocked to the point of impairing activation of the NFκB and NF-AT transcription factors in addition to AP-1. A recent report has suggested that this deeper state of

anergy can also be achieved in vitro if the T cell clones are exposed to IL-10 during their stimulation through the T cell receptor. The molecular mechanism for this IL-10 enhancement is not known.

The second in vivo system in which anergy has been identified involves TCR transgenic mice. CD4 cells from such animals have been transferred to normal recipients and challenged with antigen intraperitoneally in incomplete Freund's adjuvant. Cells recovered from the lymph nodes failed to proliferate in vitro when rechallenged with antigen. In a second model, H-Y specific, TCR transgenic, CD8 cells, when transferred into male nude mice, responded in an analogous way to that seen for normal T cells stimulated with superantigens. After an initial expansion and death phase the remaining cells were unresponsive to restimulation with either the antigen or an anti-TCR antibody. To date, the biochemical state of the unresponsive cells has not been examined in either transgenic model. Hence at this time one cannot be certain that the state is the same as that observed in T cell anergy studied in vitro.

Given the existence of anergic T cells in vivo, one can now ask what their biological function is. No consensus exists on this point. It was originally thought that anergy played some role in self tolerance. Naive T cells make only IL-2 following T cell activation and it was postulated that anergy induction would block this response, thus preventing the T cell from expanding and differentiating into an effector cell. At this point, however, there is no definitive evidence that naive T cells in vivo are turned off when given signal 1 in the absence of signal 2. Some experiments suggest that instead the cells may differentiate into T_H2 cells. Anergy and T_H2 differentiation can be distinguished by their responsiveness to IL-4. Anergic T cells cannot proliferate in response to IL-4, whereas T_H2 cells can. So far no investigation has clearly made this distinction. Another possible scenario for anergic T cells in vivo is that they are on their way to die. The biochemical events seen inside the T cell during and after anergy induction are not those associated with apoptosis; however, Fas ligand is upregulated in vitro and could be used in a subsequent encounter with antigen to mediate cell death. On the other hand, transfer of CD8 TCR transgenic cells into female nude recipients suggests that the cells do not die and that they can actually spontaneously come out of the anergic state in the absence of antigen. Anergy can also be reversed in vitro by stimulating the T cell clones with IL-2. Whether this reversibility would provide a useful mechanism for transiently recruiting autoreactive clones for use in an ongoing immune response to foreign antigens remains an intriguing possibility.

See also: **Anergy, B cell; Delayed-type hypersensitivity; Second signals for lymphocyte activation; Superantigens; T lymphocyte activation.**

Further reading

Alberollala J, Takaki S, Kerner JD et al (1997) Differential signaling by lymphocyte antigen receptors. Annual Review of Immunology 15: 125–154.

Boussiotis VA, Freeman GJ, Berezovskaya A, Barber DL, Nadler LM (1997) Maintenance of human T cell anergy: blocking of IL-2 gene transcription by activated Rap1. Science 278: 124–128.

Cauley LS, Cauley KA, Shub F, Huston G, Swain SL (1997) Transferable anergy: superantigen treatment induces CD4+ T cell tolerance that is reversible and requires CD4−CD8− cells and interferon gamma. Journal of Experimental Medicine 186: 77–81.

Jenkins MK (1992) The role of cell division in the induction of clonal anergy. Immunology Today 13: 69–73.

Parijs LV, Perez VL, Biuckians A, Maki RG, London CA, Abbas AK (1997) Role of interleukin 12 and costimulators in T cell anergy in vivo. Journal of Experimental Medicine, 186: 1119–1128.

Schwartz RH (1990) A cell culture model for T lymphocyte clonal anergy. Science 248: 1349–1356.

Schwartz RH (1996) Models of T cell anergy: is there a common molecular mechanism. Journal of Experimental Medicine 184: 1–8.

Schwartz RH (1997) T cell clonal anergy. Current Opinion in Immunology 9: 351–357.

Smith JA, Tso JY, Clark MR, Cole MS, Bluestone JA (1997) Nonmitogenic anti-CD3 monoclonal antibodies deliver a partial T cell receptor signal and induce clonal anergy. Journal of Experimental Medicine 185: 1413–1422.

ANNEXINS (LIPOCORTINS)

Fusao Hirata, Departments of Pharmaceutical Science, Pharmacology & Institute of Chemical Toxicology, Wayne State University, Michigan, USA

The annexin (lipocortin) family of proteins possess a highly conserved core region, consisting of four or eight repeats of approximately 70 amino acid residues, and a highly variable N-terminal region. The core region mediates Ca^{2+}-dependent binding to phospholipid membranes and forms a Ca^{2+} channel-like structure. The physical and structural properties of annexin proteins suggest that they regulate multiple aspects of cell membrane function, including involvement in membrane trafficking, signal transduction and cell–matrix interactions. Some of their actions are akin to those of glucocorticoids, including anti-inflammatory, anti-edema and immunosuppressive effects.

Historical background

Glucocorticoids are widely used as one of the most efficacious medicines against various inflammatory and immunological diseases such as rheumatoid arthritis, systemic lupus erythematosus and bronchial asthma. Their anti-inflammatory action is mediated by inhibition of arachidonic acid release, a precursor of prostaglandins (PGs), hydroxyeicosatetraenoic acids (HETEs) and leukotrienes (LTs). Phospholipase A_2 (PLA_2) and alkylphospholipids, a precursor of platelet-activating factor (PAF), in biomembranes have been considered as the key enzyme and the major source of arachidonic acid, respectively. Anti-inflammatory steroids also inhibit the formation of both PAF and its inactive lyso-form (deacylated molecule). Since most of the anti-inflammatory actions of glucocorticoids are inhibited in vivo and in vitro by inhibitors of protein synthesis as well as mRNA synthesis, it was proposed that the anti-inflammatory action of glucocorticoids is partly, if not exclusively, mediated through the induced synthesis of PLA_2 inhibitory protein(s).

Between 1980 and 1984, attempts were made by several groups to isolate a protein 1) whose synthesis is induced by glucocorticoids, 2) that inhibits the activity of PLA_2 in vitro and in vivo, and 3) that displays an anti-inflammatory action like glucorticoids. Several different proteins that inhibit PLA_2 in vitro were identified and partially purified. These included 'lipomodulin' from rabbit neutrophils (molecular weight = 40 kDa), 'renocortin' from rat kidney cells (molecular weight = 30 kDa) and 'macrocortin' from rat macrophages (molecular weight = 15 kDa). Among these proteins, lipomodulin was best characterized: a possibly glycosylated protein with an apparent molecular weight of 40 kDa and a pI value of 9.0. This protein can bind 2 mol of Ca^{2+} mol^{-1} protein, and the concentration of Ca^{2+} required for half maximal binding is approximately 1 μM. It was proposed that this protein suppresses PLA_2 activity by forming a complex with PLA_2 at the Ca^{2+}-binding site(s). Furthermore, various protein kinases including protein kinase C and tyrosine protein kinase, can phosphorylate lipomodulin to modify its function and structure as detected by the inhibitory activity against PLA_2 and the susceptibility to proteases.

Despite differences in their chemical properties, all proteins isolated as second messengers of glucocorticoid anti-inflammatory action have similar, if not identical, biological properties: 1) the synthesis of these proteins is induced by glucocorticoids, 2) preparations of these proteins, regardless of their purity, inhibit porcine pancreas and/or snake venom PLA_2 *in vitro*, 3) these protein preparations mimic some actions of glucocorticoids, especially with regard to arachidonic acid release and production of lipid mediators such as prostaglandins, and 4) some monoclonal antibodies raised in one laboratory cross-react with the proteins prepared by the other laboratories. Based upon these findings, it was proposed in 1984 that a family of PLA_2 inhibitory proteins whose syntheses are induced by glucocorticoids be named as *lipo*(modulin, macro- or reno-)*cortins* (lipocortins). In 1986, the Biogen group purified two proteins from human placenta whose properties are almost identical to those of lipomodulin. They isolated cDNA clones encoding these proteins, and described their chemical natures as follows: 1) their molecular weights are around 36 kDa, 2) they have multiple phosphorylation sites including one for tyrosine protein kinase and a potential glycosylation site, 3) they have four repeats which can bind acidic phospholipids and Ca^{2+}, and 4) they inhibit PLA_2 *in vitro*. Interestingly, these cDNA clones were almost identical to the simultaneously discovered cDNAs that encode two of the major substrate proteins (calpactins) for the EGF receptor (tyrosine) kinase.

Diversity in the annexin family

Two protein inhibitors of PLA_2, namely annexin I and II, have the same characteristic structural organization: following unique N-terminal sequences of about 40 amino acid residues, they both are composed of four repeated sequence motifs of 70–80 amino acids, in which a conserved 17 amino acid consensus (Lys-Gly-X-Gly-Thr-Asp-Gln-X-X-Leu--Ile-X-Ile-Leu-Ala-X-Arg) is thought to be important for Ca^{2+}-dependent binding to phospholipids. These features have now been identified in sequences of 18 related proteins (**Table 1**), although annexin VI has 8 repeats instead of the 4 in other annexins. Due to this conserved structure in the C-terminal domain, annexins have a high degree of identity with each other, and maintain around 40–60% amino acid sequence homology. This family of proteins is ubiquitously distributed, being present in lower organisms such as *Drosophila* and plants. They are referred to as annexins since their main property is to 'annex' (bind to) cellular membrane phospholipids in a Ca^{2+}-dependent manner. Distinct from the 'EF-hand calcium-binding proteins' such as calmodulin, their intrinsic affinity for Ca^{2+} is generally low (around 0.1–1 mM), and the number of Ca^{2+}-binding sites is between 2 and 4. However, the presence of phospholipids increases their affinity for Ca^{2+} up to 100-fold, while Ca^{2+} facilitates their binding to acidic phospholipids (phosphatidic acid > phosphatidylserine > phosphatidylinositol). Although some annexins such as annexin I and II can bind to neutral phospholipids such as phosphatidylethanolamine, their binding to phosphatidylcholine and sphingomyelin, choline lipids, is not detectable. In

Table 1 The annexin (lipocortin) family

	Previous terminology	Biological functions
Annexin I	Calpactin II, Chromobindin 9, GIF, p35	EGF receptor kinase substrate
Annexin II	Calpactin I, Chromobindin 8, p36, PAP-IV, Protein I	Src-kinase substrate
Annexin III	Calcimedin 35-α, Calphobindin III, PAP-III	
Annexin IV	Calcimedin 35-β, Calelectrin 32.5K, Chromobindin 4, Endonexin I, PAP-II, PP4-X, Protein II	F-actin-binding protein
Annexin V	Anchorin CII, Calelectrin 35K, Calphobindin I, Calcimedin 35-γ, Endonexin II, IBC, VAC-α, PAP-I, PP4	Anticoagulant protein
Annexin VI	Calcimedin 67K, Calelectrin 67K, Calphobindin II, Chromobindin 20, p68, p70, 73K, Protein III, Synhibin	
Annexin VII	Synexin	
Annexin VIII	Vascular anticoagulant (VAC-β)	
Annexin IX	*Drosophila melanogaster* annexin	
Annexin X	*Drosophila melanogaster* annexin	
Annexin XI	Calcyclin-associated annexin (CAP)-50	
Annexin XII	*Hydra vulgaris* annexin	
Annexin XIII	Intestine-specific annexin (ISA)	

contrast to the conserved C-terminal core, each annexin has a unique and extremely variable sequence in the N-terminal domain with the length varying from a few amino acids to 160 amino acids. This domain contains various sites for phosphorylation, glycosylation, acylation and other post-translational modifications. A dimer of annexin II forms a heterotetrameric structure via its N-terminus with a dimer of the p11 protein, a complex which can bind to phosphatidylserine at nanomolar Ca^{2+} concentrations. Therefore, this domain is considered as the regulatory region of the protein for various biological functions.

Results of genomic analysis suggest that annexin genes may be derived from a common ancestor gene, and that the evolution and diversification of the family arose by two consecutive duplications of a DNA sequence encoding a protein resembling a single repeat. The structure of all the annexin genes is well conserved. The 5'-flanking region of annexin genes contains sequences for the binding sites of several transcriptional factors, indicating transcriptional regulation by mitogenic stimulation, steroids and metals, while the 5'-flanking region demonstrates alu-like repeats. The presence of potential splice sites and Z-DNA structure in the C-terminal core region produces different isoforms of annexins.

Mechanism of action of annexins

In contrast to the initial proposed mechanism of phospholipase A_2 inhibition whereby annexin I (lipomodulin) was thoght to complex with PLA_2 via Ca^{2+}-binding sites, the currently accepted mechanism proposes that annexins bind phospholipids in a Ca^{2+}-dependent manner, thus depleting phospholipid substrates for phospholipase A_2. Since a certain type of PLA_2 (type II) is released in inflammatory loci, the in vivo anti-inflammatory action of annexins is also explained by a hypothetical mechanism in which annexins protect membranes from attack by PLA_2 by binding to membrane phospholipids. Since annexins bind acidic phospholipids such as phosphatidic acid, phosphatidylinositol and phosphatidylserine but not phosphatidylethanolamine or phosphatidylcholine, this interpretation does not explain their specificity for PLA_2. Lipases such as phospholipase C and phospholipase D, the enzymes that hydrolyze these phospholipids are also potentially inhibited by the same mechanism. Annexins are now found to form complex homo- and heterodimers or tetramers, with annexins or other proteins. The annexin-binding proteins are annexins, collagens, S-100, apolipoproteins, helicase, DNA methyltransferase, protein kinase C, glycero-3-phos-

phate dehydrogenase, malate dehydrogenase, calcyclin, F-actins and PLA_2. Despite the findings that ratios of annexin I to phospholipid substrate (phosphatidylserine) are an important determinant factor of the in vitro inhibition of PLA_2, the possibility of complex formation is not ruled out. Such protein–protein interaction, whether it be a specific interaction or nonspecific electrostatic interaction, alters the function and stability of these binding proteins. In this sense, annexins have some properties similar to those of 'house-keeping' proteins.

Crystallographic and molecular modeling studies demonstrate that annexins have a calcium channel-like structure. In fact, annexin V and VII are shown to function as voltage-dependent and GTP-sensitive Ca^{2+} channels, respectively. GTP-binding activity has been implicated by a homology between the amino acids 78–236 (the core region) of annexin I and the amino acids 22–171 of c-K-ras 2a, a mammalian ras-onc gene product which has GTPase activity. It is noteworthy that maize annexin has ATPase activity. It is also speculated that annexins which bind to mitochondrial dehydrogenases such as isocitrate dehydrogenase and malate dehydrogenase may act as Ca^{2+} sensors, since these enzymes are known to be activated by Ca^{2+} without apparent Ca^{2+}-binding sites. Therefore, annexins are distinct from EF-hand and Ca^{2+}-binding proteins such as calmodulin, whose major functions are Ca^{2+} buffering inside cells.

Biological actions and possible physiological roles

Initial efforts have been made to identify and characterize the annexins, particularly annexin I and II, as possible second messengers in response to anti-inflammatory steroids. The observations to date have shown that these recombinant annexins are able to mimic a part, if not all, of the anti-inflammatory action of glucocorticoids, while antibodies against annexins diminish such actions (**Table 2**). Even some of their fragments containing the N-terminus exhibit similar but weak anti-inflammatory actions. The inflammatory reactions inhibited by annexins and their fragments include not only the release of arachidonate and its metabolites and the formation of PAF but also neutrophil chemotaxis and release of lysozymes. The cytotoxic reaction by cytotoxic T cells and NK cells is also inhibited by both annexins and glucocorticoids. Although the annexin I and II genes contain GRE sequences in their 5'-flanking regions, thus implicating transcriptional regulation by glucocorticoids, induction of the synthesis of annexins by the steroids remains to be determined. Such induc-

Table 2 Biological action of annexins

1. Inflammatory responses
    a) Inhibition of *in vivo* inflammation
        Carrageenan-induced paw edema and pleurisy
    b) Inhibition of *in vitro* inflammatory response
        Inhibition of neutrophil chemotaxis
        Slight inhibition of O_2^- production
        Inhibition of lysozyme release
        Inhibition of phagocytosis
        Inhibition of arachidonic acid liberation
        Inhibition of PAF formation
2. Immune system
    a) *In vivo*
        Tumor-induced immunosuppression
        Modulation of *in vivo* pyrogenic action by
        cytokines
        Suppression of IgE synthesis
    b) *In vitro*
        Inhibition of cytotoxic reaction of cytotoxic T cells
        and NK cells
        Inhibition of *in vitro* cytotoxic T cell generation
        Inhibition of IL-1 production
        Inhibition of IL-1 action
        Inhibition of IL-2 production
        Inhibition of T cell proliferation
        Induction of maturation of suppressor T cells
        Induction of memory cells
        Inhibition of IgE synthesis
        Change from necrosis to apoptosis of H_2O_2-
        treated thymocytes
3. Cell proliferation and differentiation
        Differentiation of leukemia cell lines
        Differentiation of macrophage cell lines
        Differentiation of neuronal cell lines
        Differentiation of glial cell lines
        Differentiation of fibroblast cell lines
        Differentiation of epidermal cell lines
        Differentiation of epithelial cell lines
4. Secretion
    a) Inhibition of ACTH, TSH, prolactin and other peptide
        hormones from pituitary cells
    b) Inhibition of catecholamines from chromaffin cells
5. Other biological actions
    a) Inhibition of *in vitro* coagulation
    b) Inhibition of *in vivo* brain edema
    c) *In vitro* mucous production of tracheas
    d) *In vitro* induction of β-adrenoceptors and/or inhibition
        of β-adrenoceptor downregulation
    e) Inhibition of *in vivo* LPS induction of nitric oxide
        (NO) synthetase
    f) Enhancement of DNA replication in the oocyte cell
        free system and in mitochondria
    g) Osteoclast formation and bone reabsorption

tion has been often demonstrated in intact animals and organs, while cultured cells mostly fail to respond to glucocorticoids at either mRNA or protein levels. Since a whole family of annexin proteins which maintain a highly conserved structure in the C-terminal core with each other, occupy approximately 2% of the total cellular proteins, and since their synthesis is dependent on the cell cycle, changes in their mRNA and/or protein levels might be often

underestimated. Alternatively, an unknown mechanism beside the genomic effect of glucocorticoids might be involved in induction of the synthesis of annexin I and II.

Most annexins are localized intracellularly, particularly in the cytosol. However, various stimuli including increased intracellular Ca^{2+} are known to translocate annexins to plasma membranes and other subcellular vesicles including chromaffin granules. Glycosylation and acylation of annexins is thought to be important for such insertion and/or attachment to membranes. Some annexins are known to be extracellularly released. Autoantibodies against annexins in patients with rheumatoid arthritis and systemic lupus erythematosus (SLE) neutralize these annexins, thereby augmenting inflammatory responses in these diseases. Similar observations have been extended to inflammatory diseases such as asthma, psoriasis, and ulcerative colitis. Among these diseases, SLE may involve dysfunction of suppressor T cells in the immune system. During immunoglobulin E (IgE) synthesis *in vitro* annexin I enhances suppressor function by inhibiting the glycosylation of IgE-binding factor.

Similarly, annexins regulate the proliferation–differentiation of suppressor T cells, including cytotoxic T cells. This leads to the suggestion that the immunosuppression of animals bearing tumors can be attributed to monocytes/macrophages in which the synthesis of annexin I is stimulated. Because of the chemical nature of annexin I and II as substrates for tyrosine kinases, including EGF receptor kinase and Src kinases, annexins are associated with the proliferation–differentiation process of many cells other than suppressor T cells (**Table 2**). Effects of annexins, especially annexin I and II, are similar, if not identical, to those of glucocorticoids. However, the mechanism of action of exogenous annexins cannot be explained by their binding to plasma membrane acidic phospholipids, which are mainly located on the intracellular side of the membranes. In fact, the binding of annexin V is currently used to detect apoptotic cells which have an inverted membrane phospholipid distribution. This suggests that the existence of specific receptors for annexins mediate their actions. Alternatively, annexins may be inserted into membranes to interact with specific enzymes and/or proteins.

Annexin VII has been identified as synexin, a protein which modulates presynaptic functions including the release of neurotransmitters. Similarly, other annexins are reported to participate in exocytosis and endocytosis in a variety of cell functions such as catecholamine release from adrenal chromaffin cells and ACTH secretion from pituitary cells. Such activity is attributed to the binding of annexins to subcellular vesicle membranes and Ca^{2+} channel and/or sensor action, although the possibility of an interaction between annexins and actin-like cytoskeletal elements, thus changing their bundling, cannot be neglected.

The presence of annexins in nuclei and mitochondria has also been reported. Although annexin II can regulate the replication of DNA in cell-free systems, the detailed mechanism(s) remains to be solved. Since annexin I and II and annexin I–IV have phosphorylation sites for tyrosine protein kinases and protein kinase C (enzymes that regulate the proliferation–differentiation and/or cell cycle of cells) respectively, many reports describe their involvement in the proliferation–differentiation processes of various cells. Such phosphorylation of annexins alters their affinities for Ca^{2+} and phospholipids, and their interactions with other enzymes and/or proteins. A recent report describing the involvement of annexin I in the apoptosis of H_2O_2-treated thymocytes may also substantiate this contention, because apoptosis, a type of cell death distinct from necrosis, is explained by an abortive cell activation mechanism.

Although the structure and chemical and physical nature of annexins have been extensively studied, the mechanism of most of their biological and physiological actions remain unclear. Considering the unique distribution of certain annexins in specific cell types, it is likely that additional physiological and/or biological roles and mechanisms of actions of the annexin family of proteins will be explored in the near future.

See also: **Acute inflammatory reaction; Arachidonic acid and the leukotrienes; Autoimmune diseases; Glucocorticoids; Hypersensitivity reactions; Platelet-activating factor (PAF); Proliferation, lymphocyte; Prostaglandins.**

Further reading

Clark GB and Roux SJ (1995) Annexins of plant cells. *Plant Physiology* 109: 1133–1139.

Flower RJ and Rothwell NJ (1994) Lipocortin-1: cellular mechanism and clinical relevance. *Trends in Pharmacological Science* 15: 71–76.

Hirata F (1989) Role of lipocortins in cellular function as a second messenger of glucocorticoids. In: Lichtenstein LM, Claman H, Oronsky A and Schleimer R (eds) *Anti-inflammatory Steroid Action: Basic and Clinical Aspects*, pp 67–95. London: Academic Press.

Smith PD and Moss SE (1994) Structural evolution of the annexin supergene family. *Trends in Genetics* 10: 241–246.

Swairjo MA and Seaton BA (1994) Annexin structure and membrane interactions: a molecular perspective. *Annual Review of Biophysics and Biomolecular Structure* 23: 193–213.

Vermes I, Haanen C, Steffens-Nakken H and Reutelingsperger C (1995) A novel assay for apoptosis. Flow cytometric detection of phosphatidylserine expression on early apoptotic cells using fluorescein labeled Annexin V. *Journal of Immunological Methods* 184: 39–51.

ANTI-GLOBULIN (COOMBS') TEST

Nevin Hughes-Jones, Molecular Immunopathology Unit, Medical Research Council, Blood Transfusion Centre, Cambridge, UK

The anti-globulin test was developed to detect human blood group immunoglobulin G (IgG) antibodies by agglutination. The negative charge on the surface of red cells prevents them from coming closer than within 20 nm of each other, thus IgG antibodies are unable to cross-link red cells as the Fab arms, even when fully extended, are unable to span this distance. On the other hand, the Fc portion of cell-bound antibody projects outwards sufficiently far to allow an anti-IgG antibody to cross-link between IgG molecules on one cell and those bound to neighboring red cells, thus bringing about agglutination (**Figure 1**). The development of the test occurred following the discovery of the Rh blood group system in the early 1940s. It was soon realized that there were two types of antibody involved in this system – those that would directly agglutinate red cells in saline (retrospectively identified as IgM antibodies), and the so-called 'incomplete' or 'blocking' antibodies (now identified as IgG) which would not directly agglutinate but would block the action of the direct agglutinators.

R.R.A. Coombs, A.E. Mourant and R.R. Race, working in Cambridge in the early 1940s, were investigating the various specificities of the antibodies that appeared to be associated with the Rh system. As reported in their publication of 1945, the seminal idea was that red cells sensitized with nonagglutinating anti-Rh antibody 'had absorbed antibody globulin at some points on their surface and that an

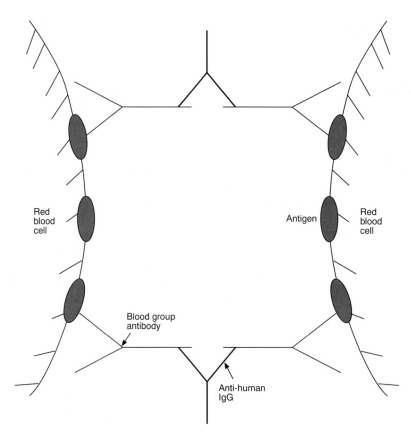

Figure 1   Cross-linking of cell bound IgG.

anti-human globulin serum might be expected to react with this in some observable way'. The principle of the test was soon established. In a later publication, they indicated that the test could probably be used to detect any nonagglutinating antibody present in serum (the indirect Coombs' test) by initially absorbing the antibody on to red cells; they also showed that it could also be used to detect antibody on the surface of fetal red cells in hemolytic disease of the newborn (direct Coombs' test).

It is interesting to note that the use of an anti-globulin serum in this way was first described by the Italian physiologist, Moreschi, in 1908. Moreschi showed that if rabbit red cells were reacted with a goat anti-rabbit red cell antibody at too low a concentration to bring about agglutination, they could subsequently be agglutinated by the addition of a goat serum-specific antibody. At that time, human nonagglutinating antibodies were unknown and hence the significance of the reagent was not appreciated and its description was forgotten.

The test is widely used in two areas in clinical immunohematology. First, it is of major importance in blood transfusion in cross-matching for determining compatibility between donor and recipient. Donor red cells are added to the recipient's serum and any nonagglutinating antibody which binds to the cells can be detected by the addition of the anti-globulin reagent. Second, it is used in the diagnosis of acquired hemolytic anemias for demonstrating the presence of antibodies bound to red cells *in vivo*.

Antiglobulin reagents can be made specific for IgM, IgA and the four subclasses of IgG. The reagents used in cross-matching also contain antibodies specific for the complement component C3, because some antibodies are best detected by testing for the bound complement which is deposited as the result of the antigen–antibody reaction.

See also: **Antibodies, detection of; Blood transfusion reactions; Gammaglobulin; Hemolytic disease of the newborn; Maternal antibodies; Rh antigens; Transfusion.**

Further reading

Coombs RRA, Mourant AE and Race RR (1945) Detection of weak and 'incomplete' Rh agglutinins: a new test. *Lancet* ii: 15–16.

Coombs RRA, Mourant AE and Race RR (1945) A new test for the detection of weak and 'incomplete' Rh agglutinins. *British Journal of Experimental Pathology* 6: 255.

Mollison PL, Englefriet CP and Contreras M (1997) *Blood Transfusion in Clinical Medicine* (10th edn). Oxford: Blackwell Science.

ANTI-INFLAMMATORY (NONSTEROIDAL) DRUGS

John L Wallace, Department of Pharmacology and Therapeutics, Faculty of Medicine, University of Calgary, Calgary, Alberta, Canada

Nonsteroidal anti-inflammatory drugs (NSAIDs) are among the most prescribed drugs and are also widely used in over-the-counter preparations. The first NSAID, aspirin, was first commercialized at the end of the nineteenth century. Since that time, dozens of more potent NSAIDs have been marketed. NSAIDs are used primarily for their anti-inflammatory, analgesic and antipyretic effects, although more recently aspirin has been used increasingly for prevention of myocardial infarction and stroke. While widely used, these drugs are not entirely safe, with well-documented toxicity in the gastrointestinal tract and kidney. In this entry, the mechanisms of action of NSAIDs are reviewed, as are the major adverse effects associated with their use.

NSAIDs and prostaglandin synthesis

NSAIDs fall into a number of different chemical classes, but despite structural heterogeneity, they share activity, toxicity and most probably, mechanism of action (**Table 1**). While some NSAIDs may have additional activities which contribute to their anti-inflammatory action, it is the ability of all NSAIDs to inhibit the enzyme cyclooxygenase (COX) that is the primary mechanism through which these drugs reduce pain, inflammation and fever. Cyclooxygenase catalyzes the conversion of arachidonic acid to prostaglandins G and H. Subsequent enzymatic and nonenzymatic reactions result in the conversion of these highly unstable prostaglandins to more stable and physiologically important prostanoids, including prostaglandin E_2, prostacyclin (PGI_2) and thromboxane A_2. Arachidonic acid is a 20 carbon, unsaturated fatty acid found in membrane phospholipids. It can be cleaved from these phospholipids through the actions of phospholipase A_2 or phospholipase C, whereupon it can react with cyclooxygenase to form prostanoids. One of the mechanisms through which glucocorticoids reduce inflammation is by inhibiting this phospholipase-mediated liberation of arachidonic acid from membrane phospholipids. Prostaglandins contribute to the inflammatory process primarily by causing relaxation of vascular smooth muscle around arterioles, thereby increasing blood flow. While prostaglandins themselves cause only minor changes in the permeability of blood vessels, the increase in blood flow they produce results in a synergistic increase in plasma exudation (edema formation) caused by other mediators, such as histamine and bradykinin. In doing so, prostaglandins contribute to three of the cardinal signs of inflammation, namely, redness, swelling and heat.

Prostaglandins also contribute to the pain associated with inflammation. Prostaglandins themselves are not particularly potent at inducing a pain response when applied, for example, to the base of a blister in human skin. However, they can produce a state of prolonged hyperalgesia and increase the sensitivity of peripheral pain receptors to chemical and mechanical stimuli. For example, the presence of prostaglandins at a site of inflammation or injury will greatly increase the sensitivity of pain receptors to mediators such as bradykinin and histamine. By inhibiting prostaglandin synthesis, NSAIDs remove this hyperalgesic component of an inflammatory reaction. NSAIDs exert analgesic effects both peripherally and centrally, although it is the peripheral action that predominates.

Prostaglandins also play a key role in the generation of fever. There is strong evidence that prostaglandins are produced in the hypothalamus in response to interleukin 1 (IL-1). These prostaglandins mediate the resetting of temperature-regulating systems in the hypothalamus. Blockade of

Table 1 Chemical classes of NSAIDs and examples

Chemical class	Examples
Salicylic acid derivatives	Aspirin
	Diflunisal
Proprionic acids	Ibuprofen
	Naproxen
	Flurbiprofen
	Ketoprofen
Indole acetic acids	Indomethacin
	Etodolac
	Sulindac
Enolic acids	Piroxicam
	Meloxicam
Heteroaryl acetic acids	Diclofenac
	Ketorolac
Fenamates	Mefenamic acid

prostaglandin synthesis by NSAIDs results in a blockade of this effect of IL-1 and other pyrogenic substances. Interestingly, acetaminophen (paracetamol) shares this ability to inhibit prostaglandin synthesis in the hypothalamus and therefore reduce fever, but this drug is a poor inhibitor of prostaglandin synthesis in the periphery, so is not an effective anti-inflammatory drug.

Interaction of NSAIDs with cyclo-oxygenase

The inhibition of COX activity by NSAIDs occurs in two main ways. Most NSAIDs inhibit this enzyme by binding in a reversible manner to a site within the channel through which arachidonic acid must insert to be metabolized (**Figure 1**). In contrast, aspirin produces an irreversible alteration in the conformation of the active site such that arachidonic acid can no longer gain access. Aspirin produces this effect by acetylating a serine residue in COX. Thus, the recovery of prostanoid synthesis after administration of aspirin is a function of the rate of turnover of COX in each tissue. The irreversible blockade of COX by aspirin accounts for the utility of this drug in the prophylaxis of stroke and myocardial infarction. Due to their reversible binding to COX, most NSAIDs are competitive inhibitors of COX. When plasma levels of the NSAID decline below a critical level, COX activity is restored. On the other hand, COX activity is only restored following aspirin administration through the synthesis of new enzyme. Platelet aggregation is regulated by two key prostanoids. Thromboxane produced by the platelet stimulates aggregation, while prostacyclin produced by the vascular endothelium inhibits platelet aggregation. Following aspirin administration, endothelial prostacyclin synthesis is inhibited until such time as new COX is synthesized (the plasma half-life of aspirin is only ~15 min). However, platelets lack the nuclear machinery to synthesize new COX, so aspirin effectively blocks their ability to synthesize thromboxane permanently. Thromboxane synthesis only returns with the appearance of new platelets in the circulation. Thus, giving small doses of aspirin daily leads to marked suppression of thromboxane synthesis with little or no effect on endothelial prostacyclin synthesis, thereby producing a net antithrombotic effect.

In recent years, it has become clear that COX exists in at least two distinct forms. COX-1 is constitutively expressed in many tissues, including the stomach, kidney and platelet, and is believed to produce the prostaglandins that mediate important physiological functions in these tissues (**Figure 2**). On the

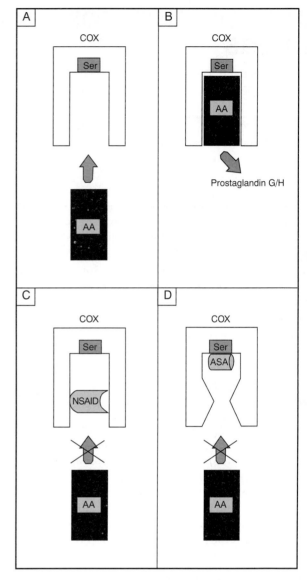

Figure 1 Cyclooxygenase metabolizes arachidonic acid to prostaglandins G and H, which are in turn converted to a number of bioactive prostanoids (PGE_2, PGI_2, TXA_2). Arachidonic acid inserts into a channel in COX (panel A) and can then undergo conversion to PGG_2/PGH_2 (panel B). Most NSAIDs bind to a site within the channel through which arachidonic acid must insert to be metabolized, thereby blocking the activity of COX (panel C). Aspirin acetylates a serine residue in COX resulting in a conformational change in the active site, such that arachidonic acid can not be converted to PGG_2/PGH_2 (panel D).

other hand, COX-2 is not constitutively expressed in many tissues, but can be induced in many tissues by a number of cytokines and mitogens. NSAIDs currently on the market are nonselective, inhibiting both isoforms of COX. As mentioned above, aspirin is able to produce its inhibitory effects on both COX-1 and COX-2 through acetylation of a serine residue, although the position of this residue differs slightly between the two COX isoforms. COX-2 has also

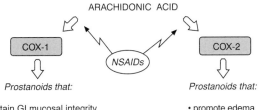

Figure 2 Arachidonic acid is metabolized by the enzyme cyclo-oxygenase (COX) to form prostaglandins. It has been suggested that the COX-1 isoform is responsible for producing prostaglandins important to the function of the gastrointestinal (GI) tract, kidney and platelet, while COX-2 is expressed at sites of inflammation and produces the prostaglandins that contribute to the associated pain, swelling and redness. Currently marketed NSAIDs show little selectivity for COX-1 versus COX-2, perhaps explaining their detrimental effects on the gut and kidney when used at doses required to reduce inflammation.

been shown to be the predominant form of COX expressed at sites of inflammation. This has given rise to the hypothesis that NSAIDs reduce inflammation through their inhibitory effects on COX-2, while producing their toxicity in the gastrointestinal tract and kidney through inhibitory effects on COX-1. If this is true, highly selective inhibitors of COX-2 should produce the beneficial effects of NSAIDs without the toxicity they exhibit in some tissues. This hypothesis is supported by considerable data, although there is evidence of prostaglandins derived from COX-2 performing important physiological functions in some circumstances, such as in situations in which the gastrointestinal tract is inflamed (see below).

Other mechanisms of action of NSAIDs

While there is very strong evidence supporting the hypothesis that NSAIDs produce their anti-inflammatory, analgesic, antipyretic and antithrombotic effects through inhibition of prostanoid synthesis, there is also evidence for other mechanisms of action. These other mechanisms of action may explain the differences in activity from one NSAID to another. For example, NSAIDs such as indomethacin have been shown to inhibit other enzymes, including phospholipase A_2, diacylglycerol kinase and diacylglycerol lipase. These effects are observed at concentrations achieved by therapeutic doses of these drugs, and may explain the observation that some drugs, including indomethacin, are more potent as anti-inflammatory agents than they should be based solely on their potency as inhibitors of COX.

Many NSAIDs have also been shown to inhibit the motility of neutrophils and monocytes, which could explain their ability to reduce the number of inflammatory cells emigrating to sites of injury. Some NSAIDs have also been shown to suppress the function of helper T cells and B cells. However, at least in some cases, these effects are seen only with supratherapeutic concentrations of the drugs.

There may also be COX-related effects of some NSAIDs that contribute to their beneficial effects, but are not due to inhibition of the activity of this enzyme. For many years, researchers have been puzzled by the observation that salicylic acid, the metabolite of aspirin, could reduce inflammation without having significant effects on COX activity. It appears that one of the mechanisms through which salicylate acid produces this effect is by inhibiting the induction of COX-2 at sites of inflammation, possibly by blocking the activity of the transcription factor NFκB (which regulates the expression not only of messenger RNA for COX-2, but also of a number of other proinflammatory mediators).

Proinflammatory effects of NSAIDs

Ironically, while prostaglandins are typically described as mediators of inflammation, these substances exert a wide range of anti-inflammatory effects (**Figure 3**). For example, prostaglandins are potent inhibitors of the release of tumor necrosis factor α (TNFα) and IL-1 from macrophages, and potent inhibitors of TNFα and platelet-activating factor from mast cells. Prostaglandins also suppress the release of a number of proinflammatory mediators from platelets. On the other hand, NSAIDs, by suppressing endogenous prostaglandin synthesis, can increase the release of a number of proinflammatory mediators from various cells, and can therefore enhance an inflammatory reaction (while simultaneously reducing edema and pain). Prostaglandins have also been shown to be potent inhibitors of adhesion molecule expression on the vascular endothelium (e.g. ICAM-1) and on leukocytes (e.g. CD11/CD18), thereby reducing the ability of leukocytes to extravasate. Conversely, NSAIDs have been shown to increase adhesion molecule expression in some experimental models, and to cause a corresponding increase in leukocyte adherence to the vascular endothelium. Actions such as these might explain the observation that NSAIDs can actually lead to increased tissue injury in some forms of inflammation, as well as some of the adverse reactions to NSAIDs in settings of inflammation (e.g. inhibition of the healing of peptic ulcers). Removal of the immunomodulatory effects of endogenous prostaglandins through NSAID administration may

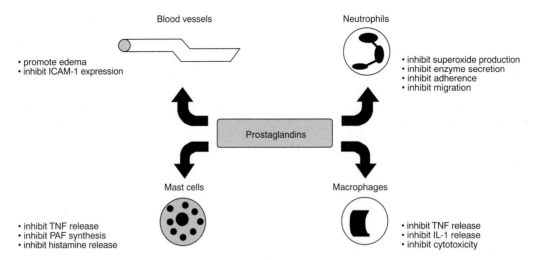

Figure 3 Prostaglandins exert both pro- and anti-inflammatory effects. Prostaglandins, through vasodilation, increase edema forma-tion. However, prostaglandins can reduce inflammatory reactions through inhibition of adhesion molecule expression on the vascular endothelium, and inhibition of inflammatory mediator release from macrophages, mast cells and platelets. Prostaglandins can also reduce tissue injury through inhibition of oxygen-derived free radical production by leukocytes and monocytes.

also contribute to the hypersensitivity reactions to these drugs (see below).

Adverse effects of NSAIDs

Like the beneficial effects of NSAIDs, the adverse effects of these drugs can be largely attributed to their effects on prostaglandin synthesis. The most common detrimental effects of NSAIDs are ulcer-ation in the gastrointestinal tract, renal damage, delayed labor and hypersensitivity reactions (often manifest as asthma). NSAIDs can cause gastric and duodenal ulceration and can exacerbate or delay the healing of pre-existing ulcers. Inhibition of prosta-glandin synthesis in the upper gastrointestinal tract is central to the pathogenesis of this ulceration. On the other hand, small intestinal damage caused by NSAIDs may be more a consequence of their topical irritant properties and enterohepatic recirculation than to inhibition of prostaglandin synthesis. Renal injury by NSAIDs, which includes papillary necrosis and chronic interstitial nephritis, is also believed to be, at least in part, attributed to inhibition of prosta-glandin synthesis. Prostaglandins play an important role in autoregulation of renal blood flow, with a particularly important role being played in indi-viduals with renal and/or hepatic insufficiency. In the case of delayed labor, once again it is the suppression of prostaglandin synthesis that causes alterations in uterine contraction; however, there is evidence that the prostaglandins in this case are derived largely from COX-2, which is induced in labor. Similarly, in settings of gastrointestinal inflammation, such as in inflammatory bowel disease and peptic ulcer dis-ease, the exacerbation of inflammation and delayed

healing of ulcers may be due to inhibitory effects of NSAIDs on COX-2. Because of this, the notion that selective COX-2 inhibitors will be devoid of toxicity, particularly in the gastrointestinal tract, may have to be reconsidered in cases where individuals have a pre-existing inflammatory disease in those tissues in which COX-2-derived prostaglandins appear to play an important immunomodulatory and anti-inflammatory role.

Hypersensitivity reactions to NSAIDs are not com-mon in children, but may occur in up to a quarter of middle-age patients. The reaction, which can range in severity from rhinitis and bronchial asthma to hypotensive shock, can be life-threatening and can occur following ingestion of small doses of these drugs. While often regarded as occurring only with aspirin, hypersensitivity reactions can occur with any NSAID. The mechanism responsible for this reaction has not been firmly established, but does not appear to be immunological in nature. However, as it can occur with NSAIDs with diverse chemical structures, the reaction may be related to suppression of COX. There is evidence that administration of NSAIDs to susceptible individuals results in a profound increase in the production of peptido-leukotrienes, which are potent proinflammatory and bronchoconstrictive agents. These substances are also derived from arach-idonic acid, so the increase in leukotriene synthesis may be a consequence of 'shunting' of substrate to that pathway when COX is inhibited, or due to the removal of the inhibitory effects prostaglandins can exert on leukotriene synthesis.

See also: **Arachidonic acid and the leukotrienes; Fatty acids (dietary) and the immune system; Glucocort-**

icoids; Prostaglandins; Rheumatoid arthritis, animal
models; Rheumatoid arthritis, human.

Further reading

Brooks PM and Day RO (1991) Drug therapy: nonsteroidal antiinflammatory drugs – Differences and similarities. *New England Journal of Medicine* 324: 1716–1725.

Cronstein BN and Weissmann G (1995) Targets for anti-inflammatory drugs. *Annual Review of Pharmacology and Toxicology* 35: 449–462.

Mitchell JA, Larkin S and Williams TJ (1995) Cyclooxygenase-2: Regulation and relevance in inflammation. *Biochemistry and Pharmacology* 50: 1535–1542.

Vane JR, Flower RJ and Botting RM (1990) History of aspirin and its mechanism of action. *Stroke* 21: IV12–IV23.

Wallace JL (1997) Nonsteroidal anti-inflammatory drugs and gastroenteropathy: the second hundred years. *Gastroenterology* 112: 1000–1016.

Weissmann G (1993) Prostaglandins as modulators rather than mediators of inflammation. *Journal of Lipid Mediators* 6: 275–286.

ANTI-LYMPHOCYTE SERUM

Göran Sandberg, Lymphocyte Unit, Department of Neuroscience, Karolinska Institute, Stockholm, Sweden

Anti-lymphocyte serum (ALS) is a serum which contains antibodies against lymphocytes, and is usually prepared in horse, goat or rabbit by immunization with human lymphoid cells. ALS may be obtained by immunization with, for example, lymph node cells, T cell lines, B cell lymphoblasts, thoracic duct lymphocytes or thymocytes. In the latter case the produced serum is referred to as antithymocyte serum (ATS). Most often, the immunoglobulin (Ig) fractions of ALS or ATS were isolated and used as antilymphocyte globulin (ALG) or antithymocyte globulin (ATG). Removal of cross-reacting antibodies (such as to erythrocytes or platelets) reduces the side-effects. Some frequently used preparations are ATGAM (equine ATG), Lymfoser, Minnesota anti-lymphoblast globulin (MALG), and different RATG (rabbit ATG) preparations, such as ATG Fresenius, Nashville antithymocyte serum (nATS), and thymoglobulin. In this text, all these different preparations are referred to as ALS. With modern techniques, highly specific monoclonal antibodies (mAbs) against different cell surface molecules have been prepared, and are used in a similar fashion as ALS. Both with polyclonal ALS and mAbs, the effects may be counteracted by sensitization against the xenogeneic proteins.

ALS as an immunosuppressive agent

ALS is used, often in combination with other immunosuppressive agents, to avoid allograft rejection. In a quadruple therapy protocol it is used with azathioprine, steroids and cyclosporine. ALS is used both as a preventive immunosuppressant, for initial treatment of rejections, and to treat steroid-resistant rejection. The mechanism of action is not fully clarified, but depletion of circulating lymphocytes does occur. This may result from either cytotoxic mechanisms or opsonization. The widest experience with ALS is from kidney transplantation, but ALS has also been used in connection with transplantation of small bowel, heart, bone marrow, liver, pancreas (or islet cells), cornea and skin.

ALS in bone marrow disease and bone marrow transplantation

ALS is widely used in the treatment of bone marrow disorders, particularly severe aplastic anemia. When bone marrow transplantation is not possible, ATG represents the second-best therapeutic alternative in aplastic anemia. It has also been used together with bone marrow transplantation and with good results.

The graft-versus-host reaction is a persistent problem in bone marrow transplantation. The removal of mature T cells and T cell precursors with different lymphocyte-specific antibodies has been a way of preventing it. There are, however, studies that claim that the removal of T cells from bone marrow before transplantation does not improve survival rates, and in fact can cause a higher frequency of graft failure.

An antigen on T lymphocytes which is a very good target for cell lysis is the CDw52 antigen. mAbs to this antigen, prepared in the rat (CAMPATH-1), have been used successfully to deplete donor bone marrow of T lymphocytes. The variants CAMPATH-1G (IgG2b) and CAMPATH-1M (IgM) exist, as well as the humanized CAMPATH-1H (human IgG1).

Therapeutic use of ALS in other diseases

Other cases in which ALS has been reported of value include autoimmune disease such as rheumatoid arthritis and multiple sclerosis, autoimmune thrombocytopenic purpura, Omenn's syndrome, Wegener's granulomatosis, pure red cell aplasia and familial hemophagocytic lymphohistiocytosis. The use of ALS in these conditions is not widespread, however, possibly because of problems related to repeated treatment, such as reduced effect, or anaphylactic reactions. In mice, ALS (or anti-CD4 mAbs) prevents the development of spontaneous systemic lupus (NZB strain) and diabetes (NOD strain). Experimentally induced diabetes (BALB/c strain), arthritis and myasthenia gravis are also prevented this way. In addition, ALS or more specific antibodies may prove to be useful in leukemia. A monovalent, CD3-specific mAb has been shown to deplete CD3$^+$ tumor cells effectively in a patient with T cell leukemia. CAMPATH-1 is very effective in the treatment of lymphoid malignancy and lymphoproliferative diseases. This mAb has also been tried in the treatment of rheumatoid arthritis and multiple sclerosis.

Monoclonal anti-lymphocyte antibodies

Although the polyspecific ALS (shown to contain antibodies to a great number of T lymphocyte surface antigens) is still very useful, with the advent of monoclonal antibodies to various surface molecules on lymphocytes, more specific tools are available. Antibodies specific for epitopes on molecules such as CD2, CD3/TCR components, CD4, CD6, CD8, IL-2R (CD25), LFA-1, and HLA class II have been tried. OKT3 (anti-CD3), which is by far the most commonly used mAb to lymphocytes, has been used for immunosuppression in clinical practice for about 15 years. It has a half-life after injection of 18 h. As with ALS, such mAbs will be used for depletion of lymphocyte populations, but may also be used to modulate the function of lymphocytes by way of interacting with the respective surface molecules. Many studies have compared the therapeutic use of OKT3 and ALS, and in many cases they were found to be equivalent. OKT3 has been effective in cases where graft rejection was both steroid and ALS resistant. Many factors influence the effectiveness of lymphocyte-specific mAbs, such as the properties of preparation itself, the pharmacokinetics, the rate of production of the target molecules, the presence of blocking antibodies, etc. Advantages with mAbs are that they are uniform in immunoglobulin subclass and have a better defined specificity and more reproducible effects. A problem is the production of antiantibodies which counteract the effect of the administered mAb (**Figure 1**). It is a smaller problem when using polyclonal ALS, and is to some extent prevented by the use of concomitant immunosuppression. The problem with antiantibodies may be circumvented by changing to a mAb against a different epitope or by using mAbs with a human type of molecular structure. In an experimental system, pretreatment with ALS was found to suppress formation of neutralizing antiantibody to a mAb administered later. Only mAbs against CD4 seem to avoid stimulating the production of antiantibodies by the recipient. This may reflect the unique ability of CD4-specific mAbs to induce tolerance. A humanized CD4-specific mAb has been used in clinical trials on patients with autoimmune disease. The effect of mAbs may be modified by removing the Fc fragment, which is of importance for the elimination of the target cells by phagocytes. Thus, CD3-specific mAbs which lack the Fc part cause immune activation rather than immunosuppression. Antibodies may be raised against the antigen-binding epitope of the T cell receptor. This will probably become of value in the treatment of autoimmune disease. In the comparison between ordinary, polyclonal ALS and mAbs, contradictory opinions have been published regarding the effectiveness and severity of side-effects.

Side-effects

ALS is administered via a central nervous catheter to avoid irritation following intramuscular or ordinary intravenous injection. Many side-effects seen after administration of polyclonal or monoclonal antibodies against lymphocytes are probably due to antibodies cross-reacting with other tissues. A common problem is serum sickness (fever, malaise, dyspnea, hypotension, edema, cutaneous eruptions, lymphadenopathy, arthralgia and headache). Histologically there may be signs of vasculitis. Many of these symptoms seem to be associated with occurrence of immune complexes. Monoclonal antibodies also have side-effects, even in their humanized forms. The first few injections of anti-CD3 often cause fever, gastrointestinal and respiratory disturbances, headache and anorexia, symptoms sometimes referred to as 'the first-dose syndrome'. The side-effects caused by both ALS and anti-CD3 are thought to be mediated by release of tumor necrosis factor (TNF), interferon γ (IFNγ) and possibly interleukin 2 (IL-2). Transient renal dysfunction attributed to cytokine-induced renal capillary leakage, has also been reported. Other T cell-specific mAbs do not cause

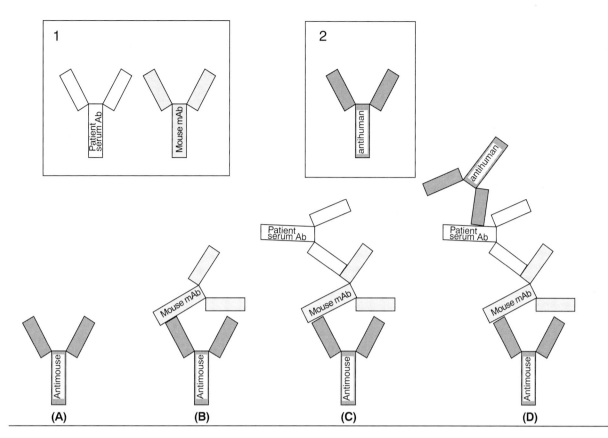

Figure 1 Measurement of a human antimouse antibody response to therapeutic Mabs. An antimouse antibody is first bound to a surface (A). The therapeutic mouse Mab is then added, together with the human serum to be examined (1; B, C). Lastly, an antihuman Ig antibody is added (2; D). The binding of this last antibody is dependent on the presence of antimouse antibodies in the patient's serum.

cytokine release and do not result in so many side-effects. More rarely, symptoms from the central nervous system may occur. There is a risk of lympho-proliferative conditions with both ALS and OKT3, at least after extended use. It has been suggested that side-effects of ALS may be minimal with a remaining therapeutic effect if the administration of ALS is adjusted according to the daily level of T lymphocytes in the blood. Of course, the immunosuppressive effects of both polyclonal and monoclonal lymphocyte-specific antibodies are associated with a risk of opportunistic infections.

Mechanism of action and methods of monitoring ALS before and during clinical use

There is a great need for reliable methods of evaluating the effectiveness of various ALS preparations before they are used on patients. However, as long as the mechanism of action is not clearly established, it is hard to identify the method of choice. The immunosuppressive effect of ALS may be mediated by depletion of lymphocytes from blood and lymph-oid tissue. This is accomplished by the opsonizing effect of antibodies, stimulating phagocytosis of the lymphocytes. Other possibilities are blocking or modulation of receptors on lymphocytes. While OKT3 causes depletion of blood T lymphocytes, these cells, although antigenically modulated, may persist in peripheral lymphoid organs. It has also been reported that ALS may induce expansion of unusual subpopulations of lymphocytes. Also, donor-specific antigen-dependent suppressor cells may maintain the allograft tolerance induced by ALS. The effect of ALS on severe aplastic anemia has been ascribed to the release of hematopoietic growth factors (such as granulocyte-macrophage colony-stimulating factor (GM-CSF) and IL-3), stimulation of hematopoietic cells via CD45RO, blocking of Fc receptors for IgG on T cells, or interference with activated T lymphocytes which inhibit hematopoiesis.

Among the *in vitro* methods used for tests of ALS activity are the study of specificity for different epitopes, the monitoring of cytotoxic or mitogenic effects, inhibition of the binding of sheep erythrocytes to T cells via CD2 (rosette inhibition), opsonizing effect on lymphocytes, quantitation of antibodies bound to lymphocytes or of macrophage-cytophilic antibody, or methods based on complement binding. The potential of an ATG preparation can be estimated by titration of the dose which gives a 50% inhibition of binding of a panel of mAbs to lymphocyte markers. Owing to relatively poor correlation between *in vitro* tests and the immunosuppressive effect of ALS, *in vivo* testing of antihuman ALS preparations has also been performed. For instance, effects on graft-versus-host reactions in rats, and the rejection of skin allografts in monkeys, were shown to correlate well with immunosuppressive effects on patients. It is possible to examine the effectiveness of treatment by measuring target cell concentrations in the blood, or the density of target antigens on such cells. Also, the immunological response to the administered ALS or mAbs may be quantitated by various methods such as ELISA. Such measurements are important in the planning of a repeated treatment with ALS.

Experimental use of ALS

In addition to the wide clinical use of ALS, it can be used for both the identification of lymphocyte subsets and for isolation of such populations. This can be achieved either by negative selection (complement-mediated lysis) or positive selection (e.g. by means of adherence to antibody-coated surfaces). However, mAbs are mainly used for these purposes today. ATS-treated mice can be used in an assay for tumorigenicity and metastatic capacity of cancer cells.

Natural and disease-associated lymphocyte-specific antibodies

In the blood of normal individuals one finds lymphocyte-specific antibodies which, under certain conditions, may be cytotoxic to all, or to subpopulations of, lymphocytes. These antibodies are part of the natural antibodies found in nonimmunized individuals. The significance of these antibodies is not clear, but their presence may induce acute rejection of a transplanted tissue. Autologous antibodies against lymphocytes seem to be induced by virus infections. They also occur in increased frequency in autoimmune disease (systemic lupus erythematosus, rheumatoid arthritis, ankylosing spondylitis), cancer, and in patients exposed to alloantigen, such as multiple transplanted uremic patients, multiparous dialysis patients, hemophiliacs and male homosexuals. A large percentage of patients with Behçet's syndrome have lymphocytotoxic antibodies, as do some of their healthy children. The presence of lymphocyte-

specific antibodies in human immunodeficiency virus (HIV) infection is associated with increased risk for developing acquired immune deficiency syndrome (AIDS). Such antibodies may have been produced as a result of an immune response against lymphocyte-bound HIV determinants (such as gp41) and may directly cause the lymphopenia in AIDS patients. Autoantibodies to CD4, found in some HIV patients, do not however appear to have a prognostic significance. Autoantibodies to the GM3 ganglioside on AIDS patients' lymphocytes have been detected which do not bind to normal GM3.

Sera with natural lymphocytotoxic antibodies to heterologous cells have not been used therapeutically but may have an experimental value. For instance, natural thymocytotoxic antibodies from rabbits have been used in experiments on guinea pigs to deplete thymus cells of immature populations.

See also: **Antiserum; Bone marrow and hematopoiesis; CD antigens; Graft rejection; Graft-versus-host reaction; Immunosuppression; Lymphocytes; Monoclonal antibodies (mAbs); Natural antibodies; Plasma; Serum sickness; Transplantation.**

Further reading

Copeland JG, Icenogle TB, Williams RJ *et al* (1990) Rabbit antithymocyte globulin – a 10-year experience in cardiac transplantation. *Journal of Thoracic and Cardiovascular Surgery* 99: 852–860.

Forsythe JLR (1994) ATG – a polyclonal sledgehammer? *Transplant Immunology* 2: 148–152.

James K (1968) Anti-lymphocyte serum. *Clinica Chimica Acta* 22: 101–113.

Jeejeebhoy HF (1971) Heterologous antilymphocyte serum, a review. *Canadian Journal of Surgery* 14: 5–18.

Keown PA and Stiller CR (1986) Control of rejection of transplanted organs. *Advances in Internal Medicine* 31: 17–46.

Kreis H (1992) Antilymphocyte globulins in kidney transplantation. *Kidney International* 42: s188–s192.

Najarian JS (1971) The clinical use of antilymphocyte globulin. *New England Journal of Medicine* 285: 158–166.

National Kidney Foundation Conference (1988) Use of monoclonal antibodies in organ transplantation. Proceedings of a consensus conference. *American Journal of Kidney Diseases* 11: 85–165.

Norman DJ (1992) Antilymphocyte antibodies in the treatment of allograft rejection: targets, mechanisms of action, monitoring, and efficacy. *Seminars in Nephrology* 12: 315–324.

Seaman WE and Wofsy D (1988) Selective manipulation of the immune response *in vivo* by monoclonal antibodies. *Annual Review of Medicine* 39: 231–241.

ANTI-NUCLEAR ANTIBODIES

RJT Smeenk, Central Laboratory of the Netherlands Red Cross, Amsterdam, The Netherlands

TEW Feltkamp, Research Center for Rheumatic Diseases, Amsterdam, The Netherlands

Antibodies against antigens of cell nuclei probably occur in the blood of all human beings. Since such antibodies generally react with all kinds of nuclei, whatever their origin, they are also directed against antigens in the nuclei of the host, and are therefore considered to be 'autoantibodies'. If the anti-nuclear antibodies (ANAs) occur in titers elevated significantly above the normal serum level, the employed test is considered 'positive'. Such high titered autoantibodies are especially associated with the autoimmune disease systemic lupus erythematosus (SLE), although they also occur in high frequencies in patients with rheumatoid arthritis (RA), Sjögrens syndrome, scleroderma, polymyositis, mixed connective tissue disease (MCTD), myasthenia gravis and chronic active hepatitis.

ANA were first demonstrated in 1957 by Holborow and by Friou, using the indirect immunofluorescence technique (IFT) as developed by Coons. This method is still the method of choice as a screening technique, before more specific methods are used. The distinct ANAs and the assays used to demonstrate their presence are listed in **Table 1**.

Nuclear antigens

Nucleus

Many distinct structures in the cell nucleus serve as antigen for different populations of ANAs. Most ANAs are directed against nucleic acids or against proteins associated with nucleic acids. Only nucleoli and centromeres of chromosomes can readily be distinguished by the IFT as separate antigenic entities, all other antigens for autoantibodies have to be determined with more specific methods. The centromere antigen complex contains at least three antigenic proteins: CENP-A (18 kDa), CENP-B (80 kDa) and CENP-C (140 kDa).

Nucleosome

The nucleosome is the basic structure of chromatin and has an important function in the compaction of DNA in the nucleus of the cell. It consists of dimers of the four core histones, H2A, H2B, H3 and H4, together forming a histone-octamer around which 146 base pairs of DNA are wrapped twice (**Figure 1**). Two nucleosome subunits are connected via a

Table 1 Assays used for the detection of ANAs

ANA	Assay							
	LE cell test	IFT	CIE	IBT	RNA precipitation	Farr assay	PEG assay	ELISA
Anti-DNP	✓							
Antinucleosome								✓
Anti-DNA		✓				✓	✓	✓
Antihistone				✓				✓
Anticentromere		✓		✓				
Anti-Sm			✓	✓	✓			✓
Anti-U1RNP			✓	✓	✓			✓
Anti-Ro/SS-A			✓	✓	✓			✓
Anti-La/SS-B			✓	✓	✓			✓
Anti-Scl70			✓	✓				✓
Anti-Jo1			✓	✓	✓			✓
Anti-PL12				✓				
Anti-PL7				✓				
Anti-rRNP			✓	✓				✓
Anti-RA-33				✓				
Anti-Ku				✓				
Anti-PCNA			(✓)	✓				

IFT, Immunofluorescence technique; CIE, Counterimmunoelectrophoresis; IBT, immunoblotting technique; PEG, polyethyleneglycol.

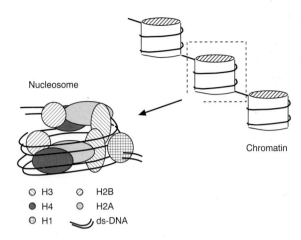

Figure 1 Schematic drawing of chromatin and its subunit, the nucleosome.

stretch of linker DNA to which histone H1 is bound. The four core histones are single-chain polypeptides with molecular weights ranging from 11 to 15 kDa. Clustered at the N-terminal regions of the core histones are basic residues, which, therefore, are located at the outside of the nucleosome. These positive charges on the cylindrical surface of the histone octamer form a left-handed spiral, situated along the DNA and are partly involved in the binding of DNA.

Small nuclear RNP (snRNP)

Eukaryotic cells contain a number of distinct small RNA molecules, which can be broadly divided into two classes: the capped small nuclear RNAs (snRNAs or U-RNAs) and the noncapped small cytoplasmic RNAs (scRNAs). Mammalian cells contain at least 14 different U-RNAs, organized into ribonucleoprotein particles (U-snRNPs; **Figure 2**). The

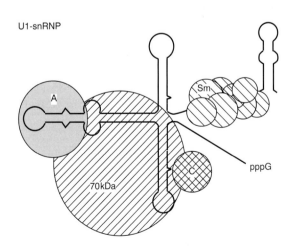

Figure 2 Schematic drawing of a U-snRNP particle. To the U1-RNA molecule the proteins 70 kDa, A, C and those of the Sm complex are bound; the Sm complex encompasses the proteins BB', D1, D2, D3, E, F and G.

U1–U6 snRNPs, with the exception of U3 snRNP, have an important role in messenger RNA processing.

More than 25 different polypeptides have been identified as constituents of the major snRNPs U1, U2, U5 and U4/U6. Of these proteins, nine are present in each of the individual snRNPs, and are designated as Sm or core proteins (**Table 2**). These include the BB' doublet, the D1/D2/D3 triplet and the E, F and G polypeptides. In addition to the core proteins, most of the snRNPs contain a number of unique polypeptides, designated 70 kDa protein, A and C (found in U1 snRNP only), A' and B" (found only in U2 snRNP).

RA-33

So-called heterogeneous nuclear ribonucleoproteins (hnRNPs) are complexes of RNA-polymerase II transcripts and a number of proteins. In these complexes, the processing of hnRNA into mature RNA takes place. Amongst the proteins in the hnRNP-complexes are the hnRNP-A1 and -A2. The latter has been shown to be identical to the RA-specific antigen RA-33.

Ku

The Ku antigen is localized in a particle composed of two noncovalently linked proteins of 70 and 80 kDa that bind DNA. The antigen is identical to nuclear factor IV (NF IV). Both proteins have been cloned and epitope mapping studies indicate that the major epitopes recognized by anti-Ku antibodies are conformational.

PCNA

Proliferating cell nuclear antigen (PCNA), also named cyclin, is a protein of 29 kDa that is primarily present in dividing cells. It has been identified as an auxiliary protein of DNA polymerase δ, a particle involved in DNA replication.

Nuclear enzymes

Several nuclear enzymes serve as antigen for autoantibodies. Topoisomerase I is the most important of these. It is an enzyme of 100 kDa which is involved in the relaxation of supercoiled DNA, by nicking and releasing one strand of the DNA duplex.

Cytoplasmic antigens

ANAs are, by definition, directed to antigens in the cell nucleus. Since many patients with generalized autoimmune diseases not only have antibodies to nuclear antigens but also to cytoplasmic antigens,

Table 2 Presence of proteins in U-snRNP particles

	70 kDa	A	A'	B	B'	B"	C	D1-3	E	F	G
U1-RNP	✓	✓		✓	✓		✓	✓	✓	✓	✓
U2-RNP			✓			✓		✓	✓	✓	✓
U5-RNP				✓	✓			✓	✓	✓	✓
U4/U6-RNP				✓	✓			✓	✓	✓	✓

these are generally also loosely included under the term 'ANA'.

Small cytoplasmic RNP (scRNP)

One of these cytoplasmic antigens is called La/SS-B. It functions as a termination factor for RNA polymerase III. Therefore, La/SS-B scRNPs are composed of an RNA polymerase III transcript to which the La/SS-B protein is bound (**Figure 3**). The RNA transcripts include 7S RNA, 5S RNA, tRNA, U6-RNA, the Y-RNAs as well as a number of viral RNAs.

Ro/SS-A scRNPs are composed of several proteins complexed with a subset of the La/SS-B associated RNAs, the so-called Y-RNAs (**Figure 3**). In human cells four different Y-RNAs have been identified, together with two different Ro/SS-A proteins, designated Ro52 and Ro60. The Ro60 protein is unusual in containing both an RNP consensus motif for binding RNA and a zinc finger motif for binding to DNA. The Ro52 protein contains multiple zinc fingers and a leucine zipper sequence, but no RNP consensus motif. Most probably, this protein is complexed to Y-RNPs via binding to the Ro60 protein. The 50 kDa La/SS-B protein contains, as expected, an RNP consensus motif.

About 30% of both Ro/SS-A and La/SS-B is localized in the nucleus of the cell, which explains the nuclear immunofluorescence of anti-Ro/SS-A and anti-La/SS-B. Contrarily, Y-RNAs are predominantly cytoplasmic. Presumably, Ro/SS-A and La/SS-B bind to newly synthesized Y-RNA in the nucleus, after which the mature complex, termed scRNP is transported to the cytoplasm.

No function has as yet been associated with the Ro/SS-A proteins.

rRNP

Ribosomal P-proteins are phosphorylated proteins that are present, often in multiple copies, on the ribosome. P1 (19 kDa) and P2 (17 kDa) interact with the eukaryotic elongation factors EF1 and EF2 and play a role in aminoacyl-tRNA binding and polypeptide synthesis. These proteins share a 22 amino acid sequence at the C-terminal that contains an epitope recognized by so-called anti-rRNP or anti-P antibodies.

Cytoplasmic enzymes

Aminoacyl-tRNA synthetases are a group of cytoplasmic enzymes that catalyze the binding of tRNA to their respective amino acids. A number of them have been identified as antigens for a special class of ANA.

Detection, identification and clinical significance of ANAs

ANAs with IFT

The IFT is generally used as a screening assay for the presence of ANAs. The method is highly sensitive and detects almost all ANA specificities. Most laboratories now use cultured cells as substrate instead of tissue sections. Sera from patients with generalized autoimmune diseases mostly have several distinct ANAs at the same time. Since the titers of these antibodies differ, titration of the serum can reveal the strongest ANAs giving a certain pattern of nuclear fluorescence. Homogeneous patterns are frequently observed in patients with SLE or rheumatoid arthritis (RA), speckled or granular patterns in sera from patients with Sjögren's syndrome or scleroderma. Nucleolar fluorescence is often seen in patients with progressive systemic sclerosis (PSS). These associations, however, are of limited value to the clinician.

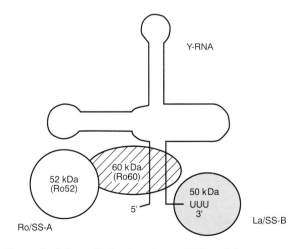

Figure 3 Schematic drawing of an scRNP particle.

Only the discrete speckled pattern of nuclear fluorescence is informative, since this points to the presence of antibodies to centromeres. This should be confirmed by performance of the IFT on mitotic cells or chromosome spreads. Also the presence of other types of nuclear fluorescence is mostly the start of studies to specify the kind of the ANA.

Nearly all patients with SLE have ANAs, mostly in high titers. In RA, Sjögren's syndrome, PSS, MCTD, myasthenia gravis and chronic active hepatitis the frequency of the ANAs and the titers of these antibodies are considerably lower (Table 3).

A negative result in the IFT does not necessarily mean that ANAs are not present. It is known that low titered reactivities to Ro/SS-A, rRNP and Jo-1 are relatively difficult to detect in this assay.

Most laboratories have tested sufficient sera from healthy individuals to be aware of the statistical limits between normal and pathological ANA titers. Nevertheless, it should be noted that not only generalized autoimmune diseases show a preponderance for women and adults, but that also healthy elderly women have a far greater tendency to show these antibodies than young boys. A positive ANA in a boy, therefore, draws more attention than the same ANA in a woman over 60 years of age.

LE cell test

In 1948 Hargraves described for the first time the occurrence of LE cells. The demonstration of these cells was a great help to define the complicated clinical picture of SLE (Table 3). Later on, the 'LE cell factors' were identified as autoantibodies and the 'LE cells' as granulocytes which had phagocytosed complexes of these autoantibodies and nuclei of other cells. Nucleosomes are able to inhibit the formation of 'LE cells', in contrast to free dsDNA or histones. Thus, it appears that the LE cell phenomenon is related to the presence of antinucleosome autoantibodies. After 45 years the test is still in use but with the introduction of more specific methods, it has become somewhat redundant.

Anti-DNA

Antibodies to DNA can be found in the circulation of the majority of patients with SLE. They are quite specific for this disease, which makes their detection an important diagnostic aid to the clinician (Table 3). Fluctuations in the level of anti-dsDNA in an individual patient generally parallel the clinical status of that patient. Under defined conditions, increases in the level of anti-DNA predict an upcoming flare of the disease. Indeed, it has recently been shown that instalment of (prednisone) treatment on the basis of increasing levels of anti-DNA may prevent the exacerbation from becoming overt. Furthermore, the presence of anti-dsDNA may precede the diagnosis of SLE by more than a year.

Table 3 Frequencies of ANA in various autoimmune diseases (percentages in round figures)

ANA	Autoimmune disease						
	SLE	RA	SS	MCTD	PSS	CREST	PM-DM
ANA	90	35	30	100	60	70	15
LE cell test	45	5	nk	20	nk	nk	nk
Anti-dsDNA	60	10	0	15	0	0	5
Anti-ssDNA	75	10	0	10	0	0	30
Anti-nucleosome	nk	nk	nk	nk	nk	nk	nk
Anti-histone	60	15	nk	nk	nk	nk	nk
Anti-centromere	2	0	0	5	10	95	nk
Anti-Sm	20	0	0	5	1	1	0
Anti-U1RNP	20	3	0	100	5	2	0
Anti-Ro/SS-A	40	5	70	50	30	nk	nk
Anti-La/SS-B	15	1	60	0	5	0	nk
Anti-Scl70	0	0	0	0	35	5	0
Anti-Jo1	0	0	0	0	0	0	30
Anti-P	10	2	2	0	0	0	0
Anti-RA-33	20	40	4	40	6	0	10
Anti-Ku	6	0	0	30	3	nk	4
Anti-PCNA	3	0	nk	nk	nk	nk	nk

nk, not known. SLE, Systemic lupus erythematosus; RA, rheumatoid arthritis; SS, Sjögren's syndrome; MCTD, mixed connective tissue disease; PSS, progressive systemic sclerosis; CREST, CREST syndrome (variant of scleroderma); PM-DM, Polymyositis-dermatomyositis.

A multitude of assays have been developed to detect the presence of antibodies to DNA. Currently, the most commonly used assays are the IFT on *Crithidia luciliae*, radioimmunoassays (RIAs) such as Farr assay and PEG assay, and enzyme-linked immunosorbent assays (ELISAs). These methods can either be obtained in kit form or be employed as in-house assays. The hemoflagellates *Crithidia luciliae* which are used in the IFT contain a giant mitochondrion, the kinetoplast, which consists of only double-stranded DNA. To facilitate discrimination between nuclei and kinetoplasts, the slides are counterstained by propidium iodide, which intercalates in the dsDNA helices. Fluorescence of kinetoplasts is taken as an indication of the presence of anti-DNA. After 20 years, this method still is one of the most frequently employed techniques for the detection of anti-DNA. The method is specific and quite sensitive. In RIAs the choice of antigen again is of great importance. The DNA employed has to be bigger than 10^5 but smaller than 10^7 kDa. Furthermore, the DNA must be double stranded and, to allow quantitation of antibody reactivity, monodisperse in size. This indicates that circular double-stranded bacteriophage DNA (such as from PM2) or plasmids (such as pUC9) are to be preferred.

In ELISA systems, DNA has to be coated to plastic. ssDNA can easily be coated directly, but dsDNA is mostly coated via intermediates such as poly-L-lysine, protamine or methylated BSA. Such precoats introduce problems related to the binding of immune complexes and/or immunoglobulins not directed against DNA to the plates (via the intermediate molecule). An alternative is to make use of biotinylated DNA and coat this via streptavidin to the plates.

Different assay systems are not always comparable, for the following reasons:

1. The source of antigen differs: DNA may be from eukaryotic or prokaryotic origin, be double stranded or single stranded, be polydisperse in size or homogenous, etc.

2. Presentation of the antigen to the antibody differs: in RIAs it is generally in solution, in ELISAs it is coated to plastic; in the *Crithidia* test DNA is mostly presented intact in cells.

3. Reaction conditions are different: e.g. due to the employed ammonium sulfate precipitation step used in the Farr assay, anti-dsDNA of low avidity is missed with this method; in second antibody techniques such as IFT and ELISA the choice of conjugated antibody is of importance; often, only IgG anti-DNA is measured with these techniques.

General comparison of four different assays using sera of patients with defined SLE leads to high levels of correlations between the various assays (**Table 4**). However, upon routine screening of sera from patients suspected as having generalized autoimmune diseases, large discrepancies between the different assays are also seen: out of 16 possible reactivity combinations, 11 actually occurred. Sensitivity differences can only partly explain the discrepancies observed between the assays. An important cause is to be found in the avidity of the antibodies (**Figure 4**). Furthermore, histones or nucleosomes complexed to antinucleosome antibodies may also cause a positive reaction in the Farr assay. It is advisable to quantitate anti-DNA levels and express these in International Units, to allow comparison between different studies. A World Health Organization (WHO) standard serum to serve this purpose is available from the Central Laboratory of the Blood Transfusion Service (CLB) in Amsterdam. The CLB is the custodian of WHO standards for rheumatology.

Of the methods described, the ELISA is the most

Table 4   Comparison of the disease specificity of four anti-dsDNA assays

Disease	Number	Percentage of sera positive in			
		Farr assay	Crithidia	PEG assay	ELISA
Active SLE	96	98	96	96	100
Rheumatoid arthritis	62	1	0	5	3
Sjögren's syndrome	14	0	0	7	20
Scleroderma	12	0	0	0	30
Autoimmune hepatitis	61	0	0	20	15
Myasthenia gravis	25	0	0	32	20
Autoimmune thyroiditis	66	0	0	7	13
Autoimmune gastritis	32	0	0	0	18
Autoimmune hemolytic anemia	40	0	0	10	8
Normal donors	192	0	0	0	0

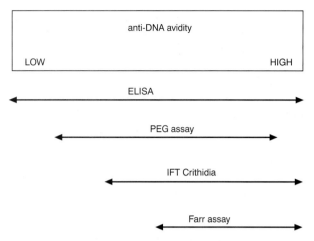

Figure 4 Relation between anti-DNA avidity and assay behavior.

sensitive, whereas the Farr assay is the most specific for SLE. Using the latter method, only antibodies of a relative high avidity for DNA are detected. Mild forms of SLE, where patients only have anti-dsDNA of a low avidity in their circulation, may easily be missed by this technique. On the other hand, if screening for the presence of anti-DNA takes place using an assay that is not selective for anti-DNA of high avidity, then a positive assay result does not always indicate that the patient has SLE: anti-DNA of lower avidity occurs in diseases other than SLE. An evaluation of the diagnostic value of low avidity anti-dsDNA has shown that half of the patients in whom anti-dsDNA is PEG positive but Farr negative have SLE. When high-avidity anti-dsDNA is present as well, nearly 90% of the patients were found to have SLE. Therefore, screening using a 'broad-spectrum' method should be followed by an assay selective for high-avidity anti-dsDNA.

Because the Farr and PEG assays may readily be compared, as they only differ with respect to the way DNA/anti-dsDNA complexes are precipitated, a relative avidity index can be acquired by calculating the ratio between results (in IU ml^{-1}) of both assays. An optimal discrimination between low- and high-avidity DNA was obtained using a cut-off Farr:PEG ratio of 5. Using this approach anti-dsDNA of SLE patients with nephritis was found to have significantly higher avidity than that from patients with CNS involvement.

Antibodies to DNA have always been claimed to play an important role in the pathogenesis of SLE. Traditionally, SLE is considered to be an immune complex disease. In this concept, anti-DNA binds DNA and the resulting immune complexes are deposited in the tissues. This binding of DNA by antibodies may occur in the circulation, but it may also happen *in situ*. At the site of deposition, subsequent complement activation then leads to inflammation and the characteristic disease features of SLE. In the past few years this concept of the pathophysiology of SLE has been challenged, and a modified hypothesis concerning the pathogenesis of SLE has been proposed. This new concept is based on studies that have shown that anti-DNA may interact with tissue structures such as heparan sulfate (HS), the major glycosaminoglycan side-chain of the glomerular basement membrane (GBM). Although it was originally thought that the binding of anti-DNA to HS was based on cross-reactivity, more recently it has been shown that this binding is in fact mediated by nucleosomes. Increased levels of nucleosomes have been demonstrated in the plasma of SLE patients, perhaps due to increased or defective apoptosis leading to their release into the circulation. Renal perfusion studies in the rat have shown that anti-DNA can only bind to the GBM after prior perfusion with histones followed by DNA, or with nucleosomes. Thus, complexes composed of antibodies and nucleosomal material interact via their histone part with heparan sulfate in the GBM. In contrast to anti-nucleosome and anti-DNA antibodies, antihistone monoclonal antibodies do not localize in the GBM after complexation with nucleosomes. Therefore, the specificity of the antibody bound to the nucleosome appears to be a critical determinant for the nephritogenic potential of the complex.

Anti-nucleosome

Anti-nucleosome antibodies are defined as antibodies which are directed exclusively (or predominantly) against nucleosomes or subnucleosomal structures, consisting of DNA plus core histones. These antibodies were in fact the first autoantibodies described in association with SLE, being the LE factors that were responsible for the so-called 'LE cell phenomenon'.

For the specific detection of antibodies to nucleosomes, ELISAs have been developed in which purified nucleosomes are used as antigen. Several purification protocols have been described, all using micrococcal nuclease digestion which causes internucleosomal cleavage. All eukaryotic cells can be used as starting material, but most frequently calf thymus or rat liver is used. After preparation, the purity should be checked, both for the histones by PAGE analysis and for DNA by extraction and analysis on agarose gels. For screening purposes, H2A–H2B/DNA can be used as a substitute for nucleosomes. To this end, commercially obtained H2A and H2B can be mixed in equal amounts; the dimer is then coated to ELISA plates, subsequently followed by addition of dsDNA.

A problem in the measurement of antibodies to nucleosomes is, of course, that both anti-dsDNA and antihistone will also react with nucleosomes. So far, this can only be solved by prior absorption of anti-DNA and anti-histone from the serum or plasma sample. In this way, the presence of nucleosome-specific antibodies has unequivocally been demonstrated in SLE patients. From analysis of the epitope specificity of a number of lupus-derived nucleosome-specific monoclonal autoantibodies, it is clear that these antibodies recognize a multitude of conformational epitopes formed by the interaction between DNA and core histones.

Anti-histone

Anti-histone antibodies occur in a number of autoimmune diseases, including SLE, drug-induced lupus, juvenile rheumatoid arthritis and RA (**Table 3**). The frequency of autoantibodies to individual histones vary according to the type of autoimmune disease. In general, antibodies to H1 are the most frequent in SLE, followed by anti-H2B, anti-H2A, anti-H3 and anti-H4, respectively. Antibodies to histones are generally measured by means of specific ELISAs, using purified histones as antigens. Care has to be taken regarding the purity of commercial histone preparations. Antihistone reactivity is also readily detectable in immunoblotting assays, using nuclear extracts as antigen.

Anti-centromere

These antibodies can be demonstrated with the IFT on cultured cells. A more sophisticated assay makes use of chromosome spreads on slides, to allow the specific localization of the centromeres.

Antibodies to the centromere antigens CENP-A and CENP-B are the most common and can be found in about 95% of the patients with the CREST syndrome (**Table 3**). They occur less frequently in patients with diffuse scleroderma, and are, therefore, important diagnostic markers for scleroderma with limited skin involvement. They also appear to have prognostic significance. Anti-centromere reactivity is readily measured by IFT and immunoblotting; CENP-B has been cloned and can be used in ELISA.

Anti-snRNP (Sm, U1-RNP, U2-RNP)

Sm-specific antibodies are directed to the D proteins (either all three or to a subset of them) and to the BB′ doublet of the U-snRNPs (**Figure 2**). Since these proteins are common to all major snRNPs except U3, Sm-specific antibodies precipitate U1, U2, U4, U5 and U6 snRNPs. Whereas these antibodies to Sm are exclusively found in patients with SLE, and are, therefore, disease specific, antibodies to U1-RNP are considered to be a marker antibody for MCTD (**Table 3**).

Anti-U1-RNP sera precipitate U1-snRNPs; they predominantly recognize U1-70 kDa and U1-A, and with lower frequency also U1-C. In about 50% of the cases U1-RNP sera also react with BB′. Antibodies to U2-RNP react predominantly with the U2-snRNP-specific B″ protein, and in some cases also with the U2-A′ protein.

Apart from detection by counterimmunoelectrophoresis (CIE) and immunoblotting, specific ELISAs have also been developed for the measurement of anti-Sm and anti-U1-RNP. Most of the relevant proteins are available in recombinant form, for use in ELISA systems. For some unexplained reason, the recombinant D protein(s) is (are) not immunoreactive in ELISA and cannot be used.

Presently available data on the incidence of anti-Sm and anti-U1-RNP in autoimmune diseases has been compiled using 'older' assays, such as CIE. Data obtained using immunoblotting and ELISA are not readily available.

Anti-RA-33

Antibodies to RA-33 were originally described to be quite specific to RA. More recently they have also been found in other autoimmune diseases (**Table 3**). They can be detected by immunoblotting, where they generally give rise to a trimer of around 33 kDa.

Anti-Ku

Ku-specific antibodies were originally described in Japanese patients with scleroderma–polymyositis overlap syndromes. Later, it was observed that these antibodies also occur in patients with SLE, scleroderma and MCTD (**Table 3**). They can be detected by immunofluorescence, CIE and immunoblotting.

Anti-PCNA

Antibodies to PCNA are found in the sera of about 3% of SLE patients, and can be detected by IFT in dividing cells (**Table 3**). The antibody is also readily detectable by CIE and immunoblotting, where it shows a band at 35 kDa. Epitope mapping studies have shown that the antibodies primarily bind conformational epitopes in this antigen.

Anti-topoisomerase I (Scl70)

Antibodies to topoisomerase I, mostly termed anti-Scl70, are found frequently in sera of patients with diffuse cutaneous systemic sclerosis and are quite specific to this disease (**Table 3**). Therefore, anti-Scl70 is an important marker antibody for systemic sclerosis. Anti-Scl70 can be detected by CIE, immunoblotting or a specific ELISA. The presence of this antibody in patients with Raynaud's phenomenon that eventually develop scleroderma suggests that anti-Scl70 may have prognostic significance.

Anti-scRNP (Ro/SS-A, La/SS-B)

Antibodies to La/SS-B are predominantly found in patients with Sjögren's syndrome, but also in SLE and in RA (**Table 3**). Differences in reported percentages are to be explained on the basis of patient selection and use of different methods of the detection of anti-La/SS-B. Analysis of immunoglobulin heavy and light chain usage has revealed that these antibodies are probably the result of an oligoclonal B cell expansion.

Anti-La/SS-B are almost always found in combination with anti-Ro/SS-A. The reverse is not always the case: antibodies to Ro/SS-A often occur alone in SLE and systemic sclerosis (**Table 3**).

Classically, antibodies to Ro/SS-A and La/SS-B are detected by immunodiffusion and CIE. More recently, immunoblotting, ELISA and RNA precipitation have been used for the detection of anti-Ro/SS-A and anti-La/SS-B. Autoantibody levels against Ro/SS-A and La/SS-B in patients with SLE do not correlate with disease symptoms or activity. This is in contrast to anti-dsDNA activity which correlates very well with disease activity in these patients. This also implies that the anti-Ro/SS-A and anti-La/SS-B responses are regulated independently from anti-DNA. Anti-Ro/SS-A and anti-La/SS-B responses significantly correlate. Thus, most of the time anti-Ro/SS-A and anti-La/SS-B fluctuate together. One of the few clear-cut clinical correlations between an antinuclear antibody and a clinical syndrome is found in the congenital heart block (CHB). CHB was originally reported as a rare but potentially fatal complication of offspring from mothers with connective tissue disease, especially SLE. Maternal anti-Ro/SS-A are the largest single risk factor for the development of intrauterine or neonatal complete heart block in a child. The period of pregnancy when cases of fetal bradycardia are first noted (from the 20th week of gestation) coincides with the start of transplacental immunoglobulin G (IgG) transport. The autoantibodies are thought to mediate disease by eliciting an inflammatory reaction in the conduction tissue of the fetal heart. Parameters that would allow discrimination between 'pathogenic' (i.e. CHB-inducing) and nonpathogenic anti-Ro/SS-A have not yet unequivocally been identified.

Anti-rRNP

These antibodies react with the ribosomal phosphoproteins P1 and P2. Mostly, they also recognize the neutral phosphoprotein P0 (38 kDa) that is found in the large subunit of the ribosome.

Anti-P can be found in 10% of patients with SLE (**Table 3**). Initially, its occurrence was related to the presence of lupus psychosis, but later studies have not been able to confirm this relation. Anti-P can be readily detected by CIE and immunoblotting. In the latter assay, anti-P reactivity generally gives rise to three stained bands. Anti-P reactivity can also be detected using an ELISA in which a synthetic peptide of the C-terminal 22 amino acids serves as antigen. Longitudinal studies of anti-P in SLE have shown that quantitative determination has no practical value in the follow-up of SLE patients.

Anti-Jo1 and other anti-tRNA synthetases

Antibodies to tRNA synthetases often occur in patients with polymyositis. The best known of these ANAs is anti-Jo1, which is found in 30% of the patients with adult polymyositis (**Table 3**). The antibody is directed to the histidyl-tRNA synthetase (54 kDa). Anti-Jo1 can be detected by CIE, immunoblotting and specific ELISA. Because the synthetase is associated with a tRNA molecule, RNA precipitation results in a tRNA band upon gel electrophoresis.

Antibodies related to anti-Jo1 are anti-PL12, which is directed to alanyl-tRNA synthetase (110 kDa), and anti-PL7, directed to threonine-tRNA synthetase (80 kDa). Antibodies reactive with isoleucine-tRNA synthetase and glycine-tRNA synthetase have also been reported.

Concluding remarks

It is the current view that autoantigens themselves drive the autoimmune response against them. In that view, nucleosomes are to be considered the relevant autoantigen for the genesis of antibodies to nucleosomes, histones and DNA. Indeed, it would not be expected that DNA occurs freely in the circulation or the organs of the immune system, since in the nucleus of the cell it is so tightly bound to the core histones. Evidence implicating the role of nucleosomes as the driving antigen has been obtained by several different groups. Datta and colleagues, studying the role of T cells in the induction of autoantibodies, found that in lupus mice 50% of the pathogenic T helper cells respond to nucleosomes. These nucleosome-specific T helper cells not only induced the production of nucleosome-specific autoantibodies by syngeneic B cells, but also the formation of anti-DNA and antihistone. Comparable results were obtained in studies with human T cell clones. These observations assign a central and dominant role to the nucleosome in the induction of the ANA response. The validity of this concept is underlined by observations made by Rubin and colleagues, that the formation of antibodies to nucleosomes precedes the development of anti-DNA and antihistone in MRL/lpr mice ('antigen spreading'). Sequencing of ANAs has taught us that ANAs, just like 'ordinary' antibodies show somatic mutations with increasing antibody avidity. This too, is taken as evidence for a driving role of the (auto)antigen in the immune response towards autoantigens.

See also: **Anti-inflammatory (nonsteroidal) drugs; Autoantibodies, tests for; Glucocorticoids; Molecular mimicry; Prostaglandins; Rheumatological disorders; Sjögrens syndrome; Skin, autoimmune diseases; Systemic lupus erythematosus (SLE), human.**

Further reading

Brinkman K, Termaat R-M, Berden JHM and Smeenk RJT (1990) Anti-DNA antibodies and lupus nephritis: the complexity of crossreactivity. *Immunology Today* **11**: 232–234.

Kramers C, Hylkema MN, Termaat R-M, Brinkman K,

Smeenk RJT and Berden JHM (1993) Histones in lupus nephritis. *Experimental Nephrology* **1**: 224–228.

Lahita RG (ed) (1993) *Systemic Lupus Erythematosus.* New York: John Wiley.

Panayi GS (ed) (1994) *Immunology of the Connective Tissue Diseases.* Dordrecht: Kluwer Academic.

Peter JB and Schoenfeld Y (eds) (1996) *Autoantibodies.* Amsterdam: Elsevier.

Smeenk R and Hylkema M (1992) Detection of antibodies to DNA: a technical assessment. *Molecular Biology Reports* **17**: 71–79.

Smeenk RJT, Van den Brink HG, Brinkman K, Termaat R-M, Berden JHM and Swaak AJG (1991) Anti-dsDNA: choice of assay in relation to clinical value. *Rheumatology International* **11**: 101–107.

Tan EM (1982) Autoantibodies to nuclear antigens (ANA): their immunobiology and medicine. *Advances in Immunology* **33**: 167–240.

Tan EM, Fritzler MJ, McDougal JS *et al* (1982) Reference sera for ANA. I. Antibodies to native DNA, Sm, nuclear RNP and SS-B. *Arthritis and Rheumatism* **25**: 1003–1005.

Tan EM, Chan EKL, Sullivan KF and Rubin RL (1988) Antinuclear antibodies (ANAs): diagnostically specific immune markers and clues toward the understanding of systemic autoimmunity. *Clinical Immunology and Immunopathology* **47**: 121–141.

van Venrooij WJ and Maini RN (1993–95) *Manual of Biological Markers of Disease.* Dordrecht: Kluwer Academic.

ANTI-OXIDANT MICRONUTRIENTS AND THE IMMUNE SYSTEM

Adrianne Bendich, Human Nutrition Research, Roche Vitamins and Fine Chemicals, Paramus, New Jersey, USA

In the last decade there has been growing evidence that oxidative stress impairs immune responses and that anti-oxidants can reduce many aspects of oxidant-mediated immune suppression. Oxidative stress is directly related to the concentration of highly reactive molecules, most of which contain reactive species of oxygen, which reduce the anti-oxidant capacity of the body's cells.

Free radicals, highly reactive molecules with one or more unpaired electrons, often contain reactive oxygen species. Free radicals are generated during cellular metabolism, can be ingested or inhaled as environmental pollutants, or can be generated during the metabolism of certain drugs or xenobiotics.

Essential micronutrients with anti-oxidant activities

Antioxidants interfere with the production of free radicals and/or inactivate them once they are formed. There are four enzymes which have anti-oxidant capacity and contain essential minerals. These include two types of superoxide dismutases: a manganese-containing enzyme and an enzyme containing both copper and zinc. The third enzyme, catalase, an iron-containing enzyme, catalyzes the decomposition of hydrogen peroxide. Selenium is an essential component of the fourth enzyme, glutathione peroxidase, important in the decomposition of hydrogen peroxide and lipid peroxides, termination products of free radical attack on lipids.

Three other essential micronutrients can directly interfere with the propagation of, as well as scavenge, free radicals. Vitamin E (α-tocopherol), the major lipid-soluble anti-oxidant present in all cellular membranes, protects against lipid peroxidation and prevents the loss of membrane fluidity. Vitamin E has been characterized as the most critical anti-oxidant in blood. Vitamin C (ascorbic acid) is water soluble and, along with vitamin E, can quench free radicals as well as singlet oxygen. Ascorbate can also regenerate the reduced, anti-oxidant form of vitamin E. Recent work has shown that β-carotene, a pigment found in many photosynthetic plants, is an efficient quencher of singlet oxygen and can function as an anti-oxidant. β-Carotene is the major dietary carotenoid precursor of vitamin A. Vitamin A cannot quench singlet oxygen and has less anti-oxidant activity than the other nutrients discussed; however, its importance for the immune system is well recognized.

Assessment of oxidative stress and anti-oxidant status

Noninvasive measures

The most commonly used noninvasive measure of oxidative stress is the determination of the concentration of the volatile lipid oxidation products, pentane and ethane, in the breath. Dietary recall is the most commonly used noninvasive measure of intake of anti-oxidants.

Invasive measures

Serum concentrations of lipid peroxides and other oxidative products of proteins, DNA and carbohydrates are used to assess levels of oxidative stress. Serum concentrations of the anti-oxidant micronutrients are used as indicators of *in vivo* anti-oxidant status.

Free radicals and immune cell function

There are numerous links between free radical reactions and immune cell functions. White blood cell membranes are composed of lipids containing saturated and unsaturated fatty acids. Unsaturated bonds in fatty acids are highly susceptible to free radical attack, one consequence of which is to adversely affect the integrity of the cell membranes. For instance, oxygen-containing radicals and the products of their reactions have been shown to decrease the fluidity of white blood cell membranes and synovial fluids, consequently reducing their function.

Effects of immune-generated oxidants

The most abundant circulating white blood cell, the neutrophil, utilizes reactive oxygen species to kill invading organisms. When stimulated, neutrophils have the capacity to take up molecular oxygen and generate oxygen-containing free radicals and other reactive molecules. This is often called the oxidative burst. Free radicals and singlet oxygen, along with other reactive molecules, can kill pathogens. Neutrophils can also generate highly toxic halogenated molecules (e.g. hypochlorous acid) when the myeloperoxidase halide enzyme system is activated during the oxidative burst. The halogenated species can also lyse the phagocytosed pathogen. Recently, another reactive oxygen species, peroxynitrite, has been identified as an important component in immune cell killing of pathogens.

Under normal circumstances, the reactive oxygen species generated by neutrophils and other immune cells are used for control of infection; however, in circumstances of chronic activation the reactive oxygen products can result in destruction of normal tissue, as seen in rheumatoid arthritis.

Effects of anti-oxidant deficiency

One of the most obvious factors that could reduce anti-oxidant status is an induced dietary deficiency of, for instance, vitamin C. The effects of marginal vitamin C deficiency on immune and other parameters have been determined under highly controlled conditions in healthy males. Serum, white blood cell and sperm vitamin C levels were significantly reduced when the diet contained 5–20 mg of vitamin C for 2 months. Delayed-type hypersensitivity (DTH) responses were significantly depressed during the period of low vitamin C intake.

In addition to DTH responses, an index of oxidative damage to sperm DNA was also measured; these levels were significantly increased when vitamin C intakes were low. This carefully controlled study clearly demonstrated the importance of the balance between anti-oxidant status, oxidant levels and immune response. The study is especially noteworthy since all other dietary anti-oxidants, such as vitamin E and β-carotene, were provided throughout the study at recommended daily allowance (RDA) levels.

Clinical examples of free radical, anti-oxidant and immune function interactions

Examples of immune dysfunction associated with increased oxidative stress exemplify the interactions between the immune system and the oxidant/anti-oxidant status of the individual.

Rheumatoid arthritis

Rheumatoid arthritis (RA), an autoimmune disease of unknown cause, is characterized by a chronic inappropriate immune response in articular joints, resulting in inflammation and destruction of joint tissues. At some point, the initial insult and inflammation becomes a chronic process. Infiltration of the fluid-filled joint space (synovium) with inflammatory neutrophils occurs and structural changes appear in the synovium, forming an inflamed layer called a pannus. Oxidative products reduce the viscosity of the synovial fluid, thus hindering joint movement further.

Animal models have documented the increased production of pentane in arthritic animals; vitamin E supplementation lowered the pentane exhalation as well as joint swelling. Breath pentane concentrations correlates with the severity of symptoms in RA patients and clinical improvement is associated with a significant decrease in breath pentane. Patients with RA have significantly lower values in the total radical-trapping anti-oxidant parameter ('Trap') assay, based on serum levels of anti-oxidant nutrients, than do control subjects.

With regard to intervention studies, vitamin E has been examined to the greatest extent in patients with RA and other arthritic conditions. Three studies in RA patients suggest that vitamin E at high levels, but not at dietary intake levels, reduced pain. Vitamin E supplementation produced significant pain relief in four other studies. There was also a consistent finding of vitamin E-related antiinflammatory activity, although the studies involved a limited number of subjects.

Aging

The cumulative effects of free radical damage throughout the lifespan are seen in the pigmented age spots of the elderly, which are a consequence of lipid oxidation. The overall increased oxidative stress associated with aging also adversely affects many aspects of immune responses. The consequences of suboptimal immune responses are particularly detrimental in the elderly who have an increased risk of infections as well as of autoimmune diseases.

The cell-mediated immune responses involving T lymphocyte functions (cytotoxicity, interleukin 2 (IL-2) production, proliferation) are the most sensitive to the age-related decline in immune responses. As a consequence, DTH responses to skin test antigens are diminished in the elderly, and can often result in complete loss of response to antigen challenge (anergy) in the most immunosuppressed. Clinical studies have shown that DTH can be used as a predictor of morbidity and mortality in the elderly; i.e. elderly with anergy had twice the risk of death from all causes as elderly who responded to the antigens. Moreover, in hospitalized elderly who had undergone surgery, anergy was associated with a greater than tenfold increased risk of mortality and a fivefold increased risk of sepsis.

Recently, in a placebo-controlled study, intake of a one-a-day type multivitamin/mineral supplement for 12 months significantly enhanced DTH in healthy elderly. Because the multivitamin included β-carotene, vitamin E, vitamin C and all other essential vitamins as well as several minerals, it is not possible to determine whether the anti-oxidants or the other components in the multivitamin supplement were responsible for the improved DTH responses. In another recent placebo-controlled intervention trial, elderly were given a multivitamin, daily for 1 year, which contained approximately eight times the standard level of intake of β-carotene as well as higher levels of vitamins C and E. The supplemented group had significantly less infections than the placebo group. Responses to vaccines were also improved in the supplemented group.

With respect to individual anti-oxidants, an epidemiological study in an elderly population found that the higher the plasma vitamin E levels, the lower the number of infections. Two placebo-controlled, double-blind studies showed that vitamin E supplementation alone significantly enhanced DTH responses and/or T cell proliferative responses in the elderly. Lymphocyte vitamin E levels increased over threefold with supplementation and were correlated with enhanced IL-2 production and decreased prostaglandin E_2 as well as decreased serum lipid peroxides.

Cigarette smoking

Approximately 30% of US adult women and 25% of adult men smoke. Cigarette smoke contains millions of free radicals per inhalation. Other harmful products in cigarette smoke can stimulate the formation of highly reactive molecules that further increase the free radical burden; smokers have significantly higher breath pentane levels than nonsmokers. The micronutrient most affected by cigarette smoking appears to be the anti-oxidant, vitamin C. Smokers require about four times as much vitamin C per day to reach the same blood levels as nonsmokers. In addition to vitamin C, serum levels of vitamin E, folic acid and β-carotene, as well as lung vitamin E concentrations, are significantly lower in smokers compared to nonsmokers.

Cigarette smokers have depressed immune responses compared to nonsmokers, which may in part be due to the overproduction of immuno-suppressive free radicals by neutrophils and macrophages in their lungs. The lung of the healthy non-smoker contains very few neutrophils. In smokers, there is a constant activation of neutrophils and a consequent overproduction of reactive oxygen species.

Supplementation with high levels of vitamin E resulted in a significant decrease in smoker breath pentane levels and significantly reduced the overproduction of oxidant radicals by their circulating phagocytic cells.

Summary

Immune function is dependent upon a balance between the free radical and anti-oxidant status of the individual. In healthy adults, exposure to high levels of oxidants is associated with reduction in clinically relevant immune responses; exposure to low levels of dietary anti-oxidants also reduces immune responses such as DTH.

Anti-oxidant status becomes particularly critical in conditions which result in increased oxidative stress and immune dysfunction, as illustrated in RA, aging and cigarette smoking. In all three examples, evidence of free radical damage to lipids and other cellular components has been demonstrated. At the same time, anti-oxidant status is reduced in arthritic patients and smokers compared with controls. Data suggest that elderly individuals may require higher levels of anti-oxidants to maintain DTH responses.

Several clinical studies have reported that supplemental anti-oxidants reduced indices of oxidative stress and improved various parameters of immune function.

See also: **Fatty acids (dietary) and the immune system; Phagocytosis; Vitamin A and the immune system; Vitamin C and the immune system.**

Further reading

Bendich A (1994) Role of antioxidants in the maintenance of immune functions. In: Frei B (ed) *Natural Antioxidants and Human Health and Disease*. New York: Academic Press.

Bendich A (1996) Antioxidant vitamins and human immune responses. *Vitamins and Hormones* 52: 35–62.

Bogden JD and Louria DB (1997) Micronutrients and immunity in older people. In: Bendich A and Deckelbaum R (eds) *Preventive Nutrition*, pp 317–336. Clifton, NJ: Humana Press.

Cunningham-Rundles S (ed) (1993) *Nutrient Modulation of the Immune Response*. New York: Marcel Dekker.

Klurfield D (ed) (1993) *Nutrition and Immunology*. New York: Plenum Press.

ANTIBODIES: ANTIGENICITY OF

Felix Milgrom, Department of Microbiology, State University of New York at Buffalo, New York, USA

The term anti-antibodies (AAs) refers, in a broad sense, to all antibodies combining with other antibodies, the latter acting as antigens. This also includes antibodies against immunoglobulins of unknown antibody specificity. As early as 1900, Ehrlich and Morgenroth theorized about the formation of 'true AAs' directed against antibody-combining sites and postulated that such antibodies may exert a homeostatic mechanism preventing the formation of autoantibodies that could be harmful for the host. Subsequently, since the beginning of the twentieth century several investigators performed immunization of animals with antibodies of foreign species origin, with the objective of obtaining true AAs. All these studies, however, resulted in production of AAs directed against immunoglobulin structures other than the antibody-combining sites.

AAs to native antibody molecule other than the combining site

Moreschi (1909) used AAs to achieve agglutination of erythrocytes sensitized by nonagglutinating antibodies. He showed that rabbit erythrocytes sensitized by such antibodies of goat origin would undergo agglutination when exposed to rabbit antiserum against goat serum proteins. This was the first description of what has been called later antiglobulin reactions which were introduced into routine laboratory practice by Coombs, Mourant and Race in 1945. AAs active in these tests, frequently referred to as antiglobulin antibodiess, are usually produced by immunization with immunoglobulins of animals of foreign species (e.g. rabbits or goats are immunized with human immunoglobulins). These AAs recognize clearly the species origin of the antibody with which they are reacting.

Allotypes are inherited antigens of immunoglobulins originally described by Grubb (1956). They are usually recognized by means of AAs produced by an animal of the same species. Production of such AAs occurs spontaneously in some humans, although the reasons for this are unclear, or may be achieved by intentional immunization of animals, e.g. rabbits, mice or sheep with allogeneic immunoglobulins.

AAs to altered antibody molecules

Rheumatoid factor (RF) was described by Waaler in 1940 and by Rose and his associates in 1948. It was found in sera of a majority of patients with rheumatic arthritis; it combined with rabbit antibodies sensitizing sheep erythrocytes and caused agglutination of these erythrocytes. In the second part of the 1950s, a general consensus was reached among workers in the field that RF detected in sera of patients with rheumatoid arthritis is an antibody of the immunoglobulin M (IgM) class combining with the Fc fragment of IgG originating from a variety of species; the most frequently studied IgGs were of rabbit and human origin. It was shown that RF reacting with rabbit IgG is different from RF reacting with human IgG and that there also exists a cross-reacting RF, presumably a multispecific antibody combining with IgG of both of these species. Later, in addition to IgM, RF was shown in the IgG and IgA classes. The heterogeneity of RF justified the use of the plural – RFs.

Some investigators have referred to all RFs as autoantibodies. This does not seem justified at all with reference to the RFs combining with IgG of foreign species. Furthermore, RFs combining with human IgG frequently react only with aggregated IgG or, otherwise, with IgG of the allotypic specificity other than that of the patient. Again, neither of these RFs should be called an autoantibody. The term autoantibody should be reserved for those RFs that react with the patient's own native IgG; some evidence for the existence of such RFs has been presented.

An important observation concerning specificity of RFs was made by Hannestad and his associates in the 1970s. They demonstrated RFs which in addition to IgG reacted with other unrelated antigens such as nuclear antigens or cardiolipin. Significantly, the same molecule of RF could react with IgG and these unrelated antigens. It has been proposed that such a cross-reacting RF molecule recognizes shared epitopes on these antigens; alternatively, it has been suggested that the cross-reacting RF is a multispecific antibody with separate or overlapping combining sites for different epitopes.

Another type of serum factor was described by Milgrom, Dubiski and Wozniczko in a few samples (less than 1%) of human sera in 1956. Similar to RFs, it is an IgM antibody combining with IgG antibodies, however this factor reacts only with human antibodies and only if they appear in the form of immune complexes; it does not react with free antibodies. Accordingly, this factor provided evidence for the long disputed thesis about molecular transformation of an antibody molecule in the course of its reaction with the antigen. Furthermore, the characteristics of this factor encouraged the hypothesis that this factor as well as RFs are formed in response to a stimulus exerted by the individual's own IgG antibodies altered during *in vivo* reactions with their antigens. According to this hypothesis, RFs as well as other AAs in human sera would represent stereotypes of reactions of subjects exposed to prolonged immunizing stimuli. This was consistent with the demonstration of RFs in several pathologic conditions other than rheumatoid arthritis, primarily in subacute bacterial endocarditis. This hypothesis was further supported by studies on experimental animals, which showed that immunization with partially denatured autologous IgG as well as prolonged exposure to any strong antigen resulted in formation of RF-like antibodies. Alternatively, several investigators postulated that RF may be formed as a result of polyclonal stimulation of B cells by mitogens released or created under various pathologic conditions.

The pathological role of RFs in rheumatoid arthritis has been repeatedly suggested but never substantiated convincingly. In recent years, more and more studies have been conducted on IgG RFs. It has been shown that these RFs have a propensity for self-aggregation in that each RF molecule may act as an antigen through its Fc fragment and as an antibody through its Fab fragment. Evidence has been obtained that such aggregates may form immune deposits responsible for or contributing to glomerulonephritides.

AS to the antibody-combining sites

As mentioned, early attempts to elicit production of true AS met with failure. Immunization with antibodies originating from a species foreign to the immunized animal resulted in formation of AS of antiglobulin nature. In 1957, however, immunization of rabbits with rabbit antibodies to *Proteus* and *Escherichia* was shown by Milgrom and Dubiski to result in the formation of AAs that distinguished the anti-*Proteus* from the anti-*Escherichia* antibody and accordingly, appeared to have properties of true AAs. Subsequently, in 1963 Kunkel, Mannik and Williams as well as Oudin and Michel, used various protocols of immunization of animals and succeeded in eliciting formation of what appeared to be true AAs. They called them idiotypic antibodies. Further studies, however, showed that the idiotypic specificity cannot be equated with the structure of the antibody-combining site, even if it is closely related to this structure.

See also: **Allotypes, immunoglobin; Antibodies, specificity; Antiglobulin (Coombs') test; Idiotype; Natural antibodies; Rheumatoid arthritis, animal models; Rheumatoid arthritis, human.**

Further reading

Carson DA (1993) Rheumatoid factor. In: Kelley WA, Harris ED Jr, Ruddy S and Sledge CB (eds) *Textbook of Rheumatology*, 4th edn, pp 155–163. Philadelphia: WB Saunders.

Jerne NK (1984) Idiotypic networks and other preconceived ideas. *Immunological Reviews* 79: 5–24.

Mannik M (1985) Rheumatoid factors. In: McCarty DJ (ed) *Arthritis and Allied Conditions. A Textbook of Rheumatology*, pp 660–667. Philadelphia: Lea and Febiger.

Milgrom F (1988) Development of rheumatoid factor research through 50 years. *Scandinavian Journal of Rheumatology* 17 (suppl 75): 2–12.

Moore TL, Dorner RW (1993) Rheumatoid factors. *Clinical Biochemistry* 26: 75–84.

Schrohenloher RE and Koopman WJ (1993) Rheumatoid factor. In: McCarty DJ and Koopman WJ (eds) *Arthritis and Allied Conditions. A Textbook of Rheumatology*, 12th edn, pp 861–876. Philadelphia: Lea and Febiger.

Shakib F (ed) (1989) *Autoantibodies to Immunoglobulins*, vol 26. Basel: Karger.

Vaughan JH (1993) Pathogenic concepts and origin of rheumatoid factor in rheumatoid arthritis. *Arthritis Rheumatism* 36: 1–6.

ANTIBODIES, BISPECIFIC

Constantin A Bona, Department of Microbiology, Mount Sinai Medical School, New York, USA

Bispecific (bifunctional) antibodies represent a category of artificially created immunoglobulins exhibiting a double, well-defined antigen specificity. The major application of bispecific antibodies is to focus the activity of an effector cell on a target cell by virtue of their ability to bind with one combining site to effector cell and with another to target cells.

Antibodies against the T cell receptor (TCR) of helper and cytotoxic effector cells are able to mimic the antigen and to activate the T cells to proliferate, to release lymphokines or to become cytotoxic. Bispecific antibodies which bind with one arm to the effector cell and with another to the target cell can activate the effector cell and ensure intimate contact between effector and target cells.

The preparation of bispecific antibodies was helped by the development of monoclonal antibody technology which can provide unlimited amounts of homogeneous antibody. There are three basic methods used to prepare bispecific molecules with 'à la carte' desired specificity (**Figure 1**).

Heteroconjugates

Heteroconjugates are bispecific antibodies obtained by chemical linkage of two immunoglobulin (Ig) molecules with different binding specificity. The chemical linkage of two monoclonal antibodies is carried out using cross-linkers such as N-succinimydyl-3-(2-pyridyldithio)-propionate (SPDP). High-pressure liquid chromatography (HPLC) is used for the purification of heteroconjugates made up of only dimers.

In vitro experiments demonstrated that such heteroconjugates are able to focus the activity of effector T cells on target cells bearing different antigen specificity. The presence of monocytes which can bind the heteroconjugates via Fc receptor can supply additional signals for the activation of T cells. It remains to be tested whether these antibodies are effective *in vivo*, in particular whether they could achieve the activation of local T cell contact with the target cells.

Heteroconjugates, although relatively easy to produce, are likely to be cleared quickly and may function as immune complexes, eventually causing immunopathological phenomena *in vivo*. Their stab-

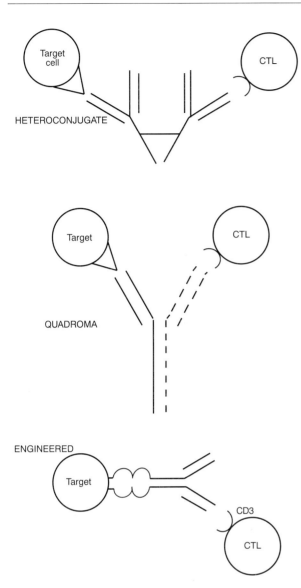

Figure 1 Structural characteristics and binding properties of various types of bispecific antibodies.

ility *in vivo* is questionable and since they are dimeric molecules they can cause antigenic modulation subsequent to cross-linking of TCR molecules associated with the surface of effector cells or of antigen molecules expressed on the surface of target cells.

Quadroma bispecific antibodies

Quadromas are bispecific antibodies synthesized by hybrid hybridomas obtained by fusion of two lymphocytes producing antibodies with different specificity. Because in hybrid hybridomas the expressed V_H and V_K genes of the parental cells are all produced there are ten molecular species of hybrid antibodies which theoretically can be formed as expected from the random association of the product of each gene. However, immunochemical studies of Ig mol-

ecules produced by quadromas showed that only six species were secreted and indicated a marginal preference for heavy–light chain homologous combination. The theoretical yield of a bispecific antibody with desired specificity produced by quadromas is 8–17% of the total Ig synthesized.

The production of quadromas is based on the principle of fusing two parental cells, each carrying a different drug resistant marker and selecting the hybrids of both type of cells in the presence of both drugs.

There have been only a few successful attempts to produce quadromas by fusing cells sensitive or resistant to various drugs such as hypoxanthine–aminopterin–thymidine (HAT)-sensitive, ouabain-resistant, neomycin (G418)-resistant, or resistant to iodoacetamide damage. Utilization of these drugs requires tedious experiments to select drug-sensitive or -resistant mutants in the population of hybridomas which will be used to generate quadromas. A new and easier method takes advantage of defective retroviruses carrying genes conferring resistance to neomycin or methotrexate.

Each partner of the fusion is infected with a retrovirus which confers a stable drug resistance at a very high frequency. The yield of quadromas using retrovirus-infected cells is generally higher than those using cells sensitive or resistant to various drugs. Utilization of hybridomas producing antibodies with different isotypes or idiotypes facilitates the purification of bispecific antibodies using anti-isotype or anti-idiotype immunoadsorbants.

Bispecific antibodies specific for the TCR of cytotoxic T lymphocytes (CTLs) and for viral antigens budding from the surface of target cells or against tumor antigens have been shown to be very efficient in small concentrations to focus CTL activity on target cells and to cause their lysis. The Fab fragment binding to the TCR is sufficient to activate the CTL, and the other Fab fragment brings the target cell in intimate contact with the CTL thereby causing lysis of the target.

It has been clearly shown that the redirected lysis mediated by bispecific antibodies circumvents the genetic restriction requirement of T cells. The efficacy of bispecific antibodies can be increased by preactivation of CTLs with specific antigens or superantigens. Bispecific monoclonal antibodies have numerous advantages when compared with chemically constructed heteroconjugates. These advantages include greater uniformity, stability and purity, and the absence of aggregates which may be cleared from the circulation as immune complexes. They also have a longer half-life *in vivo* because of their normal structure. In addition, because of the monomeric structure of the combining site it is unlikely that it will cause antigen modulation, a phenomenon which requires cross-linking of receptors or antigens associated with the membrane of effector or target cells.

Bispecific molecules produced by genetic engineering

The development of molecular biology techniques provided a new approach which permits the insertion, within or adjacent to the genes encoding an immunoglobulin molecule, of oligonucleotides encoding another immunoglobulin, a desired immunogenic epitope or an epitope responsible for interaction with a viral antigen. For example, it is possible to create a bispecific molecule in which the coding sequence for the V region of a CD3-specific antibody is combined with the sequence for the CD4 molecule which is able to bind HIVgp120. Such a bispecific molecule could activate a CTL and bring it into intimate contact with an HIV-infected cell.

Bispecific antibodies and heteroconjugates have a potential application in antitumor therapy and in the treatment of infectious diseases caused by bacteria or viruses in which the microbial antigen is expressed on the surface of infected cells. In the case of antitumour therapy, a bispecific antibody could be constructed using a monoclonal antibody specific for the TCR–CD3 complex (i.e. anti-CD3, anti-idiotype or anti-allotype) and a monoclonal antibody specific for a tumor-associated antigen. Bispecific antibodies have also been used to deliver isotopes or toxins to tumors which are difficult to remove by surgery or to tag remaining tumor cells after surgery. The efficiency of bispecific antibodies as antitumor immunotherapeutic agents are currently being evaluated in clinical trials in humans.

In the case of the treatment of infectious diseases the heteroconjugates or bispecific antibodies can be constructed using monoclonal antibodies against the TCR–CD3 complex of CTL and monoclonal antibody specific for a viral antigen. Evidence has been presented in a number of viral diseases that viral-specific CTLs reduce viral replication and dissemination. Therefore, the focusing of CTLs on virally infected cells by bispecific antibodies can prevent viral replication and spreading. It has already been shown that heteroconjugates or bispecific antibodies can redirect CTL activity against cells infected with

viruses such as human immunodeficiency virus (HIV), herpes or influenza.

Thus, it appears that bispecific antibodies have the potential to become a new category of immunotherapeutic reagents.

See also: **Antigen-binding site; Cytotoxic T lymphocytes; Hybridomas, B cell; Monoclonal antibodies (mAbs).**

Further reading

Carter P and Merchant AM (1997) Engineering antibodies for imaging and therapy. *Current Opinion in Biotechnology* 8: 449–454.

De-Jonge J, Brissinck J, Heirman C et al (1995) Production and characterization of bispecific single-chain antibody fragments. *Molecular Immunology* 32: 1405–1412.

de-Kruif J and Logtenberg T (1996) Leucine zipper dimerized bivalent and bispecific scFv antibodies from a semi-synthetic antibody phage display library. *Journal of Biological Chemistry* 271: 7630–7634.

Demanet C, Brissinck J, De-Jonge J and Thielemans K (1996) Bispecific antibody-mediated immunotherapy of the BCL1 lymphoma: increased efficacy with multiple injections and CD28-induced costimulation. *Blood* 87: 4390–4398.

DeSilva BS and Wilson GS (1995) Solid phase synthesis of bifunctional antibodies. *Journal of Immunological Methods* 188: 9–19.

Fanger MW, Segal DM and Romet-Lemonne J-L (1991) Bispecific antibodies and targeted cellular cytotoxicity. *Immunology Today* 12: 51–54.

Ito M and Moran T (1989) Sideways killing mediated by either anti-TCR or anti-T3 antibodies. *International Reviews of Immunology* 4: 133–145.

Jost CR, Titus JA, Kurucz I and Segal DM (1996) A single-chain bispecific Fv2 molecule produced in mammalian cells redirects lysis by activated CTL. *Molecular Immunology* 33: 211–219.

Jung G and Müller Eberhard HJ (1988) An *in vitro* model for tumor immunotherapy with antibody heteroconjugates. *Immunology Today* 9: 257–260.

Renner C and Pfreundschuh M (1995) Tumor therapy by immune recruitment with bispecific antibodies. *Immunology Reviews* 145: 179–209.

Starz UD and Bevan MT (1989) Redirecting the cellular immune response. *International Reviews of Immunology* 4: 159–175.

Tibben JG, Boerman OC, Massuger LF, Schijf CP, Claessens RA and Corstens FH (1996) Pharmacokinetics, biodistribution and biological effects of intravenously administered bispecific monoclonal antibody OC/TR F(ab')$_2$ in ovarian carcinoma patients. *International Journal of Cancer* 66: 477–483.

ANTIBODIES, DETECTION OF

Michael A Kerr, Department of Molecular and Cellular Pathology, University of Dundee, Ninewells Hospital Medical School, Dundee, Scotland

The widespread use of diagnostic tests which depend on the use of antibodies, together with the increasing use of antibodies in research laboratories for the detection and quantitation of all manner of biochemicals, has resulted in the development of a vast array of different techniques which can be used to detect antibodies. The nature, abundance and purity of the antigen recognized by the antibody and the number of assays to be performed will be the main factors which determine the selection of one technique rather than another. The most commonly used techniques and their relative advantages and disadvantages are summarized below.

Immunoprecipitation techniques

Antibodies were first detected by their ability to precipitate antigen when mixed at equivalence. This classical precipitin reaction of Heidelberger and Kendall is seldom used in its original form but precipitation tests adapted in many different ways are still widely used for the detection of antibody. In the double diffusion or Ouchterlony technique, antigen and antibody are placed in adjacent wells punched out of an agarose gel. Precipitation occurs when the two meet at appropriate concentrations. The simplicity of this technique makes it ideal for the initial screening of antisera raised in animals. Under appropriate conditions the test can also be used for comparing the specificity of antisera or determining the relatedness of two antigens. The test is commonly used for determining the class or subclass of monoclonal antibodies (in this case the monoclonal antibody is behaving as the antigen).

Many other techniques involving precipitation in gels are used primarily in the detection and quantitation of antigen. Counterimmunoelectrophoresis, in which the antigen and antibody are concentrated together by the effect of an electric current, is one modification of the Ouchterlony technique used for the detection of antibodies. Precipitation techniques are, in general, rather insensitive, detecting antibodies or antigens in the $\mu g\,ml^{-1}$ range. They are more useful for the detection of antibodies in polyclonal antisera rather than monoclonal antibodies which precipitate poorly.

The sensitivity of the basic precipitin reaction can be increased considerably by the use of complex optical detection systems to determine the amount of precipitation. Highly sensitive turbidometers and laser-based nephelometers are widely available. Though the equipment is expensive, these techniques are commonplace in diagnostic laboratories where high throughput can justify the initial investment.

Precipitin reactions can be accelerated by the inclusion of suitable concentrations of reagents such as ammonium sulfate or polyethylene glycol which will encourage precipitation of antibody or antibody–antigen aggregates but not free antigen. If the antigen is radiolabeled, this can be used as a sensitive and simple test for the detection of antibody – the Farr test. Radioimmunoassays have been used extensively for many years for the quantitation of antigens such as hormones and drugs which are present in very low concentrations.

Agglutination assays

If an antigen is particulate, e.g. a bacterial surface antigen or eukaryotic cell surface antigen, agglutination of the cells by the addition of antibody can provide a simple detection system. Agglutination is the standard test for blood group serology and it has other specialized applications. The technique can be extended to antibodies against soluble antigens by coupling of the antigens to particulate carriers. Initially the carrier of choice was the erythrocyte and detection systems depended on coupling of antigen on to the red cell using tannic acid. Hemagglutination assays remain the basis of several diagnostic test systems, quantitation being possible in terms of the antibody dilution of titer at which agglutination stops.

A number of synthetic carriers have been developed, including latex particles and a new generation of polymerized gelatin particles. Agglutination assays are simple to perform, requiring little or no expensive equipment. Modern versions are very sensitive and highly suitable for use outside the laboratory and in less-developed countries. They are widely used for detection of antibodies in the diagnosis of infectious disease. Tests for the human immunodeficiency virus (HIV) based on agglutination techniques compare favorably with other techniques. One drawback is that the tests can be more sensitive to the detection of polymeric immunoglobulin M (IgM) antibodies. This can be advantageous in detecting recent infections but might be a problem in autoimmune serology. Sensitivity can be down to 1 μg ml^{-1}.

Complement-dependent assays

The lytic activity of complement can be used in sensitive tests for the detection of antibodies recognizing cell surface antigens. Although now of limited application, it is still used widely in certain specialized situations, for example, the detection of antibodies recognizing histocompatibility antigens. Complement-mediated cytotoxicity is detected either by dye exclusion or by the release of ^{51}Cr from labeled cells. Complement fixation tests, once widely used, depend on the fact that antibody–antigen interaction will consume complement and the remaining complement can then be measured in a hemolytic assay. Though sensitive, these assays have declining usage.

Detection of antibodies using labeled anti-immunoglobulin reagents

The most widely used tests are those which use a second antibody, labeled in some way, to detect the binding of primary antibody to antigen. The availability of excellent, highly specific reagents from many commercial sources has made these techniques simple to apply in any laboratory. 'Second antibodies' are available which recognize imunoglobulins from humans and from most laboratory and veterinary animals. The second antibody can be labeled with radioactivity (usually ^{125}I), a fluorescent or luminescent dye, or coupled covalently to enzyme molecules. Each type of assay has its own advantages and disadvantages.

In quantitative assays, the antigen is usually coated on to plastic tubes or, more frequently, 96-well microplates to provide a solid phase on which to capture antibody. Sensitive detectors measure enzyme activity colorimetrically or detect chemiluminescence or fluorescence in this format. Flexible plates can be cut up for counting radioactivity. The enzyme-linked immunosorbent assay (ELISA) is the most widely used technique. Bound antibody is usually detected using alkaline phosphatase, horseradish peroxidase or β-galactosidase-conjugated second antibody. All of these enzymes cleave suitable substrates to yield highly colored products allowing detection of antibody in the ng ml^{-1} range.

Blotting techniques

A variation on the ELISA involves immobilization of antigen on sheets of nitrocellulose or a similar carrier. Again, filtration devices in the 96-well format give easy sample management. These 'dot blots' provide rapid, sensitive and simple tests with wide application in research laboratories. Enzyme-linked antibody systems are again most commonly used, utilizing the same conjugates as ELISA but substrates which give highly colored insoluble products. This allows easy measurement by eye, with the option that reflectance readers can be used for quantitation in a manner analogous to conventional ELISA readers. Related blotting techniques are used increasingly in rapid diagnostic tests. Most 'dipstick' techniques use this approach. Purified or recombinant antigens can be coated easily on to plastic or cellulose matrixes as the support for these rapid tests. Several antigens can be applied as discrete spots or bands to allow differential detection of specific antibodies in the same sera; ideal for many applications in infective or autoimmune serology.

In the research laboratory, the immunoblot or western blot is one of the most widely used techniques for the determination of antibody specificity. Separation of a complex mixture of antigens, for example a cellular extract, on polyacrylamide gels is followed by transfer of the separated proteins to a rigid medium such as nitrocellulose or nylon. Antibody is then added and after washing, the blot is developed with labeled second antibody and substrate. This allows characterization of the specificity of an antiserum or monoclonal antibody at the molecular level. The major drawback is that many antigenic determinants are destroyed by the SDS and denaturants used in the electrophoretic procedure. Blotting techniques can also be used for detecting antibodies against glycolipid antigens.

Immunohistochemistry

When the antigen is cell-associated, immunohistochemistry allows the detection and characterization of antibodies. For tissue sections, immunofluorescence is favored in many laboratories because of its simplicity. It is particularly useful for the detection of antibodies, including autoantibodies, recognizing antigens in intracellular organelles or where double labeling with two different antibodies (detected using two dyes of different color) is advantageous. Fluorescein and rhodamine are the standard conjugates, but a wide range of different colored dyes are available. Laser-based confocal microscopes have greatly increased the sensitivity and specificity of these techniques.

Immunofluorescent techniques for the detection of antibodies are widely used in conjunction with the flow cytometer or fluorescence-activated cell sorter. CD numbers describe leukocyte cell surface antigens recognized by monoclonal antibodies, defined initially by their cytofluorometric staining patterns on a large panel of different cell types. A wide range of different laser dyes are now available which are designed for use with the lasers commonly used in flow cytometers and confocal microscopes.

For tissue immunohistochemistry, enzyme-labeled antibodies are the choice in most laboratories. Peroxidase- and alkaline phosphatase-based techniques are used especially where the antigen detected will withstand the harsh fixation techniques often necessary to maintain tissue integrity. At the electron microscope level, immunogold techniques are used. Small, specifically sized gold particles are attached to antibody to allow localization of antigens. Colloidal gold conjugates can also be used successfully at the light microscope level, particularly in association with silver enhancement techniques. Immunogold can also be applied to blotting techniques giving sensitivity similar to that of enzyme-based detection systems.

Increasing sensitivity

Enzyme-based immunoassays, blotting techniques and immunohistochemistry have become the norm for the detection of antibodies and for characterization of their specificity. These systems have been developed in several ways to increase their sensitivity and ease of application. Biotin, a small molecule (244 Da) which binds with very high affinity to the proteins avidin or streptavidin, can itself be bound covalently to immunoglobulins without the loss of activity. A single biotinylated reagent can then be used in any test system with suitably labeled avidins. Since avidin can bind up to four biotin molecules, this gives the possibility of multilayered systems which offer increased sensitivity.

Alternative approaches to the detection of antibody utilize protein A, a bacterial surface protein which binds specifically to certain classes of IgG. Protein A in its natural or recombinant form or protein G, an IgG-binding protein from streptococci, are widely available. Protein G has broader specificity for subclasses of IgG and binds better to sheep and goat IgG than protein A. Second antibody systems do, however, remain the method of choice, particularly with the availability of good monoclonal antibodies specific for individual immunoglobulin classes or subclasses.

Although conventional detection systems are usually for sufficient sensitivity for the detection of antibodies, the detection of trace antigens such as growth factors or their receptors can require the necessity for an amplified detection system which will quantitate the binding of a primary antibody. Increased sensitivity is possible by the use of sandwich techniques involving several layers of antibody, enzyme–antienzyme complexes, biotin–avidin complexes or by newly developed specific amplification systems. One example of an enhancement system uses alkaline phosphatase conjugated to the detecting antibody to generate NAD from NADP. The NAD is then used in a pair of cycling redox reactions to reduce a colorless precursor to a colored formazan dye. The reaction product can be detected at 492 nm by conventional readers. The amplification step results in an increase in sensitivity of over 100-fold and is the basis of several rapid dipstick-type tests.

Chemiluminescence-based techniques have replaced colorimetric ELISAs and immunoblotting techniques in many laboratories because of their much greater sensitivity. A number of substrates which yield chemiluminescent products upon cleavage by peroxidase (luminol) or alkaline phosphatase (dioxetane phosphate esters) are available, usually in the form of kits containing all necessary reagents. For ELISA-based assays 96-well microplate luminometers are used. In chemiluminescence-based blotting techniques the signal can be detected using photographic film or specially designed plate detectors.

Time-resolved fluorescence techniques such as the DELFIA (Pharmacia) system, have been developed to replace the radioimmunoassay for the measurement of hormones etc. in large diagnostic laboratories. These assays are equally applicable to detection of antibodies, for example, in the diagnosis of infectious diseases. DELFIA utilizes Europium^{3+} bound to proteins through a covalently-linked EDTA derivative. Excess of the chelators naphthoyltrifluoroacetone and trioctylphosphine are then used to form a fluorescent complex in solution at low pH.

Future advances

Techniques developed for the detection of antibodies during the last few decades have sufficient sensitivity, diversity of application and robustness that they serve the vast majority of requirements. The widespread availability of highly specific, conjugated second antibodies and novel detection systems means that major gains in sensitivity are not necessary for the detection of most antibodies. It is advances in speed and ease of application which will determine the tests of the future. To this end, it is important to appreciate the potential or the instantaneous electrochemical tests based on biosensors and microelectronics which are already being developed and could make the detection of antibodies as simple and quick as the measurement of pH.

See also: **Agglutination; Autoantibodies, tests for; Complement fixation test; Enzyme-linked immunosorbent assay (ELISA); Flow cytometry; Fluorochrome labeling; Immunoassays; Western blotting.**

Further reading

Anon (1995) *Linscotts Directory of Immunological and Biological Reagents*, 8th edn. Santa Rosa, CA: Linscotts Directory.

Bjerrum OJ and Heegard NHH (1988) *CRC Handbook of Immunoblotting of Proteins*, vols I and II. London: CRC Press.

Catty D (1989) *Antibodies: A Practical Approach*, vols I and II. Oxford: IRL Press.

Delves PJ (1995) *Antibody Applications.* Chichester: John Wiley and Sons.

Harlow E and Lane D (1988) *Antibodies – A Laboratory Manual.* New York: Cold Spring Harbor Laboratory.

Herzenberg LA, Weir DM, Herzenberg LA and Blackwell C (1996) *Handbook of Experimental Immunology.* 5th edn. Oxford: Blackwell Science.

Johnstone A and Thorpe R (1996) *Immunochemistry in Practice*, 3rd edn. Oxford: Blackwell Scientific.

Kerr MA and Thorpe R (1994) *LABFAX Immunochemistry.* Oxford: Bios Scientific.

Price CP and Newman OJ (1991) *Principles and Practice of Immunoassay.* New York: Stockton Press.

ANTIBODIES, SECRETION

Roberto Sitia, DIBIT – San Raffaele Scientific Institute, 20132 Milan, Italy

As established by the classical experiments of Palade and coworkers, proteins destined to be secreted (as well as cell surface proteins) are synthesized in the endoplasmic reticulum (ER), and then transported through the Golgi complex to the extracellular space. Distinct post-translational modifications (assembly, glycosylation, etc.) take place sequentially along this pathway, allowing the intracellular location of a protein to be determined. The stepwise nature of the secretory pathway is confirmed by the existence of drugs which block intracellular transport at given stages. Similarly, several yeast temperature-sensitive mutants have been characterized in which secretion is blocked at different levels. Since mutations or drugs block the export of most secretory proteins, there appears to be only one main secretory pathway, utilized also by proteins destined to be expressed on the plasma membrane. An alternative pathway has been identified, which allows the selective secretion of certain cytosolic proteins lacking a conventional 'signal sequence' (see below).

Antibody secretion will be discussed in the context of the general problems of protein secretion. Among the many exciting questions in this field, the ones related to selectivity are maybe the most intriguing. How do cells decide what to secrete, when, and for how long?

Antibodies as a model system for protein secretion

Like all proteins destined to be synthesized in the ER, immunoglobulins are characterized by an N-terminal stretch of hydrophobic amino acids, the signal (leader) sequence, first inferred by Milstein and coworkers in 1972 in studies on immunoglobulin (Ig) light chain secretion. The signal sequence interacts with a multimeric ribonucleoprotein, the signal recognition particle (SRP). This interaction arrests translation until the complex formed by ribosome, nascent protein and SRP binds to the SRP receptor or docking protein on the ER membrane. Translocation of the nascent chain across the ER membrane occurs cotranslationally and the signal sequence is then cleaved by specific proteases located on the luminal face of the ER membrane. The first steps of N-linked glycosylation also occur cotranslationally (**Figure 1**).

The signal sequence is a paradigmatic example of 'positive' sorting: only the proteins that express it enter the secretory pathway. However, not all proteins synthesized within the ER will reach the extracellular space: some of them accumulate in the ER, some in the Golgi. Specific C-terminal sequences have been shown to cause *retention* within the ER of the proteins possessing them. This has led to the proposal of the bulk flow model, according to which all proteins in the secretory compartment will be secreted 'by default' unless they are marked with specific 'retention signals' which block them within a given organelle.

Protein secretion may be constitutive or regulated. Antibodies are secreted by plasma cells through the constitutive pathway. In the regulated pathway, pro-

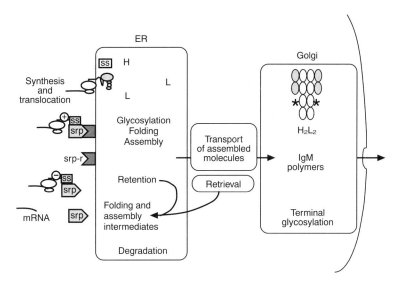

Figure 1 Assembly and secretion of immunoglobulins. The N-terminal signal sequence (ss) is recognized by the signal recognition particle (srp) on cytosolic nascent proteins. This interaction causes an arrest in translation (–). The complex binds to the srp receptor (or docking protein, srp-r), targeting the ribosome to the ER membrane, and allowing elongation of the nascent polypeptide (+). Translocation of the ER membrane and the first steps of N-linked glycosylation (addition of the $GlcNac_2Man_9Glu_3$ precursor) occur cotranslationally. Folding and assembly begin when the nascent H and L chains are still on the polysome, and are rapidly completed under the assistance of ER chaperones and folding enzymes (BiP, calnexin, PDI, ERp72, etc.). Only fully assembled molecules are transported to the Golgi, where they undergo terminal processing of their sugar moieties (∗) before being released into the extracellular space. Folding and assembly intermediates are retained in the ER, or retrieved in this organelle from the early compartments of the cis Golgi network. A proteolytic system, independent from that of lysosomes, maintains homeostasis in the ER. All transport steps occur within membrane-sealed vesicles that are thought to bud from one compartment and fuse with the next along the exocytic pathway.

teins are concentrated within intracellular stores (secretory granules) and bursts of secretion can be triggered at rates much higher than the synthetic one. In constitutive secretion there is normally little intracellular accumulation, and secretion depends largely on the rate of synthesis. However, IgM antibodies are an exception to this scheme as their secretion is developmentally regulated (see below). Constitutive secretion is common to virtually all cells, although at different levels. Like most cells specialized in secretion, plasma cells have abundant ER and a developed Golgi apparatus. By contrast, B cells have a very scarce ER.

Secreted proteins are remarkably uniform, and *only* fully assembled molecules are released extracellularly. This selectivity implies the existence of quality control steps in protein synthesis, folding and assembly, which appear to be coupled to intracellular transport. In addition, to maintain cellular homeostasis, proteins which fail these editing steps, and are hence not transported, must be degraded. Antibodies are an excellent model for understanding how cells manage to obtain high secretion efficiency and stringent quality control of the released products. This will be of interest in the general context of protein secretion, as well as for some more specific problems, namely how the onset, duration and intensity of the antibody responses are controlled.

Antibody secretion during B cell differentiation

Before it was discovered that membrane and secreted Ig contained distinct forms of heavy chains, differing at their C-termini, the problem of the differential expression of Ig during B cell differentiation was a dilemma for both immunologists and cell biologists. It was known that small, resting B lymphocytes expressed IgM on the cell surface (10^4–10^5 molecules per cell), but did not secrete IgM molecules. The same cells can be induced by mitogens or antigen to differentiate into plaque-forming cells (PFC), which lack surface Ig and secrete large amounts of antibodies (over 10^3 copies s^{-1} per cell). Since it was thought that constitutive secretion could be regulated only by changing the rate of synthesis, it was not easy to explain these results. In 1978–1981 it became clear that μ chains, as well as all other heavy chain isotypes, may be produced in a membrane (μm) or a secretory (μs) form by alternate RNA processing. The μm : μs ratio varies during B cell differentiation, μm predominating in the early (pre-B, B cells), and μs in the late stages (activated B cells and plasma cells). However, in many B lymphomas, abundant μs mRNA is present, and the rate of synthesis and assembly to light (L) chain is quite similar for μm and μs, indicating that the block in IgM secretion is due to post-translational mechanism(s). The molecular mechanisms preventing IgM secretion in B cells are related to the general problem as to how cells make sure that only fully assembled molecules are secreted or expressed on the cell surface, and will be discussed below.

Only fully assembled immunoglobulins are secreted

Antibodies are multimeric glycoproteins, made of two L and two heavy (H) chains. To maintain the clonal organization of the immune system, allelic exclusion ensures that only one H and one L chain specificity are produced by a B lymphocyte. However, the specificity of a V_H region might differ if H chains were not assembled with L chains. The mechanisms ensuring that only the fully assembled forms of antibody molecules are secreted by plasma cells (or expressed on the surface of B lymphocytes) have been understood recently, and once again information gathered on antibodies has proven of general relevance. It has been shown that, in the absence of L chains, H chains interact with BiP (heavy chain binding protein, grp 78), an abundant resident protein of the ER. BiP belongs to the protein family of chaperonins, which, together with oxidoreductases (such as PDI or ERp72) and other enzymes, assist the folding and the assembly of newly synthesized proteins in the ER. Since BiP is itself retained in the ER lumen via its C-terminal sequence Lys-Asp-Glu-Leu (KDEL), unassembled H chains are not able to leave the ER. The interaction with BiP involves the first constant domain of the H chain (C_H1), which normally interacts with the constant domain of L chains. Thus, assembly with L chains masks the BiP binding site, allowing assembled molecules to exit the ER and reach the Golgi apparatus, where terminal glycosylation takes place (**Figure 1**). Deletion of the C_H1 domain by recombinant DNA techniques allows secretion of free γ heavy chains, a finding that explains why, in the rare cases of heavy chain disease, secreted free heavy chains always lack the C_H1.

Developmental control of IgM secretion

In the case of IgM and IgA, the basic H_2L_2 structure is further assembled into polymers which contain J chain, a small cysteine-rich glycoprotein synthesized by plasma cells, but not by resting B lymphocytes. Only polymeric IgM is secreted, despite the fact that the major intracellular form is μ_2L_2. Thus, IgM (and IgA) undergo a further level of control, which blocks secretion of nonpolymeric molecules. This editing step depends on disulfide interchange reactions,

which involve the cysteine residue found at the penultimate position of both μ_s and α_s chains. This residue is responsible for the intersubunit disulfide bonds which stabilize the polymeric structure. In assembly intermediates the unbound SH group may interact with ER resident proteins, thereby blocking their transport to the Golgi. Thus, IgM is subject to a dual editing process which allows plasma cells to secrete only polymers. First, μ-L association is controlled by interactions between BiP and sequences in the $C\mu1$; then, disulfide interchange reactions control polymerization.

In B lymphocytes, polymerization is very inefficient, a finding that explains why IgM is not secreted. The requirement for polymerization might also explain why, also in myelomas, secretion of IgM is rather slow and inefficient compared with IgG. If the C-terminal cysteine of the μ_s chain is replaced by serine, the rate and efficiency of IgM secretion is increased, and intracellular degradation reduced. Furthermore, these mutant monomeric IgMs are secreted also by B cells, indicating that the presence of a developed ER is not *per se* necessary for secretion of immunoglobulin molecules.

As polymeric IgM contains J chains, it has been proposed that the failure of B cells to secrete IgM correlates with the absence of J chain synthesis. However, since B cell lines have been isolated which synthesize J chain and yet do not secrete IgM, and nonlymphoid transfectants secrete polymeric IgM lacking J chains, the latter appear to be neither essential nor sufficient for IgM secretion. Knock-out mice that lack J chains have high levels of IgA (mainly monomeric) and of hexameric IgM in the serum. Hence, J chain seems to play a key role in 1) determining the size of polymeric IgM (pentamers predominate in the presence of J chain), and 2) facilitating the transcytosis of polymeric Igs across epithelia. The problem of why B cells do not secrete IgM may thus be reduced to the single question as to why in B cells polymerization is so inefficient. Differentiation into IgM secreting plasma cells is accompanied by major changes in the ER and by a much higher rate of synthesis of μ and L chains. These events might include modification(s) of the redox potential along the secretory pathway which would favor polymerization.

Glycosylation and secretion

Despite the abundant literature on the issue, the precise function of the carbohydrate moieties of glycoproteins remains to be established. Selective inhibitors (e.g. tunicamycin) or site-directed mutagenesis of the relevant asparagines have been employed to prevent N-linked glycosylation of many glyco-proteins, including IgS. In those systems where the presence of tunicamycin blocks secretion, folding and assembly are slower, and intracellular degradation is increased. Glycosylation might increase solubility and stability of antibodies. Since many deglycosylated proteins are exported, glycosylation does not appear essential for secretion. However, the recent findings of several compartmentalized molecules with lectin activity within the secretory pathway have awakened the dormant hypothesis of a role of glycans in facilitating exocytosis.

Intracellular degradation of newly synthesized proteins

To maintain the steady state, proteins which cannot be secreted must be degraded. On the other hand, unassembled or malfolded proteins are retained in the ER via interactions with BiP or disulfide interchange reactions, and may thus not reach the lysosome. This apparent paradox was solved when it became clear that a proteolytic system, independent from the lysosomal one, exists in a pre-Golgi compartment. Heavy chains are degraded more rapidly when not assembled to L chains. Assembly might decrease the susceptibility to proteases, hide signals which target to degradation, or both.

The biochemistry of ER degradation is still largely unknown. Evidence has been recently obtained that ubiquitin and proteasomes are involved in the degradation of CFTR, a transmembrane protein retained in the ER in cystic fibrosis patients. As to the specificity of the process, in many cases, including T cell receptors and Igs, the signals that lead to degradation have been shown to coincide with those that mediate the assembly as well as the retention of unassembled subunits. However, there must be a lag while nascent proteins, that are bound to express many degradation targeting signals, are protected from proteolysis. A distinct subcompartment, specialized in proteolytic activity, may exist in the ER. Alternatively, nascent proteins maybe shielded by chaperones.

Pathologic conditions related to Ig secretion

Defects in immunoglobulin secretion might be at the basis of certain pathologic conditions such as common variable immunodeficiency (acquired hypogammaglobulinemia). In this disease, the number of membrane Ig-expressing B cells is normal but very little antibody is present in the serum: defects in γ chain glycosylation have been reported, but their pathogenic relevance remains to be established.

Immunodeficiency with hyper IgM is characterized by high levels of serum IgM and virtual absence of IgG and IgA. In these patients, mutations in the CD40 ligand perturb T cell–B cell interactions, resulting in impaired isotype switching and affinity maturation. Although it is worth recalling that considerable amounts of monomeric IgM are present in the serum of these patients, the significance of this observation is at present unclear.

Many observations on myelomas and heavy chain disease related to defects in or unbalanced Ig secretion have already been mentioned. Secretion of free L chains (Bence Jones proteins), does not appear to be a characteristic of neoplastic plasma cells, but probably reflects an important feature of the Ig assembly line, where the limiting factor is the heavy chain. While cells producing only L are frequent, myeloma mutants producing only H are exceedingly rare, an observation which led to the proposal of heavy chain toxicity. Assembly of complete Ig molecules requires an equal number of L and H chains. Although it might be thought more economical for the cell to synthesize equimolar amounts of the two chains, L chains are produced in excess to optimize HL assembly. The excess L chains can be secreted mainly as L_2 homodimers.

Mott cells are plasma cells defective in Ig secretion found in multiple myeloma and certain chronic inflammatory and autoimmune conditions. Mott cells are characterized by cytoplasmic inclusions normally containing immunoglobulin molecules, called Russell bodies, and representing dilated cisternae of the ER. Mott hybridomas have been obtained by fusing splenocytes from NZB mice, a strain highly susceptible to autoimmune diseases. Since these hybridomas express several membrane antigens, a general defect in the secretory pathway may be excluded. That the Mott cell phenotype is due to mutations in the Ig chains is indicated by the observation that Russell bodies are formed upon transfection of certain mutated heavy chains into myeloma cells. Not all nonsecretable chains induced the Mott phenotype. Thus, Russell bodies probably reflect the presence of nontransportable molecules resistant to pre-Golgi degradation.

Ig secretion by nonlymphoid cells

Immunoglobulins have been expressed in several heterologous systems, such as nonlymphoid transfectants, Xenopus oocytes, or transgenic plants. In most cases, immunoglobulin molecules were properly assembled and secreted. Mutants were handled similarly by lymphoid and nonlymphoid cells, and Russell bodies could be detected in glioma transfectants.

Thus, unlike the rearrangement of Ig genes, the complex and developmentally regulated processes of Ig assembly and secretion do not appear to require tissue-specific factors.

Secretory immunoglobulins

Antibodies in external fluids (milk, bile, saliva, lacrimal, nasal, intestinal, cervical fluids) are often called secretory Ig, as opposed to serum Ig, a definition that may generate confusion now that the same term is used to discriminate the soluble form from the membrane-bound form of antibody molecules. Polymeric immunoglobulins (IgM and IgA) in external secretions contain, in addition to J chain, a polypeptide of approximately 25 kDa, called the secretory component. The latter is not produced by lymphoid cells, but represents a portion of the poly-Ig receptor which is proteolytically cleaved during the process of transcytosis across epithelial cells.

See also: **Allelic exclusion; Antibodies, synthesis; Bence Jones proteins; Glycosylation of immune system molecules; Heavy chain diseases; IgA; IgD; IgE; IgG; IgM; Immunoglobulin, cell surface; Joining J chain; Lymphoma; Plaque-forming cell (PFC) assays; Secretory component (the polymeric Ig receptor).**

Further reading

Brewer JW, Randall TD, Parkhouse RME and Corley RB (1994) IgM hexamers? *Immunology Today* **15**: 165–168.

Carayannopoulos L and Capra JD (1993) Immunoglobulins. Structure and function. In: Paul WE (ed) *Fundamental Immunology*, 3rd edn, pp. 283–314. New York: Raven Press.

Fiedler K and Simons K (1995) The role of *N*-glycans in the secretory pathway. *Cell* **81**: 309–312.

Fra AM and Sitia R (1993) The endoplasmic reticulum as a site of protein degradation. In: Borgese N and Harris JR (eds) *Subcellular Biochemistry. Endoplasmic Reticulum*, pp. 143–168. New York: Plenum Press.

Gaut JR and Hendershot LM (1993) The modification and assembly of proteins in the endoplasmic reticulum. *Current Opinion in Cell Biology* **5**: 589–595.

Hammond C and Helenius A (1995) Quality control in the secretory pathway. *Current Biology* **7**: 523–529.

Hendrickson BA, Conner DA, Ladd DJ *et al* (1995) Altered hepatic transport of immunoglobulin A in mice lacking the J chain. *Journal of Experimental Medicine* **182**: 1905–1911.

Honjo T, Alt FW (eds) (1995) *Immunoglobulin Genes*, 2nd edn. London: Academic Press.

Kaloff CR and Haas IG (1995) Coordination of immunoglobulin chain folding and immunoglobulin chain assembly is essential for the formation of functional IgG. *Immunity* **2**: 1–20.

Melnick J and Argon Y (1995) Molecular chaperones and the biosynthesis of antigen receptors. *Immunology Today* **16**: 243–250.

Palade GE (1975) Intracellular aspects of the process of protein secretion. *Science* **189**: 347–358.

Rothblatt J, Novick P and Stevens TH (eds) (1994) *Guideline to the Secretory Pathway*. Oxford: Oxford University Press.

Sitia R and Cattaneo A (1995) Synthesis and assembly of antibodies in natural and artificial environments. In: Zanetti M and Capra JD (eds) *The Antibodies*, vol I, pp 127–168. Luxembourg: Harwood Academic.

Sitia R, Neuberger MS, Alberini CM *et al* (1990) Developmental regulation of IgM secretion: the role of the carboxy-terminal cysteine. *Cell* **60**: 781–790.

Von Heijne G (1990) Protein targeting signals. *Current Opinion in Cell Biology* **2**: 604–608.

ANTIBODIES, SPECIFICITY

Denong Wang and **Elvin A Kabat**, Department of Microbiology, College of Physicians and Surgeons, Columbia University, New York, USA

Quantitatively, the specificities of antibodies are determined by their relative binding affinities, the intrinsic property of each antibody combining site, expressed as equilibrium dissociation (K_d) or association constants (K_a) for their interactions with different antigens. The K_d values may vary significantly among different antibody–antigen interactions, ranging from 10^{-3} M to 10^{-11} M or higher, but never reach the value of the binding of biotin to avidin (K_d 10^{-15} M).

Different classes of antibodies may differ in their 'avidities', i.e. the number of combining sites on each antibody. As illustrated in **Figure 1**, an antibody molecule has a four-chain structure built of two identical heavy (H) and two identical light (L) chains. Pairing of each H and L chain forms the basic unit of antibody combining sites. In monomeric antibodies such as immunoglobulin G (IgG), IgD, IgE and the majority of the serum IgA, two pairs of H and L chains, linked by disulfide bonds in the hinge region

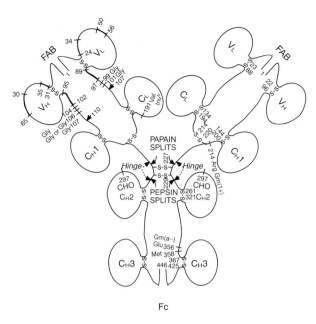

Figure 1   Schematic view of four-chain structure of human IgG1 molecule. Numbers on right side denote actual residues of protein Eu (Edelman *et al*, 1969). Numbers of Fab fragment on the left side are aligned for maximum homology; light and heavy chains are numbered according to Wu and Kabat (1970) and Kabat and Wu (1971). Heavy chains of Eu have residue 52A and 82A,B,C and lack residues termed 100A,B,C,D,E,F,G,H,I,J,K and 35A,B. Thus, residue 100 (end of variable region) is 114 in actual sequence. Hypervariable or complementarity-determining regions (CDRs) are shown by heavier lines. V_L and V_H denote light- and heavy-chain variable regions: C_H1, C_H2 and C_H3 are domains of constant region of heavy chain: C_L is constant region of light chain. The hinge region in which two heavy chains are linked by disulfide bonds is indicated approximately. Attachment of carbohydrate is at residue 297. Arrows at residues 107 and 110 denote transition from variable to constant region. Sites of action of papain and pepsin and locations of a number of genetic factors are given. (Reproduced from Kabat EA *et al* (1987).)

of H chains, form two identical antibody combining sites; secretory IgA may be dimers or trimers with four or six binding sites; IgM isotype is pentameric, bearing ten identical sites. For a given Ig isotype, the amino acid sequences in the C-terminal domains are basically identical, termed the constant region (C); those of the N-terminal domains are highly variable, called the variable region (V). Avidities of antibodies are associated with H chain C region isotypes; affinities or binding specificities are determined by V region structures.

Many kinds of substances, when introduced into the body, may induce the formation of antibodies. These include infectious agents such as bacteria and viruses, allo- or xenoantigens of blood cells or other cell types and many substances in the environment or derived from foods, e.g. pollens, shellfish and others to which some people may be allergic. Natural antigens may frequently be complex mixtures of many antigenic substances. Even highly purified substances such as proteins, polysaccharides, glycolipids or nucleic acids may contain multiple antigenic determinants (epitopes). B lymphocytes comprise an enormous population of distinct antibody-producing cells. Each cell and its descendants synthesize one antibody in response to a single epitope but different cells may recognize different aspects of the same epitope and vary in their binding affinities. Thus, the antibody response of an individual to a bacterium or virus, etc. may involve multiple B cell clones recognizing different antigenic determinants and is said to be polyclonal.

Early studies on specificity carried out on polyclonal populations of antibody yielded much information but the most definitive studies are those using monoclonal antibodies from humans or mice with multiple myeloma or macroglobulinemia and with monoclonal antibodies produced by the hybridoma technique of Köhler and Milstein. Hybridoma antibodies may be produced to any epitope; in practice this may be more difficult, particularly for producing human monoclonals. Cell–cell hybridization for making hybridomas is inefficient and often limited to certain stages of B cell differentiation. Alternative strategies for producing monoclonal antibodies, their Fv, Fab fragments and the engineered single-chain antibodies (scFv), have recently been developed by combining PCR amplification and gene expression. Using advanced flow cytometry, a single B cell, with an Ig receptor of defined specificity as well as other surface markers, may be isolated and its original pair of V_H and V_L chains identified, allowing further exploration of the repertoires of monoclonal antibodies.

Binding specificities of antibodies may be investigated using rationally designed antigens in which one or more chemically defined small substances may serve as antigenic determinants. Thus, diazotized arsanilic acid, dinitrofluorobenzene, etc. may be coupled to a macromolecule to produce an artificial antigen. The antibodies induced will generally react best with, or be most specific for, the group introduced. Thus antibodies to the arsanilic acid-containing macromolecule generally bind arsanilic acid azotyrosine, and those to the dinitrophenyl macromolecule often bind only dinitrophenyllysine. Binding specificities may be further illustrated by competitive inhibition of the reaction by corresponding low molecular weight substances. Competition with structural derivatives differing from the active molecule by defined fine modifications at given positions may allow identification of the critical structures involved in specific recognition. Such low molecular weight substances are termed haptens; the macro-molecules are called carriers.

A potential difficulty in these studies is that the introduced groups are frequently insufficient in size to fill the antibody combining site so that the new epitopes may include a portion of the carrier molecule to which it is linked. Studies with small haptenic determinants, such as phosphorylcholine (PC), 2-phenyloxazolone (phOx), 4-hydroxy-3-nitrophenyl (NP) or dinitrophenyl (DNP) and p-azophenyl-arsonate (Ars) coupled to proteins, may thus not be clearly definable as to what constitutes the antigenic determinant. For example, one may not be able to determine whether sequence differences in the V regions of antibodies induced by these conjugates reflect specificity for different antigenic determinants or are a consequence of specificity differences to a single epitope.

Better understanding of antibody diversity and specificity requires a single site-filling antigenic determinant of well-defined structure. Native dextran N279 is a near-linear macromolecule of glucose linked by 90% $\alpha(1, 6)$ and 5% $\alpha(1, 3)$ glucopyranos-idic bonds and has 5% $\alpha(1, 6)$ or other linkages for the glucoses at terminal nonreducing ends. The relative structural simplicity of the carbohydrate antigen, $\alpha(1, 6)$ dextran, provides a model system for such studies. The availability of oligosaccharides of $\alpha(1, 6)$-linked glucose, ranging from isomaltose (IM2) to $[Glc(\alpha1, 6)]_9$ (IM9), allow us to 'measure' the sizes of antibody combining sites by competitive inhibition of the dextran–antidextran interaction. The combining site is considered to be complementary in size to the smallest oligosaccharide giving maximum competition. Such an oligosaccharide is defined as an epitope or antigenic determinant. It was estimated by such immunochemical mapping that the antibody combining sites to dextran may vary in size from a lower limit of 1–2 glucoses to an upper limit of 6–7.

To accommodate epitopes with distinct structural properties, different 'shapes' or 'types' of antibody combining sites may be required. For the polysaccharide antigen $\alpha(1, 6)$ dextran, either the nonreducing end sugar or the internal chain structure may function as antigenic determinants. They may be specifically recognized by either cavity- or groove-type combining sites. This was first established by immunochemical mapping of the combining sites of two monoclonal myeloma proteins, W3129 and QUPC52, both specific for $\alpha(1, 6)$dextran. W3129 had a site saturated by isomaltopentaose, whereas QUPC52 accommodated isomaltohexaose. With W3129, the terminal nonreducing glucose contributed 50–60% of the total binding energy but with QUPC52 less than 5%. The two antibodies also dif-

fered in their ability to precipitate a synthetic linear dextran with about 200 glucoses. QUPC52 but not W3129 forms precipitins in saline. These observations indicate that the combining sites of QUPC52 might be 'grooves' into which internal chain epitopes of $\alpha(1–6)$-linked glucose could fit; in contrast, the nonreducing ends of dextran may be held by the cavity-type site of W3129. Monoclonal antibodies (mAbs) for 3-fucosyllactosamine, i.e. Le^x, may also accommodate either the nonreducing ends (PM81), or may bind to the side of the sugar chain (PMN6). Crystal structures for these mAbs are currently not available but a few antibodies for other carbohydrate antigens have been crystallized. A $\beta(1,6)$galactan-specific myeloma protein J539 displays a shallow surface pocket accommodating the polysaccharide antigen; a monoclonal antibody, Se 155-4, binds a trisaccharide of *Salmonella* with the terminal abequose totally buried in a deep pocket of the combining site. Antigen-binding sites, which may be classified as either groove- or cavity-type, are also seen in antibodies specific for other antigens. For example, BV04-01 Fab binds ssDNA with a large, irregular groove and Fab McPC603 has a cavity to accept the hapten phosphorylcholine.

Antibodies may interact with protein antigens with a relatively flat surface. Proteins differ from carbohydrate antigens in their behavior in aqueous solution. Proteins tend to fold to bring their hydrophobic side-chains together, forming an oily core with the polar side-chains exposed. Such folding may allow discontinuous amino acids clustered on the solvent-accessible surface to form discontinuous epitopes. Interior residues are usually not accessible to antibody interactions. A protein epitope may thus be formed either by several contiguous amino acid residues or by discontinuous residues. Of three lysozyme–antilysozyme complexes whose X-ray structures have been determined at high resolution, two antibody combining sites, D1.3 and HyHel-5, each interact with amino acids from two discontinuous stretches of the lysozyme polypeptide chain; the third, HyHel-10, is complementary to the exposed surface of a helix including some surrounding structures. With influenza neuraminidase, four segments of its polypeptide chain were found to interact with the antibody combining site in a resolved crystal structure of their complex. It is thus said that antibodies recognize 'conformation' rather than 'sequence' of a protein epitope.

A discontinuous conformational epitope may be mimicked by molecules having different primary structures. Indeed, antibodies which mimic the structures of other molecules exist. They may be specifically induced by idiotype–anti-idiotype interactions.

Antibodies to various antigens may have distinct epitopes in their V regions termed idiotopes, which may be antigenic upon injection. Such induced antibodies are termed anti-idiotypic antibodies. Some anti-idiotypic antibodies may mimic the external antigen that elicited the first antibody reacting with the anti-idiotype. A complex of antilysozyme D1.3 and its anti-idiotype E5.2, an internal image type, has been crystallized and its three-dimensional structure clarified. By comparison with the crystal structure of D1.3–lysozyme complex, it was shown that D1.3 contacts lysozyme and the internal image antibody E5.2 through essentially the same combining site residues. In addition, E5.2 interacts with D1.3, making contacts similar to those between lysozyme and D1.3. Functional mimicry of a small biologically active compound, taxol, by an anti-idiotypic antibody 82H has been recently reported. Like taxol, this anti-idiotypic antibody can promote and stabilize microtubule assembly. We must still learn how the three-dimensional structure of 82H can mimic a ligand molecule that bears no structural similarity to immunoglobulins.

There is also evidence that variable regions of antibodies with radically different primary structures may accommodate identical epitopes. A mouse mAb specific for blood group substance A and a human antibody to the same antigenic determinant were found to have very different amino acid sequences in their V_H and V_L domains. Their fine specificities to substance A are indistinguishable by current immunochemical analysis. More examples are seen in anti-$\alpha(1, 6)$ dextrans. mAbs to $\alpha(1, 6)$dextran may be either groove-type or cavity-type, and sites defined as the same could be very similar imunochemically. Their Ig-V region sequences were determined, showing at least 18 distinct combinations of V region genes and segments of different primary structures, 15 combinations for the groove-type combining sites and three for the cavity-type sites. A definitive answer to the paradox of 'diverse sequence-similar site' will come from X-ray crystallographic analysis of these antibodies and their ligand complexes as well as from a dynamic analysis of their solution conformers applying nuclear magnetic resonance (NMR) and other advanced methods.

To understand better the relationships of structural diversity of antibody combining sites and their complementarity and specificities, the critical structures defining the prototypes or shapes of antibody combining sites and their fine specificities should be identified. Analysis of V region sequences led to recognition of hypervariable or complementarity-determining regions (CDRs) in V domains of antibodies. In the early 1970s, Wu and Kabat examined

about 70 human V_κ and V_λ and mouse V_κ sequences and introduced an equation, termed a variability plot for analysis:

$$\text{Variability} = \frac{\text{Frequency of the most common amino acid at a given position}}{\text{Number of different amino acids at that position}}.$$

When variability was plotted against amino acid residue number for the 107 residues in the V region, three peaks of high variability were seen at positions 24–34, 50–56 and 89–97, bracketed by invariant or almost invariant residues with length variations at residues 27A–27F and 95A–95F (**Figure 2**). As V_H

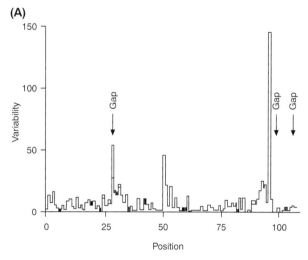

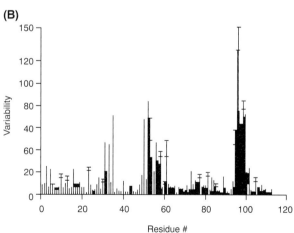

Figure 2 (A) Variability at different positions for the variable region of light chains. GAP indicates position at which differences in length have been found. (Reproduced from Wu TT and Kabat EA (1970) by copyright permission of The Rockefeller University press.) (B) Variability at different positions for the variable region of heavy chains. The plot was made by the PROPHET computer system. (Reproduced from Kabat EA, Wu TT and Bilofsky H (1979) Government Printing Office Publication NIH 80-2008. Washington DC.)

sequences of various species become available, three hypervariable regions were also found at positions 31–35, 50–65 and 95–102; with length variations listed as 35A and 35B, 52A to 52C and 100A to 100K (**Figure 2B**). Considerable three-dimensional information has now become available by X-ray crystallography. All high-resolution X-ray structures verified the prediction and showed that the hypervariable regions, as defined, formed the antibody combining site. These are termed CDRs and the rest of the V_H and V_L domains form a framework (FR). Comparison of the three-dimensional structures of variable domains of different antibodies reveals that the nonhypervariable or framework regions of these domains are essentially superimposable. Structural variations related to antibody specificity are mainly confined to the hypervariable segments. Amino acid residues of antibody in actual contact with antigenic determinants are found predominantly in the CDR regions. The antibody combining site can thus be viewed as being formed by a relatively small number of segments of variable structure grafted on to a scaffolding of essentially invariant architecture. In three dimensions, these variable segments or CDRs are seen as a loop structure situated at the N-terminal tip of an antibody. Their combination forms a continuous solvent accessible surface, the CDR surface, approximately 2800 Å^2 in area.

In the crystal structure of antibody–ligand complexes, a portion of the CDR surface may be buried by the ligand; likewise, those of the ligand covered by the antibody. Such a buried area is termed a contacting surface, representing the actual sizes and shapes of antibody combining sites. Different types of interaction, such as reacting to protein, to polysaccharide or to small haptens, may differ significantly in the area of their contacting surface as well as the nature of their three-dimensional complementarity. In Fab-Se 155-4 complexed with a branched trisaccharide α-D-Galp(1–2)[α-D-Abep(1–3)]-α-D-Manp of *Salmonella*. The terminal abequose fills the hydrophobic pocket of the antibody, with contacting surfaces of 255 Å^2 for the buried sugar epitope and 304 Å^2 for the antibody, corresponding to the lower limit of site sizes estimated by immunochemical mapping of antidextrans. For a carbohydrate–lectin complex, the interface of ligand Le^b and its receptor OMe.GS-IV shows complementarity of polyamphiphilic properties of their contacting surface, with buried areas of 237 Å^2 and 265 Å^2, respectively. The changes of contacting area of these carbohydrate receptors is similar to that for binding of haptens by antibodies but much smaller than the interfaces of proteins and their antibody combining sites. McPC603 contacts phosphorylcholine by 151 Å^2

and 138 Å^2; Fab AN02 and DNP-spin-label by 363 Å^2 and 230 Å^2; and Fab 4-4-20 with fluorescein by 338 Å^2; and 247 Å^2. Protein antigens may interact with antibody combining sites with a relatively larger surface. In Fab–lysozyme complexes, lysozyme was bound by HyHEL-5 with buried surface areas of 768 Å^2 and 723 Å^2, the HyHEL-10 complex of 699 Å^2 and 753 Å^2, and the D1.3 complex by 512 Å^2 and 524 Å^2. Their binding constants (K_d) are 5×10^{-11} M, 2×10^{-10} M and 10^{-10} M, respectively. Binding of carbohydrates by antibodies or by lectins is specific but binding constants are often several logs lower than antibody–protein interactions, generally 10^{-3} M to 10^{-6} M. Possible correlations between their limited contacting areas and the low binding affinities may be evaluated when more crystal structures become available.

The topographic properties of the contacting surface are mainly determined by the loop configuration of individual CDRs and their relative disposition. These, in turn, are determined by the number and nature of amino acid residues in CDRs. There are residue positions in CDR which are more conserved than others and were postulated to be structural or conformational elements. On the basis of comparative studies of known crystal structure of antibodies and sequences, Chothia and colleagues found that the loop conformation of CDRs is determined by a few conserved residues in a CDR segment and suggested that there is a small repertoire of main chain conformations for at least five of the six CDRs of antibody, termed canonical structures. The length variation of CDR segments is also important for their loop conformations. Among six CDRs, only the V_L-CDR2 is conserved in length, with seven amino acid residues (**Figure 2**) in all productive V_L chains so far identified. A unique canonical structure fits 95% of 69 human V_L and of 183 murine V_L analyzed. The V_H-CDR3s vary extensively not only in residue composition but also in the number of their amino acid residues. No canonical structures can be assigned to this region. For the rest of CDRs, distinct canonical structures can always be identified among segments of a given CDR when they differ in length by as little as a single amino acid residue.

To form a given prototype of antibody combining sites, a certain combination of CDR loops may be required. For example, a long V_H-CDR3 and a long V_L-CDR1 are common to the cavity-type combining sites of different specificities, including all the cavity-type anti-α(1, 6)dextrans so far sequenced, anti-phosphorylcholine mAb McPC603 and anti-3-fucosyllactosamine PM81. Modeling of these sites showed that this CDR loop combination is required to form the cavity wall of the combining sites. With the groove-type sites, a short V_L-CDR1 lacking amino acid residues 27 and 28 is predominantly seen in anti-dextrans; a few exceptions have either a long V_L-CDR3 or a long V_H-CDR, but not both. Lara-Ochoa and coworkers analyzed the combinations of the canonical CDR structures of murine Ig sequences provided by the on-line server of the KABAT database. Of 519 murine antibodies studied, only 33 combinations of at least 300 total expected combinations are actually found. About 85% of the antibodies fall into only six different combinations of canonical structures. These distinct groups correlate to the types of antigen with which they interact. It was suggested that relatively small numbers of canonical structural combinations of CDR segments may primarily determine the 'prototypes' or 'gross' specificities of the antibody combining sites. Further diversification of these structures are required to generate a wide variety of antigen-binding specificities.

The molecular mechanisms underlying antibody diversity have been extensively studied. The intact V_H or V_L chains are assembled by genetically separated elements, V_H genes, D and J_H segments or V_L genes and J_L segments, by a site-specific recombination event the V(D)J rearrangements. CDR1 and CDR2 are encoded by the V_H or V_L genes; the CDR3 regions are generated by recombination events, V_L-CDR3 joined by V_L and J_L, and the V_H-CDR3 by V_H, D and J_H. N or P element insertions may occur at either V_H-D or D-J_H junctions. D-D fusion may also occur during the V_H-D-J_H recombination but at lower frequency. Sequences and lengths of V_H-CDR3 are therefore the most variable. A rearranged antibody molecule may be further diversified by another somatic molecular process termed 'hypermutation', which may be induced during an immune response to antigenic stimulation, typically those elicited by T-dependent protein antigens. In the nonimmunized repertoire or the 'natural antibody' population, antibodies with low affinity and cross-reactivity are frequently seen. They are usually encoded by germline V region genes without or with few somatic mutations. Antibodies with relatively high affinity may be obtained during secondary immune responses or later but generally not at the stage of the primary response. Point mutations are frequently observed in their V regions. The process by which an antibody with low affinity is further diversified by point mutations to high affinity is termed 'affinity maturation'. This process is believed to occur in the germinal centers of lymphoid tissue and requires help by T lymphocytes and other accessory cells. The molecular mechanisms underlying hypermutation and how it contributes to the affinities and specificities of antibody combining sites are less understood.

Since V(D)J recombination occurs at the pre-B cell stage and secondary rearrangements appear very infrequently, a 'matured' high-affinity antibody may preserve the lengths of its six CDR loops and the canonical structural combination of its parent antibody, i.e. the rearranged unmutated germline antibody, unless mutations occurred at the conserved CDR residue positions which are considered as those critical for the canonical structure of CDRs. Comparison of such matured high-affinity sites and their low-affinity germline antibody may allow us to investigate how somatic mutation contributes to the affinity maturation. Patten and colleagues studied a catalytic antibody 48G7 and its germline partner. They reconstructed and expressed the Fab segments of 48G7 as well as the germline antibody. The active catalytic antibody 48G7 differs from the germline partner by nine replacement mutations, six in CDRs and three in FRs. None of the six CDR residues, two in V_L-CDR1, one in V_L-CDR2 and three in V_H-CDR2, examined using Chothia's definition, can be classified as 'key residues' for the canonical structure of the CDRs. Thus, the two antibodies have the same combination of canonical CDR structure. These mutations, however, resulted in increased affinity for the transition state analog by a factor of 10^4 and also enhanced catalytic activity with the rate K_{cat}/K_m, from 1.7×10^2 M^{-1} min^{-1} to 1.4×10^4 M^{-1} min^{-1}. The three-dimensional crystal structure of the 48G7 Fab–hapten complex was resolved to 2.0 Å, allowing the identification of amino acid residues which contact the bound hapten. Surprisingly, none of the nine residues generated by somatic mutation contacted the ligand directly. They are all noncontacting residues. It was suggested that these mutants played roles in fine tuning of the combining site, by optimizing the geometries for hapten binding. These studies emphasized that the relative contribution of the CDR contacting and noncontacting residues and their cooperative interaction to antibody specificity need further investigation.

Since the discovery of antibody more than 100 years ago, much has been learned about this molecule. It has become possible to ask whether an antibody combining site of a given specificity may be designed and synthesized. To realize this long-term goal, additional efforts must be made to understand further the relationship of structural diversity and complementarity, to identify the critical structures which define three-dimensional complementarity in overall shapes or gross specificities, and to define those which may further optimize the fine geometries of antibody combining sites to achieve directed specificities. To facilitate these studies, a combination of advanced approaches, including X-ray crystallography, NMR, computer modeling, molecular engineering, immunochemical analysis and other methods for determination of fine specificities should be applied in rational designed experiments.

See also: **Affinity maturation; Antigens; Carrier; Diversity, generation of; Domains, immunoglobulin-type; Epitopes; Hapten; Idiotype; Immunoglobulin class switching; Immunoglobulin structure; Antibody-antigen complexes, three-dimensional structures.**

Further reading

Chothia C, Lesk AM, Tramontano A, Levitt M *et al* (1989) Conformations of immunoglobulin hypervariable regions. *Nature* 342: 877–883.

Cygler M, Rose DR and Bundle DR (1991) Recognition of a cell-surface oligosaccharide of pathogenic *Salmonella* by an antibody Fab fragment. *Science* 253: 442.

Edelman GM and Gally J (1962) The nature of Bence Jones proteins. Chemical similarities to polypeptide chains of myeloma globulins and normal γ-globulins. *Journal of Experimental Medicine* 46: 207–227.

Edelman GM, Cunningham BA, Gall WE *et al* (1969) The covalent structure of an entire XG immunoglobulin molecule. *Proceedings of the National Academy of Sciences of the USA* 63: 78–85.

Fields BA, Goldbaum FA, Ysern X, Poljak R and Mariuzza RA (1995) Molecular basis of antigen mimicry by an anti-idiotope. *Nature* 374: 739–742.

Kabat EA and Wu TT (1971) Attempts to locate complementarity determinating residues in the variable positions of light and heavy chains. *Annals of the New York Academy of Sciences* 190: 383–393.

Kabat EA, Wu TT, Reid-Miller M, Perry HM and Gottesman KS (1991) Tabulation and analysis of amino acid and nucleic acid sequences of precursors, V-regions, C-regions, J chain, T-cell receptors for antigen, T-cell surface antigens, β2-macroglobulin. In: *Sequences of Proteins of Immunological Interest*, 5th edn, pp 1–804.

Bethesda MD: US Department of Health and Human Services, National Institutes of Health.

Lara-Ochoa F, Almagro JC, Vargas-Madrazo E and Conrad M (1996) Antibody–antigen recognition: a canonical structure paradigm. *Journal of Molecular Evolution* 43: 678–684.

Leu JG, Chen BX, Diamanduros AW and Erlanger BF (1994) Idiotypic mimicry and assembly of a supramolecular structure: an anti-idiotypic antibody that mimics taxol in its tubulin–microtubule interactions. *Proceedings of the National Academy of Sciences of the USA* 91: 10690–10694.

Padlan EA (1995) Anatomy of the antibody molecule. *Molecular Immunology* 31: 169–217.

Padlan EA and Kabat EA (1991) Modeling of antibody combining sites. In: Langone JJ (ed) Molecular Design and Modeling: Concepts and Application. *Methods in Enzymology* 203: 3–21.

Padlan EA, Silverton EW, Sheriff S *et al* (1989) Structure of an antibody–antigen complex: crystal structure of the HyHEL10 Fab–lysozyme complex. *Proceedings of the National Academy of Sciences of the USA* 86: 5938–5942.

Patten PA, Gray NS, Yang PL *et al* (1996) The immunological evolution of catalysis. *Science* 271: 1086–1091.

Snyder JG, Dinh Q, Morrison SL et al (1994) Structure–function studies of anti-3-fucosyllactosamine and anti-(Le^x) galactosylgloboside antibodies. *Journal of Immunology* 153: 1161–1170.

Souchon H, Doyen N, Riottot M-M, Rougeon F and Poljak RJ (1990) Nucleotide sequence of the V_H, V_L regions of an antiidiotypic antibody reacting with a private idiotype of the anti-lysozyme D1.3 antibody. *Molecular Immunology* 27: 429–433.

Wang D and Kabat EA (1996) Carbohydrate antigens (polysaccharides). In: Van Regenmortal MHV (ed) *Structure of Antigens*, vol 3, pp 247–276. Boca Raton: CRC Press.

Wu TT and Kabat EA (1970) An analysis of the sequences of the variable regions of Bence-Jones proteins and myeloma light chains and their implications for antibody complementarity. *Journal of Experimental Medicine* **132**: 211–250.

ANTIBODIES, SYNTHESIS

Fritz Melchers, Basel Institute for Immunology, Basel, Switzerland

The human immune system contains 10^{11}–10^{12} B lymphocytes, which synthesize the 10^{20} antibody (immunoglobulin, Ig) molecules found inside and on the surface of these cells and, most of all, in the serum. Other mammalian species contain B cells and Ig molecules in numbers relative to their body weight, e.g. mice have 10^9 B cells and 10^{17} Ig molecules. Both B cells and Ig molecules turn over; both are synthesized and degraded throughout life.

Antibodies are glycoproteins composed of glycosylated heavy (H) chains and (mostly unglycosylated) light (L) chains. The amino-terminal domains of both H and L chains are variable (V) from antibody to antibody; they bind antigen. The other, more carboxy-terminal, constant (C) domains are involved in functions of antibodies which are unrelated to their individual antigen-binding specificities, but are carried out by antibodies of a given class or subclass, e.g. complement binding and activation, binding to Fc receptors on surfaces of cells, or transport through cells. Genes encoding H and L chains are encoded by segments which have to be rearranged before the genes can be transcribed and translated. The rearrangements of gene segments occur when B cells develop from B lineage-committed progenitor cells. Therefore, rearranged Ig genes only exist in cells of the B lineage, but in no other cells of the body.

Development of B lineage cells and rearrangements of Ig gene loci

In humans (and mice) three Ig gene loci can be rearranged. The H chains on human chromosome 14 (chromosome 12 in mouse) with the μ-, δ-, γ_{1-4}, α_{1-2} and ϵ C-region genes, κ L chains on human chromosome 2 (chromosome 6 in mouse) and λ L chains on human chromosome 22 (chromosome 16 in mouse). During B cell development (in humans at around 10 weeks, in mice between day 10 and 18 of gestation) B cells are generated in waves. In the mouse a first wave in embryonic blood and placenta is succeeded by a second wave in fetal liver. Throughout life B cells continue to be generated in bone marrow at a rate of 5×10^7 cells per day in the mouse (approximately 10^3-fold more in humans), of which 0.5–5% become mature, surface Ig (sIg)-positive cells of the periphery. Most newly generated B cells therefore die at the site where they have been generated.

From pluripotent stem cells which are the ancestors of the different lineages of blood cells, progenitors develop which are committed to the B lineage.

A collection of intracellular and surface-bound marker molecules has allowed the separation of subpopulations of B lineage cells from fetal liver and bone marrow, and single-cell PCR analyses of the status of the Ig gene loci have been useful to order these cell populations on their way from a pluripotent stem cell to a mature, antigen-reactive B lymphocyte. Many early cells of B lymphocyte development find themselves, and function, in close contact with an environment of stromal cells which provides specific contacts and cytokines that regulate the proliferation and differentiation of B lineage cells. Interleukin 3 (IL-3) and IL-7 have been identified as such cytokines in the mouse, and c-kit and flk-2 are membrane-bound tyrosine kinases on B lineage precursors which interact with their corresponding membrane-bound ligands on stromal cells.

The earliest signs of a cell to be committed to the B lineage of development is the transcription of the nonrearranged, germline μ H chain gene locus, the transcription of the V_{preB} and λ_5 genes encoding the surrogate light (SL) chain and the activation of the machinery involved in rearrangements of segments of the Ig gene loci, i.e. the activation of terminal deoxynucleotidyl transferase (TdT) and the recombination activating genes RAG1 and RAG2. This occurs in cells which express B220 (CD45R), but do not yet express CD19, the two markers most commonly used in the characterization of B lineage cells. The first Ig gene rearrangements, D_H segments to J_H segments, are already detectable in these cells. TdT is responsible for N-sequence insertions at the joints of the rearrangements. TdT is active in bone marrow but not in fetal liver. Therefore antibodies derived from bone marrow-generated B cells are N-region diverse (in their H chains); those derived from fetal liver are not.

This ordered rearrangement process continues in the next distinguishable B lineage cell population, which is B220 (CD45)$^+$, CD19$^+$, also expresses c-kit and SL chain on the surface, and now has practically all H chain alleles $D_H J_H$ rearranged.

The next rearrangement in-line is V_H to $D_H J_H$ on one of the two H chain alleles. Whenever this rearrangement occurs in-frame, a μH chain can be made. The μH chain combines with SL chain and thus forms a pre-B receptor. This development has several consequences which lead to a new cell population. It induces cells into cycle, hence the pre-B receptor-expressing, so-called pre-B II cells are large. Since nonproductively rearranged cells cannot form a pre-B receptor they do not expand by proliferation. Hence, productively rearranged, μH chain expressing, pre-B receptor-positive cells outgrow this compartment, i.e. are positively selected. They no longer express c-kit and have completely downregulated the rearrangement machinery, i.e. TdT, RAG1 and RAG2. As a new surface marker, they now express CD25 (TAC), the α chain of the IL-2 receptor. Downregulation of the rearrangement machinery is likely to be part of the mechanisms by which the second H chain allele is inhibited from V_H to $D_H J_H$ rearrangement. Hence it secures allelic exclusion, i.e. that one B cell makes only one H chain sequence.

Large pre-B II cells proliferate for an estimated 3–5 cell cycles, lose pre-B receptor expression, begin to re-express RAG1 and RAG2, and begin to transcribe the nonrearranged L chain gene loci κ and λ. While doing so they fall into a resting state, become small, and hence are called small pre-B II cells. The rearrangement-active genes RAG1 and RAG2 but not TdT are active; all cells now contain V_L to J_L-rearranged L chain gene loci, but no N-region insertions can be made. Half of them are productively rearranged, express the L chains in their cytoplasm, but not (yet) on their surface. The other half contain nonrearranged, or out-of-frame rearranged L chain loci. Since the pre-B II cells have an active rearrangement machinery, they can engage in secondary V_L to J_L rearrangements which in some cells might change nonproductive to productive L chain gene loci, and which in other cells might change a productive L chain locus encoding an autoantigen-reactive Ig receptor (termed receptor editing). Secondary L chain gene rearrangements might allow a B cell to express two L chains, whenever the rearrangement process allows both L chain alleles to be used. It has been seen that no more than 1–3% of all peripheral mature B cells express two L chains. Since less than 1% of all B cells have been seen to express two H chains, it remains true that for most B cells the rule 'one B cell makes one antibody' is valid. This is the basis for clonal selection in the immune system, in which a given antigen selects from all the lymphocytes those which have a fitting receptor on their surface.

The rearrangement machinery continues to be active in the next cell population in-line, the immature, surface IgM-expressing B cells. This is probably useful in editing autoreactive B cells.

The expression of an autoreactive Ig receptor on immature B cells leads to the arrest of differentiation of this cell. Since the cell remains short lived, it will die at this site of development in the primary lymphoid organ unless it can change its receptor specificity through editing. In this way of arrest of differentiation, the emerging B cell repertoire is purged of all B cells which are autoreactive to antigens present and presented in the bone marrow. A classical case for such an autoantigen is double-stranded DNA, present in large quantities due to extensive cell death at this site of development.

Of the sIgM-expressing immature B cells which do *not* recognize an autoantigen at this point of development, a small proportion (2–3%) are chosen each day to become mature, resting antigen-sensitive, sIgM/sIgD double-expressing B cells which are allowed to migrate to the periphery and become eventually longer lived. Whether sIg is involved in this 'positive selection', i.e. whether self antigen or foreign antigens are mandatory to make all immature B cells mature, remains to be seen. However, B lineage cells which are defective in T-independent as well as T-dependent B cell activation through mutations in their btk and CD40 genes are unable to establish longer-lived peripheral, mature B cell compartments, indicating that such stimulatory pathways are involved in the establishment of the peripheral, mature B cell compartments.

It should be mentioned that other species with an immune system might use different strategies to generate antibody diversity. In chicken, as one example, there is only one functional rearrangement of one V_H to a series of different D_H segments and to one J_H segment, and one V_L to one J_L segment generates a very limited original Ig repertoire which is then altered by gene conversion with many pseudo-V_H and pseudo-V_L gene segments, respectively.

As another example, fish carry partially and fully V(D)J-rearranged genes in many copies; hence they rely much less on rearrangements and more on combinations of different H and L chains for antibody diversity.

Selection of the B cell repertoire by self antigens

Once sIg-positive cells have been generated they are subjected to selection processes by self antigens in their own environment, probably presented by cells in the B cell-generating organs. Self reactive B cells appear to be either deleted or anergized. Whether *positive* selection *for* self antigens can also occur – maybe in a special B lineage, the Ly-l+/CD5+ B cells – needs to be elucidated.

Those B cells which have been untouched by these selection processes then enter the mature B cell compartment of virgin cells involved in primary B cell responses. Such cells still turn over rather rapidly, with half-lives of less than 1 week. They can be stimulated by foreign antigens, either with the help of T cells (helper T cell dependent) or without such help (T cell independent). Stimulation results in the activation from a resting, G_0 state and entry into the proliferative cell cycle. One cell cycle lasts 20 hours at 37°C and is controlled by several interactions (see below) of antigen, helper T cells, accessory cells and cytokines. Proliferating B cells also mature to Ig-secreting cells. A single activated B cell can balance between proliferation and maturation to Ig secretion. With every successive cell cycle the contribution to Ig secretion increases, so that finally mature plasma cells develop which no longer divide.

Helper T cell-dependent stimulation of B cells

T cell-dependent antigens are often monomeric protein molecules. Stimulation of B cells by such T cell-dependent antigens begins with the binding of antigen to sIg on fitting B cells. The complex of sIg and antigen is taken up by the cell, processed by proteolytic degradation, and the processed antigen in the form of peptides combines with class II major histocompatibility complex (MHC) molecules, so that the peptides of the antigen appear associated with the MHC class II on the surface of B cells. Upregulation of MHC class II expression might be necessary to mediate effective recognition and interaction of the complex with the T cell receptor of antigen-specific helper T cells, and IL-4 produced by helper T cells (or other cells) has been recognized as one major cytokine involved in the upregulation of MHC class II expression. This interaction might result in crosslinking of MHC class II molecules followed by signaling to B cells to proceed in the cell cycle. The same helper T cells have also seen the processed antigen on accessory cells such as macrophages, again an association with MHC class II molecules. In response to the T cell-induced signaling, these accessory cells may have produced cytokines which now interact with B cells at the entry into S phase. T cell-dependent B cell stimulation is, therefore, dependent on accessory cells. Activated helper T cells contribute to B cell stimulation in various ways. Activation of resting helper T cells by the recognition of the MHC class II–antigen–peptide complex on antigen-presenting accessory cells (dendritic cells, macrophages), leads to the upregulation of expression of the ligand for CD40 and to the upregulation of cytokine expression such as IL-2 (by helper T cells of type 0 and type 1), and of IL-4 and IL-5 (by helper T cells of type 2). In addition, different cell–cell contacts mediated by, for example, CTLA-4 and CD28 on helper T cells with B7-1 and B7-2 on B cells appear to guide the responses of B cells to IgM production (T_H0 and T_H1), or IgG and IgE production (T_H2), and the memory responses of B cells. In summary, T cell-dependent activation controls the B cell cycles at four points: 1) by antigen via sIg; 2) by T cell receptor interaction via processed antigen and MHC class II molecules, both in the G_1 phase; 3) by cytokines from accessory cells and by CD40 ligand from helper T cells at the entry of S phase; and 4) by IL-2 or IL-5 from helper T cells via IL-2 and IL-5 receptors before mitosis, and by additional cell-to-cell contact.

Synthesis of antibody with different H chain classes: the problem of H chain gene switching

T cell-independent antigens stimulate IgM- and IgG-synthesizing and secreting B cell clones, without any strong switching to other classes of IgH chains. T cell-dependent antigens, however, stimulate IgM-secreting B cell clones and induce the switching to other classes of IgH chains in these clones. Different helper T cells in different lymphoid organs may induce the switching to different classes of H chains. T cells secreting IL-4 induce switching to IgG1 and IgE.

Somatic hypermutation of Ig genes

T cell-dependent stimulation generates memory for the antigen in the immune system. This may be so because T and B cells specific for the antigen are now present in higher numbers, because B cells have a longer life in the system and because B cells with better fitting sIg have been made by hypermutation of Ig V regions. With a hypermutation rate estimated to be as high as 10^{-3} per base pair per division, one nucleotide of a V gene is mutated with every B cell division. Antigen continues to select any better fitting Ig on a mutated B cell in the T cell-dependent fashion of clonal stimulation described above. Much of this appears to occur in germinal centers. T cell-dependent stimulation to germinal center formation, Ig class switching and hypermutations is abolished when CD40 is made nonfunctional in B cells by targeted disruption of the gene.

Mutations of B cells to specificities recognizing self antigens may occur, but these autoimmune B cells are not dangerous as they are not selected for further growth. This is because any processed self antigen on MHC class II is not recognized by the helper T cells which are specific for foreign antigens, and because helper T cells for self antigens are absent from the immune system due to deletion in the thymus during their generation.

T cell-independent B cell stimulation

Two types of T cell-independent antigens (types I and II) stimulate B cells without involving MHC class II molecules, i.e. in a non-MHC-restricted fashion, to proliferation and to maturation into antigen-secreting cells. Memory to these antigens is normally not induced; the responses remain mainly IgM response and little, if any, hypermutation of IgV genes is observed. The stimulated B cells remain short lived. Typical type I antigens are those connected to lipopolysaccharide (LPS), while type II antigens are often polysaccharides.

T cell-independent antigens usually consist of repeating determinants with the capacity to cross-link sIg, probably without ever being taken up and processed by the B cells. Three restriction points control the cell cycle of a B cell activated by a T cell-independent antigen: 1) antigen binds to sIg early in the G_1 phase; 2) at entry into S phase CR2 receptors are ligated; and 3) at entry into mitosis IL-2 or IL-5 bind to their corresponding receptors. T cell-independent antigens of type I do not need IL-2 or IL-5 to stimulate B cells at the third restriction point. Other cytokines, such as IL-1, IL-4, IL-6 and interferon γ (IFNγ) have positive and negative modulating functions for proliferation and/or maturation of B cells.

Synthesis, intracellular transport, surface deposition and secretion of Ig chains

When the Ig gene segments have been rearranged, the Ig gene loci can be transcribed, and the primary transcripts processed into mature mRNA. Transcription is controlled by B lineage-specific promoters and enhancers, so that 50–100 mRNA molecules for μH chains, and later for L chains, are found in a pre-B cell. This suffices to maintain the synthesis of approximately 5×10^4 μH chains of membrane bound type (μ_m), and later the same amount of L chains, in 24 hours. As long as pre-B cells divide, most of the newly synthesized molecules are incorporated into newly generated surface membranes used in cell replication. Some of the 7–8S μH$_2$L$_2$ sIgM-positive B cells shed these molecules rapidly, i.e. with a half-life of 2–4 hours, from the pre-B cells. At early stages of B cell development, before the expression of L chains, these 7–8S sIg molecules contain $V_{preB}\lambda_5$ as a surrogate L chain. Later, when B cells fall into the G_0 resting phase, the same amount of IgμH and L chain synthesis provides the 7–8S μH$_2$L$_2$ molecules shed from the cells with a slow turnover (half-life of 24 hours). The transmembrane portion of μH$_m$ determines its deposition in the surface membrane.

Within 2 hours of stimulation, resting B cells change the rate of IgM synthesis by a factor of 5, and within the next 2 days by a factor of 20–100. This is achieved by stabilization of mRNA and an increase in the rate of transcription. The increase in IgM synthesis is devoted entirely to the synthesis of the secretory form of μH chains (μ_s). Splicing of precursor RNA into mature mRNA is altered from μ_m to μ_s type. Within 4 hours of stimulation, 19S (μH$_2$L$_2$)s pentameric IgM is secreted from stimulated B cells. Synthesis of J chain is stimulated, and J chains become associated with 19S IgM. Beyond 2

days of stimulation, the rate of IgM synthesis increases by another fivefold. In these later phases of B cell maturation, plasma blasts enlarge their endoplasmic reticulum (ER) and accumulate intracellular Ig (from 5×10^4–5×10^6 molecules per cell).

IgH and L chains are synthesized and transported through the cell by the conventional pathway for secreted proteins. H and L chains are synthesized on separate polyribosomes. It takes 30–40 s to synthesize an L chain, and around 90 s for an H chain. Translation is initiated on free ribosomes. As soon as the amino terminal leader sequences of H and L have been synthesized, they allow the binding of the ribosomes to the rough endoplasmic reticulum (RER) and then, the translocation of the nascent chains through the ER membrane. On the cisternal side, the leader sequence is enzymatically cleaved, and the H chain is glycosylated by the transfer of core oligosaccharides in the form of dolichol-phosphate intermediates to Asn-X-Ser/Thr acceptor sites. The H and L chains are successfully S–S bonded, the carbohydrate portions first trimmed, then terminal sugars added, as the Ig travels from the RER to the smooth ER (SER) and the Golgi apparatus. In mature plasma cells Ig is held intracellularly, particularly in the SER. At the late stage of plasma cell maturation, a single Ig synthesizing and secreting cell contains between 1 and 4×10^6 mRNA molecules for H and L chains, from which it synthesizes and secretes 10^3–10^4 Ig molecules per second.

See also: **Antigens, T dependent and independent; B lymphocyte differentiation; Diversity, generation of; Glycosylation of immune system molecules; Immunoglobulin genes; Immunoglobulin structure; Plaque-forming cell (PFC) assays; Somatic mutation.**

Further reading

All articles in: Lymphocyte Activation and Effector Functions. *Current Opinion in Immunology* 6(3) (1994); 7(3) (1995); 8(3) (1996); 9(3) (1997).

Honjo T and Alt FW (eds) (1995) *Immunoglobulin Genes*, 2nd edn. London: Academic Press.

Melchers F, Karasuyama H, Haasner D *et al* (1993) The surrogate light chain in B-cell development. *Immunology Today* 14: 60–68.

Melchers F, Rolink A, Grawunder U *et al* (1995) Positive and negative selection events during B lymphopoiesis. *Current Opinion in Immunology* 7: 214–227.

ANTIBODY–ANTIGEN COMPLEXES, THREE-DIMENSIONAL STRUCTURES

Steven Sheriff, Bristol-Myers Squibb Pharmaceutical Research Institute, Princeton, New Jersey, USA

The advent of monoclonal antibody technology has made possible structural studies of antibody–antigen complexes by providing large quantities of unique molecular entities. Since the mid-1980s, structural studies of antibody–antigen complexes have encompassed a wide variety of antigens ranging from small molecules through peptides and oligosaccharides to proteins, including several anti-idiotype–idiotype complexes (**Table 1**). All antibody–antigen complexes have shown that the antibody has achieved specificity and affinity through interactions of an antigen-binding site, made up principally, but not exclusively, of residues from the complementarity-determining regions (CDRs), with the antigen. However, the shape of the antigen-binding site and specific interactions have varied considerably depending on the size, shape and surface polarity of the antigen.

Extent and nature of the interface between antibody and antigen

The amount of surface buried in the interaction between antigen and antibody varies with the size of the antigen, from ~1.7 nm^2 to ~9 nm^2 on each surface (**Figure 1**). The surface area of interaction may also be limited by the size of the antigen-binding site for the largest protein antigen studied (neuraminidase). In the case of protein antigens only a small percentage (~10% to ~15%) of the total antigen surface area is buried in the interaction. Conversely, for most small molecules, the interaction buries 50–90% of the total antigen surface. The surfaces of interaction vary from deep pockets (**Figure 1A**) to broad shallow pockets (**Figure 1B**) to grooves (**Figure 1C**) for small molecules including carbohydrate and peptides. In contrast, antigen-binding sites are relatively flat for protein antigens (**Figure 1D**). However, in all cases the surfaces are rather complementary with limited space for water molecules in some antibody–protein complexes.

The number of residues involved in the interaction between antibody and antigen also varies with size of the antigen. For smaller antigens, as few as eight residues may be involved on the part of the antibody. For protein antigens, typically 14–21 residues are in contact on both molecules. The antibody-binding

sites on protein antigens (epitopes) consist of 2–5 sequentially discontinuous segments that are spatially contiguous (**Figure 1D**). Similarly, antigen-binding sites on antibodies (paratopes) consist of 4–6 CDRs that are spatially contiguous (**Figure 1A–D**).

In the typical complex the heavy chain contributes more surface area and residues to the interaction with antigen, ranging from just over 50% to almost 80%. One exception to this rule is the antibody AN02, where the light chain contributes a majority of the interactions. The CDRs that typically make a preponderance of the interactions are the third CDR of the light chain and the second and third CDRs of the heavy chain. Most complexes with small molecules and some complexes with proteins do not involve the second CDR of the light chain. In contrast, the NC41–neuraminidase complex does not involve the first CDR of the light chain and a few protein complexes have rather minimal involvement of either the third CDR of the light chain or the third CDR of the heavy chain.

Chemical nature of the interactions between antibody and antigen

The interactions of antibody with antigen are generally van der Waals interactions involving surface residues, which despite being solvent exposed are relatively hydrophobic in nature. However, most antibody–antigen interactions contain at least one hydrogen bond or salt link and typically contain many. For example, protein antigens form on the order of 15–20 hydrogen bonds and/or salt links with antibody. However, it is impossible to extrapolate from the number of hydrogen bonds and salt links to the strength of the interaction between antibody and antigen. For example, the 26-10–digoxin complex has no hydrogen bonds and no salt links, but its association constant (~1×10^{10} M^{-1}) is as strong as any whose three-dimensional structure is known. In the antibody–protein complexes, some water molecules have been found to be part of the interface between antibody and antigen.

In the antigen-binding site, tyrosines and tryptophans occur more frequently than in the rest of the antibody. These two residues are both capable of forming hydrogen bonds to solvent or antigen, but have

Table 1 Antibody–antigen complexes and their Protein Data Bank (PDB) codes

Antibody[a]	Antigen[b]	PDB code Complexed	Uncomplexed
Antiprotein			
Antilysozymes			
D1.3 Fv	Hen egg lysozyme	1VFB, 1FDL	1VFA
D1.3 Fv	Turkey egg lysozyme	NA	
HyHEL-5	Hen egg lysozyme	3HFL	
HyHEL-5	Bobwhite egg lysozyme	1BQL, 2IFF	
HyHEL-10	Hen egg lysozyme	3HFM	
D11.15 Fv	Pheasant lysozyme	1JHL	
D44.1	Hen egg lysozyme	1MLC	1MLB
F9.13.7	Guinea fowl egg lysozyme	1FBI	
cAb-Lys3	Hen egg lysozyme	1MEL	
Antineuraminidases			
NC41	N9 neuraminidase	1NCA, 1NCB, 1NCC, 1NCD	
NC10	N9 neuraminidase	1NMA, 1NMB	
Antiidiotopes			
E225	D1.3	NA	
E5.2 Fv	D1.3 Fv	1DVF	
409.5.3	730.1.4	1IAI	1AIF(409.5.3)
T91AJ5	Yst9.1	NA	1MAM(Yst9.1)
Others			
JEL 42	HPr	1JEL	
HC19	Hemagglutinin	1VIR(Cα)	1GIG
N10	Staph nuclease	1NSN	
28	HIV rt–DNA	NA	
7E2 Fv	Cytochrome *c* oxidase	NA	
Antipeptide			
B13I2	Myohemerythrin, 69-87	1IGF	2IGF
17/9	Hemagglutinin, 75-110	1HIM, 1HIN, 1IFH	1HIL
26/9	Hemagglutinin, 75-110	1FRG	
131	Angiotensin II	NA	
TE33	Cholera toxin, 50-64	1TET	
50.1	HIV gp120 V3	1GGI	1GGB, 1GGC
59.1	HIV gp120 V3	1ACY	
8F5	Rhinovirus VP2, 156-170	NA	1BBD
C3	Poliovirus, 86-103	1FPT	
SD6	FMDV, G-H loop	NA	NA
Anticarbohydrate			
Se155-4	*Salmonella* O antigen	1MFA, 1MFB, 1MFC, 1MFD, 1MFE	
BR96	Le[y]	1CLY, 1CLZ	1UCB
Anti-DNA			
BV04-01	dT_3	1CBV	1NBV
Anti-small molecule			
McPC603	Phosphocholine	2MCP	1MCP
4-4-20	Fluorescein	1FLR	
NQ10/12.5	2-Phenyloxazolone	NA	
AN02	TEMPO-DNP	1BAF	
R454511	Cyclosporine	1IKF	
DB3	Progesterone etc.	1DBB, 1DBJ, 1DBK, 2DBL, 1DBM	1DBA
26-10	Digoxin	1IGJ	1IGI
40-50	Ouabain	1IBG	
JEL 103	Nucleotides	1MRD, 1MRE, 1MRF	1MRC
CHA255	EOTUBE (In^{3+},Fe^{3+})	1IND, 1INE	
NC6.8	NC174	2CGR	1CGS
N1G9	(4-Hydroxy-3-nitrophenyl) acetate	1NGP	1NGQ
1F7	Transition state analog	1FIG	
17E8	Transition state analog	1EAP	
CNJ206	Transition state analog	1KNO	2GFB
48G7	Transition state analog	1GAF	

NA = not available, although paper describing the structure has been reported. Blank in the uncomplexed column means structure has not been reported.
[a]Antibodies are Fabs unless noted as Fv.
[b]Antigen names: HPr, histidine-containing protein of the phosphoenolpyruvate:sugar phosphotransferase system; FMDV, foot-and-mouth disease virus; TEMPO-DNP, 2,2,6,6,-tetramethyl-1-piperindinyloxy dinitrophenol; EOTUBE, 4-[N'-(2-hydroxyethyl)thioureido]-L-benzyl-EDTA; NC174, N-(p-cyanophenyl)-N'-(diphenylmethyl)-N''-(carboxymethyl)guanidine.

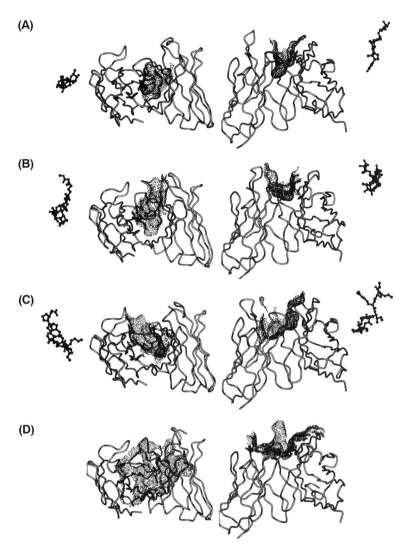

Figure 1 Binding sites and buried surfaces (represented as dots) of selected antibody–antigen complexes demonstrating different sizes and shapes of binding interfaces. For each complex, on the left the antibodies are shown with antigen-binding site face-on and on the right rotated 90° about the horizontal relative to the figure on the left. In both views the light chain is on the left. In the right image, the viewer is looking from CDR-L3 towards CDR-H3, which is in the back. Antibody backbone is represented as a ribbon. To the far left and far right of the antibody structures the small molecule antigens for the first three complexes are represented as ball-and-stick in the orientation that they are bound to the antibody. (A) 26-10–digoxin; (B) BR96–Lewis Y; (C) 50.1–HIV gp120 V3; (D) HyHEL-5–lysozyme. Note the deep pocket of 26-10, the broad pocket of BR96, the groove of 50.1 and the relatively flat and extensive surface of HyHEL-5. (Figure produced with MOLSCRIPT by Per Kraulis.)

large hydrophobic surfaces. Moreover, these large hydrophobic surfaces can be immobilized with limited entropy loss due to restricted rotation of bonds in the complex. Thus the preference for tyrosines and tryptophans is most likely due to the unique nature of the antigen-binding site, which spends part of its time accessible to solvent and part of its time buried in a complex.

Conformational change upon complexation of antibody and antigen

A range of motions have been found for antibody and for antigen upon complexation. From most global to most local these include: rotation of V_H relative to V_L, conformational rearrangement of the polypeptide backbone, rigid-body motion of polypeptide backbone segments, and side-chain motion. Examples of antibody motion have been principally found with antibodies to small molecules including peptides and carbohydrate, but this may be due to

the limited number of structures of uncomplexed antibody available for protein-specific antibodies (**Table 1**). An example of rotation of V_H relative to V_L and of conformational rearrangement of the third CDR of the heavy chain may be seen in **Figure 2A**. The effects of these motions on opening the antigen-binding site may be seen by a comparison of **Figure 2B** with **Figure 2C**.

Anti-idiotype complexes

A number of anti-idiotype complexes have been reported (**Table 1**). However, the lack of availability of the structure of the original antibody in complex with antigen has limited the ability to describe mimicry of the antigen by the idiotypic antibody. In the case of the D1.3 antibody, whose structures both uncomplexed and in complex with antigen (lysozyme) have been determined, two anti-idiotypic complex structures have also been determined. One (E225) blocks the antigen-binding site, but does not

(A)

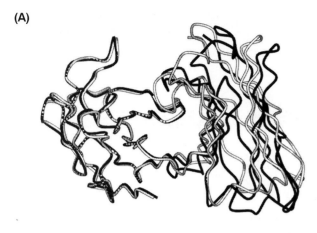

(B)

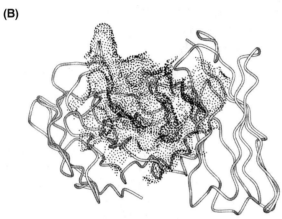

(C)

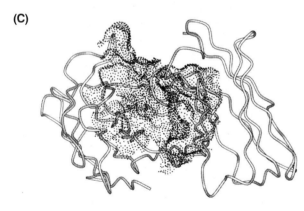

Figure 2 Comparison of complexed and uncomplexed forms of 50.1 showing the change of the binding pocket between the uncomplexed and complexed forms. (A) Superposition of V_L domains of 50.1, showing changes due to differences between relative position of V_H and conformational differences of the third CDR loop of the heavy chain (complexed antibody in black and uncomplexed antibody in white). (B) Binding site (as represented by a dot surface) of complexed form of 50.1. (C) Binding site (as represented by a dot surface) of uncomplexed form of 50.1. The third CDR of the heavy chain is towards the top center of the figures. (Figure produced with MOLSCRIPT by Per Kraulis.)

mimic the surface of the antigen. In contrast, the other (E5.2) blocks the antigen-binding site and appears to mimic the interactions of lysozyme with D1.3 to a high degree.

Future directions

The future of structural work in the antibody–antigen complex field will probably be driven by four forces: 1) the use of antibody–antigen complexes as model systems for examining protein–protein interactions, which includes the ability of the immune system to find multiple solutions to binding to the same surface (epitope); 2) the study of camelid antibodies, which have single, heavy-chain binding domains rather than the more common $V_L:V_H$ heterodimers (an example of a camel antibody–lysozyme complex has recently been determined (**Table 1**)); 3) the use of antibodies to crystallize complexes of otherwise refractory proteins, such as human immunodeficiency virus (HIV) reverse transcriptase and cytochrome *c* oxidase (**Table 1**); and 4) a desire to understand the structural basis of catalytic antibodies of which four examples already exist (**Table 1**).

See also: **Antibodies, specificity; Antibody-antigen intermolecular forces; Antigen-binding site; Diversity, generation of; Domains, immunoglobulin-type; Idiotype; Idiotype, internal image; IgA; IgE; Immunoglobulin structure; Monoclonal antibodies (mAbs).**

Further reading

Braden BC and Poljak RJ (1995) Structural features of the reactions between antibodies and protein antigens. *FASEB Journal* 9: 9–16.

Colman PM (1991) Antigen–antigen receptor interactions. *Current Opinion in Structural Biology* 1: 232–236.

Davies DR and Chacko S (1993) Antibody structure. *Accounts of Chemical Research* 26: 421–427.

Davies DR and Padlan EA (1992) Twisting into shape. *Current Biology* 2: 254–256.

Davies DR, Padlan EA and Sheriff S (1990) Antibody–antigen complexes. *Annual Review of Biochemistry* 59: 439–473.

Mariuzza RA and Poljak RJ (1993) The basics of binding: mechanisms of antigen recognition and mimicry by antibodies. *Current Opinion in Immunology* 5: 50–55.

Sheriff S (1993) Antibody–protein complexes. *Immunomethods* 3: 222–227.

Stanfield RL and Wilson IA (1993) X-Ray crystallographic studies of antibody–peptides complexes. *Immunomethods* 3: 211–221.

Webster DM, Henry AH and Rees AR (1994) Antibody–antigen interactions. *Current Opinion in Structural Biology* 4: 123–129.

Wilson IA and Stanfield RL (1993) Antibody–antigen

interactions. *Current Opinion in Structural Biology* 3: 113–118.

Wilson IA and Stanfield RL (1994) Antibody–antigen

interactions: new structures and new conformational changes. *Current Opinion in Structural Biology* 4: 857–867.

ANTIBODY–ANTIGEN INTERMOLECULAR FORCES

Carel J van Oss, Department of Microbiology, School of Medicine, State University of New York at Buffalo, Buffalo, New York, USA

The different types of bonds occurring in the specific interaction between antigen (Ag) and antibody (Ab) molecules are all of the weak physical variety. The three different classes of bonding forces in question are (not necessarily in the order of their relative importance): 1) van der Waals or electrodynamic forces; 2) hydrogen bonding or polar forces; 3) electrostatic forces. Covalent bonds are not involved in Ag–Ab interactions. These physical, noncovalent forces also provide the bonds between other biological entities, such as various ligand and cell surface receptors, carbohydrates and lectins, and enzymes and their substrates. (In enzyme–substrate reactions however, covalent bonds can also occur, in addition to the three types of physical forces mentioned above.)

Human Ab molecules (immunoglobulins) have from two (IgG, IgA, IgD, IgE), to ten identical valencies (IgM), while secretory IgA (S-IgA) has four valencies. Each paratope on an immunoglobulin molecule represents one valency. Ag molecule (or particles) can have from a few to a great many valencies (each epitope represents one valency). The multiple valencies of such Ag molecules may be all different, or all identical, or some epitopes on a given Ag may be different and others the same. Ag and Ab molecules of a given specificity can combine into Ag–Ab complexes in virtually every conceivable proportion: the Ag–Ab reaction is essentially nonstoichiometric. Thus, the valency of an Ag molecule can only be determined under conditions of excess Ag. In both cases the resulting Ag–Ab complexes will tend to be soluble; insoluble complexes only occur at intermediate Ag–Ab ratios, i.e. close to the optimal, or equivalence ratio.

Nature of antigen–antibody intermolecular forces

Van der Waals forces

Also known as electrodynamic interactions, these occur universally between all atoms and molecules, when brought close enough together. Three different but related phenomena contribute to van der Waals interactions: 1) randomly orienting dipole–dipole (orientation) interactions, or van der Waals–Keesom forces; 2) randomly orienting dipole-induced dipole (induction) interactions, or van der Waals-Debye-forces; 3) randomly fluctuating dipole-induced dipole (dispersion) interactions, or van der Waals–London forces. Keesom and Debye interactions only occur with molecules which have permanent dipole moments. The van der Waals–London interaction occurs universally and is also present in atom–atom interactions. In condensed media (i.e. in the liquid and the solid phase), on a macroscopic scale (i.e. on a supra-atomic level), it was first shown by Lifshitz that all three varieties of van der Waals forces can be grouped together; they should be treated in the same manner, and the forces decay with distance at the same rate. On a macroscopic scale, which is also the realm of Ag–Ab interactions, the three varieties of van der Waals interactions, grouped together, are alluded to as Lifshitz–van der Waals (LW) interactions. Due to the fact that the total LW interaction between Ag and Ab, in water, not only must account for the interaction between Ag and Ab, but also for the LW interactions between the Ags and the water molecules, and between the water molecules among one another, the *net* LW attraction between such biopolymers is rather strongly attenuated when occurring in water. The net free energy of LW interaction of the Ag–Ab system in water is of the order of: $\Delta G^{LW} = -0.5$ to -5 mJ m^{-2}. For the interaction between one epitope and its corresponding paratope, given an average surface area of the interaction between epitope and paratope: $A = 3$ nm^2, the LW contribution to such an Ag–Ab interaction then corresponds to $\Delta G^{LW} = -0.2$ to $-2\,kcal\,mol^{-1}$. Thus LW interactions typically represent only between 2 and 20% of the total interaction energy of average Ag–Ab reaction (which is of the order of: $\Delta G^{TOT} = -10\,kcal\,mol^{-1}$).

Hydrogen bonding, or polar forces

These are nonelectrostatic polar (Lewis) acid–base (AB) interactions, which are of considerable importance in strongly polar media such as water. In water, these polar interactions are principally of the hydrogen-bonding variety; their net outcome can be attractive (hydrophobic attraction) or repulsive (hydration repulsion), depending on the circumstances. In either case, net AB interactions are long-range, i.e. they act at a distance of up to about 10 nm. Analogous to LW or apolar interactions, taking place between two different moieties immersed in a liquid, AB interactions taking place in water are the net outcome of the polar interactions between Ag and Ab, and those between Ag and water molecules, as well as those between Ab and water molecules, and between the molecules among one another.

Hydrophilic AB interactions (also known as hydration forces) are the major cause of the net long-range macroscopic scale repulsion between cells and/or biopolymers. This is the principal repulsion force which epitopes and paratopes have to overcome before engaging in the specific microscopic scale attraction that culminates in the Ag–Ab bond.

The equally long-range hydrophobic AB interactions usually represent the principal microscopic scale attractive force between epitope and paratope. Contrary to a still fairly widely held belief, hydrophobic interactions in water need not exclusively take place between two hydrophobic sites. Hydrophobic attractions between, for example, a hydrophilic epitope and a hydrophobic paratope are quite common among Ag–Ab interactions *in vitro* and *in vivo*. As all immunodominant epitopes tend to be hydrophilic, the corresponding paratopic sites usually are hydrophobic. Such hydrophobic paratopic sites are necessarily located in cavities or clefts, thus obviating undesirable aspecific interactions between unduly exposed hydrophobic loci. The driving force for the hydrophobic attraction is the cohesive hydrogen-bonding interaction between the surrounding water molecules. Hydrophobic Ag–Ab interactions, at closest approach, range from -3 to $-25\,kcal\,mol^{-1}$ and as such usually play the dominant role in the total Ag–Ab interaction.

In contrast to hydrophobic interactions, direct hydrogen bonds are extremely short range in nature, i.e. direct hydrogen bonds only act at a distance of about 0.1–0.3 nm. Direct hydrogen bond energies range from -1.3 to $-3.4\,kcal\,mol^{-1}$.

Electrostatic interactions

Electrostatic interactions between Ag and Ab are caused by the attraction between one or more ionized sites on the epitope and one or more oppositely charged sites on the paratope. These charged sites typically are the COO^- and the NH_3^+ groups on ionized amino acids of the Ag (in such cases usually a protein or a peptide) and of the Ab. Of the three classes of forces involved, the electrostatic (or Coulombic) interaction forces are the most influenced by the pH and by the ionic strength of the liquid medium. The pH is important, as it largely determines the degree of dissociation of the COO^- or the NH_3^+ ions. The ionic strength is important, as it governs the value of the electrokinetic, or zeta-potential of the charged sites, as well as of the (Debye) thickness of the diffuse ionic double layer surrounding these sites. At the physiologic ionic strength of 0.15, electrostatic interactions have a maximum range of about 8 nm; at lower salt concentrations the range can be much longer. The free energy of attraction between one COO^- and an NH_3^+ group, at a distance of about 0.3 nm, at physiological ionic strength, is about $-7\,kcal\,mol^{-1}$; at a distance of 0.5 nm, the electrostatic (EL) energy of attraction is about $-5.5\,kcal\,mol^{-1}$.

Whilst electrostatic Ag–Ab interactions occur principally between oppositely charged sites on the epitope and paratope, rare instances have been reported of interactions between two negatively charged sites, by the intermediary of Ca^{2+} ions. Ag–Ab systems involved in Ca^{2+} bridging are, for example, polyglutamic acid Ags, recombinant proteins and (occasionally) DNA–anti-DNA complexes.

The obligatory long-range attraction between epitope and paratope

Normally all biopolymers and cells dissolved or dispersed in aqueous media under physiological conditions repel one another, which prevents them from approaching each other more closely than about 3–5 nm. This makes it necessary for specifically interacting epitopic and paratopic sites to be able to attract each other from a distance. Three factors can contribute to make this possible: 1) The specifically interacting sites are small (surface areas usually between 1 and 10 nm²) and the epitope tends to lie on a prominent edge or peak with a small radius of curvature, which enables it to pierce the general repulsion field and to bring it within less than 3 nm of the paratope. 2) The two sites have a significant electric charge of opposite signs. 3) At least one of the two (usually the paratope) is fairly hydrophobic.

The rate of decay of Ag–Ab interactions with distance

The rate of decay as a function of distance, d, varies considerably in the three different classes of physical bonds. LW interaction energies in the range of virtual contact, up to $d = 10$ nm, varies at $1/d^2$, in a configuration of two flat parallel slabs. Both polar (AB) and electrostatic (EL) energies decay exponentially with distance, d. AB energies decay as $\exp(-d/\lambda)$, where λ is the decay length of water; λ (water) has a value of about 1.0 nm. EL energies decay as $\exp(-\kappa d)$, where $1/\kappa$ is the thickness of the diffuse electrical double layer; at the physiological ionic strength of 0.15, $1/\kappa = 0.8$ nm. As such exponentially decaying forces usually are measurable at distances that are up to ten times longer than the decay length, thus epitope–paratope interactions begin to make themselves felt at a distance, d of about 8–10 nm. Beyond that distance, the generally prevailing AB and EL repulsion acts between Ag and Ab, as it does between most biopolymers and cells, dissolved or immersed in water. At very short distances between Ag and Ab (i.e. $d_0 = 0.16$ nm), the pronounced increase in strength in all three modes of physical bonding, explains why the best 'fit' between epitope and paratope correlates so strongly with the highest binding affinity.

Hybrid intermolecular Ag–Ab forces

Combinations of LW, AB and EL forces all contributing to the Ag–Ab bond in a variety of proportions are more the rule than the exception. In aqueous media, systems interacting exclusively through Lifshitz–van der Waals forces do not occur; such systems only are possible in apolar media such as alkanes, in which all immunoglobulins and most antigens would be insoluble. Exclusively interfacial interactions, i.e. those involving only LW and AB forces, do occur, for example with (electro-) neutral carbohydrates such as dextran as Ags, or with haptens such as 3-azo-pyridine, p-azo-toluidine, dinitrophenol, etc. Exclusively electrostatic Ag–Ab interactions also occur, e.g. in the case of dsDNA–anti-DNA. Otherwise, most Ag–Ab interactions involve LW + AB + EL forces in the primary binding interaction between epitope and specific paratope. Thus, in general, $\Delta G^{TOT} = \Delta G^{LW} + \Delta G^{AB} + \Delta G^{EL}$.

Primary and secondary Ag–Ab bonds

Once the repulsion front is pierced and epitope and paratope have made contact, the epitope–paratope

bond strengthens, either through the sheer effect of the small distance between the two, or because of a qualitative change in the nature of the bond; for example, through expulsion of water of hydration, or (relatively rarely) through formation of direct hydrogen bonds. Also, once epitope and paratope have approached each other closely, in many cases secondary bonds can ensue between biopolymer moieties that are in close proximity to epitope and paratope. Secondary Ag–Ab bonds occur in all cases where the energy of association is smaller than the energy required for dissociation, once the bond has been formed. Secondary bonds tend to be of the interfacial (or LW + AB, or hydrophobic) variety and hardly ever of an EL nature. If one defines ΔG^{TOT} as $\Delta G_{primary} + \Delta G_{secondary}$, and $\Delta G_{primary}$ as the free energy one needs to furnish to prevent the Ag–Ab complex from forming ($\Delta G_{primary} = \Delta G_{prevention\ of\ association}$), while ΔG^{TOT} equals the energy needed to dissociate the complex, then:

$$\Delta G_{secondary} = \Delta G_{dissociation} - \Delta G_{prevention\ of\ association} \tag{1}$$

As one can measure both the energy needed to prevent association, and the energy of dissociation (i.e. ΔG^{TOT}), $\Delta G_{primary}$ as well as $\Delta G_{secondary}$ can be determined. Consolidation of intraepitope–paratope binding (e.g. through direct H-bonding or direct EL interactions) also involves $\Delta G_{secondary}$. The bovine serum albumin (BSA) system: BSA–anti-BSA, is an example of a primary EL bond, and a secondary hydrophobic (LW + AB) bond.

Dehydration of the epitope–paratope interstitial space (which gives rise to the increase in entropy typically observed in Ag–Ab interactions) is another important aspect of the secondary part of the Ag–Ab interaction. Due to that dehydration, the distance between epitope and paratope decreases, which strengthens their attraction. Upon the disappearance of interstitial water, the epitope–water–paratope interaction becomes, at least in part, a direct epitope–paratope attraction that mainly involves high-energy direct LW forces.

Thermodynamics of antigen–antibody interactions

Law of mass action

Writing the antigen–antibody reaction as:

$$Ag + Ab = Ag.Ab \tag{2}$$

according to the law of mass action the equilibrium

association constant is expressed as (simplified for the case of monovalent haptens, or single epitopes, and monovalent, or Fab-type paratopes):

$$K_a = K_a/k_d = (Ag.Ab)/[(Ag) \times (Ab)] \qquad (3)$$

where (Ag) is the molar concentration of free Ag sites, (Ab) the molar concentration of free Ab and (Ag.Ab) the molar concentration of the Ag.Ab complex. k_a is the association kinetic constant; it tends to be rather uniform in value and fairly high (10^3–10^8 M^{-1} s^{-1}); k_d is the dissociation kinetic constant; it varies considerably from case to case (10^4–10^6 s^{-1}). To determine K_a as well as the antibody valency (n), one can use either a Scatchard or a Langmuir plot. In the Scatchard approach one plots (Ag-bound)/(Ag) $\times$ (Ab) on the ordinate versus (Ag-bound)/(Ab). The slope then yields $-n \times K_a$ and the intercept with the abscissa, n. With the Langmuir approach one plots (Ab)/(Ab-bound) on the ordinate versus 1/(Ab-bound). Here the slope yields $(1/n) \times K_a$ and the intercept with the ordinate, $1/n$. If the line obtained in a Langmuir plot is not a straight line, the (Sips) heterogeneity index α, may be obtained by determining α such that the plot of (Ab)/(Ag-bound) versus 1/(Ag-bound)$^\alpha$, forms a straight line. K_a values usually vary between 10^4 and 10^{11} l mol^{-1}. For plurivalent antigens (i.e. for most antigens), eqn (2) and concomitantly, eqn (3) become more complex. In addition, it should be kept in mind that each of the valencies of a typical protein antigen usually represents a different epitope. A polyclonal antiserum to such a protein antigen then comprises a whole collection of antibodies with different specificities, as well as with widely differing affinities. Thus, for the interaction of such a polyclonal collection of antibodies with a protein Ag, a large series of eqns (2) should be used for which, however, most of the parameters are unknown and probably unknowable. One therefore usually reverts to eqn (3) in its simple form, and tests for heterogeneity in the manner indicated above.

Energetics

For purposes of energetics, the equilibrium binding constant, K_a (see eqns (4) and (5), below) has to be expressed as a dimensionless number (K_a), in terms of inverse mole fractions. For instance in water, which comprises 55.56 mol H_2O l^{-1}, a concentration of 1 mol l^{-1} = 1/55.56 = 0.018 mole fraction. Thus, starting with the unit in which K_a is habitually expressed (i.e. in l mol^{-1}) it should be noted that 1 l mol^{-1} becomes 55.56 (mol fraction)$^{-1}$. Conversely, to find K_a (in l mol^{-1}) from K$'_a$, one has to multiply K$'_a$ by 0.018.

From the dimensionless equilibrium association constant, K'_a, the free energy of the Ag–Ab bond can be obtained via:

$$\Delta G^{TOT} = -RT \ln K'_a \qquad (4)$$

where ΔG is expressed in kcal mol^{-1}, R is the gas constant = 1.986×10^{-3} kcal K^{-1} mol^{-1} and T is the absolute temperature in degrees Kelvin. To obtain ΔG in joules, $R = 8.3144$ J K^{-1} mol^{-1}. To obtain ΔG in SI units per epitope–paratope bond, one divides R by Avogadro's number N ($N = 6.022 \times 10^{23}$), to obtain Boltzmann's constant k, where k replaces R in eqn (4). To obtain both the enthalpy (ΔH) and entropy (ΔS) components of the binding energy, $\Delta G = \Delta H - T \Delta S$, K'_a must be measured at a number of different temperatures, in which case one can use, as an approximation:

$$(d \ln K'_a)/dT = \Delta H/RT^2 \qquad (5)$$

where R again may be replaced by k when working on the molecular scale of single bonds. Once ΔH is known, one obtains $T \Delta S$ from $T \Delta S = \Delta H - \Delta G$. ΔH can also be obtained by microcalorimetric measurements of Ag–Ab reactions.

Contrary to a rather widely held belief, hydrophobic interaction energies are not necessarily mainly entropic: they can be enthalpic, or entropic, or a combination of these in any proportion. With an increase in temperature the total interaction energy tends to change from predominantly enthalpic to mainly entropic (see following section).

Temperature effects

As the reaction usually is exothermic, at room temperature or lower, ΔH is mostly negative, but it can vary from +10 to −20 kcal mol^{-1}. The entropy contribution can vary widely, from −40 to +80 entropy units per mole. In Ag–Ab interactions a positive entropy is usually taken to be due to the randomization of previously organized (oriented) water molecules of hydration which, upon closer approach between epitope and paratope, are squeezed out and become part of the bulk liquid.

In many Ag–Ab reactions, an increase in temperature causes ΔH to become less negative. However, this effect tends to be compensated by a concomitant increase in $T \Delta S$, thus leaving ΔG practically unchanged over a fairly wide range of temperatures. The increase in $T \Delta S$ with an increase in T is a consequence of the following phenomenon: At increased T, the molecular hydration energy decreases, which favors the escape of interstitial water of hydration into the bulk liquid and thus causes an increase in the entropy of the system caused by the randomization of formerly more organized water of hydration. This loss of interstitial water of hydration also causes a decrease in the distance between the epitopic and paratopic sites, which increases their mutual energy of attraction and ultimately becomes, at least in part, a higher energy direct LW bond.

Measurement of Ag–Ab interaction energies

There is a large variety of equilibrium methods by which the parameters on the right-hand side of eqn (4) can be determined, allowing the calculation of K_a and from this value, of K'_a and of ΔG. Among these methods are equilibrium dialysis or ultrafiltration, precipitation methods, analytical ultracentrifugation, gel filtration or size exclusion chromatography, affinity chromatography, fluorescence, fluorescence quenching, fluorescence polarization, immunoassay methods, hapten inhibition methods, nuclear magnetic resonance, electron spin resonance, etc. The powerful new bioaffinity sensor methods should be specially mentioned.

Bioaffinity sensors

The bioaffinity sensor methodology has, since the early 1990s, developed into one of the most powerful approaches to determining the kinetic association (k_a) and dissociation (k_d) constants, and from these the equilibrium binding constant, K_a (see eqn (3), above), and its inverse, the equilibrium dissociation constant, $K_d = k_d/k_a$. By optical means, the thickening of a layer of, for example, Ab, which is continuously deposited by means of a thin stream of an Ab solution moving across a thin layer of Ag molecules, can be monitored in real time. The graph of Ab thickness versus time thus obtained yields the kinetic association constant, k_a. Upon subsequent replacement of the Ab solution with a buffer solution, the kinetic dissociation constant, k_d, is obtained. From these the equilibrium binding constant, K_a, is derived (see eqn (3)).

Concentration dependence of K_a

With polyclonal Abs, for example, in the BSA–anti-BSA system (BSA = bovine serum albumin), 100-fold dilution (at Ag/Ab equivalence) causes an almost 40 000 fold increase in K_a, i.e. from 1.7×10^7 to 6.3×10^{11} l mol^{-1}. Even with monoclonal Abs a significant increase in K_a with dilution must be expected because greater dilution minimizes steric hindrance. Thus, if one aims to characterize an Ag–Ab system by measuring the K_a value, it is advisable to operate at the lowest practical reagent concentration. For instance in a Biosensor setting, with a constant Ag concentration in the immobilized phase, a 100-fold decrease in the mobile phase (monoclonal Ab solution) typically gives rise to a 70- to 100-fold decrease in k_a and K_a. In general, under similar circumstances, only the lowest feasible Ab concentration in the mobile phase will yield accurate k_a and K_a values.

See also: **Affinity; Antigens; Immunoglobulin structure; Precipitation reaction; Surface plasmon resonance; Valency of antigens and antibodies.**

Further reading

Absolom DR and van Oss CJ (1986) The nature of the antigen–antibody bond and the factors affecting its association and dissociation. *Critical Reviews in Immunology* **6**: 1–46.

Fägerstam LG and Karlsson R (1994) Biosensor techniques. In: van Oss CJ and van Regenmortel MHV (eds) *Immunochemistry*, pp 949–970. New York: Marcel Dekker.

Hardie G and van Regenmortel MHV (1975) Immunochemical studies of tobacco mosaic virus I. Refutation of the alleged homogeneous binding of purified antibody fragment. *Immunochemistry* **12**: 903–908.

Mukkur TKS (1984) Thermodynamics of hapten–antibody interactions. *Critical Reviews in Biochemistry* **16**: 133–167.

Pellequer JL and van Regenmortel MHV (1993) Measurement of kinetic binding constants of viral antibodies using a new biosensor technology. *Journal of Immunological Methods* **166**: 133–143.

van Oss CJ (1994) Nature of specific ligand–receptor bonds, in particular the antigen–antibody bond. In: van Oss CJ and van Regenmortel MHV (eds) *Immunochemistry*, pp 581–614. New York: Marcel Dekker.

van Oss CJ (1995) Hydrophobic, hydrophilic and other interactions in epitope-paratope binding. *Molecular Immunology* **32**: 199–211.

van Oss CJ and Walker J (1987) Concentration dependence of the binding constant of antibodies. *Molecular Immunology* **24**: 715–717.

van Regenmortel MHV (ed) (1995) Uses of biosensors in immunology. *Journal of Immunological Methods* **183**: 3–182.

ANTIBODY-DEPENDENT CELLULAR CYTOTOXICITY

Jorge Raúl Geffner, Instituto de Investigaciones Hematológicas, Academia Nacional de Medicina, Buenos Aires, Argentina

It was first shown by Moller in 1965 that a wide variety of target cells, coated with low amounts of specific immunoglobulin G (IgG) antibodies, can be lysed *in vitro* by lymphocytes not previously sensitized to target cell antigens. Further studies established that nonlymphoid cells such as polymorphonuclear leukocytes, monocytes and macrophages can also mediate this cytotoxic mechanism, known as antibody-dependent cellular (or cell-mediated) cytotoxicity (ADCC). The ability of a given effector cell population to perform this response, however, appears to be strongly dependent on several factors. They include the nature of the target cells, the isotype and density of antibodies coating the target cell surface, the class of receptor for the Fc portion of immunoglobulin molecule (FcR) involved, and the activation state of effector cells. In all cases, ADCC is induced without major histocompatibility complex (MHC) restriction and therefore it is operative in syngeneic, allogeneic and xenogeneic systems.

It should be noted that the specificity of ADCC is conferred by antibodies, which at extremely low concentrations, far below those required for complement-mediated lysis, are able to induce cytotoxicity. In fact, target cells coated with as few as 100–500 immunoglobulin molecules can be destroyed through ADCC.

Although the mechanisms involved in ADCC are still not completely understood, it is well established that ADCC is triggered by the interaction of target cell-bound IgG antibodies with the receptors for the Fc fragment of IgG (FcγR) expressed on the effector cells. These receptors, which act as signal-transducing molecules, are all members of the immunoglobulin-like superfamily of membrane receptors. They are expressed by human hematopoietic cells, including natural killer (NK), B and T lymphocytes, as well as by monocytes, macrophages, polymorphonuclear leukocytes, mast cells and platelets. Most of them express multiple types of FcγR, which fall into three main classes based on structural analysis of the genes and proteins for these receptors: the high affinity FcγRI (CD64), the low affinity FcγRII (CD32) and the low/intermediate affinity FCγRIII (CD16), which involve at least 12 different isoforms.

FcγR mediate a wide array of responses. They range from effector functions, such as ADCC, phagocytosis, pinocytosis and release of inflammatory mediators, to immunoregulatory signals, such as modulating antigen presentation, lymphocyte proliferation and antibody production. Triggering of biological responses through FcγR normally requires cross-linking of these receptors, which is usually induced by IgG immune complexes.

ADCC has been defined and characterized in several experimental models performed *in vitro*. Although its relevance *in vivo* has not been clearly established, several lines of evidence suggest that it plays an important role in host immune defense.

Nature of effector cells and antibodies involved in ADCC

NK cells are a subset of lymphocytes, morphologically identified as large granular lymphocytes, which lack typical T and B cell markers and usually express CD16 (FcγRIII) and CD56. They are able to destroy a variety of cell types, in the absence of prior stimulation, through a mechanism known as natural killer cytotoxicity. This cytotoxic response is not restricted by MHC gene products and is induced without antibody participation. NK cells, which comprise about 5% of human peripheral blood lymphocytes, also account for most lymphocyte ADCC activity. Thus, the same lymphocyte subpopulation seems to be capable of mediating distinct cytotoxic mechanisms, i.e. NK cytotoxicity and ADCC, through the activation of different recognition systems.

The ability of NK cells to perform ADCC has been demonstrated employing a wide variety of IgG-coated target cells such as normal, tumor and virus-infected cells, as well as bacteria, fungi and parasites. It is worth noting that in several human infectious diseases the presence of high levels of specific serum antibodies capable of inducing NK-mediated ADCC against the infectious agent has been described. Similarly, high concentrations of serum antibodies, competent to induce ADCC against tumor and allogeneic cells, have also been found in cancer and kidney transplant patients, respectively. These observations suggest that ADCC mediated by NK cells may play an important role in controlling some infection diseases, in antitumor immunity and, probably, in organ transplant rejection.

Although it is well established that NK cells constitute the major lymphocyte subpopulation capable of performing ADCC, the relative contribution of T and B lymphocytes, as effector cells, should be considered. Studies performed with resting T cells have shown that, with few exceptions, they are unable to mediate ADCC. However, since some T cell subsets express FcγR only during a narrow window following cellular activation, the possibility that activated T cells mediate ADCC cannot be ruled out. Regarding B lymphocytes, despite the fact that most of them bear FcγRII, they are unable to perform ADCC, suggesting that in B cells these receptors do not act as ADCC-triggering molecules.

Phagocytes can mediate the destruction of antibody-coated target cells by two major pathways: either by intracellular killing of target cells following phagocytosis or by ADCC-mediated extracellular lysis of targets. ADCC performed by mononuclear phagocytes has been largely studied employing peripheral blood monocytes, tissue macrophages and monocyte/macrophage-like cell lines as effector cells. Polymorphonuclear-mediated ADCC has been analyzed using peripheral blood neutrophils and neutrophils collected from inflammatory sites. There is general agreement that mononuclear phagocytes and neutrophils are able to mediate ADCC against a wide variety of target cells. In most of the models described, ADCC involves the participation of IgG antibodies, all IgG subclasses being able to mediate cytotoxicity. In contrast, IgM antibodies seem to play no role in the induction of ADCC. IgA antibodies are also unable to induce cytotoxicity, but they are capable of synergizing with IgG in mediating ADCC.

The relevance of ADCC performed by phagocytic cells in defense against disease is still not completely defined. Several lines of evidence strongly suggest that it plays a major role in host acquired immunity against a wide variety of infectious agents. A possible participation of macrophage-mediated ADCC in antitumor immunity has also been proposed. This possibility was recently supported by several studies which demonstrated that the therapeutic efficacy of some monoclonal antibodies, directed against tumor cell-associated antigens, strongly depends on the number of tumor-infiltrating macrophages.

For a long time it was thought that cellular interactions of IgE molecules were restricted to basophils and mast cells, which express a high-affinity receptor for the Fc fragment of IgE (FcεRI). The discovery of receptors of low-affinity for IgE (FcεRII; CD23) on mononuclear phagocytes, eosinophils, B cells and platelets suggested that these cellular populations may also be able to respond to IgE. Thus, Capron and Dessaint showed that macrophage-mediated ADCC induced by specific IgE antibodies against *Schistosoma mansoni* schistosomula led to the death of the parasite. More recent findings have indicated that not only macrophages but also eosinophils and platelets are able to perform IgE-dependent ADCC against helminths. While several lines of evidence strongly suggest that ADCC induced by IgE antibodies plays a major role in resistance to schistosomiasis, its relevance in host immunity against other parasites remains to be established.

Mechanisms involved in ADCC

The mechanisms involved in ADCC are still not well defined. As mentioned above, the cytotoxic response is triggered by the cross-linking of FcR expressed by the effector cells, which is induced by antibodies that coat target cells. It is also well established that cytotoxicity does not involve the participation of a diffusible cytotoxic factor. In fact, when mixtures of antibody-coated and uncoated target cells are incubated together with effector cells, lysis of non-sensitized targets is not observed.

Different metabolic requirements are involved in the induction of ADCC, depending not only on the nature of the effector cells but also on their activation state, the properties of antibodies and the nature of target cells. The role of Ca^{2+} in the induction of ADCC appears to differ for distinct effector cells. It is well known that the stimulation of human neutrophils and monocytes with immune complexes triggers Ca^{2+} mobilization. The increase in $[Ca^{2+}]_i$ appears to play an important role in neutrophil-mediated ADCC; however, it represents a secondary phenomenon in monocyte-mediated ADCC. Studies performed to evaluate the role of the cytoskeleton have also demonstrated major differences between neutrophils and monocytes. Thus, integrity of microfilament and microtubule systems is required for neutrophil-mediated ADCC, but it plays no role in cytotoxicity performed by monocytes.

The cytolytic mechanisms responsible for target cell destruction also seem to be quite different in distinct ADCC models. The generation of reactive oxygen intermediates (ROI), such as superoxide anion and hydrogen peroxide, plays a major role in some models of phagocytic cell-mediated ADCC. By contrast, ROI are not involved in cytotoxicity performed by lymphoid cells, which appears to be dependent on nonoxidative mechanisms, including the release of cytoplasmic granules containing perforin and granzymes. Furthermore, employing monocytes from chronic granulomatous disease patients, which generate very limited amounts of ROI, it was found that oxidative mechanisms play an important role in ADCC mediated by monocytes against red blood cells but not against lymphoblastoid cells. Interestingly, these data indicate that a single type of effector cell is able to perform ADCC towards different target cells via distinct cytolytic mechanisms.

It is possible that many of the variables observed in different models of ADCC may result from the participation of distinct types of FcγR in the induction of cytotoxicity. In this regard, it is noteworthy that FcγR share structurally related ligand-binding domains, but differ in their transmembrane and intracellular domains which mediate intracellular signaling.

Modulation of cytotoxic activity of effector cells

ADCC can be modulated by several cytokines and inflammatory products. Interferon γ (IFNγ) is one of the most important agents capable of increasing ADCC mediated by both polymorphonuclear leukocytes and mononuclear phagocytes. It causes a 5–15-fold increase in the number of FcγRI on monocytes, macrophages and neutrophils, and, moreover, significantly enhances effector cell oxidative metabolism. Both mechanisms seem to be responsible for the increase in ADCC observed after treatment with IFNγ. While interleukin-10 (IL-10) is also able to stimulate FcγRI expression and ADCC in mononuclear phagocytes, both IL-4 and IL-13 downregulate the expression of all three FcγR and strongly inhibit ADCC mediated by either untreated, IL-10- or IFNγ-treated monocytes. Tumor necrosis factor α (TNFα) can also activate ADCC mediated by neutrophils and eosinophils towards tumor cells and schistosomes, respectively. Interestingly, IL-5 has been shown to enhance antibody-dependent lysis of tumor cells mediated by eosinophils but not by neutrophils.

Colony stimulating factors are also powerful stimulators of ADCC mediated by phagocytic cells. Granulocyte-CSF (G-CSF) has been used in clinical studies for the improvement of circulating neutrophil counts. During G-CSF therapy it was observed that the expression of FcγRI is induced on circulating neutrophils. This effect, which results from G-CSF action on myeloid precursor cells, enables neutrophils to mediate high levels of ADCC against tumor cells. Monocyte-mediated ADCC, on the other hand, can be increased by treatment with macrophage-CSF (M-CSF). Measured on a cell-for-cell basis, treated monocytes are 10–100-fold more efficient than untreated monocytes. The ability of granulocyte-macrophage CSF (GM-CSF) to increase ADCC has

also been established. GM-CSF treatment enables eosinophils, neutrophils or monocytes to display high levels of ADCC against antibody-coated tumor cells and significantly increases antibody-dependent killing of parasites by eosinophils.

Other factors are also able to modulate ADCC. The C5a split product of complement activation increases both the expression of FcγRI on phagocytic cells and ADCC. Phagocytic cell-mediated ADCC can also be significantly increased by opioid peptides, such as metenkephalin. By contrast, glucocorticoids and several compounds able to increase intracellular levels of cAMP, strongly inhibit ADCC.

Even though *in vitro* studies have provided some information about the characteristics of ADCC, much more remains to be learned. As our understanding of the mechanisms involved in the regulation of ADCC increases, this knowledge should be applied to improve the therapeutic efficacy of monoclonal antibodies, not only in cancer immunotherapy but also in the treatment of some infectious diseases, which depends on the recruitment of host effector systems including ADCC.

See also: **Cytotoxicity, assays for; Cytotoxicity, mechanisms of; Fc receptors; Granzymes; Immunoglobulin, functions; Macrophage activation; Natural killer (NK) cells; Parasites, immunity to; Perforin; Tumors, immune response to.**

Further reading

Capron A and Dessaint JP (1985) Effector and regulatory mechanisms in immunity to schistosomes. *Annual Review of Immunology* 3: 455–476.

Cerottini JC and Brunner KT (1974) Cell-mediated cytotoxicity, allograft rejection, and tumor immunity. *Advances in Immunology* 18: 67–132.

Fanger MW, Shen L, Graziano RF and Guyre PM (1989) Cytotoxicity mediated by human Fc receptors for IgG. *Immunology Today* 10: 92–99.

Fridman WH (1993) Regulation of B cell activation and antigen presentation by Fc receptors. *Current Opinion in Immunology* 5: 355–366.

Fridman WH, Bonnerot C, Daeron M, Amigorena S, Teillaud JL and Sautes C (1992) Structural bases of Fcγ receptor functions. *Immunological Reviews* 125: 49–75.

Pearson GP (1978) *In vitro* and *in vivo* investigations on antibody-dependent cellular cytotoxicity. *Current Topics in Microbiology and Immunology* 80: 65–96.

Perlmann P and Holm G (1969) Cytotoxic effects of lymphoid cells *in vitro*. *Advances in Immunology* 15: 117–193.

Ravetch JV (1994) Fc receptors: rubor redux. *Cell* 78: 553–560.

Valerius T, Repp R, de Wit TPM *et al* (1993) Involvement of the high-affinity receptor for IgG (FcγRI; CD64) in enhanced tumor cell cytotoxicity of neutrophils during granulocyte colony-stimulating factor therapy. *Blood* 82: 931–939.

van de Winkel JGJ and Capel PJA (1993) Human IgG Fc receptor heterogeneity: molecular aspects and clinical implications. *Immunology Today* 14: 215–221.

ANTIGEN-BINDING SITE

Bradford C Braden and **Roberto J Poljak**, Center for Advanced Research in Technology, Rockville, Maryland, USA

Different estimates indicate that the immune system of higher vertebrates can produce antibodies capable of reacting with more than 10^8 different external antigens. Given this physiological diversity of antibody molecules, the molecular structure of their antigen-combining sites has been the object of much speculation and research. Amino acid sequences of immunoglobulin light (L) and heavy (H) chains from human and mouse myeloma proteins indicated the presence of hypervariable regions, located around sequence positions 30, 50 and 100 in each chain. These hypervariable sequences constitute the antigen-combining sites of antibodies and thus are termed complementarity determining regions (CDRs). Because of their sequence hypervariability, the CDRs must possess great conformational diversity, reflecting the potential of antibodies to respond to many different external antigens. Antibody diversity is generated at the genetic level by multiple V_H and V_L genes and segments (D and J), by a somatic recombination process and an antigen-driven somatic mutation mechanism.

The determination of the three-dimensional structure of Fab fragments of myeloma immunoglobulins by X-ray crystallographic techniques indicated that the folding of the polypeptide chain brings the CDRs into close proximity at an end of the antibody molecule. The β-barrel structures of the V domains provide a nearly constant, conformationally stable framework on which different external polypeptide loops, the CDRs, can be placed without adversely affecting the stability of the folding. Their variable lengths, in particular those of the V_L CDR1 and V_H CDR3, have a profound effect on the stereochemistry of the combining site. In addition, part of the interactions between V_H and V_L mediated by the CDRs are important in shaping antigen-combining sites and in determining the preferential pairing of H and L chains.

Molecular structures of Fabs and Fab–hapten complexes

The determination of the first three-dimensional structures of Fab complexes with the haptens phosphorylcholine and vitamin K_1OH, confirmed that the CDRs of both V_H and V_L participate in binding. The contacts of the ligands with the combining site included salt bridges, hydrogen bonds and van der Waals interactions. No conformational changes in the combining site or in other regions of the antibody could be seen by comparing free with liganded Fabs. Thus, an allosteric mechanism by which conformational signals would be transmitted from the combining site to the Fc region was not supported by these structure determinations. Such mechanisms were postulated as a way of activating secondary (effector) functions of antibodies. However, since haptens represent only a fraction of the antigenic determinants recognized by antibodies, the complete antigen-binding site could not be defined by that approach. Moreover, it was thought possible that conformational changes would be observed only if a complex with a macromolecular antigen, contacting a wider area at the combining site, could be studied.

Antibody–antigen complexes

The introduction of cell hybridization techniques leading to the development of immortalized lymphocytic cell lines (hybridomas) secreting antibodies of predefined specificity allowed the production of monoclonal antibodies (mAbs) in large quantities. These made it possible to study specific antigen–antibody reactions in greater detail, eventually providing a deeper understanding of antigenic determinants and combining site structure. Moreover, the elucidation of the antigen-binding site has been greatly facilitated by the production of antibody variable domain fragments (Fv). As the volume of Fv fragments is half that of the Fab, Fv fragments generally crystallize in smaller asymmetric units and thus diffract to higher resolution.

By 1996 more than 50 structures of antibody fragments, free and complexed with antigen, had been determined by X-ray diffraction techniques. By far the most widely studied antibodies have been of mouse origin. The mAbs were obtained after secondary responses and can be assumed to be highly specific – that is, they recognize only one antigen (and related, cross-reacting antigens sharing the antigenic determinant). Thus, their combining sites are uniquely defined by stereospecific contacts with the antigens. Several BALB/c mouse mAbs have now been studied by X-ray diffraction, including six which form complexes with hen egg-white lysozyme (HEL), two with influenza virus neuraminidase, one with HPr (a histidine-containing phosphocarrier protein), one with NC10 staphylococcal nuclease and four with anti-idiotopic antibodies. These results can be correlated with those of other crystallographic, immunochemical and sequence studies related to antigen and hapten recognition by specific antibodies. In most of the complexes above, the combining site is formed by amino acid residues from each of the CDRs of the L and H chains, although the H chain may in several cases contribute more contacts than the L chain. About 15 residues, mostly from the CDRs but including also one or two from the framework regions, are in contact with a similar number from the antigen. The general topology of the site is not that of a big cavity, but rather flat with interspersed depressions and protuberances that closely complement the surface topology of the antigenic determinant.

The nature of the chemical contacts made by the combining site includes charge bridges between ion pairs, hydrogen bonds and van der Waals interactions. If hydrogen bonds are inaccessible to solvent they should contribute appreciably to the stability of antigen–antibody interactions. In the complex of mAbs HyHEL-5 and D44.1 with HEL, two glutamic acid residues of the combining site interact closely with two arginines of the antigen. The crystal structure of HyHEL-5 complexed with a site-directed mutant of HEL (Arg68→Lys) demonstrated the specificity of electrostatic interactions. While generally considered a conservative mutation, the HEL mutant binds to HyHEL-5 with a 10^3-fold reduction in affinity. The crystal structure demonstrated that lysine is unable to form both salt bridges to a HyHEL-5 glutamate, therefore the decrease in affinity of the HyHEL-5 reaction with the mutant HEL was ascribed to the loss of one hydrogen bond. Further evidence of the electrostatic complementarity defining antibody–antigen interactions came from the crystal structure of D1.3 complexed with turkey egg-white lysozyme (TEL). In this case, an important residue in the antibody–antigen interface (HEL Gln121) is replaced by a histidine. Gln121 makes two hydrogen bonds to carbonyl oxygen and amide nitrogen main-chain atoms of D1.3 V_L CDR-3 (Oϵ1-Ser93 N; Nϵ2-Phe 91 O). The orien-

tation of TEL His121 is such that its Nϵ2 atom is positionally equivalent to the Oϵ1 atom of HEL Gln121 and therefore unable to form a hydrogen bond to the amide nitrogen of D1.3 Ser93. D1.3 was observed to compensate for this difference in the electrostatic character of HEL121 by undergoing a flip of the main-chain peptide orientation such that the carbonyl oxygen of Trp92 is exposed at the interface, allowing formation of a hydrogen bond to TEL His121 Nϵ2 (**Figure 1**).

Since hydrogen bonds and van der Waals interactions require a somewhat strict complementarity, they can be taken as the basis of antigen–antibody specificity. In the combining sites there is a high relative proportion of aromatic residues Tyr and Trp. Given their bulky size, these contribute a maximum of van der Waals contacts as well as affording the possibility of hydrogen bond formation to their polar atoms. The area of contact between antigen and antibody can be defined as that which becomes inaccessible to solvent after the formation of a complex. The surface buried by protein antigens is of about 600 Å^2 and higher, compatible with the requirements for the formation of a stable complex. This observation is in agreement with that made in other protein-interacting systems in which subunits make contacts through a closely packed interface occupying a large surface area. The crystal structure of a Trp→Asp mutation of D1.3

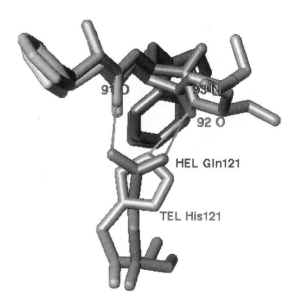

Figure 1 Conformational differences in antibody D1.3 V_L CDR3 induced by differing antigen side-chains. HEL residue Gln121 makes two main-chain hydrogen bonds; to the carbonyl oxygen of D1.3 V_L Phe91 and the amide nitrogen of D1.3 V_L Ser93. Replacement of the glutamine by histidine in TEL induces a conformational change in the backbone of V_L CDR3 which allows the formation of a hydrogen bond between the histidine and the carbonyl oxygen of V_L Trp92. (See also color **Plate 8A**.)

exemplifies the importance of interacting surface complementarity and van der Waals interactions. The V_L Trp92→Asp mutation results in a 10^3 reduction in the affinity of D1.3 for HEL. Trp92 makes extensive van der Waals contacts with the antigen. With the substitution of Asp about 150 Å² of surface are lost to the antibody–antigen complex, resulting in the reduction of affinity (**Figure 2**).

While a few buried water molecules have been reported in other antibody–antigen complexes, the D1.3–HEL complex contains a large number of bound water molecules which bridge the antibody and antigen. This water contributes to the stability of the antibody–antigen complex in two important ways: 1) the network of water molecules contributes to a favorable free energy of complex formation by mediating hydrogen bonds between antibody and antigen; and 2) the water molecules fill cavities in the interface which are destabilizing to complex formation (**Figure 3**).

No major conformational change seems to take place at the antibody site upon the binding of antigen. Small rearrangements of side-chains and CDR loops have been observed, particularly upon the binding of small antigens, most notably peptides, as well as relative displacements of V_H and V_L. Thus, antibody–antigen complexes can be viewed as a form of 'lock-and-key' association and small displacements can provide potential diversity in the conformation of the

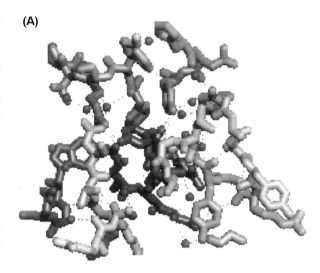

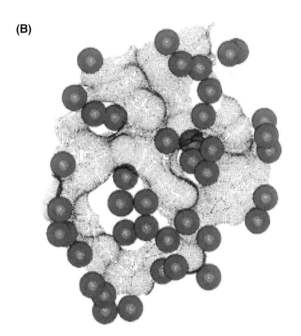

Figure 3 (A) Hydrogen bonding network of the D1.3–HEL interface mediated by bound solvent molecules; 25 water molecules form hydrogen bonds linking the antibody and antigen, directly or through other water molecules. (B) Water molecules in contact with the D1.3–HEL buried surface. Including the 25 bridging water molecules, nearly 50 solvent sites are in contact with the buried surface defined by the D1.3–HEL interface. Many of these water molecules fill internal cavities, further stabilizing the complex. (See also color **Plate 8C and D**.)

combining site and, perhaps, a mechanism by which the site could adapt to an antigenic determinant without large loss of entropy.

Molecular modeling of combining sites

Modeling of the CDRs of antibodies of unknown three-dimensional structure was attempted in several

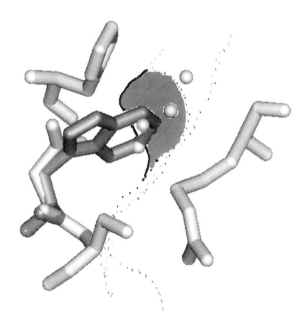

Figure 2 The effect of a Trp→Asp mutation on the interaction surface area of the D1.3-HEL complex. A thin slice through the buried surface of the wild-type D1.3–HEL complex (dots) and the mutant D1.3–HEL surface (solid line) demonstrates the loss of interaction surface area in the mutant complex. A 150 Å² loss in surface area accounts for the reduction in affinity of the mutant D1.3–HEL reaction. (See also color **Plate 8B**.)

laboratories, using different energy minimization and computer graphics approaches. The proposed models were subsequently compared with the determined crystallographic structures. The apparent occurrence of 'canonical structures' for most of the CDRs allowed successful approximation of the folding of the main polypeptide chain for the unknown antibodies. Establishing the orientation of side-chains is generally beyond the reach of these procedures, although in several cases they were correctly predicted. The biggest problems for modeling are posed by 1) the less predictable structure of the CDR3 of V_H; 2) the relative positioning of V_H and V_L; 3) the difficulty in placing solvent molecules which could be tightly bound to the combining site or its surroundings and thus contribute to its conformational stability; and 4) predicting possible conformational change that may take place upon antigen binding. Modeling attempts have been partially successful in determining the conformation of some of the CDRs compared with those observed in the crystal structures of the complexes with antigen. Thus they suggest agreement with the experimental observation that there is no major conformational change in going from the uncomplexed to the complexed antibody-combining site.

Genetic engineering of antibody-combining sites

Site-directed mutagenesis experiments performed on an antilysozyme antibody showed that a double mutant V_L Glu28→Ser, V_H Lys56→Gln increased 8- to 9-fold its affinity for the antigen. One interesting conclusion of this work was that removal of electrostatically charged side-chains and their replacement by noncharged residues with hydrogen bond potential allows formation of additional hydrogen bonds with the antigen and leads to an increase in affinity. Certainly, a prime consideration in the production of genetically engineered antibodies is an improvement in affinity for antigen. However, important questions are yet to be answered in this regard: 1) what are the structural mechanisms which lead to the increase in affinity, and 2) why don't the natural diversification mechanisms produce these same hypervariable sequences?

See also: **Affinity; Antibodies, specificity; Antibody-antigen intermolecular forces; Immunoglobulin structure; Antibody-antigen complexes, three-dimensional structures.**

Further reading

Bhat TN, Bentley GA, Boulot G *et al* (1994) Bound water molecules and conformational stabilization help mediate an antigen–antibody association. *Proceedings of the National Academy of Sciences of the USA* **91**: 1089–1093.

Braden BC and Poljak RJ (1995) Structural features of the reactions between antibodies and protein antigens. *FASEB Journal* **9**: 9–16.

Braden BC, Fields BA and Poljak RJ (1995) Conservation of water molecules in an antibody–antigen interaction. *Journal of Molecular Recognition* **8**: 317–325.

Chacko S, Silverton E, Kam-Morgan L, Smith-Gill S, Cohen G and Davies D (1995) Structure of an antibody–lysozyme complex: unexpected effect of a conservative mutation. *Journal of Molecular Biology* **245**: 261–274.

Davies DR and Cohen GH (1996) Interactions of protein antigens with antibodies. *Proceedings of the National Academy of Sciences of the USA* **93**: 7–12.

Poljak RJ (1991) Structure of antibodies and their complexes with antigens. *Molecular Immunology* **28**: 1341–1345.

Wilson IA and Stanfield RL (1993) Antibody–antigen interactions. *Current Opinion in Structural Biology* **3**: 113–118.

Ysern X, Fields BA, Bhat TN *et al* (1994) Solvent rearrangement in an antigen–antibody interface introduced by site-directed mutagenesis of the antibody combining site. *Journal of Molecular Biology* **238**: 496–500.

ANTIGEN-PRESENTING CELLS

Emil R Unanue, Department of Pathology and Center for Immunology, Washington University School of Medicine, St Louis, Missouri, USA

Antigen-presenting cells (APCs) refers to the leukocytes responsible for antigen presentation. These include three sets of cells – the mononuclear phagocytes, the Langerhans-dendritic cells and the B cells. Other cells can be made to have APC function under special conditions.

Antigen presentation is an obligatory step in the recognition of protein antigens by the T cell lineage.

The APCs bear the molecules encoded in the major histocompatibility complex (MHC), the class I and II molecules. These MHC molecules bind peptides resulting from intracellular processing of the protein. The MHC–peptide complex constitutes the antigenic determinant, the epitope, that engages the T cell receptor. Thus APCs are essential cells for the initiation and maintenance of all T cell responses. (See Antigen Presentation via MHC Class I molecules and Antigen Presentation via MHC Class II molecules.)

APCs need to have several properties in order for them to be involved in presentation to CD4 and CD8 T cells: 1) the capacity to take up the antigen; 2) the capacity to internalize the antigen and process it; 3) the synthesis and expression of MHC class I and II molecules; 4) the expression of adhesion molecules, to promote and insure the APC–T cell interaction; and 5) the expression of costimulator molecules (i.e. those molecules that promote the growth and differentiation of T cells during antigen presentation) and the release of cytokines. The APC–T cell interaction affects both cells; it is symbiotic. The APC changes its biology, becoming activated both in the case of macrophages and B cells; and the T cells respond by entering cell cycle and/or expressing cytokine genes. The activation of T cells is a 'two signal' event, dependent, first, on the engagement of its antigen receptor by peptide–MHC complex (signal 1) and, second, on interactions with the costimulatory mol-ecules (signal 2). The major cell interaction molecules are shown in **Table 1**.

Not all these properties are expressed to the same degree by all the APCs. The differentiation state of APCs, the environment of a given tissue and the nature of the antigen molecule influence APC function. The T cells may also vary in their requirements, depending on their natural history (i.e. unstimulated versus memory cells). Finally, the antigen molecules themselves dictate the extent to which one or another property becomes important, in three ways. First, the physical and chemical form of the antigen determines the extent of uptake by APCs. Whether the antigen is a small molecule or part of a complex structure like that of a bacterium or a virus makes a difference. In the former case the antigen may enter the cell by fluid phase or receptor-mediated endocytosis, while the latter case involves a phagocytic process with internalization of a large extracellular ligand. Along these lines the capacity to internalize a microbe is limited for some APC-like B cells, in contrast to macrophages. Second, the complexity of the antigen will determine the number of peptides derived from its component proteins that become available for binding to MHC proteins. There is no direct estimate of the number of peptides that can be occupied by an MHC molecule when dealing with a bacterium, a complex protein or a simple polypeptide. But the limited studies indicate that the more protein taken up by the APCs, and the more complex the protein,

Table 1 Molecules involved in APC–T cell interaction

APC	T cells	Interaction
Class I and II MHC molecules	T cell receptor for antigen (TCR)	Engagement of the TCR provides first signal for activation
Class I and II MHC molecules	CD8/CD4 molecules	Function to promote the interaction of TCR with peptide–MHC class I (CD8) or peptide–MHC class II (CD4)
ICAM-1 (CD54) ICAM-2 (CD102) ICAM-3 (CD50)	LFA-1	Major sets of adhesive molecules
LFA-3 (CD58) (in humans), CD48 (in mice)	CD2	Promotes cell interaction and costimulatory function
B7-1 and B7-2	CD28 CTLA-4	CD28 involved in early T cell activation while CTLA-4 inhibits activation
CD40	CD40L	Primarily involved in B7 cell activation → promotes B cell activation
Cytokines	Cytokine receptors	Interaction
IL-1α and β IL-6 IL-12 TNF IL-10		Secretion of early cytokines promotes vascular and tissue responses. Secreted by macrophages and DCs. Release of IL-12 promotes T_H1 differentiation. IL-10 inhibits the system
IFNγ receptor	IFNγ	IFNγ released early by T_H1 cells promotes macrophage activation

the larger is the number of peptides bound to MHC molecules. Last, the capacity of an antigen to stimulate the APC is a major factor that may lead to the enhanced response to some microorganisms. Indeed, many bacteria trigger the induction of cytokines, costimulatory and adhesion molecules that markedly influence the T cell response. In contrast, bland protein antigens are considerably less effective.

The three main APCs

Brief comments on three main APCs now follow. Macrophages are ubiquitous cells found in most tissues. They are highly active in internalization of a wide range of proteins as well as microorganisms. The extent of expression of class II MHC molecules varies among macrophages of various tissues and also among species. For example, most human monocytes and macrophages express class II MHC molecules, and are active in presenting antigens; in contrast class II MHC molecules are expressed on only a percentage of macrophages in the mouse. Here the percentage of class II-bearing cells varies from most of spleen macrophages to just a few of peritoneal macrophages. Accordingly, antigen presentation varies among them. Regardless, macrophages from all species express high levels of class II MHC molecules after their exposure to interferon γ (IFNγ).

Macrophages are highly effective in presentation of proteins and bacteria, most likely as a result of their highly developed endocytic capacity. They take up proteins by fluid-phase pinocytosis and/or receptor-mediated uptake, i.e. by their binding to specific surface receptors. Macrophages have complement receptors and Fc receptors that enable them to take up opsonized antigens as well as surface receptors for denatured proteins (scavenger receptors) or glycosylated proteins (such as the mannose receptor).

Macrophages are also highly secretory cells. Some of the secretory products are important during antigen presentation and early inductive events. These include interleukin 1α (IL-1α) and IL-β, tumor necrosis factor α (TNFα), IL-12, IL-6, IL-8 and a number of other chemokines. This group of early cytokines has effects on T cells as well as on connective tissue and vascular cells and they are believed to be involved in the early inflammatory changes in immunity. Macrophages also express adhesive and costimulatory molecules such as ICAM-1 (CD54), B7-1 (CD80) and B7-2 (CD86), respectively. Their level of expression is increased, particularly after the uptake of microbial antigens.

The Langerhans-dendritic cells constitute a single lineage, abundant in the skin and epithelia and thymus-dependent areas of lymphoid tissues. Langerhans cells are part of the family of dendritic cells (DCs). In the epidermis they constitute about 2–8% of the cells and are found between the keratinocytes, where they were first identified by morphological studies. Langerhans-dendritic cells arrive by way of afferent lymphatics to the thymic-dependent areas of lymphoid organs. In the skin they represent the local APC that takes up antigen molecules that contact the epidermis and carry the antigen by way of the lymphatic circulation to the draining lymph nodes. For example, application of protein-reactive compounds to the skin, such as dinitrofluorobenzene, ultimately results in their binding to the class II MHC of the Langerhans-dendritic cells, and with it the subsequent activation of T cells in the lymph nodes. Ultraviolet irradiation of the epidermis results in their disappearance; if such sensitizing compounds are applied to such areas, no T cell activation takes place.

DCs originate from bone marrow precursors, circulate, and seed the different lymphoid tissue and epithelia. DCs and macrophages have similar progenitors, with monocytes being a common cellular stage prior to the differentiation of the two lineages. In culture, the immature DC can differentiate to a mature state by the action of two cytokines, granulocyte-macrophage colony-stimulating factor (GM-CSF) and IL-4.

Another important immunological reaction where Langerhans-dendritic cells participate is in the allograft reaction. Their high content of MHC proteins make the Langerhans-dendritic cells the most powerful allogeneic cell in immunizing the host. Langerhans-dendritic cells are found in variable amounts in the interstitial and connective tissue of most transplanted organs (including liver, kidney, heart and, of course, skin).

DCs constitutively express high levels of class II MHC proteins, which makes them very active as APCs and as stimulator cells in the mixed leukocyte reaction. Langerhans-dendritic cells are active in presenting proteins but their degree of internalization and processing of protein antigens varies as a function of their state of maturation. As with macrophages, they mature in their antigen-presenting capacity. For example, their antigen-presenting capacity is limited when freshly harvested from the epidermis or blood but improves upon brief culture, which is one of the criteria for defining immature and mature DCs. DCs can express costimulatory molecules and release early cytokines such as IL-12.

B cells have an important antigen-presenting function that forms the basis for their interaction with T cells. B cells bind the specific antigen by way of their membrane immunoglobulin, internalize it and process it to peptides that become bound to their class II MHC molecules. The encounter with T cells reactive to the peptides results in a reciprocal activation of both cells. B cells function best as APCs if they are first activated, as they express only small amounts of costimulatory and adhesion molecules in their resting state. *In vitro* B cells become active in antigen presentation upon culture with anti-immunoglobulin antibodies and cytokines such as IFNγ. Such treatment does not affect the level of class II MHC on B cells but increases the level of adhesion molecules, including ICAM and of B7-1 and B7-2. Expression of class II MHC molecules is constitutive in B cells. This basal level is increased by IL-4 but not by IFNγ.

APC–T cell interaction in tissues

The dynamics of the encounter in tissues between a cloned T cell and the APC bearing the peptide–MHC complex is not entirely known and may depend on a number of conditions. For example, a bacterium that enters a nonlymphoid tissue, the lung alveoli, will be taken up by alveolar macrophages and an inflammatory reaction ensues as the macrophages release early cytokines. This inflammatory reaction is conducive to the encounter between APCs and T cells. A different situation may develop when a contact-sensitizing molecule reaches the skin. Here the Langerhans cells located in the epidermis will take up the sensitizer and will now move via the afferent lymphatic to the draining lymph nodes. Thus, in this reaction part of T cell induction is in part mediated by the transport of the antigen directly to the lymphoid organs.

The anatomy of APC–T cell interaction in lymph nodes and spleen has been difficult to study. A network of APCs are found in the deep cortex of the lymph nodes where presumably the productive trapping of antigen and encounter with the T cell takes place. DCs constitute many of the 'interdigitating cells' found in histological examinations. The relative importance of, and the interplay among, the three APCs described above in a physiological immune response is not entirely understood. A likely scenario is one where antigen is first trapped by the macrophages and DCs of the thymus-dependent areas of lymphoid organs and there recruit and activate antigen-specific CD4 T cells. The subsequent stage envisions B cells binding the antigen molecule via their surface immunoglobulin and interacting with the activated CD4 T cells. In follicles and germinal centers B cells interact with the follicular dendritic

cells that bear antigen–antibody complexes on their surface. This interaction is part of the reactions that lead to B cell activation and differentiation.

The case of CD8 T cells

APCs are involved in the early activation of CD8 T cells by presenting peptides via class I MHC molecules. Once activated, the CD8 T cells will be able to interact and react with class I MHC–peptide complex presented in various target cells. Thus, in the antiviral response the first encounter that recruits and activates specific antiviral clones will be that of infected APCs (either macrophages or DCs) with the CD8 T cells. Once clonal expansion and activation takes place, the CD8 T cells can kill the virally infected target cells. APCs also have the ability to capture proteins from other cells (i.e. tumor antigens, alloantigens, for example) and process it into the class I MHC presentation pathway, a process that needs to be better defined in mechanistic terms. (See Antigen Presentation via MHC Class I Molecules.)

Most epithelial, vascular and mesenchymal cells do not express class II MHC molecules or costimulatory molecules; however, there are exceptions: thymic epithelium normally expresses class II MHC molecules, and some mucosal cells of the gastrointestinal tract and proximal tubular cells of the kidney also express some levels of class II MHC molecules. During inflammation, as a result of local IFNγ production, many cells are made to express class II MHC molecules. Whether this aberrant expression is involved in tissue autoimmunity needs to be settled. Tissue cells express limited amounts of costimulatory molecules which makes them poor APCs for initiating T cell activation.

See also: **Antigen presentation via MHC class I molecules; Antigen presentation via MHC class II molecules; B lymphocyte, antigen processing and presentation; B lymphocytes; Dendritic cells; Immunogen; Langerhans cells; Macrophage activation; Microenvironment; Monocytes; Mononuclear phagocyte system; Second signals for lymphocyte activation.**

Further reading

Austyn JM (1996) New insights into the mobilization and phagocytic activity of dendritic cells. *Journal of Experimental Medicine* 183: 1287–1292.

Bevan MJ (1995) Antigen presentation to cytotoxic T lymphocytes *in vivo*. *Journal of Experimental Medicine* 182: 639–641.

Lanzavecchia A (1990) Receptor-mediated antigen uptake

and its effect on antigen presentation to class II-restricted T lymphocytes. *Annual Review of Immunology* 8: 773–793.

Lenschow DJ, Walunas TL and Bluestone JA (1996) CD28/B7 system of T cell costimulation. *Annual Review of Immunology* 14: 233–258.

Neefjes JJ and Momburg F (1993) Cell biology of antigen presentation. *Current Opinion in Immunology* 5: 27–34.

Unanue ER (1992) Cellular studies on antigen presentation by class II MHC molecules. *Current Opinion in Immunology* 4: 63–69.

ANTIGEN-SPECIFIC CELLS: ENRICHMENT AND ISOLATION

KGC Smith, Department of Medicine, University of Cambridge, School of Clinical Medicine, Addenbrooke's Hospital, Cambridge, UK

JE Layton, Ludwig Institute for Cancer Research, Melbourne Tumour Biology Branch, Post Office Royal Melbourne Hospital, Victoria, Australia

DM Tarlinton, The Walter and Eliza Hall Institute of Medical Research, Post Office Royal Melbourne Hospital, Victoria, Australia

Burnet, in his clonal selection theory of antibody formation, proposed that the precursors of antibody-forming cells carried receptors of unique specificity for a particular antigen. After 'selection' by antigen, the antigen-specific cell would proliferate and eventually give rise to a clone of antibody-secreting cells. The antibody produced would be specific for the original antigen. Given the large number of different antigens in the environment, for any single antigen the frequency of antigen-binding cells would have to be very low, and an individual antigen-binding cell should bind only one antigen. The validity of the clonal selection theory was first demonstrated for B lymphocytes, but was subsequently shown to be true for T lymphocytes, which are also antigen specific.

Antigen-binding cells were first demonstrated and enumerated with large particulate antigens such as bacteria and red blood cells. Binding of soluble antigen by lymphocytes was first visualized by Naor and Sulitzeanu, who used ^{125}I-labeled albumin and auto-radiography. The first antigen-binding lymphocytes studied were B cells, which recognize antigen with a unique antigen receptor comprising surface immunoglobulin. The fact that B cells bear this antigen receptor which recognizes antigenic epitopes in their native form has made isolation of antigen-specific B cells relatively successful. In contrast, T cells recognize antigen after processing to peptide form and in the context of major histocompatibility complex (MHC) molecules, and do not bind native antigen. This has made their isolation considerably more difficult. Problems with the isolation of antigen-specific cells are compounded by the relative scarcity of these cells. Even at the height of the B cell response to haptens such as (4-hydroxy-3-nitrophenyl)acetyl (NP) in the mouse, the antigen-specific B cells constitute no more than 1% spleen cells, declining to <0.01% of cells in the memory cell population. The other problem is that antigen-specific lymphocytes may differ only subtly from their colleagues, and detection of this subtle difference is critical to their isolation.

Early attempts to deplete antigen-specific cells were made to provide evidence in support of the clonal selection theory. These techniques are no longer in common use and will be considered only briefly. Detailed study of the immune response to both experimental immunogens and to pathogens is greatly enhanced by the isolation of antigen-specific lymphocytes. Techniques for such enrichment and isolation are more advanced for B cells, which will be considered first. Recent techniques employed for the isolation of antigen-specific T cells will then be examined.

Enrichment and isolation of B lymphocytes

Depletion

The first attempts to deplete antigen-binding cells were made by Wigzell and colleagues using antigen-coated beads in affinity columns, which depleted antigen-binding cells but also a significant number of nonspecific cells. An alternative approach was to deplete antigen-specific cells by allowing them to bind radioactive antigen of high enough specific activity to kill them; a technique sometimes referred to as 'antigen suicide'. Ada and Byrt demonstrated that incubation in the cold of lymphoid cells with ^{125}I-labeled T-independent antigens specifically abolished the response of these cells to the unlabeled antigen on adoptive transfer into irradiated syngeneic recipients, establishing that antigen-binding B cells were the precursors of antibody-forming cells. These experiments provided strong support for the clonal selection theory but did not yield purified populations of antigen-specific cells for further study. Such methods are no longer widely used.

Enrichment: historical methods

A number of approaches have been taken to enrich lymphocyte populations for antigen-specific cells. Some are now of historical interest only. Such techniques include the use of affinity matrices and columns. Two major problems with these modalities were nonspecific adsorption of cells to affinity matrices and difficulty in recovering viable, functional cells after interaction with antigen.

Another early method for isolating antigen-specific cells was the use of hapten–gelatin-coated Petri dishes ('panning'). Cell suspensions were added to the dishes, binding of hapten-specific B cells occurred, unbound cells were washed off and bound cells recovered by melting the gelatin layer at 37°C. A major disadvantage of this method was its relatively low cell yield, but combined with limiting dilution assays, it was a useful method for studying antigen-specific B cell activation.

Rosetting has also been used to enrich for antigen-specific B cells. For example, haptenated horse red blood cells (HRBCs) were allowed to bind to hapten-specific B cells, forming rosettes. The rosettes could then be separated from nonrosetted cells by buoyant density and/or sedimentation velocity centrifugation, and the HRBCs removed from the antigen-binding cells by protease digestion, followed by overnight culture of the cells to allow for receptor regeneration.

Enrichment: 'Pre-enrichment' by depletion of nonantigen-specific cells

Partial purification or enrichment of antigen-specific cells subsequently allows more rapid and accurate isolation of these cells by more time-consuming or expensive procedures, such as fluorescence-activated cell sorting (FACS: see below). The removal of unwanted cells can be achieved by physical means, such as by taking advantage of the propensity of T cells to bind to nylon wool columns or of macrophages to adhere to plastic. Depletion of unwanted cells using complement fixation is a commonly used and effective technique. To enrich for immunoglobulin G-positive (IgG+) B cells, for example, spleen cells are cultured in a cocktail of antibodies against

T cells (e.g. anti-CD3), macrophages and other B cells (e.g. anti-IgM). Provided the chosen antibodies fix complement efficiently (IgM antibodies are best) and have been properly titrated to reduce nonspecific killing, considerable enrichment and high yields can be achieved. Similar cocktails of antibodies conjugated directly or indirectly (via biotin-avidin) to magnetic beads can be used to remove unwanted cells, as cells binding the paramagnetic beads will stick to steel wool in a column or to the side of a container when a magnetic field is applied, while the desired cells will pass through the column (**Figure 1**). A potential hazard of this technique is the risk of saturating the column: if the surface area of the steel wool is inadequate to bind the number of cells to be depleted they too will pass through the column causing substantial contamination. One advantage of these 'negative selection' methods of enrichment is that they do not require antibody binding to, and thus potential activation of, the antigen-specific cells.

Enrichment: positive 'pre-enrichment'

Paramagnetic beads can also be used to enrich for antigen-specific B cells in a 'positive' fashion. If, for example, the antigen-specific B cells have a characteristic immunoglobulin isotype (such as the γ heavy and λ light chains in the response to NP) antibodies to these can be used to attach magnetic beads to the cells of interest. These cells will then attach to the column as described above, and can be washed by passage of medium through the column, followed by their removal by flushing after withdrawing the column from the magnetic field (**Figure 1**). Saturation of the column will not result in impurity of the resulting population, but only a reduced yield. In the example above, enrichment of spleen cells using anti-IgG1 and paramagnetic beads can result in a 40-fold enrichment for anti-NP-specific B cells, with a proportionate reduction in the flow cytometry time needed to complete the purification.

One problem with positive enrichment using these columns is nonspecific adhesion of dead cells to the column. If this is a problem, dead cells may have to be removed in a separate initial step, for example using density gradient separation. Direct conjugation of antigen to paramagnetic beads is currently being attempted which should improve isolation of antigen-specific cells by this method.

The flow cytometer can itself be used to pre-enrich cells prior to a further round of flow cytometry. Very rapid sorting by FACS results in a predictable number of errors and therefore impurity. Substantial enrichment is nonetheless achieved during this very rapid sorting, and the time needed for the subsequent

(A)

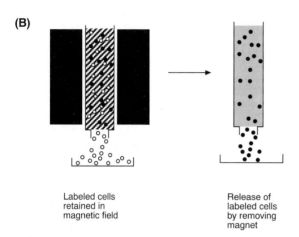

Cell of
interest

Cell labeled
with biotinylated
antibody

Biotin labeled
with avidin beads

(B)

Labeled cells
retained in
magnetic field

Release of
labeled cells
by removing
magnet

Figure 1 Schematic representation of the use of paramagnetic beads for 'positive' enrichment. (A) The desired cells are labeled with a biotinylated antibody, washed, then attached to avidin beads. (B) Labeled cells are retained when a magnetic field is applied, and unwanted cells washed through. The desired cells are then recovered after removal of the column or tube from the magnetic field.

slower and more accurate sort is reduced resulting in an overall saving of time.

Isolation: fluorescence-activated cell sorting

FACS provides the most reliable and accurate means of purifying antigen-specific B cells. B cells can be identified by a number of markers, but the ability to detect binding of a specific antigen is crucial to identifying antigen-specific cells. Initial success using this method was achieved by Hayakawa and colleagues, who immunized mice with the fluorescent protein phycoerythrin (PE), later isolating PE-binding B cells on the FACS. This technique was later advanced by Lalor, McHeyzer-Williams and Nossal, who identified NP-specific B cells by detecting binding of NP conjugated to allophycocyanin, allowing further dissection of a well-characterized stereotypic immune response.

A major drawback of this technique has been the time (and therefore expense) taken to sort substantial number of cells if these are very rare. This can now be largely overcome by using one or a combination of the pre-enrichment techniques described above.

Another advance has been the advent of techniques allowing analysis of single cells, which removes the need to sort large numbers of cells. For example, a polymerase chain reaction (PCR)-based strategy can be used to amplify single genes from cDNA which can subsequently be sequenced. This has allowed analysis of patterns of somatic hypermutation in very rare subpopulations of antigen-specific B cells, such as the bone marrow antibody-forming cells described below.

Another major problem is the potential difficulty in ensuring the purity of very rare populations of cells, as relatively few cells which are incorrectly sorted can reduce the purity of such populations dramatically. This has been overcome by making maximal use of the number of detection parameters available on modern FACS machines. Consider the example of the isolation of NP-specific bone marrow antibody-forming cells shown in **Figure 2**. First, all cells which do not have the forward and side scatter characteristics (which measure size and 'complexity' respectively) of lymphocytes are excluded. One channel is then used to identify and exclude unwanted

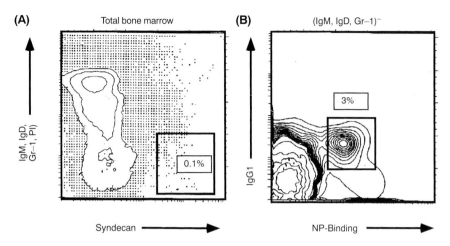

Figure 2 Identification of NP-specific antibody-forming cells in the bone marrow after 14 days of the primary immune response. (A) Cells staining for IgM, IgD and Gr-1 and propidium iodide were excluded. Antibody-forming cells were identified by their expression of syndecan. (B) This population was further partitioned into cells expressing IgG1 and able to bind the immunizing hapten NP, coupled to a fluorochrome. In the example shown, the NP-specific antibody-forming cell population represents 0.003% of nucleated bone marrow cells. Boxes indicate the criteria used for sorting cells for V_H gene sequencing.

cells. Antibodies to IgM, IgD and the myeloid-macrophage lineage marker Gr-1 are conjugated to PE, and dead cells are labeled with propidium iodide (which fluoresces in the PE channel), and all of the cells so labeled can be excluded from further analysis (a 'dump' channel). The addition of a dump channel to a single positive selection channel can decrease nonspecific contamination to less than 1 in 10^6 cells. Two further antibodies identify markers characteristic of the cells required – syndecan (a marker of antibody-forming cells, in the fluorescein channel) and surface IgG1 (in the Texas Red channel). Finally a sixth parameter is used to ensure antigen specificity, that is, the ability of the IgM⁻ IgD⁻ Gr-1⁻ syndecan⁺ IgG1⁺ cells to bind the original immunizing antigen NP bound to allophycocyanin. The probability of a nonspecifically staining cell having the same characteristics as the required cells in all six parameters is so low that populations of antigen-specific cells as rare as 1 in 200 000 cells can now be reliably and consistently sorted to >95% purity, even in the absence of pre-enrichment (see **Figure 2**).

Isolation: histology

The groups of Kelsoe, Rajewsky and others have recently isolated antigen-specific B (and germinal center T) cells by micromanipulation of single nuclei from histological sections. While this can only isolate small numbers of nuclei for PCR analysis, it does permit correlation of the molecular information obtained by PCR with the exact location of the cell in a stained histological section. This has allowed

elegant analyses to be performed of the development of the postantigenic B cell response which would not have been possible using conventional techniques.

Isolation: transgenic mice

Another approach to isolation of antigen-specific cells is the creation of mice bearing transgene-encoded antigen receptors of known specificity. Well-known examples are the mice transgenic for a T cell receptor specific for the male HY antigen, and those transgenic for immunoglobulin binding hen egg lysozyme. Thus the vast majority of the lymphocytes in such mice are of known specificity. This avoids the need to isolate rare cells, but requires careful interpretation of results since they have been obtained from mice with a markedly skewed lymphocyte repertoire.

Enrichment and isolation of T lymphocytes

T cell receptors (TCRs) recognize processed antigen (peptides) in the context of MHC. It is therefore currently not possible to isolate antigen-specific T cells by detecting antigen binding using the FACS or paramagnetic bead technology. Clearly, however, all the pre-enrichment techniques described above for B cells also apply to T cells. A traditional approach to isolating antigen-specific T cells has been to stimulate T cell populations with antigen and subsequently to clone cells activated by that antigen. The option is then available to make hybridomas from single cloned antigen-specific T cells.

A number of novel approaches have been taken to the isolation of antigen-specific T cells in the absence of an *in vitro* activation and cloning step. Monoclonal antibodies have been raised which recognize a single clonotype of TCR and which, in principle, could be used to identify antigen-specific cells in responses utilizing this clone. Some T cell responses use a limited and well-defined TCR, and detection of these cells by FACS can serve as the basis for identifying antigen-specific cells. A recent example is the identification by McHeyzer-Williams and Davis of T cells responding to pigeon cytochrome C in draining lymph nodes after immunization by staining for $V_\alpha 11 V_\beta 3$ TCR.

See also: **Cell separation techniques; Clonal selection; Flow cytometry; Fluorochrome labeling; Rosetting techniques; T cell receptor, recognition by.**

Further reading

Goodnow CC (1992) Transgenic mice and analysis of B-cell tolerance. *Annual Review of Immunology* 10: 489–518.

Hayakawa K, Ishii R, Yamasaki K, Kishimoto T and Hardy RR (1987) Isolation of high-affinity memory B cells: Phycoerythrin as a probe for antigen-binding cells. *Proceedings of the National Academy of Sciences of the USA* 84: 1379–1383.

Jacob J and Kelsoe G (1992) In situ studies of the primary immune response to (4-hydroxy-3-nitrophenyl)acetyl. II. A common clonal origin for periarteriolar lymphoid sheath-associated foci and germinal centers. *Journal of Experimental Medicine* 176: 679–687.

Kisielow P, Bluthmann H, Staerz UD, Steinmetz M and von Boehmer H (1988) Tolerance in T-cell-receptor transgenic mice involves deletion of nonmature CD4$^+$8$^+$ thymocytes. *Nature* 333: 742–746.

McHeyzer-Williams MG, Nossal GJV and Lalor PA (1991) Molecular characterization of single memory B cells. *Nature* 350: 502–505.

McHeyzer-Williams MG and Davis MM (1995) Antigen-specific development of primary and memory T cells *in vivo*. *Science* 268: 106–111.

Manz R, Assenmacher N, Pfluger E, Miltenyi S and Radbruch A (1995) Analysis and sorting of live cells according to secreted molecules, relocated to a cell surface affinity matrix. *Proceedings of the National Academy of Sciences of the USA* 92: 1921–1925.

Radbruch A and Recktenwald D (1995) Detection and isolation of rare cells. *Current Biology* 7: 270–273.

Smith KGC, Light A, Nossal GJV and Tarlinton DM (1997) The extent of affinity maturation differs between the memory and antibody-forming cell compartments in the primary immune response. *EMBO Journal* 16: 2996–3006.

ANTIGEN CLEARANCE

Antony J Cutler and **Kevin A Davies**, Rheumatology Unit, Royal Postgraduate Medical School, Hammersmith Hospital, London

The clearance of exogenous antigens constitutes one of the primary functions of the immune system. Antigens are mainly eliminated by the cells of the fixed mononuclear phagocytic system. The mechanism of removal depends on the biological and physicochemical properties of the antigen concerned, its mode of presentation to the immune system, and its ability to elicit a specific humoral or cellular immune response.

Antigen clearance by immune complex formation

Immune adherence, complement receptor type 1 and immune complex transport

Immune complexes that form within or enter the circulation may have to travel some distance around the body before reaching one of the organs of the fixed mononuclear phagocytic system. The majority of immune complexes travel through the circulation bound to receptors on the surface of circulating cells rather than free in plasma. On arrival in the fixed mononuclear phagocytic system, they are transferred from the carrier cell to fixed macrophages.

The binding of immune complexes to receptors on carrier cells was first described for complement-coated microorganisms many years ago. Pneumococci injected intravenously into immune rabbits were shown to cluster around platelets in blood taken by cardiac puncture, and it was also shown in early studies that the serum of rats which had recovered from infection with *Trypanosoma brucei* would cause blood platelets to adhere to *T. brucei in vitro*. It was subsequently found in humans and other primates that erythrocytes, rather than platelets were the main cell in blood to which opsonized trypanosomes would bind. The role of complement in mediating these binding reactions was initially suggested by Kritschewsky and Tscherikower, working in Moscow, who observed that sera inactivated at 55°C would not mediate binding. Subsequently, it was shown that erythrocyte adherence reactions could be abolished by heat treatment of sera and by dilute ammonia (inactivating C4). The observation that treatment of serum with cobra venom factor (CVF) prevented adherence reactions showed an essential role for C3. Nelson and colleagues in the 1950s rediscovered this 'immune adherence' phenomenon in studies of the reactions between human erythrocytes and specifically-opsonized treponemes and pneumococci.

Our present understanding of the immune adherence phenomenon followed the isolation by Fearon of the molecule responsible for the adherence reactions of human erythrocytes, the C3b/iC3b receptor (complement receptor type 1, CR1, CD35). This receptor bound large immune complexes and was shown to play a role in the transport of soluble immune complexes in vivo in primates. CR1 is a receptor for C3b and iC3b with diverse activities including: 1) the uptake by phagocytic cells of C3b- and iC3b-coated immune complexes and particles; 2) acting as a cofactor for factor I-mediated cleavage of C3b to iC3b and then C3dg; and 3) acting as a transport molecule for immune complexes, both soluble and particulate. Relevant to antigen clearance is the role of CR1 as a transport molecule.

There is considerable interspecies variation of the sites of expression of CR1. In humans and other primates the majority of CR1 in the circulation is located in a clustered form on erythrocytes. The actual number of CR1 molecules per erythrocyte is extremely low, varying between 50 and approximately 1000 receptors per cell in humans. This compares with 5000 to 50 000 receptors per neutrophil depending on the state of cellular activation. However, in spite of this unfavorable comparison, red cells play an important role in the binding and transport of C3b- and iC3b-coated immune complexes and particles through the circulation, partly as a result of the vast numerical majority of red cells over other cell types (approximately 1000 erythrocytes for every neutrophil) and partly as a consequence of the clustered nature of CR1 on erythrocytes which promotes very high avidity interactions with ligand, in comparison to neutrophils and lymphocytes on which the receptor is expressed as cell surface monomers. In other species a hybrid molecule sharing the activities expressed by human CR1 and CR2 is expressed on leukocytes and platelets, and no complement receptor is expressed on erythrocytes.

In vivo studies of soluble immune complex processing in animals

The major site of clearance of immune complexes is the fixed mononuclear phagocytic system. In most species, including lagomorphs, primates and rodents, the liver and spleen are the primary sites in the circulation in which tissue macrophages are located. However, pulmonary intravascular macrophages are also found in pigs, cows, sheep, goats and cats, and these have been shown to be important both in the clearance of particles and soluble immune complexes.

In lagomorphs and rodents soluble immune complexes, injected intravenously, were predominantly removed in the liver and spleen, as in humans, but the complexes were not transported in the circulation bound to erythrocytes, which in these species do not bear CR1. Platelets in these species bear C3b receptors and rapid in vivo binding of immune complexes to platelets has been observed following intravenous injection.

Evidence for the importance of antigen as well as antibody in determining the clearance kinetics of immune complexes came from studies of the clearance in mice of immune complexes containing as antigen either orosomucoid or ceruloplasmin or their desialylated derivatives. The asialo-orosomucoid-containing complexes were cleared 20-fold more rapidly than those containing the sialylated molecule, and blocking studies showed that the rapid clearance phase was mediated by a hepatocyte carbohydrate receptor.

Antigen clearance by immune complex formation in primates was first shown in a series of experiments in baboons. Large radiolabeled immune complexes comprising BSA/anti-BSA were initially employed. Following intra-aortic infusion, these complexes bound rapidly to erythrocytes, and were subsequently cleared during transit through the hepatic, but not renal circulation. The effect of complement-depletion was evaluated by CVF treatment. In decomplemented animals, the immune complexes did not bind to red cells, and were cleared more rapidly, depositing in other organs, including the kidney. It was subsequently shown that immunoglobulin A (IgA)-containing complexes, which fixed complement poorly, also failed to bind to baboon erythrocyte CR1, were cleared rapidly, and localized in other organs.

The liver and spleen are not the main sites of immune complex clearance in all species. In pigs, ruminants and cats, the anatomy of the fixed mononuclear phagocytic system is different and intravascular pulmonary macrophages play an important role in the clearance of immune complexes and also in the clearance of bacteria. Immune complex processing in pigs was associated with a fall in peripheral blood mononuclear cell numbers not seen in studies of immune complex clearance in humans.

In vivo studies of soluble immune complex processing in humans

The *in vivo* processing of exogenously administered soluble immune complexes in humans has been studied in three main model systems. These are heat-aggregated IgG, tetanus toxoid (TT)/anti-TT, and hepatitis B surface antigen (HBsAg)/anti-HBsAg immune complexes. ^{125}I-labeled heat-aggregated IgG injected intravenously into normal subjects was shown by γ scintigraphy to be cleared in the liver and spleen. The complement- and CR1-dependent natures of soluble immune complex clearance mechanisms were first studied *in vivo* using ^{125}I-labeled tetanus toxoid/anti-tetanus toxoid complexes. Either native complexes or complexes preopsonized *in vitro* with autologous serum were injected into normal volunteers, and into patients with immune complex disease or hypocomplementemia. Immune complexes bound to erythrocyte CR1 receptors in a complement-dependent manner, and CR1 number correlated with the level of uptake. Two phases of clearance were seen. In subjects with low CR1 numbers and hypocomplementemia there was a very rapid initial disappearance of immune complexes. The second phase of clearance was approximately monoexponential, and the observed elimination rate correlated inversely with CR1 numbers and the binding of immune complexes to red cells. Similar *in vivo* studies of soluble immune complex clearance have been performed using ^{123}I-labeled HBsAg/anti-HBsAg immune complexes. The fate of these immune complexes was followed by blood sampling and γ scintigraphy to define the site and kinetics of processing in normal subjects, patients with systemic lupus erythematosus (SLE) and a single patient with homozygous C2 deficiency. In normal subjects, complexes were cleared in the liver and spleen, with a median clearance half-time of 5 min. At 10 min around 40% of the injected complexes were bound in the liver in normal subjects. The majority of the injected complexes bound to red cell CR1 at 2 min. In all subjects there was a very close correlation between *in vivo* binding to red cells and CR1 number. In hypocomplementemic SLE patients there was more rapid initial immune complex uptake into the liver, but subsequent re-release of complexes back into the circulation. Defective splenic immune complex uptake was also observed in these patients, and repletion experiments in a C2-deficient subject

showed that the splenic uptake of soluble labeled HBsAg/anti-HbsAg immune complexes was entirely complement dependent. The early work of Pepys and Klaus and colleagues demonstrated that complement is critical for facilitating the localization of certain antigens to follicular dendritic cells, and for the development of a memory immune response. Defective antigen processing and splenic localization of immune complexes in hypocomplementemia may be a factor in the development of autoimmunity in SLE.

A significant criticism of all of the studies of immune complex processing described above is that they all involve large immune complex prepared *in vitro* in the absence of complement. Physiologic antigen clearance *in vivo* will frequently involve the formation of complexes between an exogenous antigen and pre-existing antibody. A number of attempts have been made to model this situation. The successive infusion of human anti-dsDNA antibodies and dsDNA into monkeys and rabbits led to rapid formation of immune complexes which bound to red cell CR1. The formation and fate of immune complex formed *in vivo* in human subjects receiving radioimmunotherapy has also been studied. Successive administration of a radiolabeled mouse antitumor antibody and a human anti-mouse antibody resulted in the formation of immune complexes comprising the two antibody species. Rapid clearance of complexes was observed with binding of approximately 10% of the complexed material to CR1. Systemic complement activation, and a 30% fall in erythrocyte CR1 numbers were observed. External γ counter monitoring indicated that clearance took place primarily in the liver.

Clearance of an autoantigen – erythrocytes

The class of antibody bound to the antigen influences the site of clearance of particulate immune complexes. This is illustrated by studies of autoimmune hemolytic anemia. Cold agglutinin disease is mediated by IgM anti-I antibodies, which stimulate efficient classical pathway activation and fixation of C4 and C3 to erythrocytes. The role of anti-I and complement in mediating cell lysis was first studied in a rabbit model. IgM cold agglutinin was injected into C3-depleted and C6-deficient rabbits. The latter developed thrombocytopenia, neutropenia and a fall in hemoglobin, with only minimal hemoglobinemia, but a sharp fall in plasma C3. Circulating red cells could be readily agglutinated with antibodies to C3, and *in vivo* immune adherence of platelets to red cells occurred. In the C3-depleted animals injection of the anti-I IgM produced no significant hematological changes. The fate of erythrocytes in cold agglutinin disease has been modeled in primates using radiolabeled cells coated with an IgM cold agglutinin. The liver was the main site of red cell uptake. Transient retention of cells in this organ occurred, thought to be mediated by reversible binding to complement receptors. In patients with cold agglutinin disease, circulating red cells are characterized by a change to a microspherocytic form, accompanied by the presence of many thousands of C3dg molecules bound per cell. Three possible conclusions may be drawn from these observations. The first is that phagocytic uptake of erythrocytes which have bound IgM and fixed C3 and C4 is very inefficient. The second is that, during the transient retention of red cells in the liver, it is probable that the C3 is catabolized to C3dg and erythrocyte shape changes occur. The third is that there is no clearance receptor in the circulation for C3dg-coated particles.

By contrast, in warm hemolytic anemia mediated by IgG, uptake of erythrocytes occurs predominantly in the spleen by Fc-dependent pathways. ^{51}Cr-labeled incompatible red cells, transfused into recipients with noncomplement fixing antibodies, were removed from the circulation monoexponentially with a half-time of 18–20 min. Splenic uptake was also monoexponential, with a similar half-time. No uptake was detectable elsewhere, notably in the liver. As the spleen exclusively removed cells, and this organ receives only a small fraction of the cardiac output, it was reasoned that the splenic extraction efficiency was very high. It was subsequently demonstrated that the site of sensitized red cell destruction was dependent on the degree of antibody coating, with more heavily coated cells being destroyed predominantly by the liver.

Radiolabeled erythrocytes, coated with IgG, have been extensively studied as a probe of the capacity of the mononuclear phagocytic system to remove particulate antigens. In humans and other species, these cells are cleared largely in the spleen. The mechanisms whereby this probe exhibits primarily splenic clearance, while cells coated with IgM and C3, and soluble immune complexes, discussed above, localize predominantly in the liver, are poorly understood. Tissue macrophages in the liver and spleen bear both Fc and complement receptors (CR1, CR3 and CR4), while follicular dendritic cells within the spleen and lymph nodes also bear CR2. The Fc receptors primarily involved in interaction with complexes or aggregated immunoglobulin are the relatively low-affinity receptors FcγRII and FcγRIII. The binding and retention of an immune complex within the liver and spleen will partly reflect the specific receptor(s) with which it interacts.

Nonclonal receptors in antigen clearance

Growing evidence suggests that initial interaction of pathogens with the innate immune system can initiate and direct the development of the adaptive immune response. As discussed, pathogens opsonized by serum proteins are phagocytosed and cleared from the body by cells of the immune system. In addition, germline-encoded receptors with the capacity directly to recognize nonopsonized microorganisms have been identified on cells of the innate immune system. Janeway proposed that such nonclonal receptors, termed 'pattern-recognition molecules', bind common constituents of pathogenic microorganisms, providing a first line of defense in the preimmune host. The wide spectrum of molecules recognized would not be expressed on the surface of normal cells, thus allowing discrimination of non-self from self. Scavenger receptors, CD36, CD14, and mannose receptors have been proposed as candidate pattern-recognition receptors.

Scavenger receptors

Initially identified for the ability to bind low-density lipoproteins (LDLs), macrophage scavenger receptors (SRs) were found to exhibit broad polyanionic ligand binding specificity, a characteristic of pattern-recognition molecules. Three independent subclasses of receptor, SR-A, B and C have been described, with expression limited to monocytes, macrophages and hemocytes. Type I and II class A SRs bind to and remove endotoxin (lipid A of LPS) from plasma. Whole gram-positive bacteria and lipoteichoic acid (LTA), a ubiquitous gram-positive cell wall constituent, were shown to be additional ligands for type I SR-As. A third recently described SR-A, 'MARCO', expressed on splenic and lymph node macrophages was also reported to interact with E. coli and Staphylococcus aureus. A primary function of SR-As on macrophages, monocytes and hemocytes appears to be the clearance of toxic shock-inducing microbial cell surface constituents and pathogenic microorganisms from the body.

The rapid phagocytosis of damaged and apoptotic cells prevents the release of noxious intracellular molecules into the body and prevents exposure of the adaptive immune system to unseen components of self. Ailing cells express surface molecular structures not characteristically found on normal cells. Growing evidence supports the proposal that SRs function in the clearance of apoptotic and damaged cells. COS cells acquired the capacity to phagocytose apoptotic cells when transfected with the class B SR CD36. CD36 has also been implicated in mediating the

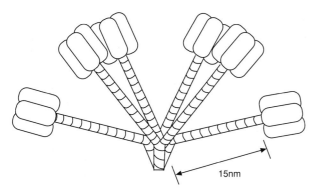

Figure 1 The structure of mannose-binding lectin.

clearance of *Plasmodium falciparum*-infected red blood cells, apoptotic neutrophils and leukocytes, and as a rhinovirus receptor. Recent reports indicated that class A SRs facilitated the uptake of

oxidatively damaged erythrocytes. The uptake of approximately 50% of apoptotic thymocytes *in vitro* was recently reported to be SR-A dependent, a finding yet to be demonstrated *in vivo*. Therefore, SRs appear to be candidate receptors for molecules expressed on damaged or apoptotic cells.

CD14

CD14 is a 55 kDa glycoprotein found as a glycosyl phosphatidylinositol (GPI)-anchored species on monocytes, macrophages and as an abundant protein in plasma. It interacts with soluble lipopolysaccharide (LPS) released from gram-negative bacteria in combination with a plasma protein, LPS-binding protein (LBP). Blockade by mAb or elimination of CD14 expression by gene knockout technology lowered the sensitivity of animals to LPS by 100–10 000 fold. CD14 exhibits many characteristics of a pattern- recognition receptor. The binding of many

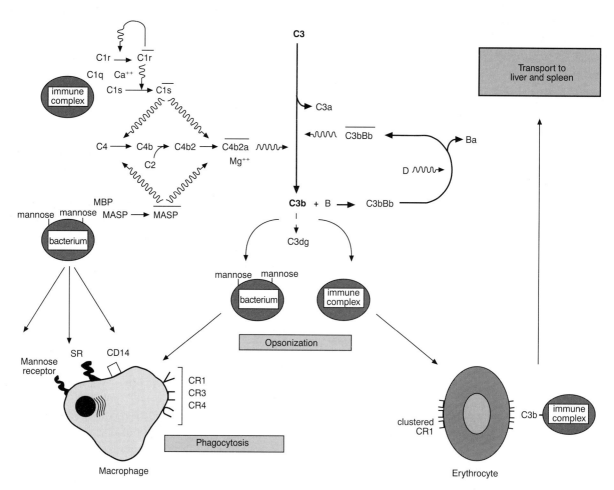

Figure 2 Adaptive and innate immune mechanisms of antigen clearance.

different components of both gram-negative and gram-positive bacteria to macrophages and monocytes has been shown to be CD14 dependent. Indeed, a nonmonocytic cell line acquired the capacity to bind intact gram-negative bacteria following transfection with the CD14 gene. Furthermore, CD14-dependent phagocytosis of whole gram-negative bacteria was recently demonstrated *in vitro*.

CD14/bacterial interaction induces activation of macrophages. The cytokines produced act to recruit lymphoid cells and possibly direct the resulting adaptive immune response. A recent report has suggested that interleukin 12 (IL-12) production following macrophage contact with LTA from gram-positive bacteria can be CD14 dependent. IL-12 is a potent stimulator of T_H1 CD4 T cells. Therefore CD14-dependent signals might exert an early influence on the nature of any resultant adaptive immune response. Furthermore, the release of the potent inflammatory cytokines tumor necrosis factor α (TNFα), IL-1β and IL-6 following bacterial activation of macrophages appears in part to be CD14 dependent. These mediators recruit phagocytic cells, principally neutrophils, to the site of infection which may enhance the clearance of antigen and influence disease progression. However, if uncontrolled, these same cytokines can contribute to the development of sepsis syndrome in humans. CD14 plays a major role in this disease as CD14-deficient mice are highly resistant to toxic shock. Numerous anti-LPS antibody reagents have been used clinically in an attempt to modify the development of septic shock in infected patients, with to date disappointing results, presumably because the cytokine-mediated physiological response responsible for the syndrome is already established in most cases by the time the therapeutic agent is administered.

Mannose receptors

The mannose receptor is a well-characterized macrophage membrane lectin expressed on tissue macrophages throughout the body but not on circulating monocytes. Evidence strongly suggests that mannose receptors play a role in the clearance of pathogens. The mannose receptor is known to bind to mannose- and fucose-containing microorganisms by carbohydrate recognition domains. Numerous reports have detailed mannose receptor recognition of yeast, bacteria and certain protozoa. Furthermore, non-phagocytic COS cells gained the capacity to bind and ingest microorganisms following transfection with mannose receptor genes, a clear indication that the mannose receptor is a professional receptor for phagocytosis. The engagement and phagocytosis of microorganisms by the macrophage mannose receptor actively stimulates the release of secretory products including IL-1, TNFα and reactive oxygen intermediates, further enhancing the clearance of antigen.

It is of interest that dendritic cells express the mannose receptor and a membrane lectin (DEC-205) with structural similarities and binding specificities to that of the macrophage mannose receptor. These receptors have a potential role in the enhancement of the capture, processing and presentation of antigen to the adaptive immune system by dendritic cells.

Mannose-binding protein/lectin (MBP/L)

MBP/L is a soluble serum protein and belongs to the collectin family of proteins, which is becoming increasingly recognized as an important component of the nonclonal immune system. MBP/L is a C-type lectin (**Figure 1**) which mediates calcium-dependent binding of certain carbohydrates. The protein recognizes mannose and N-acetylglucosamine residues on gram-positive and negative bacteria as well as yeast and certain parasites, protozoa, mycobacteria and viruses. Acting in concert with an MBP-associated serine protease (MASP), MBP/L can activate the classical complement pathway by cleaving the C4 and C2 molecules generating C4b2a complexes with C3 convertase activity. Indeed, MBP interaction with rough *E. coli* induces complement activation and bactericidal lysis. MBP can also act as an opsonin, either by inducing C3b deposition and subsequent clearance by phagocytic cells or independently by binding to C1q receptors.

The different mechanisms of antigen clearance we have described, involving both the innate and adaptive immune systems are summarized in **Figure 2**.

See also: **Bacteria, immunity to; Bacterial cell walls; Carbohydrate antigens; Chemotaxis; Complement receptors; Endotoxin (lipopolysaccharide (LPS)); Fc receptors; Immune adherence; Immune complexes; Innate immunity; Mononuclear phagocyte system; Opsonization.**

Further reading

Davies KA, Schifferli JA and Walport MJ (1994) Complement deficiency and immune complex disease. *Springer Seminars in Immunopathology* 15: 397–416.

Ezekowitz RA, Williams DJ, Koziel H *et al* (1991) Uptake of *Pneumocystis carinii* mediated by the macrophage mannose receptor. *Nature* 357: 155–158.

Fearon DT and Locksley RM (1996) The instructive role of innate immunity in the acquired immune response. *Science* 272: 50–54.

Frank MM, Lawley TJ, Hamburger MI and Brown EJ (1983) Immunoglobulin G Fc receptor-mediated clearance in autoimmune diseases. *Annals of Internal Medicine* **98**: 206–218.

Glauser MP, Tobias PS and Ulevitch RJ (1994) CD14 is a pattern recognition receptor. *Immunity* **1**: 509–516.

Janeway CA Jr (1992) The immune system evolved to discriminate infectious nonself from noninfectious self. *Immunology Today* **13**: 11–16.

Pearson AM (1996) Scavenger receptors in innate immunity. *Current Opinion in Immunology* **8**: 20–28.

Peters AM (1983) Splenic blood flow and blood cell kinetics. *Clinics in Haematology* **12**: 421–447.

Turner MW (1996) Mannose-binding lectin: the pluripotent molecule of the innate immune system. *Immunology Today* **17**: 532–540.

Walport MJ and Lachmann PJ (1987) Erythrocyte complement receptor type 1, immune complexes and the rheumatic diseases. *Arthritis and Rheumatism* **31**: 153–158.

Wright SD (1995) CD14 and innate recognition of bacteria. *Journal of Immunology* **155**: 6–8.

ANTIGEN, ENTRY INTO THE BODY

Taede Sminia and **Georg Kraal**, Department of Cell Biology, Medical Faculty of Vrije University, Amsterdam, The Netherlands

The epithelia of the skin and the mucous membranes of the respiratory, gastrointestinal and urogenital tract represent an extensive surface area. They are constantly exposed to a great variety of microorganisms and other antigenic substances. The skin constitutes a strong mechanical (keratin layer) and physiological (gland products, in particular sebum) barrier towards antigen. In the mucous membranes, which are only covered by a thin specialized epithelium, other mechanisms such as ciliary function and nonspecific and antimicrobial factors (e.g. mucin and lysozyme) are involved in preventing or combating infections. In addition, specific immune reactions play a part. The hallmark of specific mucosal immunity is the production and action of secretory immunoglobulin A (sIgA), which displays its functions at the mucosal surface ('outside' the body), and of effector T cells. Thus, the epithelia of the skin and the mucous membranes are primarily engaged in antigen exclusion; only under pathological conditions (e.g. wounding, infections) is there a 'free' exchange of antigens between the external and internal environment. Both types of epithelia possess antigen handling (uptake, processing and presentation) systems.

Antigen uptake by the skin

Several types of nonepithelial cells can be found in the skin, such as lymphocytes, macrophages and, in the epidermis, Langerhans cells. Langerhans cells are involved in the processing and presentation of antigens that enter the skin. They form an extensive network in the basal layers of the epidermis and are efficient antigen-processing cells, capable of taking up exogenous antigens by virtue of several specialized surface receptors. The display of antigenic peptides by major histocompatibility complex (MHC) molecules on the surface of the cell permits presentation to passing T cells. This process can take place in the epidermis, but Langerhans cells can also, under the influence of factors produced in the skin as a result of antigenic stimulation, leave their sentinel position in the basal layers of the epidermis. As shown in kinetic studies using fluoresceinated dyes, they can be found in lymphatic vessels and migrate into the draining lymph nodes. During this migration they show characteristic, extended membrane processes, for which they are termed veiled cells. Once they have arrived in the lymph node they localize in the paracortical areas where, as dendritic, interdigitating cells, they play a pivotal role in the primary activation of T lymphocytes. Thus Langerhans cells, veiled cells and interdigitating cells are different stages of the dendritic cell lineage (**Figure 1**). While Langerhans cells are extremely efficient at processing antigen, once they arrive in the lymph node they differentiate into potent presenting cells at the expense of their processing capacity. This is reflected in the expression of MHC molecules and accessory molecules, which increase during the differentiation into interdigitating cells.

It is only under pathological conditions that cells in the skin other than Langerhans cells are involved in antigen handling. In such cases keratinocytes can express MHC class II molecules and are able to present antigen. Studies on squamous (mucosal) epithelia have shown that antigen-processing and -presenting dendritic cells also occur in the non-keratinizing epithelium of the oral and nasal mucosa,

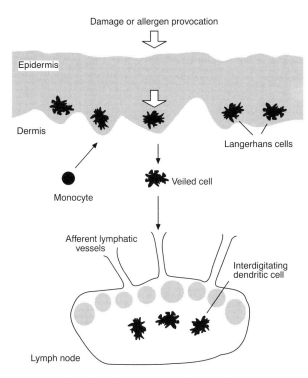

Figure 1 Migration of Langerhans cells from the epidermis into the draining lymph node. Antigens are processed in the skin by Langerhans cells, and stimuli produced by keratinocytes induce the cells to migrate to the lymph nodes. Here they differentiate into antigen-presenting dendritic cells. Langerhans cells are replaced by monocyte-derived precursors.

the trachea and bronchi, the esophagus and the tonsils, and can form comparable networks at these sites. In simple epithelial membranes, such as the epithelium lining the lung, the stomach and the gut, there is no proof for the existence of extensive networks of dendritic cells, although solitary dendritic cells have been demonstrated. In these organs other antigen-handling systems are operative (see below).

Antigen uptake by mucosal surfaces

The structure of mucosal surfaces (epithelium with tight junctions and a mucous layer) itself is an important determinant of antigen exclusion. Macromolecules are shown to transgress this barrier by endocytosis. Granulocytes, macrophages and plasma cells in the lamina propria interact with these absorbed antigens, thus forming a secondary barrier of defense against penetration of antigens into the circulation. Certain diseases or altered states (e.g. malnutrition, vitamin A deficiency, decreased gastric acidity, allergy) may allow for increased amounts of macromolecular transport. It is thought, for example, that tight junctional complexes present between the mucosal epithelial cells are broken down during malnutrition and vitamin A deficiency. In

addition to the epithelial barrier, the mucosa contains a high proportion of lymphoid cells, the so-called intraepithelial lymphocytes (IELs). These cells are mainly localized in the basal area of the epithelium and bear either cytotoxic T cell or natural killer cell markers.

In the gastrointestinal and respiratory tracts a specialized antigen transport system exists which allows for the efficient transport of macromolecules from the lumen to the organized gastrointestinal and respiratory tract lymphoid tissue (gut-associated, nose-associated and bronchus-associated lymphoid tissue – GALT, NALT and BALT, respectively). The epithelium covering these lymphoid tissues contains specialized antigen-transporting membraneous (M) cells.

Antigen uptake by the gut

The gut is constantly challenged with large doses of soluble and particulate antigens. Although it is highly antigen-impermeable, the gut possesses specialized antigen transport mechanisms in the epithelium covering the Peyer's patches (PPs), the appendix and scattered lymphoid follicles. M cells are commonly interspersed between enterocytes; their numbers vary between species. M cells are physically attached to enterocytes via conventional junctional complexes. Although the intermediate filament composition and glycosylation state of M cells is slightly different from that of the surrounding enterocytes, the junctional complexes and the presence of epithelial-specific vimentin and cytokeratin expression in M cells provide evidence for an epithelial origin of M cells, in contrast to all other types of antigen-handling cells which are bone marrow derived. M cells differ from the rest of the epithelial cells in histochemical and ultrastructural respects. At the microscope level these cells can be recognized by their close association with IELs. M cells possess large basolateral pocked domains which harbour specialized IELs. In ultrathin sections, an M cell is seen as a rim of apical cytoplasm that bridges the space between the adjacent enterocytes (**Figure 2**). This M cell forms a kind of umbrella above a space in which IELs, and sometimes macrophages and dendritic cells, are present. Antigen is absorbed at the apical side of the M cell; absorption may be aided by the lack of a 'fuzzy coat' and the absence of mucous (goblet) cells in the PP epithelium. Following absorption, antigen is endocytosed and transported into vesicles to the lateral and basal cell membrane; by fusion the antigen is released into the basolateral space, where it comes into contact with lymphocytes and macrophages or dendritic cells. Antigen is transcytosed by M cells

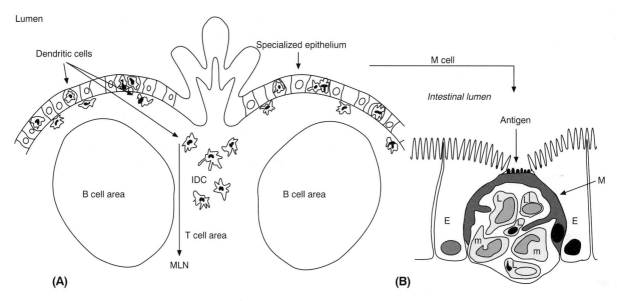

Figure 2   (A) A Peyers patch; (B) detail of an M cell within the Peyers patch epithelium. After uptake and transport by the M cell, antigen is processed by macrophages or by dendritic cells which transform into interdigitating cells (IDCs) and is then presented to lymphocytes in the T cell areas of Peyers patches and mesenteric lymph nodes (MLN). E, enterocyte; L, lymphocyte; m, macrophage/dendritic cell.

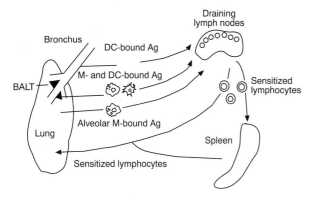

Figure 3   Interactions between the immune compartments of the lung (alveoli with alveolar macrophages, BALT macrophages (M) and dendritic cells (DC) in the lamina propria, lung-draining lymph nodes). Ag, antigen.

with little or no degradation. It is picked up by macrophages or dendritic cells and presented to local lymphocytes or transported to the interfollicular T cell areas of PPs or mesenteric lymph nodes where antigen is presented by interdigitating cells (IDCs). These antigen-presenting IDCs are derived from the dendritic cells that had picked up antigen within the epithelium.

There are indications that antigen uptake by the M cells in the PP epithelium induces a secretory IgA immune response. In addition, a systemic suppression is exerted by the generation of suppressor T cells inside PPs. It is suggested that part of the intestinal antigens – in particular soluble, low molecular weight antigens – are absorbed by the enterocytes of the villous epithelium. Enterocytes, in particular those of the small intestine, constitutively express MHC class II molecules and it has been shown that these cells are able to present antigen. There are indications that antigen presentation by enterocytes leads to the generation of T suppressor cells which are involved in systemic suppression and tolerance induction. These findings have significant implications in local gut immune responses and may explain the poorly understood phenomena of oral tolerance induction and systemic suppression.

Antigen uptake by the upper and lower respiratory tract

The nasal and oral cavities are covered by a (pseudo)stratified epithelium, that acts, due to surface protection by mucus and sIgA, as an adequate barrier. This epithelium possesses antigen-presenting Langerhans-like (dendritic) cells. Painting of this area with fluoresceinated dyes indicates that dendritic cells can bind antigen and transport it to the draining lymph nodes (in particular the cervical mandibular lymph nodes) for an adequate immune response. The epithelium of the mucosal surface of the oral and upper respiratory tract, except for the epithelium above lymphoid structures (Waldeyer's lymphoid ring), is involved in antigen exclusion rather than in antigen uptake. The epithelium above the ring of Waldeyer – in the nose the lymphoid tissue has been described under the name NALT – contains, just as BALT and GALT do, antigen-transporting M cells by which the local mucosal immune system is allowed to react adequately.

Antigen-presenting dendritic cells which constitutively express MHC class I and II molecules have also been described in the pseudostratified epithelium of the trachea and the bronchi. The majority of them are localized in the mucosa, either above or below the basement membrane, and in the lamina propria. Although there are no clear data about the migration route of these cells, there are indications that after antigen uptake dendritic cells migrate to the draining lymph nodes for antigen presentation. The lower respiratory tract, in particular the lung, is thought to be involved in antigen exclusion rather than in antigen uptake. Clearance of antigens from this part of the respiratory tract mainly depends on mucociliary activity and alveolar macrophages. The alveolar macrophage population, however, appears to be heterogeneous, both morphologically and functionally. Some macrophages act as real scavenger cells (they phagocytose and digest antigen, and leave the lungs via the mucociliary trap), some are apparently inhibitory, while others display a stimulating effect on the local immune response by presenting antigen to lymphoid cells. Most probably this latter effect is brought about by migration of alveolar macrophages from the alveoli into the lung tissue. It has been shown that antigen-laden alveolar macrophages cross the lining of the alveoli and migrate to and present antigen in the draining lymph node. In this way alveolar macrophages act as dendritic cells forming a specialized antigen handling system in the lungs. **Figure 3** illustrates the interactions between the immune 'compartments' of the lower respiratory tract. Antigens can reach the draining lymph nodes via diverse routes and there are indications that the site where antigen is taken up, processed and presented determines the outcome of the immune response.

See also: **Antigen-presenting cells; Antigen presentation via MHC class I molecules; Antigen presentation via MHC class II molecules; HLA class II; Mucosa-associated lymphoid tissue (MALT); Oral immunity; Skin, contribution to immunity.**

Further reading

Bos JD and Kapsenberg ML (1986) The skin immune system. Its cellular constituents and their interactions. *Immunology Today* 7: 235–240.

Kato T and Owen RL (1994) Structure and function of the intestinal mucosal epithelium. In: Ogra PL *et al.* (eds) *Handbook of Mucosal Immunology.* London: Academic Press.

Nicod LP (1996) Role of antigen-presenting cells in lung immunity. *European Respiratory Review* 6: 142–150.

Savidge TC (1996) The life and times of an intestinal M-cell. *Trends in Microbiology* 4: 301–306.

Sminia T (1996) A review of the mucosal immune system: development, structure and function of the upper and lower respiratory tract. *European Respiratory Review* 6: 136–141.

Van Wilsem EJG, Brevé J, Kleijmeer M and Kraal G (1994) Antigen bearing Langerhans cells in skin draining lymph nodes. Phenotype and kinetics of migration. *Journal of Investigating Dermatology* 103: 217–220.

ANTIGEN PRESENTATION VIA MHC CLASS I MOLECULES

Emil R Unanue, Department of Pathology and Center for Immunology, Washington University School of Medicine, St Louis, Missouri, USA

As described in Antigen Presentation via MHC Class II molecules, the T cell receptor for antigen, either of the CD4 or CD8 subset, must interact with peptides bound to the major histocompatibility complex (MHC) molecules. Both the class I and II MHC molecules inform the T lymphocytes of the intracellular content of peptides. CD8 T cells interact primarily with peptides bound to class I MHC molecules. As was initially shown, CD8 T cells directed to viruses can be triggered by viral peptides. Two major differences between presentation by the class I and the class II MHC molecules are, first, that the class I molecules serve to select primarily, but not exclusively, peptides derived from cytoplasmic proteins – the class II molecules select peptides from proteins found in the vesicular system; and, second, that the primary site of coupling of class I molecules with peptides is the endoplasmic reticulum (ER) – the major site of peptide coupling by class II molecules is in vesicles. In this form, the lymphocyte recognizes products from viruses and some bacteria by way of the MHC class I system, and products of intracellular bacteria or parasites (and of endocytosed/phagocytosed antigens) by the class II MHC system. Details on the biology of antigen-presenting cell (APC)–CD8 T cell interaction have been given under Antigen-Presenting Cells.

Cellular events

The interactions of CD8 T cells first involves a recognition of the peptides bound to class I MHC molecules of APC and the activation of the lymphocyte. This interaction is similar in principle to that involving CD4 T cells with APCs bearing class II MHC molecules. The interaction of the naive CD8 T cells involves the presence of adhesion molecules and the activation of the T cells by costimulatory molecules. Once activated, CD8 T cells can kill different types of target cells bearing the peptide–class I MHC complex. It is thought that very few peptide–MHC complexes are needed for recognition and cytolysis by CD8 T cells (i.e. less than a hundred per cell).

The cellular events involved in the presentation of peptides by class I MHC molecules involve four major steps. First is the catabolism of the protein antigen, which takes place in the cytoplasm. Second is the transport of peptides from cytosol to the ER, and third is the assembly of the peptide–MHC complex at that site. The last step is the transport to the cell surface.

That the cytosol is the site of generation of peptides first came from the studies on viral infections where viral peptides were found to be the main target of CD8 T cells. This recognition brought about protective antiviral immunity. Subsequently, proteins were introduced directly into the cytosol of target cells, and peptides derived from them were found to be associated with class I molecules. In contrast to presentation of peptides by class II molecules, presentation by class I molecules was not sensitive to lysosomotropic alkalinizing agents. The latter, however, was inhibited by peptide derivatives that inhibited the proteasome. Tri- or dipeptide aldehydes inhibited proteasome catabolic activity *in vitro* as well as *in vivo* generation of class I bound peptides. The proteasome is a large multicatalytic protein complex composed of multiple subunits that together form a 26S particle (~1500 kDa). The proteasome subunits are uniquely assembled into a large cylindrical structure, that is responsible for the ATP-dependent proteolysis of ubiquitin-conjugated proteins. Proteasome catabolism controls the turnover of a number of important cytosolic proteins, including transcription factors and cell cyclins. Ubiquitin is a small polypeptide that is attached by way of several enzymatic steps to lysine in cytosolic proteins. Ubiquitin marks the protein for proteasomal catabolism. Whether all peptides bound to class I MHC molecules are derived from ubiquitination of proteins is not clear at present. Peptides akin in structure to those generated by APCs have been generated *in vitro*.

Many of the class I bound-peptides are derived from proteasome catabolism. Two of the enzymes that form the proteasome are, in fact, expressed, particularly after exposure of cells to interferon γ. These two subunits, LMP2 and LMP7, influence the nature of the catabolic process favoring hydrolysis of peptides after hydrophobic or basic residues. Cells that do not express either of these two enzymes show different profiles of presentation of peptides. LMP2 and LMP7 together with the TAP transporters described below are encoded in the MHC gene locus.

Once generated, peptides cross into the lumen of the ER using the TAP molecules (Transporter Associated with antigen Processing). TAP1 and TAP2 are homologous subunits molecules belonging to the family of transporters containing ATP-binding cassettes found in both eukaryotes and prokaryotes. These two membrane-spanning molecules act in concert by binding to cytosolic peptides of a given length, usually 8–12 amino acids, and transporting them into the ER in an ATP-dependent process. The binding of peptides to TAP transporters has been studied using free microsomes or permeabilized cells. Peptides bind to TAP in an ATP-independent process, with μM affinity constants. There is some degree of specificity of peptides–TAP interaction which varies among species and different class I alleles. Interestingly, there is some concordance in peptide preference for TAP transport and that for binding to a class I MHC molecule. The importance of TAP transporters was first brought into attention by cell lines defective in class I MHC expression caused by mutations in TAP molecules. This indicated that TAP molecules were essential for the transport of peptides which is necessary for the assembly of MHC class I–peptide complex.

The site of interaction between class I MHC molecules and peptide occurs in the ER. The formation of a stable trimolecular complex (i.e. heavy chain of class I MHC molecules, β2-microglobulin and peptide) takes place following transport of peptides by the TAP molecules. Several steps have been identified in the ER leading to the formation of the peptide–class I complex. Chaperone molecules that normally are found in the ER, such as BiP and calnexin, help in the formation of a correctly folded heavy chain. BiP is a membrane of the heat shock family of proteins. Calnexin resides like BiP in the ER and participates in the correct folding of many glycoproteins. The heavy chain and the β2-microglobulin then associate physically with the TAP molecules. Involved in the final assembly are recently identified helper molecules, such as calreticulin and tapasin, which probably serve to bridge the interaction of the assembled class I molecule with TAP. Calreticulin is a resident ER chaperone molecule of 45 kDa. The precise role of tapasin is yet to be determined. The MHC class I molecules associated with TAP then establish contact with the recently transported peptides.

Once the MHC–peptide complex is assembled, it is transported to the Golgi and then rapidly to the plasma membrane. Class I MHC molecules devoid of peptide are unstable molecules at physiological temperatures. The fraction of peptide-free MHC molecules that reach the plasma membrane varies depending on the form and species of it.

Class I MHC molecules clearly present peptides derived from the cytosolic catabolism of proteins such as viral proteins or autologous cytosolic proteins. But class I molecules can also be loaded with peptides from proteins that are internalized in vesicles. These include aggregated proteins, proteins from inactivated viruses, bacteria or particulate bound proteins. The pathways that these proteins follow in the cells have been much discussed recently. It may involve transposition of the proteins from vesicles into cytosol, leading to a sequence of events similar to those described above. But an alternative pathway may result in peptides generated in endosomes or lysosomes that in some form become accessible to class I molecules. Regardless of the exact pathway of processing, the point is that proteins taken in by endocytosis/phagocytosis can also lead to peptide loading of class I molecules.

It is noteworthy that viruses have been shown to produce proteins that inhibit presentation by the class I MHC system. This may be one of the ways in which viruses try to evade the immune system. For example, adenovirus E3/19K glycoprotein binds to the class I MHC molecule directly and inhibits its transport to the cell surface. Herpes virus type I ICP47 protein binds to TAP and inhibits transport. Cytomegalovirus also produces proteins that inhibit class I presentation.

Peptide binding

Class I MHC molecules bind to peptides usually of 8 or 9 residues in length. The binding specificity is broad: many different peptides bind to a given class I MHC molecule, although there are clear preferences depending on the peptide sequence, and these vary among class I molecules of a given genotype. Binding of peptides to class I MHC molecules has been studied using purified molecules in solution but most frequently using cells deficient in TAP transporters. These cells have poor basal expression of class I MHC molecules but will increase this expression when cultured with peptides.

In common with the class II molecule, class I molecules do not discriminate between foreign and self peptides. Peptides have been extracted from class I molecules of different target cells. These peptides were isolated, fractionated, usually by reverse phase high-pressure liquid chromatography, and then sequenced. Class I molecules were found to contain hundreds of peptides, many of them representing autologous cytosolic proteins.

The biochemical basis of peptide binding has been extensively analyzed following the pioneering studies by Bjorkman and colleagues from Wiley and Strominger's laboratories. There are features in common between the structure of the binding site of both class I and II molecules. The binding site is located at the top of the molecule. It contains a cleft or 'groove', the peptide-combining site, which is made by a platform of β-pleated sheet surrounded by two helices. The groove is about 30 Å in length and 12 Å in its center. Amino acid residues responsible for the extensive allelic polymorphism contact the peptides and are responsible for their binding specificity. For class I MHC molecules, both the α_1 and α_2 domains contribute to the combining site. Each domain contributes to half the number of β sheets and one of the helices. The α_3 domain of the heavy chain and β_2-microglobulin serve to hold and give support to the top two domains.

Peptides are bound to class I molecules as a result of two sets of interaction. One is that of conserved amino acid residues of the class I heavy chain, with amino acids at each end of the peptide. Amino acid residues at the ends of the peptide form extensive hydrogen bonds with conserved residues at subsites located at each end (termed pockets A and F). The peptides bound at each end will run through the groove as an extended conformation. Depending on the particular peptide and class I molecule, the peptide may or may not bulge or kink towards the middle of it. The extensive hydrogen bonding of the main chain atoms of the peptide with the conserved residues of the MHC molecule stabilizes the complex. A second set of interactions takes place with side-chains of the peptide. These side-chain-specific interactions are responsible for the sequence binding motifs that have been identified. Particularly prominent for most class I bound peptides are interactions at the second and last residue.

Some of the residues in the peptide are solvent exposed and will establish contact with the T cell receptor. The X-ray structure of the T cell receptor bound to a class I MHC molecule shows the receptor contacting the α helices of the MHC molecules as well as the peptide. The peptide occupies about the center of the peptide-binding structure available to the T cell. The receptor is oriented slightly diagonal to the main axis of the peptide, with the CDR3 region of their α and β chains contacting the middle of the peptides and the CDR1 and CDR2 contacting the peptide ends and the MHC. Thus the structural analysis confirms the dual specificity of the T cell receptor for peptide and MHC molecules, as was predicted by the findings of MHC restriction.

See also: **Adhesion molecules; Antigen-presenting cells; Antigen presentation via MHC class II molecules; MHC peptide-binding specificity; CD8; Cytotoxic T lymphocytes; H2 class I; HLA class I; Interferon γ; MHC, evolution of; MHC, functions of; MHC restriction; T cell receptor, recognition by.**

Further reading

Bjorkman PJ, Saper MA, Samvaoui B, Bennett WS, Strominger JA and Wiley DC (1987) The foreign antigen binding site and T cell recognition regions of class I histocompatibility antigens. *Nature* **329**: 506–512.

Engelhard VH (1994) Structure of peptides associated with MHC class I molecules. *Current Opinion in Immunology* **6**: 13–23.

Sadasivan B, Lehner PJ, Ortmann B, Spies T and Cresswell P (1996) Roles for calreticulin and a novel glycoprotein tapasin, in the interaction of MHC class I molecules with TAP. *Immunity* **5**: 103–114.

Townsend ARM, McMichael AJ, Carter NP, Huddelston JA and Brownlee GG (1984) Cytotoxic T cell recognition of the influenza nucleoprotein and hemagglutinin expressed in transfected mouse L cells. *Cell* **39**: 13–25.

York IA and Rock KL (1996) Antigen processing and presentation by the class-I major histocompatibility complex. *Annual Review of Immunology* **14**: 369–396.

ANTIGEN PRESENTATION VIA MHC CLASS II MOLECULES

Emil R Unanue, Department of Pathology and Center for Immunology, Washington University School of Medicine, St Louis, Missouri, USA

During antigen presentation a protein is taken up and processed by antigen presenting cells (APCs), and is then recognized by T lymphocytes. The basic patterns of protein recognition apply to both CD4 and CD8 T lymphocytes. Both cells do not recognize protein antigens in their native state but only after the antigens are taken up by an APC. The role of the APC is to process the protein into denatured fragments or peptides that complex with their class I or II major histocompatibility complex (MHC) molecules. The peptide–MHC bimolecular complex represents the antigenic determinant recognized by the αβ T cell receptor of CD4 or CD8 T cells. However, there are notable differences between recognition by CD4 or CD8 T cells in that CD4 T cells recognize the peptides associated with class II MHC molecules, while CD8 T lymphocytes recognize the peptides associated with class I molecules. The CD4 or CD8 molecules interact with either the class II or class I molecule, respectively, favoring the interaction of the T cell receptor with the MHC–peptide complex.

Historical background

The early studies on responses to protein antigens established a relationship between the degree of uptake of the antigen by the 'reticuloendothelial system' and its immunogenicity. This was most evident in the responses to foreign albumins or gamma globulins where the antigenic preparations differed in their content of polymeric molecules. Albumin or gamma globulins with a heavy content of polymers (or aggregates) were strongly immunogenic while, in contrast, preparations made mostly of monomers were poorly immunogenic or even tolerogenic. The degree of uptake by spleen macrophages of polymers was much higher than of monomers. That these results could be ascribed to the uptake by macrophages was ascertained in experiments in which macrophages that had taken up the protein were isolated and transferred to syngeneic hosts. The recipients made strong responses to the macrophage-associated antigen. Therefore, the macrophage, a cell responsible for protein catabolism, was linked to the immunogenicity of the antigen.

An understanding of this phenomenon required the introduction of cell culture techniques. In culture, APCs were strictly required for antibody responses, or for responses by T lymphocytes to protein antigen or to plant lectins. The depletion of APCs, usually by their property of adherence to culture dishes, resulted in an absolute lack of T cell proliferation or of cytokine secretion. It was in 1973, through the studies of Shevach and Rosenthal, in the inbred guinea pig strains 2 and 13, that it became apparent that T lymphocytes not only required the presence of macrophages but of macrophages that were syngeneic. The class II MHC molecules were essential elements in this interaction. Further experiments, also first in the guinea pig, led to the concept of determinant selection: that the T cell recognizes antigenic determinants selected by APCs of a given MHC genotype. Thus, antigen presentation was related to the immune response gene phenomena reported in inbred strains of mice and guinea pigs. The 'immune response' gene experiments and those of MHC restriction and determinant selection set the base for the cellular and molecular understanding of this very early inductive phase of T cell recognition and of antigen presentation.

Antigen processing was first inferred from observations on the specificity of antigenic recognition by B and T cells. B cells usually recognize protein antigens in their native state. Much of the antibodies found in blood after immunization with a globular protein antigen bind to the protein in its three-dimensional conformation and not to the denatured protein. This indicates that the native protein antigen was selected by B cells with specific immunoglobulin (Ig) receptors for it, prior to its unfolding by the host's catabolic processes. In contrast, T cells recognize the denatured protein or fragments of it. This was first ascertained by examining a variety of T cell reactions (delayed hypersensitivity, secretion of cytokines, proliferation). In such examples there was no difference if the protein was presented in its native state, unfolded or as a peptide fragment. These phenomena are now explained by the more recent findings indicating that protein antigens are processed by APCs, that some but not all processed peptides bind to a given allelic form of class II MHC molecules, and that the MHC–peptide complex represents the antigenic determinant that engages the T cell receptor.

Cellular events

Antigen presentation takes place very rapidly upon entry of antigen into lymphoid tissues. Presumably macrophages and Langerhans-dendritic cells take up the antigen and are responsible for the early recruitment and activation of CD4 T cells. B cells that have surface immunoglobulin molecules with specificity for the antigen also participate by binding the antigen, processing it and presenting it to the CD4 T cells.

Antigen presentation comprises other events besides processing of the antigen and formation of the peptide–MHC complex. First, the antigen-specific T cells must establish physical contact with the APCs. Second, T cells require to interact with two sets of molecules provided by APCs: costimulatory

molecules, in order to enter cell cycle and to activate cytokine-specific genes; and cytokines that modulate their expression of different genes. Clearly T cell activation is a multistage process involving a 'signal 1', the engagement of the T cell receptor, and various 'signal 2'. The molecules that primarily promote physical contact are termed cell adhesion molecules (or CAMs), while those that primarily promote growth and differentiation are termed costimulators. Details of the APC–T cell interaction are given in the Antigen-Presenting Cell article which contains a table showing the molecules involved.

The interaction between the APCs and the CD4 T cells is physically manifested by close cell-to-cell contact. This intimate APC–CD4 T cell contact is favored by cell adhesion molecules the lymphocyte functional antigen-1 (LFA-1) on the T cells with its corresponding ligands, ICAM-1, ICAM-2 and ICAM-3 on the APCs; and the CD2 molecule with its counter-receptor. The functional effects of the interaction are reciprocal – macrophages will be stimulated to release cytokines, B cells will proliferate and differentiate, while the CD4 T cells will also proliferate and release cytokines.

Costimulator molecules are key in determining that the engagement of the T cell antigen receptor to the MHC–peptide complex is a productive interaction. These include the B7-1 and B7-2 molecules on APCs (and their coreceptors CD28 and CTLA-4 on T cells), and the CD40 molecule on B cells in particular, and the CD40 ligand coreceptors on T cells. These costimulator molecules may act by inducing early release by T cells of growth factors such as interleukin-2 (IL-2) and/or by regulating the expression of receptors for growth factors, and by inhibiting apoptosis. *In vitro* experiments indicate that exposure of T cells to fixed APCs (which cannot provide costimulatory molecules) results in an absent response. Such T cells, in fact, may develop an unresponsive or anergic state. Costimulatory molecules of APCs are expressed in low amounts. The representation of their expression is one component that initiates productive presentation. Finally to note is that several cytokines from APCs modulate the T cell response during antigen presentation. Included are IL-1α and β, tumor necrosis factor -α (TNFα), IL-6 and IL-12. This latter cytokine is key in the differentiation of T cells to the T_H1 subset.

Antigen processing

Processing refers biochemically to the unfolding of the proteins and/or the generation of peptides as a result of their partial proteolysis. Globular proteins in their native state do not bind to MHC class II proteins: proteins are required to have conformational flexibility in order to be able to bind and mold into the combining site of an MHC molecule. This flexibility is brought about either by denaturing the protein or partially fragmenting it to small peptides. The denatured proteins or the peptides, in contrast to the native unfolded molecule, interact and complex to the class II MHC molecules.

Processing by APCs involves several successive stages: 1) the internalization of the antigen into acid intracellular vesicles; 2) its partial proteolysis; 3) its coupling to intracellular MHC II molecules; and 4) its transport to the plasma membrane.

Protein antigens internalized by APCs are taken to deep intracellular vesicles where unfolding of the protein and/or its partial catabolism to peptides then takes place. The denatured protein and/or peptides are thus available to bind to class II MHC molecules. The most recent evidence suggests that this encounter takes place preferentially, but not exclusively, with class II MHC molecules that have been recently synthesized, and that this encounter takes place in vesicles with the properties of early lysosomes.

Class II MHC molecules assemble in the endoplasmic reticulum (ER) and traverse the Golgi vesicles associated with a nonpolymorphic polypeptide, the invariant chain. Invariant chain and the αβ dimers of class II molecules form a complex that is transported to vesicles outside the Golgi vesicles. The estimate is that a trimerized invariant chain binds to three class II molecules (i.e. three αβ dimers), thus forming a nonameric complex. The invariant chain has signal sequences in its cytosolic portion that serves to guide the complex out of the Golgi into late vesicles. The invariant chain also has the important property of covering the combining site of the class II molecule during its travel through the ER. Thus, during their sojourn through the ER and Golgi the class II molecules have less opportunity to interact with peptides derived from catabolism of self peptides. The invariant chain has different isoforms that may be involved in different ways in the fate of the complex.

Once the invariant chain–αβ complex leaves the Golgi, the invariant chain is catabolized in a proteolysis rich, acidic compartment; however, a segment of the invariant chain comprising residues 81–104 remains associated with the combining site. This peptide, termed CLIP, must be removed to make the αβ dimer competent to bind foreign (or autologous) peptides. A secondary auxiliary molecule (HLA-DM in humans or H2-M in the mouse) then associates with the αβ dimer containing the CLIP peptide. This association leads to the removal of CLIP. How this protein associates with the αβ dimer, and the basic interaction that favors a fast off-rate of the bound peptide still requires analysis. As the CLIP peptide is removed, high-affinity binding peptides found in the vesicular 'loading' compartment then bind. Thus, there is an exchange of peptides, with CLIP leaving, and strong binding peptides occupying, the class II MHC molecule. Class II molecules with bound peptides are then transported to the plasma membrane, the site of interaction with the T cell and its receptor.

Many of the class II MHC bound peptides have a very slow off-rate and, therefore, remain bound during their entire span in the APC. In fact the half-life of the class II MHC molecules reflects their content of different affinity peptides. Some of the class II molecules bearing weak binding peptides can exchange peptides in endosomal vesicles or at the plasma membrane.

Thus, a scenario that is favored is that an internalized protein (i.e. a soluble protein or a microbe containing a large array of proteins) is taken to a deep lysosomal compartment, and it is there that peptides are generated from partial proteolysis. Nascent class II molecules meet with these peptides and an effective peptide exchange reaction takes place, as described above. Peptides that are bound, i.e. 'selected', are protected from further proteolysis. Class II molecules are, therefore, peptide-binding molecules that protect from extensive catabolism. **Figure 1** illustrates the antigen-processing events depicted using the protein lysozyme.

The nature of the proteolytic event that results in the degradation of the invariant chain and of the protein antigen is still under much consideration. Most likely, cathepsins are involved in the degradation. A strong case has been made for the involvement of cathepsin S in invariant chain degradation. Concerning the protein antigen, one way of viewing the processing event is to postulate the unfolding of the protein, after which the denatured unfolded polypeptide binds to class II molecules through the segment displaying sequences that favor high binding to MHC molecules. Once bound, the portion of the unfolded peptide that spills out of the peptide-combining site is catabolized, perhaps by amino- and carboxypeptidases, up to the limit of the combining site.

There has been much discussion about the nature of the MHC–peptide loading compartment (called MIIC). An organelle containing lysosomal proteins and class II MHC molecules, and which receives internalized protein late, has been identified by electron microscopy, and also defined by subcellular fractionation. Thus, for many protein antigens this late vesicular and lysosomal-like compartment may be the site of loading to nascent class II molecules. However, it is also clear that peptides can bind class

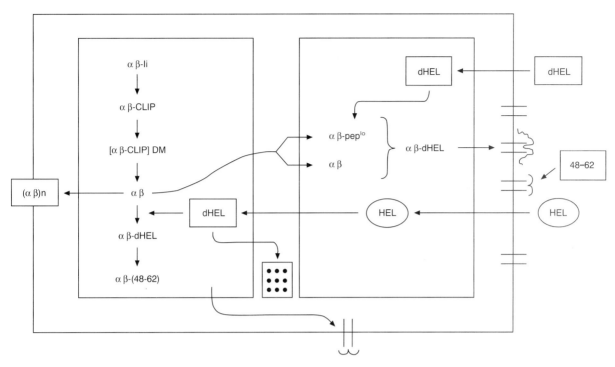

Figure 1   Processing of the protein hen egg white lysozyme (HEL). There are two functional compartments in APCs, depicted as the two squares: a deep compartment (left) and a recycling or endosomal compartment (right). HEL is a globular protein that requires denaturation by reduction of its four disulfide bonds (dHEL). This takes place after HEL reaches the deep compartment. The dHEL binds to the αβ dimers of class II MHC, after their exit for ER–Golgi. αβ dimers exit bound to the invariant chain (αβ-Ii). The invariant chain is degraded leaving CLIP peptides bound to it. The HLA-DM molecules remove CLIP making the αβ dimers competent to bind dHEL. The dHEL bound to class II molecules is trimmed by amino- and carboxypeptidases to a peptide of 15–16 residues. The peptide is transported to plasma membrane. The dHEL not bound is catabolized to amino acids (box with dots). If APCs are given HEL already denatured, it can bind to αβ dimers in endosomes where peptide exchange takes place. Peptides can also bind directly to some peptide-free αβ dimers at the cell surface.

II molecules in early endosomes or, if available, at the plasma membrane. The nature of the protein, and the ease by which the protein is subjected to denaturation and partial proteolysis, clearly are factors in determining the site of loading. Autologous proteins, which are rapidly secreted from APCs, can also load into class II molecules during their short travel through APCs. This is an indication that there is some degree of proteolysis taking place during secretion and that the loading process is very effective. Lastly, peptides derived from cytosolic molecules have been found bound to class II molecules, an indication that cytoplasmic-derived peptides are also accessible to the class II MHC system. However, whenever a comparison has been made, peptides derived from cytosolic proteins are less effective than those found in vesicular proteins in reaching the class II MHC system.

Binding properties of class II MHC molecules

The binding properties of class II MHC molecules can be studied using purified molecules, usually in detergent solutions, or directly in the APC. Purified class II molecules bind peptides in a homogeneous saturable process with binding affinity constants in the 10^{-6}–10^{-8} M range. The rate of association of peptide with the MHC molecule is slow, but once the peptide is bound it can form a very stable and long-lived complex. The complex of MHC with peptide can be assembled and isolated in free solution, and can directly trigger CD4 T cells these experiments have been done with T cell hybridomas that are triggered by the engagement of their receptor without the need of costimulatory molecules. Binding of peptides to class II MHC molecules can also be directly determined on APCs by using peptides tagged with a radioactive or fluorescent label, or with photoreactivatable probes. In live APCs the proportion of class II MHC molecules that need to be occupied by a given peptide to trigger T cells is small, usually about 0.1% of total class II MHC (about 10^2 in the APCs studied so far).

The binding of peptides takes place in the antigen-binding site of the MHC molecules, which was defined through structural studies of purified complexes pioneered in the laboratory of Don Wiley and

Jack Strominger. The main architectural features are found for both the combining site of class I and II MHC molecules. For class II molecules the binding site is at the top of the molecule and consists of a groove or pocket made up of a platform of β-pleated sheets, derived from the α_1 and β_1 domains, surrounded by α helices, also made from portions of α_1 and β_1 domains. Most of the amino acid residues responsible for allelic polymorphism, found in the α_1 and β_1 domains, are located in the helices and in the platform. These residues are believed to be involved in interaction (charge or ionic, or hydrophobic) with residues in the processed protein antigen.

Peptides are found in an extended conformation with a slight twist typical of polyproline II-like conformations. Two types of interaction determine the affinity and specificity of peptide binding: those between the peptide backbone and conserved residues of the MHC molecules; and those between side-chains of critical amino acids with sites of the MHC molecule. The first set of interactions include hydrogen bonds between the conserved residues in the MHC molecules and the peptide backbone. This extensive array of hydrogen bonds contributes to the affinity of the peptide and is dependent on the length of the peptides. In contrast, side-chains of amino acids interacting with critical areas in the combining site give specificity to the interaction. The sites or areas have preference for different amino acids side-chains. The amino acid residues of the MHC pockets characterize a given MHC genotype.

Binding kinetics and competition experiments indicate the single peptide-binding site can be occupied by peptides of 8–30 amino acid residues. The specificity of peptide binding is broad, assuring that many different peptide structures can be recognized by the T cell system. Several peptide motifs that favor binding to class II MHC molecules have been identified. Not all of these motifs so far identified predict all T cell determinants. A peptide contains amino acid residues that contact the MHC binding site and other residues that contact the T cell receptor. The contact residues for MHC and T cell receptors are intermingled in the peptide. Usually 1–3 residues are solvent exposed and serve primarily to contact the T cell receptor. To note is that although there is broad binding specificity, not all peptides bind to a given allelic form of an MHC class II protein. The weak binding, or lack of it, results, as expected, in very poor activation of the specific T cells. It is the weak or poor binding of peptides to a given allelic variant of class II MHC molecules that explains many of the immune response gene effects described from early studies on inbred mice.

An important observation first made with lysozyme peptides is that the class II MHC binding site does not discriminate between self and nonself peptides. Self peptides have been shown to bind or not to bind, depending on their structural features. Hence, self and nonself peptides behave in the same way insofar as their binding properties to a given class II protein. Moreover, it has now been shown that APCs isolated from different tissues, including the thymus, contain self peptides associated with them. Indeed, the number of different self peptides isolated from class II molecules is in the hundreds. Some peptides derive from uptake of extracellular molecules but the majority derive from membrane proteins of the vesicular system.

The binding of self peptides to MHC molecules results in three potentially important effects: 1) on the thymus stromal cells it may be instrumental in causing the death or negative selection of maturing T cells; 2) on APCs of peripheral lymphoid tissues, self peptides may compete for the binding of foreign peptides to MHC class II molecules; and 3) such MHC–peptide complexes on APCs can potentially trigger autoreactive T cells, to cause autoimmunity. Of course, reactivity to foreign or self antigens comprises multiple steps and factors of which the generation of the MHC–peptide complex is only one.

See also: **Antigen-presenting cells; Antigen presentation via MHC class I molecules; Antigens; Antigens, T dependent and independent; B lymphocyte, antigen processing and presentation; CD28; CD40 and its ligand; B7 (CD80 & CD86); Dendritic cells; H2 class I; H2 class II; HLA class I; HLA class II; Invariant chain (Ii); MHC, functions of; MHC restriction; Phagocytosis; Second signals for lymphocyte activation.**

Further reading

Brown JH, Jardetsky TS, Gorga JC, Stern LJ, Urban RG, Strominger JL and Wiley DC (1993) Three-dimensional structure of the human class II histocompatibility antigen HLA-DR1. *Nature* **364**: 33–39.

Cresswell P (1994) Assembly, transport and function of MHC class II molecules. *Annual Review of Immunology* **12**: 259–293.

Nelson CA, Viner NJ and Unanue ER (1996) Appreciating the complexity of MHC class II peptide binding: lysozyme peptide and I-A^k. *Immunological Reviews* **151**: 81–105.

Pieters J (1997) MHC class II restricted antigen presentation. *Current Opinion in Immunology* **9**: 89–96.

ANTIGENIC VARIATION

Janice E Clements and **Susan L Gdovin**, Departments of Comparative Medicine and Molecular
Biology and Genetics, Johns Hopkins University School of Medicine, Baltimore, MD, USA

Antigenic variation is a well-established mechanism among infectious organisms for escaping the immune response of the host. It is a Darwinian process in which alteration of the antigenicity of surface molecules enables infectious organisms to escape immune elimination. These alterations are the result of random mutations, and organisms that acquire surface changes that allow them to escape from host recognition will have a selective advantage and predominate. Antigenic variation is the principal means of persistence of protozoans such as African trypanosomes, *Plasmodium* spp., *Giardia* and several species of bacteria, including *Neisseria gonorrhoeae* and *Borrelia* spp., in an infected individual. This phenomenon also allows for the persistence of animal viruses. The classic example of antigenic variation of viruses is observed among the influenza A viruses. Influenza viruses do not establish persistent infections in individuals, but alterations in the surface glycoproteins as the virus spreads through a population allow for reinfection of individuals and therefore the persistence of influenza viruses in a population and worldwide.

Antigenic variation of viruses within an individual host occurs with the lentiviruses. Lentiviruses include the human immunodeficiency virus (HIV) and an increasing number of animal viruses which cause persistent infections with chronic disease. Antigenic variation has also been observed for the enteroviruses (poliovirus, Coxsackie virus, echoviruses) and for the common cold viruses (rhinovirus types 22 and 51). Even monotypic viruses, such as measles, exhibit genetic diversity in surface proteins. More detailed descriptions of the molecular mechanisms of antigenic variation of trypanosomes (an example of protozoans), influenza A viruses and lentiviruses are provided here.

Differential gene expression in trypanosomes results in antigenic variation

Trypanosomes are eukaryotic flagellates that cause sleeping sickness in humans and nagana in cattle. These protozoan parasites are transmitted by insects to the bloodstream of the host. The trypanosome has a number of developmental stages. The bloodstream-stage trypanosomes are covered with a dense coat composed of a single type of glycoprotein, the vari-

ant surface glycoprotein (VSG). Antigenic variation in trypanosomes occurs through the sequential expression of different VSG genes. During the course of infection, trypanosomes with serologically unrelated coats are periodically generated, thus allowing evasion of the humoral immune response produced against previously circulating coat VSG.

Each trypanosome has a large repertoire of different VSG genes (100–1000, depending on the species). The switch from one coat to another occurs at a low frequency (10^{-6} or 10^{-7} per cell division) and appears to be independent of immune selection. Only a single VSG gene is usually expressed at one time. The active VSG gene is invariably in a telomeric location in a VSG expression site. Although there are multiple expression sites, located on a few specific chromosomes, only one site is active at any given time. Nonexpressed or silent VSG genes are clustered at internal positions on the chromosomes and are also found at many of the chromosome telomeres. Activation of specific VSG genes occurs by two genetic mechanisms. The first is gene replacement, by duplicative transposition of a new VSG gene into a transcriptionally active expression site. This is thought to occur via homologous recombination. Selection of VSG genes is dictated by the degree of homology between two loci, which may explain the loosely defined order of appearance of trypanosome variants during an infection. The second mechanism for activation of VSG genes is the activation of an alternative expression site. The promoters of expression sites are negatively controlled, and transcriptional activation is thought to be mutually exclusive. Transcription of VSG genes is insensitive to α-amanitin, but the polymerase involved is not known. There is evidence that the presence of an unusual DNA base, pdJ, may be involved in the inactivation of expression sites.

Despite the enormous VSG gene pool available, the reproduction of variant antigenic types is limited in the trypanosome: this prevents the exhaustion of the surface glycoprotein repertoire at an early stage of disease. Antigenic variation also occurs in trypanosome surface receptors involved in food uptake. These variants are limited in number, making these proteins a better target for vaccine development. The bacterium *Borrelia hermsii*, which causes relapsing fever, uses DNA rearrangement mechanisms for producing antigenic variants similar to those seen with trypanosomes.

Antigenic 'shift' and 'drift' in the influenza viruses

Among the influenza A viruses, both of the surface glycoproteins (the hemagglutinin and neuraminidase) undergo two types of variation: antigenic drift and antigenic shift. Antigenic drift involves minor changes in the antigenicity of the surface protein and is thought to be responsible for the persistence of the virus in a susceptible population. Antigenic shift involves major genetic changes that are responsible for the development of the 'new' viruses in the host species. Antibodies to the hemagglutinin neutralize the infectivity of the virus, and variation in this protein is mainly responsible for recurring outbreaks of influenza and for the failure to produce an effective vaccine. Extremely high concentrations of antibodies to the neuraminidase can also neutralize the infectivity of influenza viruses. This neutralization may occur by a saturation of antibody-binding sites on the neuraminidase resulting in steric inhibition of the hemagglutinin.

Antigenic drift of either surface molecule occurs by the accumulation of point mutations in the respective gene; however, single point mutations appear to have little effect on the antigenic properties of the proteins. Nucleotide sequence analyses of epidemiologically significant strains suggest that single amino acid changes in two or more epitopes of the hemagglutinin are necessary for a significant antigenic change. The most likely mechanism for mutations in multiple epitopes is single mutations occurring sequentially during the spread of the virus from person to person. Strains with single mutations in one epitope must escape the immunity of an individual, possibly because the humoral immune response in humans is heterogeneous and the limited antibody repertoire against influenza virus in children probably permits such selection.

Antigenic shift involves replacement of at least the hemagglutinin gene via genetic exchange with an avian or animal virus. The new shift variant can cause a pandemic, as no neutralizing antibodies are present in the human population. There is evidence for genetic reassortment between human and animal influenza viruses *in vivo*. A shift virus which emerged in 1968 contained a human neuraminidase gene, but the hemagglutinin was 98% homologous at the nucleotide level with an avian influenza A virus. It is believed that new pandemic strains are produced by co-infection of pigs with avian and human influenza virus strains.

Antigenic variation in lentiviruses

Antigenic variation in an individual host occurs with animal lentiviruses. The first report of antigenic drift was in equine infectious anemia virus (EIAV). Horses infected with EIAV develop sequential episodes of acute hemolytic crises during persistent infections. Sera taken at various times from an infected animal were able to neutralize isolates from previous clinical episodes, but failed to neutralize subsequent viral isolates. Visna virus in sheep also causes persistent infection, although episodic disease is not observed. Like EIAV, antigenic variants of visna virus emerge over time in persistently infected sheep. This antigenic drift can be duplicated in cell culture using plaque-purified virus and monospecific antibody for the selection of variants.

The molecular mechanism of antigenic variation in the lentiviruses is the accumulation of single nucleotide changes in the surface glycoprotein genes. In visna virus the accumulation of point mutations appears to be progressive. Antigenic variant viruses sequentially isolated from a single animal contained the same point mutations when compared to the input virus. Antibodies produced by the animal to a particular variant recognized all changes found in the other preceding variants, supporting the cumulative and progressive nature of antigenic drift in visna virus.

In both visna virus and EIAV, point mutations are seen throughout the surface glycoprotein gene, but hypervariable regions have been identified. Antigenic variation in visna virus can be detected 1 year after infection and continues throughout the infection. In contrast, antigenic drift in EIAV occurs more rapidly, in the first weeks after infection, and continues until the host develops a broad antibody response against the virus. Distinct EIAV variants can be associated with each clinical episode. However, unlike visna virus, no accumulation of point mutations has been observed; variation is more random.

Extensive genetic heterogeneity of HIV isolates from infected individuals has also been observed, and may provide evidence for antigenic drift *in vivo*. Genetically diverse viruses, or 'quasispecies', are produced in infected individuals due to the infidelity of the viral reverse transcriptase. Recent studies have shown that the evolutionary dynamics displayed by these heterogeneous virus populations *in vivo* is consistent with adaptive evolution. Also, antigenic variants of HIV have been isolated in cell culture using a molecularly cloned virus and sera from an immune individual. Host neutralizing antibodies appear to be at least one of the selective pressures responsible for the emergence of antigenic variants. However, other selective forces, such as cell-mediated immune responses, may also play a role in the production of variants. The role of these antigenically-distinct viruses in the pathogenesis of HIV is unclear.

Antigenic variation and immunity

Antigenic variation of protozoans, bacteria and animal viruses provides a mechanism for persistence of the organism in its host, but makes immunological control difficult. The strategy used for the development of influenza A virus vaccines has been to identify the circulating strains early in the influenza season and to rapidly produce a vaccine against the predominant strains. In lentiviruses this strategy cannot be used because mutation and selection occur in a single infected host. Thus a wide repertoire of neutralizing epitopes must be included in a vaccine to prevent the evolution of lentiviruses that can evade the host immune response.

See also: **Influenza virus (*orthomyxovirus*), infection and immunity; Parasites, immunity to; Rhabdovirus, infection and immunity; Trypanosomiasis, African; Vaccines; Viruses, immunity to.**

Further reading

Bellini WJ, Rota JS and Rota PA (1994) Virology of measles virus. *Journal of Infectious Diseases* 170 (suppl 1): S15–S23.

Borst P, Gommers-Ampt JH, Ligtenberg MJL *et al* (1993) Control of antigenic variation in African trypanosomes. In: *Cold Spring Harbor Symposia on Quantitative Biology* LVIII: 105–114.

Borst P, Bitter W, McCulloch R, van Leeuwen F and Rud-

enko G (1995) Antigenic variation in malaria. *Cell* 82: 1–4.

Brunham RC, Plummer FA and Stephens RS (1993) Bacterial antigenic variation, host immune response, and pathogen–host coevolution. *Infection and Immunity* 61: 2273–2276.

Burns DPW and Desrosiers RC (1994) Envelope sequence variation, neutralizing antibodies, and primate lentivirus persistence. *Current Topics in Microbiology and Immunology* 188: 185–219.

Clements JE, Gdovin SL, Montelaro RC and Narayan O (1988) Antigenic variation in lentiviral disease. *Annual Review of Immunology* 6: 139–158.

Donelson JE (1995) Mechanisms of antigenic variation in *Borrelia hermssi* and African trypanosomes. *Journal of Biological Chemistry* 270: 7783–7786.

Murphy BR and Webser RG (1990) Orthomyxoviruses. In: Fields BN and Knipe DM (eds) *Virology*, pp 1091–1152. New York: Raven Press.

Nash TE (1989) Antigenic variation in *Giardia lamblia*. *Experimental Parasitology* 68: 238–241.

Pays E, Vanhamme L and Berberof M (1994) Genetic controls for the expression of surface antigens in African trypanosomes. *Annual Review of Microbiology* 48: 25–52.

Saunder JR, O'Sullivan H, Wakeman J *et al* (1993) Flagella and pili as antigenically variable structures on the bacterial surface. *Journal of Applied Bacteriology Symposium Supplement* 74: 33S–42S.

Scholtissek C (1994) Source of influenza pandemics. *European Journal of Epidemiology* 10: 455–458.

Wiley DC and Skekel JJ (1987) The structure and function of the hemagglutinin membrane glycoprotein of influenza virus. *Annual Review of Biochemistry* 56: 373–378.

Wolinsky SM, Korber BTM, Neumann AU *et al* (1996) Adaptive evolution of human immunodeficiency virus-type 1 during the natural course of infection. *Science* 272: 537–542.

ANTIGENS

Michael Sela, Department of Chemical Immunology, The Weizmann Institute of Science, Rehovot, Israel

Antigen is any substance (molecule) that provokes the production of specific antibody or immunocyte (immune cell), or that interacts specifically with these products of the immune response, when penetrating the body of a vertebrate. The first part of this definition, namely, the capacity to provoke an immune response is also called immunogenicity and the substance provoking such a response is called immunogen. The second part, the specific interaction, is called antigenic specificity. A chemical or physical change in a molecule that will result in an increased immune response will increase its immunogenicity, even though it may or may not change its antigenic specificity. It is the antigenic determinant (also called epitope) which is responsible for the specificity.

The ability to mount an immune response depends ultimately upon the interplay between the chemistry of the antigen and the physiologic state of the host. Thus, immunogenicity is operationally dependent on the experimental conditions of the system, including parameters such as the antigen, the mode of immunization, the organism being immunized and its genetic background, as well as the sensitivity of methods used to detect a response.

It is worth stressing that we are using the word antigen sometimes for a molecule, sometimes for a virus or a bacterium, and sometimes for an organ or a tissue, but the antibodies have a *combining site* (also defined as *paratope*), with all its distinctive features, of a more or less similar size and cavity. These combining sites are not complementary to a complete bacterium or a complete heart, but they are always complementary to a unique antigenic determinant which is of a limited molecular size.

Among the immunocytes we recognize B cells (the precursors of antibody-producing cells) and T cells. The combining sites on B cells are essentially the same as those of the antibodies which their progeny will produce. On the other hand, the combining sites of the T cell receptors are distinct from those of antibodies. What is characteristic of the T cell receptors is that they recognize generally the antigen after it has been processed within a cell and presented to the T cell receptor in conjunction with either class I or class II antigens. These are antigens defined by immune response genes which are part of the major histocompatibility complex (MHC). Most antigens are thymus dependent, which means that they need to be recognized in the above manner. A minority of antigens, called thymus independent, do not need the recognition by T cells, and may lead to efficient antibody formation after interacting exclusively with B cells.

The notion of antigen includes also the capacity to induce specific immunological tolerance, or anergy, defined as a state of T lymphocyte unresponsiveness characterized by the absence of proliferation (human T cell clonal anergy).

The recognition of antigens by the T cell compartment of the immune system is a multistep process culminating in the formation of a ternary complex between the T cell receptor for antigen (TCR) and the binary complex of class I or II MHC encoded molecules, with short peptides derived from the antigen. Thus, the specificity of the TCR is for a *neo*antigen determinant composed of both, the genetically restricting MHC molecule and the bound peptide. The recognition process may therefore be considered as consisting of two distinct phases, the first in which peptides are produced and get bound to the MHC encoded proteins, and the second where the TCR binds this binary complex. Since MHC encoded molecules may bind peptides derived from both self and nonself proteins, the fundamental implication of the above is the need for a selection process where cells with TCR that bind self-peptides are eliminated during the development process in the thymus, yielding a repertoire of mature T cells that recognize MHC complexes with nonself peptides.

The antigenic determinants leading to the formation of antibodies by B cells may be parts of proteins, nucleic acids, polysaccharides, lipids or glycolipids, or other biological macromolecules. Very often they have unique steric conformations and are part of a native structure. We have thus to distinguish between sequential determinants (epitopes) and conformation-dependent (or conformational) determinants (epitopes). The operational definition holds that if antibodies against, e.g. a protein, react well with a tetra-, penta- or hexapeptide derived from that protein, then the antibody is against a sequential determinant. The antibody, on the other hand, is against a conformation-dependent determinant if it is made against a juxtaposition of atoms in space which results from a unique conformation of the macromolecule, and any peptide derived from such a protein will not be able, after denaturation, to react with the antibody.

If is of interest that for most globular proteins and native nucleic acids, almost all the antigenic determinants are conformation dependent, whereas for most polysaccharides, fibrilar proteins such as silk fibroin, and single-stranded nucleic acids, the determinants are sequential. The use of homopolymers of amino acids or sugars, and of peptidyl proteins as antigens has established that the sequential determinant is composed of 4–6 amino acid or sugar residues which contribute unequally to binding with the antibody combining site.

Not all the antigenic determinants express themselves all the time: some are more immunopotent than others. Some do not express themselves at all under a certain set of conditions, and we call them immunosilent, even though under other conditions they may provoke an efficient immune response. Thus a determinant may be immunosilent within a complete macromolecule, but may be quite immunopotent when a segment of that macromolecule on which it is present is used for immunization. Situations are also known where a determinant is immunosilent but becomes immunopotent in animals made tolerant to other parts of the immunogenic macromolecule of which the determinant discussed forms a part. We may thus define immunopotency as the capacity of a region of an antigen molecule to serve as an antigenic determinant and induce the formation of a specific immune response.

The term hapten, in its strictest sense, designates any substance, large or small, which does not elicit an immune response by itself but can be shown to react with antibody provoked by immunization with a complete immunogen of which the hapten formed a part. In practice, most haptens investigated are small chemical substances, in most cases of a size definitely smaller than that of a complete antigenic determinant. When attached to a protein, haptens such as dinitrophenyl or penicilloyl might be defined as immunodominant parts of an antigenic determinant (an epitope). In studies of determinants of polysaccharide or polypeptide nature, it is of interest to establish which is their immunodominant portion.

Generally an organism distinguishes between self (material which is its own) and nonself (any foreign material). The immune system of an organism reacts against any foreign compound (antigen), and is tolerant (unable to react) towards its own body components, which may be good immunogens in other organisms. This self-tolerance is acquired during fetal or neonatal development, and the immune system can be made tolerant even to foreign material or tissue introduced during this period. Such material, which can induce immunological tolerance or unresponsiveness, is called a tolerogen.

Another phenomenon which should be mentioned here is antigenic competition. This may occur between different antigens (intermolecular), or between different specificity determinants on the same antigen (intramolecular), in which case we define it as competition between antigenic determinants. The existence of this phenomenon may account for some determinants being immunosilent under certain circumstances. Antigenic competition may be defined as the inhibition of the immune response to one antigen or determinant by the administration of another antigen or determinant.

Molecules as antigens

The two types of natural macromolecules most investigated as antigens are proteins and polysaccharides. These also include glycoproteins, nucleoproteins, lipoproteins, etc., as well as peptidoglycans, glycolipids and other conjugates. Nucleic acids are also antigenic. Lipids are poor immunogens, but antibodies against them can be obtained, and liposomes play a role here, as they do in enhancing the immunogenicity of various other antigens. Synthetic antigens, especially synthetic polypeptides, have played an important role in the elucidation of the molecular basis of antigenicity and many other immunological phenomena, and they will be discussed here in more detail below. Other synthetic polymers have also been shown to be immunogenic, e.g. polyvinylpyrrolidone.

All proteins are probably immunogenic, although individual proteins differ markedly in their immunogenicities. Denatured proteins are often less immunogenic than the corresponding native proteins. Self-aggregation of a protein is usually associated with a negligible change in its antigenic specificity, but with a considerable increase in immunogenicity. Like other antigens, proteins possess a continuous spectrum of antigenic determinants that correspond to discrete portions of the surface structure and that are preferentially located in those regions most exposed to the external environment. The relationship between structure and antigenicity is, however, more complex for globular proteins than for other antigens, in that it depends to a very large extent upon the overall conformation of the molecule. The exploration of antigenic regions on the surface of proteins has become easier with the advent of monoclonal antibodies and rapid methods of peptide synthesis. The antigenic sites may be described as surface domains made up from amino acid side chains which may be distant in sequence but close in space (conformation-dependent determinants). Such domains are probably overlapping and cover most of the protein surface. On the other hand, fibrous proteins possess sequential determinants, of three to six amino acid residues.

Special attention has been paid by immunologists to those proteins which possess distinct and easy-to-measure biological properties. These include enzymes and enzyme inhibitors, protein hormones, toxins, antibodies (i.e. immunoglobulins as antigens), as well as proteins composing viral coats. Immunologic studies have also been successful in following the evolution of proteins.

The other class of substances that was readily shown to be antigenic comprises the polysaccharides. Although complex, they nevertheless provide antigens of relatively simple structure by which many of the detailed structural aspects of antigenic determinants and antibody combining sites have been worked out. Microbial polysaccharides are located on the cell surface and are, therefore, of importance in recognition and immune responses of a higher organism to microbial infection. The simplest polysaccharide antigens are dextran, a polymer composed entirely of glucose, and levan, composed entirely of fructose. Another important group contains the capsular polysaccharides of pneumococci. Complex lipopolysaccharide antigens, endotoxins, are found in a large variety of microorganisms, notably in gram-negative Enterobacteriaceae, such as *Salmonella* and *Shigella*. The polysaccharide determinants are predominantly sequential, consisting usually of 4–6 sugars, but some antibodies may have combining sites which are smaller.

Blood group antigens are the other important category of polysaccharide antigens. They are gene-dependent structures expressing the individuality of cell surfaces, body fluids and secretions. Chemical characterization of blood group structures has been fully developed. The chemical structures of ABH and Lewis antigens have been elucidated using water-soluble blood group substances isolated from secretions (ovarian cyst mucin, gastric mucin). These structures, when on erythrocytes and other cells, are part of more complete glycolipid or glycoprotein antigens.

Antigenic functions of nucleic acids were only recognized much later than those of proteins or poly-saccharides. No immunogen has yet been prepared that would be capable of inducing in experimental animals antibodies to double-stranded DNA. Such antibodies are, nevertheless, available in humans suffering from systemic lupus erythematosus, as well as in mice and dogs with similar diseases. Their sera usually also contain antibodies to single-stranded, denatured DNA, as well as to RNA, double-stranded RNA, histone and nucleoprotein. It is possible to induce antibodies to single-stranded RNA or DNA, either by immunizing these, complexed with a macromolecule of opposite electrical charge, or by preparing conjugates of nucleosides, nucleotides or oligonucleotides, with proteins or synthetic poly-peptide antigens, and using them as immunogens. Complex formation of methylated bovine serum albumin with synthetic polynucleotides, including some that were double-stranded and triple-stranded, yielded a mosaic of antigens, some of which recognized the higher order structure of these macro-molecules.

Progress in the field of lipid immunology is more recent, and largely due to advances in lipid and membrane chemistry. This led to a heightened awareness of lipids as important cellular antigens. Among the lipids, most important immunologically are phosphatides, such as sphingomyelin and cephalin, as well as glycosphingolipids such as galactocerebroside. Antibodies against lipoidal extracts of various tissues appear during the course of syphilitic infection, and this led to a standard serological test for syphilis. Another lipid antigen is the Forssman antigen, mainly responsible for hemolysis of sheep erythrocytes in the presence of antiserum and complement. The greatest barriers to advancement in the field of lipid immunology have always been the chemical and physical properties of the lipids themselves, particularly water insolubility. The problem of reactivity of soluble antibodies with lipid antigens was partially overcome by the inclusion of 'auxiliary lipids' such as lecithin and cholesterol in the antigen suspension. Mixtures of lipids in the form of liposomes, consisting of concentric spherules of lipid bilayer membranes, can mimic precisely many of the immunological aspects of intact cell membranes. The availability of liposomes has permitted the study of the immunogenicity of membrane-associated lipids.

Immunoglobulins

Immunoglobulins (Igs) are mentioned here exclusively in terms of their antigenicity. Usually immunological data preceded structural information, and they were crucial, e.g. in the discovery of allotypy and idiotypy. The availability of monoclonal antibodies permits today a detailed antigenic analysis of immunoglobulins of every class and type. The epitopes within one immunoglobulin molecule vary much in their relative immunopotencies. Thus some determinants on the Fc fragment of an IgG are immunodominant compared with determinants on Fab, but when Fab is injected, in the absence of Fc, either by itself or as the dimer $(Fab)_2$, antibodies are produced efficiently against epitopes on the Fab fragment of IgG.

Antigenic analysis helped not only to distinguish between the various classes (IgG, IgM, IgA, IgE, IgD) and subclasses of immunoglobulins, but also to define their phylogeny. Allotypes are immunologically detectable genetic differences in particular constant regions, whereas idiotypes are the unique antigenic determinants found on the variable regions of antigen binding receptors, i.e. they represent paratopes of different specificities (idiotypes) in terms of their antigen variation. The regulation of the immune system through idiotype–anti-idiotype interactions can be achieved without the presence of the antigen, and, thus, is particularly well suited to the maintenance of steady states in lymphoid populations after the antigenic stimulus has been removed. Indeed, idiotype–anti-idiotype relationships have the potential to link diverse members of the immune system into a network, so that the activation of one set of clones within the system may have far-reaching and quite unanticipated effects elsewhere within the 'immunological network'.

Synthetic antigens

Landsteiner first showed that small molecules (e.g. 2,4-dinitrophenol) when injected into animals do not elicit antigen formation. However, dinitrophenyl proteins, in which dinitrophenyl is attached to a macromolecular carrier, elicit the formation of antibodies reacting specifically with the dinitrophenyl group. Such small molecules were termed haptens.

Thus a new antigenic specificity may be grafted on an antigen. On the other hand, a limited enrichment of gelatin with tyrosine increased its immunogenicity without significantly changing its specificity. Thus by chemical modification it is possible to change both immunogenicity and antigenic specificity. Increase in immunogenicity by means of appropriate adjuvants has developed significantly due to synthetic adjuvants which may also be attached covalently to the antigen.

Synthetic polypeptides (polymers of amino acids), linear and branched, have been used extensively in immunological research, as their structures were both simple and well known. This permitted the construction of literally hundreds of antigens for the purpose of elucidating the molecular basis of antigenicity, and later the molecular basis of manifold immunological phenomena.

Knowing the chemistry of the copolymers made it possible to arrive at conclusions concerning the role of various structural features in their antigenic function. It is, nevertheless, important to stress that the immunogenicity of a chemical substance depends not only on its structure but also on the biological background of the animal immunized, including its genetic features. It was thus learned that the immunogenically important area of the molecule must be readily accessible to the B cell and cannot be hidden in the interior of the molecule. By chemical modification, antigenic materials may be converted into nonantigens (e.g. by attachment of poly(ethylene glycol) or by poly(DL-alanylation)), whereas nonantigenic materials may become immunogenic.

The overall shape of the molecule does not seem to be a crucial factor in immunogenicity, whereas the size seems to be important: very few molecules of less than 2000 Da are immunogenic, and the immunogenicity increases steadily with the molecular size. The presence of electrical charges on a macromolecule is not a minimum requirement for it to be immunogenic.

Appropriately constructed polymers of D-amino acids may be immunogenic in a similar way to polymers of the natural L-amino acids, but to detect this antigenicity, it is necessary to immunize animals with very low doses, as in the dose range required to prove the immunogenicity of L-amino acid polymers, the D-polymers induce immunological tolerance, also called paralysis. This is probably due to their being very slowly, if at all, metabolized. Through studies of structurally related immunogens, it was possible to establish that those antigens, such as pneumococcal polysaccharides, Escherichia coli lipopolysaccharides or D-amino acid polymers, which possess repeating antigenic determinants and are slowly metabolized, are T independent, i.e. they do not need the cooperation of the helper T cells with B cells, whose progeny produce antibodies, for an efficient immune response. In contrast, most antigens – including L-amino acid copolymers – are T dependent. The purely cellular immune response is limited to the T cell population, of which several subpopulations are now known, and it probably involves the cooperation of helper T cells with effector T cells.

Antigens leading to an immune response of essentially any specificity desired can be prepared synthetically, and this includes the production of antibodies against peptides, oligosaccharides, oligonucleotides, tRNA, lipids, as well as haptens such as penicillin, prostaglandin, dinitrophenol, pyridoxal or ferrocene. Similarly, antibodies have been obtained against many biologically active peptides such as angiotensin, bradykinin or vasopressin. Moreover, in recent years totally synthetic immunogens, including peptide segments of viral coat proteins, e.g. MS2 bacteriophage, hepatitis virus or bacterial toxins (diphtheria, cholera) have been produced, and they have led to the production of antibodies capable of neutralizing the virus, or inducing in experimental animals protection against diphtheria and cholera.

The spatial folding of proteins plays a decisive role in determining their antigenic specificity. With synthetic models, it has been possible to build with the same peptides, immunogens which possessed either exclusively sequential or conformation-dependent antigenic determinants. In globular proteins, most of the antigenic determinants are conformational, as is evident by loss of reaction with their antibodies after denaturation. Antibodies are, therefore, good probes for the conformational state of proteins, and there are many reported cases in which antibodies have been used for detection of different conformations in proteins. Working from these considerations, we have shown that a peptide analogous to a stretch of the hen eggwhite lysozyme sequence can be synthesized, closed into a 'loop' by a disulfide bridge and attached to a synthetic branched polymer. The resulting macromolecule leads to production of antibodies which cross-react efficiently with a unique conformation-dependent region of a native protein. In conceptual terms this opened the road to the synthetic vaccines of the future as it pinpointed the possibility of synthetically preparing relevant determinants that could lead to protection against diseases.

To give just one of the many examples where synthetic antigens were of crucial importance in detecting, or elucidating, a defined immunological phenomenon, the genetic control of immune response should be mentioned. It is clear today that the capacity to respond well or poorly to a certain antigenic stimulus is under strict genetic control. This observation has been made largely thanks to synthetic antigens (simple chemically) and inbred strains of animals (simple genetically). Using defined branched synthetic polypeptides, differing only in a limited manner within their antigenic determinants, it was possible to prove conclusively that the genetic control of the immune response is determinant specific. McDevitt showed later that the immune response to these synthetic antigens was linked to the MHC locus of the species. The newly discovered immune response (Ir) genes and their products (Ia) have been extremely important in enabling us to understand the phenomena of immunity and resistance to diseases. The Ir gene products (Ia antigens) are present on the cell surface and are important in controlling interactions between cells of the immune system.

Complex antigens

Antigens of importance in practical immunology are mostly not dispersed molecules but cellular or multicellular structures. Of course, the specificity is ultimately definable in all cases in molecular terms. Viruses, sometimes even crystallizable, are among the simplest of such structures, with most of the antigenic specificity residing in their coats, sometimes of purely protein nature, but often including lipids or polysaccharides. In some cases, inner core proteins are also efficient antigens, capable of providing a protective immune response. More has been learned about immunology from studies on bacteria than from any other group of natural antigens, and their antigenic determinants have been in many cases elucidated in great detail, most of it of a polysaccharide nature, but also involving proteins and teichoic acids. Lipids often participate in these specificities. More limited progress has been made in the investigation of mycoplasms and chlamydiae. On the other hand, recent years have seen a tremendous progress in the immunology of parasite diseases, due to both helminths and protozoa, including the great antigenic variations characteristic of some agents. Fungi are another group of antigens that express an enormous number of antigenically different entities, about whose molecular nature relatively little is known.

Vaccines used in medical practice include four main types of antigen preparations: toxoids (the soluble exotoxins of bacteria such as diphtheria and tetanus bacilli, which have been modified and rendered less toxic by the addition of formalin or gentle heating); antigens isolated from infectious agents (such as the capsular polysaccharide of the pneumococci); killed vaccines (cultured organisms killed by heat, ultraviolet irradiation or chemicals such as phenol, alcohol or formalin); and attenuated living vaccines (made from strains of organisms that have lost their virulence by growth in culture).

Allergens are antigens which cause allergic reactions either of the immediate or delayed type. They may be of widely different origins such as dust, fungi, hair, pollen, bacterial proteins, food or drugs. The immediate-type allergy is induced mainly through a mechanism triggered by IgE class antibodies, whereas the delayed-type allergy is T cell mediated.

All plant and animal cells possess antigens that can express themselves in a foreign host. Many animal and human antigens may trigger autoimmune phenomena. Some antigens may be organ specific, whereas others are present essentially on all cells (e.g. histocompatibility antigens). In the past two decades the central role of the MHC in immune processes has been recognized. The MHC, a cluster of diverse genes which mediate and regulate a variety of immune mechanisms, appears to exist in all higher vertebrate species (HLA in humans; H2 in mice). Genetic, structural and functional studies of the multiple MHC products have defined three broad classes of genes and molecules. The class I products are glycoproteins expressed on the membranes of all nucleated cells (histocompatibility, or transplantation, antigens). These are the main targets of the graft rejection reaction, and they mediate the recognition and destruction of virus-infected or neoplastic cells. Class II products, defined by immune response (Ir) genes, are expressed principally on the membranes of antigen-presenting cells (e.g. macrophages, dendritic cells, B lymphocytes) and mediate the regulation, through so-called helper and suppressor effects, of a variety of humoral and cellular immune responses. When incompatible, these Ir gene products also play a potentiating role in transplant rejections. Class III genes determine the structures of several discrete proteins including certain components of the complement system which cause destruction and elimination of bacteria and other foreign cells.

No listing of natural antigens would be complete without mentioning all the cellular markers, receptors and tissue antigens. There is a growing number of immunologically and chemically defined antigens characteristic of various types of T cells, and also B cells and macrophages. There are also all the cytokines, molecules provoked in cells and secreted into body fluids, such as interleukins, interferons, thymic and tumor factors, etc.

There are many indications that the cancer patient's immune response may affect tumor growth.

In the study of tumor immunity, the identification of new tumor-specific antigens not present in normal tissues is a primary task. One has to distinguish them from organ-specific antigens and histocompatibility antigens. Tumor antigens are often tumor selective rather than tumor specific, i.e. their concentration may be much higher on cancer cells than on normal cells. Tumor antigens are classified according to the origin of the tumor: experimentally induced (by chemical, physical or viral carcinogens) or spontaneous. The category of oncodevelopmental antigens is of special interest. These, exemplified by α-fetoprotein and by the carcinoembryonic antigen of the colon, are present in normal individuals before birth but disappear thereafter (or stay at an extremely low level), and reappear in the body fluids in adult life only concurrently with specific cancers. Their quantification may, therefore, be of diagnostic value. Antitumor antibodies may be used for immunotargeting of toxins (immunotoxins) and chemotherapeutic drugs.

See also: **Allergens; Allotypes, immunoglobin; Antibodies, specificity; Antigen-binding site; Antigens, cell surface; Antigen presentation via MHC class I molecules; Antigen presentation via MHC class II molecules; Antigens, T dependent and independent; Autoimmunity; Carbohydrate antigens; Carrier; Epitopes; Hapten; Idiotype; Immune response; Immune response (Ir) genes; Immunogen; MHC restriction; Specificity; Tolerance, peripheral; Vaccines; Valency of antigens and antibodies.**

Further reading

Benacerraf B (1981) Role of MHC gene products in immune regulation. *Science* **212**: 1229–1238.

Berzofsky JA (1985) Intrinsic and extrinsic factors in protein antigenic structure. *Science* **229**: 932–940.

Germain RN (1993) Antigen processing and presentation. In: Paul WE (ed) *Fundamental Immunology*, pp 629–676. New York: Raven Press.

Geysen HM, Fainer JA, Rodda SJ *et al.* (1987) Chemistry of antibody binding to a protein. *Science* **235**: 1184–1190.

Gimmi CD, Freeman GJ, Gribben JG, Gray G and Nadler LM (1993) Human T-cell clonal anergy is induced by antigen presentation in the absence of B7 costimulation. *Proceedings of the National Academy of Sciences of the USA* **90**: 6586–6590.

Kabat EA (1976) *Structural Concepts in Immunology and Immunochemistry*. New York: Holt, Rinehart and Winston.

Langone JJ (ed) (1989) Antibodies, antigens and molecular mimicry. *Methods in Enzymology* **178**: 1–835.

McConnell I, Monro A and Waldmann H (1981) *The Immune System*, 2nd edn. Oxford: Blackwell Scientific.

Novotny J, Handschumacher M and Bruccoleri RE (1987) Protein antigenicity: a static surface property. *Immunology Today* **8**: 26–31.

Rammensee HG, Falk K and Rotzschke O (1993) Peptides naturally presented by MHC class I molecules. *Annual Review of Immunology* **11**: 213–214.

Rothbard JB and Gefter M (1991) Interactions between immunogenic peptides and MHC proteins. *Annual Review of Immunology* **9**: 527–565.

Sela M (ed) (1973–1987) *The Antigens*, vols 1–7. New York: Academic Press.

Sela M (1989) Antigenicity: some molecular aspects. *Science* **166**: 1365–1374.

Sutcliffe JG, Shinnick TM, Green N and Lerner RA (1983) Antibodies that react with predetermined sites on proteins. *Science* **219**: 660–666.

Swat W, von Boehmer H and Kisiebow P (1994) Central tolerance: clonal deletion or clonal arrest? *European Journal of Immunology* **24**: 4485–4487.

Todd PEE, East IJ and Leach SJ (1982) The immunogenicity and antigenicity of proteins. *Trends in Biochemical Sciences* **7**: 212–216.

van Regenmortel MHV (1989) Structural and functional approaches to the study of protein antigenicity. *Immunology Today* **10**: 266–272.

Herzenberg LA, Weir DM, Herzenberg LA and Blackwell C (eds) (1996) *Handbook of Experimental Immunology*. 5th edn. Vol 1, *Immunochemistry and Molecular Immunology*. New York Blackwell Scientific.

ANTIGENS, CELL SURFACE

Wolfgang J Rettig, Dr Karl Thomae GmbH, Germany

The basic structure of the plasma membrane is a lipid bilayer with intercalated proteins and carbohydrate side-chains extending from the external membrane surface. Chemical studies with SDS-polyacrylamide gel electrophoresis, lectin chromatography and glycolipid analysis have shown that plasma membranes isolated from various tissues differ widely in their protein and carbohydrate composition. However, by far the most detailed picture of plasma membrane diversity, especially with regard to the diversity displayed on the external membrane surface, has come from immunologic studies.

Immunogenetic classification of cell surface diversity

Four genetically distinct categories of cell surface diversity have been identified with serologic and cell-mediated immune reactions (**Table 1**). First, the discovery of the human ABO blood group antigens and mouse H-2 major histocompatibility antigens established precedents for allogeneic diversity. Allogeneic diversity is specified by genetic polymorphism, i.e. the presence and mendelian inheritance of different alleles of a common gene in members of the same species. The allelic variation may reside in 1) the structural gene for a cell surface protein, as illustrated by major histocompatibility complex (MHC) class I and class II molecules; 2) the activity of an enzyme involved in carbohydrate synthesis, as illustrated by blood group antigens; or 3) a regulatory gene or DNA sequence controlling the expression of a structural gene, as suggested for the TL antigens of TL$^+$ and TL$^-$ mouse strains.

Second, xenogeneic diversity reflects genotypic differences between members of different species and includes instances in which homologous cell surface molecules in disparate species show structural diversity (e.g. mouse versus human Thy 1) and instances in which an antigen in one species has no apparent structural homolog in another species (e.g. apparent lack of genes homologous to mouse Tla in several other species). A special case of xenogeneic diversity detected on the plasma membrane of mammalian cells is antigens encoded by viral genes integrated into the host cell genome. Despite the clear genetic distinction, the observed patterns of viral antigen expression may be deceptively complex, as illustrated by the murine leukemia virus (MuLV)-encoded gp70 cell surface antigens of mouse leukemias. MuLV genetic information is ubiquitous in the mouse, but whether these endogenous viral genes are expressed or not is determined by a variety of viral and host gene functions. For example, the expression of specific gp70 determinants differs between mouse strains with low and high leukemia incidence and between differentiated normal tissues in the same animal, thus mimicking the distribution of alloantigens or restricted differentiation antigens encoded by host genes. Apart from direct insertion of viral proteins into the plasma membrane, peptides generated from the intracellular degradation of viral proteins may bind to MHC molecules and be presented on the cell surface, where they can be recognized by T cells.

Third, clonogenetic diversity is determined by somatic genetic changes in gene structure, such as mutations and recombinational events. Genetic recombination is a normal step in immunoglobulin (Ig) and T cell receptor (TCR) gene expression, whereas mutations due to hits by external mutagens or errors in replication may affect any surface antigen gene in somatic cells. Such changes will escape notice unless an affected cell undergoes clonal expansion. For example, malignant transformation of individual B cell or T cell clones has allowed serologic detection of clonotypic determinants on surface Igs and TCRs. The individually distinct tumor rejection antigens of chemically induced sarcomas of mice, the unique antigens of human melanoma detected by autologous typing, and the tum$^-$ antigens of mutagenized mouse tumors may represent clonogenetic diversity of this sort on nonlymphoid cells. In the case of unique antigens of human melanoma, the serologic specificity has been traced to a variant of a normal melanocyte surface antigen, melanotransferrin. In the case of tum$^-$ antigens, the mutations affect genes encoding for intracellular rather than cell surface components, and the clonotypic determinants appear to reside on endogenous peptides that are presented on the cell surface by MHC molecules and recognized by T cells.

The fourth category of cell surface diversity can

Table 1   Immunogenetic classification of cell surface antigen diversity

Designation	Genetic basis	Prototype antigens	Reagents (examples)
Allogeneic	Allelic differences	MHC class I, II antigens	Alloantisera
		Blood groups	mAbs
			T cell clones
Xenogeneic	Species divergence for homologous genes	Most surface proteins	Heteroantibodies
	Endogenous viral genes	Virus-coded tumor antigens	Heteroantibodies
Clonogenetic	Gene recombination	TCR; Igs	mAbs
	Somatic mutations	Unique tumor antigens	Autologous antibodies
			T cell clones
Epigenetic	Regulated expression	CD antigens	mAbs
			Heteroantibodies

be referred to as epigenetic ('differentiation-related') diversity and reflects differences in gene expression, rather than disparity of gene structure. (In this context, the term differentiation can be used for all processes that lead to diversity in the patterns of proteins synthesized in cells harboring the same genome, such as embryonic and fetal development, normal self-renewal and terminal differentiation in adult tissues, inflammation, tissue repair and malignant transformation.) Prior to the impact of serologic analysis, there was a general notion coming from transplantation studies with tolerant and chimeric animals that cells from different lineages shared a common surface antigenic phenotype. The first examples of cell surface antigens that distinguish different cell types in the same animal were discovered some 25 years ago in the search for tumor-specific antigens of mouse leukemias. At that time, H-2 was the only known cell surface antigen on these tumor cells. However, specific immunization and testing schemes devised to obviate anti-H-2 responses, led to the detection of several new antigenic systems, including TL, Thy-1, Lyt-1 and Lyt-2,3. Like H-2, these antigens were found both on leukemic cells, which in the mouse are commonly of T cell origin and arise in the thymus, and on normal thymocytes. Unlike H-2, the newly defined antigens showed a restricted distribution among other lymphoid cells and in non-lymphoid tissues and came to be known as differentiation antigens. Enormous interest was generated by the finding that specific cell surface phenotypes not only permitted a distinction between T and B cells, but also between T cell subsets with cytotoxic (Lyt-2,3$^+$) and helper cell (Lyt-2,3$^-$) activities. This gave rise to the now widely accepted idea that the surface of cells reflects their differentiated state and that cells undergoing distinct pathways of differentiation or serving disparate functions have unique surface phenotypes.

The terms used here to classify cell surface diversity apply to the epitopes defined by specific antibodies or T cells rather than to entire molecules. Any individual cell surface molecule, be it a differentiation antigen or not, may combine structural features that are xenogeneic, allogeneic and clonogenetic in nature.

Test systems and approaches to cell surface antigen characterization (Table 2)

Initial interest in cell surface antigens came from studies of blood group antigens, histocompatibility antigens and tumor rejection antigens and their role in blood transfusion, organ transplantation and tumor immunity. The discovery of differentiation antigens established cell surface serology as a new approach to studying general aspects of cellular differentiation, first in cells of hematopoietic origin and subsequently in other cell lineages. With recent developments in serologic, biochemical and genetic techniques and test systems, the study of cell surface differentiation has been vastly expanded and it is now possible to carry out a comprehensive survey of tissue-specific cell surface antigen display. First, hybridoma technology permits sampling of common and rare immune responses and permits rapid analysis of large numbers of monoclonal antibodies (mAbs) without the elaborate specificity controls required for complex hetero- and xenoantisera. Thus, over the past years, mAbs have been used to define hundreds of new cell surface antigens, primarily in humans and mice. Second, indirect immunofluorescence staining combined with cytofluorometry and cell sorting and other techniques allow detailed analysis of hematopoietic cells and other tissues that can be prepared as free-cell suspensions. Cytofluorometry does not lend itself to the analysis of intact tissues. To test substrate-adherent cultured cells, procedures such as radiobinding assays or immunocytochemistry are available. For solid tissues, highly sensitive immunohistochemical procedures have been developed, including indirect immunofluorescence, avidin–biotin complex immunoperoxidase, and alkaline phosphatase (ALP)–anti-ALP procedures. These largely replace absorption assays and other methods that do not permit antigen localization to specific cell types or subcellular structures within tissues. Third, a large number of human and rodent tumor cell lines have been established, representing a wide range of distinct cellular lineages, and much progress has been made in culturing differentiated normal cells. They are used as standard typing panels for antigen specificity and as a source of homogeneous cell populations for biochemical and genetic studies. Fourth, the development of sensitive immunochemical techniques in conjunction with mAbs has led to the definition of a host of plasma membrane proteins, glycolipids and carbohydrates and it has permitted their chemical characterization. For a host of proteins, this analysis has yielded information on their primary structure and facilitated the cloning of antigen-coding cDNAs. In addition, it has allowed distinct cell surface proteins to be placed into families with shared structural features and possibly, common evolutionary ancestry, as exemplified by the immunoglobulin superfamily. Some cell surface antigen genes show alternative mRNA splicing to generate transmembrane, glycosylphosphatidylinositol

Table 2   General approach to cell surface antigen classification

Antigen characteristics	Examples and methodologies
Cell-type specificity	
Cultured cells	Binding assays with short-term cultures of normal cells and tumor cell lines (cotyping)
Tissues	Immunohistochemistry; immunofluorescence staining and flow cytometry (cell suspensions)
Biochemistry	
Proteins	Immunochemistry (immunoprecipitation, Western blotting, purification, amino acid sequencing)
	Biosynthesis and subunit composition
	Membrane anchoring
Glycolipids	Carbohydrate and lipid analysis (immuno-thin layer chromatography)
Carbohydrates	Sugar analysis, carrier analysis (lipids, proteins)
Epitope structure	Competition studies with multiple mAbs (radiobinding assay, surface plasmon resonance)
	Species comparison
	Molecular structure (amino acid sequence, carbohydrate determinants, conformation-dependence, combinatorial epitope for multimeric antigens)
	Active site mapping for biochemical functions
Membrane dynamics	
Internalization	Coated pits, caveolae, macropinosomes
	Surface recycling and processing/degradation of internalized antigen
Extracellular release	Secretion of splice variants lacking membrane anchors
	Proteolytic release of membrane-bound forms
Genetics	
Molecular cloning	cDNA cloning, sequence analysis for homologies (gene families) and functional domains
	Alternative mRNA splicing
Gene locus	Chromosome mapping
	Exon–intron structure, regulatory elements, species comparison
	Disease-related mutations, deletions and polymorphisms
Biochemical function	Signaling receptors or ligands (cell-bound versus soluble forms)
	Adhesion molecules
	Membrane-bound enzymes
Biological function	Growth, differentiation of cultured cells
	Transgenic animals, knockout animals
	Altered structure or regulation during development, physiologic activation, or in diseased tissues (inflammation, cancer, immunologic diseases)

(GPI)-linked, and secreted forms of the antigen, or antigens that differ in the length of their cytoplasmic or extracellular domains. Examples of antigens that show this sort of isoform diversity include the neural cell adhesion molecule (NCAM) and the leukocyte common antigen (CD45). Additional diversity within antigenic systems may result from cell type-specific patterns of glycosylation or from differences in subunit assembly in the plasma membrane, as illustrated by the combinatorial diversity of T cell antigen receptor complexes or integrin heterodimers. Analysis of this level of structural diversity is greatly facilitated by the availability of mAbs specific for individual subunits or isoforms carrying shared and unique epitopes. Finally, chromosome mapping and genetic linkage studies that employ 1) serologic analysis of somatic cell hybrids, 2) cytogenetic analysis of inbred and congenic animals, 3) cytogenetic analysis with DNA probes (in situ hybridization to somatic and meiotic chromosomes), and 4) physical mapping with yeast artificial chromosomes and other large DNA fragments have permitted the construction of genomic maps for cell surface antigen genes.

The plasma membrane is a dynamic structure, with extensive lateral diffusion of surface antigens in the lipid bilayer. Nevertheless, many membrane antigens are not evenly distributed over the entire cell surface (**Figure 1**). Thus, the paradigm of a 'fluid mosaic' of cell surface molecules freely diffusing within the plane of the plasma membrane has been modified. Complex assemblies of multiple cell membrane components that appear to be organized into specialized cell surface domains have been identified, some of which are anchored to intracellular structures via cytoskeletal proteins. Spatial restriction of cell surface molecules has been documented in detail for polarized epithelial cells and vascular endothelial cells, in which many antigens show preferential localization either to the apical (luminal) surface or to the basolateral surface membranes. Other antigens are targeted to sites of cell–cell or cell–extracellular matrix contacts, to membrane protrusions of invading cells (invadopodia), or to the leading or trailing edges of migrating cells.

Cell surface antigens are not strictly confined to the outer surface of cells. Instead, they are taken up into intact cells by one of several modes of vesicular internalization (**Figure 2**). The best-studied uptake mechanism is via clathrin-coated pits and vesicles, a pathway utilized, for example, by the receptors for epidermal growth factor and transferrin. Additional pathways of internalization use caveolae, as shown for the membrane-bound folate-binding protein (FBP) and other GPI-linked surface molecules, or macropinosomes, as shown for the A33 colon cancer antigen. Viruses exploit a number of internalizing cell surface antigens as receptors to gain access to the cell interior, with human immunodeficiency virus (HIV) binding to CD4 being one example. Finally, the clear distinction between surface-bound antigens and secreted antigens has been abandoned because genes encoding *bona fide* integral membrane antigens may also encode soluble antigens found in the extracellular space, either as a result of alternative splicing of membrane-anchoring, transmembrane domains or due to cleavage of the extracellular domains of the membrane-bound forms by specific proteases. These principles apply to a number of cell surface receptors for cytokines that are also found as soluble cytokine-binding proteins and for cytokines that are derived from membrane-bound precursors.

With the new techniques and test systems, the following questions can now be addressed.

1. What is the size of the surface antigen repertoire expressed on normal cells?
2. Which surface molecules are constitutively expressed on all cell types and which are differentially expressed?
3. Of the differentiation antigens, how many follow a single lineage or phase pattern and how many show complex patterns?
4. How is the biochemical function of a cell surface antigen correlated with its cell type specificity?
5. Are the repertoires of cell surface antigens conserved in different species, and are structural homologs expressed with the same tissue specificity and serve the same functions?
6. What is the hierarchy of intrinsic and extrinsic factors that control cell surface differentiation and the coordinate expression of multiple antigenic systems?
7. What is the significance of quantitative variations in the expression of individual antigens on different cell types?
8. Do the various antigens that make up the cell surface have preferrential locations as part of a prescribed organization of surface elements, and what information is encoded by such supramolecular associations?
9. Which alterations in surface phenotype are associated with malignant transformation and other perturbations in normal cell growth and function?

Emerging view of cell surface differentiation

The wealth of information coming from serologic studies of cell surface antigen expression in different species and in diverse cell and tissue types has led to the demise of earlier concepts about how the surface of cells is constructed. Chief among these is the notion that developmental cell lineage patterns provide the general organizing principles for differentiation-related cell surface diversity. The expectation was that distinct cell lineages in developing embryonic and fetal tissues and in self-renewing adult tissues would be marked by unique surface antigens (e.g. lymphoid or neuroectodermal lineage markers) and that discrete phases in these lineages would be marked by differential expression of additional antigens (phase markers). These molecules would serve cell functions unique to the respective lineages and phases and provide convenient histogenetic markers for the study of embryonic development, tumor classification and other cell type analyses. One early exception to this concept was the mouse Thy-1 antigen, which was found not only on thymocytes and peripheral T cells but also on fibroblasts, in brain tissue, and on a few additional cell types. Thus, Thy-1 shows the restricted expression of a differentiation antigen, yet its tissue distribution is complex, overlapping several distinct embryological lineages and showing differences in developmental regulation within these lineages. Subsequent studies have shown that lineage-restricted antigens are the exception and antigens like Thy-1, whose distribution does not conform to embryonic derivation or lineage are the ones commonly found. The reluctance of differentiation antigens to fit into established cell lineage patterns means that comprehensive maps of antigen distribution are required before conclusions can be reached with regard to cell type, tissue type or disease-related specificity.

Apart from normal differentiation antigens, tumor cell surface antigens have been the subject of much research, and the question of their normal tissue distribution has been of key importance. One suggestion has been that tumors re-express molecular and biological traits of fetal cells that are absent from normal adult cells. This theory has not held up for

(A) General cell surface distribution

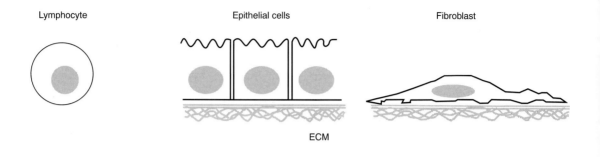

Lymphocyte   Epithelial cells   Fibroblast

ECM

(B) Restricted cell surface distribution

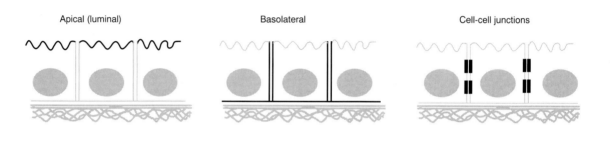

Apical (luminal)   Basolateral   Cell-cell junctions

Focal adhesion contacts   Leading (trailing) edge

(C) Cell surface shift of cryptic antigens

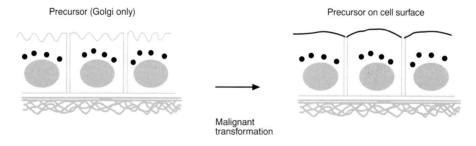

Precursor (Golgi only)   Precursor on cell surface

Malignant
transformation

Figure 1 Differential localization of cell surface antigens. Examples of antigen expression on lymphoid, epithelial and fibroblastic cells are illustrated as follows. (A) Uniform antigen distribution on the surface membrane, as seen for MHC class I molecules. (B) Spatially restricted cell surface distribution on polarized cells growing on extracellular matrix (ECM). In epithelial cells, apical, basolateral and cell junctional patterns are distinguished. For fibroblastic cells, antigen localization to focal adhesion contacts and the leading (or trailing) edge of migrating cells are indicated. (C) Cryptic antigens may be present in intracellular compartments of some cells but become exposed on the surface of other cells. The example shown here represents a mAb-defined carbohydrate structure, lacto-*N*-tetraose (type I blood group precursor), carried by glycolipids and glycoconjugates, that is detectable in the Golgi apparatus of normal adult cells, but becomes further glycosylated and 'cryptic' before reaching the cell surface. By contrast, in fetal endoderm and teratocarcinomas, the glycosylation of lacto-*N*-tetraose moieties is deficient and large numbers of the precursor structure reach the cell surface.

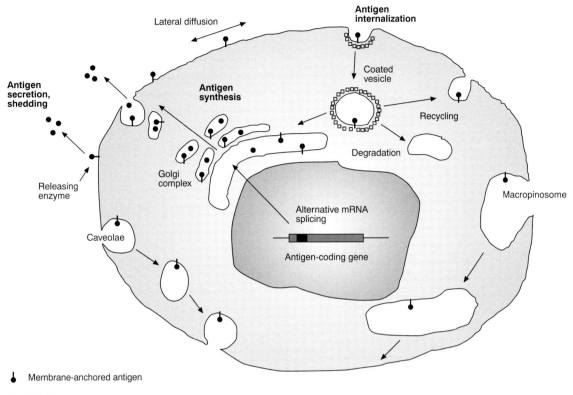

Figure 2 Dynamic view of cell surface antigen expression on the plasma membrane. Using immunocytochemical staining methods with permeabilized cells, some antigens are detected as biosynthetic precursors in the cytoplasm and Golgi complex, prior to their appearance on the cell surface. Similarly, antigens that are internalized through clathrin-coated vesicles, macropinosomes, or caveolae can be followed by these methods until they are either degraded (e.g. lysosomal pathway) or recycled in intact form to the cell surface. Alternative splicing of antigen-coding mRNAs with removal of membrane-anchoring transmembrane domains or cleavage of membrane-bound antigens by specific proteases may result in secreted or shed variants of the antigen.

most cancer antigens when the analysis of normal adult tissues has been sufficiently detailed. Antigens that fit an 'oncofetal' pattern in one system are invariably found in other systems with a different mode of expression and control. Similar departures from the presumed modes of expression have been found for other categories of 'transformation-related' or 'proliferation-related' antigens of cancer cells. (Much of the current interest in tumor-specific antigens focuses on clonogenetic determinants on cell surface differentiation antigens detected by the host immune system, as described above.) Even for those antigens for which a biochemical function has been identified, such as various cell surface receptors, membrane-bound enzymes and adhesion molecules, the unpredictable cross-lineage patterns are observed.

Understanding the genetic and biochemical control of the complexity in cell surface antigen display will require decoding the signals that initiate, regulate and maintain the differentiated state. Understanding

the physiologic role of a cell surface antigen in the organism, even if it has been assigned an *in vitro* biochemical function and its mode of genetic control is known, may require highly specialized test systems. A search for genetic diseases caused by abnormalities in a single cell surface antigen locus may facilitate the study of physiologic function for some molecules, as illustrated by the analysis of patients with leukocyte adhesion deficiency due to defects in the CD18 gene. However, it is tempting to speculate that many common biological functions of the cell surface are not assigned to individual proteins. They are the responsibility of integrated circuits comprising multiple components, both in the plasma membrane and inside and outside of the cell, in which individual proteins serve as structural and functional modules. The same module may be used over and over in different cell types and different circuits to serve different functions, and similar functions may be mediated, in parallel or alternatively, by separate molecular mechanisms. Such a concept is consistent with the experience that targeted inactivation of genes in knockout mice is commonly associated with unexpectedly subtle phenotypes.

What lessons can be drawn at this stage of the analysis?

1. From the large pool of genes coding for cell surface antigens, distinct but widely overlapping sets are activated during differentiation in disparate lineages.
2. The distinctive surface phenotype of differentiated cells is achieved not by the display of unique lineage-restricted antigens but rather through unique combinations of antigens that are drawn from a common pool.
3. Although the surface phenotype of differentiated cells is quite stable, there is considerable flexibility in reprogramming individual antigens. Surface antigens are not irreversibly silenced or expressed during differentiation but can be induced or suppressed by specific extrinsic/intrinsic signals.
4. Individual surface antigens can be viewed as modular elements that together generate complex and unique surface patterns. This concept of modularity in the construction of cell surfaces could explain unique functions achievable with common elements, as the same module in different cell types would come under different regulatory control and could impart different information.

See also: **ABO blood group system; Alloantigens; B-lymphocyte differentiation; Carbohydrate antigens; CD antigens; Flow cytometry; Immunocytochemistry and enzyme markers; Monoclonal antibodies (mAbs); T lymphocyte differentiation; Thy-1; Tumor antigens.**

Further reading

Holmes KL and Morse HC (1988) Murine hematopoietic cell surface antigen expression. *Immunology Today* 9: 344–350.

Magnani JL (1987) Mouse and rat monoclonal antibodies directed against carbohydrates. *Methods in Enzymology* 138: 484–492.

Oettgen HF, Rettig WJ, Lloyd KO et al (1990) Serologic analysis of human cancer. In: Oettgen HF (ed) *Human Cancer Immunology I. Immunology and Allergy Clinics of North America*, vol 10, no 4. Philadelphia: WB Saunders.

Old LJ (1981) Cancer immunology: the search for specificity. *Cancer Research* 41: 361–375.

Old LJ and Stockert E (1977) Immunogenetics of cell surface antigens of mouse leukemia. *Annual Review of Genetics* 11: 127–160.

Schlossman SF, Boumsell L, Gilks W et al (eds) (1995) *Leukocyte Typing V. White Cell Differentiation Antigens*. Oxford: Oxford University Press.

ANTIGENS, T DEPENDENT AND INDEPENDENT

Rudolf H Zubler, Division of Hematology, Department of Medicine, University Hospital, Geneva, Switzerland

Defense mechanisms against microbial invaders form a spectrum ranging from relatively primitive innate immunity to highly sophisticated acquired immune responses. The innate immunity uses only invariant, germ line-encoded receptors for the recognition of foreign substances. The T cell-dependent B cell response, on the other hand, produces somatically mutated, high-affinity antibodies with an enormous range of specificities and a variety of constant regions for different effector functions. The B cell response to T-independent antigens occupies an intermediate position in this scheme; it generates essentially low-affinity antibodies of the immunoglobulin M (IgM) class with germ line specificities. The elaboration of high-affinity antibodies by somatic mutation carries the risk of creating dangerous self-reactive antibodies; the B lymphocytes must be controlled by helper T lymphocytes via 'cognate' T–B interaction (linked recognition of T and B epitopes of the same antigen). Most natural proteins are T-dependent antigens, and B cells can not respond to such antigens without costimulatory signals from cognate T help. T-independent antigens bypass the requirement for cognate T help. They do this by reacting with both B cell antigen receptors and receptors of innate immunity (on B cells or accessory cells) which provide other costimulatory signals. Typical T-independent antigens are microbial sugars, lipid structures and certain nucleic acids which can not be presented to T cells on major histocompatibility complex (MHC) molecules for linked recognition and must be handled otherwise. Type 1 T-independent antigens (such as endotoxin, lipopolysaccharide) are directly mitogenic for B cells of certain species, while type 2 antigens (e.g. polysaccharides) activate B cells in conjunction with accessory cells, cytokines and other factors, such as complement. However, the T-independent antibody responses, compared to those benefiting from cognate T help, are limited with regard to affinity, isotype pattern and immunologic memory.

Role of costimulatory signals

The immune system should discriminate between self and nonself. It copes with this problem at different levels. Immature lymphocytes which react with self antigens undergo apoptotic cell death, but not all self antigens are present in the lymphopoietic microenvironments. Therefore, the cellular activation processes during immune responses depend on the cotriggering of lymphocytes by different signals, via the antigen receptor and other receptors; triggering at the antigen receptor only, leads to apoptosis or tolerance. Usually, microorganisms or their products generate costimulatory signals for T cells at the level of the antigen-presenting cells. In the case of B cells responding to T-dependent antigens, the critical costimulatory signals are then provided by helper T cells. In particular, the functions of B cells, 1) to generate high-affinity antibodies by somatic mutation (with the risk of producing novel self-reactive antibodies), 2) to switch from IgM to other immunoglobulin isotypes, and 3) to extensively proliferate and generate a memory cell population in addition to antibody secreting cells – depend on cognate T help and take place in the germinal centers of secondary lymphoid organs. However, cognate T–B interaction only occurs if the antigen, after recognition via a B cell epitope, and then internalization and processing by the B cell, produces a T cell epitope (a short peptide) which can then be presented as a complex with an MHC class II molecule on the surface of the B cell. The most important costimulatory signal during cognate T–B interaction is mediated by CD40 ligand (CD40L) on the T cell binding to CD40 on the B cell. CD40 knockout mice generate no germinal center responses and only respond to T-independent antigens. Humans with nonfunctional CD40L mutations suffer from the X-linked hyper IgM syndrome: the germinal center response is lacking and the immune system is overstimulated by T-independent bacterial antigens.

T-independent antigens can provide other costimulatory signals for B cells, directly or via accessory cells (**Figure 1**). On the other hand, obligatory T-independent antigens do not induce a germinal center response and, consequently, do not induce either somatic hypermutation or memory. Only certain isotype switches occur (see below).

Type 1 T-independent antigens

Type 1 antigens are directly mitogenic for B cells from certain species. LPS (lipopolysaccharide, endotoxin) of gram-negative bacteria is the prototypic type 1 antigen for murine B cells. CD14, a 55 kDa glycosylphosphatidylinositol (GPI)-anchored glycoprotein, is the major cell surface receptor for the activating effects of LPS on macrophages, B cells and various other cells. Serum lipid transfer protein or LPS-binding protein (LBP) accelerates the transfer of LPS to CD14 in a catalytic fashion. LPS then probably exerts its mitogenic activity by incorporating itself into the cell membrane. Because the lipid A/core portion of LPS bears structural resemblance to the second messenger ceramide, LPS could interact with ceramide-activated protein kinases. However, while LPS is a potent activator of human macrophages, it is not directly mitogenic for human B cells; it acts like a type 2 antigen for human B cells. For murine B cells, one can distinguish between the polyclonal B cell activator function of LPS, which occurs at a high LPS concentration, and the proper type 1 antigen function which occurs at a 1000-fold lower concentration. At the low dose, B cells with the appropriate antigen receptors have the advantage of focusing the mitogen on to themselves; the response, e.g. to DNP-haptenated LPS, then occurs only in hapten-specific B cells.

CD14 functions as a 'pattern recognition receptor' for a range of microbial constituents from gram-negative as well as gram-positive bacteria which, like LPS, activate macrophages. The B cell mitogenic properties of these substances are not yet well characterized. On the other hand, LPS reacts with a variety of receptors, including the CD11b/CD18 integrin, the animal lectin galectin-3 (expressed by activated macrophages) and others. *In vivo*, cytokines, inflammatory mediators and cell adhesion/cell interaction molecules from various accessory cells (macrophages, dendritic cells, natural killer (NK) cells, mast cells, activated bystander T cells, etc.) can participate in a T-independent antigen type 1 response. *In vitro*, high concentrations of appropriate cytokines induce all types of immunoglobulin class switches in LPS-activated B cells.

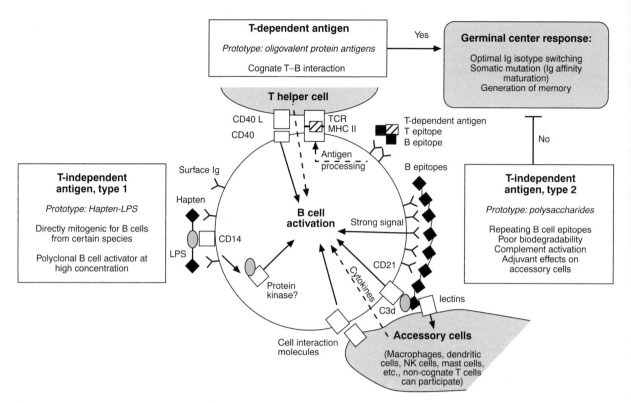

Figure 1　T-dependent and -independent B cell activation: properties of type 1 and type 2 T-independent antigens compared to T-dependent antigens.

Type 2 T-independent antigens

Although the presence of repeating B cell epitopes, leading to extensive cross-linking of B cell antigen receptors, is a common feature of type 2 antigens, they are not by themselves mitogenic for B cells. They bypass cognate T help only by synergy with the soluble factors and/or cell interaction molecules from accessory cells like those mentioned above; their effects on the B cell antigen receptor and on nonantigen receptors are equally important. Polysaccharides from encapsulated bacteria are the prototypic type 2 antigens in nature.

Effects of type 2 antigens on the B cell antigen receptor

Type 2 antigens are high molecular weight substances with many repeating B epitopes; they can be sugars (dextran, inulin), proteins (polymerized flagellin, viral capsids) or synthetic polymers (polyacrylamide). The number of identical epitopes is an important variable for B cell activation. Monovalent antigens simply occupy the antigen receptors. Bivalent/low-multivalent antigens can be internalized and their T cell epitopes presented to helper T cells. Cognate T help is required for these antigens, to which most natural proteins belong. Too extensively multivalent antigens can inactivate B cells. However,

somewhere in between, multivalent antigens optimally sensitize B cells to various T-independent costimulatory signals. Cross-linking of surface Ig leads to intracellular clustering of protein kinases, phosphatases and other receptor-associated proteins. The outcome depends on the extent of cross-linking and additional variables, such as the rigidity of the antigen backbone, allosteric effects on individual antigen receptors, and persistence of the interaction; type 2 antigens usually have a poor biodegradability.

Historically, type 2 antigens were defined as antigens which produce no antibody response in those mice which later turned out to have the xid defect (X chromosome-linked immunodeficiency). Interestingly, whereas humans with X-linked agammaglobulinemia, caused by mutations of the tyrosine kinase Btk, have a profound B cell maturation defect, the xid mice, with another Btk mutation, only show a defect of B cell activation by type 2 antigens. The signaling defect after Ig cross-linking is irrelevant for the response to T-dependent antigens in these mice.

Effects of type 2 antigens on nonantigen receptors

Polysaccharides are activators of the alternative pathway of the complement system. Via bound complement fragment C3d, they can react with the complement receptor 2, CD21 (the Epstein–Barr virus receptor on human B cells). CD21 is associated in the B cell membrane with the CD19 signal transduction complex, and thus can generate an activatory signal. In addition, B cells, macrophages and other cells express carbohydrate receptors of various kinds/specificities: C-type lectins (selectins, collectins) and others (e.g. galectins). These animal lectins play a role in cell adhesion, phagocytosis and cell activation as well as in interactions of cells with glycosylated serum proteins. In addition, they can recognize carbohydrates on microbial antigens, and thus probably participate in T-independent polysaccharide-specific antibody responses (e.g. the B cell signaling molecules CD23 and CD72 have C-type lectin domains. More generally, the 'adjuvant effect' of type 2 antigens is their capacity to activate accessory cells and induce cytokine secretion by such cells (phagocytes, inflammatory cells, etc.). In principle, activated bystander T cells can also participate in type 2 antigen-dependent B cell activation via cytokines. Moreover, activated B cells themselves are now known to produce a variety of cytokines, including typical 'T cell cytokines' like interleukin 2 (IL-2).

Immunodeficiencies for type 2 antigens

Neonatal mammals generate antibody responses to type 2 antigens either not at all or weakly; human infants under 2 years old respond very poorly to polysaccharides. Thus, some maturation of B cells and/or accessory cells (microenvironments) is necessary. Poor antipolysaccharide responses also occur in common variable immunodeficiencies and in the Wiskott–Aldrich syndrome. In the latter, a mutation in the WASP gene prevents correct expression of a whole series of cell surface molecules. In normal adults, antipolysaccharide responses are greatly compromised after splenectomy. Splenic B cells are important, particularly marginal zone B cells and CD5$^+$ B cells. Some investigators consider that CD5$^+$ (also called B1) B cells belong to a separate B cell lineage which preferentially expresses certain germ line-encoded (low-affinity, polyreactive) antibody specificities. Alternatively, since CD5 is an (early, pregerminal center) activation marker for B cells, one could conceive that conventional B cells expressing certain (i.e. polyreactive) antigen receptor specificities would be frequently activated in vivo. In any case, antipolysaccharide responses, in accordance with their generation outside germinal centers, typically produce only germline antibody specificities, are oligoclonal and primarily restricted to IgM. But isotype switching to IgG2 in humans and IgG3 in mice does occur; interferon γ (IFNγ), IL-3 and granulocyte-macrophage colony-stimulating factor

(GM-CSF) synergistically induce the IgG3 switch in murine B cells exposed to polysaccharides. Conjugate vaccines of polysaccharides linked to proteins induce cognate T–B interaction. Their utilization to enhance defense against encapsulated bacteria in infants and splenectomized or otherwise immunocompromised adults is of medical importance.

Immunogenicity of microbial DNA

dG polynucleotides can form four stranded conformations which are recognized by the scavenger receptor of macrophages. Moreover, certain palindromic DNA motifs, with sequences rarely present in mammalian DNA, can activate macrophages as well as be directly mitogenic for B cells. The mitogenic effect occurs via interaction with presently unknown intracellular receptors following internalization. The presence of an unmethylated CpG core in the active motifs seems to be relevant to self–nonself discrimination; the CpG content is higher in bacteria than in mammalian DNA and cytosine is not methylated in bacteria. The possibility (still theoretical) exists that bacterial surface molecules could be converted into T-independent antigens by complex formation with a mitogenic DNA motif.

B cell superantigens

Other microbial substances act as superantigens by binding to the B cell antigen receptors outside the antigen binding site. *Staphylococcus aureus*-derived protein A is the prototype for this interaction at the B cell level. Polymerized protein A induces strong B cell proliferation and Ig secretion in conjunction with cytokines such as IL-2. Superantigens are polyclonal activators but, rather than stimulating protective immunity, they could deviate the B cell response away from important antigens in the interest of the microorganism.

See also: **B lymphocyte activation; B lymphocyte repertoire; B lymphocyte, antigen processing and presentation; CD5; CD40 and its ligand; Cytokines; Endotoxin (lipopolysaccharide (LPS)); Germinal center; Helper T lymphocytes; Immunoglobulin class switching; Innate immunity; Lectins; Memory, immunological; Polyclonal activators; Selectins (CD62-E/L/P); Somatic mutation; Superantigens; Vaccines.**

Further reading

Bachmann MF and Zinkernagel RM (1996) The influence of virus structure on antibody response and virus serotype formation. *Immunology Today* **17**: 553–558.

Fearon DT and Locksley RM (1996) The instructive role of innate immunity in the acquired immune response. *Science* **272**: 50–54.

Gordon J (1994) B-cell signalling via the C-type lectins CD23 and CD72. *Immunology Today* **15**: 411–417.

Holmskov U, Malhotra R, Sim RB and Jensenius JC (1994) Collectins: collagenous C-type lectins of the innate immune defense system. *Immunology Today* **15**: 67–73.

Kindler V, Matthes T, Jeannin P and Zubler RH (1995) Interleukin-2 secretion by human B lymphocytes occurs as a late event and requires additional stimulation after CD40 cross-linking. *European Journal of Immunology* **25**: 1239–1243.

Mond JJ, Lees A and Snapper CM (1995) T cell-independent antigens type 2. *Annual Review of Immunology* **13**: 655–692.

Pisetsky DS (1996) The immunologic properties of DNA. *Journal of Immunology* **156**: 421–423.

Pleiman CM, D'Ambrosio D and Cambier JC (1994) The B-cell antigen receptor complex: structure and signal transduction. *Immunology Today* **15**: 393–399.

Wright SD (1995) CD14 and innate recognition of bacteria. *Journal of Immunology* **155**: 6–8.

ANTISERUM

Yasmin Thanavala, Department of Molecular Immunology, Roswell Park Cancer Institute, Buffalo, New York, USA

An antiserum is simply a serum obtained from an immunized animal or vaccinated human. Immunization is the process of introducing an antigen, often repeatedly, and via a variety of routes (intraperitoneal, subcutaneous, intramuscular, intravenous or oral) into an experimental animal. An immunogen is a molecule which is recognized by the immune system and is capable of inducing an immune reaction. The immune response elicited usually consists of a humoral component and a cellular component. The term antibody was coined to designate the serum proteins that are responsible for humoral immunity. Antibodies are synthesized by plasma cells (terminally differentiated B cells) and can be detected in the serum. Thus a serum that contains a greater than usual concentration of antibodies to a particular antigen, usually as a result of immunization (although natural infection can also generate convalescent antisera), is an antiserum against that antigen. Serology is the term classically used to refer to the study of reactions between an antigen and its antiserum.

The antibody response

Initial immunization of an animal results in a slowly rising, limited response consisting mainly of immunoglobulin M (IgM) class antibodies in the serum. Further injections of antigen boost the antibody level, resulting in a long-lasting enhanced response. This secondary response is composed primarily of IgG class antibodies. Antibodies that comprise the secondary response possess a higher affinity for antigen and hence most sera are collected after the onset of a secondary response.

Passive transfer of immunity

Specific immunity can also be conferred upon an animal or human by the passive transfer of antiserum from a specifically immunized donor. The recipient of such an adoptively transferred antiserum becomes immune to the particular antigen, without ever having being directly exposed to the antigen or having responded to the antigen itself. The immunity thus acquired is of short duration and no memory cells are generated. This approach is useful for conferring immunity rapidly, without the time delay needed to generate an active immune response. The main disadvantage of passive immunization was first observed by a physician named Clemens von Pirquet who reported on a phenomenon we now call serum sickness. He observed that patients repeatedly treated by passive immunization with horse serum, containing antibodies to diphtheria toxin, developed fever, skin rashes and joint pains.

Specificity, titer and affinity

Several parameters have to be evaluated to establish the quality and usefulness of an antiserum. These are specificity, titer and affinity.

The most outstanding feature of a good antiserum is specificity. Most antigens express a large number of epitopes and, against each of these, different antibodies may be elicited. A highly specific antiserum is one that reacts only with epitopes on the antigen used to raise it and not to other antigens that resemble it. In practice an antiserum reacts with antigens that in one way or another resemble the immunizing antigen. Extensive absorption against these cross-reacting antigens will yield a monospecific antiserum.

A high titer antiserum is one which has a large number of antibodies that are specific for the antigen being tested. The titer of an antiserum is generally expressed as the reciprocal of the highest dilution that reacts with antigen to a predetermined end-point in a given assay system.

The affinity of an antibody reflects the strength of binding between a single antibody-combining site (paratope) and an antigenic determinant (epitope). The term avidity is thus used to describe the overall strength of binding between the antigen and antibody. Avidity is influenced by the intrinsic affinity of the antibody for an epitope on its antigen and the valency of both the antibody and the antigen. As a rule, when an antibody and antigen can form multivalent complexes, the overall strength of the interaction (avidity) is greatly increased.

Making antigens immunogenic

There is no perfect recipe for the generation of a good antiserum. Many foreign molecules (viruses, bacteria and cells) elicit strong antibody responses but some foreign substances fail to induce a good antiserum. In some of these instances the immune system can be manipulated to generate a response, and this can be achieved either by modifying the antigen or varying the host animal. Many of these modifications have been established empirically over the years; however, our increased understanding of the molecular events controlling an immune response should allow more rational approaches for the generation of high titer, specific antisera. Before attempting to produce an antiserum, consideration should be given to the following points: the nature of the antigen and its purity, the site/route of immunization, the dose of the antigen, the choice of adjuvants and the genetic background of the animal to be immunized.

In general, particulate antigens and higher molecular weight proteins tend to be more immunogenic than soluble antigens and proteins of low molecular weight. Converting small soluble molecules into large aggregates is an effective way of enhancing their immunogenicity. The physical coupling of a small molecule which is nonimmunogenic on its own (hapten) to a larger immunogenic carrier molecule also achieves the same result. The most common routes of immunization are subcutaneous, intramuscular, intradermal, intraperitoneal and intravenous. Other routes of immunization include oral ingestion of antigen, antigen inhalation, topical application to the skin and the direct injection into an organ such as the spleen. The dose of the antigen to be administered can profoundly influence the outcome of the procedure. Thus either very low or high doses of antigen may induce tolerance rather than the successful production of an antiserum. One should also bear in mind that with multiple injections, trace contaminants within an antigenic preparation may eventually elicit responses which will be detected in later bleeds collected from the animal and may result in an antiserum with multiple specificities. The degree of specificity of an antiserum depends largely on the degree of purity of the antigen used. The decision about antigen purity is often based on the intended use of the antiserum. If a highly specific antiserum that will only recognize the appropriate antigen is needed, then before commencing immunization the antigen must be purified to homogeneity.

Choice of species

Antisera can be raised in a wide variety of vertebrate animals: mice, rats, guinea pigs, hamsters, rabbits, chickens, sheep, pigs, goats, donkeys and horses. The choice of animal for immunization tends to be determined by how much serum is needed, how much antigen is available and the extent of foreignness of the antigen to the immunizing animal. Sheep, goats, pigs, donkeys and horses yield larger quantities of antiserum but are expensive to maintain and are generally used only for the production of commercially available antisera. Rabbits are most commonly used in the laboratory setting when individual investigators need to generate larger volumes of a particular antiserum. Exsanguination is the recommended method for collection of large amounts of antiserum from an animal to be sacrificed but this should only be performed by individuals well versed in the correct technique and as approved by institutional and national guidelines. The production of limited quantities of antisera in the mouse can be overcome by the production of ascites fluid where high antibody titers, equivalent to those achieved in serum, can be obtained. When only tiny amounts of antigen are available, the use of mice is also a clear advantage. A further advantage is that most investigators use inbred mouse strains and the genetics of the immune response for most of the strains have been well documented. If a weak response to an antigen is obtained in a particular mouse strain, changing the strain may help overcome the problem. If the amount of antigen is not limiting, several animals should be used as, even in inbred animal strains, a single antigen preparation will produce differing responses. The most important rule in the choice of animals is that immunization should be done in animals that are furthest in evolutionary distance from the source of antigen.

Adjuvants

The judicious use of adjuvants (L. *adjuvare*, to help) allows for the generation of early, strong and sustained immune responses. In fact the use of an adjuvant can often determine the difference between success and failure. The adjuvants that are available are highly heterogeneous agents and exert their effects in diverse ways, such as causing depot formation at the site of injection (e.g. oil-based adjuvants), causing immunostimulation (e.g. lipopolysaccharide) and serving as delivery vehicles by facilitating the targeting of antigens (e.g. liposomes, biodegradable polymers). The most commonly used adjuvant is Freund's complete adjuvant, in which the immunogen is prepared as a water-in-oil emulsion. The main disadvantage of Freunds complete adjuvant is that it evokes aggressive granuloma formation in the animal and is thus completely unacceptable for use in human vaccine programs. A common alternative, and one licensed for human use, is alum. Here antigen is adsorbed on to an aluminum salt, aluminum hydroxide being most commonly used. Other adjuvants include Freund's incomplete adjuvant, *N*-acetylmuramyl-L-alanyl-D-isoglutamine (common name MDP) and its derivatives, lipid A, lipopolysaccharide, saponin, Quil A, ISCOMS, liposomes and micropheres made of biodegradable polymers. It should be stressed that the use of adjuvants is not only important for the humoral arm of the immune response (i.e. in generation of a superior antiserum) but also for activation of cellular immune responses. The single most important issue determining the acceptability of an adjuvant for human use is safety and the severity of side-effects, especially when implemented for routine childhood immunizations.

Uses of antisera

A final word about the use of antisera. They are used in medicine both for diagnostic purposes and for patient treatment, and in the laboratory they are used as analytical and preparatory tools. Thus the injection of antisera against toxins such as diphtheria and tetanus, against the venoms of snakes, and against rabies still remains a mainstay of treatment. Equally, the use of specific antiserum allows for the detection and quantitation of minute quantities of telltale antigens such as meningococus in the cerebrospinal fluid or hormones and drug levels in urine or sera. Specific antisera are used for tissue typing and cells can be phenotyped using antisera raised against specific cell surface molecules. Antisera coupled to radionuclides are used in the detection and treatment of some tumors.

See also: **Adjuvants; Affinity; Antigens; Antilymphocyte serum; Carrier; Epitopes; Hapten; Immunoassays; Immunogen; Liposomes; Plasma; Serum sickness; Specificity; Tissue typing; Tolerance, peripheral; Toxins; Vaccination, methods of administration; Venoms.**

Further reading

Catty D and Raykundalia C (1988) Production and quality control of polyclonal antibodies. In: Catty D (ed) vol I: *A Practical Approach*, Chap. 2. Oxford: IRL Press.

Delves PJ (1997) *Antibody Production*. Chichester: Wiley.

Dresser DW (1986) Immunization of experimental animals. In: Weir DM, Herzenberg LA, Blackwell C and Herzenberg LA (eds) *Handbook of Experimental Immunology*, 4th edn, chap 8. Oxford: Blackwell Science.

Harlow E and Lane D (eds) (1988) *Antibodies: A Laboratory Manual*. New York: Cold Spring Harbor Laboratory Press.

Stewart-Tull DES (ed) (1995) *The Theory and Practical Application of Adjuvants*. Chichester: Wiley.

APOPTOSIS

Seamus J Martin, Molecular Cell Biology Laboratory, Maynooth College, Co Kildare, Ireland

In a multicellular organism cell death occurs in many contexts – during development, tissue homeostasis, terminal differentiation and disease. In most of these cases cells are eliminated due to the triggering of a process that results in the dismantling of the cell from within. This demolition process results in a very distinctive and easily recognizable cellular phenotype that, in 1972, led John Kerr, Andrew Wyllie and Alister Currie to propose that this mode of cell death was different from that which occurred in response to severe cellular insults (necrosis), and for which they coined the term apoptosis. Apoptosis – a word derived from the Greek where it is used to describe the process of leaves falling from trees or petals from flowers – perfectly encapsulates a process where cells quietly shrink and fall away from the tissues they were once an integral part of, with little damage to the main organism. Although the features of apoptosis were originally described in mammalian cells, the morphologic characteristics of dying cells are strikingly similar in birds, amphibians and insects. This suggests that at least some of the genes controlling this process have been well conserved through evolution, and indeed, evidence for this is now emerging.

Apoptosis can be triggered by diverse stimuli, both physiologic and pathologic, all of which seem to engage the same cellular machinery that is responsible for the destruction of the cell from within. Thus, although the proximal signaling events that can lead to apoptosis may vary from one stimulus to another, it is likely that different signals converge on a common set of effector molecules at some point. Recent developments in this field heavily implicate members of the interleukin 1β (IL-1β)-converting enzyme (ICE) family (caspases) as the end-stage effectors of apoptosis.

Apoptosis: form and function

Morphology

During apoptosis, a cell typically condenses its nucleus and cytoplasm, its DNA is degraded into many small (200 bp–250 kbp) pieces, marked blebbing of the plasma membrane occurs, and, in the final stages, the cell collapses into multiple intact fragments that are eaten by phagocytes *before* the cellular contents have had a chance to escape (**Figure 1**). Probably the most striking morphologic feature of apoptosis is the marked condensation and disintegration of the nucleus into numerous, intensely staining, spheres scattered throughout the cytoplasm

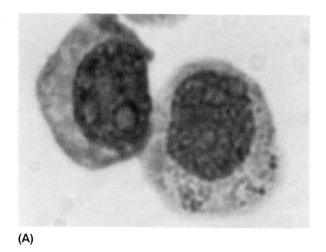

(A)

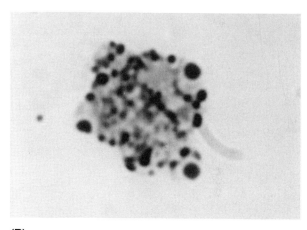

(B)

Figure 2 Morphological features of (A) a live versus (B) an apoptotic cell. Note particularly the disintegration of the nucleus into numerous discrete fragments.

(**Figure 2**). This contrasts starkly with the process of necrosis, where the nucleus typically swells to occupy most of the cytoplasm, and the chromatin decreases rather than increases in staining intensity. Plasma

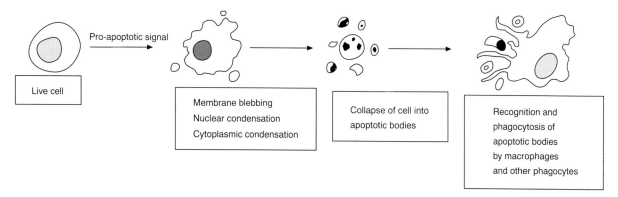

Figure 1 Schematic representation of apoptosis.

membrane blebbing and disintegration of the cell into numerous apoptotic bodies are other highly characteristic features of apoptosis (**Figure 3**). The collapse of the cell into apoptotic bodies, that retain membrane integrity for several hours, likely facilitates phagocytosis and removal of the dying cell by surrounding phagocytes (**Figure 1**). In essence, apoptosis represents a clean and efficient way of removing unwanted or diseased cells while minimizing an inflammatory response.

Recognition and removal of apoptotic cells by phagocytes

Changes to the composition of the plasma membrane have long been suspected to mediate early recognition of apoptotic cells by phagocytes – thereby triggering their safe removal. In many ways this stage of apoptosis is the most critical, since the essential functional difference between an apoptotic and a necrotic cell is that the former is somehow recognized as being in the throes of death several hours before any cytoplasmic contents leak out. Necrotic cells, on the other hand, undergo early lysis, thereby

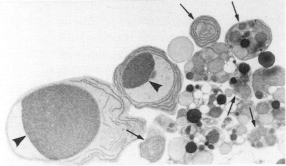

Figure 3 Transmission electron micrographs of a healthy (top) versus an apoptotic (bottom) mouse hepatocyte. Apoptosis was induced by ligation of CD95 (Fas/APO-1) on these cells with cross-linking antibody. Note the dramatic collapse of the apoptotic cell into many discrete apoptotic bodies (arrows) and the marked condensation of the chromatin (arrowheads). N, indicates the position of the nucleus in the live cell. (Reproduced with permission from Ni *et al.* (1994) *Experimental Cell Research* **215**: 332–337. Figure kindly provided by Professor Shigekazu Nagata.)

causing damage to surrounding cells and eliciting an inflammatory response. When apoptotic cells are formed in culture, where there are no phagocytic cells around to eat them, they eventually undergo secondary necrosis, which would probably be just as damaging as primary necrosis were it to occur *in vivo*. Thus, the membrane changes that signal to phagocytes that a cell is undergoing apoptosis are of paramount importance in this process.

Membrane changes that occur on apoptotic cells have proved elusive. To date it appears that there are two main alterations that occur on the surface of apoptotic cells that may be mutually exclusive in their usage. One mechanism used by apoptotic cells to signal their plight to surrounding cells is to export phosphatidylserine – a lipid normally confined to the inner plasma membrane leaflet on healthy cells – to the external surface of the plasma membrane. This appears to trigger phagocytosis of these cells, presumably by recognition of surface phosphatidylserine via a putative phosphatidylserine receptor on the macrophage. The other mechanism that has been comparatively well characterized involves the appearance of, an as yet unidentified, thrombospondin-binding ligand on the surface of the apoptotic cell. This ligand is bound by thrombospondin-bearing macrophages (thrombospondin being bound to the macrophage via a vitronectin receptor-CD36 interaction) and facilitates uptake of the apoptotic cell by the latter. Interestingly, the CD36-associated mechanism also appears to operate in *Drosophila*, as recent studies have discovered a CD36-related molecule (Croquemort) involved in macrophage removal of apoptotic cells in this organism. Other apoptosis-associated membrane changes have also been described, such as alterations to the carbohydrate composition of the plasma membrane, but these changes remain poorly characterized.

Towards a molecular mechanism

Due to the widespread importance of apoptosis in many biological processes there has been intense interest in understanding how this process works at a molecular level. By 1993, although much of the cell biology of apoptosis had been established and several key apoptosis regulatory molecules, such as Bcl-2 and p53, had been discovered, very little was known concerning the nature of the cell death machinery itself. In 1993 a major breakthrough occurred when it was reported that CED-3, one of the genes that was known to be required for all the developmental-related programmed cell deaths in the nematode worm *Caenorhabditis elegans*, was homologous to ICE (caspase-1). ICE is a cysteine protease that has been implicated in the processing of IL-1β to its mature form and is unusual as it was the first protease described that cleaves after aspartate (Asp) residues. Recent studies suggest that ICE itself probably does not play a pivotal role in apoptosis: rather several of its mammalian homologs (including CPP32 (caspase-3), Mch2 (caspase-6), Mch3 (caspase-7) and mch5 (FLICE/Caspase-8)) are involved in the cell death signal. These caspases, which cleave after Asp residues, appear to be constitutively expressed in most cells as inactive precursors that require proteolytic processing to achieve their active forms (**Figure 4**).

Evidence that proteases are central to apoptosis

The evidence that proteases may be key components of the cell death machinery is derived from several lines of investigation. Early indications that proteases may participate in apoptosis was suggested by observations that several proteins underwent proteolytic cleavage during this process. Additional evidence was provided by the discovery that certain broad-spectrum protease inhibitors could block or delay apoptosis. Strong support for a role for caspases in apoptosis has subsequently been provided by studies that have examined the effects on apoptosis of CrmA, a cowpox virus-derived serpin (serine protease inhibitor) that was known for its ability to act as a pseudosubstrate for, and thereby neutralize, ICE. Several groups have independently reported that CrmA potently blocks several forms of apoptosis, including that induced by ligation of the CD95 molecule (Fas/APO-1) as well as due to CTL attack. Another pseudosubstrate for caspases was recently discovered in the form of the baculovirus

p35 protein, which was already known for its ability to act as a potent repressor of apoptosis.

Many recent studies have also found that specific peptide inhibitors of caspases (YVAD, DEVD, DEAD, VAD) inhibit many forms of apoptosis. All of this evidence for protease involvement in apoptosis is supported by the ongoing discovery of new proteins that are cleaved during this process. Together these data heavily implicate proteases as central components of the cell death machinery and suggest that the caspases play a critical role in apoptosis (**Figure 5**).

How protease activation may lead to the apoptotic phenotype

So how do proteases produce the apoptotic phenotype in a cell? The short answer is that we do not know as yet. Some informed guesses can be made by looking at the nature of the substrates that are cleaved during apoptosis. To date, most of the substrates that have been documented to undergo proteolytic cleavage during apoptosis are localized in the nucleus. It is likely that many of these cleavage events are not contributory to the apoptotic phenotype but are merely bystander effects due to these proteins possessing the appropriate cleavage sites. This idea is strongly supported by the observation that enucleated cells can also undergo apoptosis. However, it is relatively easy to conceive how cleavage of some of these proteins may directly lead to changes in the cell that frequently occur during apoptosis. For example, cleavage of the nuclear lamins, proteins that are largely responsible for the maintenance of the integrity of the nuclear envelope, could be directly responsible for the collapse (condensation) of the nucleus that is seen during apoptosis. Proteolysis of fodrin, a cytoskeletal protein that plays a major role in the cortical cytoskeleton, could lead to the plasma membrane blebbing that is typical of apoptosis (**Figure 3**). Proteases could also serve to degrade an inhibitor of the endonuclease that cleaves DNA at internucleosomal sites during apoptosis. Indeed, a protease with nuclease-activating properties has been described. Further studies are required in order to fully investigate the impact of each of the cleavage events upon cell integrity and to elucidate how they impact upon the cell death process.

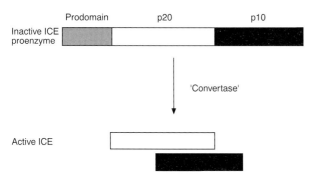

Figure 4 Caspase (ICE/CED-3) family proteases require proteolytic processing to achieve their mature forms. Most caspases are probably constitutively expressed as inactive precursor proteins that require further proteolytic processing at Asp residues in order to achieve their active heterodimer forms (that may further associate to form dimers of heterodimers). Maturation of some caspases is seen during the early stages of apoptosis (CPP32 and Mch3, for example).

Apoptosis in immunity

In the immune system, apoptosis is used as a means to dispose of unwanted cells time and again. In many cases the CD95 molecule (Fas/APO-1), a member of the TNF/NGF receptor family, is used to transduce the death signal. Some of the situations where

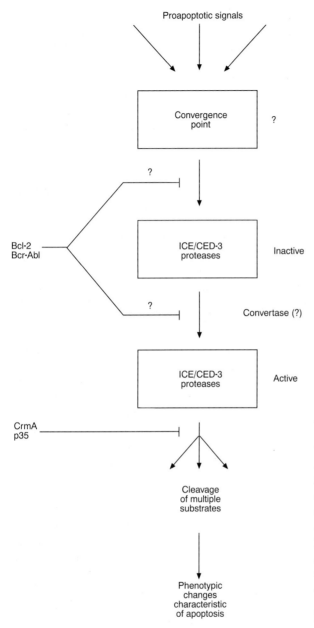

Figure 5 Molecular events in apoptosis. Members of the caspase (ICE/CED-3) protease family are depicted as being at a point just below the convergence point for diverse proapoptotic stimuli. Activation of ICE/CED-3 family proteases may lead directly to the apoptotic phenotype through cleavage of specific substrates, although this is speculative. From current evidence, some apoptosis-repressor proteins (Bcl-2) appear to act upstream of the point of activation of at least some of the members of the ICE/CED-3 family, while others (CrmA, p35) act directly as inhibitors of these proteases.

apoptosis plays a key role in immunity are described below.

Thymic selection

It has been estimated that approximately 95–98% of thymocytes that enter the thymus are eliminated there. Thymocytes die at several stages of the maturation process; either because they fail to rearrange their TCR genes successfully, because they exhibit strong reactivity with self (negative selection), or because they fail to recognize self-MHC at all (death by neglect). Studies in the late 1980s and the early 1990s established that thymocytes die in all of these cases due to the induction of apoptosis in these cells. Most of the cell deaths that occur in the thymus do so in the cortex and at the corticomedullary boundary at the double-positive stage (CD4+CD8+) of thymocyte development. Upon entry into the medulla, single-positive thymocytes (CD4+CD8− or CD4−CD8+) become much more resistant to the induction of apoptosis. The precise nature of the signal that provokes death of cortical thymocytes has not been established. The possible involvement of CD95–CD95 ligand interactions is ruled out due to the fact that thymocyte maturation is largely unaffected in mice that carry loss-of-function mutations in CD95 (lpr/lpr) or the CD95 ligand (gld/gld). The thymocyte death signal is similarly unaffected by overexpression of Bcl-2, a 26 kDa protein that blocks many other forms of cell death.

Despite the enormous amount of cell death that goes on in the thymus, it is remarkable how few apoptotic cells are actually detectable in tissue sections of this organ. This puzzle can be explained if it is recalled that apoptotic cells are readily recognized by cells with phagocytic capability – by virtue of the membrane changes on these cells – and are eaten before they exhibit the morphologic features of apoptosis. Recent studies have implicated resident F4/80− macrophages as the effectors of this efficient clearance process for thymocytes undergoing negative selection, whereas F4/80+ macrophages appear to remove thymocytes that have died by neglect.

Peripheral deletion

The small minority of thymocytes that are positively selected exit the thymus and migrate to the peripheral lymphoid organs. Here they are faced with the possibility of reacting with previously unencountered self-antigens. Should this happen, the autoreactive mature T cell, all going to plan, should then undergo apoptosis, probably as a result of receiving an inappropriate activation signal (such as TCR engagement in the absence of CD28 costimulation). Should this peripheral deletion process fail for any reason, then autoimmunity can result. Unlike in the thymus, CD95–CD95L interactions do appear to be important for peripheral deletion, as both lpr and gld mice are impaired in peripheral deletion and develop a systemic lupus erythematosus (SLE)-like autoimmune disease as a result.

Peripheral T and B lymphocytes are also eliminated after an immune response, otherwise the numbers of these cells would steadily increase after each successive encounter with antigen. While such an increase does happen to some extent (i.e. precursor frequencies to recall antigens are higher than to previously unencountered antigens), clearly the majority of clonally expanded lymphocytes do not survive long after an immune response has ended. Studies in recent years have established that these excess lymphocytes die by apoptosis. Once again, CD95–CD95L interactions have been implicated in this process. While mature peripheral T cells constitutively express CD95 on their surface, they are largely resistant to CD95L-mediated killing until they are activated, whereupon they now acquire sensitivity to CD95 ligation. Thus, activated T cells die upon encounter with CD95L-bearing cells. Since the expression of CD95L is strictly restricted to certain tissues, it is not clear what cells do the actual killing. It may be the activated T cells themselves, since CD95L is upregulated on lymphocytes upon activation, or a subset of dendritic cells or other antigen-presenting cells.

CTL and NK killing

Cytotoxic lymphocytes (CTLs and natural killer (NK) cells) are capable of killing target cells via two distinct pathways: by delivering cytotoxic granules on to the plasma membrane of the target cell, or by cross-linking the CD95 molecule on the target cell surface via CD95 ligand. In both cases, the end-result is the activation of the endogenous death machinery in the target cell, resulting in death from within – a kind of assisted suicide.

Granule-dependent killing is thought to be the major mechanism of cytotoxic lymphocyte killing. Cytotoxic cell granules contain perforin, a pore-forming protein similar to the C9 component of complement, as well as a series of enzymes – several of which are serine proteases – called granzymes. Perforin is thought to act as a conduit or channel to allow the entry of granzymes into the target cell cytoplasm. Of the seven or so granzymes that have been characterized to date, only one of these, granzyme B, has been shown to be both necessary and sufficient, in combination with perforin, to induce apoptosis of target cells. Granzyme B is an unusual protease in that it cleaves after Asp residues, a property that it shares with the caspase family of cysteine proteases discussed earlier. Recent studies have shed light on the mechanism whereby granzyme B activates the endogenous death machinery in the target cell. A number of groups have found that granzyme B is capable of directly cleaving and activating several members of the caspase family, but not ICE itself. Thus, granule-dependent killing operates by directly activating the endogenous cell death machinery in the target cell by processing members of the caspase family to their active forms.

The other mechanism of cytotoxic lymphocyte killing involves a CD95 ligand-bearing cell interacting with, thereby cross-linking, CD95 on the target cell surface. As mentioned above, CD95 is a member of the TNF/NGF receptor family that transduces, upon trimerization, a death signal into cells bearing this receptor. CD95 was originally identified in 1989 by two separate groups and is commonly called two different names as a result: Fas or APO-1. The molecular mediators of the CD95-associated death signal have recently begun to emerge. Briefly, the cytoplasmic tail of CD95 contains a stretch of amino acids that are critical for the CD95-mediated death signal (the death domain), but this region does not have any obvious signaling function (such as kinase or phosphatase activity). Other death domain-containing proteins have since been discovered, such as FADD (Fas-associated death domain), that can associate with the CD95 death domain, thereby propagating the apoptotic signal. Thus, the death domain appears to be a protein–protein interaction domain. FADD then recruits caspase-8 (MACH-1/FLICE) which becomes processed to its active form, thus propagating the death signal.

Maintenance of immune privilege

It has been known for over a hundred years that certain sites in the body enjoy immune privilege. That is to say, immune responses do not generally occur at these sites. Classically, an immune-privileged site is defined as an area where introduction of allogeneic or xenogeneic cells does not result in immediate rejection as it would in other areas of the body. This definition has subsequently been broadened to include infectious organisms and tumors. Examples of immune-privileged sites include the eye, the testis and the central nervous system – all of which are tissues where the benefits of an immune response are outweighed by the dangerous consequences of a vigorous immune reaction in such delicate and vital tissues. While it was initially thought that immune privilege was maintained by physical barriers that contained antigen and prevented infiltration of the site by myeloid cells and lymphocytes, this is now known to be untrue because these cells do enter privileged sites but are somehow inactivated. Recent studies on the eye and the testes appear to have solved this puzzle. In these organs, it transpires that CD95 ligand is abundantly expressed such that infiltrating lymphocytes and neutrophils – both of which express surface CD95 – are induced to undergo apoptosis upon entry into these sites. As elegant proof of this, mice carrying a non-functional CD95-ligand (gld) do not enjoy immune privilege and, in the case of the eye, display marked infiltration upon introduction of a virus (herpes simplex virus type 1, HSV-1) into the anterior chamber of this organ – resulting in keratitis. In stark contrast, introduction of HSV-1 into the eye of wild-type mice results in death of infiltrating lymphocytes and neutrophils and containment of the infiltrating cells to the anterior chamber. Similarly elegant transplantation experiments of testes from lpr and gld mice yielded a similar conclusion that CD95 ligand was responsible for maintaining immune privilege in this organ also. Other studies have demonstrated that CD95L is also abundantly expressed in other immune-privileged sites such as the brain, ovary, uterus, adrenal gland and prostate, suggesting that a similar protective mechanism from immune responses operates in these tissues also.

B cell development and affinity maturation

Like T lymphocytes, the majority of newly formed B lymphocytes fail to migrate to the peripheral lymphoid organs due to the induction of apoptosis in these cells. B cells are produced throughout life in the bone marrow but only a small minority of these cells, as is the case with thymocytes, will be allowed to enter the peripheral blood. Most developing B-lineage cells die by apoptosis, either because of aberrant immunoglobulin (Ig) gene rearrangements or due to encounter with high concentrations of high-affinity antigens (akin to negative selection). It has been estimated that approximately 75% of developing B cells die in the bone marrow at the transition between large pro-B to small pre-B cell stage. The small fraction of virgin B cells that exit the bone marrow travel to the spleen and then on to the lymph nodes. In the peripheral lymphoid tissues B cells fall into two compartments, short-lived (2–3 days) and long-lived (several weeks). Short-lived B cells probably die (by apoptosis) through failure to encounter antigen and are rapidly replaced by newly formed B cells from the bone marrow. B cells that receive a survival signal (antigenic stimulation) likely switch to the long-lived state, although there has been some debate concerning whether short-lived and long-lived B cells are derived from separate bone marrow precursors or a common progenitor. In either case, long-term survival of B cells appears to require repeated re-stimulation with antigen. Long-term B cell survival appears to be regulated, at least in part, by expression of the Bcl-2 protein. Bcl-2 transgenic mice

display elevated peripheral B cell numbers and extended B cell memory.

B cells that manage to persist also run the gauntlet of apoptosis during affinity maturation in the germinal centers. During the germinal center reaction, activated B cells acquire point mutations in the V regions of their immunoglobulin genes that may or may not increase their affinity for antigen and can even result in autoreactivity. The majority of B cells that undergo this hypermutation process are eliminated via apoptosis, with mutants that have a high affinity for antigen being rescued from a similar fate due to encounter with their specific antigen in the context of CD40 ligand (gp39) costimulation. CD95 also appears to play a role in this elimination process because activated B cells acquire sensitivity to CD95 unless they receive concurrent engagement of the CD40 molecule. This may also explain why lpr mice (that are defective in CD95) also display a B cell defect and develop and SLE-like autoimmune disease.

Resolution of inflammation

One of the earliest events in an immune response involves the dramatic accumulation of infiltrating neutrophils and other cells of the myeloid lineage at the site of infection. Neutrophils form a very important first line of defense and these cells appear to be well equipped for this task, with a barrage of toxic enzymes and reactive oxygen intermediates within their secondary granules. But what happens to all of these cells when they have completed their task and are no longer required? It is well known that neutrophils have a very short half-life of approximately 12–18 hours. But where do they die and how are they disposed of? By now it will come as no surprise to learn that old unwanted neutrophils die by apoptosis and that damage to cells in the vicinity of dying neutrophils is minimized as they are programmed to die around the time that the wave of macrophage infiltration reaches its peak. Thus, inflammatory macrophages are charged with the task of removing the dying neutrophils and of safely disposing of their potentially destructive contents. The trigger for macrophage recognition of senescent neutrophils, as discussed earlier, appears to be either phosphatidylserine externalization at the surface of the plasma membrane or the appearance of a thrombospondin-binding moiety on the surface of these cells – depending on whether the phagocytic cells are inflammatory or resting macrophages, respectively. Interestingly, macrophages respond very differently when they phagocytose apoptotic cells, as opposed to yeast particles, for example, as the former do not elicit the release of inflammatory mediators by the macrophage. Whether a distinct phagolysosomal compartment is used for digestion of apoptotic cells has not been explored as yet.

Apoptosis in disease

We now know that proper control of cell death is just as important for the maintenance of dividing cell populations at equilibrium as control of cell division is. Therefore, just as loss of normal controls on cell division can result in disease, so can defects in the regulation of cell death. Obviously, cell death defects can take two forms – too much or too little. Situations where excessive or inappropriate apoptosis may contribute to disease include neurodegenerative diseases such as Alzheimer disease, Parkinson disease and spinal muscular atrophy. In the latter case, this appears to be due to loss-of-function mutations in an endogenous inhibitor of apoptosis (neuronal apoptosis inhibitory protein). It has also been proposed that the loss of CD4+ T cells that is observed during human immunodeficiency virus (HIV)-1 infection is due to excessive apoptosis (although this is a debatable point). The development of some forms of autoimmunity may either be the result of a block in apoptosis – that allows autoreactive lymphocytes to survive – or defective apoptosis – that allows the release of proteins that could potentially break self-tolerance. On the other side of the coin, over-expression or dysregulation of genes that can block apoptosis (such as bcl-2 or bcr-abl) or mutations in genes that can facilitate apoptosis (p53) may also contribute to the development of malignancy by synergizing with proliferation-associated oncogenes (such as c-*myc*). Thus, intensive investigation is currently underway to understand how apoptosis works at a molecular level and to explore how this process can be modulated in situations where this may be desirable.

See also: **B lymphocyte activation; Cytotoxic T lymphocytes; Thymic epithelium: potential role in regulatory T cell tolerance; Fas (CD95) and fas ligand; Germinal center; Lifespan of immune cells and molecules; Membrane-associated cytoskeleton: role in regulating immune cell function; Memory, immunological; Natural killer (NK) cells; Perforin; Privileged sites; T lymphocyte activation; T lymphocytes, autoreactive.**

Further reading

Abbas AK (1996) Die and let live: eliminating dangerous lymphocytes. *Immunity* 84: 655–657.

Cohen JJ, Duke RC, Fadok VA and Sellins KS (1992) Apoptosis and programmed cell death in immunity. *Annual Review of Immunology* 10: 267–293.

Cotter TG and Martin SJ (eds) (1996) *Techniques In Apoptosis: A User's Guide*. London: Portland Press.

Duvall E and Wyllie AH (1986) Death and the cell. *Immunology Today* 7: 115–119.

Gregory CD (ed) (1995) *Apoptosis and the Immune Response*. New York: Wiley-Liss.

Kerr JFR, Wyllie AH and Currie AR (1972) Apoptosis: a basic biological phenomenon with wide-ranging implications in tissue kinetics. *British Journal of Cancer* 26: 239–257.

McGahon AJ, Cotter TG and Green DR (1994) The *abl* oncogene family and apoptosis. *Cell Death Differentiation* 1: 77–83.

Martin SJ and Green DR (1995) Apoptosis and cancer: the failure of controls on cell death and cell survival. *Critical Reviews in Oncology/Hematology* 18: 137–153.

Martin SJ and Green DR (1995) Protease activation during apoptosis: death by a thousand cuts? *Cell* 82: 349–352.

Martin SJ, Green DR and Cotter TG (1994) Dicing with death: dissecting the components of the apoptosis machinery. *Trends in Biochemical Sciences* 19: 26–30.

Nagata S and Goldstein P (1995) The Fas death factor. *Science* 267: 1449–1456.

Raff MC (1992) Social controls on cell survival and cell death. *Nature* 356: 397–400.

Savill JS, Fadok V, Henson P and Haslett C (1993) Phagocyte recognition of cells undergoing apoptosis. *Immunology Today* 14: 131–136.

Tan EM (1994) Autoimmunity and apoptosis. *Journal of Experimental Medicine* 179: 1083–1086.

Thompson CB (1995) Apoptosis in the pathogenesis and treatment of disease. *Science* 267: 1456–1462.

Williams GT and Smith CA (1993) Molecular regulation of apoptosis: genetic controls on cell death. *Cell* 74: 777–779.

Wyllie AH, Kerr JFR and Currie AR (1980) Cell death: the significance of apoptosis. *International Review of Cytology* 68: 251–306.

ARACHIDONIC ACID AND THE LEUKOTRIENES

Marek Rola-Pleszczynski, Faculty of Medicine, Université de Sherbrooke, Sherbrooke, Quebec, Canada

Arachidonic acid (AA) is an important constituent of mammalian cell membranes. Following membrane perturbations or receptor-mediated signaling which leads to activation of phospholipase A_2 (PLA_2), AA is released from membrane phospholipids. It may undergo oxidative metabolism through cyclo-oxygenase, which results in the formation of the various prostaglandins, through the cytochrome P450 system, or through one of several lipoxygenases. Borgeat and Samuelsson first identified a novel class of molecules derived from this latter metabolic pathway of AA, which they named leukotrienes, because of their leukocytic origin and their characteristic triene structure. Leukotrienes (LTs) are derived from the combined actions of 5-lipoxygenase (5-LOX) and 5-LOX-activating protein (FLAP), with initial formation of 5-hydroperoxyeicosatetraenoic (5-HPETE) acid, followed by LTA_4. LTB_4, which is an enzymatic, hydrolytic product of LTA_4, differs from the other leukotrienes, LTC_4, LTD_4 and LTE_4, in that it has no peptidic component. It is a more stable molecule than the peptidoleukotrienes, but can be rapidly degraded through ω-oxidation by polymorphonuclear leukocytes (PMNs) to the relatively inactive metabolites, $20\text{-}OH\text{-}LTB_4$ and $20\text{-}COOH\text{-}LTB_4$.

While sharing some of the myotropic properties of the other leukotrienes, LTB_4 has been found to exert very strong leukocytotropic activities. It is one of the most powerful chemokinetic and chemotactic agents and it can induce neutrophil aggregation, degranulation, hexose uptake and enhanced binding to endothelial cells. It can also induce cation fluxes, augment cytoplasmic calcium concentrations from intracellular pools and activate phosphatidylinositol hydrolysis. LTB_4 can also synergize with prostaglandins E_1, (PGE_1) and PGE_2 in causing macromolecule leakage in the skin, through increased vascular permeability, and, when injected into guinea pig skin, it induces leukocytoclastic vasculitis. Two sets of plasma membrane receptors for LTB_4 have been described on human PMNs. The high-affinity receptor set mediates aggregation, chemokinesis and increased adherence to surfaces, while the low-affinity receptor set mediates degranulation and increased oxidative metabolism. In contrast to human cells, rat leukocytes lack the lower affinity receptor set. Signal transduction via high-affinity receptors appears to involve a guanine nucleotide regulatory protein. In contrast to PMNs, little is known at present about potential LTB_4 receptors on lymphocytes, although a fraction of $CD4^+$ and $CD8^+$ T cells bind LTB_4.

Cellular sources of LTB_4

LTB_4 is rapidly synthesized by phagocytic cells, principally PMNs and aveolar macrophages, upon challenge with a variety of stimuli such as microbial pathogens, toxins, aggregated immunoglobulin, tumor necrosis factor α (TNFα), particulate material or ionophores, especially when exogenous AA is available. Its synthesis can also be induced by platelet-derived 12-HPETE or platelet-activating factor (PAF). Induction by natural stimuli of LTB_4 production by PMNs *in vitro* is relatively modest, unless the cells are primed by granulocyte-macrophage colony-stimulating factor (GM-CSF), TNFα or bacterial lipopolysaccharide (LPS) (**Table 1**). Under these conditions, enhanced LTB_4 production appears to be the result of both an immediate activation of PLA_2, with subsequent generation of AA, and a later, transcriptional induction of 5-LOX and FLAP gene expression. In contrast, PMNs exposed to transforming growth factor β (TGFβ) lose the capacity to produce LTB_4 through a selective downregulation of 5-LOX (but not FLAP) mRNA expression. Such an interaction between priming events and direct stimuli of LT generation may also be operative *in vivo* in the context of infection and inflammation.

LTB_4 is predominantly a product of cells of myeloid origin. PMNs are the main source of the mediator: when stimulated by LPS, PMNs can produce five times more LTB_4 than monocytes. In con-

Table 1 Production of LTB_4 by PMNs as a function of stimulus and priming

Stimulus	Priming	LTB_4 production
Ca^{2+} ionophore	–	++
PAF or fMLP	–	±
PAF or fMLP	GM-CSF, TNFα or LPS	++
PAF or fMLP	TGFβ	–

fMLP, N-formylmethionine leucine phenylalanine.

trast, the latter produce a wider variety of AA metabolites, including the peptido-LT and prostanoids. B lymphocytes can also produce LTB_4 and 5-HETE. Unlike PMNs or monocytes, they require particular stimulation conditions, including an oxidative environment, in addition to a source of AA. T lymphocytes, on the other hand, do not produce LTs, as they lack 5-LOX. Similarly, endothelial cells and epithelial cells of different origins cannot directly synthesize LTB_4 from AA, because they lack both 5-LOX and FLAP (**Table 2**). They can and do, however, produce LTB_4 when supplied with LTA_4, through what is known as transcellular metabolism, since they have LTA_4 hydrolase. That the genes involved in LT synthesis can be derepressed is suggested, however, by the observed production of LTC_4 by a human hybridoma formed by fusing $CD8^+$ T cells with $CD4^+$ CEM-6 lymphoma cells.

LTB_4 has been detected in significant concentrations in inflammatory synovial exudates, psoriatic skin lesions, peritonitis and inflammatory bowel disease. In an animal model of colitis, local production of LTB_4 and LTC_4 correlates with inflammatory cell infiltrates. Globally, LTB_4 thus appears to be a potent proinflammatory agent. It may also affect many immunoregulatory functions via interactions with a variety of cell populations, as presented in the next sections.

Cellular actions of LTB_4

T lymphocytes

When LTB_4 is added to human peripheral blood mononuclear leukocyte cultures stimulated with mitogenic lectins, an inhibition of the proliferative response can be observed. Similar findings are also observed for LTD_4 and LTE_4, and for 15-HETE in mice. A significant suppressor cell activity can indeed be generated at picomolar concentrations of LTB_4.

Table 2 Expression of 5-LOX and FLAP in various cell populations

Cell population	FLAP	5-LOX
PMNs	+	+
Monocytes/macrophages	+	+
Myeloid cell lines		
THP-1	–	+
U937	+	–
HL-60 (differentiated)	+	+
B cells/B cell lines	+	+
T cells	±	–
T cell lines (Jurkat, MOLT)	+	–
Endothelial cells	–	–

LTD_4 induces no such suppressor cell activity. The magnitude of the suppressor cell activity generated by LTB_4 is comparable to that seen with histamine, but the concentrations at which it occurs are orders of magnitude lower than those needed with the latter. LTB_4-induced suppressor T cells can also inhibit immunoglobulin production by B cells and leukocyte migration inhibitory factor production by T cells.

When LTB_4 induces the appearance of suppressor cells, the effective suppressor cells bear finally the $CD8^+$ phenotype. Proliferation of $CD4^+$ cells is inhibited by LTB_4, whereas the proliferation of $CD8^+$ cells is enhanced. Further analysis of the cellular requirements for LTB_4-induced suppressor cell activity reveals that, whereas only T cells need to interact with LTB_4, the expression of their suppressor activity requires the presence of monocytes in the responding cell population. Only purified $CD8^+$ T cells can bypass this requirement. For preincubated $CD4^+$ T cells or unfractionated T cells, little suppression is seen in the absence of monocytes, whereas a helper effect is evident in the presence of monocytes plus the cyclo-oxygenase inhibitor indomethacin. This phenomenon could be explained by a dual stimulation of monocytes to produce both PGs and interleukin-1 (IL-1) by LTB_4-preincubated T cells. Indeed, LTB_4-pulsed T cells release a soluble factor which stimulates monocytes to produce PGE_2 and/or IL-1, and most of the activity of such T cell supernatants is attributable to interferon γ (IFNγ). LTB_4 can indeed enhance, at nanomolar concentrations, IFNγ production by $CD4^+$ T cells and inhibit IFNγ production by $CD8^+$ T cells. In the mouse, LTB_4 (as well as other leukotrienes and AA itself) can replace a requirement for helper cells or IL-2 in IFNγ production. LTB_4 can also induce proliferation of IL-2-dependent T cells in the presence of suboptimal IL-2 and restore such proliferation after inhibition with lipoxygenase inhibitors or hydrocortisone. LTB_4 can also induce T cells to produce IL-2 and IL-5 (**Figure 1**).

B lymphocytes

Purified human B cells show amplified proliferative responses to IL-2, IL-4 and B cell stimulatory factor, when exposed to picomolar concentrations of LTB_4. Immunoglobulin G (IgG) production is also enhanced by LTB_4, but not by LTC_4. Moreover, in the presence of IL-4, LTB_4 stimulates IgE production, suggesting a central role for this mediator in allergy. In contrast, LTC_4 can affect B cells directly and suppress Ig production. LTB_4 also induces enhanced CD23 and major histocompatibility complex (MHC) class II antigen expression on B cells (**Figure 1**).

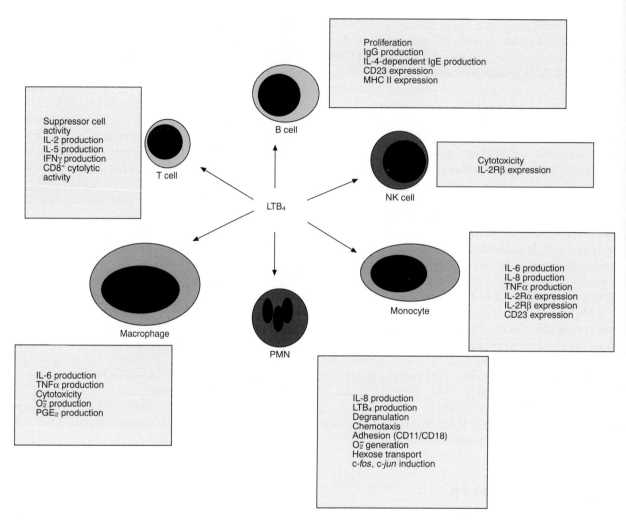

Figure 1   Stimulatory proteins of LTB$_4$ on cells of the immune system.

NK cells

LTB$_4$ can modulate the activity of natural killer (NK) and natural cytotoxic (NC) lymphocytes. At picomolar concentrations, LTB$_4$ and, to a lesser extent, LTA$_4$, markedly augment NK and NC activities. Lipoxygenase inhibitors can reversibly block NK and NC activity, and this inhibition can be effectively reversed by LTB$_4$, indicating that exogenous lipoxygenase products can compensate for endogenous lipoxygenase inhibition. However, whereas human NK cells pretreated with interferons or poly I:C are partially resistant to suppression by lipoxygenase inhibitors, lymphokine (IL-2)-activated killer (LAK) cells can be reversibly inhibited by these drugs. LTB$_4$ acts on effector NK or NC lymphocytes rather than on their target cells, increasing both the binding of effector lymphocytes to their target cells and the rate of target cell killing. No IL-2 or IFNγ is detectable in these cultures.

LTB$_4$ can also enhance IL-2-induced cytolytic activity on both NK (CD56$^+$) cells and cytotoxic T (CD8$^+$) cells. Twenty-four hours after exposure to 10^{-10} M LTB$_4$, the cells respond to 100-fold lower concentrations of IL-2 with enhanced cytotoxicity. This is accompanied by an LTB$_4$-dependent increase in expression of IL-2Rβ on CD56$^+$ and CD8$^+$ cells, suggesting a receptor-mediated sensitization of NK and cytotoxic T cells (**Figure 1**).

Monocytes/macrophages

Cytotoxicity   The potential regulatory role of endogenous and exogenous LTs on functions of monocytes/macrophages has also come under study, in view of the findings that LTs are synthesized and released by these cells after receiving immunological and nonimmunological stimuli. For instance, as assessed by use of lipoxygenase inhibitors, activation of macrophage phagocytic capacity by endotoxins appears to be dependent on lipoxygenase metabolites of AA. LTs can also induce the release of PGs and lysosomal enzymes by macrophages. When appropriately stimulated, monocytes/macrophages can produce a variety of cytokines, as well as inhibit tumor cell growth or destroy susceptible target cells by a number of different mechanisms. For instance, when mouse-resident peritoneal macrophages are cocultured with MOPC-315 myeloma cells, the cytostatic activity of the former is enhanced by either LTD_4 or indomethacin, whereas both LTD_4 and indomethacin together are additive in causing a more than 80% inhibition of tumor cell proliferation.

Human peripheral blood monocytes can also lyse several types of tumor target cells. When they are incubated with LTB_4, a very significant augmentation of cytotoxicity is observed. This is associated with enhanced binding of monocytes to target cells and augmentation in the rate of killing of target cells by the culture supernatants. Inhibitors of lipoxygenase cause a marked inhibition of monocyte-mediated cytotoxicity. Exogenous LTB_4 can restore the activity, suggesting that both endogenous and exogenous LTs have a positive effect on cytotoxic functions of mononuclear phagocytes.

Cytokine production LTB_4 is a powerful stimulator of IL-6 production by monocytes. At nanomolar concentrations, LTB_4 induces a fivefold increase in IL-6 gene transcription and a threefold extension of IL-6 mRNA half-life. This effect is dependent on activation of a tyrosine kinase and involves induction of the transcription factors NF-κB and NF-IL6. Although LTB_4 also stimulates the accumulation of IL-1β mRNA, it preferentially augments IL-6 production as compared to IL-1. LTB_4 can also affect cytokine production indirectly, via T lymphocyte activation: human T cells pulsed with LTB_4 modulate IL-1 production by human monocytes by secreting IFNγ.

TNFα is a potent mediator of cytotoxic activity exerted by monocytes and macrophages, as well as NC lymphocytes. LTB_4 markedly enhances cytotoxicity mediated by NC cells and monocyte-mediated cytotoxicity is also augmented by LTB_4. Addition of LTB_4 to monocyte cultures enhances TNFα activity of their supernatants. Addition of indomethacin to the cultures augments TNFα production, whereas lipoxygenase inhibitors diminish TNFα production. LTB_4 may thus affect cytotoxic activity of human monocytes by augmenting their production of the cytolytic cytokine TNFα.

Alveolar macrophages can play a crucial role in the pathogenesis of pulmonary disease via their ability to produce potent inflammatory and fibrogenic mediators. When alveolar macrophages are cultured with silica particles or asbestos fibers they produce TNFα and LTB_4 in a concentration-dependent fashion. Increased amounts of LTB_4 precede the rise in TNFα activity. The lipoxygenase inhibitors NDGA and AA861 reduce in a concentration-dependent fashion asbestos- or silica-stimulated TNFα release. On the other hand 'reconstitutive' experiments in which exogenous LTB_4 is added to alveolar macrophages treated with lipoxygenase inhibitors show partial restoration of TNFα production induced by chrysotile or silica. Alveolar macrophages are also stimulated by PAF to produce IL-1β, TNFα and IL-6. Lipoxygenase inhibitors, including the FLAP antagonist MK-886, prevent this effect of PAF, whereas exogenous LTB_4 partially reconstitutes the responses.

LTB_4 can induce the expression of IL-2Rα in human monocytes by activating IL-2Rα gene transcription. It can also stimulate the expression of IL-2Rβ through post-transcriptional regulation. This augmented expression of both α and β chains of IL-2R is associated with enhanced sensitivity of monocytes to IL-2 in terms of TNFα production, and may be relevant to some of the proinflammatory actions of LTB_4.

In addition to modulating cytokine production and cytokine receptor expression, LTB_4, as well as LTC_4 and LTD_4, can stimulate human myelopoiesis and play a role as essential intermediates in GM-CSF-stimulated myeloid colony formation.

Polymorphonuclear leukocytes

AA induces PMNs to aggregate, generate superoxide anion and release the contents of lysosomes, by mechanisms which do not appear to involve any of its metabolites. LTB_4 also activates PMNs in a number of ways: it induces chemotaxis, aggregation, degranulation, cation fluxes and superoxide anion production. LTB_4 induces migration and adhesion of PMNs to endothelium, secondary to expression of CD11/CD18 adhesion molecules. Moreover, LTB_4 constitutes a powerful stimulus for its own production, as well as for the production of PMNs of certain cytokines, in particular IL-8.

AA and LTs as second messengers

AA can exert a variety of direct effects on leukocytes that do not depend on the metabolism via cyclooxygenase or lipoxygenase pathways. AA can directly activate protein kinase C, an effect it shares with diacylglycerol. AA can also directly activate a pertussis toxin-sensitive GTP-binding protein in the PMN plasma membrane and may thereby act as a second messenger in signal transduction.

LTB_4 and possibly other 5-LOX metabolites may also play central roles as internal 'second messengers'. LTB_4 can induce c-*fos* and c-*jun* proto-oncogene expression in monocytes and PMNs. This is accompanied by enhanced binding of LTB_4-induced nuclear proteins to the AP-1 consensus site, suggesting that LTB_4 may play a role in the transactivation of genes containing the AP-1 binding site in their promoter region. Through intracellular formation of H_2O_2, LTB_4 can also activate the transcription factors NF-κB and NF-IL6.

LTB_4 may also play a role as an endogenous Ca^{2+} ionophore, and the sensitivity to LT synthesis inhibition of a number of cellular responses to a variety of stimuli strongly suggests that LTs may act as second messengers for the regulation of certain immune functions, including cytokine production. The recent development of a 5-LOX knockout mouse model should prove particularly useful in defining the selective involvement of LTs in immune and inflammatory conditions.

Conclusion

An increasing body of evidence suggests that LTB_4 may be an important modulator of many immune cell functions, either as an internal messenger within some cells, or as an external signal, linking inflammatory cells to lymphocytes. LTB_4 and, to some extent, other LTs, are known protagonists of numerous inflammatory processes. They can also mediate varied and powerful effects on many cells involved in immunological reactions.

See also: **Anti-inflammatory (nonsteroidal) drugs; B lymphocytes; Cytokines; Glucocorticoids; Lymphokine-activated killer (LAK) cells; Macrophage activation; Monocytes; Natural killer (NK) cells; Prostaglandins; T lymphocytes; Tumor necrosis factor α.**

Further reading

Chen X-S, Sheller JR, Johnson EN and Funk CD (1994) Role of leukotrienes revealed by targeted disruption of the 5-lipoxygenase gene. *Nature* 372: 179–181.

Goetzl EJ, Lewis RA and Rola-Pleszczynski M (eds) (1994) Cellular Generation, Transport and Effects of Eicosanoids. *Annals of the New York Academy of Sciences* 744.

Rola-Pleszczynski M (1985) Immunoregulation by leukotrienes and other lipoxygenase metabolites. *Immunology Today* 6: 302–307.

ARENAVIRUS, INFECTION AND IMMUNITY

Maria S Salvato, Pathology Department, University of Wisconsin Medical School, Madison, Wisconsin, USA

Igor S Lukashevich, Belarussian Research Institute for Epidemiology and Microbiology, Minsk, Belarus

Discussions of cell-mediated immunity and immunopathogenesis frequently cite the prototype arenavirus, lymphocytic choriomeningitis virus (LCMV). The 1996 Nobel Prize in Physiology or Medicine went to Peter Doherty and Rolf Zinkernagel who used LCMV-infected mice to show that cytotoxic T lymphocytes (CTLs) only kill cells that are syngeneic at the major histocompatibility complex (MHC) (murine H2) locus. Two properties of LCMV facilitated this landmark finding: first, LCMV is noncytopathic in cell culture, enabling 15 h chromium-release assays in which cell lysis is entirely due to CTLs, and second, LCMV elicits a vigorous CTL response, peaking 7 days after infection and causing very high specific lysis in chromium-release assays. Several other viruses elicit cell-mediated immunity, but usually their virus-specific CTL activity cannot be detected without secondary stimulation. This entry summarizes research primarily on the less virulent arenaviruses – LCMV, Pichinde and Tacaribe – and, to a lesser extent, on the virulent 'emerging viruses' such as Lassa, Machupo, and Junin.

Characteristics of the arenaviruses and their antigens

The arenaviruses are enveloped viruses with two single-stranded RNA genomic segments. They are classified as 'negative-strand viruses' because their genomic RNA cannot function as a messenger RNA, i.e. transcription by the viral RNA-dependent RNA polymerase (RdRp) must precede translation. The arenaviruses encode four gene products; a nucleocapsid protein (NP) that encapsidates the genomic RNA, an envelope glycoprotein (GP) that undergoes a maturation cleavage to become GP1 and GP2, a small zinc-binding protein (Z) and a large RdRp (L). The small (S) RNA segment is 3.4 kb and encodes

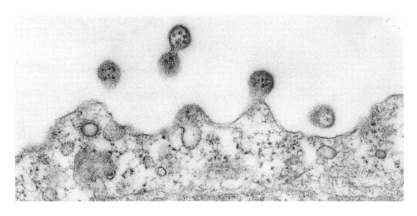

Figure 1 The arenaviruses are noncytopathic and bud from the host cell. They have a granular appearance from which the name (L. *arena*, sandy) is derived. (Reproduced by permission from M Buchmeier, La Jolla, CA.)

GP and NP in an ambisense arrangement (using sense and antisense (complementary) mRNAs). The large (L) RNA segment is 7.2 kb and encodes the Z and L proteins, also in an ambisense arrangement. The morphological characteristics of arenaviruses are depicted in **Figure 1**.

Immune responses of the host

Arenaviruses are generally carried by rodents with little ill-effect to the carrier; however, transmission from rodents to primates can cause severe encephalitis, hepatitis or hemorrhagic syndrome. Thus, rodent and humans can have drastically different immunologic and pathologic responses to infection. We will describe the classical studies of cell-mediated immunopathology in the LCMV/murine model with the caveat that it does not apply to arenavirus disease in primates.

LCMV was first isolated in the early 1930s from a man who died of encephalitis in St Louis, Missouri. It was never entirely clear whether the virus came from the deceased person or from the laboratory mice used for passage, because similar stocks of LCMV were isolated from mice in other laboratories around the same time. Electron microscopy and serological studies confirmed the familial relatedness of the various laboratory isolates and some new viruses from outbreaks in Africa (Lassa virus) and South America (Machupo and Junin).

Ever since the 1960s, LCMV was used to study virus-induced cell-mediated immunity. There are two types of murine infection: an acute infection that correlates with vigorous cell-mediated immunity (as measured by CTL assay) or a persistent infection that correlates with little cell-mediated immunity (**Figure 2**). The immune response to the acute infection either kills the mouse by engendering meningitis, or subsides and leaves the mouse LCMV-immune. Adoptive transfer of splenocytes from an LCMV-immune mouse can clear infection in a persistently infected mouse. Clearance is mediated by CD8$^+$ and not

CD4$^+$ splenocytes, as shown by antibody depletion of lymphocyte subsets. In contrast to their beneficial effects in clearing virus infection, the CD8$^+$ cells mediate pathology (choriomeningitis) when injected intracerebrally. Thus the LCMV/murine model offered a paradigm for the positive and negative effects of CTL-mediated immunity. Even though LCMV has an acid-sensitive envelope, it has recently been shown to infect the gastric mucosa at very low doses; thus expanding its usefulness to studies of mucosal immunity.

LCMV-specific cell-mediated immunity was defined by studies with transgenic mice, synthetic peptides, and recombinant vaccinia expression vectors. BALB/c (H-2^d) mice make a CTL response primarily to epitopes on the viral envelope, GP, whereas C3H (H-2^b) mice respond primarily to epitopes on the NP. Synthetic peptides were used to define the most important residues for these CTL epitopes. Transgenic mice lacking CD8$^+$ expression (either by CD8 gene knockout or by knockout of β_2-microglobulin) have greatly reduced CTL responses, resulting in virus persistence. Intracerebrally infected mice lacking CD8$^+$ lymphocytes die later than normal mice, thus the CD8-mediated immunopathology is reduced but not entirely eliminated. Knockout mice lacking perforin are also unable to clear infections, indicating that virus clearance is dependent on the perforin-mediated destruction of virus-infected cells. Mice lacking CD4$^+$ cells or B cells are able to clear virus-infected cells initially, but virus reappears and the mice then succumb to acute infection.

LCMV infection induces inflammatory intermediates such as interferon γ (IFNγ) and tumor necrosis factor α (TNFα), both of which influence the host's immune response to other pathogens. IFNγ stimulates the proliferation of natural killer (NK) cells that serve to eliminate certain pathogen-infected cells and some tumors. TNFα produced in the liver as a result of LCMV infection can clear hepatitis B virus infection, even in perforin-negative mice, probably by

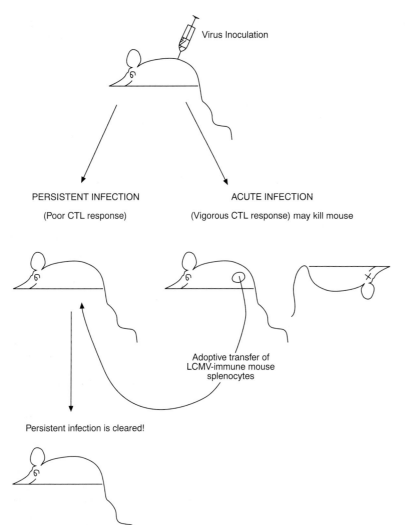

Figure 2 In the murine/LCMV model, acute and persistent infections are correlated with vigorous and poor virus-specific CTL responses, respectively. Acute infection generally requires an adult immunocompetent mouse, whereas persistent infection generally occurs in a neonatal or immunosuppressed mouse, or in an adult mouse given an immunosuppressive variant of LCMV. Vigorous CTL response can mediate lethal immunopathology, but adoptive transfer of CTL can also mediate virus clearance.

inducing an RNase that destroys the hepatitis viral nucleic acid.

Junin, Machupo and Lassa viruses can cause hemorrhagic fever in primates, the severity of which is directly proportional to virus titer. Arenavirus disease in primates is not alleviated by immunosuppressive cyclophosphamide. The Junin and Machupo diseases are primarily treated with convalescent serum, whereas Lassa disease is primarily treated with ribavirin, since antisera are only effective early in the disease.

Virus evasion of host immune responses

The ability of arenaviruses to persist in their long-term carriers is facilitated by antigenic variation that allows evasion of host immune responses. Neutralization-resistant variants of Junin and Tacaribe viruses escape the humoral immune response, and certain epitope variants of LCMV escape the CTL response. In addition to viral variants that can escape host immune surveillance, variants have been described that suppress the immune response and thereby persist. Docile is a variant of the Aggressive isolate of LCMV (UBC), and Clone 13 is a variant of the LCMV (Armstrong strain). Both Docile and Clone 13 replicate very well in the spleen and poorly in the brain in contrast to their parental viruses. Both Docile and Clone 13 elicit poor CTL responses when tested 7 days after infection, and consequently, both persist in the mouse longer than their parental viruses. Docile and Clone 13 isolates actually do elicit CTL by day 3 after infection, but these viruses replicate so vigorously in the spleen that they cause high-dose immune suppression, i.e. high immune stimulation leading to massive apoptosis of immunocytes, leading to little CTL response by day 7. Thus, virus isolates that were thought to be immunosuppressive are in fact evading host immune responses by overstimulating and destroying the immune response.

Vaccines

Mice can be protected from lethal LCMV challenge either by peptide vaccination or by vaccinia vectors that express viral epitopes. Guinea pigs can be protected from lethal Lassa virus challenge by inoculation with vaccinia vectors that express either Lassa glycoprotein or Lassa nucleoprotein; however primates are only protected by the vector expressing glycoprotein. Primates are protected from the Junin virus disease, Argentine hemorrhagic fever, by injection with attenuated strains of Junin or with the related strain Tacaribe. Tacaribe or its subunits would make an excellent vaccine for Argentine hemorrhagic fever because it is unlikely to revert to pathogenicity, and causes a brief infection.

Vaccine research using arenaviruses established important negative as well as positive results. Vaccination of guinea pigs with both the Lassa NP and GP-expressing vector does not give double protection against virus challenge, but instead gives less protection than a single vaccination. Vaccination of mice with a GP-expressing vector can sometimes exacerbate virus-mediated pathogenesis. Despite the setbacks, there is considerable optimism that effective subunit vaccines may eliminate some problems that arise when attenuated viral strains are used for vaccination.

See also: **Antigen presentation via MHC class I molecules; Cell-mediated immunity; Fever; Cell-mediated lysis; Immunopathology; Immunosuppression; MHC restriction; Mucosal immunity; T lymphocyte activation; Transgenic animals; Viruses, immunity to.**

Further reading

Borrow P and Oldstone MBA (1995) Lymphocytic choriomeningitis virus. In: Nathanson N (ed) *Viral Pathogenesis*, pp 593–627. Philadelphia, PA: Lippincott-Raven.

Doherty P and Ahmed R (1995) Immune responses to viral infection. In: Nathanson N (ed) *Viral Pathogenesis*, pp 143–161. Philadelphia, PA: Lippincott-Raven.

Oldstone MBA (ed) (1987) *Arenaviruses. Current Topics in Microbiology and Immunology*, vol 133, pp 1–116. Berlin: Springer-Verlag.

Oldstone MBA (ed) (1987) *Arenaviruses. Current Topics in Microbiology and Immunology*, vol 134, pp 1–242. Berlin: Springer-Verlag.

Peters CJ (1995) Viral hemorrhagic fevers. In: Nathanson N (ed) *Viral Pathogenesis*, pp 779–799. Philadelphia, PA: Lippincott-Raven.

Peters CJ, Buchmeier M, Rollin P and Ksiasek T (1995) Arenaviruses. In: Fields B, Knipe D and Howley P (eds) *Fields' Virology*, 3rd edn, pp 1521–1551. New York: Raven Press.

Salvato MS (ed) (1993) *The Arenaviridae*. New York: Plenum Press.

Southern PJ (1995) Arenaviridae: The viruses and their replication. In: Fields B, Knipe D and Howley P (eds) *Fields' Virology*, 3rd edn, pp 1505–1519. New York: Raven Press.

Thomsen AR, Johansen J, Marker O and Christensen JP (1996) Exhaustion of CTL memory and recrudescence of viremia in lymphocytic choriomeningitis virus-infected MHC class II-deficient mice and B cell-deficient mice. *Journal of Immunology* 157: 3074–3080.

Zinkernagel R (1995) Virus-induced immunopathology. In: Nathanson N (ed) *Viral Pathogenesis*, pp 163–179. Philadelphia, PA: Lippincott-Raven.

ARGININE AND IMMUNITY

Stephen J Kirk and **Adrian Barbul**, Department of Surgery, Sinai Hospital and The Johns Hopkins Medical Institutions, Baltimore, Maryland, USA

Arginine, a dibasic nitrogen-rich amino acid, is classified as semidispensable. In health it is synthesized in adequate amounts for the maintenance of nitrogen balance. Dietary requirement is essential only for the optimal growth of the young of some species. In certain circumstances, such as immaturity and severe stress (sepsis, trauma, nitrogen overload), arginine becomes indispensable, being required for maintenance of nitrogen balance and physiologic functions in humans. More importantly, arginine has several unique and remarkable pharmacologic properties, including a marked immunomodulatory function.

Immune function

Supplemental administration of arginine (approximately 500 mg kg^{-1} per day) to rodents either enterally or parenterally enhances thymic size, lymphocyte count and lymphocyte mitogenesis in response to mitogens and alloantigens. This is accompanied by enhanced interleukin 2 (IL-2) synthesis. Following injury, arginine reduces or abrogates post-traumatic thymic involution and the impairment of T lymphocyte function. Other immune effects of arginine include enhanced delayed-type hypersensitivity reactions, amplified *in vitro* and *in vivo* allogeneic responses and increased survival following lethal septic challenges, experimental burn injuries and trauma. Arginine also promotes host antitumor responses in a variety of tumor models (solid transplanted, chemical- or viral-induced) by decreasing the rate of tumor growth and metastatic spread, and by increasing the latency period to tumor appearance following induction. Survival is also increased. Similarly, in humans, supplemental arginine stimulates T lymphocyte mitogenesis, increases T helper to T suppressor cell ratio and improves wound healing.

Arginine is required *in vitro* for optimal lymphocyte mitogenic response, cytokine production, and for induction of cytotoxic T lymphocyte (CTL) and natural killer (NK) cell function. Maximum mitogenic stimulation and IL-2 production occur at an arginine concentration of 0.04 mM, further increases do not result in enhanced responses. Maximal NK and CTL generation and activation *in vitro* is observed at an arginine concentration between 0.4 and 0.9 mM. Plasma arginine concentrations in human adults range from 0.04 to 0.1 mM, suggesting that the effects observed with *in vivo* arginine supplementation are not related to elevation of plasma levels, since they are already optimal for lymphocyte function.

Within the rodent immune system macrophages, neutrophils and lymphocytes utilize the arginine–nitric oxide (NO) pathway. In macrophages this pathway is essential for the expression of cytotoxicity against tumor cells and pathogenic fungi. Inhibition of NO generation using a specific inhibitor (L-mono-N-methylarginine) results in abrogation of cytotoxic response. Cytotoxic macrophages generating NO destroy target cells by inhibiting aconitase activity (a citric acid cycle enzyme), DNA synthesis, and mitochondrial respiration. A similar pathway has been identified (*in vitro*) in cloned T cells. In these cells NO has an autocrine function in the regulation of cell mitogenesis. The role of the arginine–nitric oxide pathway in humans is less well defined.

The presence of arginine is essential for the function of a variety of immunoregulatory proteins such as thymosin, thymopentin and tuftsin. Production of activated C3a and C5a (both powerful vasoconstrictors and fundamental in the inflammatory process) occurs when the C3 and C5 α chains, respectively,

are split at the N-terminal end by convertase enzymes, thus exposing a C-terminal arginine molecule. Subsequent arginine removal by carboxypeptidase B inactivates C3a. Removal of the arginine from C5a produces C5a-desarginine, which maintains (at a much reduced level) the cell-activating properties of C5a (neutrophil chemotaxis, activation of neutrophil leukotrienes and mast cell degranulation), but there is loss of vasoconstrictive properties.

Mechanism of action

The mechanism for the diverse actions of arginine on the immune system are not fully understood. Nonetheless several hypothesis exist. Arginine via its secretagogue effects promotes growth hormone and prolactin release from the pituitary, and insulin and glucagon release from the pancreas. Convincing *in vivo* and *in vitro* evidence suggests an immunopermissive role for prolactin. Hypophysectomized rats fail to mount an adequate immune response to antigenic challenge, a failure reversed by giving them prolactin or growth hormone. Prolactin-like receptors have been identified on the surface of T cells, as has the production of a prolactin-like protein by stimulated T cells. It is likely that arginine (*in vivo*) exerts some effect on the immune system via increased pituitary release of prolactin and/or growth hormone. However, hypophysectomized rats supplemented with growth hormone, thyroxine and testosterone do not demonstrate increased immune responses secondary to arginine supplementation. There are no similar data available for the human immune system. The *in vitro* arginine requirement for optimal lymphocyte responses to lectins also suggests a local cellular response to arginine, possibly via the nitric oxide pathway.

It has been postulated that arginine is required as a precursor for polyamines which are necessary for lymphocyte proliferation. This does not explain why many of the *in vivo* immune effects of arginine are replicated by ornithine but not by citrulline, spermine or putresceine (other precursors of polyamine synthesis). Finally, when looking at macrophage function, intracellular NO formation from arginine explains much of their activities. Within the liver (in rodents), activated Kuppfer cell secretory function (TNFα, IL-6) but not phagocytosis is enhanced up to twice normal following dietary supplementation with arginine. Again, the exact mechanism of action is not fully understood. Elsewhere within the immune system the arginine NO pathway is responsible for inhibition of neutrophil aggregation and may on the basis of *in vivo* studies be a requirement for T cell mitogenesis. However, the exact mechanism by which arginine influences lymphocyte function *in vivo* remains unknown.

Despite insufficient knowledge regarding its mechanism of action, it is clear that arginine has a potent effect on multiple cells and molecules involved in immune responses. In the future it is likely that arginine may be used as a pharmacologic agent in immunocompromised states.

See also: **Thymic hormones and peptides.**

Further reading

Barbul A (1986) Arginine: biochemistry, physiology and therapeutic implications. *Journal of Parenteral and Enteral Nutrition* 10: 227–238.

Moncada S and Higgs EA (1993) The L-arginine–nitric oxide pathway. *New England Journal of Medicine* 329: 2002–2012.

Moncada S, Palmer RMJ and Higgs EA (1989) Biosynthesis of nitric oxide from L-arginine: A pathway for the regulation of cell function and communication. *Biochemistry and Pharmacology* 38: 1709–1715.

ARTHUS REACTION

Paul G Hellewell, Applied Pharmacology, Imperial College School of Medicine at the National Heart and Lung Institute, London, UK

Adriano G Rossi, Respiratory Medicine Unit, Department of Medicine, Rayne Laboratory, Edinburgh, UK

The Arthus reaction was first described by Maurice Arthus as an acute inflammatory response induced in rabbit skin by a local injection of horse serum in rabbits sensitized by previous injections of the same substance. Although the reaction described originally could have had components of anaphylactic and delayed hypersensitivity responses, the term Arthus reaction best describes the acute response initiated by local deposition of immune complexes and is an example of type III hypersensitivity. Strictly speaking, the Arthus reaction is restricted to the skin and Arthus-like or Arthus-type reactions occur in other organs.

Antibody–antigen complexes are believed to be principal in the inflammatory response associated with a number of diverse diseases which are listed in **Table 1**. Some of these are well known while others are more obscure and are complications of other diseases (e.g. erythema nodosum leprosum is a serious complication of lepromatous leprosy) or can be adverse reactions to drugs. In the Arthus reaction as originally described, antigen was injected intradermally into sensitized animals and, as antibody diffused from cutaneous microvessels, immune complexes were deposited in and around the vessel wall. Experimentally it is convenient to induce the reaction passively and in reverse, such that antibody is injected intradermally and antigen intravenously – the so-called reversed passive Arthus reaction.

The Arthus reaction can be dissected into three fairly distinct stages: a rapid increase in vascular permeability and extravasation of plasma protein, which is maximal at 1–2 hours, infiltration of leukocytes (initially neutrophils) and hemorrhage which peak in intensity after 4–8 hours. Longer reactions are sometimes associated with necrosis. Experimentally, hemorrhage is the most notable feature of the reaction in transparent tissues such as skin.

Role of complement

Immune complex-mediated tissue injury is thought to be mediated in the initial stages by activation of primarily the classical pathway of the complement system. In the Arthus reaction the formation of immune complexes in and around the wall of microvessels (**Figure 1**) results in the activation of complement and the generation of C3a and C5a as well as assembly of the membrane attack complex C5–C9. Depletion of complement (e.g. with cobra

Table 1 Diseases and conditions which have features of the Arthus reaction

Systemic lupus erythematosus
Rheumatoid arthritis
Immune glomerulonephritis
Vasculitis
Kawasaki disease
Erythema nodosum leprosum
Inflammatory demyelinating neuropathies
Hypersensitivity pneumonitis
Reaction to immunization with diphtheria toxoid
Drug hypersensitivity

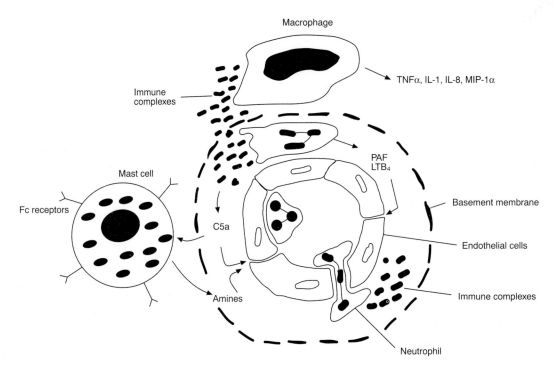

Figure 1   Some of the mechanisms involved in the pathological changes associated with an Arthus reaction. Although considered to be driven primarily by complement components (in particular C5a), recent studies suggest that the mast cell Fc receptor plays a crucial role (see text for details). Evidence that amines, PAF and LTB$_4$ contribute to the edema formation and neutrophil accumulation has been obtained from pharmacological studies. A similar approach (using neutralizing antibodies) has demonstrated a role for the cytokines and chemokines listed.

venom factor) reduces the magnitude of the Arthus reaction and has led to the idea that C5a plays a key role in orchestrating the early stages of the reaction. Thus, generation of C5a could act on mast cells to release bioactive amines which increase vascular permeability and C5a itself increases permeability by a mechanism that depends on circulating neutrophils. This would supply more plasma proteins, including complement components, leading to further C5a generation. In support of this idea, both antibodies to C5a and soluble CR1, which inhibits the generation of C5a, provide partial protection against immune complex-induced lung and skin inflammation in animal models. However, this concept has been challenged recently by studies in mice genetically deficient in complement components C3, C4 or C5. In these animals the Arthus reaction is indistinguishable from that in wild-type controls, suggesting that complement is not required.

Role of blood elements and adhesion molecules

One of the characteristic features of the reaction is the accumulation of neutrophils. Experimentally this peaks 4–8 hours after initiating the reaction and an early observation was that edema formation and

hemorrhage in the Arthus reaction could be suppressed by depletion of circulating neutrophils. Similar findings have been made using monoclonal antibodies directed against neutrophil β_2-integrins and endothelial ICAM-1, which prevent neutrophil recruitment to sites of Arthus reactions, presumably by preventing firm adhesion and migration. Neutrophils contribute to inflammatory changes in the Arthus reaction in several ways: neutrophil-dependent edema formation induced by C5a; neutrophil-derived proteases which could cleave C5 in tissue fluid leading to the generation of C5a; neutrophil proteases such as elastase which could lead to tissue destruction and hemorrhage; neutrophil production of lipid mediators (such as platelet-activating factor (PAF) and leukotriene B$_4$ (LTB$_4$)) and chemokines (e.g. interleukin-8, IL-8).

Arthus reactions are also suppressed by reagents that interfere with selectin function, for example an anti-E-selectin monoclonal antibody, which reduce neutrophil accumulation and the attendant pathological changes. This has been attributed to the capacity of selectins to mediate neutrophil rolling, the first stage in the process of leukocyte recruitment. An unexpected finding was the ability of a monoclonal antibody against the leukocyte β_1-integrin VLA-4 to decrease neutrophil accumulation in immune complex-induced lung inflammation. As neutrophils do not express VLA-4, the protective effect of the antibody might be due to suppression of macrophage function.

Platelet depletion also reduces neutrophil accumulation in the Arthus reaction. The reason for this is not entirely clear but platelets are suggested to facilitate efficient recruitment of neutrophils into tissues, perhaps via lipid mediator interactions and P-selectin-mediated adhesion.

Mediators involved in the Arthus reaction

A list of inflammatory mediators demonstrated (using a pharmacological approach) to have a role in the pathology of the Arthus reaction is given in Table 2. Biogenic amines (histamine and 5-hydroxytryptamine) released from mast cells, usually in response to the anaphylatoxins C3a and C5a, can increase vascular permeability, although this action is greatest in rodents. Antagonists of these amines have no effect on neutrophil recruitment and hemorrhage. A role for PAF in the Arthus reaction was discovered almost a decade ago and it appears to be an important mediator of plasma leakage. The site of deposition of immune complexes may be important in this regard; in the Arthus reaction neutrophil phagocytosis of immune complexes in the vessel wall releases PAF adjacent to endothelial cells leading to plasma leakage. In contrast, phagocytosis of immune complexes away from the vessel wall does not reveal a role for PAF. The same consideration may apply for LTB$_4$ because specific receptor antagonists reduce edema formation in an Arthus reaction. Vasodilator prostaglandins (e.g. PGE$_2$, prostacyclin) produced in the Arthus reaction may modulate edema formation and neutrophil accumulation by augmenting the blood supply; this increases hydrostatic pressure in postcapillary venules and increases the delivery of neutrophils to the tissue.

Of the cytokines, IL-1 is involved in the edema formation, neutrophil accumulation and hemorrhage

Table 2 Mediators demonstrated to be involved in the Arthus reaction

Class	Examples
Lipid-derived	PAF, LTB$_4$, prostaglandins
Amines	Histamine, serotonin
Complement-derived	C5a
Cytokines	TNFα, IL-1
Chemokines	IL-8, MCP-1, MIP-1α
Others	Nitric oxide

in the Arthus reaction and immune complex-induced lung injury. In contrast, tumor necrosis factor α (TNFα) appears to have a more important role in the lung as a number of TNFα inhibitors have no effect on Arthus reactions in skin. The source of these cytokines is speculated to be macrophages which are stimulated by immune complexes. Macrophages are also likely to be one of the sources of chemokines, including IL-8 and macrophage-inflammatory protein 1α (MIP-1α), which appear to play a role in the Arthus reaction. However, other cells, including endothelial cells, fibroblasts and even neutrophils themselves, could contribute to production of these mediators.

Other neutrophil-derived factors that contribute to the pathological changes in the Arthus reaction include proteases, particularly elastase which may cleave C5 but also destroys tissue and leads to hemorrhage. Indeed, an elastase inhibitor prevents immune complex-induced hemorrhage in the lung. Nitric oxide (NO) can enhance blood flow and exacerbate the Arthus reaction in a similar manner to PGE$_2$. Moreover, on interaction with superoxide anion, NO forms the highly reactive peroxynitrite anion (ONOO$^-$), which in turn can be protonated to form the tissue damaging hydroxyl radical.

Recent advances in mechanisms underlying the Arthus reaction

As discussed above, recent data suggest that in the mouse the presence of an intact complement system is neither necessary nor sufficient to trigger or propagate an Arthus reaction. This is a surprising finding given that antibodies to C5a are effective at attenuating the reaction in rat and rabbits, and treatment with an anti-C5 mAb for 6 months prevents the spontaneous development of an autoimmune syndrome with features of systemic lupus erythematosus (SLE) in NZB/W mice. In addition, a soluble form of the complement regulatory protein CD46 (membrane cofactor protein), which inhibits complement activation *in vitro*, reduces inflammatory cell influx and edema formation in the Arthus reaction. In the same model, soluble CD35 (CR1) and CD55 (decay-accelerating factor) were also effective as anti-inflammatory agents.

An alternative mechanism has been proposed based on the greatly diminished capacity of mice deficient in the γ subunit of Fc receptors to develop Arthus reactions. Mast cell reconstitution of the mast cell-deficient mouse strain W/W^v reveals that FcγRIII on this cell is responsible for triggering the inflammatory response in the Arthus reaction. Other FcγRIII-expressing resident tissue cells (macrophages and Langerhans cells) and neutrophils could be involved in later stages of the reaction. Similarly, FcγRII is involved in aspects of the Arthus reaction. A soluble form inhibits hemorrhage and perivascular neutrophil recruitment; this may be related to suppression of neutrophil activation *in vivo*.

Although much progress has been made in understanding the physiological and cellular mechanisms underlying the Arthus reaction, clearly much has still to be elucidated concerning the relevant inflammatory and hemorrhagic response process to be targeted clinically.

See also: **Acute inflammatory reaction; Adhesion molecules; Anaphylatoxins; Autoimmune diseases; Mast cells; Chemokines; Cobra venom factor; Complement, classical pathway; Cytokines; Fc receptors; Histamine; Hydrostatic pressure, effect on immune system; Immune complexes; Integrins; Intercellular adhesion molecules: ICAM-1, ICAM-2 and ICAM-3; Interleukin 8 and its receptor; Neutrophils; Nitric oxide; Phagocytosis; Platelet-activating factor (PAF); Prostaglandins; Selectins (CD62-E/L/P); Serotonin; Systemic lupus erythematosus, experimental models; Tumor necrosis factor α; Chemotaxis of neutrophils.**

Further reading

Arthus M (1903) Injections repetées de serum de cheval chez le lapin. *Comptes Rendes des Seances de la Societe de Biologie et de ses Filiales (Paris)* 55: 817–820.

Christiansen D, Milland J, Thorley BR, McKenzie IF and Loveland BE (1996) A functional analysis of recombinant soluble CD46 *in vivo* and a comparison with recombinant forms of CD55 and CD35 *in vitro*. *European Journal of Immunology* 26: 578–585.

Cochrane GC and Janoff A (1974) The Arthus reaction: a model of neutrophil and complement-mediated injury. In: Zweifach BW, Grant L and McCluskey RT (eds) *The Inflammatory Process*, pp 85–162. New York: Academic Press.

Crawford JP, Movat HZ, Narendranath SR and Hay JB (1982) Pathways to inflammation induced by immune complexes: development of the Arthus reaction. *Federation Proceedings* 41: 2583–2587.

Fletcher DS, Osinga DG, Keenan K *et al* (1995) An inhibitor of leukocyte elastase prevents immune complex-mediated hemorrhage in the rat lung. *Journal of Pharmacology and Experimental Therapeutics* 274: 548–554.

Hellewell PG and Williams TJ (1986) A specific antagonist of platelet-activating factor suppresses oedema formation in an Arthus reaction but not oedema induced by leukocyte chemoattractants in rabbit skin. *Journal of Immunology* 137: 302–307.

Humphrey JH (1955) The mechanism of Arthus reactions. I. The role of polymorphonuclear leucocytes and other factors in reversed passive Arthus reactions in rabbits. *British Journal of Experimental Pathology* 36: 268–282.

Ierino FL, Powell MS, McKenzie IFC and Hogarth PM (1993) Recombinant soluble human FcγRII: production, characterisation, and inhibition of the Arthus reaction. *Journal of Experimental Medicine* 178: 1617–1628.

Mulligan MS and Ward PA (1992) Immune complex-induced lung and dermal vascular injury. Differing requirements for tumor necrosis factor-α and IL-1. *Journal of Immunology* 149: 331–339.

Mulligan MS, Varani J, Dame MK *et al* (1991) Role of endothelial-leukocyte adhesion molecule 1 (ELAM-1) in neutrophil-mediated lung injury in rats. *Journal of Clinical Investigation* 88: 1396–1406.

Mulligan MS, Wilson GP, Todd RF *et al* (1993) Role of β_1, β_2 integrins and ICAM-1 in lung injury after deposition of IgG and IgA immune complexes. *Journal of Immunology* 150: 2407–2417.

Norman KE, Williams TJ, Feldmann M and Rossi AG (1996) Effect of soluble P55 tumour-necrosis factor binding fusion protein on the local Schwartzman and Arthus reactions. *British Journal of Pharmacology* 117: 471–478.

Rossi AG, Norman KE, Donigi Gale D, Shoupe TS, Edwards R and Williams TJ (1992) The role of complement, platelet-activating factor and leukotriene B4 in a reversed passive Arthus reaction. *British Journal of Pharmacology* 107: 44–49.

Sylvestre D and Ravetch JV (1996) A dominant role for mast cell Fc receptors in the Arthus reaction. *Immunity* 5: 387–390.

Sylvestre D, Clynes R, Ma M, Warren H, Carroll MC and Ravetch JV (1996) Immunoglobulin G-mediated inflammatory responses develop normally in complement-deficient mice. *Journal of Experimental Medicine* 184: 2385–2392.

ASCARIASIS

Malcolm W Kennedy, Division of Infection and Immunity, Institute of Biomedical and Life Sciences, University of Glasgow, Glasgow, UK

The organism and its antigens

Ascaris lumbricoides is among the most widespread and common of all pathogens of humans, infecting over 1.3 billion people. It is a nematode, or 'roundworm', and can arguably present the human host with a greater burden of foreign biological material than does any other parasite. Sexually-producing adult worms develop in the intestine to a maximum size of about 400 mm long by 6 mm thick, and females release eggs at the rate of 200 000 per day. These take about 2–3 weeks to embryonate and produce the infective larvae. Following ingestion, the larvae emerge from the egg, invade the mucosa, migrate to the lungs via the liver, break out into the alveoli, move up the trachea and are swallowed. Upon re-entry to the intestine, they develop to mature adult worms, mate, and eggs usually begin to be released in the feces by about 60–70 days of infection.

It has often been written that the vast majority of ascariasis cases are symptomless, but it is becoming clear that chronic malabsorbtion and malnutrition can result, and even single worms can prove lethal by penetrating the bile or pancreatic ducts. Rupture and/or blockage of the intestine by the sheer mass of worms is estimated to kill about 20 000 children a year, but this is almost certainly a gross underestimate. Treatment by anthelmintics is effective but parasite infections can return to pretreatment levels within 1 year because of contamination of the environment with the highly persistent eggs. There is, therefore, little evidence for the acquisition of a sterile immunity to the parasite in humans, although certain individuals appear to remain consistently uninfected. A characteristic of most helminthiases, including ascariasis, is that the parasite population is overdispersed within a host population. That is, most of the parasites are present in a small proportion of potential hosts, and the majority of people are parasite-free or have only small burdens. Among infected individuals, children tend to suffer infections of greater intensity than do those in older age groups. Recent genetic studies on the parasites have shown that the closely related parasite of pigs, *A. suum*, probably does not reach maturity in humans, but exposure to it might nevertheless influence the immune response to *A. lumbricoides*.

The first clinical signs of infection are associated with the pulmonary phase and include pneumonitis, cough, dyspnea, substernal pain and sometimes a blood-stained sputum. This is known as the Löffler syndrome and has some of the characteristics of an immediate-type hypersensitivity response. There can be a dense pulmonary infiltrate at this time, and a rising eosinophilia. Pulmonary hypersensitivity can cause significant mortality among children in arid regions where high-level seasonal transmission occurs. The intestinal phase is associated with digestive disorders, nausea and colic. Villous atrophy has been demonstrated in infected children and pigs, and is probably immune-associated.

Until recently, work on the antigens of *Ascaris* has been confined to somatic materials of the parasite. These have been shown to be rich in the phosphorylcholine hapten, and antibody responses to it are a major part of the response to infection in mice. The determinant is found internally and is not thought to be exposed on the parasite surface. *Ascaris* is renowned among laboratory workers for its content of allergens, and proteinaceous allergens ranging between 14.4 and 360 kDa have been described. A nonspecific mast cell-degranulating factor of about 9 kDa has also been described from *Ascaris*. The extent to which these substances contribute to pathology is not clear, but there is one report of lethal intestinal anaphylaxis following chemotherapy for ascariasis, and it is likely that parasite allergens contribute to pulmonary hypersensitivity.

It is now clear, however, that antigens released by the tissue-invasive larvae of the parasite (usually termed 'excretory/secretory' (ES) products) are potently immunogenic and that the set of (glyco) proteins of which they are comprised changes radically during the migration from intestine to lungs. The larvae also release several proteinases, the biochemical activity of which are inhibitable by antibody elicited by the infection. ES products contain components ranging from 14 to 410 kDa, the 14 kDa component also being found in abundance internal to the worm, and is a potent allergen named ABA-1. This protein is now known to be a fatty acid and retinoid-binding protein which appears to have no homolog in vertebrates, and has highly unusual binding characteristics. It is thought to be a four-bundle α-helix protein with its binding site in its core (**Figure 1**). ABA-1 is a member of the nematode

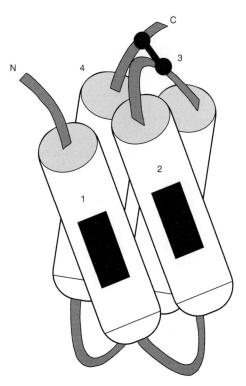

Figure 1 Model of the ABA-1 allergen of *Ascaris*, showing the proposed four α-helix bundle structure. The protein is known to form dimers and the position of putative external hydrophobic patches on helices 1 and 2, which may act as the subunit interface, are shown as black rectangles. (Courtesy of Dr A Brass, University of Manchester, UK.)

polyprotein antigens/allergens which appear to be produced by all nematodes as a polyprotein that is cleaved by proteinases during post-translational processing into multiple copies of the active allergen protein.

Immune response of the host

Infected humans produce strong immunoglobulin G (IgG) and IgE antibodies against the parasite, but most people respond only to a subset of parasite components. For instance, only about one in five infected people appear to respond to the ABA-1 antigen/allergen. This heterogeneity has been modeled in laboratory rodents in which the immune repertoire to *Ascaris* antigens is restricted by the class II region of the major histocompatibility complex. A surprising feature of the restriction is that it applies to whole molecules as large as 220 kDa. A similar genetic restriction probably explains the limited repertoire seen in humans, but heterogeneity in recognition of individual parasite components might mean that people will vary in the specificity of their hypersensitivity reactions to *Ascaris*. Moreover, there is growing evidence that the IgE response is protective

in ascariasis, as is thought to be the case in some other helminth infections. Experiments in mice have shown that the immune response in *Ascaris* infection is dominated by T_H2 cells, which presumably explains the high IgE, mastocytosis and eosinophilia of the infections. In experimental infections in mice with other species of intestinal nematode, the T_H2 response is crucial to the immune elimination of the parasites.

Evasive strategies by the organism

Anything written on evasion strategies in nematodiases remains speculative. The parasite alters its surface and secreted antigens during its tissue migrations, and it has been suggested that this functions to keep the parasite ahead of the immune response. This would not, however, be compatible with the continuous recruitment of parasites known to occur in infected humans. The larvae secrete proteinases which could cleave bound antibody and/or complement. Parasitic nematodes commonly secrete antioxidants, such as superoxide dismutase, but this has not been examined for *Ascaris*. If, like the related nematode *Toxocara canis*, *Ascaris* has a surface that rapidly sheds antigens, then continuous loss of bound antibody, complement and/or cells would provide an immune evasion mechanism. It also might simply be that it is not possible for the immune system to deal with a rapidly migrating multicellular parasite. The intestinal stage of *Ascaris* is thought to live for at least 1 year, and there appear to be successive waves of recruitment. It is not known how these worms evade the immune response, although it is known from experimental models that some species of gastrointestinal nematodes are able to suppress local and sometimes systemic immune responses. Another possibility is that T cell tolerance to these long-term occupants of the gut is generated.

Vaccines

There is no vaccine, and no immediate prospect of one. ES antigens are known to be partially protective in rodents and pigs, and are therefore attracting attention. It has become conventional that parasite surface antigens be investigated, but their activity as protective antigens has not been examined for *Ascaris*. Only one vaccine against any nematode parasite is currently available, the irradiation-attenuated vaccine against the lungworm of cattle and sheep, *Dictyocaulus viviparus* and *Dictyocaulus filariae*. Ultraviolet-irradiated larvae of *Ascaris* confer partial resistance in pigs, but such a preparation would probably not be acceptable for human or veterinary use because of the associated pathology, particularly in the liver. The design of a vaccine against *Ascaris* (as with all pathogens) comprising recombinant proteins would have to take into account the genetic restriction of the immune repertoire. Some new generation vaccines are thought to circumvent this restriction, but this has not yet been found to be the case for nematode antigens. Likewise, the importance of IgE antibody to protection will need to be considered, although immunization regimens designed to generate an IgE response may be necessary; they would need to be designed to avoid unacceptable hypersensitivity responses in vaccinated subjects who may already have been sensitized by infection.

See also: **Allergens; Gastrointestinal tract infections; Hookworm disease; Parasites, immunity to; Toxocariasis; Trichuriasis**

Further reading

Coles GC (1985) Allergy and immunopathology of ascariasis. In: Crompton DWT, Nesheim MC and Pawlowski

ZS (eds) *Ascariasis and its Public Health Significance*, pp 167–184. London: Taylor and Francis.

Fraser EM, Christie JF and Kennedy MW (1993) Heterogeneity amongst infected children in IgE antibody repertoire to the antigens of the parasite nematode *Ascaris*. *International Archives of Allergy and Immunology* 100: 283–286.

Kennedy MW (1992) Genetic control of the antibody response to parasite allergens. In: Moqbel R (ed) *Allergy and Immunity to Helminths: Common Mechanisms or Divergent Pathways?* pp 63–80. London: Taylor and Francis.

Kennedy MW, Brass A, McCruden AB, Price NC, Kelly SM and Cooper A (1995) The ABA-1 allergen of the parasitic nematode *Ascaris suum*: fatty acid and retinoid binding function and structural characterization. *Biochemistry* 34: 6700–6710.

Ogilvie BM and de Savigny D (1982) Immune response to nematodes. In: Cohen S and Warren KS (eds) *Immunology of Parasitic Infections*, pp 715–757. Oxford: Blackwell Scientific.

ASTHMA

David M Essayan and **Lawrence M Lichtenstein**, Division of Clinical Immunology, Department of Medicine, Johns Hopkins University School of Medicine, Baltimore, Maryland, USA

Asthma is a disease of the lungs affecting both children and adults and characterized by: 1) airway obstruction that is partially or completely reversible, 2) airway inflammation, and 3) airway hyperresponsiveness. A persistent rise in disease prevalence, hospitalizations due to disease exacerbation, and disease mortality over the last two decades underscores the importance of an increased understanding of disease pathogenesis and the development of improved therapeutic agents. This entry summarizes our current understanding of this disease entity.

Epidemiology

There is a close concordance between asthma, allergic rhinitis and atopic dermatitis; the presence of one of these entities increases the relative risk of the other two by 3- to 30-fold over the lifetime of the subject. All three of these diseases are associated with high levels of nonspecific and antigen-specific serum immunoglobulin E (IgE).

The worldwide prevalence of asthma in childhood ranges from approximately 1.4 to 11.4%, but varies widely by racial and geographic factors and ascertainment methods. The overall prevalence of asthma is approximately equal in industrialized and nonindustrialized nations; however, prevalence tends to be less in rural than in urbanized communities. Moreover, children emigrating from rural to urbanized areas tend to assume the relative risk associated with their new environment, implicating exposure to extrinsic agents in disease pathogenesis. In developed countries, asthma is the second leading cause of hospitalization in children. Finally, greater than 70% of bronchial hyperresponsiveness (BHR) in adults and greater than 85% of BHR in children is associated with IgE sensitivity to various, predominantly inhalant, allergens.

A strong genetic influence on the development of asthma has also been described in studies of mono- and dizygotic twins. Vertical transmission studies show a 25–35% relative risk of asthma conveyed to each child by each affected parent. Finally, a synthesis of data from various linkage studies in affected kindred have shown associations of the asthma phenotype to microsatellite markers on chromosomes 4, 6, 7, 11, 13 and 16, with more specific mapping to 11q13 (FcεR1β), 5q31 (IL-4, -5 and -13 gene cluster), 6p21 (HLA-DR), 14q11.2 (T cell receptor α/δ chains) and 12q15. Thus, our understanding of disease pathogenesis must take into consideration the multifactorial nature of this clinical entity.

Pathogenesis

The key initiating event in the pathogenesis of asthma is currently felt to be inflammation of the conducting airways. T lymphocyte activation is suggested by increased surface expression of CD25, CD45, HLA-DR and VLA-1 on lymphocytes from bronchoalveolar lavage (BAL) and bronchial biopsy specimens of asthmatic subjects. Moreover, expression of interleukin-4 (IL-4) and IL-5 but not interferon γ (IFNγ), in a pattern consistent with a T_H2 response, has been shown in asthmatic subjects; this expression is greater in symptomatic subjects, increased after allergen challenge, positively correlated with asthma symptoms, and negatively correlated to FEV_1 (forced expiratory volume in 1 second). Early activation of pulmonary mast cells is suggested by elevations of both histamine and tryptase in BAL samples immediately following allergen challenge. IgE-dependent activation of mast cells results in the generation of sulfidopeptide leukotrienes that contribute to mucus hypersecretion, increased microvascular permeability and smooth muscle contraction. The participation of tryptase in neuropeptide metabolism may further contribute to neuronally mediated increases in airway smooth muscle tone. The late inflammatory response is associated with a marked influx of eosinophils and basophils into the asthmatic airway. Eosinophil degranulation is suggested by increases in major basic protein, eosinophil peroxidase, and eosinophil cationic protein in asthmatic airways. These highly toxic substances may promote BHR through direct damage to airway epithelium, resulting in exposure of mast cells and nerve endings. Activation of basophils recruited to these sites of inflammation result in both the generation of mediators of bronchoconstriction and mucus hypersecretion and the elaboration of proinflammatory cytokines such as IL-4 and IL-13. Selective and coordinated recruitment of these various effector cell types may be achieved through the upregulation of specific members of the integrin and selectin superfamilies of cellular adhesion molecules and the elaboration of specific cellular chemoattractants (**Figure 1**).

The pathology of asthma reflects these basic principles of allergic inflammation. Those airways most affected in asthmatics are the large and medium conducting airways. Classic changes seen on biopsy of severe asthmatic subjects, as well as postmortem examination of subjects suffering fatal asthma, include vascular congestion, mucosal edema with exudation of fluid and proteins from the microvasculature, and infiltration of inflammatory cells into interstitial tissue. Mucus hypersecretion with disruption of pulmonary epithelial cells results in luminal obstruction. Chronic inflammation may also result in airway remodeling with thickening and fibrosis in the region of the basement membrane. Curschman spirals (expectorated casts of inflamed airways), Creola bodies (compact clusters of sloughed epithelial cells), and Charcot–Leyden crystals (condensed eosinophil granular proteins) are considered classic findings in severe asthma. Squamous metaplasia may occur as a response to epithelial disruption. The functional

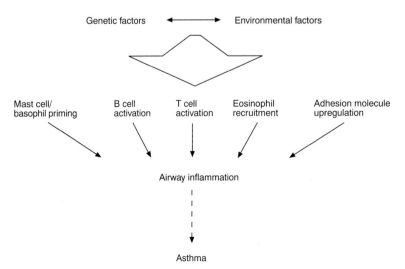

Figure 1 The pathogenesis of asthma.

consequences of these pathological changes include early airway closure with distal air trapping and increased residual volume, reduced FEV$_1$ values, and abnormal gas distribution and exchange. Increased airway resistance and tidal volumes closer to inspiratory plateau contribute to an increased work of breathing that is only partially compensated by the use of accessory muscles for respiration. Finally, defects in smooth muscle relaxation may contribute to the pulmonary mechanical dysfunction characteristic of asthma.

Clinical presentation

Asthma may present acutely or as a chronic pulmonary disease. Symptoms of acute asthma include shortness of breath, chest tightness, wheezing and cough, often productive of clear or slightly colored sputum. When present, chest pain is usually musculoskeletal in origin. Audible wheezing may not be present in mild asthma, but may be elicited by forced expiratory maneuvers. Increased diurnal variations in pulmonary function are often associated with nocturnal exacerbations. Triggers for worsening asthma include cold air exposure, exercise, viral respiratory infections, sinusitis, gastroesophageal reflux, exposure to seasonal or perennial inhalant allergens, and exposure to inhaled irritants such as cigarette smoke. Seasonal variations in asthma severity often correlate with seasonal allergen exposure. Finally, a number of medications, including β adrenergic blockers and nonsteroidal anti-inflammatory agents, as well as sulfite preservatives, may exacerbate asthma in susceptible subjects. A correlation of total suspended particles and levels of various air pollutants to exacerbation rates for asthma has been reported.

Physical signs of acute asthma include tachypnea, tachycardia, pulsus paradoxicus, hyperinflation of the chest, audible wheezing, and the use of accessory muscles of respiration. Chest roentgenogram may show flattening of the diaphragms bilaterally and increased anteroposterior dimension. Pulmonary function studies reveal an obstructive pattern which may be partially or completely reversed by the administration of β-adrenergic agonists. Diurnal variations in peak expiratory flow rate greater than 20% are highly suggestive of asthma. Bronchoprovocation with a variety of agents, including methacholine and histamine, may identify subjects with BHR. However, it should be noted that the perception of asthma by an affected subject may not correlate to the degree of pulmonary dysfunction due to an impaired sensitivity to hypoxia and hypercarbia.

The differential diagnosis of asthma includes mechanical obstruction of the airway (extrathoracic and intrathoracic), laryngeal dysfunction, chronic obstructive pulmonary disease, cardiac dysfunction, pulmonary embolism, pulmonary infiltrates and eosinophilia (PIE syndrome), cough due to drugs (angiotensin-converting enzyme ACE inhibitors), and carcinoid tumors. The majority of these entities may be readily differentiated from asthma on the basis of clinical presentation, physical examination, roentgenographic studies and pulmonary function testing.

Treatment

Nonpharmacologic

Optimal management for asthma of any stage should include a number of nonpharmacologic measures. Paramount among these is education of the patient and family concerning basic issues of disease pathogenesis, mechanisms of action of medications, and the proper technique for the use of metered-dose inhalers. Avoidance of allergic and irritant triggers of asthma, particularly indoor allergens (dust mite, animal danders, cockroach and mold) and indoor irritants (cigarette smoke, colognes) should be encouraged. Finally, every patient should be instructed in the proper use of step care for asthma exacerbations due to exposures and viral illnesses, with the objective of reducing the necessity for acute and subacute care (**Figure 2**).

Pharmacologic

Nonacute asthma may be classified as mild, moderate or severe on the basis of clinical parameters. Mild asthma is defined as exacerbations of cough and wheezing less than twice a week with few clinical signs or symptoms between exacerbations, good exercise tolerance, nocturnal symptoms less than

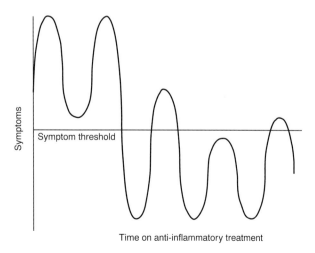

Figure 2 The beneficial effects of anti-inflammatory therapy on frequency, duration and severity of exacerbations in asthma.

twice a month, and a resting peak expiratory flow rate (PEFR) of >80% of predicted with less than 20% diurnal variability. Moderate asthma is defined as exacerbations more than twice a week, resulting in urgent care treatment less than three times a year, with periods of minimal symptoms between exacerbations; exercise tolerance in these patients is slightly diminished, nocturnal symptoms may be present 2–3 times a week, and resting PEFR may be 60–80% of predicted with diurnal variability of 20–30%. Severe asthma is characterized by daily symptoms with frequent exacerbations and frequent utilization of urgent care facilities or a history of respiratory failure. Patients with severe asthma have poor exercise tolerance, frequent nocturnal symptoms, resting PEFR <60% of predicted with diurnal variability >30%. Risk factors for fatal asthma include hospital admission for severe asthma within the preceding year, a history of respiratory failure with hypercarbia due to asthma, and a history of barotrauma. Pharmacologic therapy should be targeted to clinical stage, as summarized in **Table 1**. A synthesis of available studies suggests that immunotherapy for inhalant allergens reduces BHR, frequency and/or severity of exacerbations, and medication usage in all three clinical stages of chronic asthma. Leukotriene antagonists may be useful for all stages of asthma, and particularly effective for aspirin sensitive asthmatics. Agents considered investigational at this time for the treatment of severe asthma include methotrexate, gold, macrolides and cyclosporine.

The treatment of acute asthma should focus on intensification of pharmacologic therapies and maintenance of respiratory function with the use of ventilatory support and neuromuscular paralysis as necessary. Therapeutic BAL may be useful in selected patients. Mucolytic agents and iodides are contraindicated.

Special considerations

Occupational asthma

Approximately 2% of all asthma is related to occupational exposures. A large and growing list of agents may precipitate this syndrome, including vegetable materials, chemicals, animal materials, metals and pharmaceuticals. While the high molecular weight compounds are complete antigens that elicit IgE synthesis, many of the low molecular weight compounds are haptens, creating a complete antigen only when bound to carrier proteins. There is often a latency period between the onset of exposure and the development of clinical disease. Symptoms tend to be worse on work days and better on weekends and holidays. Bronchoprovocation testing with the specific agent may confirm the diagnosis. Subjects with long exposure histories may suffer chronic pulmonary dysfunction despite removal from the environment.

Asthma during pregnancy

Poorly controlled asthma poses significant risks to both mother and fetus. The primary goals of asthma therapy during pregnancy are stabilization of disease with prevention of exacerbations and rapid, early intervention for acute exacerbations should they occur. Intensification of nonpharmacologic therapies is indicated: risk/benefit analysis suggests a positive profile for most asthma medications, particularly the inhaled medications.

See also: **Acute inflammatory reaction; Allergens; Atopic allergy; Basophils; Drugs, allergy to; Eczema; Eosinophils; Food allergy; Glucocorticoids; Helper T lymphocytes; Histamine; Hypersensitivity reactions; Mast cells; Rhinitis, allergic.**

Table 1 Pharmacologic therapy of chronic asthma

Asthma grade	β Agonists	Cholinergic blockers	Cromoglycates	Steroids	Methylxanthines	Immunotherapy
Mild	As needed pre-exercise pre-exposure	As needed; may be useful	May be useful pre-exercise pre-exposure	Rarely needed	May be useful for nocturnal symptoms	Indicated
Moderate	As needed or regular use; consider long-acting agents		Regular use	Regular use of inhaled; systemic as needed	May be useful adjunct therapy	Indicated
Severe	As needed and regular use; consider long-acting agents		Regular use	High dose inhaled; systemic as needed	Regular use	Indicated

Further reading

Barnes KC, Neely JD, Duffy DL et al (1996) Linkage of asthma and total serum IgE concentration to markers on chromosome 12q: Evidence from Afro-caribbean and caucasian populations. Genomics 37: 41–50.

Barnes PJ (1995) Inhaled glucocorticoids for asthma. New England Journal of Medicine 332: 868–875.

Busse WW and Reed CE (1993) Asthma definition and pathogenesis. In: Middleton E, Jr., Reed CE, Ellis EF, Adkinson NF, Jr., Yunginger JW and Busse WW (eds) Allergy Principles and Practice 4th edn, pp. 1173–1201. St Louis: Mosby.

Creticos PS, Reed CE, Norman PS et al (1996) Ragweed immunotherapy in adult asthma. New England Journal of Medicine 334: 501–506.

Daniels SE, Bhattacharrya S, James A et al (1996) A genome-wide search for quantitative trait loci underlying asthma. Nature 383: 247–250.

Holgate ST, Bradding P and Sampson AP (1996) Leukotriene antagonists and synthesis inhibitors: New directions in asthma therapy. Journal of Allergy and Clinical Immunology 98: 1–13.

Nelson HS (1995) β-Adrenergic bronchodilators. New England Journal of Medicine 333: 499–506.

Paul WE and Seder RA (1994) Lymphocyte responses and cytokines. Cell 76: 241–251.

Robinson DS, Hamid Q, Ying S et al (1992) Predominant Th2-like bronchoalveolar T-lymphocyte population in atopic asthma. New England Journal of Medicine 326: 298–304.

Schroeder JT and MacGlashan DW, Jr. (1997) New concepts – the basophil. Journal of Allergy and Clinical Immunology 99: 429–433.

Sheffer AL (chair) (1991) NHLBI Guidelines for the diagnosis and management of asthma. Journal of Allergy and Clinical Immunology 88: 427–534.

ATAXIA TELANGIECTASIA

Richard A Gatti, Department of Pathology, UCLA School of Medicine, Los Angeles, California, USA

Ataxia telangiectasia (AT) is a rare (1:40 000 live births) pleiotropic disorder whose various phenotypic manifestations include a progressive cerebellar ataxia, ocular apraxia, and oculocutaneous telangiectasia (**Figure 1**). Almost all patients have an elevated serum α-fetoprotein (AFP). Translocations involving chromosomes 7 and 14 are characteristic. About half of the patients have a moderate to severe immunodeficiency, involving both B and T cell compartments. One-third of patients develop cancer, usually lymphoid. Because these patients are hypersensitive to ionizing radiation and are cancer susceptible, they are in grave danger of being overtreated with conventional doses of radiation therapy. The disease is inherited as an autosomal recessive trait. Despite previous work describing four complementation groups, only a single AT gene exists, ATM (AT, mutated). Most patients are compound heterozygotes, i.e. they inherit a different mutation from each parent. The function of the ATM gene is presently unknown; however, much evidence suggests that one of its primary roles is to sense double-stranded DNA breaks and alert the cell, via signal transduction pathways upstream of p53, not to enter the S (synthesis) phase of the cell cycle until the DNA damage has been repaired. No doubt the ATM gene product will have other roles as well. AT cells have G_1, S, and G_2/M checkpoint defects. All DNA repair mechanisms that have been tested in AT patients have been normal.

Neuropathology

The most apparent characteristic of the AT syndrome is the ataxia. Shortly after learning to walk, AT children begin to stagger; by 10 years of age, they are confined to a wheelchair for the remainder of their lives. The most obvious lesion in the central nervous system at postmortem examination is a paucity of Purkinje cells in the cerebellum. These cells are present in normal numbers at birth but degenerate progressively. Purkinje cell migration and arborization are also abnormal, lesions that would have had to have been expressed during the third trimester of pregnancy, long before symptoms appear. It is not known whether the Purkinje cell degeneration is central or results from anteriograde or retrograde degeneration.

Radiosensitivity

Radiation therapists have observed that when AT patients with cancer are treated with conventional doses of ionizing radiation, they develop sequelae characteristic of much higher dosages. The radiosensitivity can be demonstrated in vitro as well, usually

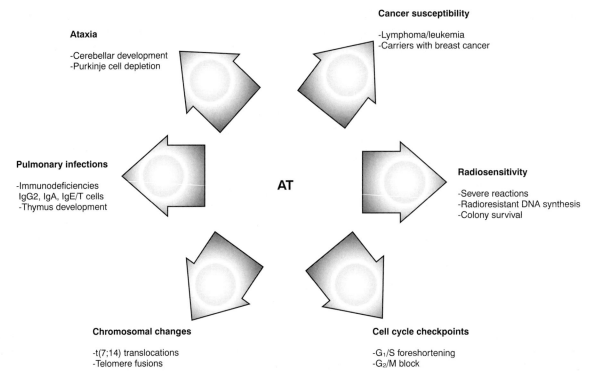

Ataxia

-Cerebellar development
-Purkinje cell depletion

Cancer susceptibility

-Lymphoma/leukemia
-Carriers with breast cancer

Pulmonary infections

-Immunodeficiencies
IgG2, IgA, IgE/T cells
-Thymus development

AT

Radiosensitivity

-Severe reactions
-Radioresistant DNA synthesis
-Colony survival

Chromosomal changes

-t(7;14) translocations
-Telomere fusions

Cell cycle checkpoints

-G_1/S foreshortening
-G_2/M block

Figure 1 The AT syndrome.

by 'radioresistant DNA synthesis' or by colony survival efficiency following radiation. In the laboratory, carriers are intermediate in radiosensitivity between homozygotes and normals. AT cells are sensitive not only to ionizing radiation but to a variety of radiomimetic agents as well. Testing for radiation hypersensitivity can be used to confirm the diagnosis; however, few laboratories test clinical specimens. Our laboratory uses an Epstein–Barr virus (EBV)-transformed lymphoblastoid cell line (LCL) to measure *in vitro* radiosensitivity (**Figure 2**).

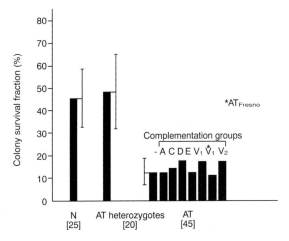

Figure 2 Colony survival assay (CSA) measures radiosensitivity of LCLs to 1 Gy on patients with AT, AT heterozygotes, and normals. Also included are results on patients with NBS (V_1), BBS (V_2) and AT$_F$ (V_1).

Heterozygotes cannot be distinguished by this method under the conditions used.

Cancer susceptibility

During the shortened lifetimes of AT homozygotes, 38% develop a malignancy, usually lymphoid. This represents a 61-fold and 184-fold increase in Euro-American and Afro-American patients, respectively. About half of the malignancies observed are lymphomas, usually of the B cell type. Leukemias account for another quarter of the malignancies. These are usually T cell leukemias. Young AT patients develop a less aggressive T cell leukemia than older patients, who develop a prolymphocytic leukemia (T-PLL); the latter was formerly described as T-CLL because the cells histologically resemble those of chronic lymphocytic leukemia. However, the T-PLL cells are T cells. Myeloid leukemias have not been described in AT patients. AT heterozygotes are also cancer prone, although not to the extent that homozygotes are. Breast cancer was observed to be five-fold higher among heterozygotes in US families. Based on this observation and an estimated carrier frequency of 1%, it has been postulated that between 8 and 18% of all breast cancer patients may be AT heterozygotes. Despite this prediction, recent genetic screening of breast cancer patients for ATM mutations has failed to reveal increased numbers of AT heterozygotes. Further studies are in progress to answer this question. Meanwhile, ATM knockout mice all die with malignant thymic lymphomas, closely mimicking the cancer susceptibility of AT patients.

Chromosomal instability

Almost all AT patients have translocations involving the T cell receptor gene complexes at 14q11, 7q35 or 7p14, making up about 10% of metaphases counted. AT heterozygotes have similar translocations in about 1% of their T cells. Normals also have such translocations in about 0.1% of their T cells. Chromosomal aberrations in fibroblasts and amniocytes of AT patients are random and do not show the characteristic translocations. The T-PLL leukemia of AT patients is frequently associated with translocations or inversions involving the same sites described above. These translocations juxtapose part of a T cell receptor gene to a site just proximal to either the TCL-1 (T cell leukemia 1) gene at 14q32 or the c6.1B/MTCP-1 (mature T cell proliferation 1) gene at Xq28. Other factors must also be necessary for leukemia to develop since some AT patients have these clonal expansions in 100% of their T cells for many years and yet do not have leukemia. The frequencies of both mitotic and meiotic recombination are increased in AT cells, as is intrachromosomal recombination. Gametogenesis may be abnormal. ATM knockout mice have gonadal streaks, female animals do not ovulate, and male animals are sterile. Despite this, most AT patients reach normal sexual maturity, with normal menstrual cycles in females, and the ability to produce sperm in at least some males.

Immunodeficiency

At postmortem examination, virtually every AT homozygote has had a small embryonic-like thymus. No single uniform immunological abnormality has been found in AT patients. Indeed, even affected siblings often have different degrees of immunodeficiency. IgA and IgG2 deficiencies have been described in 60% and 80% of patients, respectively. Occasional AT patients have hyper-IgM, with hyperviscosity of blood and splenomegaly. T cell levels are normal to slightly reduced in AT patients. A suggestion that a $\gamma\delta$ T cell subset is increased in AT patients has not been generally confirmed. CD4$^+$/CD45RA$^+$ (naive) T cells are decreased in some patients. Responses to mitogens, antigens and allogeneic cells are usually slightly reduced, although a few patients have profound deficiencies of T cell responses. T cells show abnormally fast capping of FITC-labelled con-

canavalin A. Natural killer (NK) cell activity and NK cell levels have been described as normal, decreased, or increased in various studies. Some of these discrepancies may reflect transient immunological changes during infections. Unlike all other immunodeficiency symptoms, opportunistic infections are not seen in AT patients.

The ATM gene and mutations

The AT gene was isolated in 1995, culminating a 14-year positional cloning effort by an international consortium of investigators. The ATM gene and gene products are very large: 3056 amino acids, 350 kDa protein, and a 13 kb transcript that may be alternatively spliced in some tissues. The ATM gene is expressed in all tissues tested. The gene has 66 exons, each of about 100–300 base pairs in length; these are spread over about 150 kb of genomic DNA at chromosome 11q23.1. Eighty-five per cent of mutations result in a shortened (truncated) protein. Since the gene has a phosphotidylinositol 3-kinase domain at the 3' end, truncated proteins probably will be lacking this important functional domain. Many of these truncations result from deletions of 1, 2 and 3 exons because of mutations at splice sites. About 200 mutations have been characterized thus far (**Figure 3**); only two potential hotspots can be appreciated at exons 54 and 16. The rest of the mutations are found across the entire gene, making it difficult to identify each patient's mutations without a great deal of screening of the gene. The most useful screening techniques thus far have been protein truncation testing (PTT), single-strand conformational analysis (SSCA), heteroduplex analysis (HA), conformation-sensitive gel electrophoresis (CSGE), RNAase cleavage assay (RCA), and restriction endonuclease fingerprinting (REF). Each of these must then be followed by DNA sequencing to identify the actual site of the mutation. A few common mutations have been identified and can be tested easily among Amish, Central-Southern Italians, Moroccan Jews, Midland English, Norwegians, Costa Ricans and Polish.

Related syndromes

Several related syndromes overlap with AT. Nijmegen breakage syndrome (NBS) shares t(7;14) translocations, radiosensitivity, immunodeficiency and cancer susceptibility with AT but these patients do not have ataxia, telangiectasia, nor elevated AFP; NBS patients are microcephalic and mentally retarded. AT patients are usually not mentally retarded. Berlin breakage syndrome is very similar

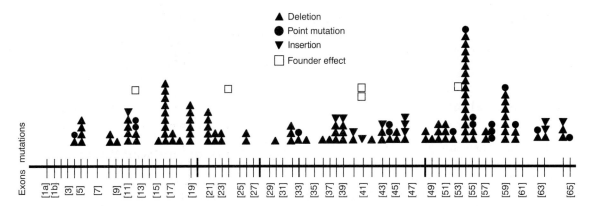

Figure 3 Spectrum of ~120 ATM mutations based on studies of cDNA from cells of patients from many countries. Mutations seen in related (i.e. shared haplotypes) families are indicated only once (boxes) so as not to bias the distribution.

to NBS but sometimes includes syndactyly or anal stenosis. AT$_{Fresno}$ combines the AT and NBS syndromes. AT$_{Fresno}$ patients have ATM mutations. NBS and BBS families do not link to 11q23.1 and, therefore, are probably caused by mutations at another (AT-related) gene.

Therapy

There is no effective therapy for the progressive ataxia. Spasticity can be controlled in some patients with bromocriptine; however, the safety of this medication has not been established for children under 15 years. Valium has been used to ameliorate chronic jerks and tremors but its effects are short-lived. Vitamin E (α-tocopherol) is sometimes prescribed to minimize nonspecific free-radical damage to tissue, although its efficacy is unproven. Immunotherapy is only indicated for patients with frequent recurring infections. Intravenous gamma globulin is effective in reducing the frequency and severity of infections in such patients. Conventional dosages of radiation therapy and radiomimetic agents are contraindicated and life-threatening.

Physical activities such as swimming and calasthenics maintain muscle tone, prevent fractures and slow the side-effects of long-term confinement to a wheelchair – most notably, contractions of hands and feet. Speech therapy helps articulation and voice volume. Good pulmonary hygiene and regular breathing exercises minimize lung impairment, although there is a bit of evidence that the lungs of AT patients may be anatomically compromised by the disease itself. Parental counselling is of paramount importance in alleviating confusion and anxiety. Bringing members of AT families together periodically as a *de facto* support group is also effective therapy. Prenatal diagnosis is now feasible and is quite accurate, with a turnabout time of 1–2 weeks.

See also: **Chromosome translocations of immune genes; Immunodeficiency, primary.**

Further reading

Boder E and Sedgwick RP (1958) Ataxia-telangiectasia: a familial syndrome of progressive cerebellar ataxia, oculocutaneous telangiectasia and frequently pulmonary infection. *Pediatrics* **21**: 526–554.

Burgt I, Chrzanowska K, Smeets D and Weemaes C (1996) Nijmegen breakage syndrome. *Journal of Medical Genetics* **33**: 153–156.

Gatti RA (1996) Ataxia-telangiectasia. In: Scriver CR, Beaudet AL, Sly WS and Valle D (eds) *Metabolic and Molecular Basis of Inherited Disease*, New York: McGraw-Hill CD-ROM.

Gatti RA and Swift M (eds) (1985) *Ataxia-telangiectasia: Genetics Neuropathology, and Immunology of a Degenerative Disease of Childhood*. New York: Alan R Liss.

Gatti RA, Boder E, Vinters HV, Sparkes RS, Norman A and Lange K (1991) Ataxia-telangiectasia: an interdisciplinary approach to pathogenesis. *Medicine* **70**: 99–117.

Gatti RA, Lange E, Rotman G et al (1994) Genetic haplotyping of ataxia-telangiectasia families localizes the major gene to an ~850 kb region on chromosome 11q23.1. *International Journal of Radiation Biology* **66**: S57–S62.

Huo YK, Wang Z, Hong J-H et al (1994) Radiosensitivity of ataxia-telangiectasia, X-linked agammaglobulinemia and related syndromes. *Cancer Research* **54**: 2544–2547.

Kojis TL, Gatti RA and Sparkes RS (1992) The cytogenetics of ataxia-telangiectasia. *Cancer Genetics and Cytogenetics* **56**: 143–156.

Lavin MF and Shiloh Y (1997) The genetic defect in ataxia-telangiectasia. *Annual Review of Immunology* **15**: 177–202.

Meyn MS (1995) Ataxia-telangiectasia and cellular responses to DNA damage. *Cancer Research* **55**: 5991–6001.

Painter RB (1993) Radiobiology of ataxia-telangiectasia. In: Gatti RA and Painter RB (eds) *Ataxia-Telangiectasia*. NATO ASI Series, pp 257–268.

Rotman G and Shiloh Y (1997) The ATM gene and protein: possible roles in genome surveillance, checkpoint controls and cellular defense against oxidative stress. *Cancer Surveys* 29: 285–304.

Savitsky K, Bar-Shira A, Gilad S *et al* (1995) A single ataxia-telangiectasia gene with a product similar to PI-3 kinase. *Sceince* 268: 1749–1753.

Sedgwick RP and Boder E (1991) Ataxia-telangiectasia. In: de Jong JMBV (ed) *Handbook of Clinical Neurology*, vol. 16: *Hereditary Neuropathies and Spinocerebella Atrophies*, pp 347–423. Amsterdam: Elsevier Science.

Spector BD, Filipovich AH, Perry GS and Kersey JH (1982) Epidemiology of cancer in ataxia-telangiectasia. In: Bridges BA and Harnden DG (eds) *Ataxia-telangiectasia – Cellular and Molecular Link between Cancer, Neuropathology and Immune Deficiency*, pp 103–107. Chichester: John Wiley.

Swift A, Morrell D, Massey RB and Chase CL (1991) Incidence of cancer in 161 families affected by ataxia-telangiectasia. *New England Journal of Medicine* 325: 1831–1836.

Taylor AMR, Metcalfe JA, Thick J and Mak Y-F (1996) Leukemia and lymphoma in ataxia telangiectasia. *Blood* 87: 423–438.

Telatar M, Wang Z, Udar N *et al* (1996) Ataxia-telangiectasia: mutations in ATM cDNA detected by protein-truncation screening. *American Journal of Human Genetics* 59: 40–44.

Virgilio L, Narducci MG, Isobe M *et al* (1994) Identification of the TCL1 gene involved in T cell malignancies. *Proceedings of the National Academy of Sciences of the USA* 91: 12530.

ATOPIC ALLERGY

Glenis Scadding, Royal National Throat, Nose and Ear Hospital, London, UK

Definition

Allergy was originally defined in 1906 by Clemens von Pirquet as 'altered reactivity' to denote the different reaction which occurs on second exposure to an antigen, due to the formation of antibodies, when compared to the first exposure. Used in this way the term covered all imune reactions; however, its use has since become restricted to certain hypersensitivity reactions. The term atopy (from the Greek 'out of place') was introduced by Coca and Cooke in 1923. They had observed that certain disorders, such as asthma, eczema and urticaria, run in families and that affected subjects show positive wheal and flare skin reactions to common inhalant antigens, but lack precipitating antibodies.

Prausnitz and Kustner in 1921 demonstrated the transfer of atopic reactivity to normal skin by means of serum. The serum factor, called 'reagin' was identified as a new class of immunoglobulin, IgE, in the 1960s.

Immunoglobulin

IgE has the usual immunoglobulin structure of two heavy and two light chains and is heavily glycosylated, containing about 12% carbohydrate. There are five domains in the heavy chain, compared to four in IgG1. A part of the Fc region of IgE (C_H3 and C_H4) is the binding site for high affinity Fcε receptors on mast cells and basophils. This activity is destroyed by heating at 56°C for 30 min; however, antigen binding activity, which resides in the Fab part of the molecule is not heat labile. Serum levels of IgE are far lower than for other immunoglobulins, being measured in nanograms as opposed to milligrams per milliliter. The half-life of IgE in serum is short (2.5 days); once cell bound, this is increased to several weeks.

Individuals produce IgE in response to certain stimuli, such as parasitic worms, but atopic individuals produce it in response to harmless airborne and/or ingested antigens, which are termed allergens. These include grass pollen, animal dander, house dust mite feces, moulds, food antigens and also industrial substances such as toluene di-isocyanate, plicatic acid and platinum salts. Guidelines for allergen nomenclature recommend the use of the first three letters of the genus, plus the initial of the species, followed by a roman numeral which usually reflects the order in which the allergen was isolated. Major allergens are however designated I. Thus the major house dust mite allergen is known as Der pI, the major cat allergen as Fel dI, etc.

Basis of atopy

The incidence of atopy is closely related to the serum IgE concentration, with less than 5% of the individuals with levels less than 60 iu/ml (1 iu = 2.4 µg) being affected, but over 95% of those with values over 450 iu/ml. There is also an obvious genetic influence, with over 50% of individuals having two allergic parents being atopic, compared with 15% in the normal population. There are several genetic influences determining IgE production: an autosomal dominant gene codes for low IgE levels, HLA-linked genes control IgE and IgG production against specific allergenic proteins (most noticeable for minor determinants when total IgE is low), and HLA-B8 and DRW3 are associated with general immune hyper-responsiveness, possibly via decreased T suppressor activity. Genetic linkage of atopic IgE responses to chromosome 11q13, now observed by several groups, is strongest in maternally derived alleles and may contribute to the maternal inheritance of atopy seen in many studies. The gene for the β chain of the high affinity IgE receptor is a candidate for the chromosome 11q13 effect. A polymorphic variant Leu181/183 was present in 4.5% of the population of Busselton, Western Australia, and when inherited maternally carried a significant risk of atopy and bronchial hyper-responsiveness, but accounted for only a part of the atopy and asthma in that population. Other candidate genes are the TCRα region on chromosome 14 and the interleukin-4 (IL-4) cluster on chromsome 5, both of which show linkage to IgE responses.

Environmental influences are also important: smoking and the use of β-blocking drugs in pregnancy increase the incidence of atopy in offspring. Early contact with highly allergenic proteins (as in cow's milk, eggs, fish, nuts, Der pI, Fel dI) before mucosal protective mechanisms, especially IgA, are fully established appears to contribute to allergy in genetically predisposed infants. Environmental risk factors for seasonal rhinitis include higher social class, being the first-born child and not having to share a bathroom. These suggest that early infections may have a protective antiallergic effect, possibly by interferon γ production.

The incidence of allergic diseases (hay fever, asthma and eczema) in the population is increasing, possibly caused by increased exposure to indoor allergens, or by the adjuvant effect of atmospheric pollutants such as diesel fumes, or possibly by dietary changes. Disruption of mucosal surfaces, allowing increased antigen entry and IgE production can occur following exposure to pollutants such as sulfur dioxide or during viral infections. Viruses can precipitate allergic symptoms, especially following respiratory syncytial virus infections in childhood.

Type I hypersensitivity

The central mechanism of atopic allergy is type I hypersensitivity (**Figure 1**). Mucosal contact with allergen results in uptake by an antigen-presenting cell (APC) and presentation in the form of an allergenic peptide held in the groove of the major histocompatibility complex (MHC) class II molecule to a helper T lymphocyte. This then provides help for a previously committed B cell, which is capable of recognizing the antigen, to make IgE antibody.

Factors determining IgE rather than IgG production are not fully understood; however, the nature of the antigen-presenting cells may be relevant. In atopic eczema and allergic rhinitis Langerhans cells which are HLA-DR positive and bear high-affinity IgE receptors have been described. Class switching to IgE is promoted by cytokines IL-4 and IL-13 and is inhibited by interferon γ. In atopics increased levels of T_H2 type T cells producing IL-4 have been described, e.g. in vernal conjunctivitis.

A second signal required for IgE expression is delivered by a soluble fragment of FcεRII (CD23). This is also upregulated by IL-4. Class switching

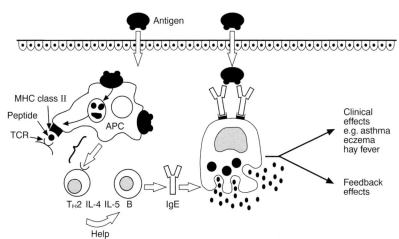

Figure 1   Type I hypersensitivity.

with the production of mRNA for IgE has been described within 30 min of allergen contact. Initial IgE production probably takes place in the local lymphoid tissues. Once produced, the IgE is rapidly and avidly bound by its Fc piece to mast cells and basophils, which are then sensitized. Subsequent contact with the same allergen results in cross-linking of IgE molecules by their Fab portion, calcium ion influx, cell degranulation and mediator release.

Certain mediators exist preformed in granules within the cell, others are formed after activation by phospholipase A_2 breakdown of the cell membrane to release arachidonic acid. This is then metabolized by the cyclo-oxygenase or lipoxygenase pathways, depending on the cell type, to produce prostaglandins and thromboxanes, or leukotrienes respectively. Recent research suggests that there is a third phase of cytokine production taking place in the mast cell during the hours after degranulation. This involves de novo protein synthesis and results in the generation of several cytokines, including IL-3, IL-4 and IL-5. Storage of IL-4 has also been demonstrated within mast cells and its release can occur on degranulation.

Degranulation of mast cells and basophils can also occur following cross-linking of adjacent membrane-bound IgE molecules by anti-IgE, by anti-idiotype, or by lectins. Fab portions of anti-idiotype could occupy IgE antigen-binding sites without causing cross-linking and degranulation, and can thus theoretically protect against allergen challenge.

Pseudoallergy

Certain substances can affect mast cell membranes directly, allowing Ca^{2+} ion influx and release of granule contents. These include the anaphylatoxins, C3a and C5a, secretagogues such as calcium ionophore A23187 and mellitin (a component of insect venom) and drugs such as codeine, morphine and synthetic adrenocorticotropin. Physical stimuli such as pressure, heat, cold and sunlight can cause mast cell degranulation in certain individuals.

Late-phase response

The above mechanism accounts for the immediate allergic reaction; however, in many cases inflammation with ingress of many cell types, including eosinophils, further mast cells, basophils, neutrophils and lymphocytes, occurs within hours of allergen contact. The mechanisms for this depend partly on chemotactic factors released by mast cells, but probably more on cytokine production by T lymphocytes (IL-3, IL-5, IL-10, granulocyte-macrophage colony-stimulating factor (GM-CSF)), macrophages (GM-CSF) and endothelial cells (GM-CSF), together with mast cells (IL-2, IL-3, IL-4, IL-5) (Figure 2). This cytokine network provides the basis for clonal amplification of T cells, B cells and inflammatory cells such as mast cells, basophils and eosinophils. Cells passing in nearby blood vessels are recruited to the site of inflammation, becoming attached to the vascular endothelium, via expressed integrin molecules on the cell surface which interact with receptors such as ICAM-1 and iC3b on the vascular endothelium. Expression of integrins and their receptors is upregulated by inflammatory cytokines. The cells then diapedese through the vascular endothelium and migrate down a chemotactic gradient to the site of allergic inflammation.

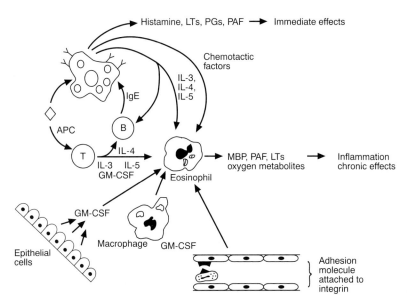

Figure 2 Some of the pathways leading to the late phase inflammatory reaction which is seen in chronic allergic disease.

Physiological effects

The physiological effects of the mast cell-derived mediators fall into three main groups: spasmogens, activators and chemoattractants. In humans the major vasoactive amine is histamine, which causes vasodilatation, increased capillary permeability and bronchoconstriction. Prostaglandin (PG) D_2, leukotrienes (LTs) C_4 and D_4 and platelet activating factor (PAF) are all newly formed bronchoconstrictors, some of which could be partly responsible for the late phase of the allergic response (see below). PAF also activates platelets, leading to microthrombi and further mediator release. Other activators include tryptase, which is a C3 convertase, and kininogenases, which generate kinins from plasma and tissue kininogens, affecting small blood vessels and leading to inflammation. The chemoattractants include neutrophil chemotactic factor (NCF), eosinophil chemotactic factor of anaphylaxis (ECF-A), which are granule derived, and leukotriene B_4, which is newly formed. These induce a cellular infiltrate which includes neutrophils, eosinophils, basophils and monocytes.

The actual mediators released depend on the cell type involved; for example, basophils do not produce prostaglandin D_2. It is apparent that there are at least two different subpopulations of mast cells in humans, with differences in their morphology and pharmacology.

Clinical effects

The clinical effects of type I hypersensitivity depend upon the site of the reaction: involvement of the nose and/or lungs results in rhinitis and/or asthma; skin involvement causes urticaria. Atopic eczema involves IgE-mediated allergy, although the histology resembles a type IV hypersensitivity reaction. It is possible that an initial type I mechanism causes increased vascular permeability, allowing the influx of lymphocytes. Type I reactions to food can cause immediate reactions involving itching and swelling of the lips, mouth and tongue or may lead to nausea, vomiting and abdominal pain, usually within an hour of ingestion. Where the allergen is injected systemically, as in insect stings and intravenous infusions, and occasionally in a very sensitive subject following ingestion, there may be overwhelming basophil degranulation causing anaphylaxis. This involves massive vasodilatation with a sudden drop in blood pressure and collapse. Other symptoms include bronchospasm, an itchy whealing urticarial rash, gut cramps and diarrhea. Anaphylaxis can prove fatal; the mainstay of treatment is epinephrine (adrenaline), either intramuscular or subcutaneous.

The inflammation of the late phase of the allergic reaction is probably of great importance in chronic allergic disease such as asthma, where the infiltrating eosinophils are thought to damage the bronchial mucosa by means of some of their granule contents: such as major basic protein (MBP) and eosinophilic cationic protein (ECP). Exposure of nerve endings could then contribute, via axonal reflexes, to bronchial hyper-reactivity. In the nose and sinuses the thickened mucosa can act as a predisposing factor to chronic or recurrent infection.

Clinical tests

The onset of the allergic reaction from the time of allergen contact with sensitized mast cells is rapid, taking place within minutes. Skin-prick testing, which is the classical test for allergy, can thus be performed as a rapid diagnostic procedure. Antigen is introduced into the skin, which is examined for the presence of a wheal some 15–20 min later; histamine is used as a positive control, saline as the negative. A positive skin test (wheal 3 mm in diameter larger than saline control) usually correlates with the laboratory test for allergen-specific IgE in blood, the radioallergosorbent test (RAST) and with provocation tests. However, the skin-prick test results must always be interpreted in the light of the patient's history, as IgE reactivity to allergen is not always associated with clinical symptoms. Conversely, a negative skin-prick test can exist where there is only local sensitization in the shock organ; such patients will only give positive results on provocation tests.

Other cells with IgE receptors

Mast cells and basophils possess high affinity ($K_d = 10^{-10}$ M) IgE receptors (FcεRI) which have a six-chain structure (two α, two β, two γ). Recently, other cells, such as Langerhans cells, activated eosinophils, monocytes and macrophages, have also been shown to possess such receptors. Many cells of the immune system bear lower affinity (10^{-6} M) IgE receptors (FcεRII, CD23) of a different structure. This is not a member of the immunoglobulin superfamily but instead shares homology with animal C type lectins such as mannose-binding protein. It is present on B and T lymphocytes, monocytes, alveolar macrophages, eosinophils, platelets and Langerhans cells. Soluble CD23 acts as the second signal for IgE production by B cells. FcεRII-bearing cells increase with allergen exposure. These may have cytotoxic properties when armed with IgE. Similarly, eosinophils and platelets are able to kill *Schistosomula* larvae when sensitized by IgE. This function of parasite killing is probably the rationale for the existence of IgE and its immune reactions, with atopic disease an unintended byproduct.

Treatment

Treatment of atopic allergic disease falls into three categories: 1) allergen avoidance; 2) pharmacotherapy; and 3) immunotherapy. The major antiinflammatory drugs used are glucocorticoids, which have a wide spectrum of activity, including reduction of cytokine production and inflammatory cell numbers and activation, a decrease in antigen presentation via a decrease in Langerhans cells in nose and skin, and reduction of mast cell mediator production from arachidonic acid; and sodium cromoglycate, which has multiple effects, including inhibition of mast cell degranulation, sensory nerve function and cytokine secretion. Immunotherapy involves repeated allergen injection; the mechanism of its action may be to induce a T_H1 rather than a T_H2 response locally. Other possibilities such as the use of peptides to produce T cell unresponsiveness, anticytokines and cytokine inhibitors are under investigation.

See also: **Allergens; Arachidonic acid and the leukotrienes; Asthma; Basophils; Eczema; Fc receptors; Food allergy; Hypersensitivity reactions; IgE; Mast cells; Prostaglandins.**

Further reading

Cooke RA and Van der Veer A (1916) Human sensitization. *Journal of Immunology* 1, 201.

Holgate ST and Church MK (eds) (1993) *Allergy.* London: Gower.

Hopkin JM (1989) Genetics of atopy. *Clinical and Experimental Allergy* 19: 263–267.

Kaplan AP (ed) (1995) Basic allergy: immunoglobulin IgE synthesis, inflammation and therapy. *Allergy* 50 (suppl 25).

Kapsenberg ML, Hilkens CM, Jansen HM, Bos JD, Snijders A and Wierenga EA (1996) Production and modulation of T-cell cytokines in atopic allergy. *International Archives of Allergy and Immunology* 110: 107–113.

Wide L, Bennich H and Johansson SGO (1967) Diagnosis of allergy by an *in vitro* test for allergen antibodies. *Lancet* ii: 1105.

ATTENUATED ORGANISMS AS VACCINES

Konstantin M Chumakov, Center for Biologics Evaluation and Research, Food and Drug Administration, Maryland, USA

Attenuation is a process of genetic changes leading to a loss of virulence by pathogenic microorganisms while retaining the capacity to induce an immune response in susceptible hosts, resulting in lasting protection from a disease. Attenuation is a part of the natural evolution of pathogenic microorganisms, and is used by man to create 'live' vaccines against infectious diseases (**Table 1**), in contrast to 'killed' vaccines consisting of inactivated pathogens or their immunogenic subunits. Both types of vaccines have advantages and shortcomings; these will be compared after a brief historical overview and discussion of the general principles behind the process of attenuation. The evolution of pathogens involves several concurrent trends, including immunological drift to escape host defense mechanisms, expansion into new populations (including cross-species adaptation), acquiring new pathogenic factors and properties, and, finally, reduction and loss of pathogenicity (attenuation). While the adaptive value of the former processes is self-evident, as they expand the habitat

of the species, the driving force behind the latter is less apparent. Such 'altruistic' behavior can, perhaps, be explained by the advantages of replicating and spreading without killing a host (which in many cases is a dead end for the microorganism).

Brief history of live vaccines

The oldest example of the use of naturally attenuated organisms for protection against diseases is provided by smallpox. 'Variolation', i.e. deliberate inoculation of susceptible people with virus-containing lymph from pustules of patients with mild forms of the disease, goes back to the early cultures of Africa and Asia. As a result of variolation, patients usually developed the disease with limited lesions, but lasting resistance to smallpox. A few of them, however, had severe disease and some died. By the seventeenth century it was being practised in Europe with the modification of using pustular liquid from cows having a closely related disease, cowpox. In 1796 the British

Table 1 Attenuated organisms as live vaccines (currently licensed)

Bacterial vaccines	Viral vaccines
Anthrax[a]	Adenovirus types 4 and 7
Chicken cholera[a]	Hepatitis A[b]
Cholera[b]	Influenza A and B[b]
Salmonella[b]	Measles
Shigella[b]	Mumps
Tuberculosis (BCG)	Parainfluenza type 3[b]
Typhoid[b]	Poliomyelitis types 1, 2 and 3
	Rabies[a,b]
	Rotavirus[b]
	Rubella
	Smallpox
	Tick-borne encephalitis[b]
	Varicella
	Yellow fever

[a] No longer used.
[b] Still under investigation.

doctor, Edward Jenner, became aware of this procedure, practised by farmers in southern England, and took the next step by propagating the cowpox through patient-to-patient transfer; he called this procedure 'vaccination' (*L. vacuum*, cow). Thus, he created the first biological and called it a 'vaccine'. This term was later broadened to include all biologicals (live, killed or synthetic) used to induce protective immunity against various pathogenic microorganisms, and to treat noninfectious diseases by stimulating the immune system.

The introduction of smallpox vaccine was responsible for a dramatic reduction of the incidence of smallpox in the nineteenth century and led to its complete eradication in the 1970s. Jenner's work was also important for demonstrating the feasibility of preventing infectious diseases and for identifying, for the first time, a method for achieving artificial attenuation. The 'jennerian' approach, involving the growth of pathogenic microorganisms in a nonhuman host and the use of closely related animal pathogens, was the basis for the creation of many other live vaccines. Recent examples are experimental vaccines made with bovine and rhesus rotaviruses which protect against human rotaviruses, and bovine paramyxovirus type 3 vaccine which protects man against human parainfluenza.

The next step in the attenuation of microorganisms was taken by Louis Pasteur, who, in 1880, developed a live vaccine against chicken cholera by exposing a bacterial strain of *Pasteurella multocida* to air. The strain could be cultivated *in vitro* and was the first wholly artificial vaccine prepared outside a living organism. In 1881, by extending this approach based on adverse treatment of the microorganism, he proposed the use of a weakened strain of anthrax

bacillus as a vaccine and demonstrated its remarkable effectiveness. In 1885, together with Emile Roux and others, he proposed to immunize against rabies, using a series of successive inoculations of virus preparations with gradually increasing virulence, a procedure similar to variolation but carried out with a vaccine artificially prepared from the virus weakened by air-drying the spinal cords of infected rabbits.

Another method of achieving artificial attenuation of pathogenic organisms by adaptation to growth in culture is exemplified by the BCG (bacille Calmette–Guérin) vaccine. This attenuated strain of *Mycobacterium bovis* was developed in the early twentieth century by the French doctors Albert Calmette and Camille Guérin. They found that the mycobacteria could be grown in culture on potatoes, cooked and supplemented with glycerol and beef bile. After 231 consecutive passages over the course of 13 years, the strain lost its virulence for animals but retained its antigenic properties and was able to stimulate protective immunity against infection with the virulent strain.

In 1935, a combination of growth in nonnatural hosts and in culture was used by Max Theiler to prepare two strains of a live vaccine against yellow fever. The French neurotropic strain (FNS) was attenuated by serial passaging in the brains of mice, and the 17D strain by intermittent passaging in rhesus monkeys and mosquitoes, followed by passaging in whole mouse embryonic tissue cultures, and then in chick embryos. Since the FNS retained a greater degree of virulence, only the 17D strain is currently used in manufacturing the vaccine.

In addition to the above-mentioned principles of attenuation, it was noted that passaging natural viral isolates in cell cultures almost invariably leads to temperature-sensitive (ts) mutations, suggesting that these may be linked to attenuation. This was one of the principles used by Albert Sabin for the creation of oral poliovirus vaccine (OPV) (**Figure 1**). In many respects OPV is a paradigm for other live viral vaccines and deserves special attention. Sabin noticed that when polioviruses were grown at a low multiplicity of infection, the wild-type strains retained their neurovirulence even after prolonged serial passaging. However, if the virus was passaged at high multiplicity, the degree of neurovirulence dropped. Sabin was also aware of the fact that natural populations of poliovirus consist of a mixture of viral particles with differing 'genetic potentialities'. The term 'quasispecies' is now used to describe this genetic diversity of viral populations. Sabin hypothesized that, while virulent virus particles in a natural mixture replicate to a higher yield and have a replicative advantage in the long run, attenuated particles may

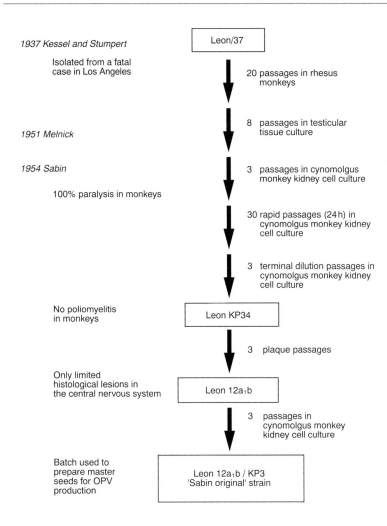

1937 Kessel and Stumpert

Isolated from a fatal
case in Los Angeles

Leon/37

20 passages in rhesus
monkeys

1951 Melnick

8 passages in testicular
tissue culture

1954 Sabin

3 passages in cynomolgus
monkey kidney cell culture

100% paralysis in monkeys

30 rapid passages (24 h) in
cynomolgus monkey kidney
cell culture

3 terminal dilution passages in
cynomolgus monkey kidney
cell culture

No poliomyelitis
in monkeys

Leon KP34

3 plaque passages

Only limited
histological lesions in
the central nervous system

Leon 12a₁b

3 passages in
cynomolgus monkey
kidney cell culture

Batch used to
prepare master
seeds for OPV
production

Leon 12a₁b / KP3
'Sabin original' strain

Figure 1 Attenuation of type 3 poliovirus by Albert Sabin.

replicate faster and be selected if replication of the virus is limited in time. Thus he carried out a series of 'rapid' (24 hours) passages in primary monkey kidney cell cultures, nonneuronal in origin, to suppress viral neutropism. The passages were done at 34°C to select for ts mutants. He was able to create strains of all three serotypes of poliovirus with markedly reduced neurovirulence. The strains were then cloned and plaques with the lowest levels of neurovirulence for monkeys were selected for making the vaccine. The attenuated strains had a number of characteristic genetic markers, including a reduced capacity to replicate at high temperatures (rct40) and at a decreased concentration of bicarbonate (d-marker), and, most importantly, very low neurovirulence even when inoculated directly into the central nervous system of monkeys. These strains were highly immunogenic and have become a major tool in the worldwide eradication of the disease, which is anticipated to occur by the year 2000.

Genetic stability

While the attenuated poliovirus strains comprise the basis of a remarkably effective vaccine, they are prone to partial reversion to neurovirulence. Attenuated virus passaged in cell cultures, and the virus excreted by healthy vaccine recipients, were found to have gradually lost their attenuation markers. This required rigorous neurovirulence safety testing during vaccine production. This potential for reversion back to virulence is a general problem inherent in all live vaccines. A similar process occurs in some strains used in the live mumps vaccine, and to a lesser degree in the yellow fever vaccine. A reduction in, and eventual elimination of, this potential for reversion can be accomplished by creating genetically stable vaccine strains using our knowledge of molecular mechanisms of virulence and attenuation.

Molecular basis of attenuation

A reduction in pathogenicity can occur either through the loss of external pathogenic factors (toxins), as is the case with some bacterial vaccines, or by impairing the invasiveness of a pathogen and limiting its access to target organs. In many cases attenuating mutations occur in capsid or envelope proteins of a virus, presumably reducing its affinity for the target cells. Detailed studies of attenuated polioviruses identified a number of mutations that distinguished vaccine viruses from their wild-type progenitor strains. The mutations linked to attenuation were located in genes for both capsid and noncapsid proteins, as well as in the untranslated regulatory regions (UTRs) of the genome. The mutations in a stem-and-loop domain within the internal ribosome entry site (IRES) of the 5'-UTRs were responsible for the attenuation of all three types of poliovirus. These mutations impaired the initiation of viral protein synthesis by decreasing the affinity of viral RNA to cellular initiation factors. This impairment was cell-type specific, as the difference in replicative capacity between attenuated and wild-type strains was much more pronounced in cultures of cells of neuronal origin than in those of nonneuronal cells.

Viruses serially passaged *in vitro* or isolated from recipients of OPV were found to have reverted at some of the attenuated sites (including the one in the IRES) back to the wild-type state. Other mutations were found which boosted the replicative capacity of the attenuated strains *in vitro* but did not contribute to increased neurovirulence in monkeys. While attenuation is generally associated with lowering the replicative capacity, 'weakening' of the virus does not necessarily lead to a loss of pathogenicity. Attenuation is linked to an inability of the virus to replicate in specific target cells (motor neurons in the case of poliovirus), while retaining the ability to replicate in noncritical organs.

Rational vaccine design

Ideally, an attenuated organism would possess the ability to replicate vigorously and induce an immune response, while being completely devoid of virulent properties. Strains with hyperattenuation (reduced vitality) and substantial or unstable residual virulence are unacceptable for use as vaccines. A knowledge of the genetic basis of virulence allows us to target virulence determinants and to create strains lacking the genes required for pathogenicity. Another challenge in vaccine development arises when dealing with viruses that have a very high rate of antigenic drift, e.g. influenza. In this case, standardized techniques for virus attenuation would be desirable in order to prepare vaccines with consistent effectiveness against the new influenza strains that emerge each year. It was found that passaging influenza virus at low temperatures results in attenuation and that the determinants of attenuation are located on the PA, M, PB2, and PB1 genes of the cold-adapted influenza A virus. Genes of influenza viruses are located on separate RNA segments, and so reassortment of the segments bearing the determinants of attenuation with the ones carrying the genes for hemagglutinin and neuraminidase, which are responsible for immunogenicity, resulted in vaccine strains with the desired antigenic structure and a predictably high degree of attenuation.

New genetically engineered bacterial vaccines provide other examples of a rational approach to vaccine design. Hybrids of *Shigella* and *Escherichia coli*, and *Salmonella* and *shigella*, devoid of toxin genes, but expressing important antigens, have been suggested for use in live vaccines. Selective mutagenesis of the cholera toxin gene results in a strain which possesses all of the antigens important for protective immunity, but with much lower pathogenicity.

Recently it has been found that artificial rearrangement of gene order in vesicular stomatitis virus led to strong attenuation of the virus, even though no changes of amino acid sequences was involved, suggesting a new rational way for creating stable vaccine strains of negative-strand RNA viruses.

Attenuated organisms versus killed vaccines

Arguments about the relative advantages of live and killed vaccines are endless and started with the invention of vaccines themselves. Live vaccines are generally less stable than killed vaccines and require freezing during transportation and storage. The possibility of contamination with live adventitious agents, including the unknown ones, is a consideration that is hard to discount. But the greatest shortcoming of live vaccines is their potential for reversion to virulence. Because of this, in the nineteenth century, variolation was considered a felony in England. Modern vaccines, especially the ones created with a knowledge of the molecular basis of virulence, are much safer than the attenuated strains of the past. In addition, sophisticated methods of quality control are now used to ensure the safety of live vaccines.

The advantages of using attenuated organisms as vaccines are numerous. Since they replicate in the body of a vaccinee, the dose of a live vaccine is usually small, which means its cost and potential for antigenic overload and allergization are low. Many live vaccines can be administered simply by oral or intranasal routes, thus avoiding the hazards of injection. In most cases, vaccination with a live vaccine results in antigenic presentation that closely mimics the natural infection. As a result, immunity is more comprehensive than that induced by killed vaccines, involving both systemic and local factors. For example, immunization with inactivated poliovirus vaccine (IPV) results in high seroconversion rates and high titers of antibodies in the blood of vaccine recipients, but does not create adequate intestinal immunity. Consequently, while the individual immunized with IPV is completely protected from poliomyelitis, the wild-type poliovirus can still replicate in the intestinal tract of the vaccinee and be excreted. Thus IPV cannot break the chain of transmission of wild-type polioviruses, in contrast to OPV, which induces intestinal immunity and results in comprehensive resistance to the poliovirus. OPV stops the circulation of wild-type polioviruses in the human population, and spreads to contacts, thus expanding the reach of immunization. Nonspecific immunity factors such as interferons are produced by live vaccines, which therefore can protect against a wide range of other diseases. For example, OPV has been successfully used to stop outbreaks of diseases caused by other serologically unrelated enteroviruses and has been shown to interfere nonspecifically with infection by other viruses.

Conclusions

As stated earlier, attenuation is a natural part of the coevolution of a host and its microorganisms. As always in symbiotic relationships, both parties benefit. The host provides a substrate for a microorganism's subsistence, which in exchange refrains from causing extensive damage to its host. As an additional payoff, this endosymbiotic microorganisms may help its host to fight off pathogenic microorganisms. This occurs with normal enteric bacterial microflora, and may also be true for naturally attenuated viruses which can temporarily enter into symbiotic relationship with their hosts. A good example of this is the large variety of nonpathogenic enteroviruses (Sabin strains of poliovirus should be regarded as members of this group) that asymptomatically infect the intestinal tract and, by stimulating a host's immune system, interfere with a wide range of pathogenic viruses and help the host fight other diseases. Thus, by acting within the framework of existing micro/macroorganism interactions, artificially attenuated viruses and bacteria are a manmade addition to the natural arsenal with which the human body protects itself against diseases.

See also: **Antigens; Bacteria, immunity to; BCG; Cell-mediated immunity; Humoral immunity; Interferon α; Interferon β; Interferon γ; Mucosal immunity; Vaccination, methods of administration; Vaccines; Vaccines, adverse reactions to; Viruses, immunity to.**

Further reading

Ada GL (ed) (1994) *Strategies in Vaccine Design*. Austin TX: RG Landes.

Domingo E, Marginez-Salas E, Sobrino F *et al* (1985) The quasispecies (extremely heterogeneous) nature of viral RNA genome populations: biological relevance – a review. *Gene* **40**: 1–8.

Guerin C (1980) The history of BCG. In: Rosenthal SR (ed) *BCG Vaccine: Tuberculosis–Cancer*, pp 35–43. Littleton MA: PSG Publishing Company.

Holland J, Spindler K, Horodyski F, Grabau E, Nichol S and VandePol S (1982) Rapid evolution of RNA genomes. *Science* **215**: 1576–1585.

Kapikian AZ, Hoshino Y, Chanock RM and Perez-Schael I (1996) Jennerian and modified Jennerian approach to vaccination against rotavirus diarrhea using a quadrivalent rhesus rotavirus (RRV) and human-RRV reassortant vaccine. *Archives of Virology* **12**: 163–175.

Levin BR and Bull JJ (1994) Short-sighted evolution and the virulence of pathogenic microorganisms. *Trends in Microbiology* **76**: 76–81.

Melnick JL (1995) Enteroviruses: polioviruses, coxsackieviruses, echoviruses, and newer enteroviruses. In: Fields BN, Knipe DM, Howley PM, Chanock RM *et al* (eds) *Fields Virology*, pp 655–712. Philadelphia: Lipincott-Raven.

Murphy BR and Chanock RM (1995) Immunization against virus disease. In: Fields BN, Knipe DM, Howley PM *et al* (eds) *Fields Virology*, pp 467–498. Philadelphia: Lipincott-Raven.

Murphy BR, Hall SL, Kulkarni AB *et al* (1994) An update on approaches to the development of respiratory syncytial virus (RSV) and parainfluenza virus type 3 (PIV3) vaccines. *Virus Research* **32**: 13–36.

Plotkin SA and Mortimer EA Jr (eds) (1988) *Vaccines*. Philadelphia: WB Saunders.

Robbins JB, Schneerson R, Klein D, Sadoff J and Hardegree MC (eds) (1987) *Bacterial Vaccines*, New York: Praeger.

Sabin AB (1955) Characteristics and genetic potentialities of experimentally produced and naturally occurring variants of poliomyelitis virus. *Annals of the New York Academy of Sciences* **61**: 924–938.

Sabin AB and Boulger LR (1973) History of Sabin attenuated poliovirus oral live vaccine strains. *Journal of Biological Standardization* **1**: 115–118.

Voroshilova MK (1989) Potential use of nonpathogenic enteroviruses for control of human disease. *Progress in Medical Virology* **36**: 191–202.

World Health Organization (1980) *The Global Eradication of Smallpox. Final Report of the Global Commission for Certification of Smallpox Eradication*. Geneva: WHO.

AUTOANTIBODIES, TESTS FOR

C Lynne Burek, Department of Pathology, The Johns Hopkins University School of Medicine, Baltimore, Maryland, USA

Autoantibodies are antibodies that have the capacity to bind to self antigens. Autoantibodies are evaluated for a number of reasons and may be used as an aid in diagnosis of disease, either by inclusion or exclusion. In some cases the autoantibodies may actually cause disease. However, they are more frequently used as markers in a variety of ways. They may help distinguish between different forms of a condition, which may result in using different therapeutic strategies. Changes in antibody quantity may be used to monitor successful therapy or disease exacerbation. They may be used as indicators of individuals at risk for future diseases in disorders that are familial. Autoantibody tests are never used by themselves for diagnosis of disease. The total picture of the patient must always be considered as autoantibodies can also be found in normal individuals. Autoantibodies in normal individuals range in frequency according to age and sex; generally, the lowest frequency is in young males, the highest in elderly females.

Methods for identifying autoantibodies

Techniques for demonstrating autoantibodies are frequently ordained by the location and properties of the antigen and the required level of sensitivity. Early assays, some of which are still used today, included agglutination and precipitation techniques. Agglutination employs stable suspensions of beads (e.g. latex) or erythrocytes coated with the appropriate soluble antigen. Autoantibodies cross-link the coated particles forming the complex lattice structure of agglutination. Thyroid autoantibodies are frequently detected by indirect hemagglutination (i.e. by using erythrocytes coated with thyroid antigens), while latex agglutination remains the most widely used test for the measurement of rheumatoid factor (i.e. by using latex beads coated with gammaglobulin). Although precipitation in fluid or gelified media (e.g. immunodiffusion) is less sensitive than agglutination, it is still appropriate for the demonstration of antibodies to complex mixtures of soluble antigens, such as certain nuclear antigens that have not yet been purified.

Indirect immunofluorescence (IIF) is the most commonly used test for the detection of tissue-specific autoantibodies because of its wide range of applications. Briefly, serum is placed on a tissue section (frozen section, 4 μm thick). If autoantibodies are present, they will bind to the appropriate antigen. Excess serum is washed away. A second reagent, antihuman immunoglobulin conjugated to a fluorescent dye (usually fluorescein isothiocyanate, FITC), is then incubated with the tissue section. Unbound reagent is again washed away. Autoantibodies are detected using a microscope (transmission or incident light illumination) with an appropriate light source (usually mercury vapor or halogen quartz) and filter system that will enable the fluorescent markers to be seen. IIF can detect multiple antibodies on a single tissue or on a multiple tissue block, and thus has considerable value as a screening test. It is particularly valuable in testing for autoantibodies for which the antigen has not yet been characterized or for unexpected antibodies. These latter antibodies may be missed by an assay employing only purified antigens. With IIF, the reaction site can be seen, and thus the location of the cellular antigen can be determined. In a few cases, however, the major autoantigen associated with a particular autoimmune disorder has been isolated. Subsequently, more sensitive quantitative tests, such as hemagglutination, enzyme-linked immunosorbent assay (ELISA) and radioimmunoassay (RIA), have been developed using the isolated antigen fraction and have replaced IIF. Autoantibody isotype can be evaluated by using heavy chain-specific anti-immunoglobulin, although this is also true for any of the indirect detection tests.

Indirect immunoperoxidase (IIP), although similar to IIF in performance, utilizes an enzyme (e.g. horseradish peroxidase) to hydrolyze a substrate to form a colored precipitate at the site of antibody binding, rather than a fluorescent marker. Another enzyme, alkaline phosphatase, can also be used in a similar fashion. Although IIP has certain advantages over IIF, as the reaction can be seen under a standard light microscope and the slide can be stored indefinitely, it is not totally without problems. Endogenous peroxidases may cause false-positive results. The same time and effort must go into establishing this technique as for IIF. IIP is reported to be more sensitive than IIF, but each individual assay model must be evaluated independently.

RIA is a highly sensitive technique for the detection of autoantibodies; however, it requires defined antigens and the use of radioisotopes, and the trend is to replace radiolabeled compounds with enzyme-labeled substances and many of the former RIAs have therefore been converted to ELISAs.

The western immunoblot has recently been introduced for clinical diagnosis. It does not require a pure antigen but is relatively slow and expensive. Briefly, the antigen solution is separated by electrophoresis in polyacrylamide gel on the basis of relative molecular weight. The proteins in the gel are electrotransferred to a nitrocellulose membrane and cut into strips. Individual strips are reacted with patient serum, washed and incubated with an anti-immunoglobulin conjugated to an enzyme. Finally, the strips are treated with an enzyme substrate and the site of antibody localization is identified by a color precipitate. Western blot will indicate the approximate molecular weight of the antigen that is recognized by the autoantibody, but will not identify the protein itself.

Autoantibodies

There is a spectrum of autoantibody reactivities ranging from organ-specific to non-organ-specific autoantibodies. Organ-specific autoantibodies react to antigens of only one tissue, such as to thyroid tissue. Non-organ-specific autoantibodies react with antigens common to all tissues, such as to different nuclear antigens, and are often associated with more generalized disorders, such as systemic lupus erythematosus. There is also a small group of intermediate autoantibodies with specificity to particular tissues but with a widespread distribution, such as smooth muscle. The description of the autoantibodies and their tests, presented below, will feature this range of reactivities, summarized in **Table 1**.

Thyroid-specific antigens

Thyroglobulin

Thyroglobulin autoantibodies can be demonstrated by several procedures, such as precipitation in agar, IIF, indirect hemagglutination of cells coated with thyroglobulin, RIA and ELISA. At present, hemagglutination is the most commonly employed technique for the detection of antibodies against thyroglobulin. The ELISA is increasingly used for the measurement of antibodies to thyroglobulin and will additionally detect antibodies that are nonagglutinating. Thyroglobulin antibodies are found in individuals with chronic thyroiditis, myxedema, Graves disease, goiter, thyroid tumors and other polyendocrine disorders. The highest titers are found in patients with autoimmune thyroid disorders. Low titers of thyroglobulin antibodies may be found in normal

individuals. The prevalence of such antibodies in subjects without overt thyroid disease is higher in women. The incidence also increases with age, so that 18% of women over 40 years old may have antibodies to thyroglobulin. Total thyroglobulin antibody is not a specific marker of autoimmune thyroiditis as so many other conditions also show the presence of this antibody. Recent evidence suggests, however, that there may be disease-related epitope specificity of the autoantibody. The disease-related antibodies were detected by competitive inhibition ELISA experiments using murine monoclonal antibodies.

Microsomal antigens (TPO) of thyroid epithelial cells

The microsomal antigen has been identified chiefly as the thyroid peroxidase enzyme (TPO) of the thyroid epithelial cell. However, purified TPO is not readily available for use in diagnostic tests. The most commonly used tests for the microsomal autoantibodies are either IIF, using primate thyroid tissue, or hemagglutination. ELISA, RIA or a chemiluminescence-based assay may also be employed. The antibodies to the microsomal antigens belong predominantly to the immunoglobulin G (IgG) class and, when detected by IIF, stain the cytoplasm of thyroid cells. The IIF test for antibodies to thyroid microsomal antigens is positive in approximately 70–90% of patients with chronic thyroiditis. It is also positive in 64% of patients with primary hypothyroidism, 50% of patients with thyrotoxicosis, 10% of patients with simple goiters, and 17% of patients with thyroid tumor. It can also be found in normals at a low frequency and titer.

Thyrotropin receptor

Autoantibodies binding to the thyrotropin (TSH) receptor on the surface of thyroid epithelial cells are believed to be the direct cause of the hyperthyroid state in Graves' disease. The thyroid-stimulating autoantibodies (TSAbs) bind near to or with the TSH receptor and mimic TSH activity, resulting in uncontrolled stimulation as there is no negative feedback control. Tests for TSAbs are primarily of two types: bioassays or binding assays. Most bioassays have limited utility because they are cumbersome and require scarce materials, such as viable slices of fresh human thyroid tissue. Bioassays, however, evaluate functional aspects of the antibodies as their endpoint. Binding assays are based on competition between ^{125}I-labeled TSH and patient autoantibodies for binding to thyroid preparations. Some confusion has been created by the heterogeneity of the autoantibodies and the diversity of the assays for their

Table 1 Detection of autoantibodies

Autoantibody to:	Primary method of detection[a]	Primary associated disorders
Thyroid		
Thyroglobulin	Hemagglutination ELISA	Autoimmune thyroiditis, primary myxedema
Microsomal (thyroid peroxidase)	IIF (mk-thyroid) Hemagglutination	Autoimmune thyroiditis, primary myxedema
TSH receptor	Bioassay Binding assay	Graves' disease
Parietal cell	IIF (ro-stomach)	Atrophic gastritis, pernicious anemia
Adrenal	IIF (mk-adrenal)	Idiopathic Addison's disease
Ovary	IIF (mk-ovary)	Infertility
Testes, sperm	IIF (mk-testes) Agglutination Immobilization	Infertility
Pancreas islet cell	IIF (hu group O or mk-pancreas)	Insulin-dependent diabetes mellitus
Parathyroid	IIF (mk-parathyroid)	Idiopathic hypoparathyroidism
Pituitary	IIF (hu- or mk-pituitary)	Growth disorders
Skin		
Basement membrane zone	IIF (hu-skin, mk-esophagus)	Bullous pemphigoid
Intercellular substance	IIF (hu-skin, mk-esophagus)	Pemphigus vulgaris
Muscle		
Smooth	IIF (ro-stomach)	Chronic active hepatitis
Cardiac striated	IIF (ro-heart)	Autoimmune cardiomyopathy
Skeletal striated	IIF (ro-skeletal)	Myasthenia gravis
Endomysial	IIF (mk-esophagus)	Celiac disease
Acetylcholine receptor	RIA, ELISA	Myasthenia gravis
Neutrophil cytoplasm (C-ANCA, proteinase 3, P-ANCA, myeloperoxidase)	IIF (hu-PMNs), ELISA	Wegener's granulomatosis, microscopic vasculitides
Nuclear antigens (ANAs)	IIF (ro-liver, Hep-2 cells), ELISA Hemagglutination Immunodiffusion	Systemic lupus erythematosus, connective tissue disorders
Mitochondria	IIF (ro-kidney)	Primary biliary cirrhosis
Phospholipids	ELISA	Antiphospholipid syndrome
Rheumatoid factor	Latex agglutination Nephelometry	Rheumatoid arthritis

PMN, polymorphonuclear leukocyte.
[a]Species and tissue substrate used: mk, monkey; ro, rodent; hu, human.

demonstration. Different specificities of auto-antibodies to the thyroid epithelial cell surface on or near the TSH receptor may be represented.

The detection of these antibodies in Graves' patients ranges from 55 to 95%, depending on the assay. The TSAb assay is of greatest utility in conditions where conventional test results are equivocal or where clinical signs and symptoms are not readily apparent (e.g. ophthalmopathy in the absence of other features). Moreover, the TSAb assay is usually negative in patients with thyrotoxicosis in association with thyroid nodules, with cancer, or in patients with subacute thyroiditis. Therefore, a positive test confirms a diagnosis of Graves' disease with a high degree of confidence. The assay can be used to monitor patient therapy, as successful treatment of Graves' disease with propylthiouracil may result in lowering levels of TSAb antibodies. The assay has also proven useful in the diagnosis of neonatal thyrotoxicosis.

Gastric parietal cells

Autoantibodies to antigens of gastric parietal cells (parietal cell antibodies) occur with high frequency in patients with pernicious anemia and atrophic gastritis. Autoantibodies to gastric parietal cells are frequently found simultaneously with thyroid antibodies, although these cells are not usually considered as part of the endocrine system. These autoantibodies are readily detected by IIF with sections of rodent stomach (mucosa) as tissue substrate. The pattern of staining resembles that seen with mitochondrial antibodies; therefore, a control test on kidney should also be performed. Parietal cell antibodies are found in 90% or more of patients with pernicious anemia. Recently, the autoantigen has been identified as the α and β subunits of gastric H^+,K^+-ATPase. An ELISA using this enzyme and a western blotting technique using gastric extracts have been developed. These antibodies are also present in a number of other conditions, such as chronic thyroiditis (33%), Sjögren's sicca syndrome (15%), atrophic gastritis (60%), gastric ulcer (22%), etc. The antibodies are also found in the normal population, with an incidence that varies according to age and sex; i.e. from 2% in subjects under 20 years old to 16% in subjects over 60 years old. They are more frequent in women than in men.

Other endocrine organs

Autoimmunity also develops against other endocrine organs such as the adrenal gland, pancreas islet cells, parathyroid, pituitary and ovary. The autoantibodies are much less prevalent than with thyroid disease but, if present, help in diagnosis. The reactivities, assays and primary associated disorders are summarized in **Table 1**.

These autoantibodies share certain characteristics. Antibodies bind to antigens associated with the cytoplasm of cells, usually to unidentified antigens. The antibodies belong predominantly to the IgG class and, in general, have rather low titers (not higher than 100) and are rarely found in normal individuals.

The presence of antibodies to particular endocrine organs suggests that the disease is idiopathic and not of malignant, infectious or other nature. However, it is not uncommon for patients with autoantibodies to one endocrine organ to have multiple endocrine reactivities. Furthermore, not all patients with a particular disorder have the autoantibodies, so that a negative test obviously does not exclude a particular diagnosis. On the other hand, a positive test is not necessarily diagnostic, in that the patient might have other autoantibodies to endocrine organs without clinical disease. An interesting feature of autoantibodies to islet cells of the pancreas is that the percentage of positive sera decreases with time after onset of disease.

Skin antigens

Patients with autoimmune skin disease, such as pemphigus vulgaris or bullous pemphigoid (BP) develop autoantibodies that bind to epidermal antigens. These antibodies are identified by IIF, using tissue sections of skin (e.g. foreskin) or other squamous epithelium (e.g. monkey esophagus) as tissue substrate. Patients with pemphigus vulgaris show serum autoantibodies to the intracellular area of the epidermis in 80–90% of cases. These antibodies are IgG, most of them bind complement, and they are pathogenic, as demonstrated by serum transfer experiments. Low levels of pemphigus-like autoantibodies are sometimes found in other conditions, such as burns and systemic lupus erythematosus, as well as in normal individuals. These antibodies appear to correlate with disease activity and may be used to monitor therapy.

Over 70% of BP patients exhibit autoantibodies that bind to the basement membrane zone between the dermis and the epidermis, appearing as a linear band of staining. False positives are rare. Evidence from *in vitro* and *in vivo* studies shows that these autoantibodies are pathogenic.

Muscle antigens

Smooth muscle

Sera from patients with chronic active hepatitis contain antibodies to smooth muscle antigens that are detectable by IIF and bind smooth muscle of all organs. The major antigen of the smooth muscle is actin. The antibodies belong mainly to the IgG class, but they can also be found in the IgM class. The test is performed on unfixed cryostat sections of rodent stomach as substrate. Smooth muscle antibodies are found in 40–70% of patients with active chronic hepatitis, with lower titers found in 50% of patients with primary biliary cirrhosis, and 28% of patients with cryptogenic cirrhosis. These antibodies are also found at low titer in patients with acute viral hepatitis, infectious mononucleosis, asthma, yellow fever and malignant tumors (carcinomas of the ovary, malignant melanoma). They have been found in less than 2% of the normal population.

Cardiac muscle

The presence of antibodies to cardiac striated muscle in patients with cardiomyopathy may help to distinguish autoimmune myocarditis from other forms of myocarditis (e.g. viral). This finding, in turn, may influence therapy. These antibodies are most readily detected by IIF with sections of rat heart as tissue substrate and bind to fibrillary antigens as well as to sarcolemma or subsarcolemma antigens. The most severe cases of myocarditis or dilated cardiomyopathy have been associated with high titers of IgG antibodies specific for cardiac and not skeletal striated muscle. Many normal individuals may have low titers of antistriated muscle antibodies, but they are generally of the IgM class and react with both skeletal and cardiac striated muscle.

Endomysial

Autoantibodies to endomysial membranes, the outside lining of smooth muscle bundles, are found in patients with dermatitis herpetiformis and with celiac disease, and are primarily IgA. The major test is IIF using the lower part of monkey esophagus as tissue substrate. It appears to be a more specific and sensitive marker of celiac disease than testing for reticulin autoantibodies. In a few patients with celiac disease that have an IgA immunodeficiency, the antibody to endomysial antigens were found to be IgG. Isotype-specific anti-immunoglobulins conjugated to FITC are used as specific reagents to determine the relevant autoantibodies.

Acetylcholine receptor

Autoantibodies to acetylcholine receptor (AchR) are present in 80–95% of sera from patients with myasthenia gravis. Variations in the reported incidence of these antibodies are due to the different methods (complement fixation, passive hemagglutination, and various RIAs and ELISAs) used for their detection. In addition, there are heterogeneous specificities of antibodies to AchR; i.e. some that react to determinants other than the neurotoxin-binding site, others that react with the neurotoxin-binding site or the extrajunctional receptors, and others that are species specific. Since the cross-reactivity of human antibodies to AchR with receptors from other species is limited, human skeletal muscle is preferred as the source of AchR.

The procedures usually employed to detect circulating antibodies to AchR are RIAs. A direct binding assay is based on the inhibition of toxin binding to the receptor by the antibodies. A double antibody assay is based on the use of a labeled neurotoxin–receptor complex and thus quantitates receptor antibodies by measuring their binding to sites other than the acetylcholine- or neurotoxin-binding site.

Neutrophil cytoplasmic antigens

Antineutrophil cytoplasmic autoantibodies (ANCAs) have recently become an important diagnostic tool for vasculitis associated with Wegener's granulomatosis and certain other microscopic vasculitis and glomerulonephritis disorders. The antibodies are detected primarily by IIF on isolated human neutrophils as substrate. Differences in fixation of the cells can separate the antibodies into two distinct groups with different specificities: C-ANCA and P-ANCA. Ethanol fixation causes a redistribution of the antigens of the P-ANCA specificity causing a 'perinuclear' (P) picture of the fluorescent staining, while C-ANCA remains cytoplasmic (C). Formaldehyde fixation prevents the redistribution of the P-ANCA antigens so that the binding of both antibodies appears cytoplasmic. The major antigen of the C-ANCA specificity has been reported as proteinase 3 of the α granules, while the major antigen of P-ANCA has been identified as myeloperoxidase. ELISA tests using specific antigens are currently being developed. The appearance and change in titer of these antibodies appear to be good indicators of remission/exacerbation and severity of disease.

Mitochondrial antigens

Autoantibodies to mitochondrial antigens, detectable by IIF on rat kidney sections, are primarily associated with patients with primary biliary cirrhosis. The major antigen is reported to be a component of the pyruvate dehydrogenase enzyme complex. The antibodies belong to the IgG, IgA and IgM classes. The mitochondrial antibodies stain the cytoplasm of cells from different organs, such as thyroid or kidney, that varies with the mitochondrial content of the cells. Distal tubules of kidney and gastric parietal cells show a bright, uniform, cytoplasmic fluorescence, whereas renal proximal tubules show a characteristic coarse, granular, duller staining.

Mitochondrial antibodies are detected in 87–98% of patients with primary biliary cirrhosis. They are also observed in 25–28% of patients with active chronic hepatitis and in 25–30% of patients with cryptogenic cirrhosis. They are only seldom observed in patients with extrahepatic biliary tract obstruction and occur very rarely in normal subjects.

Nuclear antigens

A wide range of antinuclear antibodies (ANAs) occur against antigens associated with cell nuclei, including autoantibodies to DNA, histones, small nuclear RNP (snRNP), Ro/SS-A, La/SS-B, and tRNA synthetase. Many fine specificities have been defined amongst the various types of ANA. Diseases in which ANAs are particularly prevalent include mixed connective tissue disease, systemic lupus erythematosus, the CREST syndrome and progressive systemic sclerosis.

They are also commonly seen, although at a lower frequency, in rheumatoid arthritis and Sjögrens syndrome. IIF is used as an initial screening test for the occurrence of ANAs. Antibodies to many of the specific antigens can be measured in ELISA, although RIA (including the Farr assay and PEG assay), immunoblot, immunoelectrophoresis, RNA precipitation, and the LE-cell test are all commonly employed.

Phospholipid antigens

Antiphospholipid autoantibodies are a heterogeneous group of antibodies with specificity to a phospholipid–protein complex. The protein associated with cardiolipin has been identified as a β_2-glycoprotein (β_2-GPI). Some investigators suggest that this is the relevant autoantigen in patients with antiphospholipid syndrome, although the relative importance of these two molecules has not yet been fully clarified. The most sensitive test used is an ELISA using cardiolipin or other phospholipids to coat ELISA plates. Standardization of the various tests for the different phospholipids has been a problem. However, even so, the clinical utility has been established for antiphospholipid syndrome.

Rheumatoid factor

Rheumatoid factor represents a group of antibodies characterized by their ability to react with antigenic determinants on the Fc portion of immunoglobulin. Serum from patients with rheumatoid arthritis agglutinate sheep red blood cells (SRBCs) sensitized by rabbit anti-SRBC and this is the basis of the Waaler–Rose test. However, latex beads coated with Cohn fraction II as the source of IgG antigen, devised by Singer and Plotz, is the most widely used test today.

Other techniques for demonstrating rheumatoid factor include nephelometry and ELISA. Laser nephelometry and rate nephelometry utilize the changes in light-scattering properties of aggregated IgG when exposed to sera containing rheumatoid factor. These tests are reported to be equally sensitive and specific and more reproducible than established agglutination techniques, and they lend themselves well to automation.

See also: **Agglutination; Antibodies, detection of; Antiglobulin (Coombs') test; Antinuclear antibodies; Autoantigens; Autoimmune diseases; Autoimmunity; Enzyme-linked immunosorbent assay (ELISA); Immunoassays; Immunodiffusion, single radial; Nephelometry; Precipitation reaction; Western blotting.**

Further reading

Bigazzi PE, Wick G and Wicher K (eds) (1990) *Organ Specific Autoimmunity*. New York: Marcel Dekker.
Bigazzi PE, Burek CL and Rose NR (1992) Tests for antibodies to tissue-specific endocrine, gastrointestinal, and neurological antigens. In: Rose NR, Conway de Macario E, Fahey J, Friedman H and Penn GM (eds) *Manual of Clinical Laboratory Immunology*, 4th edn, pp 762–770. Washington DC: American Society for Microbiology.
Blecher M (1984) Receptors, antibodies, and disease. *Clinical Chemistry* 30: 1137–1156.
Burek CL and Rose NR (1995) Autoantibodies. In: Colvin RB, Bhan AK and McClusky RT (eds) *Diagnostic Immunopathology*, 2nd edn, pp 207–230. New York: Raven Press.
Cook L and Agnello V (1992) Tests for detection of rheumatoid factors. In: Rose NR, Conway de Macario E, Fahey J, Friedman H and Penn GM (eds) *Manual of Clinical Laboratory Immunology*, 4th edn, pp 762–764. Washington DC: American Society for Microbiology.
Flotte TJ, Margolis RJ and Mihm Jr MC (1995) Skin diseases. In: Colvin RB, Bhan AK and McClusky RT (eds) *Diagnostic Immunopathology*, 2nd edn, pp 123–128. New York: Raven Press.
Irvine WJ, McCallum CJ, Gray RS et al (1977) Pancreatic islet cell antibodies in diabetes mellitus correlated with the duration and type of diabetes, coexistent autoimmune disease, and HLA-type. *Diabetes* 26: 138–147.
Lefvert AK, Bergstrom K, Matell G, Osterman PO and Pirskanen R (1978) Determination of acetylcholine receptor antibody in myasthenia gravis: clinical usefulness and pathogenic implications. *Journal of Neurology, Neurosurgery and Psychiatry* 41: 394–403.
Mackay IR (1989) Hepatic and biliary autoantigens. *Immunological Investigations* 18: 253–267.
Maisch B, Trostel-Soeder R, Stechemesser E, Berg PA and Kochsiek K (1982) Diagnostic relevance of humoral and cell-mediated immune reactions in patients with acute viral myocarditis. *Clinical and Experimental Immunology* 48: 533–545.
Peters JB and Shoenfeld Y (eds) (1996) *Autoantibodies*. New York: Elsevier.
Zakarija M and McKenzie JM (1981) Assays for thyroid-stimulating antibody and their clinical application. In: Soto RJ, De Nicola A and Blaqier J (eds) *Physiopathology of Endocrine Diseases: Mechanisms of Hormone Action*, pp 147–152. New York: Liss.

AUTOANTIGENS

Ian R Mackay, Department of Biochemistry and Molecular Biology, Monash University, Melbourne, Australia

Antigens, and autoantigens, are detected by their capacity to participate in immunological reactions. When antigens provoke an immune response they behave as immunogens. Immunogenicity depends on various properties of the antigen, including its mode of presentation, local concentration and the immune capacity of the responding individual. For autoantigens there is an additional constraint on the response, this being the degree of natural tolerance to the autoantigenic particle.

Just as there is reciprocity between antigen and antibody, so too is there reciprocity between autoantigen and autoantibody. In addition, autoantigen is a self constituent, and thus the autoantibody reactive with it *in vitro* is assumed to be reactive *in vivo* as well. The individual's immune system scrutinizes a 'universe' of potential antigens: those that are foreign, extrinsic or nonself, and those that are constitutive, intrinsic or self, i.e. autoantigens. However, differences between 'foreign' and 'constitutive' antigens may be slight. Thus, some bodily constituents are absolutely specific or unique to an individual but others may be shared, at least within the species, or across species, or may be so conserved as to be represented throughout most living organisms.

When speaking of autoantigens, the context is usually that of reactivity with autoantibody, i.e. a product of the B cell lineage; however, most autoantigens would also need to be reactive with a T lymphocyte for induction of an immune response and for expression of pathogenic effects. T cell reactivity with antigen and especially with autoantigen, compared with B cell reactivity, is harder to detect and quantify; however, current assays based on proliferative responses or release of cytokines are becoming increasingly reliable.

The interaction *in vivo* between autoantibody and antigen is a potential cause of disease – autoimmune disease. Whether all self constituents behave as autoantigens is uncertain; for some, autoantibody is never demonstrable, so that tolerance to them is absolute. For many self constituents there may be autoantibodies demonstrable but seldom or ever is there any associated disease; indeed there is an increasing awareness of the wide range of 'natural' autoantibodies in health to various autologous constituents. In other instances autoantibody is only transiently present, e.g. after injury. The development of disease after an autoimmune response may thus depend on additional factors, of which many are under genetic control. These include abundance and accessibility of the autoantigen, the capacity for presentation by antigen-presenting cells, the appropriate stimulation of cognate T cells, the efficiency of regulation of the immune response, the affinity and subclass of the autoantibody produced by B cells, and others.

Autoantigens have accrued a rather loose terminology among clinical immunologists who, hitherto, have referred to large cellular organelles as 'antigens', for example nuclear, mitochondrial, microsomal, etc. This parlance was convenient for clinical diagnostic purposes, since antinuclear, antimitochondrial and other tissue antibodies had disease associations, but it reflected ignorance of the constituents of cellular organelles to which autoimmune responses are directed. This is changing with molecular immunology leading to the cloning of cDNAs which code for autoantigenic polypeptides. An antigen, of whatever provenance, is actually a mosaic of determinant groups or epitopes, described by N. K. Jerne as follows: 'An antigen particle carries several *epitopes* (= surface configurations, single determinants, structural themes, immunogenic elements, haptenic groups, antigenic patterns, specific areas). An antibody molecule normally carries, apart from its epitopes, two paratopes (= combining sites, reactive segments, complementary cavities, specific receptors). Epitopes are potentially immunogenic when present on an appropriate carrier: they may induce the formation of paratopes.'

The several or more epitopes of autoantigens are called autoepitopes. These may be reactive with paratopes of the autoantibody, and with the corresponding cell surface immunoglobulin molecule which serves as the antigen receptor for B cells: these are B cell epitopes. Also there are epitopes which engage T cells, T cell autoepitopes; the (moderately) predictive algorithms proposed for identifying T cell epitopes of foreign antigens are applicable also to autoantigens.

Epitopes, including autoepitopes, for B cells may be represented by linear sequences of peptides but more often are created by the conformational structure of the protein, and may require a substantial sequence of the antigenic molecule for their formation. Examples among the autoantigens include the

Ro(SS-A) and La(SS-B) ribonucleoproteins, the E2 subunit of pyruvate dehydrogenase complex (PDC-2) and glutamic acid decarboxylase.

Epitopes for T cells are represented by short linear sequences, nine or more amino acids, that are products of the processing of antigenic molecules, yielding peptides that bind into the polymorphic antigen-binding cleft created by the molecular configuration of major histocompatibility complex (MHC) molecules; particular residues, 'anchor' residues, are critical for this binding. A conformation of amino acids, known as a disease susceptibility motif, in the antigen-binding cleft of the MHC molecule, that can effectively bind a T cell epitope of an autoantigen may explain some of the well-known HLA associations with disease. Molecular sequences that bind to MHC molecules (in reality T cell epitopes) were formerly called agretopes but, with newer knowledge, this term has lapsed. Epitopes of antigens including autoantigens that react with and stimulate T cells can be recognized by assays that depend on cellular proliferation or release of lymphokines; however, progress has been slow.

The question often arises as to whether autoantigens actually function as immunogens. The focused nature of autoimmune responses strongly suggests that these are 'antigen driven' and, if this were so, the drive would be directed to the helper CD4 T cell. It remains uncertain whether the antigen drive, for B or T cells, is derived from autoantigen or a cross-reactive extrinsic structure with a closely similar molecular shape, as postulated by the mimicry hypothesis; alternatively, anti-idiotypic antibody against, say, antibody developed to an infectious agent could act as an 'internal image' of an autoantigen and so provide an immunogenic stimulus.

Autoantigens are so numerous and diverse that classification is hardly feasible, but this could be based on their site of origin (**Table 1**) as follows: cell membranes; cell cytoplasm; cell nuclei; specialised tissue constituents; secreted molecules; neural products.

From the standpoint of pathology, the autoantigens listed in **Table 1** have varying degrees of relevance. The reactivity of various 'natural' autoantibodies present in normal sera is irrelevant to actual pathogenesis. Then there are autoantibodies that can be termed 'marker' antibodies, as they point to a disorder of immune tolerance as a cause of the disease with which they are associated, but do not *per se* appear to be pathogenic; and there are other autoantibodies which are truly pathogenic, such as those reactive with cell membrane structures including receptors for neurotransmitters and hormones.

Autoantigens associated with intracellular organelles, nuclear or cytoplasmic, raise interesting issues in that many of these have a close if not specific relationship with a particular disease, and are therefore useful diagnostically. Examples include autoantibodies to centromere or Scl-70 antigens which occur in scleroderma, to ribonucleoprotein antigens in lupus-related diseases, and to mitochondrial antigens in primary biliary cirrhosis (PBC). However, for pathogenicity to be ascribed to such antigens, one or even both of two requirements should be fulfilled. One would be that the autoantigen becomes translocated to the cell surface, and here the PDC-E2 autoantigen of primary biliary cirrhosis is an interesting example as it is demonstrable at the surface of biliary ductular cells of patients with PBC; this observation foreshadows interests for autoimmunity in mechanisms that may influence intracellular transport of molecules between nucleus, cytoplasmic organelles and cell membranes. The other requirement would be a capacity for autoantibody to penetrate the membrane of intact cells to access intracellular organelles; there are data supporting this but the matter is controversial.

The category 'neural products' (**Table 1**) contains reactants for interesting autoantibodies in paraneoplastic autoimmune neurodegenerations, central or peripheral, that are rare accompaniments of ovarian, lung and breast cancers. The cancer itself presumably generates the neural antigen and facilitates its immunogenic presentation.

A better understanding of the structure of autoantigens has come from advances in analytical biochemistry, including gel chromatography and transfer western immunoblotting, and also molecular biology, including antibody probing of gene expression libraries and phage display libraries. These techniques have identified the reactive polypeptide antigens in various of the cellular organelles and have yielded cloned cDNAs which allow for gene sequencing and mapping of autoepitopes; screening of phage display libraries may occasionally reveal linear mimotopes of conformational autoantigens. There have been interesting outcomes, as follows:

1. There is an increasing availability of recombinant proteins for diagnostic assays, ELISAs and radioimmunoprecipitation which, by reason of greater sensitivity and versatility, are supplementing detection of autoantibodies by immunofluorescence.

2. Epitope mapping is revealing that, for most autoantigens, there are multiple and apparently structurally different epitopes recognized by antibody. This impinges on the concept of 'molecular mimicry', which holds that resemblances between a sequence in a host protein and a microorganism can result in production of autoantibody. The presence

Table 1 Examples of autoantigens and disease associations

Autoantigen	Related diseases
Cell membranes	
Blood cells	Hemocytolytic diseases: hemolytic anemia, thrombocytopenic purpura, neutropenia
Receptor structures for	
acetylcholine	Myasthenia gravis
thyrotropin (TSH)	Graves disease (thyrotoxicosis), goiter (?)
insulin	Diabetes, insulin-resistant type
Nerve cells: myelin of oligodendroglia, Schwann cells	Experimental autoimmune encephalomyelitis, neuritis
Liver cells: asialoglycoprotein receptor	Autoimmune hepatitis, type 1 (?)
Cytoplasm, organelles	
Tissue specific	
gastric H^+, K^+-ATPase, α and β subunits	Autoimmune gastritis, pernicious anemia
thyroid peroxidase (microsomal antigen)	Hashimotos thyroiditis
adrenal 21-hydroxylase	Addisons disease
pancreatic islet glutamic acid decarboxylase; ICA512/IA-2/37-40k; insulin	Type I diabetes mellitus
salivary duct cell	Sjögrens syndrome with rheumatoid arthritis
neutrophil cytoplasmic proteinase 3 and myeloperoxidase (ANCA)	Wegener's disease, vasculitic diseases and others
Non-tissue specific	Autoimmune hepatitis, type 2
cytochrome P450 2D6 (liver–kidney microsomes)	Primary biliary cirrhosis
2 oxo-acid dehydrogenase enzymes (mitochondria, M2)	
phosphoproteins P0, P1, P2 (ribosomes)	Systemic lupus erythematosus (SLE)
cytoskeletal actin (smooth muscle antibody)	Autoimmune hepatitis, type 1
stress (heat-shock) proteins	Rheumatic diseases (?)
transfer RNA synthetases (Jo1)	Polymyositis and variants
Nuclei	
DNA	SLE
Histones	SLE, particularly drug related; various rheumatic diseases
U (uridine-rich) RNA–protein complexes	
U1-RNP	Mixed connective tissue disease
U1, U2, U4-6 RNPs (Sm antigen, various epitopes have been mapped)	SLE
Ro-La	
Ro(SS-A)	Primary Sjögrens syndrome; cutaneous LE; fetal heartblock
La (SS-B)	Primary Sjögrens syndrome; SLE
Centromere	Scleroderma, CREST variant
Topoisomerase I (Scl-70)	Scleroderma, systemic sclerosis
Nucleolus	Systemic sclerosis; undifferentiated rheumatic diseases
fibrillarin	
nucleolar RNP	
Proliferating cell nuclear antigen (cyclin)	SLE (rarely)
Specialised tissue products	
Squamous epithelium	
desmosomes (desmoglein 1,3)	Pempiphigus vulgaris, pemphigus foliaceus
hemidesmosomes (BPAg 1 & 2)	Bullous pemphigoid
Striated muscle, sarcomere, cytoskeletal proteins	Myasthenia gravis, with thymoma
Cardiac muscle, sarcolemma	Myocarditis, rheumatic carditis
Chondrocytes, collagen type II	Rheumatoid arthritis
Glomerular basement membrane, collagen type IV	Glomerulonephritis (Goodpasture type)
Retina, S antigen	Uveitis
Sperm antigens	Male infertility; orchitis (?)
Colon mucosal cell	Ulcerative colitis (?)
β_2 glycoprotein 1 (cardiolipin)	Antiphospholipid syndrome, thromboembolism
Secreted products	
Gastric intrinsic factor	Atrophic gastritis, pernicious anemia
Immunoglobulin G, Fc region	Rheumatoid arthritis
Thyroid colloid	Atrophic hypothyroidism; Hashimotos thyroiditis
Insulin	Type I diabetes mellitus

Table 1 Continued

Autoantigen	Related diseases
Neural products	
Glutamic acid decarboxylase	Stiff man syndrome
Calcium channels, synaptotagmin	Lambert–Eaton myasthenic syndrome
Purkinje cell cytoplasm (Yo)	Paraneoplastic (PN) cerebellar degeneration
Cerebellar neuronal nuclei	
ANNA 1 (Hu)	PN sensorimotor neuropathy
ANNA 2 (Ri)	PN midbrain encephalitis/ataxia/myelopathy

(?) Indicates incomplete consensus.

of several epitopes on autoantigens, and/or the existence of conformational epitopes, could limit the appeal of the molecular mimicry hypothesis because it is unlikely that the several epitopes of the autoantigen would be conformationally similar, or that the extrinsic antigen would have multiple mimicry epitopes; however, mimicry could exist for a single shared or cross-reactive epitope recognized by the CD4 helper T cell that could then recruit successive B cell epitopes into the autoimmune response, a process known as epitope spreading.

3. The epitope recognized by autoantibody is frequently associated with an active site of an enzyme or other functional molecule, and the antibody can be shown to inhibit the function *in vitro* of the cognate autoantigenic enzyme. For example, the major epitope of PDC-E2, the M2 autoantigen of PBC, is the functional lipoyl domain, and the reaction of PBC serum with this domain specifically abrogates the catalytic function of the PDC enzyme *in vitro*.

4. There is a possibility that autoantigens may have 'disease-specific' epitopes that differ in site or structure from epitopes that are reactive with non-disease-specific natural autoantibodies.

5. Various intracellular antigenic molecules have been functionally characterized at the molecular genetic level by the use of autoantibodies as research reagents. Examples, of which there are many, include the U-ribonucleoproteins which splice out introns from mRNA, the La ribonucleoprotein which participates in the termination of transcription of RNA polymerase III, and the Ku antigen which participates in recombination and repair of DNA.

One major need at present is to verify T cell responses to autoantigens and map the relevant epitopes, noting that autoepitope-responsive T cells have a low representation among peripheral blood cells and, even in affected tissues, will be 'diluted' by nonspecifically reactive cells in inflammatory exudates. Another need is to understand why particular molecules or related groups of molecules are singled out among numerous others as autoantigenic reactants, i.e. why there is failure of tolerance to these particular tissue constituents. This will require better understanding of how 'nascent' self reactive T or B lymphocytes are deleted in the thymus or bone marrow respectively during ontogeny, and how self reactive lymphocytes that escape this process are tolerized in the periphery in postnatal life.

See also: **Adrenal autoimmunity; Anemia, autoimmune hemolytic in human; Anemia, pernicious; Antiglobulin (Coombs') test; Antinuclear antibodies; Autoantibodies, tests for; Autoimmune disease, induced experimental models; Autoimmune disease, pathogenesis; Autoimmune disease, spontaneous experimental models; Autoimmune diseases; Autoimmunity; Cardiac disease, autoimmune; Epitopes; Experimental autoimmune encephalomyelitis (EAE); Eye, autoimmune disease; Goodpasture's syndrome; Idiopathic thrombocytopenic purpura; Insulin-dependent diabetes mellitus, animal models; Insulin-dependent diabetes mellitus, human; Molecular mimicry; Neuromuscular junction autoimmunity; Neurological autoimmune diseases; Polyendocrine autoimmunity; Rheumatoid arthritis, animal models; Rheumatoid arthritis, human; Sjögrens syndrome; Skin, autoimmune diseases; Systemic lupus erythematosus, experimental models; Systemic lupus erythematosus (SLE), human; Thyroid autoimmunity, experimental models; Thyroid autoimmunity, human; Vitiligo; Primary biliary cirrhosis; Chronic active and autoimmune hepatitis.**

Further reading

Möller G (ed) (1986) Autoimmunity. *Immunological Reviews* 94: 5–169.

Naparstek Y and Plotz PH (1993) The role of autoantibodies in autoimmune disease. *Annual Review of Immunology* 11: 79–103.

Rose NR and Mackay IR (eds) (1998) *The Autoimmune Diseases*, 3rd edn. Orlando: Academic Press.

Von Mühlen CA and Tan EM (1995) Autoantibodies in the diagnosis of systemic rheumatic diseases. *Seminars in Arthritis and Rheumatism* 24: 323–356.

AUTOIMMUNE DISEASE, INDUCED ANIMAL MODELS

W J Penhale, Institute of Molecular Genetics and Animal Disease, School of Veterinary Studies, Murdoch University, Murdoch, Australia

The first indication that the immune system could be experimentally provoked into dangerous self reactivity stems from the early 1930s when Rivers and his colleagues induced encephalomyelitis in monkeys by the injection of brain material. Some 20 years later, Voisin and coworkers made the, quite literally, seminal observation that testicular lesions could be similarly induced by testicular extracts including spermatozoa. Although these studies provided the prototype animal models of autoimmune diseases, the foundations of experimental autoimmunity were not truly laid until Rose and Witebsky demonstrated in a series of classical studies that both antibodies to thyroid constituents and thyroiditis could be induced by immunizing rabbits with thyroid extracts in Freund's complete adjuvant. Since then, many experimental models have been developed in a broad range of animal species and, consequently, the 1975 prediction of Wick – that autoimmune disease may be induced in any organ provided the investigator tries hard enough – seems ever more likely. In addition, new experimental approaches not involving specific immunization have been introduced and these have widened the scope and range of disease models now available for study. These later models have opened alternative avenues for investigation and, in consequence, new conceptual insights into the autoimmune process have been made.

As a group, induced models may be defined as those in which an autoimmune process is superimposed on otherwise normal, unaffected animals by a variety of treatments or manipulations. They contrast with the spontaneous models where disease occurs without intervention and is largely, although not entirely, determined by genetic composition. In consequence, whilst spontaneous models are limited to a particular genome, induced models are well suited to the investigation of genetic influences by their imposition on inbred strains of differing genetic constitution. They also have the particular advantages that normal syngeneic animals are available for parallel control studies, as recipients in adoptive transfer experiments, and also for the provision of cells for reconstitution studies in depleted animals.

The extensive range of induced animal models that is currently available has resulted from an expanding variety of induction strategies and can be conveniently grouped on this basis. Since the methods employed often reflect fundamental differences in both the triggering and pathogenic mechanisms, each type provides its own insight into autoimmune pathogenesis and has particular advantages for research in selected areas. Despite these widely differing inductive procedures, however, it is likely that the terminal pathogenic pathways coincide when a common organ is involved. These aspects will be discussed in the following sections which briefly review the various models currently available.

Methods of experimentally inducing autoimmunity

1. Induction of autoimmunity by immunization ('immunization models')

This approach, the first to be introduced, has been of primary importance in establishing the validity of the autoimmune concept. Furthermore, since it has been possible by this means to raise autoimmune responses to an extensive range of self components (**Table 1**), it is evident that potentially autoreactive cells are not only a normal component of the immune repertoire of every individual but also that they are quite capable of being activated under appropriate conditions. As a corollary, it also follows that, under normal circumstances, these cells are effectively subjugated by one or more regulatory mechanisms. In consequence, it is generally necessary to inject native autoantigens in combination with powerful nonspecific immunostimulants such as Freund's water-in-oil adjuvant in order to override these inhibitory influences. As an alternative procedure, the immunogen can be altered self components or material derived from other species which may provide a more effective autoimmune stimulation by way of 'modified self' or cross-reactive antigenicity. Weigle, for example, used rabbit thyroglobulin to induce thyroiditis in mice and the injection of rat erythrocytes into mice also induces antibodies to mouse erythrocytes and transient anemia. Presumably, under these circumstances, the inclusion of new antigenic determinants can provide a bypass mechanism permitting new T cell help for the generation of autoimmune responses.

Immunization models have been extensively used

Table 1 Induction of experimental autoimmunity by immunization with autoantigens

Target organ/tissue	Animal species	Analogous human disease
Thyroid follicles	Rabbit, mouse, guinea pig, rat, monkey, chicken, dog	Hashimoto's thyroiditis
Adrenal cortex/medulla	Guinea pig, rabbit, rat (Lewis, BN), mouse (CF1, BSVS), monkey, dog	Autoimmune adrenal failure (Addison's disease)
Pituitary/adenohypophysis	Rat, rabbit	Lymphocytic adenohypophysitis
Parathyroid	Rat, dog, chicken, mouse	Autoimmune parathyroiditis
Pancreas (islet cell)	Rat, mouse, rabbit	Type I diabetes
Central nervous system neurons	Rat (Lewis), guinea pig (strain B), mouse, sheep, monkey	Multiple sclerosis
Eye (uvea/retina)	Guinea pig (Hartley and NIH)	Autoimmune uveitis
Kidney (tubules/glomeruli)	Rat (BN)	Autoimmune tubulointerstitial nephritis
	Rat	Autoimmune glomerulonephritis
Joint (articular surface)	Mouse (DBA), rat, rabbit	Rheumatoid arthritis
Liver (hepatocytes)	Mouse	Chronic active hepatitis
Testes (spermatozoa)	Mouse (C57 black)	Autoimmune orchitis
Heart (myocardium)	Guinea pig, mouse	Autoimmune myocarditis
Thrombocytes	Rat (BN)	Idiopathic thrombocytopenia
Erythrocytes	Mouse	Autoimmune hemolytic anemia
Neuromuscular junction	Rat, guinea pig	Myasthenia gravis

to study genetic influences on autoimmune susceptibility. As might be expected, strong major histocompatibility complex (MHC) influences have been observed in some models as, for example, in mouse thyroiditis and experimental autoimmune encephalomyelitis (EAE) in rats. However, this does not seem to apply to the mouse antierythrocyte/anemia model mentioned above, although non-H2 genetic associations are evident.

One major disadvantage of this procedure is that the pathological effects induced are often transient in nature, presumably due to the imposition of autoimmunity on the normal animal with intact immunoregulatory feedbacks. As a consequence, overt clinical disease is not observed in many immunization models, even though short-term tissue infiltration is readily apparent histologically. However, EAE is a notable exception in that severe nervous signs can be readily induced by immunization of susceptible animals with myelin basic protein or its peptide derivatives. Clearly, the nervous system is more sensitive to the effects of immunological attack and these are more apparent clinically than, for example, those involving the endocrine tissues.

Although the relapsing form of EAE can be induced in guinea pigs by this method, in most experimental systems autoimmunity is rarely reactivated even by further immunization. There is evidence in a number of models that this effect may be due to the generation of antigen specific 'suppressor' cells, as demonstrated by adoptive cell transfer stud-

ies. Evidence for such activity has been found in mouse thyroiditis, mouse antierythrocyte autoimmunity and EAE in rats.

Although the injection of autoantigens in adjuvant can clearly have little relevance to the natural triggering events leading to human autoimmune disease development, immunization models continue to provide a wealth of information on many other aspects of autoimmunity. Currently, with the rapid accumulation of information at the molecular level concerning the subcellular components involved in autoimmunity, this procedure is likely to be utilized as a requisite step in the evaluation of purified recombinant polypeptides derived from such structures as potential B or T autoepitopes.

2. Induction of autoimmunity by impairment of immunological function ('immune depletion models')

It is now accepted that partial impairment of normal immunological function can lead to the onset of autoimmune reactivity, particularly of the organ-specific type. The earliest evidence in this context was the observation that thymectomy of certain mouse strains leads to the appearance of antinuclear antibodies. However, this relationship was firmly established in 1973 by two groups who independently reported the induction of organ-specific autoimmunity by procedures causing partial immunodepletion. Penhale and coworkers found that autoimmune thyroiditis could be induced by thymectomy of 3-week-old Wistar rats followed by repeated low-dose irradiation. In a similar vein, Nishizuka and colleagues made the observation that thyroiditis spontaneously developed in mice following thymectomy alone, provided that this was carried out in the neonatal period. The autoimmune basis of these conditions was evident from the presence of infiltrating lymphocytes in the target tissue, circulating tissue-specific autoantibodies and the ability to transfer the disease to naive recipients with lymphocytes from affected animals. From 1975 onwards a number of other manipulations and treatments involving the immune system were shown to induce organ-specific autoimmune disease in rodents. A feature of all these procedures is either a deficiency of circulating T lymphocytes or their functional impairment as, for example, by a reduction in the range of the T cell receptor (TCR) repertoire. The spectrum of autoimmune diseases induced by this means is now impressive and includes diabetes, thyroiditis, gastritis, orchitis, oophoritis, prostatitis and coagulating adenitis. These conditions are rarely, if ever, seen in normal unmanipulated rodents of the same strains. The various depletion methods employed to induce these diseases are shown in **Table 2**.

A central question in understanding the process of autoimmunity is how the aberrant immune response is initiated. The development of immunodepletion models has been conceptually important in demonstrating the critical requirement for regulatory elements in the control of potential autoimmune reactivity in the normal individual. They also strongly suggest that neither aberrant antigen modification nor presentation are likely to be necessary antecedents of the autoimmune process. In consequence, they provide a powerful tool for studying the basis for the loss of self tolerance to peripheral self antigens and the development of destructive autoimmune lesions. In this regard they have proved particularly suitable for studying the immunological regulation of autoimmunity by reconstitution studies

Table 2 Manipulations of the immune system leading to the development of organ-specific autoimmunity

Experimental manipulation
Combined sublethal irradiation/thymectomy of adult rodents
Neonatal thymectomy of rodents
Neonatal administration of cyclosporine in mice
Combined cyclophosphamide/thymectomy of adult rodents
High dose (42.5 Gy), fractionated total lymphoid irradiation of adult mice
Single-chain TCR transgenic mice
T cell transfer to syngeneic, T cell-deficient mice

using syngeneic lymphocytes derived from normal animals.

Immunodepletion models do not require immunization with putative autoantigens in adjuvant, as in the previous model above, but presumably involve the appropriate targeting of natural autoantigens rather than surrogate model antigens. In addition, they are also similar to their clinical counterparts in humans in that, once initiated, the disease is sustained and chronic. Furthermore, an association between various immunodeficient states and clinical autoimmunity in humans has been recognized. Because of these similarities in many pathological and immunological features they are providing invaluable insights into the pathogenesis of their human disease counterparts.

3. Induction of autoimmunity by infectious agents ('infection models')

The natural history of autoimmune disease in some individual patients strongly suggests the involvement of environmental or infectious agents in the inductive process. For example, postmeasles encephalomyelitis may result from an autoimmune response to myelin basic protein, and infection with Coxsackie virus group B has been associated with myocarditis in which there are autoantibodies to heart antigens. Despite this circumstantial evidence in isolated instances, direct evidence for the involvement of infectious agents in human autoimmune disease is unavailable. In contrast, experimental studies in animals provide some compelling evidence of the involvement of infectious agents, particularly viruses, in the triggering of certain forms of autoimmunity. Several viruses have been shown to induce diabetes-like conditions in inbred strains of mice with evidence of associated autoimmunity. Polyendocrine syndromes and diseases of nonendocrine organs have also been observed in certain infections. Certain bacteria or their products may also cause experimental autoimmune effects. For example, the injection of mycobacterial proteoglycan may induce arthritis, several bacterial products may similarly cause myasthenia (see below) and the injection of live *Listeria* directly into the testes can provoke an autoimmune orchitis.

The phenomenology of infection models require further investigation before a detailed understanding of their mechanisms can be gained and an autoimmune basis for their pathogenesis is unequivocally established. However, a number of immunological processes may underlie their pathogenicity, including:

1. The effect infectious agents have on host cells.

Apart from the expression of virus gene products in persistently infected cells which may target them for host immune responses, virus may also have subtle effects on cell genes and the resulting enhanced or altered expression of host cell proteins could induce an autoimmune response. A further possibility is interaction of microorganisms with immunocompetent cells, leading to their polyclonal activation or reduced susceptibility to regulation. They may also cause a loss of function of regulatory cells with autoimmune consequences.

2. Molecular mimicry. Partial sequence homology between microbial antigens and self determinants may lead to the generation of host-specific responses by T helper cell bypass.
3. Idiotype–anti-idiotype interactions (see below).
4. Tissue injury induced by infection may lead to the breaking of tolerance to self antigens and subsequent perpetuation of injury by autoimmune mechanisms. This mechanism could account for the induction of autoimmune disease by an acute, nonpersisting infection.
5. Enhanced expression of MHC antigen by microbial influences directly on the target cell or indirectly via lymphocytes.

4. Induction of autoimmunity by chemical agents ('chemically induced models')

A number of chemical substances appear to give rise to autoimmune effects in patients after prolonged use as therapeutic agents; for example, methyl dopa may cause a Coombs'-positive hemolytic anemia. Similarly, in the experimental context, several chemical agents have been shown to induce autoimmune-like syndromes, such as streptozotocin-induced diabetes in mice and mercuric chloride-induced glomerulonephritis in brown Norway rats. There are several possible mechanisms whereby chemicals may be involved in generating autoimmune manifestations, including: 1) modification of tissue components, particularly cell membrane structures; 2) breaking of self tolerance following liberation of cellular constituents by direct tissue damage; and 3) modification of immune function, particularly affecting regulatory cells. In general, withdrawal of the chemical agent results in recovery and diseases induced by this means have few clear analogies with naturally occurring human disorders. Low dose streptozotocin-induced diabetes mellitus in mice is a possible exception to the above statement, although the actual pathogenesis, whether direct toxicity or true autoimmunity, is still in doubt.

5. Induction of autoimmunity by anti-idiotype (Id) responses ('anti-idiotype models')

Theoretically, several mechanisms of induction of autoimmunity through Id interactions appear to be possible, although few examples of such are currently documented and none established as regularly utilized models for inducing autoimmunity. First, an anti-Id antibody may resemble an autoantigen sufficiently to be cross-reactive. This is exemplified in the insulin system, where it has been found that an antibody to the Id of anti-insulin antibody may interact with and actually trigger insulin receptors. Another, more dramatic example of the same mechanism appears to be the myasthenia gravis-like syndrome observed when rabbits are injected with a synthetic agonist (Bis Q) of the acetylcholine receptor. A second way in which the Id network can stimulate autoimmunity is through the development of 'parallel sets'. These may arise when immunologically distinct antibodies share a 'public' idiotype. As an example, extensive idiotypy has been discovered between the antibodies to the acetylcholine receptor and the DEX antigen (1,3-dextran) present on the surface of many bacteria. Thus, the injection of such bacteria may induce autoantibodies to the receptor and hence myasthenia gravis. It may be no coincidence that many examples of autoimmune anti-Id effects involve receptor molecules.

6. Induction of autoimmunity by genetic manipulation ('transgenic models')

Transgenic technologies have provided new opportunities for developing animal models of autoimmune diseases. To date their development has been largely directed at obtaining new insights into the fundamental questions of autoimmunity, such as the nature of self tolerance, rather than the provision of relevant models of human disease. Expression of well-defined molecules can be induced in specific cell types by this technology and three broad approaches have been utilized to study aspects of autoimmunity:

1. The genes selected may code for a normally foreign antigen which will be synthesized at a particular development stage and behave essentially like a self antigen. The gene may be linked to a tissue-specific promoter which ensures its expression in a particular tissue while simultaneously avoiding thymic expression. Thus it is possible to generate cells expressing a genuine self molecule without concurrent thymic deletion of the complementary lymphocytes.
2. The genes selected may be rearranged T cell receptor or immunoglobulin genes coding for recognition molecules with specificity for a self

component. This procedure has the potential to generate antiself lymphocytes at high frequency, allowing the fate of such cells to be followed during and after ontogeny. Alternatively, the TCR repertoire can be greatly restricted by introducing the gene coding for an irrelevant nonself specificity. Thus the T cell compartment can be functionally depleted, leading to autoimmunity (see method 2 above).

3. The transgene may code for MHC molecules in order to address the question of the significance of their upregulation on target tissues during autoimmunity. This has led to the surprising finding that diabetes of nonimmune origin can be induced by overexpression of these molecules on the islet β cells. This is presumably due to derangement of cell metabolism as a consequence of high class II expression.

These strategies can also be combined to produce multiple transgenic animals in which, for example, an antigenic molecule can be directed to a specific cell type and the complementary TCR introduced into lymphocytes simultaneously.

The β cell of the pancreatic islet currently appears to be the most popular location for transgenic modification. Apart from the importance of type I diabetes as a human autoimmune syndrome, this cell is particularly convenient in that the transgene can be linked to the specific promoter for insulin production. Studies with transgenically modified β cells have been revealing in a number of respects. For example, experiments with lymphocytic choriomeningitis virus (LCMV) glycoprotein antigen expression on these cells point to immunological ignorance rather than tolerance as the mechanism responsible for the absence of reactivity to islet cell antigens, as diabetes does not occur spontaneously in this model and can only be induced by subsequent infection with LCMV. Furthermore, a number of additional lines of evidence indicate strongly that the virus is not breaking immunological tolerance in this experiment. New generations of these transgenic models are likely to revolutionize our understanding of this central phenomenon of autoimmunity.

Conclusions

Study of human autoimmune disease presents the considerable problem of deciding whether the changes observed are the cause or consequence of the disease process. The use of animal models avoids this difficulty and their manipulative potential has yielded many valuable insights into the autoimmune process. The disease range of induced models now available covers a wide spectrum of human autoimmune diseases and, although differing in detail from the human conditions, they have been instrumental in clarifying basic pathogenic mechanisms and, perhaps more importantly, in demonstrating that multiple and converging pathways to autoimmune disease development exist. They have also demonstrated that, in addition to a specific triggering event, disturbances of normal regulatory function may be prerequisite for chronic, sustained autoimmunity.

Finally, despite the multifactorial nature of autoimmune disease clearly revealed by modeling, this approach also offers the prospect that autoimmune disease might be controlled by interfering with the final common pathways without necessarily eliminating all the anteceding immune abnormalities.

See also: **Adjuvant arthritis; Anemia, autoimmune hemolytic in animal models; Autoantigens; Autoimmune disease, spontaneous experimental models; Autoimmunity; Contrasuppression; Experimental autoimmune encephalomyelitis (EAE); Idiotype network; Immunosuppression; Insulin-dependent diabetes mellitus, animal models; Multiple sclerosis; Neuromuscular junction autoimmunity; Rheumatoid arthritis, animal models; T cell vaccination; Thyroid autoimmunity, experimental models; Transgenic animals.**

Further reading

Sabato GD (ed) (1988) Methods for the study of the cellular phenomena of inflammation and experimental models of inflammation. *Methods in Enzymology* **162**: 339–478.

Shoenfeld Y and Isenberg D (1989) *The Mosaic of Autoimmunity*. Amsterdam: Elsevier.

AUTOIMMUNE DISEASE, PATHOGENESIS

Konrad Schauenstein, Institute for Functional Pathology, Karl-Franzens University, Graz, Austria

Now as ever, autoimmune diseases constitute one of the main unsolved problems in human clinical medicine. This is because our knowledge of their etiology and pathogenesis is still not sufficient to provide new concepts towards specific therapy. They are considered to be pathological consequences of immune reactions directed towards autologous antigens.

Over 30 years ago, Witebsky and Milgrom formulated their well-known criteria for autoimmune diseases, the most important of which are that: 1) antibodies or lymphocytes specifically reacting with a defined autoantigen can be detected; 2) immunization of animals with an autoantigen results in an autoimmune disease corresponding to its original tissue distribution, and 3) experimental autoimmune disease is inducible in healthy recipients by passive transfer of autoreactive antibodies or lymphocytes. These postulates, essentially still valid today, pointed to the importance of animal models, and our present knowledge about etiopathogenesis is indeed mainly derived from the study of animals, in which autoimmune diseases are either experimentally induced by immunization with autoantigen, or occur spontaneously at high incidence.

Autoimmune diseases are a heterogeneous group of diseases. According to manifestation we can distinguish systemic diseases affecting various different tissues from organ-specific diseases, where the autoimmune process is restricted to single organ systems. There is good evidence that these two types differ considerably in etiology and pathogenesis.

Breakdown of autotolerance

The ability to tolerate autologous antigens, a central feature of the adaptive immune system, is guaranteed in redundant ways at the level of both the B and T lymphocyte system. It is thought to be the result of negative selection within the central lymphoid organs, i.e. bone marrow and thymus, where sensitive stages of developing B ($sIgM^+$ $sIgD^-$) or T ($CD4^+$ $CD8^+$) cell clones are eliminated by apoptosis due to high-affinity binding to autologous antigens. Autoreactive cell clones that escape these central selection processes for whatever reason are effectively controlled in their reactivity in the periphery, either passively by virtue of insufficient costimulatory signals or by active suppressive immunoregulation. These peripheral mechanisms are not specific for autoantigens, but are identical to those that induce tolerance against any given foreign antigen. With regard to autoimmunity the interest has focused primarily on T lymphocytes, because of the central regulatory role of T helper cells in the immune response against protein antigens, and in view of the well-known association of autoimmune diseases with major histocompatibility complex (MHC) alleles differing in effectivity of antigen presentation to T cells.

Defective differentiation

According to the aforementioned concepts a breakdown in autotolerance can occur due to failures in thymic selection, and any factors that influence the survival of thymic lymphocytes could principally be expected to result in shifts in the peripheral T cell repertoire. As MHC molecules play an important role in the presentation of thymic autoantigens, changes in thymic selection may be one mechanism by which genes of the MHC influence autoimmune diseases. Nevertheless, it has to be stated that experimental data directly proving the occurrence of autoimmune reactions as a consequence of a disturbed intrathymic differentiation are lacking as yet.

Based on the finding that autoreactive lymphocytes of patients and experimental animals with organ-specific autoimmune diseases exhibited a limited number of V genes, it was debated whether autoimmunity may be the result of an abnormal immunoglobulin (Ig) or T cell receptor (TCR) repertoire. However, restriction fragment length polymorphism (RFLP) analysis performed in humans with autoimmune diseases did not indicate associations to certain Ig or TCR genes, and no consistent differences were detected in germline Ig genes of autoimmune mouse strains.

Peripheral loss of autotolerance

As to peripheral mechanisms, the loss of anergy against autoantigens may be the result of abnormal activation of T cells by antigen-presenting cells (APCs), such as dendritic cells, macrophages and B cells, that increase the expression of costimulatory surface molecules as a result of irritation, e.g. in the course of infections or local inflammatory reactions. In accordance with this notion is the established fact that the induction of experimental autoimmune diseases in animals requires immunization with autoantigens together with strong adjuvants that lead to activation of APCs. Also, nonprofessional APCs, such as epithelial cells, may lead to local activation of autoreactive T cells by virtue of inappropriate expression of immunostimulatory molecules, such as MHC class II determinants. Another strong indication for a crucial role of T cell activation comes from results proving that enhanced levels of interleukin-2 (IL-2) are able to abrogate a state of anergy against tissue autoantigens. Further peripheral mechanisms, not related to T cell activation, may be a resistance of lymphocytes to apoptosis as described in the MLR-*lpr/lpr* mouse with systemic lupus erythematosus (SLE) symptoms and a defect in the expression of the fas apoptosis gene. However, no such association has been found in human SLE patients.

Peripheral tolerization of B lymphocytes results from antigenic stimulation without proper T cell help. Thus, a stimulus from autoreactive T helper cell clones may end the state of B cell autoanergy. Alternatively, certain foreign antigens may exhibit shared epitopes with autoantigens, and T helper cells specific for these shared epitopes may drive autotolerant B cells into activation.

Immunological cross-reactions between foreign microbial antigens and autoantigens are well known to be able to elicit humoral or cellular autoimmune responses, the classical example being rheumatic fever due to a 'normal' immune response against streptococcal antigens that is cross-reactive with myocardial protein. More recently, mycobacterial heat shock protein (hsp65) has gained interest as an antigen of possible relevance to pathogenic autoimmune responses in several diseases, including atherosclerosis.

Polyclonal, antigen-independent lymphocyte activation has been implicated in the activation of autoreactive lymphocytes and elicitation of autoimmune responses. Injection of mice with bacterial lipopolysaccharide (LPS), which is a polyclonal B cell activator in mice, has been shown to lead to the production of autoantibodies of various specificities. Even though these antibodies, due to the lack of T cell help, are of low affinity and nonpathogenic, the polyclonal B cell activation by 'LPS-like' bacterial substances may be at least one of the reasons for the close association of autoimmune and infectious diseases. Similarly the binding of bacterial superantigens to certain V_β chains of the T cell receptor has been discussed as a possible mechanism of autoimmunity at the T cell level. Finally, autoimmune phenomena are observed in the course of graft-versus-host reactions, supposedly due to polyclonal B cell activation induced by alloactivated donor T helper cells.

A disturbed balance in helper and suppressor influences exerted by T regulator cells has long been implicated in the pathogenesis of autoimmune diseases. While the classical T helper/suppressor cell model was abandoned several years ago, it is now thought that the balance between T helper1 (T_H1) and T helper2 (T_H2) cells is relevant to the maintenance of autotolerance, whereby T_H2 cells under normal conditions are thought to keep autoreactive effector T_H1 cells in line. Accordingly, quantitative or functional abnormalities in this balance may allow autoimmune reactions to occur. Investigations of joint lesions in rheumatoid arthritis (RA) patients seem to support this concept, as cloning studies identified the vast majority of infiltrating T cells as belonging to the T_H1 subtype, whereas T_H2 clones were only rarely found. In contrast, synovial specimens from more benign, nondestructive types of arthritis were found to contain high levels of IL-4 mRNA. From this it was concluded that the local presence of functional T_H2 cells may be critical for the self-limitation of the autoimmune process in the affected joints.

Besides their central roles in the effector phase of autoimmune processes (see below) cytokines are certainly critically involved in systemic and local immunoregulation and thereby modulate the clinical outcome of an autoimmune disease. Furthermore, the above mentioned data on IL-2 suggest that they may also take part in the breakdown of self-tolerance. Recently, enhanced systemic levels of inflammatory cytokines (IL-1β, IL-6, tumor necrosis factor α (TNFα)) and soluble cytokine receptors (sIL-2R, sTNFR) were reported to significantly correlate with the clinical activity of RA in children, whereby the different clinical subtypes displayed different patterns.

Effector mechanisms

As to effector mechanisms, autoimmune diseases are no different from any other pathogenic immune response against foreign antigens involving reactions of types II (cytotoxic antibodies), III (immune complexes), IV (cellular-mediated immunity) and V (stimulating antibodies) according to the Gell/Coombs nomenclature. Furthermore, antigen nonspecific mechanisms secondarily activated by autoantigen-activated lymphocytes play an important pathogenetic role.

The role of autoantibodies

The detection of circulating and/or tissue-bound autoantibodies is undoubtedly one of the most consistent findings in autoimmune diseases in human and animal models. Although low levels of autoanti-bodies can be detected in healthy individuals, and, on the other hand, autoimmune diseases can exist without detectable autoantibodies, there is in general a good correlation between peripheral levels of auto-antibody and activity of an autoimmune disease, whereby the spectrum of specificities may be charac-teristic, sometimes even diagnostic, for a particular autoimmune disease. There are several ways by which autoantibodies can be involved in the patho-genesis of autoimmune diseases:

- Tissue-specific autoantibodies may activate com-plement and lead to cytolysis of the target cell (type II), as is observed for example in spon-taneous or drug-induced autoimmune lysis of red or white blood cells. In organ-specific diseases cytotoxic autoantibodies are thought to contribute to tissue destruction, e.g. in autoimmune diseases of endocrine glands, in Goodpasture's syndrome and in myasthenia gravis.
- The binding of autoantibodies to tissues leads to triggering of the natural immune system by attracting and activating Fc receptor and com-plement receptor bearing cells to phagocytosis, cytotoxicity and antibody-dependent cellular cyto-toxicity. Furthermore, the amplification system of inflammatory mediators involving the clotting fibrinolysis and kallikerin–kinin systems can be induced by autoantibodies and complement via activation of factor XII.
- Autoantibodies specific for cell surface structures, e.g. hormone receptors, can stimulate or block the growth and functions of target cells. Stimulatory autoantibodies were first recognized in auto-immune disease of the thyroid gland being directed against the thyroid-stimulating hormone (TSH) receptor, blocking autoantibodies are found for example in myasthenia gravis, and bind specifically to the motor end-plate.
- Autoantibodies specific for soluble cell products can give rise to high levels of circulating immune complexes (type III reactions) causing inflamma-tory tissue damage at the sites of deposition as seen in both systemic and organ-restricted auto-immune diseases. The localization of immune complexes is dependent on hemorheological fac-tors, Fc binding, and on nonspecific binding characteristics of certain tissues. Hence, an enhanced binding of DNA to basement mem-branes appears to be responsible for the character-istic deposition of DNA–anti-DNA complexes.
- Autoantibodies with specificity for the idiotype of autoantibodies have been detected in several auto-

immune diseases. Treatment with such autoanti-idiotypes has been shown to suppress spontaneous autoimmune disease in animal models, which points to the potential of these autoantibodies to control the course of an autoimmune disease. On the other hand, as anti-idiotype antibodies can mimic the primary antigen (i.e. autoantigen) auto-anti-idiotypes could enhance autoimmune disease by eliciting and/or perpetuating an autoimmune response.

The role of T cells

For a long time autoantibodies were thought to play the major role in autoimmune effector mechanisms. Results in both experimental and spontaneous ani-mal models, however, revealed that autoreactive T lymphocytes are both necessary and often sufficient to cause autoimmune disease. This was shown for example in the obese strain of chickens afflicted with spontaneous Hashimoto-like thyroiditis, where erad-ication of the T cell system by neonatal thymectomy plus treatment with T cell-specific antibodies resulted in prevention of disease. On the other hand, it was shown that the disease could be effectively trans-ferred to healthy recipients of the same genetic back-ground by injection of autospecific thymocytes, or purified T cells derived from infiltrated thyroid glands of B cell-deprived (bursectomized) obese strain chickens. The dominance of the autoreactive T effector cell also emerged from the work on experi-mentally induced autoimmune diseases in rats and mice, where autoantigen-specific T cell lines could be developed that were instrumental in the study of the pathogenetic role of T cell immunity. Transfer of low numbers of viable autoreactive T cells induces vigor-ous autoimmune disease in several models. If such cells are growth arrested by irradiation prior to transfer, the recipient becomes protected against induction of the disease by immunization with the autoantigen. Taken together, these data clearly point to the fact that both the induction and effector phases of an autoimmune disease can primarily involve autoantigen-specific T lymphocytes. The appearance of autoantibody may often be secondary and have only a modulatory role in the disease.

As to the effector mechanisms by which auto-reactive T cells mediate tissue damage, the evidence obtained suggests that it is mainly the CD4$^+$ T_H1 phenotype (T_{DTH}) that upon activation by autoanti-gen in the context of MHC class II molecules releases cytokines, such as IL-2, IFNγ, TNFα/β and others, and which by themselves or by activation of other specific (autoreactive CD8$^+$ cells) and nonspecific (NK cells, macrophages) inflammatory cells destroy the target tissue. T_H2 cells, as mentioned above, supposedly suppress T_H1 effector cells, but, on the other hand, may exert helper functions to autoreactive B cells via IL-4, IL-5, IL-6, and may keep autoreactive T cells alive by IL-10, which – besides its immunosuppressive effects – prevents apoptosis.

Nonspecific mechanisms

Pathogenetic mechanisms of natural immunity were long ago recognized as important in autoimmune disease. This is confirmed by a number of more recent investigations showing the crucial roles of inflammatory monokines IL-1β, IL-6, and particularly of TNFα, as well as several chemokines in autoimmune tissue destruction. Furthermore, IL-12 produced by several professional antigen-presenting cells has been shown to be critical in the development of autoimmune disease, as it promotes the differentiation of T_H1 cells. The essential role of the monocyte/macrophage series is further underscored by more recent findings in certain animal models, where autoimmune diseases were effectively controlled by antioxidants or by inhibition of nitric oxide synthesis. Until recently, it was thought that nonspecific effector cells were secondarily activated by autoantibodies, autoimmune complexes with or without activation of complement, and cytokines derived from activated T helper cells. The newer concepts of how autotolerance can get lost in the periphery (see above), however, make it likely that a primary abnormal activation of monocytes/macrophages may lead to loss of autotolerance and thereby initiate an autoimmune disease. This view is supported by recent data in the obese strain of chickens with spontaneous autoimmune thyroid disease, and by the induction of lupus-associated autoantibodies in BALB/c mice by i.p. injection of pristane.

It should be stressed that the tissue destruction process in autoimmune diseases with few exceptions has to be regarded as the result of a combination of several humoral and cellular pathogenetic mechanisms.

Modulating factors in autoimmune disease

In discussing factors or conditions that can modify the severity and course of autoimmune disease a clear distinction between etiology and pathogenesis becomes often difficult. This is due to the fact that autoimmune diseases have a multifactorial etiology requiring both genetic features and environmental conditions to occur. The question as to whether a given genetic or epigenetic factor is permissive to an autoimmune disease or only modifying the pathogenesis is open in most cases.

Genetic predisposition

The first evidence for an involvement of certain genes in the development of autoimmune diseases came from clinical experiences in humans revealing familial incidence of certain autoimmune diseases. This was confirmed by the observations that certain strains of experimental animals spontaneously exhibit enhanced frequencies of certain autoimmune disorders, and that selective breeding for the autoimmune phenotype resulted in further enhanced incidence and severity. The best-established animal models for spontaneous autoimmune diseases are strains of mice with manifestations of systemic lupus erythematosus, and the obese strain chickens afflicted with an organ-specific disease, i.e. autoimmune thyroiditis. Also the susceptibility to the induction of experimentally induced autoimmune disease has been shown to be genetically determined.

Various loci have been found to be involved in the development of autoimmune diseases, some of them are associated with the major histocompatibility complex (MHC). The best example for the association of an autoimmune disease with a certain MHC allele is HLA-B27, which confers an 85–90-fold relative risk of ankylosing spondylitis. Further examples include rheumatoid arthritis associated with HLA-DR4 and insulin-dependent diabetes mellitus (IDDM), with HLA-DR4 and DR3. In the latter it was shown that a certain allele, i.e. HLA-DR2, confers protection with a relative risk of 0.2. Mechanisms that are discussed to explain MHC associations of autoimmune diseases include 1) insufficient thymic presentation of autoantigens, 2) abnormal presentation of autoantigens to peripheral T helper cells, 3) association with alleles of non-MHC loci, such as the genes for TNFα/β, that map to the MHC and are linked with certain MHC alleles, and 4) antigenic mimicry between microbial antigens and autologous MHC molecules.

Another set of genes – not associated with the MHC – is involved in different mechanisms of immunoregulation, and, finally, the susceptibility of the respective target organ in organ-specific autoimmune diseases appears also to be under genetic control. The latter two types of genes have been defined by classical genetic analysis of experimental and spontaneous autoimmune diseases in animal models.

Endocrine and neuroendocrine influences

Immune responses in general are not only regulated by mechanisms intrinsic to the immune system, but also by endocrine and neuroendocrine signals. It has long been recognized that many autoimmune diseases preferentially occur in females, whereas males appear protected probably due to immunosuppressive properties of androgens. Similar observations were made when obese strain chickens were first developed. However, with continuous selective breeding this sex difference disappeared, which suggests that sex hormones only have a modifying role in this disease.

Hormones involved in stress responses, such as glucocorticoids, catecholamines, endogenous opiates and most of the anterior pituitary hormones, have strong effects on specific and natural immune functions. It is well known that acute or chronic stress can exacerbate certain autoimmune diseases in humans. Chemical sympathectomy (by means of 6-OH-dopamine) has been shown to influence the course of experimental autoimmune disease in animals. Obese strain chickens were found to have enhanced plasma levels of corticoid-binding globulin leading to a diminished availability of free glucocorticoids. Early *in vivo* supplementation with free corticosterone prevented the onset of thyroiditis. Further to this, obese strain chickens were shown to have a central defect in the responsiveness of the hypothalamo-pituitary-adrenal axis to signals of the activated immune system, resulting in the lack of the peripheral glucocorticoid response after immunization as it is observed in healthy controls, and it was concluded that the defect in this negative feedback may predispose to autoimmunity. Findings in two experimentally induced models, i.e. experimentally induced encephalomyelitis and experimentally induced arthritis in rats, strongly supported this concept, and there is now good evidence that human patients suffering from rheumatoid arthritis show endocrine abnormalities indicating altered pituitary functions, which may contribute to etiology and/or pathogenesis of the disease.

Age

Aging is known to be associated with increased autoimmune phenomena. However, these increased 'forbidden' responses as manifested in mildly elevated levels of autoantibodies are not necessarily pathogenic. Some authors have assigned this age-associated autoimmunity even a physiological role as a possible scavenger mechanism for cell and tissue constituents that accumulate due to enhanced tissue damage at higher age. Most of the acute severe autoimmune diseases usually start at young to middle ages, only certain chronic processes, e.g. chronic polyarthritis, tend to severe at higher ages.

Environmental influences

Little is known about environmental influences on autoimmune disease. In general, any exogenous agent or condition that affects the immunogenic properties of autoantigens and/or the regulation of the immune response can be expected to modify autoimmune diseases. Modification of autoantigens and/or immune reactivity can occur by several bacterial and viral infections, and the outbreak of several autoimmune diseases indeed appears to be associated with certain infectious diseases, such as IDDM or multiple sclerosis following certain viral infections. Another way by which bacterial or viral infections may induce autoimmune disease is the abovementioned antigenic cross-reaction with autoantigens.

Autoimmune diseases as side-effects of drugs comprise type II reactions against drug-modified autologous white or red blood cells, but also lupus-like phenomena in patients taking β-adrenergic blockers or drugs like hydralazine and procainamide. While the mechanism(s) of action of β-blockers in this respect is not clear, *in vitro* investigations have shown that hydralazine and procainamide induces self-reactivity in cloned, heteroantigen-specific T cell lines by DNA methylation. This suggests that DNA methylation as a mechanism of gene expression plays a role in the specificity of immune responses, and that drugs or substances that interfere with the regulation of gene expression in general may have the potential to induce forbidden immune responses leading to autoimmune disease.

See also: **Aging and the immune system; Autoantigens; Autoimmune disease, induced experimental models; Autoimmune diseases; Autoimmunity; Glucocorticoids; Goodpasture's syndrome; Hypersensitivity reactions; Immune complexes; Insulin-dependent diabetes mellitus, human; MHC disease associations; Neuromuscular junction autoimmunity; Neuroendocrine regulation of immunity; Sex hormones and immunity; Systemic lupus erythematosus, experimental models; Systemic lupus erythematosus (SLE), human; Thyroid autoimmunity, experimental models; Thyroid autoimmunity, human; Tissue typing.**

Further reading

Berczi I, Baragar FD, Chalmers IM, Keystone EC, Nagy E and Warrington RJ (1993) Hormones in self tolerance and autoimmunity: a role in pathogenesis of rheumatoid arthritis? *Autoimmunity* 16: 45–56.
Cornacchia E, Golbus J, Maybaum J, Strahler J, Hanash S and Richardson B (1988) Hydralazine and procaina-

mide inhibit T cell DNA methylation and induce auto-reactivity. *Journal of Immunology* **140**: 2197–2200.

Hala K, Malin G, Dietrich H *et al* (1996) Analysis of the initiation period of spontaneous autoimmune thyroiditis (SAT) in obese strain (OS) of chickens. *Journal of Autoimmunity* **9**: 129–138.

Karopoulos C, Rowley MJ, Handley CJ and Strugnell RA (1995) Antibody reactivity to mycobacterial 65 kDa heat shock protein: relevance to autoimmunity. *Journal of Autoimmunity* **8**: 235–248.

Mangge H, Kenzian H, Gallistl S *et al* (1995) Serum cytokines in juvenile rheumatoid arthritis (JRA). Correlation with conventional inflammatory parameters and clinical subtypes. *Arthritis and Rheumatism* **38**: 211–220.

Matzinger P (1994) Tolerance, danger, and the extended family. *Annual Review of Immunology* **12**: 991–1045.

Posnett DN (1993) Do superantigens play a role in autoimmunity? *Seminars in Immunology* **5**: 65–72.

Rose LM, Latchman DS and Isenberg DA (1994) Bcl-2 and Fas, molecules which influence apoptosis. A possible role in systemic lupus erythematosus? *Autoimmunity* **17**: 271–278.

Schattner A (1994) Lymphokines in autoimmunity – a critical review. *Clinical Immunology and Immunopathology* **70**: 177–189.

Takahashi S, Fossati L, Iwamoto M *et al* (1996) Imbalance towards Th1 predominance is associated with acceleration of lupus-like autoimmune syndrome in MRL mice. *Journal of Clinical Investigation* **97**: 1597–1604.

AUTOIMMUNE DISEASE, SPONTANEOUS ANIMAL MODELS

Georg Wick and **Roswitha Sgonc**, Institute for General and Experimental Pathology, University of Innsbruck, Innsbruck, Austria

Guido Kroemer, Centre National de la Recherche Scientifique – UPR 420, Villejuif, France

Autoimmune diseases can be experimentally induced by immunization of normal animals with the respective antigens combined with appropriate adjuvants. By this means organ-specific experimental autoimmune diseases can be produced in animals of many different strains and in nearly every organ. There is no doubt that such experimentally induced autoimmune diseases, e.g. experimental allergic encephalomyelitis (EAE) or experimental autoimmune thyroiditis (EAT), have contributed considerably to our understanding of the pathogenesis of autoimmune diseases in general and these models in particular. It is, however, also clear that most of these artificially produced autoimmune diseases often do not parallel their human counterparts with respect to all essential characteristics.

Fortunately, there are several animal strains available that – based on many years of selective breeding – develop certain organ-specific or systemic autoimmune diseases spontaneously, i.e. without any experimental manipulation. These models mimic the human situation much more closely and thus serve as apt objects of study for the pathogenetic mechanisms underlying the development of these diseases as well as the establishment of new diagnostic and therapeutic strategies. In this entry, spontaneous animal models for four types of diseases, two systemic and two organ specific, will be presented. This selection is based on the large body of literature on these models, but it should be emphasized that several other promising strains exist which have not yet been investigated in such depth but may also turn out to be very useful in the future, such as the Buffalo (BUF) rat that develops an autoimmune thyroiditis in high frequency, the autoimmune glomerulonephritis, arthritis and orchitis emerging in Aleutian minks, the delayed amenalosis (DAM) chicken with autoimmune depigmentation, and several others.

In principle, spontaneous autoimmune models arose due to a combination of serendipity (spontaneous mutations causing autoimmune phenotypes) and inbreeding plus selection procedures. As a consequence, inbred animal strains afflicted by spontaneous autoimmune diseases usually manifest disease phenotypes that are compatible with breeding programs, i.e. that do not cause severe pathology before animals reach sexual maturity, although they sometimes may need special dietary, hormonal, etc. supplementation. Alternatively, autoimmune phenotypes are studied in severely diseased F1 crosses of relatively normal parental inbred strains. This particular feature of spontaneous autoimmune disease models may explain why certain laboratory-produced mutations (e.g. disruption of the CTLA4 gene) that give rise to an acute, fulminant autoimmune disorder have not been observed spontaneously.

Spontaneous animal models for organ-specific autoimmune diseases

Obese strain of chickens as an animal model for Hashimoto's thyroiditis

During the first few weeks after hatching, obese strain (OS) chickens develop a hereditary spontaneous autoimmune thyroiditis (SAT) that resembles human Hashimotos disease in all clinical, histopathological, endocrinological and immunological aspects. The thyroid glands of OS chickens become heavily infiltrated by mononuclear cells, finally resulting in complete destruction of their architecture entailing clinical symptoms of hypothyroidism (**Figure 1**), such as small body size – albeit with relatively high body weight due to the deposition of subcutaneous and abdominal fat – lipemic serum, long silky feathers, cold sensitivity, low laying capacity, diminished fertility and poor hatchability. In common with Hashimoto's thyroiditis, the infiltrated thyroid glands show high numbers of well-developed germinal centers as a characteristic hallmark that is unique to this model and absent in EAT. The serum of OS chickens contains autoantibodies to thyroglobulin (Tg-AAb), to thyroid microsomal antigens (MSAs) and to tri-iodothyronine (T_3) and thyroxine (T_4). The hypothyroid symptoms can be prevented or reversed by appropriate supplementation of the diet with thyroid hormones.

The infiltrated thyroid gland itself has been identified as a major Tg-AAb producing organ and complement-binding Tg-AAbs are also vertically transferred from the mother hen via the egg yolk into the newly hatched chick. The main initial effector mechanism for the development of SAT is, however, the infiltration by interleukin-2 receptor $(IL-2R)^+$ $CD4^+$ T cells, and Tg-AAbs only play an accelerating role.

OS chickens also develop autoantibodies against a variety of nonthyroid organ-specific or systemic autoantigens, but without concomitant histopathological or functional lesions. Adoptive transfer experiments have shown that thyroid-infiltrating lymphocytes are most effective in transferring the disease into histocompatible recipients of the Cornell C strain (CS), the nearly normal mother strain from which the OS was originally developed by R.K. Cole by selective breeding. Functional studies revealed a general hyperreactivity of the OS immune system against autoantigens, but also against exogenous antigens, such as sheep red blood cells and Rous sarcoma virus-induced tumors, as well as the T cell mitogens concanavalin A (con A) and phytohemagglutinin (PHA). This hyperreactivity is paralleled by a significantly increased production of IL-2 by OS peripheral blood lymphocytes and spleen cells compared with normal controls.

OS macrophages also show signs of hyperreactivity, such as an increased oxidative burst activity. Coculture experiments combining thymocytes and autologous peripheral blood lymphocytes revealed a

Figure 1 Normal White Leghorn chicken (left), and 6-month-old female OS chicken (right). Note the smaller size and the long silky feathers of the OS bird.

defect of the suppressive activity in the OS thymus that contributes to the general immunological hyper-reactivity in this strain.

Furthermore, OS chicken thymocytes are relatively resistant against glucocorticoid-induced thymocyte apoptosis, even if high pharmacological doses are applied. This phenomenon may be involved in the inefficient thymic negative selection process in this strain, leading to insufficient deletion of auto-reactive clones.

In addition, factors extrinsic to the immune system that also affect immunoregulation are altered in OS chickens, such as a significantly increased serum concentration of corticosteroid-binding globulin (CBG) and, therefore, decreased free, metabolically active glucocorticoids. Furthermore, OS chickens show a malfunctioning immunoendocrine feedback loop: injections of antigen or IL-1 do not lead to the surge of blood corticosterone levels observed in normal birds. This altered glucocorticoid response is due neither to a defective production of glucocorticoid increasing factors (mainly IL-1) by the immune system of the OS, nor to a disturbed release of adreno-corticotropic hormone (ACTH) by the pituitary, nor to insufficient responsiveness of the adrenal glands, but can rather be attributed to an altered responsive-ness of the hypothalamus to glucocorticoid-increasing factors or of the pituitary to corticotropin-releasing hormone (CRH).

Transfer experiments and cross-breeding studies between OS and inbred normal chickens led to the assumption that *both* autoreactivity of the immune system and a genetically determined primary suscep-tibility of the target organ are prerequisites for the development of severe SAT.

Various functional abnormalities of OS thyroid glands, such as an increased ^{131}I uptake before the onset of infiltration, an autonomous thyroid function that cannot be suppressed by high doses of T_4, and a decreased growth rate of OS thyroid epithelial cells *in vitro* with insufficient release of growth-promoting autocrine factors, can be demonstrated, but have not been found to be essential for the development of SAT. There is also no indication for an abnormal composition of OS thyroglobulin.

The question of whether there is a genetically determined primary aberrant expression of major histocompatibility complex (MHC) class II antigens on thyroid epithelial cells of OS chickens has not yet been unequivocally clarified. OS thyroid epithelial cells do, however, clearly show a lower threshold for interferon γ-induced MHC class II expression com-pared with those of normal chickens, a phenomenon that is restricted to the thyroid gland and cannot be

found with cell suspensions of other organs, such as the adrenal gland and the kidney.

Investigations on the putative role of viruses dur-ing the development of SAT led to interesting find-ings in two directions. First, C-type particles have been demonstrated electronmicroscopically in the thyroid gland of OS but not of normal chickens, and this indication for a possible presence of a thyro-tropic virus has recently been corroborated by the demonstration of 2′, 5′-adenylate synthetase in the thyroid, an enzyme that is induced by interferon γ and activated by double-stranded RNA. Second, par-allel studies have led to the discovery of a new endogenous virus (*ev22*) locus that seems to be spe-cific for the OS and the presence of which (in South-ern blots of OS DNA digests) correlates significantly with the above-mentioned decreased corticosterone response to IL-1 or antigen. It is not yet clear if this latter observation has any pathophysiological significance.

OS chickens possess three MHC (*B*-locus in the chicken) haplotypes (*B5*, *B13* and *B15*) but each of the homozygous sublines carrying these haplotypes still segregates for other major and minor histocom-patibility antigens. The haplotypes were found to have only a modulating effect on the severity and incidence of SAT.

Genetic analyses that were aimed at the identifi-cation of the number and nature of genes that poss-ibly contribute to the development of SAT have led to the formulation of a hypothesis postulating the contribution of both essential and modulatory genes. From these studies it became clear that *one essential recessive autosomal 'thyroid susceptibility gene'* is a prerequisite for the development of SAT. So far, this gene or the product of it, has not been identified. Possible candidates for additional modulating, non-essential genes are those that regulate CBG levels and T cell hyperresponsiveness, those determining excess-ive macrophage function, the *ev22* locus which cosegregates with the altered corticosterone response to cytokines, the primary altered iodine thyroid metabolism, and MHC-linked immune response genes.

Finally, it should be mentioned that the OS model has proven to be of great value for the assessment of new immunosuppressive drugs, such as synthetic androgen analogs that possess immunosuppressive and anti-inflammatory properties but are devoid of undesired endocrinological side-effects.

Animal strains with spontaneous insulin-dependent diabetes mellitus (IDDM)

Many animal species may be afflicted with spon-taneous IDDM, but so far only two inbred models of IDDM have been subjected to detailed immunological and genetic analysis: the nonobese diabetic mouse (NOD) mouse and the diabetes-prone biobreeding (DP-BB) rat. In both cases the autoimmune etiology of IDDM has been clearly established based on histological (mononuclear cell infiltration of the islets of Langerhans before the development of clinically manifest diabetes) as well as functional evidence. DP-BB rats and NOD mice exhibit both humoral and cellular autoimmune responses against islet β cells, although the pathogenetically relevant antigens remain to be identified. Disease development is inhibited by immunosuppressive intervention (neonatal thymectomy, administration of cyclosporin A, monoclonal antibodies against CD4, class II molecules, or the IL-2R knockout of the β_2-microglobulin gene) and autoimmune insulitis and β cell destruction can be adoptively transferred to healthy histocompatible recipients by bone marrow or spleen cells from NOD or DP-BB donors. The role of T cells is further underlined by the predominance of T cells in infiltrated islets, the absence of diabetes in NOD nu/nu mice, and the efficient transfer of disease into B cell-deprived recipients. Recent studies on the cell type responsible for diabetes transfer indicate that CD4$^+$ T$_H$1 but not T$_H$2 cells are responsible for β cell destruction, both in NOD mice and in DP-BB mice. Thus, autoimmune diabetes is a T$_H$1 disease. Whether T$_H$2-like cells may act as endogenous immunosuppressors is, however, still a matter of debate.

About 40% of male and 70% of female NOD mice develop overt IDDM at 7 months of age, whereas the DP-BB model lacks a female preponderance. Interestingly, a low percentage of DP-BB rats also develop autoimmune thyroiditis. Interindividual differences in the expression of disease may be attributed to unknown environmental factors or to the stochastic process of T cell receptor and antibody gene rearrangement which creates genetic heterogeneity between individuals with identical germline genes. Extensive studies have addressed the genetics of IDDM and the molecular defects implicated in the etiopathogenesis of the disease. In the NOD model, one dominant gene confers predisposition to lymphoid infiltration of pancreatic islets, whereas the development of manifest IDDM requires at least several further genes, one of which is linked to the NOD MHC. NOD mice lack messenger RNA transcribed from the I-Eα gene and, consequently, do not express I-E products on the cell surface. Moreover, the NOD class III-Aβ chain is mutated in positions 56 and 57 of the first external domain. Expression of I-Eα transgenes in NOD mice prevents insulitis, whereas I-Aβ of a normal haplotype fails to do so, thus

underlining the importance of the I-E defect for IDDM development. In addition to the diabetogenic NOD MHC (termed *Idd1*), at least 10–14 different IDDM susceptibility loci (*Idd2* through *Idd14*) influence the incidence and the severity of insulitis and diabetes. The best fitting model for these loci is a multiplicative (epistatic) model. Thus far, the pathogenic contribution of these loci remains elusive at the molecular level. It may be significant that one of the insulitis susceptibility loci has been mapped close to the apoptosis-inhibitory oncogene *bcl-2*. Moreover evidence was obtained for linkage of *Idd3* with IL-2 and *Idd10* with IgG-Fc receptor polymorphisms. In the DP-BB rat, two recessive diabetogenic loci have been postulated. One of them (*Iddm2*) appears to be associated with the class II subregion of the MHC, the other (*Iddm1*) with a gene responsible for a profound T cell lymphopenia which may be caused by defects in prothymocyte differentiation and/or thymic antigen-presenting cells. The pathogenetic relevance of ectopic MHC class II expression on islet β cells is still a matter of debate, but experiments with transgenic animals carrying class II genes under the control of the insulin promoter suggest that the presence of such molecules on β cells *per se* is insufficient to initiate autoimmune insulitis. In contrast, expression of the costimulatory molecule B7-1 markedly accelerates diabetes in transgenic NOD mice.

Spontaneous animal models with systemic autoimmune diseases

University of California at Davis (UCD) 200 strain as an animal model for progressive systemic sclerosis (SSc) – scleroderma

SSc is a human disease that is classified among the autoimmune connective tissue diseases that also comprise systemic lupus erythematosus (SLE), dermatomyositis and polymyositis, rheumatoid arthritis and several others. While there are several well-established, spontaneously occurring animal models available for SLE, models for the other conditions in this group are either nonexistent or of questionable significance. This is also true for SSc for which homologous disease of rats has been proposed as a model, as it is associated with chronic skin lesions with increased thickening and collagenization of the dermis. Significant titers of antinuclear antibodies (ANAs) are, however, lacking and the presence of immune complexes in vascular walls is also not characteristic for SSc. Another model for human scleroderma is the tight-skin (TSK) mouse, a dominant mutant of the inbred B10.D2 (58N/SN) mouse strain. The TSK mouse is characterized by cutaneous and skeletal hyperplasia but – in contrast to human SSc – these animals do not show gastrointestinal involvement, particularly the characteristic vascular pathology. There is also no evidence in these mice of early mononuclear cell infiltration of the skin.

The UCD 200 chicken model, described below, has many more similarities with SSc than all the models described so far, but it has to be emphasized that there are also some dissimilarities, including the development of glomerulonephritis, particularly in older animals, that may, however, be a sequel of secondary infection.

The first (male) chickens showing signs of a genetically determined fibrotic disease resembling SSc were discovered in 1942 by P. Bernier at the Department of Poultry Husbandry, Oregon State University, Corvallis. These birds exhibited comb and dermal swelling accompanied by fibrosis. The affected birds were then selectively bred for over 40 years and a new strain, now denoted UCD 200, was developed where males and females are affected to about the same extent.

200 strain UCD chickens exhibit severe alterations of the comb, neck and extremities. The comb already becomes visibly swollen and red 1–2 weeks after hatching, and at the age of 4 weeks about 90% of all birds develop comb necrosis with subsequent resorbtion ('self-dubbing'). Similar events occur in the digits of 30–40% of the birds, again beginning at 2–3 weeks of age, including polyarthritis of peripheral joints. At 2–4 weeks of age the skin of the neck also becomes involved, but the constant mechanical irritation of the neck in the outlets of the cages to gain access to food and water may also contribute to the lesions at this particular location.

A mononuclear cell infiltration is first observed in the affected skin areas and can be demonstrated in about 70% of line 200 birds at 1 week of age. Mononuclear cell infiltration starts perivascularly and is followed by vessel occlusion, similar to one of the hallmarks of human SSc. This acute inflammatory process reaches a peak at 2 weeks of age and subsides at the age of 5 months, when no more skin inflammation can be shown macroscopically or microscopically. At 5 months of age the esophagus becomes involved with a severe cellular infiltration around vessels and in the lamina propria of mucous glands in about 50% of the animals, increasing to 70% or more at the age of 1 year. Similar changes can be observed in the lamina propria of the small intestine, albeit at a lower frequency of about 30%. Furthermore, mononuclear cell accumulations can be found in the lung, starting at 1 week of age (60%) and decreasing to about 30% at 4–6 weeks, in the heart

and kidney (30–40% at 5–6 weeks of age) and the testes, beginning at 4–6 weeks of age.

The early mononuclear cell infiltrates in the skin are composed mainly of T cells expressing the γ/δ receptor. An influx of α/β T cell receptor-positive cells is first observed later, i.e. at the age of 20 days. While γ/δ-positive T cells occur mainly in the upper layers of the dermis, α/β-positive cells prevail in the deeper areas. Most of these latter cells express B-L, the chicken MHC class II analog.

The vascular changes are very characteristic in UCD 200 birds and can be found in most of the organs mentioned above. They are first noted in the comb and the feathered skin at 1 week of age, where the vessels show hyperplasia of the media and intimal thickening. In the internal organs the vascular changes are found later but always precede the macroscopic and clinical symptoms.

The nature of the increased deposition has not yet been studied in great detail by chemical and molecular biological methods but only by immunohistology on frozen sections, using specific antibodies against the different collagen variants. With this approach an increase of type III and type VI collagens can be noted in the skin and the terminal vascular rarification becomes clearly evident when antibodies against basement membrane components, such as type IV collagen or laminin, are applied. The accumulation of connective tissue, as manifested by fibrosis of the lung, severe myocardial muscle fiber destruction, subpericardial fibrosis, thickening of the esophageal wall and effects on other internal organs, leads to the premature death of these birds. In addition, they are prone to secondary infections and show a low fertility rate due to the massive involvement of the gonads, particularly the testes.

As in the human disease, no gross alteration at the genomic level of collagen genes has been found by means of restriction fragment length polymorphism (RFLP) analysis, thus suggesting that the UCD 200 model is an appropriate counterpart for studying the altered collagen metabolism in SSc. Investigation of the putative role of endogenous viruses (ev) for the development of SSc led to the discovery of ev23, which is found only in UCD 200 chickens. So far, the role of ev23 in the development of avian scleroderma is unclear.

Similar to human patients with SSc, sera from UCD 200 chickens contain ANAs in high frequency. At 1 month of age over 70% of the birds show ANAs with various staining patterns, including speckled centromeric and nucleolar fluorescence that are also characteristic of human SSc. These antibodies belong mainly to the IgY isotype, homologous to mammalian IgG, and can also be demonstrated on mammalian substrates, such as HEp-2 cells.

Although the UCD 200 chickens have now been kept for over 40 years, there are only a very few reports in the literature addressing the possible pathogenetic mechanisms leading to the SSc-like disease in this strain. The group of Gershwin and colleagues has shown that thymectomy on the day of hatching significantly reduces – but not completely abolishes – the comb/neck lesions, when assessed at the age of 8 weeks. Furthermore, the severity of the lesions in general was significantly reduced by this manipulation.

In vitro, UCD 200 peripheral blood T lymphocytes show a significantly decreased mitogen-induced proliferation associated with a decreased capacity to produce IL-2 and to express IL-2 receptors compared with normal White Leghorn chickens. In contrast to the deficient *in vitro* IL-2 production, the sera of UCD 200 chickens contain significantly higher levels of IL-2 bioactivity.

UCD 200 chickens also show a disturbed immunoendocrine feedback, characterized by a prolonged secretion of corticosterone after application of certain cytokines. Although the peak serum concentrations of the glucocorticoids are equal to that of controls, UCD 200 have to secrete twice as much ACTH to achieve this corticosterone serum level, owing to an apparent hyporesponsiveness of the adrenal gland to this secretagogue. The altered cytokine-induced glucocorticoid secretion is found in early as well as in chronic, sclerotic stages of the disease.

Recent studies by Sgonc and coworkers brought forward an interesting aspect on the pathogenesis of SSc: simultaneous *in situ* analysis of frozen skin sections for apoptosis and immunofluorescence staining for cell markers show that endothelial cells are clearly the first cells to undergo apoptosis in the skin of UCD 200 chickens, a process that seems to be induced by antibody-dependent cytotoxicity. Endothelial cell apoptosis is found before any other macroscopical or microscopical alterations are visible. Analysis of early lesion skin biopsies from human SSc patients shows a similar course of events.

The UCD 200 chickens are homozygous for a variation of the MHC haplotype B17. In addition they have been typed for some of the other blood groups and found to carry A1, C2, D3, E7 and P2. They are homozygous for the immunoglobulin 7S Ig (homologous to mammalian IgG) allotype 1.7. Since UCD 200 chickens are still segregating at the B locus and some other major blood group loci, attempts have been made in recent years to develop a subline that matches one of the related inbred normal lines

(line 058) in order to allow for mutual cell transfer experiments. Such a subline, denoted line 206, carrying the B15 haplotype has now been established.

In summary, the UCD 200 line of chickens seems to provide the best model for human SSc available so far. It mimics most of the clinical, histopathological and immunological hallmarks of SSc, albeit in an accelerated fashion. With respect to more detailed further studies, particularly the development of new therapeutic strategies, this accelerated course of the disease is an experimental advantage.

Murine strains with SLE-like autoimmunity

Several models of spontaneous SLE in mice have been extensively studied, namely New Zealand Black [NZB], (NZB × New Zealand White [NZW])F1, (NZB × SWR)F1, BXSB, and MRL mice, which exhibit two forms of disease, a late-life variety appearing during the second year of life (male [NZB × W]F1, female BXSB, MRL/Mp-+/+ of both sexes, NZB mice of both sexes) and an acute form beginning a few weeks or months after birth (female [NZB × W]F1, male BXSB, MRL/Mp mice of both sexes homozygous for the lymphoproliferation [*lpr*] gene, female and male [NZB × SWR]F1 mice). Accelerating factors are female sex hormones in (NZB × W)F1, a gene located on the Y chromosome (*Yaa* = Y chromosome-lined autoimmunity accelerator) of BXSB mice, the *lpr* gene in MRL mice, or genes from phenotypically normal SWR or minimally affected NZW mice in crosses with the NZB strain. All these models are characterized by hypergammaglobulinemia, anti-DNA and other ANAs, antiretroviral gp70 antibodies, circulating immune complexes, glomerulonephritis, and a low percentage of coronary arthritis. MRL/Mp-*lpr/lpr* mice also develop necrotizing polyarteritis and a rheumatoid arthritis (RA)-like disease accompanied by rheumatoid factors in serum. The NZB strain develops autoimmune hemolytic anemia.

Experiments addressing the genetics and the cellular or molecular mechanisms of SLE in these murine strains revealed that murine lupus is a polygenetic and multifactorial process, involving a combination of various genetically determined defects, which at least in part are different in each of the five models mentioned above. Studies of bone marrow irradiation chimeras indicate that murine lupus is caused by abnormalities at the hematopoietic stem cell level. The relative roles of T and B cells in the initiation and perpetuation of autoaggression are still a matter of debate. However, it appears clear that B cell hyperreactivity of lupus-prone mice is not due to defects intrinsic to immunoglobulin genes, but rather depends on T helper cells and/or polyclonal activation signals. Autoantibodies are of poly- or oligo-clonal origin, the nephritogenic ones belonging to the IgG isotype and being cationic in charge. On the cellular level, dependent of the strain investigated and the age of donors, conflicting results have been obtained as far as the production of cytokines (e.g. IL-2), the response to them (e.g. IL-2 and IL-5), the cooperation between T and B cells, and the distribution of lymphocyte subsets are concerned. Both the *lpr* and the phenotypically similar, but non-allelic, *gld* (generalized lymphoproliferative disease) genes result in a massive accumulation of abnormal Thy-1$^+$ CD5$^+$ CD4$^-$ CD8$^-$ CD3$^+$ TCR-$\alpha\beta^+$ T cells, which anomalously express B cell markers (B220, PC1) and appear to be of polyclonal origin, the Vβ8.2 and Vβ8.3 T cell receptor genes being over-represented. Homozygosity in the recessive *lpr* or the *lpr*^{cg} mutations affects the expression (*lpr*) or signal-transducing capability (*lpr*^{cg}) of the CD95/Fas/Ap-1 surface receptor that initiates apoptosis-inducing pathways upon interactions with its ligand FasL, the molecule affected by the *gld* mutation. Since Fas is involved in the activation-induced cell death of T lymphocytes it is assumed that peripheral deletion is at least partially compromised in *lpr/lpr* and *gld/gld* mice. Moreover, it is known that Fas expressed on anergic B cells can receive apoptosis-inducing signals via interaction with FasL on T cells. Therefore, the *lpr* or *gld* mutation may compromise both T and B cell tolerance.

A dominant NZW locus contributing to severe SLE in (NZB × W)F1 maps within the H-2 region. This may be either due to the unique sequence of the NZW I-Eβ chain gene or to reduce production of the MHC class III product tumor necrosis factor (TNF). This latter finding could be pathogenetically relevant since treatment with TNF postpones the development of nephritis. Heterozygosity for the I-Aβ haplotypes of NZB and SWR has also been shown to correlate with the development of glomerulonephritis in crosses of the NZB strain with SWR mice. In other strains, no strong correlation with a particular H-2 haplotype was observed. Heterozygosity for the T cell receptor strongly correlates with nephritis in (NZB × SWR)F1 × NZB backcrosses, thus suggesting that the deletion of about half the T cell receptor Vβ genes which is found in healthy SWR parents might contribute to the development of SLE. In contrast, the NZW T cell receptor β chain locus, the Cβ1, Dβ1 and Jβ1 regions of which have been deleted, probably does not contribute to the SLE of (NZB × W) hybrids.

In summary, the etiology of murine lupus appears to be rather complex and awaits further elucidation. Multiple loci accounting for different disease mani-festations are currently under molecular study using a combination of classical genetic approaches (phenotyping of intercrosses or backcrosses) and microsatellite-based chromosomal maps. Interestingly, some of the loci determining lupus of (NZB × NZW)F1 mice map close to loci determining glomerulonephritis in MRL/*lpr* mice or diabetes in NOD mice, suggesting the existence of shared genetic mechanisms for some autoimmune disorders.

Conclusions

Animal models of spontaneous autoimmune disease have substantially contributed to our knowledge on the etiopathogenesis, genetics and molecular defects ultimately responsible for autoaggression. A variety of different mechanisms, including defects in the lymphoid lineages, endocrinological alterations, target organ defects, endogenous viruses or mutations in immunologically relevant molecules (e.g. MHC, T cell receptor genes), have been implicated in animal autoimmune disease and, in part, are also being described in human disease. Furthermore, the avant-garde position of animal models on the frontier of immunopathological research has allowed for the development of new therapeutic strategies for the treatment of autoaggression.

See also: **Autoantigens; Autoimmune disease, induced experimental models; Autoimmune disease, pathogenesis; Autoimmune diseases; Autoimmunity; Insulin-dependent diabetes mellitus, animal models; MHC disease associations; Systemic lupus erythematosus, experimental models.**

Further reading

Brezinschek HP, Gruschwitz M, Sgonc R *et al.* (1993) Effects of cytokine application on glucocorticoid secretion in an animal model for systemic scleroderma. *Journal of Autoimmunity* 6: 719–733.

Cohen PL and Eisenberg RA (1991) lpr and gld: single gene models of systemic autoimmunity and lymphoproliferative disease. *Annual Review of Immunology* 9: 243–289.

Diabetes Task Force (1982) Section I. Animal models presently used in diabetes mellitus research. *Diabetes* 31: S1–S53.

Dotta F and Eisenbarth GS (1989) Type I diabetes mellitus: a predictable autoimmune disease with interindividual variation in the rate of β cell destruction. *Clinical Immunology and Immunopathology* 50: S85–S95.

Gershwin ME, Abplanalp H, Castle JJ *et al.* (1981) Characterization of a spontaneous disease of White Leghorn chickens resembling progressive systemic sclerosis (scleroderma). *Journal of Experimental Medicine* 153: 1640–1659.

Gruschwitz MS, Moormann S, Kroemer G *et al.* (1991) Phenotypic analysis of skin infiltrates in comparison with peripheral blood lymphocytes, spleen cells and thymocytes in early avian scleroderma. *Journal of Autoimmunity* 4: 577–593.

Kroemer G (1994) *Mechanisms of Self-Tolerance*, p 177. Austin TX: RG Landes.

Sgonc R, Dietrich H, Gershwin ME, Colombatti A and Wick G (1995) Genomic analysis of collagen and endogenous virus loci in the UCD 200 and 206 lines of chickens, animal models for scleroderma. *J Autoimmunity* 8: 763–770.

Sgonc R, Gruschwitz M, Dietrich H, Recheis H, Gerschwin ME and Wick G (1996) Endothelial cell apoptosis is a primary pathogenetic event underlying skin lesions in avian and human scleroderma. *Journal of Clinical Investigation* 98: 785–792.

Theofilopoulos AN (1995) The basis of autoimmunity. Part II. Genetic predisposition. *Immunology Today* 16: 150–159.

Theofilopoulos AN and Dixon FJ (1985) Models of systemic lupus erythematosus. *Advances in Immunology* 37: 269–353.

Theofilopoulos AN, Kofler R, Singer PA and Dixon FJ (1989) Molecular genetics of murine lupus models. *Advances in Immunology* 46: 61–109.

Van de Water J, Gershwin ME, Abplanalp H, Wick G and Von der Mark K (1984) Serial observations and definition of mononuclear cell infiltrates in avian scleroderma, an inherited fibrotic disease of chickens. *Arthritis and Rheumatism* 27: 807–815.

Wick G, Brezinschek HP, Hála K, Dietrich H, Wolf H and Kroemer G (1989) The obese strain (OS) of chickens. An animal model with spontaneous autoimmune thyroiditis. *Advances in Immunology* 47: 433–500.

Wick G, Hu Y, Schwarz S and Kroemer G (1993) Immunoendocrine communication via the hypothalamo–pituitary–adrenal axis in autoimmune disease. *Endocrine Reviews* 14: 539–563.

Wicker LS, Todd JA and Peterson LB (1995) Genetic control of autoimmune diabetes in the NOD mouse. *Annual Review of Immunology* 13: 179–200.

AUTOIMMUNE DISEASES

Ian R Mackay, Department of Biochemistry and Molecular Biology, Monash University, Melbourne, Australia

Autoimmunity and autoimmune disease

Autoimmune reactions to autologous molecules occur in health and may well be ubiquitous. Autoimmune disease is defined when such reactions become uncontrolled and result in structural or functional pathology. Normally there exists a physiological (natural) immunological tolerance to self constituents; previously, this was thought to be absolute, such that any immunological reactivity with autologous molecules would be abnormal. However, currently, tolerance can be expressed either as an *absolute absence*, or a *controlled level*, of autologous reactivity. Pathogenic autoimmunity might thus represent either an amplification of naturally occurring autologous reactivity, or be in some way qualitatively different.

Natural autoimmunity could serve physiological purposes: 1) early defense against infection with microorganisms that share cross-reactive epitopes with autologous molecules; 2) disposal of products of injury or tissue catabolism; or 3) facilitation of expansion in early life of immunological repertoires through mutual stimulation of the antigen receptors on B cells due to anti-idiotype connectivities. Natural autoimmunity includes both humoral (autoantibody) and cellular (T cell) activities. Natural autoantibodies are usually described as being of immunoglobulin M (IgM) isotype, broadly reactive, nonpathogenic and, to some degree, products of a particular lineage (B-1) of B cells characterized by the CD5 marker; in contrast, disease-related autoantibodies are class-switched to the IgG isotype, of focused reactivity, often pathogenic and are derived from somatically mutated Ig variable region (V) genes. However, some naturally occurring autoantibodies also exhibit these properties and, accordingly, would be difficult to distinguish from disease-related IgG autoantibodies in presymptomatic stages of autoimmune disease. Likewise, there are naturally occurring T lymphocytes reactive to various autoantigens, albeit at much lower numbers in blood than those observed in autoimmune disease. This is relevant to the diagnosis of autoimmune disease (see below), for which a major criterion is the coassociation of an 'appropriate' autoantibody; discriminatory cut-off levels must optimally distinguish between natural background reactivity and pathogenetically significant titers. Where T cell reactivity to autoantigen is applicable to the definition of an autoimmune disease, similar considerations will apply.

Designation of autoimmunity as a cause of a disease

Some authors, in discussing a particular disease, refer to it as 'an autoimmune disorder of unknown etiology'! Others even question whether autoimmunity is a legitimate etiology for any disease, perhaps forgetting Harrington's experiment in the 1950s wherein plasma transferred from a donor with 'idiopathic' thrombocytopenic purpura caused, in volunteer recipients, an immediate fall in blood platelet levels due to pathogenic anti-platelet autoantibodies. Witebsky in 1956 presented four 'postulates' to nominate a disease as autoimmune: 1) demonstration of free circulating antibodies that are active at room temperature, or of cell-bound antibodies detected using indirect means; 2) the recognition of the specific antigen against which these are directed; 3) the production of antibodies against the analogous antigen in actively immunized animals; and 4) pathological changes in the tissues of the actively sensitized animal resembling those of the corresponding human disease. However, the lack of models (components 3 and 4) precludes fulfillment of these postulates in many human autoimmune diseases.

Bayesian reasoning provides clinical and/or pathological features that can be factored in to presume an autoimmune basis for a given disease. These include: female gender; coassociation in the patient or family members of other diseases of autoimmune nature; histological evidence of 'organized' lymphoid infiltrates in the affected tissue including germinal centers, or deposition of immune complexes that contain autoantigen; association of the disease with particular alleles (usually class II) or the major histocompatibility complex (MHC), HLA in humans; and brisk responsiveness to corticosteroid drugs. As further evidence for an autoimmune basis for a given disease, there are models in animals, either spontaneous (lupus, hemolytic anemia or diabetes in particular strains of mice) or induced by immunization with the corresponding tissue in adjuvants (thyroiditis or encephalomyelitis in various species). Finally, in diseases designated as autoimmune, no other provocative causes should be demonstrable. Indeed, in chronic destructive diseases that *are* demonstrably due to a persisting microorganism, hallmarks of autoimmunity tend to be conspicuously absent, e.g. gastric mucosal destruction due to infection with *Helicobacter pylori* does not provoke the

parietal cell antibody response characteristic of autoimmune (pernicious anemia-type) gastritis. But there are exceptions, including spirochetal infection (cardiolipin antibody), hepatitis C virus infection (liver microsomal antibody, occasionally) and others.

In the absence of firm nominative criteria, a listing of likely autoimmune diseases is necessarily provisional (Table 1). A somewhat imperfect classification is as follows:

1. Organ and autoantibody specific, i.e. diseases in the 'thyrogastric cluster'.
2. Tissue and autoantibody specific, i.e. diseases in which a 'disease-relevant' target autoantigen exists, but this is widely 'dispersed' throughout the body e.g. hemolytic anemia (erythrocytes), myasthenia gravis (acetylcholine receptor).
3. Diseases that are organ or tissue specific, and in which there is a disease-specific autoantigen(s), but this is distributed in all cells and thus not 'disease relevant', e.g. primary biliary cirrhosis and mitochondrial autoantigens, or Sjögren's syndrome and ribonucleoprotein autoantigens.

Table 1   A partial list of autoimmune diseases

Hashimoto's thyroiditis
Primary myxedema
Graves' disease
Pernicious anemia
Autoimmune atrophic gastritis, pernicious anemia
Addison's disease
Ovarian failure, premature menopause
Insulin-dependent diabetes mellitus
Goodpasture's syndrome
Myasthenia gravis, Lambert-Eaton syndrome
Male infertility (few cases)
Pemphigus, bullous pemphigoid
Psoriasis (possibly)
Crohn's disease (possibly)
Sympathetic ophthalmia
Autoimmune uveitis
Multiple sclerosis
Autoimmune hemolytic anemia
Autoimmune thrombocytopenic purpura
Autoimmune neutropenia
Primary biliary cirrhosis
Chronic active hepatitis, 'cryptogenic' cirrhosis
Ulcerative colitis (possibly)
Sjögren's syndrome
Rheumatoid arthritis
Dermatomyositis
Polymyositis
Scleroderma
Anti-phospholipid syndrome
Mixed connective tissue disease
Vasculitis
Vitiligo
Systemic lupus erythematosus

4. Diseases that are multisystem and 'nonfocused', with autoimmune reactivity against antigens associated with various non-tissue-specific intracellular organelles, e.g. systemic lupus erythematosus (SLE).

Etiology and pathogenesis

Germline genetic influences

An important genetic component in autoimmune disease is female gender, with the female:male ratio ranging up to tenfold, although a notable exception is insulin-dependent diabetes mellitus (IDDM) that occurs at prepubertal ages with an equal gender incidence. The influence of female sex hormones on immune responsiveness, and perhaps an immunopotentiating gene on the X chromosome, explains the female predisposition to autoimmunity. A strong genetic predisposition to autoimmunity is conferred by alleles of the MHC, in humans and in experimental models, particularly at the class II loci, HLA-DR, -DQ, -DP rather than the class I loci, HLA-A or -B. Class II alleles encode heterodimers that present antigenic epitopes to T cell receptors, and such MHC molecules may contain, in their hypervariable regions, a sequence of amino acids that represents the disease susceptibility motif (DSM); this explains for example the HLA associations, DR1, DR4, with rheumatoid arthritis. The DSM may confer a high binding affinity for an autoepitope that can engage the T cell receptor, or may act to bias the thymic selection of the T cell repertoire.

Studies on genetic linkages in families with multiple members with an autoimmune disease e.g. IDDM, or in animals using backcrossing and chromosomal localization, e.g. lupus mice, indicate the existence of many other gene loci, encoding either 'immunologically relevant' genes or 'nonimmunologic' (background) genes, that confer or alleviate risk for autoimmunity. Examples would be genes that govern expression of cytokines, chemokines or adhesion molecules, or genes that influence expression of molecules that promote or inhibit apoptosis, *fas* and *bcl*. Still further genetic effects on autoimmunity could relate to the antigenic composition of the target organ itself, or to autoantigenic molecules as products of alternatively spliced genes, isoforms of enzymes, or to other structural or functional polymorphisms of potential autoantigens.

Somatic genetic influences

Susceptibility to autoimmune disease may depend on somatic genetic effects (mutations) in postnatal life. The best example is antigenic stimulation of B lymphocytes in germinal centers of lymph nodes, with ensuring hypermutation of antibody V region genes to generate affinity maturation of antibodies. Thus B lymphocytes with reactivity with autoantigens may emerge as a 'byproduct' of affinity maturation of antibodies to bacterial antigens, and may persist if tolerogenic processes fail, with ensuing 'rescue' of such autoimmune B cells from apoptosis. Various other somatic genetic mutations in postnatal life could predispose to autoimmunity, e.g. those that influence patterns of cytokine secretion, or processes of apoptosis.

Environment

The environment can interact with genetic predisposition to induce autoimmune disease. Viewed most simply, any cause of tissue damage can result in release of cellular products which, if exposed to antigen-presenting cells of individuals with 'susceptibility genotypes', in an appropriate microenvironment such as cytokine excess, could stimulate self-reactive T cells that normally circulate at low levels. In the case of infectious damage, there is the added possibility of antigenic (or epitope) mimicry. This idea is based on molecular homologies between a constituent protein antigen of a microorganism and host being sufficiently close that the 'protective' response to the organism becomes cross-reactive with 'self'. An example of a break in tolerance initiated by molecular mimicry is the provocation by streptococcal cell wall antigens of rheumatic endomyocarditis. Currently, molecular biological techniques for identifying sequences of autoantigenic epitopes have been combined with searches of gene and protein databanks to reveal potentially informative homologies; however, such comparisons often fail to acknowledge that B cell epitopes, including autoepitopes, are usually conformational rather than linear. Thus molecular mimicry may be more applicable to short linear T cell epitopes.

Other relevant environmental influences are ultraviolet radiation, chemicals including mercuric chloride that induce autoimmunity in rodent models, and medicinal drugs that induce various autoimmune syndromes including SLE, hepatitis and myasthenia gravis. Good explanations for the induction of autoimmunity by these influences are lacking: sunlight might act to create neoepitopes in skin cells, mercuric chloride may cause structural alterations in MHC molecules on antigen-presenting cells, and medicinal drugs may yield molecules that generate compound epitopes with cellular constituents.

Induction of autoimmune disease

The critical elements for the induction of autoimmune responses are: 1) the autoantigenic epitope;

2) processes that facilitate the presentation of the autoantigenic epitope to the immune system; and 3) recognition of the epitope by T and B lymphocytes that have evaded tolerogenic influences.

To serve as an autoantigen, a self molecule should activate both T and B lymphocytes. Autologous molecules will not be recognized as autoantigens if deletional processes have completely removed any cognate responsive T cells in the thymus, or B cells in the bone marrow. T cells can escape deletional tolerogenesis in the fetal thymus if the requisite self molecule is either not represented there, or is not adequately processed by antigen-presenting cells, or if its affinity for the antigen receptor on intrathymic T cells is too low. Thus some self-reactive T cells do exit from the thymus to the periphery: however, these are not necessarily dangerous as they may have only a low affinity for autoantigens and are not readily activated; or, being of a naive phenotype, will not express the surface adhesion molecules required for their transit into tissue parenchyma.

Autoreactive B cells can arise in two sites, the bone marrow during lymphogenesis, or lymph node germinal centers by affinity maturation during responses to extrinsic antigens (see above). B cells at both sites are subject to various tolerogenic influences, including antigen in excess, which induces cell death by apoptosis. Again, however, there is 'leakage' in health of self-reactive B cells from these sites into the periphery; evidence for this is the presence in the circulation, particularly in aging, of various autoantibodies, and also B cells capable of binding labeled autoantigens. A low degree of B cell autoimmunity may well be 'innocuous', if not beneficial (see above), provided that there is no source of potent contiguous T cell help.

Effector activities in autoimmunity

Effector activities depend on the various functions of B or T lymphocytes or, probably, both sets of cells, in unison. B cells and circulating autoantibody are the clear cause of autoimmune pathology in hemocytolytic diseases, or SLE in which damage results from deposition of immune complexes, or diseases in which autoantibody binds to cell surface receptors, either to inhibit a neurotransmitter, e.g. acetylcholine receptor in myasthenia gravis, or to stimulate a hormone receptor, e.g. the thyrotropin receptor in Graves' disease. Another role for B cells is to act as antigen-presenting cells, in a focused way, as autoantigen can be specifically captured by the B cell immunoglobulin receptor for presentation to autoimmune T cells, thus sustaining the autoimmune reaction. $CD4^+$ helper T cells are the likely effectors of damage in autoimmune disease of parenchymal

tissues, thyroid gland, stomach, brain, synovium, pancreatic islets, etc., presumably by release of injurious cytokines, particularly tumor necrosis factor (TNF), or injurious enzymes (granzymes). $CD8^+$ cytotoxic T lymphocytes (CTLs) are less easily studied functionally as effectors of autoimmune damage and data are scarce. As judged by the infrequency of MHC class I associations with autoimmune disease, $CD8^+$ CTL-mediated damage might be relatively less important in autoimmunity. However, immunohistochemical studies of tissue lesions often show a striking infiltration of $CD8^+$ T cells in contiguity with damaged cells and, in animal models, cell transfer studies have implicated $CD8^+$ CTLs as early effectors, e.g. in autoimmune islet cell damage in nonobese diabetic (NOD) mice.

Regulation of autoimmunity

Self tolerance and avoidance of autoimmunity are of such fundamental importance to the organism that several 'layers' of tolerogenesis are in place. The first and fundamental layer, 'central' tolerance, is deletion of lymphocytes in the primary lymphoid organs, thymus or bone marrow, consequent on high-affinity contact between autoantigen as ligand and antigen receptors on nascent T or B cells, i.e. negative selection. Deletional self tolerance has been elucidated by recent studies on transgenic mice in which cDNA for a marker antigen, e.g. hen-egg lysozyme, is introduced in embryonic life, and hence is treated as self; in 'double' transgenic mice there are additionally introduced genes that encode T cell or B cell antigen receptors for the transgenic molecule.

Processes of 'peripheral' tolerance operate to limit the activity of autoreactive cells that have escaped deletion in the thymus or bone marrow. Thus 1) thymic emigrant T cells have a 'naive' phenotype and lack activation molecules needed for extravasation through vascular endothelium into tissue parenchyma; 2) T cells that encounter autoantigens in the blood or on the surface of tissue cells do not receive a critical 'second signal' that is provided only by 'professional' antigen-presenting cells, and respond by anergy rather than activation; 3) particular cytokines may deflect a damaging autoreactive CD4 T helper cell response from the T_H1 inflammatory type to the more benign T_H2 antibody dominated type; 4) autoimmune B cells remain innocuous if they fail to obtain adequate helper signals from T cells that may be adequately tolerized; and, finally, 5) there are mechanisms of 'dominant' tolerogenesis, also called suppression, which can prevent autoimmunity or even override established self-reactive effector processes. Autoimmunity in states of natural and experimentally induced T cell lymphopenia is evidence for the existence of a regulatory/suppressive subset of T lymphocytes. Dominant tolerogenesis may also be mediated by anti-idiotype antibodies; such antibodies are directed against the combining site of the antibody molecule itself. Anti-idiotype antibodies to autoantibody molecules appear to exist in normal sera, and are considered to explain the beneficial therapeutic effect in certain autoimmune diseases of pooled normal human immunoglobulins given intravenously.

Diagnosis

Autoimmune diseases are usually diagnosed according to the functional deficits that ensue in affected organs, rather than by their immunological features *per se*. This applies to autoimmune disease affecting the thyroid gland, adrenal gland, pancreatic islets, stomach, liver, kidney, muscles, neural transmitters, etc. However, testing for the disease-relevant autoantibody will in many instances provide specific and decisive diagnostic information, exemplified by testing for the antiglobulin reaction in hemolytic anemia, and for autoantibodies to acetylcholine receptor in myasthenia gravis, adrenal cortical cells in Addison's disease, dsDNA in SLE, mitochondrial pyruvate dehydrogenase enzyme complexes in primary biliary cirrhosis, or to the combination of nuclei and F actin in type 1 autoimmune hepatitis. An interesting application of modern sensitive and automated tests for autoantibodies, utilizing recombinant autoantigens, is screening for presymptomatic autoimmune disease, e.g. assays for anti-GAD (glutamic acid decarboxylase) and other islet autoantigens to detect presymptomatic IDDM among first-degree relatives, or even among populations.

Treatment

Many of the organ-specific autoimmune diseases are adequately treated by replacement therapy when terminal destruction ensues, e.g. thyroiditis, adrenalitis, gastritis, insulitis, etc.; however, the state of autoimmunity must be 'controlled' when disease affects vital organs or tissues, such as the liver in autoimmune hepatitis or muscles in autoimmune polymyositis, or when the disease is systemic and many tissues are at risk, as in SLE.

Traditionally, 'control' over the immunologic activity in autoimmune disease has been with corticosteroid drugs, which have particular efficacy in blocking unwanted effects of antigen–antibody reactions. The action of corticosteroids can be supplemented by 'immunosuppressive' drugs of the types used to prevent rejection of transplanted allografts: azathioprine, cyclophosphamide and cyclosporine; however, because prolonged usage of these drugs can have various adverse effects, therapists are seeking more subtle immunological interventions. These include blockage by monoclonal antibodies of critical components of the immune response, and particularly the receptor complex of CD4 T cells, T cell cytokines including TNFα, or B cell/antibody receptors by infusion of normal polyclonal human IgG that is presumed to contain anti-idiotypes to autoantibody molecules. There is theoretical, and some practical, promise in 'at source' therapy which is to re-establish broken tolerance to culprit autoantigens. This depends on the autoantigen being administered as preparations and by routes that are more conducive to tolerance than to immunity – the 'negative vaccine' idea. Delivery of the autoantigen via the intestine, 'oral tolerance', is currently favored. The obvious benefits of this approach for the prevention of autoimmune disease should justify the years of developmental study that seem needed to bring it into routine use.

See also: **Autoantigens; Autoimmune disease, induced experimental models; Autoimmune disease, pathogenesis; Autoimmune diseases; Autoimmunity; Avian immune system; Insulin-dependent diabetes mellitus, animal models; Rheumatological disorders; Systemic lupus erythematosus, experimental models; Systemic lupus erythematosus (SLE), human; Thyroid autoimmunity, human; Tolerance, peripheral.**

Further reading

Behar SM and Porcelli SA (1995) Mechanisms of autoimmune disease induction. The role of the immune response to microbial pathogens. *Arthritis and Rheumatism* 38: 458–476.

Bona CA, Siminoveitch KA, Zanetti M and Theofilopoulos AN (eds) (1993) *The Molecular Pathology of Autoimmune Diseases*. Chur: Harwood.

Coutinho A and Kazatchkine MD (eds) (1994) *Autoimmunity, Physiology and Disease*. New York: Wiley-Liss.

Gallagher R, Gilder J, Nossal GJV and Salvatore G (eds) (1995) *Immunology: The Making of a Modern Science*. London: Academic Press.

Mackay IR and Gershwin ME (1997) The nature of autoimmune disease. *Seminars in Liver Disease* 17: 3–11.

Matzinger P (1994) Tolerance, danger and the extended family. *Annual Review of Immunology* 12: 991–1045.

Möller G (ed) (1996) Dominant Immunological Tolerance. *Immunological Reviews* 149.

Naparstek Y and Plotz PH (1993) The role of autoantibodies in autoimmune disease. *Annual Review of Immunology* 11: 79–104.

Peter JB and Shoenfeld Y (eds) (1996) *Autoantibodies*. Amsterdam: Elsevier.

Talal N (ed) (1993) *Molecular Autoimmunity*. London: Academic Press.

Rose NR and Mackay IR (eds) (1998) *The Autoimmune Diseases*, 3rd edn. Orlando: Academic Press.

Van Venrooij WJ and van Gelder CWG (1994) B cell epitopes on nuclear autoantigens. What can they tell us? *Arthritis and Rheumatism* 37: 608–616.

AUTOIMMUNITY

Peter J Delves, Department of Immunology, University College London Medical School, London, UK

At the beginning of this century Paul Ehrlich used the expression 'horror autotoxicus' to describe the body's apparent inability to respond to self antigen and he suggested that nonreactivity may be mediated by the lymphoid system. Evidence that these control mechanisms can sometimes fail was provided afterward by the observation of Donath and Landsteiner that patients with paroxysmal cold hemoglobulinemia possess antibodies against their own erythrocytes.

The experiments of Rivers, Sprunt and Berry in the early 1930s showing that injection of monkey brain antigens back into monkeys provoked encephalomyelitis provided the first experimental model of autoimmune disease. A decade later, Owen's observation that dizygotic cattle twins sharing the same blood supply during embryonic life did not destroy each other's nonidentical erythrocytes (even if these were injected in adult life) suggested that self tolerance is acquired during ontogeny. Such chimeric cattle are able to exchange skin grafts without subsequent tissue rejection. In 1953 Billingham, Brent and Medawar demonstrated that neonatal injection of cells from CBA strain mice into A strain mice allowed the mice to later accept CBA skin grafts. Three years after these experiments, a series of classical papers on thyroid autoimmunity were to firmly establish the role of autoimmune phenomena in producing disease. Rose and Witebsky induced both autoantibodies and thyroiditis by immunizing rabbits with thyroid extract in Freund's adjuvant; Roitt, Doniach and Campbell demonstrated autoantibodies to thyroglobulin in Hashimoto's disease; and Adams and Purves discovered stimulatory autoantibodies directed against the thyroid-stimulating hormone (TSH) receptor.

Consequences of autoimmunity

Autoimmunity is defined as an immune response leading to reaction with self antigen, i.e. any molecule that is a normal body constituent of the animal mounting the response. Self reactivity can arise either through the triggering of receptors directly by autoantigen or by virtue of cross-reaction between foreign and self antigens. Topographic similarity of B cell epitopes or sequence homologies of linear T cell epitopes may lead to such cross-reactions and it is highly unlikely that the immune system is able to recognize all foreign antigens specifically without some recognition of self epitopes also occurring.

Techniques such as polyclonal activation of cells with mitogens, and the establishment of lymphocyte clones and hybridomas, have established that self reactive T and B lymphocytes are frequently found in individuals who lack readily detectable autoantibodies in their serum. Indeed, at least some degree of self reactivity appears to be a normal physiological phenomenon during lymphocyte development and perhaps may be necessary in preparing the immune system for its future encounters with foreign antigen. The B-1a (CD5$^+$, Mac-1$^+$, CD23$^-$, strongly sIgM$^+$) subset of B lymphocytes are found mainly in the peritoneal cavity where they are self-renewing and express germ line V genes encoding polyspecific low affinity IgM autoantibodies bearing cross-reactive idiotypes. This B cell subset is elevated in, for example, the autoimmune NZB mouse and in patients with rheumatoid arthritis. Low affinity IgM autoantibodies are probably not pathogenic. Encounter with nonidentical cross-reacting foreign antigen will, in the presence of T cell help, lead to affinity maturation within germinal centers, thereby generating antibodies with high affinity for foreign antigen which simultaneously lose their original self-reactivity. However, as certain self antigens such as idiotypes form key recognition structures for immunological regulation it is crucial that the immune system retains the ability to recognize these particular self components.

The pathogenicity of an autoimmune response is determined not only by the magnitude but also by the nature of the response. For instance, although 10–20% of clinically normal individuals possess low titers of autoantibodies specific for thyroglobulin, and although these antibodies are present at higher titers in about 70% of Hashimoto's disease patients, it is autoantibodies to another thyroid component, thyroid peroxidase, which show a stronger correlation with histopathological lesions. These autoantibodies occur in 95% of patients with Hashimoto's disease and, unlike most thyroglobulin autoantibodies, are complement fixing and therefore potentially cytotoxic to thyroid epithelial cells. Another example underlining the distinction between autoimmunity and disease is seen in patients treated for longer than 1 year with the drug procainamide (used to control cardiac arrhythmia). Over 90% of these patients develop IgM antibodies reactive with a broad spectrum of self histones but it is only in the 10–20% of patients who develop high levels of IgG antibodies specific for the H2A-H2B histone dimer bound to DNA that a lupus-like autoimmune disease arises. In the case of immunoglobulin, different parts of the same molecule can elicit both physiological (idiotypic) and potentially pathogenic (rheumatoid factor) autoantibodies.

Animal models have confirmed the importance of cell-mediated immune responses in the development of autoimmune disease; the adoptive transfer of autoantigen-specific T cell clones is often sufficient to induce disease in normal recipients. Most autoimmune diseases probably have both T and B cell components and in some situations other mechanisms involving natural killer (NK) cells or antibody-dependent cellular cytotoxicity may play a role in the pathogenic process.

Mechanisms controlling autoimmunity

Because pathogenic autoimmunity is the exception rather than the rule, mechanisms must exist which normally prevent the development of autoimmune disease. In this respect the immune system is able to distinguish self from nonself and, ultimately, becomes 'tolerant' towards most self antigens. However, as alluded to above, many of the tolerance mechanisms controlling autoimmunity may be less concerned with repression of all self reactive lymphocytes than with preventing the development of pathogenic T cells and autoantibodies. Indeed, there is evidence from studies in transgenic mice to suggest that, in situations in which high-affinity antiself B cells are anergized, low-affinity antiself B cells escape this tolerization process.

The danger model of immune responses proposes that, rather than discriminating self from nonself, the immune system primarily distinguishes between harmless and harmful. In this scenario, self would normally be considered harmless and would fail to trigger a response. However, a response to harmful situations would occur due to upregulation of costimulatory molecules on antigen-presenting dendritic cells following signals induced by microbial antigens, cell stress or necrotic cell death.

Although evidence for several different tolerance mechanisms exists, the relative role of each of these in controlling autoimmunity remains to be firmly established. For a long time it was thought that many self antigens were sequestered in 'privileged sites' and therefore shielded from the immune system. The advent of sensitive assay techniques allowed the detection of, for example, low levels of circulating thyroglobulin (an autoantigen previously thought to be completely sequestered within the thyroid). Nevertheless, it is believed that for a few self molecules, such as lens proteins, sperm and brain antigens, this concept largely holds true.

The 'forbidden clone' theory put forward by Burnet in the 1950s suggested that deletion of self reactive clones led to self tolerance. Although it is now clear that this is not a universal mechanism for avoiding autoimmunity, clonal deletion is known to occur for some self antigens. Mice bearing, for example, particular Mls antigens eliminate any T cells which are expressing T cell receptor β chain variable region genes associated with recognition of these antigens. In situations where self reactive cells are not deleted they either become anergic or are actively suppressed by regulatory mechanisms which have evolved in order to restrain harmful autoimmunity. T cell-mediated suppression maintains control over both B lymphocyte and effector T lymphocyte responses, so that any defect in antigen-specific or idiotype-specific suppression might allow autoimmune responses to occur. Conversely, increases in helper T cell activity may allow normally quiescent self reactive lymphocytes to mount an autoimmune attack. In instances in which potentially autoreactive B lymphocytes normally remain inactive due to tolerance of the relative helper T cells, the provision of new carrier determinants can provide a 'bypass' mechanism allowing T cell help for autoantibody production. It has been shown that tolerance can be broken experimentally using chemically modified or hapten-conjugated protein antigens and it has been suggested, for example, that the Coombs' positivity of some patients treated with methyl dopa may be due to the drug complexing with erythrocyte antigens, thereby providing carrier determinants which will stimulate cognate T cell help. In other cases, T cell epitopes on the autoantigen may not be effectively presented during tolerance induction in the thymus and so potentially autoreactive T cell clones escape deletion. Only if higher levels of these normally 'cryptic' epitopes later become effectively presented in the periphery, due perhaps to altered processing or presentation of the self antigen, will autoimmune reactivity manifest itself. Furthermore, once initiated, the autoimmune response may spread to other epitopes on the same or different antigens, a process that could be fueled by the local production of inflammatory cytokines which might further lead to upregulation of cell surface molecules involved in antigen presentation and cellular activation.

Idiotypic networks may be important in the control of immune responses to autoantigen; defects in this regulatory network could provide a pathway by which self reactivity can arise. For example, anti-idiotypes to DNA-specific autoantibodies have been described in the sera of patients with inactive systemic lupus erythematosus (SLE) which were absent in those with active disease, suggesting that the presence of these antibodies may influence the course of the disease. In the anti-insulin response seen in patients with insulin-dependent diabetes mellitus (IDDM), idiotypic determinants have been reported to be cyclically expressed even though the total amount of anti-insulin remained constant, again suggesting that idiotypic interactions are involved in regulating this response. In some instances pathogenic autoantibodies may be internal image anti-idiotypes which are directed against antiviral antibody and bind to the same cell surface molecule that is used as a receptor by the virus.

Major histocompatibility complex (MHC) class II gene products are normally expressed only on 'professional' antigen-presenting cells (APCs) but they are sometimes also aberrantly expressed on a variety of cell types during autoimmune disease. It has been shown that such cells themselves are then also able to present antigen. Aberrant expression of MHC class II may be the result of cytokine secretion by cells already involved in an ongoing inflammatory response, and might provide a mechanism for perpetuation of the disease.

Regardless of the cell type expressing MHC class II it is known that autoimmune disease is influenced by MHC (particularly class II) haplotype. As the majority of autoantigens are likely to be T dependent, the ability of self peptides to associate with self-MHC at a concentration necessary for T cell activation will be central to the induction of an immune response.

Individuals bearing HLA-DR4 are nearly six times more likely to develop rheumatoid arthritis (RA) than those lacking this haplotype. For some autoimmune diseases there appears to be a synergistic effect between MHC genes; individuals who bear HLA-DR3 or HLA-DR4 have an increased risk (of

between 2 and 7) of developing IDDM but for someone bearing both these haplotypes the relative risk increases to 14. In IDDM the particular residue at position 57 of the DQβ chain appears, in concert with other residues, to be important in determining disease susceptibility in some caucasian populations.

Molecular mimicry of self antigen by invading organisms can lead to a breakdown of self tolerance as seen in the cross-reactions between streptococcal M protein and cardiac myosin in rheumatic fever and between both brain and heart tissue and *Trypanosoma cruzi* in Chagas disease. Many other examples of autoantibodies cross-reacting with pathogens have been described. Cross-reactivity between self and foreign antigens is also seen for T lymphocytes as demonstrated by the existence of T cell clones specific for determinants on a mycobacterial hsp65 and a human hsp60 which share 48% amino acid sequence homology. Polyclonal lymphocyte activation occurs in response to some infections, for example with Epstein–Barr virus, and has been proposed as a possible mechanism involved in the development of autoimmunity. However, although some of the clones activated may be specific for self antigen these will usually be short lived and produce IgM antibodies of low affinity. Experiments involving neonatal thyroidectomy of autoimmune obese strain chickens demonstrated that the presence of autoantigen is required for the development of thyroglobulin autoantibodies and therefore in this instance these antibodies are not induced by nonspecific activation of B cells.

Somatic mutation of antibody variable region genes is a further mechanism by which autoantibodies may arise. It is known that a single, naturally occurring, point mutation can change an antibody with specificity for phosphorylcholine into an antibody that recognizes double-stranded DNA, protamine and cardiolipin. This antibody has therefore lost the ability to bind to bacterial antigen but acquired binding for self antigen. Despite the fact that autoantibodies are normally restricted in their epitopic specificity (for example to two or three paired determinants on human thyroglobulin) they are usually polyclonal. It is therefore unlikely that somatic mutation on its own provides an explanation for autoimmune disease, although triggering of idiotype-specific T helper cells might allow a single clone to initiate a polyclonal response via network interactions. It is generally accepted that the development of most autoimmune disease is multifactorial in nature. Some of the animal models suggest a role for ADCC or NK cells. Other factors that may influence the initiation and development of the disease are defects in immune regulation (for example T_H1/T_H2

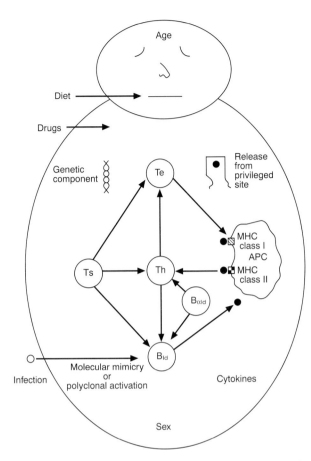

Figure 1   The multifactorial nature of autoimmunity. ●, Autoantigen; APC, antigen-presenting cell ('professional' or aberrant class II expression); Th, helper T cell (antigen- or idiotype-specific; Te, effector T cell (for example cytotoxic T cell); Ts, suppressor T cell; B$_{Id}$, autoantibody-secreting Id$^+$ B cell; B$_{\alpha Id}$, anti-idiotypic B cell.

imbalance) and in the target antigen, sex hormones (autoimmunity is more common in females than in males), diet, and the time and nature of exposure to infectious agents. Some of the above concepts are drawn together in **Figure 1**.

Intervention in autoimmunity

As a clearer picture emerges of the precise mechanisms involved in the breakdown of self tolerance, therapeutic approaches for the autoimmune diseases can begin to address the underlying defect, i.e. the specific autoimmunity. At present, when endocrine tissues are destroyed, as in Hashimoto's disease or IDDM, hormone replacement therapy is utilized. Antithyroid drugs, thyroidectomy and radioactive ablation are used in Graves disease rather than elimination of the TSH receptor autoantibody response. The immunosuppressive regimens used for systemic autoimmune conditions such as SLE and rheumatoid arthritis are crude attempts to dampen the whole

immune system rather than control the specific autoimmune response. More rational approaches to therapy are now beginning to emerge based upon, for example, oral or nasal tolerance induction, the use of cytokine antagonists, and intervention using peptide-based therapeutics to directly block T cell activation.

See also: **Adhesion molecules; Autoantigens; Autoimmune diseases; Cytokines; Idiotype network; Oral tolerance; Privileged sites; T cell vaccination; Tolerance, peripheral; Tolerance, central; Immunotherapy of autoimmune diseases; Relative risk.**

Further reading

Chiorazzi N, Lahita RG, Pavelka K and Ferrarini M (eds) (1997) B lymphocytes and autoimmunity. *Annals of the New York Academy of Sciences* **815**.

Coutinho A and Kazatchkine MD (1994) *Autoimmunity: Physiology and Disease*. New York: Wiley-Liss.

Friedman H, Rose NR and Bendinelli M (eds) (1996) *Microorganisms and Autoimmune Diseases*. New York: Plenum Press.

Gianani R and Sarvetnick N (1996) Viruses, cytokines, antigens, and autoimmunity. *Proceedings of the National Academy of Sciences of the USA* **93**: 2257–2259.

Goodnow CC, Cyster JG, Hartley SB et al (1995) Self-tolerance checkpoints in B lymphocyte development. *Advances in Immunology* **59**: 279–368.

Janeway CA Jr, Goodnow CC and Medzhitov R (1996) Danger – pathogen on the premises! Immunological tolerance. *Current Biology* **6**: 519–522.

Kuhr T, Hala K, Dietrich H, Herold M and Wick G (1994) Genetically determined target organ susceptibility in the pathogenesis of spontaneous autoimmune thyroiditis: aberrant expression of MHC-class II antigens and the possible role of virus. *Journal of Autoimmunity* **7**: 13–25.

Lydyard PM and Brostoff J (eds) (1994) *Autoimmune Disease: Aetiopathogenesis, Diagnosis and Treatment*. Oxford: Blackwell Science.

Moller G (ed) (1992) V gene usage of autoantibodies. *Immunological Reviews* **128**: 1–149.

Moller G (ed) (1994) Chronic autoimmune diseases. *Immunological Reviews* **144**: 1–314.

Pulendran B, van Driel R and Nossal GJ (1997) Immunological tolerance in germinal centres. *Immunology Today* **18**: 27–32.

Ridge JP, Fuchs EJ and Matzinger P (1996) Neonatal tolerance revisited: turning on newborn T cells with dendritic cells. *Science* **271**: 1723–1726 (see comments *Science* 1996; **272**: 1405–1408).

Rubin RL, Burlingame RW, Arnott JE, Totoritis MC, McNally EM and Johnson AD (1995) IgG but not other classes of anti-[(H2A-H2B)-DNA] is an early sign of procainamide-induced lupus. *Journal of Immunology* **154**: 2483–2493.

Schoenfeld Y and Isenberg D (1989) *The Mosaic of Autoimmunity*. Amsterdam: Elsevier.

Steinman L (1996) A few autoreactive cells in an autoimmune infiltrate control a vast population of nonspecific cells: a tale of smart bombs and the infantry. *Proceedings of the National Academy of Sciences of the USA* **93**: 2253–2256.

Tankersley DL (1994) Dimer formation in immunoglob-
ulin preparations and speculations on the mechanism of action of intravenous immune globulin in autoimmune diseases. *Immunological Reviews* **139**: 159–172.

Vanderlugt CJ and Miller SD (1996) Epitope spreading. *Current Opinion in Immunology* **8**: 831–836.

AUTORADIOGRAPHY

Manoj Raje and **Gyan C Mishra**, Institute of Microbial Technology, Chandigrah, and National Centre for Cell Sciences, Pune, India

Autoradiography is a method of localizing radioactive atoms in a specimen. The method briefly comprises of:

1. *Labeling* of a suitable molecule with a radionuclide, serving as a tracer.
2. *Incorporation* of the radioactive tracer into the sample under study.
3. *Processing* of the sample by some suitable means.
4. *Exposure* by placing the prepared sample in close approximation with a special photographic emulsion so that the products of radioactive decay in the sample may interact with the silver halide crystals of the emulsion to form latent images.
5. *Developing* the latent images to convert them into silver grains.
6. *Fixing* the resultant autoradiogram by washing away unreacted silver halide crystals.

The silver grains thus deposited are visualized and their position noted in relation to the underlying sample structure to try and understand the distribution of the label in the sample. Depending upon the nature of the information sought, autoradiography can be carried out at three levels:

1. *Gross level*: in the case of samples such as entire organs, large tissue slices, leaves, gels, etc., where the resolution required is of the order perceived by the naked eye (0.2 mm)
2. *Microscopic level*: cellular and tissue level localization, resolution of around 1–5 μm required.
3. *Ultrastructural level*: subcellular detection and localization with a resolution in the submicron range.

Further discussion will be confined to autoradiography of the microscopic and ultrastructural levels only.

For the successful application of the autoradiographic technique to accurately localize and quantify a biological molecule of interest it is necessary to have detailed information of the biochemical, physiological and pharmacological processes involved in its uptake, distribution and clearance. Also important is the need to have knowledge of the efficiency and resolution obtainable by the experimental technique. Efficiency is defined as the number of silver grains formed per radioactive disintegration in the sample. It depends upon:

- Dose, nature and energy of the radioactive emission.
- Thickness of the sample and emulsion.
- Developing parameters.

The resolution obtainable can be considered in three ways:

- Distance of separation between the points of radioactive decay and grain formed.
- Ability to separate two points of radioactive decay.
- Ability to separate the individual grains formed.

Resolution is also modulated by the nature and energy of the radioactive emission and developing parameters; it also depends upon the size of silver halide crystals in the photographic emulsion.

Commonly used radioisotopes in biological studies

Not every radioisotope will be suitable for a particular autoradiography procedure. The criteria for determining suitability are:

1. *Nature of emission*. Particle emitters are preferred. Gamma and X-ray emitters have very poor efficiency. Electron emitters are usually the most favorable.
2. *Particle energy*. Generally the higher the energy the lower is the efficiency of detection. This is because high-energy particles have a tendency to

escape from the sample and emulsion. β Particles with energies above 0.5 MeV are usually very difficult to detect. A 'high' energy will also mean that the particle will travel further before forming a latent image, hence resolution will also be poor.

3. *Half-life.* If the half-life of the radioisotope used is too short (less than 30 days), most of the radioactivity will disappear during sample processing. On the other hand, use of isotopes with very long half-lives will mean a very low specific activity (few radioactive decay events per unit time) and hence the exposure time would have to be lengthened unduly to collect the requisite number of latent images in the emulsion.

Some of the commonly used radioisotopes in biology are listed in **Table 1**. The exact choice of a particular radionuclide is dependent upon its biological relevance. The final decision in determining a suitable isotope should be made keeping in mind the nature of the biological process under study. The radiolabeled biomolecule prepared has to be purified, checked for specific radioactivity and assayed for biological activity before use for autoradiography.

Dose and administration of radiochemicals

The dose of radioactivity to be administered depends upon the detection system and resolution sought. High-resolution autoradiography is usually carried out with thin films/sections of the sample where the mass of the tissue present is very small. It is therefore necessary to use a high radioisotope concentration and extended exposure time. Although methods are available for the estimation of exposure time for a given level of radioactivity in a sample block, it is usually the practice to prepare autoradiographs in batches. Administration of the radiomolecules can be by one of several routes. In the case of animals, oral intake, direct infusion into arteries/veins or ventricular spaces, injection into peritoneum, etc., can all be considered. For labeling cell suspensions, *in vitro* incubation in culture medium is by far the most rapid, efficient and inexpensive method.

Emulsions used

Photographic emulsions used for high-resolution autoradiography are characterized by a small size of silver halide crystal. The larger the crystal diameter, the poorer is the resolution obtainable; however, greater efficiency is obtainable with larger crystals. Apart from small size, for high resolution work in an electron microscope the emulsion of crystals has to be applied in a monolayer over the sample. There are several suppliers of autoradiography emulsions (Kodak, Sakura, Ilford) with various crystal diameters available.

Application of emulsion to radiolabeled samples

Once a sample has been prepared for autoradiography it is brought into intimate contact with the emulsion. There are primarily two methods for forming a monolayer of emulsion on the sample.

Loop method

A drop of liquefied emulsion in the form of a bubble in a wire loop is applied on to the surface of a sample. This method is commonly used in ultrastructural analysis. The sample is in the form of ultrathin sections/film mounted on a grid.

Flat substrate method

Frequently used in light microscopic studies, here samples mounted on glass slides are dipped into a beaker of liquefied emulsion to form a uniform coat of silver halide crystals. A variation of this method involves first casting of the emulsion films on glass slides, from where they are floated on water and allowed to settle on to the sample.

Exposure

Exposure of emulsion-coated samples is carried out in dessicated light tight boxes at 4°C. The emulsions must be shielded from stray light and radiation. Low temperature and humidity is important to prevent

Table 1 Radioisotopes used in biology

Isotope	Nature of emission	Energy (MeV)	Half-life
^{3}H	β	Low: 0.018	Long: 12.26 years
^{14}C	β	Medium: 0.159	Very long: 5760 years
^{35}S	β	Medium: 0.167	Moderate: 87.2 days
^{32}P	β	High: 1.71	Short: 14.3 days
^{125}I	Auger electron from electron capture reaction	Low: 0.008	Moderate: 60 days

the fading of latent images (resulting in lowered efficiency). The time of exposure can vary from a few weeks to a year and depends upon the nature of the experiment and the radioisotope used. In our laboratories we usually check batches of samples after every few weeks of exposure.

Development

Development involves precipitation of silver atoms at the site of the latent image to form silver grains, which are visualized in a microscope. A generalized method of development involves immersion of the emulsion coated sample in a suitable fine grain developer (for example Kodak D-19 or Microdol X) for a standardized period of time (usually for a few minutes). After rinsing in distilled water the emulsion is fixed in sodium thiosulfate solution for at least 20 minutes and then washed extensively in distilled water. Care has to be taken to ensure that at no point is the surface of the sample contaminated with any precipitate or other material. After washing, the sample can be stained before examination under the light or electron microscope. It should be noted that different developers yield different numbers of grains (different sensitivity); moreover, the shape of the silver grains deposited also varies with developer, a factor which affects the resolution.

Control observations

The successful validation of any autoradiographic experiment requires a proper set of control observations for determination of background and presence of chemography.

Background

Silver grains deposited due to radioactivity of the tracer molecules incorporated into the sample constitute the signal. However, some additional grains can also develop for nonspecific reasons. These constitute the noise or background of the system. Generally the background should not exceed more than 5% of the signal grain density. Background can be estimated by taking the ratio of the grains present over the target tissue to the grains present over the same area of empty section (only embedding material coated with emulsion). The factors contributing to background are:

- Exposure to stray light or radiation.
- Pressure during drying of emulsion film.
- Static discharges in the vicinity (common in low-humidity workplaces).
- Overdevelopment (excessive time and/or temperature).

Chemography

Induction of grain formation by the chemical action of sample components on silver halide crystals is known to occur and is called positive chemography. The reverse process, of eradication of latent images by chemicals in the sample, is known as negative chemography. The former causes an increase in the background, while the latter lowers the efficiency. Interposing a thin inert layer of carbon between the sample and the emulsion usually minimizes the problem. A control for positive chemography is a non-radioactively-labeled, identically-treated sample. For negative chemography a control would be a light-fogged, identically-treated sample.

Interpretation of results

The simplest method is to assume that the grain observed overlies the point of radioactive decay and hence represents the site of the target molecule. For lower resolution studies at the light microscopic level this assumption may work; however, in the case of electron microscopy autoradiography this assump-

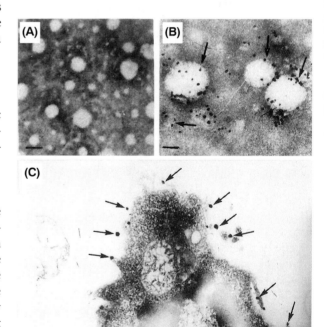

Figure 1 Binding and distribution of B3 (a costimulatory molecule) on the surface of T cells. B3 coupled to liposomes was labeled with ^{125}I and incubated with anti-CD3-activated CD4$^+$ T cells and electron microscopic autoradiography was performed using Ilford nuclear L4 emulsion. (a) Negative staining of liposomes by phosphotungstic acid (bar = 200 nm); (b) ^{125}I-labeled B3 coupled to liposomes; arrows show the liposomes bearing the iodinated B3 (bar = 200 nm); (c) CD4$^+$ T cell labeled with B3 (arrows) (bar = 200 nm). (Reproduced from Vinay, Raje, Verma and Mishra (1995).)

tion need not hold true and careful analysis of the images obtained has to be made. There are two methods in common use for localization of the radioactive decay event in a sample with relation to the observed grain density. These are known as the probability circle analysis and the cross-fire method (see Williams (1985) for detailed methodology).

Some areas of application

Autoradiographic techniques have been used extensively to study the binding of a variety of small molecules such as peptides, drugs and hormones to a variety of target sites in cells and tissues. The number of conserved subunits in chromosomes was demonstrated using autoradiography. Many important observations have been made on macromolecular metabolism, synthesis and secretion using these techniques. The method has also been successfully applied to the study of virus particles and nucleic acids. In our laboratories we have used autoradiography and electron microscopy to demonstrate the binding of a costimulatory protein to its receptor on the surface of CD4$^+$ T lymphocytes (**Figures 1** and **2**).

See also: **Immunodiffusion, single radial; Immunoelectrophoresis; Isoelectric focusing; Lymphocyte trafficking; Northern blotting; Radiolabeling; SDS-polyacrylamide gel electrophoresis (SDS-PAGE); Southern blotting; Western blotting.**

Further reading

Caro JJ and Skipper SJ (1954) *Science* **119**: 141.

Chabot J-G, Morel G, Belles Isles M, Jeandel L and Heisler S (1988) ANF and exocrine pancreas: ultrastructural autoradiographic localization in acinar cells. *American Journal of Physiology* **254**: E301–309.

Downs A and Williams MA (1984) An improved approach to the analysis of autoradiographs containing isolated sources of simple shape: method, theoretical basis and reference data. *Journal of Microscopy* **136**: 1–22.

Levinthal C and Thomas CA (1957) *Biochimica et Biophysica Acta* **22**: 453–465.

Morel G and Heisler S (1988) Internalization of endogenous and exogenous atrial natriuretic peptide by target tissues. *Electron Microscopy Reviews* **1**: 221–259.

Morel G, Pelletier G and Heisler S (1986) Internalization and subcellular distribution of radiolabeled somatostatin-28 in mouse anterior pituitary tumor cells. *Endocrinology* **119**: 1972–1179.

Morel G, Dihl F, Aubert ML and Dubois PM (1987) Binding and internalization of native gonadoliberin (GnRH) by anterior pituitary gonadotrophs of the rat. A quantitative autoradiographic study after cryoultramicrotomy. *Cell and Tissue Research* **248**: 541–550.

Morel G, Chabot J-G, Belles-Isles M and Heisler S (1988) Synthesis and internalization of atrial natriuretic factor in anterior pituitary cells. *Molecular and Cellular Endocrinology* **55**: 219–231.

Saltpeter MM and Bachmann L (1964) *Journal of Cell Biology* **22**: 469.

Saltpeter MM, Budd GC and Mattimoe S (1974) *Journal of Histochemistry and Cytochemistry* **22**: 217.

Taylor JH (1963) *Molecular Genetics*, part 1. London: Academic Press.

Vinay DS, Raje M, Verma RK and Mishra GC (1995) Characterization of novel costimulatory molecules. A protein of 38–42 kDa from B cell surface is concerned with T cell activation and differentiation. *Journal of Biological Chemistry* **270**: 23429–23436.

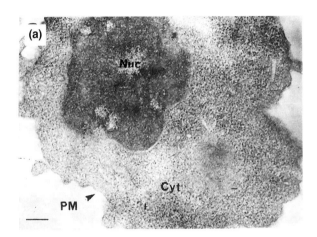

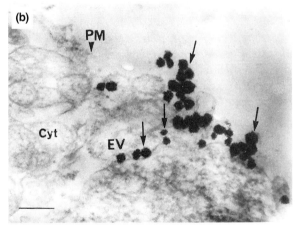

Figure 2 Murine anti-IgM coupled to liposomes and ^{125}I-labeled was incubated with T cells and A20 cells. Electron microscopic autoradiography was carried out using ultrathin sections coated with Ilford nuclear L4 emulsion. The period of exposure was 3 weeks and development was carried out using Kodak D-19 developer. PM, plasma membrane; Cyt, cytoplasm; Nuc, Nucleus; EV, endocytotic vesicle. (a) anti-CD3-activated T cells incubated with liposomized and ^{125}I-labeled murine anti-IgM (immunoglobulin M) (bar = 200 nm); (b) A20 cells incubated with liposomized and ^{125}I-anti-IgM (bar = 200 nm). Note the absence of labeled anti-IgM binding on the T cell membrane. Also note the distribution of labeled anti-IgM in and on the surface of A20 cells. (Reproduced from Vinay, Raje, Verma and Mishra (1995).)

Vinay DS, Raje M and Mishra GC (1996) Characterization of a novel co-stimulatory molecule: a 155–
160 kDa B cell surface protein provides accessory help
to CD4$^+$ T cells to proliferate and differentiate. *Molecular Immunology* 33: 1–14.
Williams MA (1985) In: Glauert AM (ed) *Autoradiography and Immunocytochemistry. Practical Methods
in Electron Microscopy*, vol 6, part 1. Amsterdam:
North Holland.
Williams MA, Downs A and Junger E (1983) *Acta
Stereologica* 2: 249.

AVIAN IMMUNE SYSTEM

J Richard L Pink, Pharma Research PRPN, F Hoffmann-La Roche Ltd, Basel, Switzerland

Olli Vainio, Department of Medical Microbiology, University of Turku, Turku, Finland

The species studied by avian immunologists include
turkeys, ducks, pigeons and Japanese quail. However, the contributions of the domestic chicken
(*Gallus gallus*) to immunology far outweigh those of
other birds, and indeed exceed those of other species
except humans and mice. The contributions date
back to 1880 (Pasteur's key observation of fowl
cholera attenuation, on which much vaccine development is based), and are continuing at present with
the para-aortic localization of hematopoietic precursors in very early embryos. Some important immunological results obtained using chickens or chick
embryos are the discoveries of tumor viruses
(including endogenous viruses) and interferon; the
association of the major histocompatibility complex
(MHC) with resistance to viral disease; induction of
tolerance by embryonic parabiosis; the definition of
separate B and T lymphocyte lineages following
Glick's elucidation of the role of the bursa; quantitation of graft-versus-host reactions and frequencies
of alloreactive T cells; and evidence that the primary
lymphoid organs are colonized by bloodborne hematopoietic stem cells, that a gene conversion-type
mechanism can play a major role in the development
of antibody variability, and that immunoglobulin G
(IgG)- and IgA-producing cells are derived from IgM-
positive precursors.

Avian and mammalian immune systems have much
in common. However, there are important differences,
emphasized in this entry, between them, notably in the
structure of lymphoid organs, the ways in which antibody variability is generated, and the arrangements of
Ig and MHC genes. The main advantages of chickens
in immunological experiments are the accessibility of
the embryo, the ease of manipulating B cell development in the bursa, and the ready availability of peripheral blood and lymphoid organs from birds with
defined genetic background. Young chicks are easy to
immunize, bleed and operate, and can be kept in standard animal housing, whereas maintaining adult chickens and establishing a breeding program requires facilities designed for this purpose, and is necessarily a long-
term project since the generation time is 6–12 months.

Chicken strains and genetic variability

Over a dozen highly inbred chicken strains, representing at least 10 of the approximately 30 characterized different MHC (B locus) haplotypes are available. Skin grafts between birds of the same inbred
strain are permanently accepted, with the exception
of female to male grafts, which are slowly rejected,
hens being the heterogametic sex. MHC-congenic
and recombinant haplotypes are available on some
of the highly inbred backgrounds. Four μ chain, 10
γ chain and two light chain Ig allotypic variants are
described, and Ig allotype-congenic and recombinant
strains exist. Variation also occurs at non-MHC or
Ig locus-linked loci of interest to immunologists, such
as loci controlling blood group antigens or responsiveness to T cell mitogens.

With very few exceptions, the inbred strains are
based on the White Leghorn type of domestic
chicken. Attempts to inbreed other types of chicken
or species of bird (ducks, Japanese quail) have been
made, but have not generally been successful. There
are lines of chickens with hypogammaglobulinemia
resulting from abnormal bursal development, a line
in which a disease similar to systemic scleroderma
can be induced, and 'obese' chicken strains which
develop a spontaneous autoimmune thyroiditis similar to Hashimoto's disease. Transgenic chickens can
be produced by DNA transfer into fertilized eggs;
viral vectors which can give high levels of somatic
transgenesis are available. A chicken genome mapping project is under way.

Immune responses and tolerance

Chickens are generally good antibody producers, and
their evolutionary distance from us enables them to

respond to some proteins (e.g. cytoskeletal elements) whose sequences are highly conserved in mammals. Immune responses develop early in chickens. They can respond to some protein antigens injected on the day of hatching, and in some cases to viruses or allogeneic or xenogeneic cells introduced into the egg. Responses to individual protein antigens develop at different times after hatching. As in mammals, IgM responses precede IgG; however, in some (but not all) antihapten responses, only poor affinity maturation is observed, consistent with the idea that there is not extensive generation of antibody variability in peripheral tissues (see below). Because of the difficulty of preparing monoclonal antibodies from chickens, their idiotypes and antibody repertoire have not been extensively studied.

Avian T cell-dependent responses (mixed lymphocyte reaction (MLR), skin graft rejection, delayed-type hypersensitivity given by cells injected into the wattle, responses to T cell mitogens) can be assayed essentially as for mammalian cells, while graft-versus-host reactions can be quantitated by the embryonic splenomegaly assay or by pock formation on the chorioallantoic membrane. T cell-dependent cytotoxic assays are established, and spleen cells from chickens infected with leukosis or reticuloendotheliosis viruses can kill infected target cells in an MHC-restricted, antigen-specific manner. Cytotoxic CD8$^+$ cells play an important role in regression of some virally induced tumors.

Depending on the antigen and mode of injection, tolerance can be induced in chick embryos or newly hatched birds. Several interesting tolerance models have been studied. The antigens used include mammalian serum albumins (large doses given to newly hatched chicks lead to B cell tolerance, which is not suppressor cell dependent); quail embryo wing buds grafted into chick embryos (tolerance is induced only if a quail thymus is also grafted with the wing bud, and may be suppressor cell dependent); parabiosed allogeneic chick embryos (leads to tolerance in early embryos, but to development of leukemias and other abnormalities in later embryos); and allogeneic bursa cells injected into cyclophosphamide-treated 4-day-old chicks, leading to long-lasting and specific B cell chimerism. This model has been useful in studies of B cell development, requirements for T–B cell collaboration and antigen presentation by B cells.

Lymphoid organs

The development of B lymphocytes in a distinct primary lymphoid organ, the bursa of Fabricius, distinguishes the avian from other immune systems. Other differences between the lymphoid organs of chickens and mammals are the multilobe structure of the bird's thymus, which consists of 6–7 distinct lobes on each side of the neck, making thymectomy technically difficult; the absence of organized lymph nodes in many avian species (they exist in a primitive form in ducks, but are replaced by numerous small lymphoid foci in chickens); the higher percentage of immigrant B cells in the avian than in mammalian thymus; the presence of a distinct gland (Harder's gland), located above the eye, which is full of plasma cells secreting IgM and IgA; and the presence of two appendix-like structures, the cecal tonsils, which branch from the gut and contain many lymphocytes. The thymus develops from an epithelial outgrowth of the pharyngeal pouches, and the bursa from an outgrowth of the cloacal epithelium starting at around day 5 of incubation. Epithelio-mesenchymal interaction is important in formation of the bursa. It has been postulated, but is not firmly established, that soluble factors (bursin, bursapoietin, thymopoietin) also play a role in genesis of these organs. Intrabursal B cell development is largely independent of exogenous antigens, although antigens introduced into the bursa can induce a local immune response in the bursal medulla.

Cells

B cell precursors located in embryonic mesenchyme enter the bursa between about days 8 and 15 of incubation. The presence of the Bu-1 antigen on at least some of these precursors (prebursal stem cells) suggests that they are already committed to the B cell lineage. Antibody variability is generated by gene conversion in the bursa (see below), probably until the organ involutes at sexual maturity. There is no evidence for development of B cells from Ig-negative precursors after hatching in any anatomical site. Instead, B cells arise in the bursa from Ig-positive bursal stem cells, and later in the periphery from postbursal stem cells, which can restore the peripheral, but not bursal B cell compartment after transfer to a cyclophosphamide-treated host. In their early formation and capacity for self-maintenance, chicken B cells differ from the majority of mouse and human B lymphocytes, although they do share some properties, e.g. CD5 expression, with the B-1 cells of these species. In spite of these differences, chicken B lymphocytes are functionally very similar to their mammalian counterparts in terms of capacity to differentiate into plasma cells and secrete antibodies at high levels. Chicken B cell subsets differing in surface phenotype and physiological criteria, such as mode of emigration from the bursa and turnover rate, have been described.

Chicken T cells develop from precursors which enter the thymus in several waves, starting at about day 6 of embryonic development, and formation of mature T cells appears to follow a course similar to that observed in mammals. Cells expressing $\alpha\beta$ T cell receptors (TCRs) have helper, cytotoxic or suppressor activities, and their functions, at least for helper and cytotoxic T cells, are MHC-restricted. Cells with a helper phenotype (carrying the CD4 antigen), as well as virally transformed CD8-bearing cells have been cloned. T cell-mediated suppression is most clearly shown in models where transfer of T cells from bursectomized birds into normal birds can induce B cell deficiency in the recipients; however, the mechanism of this suppression is not clear. Natural killer (NK) cell and antibody-dependent cellular cytotoxicity (ADCC) activities are readily detectable in chicken spleen and blood. Chicken NK cells have been identified as cytoplasmic $CD3^+$, surface $CD3/TCR^-$ and $CD25^+$ cells. A subset of these cells expresses $CD8\alpha$.

Avian nonlymphoid hematopoietic cells (monocytes, granulocytes, thrombocytes, erythrocytes) are clearly defined morphologically and functionally, and bear characteristic cell surface markers detectable by monoclonal antibodies. All of these are nucleated cells, including the erythrocytes and thrombocytes, so that separation procedures designed for mammalian lymphocytes may need modification for avian cells.

In experiments involving cell or organ transfers, the types of cell marker used to follow cellular origin include strain- or species-specific monoclonal antibodies, the sex chromosome marker, and the quail-chick nuclear marker, useful because of its independence of cell cycle and lineage.

Proteins

The well-defined chicken Ig classes (IgM, IgA and an IgG-like class, also referred to as IgY) are functionally comparable to their mammalian counterparts. A truncated IgG/Y (IgY(ΔFc)), derived by alternative RNA splicing, is found in ducks and geese. Whether a chicken IgD homolog exists is unclear. The chicken IgG/Y heavy chains have one more domain than mammalian γ chains and show about equal sequence homology to mammalian ϵ and γ chains. The IgG/Y molecules aggregate in high salt concentrations, a property which can be exploited to increase the sensitivity of assays dependent on immunoprecipitation. IgG/Y, but not IgM, is transported into the egg, from which antibody can be purified as readily as from serum. As in mammals, secretory IgA is polymeric and associated with a secretory component.

Chicken β_2-microglobulin and MHC class Iα (B-F) and class II (B-L) molecules are structurally and functionally homologous to their mammalian counterparts. The β_2-microglobulin is synthesized in the embryonic thymus around day 6 of incubation. B-F molecules are first detected on lymphoid and myeloid cells in 10- or 11-day embryos, and appear on erythrocytes around the time of hatching, whereas B-L molecules are first seen on bursal cells and macrophages about day 11 of incubation. A third type of polymorphic MHC product, B-G molecules, are disulfide-linked dimers of polypeptides which are not glycosylated and not associated with β_2-microglobulin, and whose molecular weights vary in different strains between about 30 and 55 kDa. B-G molecules are present on the surface of embryonic and adult erythrocytes and their precursors, and on thrombocytes. On other cells, e.g. lymphocytes and intestinal epithelial cells, B-G or B-G-like antigens have also been detected. The function of B-G antigens is unknown, although they show some sequence homology to myelin oligodendrocyte glycoprotein and butyrophilin.

Chicken T cell surface components which resemble mammalian T cell TCR, as well as the CD3, CD4, CD5, CD6, CD8, CD28 and CD45 antigens and the interleukin 2 (IL-2) receptor α chain (CD25), have been identified. Sequence identities with the corresponding human homologs range from 23% (CD4) through 30–40% (CD3, 5, 8) to 50% (CD28). Three subpopulations of T cells, of which two carry $\alpha\beta$ and one $\gamma\delta$ TCR heterodimers, have been defined with monoclonal antibodies. Many (20–50%) peripheral T cells express $\gamma\delta$ TCRs. Monoclonal antibodies have also been used to characterize B and T cell surface markers without known functions or mammalian homologs, e.g. the Bu-1 (chB6) B cell alloantigen and the chT1 cortical thymocyte antigen, as well as 'oncodevelopmental' antigens present, for example, on lymphoid tumor cells as well as immature (but not mature) normal erythrocytes.

Chicken IL-1, IL-2, interferon α/β, interferon γ and complement components C1, C3 and factor B of the alternative complement pathway have been characterized and resemble their mammalian counterparts. However, there is no evidence yet for a functional C2- and C4-mediated classical complement pathway in chickens. Fc receptors have been defined by their function on several cell types.

Genes

The Ig and MHC gene complexes of the chicken differ in interesting ways from their mammalian counterparts. In the case of the Ig light (λ) chains,

DNA rearrangement during embryonic development joins a unique functional V_L gene to a single J_L sequence adjacent to the single C_L gene. Light chain variability is generated principally by gene conversion (or a mechanism with similar effect), which leads to replacement of sequences in the rearranged V_L gene by sequences from one or more of a series of 25 V_L pseudogenes located 5' of the rearranged V_L. The whole light chain gene complex has been isolated, and all the pseudogenes as well as the functional V, J and C_L genes sequenced. A similar gene conversion mechanism generates heavy chain V region diversity, although in this case only 30 of an estimated 70 V pseudogenes have been sequenced (in addition to the single functional V_H, D and J_H regions and the unique C_μ and C_γ genes). D regions fused to the pseudogenes also contribute to variability. Recent evidence suggests that gene conversion and somatic point mutations additionally diversify the peripheral B cell repertoire in splenic germinal centers. As in mammals, the light and heavy chain gene complexes are not linked, whereas μ and γ chain genes are closely linked.

Chicken TCR α, β, γ and δ genes have been cloned and sequenced. As in mammals, δ and β genes comprise rearranged VDJC elements, whereas α and γ genes result from VJC rearrangement. There are only two V_α, two V_β, two V_δ and probably three V_γ families in chicken. The TCR α/δ locus organization is similar to that of mammals. Preliminary results indicate that both $V_\alpha 1$ and $V_\alpha 2$ gene segments can be used to encode TCR δ chains. The TCR repertoire is generated, in contrast to the B cell receptor repertoire, by combinatorial and junctional diversity, as in mammals.

The chicken MHC (B complex) is located on microchromosome 16, which carries the nucleolar organizer region (NOR). The B complex is smaller and simpler than mammalian MHCs. The average distance between genes in the complex is only about 10–20 kB, and typical intron sizes are about 100 bp. The class I α and class II β genes (two of each in the B complex of the B12 strain) are closely spaced, interspersed and G+C-rich. The single class II α gene is situated on the same microchromosome, some distance (about 5 cM) away from the MHC. In most MHC haplotypes there is a preferential expression of only one class I α and one class II β gene, although the number of expressed genes may be strain-dependent. Within the MHC, the BF/BL region containing class I α and class II β genes can be separated from a region encoding polymorphic B-G antigens, although the frequency of recombination between the two regions is low (about 0.05%). The B-G region contains multiple B-G genes, of which at least two are transcribed and presumably give rise by multiple splicing, processing or other mechanisms to the multiple B-G products seen in protein analyses. At least one expressed B-G-like gene is also located within the B-F/B-L region. Other genes, one coding for a protein homologous to a G protein subunit, are also present in this region. In contrast to the mammalian situation, factor B polymorphism is not linked to the MHC in chickens.

Rfp-Y, a second region bearing MHC-type (two class I α and three class II β) genes, is also located on chromosome 16. It is separated from the B complex by a region which contains the NOR and exhibits frequent recombination. These MHC genes seem to be neither highly polymorphic nor highly expressed.

The chicken β_2-microglobulin gene has been cloned and sequenced. It shows little polymorphism and is located on a large microchromosome (either 10 or 11).

Pathology

Diseases which specifically affect the avian immune system include the avian leukoses, Marek's disease and infectious bursal disease (IBD). The avian leukosis viruses (ALV) are closely related to the acutely transforming, *onc*-gene carrying viruses such as Rous sarcoma virus, which carries the *src* oncogene, and the replication-defective myelomacytosis viruses. The latter carry the v-*myc* oncogene and produce a spectrum of myeloid and lymphoid tumors. The ALVs do not carry their own oncogenes, but early studies of the slowly-transforming leukosis viruses showed that tumors developed in bursal cells when the virus was integrated next to the c-*myc* oncogene, leading to its aberrant activation, as in Burkitt's lymphoma cells. Reticuloendotheliosis viruses are also capable of inducing lymphomas in immunologically compromised birds, but are retroviruses not belonging to the ALV family. Marek's disease is caused by a very contagious DNA virus of the herpesvirus family. The virus infects both B and T cells, but specifically induces T lymphocyte transformation, and also leads to peripheral nerve degeneration, perhaps due to autoimmune attack. Resistance to Marek's disease is strongly correlated with presence of the B21 MHC allele, in both heterozygotes and homozygotes, and with low MHC class I antigen expression. Vaccination against the disease by infection of newly hatched chicks with a turkey herpesvirus is very effective, and provided the first example of a practical antitumor vaccine. The IBD virus is a double-stranded RNA virus which infects bursal cells, producing extensive necrosis and immunodepression. An attenuated IBD vaccine is available.

Vaccines effective against other diseases of chicks exist: Newcastle disease (caused by an influenza-like virus), fowl pox and cholera, infectious bronchitis, avian encephalomyelitis, egg drop syndrome and coccidiosis, which is caused by a gut parasite. There is considerable interest in defining coccidial antigens which render birds immune after a single coccidial infection, since the current attenuated vaccine needs more care in storage and delivery than would a sub-unit-based vaccine. T cell clones with specificity for coccidial antigens have been cloned and in some cases shown to have helper activity *in vitro*. Defining the mechanisms of resistance to this and other avian diseases is currently an important task.

See also: **Autoimmune diseases; Bursa of Fabricius; Immunoglobulin, evolution of; MHC, evolution of; Phylogeny of the immune response; T cell receptor, αβ; T cell receptor, γδ; T cell receptor, evolution of; Thyroid autoimmunity, experimental models.**

Further reading

Arakawa H, Furusawa S, Ekino S and Yamagishi H (1996) Immunoglobulin gene hyperconversion ongoing in chicken splenic germinal centers. *EMBO J* **15**: 2540–2546.

Davison TF, Morris TR and Payne LN (eds) (1996) *Poultry Immunology*. Poultry Science Symposium Series, vol 24. Abingdon: Carfax.

Kaufman J, Völk H and Wallny HJ (1995) A 'Minimal essential Mhc' and an 'Unrecognized Mhc': Two extremes in selection for polymorphism. *Immunological Reviews* **143**: 63–88.

Reynaud CA, Bertocci B, Dahan A and Weill JC (1995) Formation of the chicken B-cell repertoire: ontogenesis, regulation of Ig gene rearrangement, and diversification by gene conversion. *Advances in Immunology* **57**: 353–378.

Roslin Institute Chicken Genome Map Home Page. http://www.ri.bbsrc.ac.uk/chickmap/

Vainio O and Imhof BA (1995) The immunology and developmental biology of the chicken. *Immunology Today* **16**: 365–370.

Vainio O and Imhof BA (eds) (1996) *Immunology and Developmental Biology of the Chicken*. Current Topics in Microbiology and Immunology, vol 212. Berlin: Springer.

B7 (CD80 AND CD86)

Gordon J Freeman, Vassiliki A Boussiotis, John G Gribben and **Arlene H Sharpe**, Department of Pathology, Brigham and Women's Hospital, Harvard Medical School, Boston, Massachusetts, USA

Lee M Nadler, Department of Adult Oncology, Dana-Farber Cancer Institute, Department of Medicine, Harvard Medical School, Boston, Massachusetts, USA

Two signals are required for optimal T cell activation. Specificity is provided by the interaction of the T cell receptor (TCR) with major histocompatibility complex (MHC)–peptide but a second, antigen-unrestricted costimulatory signal is also required. The B7 family of proteins, B7-1 (CD80) and B7-2 (CD86 or B70) provide the major costimulatory signal for T cell activation and clonal expansion via their interaction with CD28. Engagement of the TCR in the absence of B7 costimulation results in T cell clonal anergy.

Structure

B7-1 and B7-2 are type I membrane proteins with an extracellular domain consisting of one immunoglobulin V (IgV)-like and one IgC-like domain, followed by a transmembrane anchor and short cytoplasmic tail. Mature B7-1 has 254 amino acids, is heavily glycosylated, and has a molecular weight of 45–70 kDa. Mature B7-2 has 304 amino acids, is heavily glycosylated, and has a molecular weight of 60–100 kDa. The genes for both B7-1 and B7-2 are located on human chromosome 3q21 and mouse chromosome 16B5.

Both B7-1 and B7-2 are counter-receptors for CD28, expressed on resting as well as activated T cells, and for CTLA4 (CD152), expressed on activated T cells. Dimeric CD28 has equivalent low avidity for both B7-1 and B7-2 (2400 nM) but dimeric CTLA-4 has a greater than 400-fold higher avidity for B7-1 than B7-2 (1 and 4 nM). Both B7-1 and B7-2 have very fast on/fast off rates but the binding kinetics differ, with B7-1 binding and dissociating more slowly.

B7-1 and B7-2 bind to the same general region on CD28 and CTLA4 but the amino acids critical for B7-1 or B7-2 binding are different. The CDR3 loop of the IgV-like domain of CD28 and CLTA4 contains a conserved MYPPPY motif (amino acids 99–104) important for both B7-1 and B7-2 binding. Tyrosine 104 is critical for binding to both B7-1 and B7-2. Residues 100, 99, 101 and 102 are important for differential binding of B7-1 versus B7-2.

Though B7-1 and B7-2 have similar structures, their extracellular domains have only 27% amino acid identity and other regions are even less conserved. B7-1 and B7-2 function well across species, suggesting that the ligand binding site is highly conserved. Conserved residues on the GFCC′C″ face of the B7 IgV domain and on the ABED face of the B7 IgC domain are important for binding. The eight N-linked glycosylation sites of B7 are on the opposite side from the B7/CD28 interaction surface and do not contribute to binding. Thus, CD28 and CTLA4 use sequences in their CDR3 and CDR1 regions, much like antibodies, to bind to a surface on the side of the B7 IgV and IgC domains.

Expression

B7 expression is tightly regulated and mainly restricted to antigen presenting cells. B7 on the cell surface is a monomer but is locally concentrated in small foci. B7-2 is constitutively expressed on unstimulated dendritic cells and blood monocytes. B7-1 is generally absent from unstimulated cells. B7-1 mRNA transcription is regulated by a cell-type specific enhancer responsive to NFκB family members. B7 expression is upregulated by 'danger' signals such as bacterial DNA or lipopolysaccharide and by the innate immunity receptor, Toll. On dendritic cells, both B7s are rapidly upregulated by granulocyte-

monocyte colony-stimulating factor (GM-CSF) or CD40L/CD40 signaling. On monocytes, B7 levels are increased by interferon γ (IFNγ). Unstimulated human B and T cells do not express B7. B7-1 and B7-2 are induced in B cells by cross-linking of CD40, surface Ig, or MHC class II, and by interleukin-2 (IL-2), IL-4, IL-5, tumor necrosis factor α (TNFα) and lymphotoxin (TNFβ). Memory B cells constitutively express B7-1 and B7-2 and rapidly upregulate them, permitting memory B cells to rapidly activate T cells. B7-1 and B7-2 are induced in T cells following activation and are upregulated by IL-7. Other cells also can express B7, including IFNγ-treated fibroblasts (B7-1), vascular endothelial cells (B7-2), IFNγ-treated astrocytes (B7-2) and gastric epithelial cells. Adjuvants (e.g. Freund's adjuvant, Neisserial porins) strongly induce B7 expression, providing an important mechanism for their stimulation of an immune response. Generally, B7-2 is expressed more rapidly and at higher levels than B7-1. B7-2 is expressed at sites of inflammation and B7-1 expression is found when chronic inflammation progresses to tissue damage.

B7 expression is downregulated by IL-10, transforming growth factor β (TGFβ), ultraviolet light, the environmental toxin, dioxin, and cross-linking of the low-affinity IgG receptor, CD32, by immune complexes. Microorganisms (e.g. *Leishmania donovani*, *Mycobacterium tuberculosis*) can inhibit B7 expression. These agents are immunosuppressive, presumably in part because they reduce B7 costimulatory signals.

Function

The B7/CD28 pathway is important for cellular and antibody responses to viral and microbial infections, cancer, graft rejection and the development of autoimmunity. During antigen presentation, B7 bound to CD28 or CTLA4 coassociates on the cell surface with MHC–peptide bound to TCR in the activation cap between T cell and antigen-presenting cell (APC) but engages a distinct signaling pathway. For B7-1, this colocalization depends on the short but highly positively charged cytoplasmic tail which interacts with cytoskeletal components.

Binding of B7 to CD28, in conjunction with a TCR signal, stimulates production of multiple cytokines, including IL-1, 2, 3, 4, 5, 6, 8, 10, 13, TNFα, TNFβ, GM-CSF, CSF-1 and IFNγ. B7/CD28 signaling upregulates expression of growth factor receptors including α, β and common γ chain of the IL-2 receptor. B7/CD28 signaling upregulates chemokines (MIP-1α, MIP-1β and RANTES) and chemokine receptor CXCR4, but downregulates expression of chemokine receptors CCR1, CCR2a, CCR2b and CCR5. B7/CD28 interaction stimulates production of the anti-apoptotic proteins bcl-x_L and bcl-2, leading to enhanced T cell survival and upregulates telomerase expression, thereby contributing to T cell clonal expansion. B7/CD28 interaction activates cyclic AMP-responsive element-binding protein which regulates proliferating cell nuclear antigen, DNA polymerase δ and cyclin A. While some of these proteins can be induced by a strong TCR signal alone, B7/CD28 signaling greatly hastens and augments the level of expression. B7/CD28 interaction lowers the threshold for T cell activation by approximately 2 logs of antigen concentration and is thus most important for low antigen doses and weaker antigens. Nevertheless, B7/CD28 interactions are not essential for T cell activation as strong TCR signaling alone can activate T cells. While B7 can prime T cells, it is not essential for T cell priming. B7/CD28 interactions are critical for T cell clonal expansion, high-level lymphokine production, and T cell help for B cells.

The B7/CD28 and CD40/CD40L pathways crosstalk to reinforce immune activation. CD28 signaling induces CD40L expression and CD40 signaling induces B7 expression, and in dendritic cells and macrophages also induces IL-12 secretion. The crosstalk and synergistic function of these pathways is supported by the observations in some transplant models which show that optimal tolerization is achieved by blockade of both the B7/CD28 and CD40/CD40L pathways.

B7/CD28 interaction is also critical for the differentiation of precursor CD8 T cells into cytolytic effectors and induces cytolytic proteins such as granzyme B. Following the development of cytolytic effectors, B7 expression is not needed on the target cell for cytotoxic T lymphocyte killing.

CTLA4-Ig, a fusion protein in which the extracellular domain of CTLA4 is fused to IgG, binds to B7-1 and B7-2, and is a potent blocker of immune responses. While high concentrations of CTLA4-Ig completely inhibit both B7-1 and B7-2 mediated costimulation, lower concentrations inhibit B7-1- but not B7-2-mediated responses.

CTLA4-Ig or a combination of anti-B7-1 and B7-2 monoclonal antibodies (mAbs) have shown great promise in blocking autoimmune disease or tolerizing for transplantation. CTLA4-Ig or anti-B7-1 and B7-2 mAbs have been used to tolerize successfully for pancreatic islet cell xenotransplants, heart transplants and bone marrow transplants. Following cessation of CTLA4-Ig treatment, donor antigen-specific tolerance is seen. The mechanism for this tolerance is hypothesized to be T cell clonal anergy.

A competent immune response to other antigens and infections remains.

B7-2 is the major costimulator for initiating both T_H1 and T_H2 immune responses because of its constitutive expression and more rapid upregulation. The need for two B7 proteins is unclear but many studies with murine models of autoimmunity show different effects of blocking B7-1 or B7-2. Whereas complete blockade with CTLA4-Ig or anti B7-1 plus anti-B7-2 mAbs prevents the development of disease in murine models of nonobese diabetes (NOD), systemic lupus erythematosus (SLE) and experimental autoimmune encephalitis (EAE), and alleviates symptoms in established disease, different effects are seen when either B7 is blocked. In NOD and SLE, anti-B7-2 mAb is sufficient to alleviate disease but in NOD, anti-B7-1 mAb alone exacerbates disease. In contrast, anti-B7-1 mAb alleviates EAE, whereas anti-B7-2 mAb exacerbates EAE. B7-1 is a more effective costimulator for weak peptide ligands and this may explain the importance of B7-1 in the progression of autoimmunity to subdominant epitopes.

Alternatively, these differences may be due to timing of expression, as, in NOD and SLE, B7-1 and B7-2 are regulated by normal genetic mechanisms but, in EAE, B7-1 and B7-2 are artificially upregulated by adjuvant. Differences in function also may be due to differences in strength or quality of signal delivered upon binding to CD28/CTLA4. B7-1 and B7-2 can equivalently stimulate IL-2 and IFNγ production, however, the level of IFNγ is only moderate, with IL-12 being critical for the high-level IFNγ production characteristic of T_H1. B7-2 costimulation along with antigen concentration and affinity are important for the differentiation of naive T cells into the initial producers of the IL-4 that primes for further IL-4 synthesis. Three studies show that B7-2 more effectively induces IL-4, but two others find that B7-1 and B7-2 induce IL-4 equally. However, after T_H2 differentiation, a TCR signal alone can be sufficient for IL-4 production. B7/CD28 signaling also regulates proliferation of T_H2 cells via the induction of IL-1 which makes T_H2 cells responsive to IL-4.

Studies on antibody production using mice lacking both B7-1 and B7-2 show a loss of germinal center formation and reductions in IgG1 (IL-4 dependent) and IgG2a (IFNγ dependent) of 99% and 95%, respectively. Deletion of B7-1 alone has no effect on antibody production, whereas deletion of B7-2 alone results in a loss of IgG production when mice are immunized in the absence of adjuvant. When B7-2 deficient mice are immunized in the presence of adjuvant, which induces B7-1, IgG levels are normal. These studies show that if it is induced, B7-1 can replace B7-2 in stimulating help for antibody production.

Productive infection by human immunodeficiency virus (HIV) requires activated memory CD4 T cells. Blockade of B7/CD28 prevents HIV transmission in an *in vitro* T cell/dendritic cell system. CD28 signaling promotes viral cDNA synthesis, transport of viral DNA to the nucleus, and provirus expression, and enhances HIV-Tat protein-mediated IL-2 production. CD28 signaling upregulates expression of CXCR4, the T-tropic fusion coreceptor, but not CCR5, the macrophage-tropic coreceptor. Progression of HIV-infected individuals to the acquired immune deficiency syndrome (AIDS) is associated with loss of M-tropic strains and appearance of T-tropic strains. Before progression, *in vitro* expansion of T cells from HIV-infected individuals with anti-CD3 and anti-CD28 mAbs leads to loss of HIV through downregulation of CCR5, and production of MIP-1α, MIP-1β and RANTES, and provides a source of healthy T cells. However, following progression to a T-tropic strain of HIV, CD28 stimulation might increase virus load. Using HIV antigens and either B7-1 or B7-2 in naked DNA vaccines, B7-2 but not B7-1 stimulated both cytotoxic T lymphocyte and delayed-type hypersensitivity responses against HIV antigens in mice.

Tumors generally do not express costimulatory molecules. The B7 gene has been transfected into tumor cells in the hope that the tumor cells will gain costimulatory function and stimulate an antitumor response. Many B7-transfected tumor cell lines are rejected by their host. When an animal that has rejected a B7$^+$ tumor is challenged with parental tumor not expressing B7, the tumor is rejected, demonstrating that B7 can stimulate antitumor immunity. Immunity is best induced by live B7$^+$ tumor cells and is primarily CD8 T cell mediated. B7-transfected tumor cells can stimulate a successful immune response against established wild-type tumor if the tumor burden is small. Some studies find that B7-1 and B7-2 equivalently stimulate antitumor immunity, whereas others report that B7-1 is more effective.

CTLA4 has a greater than 400-fold higher avidity for B7 than does CD28 but is expressed only after T cell activation and at only 2–5% of the level of CD28 cell surface expression. In contrast to the stimulatory signal delivered by B7/CD28 interaction, the B7/CTLA4 interaction results in a downregulatory signal leading to inhibition of IL-2 production and cell cycle progression and to T cell death. An mAb with dual specificity that recognizes a common epitope shared by CTLA4 and CD28 positively stimulates T cell proliferation, suggesting that B7/CD28 signaling dominates over B7/CTLA4 signaling.

The differing avidities of B7 for CD28 and CTLA4 and their highly regulated temporal expression has led to a model in which moderate levels of B7 engage CD28 on resting T cells and costimulate T cell activation. Following activation, the T cell expresses CTLA4 and CD28, and with moderate to high levels of B7, both are engaged, with the stimulatory CD28 response dominating. As B7 expression declines to low levels, all available B7 is engaged by higher avidity CTLA4 and CTLA4 signaling leads to downregulation of the T cell response.

See also: **Anergy, T cell; Antigen-presenting cells; Autoimmunity; B lymphocyte activation; CD28; CD40 and its ligand; Cytotoxic T lymphocytes; Dendritic cells; Graft rejection; Human immunodeficiency viruses; Humoral immunity; Immunotherapy of tumors; Second signals for lymphocyte activation; T lymphocyte activation; Tolerance, peripheral; Tumors, immune response to.**

Further reading

Azuma M, Cayabyab M, Buck D, Phillips JH and Lanier LL (1992) CD28 interaction with B7 costimulates primary allogeneic proliferative responses and cytotoxicity mediated by small, resting T lymphocytes. *Journal of Experimental Medicine* **175**: 353–360.

Boise LH, Minn AJ, Noel PJ et al (1995) CD28 costimulation can promote T cell survival by enhancing the expression of bcl-xL. *Immunity* **3**: 87–98.

Borriello F, Sethna MP, Boyd SD et al (1997) B7-1 and B7-2 have overlapping, critical roles in immunoglobulin class switching and germinal center formation. *Immunity* **6**: 303–313.

Boussiotis VA, Freeman GJ, Gribben JG and Nadler LM (1996) The role of B7-1/B7-2:CD28/CTLA4 pathways in the prevention of anergy, induction of productive immunity and down-regulation of the immune response. *Immunological Reviews* **153**: 1–26.

Carroll RG, Riley JL, Levine BL et al (1997) Differential regulation of HIV-1 fusion cofactor expression by CD28 costimulation of CD4$^+$ T cells. *Science* **276**: 273–276.

Freeman GJ, Gribben JG, Boussiotis VA et al (1993) Cloning of B7-2: a CTLA4 counter-receptor that costimulates human T cell proliferation. *Science* **262**: 909–911.

Freeman GJ, Boussiotis VA, Anumanthan A et al (1995) B7-1 and B7-2 do not deliver identical costimulatory signals since B7-2 but not B7-1 preferentially costimulates the initial production of IL-4. *Immunity* **2**: 523–532.

Gimmi CD, Freeman GJ, Gribben JG, Gray G and Nadler LM (1993) Human T-cell clonal anergy is induced by antigen presentation in the absence of B7 costimulation.

Proceedings of the National Academy of Sciences of the USA 90: 6586–6590.

Gribben JG, Freeman GJ, Boussiotis VA *et al* (1995) CLTA4 mediates antigen-specific apoptosis of human T cells. *Proceedings of the National Academy of Sciences of the USA* 92: 811–815.

Kuchroo VK, Das MP, Brown JA *et al* (1995) B7-1 and B7-2 costimulatory molecules activate differentially the Th1/Th2 developmental pathways: application to auto-immune disease therapy. *Cell* 80: 707–718.

Lenschow DJ, Zeng Y, Thistlethwaite JR *et al* (1992) Long-term survival of xenogeneic pancreatic islet grafts induced by CTLA4Ig. *Science* 257: 789–792.

Lenschow DJ, Ho SC, Sattar H *et al* (1995) Differential effects of anti-B7-1 and anti-B7-2 monoclonal antibody treatment on the development of diabetes in the non-obese diabetic mouse. *Journal of Experimental Medicine* 181: 1145–1155.

Linsley PS, Greene JL, Brady W, Bajorath J, Ledbetter JA and Peach R (1994) Human B7-1 (CD80) and B7-2 (CD86) bind with similar avidities but distinct kinetics to CD28 and CTLA-4 receptors. *Immunity* 1: 793–801.

Townsend SE and Allison JP (1993) Tumor rejection after direct costimulation of CD8$^+$ T cells by B7-transfected melanoma cells. *Science* 259: 368–370.

Tsuyuki S, Tsuyuki J, Einsle K, Kopf M and Coyle AJ (1997) Costimulation through B7-2 (CD86) is required for the induction of a lung mucosal T helper cell 2 (T$_H$2) immune response and altered airway responsiveness. *Journal of Experimental Medicine* 185: 1671–1679.

Walunas TL, Lenschow DJ, Bakker CY *et al* (1994) CTLA-4 can function as a negative regulator of T cell activation. *Immunity* 1: 405–413.

Wu Y, Guo Y, Huang A *et al* (1997) CTLA-4-B7 interaction is sufficient to costimulate T-cell clonal expansion. *Journal of Experimental Medicine* 185: 1327–1335.

BABESIOSIS

Jeffrey A Gelfand and **Michael V Callahan**, Department of Medicine, Tufts University School of Medicine, Boston, Massachusetts, USA

Babesiosis is a malaria-like disease transmitted by parasitized ticks of the genus *Ixodes* during blood feeding. There are over 100 species of Babesia which, with Theileria, comprise the family Piroplasmorida. Both adult and nymph stages of the *Ixodes* ticks (*I. scapularis, I. pacificus, I. ricinus*) transmit the disease from reservoir competent-species, principally rodents, to humans (**Figure 1**). The rodent strain, *Babesia microti* (in the United States), and the cattle strains, *B. divergens* and *B. bovis* (in Europe), are responsible for the majority of human cases. Conditions favorable for human infection include presence of disease reservoir species (rodents), of suitable hosts for blood feeding (deer, cattle) and proximity to human populations. Disease transmission through blood products and transplacental and possible perinatal infection have been described. In the United States, the majority of cases occur in the Northeast, upper Midwest and Pacific Northwest. Recently, a new species of *Babesia*, designated WA-1, has been implicated in human babesiosis in Washington and northern California. Phylogenetic analysis of DNA isolated from this species demonstrates greater similarity with *B. gibsoni*, a canine form, and to theileria species than to species known to infect humans. A fatal case of babesiosis has also been reported from Missouri. The isolate, designated MO-1, was found to have antigenic similarities and ribosomal DNA

sequences similar to *B. divergens*, a strain that causes disease in cattle and humans in Europe.

Infection with the murine strain, *B. microti*, is typically a mild illness in healthy people; however, in the asplenic or immunocompromised patient, such as those with AIDS, lymphoma or transplant patient, the disease may be overwhelming. Infection with bovine strains *B. divergens* and *B. bovis*, as seen in Europe, occurs in asplenic patients and is often fatal. Initial symptoms of babesiosis are nonspecific and include fever, chills, nausea, vomiting, arthralgia, myalgia, headache, fatigue and dark urine. The presence of a rash similar to erythema chronicum migrans probably reflects simultaneous infection with *Borrelia burgdorferi*, which is transmitted by the same vector. Laboratory studies may show decreased haptoglobin, elevated reticulocytes and parasitized red cells on blood films. Leukocytosis is rare; however, thrombocytopenia is common. Patients often have a positive direct Coombs test, and urine studies reveal proteinuria and hemoglobinuria. Liver function tests often show mild elevations of alkaline phosphatase, serum bilirubin, aspartate transaminase, alanine transaminase and lactate dehydrogenase. Successful treatment involves combination drug therapy with clindamycin plus quinine, or atovaquone plus azithromycin. Emergence of resistant strains has been documented following monotherapy. Life-

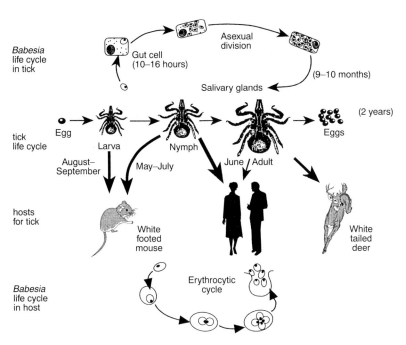

Figure 1 Life cycle of *Babesia*. The parasite requires the presence of *Ixodes* ticks, a reservoir-competent host animal such as rodent species, and large mammals for nymph and adult stages of the tick. Human infection occurs following the bite of infected nymph or adult ticks.

threatening cases may benefit from exchange blood transfusion.

The pathogen

After passage from the salivary glands of the tick into the vertebrate bloodstream, sporozoites penetrate and infect host erythrocytes (**Figure 1**). Following infection, *B. microti* undergo asynchronous, asexual budding and divide into two or four merozoites (daughter cells) (**Figure 2**). Intraerythrocyctic merozoites often appear in a ring form morphologically similar to *Plasmodium falciparum*, which has resulted in diagnostic confusion (**Figure 3**). Infection by the rodent species, *B. rhodaini*, has been shown

to involve the alternative complement pathway and the C3b receptor on rat erythrocytes. The parasite activates complement and fixes C3b to its surface, which in turn binds to the rat erythrocyte C3b receptor, leading to intracellular infection. Additionally, erythrocytes with C3 on their surface are infected, thus suggesting that complement facilitates the parasite–erythrocyte interaction. Following intracellular maturation, merozoites exit the erythrocyte, resulting in perforations and damage to the red cell membrane. The actual mechanism of hemolysis is unknown. Circadian hemolysis from synchronous schizogony, typified by the cyclic fevers of *Plasmod-*

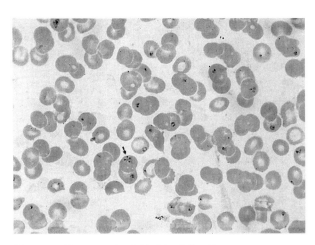

Figure 2 Giemsa-stained thin blood film. Four mature merozoites form the 'tetrad' or 'Maltese cross' prior to schizogony (single arrow). (Courtesy of Philip R. Daoust MD.)

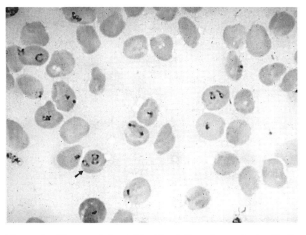

Figure 3 Giemsa-stained thin blood film of a patient with *B. microti*. Parasites often adopt intracellular ring forms that resemble *Plasmodium falciparum*. (Courtesy of Philip R. Daoust MD.)

ium infection, does not occur because schizogony is asynchronous.

Host response to babesia is poorly understood; however, the spleen is known to play a central role in immune defense. Asplenic patients and animals are more susceptible to infection by babesia and have increased parasitemia. Splenectomy and steroid therapy in animals and patients that have recovered from babesiosis may result in recrudescence of disease. As blood percolates through the spleen it is in close contact with splenic endothelium, macrophages and macrophage products. Erythrocytes must squeeze through intraendothelial spaces. Infected, deformed and potentially more rigid infected erythrocytes are more likely to be retained, where ingestion by macrophages or the action of macrophage products may serve to control the infection. Complement-sensitized erythrocytes would likely bind under these circumstances. Furthermore, complement activation by babesia could theoretically lead to the generation of tumor necrosis factor α (TNFα) and interleukin-1 (IL-1), enhancing local defense. Decreased complement levels, presumably secondary to activation, are frequently found in babesiosis. In addition, increased circulating C1q binding activity, presumably due to immune complexes, with a commensurate decrease in C4, C3 and CH50 levels, are seen in patients. The generation of these primarily macrophage-produced mediators (TNFα and IL-1) in turn could explain many of the clinical features (fever, anorexia, arthralgias, myalgias) of babesiosis, especially the fulminant shock syndrome of bovine babesiosis. It is likely that, in the less fulminant situation, TNFα functions to enhance the killing of *Babesia*, as with malaria. In addition to macrophage factors, other cellular immune functions appear to be important in the host response to *Babesia*. Nude mice and mice with greatly reduced T lymphocyte responses due to thymectomy, lethal irradiation or anti-T-lymphocyte serum develop significantly greater parasitemia. The disease itself alters cellular immune function. Patients with acute babesiosis have an increase in T suppressor/cytotoxic lymphocytes and decreased responses to lymphocyte mitogens with a polyclonal hypergammaglobulinemia.

See also: **Parasites, immunity to; Ungulate immune systems.**

Further reading

Benach JL, Habicht GS and Hamburger MI (1982) Immunoresponsiveness in acute babesiosis in humans. *Journal of Infectious Diseases* 146: 369–380.

Benach JL, Coleman JL, Habicht GS *et al* (1985) Serological evidence for simultaneous occurrences of Lyme disease and babesiosis. *Journal of infectious Diseases* 152: 473–477.

Dammin GJ (1978) Babesiosis. In: Weinstein L and Fields B (eds) *Seminars in Infectious Disease,* pp 169–199. New York: Stratton.

Esernio-Jenssen E, Scimeca PG, Benach JL *et al.* (1987) Transplacental/perinatal babesiosis. *Journal of Pediatrics* 110: 570–572.

Herwaldt B, Persing DH, Precigout EA *et al.* (1996) A fatal case of babesiosis in Missouri: identification of another piroplasm that infects humans. *Annals of Internal Medicine* 124: 643–650.

Jack RM and Ward PA (1980) *Babesia rodhaini* interactions with complement: relationship to parasitic entry into red cells. *Journal of Immunology* 124: 1566–1573.

Looareesuwan S, Ho M, Wattanagoon MB *et al* (1987) Dynamic alteration in splenic function during acute falciparum malaria. *New England Journal of Medicine* 312: 675–679.

Machtinger L, Telford SR III, Inducil C *et al* (1993) Treatment of babesiosis by red blood cell exchange in an HIV-positive splenectomized patient. *Journal of Clinical Apheresis* 8: 78–81.

Mintz ED, Anderson JF, Cabel RG *et al* (1991) Transfusion-transmitted babesiosis: a case report from new endemic area. *Transfusion* 31: 365–368.

Okusawa S, Yancey KB, van der Meer JWM *et al* (1988) C5a stimulates secretion of tumor necrosis factor from human mononuclear cells *in vitro*: comparison with secretion of interleukin-1β and interleukin-1α. *Journal of Experimental Medicine* 168: 443–448.

Persing DH and Conrad PA (1995) Babesiosis: new insights from phylogenetic analysis. *Infectious Agents and Disease* 4: 182–195.

Persing DH, Herwaldt BL, Glaser C *et al* (1995) Infection with a babesia-like organism in northern California. 332: 298–303.

Popovsky MA, Lindberg LE, Syrek AL *et al* (1988) Prevalence of *Babesia* antibodies in a selected blood donor population. *Transfusion* 28: 59–61.

Quick RE, Herwaldt BL, Thomoford JW *et al* (1993) Babesiosis in Washington State: a new species of *Babesia? Annals of Internal Medicine* 119: 284–290.

Sun T, Tenenbaum MJ, Greenspan J *et al* (1983) Morphologic and clinical observations in human infection with *Babesia microti. Journal of Infectious Diseases* 148: 239–248.

Takabayashi T, Vannier E, Margolis NH, Dinarello CA, Burke JF and Gelfand JA (1996) A new biologic role for C3a and C3a desArg: regulation of TNF-α and IL-1β synthesis. *Journal of Immunology* 158: 3455–3460.

Taverne J, Matthews N, Depledge P *et al* (1984) Malarial parasites and tumor cells are killed by the same component of tumor necrosis serum. *Clinical and Experimental Immunology* 57: 293–300.

Wittner M, Lederman J, Tanowitz HB *et al* (1996) Atovaquone in the treatment of *Babeisa microti* infections in hamsters. *American Journal of Tropical Medicine* 55: 219–222.

BACILLUS, INFECTION AND IMMUNITY

Brian W McBride and **Peter CB Turnbull**, Centre for Applied Microbiology and Research, Porton Down, UK

The best known member of the genus *Bacillus*, *Bacillus anthracis*, the causative agent of anthrax, was a major scourge for humans and animals from antiquity to just a few decades ago. The extensive history associated with anthrax dating back to about 1250 BC has been well reviewed. It features in classical writings, and several pandemics evidently occurred in Europe and Russia from medieval times to the mid-1800s. By the time it was realized at the end of the nineteenth century that one agent was responsible for several manifestations, the disease had become known by a wide variety of names, such as black bane, malignant carbuncle, rag picker's disease, Siberian plague, woolsorter's disease and numerous equivalents in other languages. It was with anthrax that Koch established his famous postulates in 1876, and history's first bacterial vaccines were against anthrax.

Other members of the genus only began to feature in literature in the early part of the twentieth century and, because of the extreme diversity of the species comprising it, organization of the taxonomy and classification within the genus has only developed very slowly and remains a challenge for today's taxonomists. For most practical purposes, the classification and identification system laid down by Gordon and colleagues in 1973 continues to be the most helpful for the principal species encountered in the context of infection and immunity.

Description and distribution of the genus

The family Bacillaceae comprises the rod-shaped bacteria which form endospores. The two principal subdivisions are the anaerobic spore-forming bacilli of the genus *Clostridium* and the aerobic or facultatively anaerobic endospore formers constituting the genus *Bacillus*. Familiarly known as aerobic spore-bearing bacilli (ASB), they are gram positive or gram variable and the majority are motile by peritrichous flagella. The endospores, one per vegetative mother cell, are resistant to adverse physical and chemical conditions. They are mostly saprophytes, having a wide diversity of physiological characteristics, which, together with their ability to form hardy spores, enables them to be widely distributed in nature from Arctic environments to hot springs and desert sands and from fresh water to salt or marine sediments. Thermophilic and psychrophilic, acidophilic and alkaliphilic, and halophilic representatives exist which are capable of growing at extremes of temperature, pH or salt concentration that would inhibit or destroy life processes in other living organisms. The spores are dispersed in dust, water and on materials of plant or animal origin.

Importance

As a result of their wide-ranging physiological characteristics and the myriad of enzymes, antibiotics and other metabolites they elaborate, *Bacillus* species are important in a host of medical, agricultural, pharmaceutical or other industrial applications and processes. Among the better known antibiotics are bacitracin from *B. licheniformis* or *B. subtilis*, polymyxin from *B. polymyxa* and gramicidin from *B. brevis*. Several are important in antibiotic assays (*B. pumilus*, *B. cereus*, *B. stearothermophilus*) or other health-related assays, e.g. folic acid (*B. coagulans*), aflatoxin (*B. megaterium*) and hexachlorophene (*B. subtilis*). Certain *Bacillus* species are utilized for degradation of pollutants and waste materials. One strain of *B. cereus* is the active ingredient of an antidiarrheal formulation prescribed in certain countries of Europe. The spores of the thermophilic *B. stearothermophilus* are particularly well suited to checking heat sterilization procedures for laboratory, surgical, pharmaceutical and food preservation processes, and *B. subtilis* var *globigii* (NCTC 10073), having a high resistance to heat, radiation and chemical disinfectants, is used for validating alternative sterilization and fumigation procedures. Contrariwise, the resistance of spores to heat, radiation, disinfectants and desiccation results in *Bacillus* species being troublesome contaminants in pharmaceutical products, foods, surgical theatres and dressings, etc. *B. thuringiensis*, *B. popilliae*, *B. sphaericus*, *B. larvae* and *B. lentimorbus* are insect pathogens. The first three are utilized in commerical insecticides for controlling crop-destroying and disease-carrying insects; *B. thuringiensis* has the widest use in this context, providing control of an extensive range of pests on many different crop types.

Bacillus species and diseases

That the etiological agent of anthrax is a *Bacillus* species, namely *B. anthracis*, was mentioned at the outset. The pathogenic potential of ASB other than *B. anthracis* has become increasingly recognized in the past three decades with a proliferation of reports implicating *Bacillus* species, particularly *B. cereus*, in distinct emetic and diarrheal types of food poisoning and in infections of immunocompromised or otherwise debilitated hosts (e.g. alcoholics, diabetics), in mixed or secondary infections or occasionally in primary infections in otherwise healthy humans or animals.

Species in addition to *B. anthracis* that have been implicated on one or more occasions in published reports on infections are *B. cereus* (numerous reports), *B. licheniformis* and *B. subtilis* (several reports), *B. alvei*, *B. brevis*, *B. circulans*, *B. coagulans*, *B. macerans*, *B. pumilus*, *B. sphaericus* and *B. thuringiensis* (a few reports). Among the types of infection involved apart from food poisoning are bacteremia/septicemia, endocarditis, meningitis, ophthalmitis, respiratory and urinary tract infections and severe wound infections.

Virulence factors in anthrax

Bacillus anthracis depends for its virulence on two factors: 1) a polypeptide (poly-γ-D glutamic acid) capsule protecting it from phagocytosis, and 2) a toxin comprised of three protein components termed protective antigen (PA – 83 kDa), lethal factor (LF – 90 kDa) and edema factor (EF – 89 kDa). By the currently accepted model, PA binds to host cell surface receptors and is activated by a host cell protease, furin, which cleaves off a 20 kDa piece, thereby exposing a secondary receptor site for which LF and EF compete to bind on the active PA (PA63). Complexes of PA + LF (lethal toxin) or PA + EF (edema toxin) are then internalized, apparently in heptameric complexes, by receptor-mediated endocytosis, with the LF or EF being released into the cytosol from the endosome following acidification. There is some analogy here to the A–B complex of cholera toxin, with EF and LF acting as alternate 'A' (active) moieties competing for the same entry mechanisms and with PA as the 'B' (binding) moiety, with PA probably creating ion-conductive channels across the eukaryotic cell membrane through which LF and EF gain access to the interior of the cell. Edema factor is a calmodulin-dependent adenylate cyclase (calmodulin only being present in eurkaryotic cells). The only other known bacterial adenylate cyclase toxin component is that of *Bordetella pertussis* but the two do not appear to be closely related structurally, genetically or antigenically, although some genetic and antigenic homologies have been noted.

LF appears to be a calcium- and zinc-dependent metalloenzyme. It is generally believed that the LF + PA complex is the major cause of tissue damage and death, with systemic shock and death seemingly resulting from the effects of high levels of cytokines (see below).

The precise kinetics of production of PA, LF and EF are not known; they appear to be elaborated concurrently and can be detected in cultures from early log phase onwards. Virulence differences among strains have not been associated with differences in quantity or rate of toxin production by different strains, and the toxin from different strains appears identical in all respects – attributable to it being encoded on a plasmid. The origin of the toxin components in the *B. anthracis* cell has not been elucidated.

The two virulence factors of *B. anthracis*, toxin and capsule, are genetically encoded on two large plasmids, respectively pX01 (175 kb) and pX02 (90 kb). The genes for each of the toxin components *pag*, *lef* and *cya* and for the membrane associated enzymes mediating D-glutamic acid polyermization have all been sequenced.

Pathogenesis and host resistance in anthrax

Lethal toxin (LF + PA) and edema toxin (EF + PA) are now regarded as being responsible for the characteristic symptoms and course of anthrax. LF + PA is cytolytic for mouse peritoneal macrophages and kills certain mouse macrophage cell lines; EF + PA impairs the phagocytic function of neutrophils but EF + PA, LF + PA, or EF + LF + PA stimulate neutrophil chemotaxis.

There has long been fascination over the seemingly inverse relationship between susceptibility to toxin and susceptibility to infection. Rats, for example, are highly susceptible to the toxin (LD_{50} (median lethal dose) of Fischer 344 rat = 0.5 µg LF + $\approx$2.5 µg PA) but highly resistant to the infection (intramuscular $LD_{50} \sim 10^6$ spores), while guinea pigs are relatively resistant to the toxin (LD_{50} = 50 µg LF + $\approx$ 250 µg PA) but highly susceptible to infection (intramuscular $LD_{50} < 10$ spores). The underlying host defense mechanisms responsible for this paradox have not been elucidated but it indicates that resistance to infection may involve a separate mechanism than that required for resistance to lethal toxicity. If resistance to infection is due to the number and availability of macrophages then this protective mechanism would also provide a larger target population of macrophages for the effect of LF toxin.

The *in vivo* depletion of mouse macrophages by the use of repeated injections of silica has elucidated the key role macrophages play in the disease process. BALB/c mice depleted of macrophages are resistant to lethal toxin (LT) but can be made sensitive to it by adoptive transfer of 10^8 RAW264.7 cells (a toxin-sensitive monocyte/macrophage cell line). The *in vivo* transfer of the same number of the LT-resistant mouse macrophage line IC-21 cells does not restore sensitivity. Resistant cells have been shown to possess normal numbers of receptors for PA and are able to activate PA and bind and internalize LF and EF. In addition, introduction of LF into the cytosol of resistant cells does not result in cell death, indicating that these cells may lack the cytosolic target of LF. Genetic studies involving resistance to nonencapsulated bacilli indicate that resistance may be controlled by a single dominant locus or gene complex.

Analysis of cytokine levels produced by RAW264.7 cells *in vitro* has revealed that levels of LT as low as 10^{-9} µg ml^{-1} LF with 0.1 µg ml^{-1} PA induce synthesis of high levels of tumour necrosis factor (TNF) and interleukin-1. Neutralizing antisera to each of these cytokines injected into mice 24 hours before challenge with LT provides partial protection, while complete protection is achieved when the antisera are combined. These results strongly implicate the release of these factors in the cause of death of toxin-treated animals by a septic shock-type mechanism. Whether this and differences in susceptibilities of macrophages to LF + PA/EF + PA are related beyond mouse models to inter- and intraspecies differences in susceptibility to *B. anthracis* or its toxin remains to be determined.

Virulence factors and pathogenesis of other *Bacillus* species

The state of knowledge on virulence factors of *Bacillus* species other than *B. anthracis* is less advanced owing to the relatively spasmodic association between these species and infections and to the absence of adequate models for analyzing the candidate factors and determining their actions in the laboratory.

Bacillus species characteristically produce a host of enzymes and other extracellular metabolites. Among those of *B. cereus*, four groups of what are broadly described as toxins have been distinguished and most of these are believed also to be virulence determinants in infections. These are:

1 Three phospholipases C (alias lecithinase, egg-yolk turbidity factor), phosphatidylcholine hydrolase (23 kDa), phosphatidylinositol hydrolase (phosphatasemic factor, 29 kDa) and sphingomyelinase (29 kDa). Although under normal *in vivo* circumstances they cannot reach their phospholipid substrates in the eukaryotic cell membrane, they may conceivably act secondarily after exposure of the phospholipids in wounds or other infections. Sphingomyelinase is also hemolytic.

2 Hemolysin I (alias cereolysin), a thiol-activated thermolabile protein cytolysin with a single 518 amino acid polypeptide chain of 55 kDa. The binding-site of the thiol-activated cytolysins on the eukaryotic cell membrane is cholesterol and binding results in pitting and micropuncturing of the cell membrane, leading to loss of control of ion exchange. The net flow of ions and water into the cell leads to swelling and rupture. However, cereolysin is inactivated by free cholesterol in the blood, which presumably limits its activities in natural infections. It is almost instantly lethal on intravenous injection in mice and causes necrosis if injected into skin.

3 Hemolysin II (HBL), consisting of a protein (component B, 36 kDa) which binds to or alters cells, allowing subsequent lysis by a second protein (component L, 45 kDa). This appears also to be the necrotic enterotoxin responsible for diarrheal-type *B. cereus* food poisoning and occasional severe wound, eye and other infections. It is almost instantly lethal if injected intravenously in mice; unlike cereolysin, this activity is not neutralized by cholesterol.

4 Emetic principle. This is a highly stable, small molecular weight entity, or group of entities, capable of surviving extremes of heat and pH and not susceptible to proteolytic enzymes. It may be associated with breakdown products from the implicated food, although it has recently been proposed that it is now identifiable as 'cereulide', a novel dodecadepsipeptide.

The protein cytotoxin enterotoxin identified by Japanese workers in 1991 may represent a fifth group. The different toxins appear to be produced to different extents by different strains, which may account for the varying degrees of seriousness of *B. cereus* infections.

Toxins have not been demonstrated in culture fluids or extracts of other *Bacillus* species periodically implicated in infections and, assuming they did play active roles in the infections from which they were isolated, the basis of their pathogenic activity is not clear.

Acquired immunity: vaccines

The polypeptide capsule of *B. anthracis* is only weakly antigenic and there is little evidence to suggest it contributes to naturally acquired immunity or can produce artificially induced protection against anthrax. Pasteur derived his vaccine strains by subculturing at 42–43°C and was inadvertently curing the bacilli of pX01. However, cap⁺/tox⁻ strains are, in fact, not protective and both the partial efficacy and the residual virulence of Pasteur's vaccines are now explained in terms of mixed cultures with residual uncured forms. Cap⁻/tox⁺ strains of *B. anthracis* are protective and one such strain, produced by Sterne in 1937, has remained to this day the basis of a highly successful live-spore animal vaccine, although this vaccine too retains some residual virulence in certain susceptible species (albeit considerably less than wild type tox⁺/cap⁺ *B. anthracis*), such as guinea pigs, a number of inbred strains of mice and certain livestock species, notably goats and llamas. As a result of this, it is considered unsuitable in the West for use in humans, although a live-spore vaccine similar to the animal vaccine is administered by scarification to people in the countries of the former USSR and in China. In the West, human vaccines developed in the 1950s and 1960s are available and consist essentially of aluminum hydroxide-adsorbed cell-free filtrates of cultures of a noncapsulating, nonproteolytic derivative of strain V770 originating from a case of bovine anthrax in 1951 (US vaccine) and alum-precipitated cell-free filtrates of Sterne strain cultures (UK vaccine). Several doses are required, however, for these to take effect and the results of animal tests suggest it may be possible to improve their efficacy; attempts are now being made to do this using the rapidly expanding knowledge of what is and what is not needed for protection.

With recently acquired techniques for purification and genetic manipulation of the toxin components, it has become clear that immune responses to PA, but not to LF or EF, are essential for protection. However, studies have also indicated that, while antibody responses to EF and LF are weak in mice immunized with spores of *B. anthracis* strains capable of only producing either EF or LF, immunization with strains producing either PA or EF or PA and LF resulted in higher antibody responses to EF or LF, respectively. In addition, studies have indicated a synergistic relationship between PA and LF or EF in immunoprotection. These results may indicate a requirement for EF and LF to be internalized, via PA, and intracellularly processed in order to produce substantial antibody responses. Notwithstanding this, the protection induced by PA alone can be raised to levels equivalent to and as long-lasting as that conferred by the live-spore vaccine if purified PA is administered together with killed whole-cell microbial supplements such as Freund's complete adjuvant, *Bordetella pertussis* or *Corynebacterium ovis*, or complex cell wall extracts from the tubercle bacillus ('Tri-Mix' and 'De Tox', Ribi ImmunoChem Research, Hamilton, Montana, USA). This nonspecific stimulation of protection indicates involvement of some cellular immune mechanisms – more than that simply produced by inciting a coincidental inflammatory response as the performance of PA is not enhanced by an irritant such as saponin.

To date, PA is the only antigen shown to induce substantial protective immunity. Studies on monoclonal antibodies directed against PA, which neutralize lethal toxin activity, either *in vivo* or *in vitro*, have identified at least three nonoverlapping antigenic regions. Two of these regions are involved in the binding of LF to cell-bound PA (the first region mapping between amino acids Ile581 or Asn601 and the second within the PA17 fragment produced by limited chymotrypsin digest of PA63). The third region is involved in the binding of PA to cells and maps between amino acids Asp671 and Ile721 of the carboxy-terminus of PA. The elucidation of the protective motifs on PA may eventually lead to the introduction of a subunit-based vaccine. The relationships between the toxin, the development of the characteristic massive bacteremia of anthrax and the mechanism by which antibodies to PA, a log phase metabolite, prevent this bacterial multiplication, remain to be elucidated. The development of a vaccine dependent on an antigen apparent to the immune system at the outset of the infection, rather than during the log phase of growth, appears to be unachievable.

Passive immunity was tried in Europe in the early part of the twentieth century in the treatment of anthrax but was discontinued many years ago as being of negligible value. In the light of modern plasmapheresis technology, it may be appropriate to reconsider this; it is possible that plasma from vaccinated individuals may offer a life-saving supplement to treatment in individuals diagnosed late in the course of a fulminating anthrax infection. Interestingly, antianthrax (horse) serum is still administered together with penicillin in the treatment of human anthrax in China.

Infections by *Bacillus* species other than *B. anthracis* are too infrequent and varied to merit development of any vaccines; consequently the topic of immunity in relation to such infections is an area that has not been studied.

See also: **Attenuated organisms as vaccines; Bacterial cell walls; Toxins.**

Further reading

Beecher DJ and MacMillan JD (1990) A novel bicomponent hemolysin from *Bacillus cerus*. *Infection and Immunity* 58: 2220–2227.

Ezzell JW, Ivins BE and Leppla SH (1984) Immunoelectrophoretic analysis, toxicity, and kinetics of *in vitro* production of the protective antigen and lethal factor components of *Bacillus anthracis* toxin. *Infection and Immunity* 45: 761–767.

Gordon RE, Haynes WC and Pang GH-N (1973) *The Genus* Bacillus. USDA, ARS, Agricultural Handbook, No. 427. Washington DC: US Government Printing Office.

Hanna PC, Acosta D and Collier RJ (1993) On the role of macrophages in anthrax. *Proceeding sof the National Academy of Science of the USA* 90: 10198–10201.

Ivins B, Fellows P, Pitt LW *et al* (1995) Experimental anthrax vaccines: efficacy of adjuvants combined with protective antigen against an aerosol *Bacillus anthracis* spore challenge in guinea pigs. *Vaccine* 13: 1779–1784.

Kramer JM and Gilbert RJ (1989) *Bacillus cerus* and other *Bacillus* species. In: Doyle MP (ed) *Foodborne Bacterial Pathogens*, pp 21–70. New York: Marcel Dekker.

Leppla SH (1995) Anthrax toxins. In: Moss J, Iglewski B, Vaughan M and Tu AT (eds) *Handbook of Natural Toxins*, vol 8, pp 543–572. New York: Marcel Dekker.

Little SF, Novak JM, Lowe JR *et al* (1996) Characterization of lethal factor binding and cell receptor binding domains of protective antigen of *Bacillus anthracis* using monoclonal antibodies. *Microbiology* 142: 707–715.

Milne JC, Furlong D, Hanna PC, Wall JS and Collier RJ (1994) Anthrax protective antigen forms oligomers during intoxication of mammalian cells. *Journal of Biological Chemistry* 269: 20606–20612.

Pezard C, Weber M, Sirard J-C, Berche P and Mock M (1995) Protective immunity by *Bacillus anthracis* toxindeficient strains. *Infection and Immunity* 63: 1369–1372.

Proceedings of the International Workshop on Anthrax, 19–21 September 1995, Winchester, England. Salisbury Medical Bulletin No. 87 (special suppl) 1996.

Turnbull PCB (1986) *Bacillus cereus* toxins. In: Dorner F and Drews J (eds) *Pharmacology of Bacterial Toxins. International Encyclopedia of Pharmacology and Therapeutics*, section 119, pp 397–448. Oxford: Pergamon Press.

Turnbull PCB (1990) Anthrax. In: Smith GR and Eason CR (eds) *Bacterial Diseases, Topley and Wilson's Principles of Bacteriology, Virology and Immunity*, vol 3, pp 365–379. Sevenoaks: Edward Arnold.

Turnbull PCB and Kramer JM (1995) *Bacillus*. In: Murray PR (ed) *Manual of Clinical Microbiology*, 6th edn, pp 349–356. Washington DC: ASM Press.

BACTERIA, IMMUNITY TO

Graham AW Rook, Department of Bacteriology, University College London Medical School, London, UK

Bacteria cause disease because of toxicity, invasiveness, immunopathology, or blends of these three mechanisms. Thus much of the interaction between a given bacterial species and the immune response can be predicted by considering the immunological mechanisms available in relation to the mechanism of pathogenicity, and the structure of the bacterium. For a toxigenic bacterium, neutralizing antibody may be all that is needed. Otherwise destruction of the organism itself may be required.

Nonspecific defenses

Nonspecific recognition of common bacterial structures

Much of the defense against bacteria depends on pathways which have nothing to do with the specific antigen receptors of either B cells or T cells, and probably antedate these in evolution. Many bacteria are simply excluded by barriers such as skin, acidity in gut and vagina, commensals occupying the relevant niche, entrapment by mucus, etc. If not excluded, the organism may be recognized by:

1. Acute phase proteins, C-reactive protein and mannose-binding protein which also fix complement.
2. Receptors for the formyl peptides released by bacteria which are chemoattractants and activators of phagocytes.
3. Receptors for bacterial cell wall components, glycolipids, glucans and other polysaccharides that nonspecifically enhance the immune response, and can be used as immunological adjuvants.
4. Complement, activated in the absence of antibody by a wide range of bacterial components.

5. Receptors that lead to cytokine release. The bacterial products which do this include endotoxin (lipopolysaccharide, LPS) of gram-negative organisms, lipoteichoic acids of gram-positive cocci, and the lipoarabinomannan of mycobacteria. It is probable that all bacteria contain cytokine triggers.

Nonspecific recognition and selection of response mechanism   Collectively these nonspecific recognition pathways perform crucial functions. First, the pattern of nonspecific recognition events, cytokines and bacterial products supplies information as to the type of immune response that needs to be activated. This immunoregulatory 'decision' is particularly important because activation of inappropriate effector mechanisms can lead to enhanced susceptibility rather than to protection. These features account for the 'adjuvant' properties of bacterial components, which are often used by immunologists to boost or direct responses to other antigens. For example, the adjuvant properties of *Bordetella pertussis* and *Mycobacterium tuberculosis* impose different balances of T_H1 to T_H2 cytokines on the T cell response to any simultaneously administered antigen. If the immune system activates a T_H2 pattern of response to a mycobacterial pathogen, accelerated disease will result.

Other factors influencing the T_H1/T_H2 balance of the T cell response   Dose and the different handling of soluble versus particulate antigen are also important. Low dose soluble antigen selectively primes T_H2, while low dose particulate antigen selectively primes T_H1. These relationships reverse as dose is increased. The reason appears to be that presentation of low dose soluble antigen is mostly by B cells, which tend to drive T_H2, while presentation of low dose particulate antigen (such as bacteria, or *Leishmania*) is mostly by macrophages, which tend to drive T_H1.

Local metabolism within lymph nodes of glucocorticoids (cortisol), and of dehydroepiandrosterone (which yields metabolites that oppose some effects of cortisol), also profoundly influences T_H1/T_H2 cytokine balance. Cortisol diverts the response to T_H2, and is partly responsible for increased susceptibility to certain infections in stressed individuals.

Nonspecific recognition and early defense: the protective role of cytokines   The nonspecific recognition events cause sufficient activation of the immune system to mobilize a 'holding operation' that can control bacterial growth while specific immunity develops. The cytokines released have rapid protective effects, but if their release is excessive or prolonged, they can cause severe immunopathology, and even death (see below). Nevertheless tumor necrosis factor α (TNFα) protects mice from *M. avium, Legionella pneumophila, Streptococcus pneumoniae* and *Klebsiella*. The mechanisms of protection by cytokines, particularly TNFα, include rapid induction (<5 min) of increased adhesion of neutrophils to endothelial cells, increased expression of CR3 and other cell adhesion molecules, priming of neutrophils for enhanced production of oxygen reduction products, and activation of macrophages. Cytokines also affect 'nonprofessional' phagocytes, and exposure of Hep-2 cells (derived from a human carcinoma of the larynx) to TNFα renders them resistant to invasion by *Salmonella typhimurium*. Similarly, interferon γ (IFNγ) derived from natural killer (NK) cells will activate killing mechanisms in macrophages.

Interactions of bacteria with complement   Numerous bacterial components can activate the alternative pathway. This results in three categories of protective function:

1. Release of the chemotactic products. C3a and C5a. These cause smooth muscle contraction, mast cell degranulation, and neutrophil chemotaxis and activation.
2. Attachment to the organism of derivatives of C3, which play an important role in the subsequent interaction with phagocytes.
3. Killing of some gram-negative organisms if the lytic complex C5b–C9 gains access to the outer lipid bilayer.

Many organisms have devised strategies to resist these effects of complement. Some capsules are very poor activators of the alternative pathway. Alternatively, long side-chains (O antigens) on LPS may fix C3b at a distance from the vulnerable lipid bilayer. Similarly, smooth gram-negative organisms (*Escherichia coli, Salmonella, Pseudomonas*) may fix but then rapidly shed the C5b–C9 membrane complex. Capsules rich in sialic acid (like host cell membranes) promote the inactivation of C3b by interaction with factors H and I, and *Neisseria meningitidis, E. coli* K1 and group B streptococci resist complement attachment in this way. The M protein of group A streptococci acts as an acceptor for factor H and there is a gene for a C5a protease close to the M protein gene.

Role of antibody

Antibody clearly plays a crucial role during infections with toxigenic organisms. It neutralizes diphtheria toxin by blocking the attachment of the binding portion of the molecule to its target cells. Similarly it may block locally acting toxins, extracellular matrix-degrading enzymes which act as spreading factors, and motility due to flagella. An important function on external surfaces, often performed by secretory immunoglobulin A (IgA), is inhibition of binding of bacteria to epithelial cells. It is also likely that some antibodies to the bacterial surface can block functional requirements of the organism such as receptors for iron-chelating compounds or the intake of nutrients. However, the most important role of antibody in immunity to nontoxigenic bacteria is the more efficient targeting of complement so that even organisms that resist the alternative pathway by the mechanisms described in the previous section are damaged by complement, or become coated with C3 products.

Interactions between bacteria and phagocytic cells

The important consequence of the inflammatory and chemotactic events triggered by bacteria in the tissues is the enhanced exposure of the bacteria to phagocytic cells.

Binding, uptake and the triggering of killing

The first stage in the intracellular killing is the attachment of the organism to the surface of the phagocyte. This important and complex interaction determines whether uptake occurs, and whether killing mechanisms are triggered. In addition to complement and antibody, this interaction can involve C-reactive protein, lectins on the organisms and on host cell membranes, the family of adhesion-promoting receptors CR3, LFA-1, p150,95 and the integrins. Some organisms are able to enter cells via unconventional receptors, such as integrins, and so avoid triggering killing mechanisms.

Antimicrobial mechanisms of phagocytic cells

Activation of antimicrobial functions

Monocytes and polymorphonuclear cells possess a number of oxygen-dependent and oxygen-independent antimicrobial mechanisms. These, while often constitutively expressed, can be activated directly by bacterial products or by cytokines such as IFNγ.

Oxygen-dependent pathways: derivatives of superoxide anion   Oxygen is reduced by a membrane-associated cytochrome system which transfers an electron onto molecular oxygen to form superoxide anion ($O \cdot \frac{-}{2}$), usually during phagocytosis. Subsequent interactions give rise to hydrogen peroxide (H_2O_2), hydroxyl radicals ($\cdot OH$), and perhaps singlet oxygen ($\Delta^1 O_2$), which is oxygen with one electron in a high energy state. These toxic intermediates are generated in the absence of myeloperoxidase (MPO) and therefore do not require fusion of the MPO-containing lysosomes with the phagosome. If fusion does occur, MPO catalyzes the formation of hypohalous acids from H_2O_2 and halides.

Oxygen-dependent pathways: nitric oxide   Nitric oxide (NO) is formed from the guanidino nitrogen of L-arginine, by NO synthase, yielding citrulline as the other product. Formation of NO is enhanced by exposure to IFNγ and a trigger of TNFα release such as endotoxin, or the equivalent cytokine triggers of other organisms. The NO is a relaxant of vascular smooth muscle and has poorly understood roles in intracellular signaling. Within macrophages it probably acts as an antimicrobial agent, though such effects are difficult to distinguish from its signaling role. Whatever the mechanism, agents that block NO synthase enhance growth of *M. tuberculosis* within macrophages both *in vivo* and *in vitro*. It is more difficult to make human macrophages generate high levels of NO, but it is now clear that they can do if stimulated with mixtures of cytokines (interleukin 4 (IL-4) and IFNγ) or further triggered by cross-linking CD23.

Oxygen-independent pathways

Some oxygen-independent killing may be due to the sequential exposure to lysozyme and neutral proteases at pH 7.0–8.0, followed by acid hydrolases after the acidification step, but several more specific pathways have now been defined.

Cationic proteins   Human granulocytes contain cationic proteins with microbicidal activity. Six have been sequenced and are cysteine- and arginine-rich peptides of 32–34 amino acids with molecular weights of about 4 kDa. They are representatives of a conserved family of related mammalian 'antibiotics' which have been named 'defensins'. Similar proteins are found in the granules of rabbit alveolar macrophages but not in human macrophages, although these contain other cationic antibacterial substances, some of which are enzymes, which kill gram-positive and -negative bacteria and fungi by mechanisms quite independent of their enzymatic activity. Moreover, it is likely that the uptake of enzymes and cations from other cells plays a significant role in macrophage antibacterial function *in vivo*. The defensins will kill organisms as diverse as *Staphylococcus aureus*, *Pseudomonas aeruginosa*, *E. coli*, *Cryptococcus neoformans* and even the enveloped virus, *Herpes simplex*.

Tryptophan deprivation   Exposure to IFNγ causes degradation of tryptophan in monocytes and fibroblasts. This amino acid is essential for some pathogens.

Cell-mediated immunity

This term is usually reserved for immunity that involves direct intervention of T lymphocytes. One of their functions is the release of lymphokines, which has several types of consequence.

1. Lymphokines attract monocytes and polymorphonuclear cells to the site of infection.
2. Lymphokines enhance antimicrobial functions of phagocytic cells. The major lymphokine for these functions is IFNγ.
3. It is likely that the mechanisms described in 1) and 2) constitute the basis for the delayed hypersensitivity reaction to skin-test challenge with soluble antigen, typified by the Mantoux test.
4. When release of lymphokines and accumulation of mononuclear cells is persistent, the characteristic T cell-dependent tuberculoid granulomas are formed. These granulomas can be isolated and the release of cytokines monitored *in vitro*. *In vivo* TNFα also seems to be involved and neutralizing antibodies to TNFα will block granuloma formation in response to BCG. It is likely that granulomas serve to isolate organisms within a focus of activated macrophages.
5. IFNγ also evokes antimicrobial mechanisms in other cells, such as endothelial cells which are incapable of the oxidative burst, as shown with *Rickettsia* and *Chlamydia psittaci*. Many cell types are capable of activation to produce nitric oxide.

Cytotoxic T cells

Cytotoxic T cells are also generated during the cell-mediated response to intracellular pathogens. These can kill infected or antigen-pulsed macrophages. It is becoming apparent that this phenomenon is at least as important as macrophage activation and may serve to release bacteria from macrophages that are failing to kill ingested bacteria and are merely acting as sites for intracellular growth. Following the death

of such cells, the bacteria can be taken up by fresh activated phagocytes.

Until recently the term 'cytotoxic T cell' was almost synonymous with CD8$^+$ T cells with α/β receptors, recognizing peptide epitopes presented by major histocompatibility complex (MHC) class I. Now several other T cell types are known to be potentially cytotoxic, including some CD4$^+$ cells.

γ/δ T cells   In the mouse, mycobacterial infection leads to a disproportionate increase in the γ/δ T cell receptor-bearing population. Moreover γ/δ T cells which respond to mycobacterial antigens can be isolated from the lesions of some types of leprosy, and a strikingly high percentage of the circulating γ/δ T cells from normal donors respond to *M. tuberculosis*. Among the antigens recognized by these cells are heat shock proteins, compounds containing 5′-triphosphorylated thymidine, and phenyl pyrophosphate derivatives. They are cytotoxic and usually IFNγ secreting.

CD4$^-$CD8$^-$ CD1-restricted α/β T cells   These T cells recognize antigens presented by CD1, which is a remotely MHC class I-like membrane glycoprotein. Clones have been identified that respond to mycobacterial glycolipids and lipids, so like γ/δ cells they indicate that recognition of bacteria by T cells does not depend only on recognition of peptide epitopes.

NK cells   These lymphocytes kill cells that fail to express self MHC class I. There is unconfirmed evidence that some NK cells can directly damage certain bacteria. NK cells also play a role in macrophage activation through release of IFNγ. This pathway may provide the source of IFNγ in severe combined immunodeficiency (SCID) mice, which are unexpectedly resistant to many infections.

Avoidance of antimicrobial mechanisms of phagocytic cells

Organisms may secrete toxins which repel or kill the phagocytes. Capsules of carbohydrate (*Str. pneumoniae*) or polypeptide (*Bacillus anthracis*) may impede complement deposition and phagocytosis. The M proteins of group A streptococci limit uptake by phagocytes, while permitting specific attachment to the epithelium of the oropharynx. Other organisms are taken up, but fail to trigger the oxidative burst. Secretion of polyanions or ammonia have been reported to block phagolysosome fusion, although the methods used to demonstrate these phenomena have recently been re-evaluated. Superoxide dismutase and catalase can degrade oxygen intermediates, and the phenolic glycolipid secreted by *M. leprae* may act as a scavenger of oxygen radicals. The lipoarabinomannan released from mycobacteria may inhibit lymphokine-mediated macrophage activation, as murine macrophages heavily infected with *M. leprae* cannot be activated to kill a protozoan. Other organisms avoid antimicrobial mechanisms by escaping from the phagosome. *M. leprae* and *Shigella flexneri* can multiply free in the cytoplasm, while *Brucella abortus* and *Legionella pneumophila* are found in the rough endoplasmic reticulum.

It is increasingly apparent that many bacteria, like viruses, hijack cellular machinery for their own use. *Listeria monocytogenes* uses 'hemolysins' to lyse the phagosome, and then interacts with actin in the cell in order to propel itself towards and into neighbouring cells. Finally, some organisms, such as *M. tuberculosis* tend to kill the macrophage, perhaps by rendering them sensitive to the TNFα which they themselves are induced to release.

Mechanisms of immunopathology

Septicemic shock and the adult respiratory distress syndrome

The cytokine release triggered by bacterial components has a protective and immunoregulatory role as described above, but when excessive, as during septicemia, there can be excessive systemic activation of phagocytes and of endothelial cells. The latter leads to adhesion of phagocytes to the endothelium, initiation of the clotting cascade via expression of tissue thromboplastin, and eventually to diffuse intravascular coagulation that exhausts the clotting system and leads to a clotting defect. Mediators such as platelet-activating factor (PAF) and NO are released, blood pressure falls and hemorrhage may occur. Neutralizing antibodies to tissue thromboplastin or inhibitors of PAF can attenuate this syndrome. A neutralizing antibody to TNFα is protective in a model of septicemic shock in the baboon. The systemic toxicity of TNFα is greatly increased in the presence of IL-1 or LPS and these are both likely to be present during bacterial infections. High serum levels of TNFα correlate with a poor clinical outcome in septicemia, and in the adult respiratory distress syndrome (ARDS), which is a similar condition that targets the lungs.

Shwartzman reaction

Cytokine release can also cause local rather than systemic pathology. Microbial products and certain types of inflammatory response (both T cell dependent and independent) 'prepare' tissue sites so that they become exquisitely sensitive to cytokines, particularly TNFα, and liable to undergo hemorrhagic necrosis if TNFα release is subsequently induced systemically, or if TNFα is directly injected into the same site. This may explain the rash often seen during meningococcal septicemia. If bacteria released during a previous subclinical septicemic episode have lodged in skin capillaries, these will become 'prepared' sites, and a later septicemic episode severe enough to trigger systemic cytokine release will cause these sites to undergo necrosis via a cascade of events similar to those occurring systemically in endotoxin shock.

Koch phenomenon and necrotizing T cell-dependent granulomas

Robert Koch observed that when tuberculous guinea pigs were skin-tested with tuberculosis bacilli or culture supernatant (tuberculin), there was a necrotic reaction at the skin-test site within 24–48 h, and if a large dose of tuberculin was used there was additional necrosis in distant tuberculous lesions. The same is true in human tuberculosis patients. This phenomenon is described in the section on mycobacteria, and probably represents a pattern of tissue destruction and eventual fibrosis that occurs when there is local release of TNFα and other cytokines into T cell-dependent inflammatory sites mediated by a mixed T_H1 plus T_H2 lymphocyte response. A similar argument holds for tissue damage around granulomas evoked by schistosome ova, so the Koch phenomenon may be a model of an important immunopathological entity.

Heat shock proteins and the possibility of autoimmunity

It was discovered recently that several dominant antigens of infectious agents are 'heat shock' or 'stress' proteins. The sequences of these microbial antigens are similar to the sequences of the mammalian homologs. The fact that the immune response focuses much 'attention' on these conserved proteins may increase the chances of recognizing any pathogen, but also increase the chance of autoimmunity.

See also: **Bacillus**, infection and immunity; Bacterial cell walls; **Bacteroides**, infection and immunity; **Bordetella**, infection and immunity; **Borrelia**, infection and immunity; **Brucella**, infection and immunity; **Campylobacter**, infection and immunity; Complement, alternative pathway; **Chlamydia**, infection and immunity; **Coccidioides**, infection and immunity; Complement, classical pathway; Complement deficiencies; Complement fixation test; Complement, genetics; Complement, membrane attack pathway; Complement receptors; Coryneform bacteria, infection and immunity; Cryptococcus, infection and immunity; Cytokines; Cytotoxicity, assays for; Cytotoxicity, mechanisms of; Effector lymphocytes; Endotoxin (lipopolysaccharide (LPS)); *Escherichia coli*, infection and immunity; *Francisella*, infection and immunity; *Fusobacterium*, infection and immunity; Granuloma; *Haemophilus*, infection and immunity; *Klebsiella*, infection and immunity; *Legionella*, infection and immunity; *Leptospira*, infection and immunity; *Listeria*, infection and immunity; Microbicidal mechanisms, oxygen-dependent; Microbicidal mechanisms, oxygen-independent; *Mycobacteria*, infection and immunity; *Neisseria*, infection and immunity; *Nocardia*, infection and immunity; Opsonization; Pasteurella, infection and immunity; Phagocytosis; *Proteus*, infection and immunity; *Pseudomonas aeruginosa*, infection and immunity; *Rickettsia*, infection and immunity; *Salmonella*, infection and immunity; *Shigella*, infection and immunity; *Staphylococcus*, infection and immunity; *Streptobacillus*, infection and immunity; *Streptococcus*, infection and immunity; Stress and the immune system; T lymphocyte differentiation; *Treponema*, infection and immunity; *Vibrio cholerae*, infection and immunity; Vitamin D and the immune system; *Yersinia*, infection and immunity.

Further reading

AlonsoDeVelasco E, Verheul AF, Verhoef J and Snippe H (1995) *Streptococcus pneumoniae*: virulence factors, pathogenesis, and vaccines. *Microbiological Reviews* 59: 591–603.

Beckman EM and Brenner MB (1995) MHC class I-like, class II-like and CD1 molecules: distinct roles in immunity. *Immunology Today* 16: 349–352.

Chatfield S, Roberts M, Li J, Starns A and Dougan G (1994) The use of live attenuated *Salmonella* for oral vaccination. *Developments in Biological Standardization* 82: 35–42.

Frank MM (1989) Evasion strategies of microorganisms. In: Melchers F *et al* (eds) *Progress in Immunology*, vol 7, pp 194–201. Berlin: Springer-Verlag.

McDonnell WM and Askari FK (1996) DNA vaccines. *New England Journal of Medicine* 334: 42–45.

Moors MA and Portnoy DA (1995) Identification of bacterial genes that contribute to survival and growth in an intracellular environment. *Trends in Microbiology* 3: 83–85.

Rook GAW, Hernandez-Pando R and Lightman S (1994) Hormones, peripherally activated prohormones, and regulation of the T_H1/T_H2 balance. *Immunology Today* 15: 301–303.

Roth JA (ed) (1988) *Virulence Mechanisms of Bacterial Pathogens*. Washington DC: American Society for Microbiology.

Verhoef J and Mattsson E (1995) The role of cytokines in gram-positive bacterial shock. *Trends in Microbiology* 3: 136–140.

Wurfel MM, Hailman E and Wright SD (1995) Soluble CD14 acts as a shuttle in the neutralization of lipopolysaccharide (LPS) by LPS-binding protein and reconstituted high density lipoprotein. *Journal of Experimental Medicine* 181: 1743–1754.

BACTERIAL CELL WALLS

Alan Cockayne, Department of Microbiology, University of Nottingham, Nottingham, UK

The bacterial cell wall is a rigid, complex macromolecular structure which surrounds the bacterial cytosol and determines the characteristic shape of different bacteria. The cell wall and associated membrane(s), often referred to as the cell envelope, in addition to maintenance of cell shape, perform several important physiological functions involved in the regulation of interactions between the organism and its environment. In particular, the bacterial surface is the site of interaction of the organism with host tissues, and the molecular architecture of the cell envelope is of key importance in the pathogenesis of bacterial infection. Some components act as receptors or adhesins and mediate attachment to host cell surfaces. Many cell envelope components are antigenic and stimulate host immune responses which may be important in controlling or eradicating infection. In contrast, other components inhibit immune interactions and contribute both to the initiation of infection and persistence of the organism in host tissues. Expression of many envelope components is influenced by environmental conditions. Products expressed under conditioins which most closely mimic those found *in vivo* are of increasing interest in understanding the pathogenesis of bacterial infections.

The majority of bacteria can be classified into one of two types, gram-positive or gram-negative, using a simple staining technique which exploits fundamental differences in the structure of the cell envelope to differentiate between the two groups. The principal components of the cell envelopes of gram-positive and gram-negative bacteria are shown in **Figure 1**.

Cytoplasmic membrane

This bounds the bacterial cytoplasm. Proteins present in the membrane are involved in selective transport of nutrients and synthesis of peptidoglycan and periplasmic and outer membrane proteins. In gram-negative organisms, the space between the cytoplasmic membrane and the outer membrane – the periplasmic space – contains proteins with catabolic, binding and degradative functions.

Peptidoglycan

This is the major component of the cell wall involved in maintenance of cell rigidity, shape and osmotic stability and may be referred to as murein or mucopeptide. It consists of a polymer of $\beta 1 \rightarrow 4$-linked N-acetylmuramic acid and N-acetyl-D-glucosamine residues which are cross-linked by peptide bridges. The antibiotic penicillin interferes with peptidoglycan synthesis by inhibiting peptide bridge forma-

tion. Peptidoglycan is present in all bacteria except mycoplasmas and some halophilic archaebacteria. In gram-negative bacteria the peptidoglycan layer may be only one or two molecules thick but in gram-positive bacteria it is much thicker. Removal of the peptidoglycan by treatment of bacteria with lysozyme generates osmotically fragile structures termed protoplasts in gram-negative bacteria and spheroplasts in gram-positive organisms; L-forms are bacterial variants that have lost the ability to synthesize peptidoglycan. Peptidoglycans of many bacteria are antigenic, and a degradation product of mycobacterial peptidoglycan – muramyl dipeptide (MDP) – has adjuvant properties.

Gram-negative outer membrane

In gram-negative bacteria such as *Escherichia coli*, the peptidoglycan layer is surrounded by a second bilayer lipid membrane, the outer membrane. The outer membrane is linked to the peptidoglycan layer by a lipoprotein and contains proteins and a highly immunoreactive molecule called lipopolysaccharide (LPS) or endoxotin.

Some outer membrane proteins (OMPs) function as receptors or ligands, and one group – the porins –

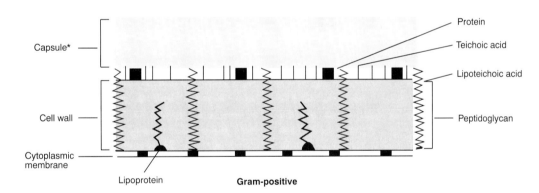

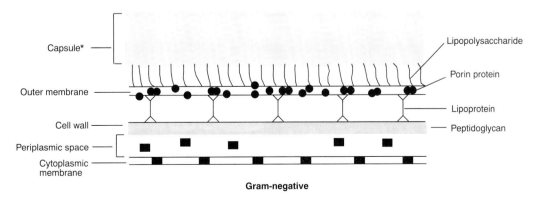

Figure 1 Components of the cell envelope of gram-positive and gram-negative bacteria. *Not always present.

form transmembrane channels involved in the non-specific transport of small hydrophilic solutes across the membrane. Other proteins mediate specific uptake of larger metabolites. Expression of some OMPs is regulated by environmental factors, such as growth medium composition. For example, many gram-negative bacteria express iron-regulated OMPs when growing in iron-deficient media. *In vivo* such proteins are involved in scavenging iron in mammalian tissues, a prerequisite for bacterial growth, and are therefore important virulence determinants of bacterial pathogens. Many OMPs are antigenic, and antigenic variation in these proteins is important in the pathogenesis of diseases such as gonorrhea (caused by *Neisseria gonorrhoeae*) and relapsing fever (caused by *Borrelia* spp.). Some OMPs contain T cell epitopes and stimulate cell-mediated responses which may modulate the immune response during infection. OMPs are also involved in the resistance of some intracellular bacteria to the bactericidal effects of phagocytic cells.

LPS or endotoxin is a complex molecule present in the outer leaflet of the outer membrane. It contains a unique lipid moiety – lipid A – which is responsible for its diverse biological activities including pyrogenicity and activation of macrophages. Many of its effects are nonspecific and are mediated through cytokines such as tumor necrosis factor α (TNFα) and interleukin-1 (IL-1) produced following interaction of LPS with lymphocytes or macrophages. LPS also contains oligosaccharides that confer antigenic specificity on the molecule and constitute the 'O' or somatic antigens of gram-negative bacteria such as *Salmonella*. The oligosaccharide side-chains are also important in preventing access of activated complement components to the bacterial outer membrane. Recent studies have shown that LPS of some bacteria, e.g. *Helicobacter pylori*, contain sugar sequences identical to human blood group antigens, which may play a role in modulating the immune response to the bacterium. The LPS of some bacteria, e.g. *Neisseria* spp., naturally lacks the oligosaccharide side-chains and these molecules are referred to as lipo-oligosaccharides (LOS).

Other components of gram-positive cell envelopes

Gram-positive bacteria lack an outer membrane but proteins, lipoproteins and other macromolecules are associated with the cytoplasmic membrane and peptidoglycan. Many wall proteins are anchored directly to the peptidoglycan, and contain a conserved amino acid motif – LPXTG – which is involved in transporting these proteins across the cytoplasmic membrane. Lipoproteins, which may be highly immunogenic, are anchored to the cytoplasmic membrane by the N-terminus which is lipid modified. Expression of both wall and cytoplasmic membrane proteins may be influenced by environmental factors such as iron availability. Also associated with the surface of some gram-positive bacteria are immunglobulin-binding proteins such as staphylococcal protein A and streptococcal protein G, which bind the Fc region of antibody molecules. Proteins with analogous function are now being detected in some gram-negative bacteria. Release of such proteins may protect the organism by binding to antibody and preventing its deposition on the bacterial surface. Other proteins such as the M protein of *Streptococcus pyogenes* have an antiphagocytic function.

Teichoic and lipoteichoic acids are acidic polymers of glycerol or ribitol and are bound to the peptidoglycan and cytoplasmic membrane respectively. They may be important antigens in staphylococci and streptococci, stimulating both humoral and cell-mediated immune responses.

Bacterial capsules

The outermost layer of many bacteria consists of a capsule. Capsules are usually, but not exclusively, acidic polysaccharides and are only loosely associated with the bacterial surface. Capsules may act as adhesins or have antiphagocytic functions due to their acidity and hydrophilic nature. In addition, capsular material may be poor antigenic (e.g. the hyaluronic acid capsule of *Streptococcus pyogenes*) and may mask more antigenic deeper layers of the cell envelope. The presence of a capsule may also sterically hinder access of complement components to the bacterial outer membrane. Other capsular antigens induce opsonizing antibody which promotes clearance of the bacteria. Although successful vaccines based on conjugated capsular polysaccharides have been developed, e.g. *Haemophilus influenzae* serotype b, some bacteria, e.g. *Streptococcus pneumoniae*, produce more than 30 antigenically distinct capsular types, which makes development of cross-protective capsular vaccines very difficult.

Other components associated with the bacterial cell envelope

Also associated with the surface of many gram-negative bacteria and some gram-positive organisms are filamentous appendages called pili or fimbriae. These are proteinaceous and are involved in mediating specific attachment of some bacteria to cell surfaces. Antigenic variation in pili may also be important in the pathogenesis of gonorrhea.

In both gram-positive and gram-negative bacteria, flagella – organelles involved in motility – are anchored into the cell envelope. Flagella are antigenic and constitute the 'H' antigens of gram-negative bacteria.

Mycobacteria do not readily stain by Gram's method and have a cell envelope which is unusually rich in lipids. This property confers the property of 'acid fastness' on these organisms since they resist decolorization with acids following staining. The lipid component of mycobacteria probably contributes to their resistance to phagocytic killing and the difficulty encountered in their degradation by these cells. Included among the lipids are mycolic acids or cord factors which may be toxic for mammalian cells.

See also: **Bacteria, immunity to; Endotoxin (lipopolysaccharide (LPS)); Muramyl dipeptide; Phagocytosis; Bacterial immunoglobulin-binding proteins.**

Further reading

Fath MJ and Kolter R (1993) ABC-transporters – bacterial exporters. *Microbiological Reviews* 57: 995–1017.

Fischetti VA, Pancholi V and Schneewind O (1994) Conservation of a hexapeptide sequence in the anchor region of surface proteins from Gram-positive cocci. *Molecular Microbiology* 4: 1603–1605.

Ghuysen JM and Hakenbeck R (eds) (1994) *Bacterial Cell Wall.* Amsterdam: Elsevier.

Lugtenberg B and Van Alphen L (1983) Molecular architecture and functioning of the outer membrane of *Escherichia coli* and other Gram-negative bacteria. *Biochimica Biophysica Acta* 737: 51–115.

Morrison DC and Ryan JL (1987) Endotoxins and disease mechanisms. *Annual Review of Medicine* 38: 417–432.

Moxon R and Kroll JS (1990) The role of bacterial polysaccharide capsules as virulence factors. *Current Topics in Microbiology and Immunology* 150: 65–85.

Puzo G (1990) The carbohydrate and lipid-containing cell wall of Mycobacteria, phenolic glycolipids: Structure and immunological properties. *Critical Review of Microbiology* 17: 305–327.

Sherburne R and Taylor DE (1995) *Helicobacter pylori* expresses a complex surface carbohydrate, Lewis x. *Infection and Immunity* 63: 4564–4568.

Sleytr UB, Messner P, Minnekin DE *et al* (1988) Structure of bacteria and their envelopes. In: Hancock I and Poxton I (eds) *Bacterial Cell Surface Techniques (Modern Microbiological Methods)*, pp 1–32. Chichester: John Wiley.

Wiertz EJHJ, Delvig A, Donders EMLM *et al* (1996) T-cell response to outer membrane proteins of *Neisseria meningitidis*: comparative study of the Opa, Opc, and PorA proteins. *Infection and Immunity* 64: 298–304.

Williams P (1988) Role of the cell envelope in bacterial adaptation to growth in infections. *Biochimie* 70: 987–1101.

BACTERIAL IMMUNOGLOBULIN-BINDING PROTEINS

Michael DP Boyle, Medical College of Ohio, Department of Microbiology and Immunology, Toledo, Ohio, USA

Bacterial immunoglobulin-binding proteins represent a family of functional molecules expressed by certain microorganisms that can interact with immunoglobulins (Igs) at sites unrelated to their antigen-combining regions. The study of these molecules was initially driven by their utility as immunochemical reagents but has now expanded to address more basic scientific questions of structure–function and biological activities.

Six types of IgG-binding proteins have been described on gram-positive bacteria. These different types have been classified by their ability to bind with the Fc region of different mammalian species and subclasses of IgG (**Figure 1**). The most extensively studied IgG-binding protein is protein A (the type I).

Protein A is expressed by the majority of human isolates of *Staphylococcus aureus*. The type II receptors are found on the surface of the majority of human isolates of group A streptococci and display a large amount of variability in their immunoglobulin-binding profiles (**Table 1**). Protein G, the type III IgG-binding protein, is expressed by the majority of human group C and G streptococcal isolates and displays the widest range of species and subclass reactivities of any of the immunoglobulin-binding proteins identified to date (**Figure 1**). The type IV, V and type VI immunoglobulin-binding proteins are associated with animal isolates of streptococci and have not been studied extensively.

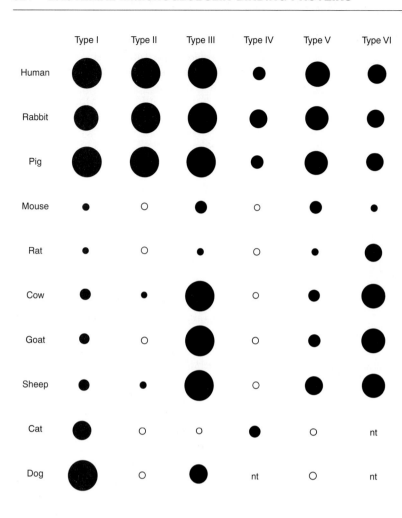

Figure 1 Profile of species reactivities of different bacterial IgG-binding protein types. Larger dots represent greater binding activity: o, no reactivity; nt, not tested. Note these reactivities have been determined using polyclonal IgG preparations. Occasional differences have been noted in the reactivity of samples from individual animals. (Reproduced with permission from Reis *et al* (1988).)

Table 1 IgG-binding profiles of type II IgG-binding proteins expressed by certain group A streptococci

Functional designation	Binding profiles						
	Human IgG1	Human IgG2	Human IgG3	Human IgG4	Rabbit IgG	Pig IgG	Horse IgG
IIo	✓	✓	✓	✓	✓	✓	✓
II′o*	✓	✓	✓	✓	✓		
IIa	✓	✓		✓	✓	✓	✓
IIb			✓				
IIc	✓			✓	✓	✓	

*Also designated protein H.
Adapted from Boyle and Raeder (1993).

IgG Fc-binding proteins have also been described on the surface of other bacteria, including *Haemophilus somnus*, *Clostridium perfringens*, *Brucella abortus*, *Taylorella equigenitalis* and *Gardnerella vaginalis*. In addition, bacterial binding proteins that display nonimmune reactivity with immunoglobulin isotypes other than IgG have been described (**Table 2**). These include proteins that bind constant regions in IgD or IgA. Other proteins have been recognized that bind regions within constant portions of the F(ab)′$_2$ fragments as well as molecules that show selective reactivity with immunoglobulin light chains. To date, a bacterial protein with absolute selectivity for the Fc region of IgM from any species has not been described. A *B. abortus* protein with reactivity for certain bovine IgM allotypes, a *Clostridium difficile* toxin protein that displays preferential reactivity with murine IgM, and a potential IgM-specific lectin-like molecule of *Borrelia burgdorferi* have been reported.

Table 2 Representative bacteria that bind immunoglobulin in a nonimmune fashion

Bacteria	IgG	IgM	IgA	IgD	IgE
Staphylococcus aureus	+				
Streptococcus, group A	+		+		
Streptococcus, group B			+		
Streptococcus groups C and G	+				
Branhamella catarrhalis				+	
Clostridium perfringens	+	+	+		
Taylorella equigenitalis	+	+			
Brucella abortus		(+)*			
Coprococcus comes	+				
Peptococcus magnus	+	+	+	+	+
Haemophilus somnus	+				

*Reactivity limited to a subgroup of bovine IgM antibodies.

Protein A – the type I IgG-binding protein

The initial IgG-binding protein described and characterized was the type I binding protein expressed on the surface of the majority of *Staphylococcus aureus* isolates and more frequently designated as staphylococcal protein A. Protein A and its interaction with the Fc region of reactive IgG antibodies has been extensively studied and detailed structure–function analysis by X-ray crystallography and nuclear magnetic resonance has mapped the key binding amino acids in the selective interaction of protein A with the C_H2–C_H3 domain of IgG.

The interaction of protein A and IgG is of relatively high affinity 10^8–10^9 M^{-1} and a lower affinity interaction has also been noted for protein A binding to F(ab)$'_2$ regions of IgG. In addition, reactivity of protein A with certain subtypes of IgM and IgA have also been described. The gene encoding protein A has been cloned and contains four or five homologous regions capable of binding to IgG.

Protein A is bivalent in its IgG-binding activity and in the presence of excess IgG forms $(IgG)_2$ (PA) complexes. When protein A is present in excess the predominant complex is $(IgG)_1$ $(PA)_2$, indicating the presence of two protein A binding domains on each IgG molecule. These different protein A–IgG complexes display different potentials for binding C1 and activating the classical complement pathway. The $(IgG)_1$ $(PA)_2$ complexes do not bind C1 indicating, that protein A and C1q target a similar site on the Fc region of IgG, whereas a dimer of the $[(IgG)_2 (PA)_1]_2$ complex is extremely efficient in binding and activating C1 and behaves in complement fixation assays with the characteristics of an IgM antibody. The ability to form such IgM-like complexes may explain the ability of protein A to induce wheal and flare reactions when injected into humans intradermally or to induce anaphylactic reactions in guinea pigs.

In addition to effects of protein A on the humoral immune system, the bacterial protein has also been reported to have T cell mitogenic properties and to act as a B cell superantigen. The T cell effects of protein A, however, are based on earlier studies of responses induced by heat-killed and/or formalin-fixed *S. aureus* Cowan strain bacteria or wild-type preparations of protein A. These sources of protein A have the potential to be contaminated with staphylococcal enterotoxins, which could account for many of the observed effects. Studies with recombinant protein A, which demonstrates all of the expected IgG-binding activities, failed to show T cell mitogenic activity, suggesting protein A may not be a T cell mitogen. By contrast, the elegant studies of Silverman and colleagues indicate that protein A can induce proliferation of a subset of human B cells and this is restricted to B cells expressing surface immunoglobulin containing certain V_H3 Fab regions.

The majority of studies of protein A have focused on its utility as a reagent for detection of antigen–antibody complexes or, once immobilized, as a reagent for affinity purification. The high selectivity of protein A for the Fc region of antibodies in immune complexes has resulted in protein A tracers replacing conventional second antibody reagents in many immunotechnological applications. Protein A has proved to be extremely valuable for procedures involving screening of hybridoma supernatants for a desired monoclonal antibody with a desired specificity as well as for the subsequent purification of that antibody.

Analysis of the infectivity of *S. aureus* isolates and paired mutants in which the protein A gene was nonfunctional have failed to provide any evidence that protein A is a virulence factor.

Type II IgG-binding proteins

Group A streptococci express an array of functionally distinct IgG-binding proteins (**Table 1**). The majority of the functional types of type II IgG-binding proteins have been cloned and sequenced. All of these IgG-binding proteins are encoded by M or M-related protein genes that are present in a virulence regulon of group A streptococci, suggesting a potential role for these proteins in pathogenesis. In addition to binding IgG, the majority of type II binding proteins also bind other plasma proteins, e.g. albumin, factor H, fibrinogen, plasminogen and IgA. Analysis of the binding domains of these proteins suggest they consist of different combinations of distinct functional modules that react with different IgG subclasses or other plasma proteins. Expression of type II IgG-binding proteins is associated more frequently with group A streptococcal skin isolates than with throat isolates. Studies in mice have indicated an association between IgG-binding protein expression and skin infectivity, while no such association occurs when the bacteria are injected intraperitoneally.

Type III IgG-binding proteins

The type III IgG-binding proteins are more frequently designated as streptococcal protein G. Protein G is expressed by the majority of human isolates of group C and group G streptococci. A number of variant forms of protein G have been described at both the gene and protein level. All forms of protein G are antigenically related and the majority also bind human serum albumin. The gene encoding protein G has been cloned and the albumin-binding and IgG-binding domains have been shown to be distinct. This has enabled nonalbumin-binding forms of protein G to be genetically engineered.

Protein G demonstrates the widest species and subclass reactivity of any bacterial IgG-binding protein (**Figure 1**). Protein G, like protein A, can form a number of different-sized complexes with IgG and these demonstrate a similar pattern of complement-fixing potential to that observed with protein A. Protein G has been shown to mediate mitogenic responses when added to human peripheral blood lymphocytes. This activity, however, could not be correlated with either the albumin or IgG-binding domain of the protein.

By virtue of its broad species and subclass reactivity profile, protein G is an extremely useful reagent as a tracer and for affinity purification of antibodies that are not reactive with protein A.

Type IV, V and VI IgG-binding proteins

Type IV, V and VI IgG-binding proteins have not been extensively studied. They are all antigenically distinct proteins that demonstrate different patterns of nonimmune IgG binding (**Figure 1**). The type IV binding protein is associated with certain β hemolytic isolates of streptococci from cattle; however, this protein demonstrates no detectable reactivity with bovine immunoglobulins. The type V and VI proteins have been isolated from different *S. zooepidemicus* isolates. It is probable that, like type II IgG-binding proteins, there will be extensive heterogeneity in the IgG-binding proteins expressed by different *S. zooepidemicus* isolates. To date, there is no evidence that any type IV, V or VI IgG-binding protein associates with disease in any animal species and none of these proteins have been tested for their utility as immunochemical reagents.

Other bacterial immunoglobulin-binding proteins

In addition to the IgG-binding proteins associated with staphylococci and streptococci, an increasing number of both gram-positive and gram-negative bacteria have been reported to express immunoglobulin-binding proteins with reactivity for IgA, IgD and IgM, as well as a protein that binds to certain κ light chains (**Table 2**). To date, no disease association has been suggested for any of the putative IgA-, IgM- and IgD-binding proteins. The Fc binding protein associated with *H. somnus* has been implicated as a virulence factor in cattle and an association between expression of protein L, a light chain-binding protein, by *Peptococcus magnus* and vaginal infections has been proposed.

As might be anticipated, based on the utility of protein A and protein G, many of these immunoglobulin-binding proteins may find applications for the purification and detection of specific immunoglobulin classes or subclasses. To date, the light chain-binding protein (protein L), a hybrid of protein L and protein G (LG), and a group B streptococcal IgA-binding protein (protein B) have demonstrated practical utility in certain immunological procedures.

Summary

Immunoglobulin-binding proteins represent a family of diverse molecules capable of interacting with antibody without impairing the ability of the antibody to bind its cognate antigen. By virtue of these properties, these molecules are potentially valuable immunochemical reagents. There is limited understanding of the role of IgG-binding proteins in bacterial virulence. Studies of *H. somnus* in cattle and *S. pyogenes* and *Peptococcus magnus* in humans have suggested a possible association between expression of IgG-binding proteins and the course of infection.

See also: **Affinity chromatography; Bacterial cell walls; IgG; Immunoassays; Immunocytochemistry and enzyme markers.**

Further reading

Boyle MDP (1984) Application of bacterial Fc receptors in immunotechnology. *Biotechniques* 2: 334–340.

Boyle MDP (ed) (1990) *Bacterial Immunoglobulin Binding Proteins*, vols I and II. San Diego: Academic Press.

Boyle MDP (1993) Bacterial IgG-binding proteins. *ImmunoMethods* 2: 1–3.

Boyle MDP (1995) Variation of multifunctional surface binding proteins – a virulence strategy for group A streptococci? *Journal of Theoretical Biology* 173: 415–426.

Boyle MDP and Metzger DW (1994) Antibody-binding bacterial proteins as immunoreagents. In: Lillchoj EP and Malik VS (eds) *Antibody Techniques. A Guide for Nonimmunologists*, pp 177–209. San Diego: Academic Press.

Boyle MDP and Raeder R (1993) Analysis of heterogeneity of IgG-binding proteins expressed by group A streptococci. *ImmunoMethods* 2: 41–55.

Boyle MDP and Reis KJ (1987) Bacterial Fc receptors. *Biotechnology* 5: 697–703.

Boyle MDP, Faulmann EL and Metzger DW (1993) Applications of bacterial immunoglobulin-binding proteins to the purification of immunoglobulins. In: Ngo TT (ed) *Molecular Interactions and Bioseparation*, pp 91–112. New York: Plenum Press.

Derrick JP and Wigley DB (1993) Analysis of bacterial immunoglobulin-binding proteins by x-ray crystallography. *ImmunoMethods* 2: 9–15.

Faulmann EL, Duvall JL and Boyle MDP (1991) Protein B: a versatile bacterial Fc-binding protein selective for human IgA. *Biotechniques* 10: 748–755.

Kastern W, Holst E, Nielsen E, Sjöbring U and Björck L (1990) Protein L, a bacterial immunoglobulin-binding protein and possible virulence determinant. *Infection and Immunity* 58: 1217–1222.

Kihlberg BM, Sjoholm AG, Björck L and Sjöbring U (1996) Characterization of the binding properties of protein LG, an immunoglobulin-binding hybrid protein. *European Journal of Biochemistry* 240: 556–563.

Reis KJ, Siden EJ and Boyle MDP (1988) Selective colony blotting to expand bacterial surface receptors: applications to receptors for rat immunoglobulins. *Biotechniques* 6: 130–136.

Silverman GJ, Sasano M and Wormsley SB (1993) The variable-region specificity of bacterial Fab-binding proteins: the search for B-cell superantigens. *Immuno Methods* 2: 17–32.

Widders PR, Dorrance LA, Yarnall M and Corbeil LB (1989) Immunoglobulin-binding activity among pathogenic and carrier isolates of *Haemophilus somnus*. *Infection and Immunity* 57: 639–642.

BACTEROIDES, INFECTION AND IMMUNITY

Michael E Shapiro, Harvard Medical School, Beth Israel Hospital, Boston, Massachusetts, USA

The importance of anaerobic bacteria in clinical human disease, particularly intra-abdominal infection, has been well established over the past two decades. Much of the interest has focused upon the various *Bacteroides* species because of their prevalence in clinical isolates and their requirements for particular antiobiotic therapy. Once classified as subspecies of *Bacteroides fragilis*, six distinct species of *Bacteroides* are now recognized based on distinctive patterns of DNA homology: *B. fragilis*, *B. distasonis*, *B. vulgatus*, *B. thetaiotaomicron*, *B. ovatus*, and *Bacteroides* species. Although *B. vulgatus* and *B. thetaiotaomicron* are the numerically dominant species of the fecal flora, *B. fragilis*, a numerically minor member of the normal flora, is the most frequently isolated anaerobic species in many infectious processes, including intra-abdominal sepsis. This sug-

gests that *B. fragilis* must possess virulence factors not present in the other species.

Examination of clinical isolates of *B. fragilis* has demonstrated the presence of a polysaccharide capsule, rarely found on other *Bacteroides* species. The capsular polysaccharide of *B. fragilis* has been well characterized chemically. Prolonged laboratory culture of encapsulated strains of *B. fragilis* may result in loss of the capsule and a marked diminution in virulence.

Much of our knowledge about *Bacteroides* virulence comes from a rat model of intra-abdominal sepsis, in which bacterial isolates are placed in a gelatin capsule along with adjuvants and implanted intraperitoneally. Using complex mixtures of fecal flora, an early peritonitis phase, with bacteremia and high mortality, is followed by an abscess phase. This latter phase has been shown to be dependent upon the presence of anaerobes in the inoculum. When various isolates were tested in this model, it was shown that encapsulated strains of *B. fragilis* were the only organisms capable of abscess formation as single isolates. Unencapsulated strains of *B. fragilis* and other anaerobes only led to abscess formation when combined with other facultative organisms, such as enterococcus. In fact, heat-killed preparations of encapsulated *B. fragilis* strains led to abscess formation in the majority of cases, as did inocula containing purified capsular polysaccharide, clearly demonstrating the role of the capsule in virulence.

The apparent central role of capsular polysaccharide in *B. fragilis* virulence led to studies using the polysaccharide as a vaccine. Rats immunized with *B. fragilis* capsular polysaccharide with or without complete Freund's adjuvant developed significant antibody titers against the polysaccharide. These animals were protected against abscess formation when challenged with *B. fragilis* or *B. distasonis*. Animals challenged with more complex bacterial inocula still formed abscesses; however, *B. fragilis* was eliminated from the abscesses in those animals. Surprisingly, when serum from immunized animals with high-titer antibody to the capsular polysaccharide was transferred to nonimmunized animals, no protection against abscess formation was conferred. On the other hand, transfer of spleen cells from immunized animals did confer protection and this result could be repeated with spleen cells enriched for T cells with nylon-wool columns. Similarly, immunization of athymic nude rats with capsular polysaccharide, although producing excellent antibody levels, did not prevent abscess formation whereas phenotypically normal littermates were protected. Thus, in the rat model, there was a strong suggestion for the role of T cell immunity in the immune response to *B. fragilis* and abscess prevention.

A murine model of intra-abdominal abscess formation was developed in order to better dissect the cellular immune response to *B. fragilis*. This model has the further advantage that the bacterial inoculum can be introduced without surgical implantation. It was possible to confirm all of the rat observations in the murine system, namely, that immunization with capsular polysaccharide was protective against *B. fragilis* abscesses, that protection could not be transferred passively with serum, but could be conferred by spleen cell transfers. The cell responsible for protection was, in fact, a T cell, of the Ly-1^- Ly-2^+I-J$^+$ phenotype. The immune T cells are antigen specific, that is, they only protect against *B. fragilis* abscesses, but are not major histocompat-ibility complex (MHC)-restricted. This immune T cell produces a factor and transfer of cell-free lysate of immune T cells are protective against abscesses as well. The factor is polypeptide in nature and of relatively low molecular weight (<12 kDa).

Because of the immune T cell phenotype and the elaboration of a soluble factor, the possibility that abscess prevention might be mediated by a T cell suppressor circuit was raised. This possibility raised two questions: what was being suppressed, and on what was the T cell factor acting. Both nude mice and rats are able to form abscesses in response to *B. fragilis* challenge, suggesting that T cells are not necessary for abscess formation. It is known that nude animals do have early T cell precursors, however. Treatment of mice with low doses of cyclophosphamide abolished their ability to form abscesses, and reconstitution of the cyclophosphamide-treated animals with Ly-1^+2^+ T cells restored this ability. Thus T cells are required at an early stage in the generation of *B. fragilis* abscesses, and the cell required for abscess induction is a relatively early precursor T cell as one might expect from the nude mouse data. It is presumed that this precursor T cell is being acted upon by the T suppressor cells in the prevention of abscess formation.

Although nude mice are capable of developing abscesses in response to challenge with *B. fragilis*, the transfer of the usual small number of immune T cells (2.5×10^6) or immune factor does not induce protection as in normal mice. This suggested that a second T cell might be required to induce abscess protection. This possibility was investigated with reconstitution experiments in nude mice. Transfer of 25×10^6 naive spleen cells into nude recipients reconstituted the ability of these mice to be protected against abscesses by the further transfer of 2.5×10^6 immune cells. The cells capable of reconstituting the nude mice were also Ly-1^-2^+ by phenotype.

Thus, it appears that abscess production and prevention in response to *B. fragilis* occurs by a T cell-mediated mechanism. Abscess induction requires a precursor-type T cell. Preliminary evidence suggests that the earliest cells entering the peritoneum in response to bacterial challenge may be lymphocytes. The mechanism by which they may act to elicit abscess formation is not yet identified. Prevention of abscesses require at least two T cells, of suppressor phenotypes, which communicate via a small polypeptide factor. These cells are antigen specific, but not MHC-restricted.

One additional question is the potential benefit of abscess formation to both the host and the bacterium. Animals which do not form abscesses do not develop diffuse overwhelming infection and death.

On the contrary, the *B. fragilis* in these animals is cleared without sequelae. This raises the possibility that abscesses are an adaptive mechanism by which the bacteria create a milieu favorable to survival rather than a particularly useful protective mechanism for the host.

See also: **Bacteria, immunity to; T lymphocytes.**

Further reading

Onderdonk AN, Kasper DL, Cisneros RL and Bartlett JG (1977) The capsular polysaccharide of *Bacteroides frag-* *ilis* as virulence factors: Comparison of the pathogenic potential of encapsulated and unencapsulated strains. *Journal of Infectious Diseases* **136**: 82–89.

Shapiro ME, Kasper DL, Zaleznik DF *et al* (1986) Cellular control of abscess formation: Role of T cells in the regulation of abscesses formed in response to *Bacteroides fragilis*. *Journal of Immunology* **137**: 341–346.

Shapiro ME, Onderdonk AB, Kasper DL and Finberg RW (1982) Cellular immunity to *Bacteroides fragilis* capsular polysaccharide. *Journal of Experimental Medicine* **154**: 1188–1197.

[This article is reproduced from the first edition (1992)]

BARE LYMPHOCYTE SYNDROME

Janice S Blum, Department of Microbiology and Immunology, Indiana University School of Medicine, Indianapolis, USA

Bare lymphocyte syndrome (BLS) encompasses a series of rare autosomal recessive disorders in which patients display low or null expression of HLA major histocompatibility proteins. Three types of BLS have been classified, with the severity of these disorders varying both in phenotypic HLA expression and loss of immune function. In BLS type I, low or no expression of HLA class I molecules are displayed on peripheral blood cells. The degree of immunodeficiency is most variable in BLS type I, with some individuals displaying essentially normal immunity. Type II BLS is defined as a reduction or complete loss of HLA class II protein expression on all cells. This disorder typically manifests as a severe combined immunodeficiency. In BLS type III disorders, both HLA class I and class II antigen expression are diminished and these individuals are severely immunodeficient. Studies of BLS patients have proven to be exceptionally informative, yielding insights into the effects of selective disruption of histocompatibility antigen function, as well as offering clues to the transcriptional and post-translational regulation of histocompatibility molecules.

Bare lymphocyte syndrome Type I

Class I histocompatibility antigens are constitutively found on all normal nucleated cells, however surface expression of these proteins may be down-modulated by viruses and in some tumors. In normal peripheral blood lymphocytes, diminished class I antigen expression with normal levels of class II proteins is an established hallmark of BLS type I. The levels of class I antigen cell surface expression are quite variable among type I patients. Immunodeficiency does not always correlate with the level of class I antigen cell surface expression, and individuals with no or low class I antigen expression and no signs of immune dysfunction have been identified. Remarkably, Epstein–Barr virus transformation of B cells from patients with this latter phenotype resulted in partial restoration of class I expression. In other patients, severe immunodeficiency has been associated with BLS type I, including persistent bacterial and yeast infections, low numbers of peripheral blood T lymphocytes, and death within one year of birth. In the majority of these patients, the specific genetic factors responsible for the loss of class I antigen expression remain unclear.

Molecular studies to identify the genetic lesion in type I BLS have been carried out in patients with very low class I expression (1–3% of normal levels) and recurring sinopulmonary infections as well as bronchiectasis. In all cases, these individuals suffer from chronic bacterial infections and require antibiotic therapy. Investigations of two related type I patients revealed a truncation mutation in TAP2 (transporter associated with antigen processing), a molecule required for class I protein assembly and function. Class I heavy chains are synthesized by these patients; however these molecules are trapped intracellularly and only loosely associated with β_2-microglobulin. In normal individuals, both surface expression of class I proteins and the stable association of class I heavy chains with β_2-microglobulin is dependent upon binding of antigenic peptides.

Antigenic peptide delivery to nascent class I proteins typically occurs via a heterodimeric transporter consisting of TAP1 and TAP2 proteins localized in the endoplasmic reticulum. Murine and human mutant cell lines, as well as knockout animals lacking TAP proteins, display a phenotype almost identical to BLS type I patients. A low level of class I antigen surface expression is observed in both these BLS type I patients and the laboratory mutants. Studies with TAP-deficient cell lines indicate a small population of peptides exists within the endoplasmic reticulum which can bind class I complexes and promote stable transport and surface expression.

Clinical investigations of these type I BLS patients are remarkable in that susceptibility to pulmonary bacterial infections predominate. Peripheral blood CD8[+] T lymphocyte levels are low and there appears to be no or very low natural killer cell function in these individuals. In contrast, high antibody titers against bacteria and viruses, as well as good responses to vaccination are found in these BLS type I patients. The enhanced frequency of respiratory tract bacterial infections in these patients suggests class I antigens on phagocytic cells such as macrophages must play a key role in immunity against these pathogens.

Bare lymphocyte syndrome type II

Class II histocompatibility antigens are expressed on professional antigen-presenting cells such as B lymphocytes, dendritic cells and macrophages. Expression of class II proteins on other cell types can be induced in response to cytokine treatment while a small number of viruses are capable of downregulating cell surface levels of class II antigens. In humans, heterodimers of class II α and β subunits are synthesized from highly polymorphic DR, DP and DQ loci encoded within the major histocompatibility gene complex. BLS type II is classically defined as a global loss of class II antigen expression. However, this definition has been broadened to encompass individuals with a loss of specific class II subunits as well as restricted class II expression on discrete cell types. Patients displaying very low or no class II proteins on their peripheral blood cells all have severe immunodeficiencies and suffer from chronic viral, bacterial, fungal and protozoal infections of the respiratory and gastrointestinal tract. Clinical onset of disease symptoms occurs within the first year of life and most patients do not survive beyond the age of four without therapeutic interventions such as bone marrow transplantation.

BLS type II patients display strong allograft rejection responses without immunosuppression, presumably because class I antigens are expressed by these patients along with, in some cases, low levels of class II molecules. Thus, the success of bone marrow transplantation is reduced in these individuals compared with other patients suffering from combined immunodeficiencies. Total numbers of peripheral blood T cells are normal in BLS type II patients, with very low numbers of circulating CD4[+] T lymphocytes and enhanced levels of CD8[+] T cells. This observation differs from the phenomena observed in mice lacking class II structural genes, where no single positive CD4 T cells mature. Possible explanations may include low expression of class II antigens on thymic cells in BLS type II patients, resulting in limited CD4[+] T cell selection. Alternatively in humans, class I molecules in the thymus may play a role in the selection of CD4[+] T cells. Most interestingly, following bone marrow transplantation of these patients, the circulating levels of CD4[+] T cells remain low, yet immunity is restored. The implications of this finding are twofold: 1) that bone marrow-derived cells are not critical in the efficiency of thymic selection of T cells in these patients; and 2) that restoration of class II antigen expression on bone marrow-derived cells is critical to host defense. The number of peripheral blood B lymphocytes in BLS type II patients are normal, but antibody production is severely deficient in these individuals, presumably due to a lack of helper CD4[+] T cells. In some individuals, autoreactivity including polyarthritis, eczema and psoriasis is also associated with the absence of class II antigen expression.

Analysis of BLS type II at a molecular level has led to the clustering of patients within multiple complementation groups, each group lacking a distinct gene regulating class II protein expression. In all cases of BLS type II, class II structural genes are intact, yet the transcription of mRNA from these loci is perturbed. Family studies suggest the genetic defects in all patients lie outside the major histocompatibility gene complex on chromosome 6. Fusion of patient cell lines with cells from normal individuals restores the expression of class II alleles derived from the BLS type II individual. This finding supports the conclusion that the defective gene is a *trans*-acting factor that controls the transcription of class II molecules. Fusion of B cell lines from different type II patients has firmly established three genetic complementation groups in this disorder (groups A, B and C (also termed II, I and IV respectively)). A mutagenized B cell line selected for its lack of surface class II antigens has been generated in the laboratory, and this cell comprises a fourth complementation group (group D or III). Additional complementation groups may exist, including patients selectively expressing only a subset of class II subunits on distinct cell types. The majority of the patients identified fall within complementation groups A and B. In two of the complementation groups (B and C), patients also have substantially reduced class I antigen expression on peripheral blood cells. These individuals have been classified both as BLS type II and type III by different investigators. Immortalization of B cells from group B and C individuals using Epstein–Barr virus typically restores class I antigen surface expression to wild-type levels, but this viral transformation does not influence class II antigen transcription.

Molecular and functional studies have defined in part the genetic defects in BLS type II. *In vivo* analysis of class II promoters from type II groups B, C and D reveals a lack of transcription factors stably binding these regions of DNA, a phenotype referred to as 'bare' promoters. This result suggests that the class II gene promoter regions are inaccessible in these mutants. By contrast in BLS type II group A, normal occupancy of class II gene promoters is observed. To date, only the transcription factors defective in BLS type II groups A and C have been definitively identified. Using complementation cloning, the transcription factor defective in group A patients has been identified as a 1130 amino acid protein, CIITA (MHC class II trans-activator). Studies of several group A patients revealed point mutations, defects in exon splicing and genomic deletions in this protein. CIITA does not bind directly to DNA and may serve instead as a coactivator to facilitate the interaction of other transcription factors. Expression of CIITA in only group A mutants restores class II antigen expression and this transcription factor is critical in interferon γ (IFNγ) induction of class II antigen mRNA. CIITA is the only transcription factor at this time whose expression directly correlates with class II antigen mRNA levels in cells. For example, CIITA synthesis is ablated during the transition of B lymphocytes to plasma cells, coincident with a loss in class II antigen expression. The C-terminus of CIITA encodes a transcription-activating domain while the N-terminus confers specificity for class II promoter regions.

BLS type II group C patients have mutations in a 75 kDa transcription factor, RFX5. This protein serves as a key subunit in a multimeric complex termed RFX which binds the X-box region of class II promoters. Disruption of the RFX complex results in the 'bare' class II promoter phenotype of group C patients. These findings suggest another component of RFX may also be defective in group B or D patients which also display the 'bare' promoters phenotype. Questions remain as to whether RFX plays any role in regulating class I antigen transcription in groups B and C, where reduced class I levels are observed on peripheral blood cells.

Both CIITA and RFX5 are essential for the synthesis of cell surface class II DR, DP and DQ alleles, however these transcription factors also have been shown to regulate the production of other molecules required for presentation via the class II pathway. The assembly and intracellular transport of class II proteins is mediated by a chaperone protein, the invariant chain. Despite its chromosomal location outside the major histocompatibility gene complex, the invariant chain shares some promoter elements with class II proteins. Expression of class II proteins and invariant chain is tightly linked in all cells and in BLS type II, synthesis of invariant chain mRNA is severely reduced but not completely ablated. The invariant chain must be proteolytically released from class II molecules to allow peptide binding and antigen presentation. Release of invariant chain peptides from the groove of class II proteins is mediated in endosomal/lysosomal compartments by HLA-DM. Functional and molecular analyses indicate that HLA-DM is also deficient in BLS type II patients. The absence of functional DM molecules renders cells unable to present exogenous antigens. While gene therapy and the replacement of class II structural genes has been discussed as a potential curative therapy for BLS type II, the requirement for multiple factors in antigen presentation suggests that restoration of the defective transcription factors is a more promising approach for this disorder.

Bare lymphocyte syndrome type III

Patients with BLS type III display no cell surface class II antigens as well as little or no class I proteins. The phenotype of these patients is most variable and many of these patients are classified as BLS type II due to their residual class I antigen expression. The immunodeficiency of these individuals mirrors that of BLS type II patients including susceptibility to chronic infections and early death without intervention. Peripheral blood levels of CD4+ T cells are low and antibody responses dramatically reduced in BLS type III.

While multiple patients with BLS type III have been identified, little progress has been made in elucidating the genetic defect(s) in these individuals. Class I antigen expression in some patients can be induced using IFNγ but this does not restore class II antigen levels. Molecular studies of a transformed fibroblast line from a type III individual revealed interferon treatment induced low levels of mRNA for class I heavy chain, β2-microglobulin and the proteosome subunits LMP2 and LMP7. Interestingly, interferon induced normal levels of mRNA production for both TAP1 and TAP2 in fibroblasts from this type III patient. No induction of class II mRNA and little synthesis of invariant chain were observed in these interferon-treated cells. *In vitro* fusion of these type III fibroblasts with B cell lines from each of the four BLS type II complementation groups restored class II antigen expression. These results suggest that the defect in this type III individual is genetically distinct from BLS type II mutations. Elucidation of the defects in these cells will be important as approaches for gene therapy and transplantation biology are advanced.

See also: **Antigen-presenting cells; Antigen presentation via MHC class I molecules; Antigen presentation via MHC class II molecules; HLA class I; HLA class II; Invariant chain (Ii); Severe combined immunodeficiency.**

Further reading

Bénichou B and Strominger JL (1991) Class II-antigen-negative patient and mutant B-cell lines represent at least three, and probably four, distinct genetic defects defined by complementation analysis. *Proceedings of the National Academy of Sciences of the USA* 88: 4285–4288.

Chang CH, Guerder S, Hong SC, van Ewijk W and Flavelle RA (1996) Mice lacking the MHC class II transactivator (CIITA) show tissue-specific impairment of MHC class II expression. *Immunity* 4: 167–178.

Glimcher L and Kara CJ (1992) Sequences and factors: a guide to MHC class-II transcription. *Annual Reviews of Immunology* 10: 13–49.

Hauber I, Gulle H, Wolf HM, Maris M, Eggenbauer H and Eibl MM (1995) Molecular characterization of major histocompatibility complex class II gene expression and demonstration of antigen-specific T cell response indicate a new phenotype in class II-deficient patients. *Journal of Experimental Medicine* 181: 1411–1423.

Klein C, Cavazzana-Calvo M, Le Deist F *et al* (1995) Bone marrow transplantation in major histocompatibility complex class II deficiency: a single-center study of 19 patients. *Blood* 85: 580–587.

Kovats S, Nepom GT, Coleman M, Nepom B, Kwok WW and Blum JS (1995) Deficient antigen-presenting cell function in multiple genetic complementation groups of type II bare lymphocyte syndrome. *Journal of Clinical Investigation* 96: 217–223.

Payne R, Brodsky FM, Peterlin BM and Young LM (1983) Bare lymphocytes without immunodeficiency. *Human Immunology* 6: 219–227.

Peijnenburg A, Godthelp B, van Boxel-Dezaire A and van den Elsen PJ (1995) Definition of a novel complementation group in MHC class II deficiency. *Immunogenetics* 41: 287–294.

Reith W, Steimle V and Mach B (1995) Molecular defects in the bare lymphocyte syndrome and regulation of MHC class II genes. *Immunology Today* 16: 539–545.

de la Salle H, Hanau D, Fricker D *et al* (1994) Homozygous human TAP peptide transporter mutation in HLA class I deficiency. *Science* 265: 237–241.

Schwartz RS (1997) The case of the bare lymphocyte syndrome-tracking down faulty transcription factors. *New England Journal of Medicine* 337: 781–783.

Touraine JL, Betuel M, Souillet G and Jeune M (1978) Combined immunodeficiency disease associated with absence of cell-surface HLA-A and -B antigens. *Journal of Pediatrics* 93: 47–51.

BASOPHILS

Reuben P Siraganian, Receptors and Signal Transduction Section, Laboratory of Immunology, National Institute of Dental Research, National Institutes of Health, Bethesda, Maryland, USA

Basophils are a member of the granulocytes, the white blood cells in the circulation, and constitute less than 1% of the circulating leukocytes. Basophils share many features with mast cells. They both develop from a common bone marrow-derived hematopoietic precursor cell that is CD34[+], have granules containing histamine, proteolytic enzymes and other inflammatory mediators, have high-affinity receptors for immunoglobulin E (IgE) (FcεRI) and are stimulated to release inflammatory mediators when they react with secretagogues. Therefore, both types of cell play a role in immediate hypersensitivity and inflammatory reactions. However, there are a number of differences between basophils and mast cells. In contrast to mast cells, which mature in the tissues where they finally reside, basophils differentiate in the bone marrow and enter the circulation as mature, functionally active cells. Basophils have the capacity for chemotaxis and are recruited into tissues during inflammatory reaction. However, even in tissues they can be identified as basophils and there is no evidence that they transform into mast cells. Basophils are smaller than mast cells, are short lived (<2 weeks) and are probably end-cells. In contrast, the mast cells are distributed in connective tissues, often adjacent to blood vessels and beneath epithelial surfaces (e.g. the gastrointestinal and respiratory tracts, and the skin). Mast cells normally do not circulate, are long lived and appear to retain the capacity to proliferate. Connective tissue-type mast cells in general contain much more histamine than basophils (a human basophil contains approximately 1 pg histamine). Unlike mast cells, chondroitin monosulfates are the major proteoglycan of basophils. There are also differences in the surface proteins found on basophils compared with those on mast cells. Studies in several mammalian species suggest an inverse quantitative relationship between basophils and mast cells, e.g. species that have abundant mast cells have few basophils. Humans however, have significant numbers of both mast cells and basophils.

The entry on mast cells describes the mediators released from basophils or mast cells, the high-affinity IgE receptor FcεRI, stimuli that activate the cells for secretion and the biochemical mechanisms of the release reaction. The present section describes the unique features of basophils and relies heavily on studies with human cells.

Morphology

Human basophils have a polylobed nucleus with condensed nuclear chromatin and absent nucleoli. They have little endoplasmic reticulum and free ribosomes. The cytoplasm contains a large number of granules that are heterogeneous in size. By electron microscopy some granules are filled uniformly with electron dense material, whereas others lack this dense material. When antigen is added *in vitro*, the basophils lose their oriented motility and extend pseudopodia. The degranulating basophils develop small cytoplasmic 'vesicles' that rapidly increase in size and coalesce. The granular membranes fuse with the plasma membrane, resulting in the development of narrow openings between the cell surface and individual granules. This results in the extrusion of membrane-free granular material through multiple openings in the circumference of the cell. However, there are some rare interconnected chains of granules opened to the exterior at a single point on the cell surface. The granule matrix is released as a whole to the outside, but the granule membrane is left behind. Frequently, membrane-free granular contents are seen attached to the cell exterior. The degranulation of mast cells is of the 'compound' type with granules fusing with each other, whereas in basophils most of

the granules fuse directly with the plasma membrane (**Figures 1 A & B**).

Basophils infiltrate and occasionally constitute a significant proportion of the total cells at sites of delayed hypersensitivity reactions. Such reactions are termed *cutaneous basophil hypersensitivity*. The T cells in such reactions probably release factors that are chemotactic for basophils and might also induce the basophils to degranulate slowly: the granules never fuse with the cell membrane, but lose their matrix in a 'piecemeal' manner over a period of days. Small packages of granular content appear to bud from granule membranes, traverse the cytoplasm and fuse with the plasma membrane, leaving completely degranulated cells.

Basophil releasability

Releasability of basophils refers to the variation in the extent of histamine release from the cells of different donors. The extent of histamine release from the cells of any one individual can vary from none to values as high as 90–100% of the total cellular content. There is good positive correlation between antigen-induced histamine release *in vitro* with the

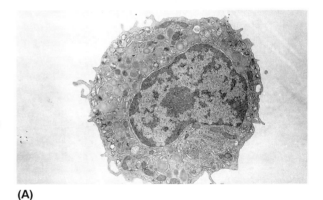

(A)

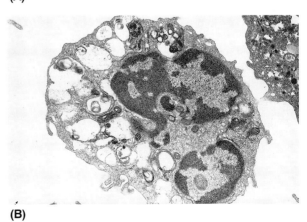

(B)

Figure 1 Human basophils; (A) non-activated; (B) after degranulation. Photomicrographs kindly provided by Dr. Connie Oliver.

basophils of allergic patients and the extent of their symptoms. The releasability of the same cells can also vary with different secretagogues. There are also differences in the extent of release from basophils compared with mast cells. There is no correlation between the number of IgE molecules present on the surface of basophils and releasability. Recent evidence suggests that these differences in secretion are regulated by intracellular factors. For example, the cells of donors who are high responders release histamine with chemically cross-linked IgE dimers; whereas the cells of the donors who are low responders release with chemically cross-linked trimers, but very poorly with dimers. The sensitivity of cells to different stimuli can be modified by factors such as adherence of the cells to other cells or extracellular matrix proteins, by cytokines, by steroids or by dietary lipids that are incorporated into the membranes.

Cell desensitization

The cross-linking of the IgE receptors on the basophil or mast cell causes the activation of enzymes that result in secretion of mediators. Some of these biochemical reactions also regulate the extent of the release reaction. This process is called *cell desensitization*. Experimentally, desensitization is initiated by addition of the secretagogue under conditions that do not result in secretion, and after a defined incubation period the permissive conditions are restored. Desensitization is an active process, blocked by some pharmacologic agents, and is secretagogue-specific. The IgE receptor-mediated desensitization requires receptor aggregation, and can be either specific to the one antigen or for all IgE-mediated release reactions. At low cell surface IgE densities there is antigen-specific desensitization, whereas at high surface IgE levels there is desensitization for all IgE-mediated reactions. Desensitization is not due to the loss of cell surface antigen-specific IgE caused by endocytosis or shedding of IgE–antigen complexes. It is probably due to the decay of an unstable intermediate formed by the cross-linked receptors interacting with a secondary component. The degree of desensitization probably regulates the extent of the release process.

The mechanism for mediator release is similar in the various cell systems studied, e.g. human mast cells, basophils or rat mast cells. All systems respond to the physiologically relevant stimulus of IgE–antigen. However, there are differences in the response to miscellaneous secretagogues that could be related to the presence of surface receptors, and there are differences in the rate of release with various cells. Some pharmacologic agents inhibit release from human basophils but not from mast cells. There are differences in the spectrum of mediators released by mast cells compared with basophils. In contrast to mast cells, human basophils release very little, if any, of the cyclo-oxygenase-derived products of arachidonic acid such as prostaglandin D_2. However, both mast cells and basophils release the leukotriene C_4. Mast cells but not basophils release the enzyme tryptase. There is little evidence to suggest that the secretory process is fundamentally different in the basophils compared with that in the mast cells.

See also: **Allergens; Anaphylatoxins; Arachidonic acid and the leukotrienes; Exocytosis; Histamine; Hypersensitivity reactions; IgE; Interleukin 3; Platelet-activating factor (PAF); Serotonin.**

Further reading

Charlesworth EN (1997) The role of basophils and mast cells in acute and late reactions in the skin. *Allergy* 52: 31–43.

Hirai K, Miyamasu M, Takaishi T and Morita Y (1997) Regulation of the function of eosinophils and basophils. *Critical Review of Immunology* 17: 325–352.

Marone G (ed) (1995) Human basophils and mast cells: biological and clinical aspects. *Chemical Immunology* 61, 62.

Siraganian RP (1988) Mast cells and basophils. In: Gallin JI, Goldstein IM and Snyderman R (eds) *Inflammation: Basic Principles and Clinical Correlates*, pp 513–542. New York: Raven Press.

BCG

Jacob George, Department of Medicine 'B' and the Research Unit of Autoimmune Diseases, Sheba Medical Center, Tel-Hashomer, Sackler Faculty of Medicine, Tel-Aviv University, Tel-Aviv, Israel

Michael Alkan, Department of Medicine 'B' and the Research Unit of Autoimmune Diseases, Sheba Medical Center, Tel-Hashomer, Sackler Faculty of Medicine, Tel-Aviv University, Tel-Aviv, Israel

Yehuda Shoenfeld, Department of Medicine 'B' and the Research Unit of Autoimmune Diseases, Sheba Medical Center, Tel-Hashomer, Sackler Faculty of Medicine, Tel-Aviv University, Tel-Aviv, Israel

Calmette and Guérin first described bacille Calmette–Guérin (BCG) in 1908. A bovine strain of *Mycobacterium tuberculosis* was grown on a piece of potato cooked at 70°C in bile containing 5% glycine. After 231 subcultures on this special medium and 13 years later, the bacilli were found to be nonpathogenic, but otherwise indistinguishable from the virulent strain. In 1921, this bacillus was first advocated as a live vaccine against tuberculosis (TB). Since then, BCG constitutes one of the mainstays of any TB control program. Evidence for successful vaccination is development of a delayed-type hypersensitivity reaction to a purified protein derivative (PPD) of *M. tuberculosis*.

Recommendations, administration and efficacy

The inconsistent policies among countries with regard to the indication for administering BCG vaccine reflect the contradicting and inconclusive data on the prevention of TB and the drawback of a resultant tuberculin seroconversion preventing the interpretation of the tuberculin skin test.

BCG is presently recommended in the USA for tuberculin-negative infants and children who have continuous exposure to isoniazide- and rifampin-resistant active TB, who cannot take isoniazid and are exposed to TB, or who belong to population groups with rates of new *M. tuberculosis* infections exceeding 1% per year. Vaccination is also advised for groups residing in high-prevalence areas such as military and foreign service personnel. Vaccination should be avoided in immunosuppressed individuals, with special regard to patients with established human immunodeficiency virus (HIV) infection because of the increased risk of disseminated infection.

The administration protocol recommended by the World Health Organization's expanded program is a single dose at birth. However, this recommendation is not implemented universally; for example, in the UK a single dose is administered at the age of 13, whereas in eastern Europe repeated doses are given through childhood.

The efficacy of BCG against TB has been debatable since its initial use in 1921, although, to date, well over 3 billion doses have been administered. A recent comprehensive meta-analysis from 14 prospective trials and, separately, 12 case–control studies, addressing the efficacy of BCG, pointed towards an overall protective effect of 50% against TB infections. The protective effect against pulmonary and disseminated infection was 78%, against tuberculous meningitis 64% and against death 71%.

Antigenic properties and immunologic aspects

The mycobacterium is an acid-fast, slow-growing bacillus. Most of its antigens are firmly attached to the cell wall. These have been classified into three groups: 1) antigens common to all mycobacteria, which can also be found in other bacteria such as *Listeria*, *Corynebacterium* and *Nocardia* spp.; 2) common antigens present on slow-growing bacteria; 3) species-specific antigens. Most studies on the soluble antigens have been based on vigorous experimental methods by which the cell wall was disrupted and solubilized. This crude antigen preparation was found to be a nonspecific stimulant of cell-mediated immunity, as well as a powerful adjuvant to vaccines used in experimental animals.

Repeated injection of Freund's complete adjuvant containing killed mycobacteria results in a response resembling autoimmune disorders (the so-called adjuvant arthritis in rats). BCG itself can induce nonspecific resistance to certain infections (or enhancement of others) and tumor growth suppression, attributed to various influences of the vaccine such as enhancement of macrophage cytotoxicity, increased production of natural killer cells, cytokines and cytotoxic T cells. Most of the above-mentioned properties are related to the high lipid content of the bacteria, up to 40% of its dry weight. These lipids include a variety of biologically active substances: trehalose 6,6′-dimycolate or 'cord factor', neutral red reactive sulfolipid, 6-O-methylglucose lipopolysaccharide, phosphatides and waxes. A group of substances which have been studied extensively are the mycolic acids. β-Mycolic acid is typical of BCG. It consists of three aliphatic chains of 11–28 carbons, linked by ester or hydroxyl residues to extensive hydrocarbon chains with a carboxyl side-chain at the link and at the end of the chain. A cyclopropyl group is present between the first two short chains. In the cell wall, these molecules are connected to sugars, containing arabinose and galactose, and with wax D. This complex is the molecule that gives the adjuvant activity. The nonspecific immune stimulation has been used in cancer management. Animal studies have demonstrated tumor regression following repeated local BCG infection. Viable BCG cells, injected into metastases of human malignant melanoma, led to marked tumor regression. Probably the most abundant use of BCG in cancer therapy is in bladder cancer. Intravesical administration is used for three purposes: 1) adjunctive therapy as a single treatment after complete tumor resolution to prevent tumor cell implantation and recurrence; 2) prophylactically, in repeated doses to prevent *de novo* recurrence of tumor following complete excision; 3) therapeutically, in repeated administrations to treat residual unresected tumor. Known adverse effects include regional adenitis, disseminated BCG infection and osteitis due to the BCG organism.

See also: **Adjuvants;** *Mycobacteria*, **infection and immunity; Vaccines.**

Further reading

Brennan PJ and Nikaido H (1995) The envelope of mycobacteria. *Annual Review of Biochemistry* **64**: 29–63.

Colditz GA, Brewer TF, Berkey CS *et al* (1994) Efficacy of BCG vaccine in the prevention of tuberculosis. *JAMA* **271**: 698–702.

Eickhoff TC (1988) Bacille Calmette–Guérin (BCG) vaccine. In: Plotkin SA, Mortimer EA (eds) *Vaccines*, pp 372–386. Philadelphia: WB Saunders.

Fine PEM and Rodrigues LC (1990) Modern vaccines: mycobacterial diseases. *Lancet* **335**: 1016–1020.

Herr HW, Badalament RA, Amato DA *et al* (1989) Superficial bladder cancer treated with bacillus Calmette–Guérin: a multivariate analysis of factors affecting tumor progression. *Journal of Urology* **141**: 22–29.

BEHAVIORAL REGULATION OF IMMUNITY

Nicholas Cohen, Jan A Moynihan and **Robert Ader,** Center for Psychoneuroimmunology Research and the Departments of Microbiology and Immunology and of Psychiatry, University of Rochester Medical Center, Rochester, New York, USA

Although immune responses can readily occur and be analyzed *in vitro*, the immune system normally functions in an intact organism where it has the opportunity to interact with other physiological systems. A significant body of recent data points out that indeed such interactions do occur *in vivo*. For example, the central nervous system (CNS) is in dynamic communication with the immune system. Lymphoid tissues are richly innervated, and abrogation of this sympathetic innervation alters expression of natural and acquired immunity. Cells of the CNS produce proinflammatory cytokines (e.g. interleukin-1 (IL-1) and IL-6), and mitogen- or antigen-stimulated lymphocytes produce different hormones (e.g. proopiomelanocortin-derived peptides, growth hormone, prolactin, luteinizing hormone) and neuropeptides (e.g. substance P, vasoactive intestinal peptide). Lymphocytes and macrophages express cell surface receptors for a diversity of hormones and neuropeptides, suggesting autocrine and paracrine regulation by these molecules. Experimental manipulation of hormone– or neurotransmitter–immunocyte receptor interactions can evoke alterations in immunologically relevant events such as lymphocyte proliferation, activity of natural killer (NK) cells, production of antibody, synthesis and release of cytokines, and expression of cytokine receptors.

There is now incontrovertible evidence that the immunomodulatory interactions between the CNS and the immune system can be 'regulated' by the behavior of the organism. Such evidence has been provided by predominantly phenomenological studies on the influences of classical (Pavlovian) conditioning and on the effects of 'stress' on immunity.

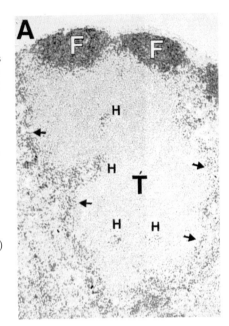

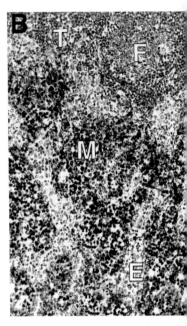

Plate 1 Lymph node. (A) Section of mouse lymph node showing recirculating IgD+ B cells around their portal of entry. The high endothelial venules (H) located in the T zone (T) are stained blue. IgD+ cells are also seen in the walls of the intranodal lymphatics in the edge of the T zone and in the follicles (F). En route to the follicles recirculating B cells travel along the walls of the intranodal lymphatics (arrows) where encounter with antigen from the lymph may occur. (B) Section of a formalin-fixed rat lymph node demonstrating large numbers of plasma cells in the medullary cords (M). These are stained brown with anti-Ig. Formalin-fixation has destroyed the surface Ig on the B cells. T - T zone; F - follicle; E - efferent lymphatic. (Kindly provided by Ian MacLennan, University of Birmingham Medical School, UK. Reproduced from MacLennan et al., 1997, *Immunological Reviews* **156**, 53-66 with permission.)

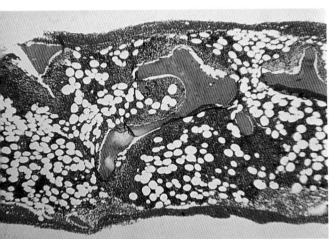

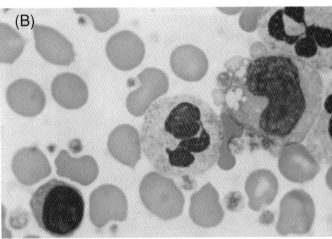

Plate 2 (A) (*above*) **Bone marrow.** Trephine biopsy from a 45 year old man (Haematoxylin and eosin stain) Trephine biopsy examination of bone marrow is used commonly to diagnose both hematological and nonhematological conditions. (Kindly provided by Michael Watts, University College Hospitals, London, UK with permission.)

Plate 2 (B) (*above right*) **Lymphocyte, neutrophil and monocyte.** Bottom left is a small lymphocyte, center is a polymorphonuclear neutrophil and top right is a monocyte showing the characteristic 'horseshoe-shaped' nucleus and moderately abundant pale cytoplasm. Two additional neutrophils are partly in the field of view at the top right. Romanowsky stain. (Kindly provided by Michael Watts, University College Hospitals, London, UK with permission.)

Plate 3 (*right*) **Tonsil.** Section of a normal human palatine tonsil. At upper right (pink) is the stratified squamous epithelium of the surface of the tonsil. This epithelium is highly folded. Beneath it is a collagen fiber layer (blue). At lower center is the lymphoid tissue (red). Apart from the pair of palatine tonsils, there is a pair of lingual tonsils and a pair of pharyngeal tonsils (adenoids) which contribute to the Waldeyer's ring of lymphoid tissue. (With permission from Photo Science Library.)

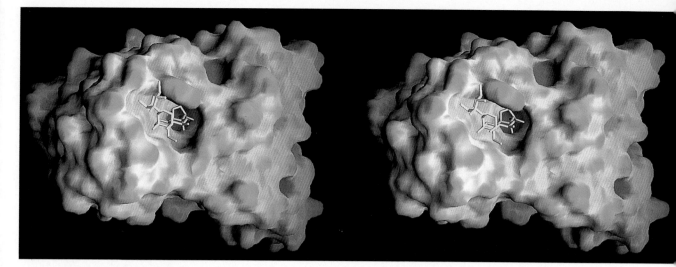

Plate 4 Antibody binding to a hapten. Stereo view of the 40-50 antibody combining site with V_L on the left and V_H on the right and colored to display concave (dark gray) and convex (green) molecular surfaces. The 40-50 binding site is a groove mostly on the surface of the light chain. The bound hapten, ouabain, is shown in yellow. (Kindly provided by Steven Sheriff, Bristol-Myers Squibb Pharmaceuticals Research Institute, Princeton, USA. Reproduced from Jeffrey *et al.*,1995, *Journal of Molecular Biology* **248**, 344-360 with permission.)

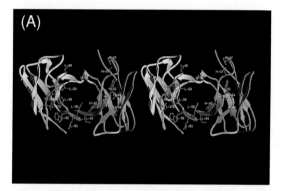

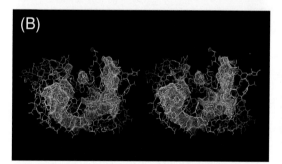

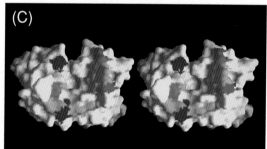

Plate 5 Antibody paratope. (A) Stereo diagram of a ribbon structure of the V_H: V_L domain showing the side-chains of the contact residues that comprise the paratope of the N10 anti-Staphylococcal nuclease antibody. The heavy chain is colored green, the light chain yellow, CDR regions silver and contact residues (with side-chains shown) are magenta. Figure produced with RIBBONS (Carson 1991). (B) Contact molecular surface (cyan dots) of the N10 antibody (blue with contact residues in yellow) calculated by the method of Connolly (1983) and displayed using GRASP (Nicholls et al 1991.) Note the U-shape of the contact surface with the single heavy chain CDR3 contact residue Asn H-96 located just inside the open end of the U. (C) The N10 antibody paratope with the light chain on the left. Surface representation of the calculated ΔG residue contribution to binding by the N10 antibody and the Staphylococcal nuclease antigen residues. A color scale was constructed of the ΔG residue values, from blue (–2.0 kcal/mol) to red (+2.0 kcal/mol). Thus, blue colors represent negative ("attractive") residue contributions, red colors represent positive ("repulsive") contributions. Figure produced with GRASP (Nicholls et al 1991). (Kindly provided by Steven Sheriff, Bristol-Myers Squibb Pharmaceuticals Research Institute, Princeton, USA. Reproduced from Bossart-Whitaker *et al.*, 1995, *Journal of Molecular Biology* **253**, 559-575 with permission.)

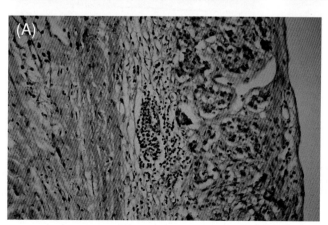

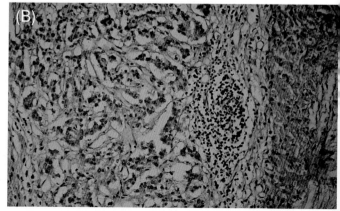

Plate 6 (A) **Addison's Disease**. Adrenal gland from patient with Addisons disease, showing atrophy of the cortex and infiltration with mononuclear cells.(B) Another area from same adrenal gland, photographed at higher magnification. (Kindly provided by P E Bigazzi, University of Conneticut Health Center, USA with permission.)

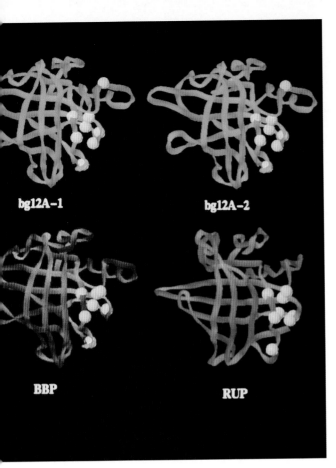

bg12A-1   bg12A-2

BBP   RUP

Plate 7 (*left*) **Allergens**. Molecular modeling of the cockroach calycin allergen, Bla g 4. The Cα backbone structures for two models of Bla g 4 (designated bg12A-1 and bg12A-2) were modeled on the X-ray crystal coordinates for butterfly bilin-binding protein (BBP) and are compared with rat urinary protein allergen (RUP), for which the X-ray crystal structure has also been determined. The yellow spheres are conserved amino acid residues that form motifs which define the ligand-binding proteins, or calycins. (Kindly provided by M D Chapman, University of Virginia, USA with permission.)

Plate 8 (*below*) **Antibody-antigen interaction.** (A) Conformational differences in antibody D1.3 V$_L$ CDR3 induced by differing antigen side-chains.Hen egg lysozyme (HEL) residue Gln121 makes two main-chain hydrogen bonds; to the carbonyl oxygen of D1.3 V$_L$ Phe91 and the amide nitrogen of D1.3 V$_L$ Ser93. Replacement of the glutamine by histidine in Turkey egg lysozyme (TEL) induces a conformational change in the backbone of V$_L$ CDR3 which allows the formation of a hydrogen bond between the histidine and the carbonyl oxygen of V$_L$ Trp92. (B) The effect of a Trp-Asp mutation on the interaction surface area of the D1.3-HEL complex (dots) and the mutant D1.3-HEL surface (solid line) demonstrates the loss of inter-action surface area in the mutant complex. A 150 Å^2 loss in surface area accounts for the reduction in affinity of the mutant D1.3-HEL reaction. (C) Hydrogen bonding network of the D1.3-HEL interface mediated by bound solvent molecules; 25 water molecules form hydrogen bonds linking the antibody and antigen, directly or through other water molecules. (D) Water molecules in contact with the D1.3-HEL buried surface. Including the 25 bridging water molecules, nearly 50 solvent sites are in contact with the buried surface defined by the D1.3-HEL interface. Many of these water molecules fill internal cavities, further stabilizing the complex. (Kindly provided by B C Braden and R J Poljak, Center for Advanced Research in Technology, USA with permission.)

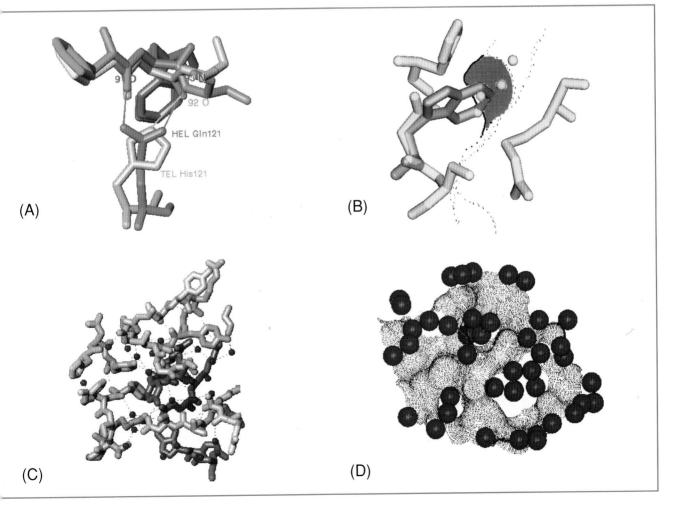

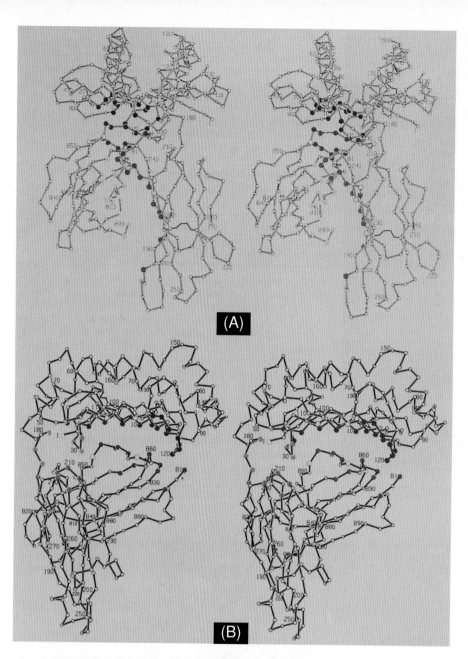

(A)

(B)

Plate 9 (*left*) **HLA-A2.** The residues forming the domain interfaces are highlighted in color on the C_α backbone stereogram. Filled and colored C_α atoms make contacts ≤ 4 Å. Red, α_1, α_2 residues in interface with $\beta_2 M$; green, $\beta_2 M$ residues in interface with $\alpha_1 \alpha_2$; blue α_3 residues in interface with $\beta_2 M$; yellow, $\beta_2 M$ residues in interface α_3; pink, $\alpha_1 \alpha_2$ residues in interface with α_3; orange, α_3 residues in interface with $\alpha_1 \alpha_2$. (A) A view perpendicular to $\alpha_1 \alpha_2$ pseudodyad with the binding cleft viewed end-on ($\alpha_1 \alpha_2$-α_3 interface not shown). (B) A side view with the molecule rotated 90° about the pseudodyad (α_3–$\beta_2 M$ interface not shown). (Reprinted with permission from Saper MA, Bjorkman PJ and Wiley DC (1991) Refined structure of the human histocompatibility antigen HLA-A2 at 2.6 Å resolution. *Journal of Moleular Biology* **219**: 277-319.)

Plate 10 (*below*) **CD8.** Three-dimensional molecular model of the N-terminal region of a CD8 homodimer consisting of two α chains; (A) ribbon presentation, (B) stick presentation. The structural data for the N-terminal 113 amino acids are based on crystallography (protein data base: 1CD8). The three-dimensional model for each monomer was generated with RasMol version 2.5 (Roger Sayle, Greenford, Middlesex, UK), and the two monomers were combined as described (Leahy *et al* (1992) *Cell* **68**: 1145). The color coding represents groups; blue corresponds to the CDR1-like loop, light blue to the CDR2-like loop, and lime to the CDR3-like loop. The monomers are distinguished in brightness of color. (Kindly provided by GF Weber and H Cantor, Dana-Faber Cancer Institute, USA with permission.)

(A)

(B)

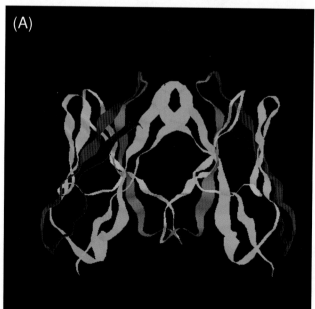

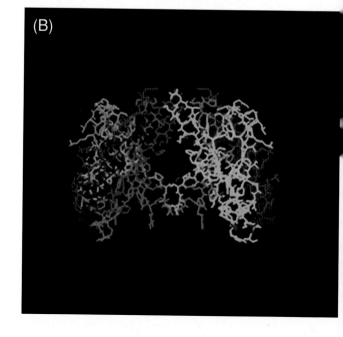

Pavlovian conditioning and immunomodulation

Classical (Pavlovian) conditioning is perhaps the first behavioral approach that has been used experimentally to reveal a relationship between the CNS and the immune system. In the classical Pavlovian paradigm, a stimulus (e.g. food) that unconditionally elicits a particular response (salivation) is repeatedly paired with a neutral stimulus that does not elicit that same response. Eventually, the neutral stimulus becomes a conditional stimulus, in that it will elicit salivation in the absence of food, the unconditional stimulus. Since Pavlov's experiments in the 1920s, a wide range of behavioral, physiologic and pharmacologic processes have been conditioned in a wide diversity of species. The first conditioning studies that involved nonspecific arms of the defense system were conducted in the Soviet Union in 1926, as extensions of Pavlov's work on the conditioning of physiologic responses. In these early studies, Metalnikov and Chorine conditioned an increase in polymorphonuclear leukocytes (PMNs) in a peritoneal exudate by repeatedly pairing the intraperitoneal injection of foreign material, in guinea pigs, with the scratching or heating of the animals' skin. After multiple pairings, and after the number of PMNs returned to baseline levels, re-exposure to the conditional stimulus alone was reported to evoke an increase in the number of PMNs. Several variations on these types of experiments, plus those in which increased levels of specific antibody were attributed to conditioning, appeared in the Russian literature in the next decade and then again in the 1950s.

The first rigorously controlled and immunologically relevant conditioning experiments in the West were published in 1975 by Ader and Cohen. In their initial study, rats were subjected to a single learning trial in which an injection of cyclophosphamide (CY), a potent immunosuppressive drug that served as an unconditional stimulus, was paired with the consumption of a novel, distinctly flavored saccharin (SAC) solution, the conditioning stimulus. When rats conditioned in this fashion were re-exposed to the conditional stimulus at the time of antigenic challenge, conditioned immunopharmacologic effects were revealed by a significantly depressed antibody response relative to the appropriate controls (i.e. nonconditioned animals, or conditioned animals that were never re-exposed to the conditional stimulus). Similar and subsequent conditioning protocols involving mice as well as rats, CY or other immunosuppressive drugs as unconditional stimuli, and different novel tastes as conditional stimuli, have revealed a conditioned: depression of

graft-versus-host reactions; enhancement of delayed hypersensitivity responses; depression of humoral immune responses to thymus-independent as well as thymus-dependent antigens; and depression of mitogen- and alloantigen-induced lymphocyte proliferation, heart and skin allograft rejection, plasmacytoma growth, NK cell activity, numbers of white cells and arthritic inflammation.

Exposure of conditioned animals (conditioned by pairing SAC with CY) to the conditional stimulus appears to create an immunomodulatory environment. This was suggested by experiments in which conditioned rats, exposed to the conditional stimulus a few weeks before they were immunized, still displayed a conditioned immunosuppressive response to the antigen. More direct evidence that conditioning alters the internal milieu (and may primarily affect T cells) comes from the use of classic lymphocyte transfer and cell-mixing protocols by Gorczynski. In these, and in other conditioning studies in which the unconditional stimulus was the injection of either CY or some other immunosuppressive drug, it seems reasonable to propose that the actual unconditional stimuli being perceived by the CNS as deviations from homeostasis are some secondary or tertiary immunologic consequence(s) of the direct effect of CY on the lymphocyte (e.g. changes in lymphocyte number and/or traffic).

That conditioned immunopharmacologic effects are of biological importance is apparent from Ader and Cohen's observations that the development of a systemic lupus erythematosus (SLE)-like autoimmune disease in (NZB × NZW)F_1 hybrid mice could be markedly delayed by treating animals under a partial schedule of pharmacologic reinforcement. That is, by substituting conditional stimuli that had been paired with CY for a proportion of the trials on which animals would normally have received active drug therapy, conditioned mice showed a significant delay in the onset of lupus using a cumulative dosage of CY that was, by itself, insufficient to alter the course of the autoimmune disease. Moreover, conditioned mice repeatedly re-exposed to the taste stimulus that had been paired with CY following the termination of active drug therapy survived significantly longer than conditioned animals that received no 'medication'.

Although in the not-too-distant future, conditioned immunopharmacologic effects may prove to be significant in clinical situations where one wishes to reduce the amount of actual drug administered to a patient with an autoimmune disease or an organ transplant, this model of conditioned immunosuppression may be of limited help in trying to understand the basic impact and physiology of conditioning on 'normal' immune responses. More revealed models would be those in which immune responses are altered in animals that are conditioned by pairing a conditional stimulus with a naturally occurring immunologic response modifier (e.g. a cytokine) or with a substance that itself unconditionally elicits an immune response, namely an antigen. Since conditioning is an example of feed forward control in which the organism reacts physiologically based on an anticipated need, a conditioned immune response in the absence of an externally administered cytokine or an immunogenic concentration of antigen would indeed highlight the physiological importance of CNS regulation of immunity during the normal life of an organism. At this time, only a handful of such studies have been performed, and several of these have involved the conditioned release of histamine or protease II from mast cells of animals sensitized with protein antigens. In one study, however, a conditioned change in antigen-specific lymphocytes was reported. In this experiment, Gorczynski, Macrae and Kennedy repeatedly grafted CBA mice with allogeneic skin from C57BL/6J mice. During the 40 day interval between first, second- and third-set grafting, the number of cytotoxic T lymphocyte precursors (CTLp) specific for the alloantigens of the sensitizing donor increased and then returned to baseline levels. Each recipient mouse was anesthetized, shaved, had a graft bed surgically prepared on to which the skin allograft was placed, and was then bandaged. That is, the grafting procedure itself served as a complex of conditional stimuli. On the fourth (test) trial, animals in all groups were exposed to just the conditional stimuli (i.e. they were sham grafted). Only conditioned mice displayed an increase in CTLp in response to the stimulus conditions associated with grafting in the absence of an actual graft. In each of several replications of this experiment, only about half of the conditioned mice showed the conditioned change in CTLp. These 'responder' mice were then divided into subgroups that either experienced two extinction trials (unreinforced exposure to the conditional stimulus) or two additional learning trials (i.e. two separate trials in which there were pairings of the conditional and unconditional stimuli). All 'responder' animals that received additional conditioning trials displayed an increase in CTLp in response to the conditional stimulus; none of the 'responders' given extinction trials showed the conditioned response.

In a recent study by Ader and his colleagues, an enhanced antibody response provided the immunologic readout of a conditioning protocol in which antigen itself served as the conditioned stimulus. In

this study, injection of a very small amount of key-hole limpet hemocyanin (KLH) was paired with a novel taste on each of several learning trials. In between each learning trial, the serum antibody response increased and then decreased. On the test trial, mice were given an amount of KLH (0.5 ng) that only elicited a modest antibody response by itself, but when it was given to conditioned animals in association with the conditional stimulus, KLH-specific antibody titers increased significantly over baseline. To confirm that this was a *bona fide* conditioned response, mice were pre-exposed to the conditional stimulus before the initiation of the first and subsequent learning trials. When such animals were presented with the small antigen boost plus the conditional stimulus, they did not produce antibody, an observation totally consistent with learning theory.

Given that we do not fully understand the mechanisms that underlie these examples of conditioning, one can only speculate about: 1) the nature of the neurochemical consequences of various conditional stimuli in the nervous system: 2) which (and how the) relevant internal physiologic consequences of an antigenic, pharmacologic or physical unconditional stimulus become associated internally with the neurologic sequelae of a conditional stimulus; and 3) how presentation of the conditional stimulus evokes the immunomodulatory responses that many investigators have observed. Regardless of our ignorance of the constellation of mechanisms that may be involved in conditioned alterations of immunity, it is clear that, since learning involves higher centers of the brain, the ability to effect changes in immune responses by conditioning must mean that, *in vivo*, the immune system receives and responds to signals (either directly and/or indirectly) from the CNS.

Stressor-associated regulation of immunity

Stress, as defined by Hans Selye, is the response to deviation from the normal resting condition (i.e. homeostasis). It is generally accepted that stressor administration causes complex neurologic and neurochemical changes as the host attempts to adapt to the demands of the situation. These CNS changes regulate many physiologic processes, including those involved in the generation of an immune response. Immunomodulatory 'stress' protocols have involved different periods of exposure to either physical stimuli (e.g. electric shock, rotation, restraint, temperature, noise) or so-called psychosocial stressors (e.g. differential housing, maternal separation and handling in experimental animals; bereavement, divorce and school examinations in humans). Immunologic outcomes measured in such studies have been: the development of primary and secondary antibody and cell-mediated immune responses to experimental antigens, microbial pathogens and tumor cells *in vivo*; the numbers of B cells and T cell subsets in various lymphoid compartments; the magnitude of mitogen- and/or antigen-induced lymphocyte proliferation *in vitro*; the production of, and response to, cytokines; NK cell cytotoxicity; and macrophage activation. Considering the variability among these studies with respect to the nature, duration and intensity of the stressor, the age, sex, species and strain of the stressed organism and the parameters of the immune function studied, it is not surprising that different effects of stress on immunity have been reported. Thus, the same stressor can effect enhancement or suppression of different immune responses; different stressors can have different effects on the same parameter of immunity; the same stressor applied for varying periods of time may have different effects on the same parameter of immunity; and changes in a single parameter of immunologic reactivity in response to different stressful stimuli are not necessarily unidirectional. By and large, however, stress in experimental animals and humans has been reported to depress the particular parameters of immunity that were being examined.

Stress has a variety of neuroendocrine effects, and immune responses are affected by the neuroendocrine milieu in which leukocytes function. However, it is far from clear which (and how) stress-associated neuroendocrine changes are responsible for which stress-associated immunomodulatory events. For example, the hypothalamo–pituitary–adrenal (HPA) axis is activated during stressful situations, and there are numerous reports of stress-induced adrenocortically-mediated immunosuppression. However, there are also several reports of stress-induced alterations of immunologic reactivity that occur in adrenalectomized animals. Although hypophysectomy obviates the effects of stress on some measures of immune function, stress-induced suppression of others are potentiated by this procedure. Because of the involvement of the HPA axis in stress-induced analgesia, many investigators have looked for, and found, a role of endogenous opioids in stress-associated immunomodulation in a variety of species including fish, mice, rats and humans. However, not all stress effects on immunity can be blocked by naloxone or naltrexone and/or mimicked by exogenous opioids such as endorphins and morphine. Finally, although levels of catecholamines and other neurotransmitters are known to be altered in response to stress, and many studies have revealed a role of norepinephrine on immune function, few studies have attempted to correlate stress-induced changes in plasma catecholamines with altered immune function.

For immunologists, the fact that physiologic responses to stressors are immunomodulatory has practical implications that relate to experimental design as well as experimental theory. For example, putative pheromones from stressed (footshocked) mice conveyed to KLH-immunized recipients can affect cytokine production by lymphocytes *in vitro* and the immune responses they regulate *in vivo*. An extension of these observations to a situation in which manipulations of mice in an animal room can be communicated to and effect immune responses of other animals in that same room is not an unwarranted assumption. A second example of practical import for immunologists is that the differential housing of mice (housed one versus four per cage from the time of weaning) reproducibly and significantly influences antigen-stimulated *in vitro* production of T_H1- and T_H2-derived cytokines by splenocytes from mice immunized with either KLH or herpes simplex virus (HSV).

In the pheromone studies mentioned above, the immunologic effects on recipients of 'stress odors' occurred in a manner consistent with the theory that depressed cellular but enhanced humoral immune responses in pheromone-exposed BALB/c mice are reflective of an altered 'balance' between production of T_H1 and T_H2 lymphocyte-derived cytokines. However, the immunologic effects of differential housing on immune responses of either BALB/c or C57/BL6 mice to either KLH or HSV do not fit all predictions inherent in the theory of a differentially 'balanced' cytokine response and strain-associated dominance of humoral or cellular immunity. That is, regardless of strain or antigen, individually housed animals produce more antibody, have greater delayed-type hypersensitivity responses, and make more interleukin-2 (IL-2), IL-4, interferon γ (IFNγ) and IL-10 than do group-housed animals.

The observations that physical and psychosocial stressors can modulate immunity on the one hand, and modify disease progression on the other, has led to popularization of the idea that stress plays an important role in the pathogenesis of immunologically relevant diseases (e.g. cancer, viral and bacterial infections, autoimmunity, allergy). At this time, however, the cause–effect relationships between a stressor-altered immune system and disease progression must be viewed more as a reasonable and attractive hypothesis than as hard fact. Specifically, it has yet to be reproducibly documented in experimental animals (let alone in humans) that stress-associated alterations of some facet of immuno-competence are, at least partially, responsible for disease pathophysiology.

Immunity can modulate behavior

The previous material has reviewed data indicating that behavioral triggers of the nervous system can regulate immunity. Several lines of evidence also indicate that components of an immune response can also signal the CNS. For example, many investigators have reported electrical changes in the hypothalamus following the administration of antigen. Others have reported that IL-1 stimulates release of corticotropin-releasing hormone from the hypothalamus into the hypophyseal portal circulation, where it can then activate the HPA axis. Moreover, the response to antigenic stimuli appears to be associated with the release of neurotransmitters and hormones produced by lymphocytes themselves. Finally, evidence suggests that these and/or other signals from an activated immune system may be directly or indirectly signaling the CNS to actually modify the behavior of the organism. The most intriguing observations are those suggesting that the immunologic abnormalities of the lupus-prone strains of congenic MRL mice modify (directly or indirectly) the animals' behavior, which in turn can act to 'correct' homeostatic imbalances within the immune system.

Summary

The current data on conditioned and stress-associated alterations of immunologic reactivity produce compelling evidence of a fundamental integration of behavioral, neuroendocrine and immune processes of adaptation. It now appears that, like all other biological systems functioning in the interests of homeostasis, the immune system is integrated with other psychophysiologic processes and therefore is subject to regulation or modulation by the brain. Conversely, immune processes seem to have implications for neural and endocrine function, including behavior. As such, they provide evidence for the *in vivo* bidirectionality of interactions between the immune system and the central nervous system.

See also: **Cytokines; Immunosuppression; Neuroendocrine regulation of immunity; Stress and the immune system.**

Further reading

Ader R and Cohen N (1982) Behaviorally conditioned immunosuppression and murine systemic lupus erythematosus. *Science* 215: 1534–1536.

Ader R and Cohen N (1993) Psychoneuroimmunology: conditioning and stress. *Annual Review of Psychology* 44: 53–85.

Ader R, Felten DL and Cohen N (eds) (1991) *Psychoneuroimmunology*, 2nd edn. San Diego: Academic Press.

Ader R, Kelly K, Moynihan JA, Grota L and Cohen N (1993) Conditioned enhancement of antibody production using antigen as the unconditioned stimulus. *Brain, Behavior, and Immunity* 7: 334–343.

Ader R, Cohen N and Felten DL (1995) Psychoneuroimmunology: interactions between the nervous system and the immune system. *Lancet* 345: 99–103.

Cohen S and Herbert TB (1996) Health psychology: psychological factors and physical disease from the perspective of human psychoneuroimmunology. *Annual Review of Psychology* 47: 113–142.

Friedman H, Klein TW and Friedman AL (eds) (1995) *Psychoneuroimmunology, Stress, and Infection*. Boca Raton: CRC Press.

Gorczynski RM (1987) Analysis of lymphocytes in, and host environment of, mice showing conditioned immunosuppression to cyclophosphamide. *Brain, Behavior, and Immunity* 1: 21–35.

Grota LJ, Schachtman T, Moynihan JA, Cohen N and Ader R (1989) Voluntary consumption of cyclophosphamide by MRL mice. *Brain, Behavior, and Immunity* 3: 263–273.

Karp JD, Cohen N and Moynihan JA (1994) Quantitative differences in IL-2 and IL-4 production by antigen-stimulated splenocytes from individually- and group-housed mice. *Life Sciences* 55: 789–795.

Moynihan JA, Karp JD, Cohen N and Cocke R (1994) Changes in humoral immunity following exposure to pheromones from stressed mice: role of glucocorticoids. *Journal of Neuroimmunology* 54: 51–78.

Moynihan JA, Brenner GJ, Cocke R *et al* (1995) Stress-induced modulation of immunity in mice. In: Glaser R and Kiecolt-Glaser J (eds) *Handbook of Human Stress and Immunity*, pp 1–22. San Diego: Academic Press.

BENCE JONES PROTEINS

Jean-Louis Preud'homme, Laboratory of Immunology and Immunopathology (CNRS ESA 6031), Poitiers University Hospital, Poitiers, France

Bence Jones proteins (BJP), initially known as urinary proteins precipitating at 56–64°C and redissolving on boiling, are now defined as monoclonal free immunoglobulin (Ig) light chains (LC) (polyclonal free LC that may be found in urine are not BJP). Their characterization and quantification is of importance because of their diagnostic and prognostic significance.

Characterization

Bence Jones proteins are usually present in urine as monomers and dimers. Search for BJP often requires a concentration step which is best achieved by vacuum dialysis preferably of daily urine. This results in minimal denaturation and does not bias against certain proteins (including some BJP). Electrophoresis of concentrated urines typically shows a narrow band with a mobility generally different from that of the entire monoclonal Ig which may be present in the serum. Bence Jones proteins are sometimes heterogeneous in charge and are easily and reliably quantified by scanning the electrophoresis. Immunoelectrophoresis shows one or several contiguous narrow precipitating lines with the relevant anti-LC serum and no reactivity with anti-heavy chain sera. Being monoclonal in origin, the BJP are of either κ or λ type. When part of a κ type BJP displays a fast migration, this usually results from an interaction with α_1-antitrypsin. Immunofixation may be useful in the diagnosis of BJP. Western blotting of high-resolution agarose electrophoresis followed by detection with enzyme-coupled Ig-specific antibodies is more sensitive and more accurate.

Bence Jones proteins are detectable in the serum when they are secreted in very large amounts, when they polymerize and in the case of renal failure. Antisera that react with free LC and not with LC in whole Ig molecules may be helpful.

Diagnostic significance

Normal plasma cells most often produce balanced amounts of heavy and light chains. In contrast, malignant plasma cells often secrete free LC. Hence, the presence of significant amounts of BJP ($\geqslant 0.3$ g l^{-1} of urine) is indicative of malignancy. Minute amounts of BJP detected after $1000 \times$ concentration of proteins present in urine in physiologic concentrations are also mostly observed in malignant diseases. In myeloma, BJP are found as the only monoclonal Ig in about 20% of cases. In IgD myeloma (of the λ type in 9 out of 10 cases), there is usually a large output of BJP, whereas the serum monoclonal IgD is often present in small amounts. Hence, the finding of an apparently isolated λ BJP should lead to a search for IgD myeloma. Bence Jones proteins may be observed in B cell lymphomas and leukemias, in small amounts in virtually every patient with Waldenström macroglobulinemia, and in about 50% of cases of μ heavy chain disease.

Pathogenetic implications

Bence Jones proteins play a direct role in myeloma-associated kidney disease and their measurement is of important prognostic significance. They are also involved in visceral diseases featuring tissue deposition of LC-related material. Combined study of serum and urine by sensitive methods reveals evidence of BJP in almost all cases of AL (amyloid light chain) amyloidosis. In LC deposition disease, tissue deposits of monoclonal LC (and of monoclonal heavy chains in some patients) correlate with the presence of a monoclonal population of bone marrow plasma cells, whatever the clinical context. In some cases, the LC are normal-sized and present in urine but in about 60–70% of patients they display an abnormal (short or enlarged by glycosylation) size, polymerize and are undetectable in serum and urine. In both instances there are numerous mutations in the variable (V) regions of the LC, especially in the hypervariable regions (with probably a direct pathogenic role), together with an abnormal subgroup distribution (VκIV predominance). V region abnormalities, with a V domain (of the VκI subgroup) highly resistant to proteolysis and prone to readily form crystals, are also involved in myeloma-associated Fanconi syndrome.

See also: **Amyloid; Heavy chain diseases; Immuno-electrophoresis; Immunoglobulin structure; Lymphoma; Western blotting.**

Further reading

Buxbaum J (1992) Mechanisms of disease: monoclonal immunoglobulin deposition. Amyloidosis, light chain deposition disease, and light and heavy chain deposition disease. *Hematology/Oncology Clinics of North America* **6**: 323–346.

Minetii L, D'Amico G and Ponticelli C (eds) (1988) *The Kidney in Plasma Cell Dyscrasias*. Dordrecht: Kluwer.

Preud'homme JL, Aucouturier P, Touchard G *et al* (1994) Monoclonal immunoglobulin deposition disease (Randall type). Relationship with structural abnormalities of immunoglobulin chains. *Kidney International* **46**: 965–972.

Rocca A, Khamlichi AA, Touchard G *et al* (1995) Sequence of Vκl subgroup light chains in Fanconi's syndrome. Light chain V region gene usage restriction and peculiarities in myeloma-associated Fanconi's syndrome. *Journal of Immunology* **155**: 3245–3252.

Solomon A, Weiss DT and Kattine AA (1991) Nephrotoxic potential of Bence-Jones proteins. *New England Journal of Medicine* **324**: 1845–1851.

BIOZZI MICE

Gino Doria, Laboratory of Immunology, AMB-BIO-MED, ENEA, Rome, Italy

Biozzi mice are lines of mice genetically selected for high (H) or low (L) antibody responsiveness. From the initial study in 1968 by Biozzi and his group, five different selections, referred to as selections I, II, III, IV and V, were carried out by Biozzi and colleagues.

The character selected was the maximal or minimal antibody response at a given time after an optimal dose of the various antigens used in the different selections. The antibody response was measured by direct or passive agglutination. In every population the frequency of the $\log_2$ of the agglutinin titer (the highest doubling serum dilution giving a positive agglutination) was normally distributed.

Except for selection II, two non-cross-reactive antigens were alternated in consecutive generations in order to avoid the specific interference of maternal antibodies passively transmitted to the progeny. In selection I the antigen used was sheep red blood cells (SRBC) for the first six generations; subsequently SRBC and pigeon erythrocytes were alternated at each generation. In all generations of selection II, mice were immunized with SRBC but the period between weaning and immunization was prolonged to allow elimination of the maternal antibodies. Selections III and IV were carried out for responses to flagellar and somatic antigens, respectively, of two non-cross-reactive *Salmonellae* (*S. typhimurium* and *S. oranienburg*) given alternately. The antigens used for selection V were bovine serum albumin and rabbit gammaglobulin, alternately.

High and low antibody responder lines were produced by bidirectional selective breeding. Starting from a foundation population (F0) of outbred albino mice displaying great variability in antibody response, the two-way selective breeding was performed for maximal or minimal antibody response and repeated in each consecutive generation. Assortative mating of the highest responder mice produced the H line, while that of the lowest responder mice produced the L line. In each line several pairs were culled at each generation and were issued from different families to delay the increase in consanguinity. The two lines diverged progressively until the maximal interline separation was reached at a given generation (selection limit).

According to the principles of quantitative genetics as applied in these studies, at the selection limit the two lines are considered homozygous for all independent loci controlling the antibody response, owing to the progressive accumulation of high-effect alleles in the H line and low-effect alleles in the L line.

The total response (*TR*) to selection is the interline difference at the selection limit, while the response (*R*) to selection is the difference between the mean values of two successive generations of each line. The selection differential (*S*) is the difference between the mean of the selected parents and that of the total population out of which they have been culled. The mean realized heritability (h^2) is calculated by the linear regression coefficient of cumulated *R* versus cumulated *S* over the generations between F0 and the selection limit, and is equal to *R/S*.

Once the selection limit was attained, the following interline hybrids were derived from H and L parents: (H × L) = F1; (F1 × F1) = F2; (F1 × H) = BcH; (F1 × L) = BcL. Using mean values (*x*) and variances (*V*) of the character measured in these mouse populations, relevant genetic parameters were estimated. The total additive effect (*a*) of all the homozygous loci in H and L lines at the selection limit in the absence of dominance is given by

$$a = \tfrac{1}{2}\,(xH - xL).$$

The global dominance deviation (d) in F1 hybrids is given by

$$d = xF1 - \tfrac{1}{2}(xH + xL).$$

The dominance effect is d/a.

The environmental variance (VE) is the mean phenotypic variance of the genetically homogeneous populations: H and L lines at the selection limit and their F1 hybrids. Therefore,

$$VE = \frac{VH + VL + VF1}{3}.$$

The phenotypic variance of the genetically heterogeneous populations, F0, F2, BcH and BcL, is contributed by both genetic and environmental factors. The variance of F2 hybrids is

$$VF2 = VA + VD + VE$$

where VA is the additive variance and VD the dominance variance. The summed variance of the two backcrosses ($VBcH + VBcL$) is

$$VBcs = 2(\tfrac{1}{2}VA + VD + VE) = VA + 2VD + 2VE.$$

Since

$$VF2 - VA = VD + VE, \text{ then } VBcs = 2VF2 - VA.$$

It follows that $VA = 2VF2 - VBcs$.

Knowing VA, the number (n) of independent loci controlling the character is calculated as

$$n = \frac{a^2}{2VA}$$

Since the h^2 value results from the additive effect of homozygous loci occupied by either high- or low-effect alleles, the heritability of the character can also be measured in the progeny of interline crosses (F2 or backcrosses) by the ratio of the additive variance to the total phenotypic variance, as follows:

$$h^2 = \frac{VA}{VA + VD + VE}.$$

Comparison of the immunogenetic parameters in the five selections (**Table 1**) revealed a remarkable

Table 1 Genetic parameters of the five selections

Selection	TR	Selection limit	h^2	n
I	7.8	F16	0.20	9–11
II	6.7	F13	0.21	5–7
III	6.3	F16	0.20	4–7
IV	6.5	F13	0.21	2–4
V	9.8	F7	0.22	2–4

TR, total response to selection; h^2, realized heritability; n, number of independent loci.

similarity in the total response to selection, selection limit and realized heritability. Only in selection V was the total response greater and attained after fewer generations. The number of independent loci controlling antibody responsiveness differed in the five selections, owing to the different nature of the antigens and immunization procedures used. Mapping studies associating polymorphic microsatellite markers with antibody response in selection I have shown that some segregating loci are linked to genes on chromosomes 4 and 8 but also to genes certainly involved in major immune functions, such as genes on chromosome 6 coding for the TCR β chain, Igκ and CD8, genes on chromosome 12 coding for the Igh allotypes, and genes on chromosome 17 coding for the MHC, TNFα, TNFβ, C2 and C4.

The antibody response in H, L lines, and interline hybrids of the five selections (**Table 2**), indicates that the additive effect (a) was similar, whereas the dominance deviation (d) was different in all selections, yielding a different dominance effect (d/a) in each selection. Thus, the high responsiveness was incompletely dominant, to a variable extent, in selections I, II, III and IV, whereas it was incompletely recessive in selection V.

In all selections, the high or low effects of the alleles at the n loci are not limited to the selection antigen but may also influence the immune response to immunogens non-cross-reactive with the selection antigen. This multispecific effect is not general, as the difference in antibody response between H and L responder mice to various unrelated antigens may be identical, smaller, insignificant or even inverse as compared with the difference in response to the selection antigen. Comparison of the results obtained in the five selections indicates that the multispecific effect is large in selections I and III, intermediate in selections II and IV and restricted in selection V.

Selective breeding was also carried out for mitotic responsiveness of lymph node cells to *in vitro* stimulation by phytohemagglutinin (PHA). The selection limit was reached after ten generations, the realized heritability was 0.24, the low responsiveness was incompletely dominant, and the character was under the control of 10–19 independent loci. These H and L responder mice also displayed a similar difference in responsiveness to concanavalin A, in mixed lymphocyte reaction and graft-versus-host reaction, but produced the same antibody titer when immunized with SRBC.

Whether selective breeding for a polygenic character, such as antibody or mitotic responsiveness, also affects lifespan was investigated in selections I, II, III and PHA. The lifespan was longer in H than in L mice of selections I and II, but no difference was

Table 2 Antibody titers (log$_2$) in H, L lines and interline hybrids of five selections

Mice	Selection I Mean ± SD	Selection II Mean ± SD	Selection III Mean ± SD	Selection IV Mean ± SD	Selection V Mean ± SD
H	12.5 ± 0.8	11.6 ± 1.0	12.8 ± 0.7	11.4 ± 1.0	14.2 ± 1.9
L	4.7 ± 1.1	4.9 ± 1.2	6.5 ± 0.8	4.9 ± 1.2	4.4 ± 2.1
F1	9.6 ± 1.3	10.1 ± 1.2	10.1 ± 0.6	8.6 ± 0.9	7.4 ± 2.8
F2	8.6 ± 1.4	9.5 ± 2.1	10.7 ± 1.2	7.9 ± 1.7	6.0 ± 3.2
BcH	11.4 ± 1.0	10.3 ± 1.3	11.7 ± 0.9	10.8 ± 1.6	13.0 ± 2.1
BcL	7.6 ± 1.5	7.5 ± 2.4	8.9 ± 0.9	6.0 ± 1.4	5.2 ± 3.2
a	3.9	3.3	3.1	3.2	4.9
d/*a*	0.3	0.5	0.1	0.1	−0.4

a, additive effect; *d*, dominance deviation; *d*/*a*, dominance effect; SD, standard deviation.

found between H and L mice of selections III and PHA. The positive correlation between antibody responsiveness and lifespan was further analyzed in interline hybrids of selection II and found statistically significant in most of these mouse populations. Moreover, the lifespan of the last 30%, 20% and 10% survivors, which are scarcely affected by early disease-induced mortality and mainly influenced by genes acting on the rate of physiologic aging, appeared as a polygenic character regulated by 3–7 independent loci. Noteworthily, the long lifespan was incompletely dominant in the total population, but was longer in the last 30% and completely dominant in 20% and 10% survivors (**Table 3**). Thus, the results of this analysis suggest that antibody responsiveness and lifespan are polygenic traits regulated by a small number of the same or closely linked loci.

The incidence of spontaneous malignant lymphomas was markedly higher in L than in H mice of selections I, II and PHA, whereas no difference was found between L and H mice of selection III.

Improvement of the effect of selection was obtained by assortative breeding from two foundation populations, F0H and F0L, each of which was produced with balanced frequency of the gene pools from the H or L lines of selections I, II, III, IV and V. After 16 generations of selection for primary or secondary responses to all the antigens used in the original five selections the difference between H and L lines in antibody responsiveness was remarkably amplified and the multispecific effect of the selection was generalized to several antigens. These results, obtained in selection GP for general-primary and selection GS for general-secondary responses, suggest that more genes with upward effects had accumulated in H mice or, rather, more genes with downward effects had accumulated in L mice during both selections. The influence of immune responsiveness on lifespan and disease susceptibility was also investigated in H and L mice of the GS selection at the F16 generation. It was found that the cumulative mortality rate is remarkably higher in L than in H mice, the difference being accounted for mostly by

Table 3 Agglutinin titer (log$_2$) and lifespan of H, L lines, and interline hybrids in selection II

Mice	Total population		Lifespan of subpopulations (days)		
	Agglutinin titer Mean ± SD	Lifespan (days) Mean ± SD	Last 30% survivors Mean ± SD	Last 20% survivors Mean ± SD	Last 10% survivors Mean ± SD
H	11.4 ± 0.8	612 ± 148	694 ± 88	752 ± 64	787 ± 45
L	5.2 ± 1.0	346 ± 110	407 ± 87	444 ± 74	490 ± 61
F1	9.4 ± 0.7	549 ± 186	670 ± 90	747 ± 62	785 ± 64
F2	9.8 ± 1.2	513 ± 183	639 ± 100	681 ± 85	724 ± 87
BcH	10.8 ± 0.9	530 ± 215	693 ± 101	748 ± 71	786 ± 64
BcL	7.5 ± 1.4	464 ± 158	531 ± 106	608 ± 100	670 ± 96
a	3.1	133	144	154	149
d/*a*	0.3	0.5	0.8	1.0	1.0

a, Additive effect; *d*, dominance deviation; *d*/*a*, dominance effect; SD, standard deviation.

malignant lymphomas that are the major cause of death in L mice. The interline difference in lifespan and lymphoma incidence in mice of the GS selection is much larger than that observed in mice of selections I and II.

The cellular modifications of the immune system brought about by selection are not completely understood. At present a major difference, between selections I and II on one hand and selections III and IV on the other hand, concerns macrophages. In selections I and II macrophages of L mice show a more active antigen catabolism and less efficient antigen presentation than macrophages of H mice. Conversely, no differences in macrophage activities were found between H and L mice of selections III and IV. Natural killer (NK) cell activity was found to be lower in L than in H mice of selection I but higher in L than in H mice of selections II and III. Expression of genes regulating antibody responsiveness in lymphocytes was mostly investigated in H and L mice of selection I. It was found that high or low effect genes accumulated in H or L mice were expressed in B cells (higher rate of cell proliferation and differentiation in H than in L mice) and at the level of all Ig isotypes but not in T cells involved in helper activity, skin graft rejection, graft-versus-host reaction, PHA mitotic response, and delayed-type hypersensitivity. However, a limiting dilution assay revealed higher numbers of T cells mediating delayed-type hypersensitivity in H than in L mice.

The significance of the humoral and cellular changes induced by selective breeding stems from studies on innate and acquired immunity to infections in selection I. The conclusion from these studies is that H mice are more resistant than L mice to extracellular pathogens such as *Pneumococcus*, *Klebsiella*, *Trypanosoma* and *Plasmodium*, which are sensitive to the consequence of antibody binding, whereas L mice are more resistant than H mice to

intracellular pathogens such as *Salmonella*, *Brucella*, *Yersinia*, *Mycobacterium* and *Leishmania*, which are sensitive to the bactericidal activity of macrophages.

The Biozzi experimental approach of bidirectional selective breeding has also been used to investigate the polygenic control of inflammation and chemical carcinogenesis.

The application of bidirectional selective breeding to acute inflammatory reaction (AIR) yielded two lines of mice, one giving the maximal (max) AIR and the other giving the minimal (min) AIR. Both max AIR and min AIR were triggered by subcutaneous injection of polyacrylamide microbeads and measured by the leukocyte and serum protein accumulation in the exudate. Selection was started from a genetically heterogeneous foundation population produced by the intercrossing of eight inbred strains of mice and carried out by assortative mating of extreme phenotypes. The response to selection in 11 consecutive generations was highly asymmetrical, as AIR markedly increased in the max line whereas it remained unchanged in the min line. The h^2 mean value in the AIR max line was 0.26 for leukocyte and 0.18 for protein concentrations. The response to selection and the large interline difference resulted from the interaction of 7–9 independent loci with additive effects. The difference between max AIR and min AIR lines is not limited to inflammatory responsiveness as max AIR mice are also more inclined to produce IgE and are more resistant to *Salmonella typhimurium* and to chemical carcinogenesis than are min AIR mice.

The polygenic control of chemical carcinogenesis has been studied by bidirectional selective breeding for susceptibility and resistance to two-stage skin carcinogenesis, initiated with 9,10-dimethyl-1,2-benzanthracene (DMBA) and promoted with 12-O-tetradecanoyl-phorbol-13-acetate (TPA). The selection was started from a heterogeneous population,

Table 4 Carcinogenesis induced in Car-S and Car-R mice at F10, and in their F1 hybrids after 49 days of promotion

Line	No. of mice	DMBA (μg per mouse)	TPA (μg per mouse)	Incidence (%)	Mean number of papillomas ± SE per treated mouse
Car-S	40	25	5	100	9.07 ± 0.70
	36	2.5	1	100	6.16 ± 0.69
	33	1.0	0.5	98	3.51 ± 0.42
	33	0.5	0.25	41	0.94 ± 0.23
Car-R	40	50	20	18	0.25 ± 0.10
	40	50	10	5	0.05 ± 0.03
	40	25	5	0	0.00 ± 0.00
F1	36	50	10	89	3.72 ± 0.64
	36	25	5	75	3.50 ± 0.56
	36	2.5	1	23	0.47 ± 0.24

SE, standard error.

as produced by the intercrossing of eight inbred strains of mice, and the character chosen for the assortative mating was the number of papillomas at the end of the promotion period. Susceptible (Car-S) and resistant (Car-R) lines of mice separated by ten consecutive generations of bidirectional selective breeding display a very large difference in responsiveness to carcinogenesis (**Table 4**). The dominance effect (d/a) = 0.38) measured in (Car-S × Car-R)F1 hybrids indicates that the susceptibility of papilloma induction is an incompletely dominant character. The difference between Car-S and Car-R lines is restricted to the skin, implying that the selected genes produce a tissue-specific effect.

See also: **Immune response (Ir) genes.**

Further reading

Bangrazi C, Mouton D, Neveu T *et al* (1990) Genetics of chemical carcinogenesis. I. Bidirectional selective breeding of susceptible and resistant lines of mice to two-stage skin carcinogenesis. *Carcinogenesis* **11**, 1711–1719.

Biozzi G, Stiffel C, Mouton D, Bouthillier Y and Decreusefond C (1968) Selection artificielle pour la production d'anticorps chez la souris. *Annales d'Immunologie de l'Institut Pasteur* **115**: 965–967.

Biozzi G, Mouton D, Sant'Anna OA *et al* (1979) Genetics of immunoresponsiveness to natural antigens in the mouse. *Current Topics in Microbiology and Immunology* **85**: 31–98.

Biozzi G, Siqueira M, Stiffel C *et al* (1980) Genetic selections for relevant immunological functions. In: Fougereau M and Dausset J (eds) *Immunology 1980. Progress in Immunology*, vol IV, pp 432–457. London: Academic Press.

Biozzi G, Mouton D, Stiffel C and Bouthillier Y (1984) Major role of macrophage in quantitative genetic regulation of immunoresponsiveness and anti-infectious immunity. *Advances in Immunology* **36**: 189–234.

Covelli V, Marini S, Di Majo V *et al* (1984) Life-span, tumor incidence, and natural killer activity in mice selected for high or low antibody responsiveness. *Journal of the National Cancer Institute* **72**: 1127–1136.

Covelli V, Di Majo V, Bassani B *et al* (1985) Spontaneous lymphomas in mice genetically selected for high or low PHA responsiveness. *Journal of the National Cancer Institute* **75**: 1083–1090.

Covelli V, Mouton D, Di Majo V *et al* (1989) Inheritance of immune responsiveness, life span, and disease incidence in interline crosses of mice selected for high or low multispecific antibody production. *Journal of Immunology* **142**: 1224–1234.

Covelli V, Coppola M, Di Majo V *et al* (1995) Life span and lymphoma incidence in high or low antibody responder mice from selection GS. *Aging: Immunology and Infectious Diseases* **6**: 95–106.

Doria G, Biozzi G, Mouton D *et al* (1997) Genetic control of immune responsiveness, aging and tumor incidence. *Mechanisms of Ageing and Development* **96**: 1–13.

Ibanez OM, Stiffel C, Ribeiro OG *et al* (1992) Genetics of nonspecific immunity: I. Bidirectional selective breedings of lines of mice endowed with maximal or minimal inflammatory responsiveness. *European Journal of Immunology* **22**: 2555–2563.

Mouton D, Sequeira M, Sant'Anna OA *et al* (1988) Genetic regulation of multispecific antibody responsiveness: improvement of 'high' and 'low' characters. *European Journal of Immunology* **18**: 41–49.

Puel A, Groot PC, Lathrop MG *et al* (1995) Mapping of genes controlling quantitative antibody production in Biozzi mice. *Journal of Immunology* **154**: 5799–5805.

Puel A, Meuel JC, Bouthillier Y *et al* (1996) Toward genetic dissection of high and low antibody responsiveness in Biozzi mice. *Proceedings of the National Academy of Sciences of the USA* **93**: 14742–14746.

Saran A, Bouthillier Y, Pioli C *et al* (1996) Genetics of chemical carcinogenesis – III. Tissue-specificity of the genes controlling susceptibility and resistance to skin carcinogenesis in the mouse. *Carcinogenesis* **17**: 2463–2468.

Stiffel C, Liacopoulos-Briot M, Decreusefond C *et al* (1977) Genetic selection of mice for quantitative responsiveness of lymphocytes to phytohemagglutinin. *European Journal of Immunology* **7**: 291–297.

BLOOD TRANSFUSION REACTIONS

C Paul Engelfriet, Central Laboratory of the Netherlands Red Cross Blood Transfusion Service, Amsterdam, The Netherlands

In addition to the transmission of infectious diseases by donor blood, immunological reactions between antibodies in the blood of the patient, and sometimes in that of the donor, and the antigens against which they are directed, may cause more or less dangerous transfusion reactions. The antibodies involved are alloantibodies against products of allelomorphic genes, but immunoglobulin E (IgE) antibodies against nonhuman antigens also play a role. The various relevant antibodies and the reactions they may cause will be briefly discussed.

Alloantibodies against red cells

These include 'naturally occurring' antibodies, particularly anti-A and -B, and immune antibodies induced by previous transfusions and/or pregnancies. Except in exceptional cases (see below) blood transfusion reactions due to red cell antibodies should not occur. The correct determination of the ABO blood group of donor and recipient, correct antibody detection and cross-matching and correct patient identification should prevent such reactions. Because donor red cells are destroyed when a reaction is caused by red cell antibodies, such reactions are called hemolytic.

The signs and symptoms of the reaction are due on one hand to the liberation of hemoglobin and thromboplastic substances in stroma, and on the other to the activation of complement, leading to the liberation of C3a and C5a which increase vascular permeability, stimulate mast cells to liberate vasoactive substances such as histamine, and macrophages to liberate cytokines such as interleukin-1 (IL-1).

When ABO incompatible red cells are transfused the reaction is usually severe: the patient becomes restless and complains of a feeling of oppression, which is often accompanied by substernal pain. The patient may have abdominal pain and may vomit.

In serious cases renal function is seriously impaired and there may be uncontrollable bleeding. There is jaundice and hemoglobinuria. Reactions due to antibodies of other specificities are usually less severe, fever being the most common symptom, but jaundice and hemoglobinuria also quite frequently occur.

Exceptional cases

Delayed-type hemolytic transfusion reaction

Whereas the above hemolytic transfusion reactions begin during or shortly after a transfusion, a hemolytic reaction may also occur 3–5 days after a transfusion. In these cases the patient has been immunized in the past against a blood group antigen, but before the present transfusion is given the antibodies are either very weak or even undetectable. The transfused red cells induce a secondary immune response against the antigen and the antibody concentration rises so quickly that after 3–5 days there is enough antibody to destroy the donor cells. If the responsible antibodies are undectable before the transfusion, the reaction cannot be prevented unless it is known that

antibodies were detected in the patient's serum on a previous occasion, in which case compatible blood must be given. In some cases the direct antiglobulin test may remain positive long after the donor red cells have been eliminated, due to the formation of cross-reacting or autoantibodies secondary to the alloimmune response.

Hemolytic transfusion reaction without detectable antibodies

Rarely a typical hemolytic transfusion reaction occurs while no antibodies are detectable at any time. It has been shown that in these cases the reaction must be due to alloimmunity against a particular red cell antigen. For example only the survival of C-positive red cells is shortened in a C-negative patient. Why anti-C is not detectable in the serum of such a patient and what the mechanism is which is responsible for the sometimes rapid destruction of the donor cells is unknown. Obviously, such a reaction cannot be prevented by routine laboratory investigations.

Red cell alloantibodies in the serum of a donor may be responsible for destruction of red cells of the patient, but this has only been described for potent Anti-A and/or B.

Alloantibodies against platelets

These are of two categories: HLA class I antibodies and platelet-specific ones. Whether transfusion reactions may develop as a result of the interaction of donor platelets and HLA antibodies has not been established. Antibodies against platelet-specific antigens may cause the following reactions.

Febrile reactions

These reactions follow a typical pattern. However, such reactions, in the vast majority of cases are caused by a reaction of antibodies with granulocytes and will therefore be described below.

Post-transfusion purpura

In this serious and, from an immunological point of view, interesting reaction, severe thrombocytopenia develops 5–7 days after a transfusion. The reaction occurs in patients, nearly always women, who have become sensitized to a platelet-specific alloantigen, usually as a result of pregnancies but occasionally by blood transfusion. The reaction is thus due to platelet-specific antibodies, anti-HPA-1a in the great majority of cases, but antibodies against other HPA antigens have also been involved. In this reaction, the patient's platelets, which are of course negative for the alloantigen involved, are destroyed. The mechanism responsible for this destruction has not yet been definitely established. It may be due to the fixation of immune complexes consisting of alloantibodies and the antigen against which they are directed. These complexes may be formed with free platelet antigens present in the donor plasma or may be liberated after the destruction of donor platelets, or both. Possibly the attraction of different platelet glycoproteins for each other, e.g. GPIIb for GPIIIa, may be the basis of the fixation of such immune complexes to the patient's platelets. Another possibility is that during the secondary immune response against the alloantigen, cross-reacting or autoantibodies are formed which react with the patient's own platelets. Post-transfusion purpura can be prevented by selecting compatible platelets, which is often difficult because of the very high frequency of most of the antigens involved.

Rarely thrombocytopenia is induced by platelet-specific antibodies in the donor plasma. In contrast to post-transfusion purpura, thrombocytopenia occurs immediately after the transfusion in these cases.

Alloantibodies against granulocytes

Granulocyte-reactive alloantibodies, mainly HLA class I and granulocyte-specific ones, are the main cause of febrile transfusion reactions. Typically in this reaction the temperature begins to rise sharply a few hours after the transfusion which is often accompanied by chills. The temperature begins to decline after about 8 h. The reactions are due to antibody–antigen complexes liberated after the destruction of leukocytes. These complexes bind to and activate monocytes, which, after a delay, release cytokines with pyrogenic properties. These reactions can be prevented by removing most of the leukocytes from red cell and platelet concentrates, e.g. by filtration.

A much more serious reaction, transfusion-related acute lung injury (TRALI) is characterized by chills, fever, a nonproductive cough, dyspnea, and infiltration and edema of, particularly, the lower lung fields. The reaction, which may be fatal, is nearly always due to the presence of leukocyte antibodies in the donor plasma, although rarely it has been caused by antibodies in the recipient. Donors whose blood induced the TRALI should be removed from the donor panel.

Febrile reactions induced by cytokines in the transfused blood

Febrile reactions may be caused by cytokines derived from leukocytes, which accumulate due to active synthesis by leukocytes in platelet concentrates during storage. There is a correlation between the frequency of febrile reactions and the number of leukocytes in the platelet concentrate and the time of storage. Pre-storage removal of leukocytes from the platelet concentrate prevents these reactions.

Antibodies against plasma proteins

Most important are antibodies against IgA, which mainly occur in IgA-deficient subjects. Most of the antibodies are directed against nonpolymorphic epitopes on the α1 or α2 chains but anti-allotypic (A2m) antibodies may also occur. The interaction of these antibodies with donor IgA, even if very small quantitites are transfused, can cause a severe anaphylactic reaction which may be fatal. Patients with such antibodies can be transfused with red cells which have been washed six times. For other blood components it is necessary to select IgA-deficient donors. Also, A2m antibodies may occur in poly-transfused patients. The reaction caused by them is much less severe, urticaria usually being the only symptom. The extent to which antibodies against other plasma proteins may cause transfusion reactions is controversial.

IgE Antibodies against nonhuman antigens

In patients who are allergic to an allergen, an allergic reaction occurs if the donor plasma contains the allergen. This may particularly occur if it concerns food allergens, which may be present in the donor plasma after consumption of the food involved. The patient develops urticaria. The reactions can be prevented, in the case of red cell concentrates, by washing the cells three times. Very rarely a similar reaction is induced by donor IgE antibodies against an allergen which at the time of the transfusion is present in the patient.

See also: **ABO blood group system; Alloantigens; Erythrocytes; Neutrophils; Plasma; Platelets; Rh antigens; Transfusion.**

Further reading

Fluit CR, Kunst VA and Drenthe-Schonk AM (1990) Incidence of red cell antibodies after multiple blood transfusion. *Transfusion* 30: 532–535.

Judd WA and Barnes A (eds) (1982) *Clinical and Serological Aspects of Transfusion Reactions.* Anaheim CA: American Association of Blood Banks.

Mollison PL, Engelfriet CP and Contreras M (1997) *Blood Transfusion in Clinical Medicine*, 10th edn. Oxford: Blackwell Scientific.

Muylle L (1995) The role of cytokines in blood transfusion reactions. *Blood Reviews* 9: 77–83.

B LYMPHOCYTE ACTIVATION

Hajime Karasuyama and **Kiyoshi Takatsu**, Department of Immunology, Tokyo Metropolitan Institute of Medical Science, Tokyo, Japan

B lymphocytes, precursors of antibody-secreting cells, originate from pluripotent hematopoietic stem cells and differentiate in the fetal liver and, in adult life, principally in the bone marrow. During differentiation the diversity of antigen specificity among B cells is generated in an antigen-independent manner through the rearrangement of gene segments encoding parts of the variable region of the B cell receptor (BCR) for antigen, that is, immunoglobulin (Ig). The newly generated, surface Ig-expressing mature B cells leave the bone marrow and circulate into peripheral lymphoid organs in which they can be activated to proliferate and to differentiate into antibody-secreting cells by encounter with antigens that bear epitopes complementary to their surface Ig.

B cell responses to antigens can be classified into T cell dependent and T cell independent. Some antigens such as bacterial polysaccharides can induce vigorous B cell stimulation independently of T cells by strong cross-linking of the BCR. In contrast, efficient B cell responses to many protein antigens need an intimate interaction of B cells with 'helper' T cells. Stimulation of BCR by antigen leads to endocytosis and degradation of the antigen captured by the BCR. Peptides derived from degraded antigen are bound to major histocompatibility complex (MHC) class II molecules and transported to the cell surface to be presented to T cells. T cells expressing a particular T cell receptor (TCR) that recognizes the peptide–MHC complex presented on the B cells then become activated. The activated T cells provide help to B cells in two forms: soluble mediators (cytokines) such as interleukin-4 (IL-4), IL-5 and IL-6, and membrane-bound stimulatory molecules including CD40 ligand.

B cell activation through BCR

The BCR is a complex with a hetero-oligomeric structure in which antigen recognition and signal transduction are compartmentalized into distinct subunits. The antigen recognition subunit of the BCR is a clonally-distributed membrane-bound Ig, a tetrameric complex of heavy and light chains, whereas the signal transduction subunit is a disulfide-linked heterodimer composed of Igα (CD79a), a *mb-1* gene product, and Igβ (CD79b), a *B29* gene product (**Figure 1**). Both Igα and Igβ chains contain within their cytoplasmic domains a sequence motif (immunoreceptor tyrosine-based activation motif, ITAM), D/E-X7-D/E-X2-Y-X2-L/I-X7-Y-X2-L/I, which is also found in the cytoplasmic tails of the signal transducers of the TCR and of Fc receptors (**Figure 2**).

Stimulation of B cells through the BCR results in rapid increases in tyrosine phosphorylation on a number of proteins and induces an increase of phosphatidylinositol and mobilization of cytoplasmic free calcium. Though none of the BCR subunits contains intrinsic protein tyrosine kinase (PTK) activity, the BCR associates with two types of cytoplasmic PTKs: Src family PTKs, including Lyn, Fyn, Blk and Lck, and the more distantly related PTK, Syk (**Figure 1**). Activation of these PTKs through ligation of the BCR by antigen leads to the phosphorylation of the two tyrosine residues within the ITAM in Igα and Igβ, which in turn leads to recruitment and activation of additional PTKs. The activated PTKs including Btk appear to phosphorylate numerous cellular proteins involved in intracellular signaling pathways, such as the adaptor protein Shc in the Ras pathway, phospholipase C (PLC)-γ2, GTPase-activating protein (GAP), mitogen-activated protein kinase (MAPK), phosphoinositide 3-kinase (PI3K) and Vav as well as HS-1 (**Figure 1**). The tyrosine phosphorylation of PLC-γ2 increases its activity to convert phosphatidylinositol 4,5-bisphosphate into the two second messengers, diacylglycerol (DAG) and inositol 1,4,5-trisphosphate (IP3). DAG activates protein kinase C while IP3 causes Ca^{2+} release from intracellular stores (**Figure 1**).

The regulated signal transduction through the BCR can be achieved by coordinated actions of PTKs and protein tyrosine phosphatases (PTPs). CD45 is a transmembrane PTP expressed on hematopoietic

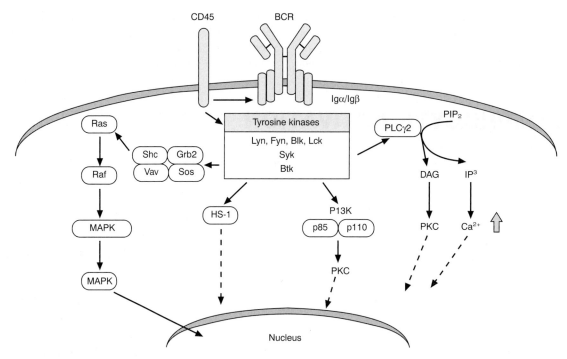

Figure 1 Signaling pathway of BCR.

cells and plays a critical role in B cell activation following ligation of the BCR (**Figure 1**). The regulation of Src family PTKs by CD45 appears to be one of the bases for requirement of CD45 in antigen-induced BCR signaling. Since Src family PTKs contain a negative regulatory tyrosine phosphorylation site at their carboxyl termini, dephosphorylation of this site by CD45 results in an increase of their kinase activity. The phosphorylated tyrosine residues within ITAM of Igα and Igβ also appear to be substrates for CD45. The importance of CD45 in BCR signaling has been confirmed by generating CD45-deficient mice in which B cells are completely refractory to proliferation stimulated by anti-IgM antibody.

Cognate T cell help for B cell activation

The CD40 ligand (CD40L) expressed by activated T cells is a 33 kDa type II membrane glycoprotein with sequence homology to tumor necrosis factor. T cells activated through TCR ligation transiently express on their surface CD40L, which interacts with CD40 expressed on B cells to deliver signals for B cell activation and proliferation. Signaling through CD40 in combination with T cell-derived cytokines such as IL-4 and IL-5 in mice leads to B cell differentiation accompanied by antibody secretion and Ig isotype switching. The CD40–CD40L interaction is also important for other B cell functions including the formation of germinal centers and the induction of

memory B cells. The physiological significance of the CD40–CD40L interaction *in vivo* has become evident from the observation of patients with X-linked hyper-IgM syndrome, who have mutations in the gene encoding CD40L and are therefore unable to express functional CD40L on their T cells. These patients fail to produce Ig of isotypes other than IgM in response to antigen challenge and also lack germinal centers in their secondary lymphoid organs.

The cognate interaction of B and T cells triggers the engagement of many other accessory molecules on both cells, which serve to stabilize the B–T conjugation and to coordinate the responses of the interacting cells. They include B7-1 (CD80), B7-2 (CD86), CTLA-4, LFA-1 (CD11a/18), LFA-2 (CD2), LFA-3 (CD58), ICAM-1 (CD54), VCAM (CD106) and VLA-4 (CD49d/29). The B7-1/B7-2 expressed on B cells interacts with the CD28 expressed on T cells to deliver a costimulatory signal to TCR-stimulated T cells, which then become fully activated to produce cytokines. T cell-derived cytokines such as IL-2, IL-4, IL-5, IL-6, IL-10, IL-13 and interferon γ (IFNγ) have been shown to enhance B cell activation and proliferation and to be essential costimuli for subsequent B cell differentiation and Ig production.

Modulation of BCR signaling

Several antigen-independent accessory molecules play an important role in the regulation and modulation of B cell activation mediated by the BCR (**Figure 2**). Key molecules include the CD19/CD21/CD81/Leu13 complex, CD22, CD38 and the Fc receptor FcγRIIB1, in addition to CD45 and CD40 discussed above.

CD19, CD21 (complement receptor 2), CD81 (TAPA-1) and Leu13 form a complex on the surface of B cells. This complex functions as a coreceptor which substantially lowers the threshold for cellular activation through the BCR. Ligation of the BCR induces the phosphorylation of tyrosine residues in the cytoplasmic tail of CD19, to which PI3K binds. The coligation of CD19 and the BCR reduces by two orders of magnitude the number of antigen receptors that must be ligated to induce B cell proliferation. Therefore, B cells that encounter antigens in the form of immune complexes containing complement components may be hyperstimulated by virtue of the coligation of the BCR and the CD19/CD21 complex. Since CD21 has been shown to also interact with CD23, antigens presented on CD23$^+$ cells such as follicular dendritic cells in germinal centers may also hyperstimulate B cells. Indeed, CD19-deficient mice showed the severe impairment of B cell responses to T-dependent antigens and lacked germinal center formation.

CD38 is a 42 kDa membrane glycoprotein expressed in many cell types, including B cells, and has been shown to associate with the BCR in humans. Ligation of CD38 with specific antibodies induces a potent proliferative signal to B cells in the presence of other growth cofactors such as IL-4, IL-5 or lipopolysaccharide (LPS). Engagement of CD38 also rescues germinal center B cells from apoptosis. CD38 stimulation activates Btk tyrosine kinase, and

it has been found that CD38 signaling is abolished in xid mice which carry a mutation in the btk gene and show a global B cell abnormality.

Immune complexes consisting of antigen and IgG antibodies are potent inhibitors of B cell responses. The coligation of the BCR and FcγRIIB1 through immune complexes leads to abortive BCR signaling (**Figure 2**). It has been shown that FcγRIIB1, when coligated with the BCR, recruits and activates a cytosolic protein tyrosine phosphatase, SHP1, through the interaction of a phosphorylated tyrosine residue within the sequence motif (immunoreceptor tyrosine-based inhibitory motif, ITIM) in the cytoplasmic domain of FcγRIIB1 and the SH2 domain of SHP1. The important role of SHP1 in negative regulation of BCR signaling has been clarified by the identification of mutated SHP1 genes as causative of the systemic autoimmune and immunodeficiency syndrome observed in motheaten (me) and motheaten viable (me^v) mutant mice. These SHP1-deficient mice are characterized by hypergammaglobulinemia and the production of multiple autoantibodies besides abnormalities of other hematopoietic cells, suggesting that SHP1 normally functions as a negative regulator of BCR signaling. Though the mechanism by which SHP1 modulates signaling through BCR has not yet been fully elucidated, SHP1 appears to be involved in FcγRIIB1-mediated negative regulation. Inhibitory signaling mediated by FcγRIIB1 is deficient in motheaten mice, indicating that SHP1 is an effector of the negative regulation of BCR signaling.

CD22, a 135 kDa B cell restricted glycoprotein, has also the sequence motif ITIM on its cytoplasmic domain, to which SHP1 is recruited after BCR ligation (**Figure 2**). B cells from CD22-deficient mice

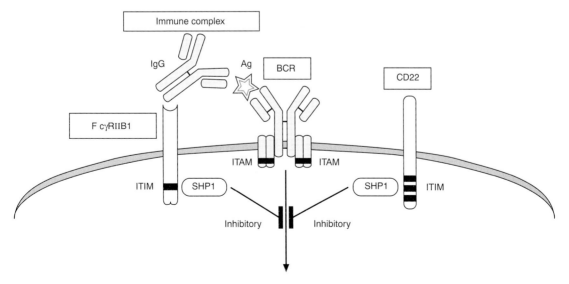

Figure 2 Negative regulation of BCR signaling.
(ITAM: immunoreceptor tyrosine-based activation motif) (ITIM: immunoreceptor tyrosine-based inhibitory motif).

show hyperresponsiveness to BCR signaling, suggesting that CD22 serves as a negative regulator of BCR signaling.

See also: **Affinity maturation; Antibodies, synthesis; Antigens, T dependent and independent; B lymphocyte, antigen processing and presentation; B lymphocyte differentiation; B lymphocytes; CD22; CD45 (the leukocyte common antigen); Helper T lymphocytes; Cytokines; Fc receptors; Germinal center; Immunoglobulin, cell surface; Interleukin 4; Interleukin 5 and its receptor; Interleukin 6; Protein kinases.**

Further reading

Armitage R and Alderson MR (1995) B-cell stimulation. *Current Opinion in Immunology* 7: 243–247.

Cambier JC, Pleiman CM and Clark MR (1994) Signal transduction by the B cell antigen receptor and its co-receptors. *Annual Review of Immunology* 12: 457–486.

Clark EA and Ledbetter JA (1994) How B and T cells talk to each other. *Nature* 367: 425–428.

DeFranco AL (1997) The complexity of signaling pathways activated by the BCR. *Current Opinion in Immunology* 9: 296–308.

Durie FH, Foy TM, Masters SR, Laman JD and Noelle RJ (1994) The role of CD40 in the regulation of humoral and cell-mediated immunity. *Immunology Today* 15: 406–410.

Justement LB, Brown VK and Lin J (1994) Regulation of B-cell activation by CD45: a question of mechanism. *Immunology Today* 15: 399–405.

Karasuyama H, Rolink A and Melchers F (1996) Surrogate light chain in B cell development. *Advances in Immunology* 63: 1–41.

Malavasi F, Funaro A, Roggero S, Horenstein A, Calosso L and Mehta K (1994) Human CD38: a glycoprotein in search of a function. *Immunology Today* 15: 95–97.

O'Keefe TL, Williams GT, Davies SL and Neuberger MS (1996) Hyperresponsive B cells in CD22-deficient mice. *Science* 274: 798–801.

Okumura M and Thomas ML (1995) Regulation of immune function by protein tyrosine phosphatases. *Current Opinion in Immunology* 7: 312–319.

Pleiman PM, D'Ambrosio D and Cambier JC (1994) The B-cell antigen receptor complex: structure and signal transduction. *Immunology Today* 15: 393–399.

Sharp AH (1995) Analysis of lymphocyte costimulation *in vivo* using transgenic and 'knockout' mice. *Current Opinion in Immunology* 7: 389–395.

Takatsu K, Takaki S and Hitoshi Y (1994) Interleukin-5 and its receptor system: implications in the immune system and inflammation. *Advances in Immunology* 57: 145–190.

Tedder TF, Zhou L-J and Engel P (1994) The CD19/CD21 signal transduction complex of B lymphocytes. *Immunology Today* 15: 437–441.

B LYMPHOCYTE ANTIGEN PROCESSING AND PRESENTATION

Nobumichi Hozumi, Samuel Lunenfeld Research Institute, Mount Sinai Hospital, Toronto, Canada

Antigen presentation by B cells: a historical view

Two different cellular populations are required for the production of antibodies, as early studies have suggested. These are thymus (T cell)- and bone marrow (B cell)-derived cells. T cells help B cells to differentiate into antibody-producing cells. *In vitro* studies have revealed that the cell populations are further subdivided. Cells from the spleen are fractionated by their ability to adhere to plastic, the adherent and nonadherent cells. The adherent cells mainly consist of macrophages, whereas the nonadherent cells are comprised of T and B cells. Further studies established that T and B cells are required for primary and secondary antibody responses, and that macrophages can also act as accessory cells involved in T cell activation. Initially, macrophages were considered to be the critical accessory cells. Subsequent experiments established the capacity of other cells to function as accessory cells, or antigen-presenting cells (APCs). These include dendritic cells (DCs), Langerhans cells, endothelial cells, Schwann cells and Kupffer cells. The expression of major histocompatibility complex (MHC) class II molecules is essential for APCs. Therefore, it is quite logical to ask whether B cells could act as APCs, as B cells express moderately high levels of the molecule. The use of rabbit antimouse immunoglobulin (RAMIg) as an antigen demonstrated that rabbit Ig-specific T cells were able to respond to B cells and macrophages with similar efficiencies in the antibody response. Macrophages presented normal rabbit Ig (NRIg) to T cells as effectively as RAMIg; however, B cells failed to present

NRIg to T cells at the same level, suggesting that antigen-specific T–B collaboration is responsible for the efficient antigen presentation by B cells. Similar experiments were conducted using a soluble antigen, keyhole limpet hemocyanin (KLH)-specific B cells. Normal resting (small) B cells from unimmunized mice were poor APCs, whereas lipopolysaccharide (LPS)-activated B cells could present KLH to KLH-specific normal T cells. Thus, it was demonstrated that normal resting B cells from unprimed mice were poor at antigen presentation.

Studies using hapten carrier systems demonstrated that antigens are recognized by two distinct cells in order to produce a hapten-specific antibody. These experiments clearly demonstrated that B cells recognize the haptenic determinant, whereas T cells recognize the carrier determinant. Based on these results an antigen bridge model was proposed, in which B cells and T cells are bridged by native antigens (hapten carrier) bound to membrane immunoglobulin (mIg) and T cell receptor (TCR). However, two important discoveries virtually destroyed the antigen bridge model. These were: 1) MHC restriction, and 2) antigen processing. The TCR makes contact with B cells via the antigen-MHC complex, thus mIg is not required for interaction with the TCR. Only processed peptides are presented to the TCR. The antigen bridge model was challenged by utilizing antigen-specific B cell and T cell clones. These experiments clearly demonstrated that antigens bound by antigen-specific mIg molecules were presented to T cells with 1000–2000-fold greater efficiency than nonspecific presentation. The antigen taken up by the B cells is processed within acidic cellular compartments and the peptides generated bind to MHC class II molecules for presentation to the TCR. Thus, the functional role of mIg on B cells for efficient antigen presentation has been firmly established. These are *in vitro* results; the role of B cells as APCs *in vivo* remains to be determined.

Antigen presentation by B cells *in vivo*

Experiments addressing this question have been carried out using mice chronically treated from birth with anti-μ antibody (anti-μ mice), a procedure which depletes Ig+ B cells. These mice fail to mount a secondary T cell proliferative response following immunization with hapten carrier, but do so if injected with hapten-coupled normal splenocytes, suggesting that the presence of B cells in lymph nodes is required for T cell priming. The antigen presentation capacity of unfractionated lymph node APCs was much stronger, however, than that of unfractionated spleen APCs.

The importance of B cells to T cell priming *in vivo* was further demonstrated by inoculating purified syngeneic normal resting B cells before priming them with antigen. B cell-depleted mice primed with antigen in the presence of exogenous B cells were shown to respond to the antigen, whereas control mice without inoculation of exogenous B cells could not respond. Anti-μ-treated mice reconstituted with fluorescein isothiocyanate (FITC)-specific B cells responded markedly better to FITC-ovalbumin than to trinitrophenyl-ovalbumin. These results suggest that B cells are involved in the generation of primary T cell responses. However, several groups have presented contradictory results to these early experiments, as described below.

Investigators agree that activated B cells are able to stimulate primed T cells. However, several experiments seem to suggest that even activated B cells are poor at stimulating naive T cells compared to DCs. The activation of antigen-specific T cells requires two signaling events which must be provided by APCs. The first signaling event consists of a cognate APC–T interaction between TCR and antigen peptide/MHC class II molecules. The second signal is provided by an interaction between costimulatory signaling molecules such as B7 molecules (B7-1 and B7-2) on APCs and CD28/CTLA-4 expressed on T cells. Deficiency in the second signaling in the APC–T interaction is thought to result in T cell tolerance. It has been demonstrated that B cells expressing high levels of CTLA-4/CD28 ligand fail to provide T cell-stimulating signals as strong as DCs. It is still possible that as yet unidentified costimulatory molecules are involved in this interaction. The form in which antigens are introduced into animals may additionally play a role in T cell activation. Transgenic mice expressing I-E molecules in different cell populations (i.e. B cells or DCs) were utilized to investigate the effect of different forms of antigen (peptide versus native protein). Peptide antigens are more efficiently presented to T cells by DCs. However, DCs show poor activity for the presentation of native protein antigens. In contrast, B cells are efficient APCs for protein antigens, but not peptides. Further, these experiments suggest that as little as 1% contamination of peptides in protein antigen preparations is sufficient for T cell activation by DCs. Previous experiments suggesting a poor ability of resting B cells for T cell priming should be re-examined in light of these new data.

The functional role of B cells as APCs was recently re-examined by using mice genetically lacking B cells. These mice (μMT knockouts) were established by depleting the μMT (membrane) region by gene targeting, which may be less abrasive than anti-μ treatment. The μMT knockouts had impaired T cell priming to protein antigens but not to peptides. Interestingly, however, KLH demonstrated an unusual ability to prime naive T cells in the B cell-depleted mice. The antigen is very potent and widely used for *in vivo* priming experiments. Investigators should pay extra attention to the experimental design when KLH is used. Antigen-specific B cells pulsed *in vivo* revealed an impressive upregulation of B7 molecules. Antigen stimulation may induce positive signaling mediated via mIg molecules; these activated B cells can then become competent APCs for the activation of naive T cells *in vivo*. Contradictory results have, however, been reported using μMT mice. T cell responses to several antigens including not only KLH, but also H-Y (male antigen), MHC and *Shistosoma mansoni* eggs have been described. However, antigens such as H-Y and MHC are expressed on the membrane surface of APCs. Concentration of these antigens by mIg molecules and subsequent internalization are not required for presentation. One can speculate, therefore, that this critical step in B cell activation is not required for presentation of these antigens. The functional role of B cells as APCs *in vivo* has yet to be firmly established; however, investigators believe B cells must be initially activated to have the capacity of APCs for T cell priming.

Processing

MHC class II molecules are transported from the endoplasmic reticulum (ER) via the Golgi to endosomal compartments as a complex with invariant chain (Ii). The Ii prevents endogenous peptides from binding to the groove of MHC class II molecules. After removal of Ii in the acidic endosomal compartments, peptides are able to bind to the MHC groove. Peptide-loaded MHC class II molecules are then transported to the membrane surface for antigen presentation. The amino acid residues 81–104 of Ii, dubbed class II-associated invariant-chain peptides (CLIP), remain bound to the class II antigen-binding grooves. In endosomal compartments, MHC class II-like DM molecules promote the dissociation of CLIP from the MHC class II complex. Because cells can utilize a different mechanism for antigen presentation from other APCs, namely mIg-mediated antigen internalization, the antigen peptide loading of MHC class II in B lymphocytes is expected to take place in a compartment accessible to mIg. The process may occur in early and late endosomes and lysosomes. However, investigators have found compartments which are distinct from the conventional vesicles described above. These compartments for peptide loading (CPLs) meet several requirements for antigen loading vesicles in B cells (**Figure 1**). mIgG and mIgM efficiently enter the compartments, and transiently accumulated MHC class II molecules are evident. MHC class II molecules in these compartments are not associated with the Ii chain. Some of the MHC class II molecules are loaded with antigen peptides. Most newly synthesized MHC class II molecules are transported through CPLs on their way to the plasma membrane. These compartments are not accessible to the transferrin receptor. Morphologically, these compartments in B cells demonstrate a physical structure with an internal vesicle membrane similar to that seen in the multivesicular bodies, an intermediate in the conventional endosomal pathway. Antigen-presenting B cells may therefore be

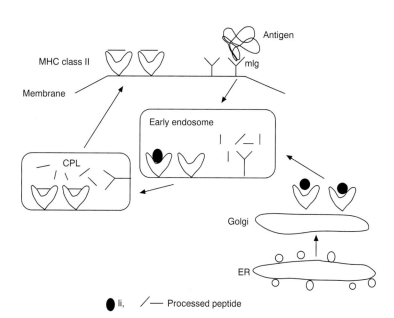

Figure 1 Antigen processing and presentation in B lymphocytes.

able to selectively target internalized antigen and increase the efficiency of antigen presentation by utilizing the CPL-mediated pathway.

See also: **Antigen-presenting cells; Antigen presentation via MHC class I molecules; Antigen presentation via MHC class II molecules; B lymphocytes; Immunoglobulin, cell surface; MHC restriction.**

Further reading

Amigorena S, Drake JP, Webster P and Mellman I (1994) Transient accumulation of new class II MHC molecules in a novel endocytic compartment in B lymphocytes. *Nature* **369**: 113–120.

Ashwell JD (1988) Are B lymphocytes the principal antigen presenting cells *in vivo*? *Journal of Immunology* **140**: 3697–3700.

Constant S, Sant'Angelo D, Pasqualini T *et al* (1995) Peptide and protein antigens require distinct antigen-presenting cell subsets for the priming of CD4+ T cells. *Journal of Immunology* **154**: 4915–4923.

Constant S, Schweitzer N, West J, Ranney P and Bottomly K (1995) B lymphocytes can be competent antigen-presenting cells for priming CD4+ T cells to protein antigens *in vivo*. *Journal of Immunology* **155**: 3734–3741.

Denzin LK and Cresswell P (1995) HLA-DM induces CLIP dissociation from MHC class II α β dimers and facilitates peptide loading. *Cell* **82**: 155–165.

Epstein MM, Di Rosa F, Jankovic D, Sher A and Matzinger P (1995) Successful T cell priming in B cell-deficient mice. *Journal of Experimental Medicine* **182**: 915–922.

Fuchs EJ and Matzinger P (1992) B cells turn off virgin but not memory T cells. *Science* **258**: 1156–1159.

Lanzavecchia A (1985) Antigen specific interaction between T and B cells. *Nature* **314**: 537–539.

Lassila O, Vanio O and Matzinger P (1988) Can B cells turn on virgin T cells? *Nature* **334**: 253–255.

Peters PJ, Neefjes JJ, Oorschot V, Ploegh HL and Geuze HJ (1991) Segregation of MHC class II molecules from MHC class I molecules in the Golgi complex for transport to lysosomal compartments. *Nature* **349**: 669–676.

Sloan VS, Cameron P, Porter G *et al* (1995) Mediation by HLA-DM of dissociation of peptides from HLA-DR. *Nature* **375**: 802–806.

Watanabe M, Wegmann DR, Ochi A and Hozumi N (1986) Antigen presentation by a B cell line transfected with cloned immunoglobulin heavy and light chain genes specific for a defined hapten. *Proceedings of the National Academy of Sciences of the USA* **83**: 5247–5251.

West MA, Lucocq JM and Watts C (1994) Antigen processing and class II MHC peptide-loading compartments in human B-lymphoblastoid cells. *Nature* **369**: 147–151.

B LYMPHOCYTE DIFFERENTIATION

John H Kehrl, Laboratory of Immunoregulation, National Institute of Allergy and Infectious Diseases, National Institutes of Health, Bethesda, Maryland, USA

B cell differentiation broadly construed encompasses both the generation of B lymphocytes from precursor or stem cells (i.e. B cell development), as well as their maturation into plasma or memory cells. B cell lymphopoiesis begins in the embryonic yolk sac, switches to the fetal liver, and shortly after birth becomes established in the bone marrow. While B-2 (conventional) B cells are continuously generated in the adult bone marrow, B-1 (CD5+) B cells are predominantly produced early in ontogeny in the fetal liver. Early B cell differentiation has been divided into steps or stages based on the status of immunoglobulin gene rearrangements, the expression of cell surface molecules, and the *in vitro* growth requirements of the developing B cells. One commonly used scheme based on the expression of the cell surface markers B220, CD43, BP-1 and HSA is shown in **Table 1.** Included in the table are the expression levels of other important B cell markers along with the status of immunoglobulin gene rearrangements in the cells at various stages.

As B cell progenitors mature, they pass through checkpoints that assess the status of their antigen receptors (see below). Those developing B cells that fail to pass die by apoptosis. Having acquired a mature phenotype, B cells enter the secondary lymphoid tissues such as spleen or lymph nodes, where they may encounter foreign antigens. Depending upon the type of antigen and the accompanying signals the B cells receive, they enter one of several different differentiation pathways that lead to the generation of plasma and/or memory B cells. B cell differentiation is a hazardous duty and relatively few cells pass all the checkpoints.

Genetic experiments in mice, both gene targeting experiments and the transgenic expression of B cell

Table 1 B lymphocyte developmental stages in mice[a]

Phenotype	Pro-B				Pre-B	Immature B	Mature B
	A	B	C	C'	D	E	F
B220	++	++	++	++	+++	+++	++++
CD43	++	+	+	+	−	−	−
HSA	−	+	+	+++	++	+	+/−
BP-1	−	−	++	++	+	−	−
sIgH	−	−	−	−	−/+	(μ+)	(μ+δ+)
sIgL	−	−	−	−	−	+	+
IgH locus	GL[b]	DJ,VDJ[c]	DJ,VDJ	VDJ	VDJ	VDJ	VDJ
IgL locus	GL	GL	GL	GL	VJ	VJ	VJ
λ5	−	+	+	+/−	+/−	−	−
VpreB	−	+	+	+/−	−	−	−
Mb-1	−	+	+	+	+	+	+
RAG-1	+++	+++	++	+	++	+/−	−[d]
TdT[e]	−	+	+	−	−	−	−
c-*kit*	+	++	++	−	−	−	−
IL-7R	−	+	+	+	+	−	−
CD19	−/+	++	++	++	+++	+++	+++
CD22	−	−	+	+	+	++	++
CD40	−	−	−	−	+	+	+

[a] See Loffert *et al* (1994) for more details.
[b] Germline.
[c] Stage D has GL as well as DJ and VDJ joints.
[d] RAG-1 is re-expressed in germinal center B cells, the functional significance unknown.
[e] TdT is not expressed in fetal liver B cells, hence their Ig genes lack N-region additions.

antigen receptors of defined specificity, have greatly deepened our understanding of the molecular and biologic processes involved in B cell differentiation. Because of the importance of these experiments they will be referred to when appropriate and the phenotypes of mice that have had molecules important in B cell differentiation altered by gene targeting have been summarized in **Table 2**. While there are some minor differences between human and mouse B cell differentiation, the overall scheme is remarkably similar.

Early B cell differentiation

Within the bone marrow microenvironment B cell development is divided into two main physiologic compartments. The small B220$^+$, CD43$^+$ population that contains many rapidly proliferating cells and the larger, but mostly resting, CD43$^-$ pre-B cell compartment, which derives from CD43$^+$ cells. The stromal cell-derived growth factors interleukin 7 (IL-7) and kit ligand help to maintain the proliferation of the CD43$^+$ cells. The recombinase machinery necessary for immunoglobulin gene rearrangements predominantly acts on the IgH loci in the CD43$^+$ compartment. The Ig rearrangements are catalyzed by a protein complex that contains two lymphoid-specific components, RAG-1 and RAG-2, that are involved in recognizing the recombination sequences and cutting the DNA. DNA joining requires the DNA-

dependent protein kinase complex. Once a B cell progenitor has successfully rearranged one heavy chain gene it terminates the rearrangement process on the other allele, a process termed allelic exclusion. Expression of μ heavy chain in conjunction with the surrogate light chains λ5 and Vpre-B results in the assembly of the pre-B cell receptor. This is a major checkpoint in B cell development. The failure to express this receptor dramatically reduces the transition of developing B from the CD43$^+$ into the CD43$^-$ compartment, stage C' to D. Whether the outside environment delivers a signal through the pre-B cell receptor or its simple expression provides the signal remains unclear although it is likely that the tyrosine kinase p72syk is required for signal transmission. The successful progression of a progenitor B cell into the CD43$^-$ compartment results in a cessation of IgH rearrangements and the completion of light chain rearrangements. The choice of κ versus λ light chain appears to be a stochastic event which in the mouse is an approximately 10:1 preference of κ over λ. A successful κ or λ rearrangement terminates the rearrangement process and the cell expresses surface IgM with either κ or λ light chains, its antigen-binding receptor. Such a cell, termed an immature B cell, must pass additional checkpoints before entering the mature B cell pool. One of those checkpoints was revealed by the analysis of mice that lack a functional mb-1 protein. Their immature B cells fail to enter the peripheral B cell pool, implying a checkpoint that assesses the competence of the antigen receptor. Evidence for another checkpoint at this stage came from the analysis of mice transgenically expressing an autoreactive antigen receptor. Immature B cells in these mice are either tolerized or deleted depending upon the nature of the autoreactive antigen. However, a mechanism may have evolved to rescue autoreactive B cells from this fate.

Table 2 Gene targeting of molecules involved in murine B cell development and differentiation

Targeted gene	Phenotype
Cell surface proteins	
BP-1	No obvious effect on B lymphocyte development and differentiation
CD19	B cell development normal, reduced responsiveness to thymus-dependent (TD) antigen, a lack of germinal centers, and failure of B1 cell development
CD21	Normal B cell development although reduced B1 cells, decreased responsiveness to TD antigens and germinal center size, increased threshold for B cell activation
CD22	Reduced number of IgM$^+$, IgD$^+$ cells, increased Ca^{2+} response to sIg signaling, and decreased thymus-independent (TI) response, expanded B1 population
CD23	No obvious effect on B lymphocyte development and differentiation
CD40	Impaired isotype switching, poor TD responses, and absent germinal centers
CD45	A decreased threshold for antigen-induced signaling resulting in the accumulation of potentially autoreactive B cells
HSA	Modest inhibition of early B cell development
Ig-α tail	A small impairment in B cell development, but a marked reduction in mature B (mb-1) cells, implying a checkpoint for the expression of the antigen receptor
Ig-β	Arrest in B cell development at CD43$^+$ stage, normal DJ joining but reduced (B29) VDJ joints
Igκ	A limited B cell repertoire, reduced number of B cells
IgD	Normal development, delayed affinity maturation of the antibody response
IL-7R	A severe block in early B cell development, failure of CD43$^+$ cells to expand
Invariant chain	Decreased response to TI antigens, development block at immature B cell stage
TNFR1	Required for germinal center formation in the spleen
λ5	Impaired expansion of pro-B cells to stage D and a lack of allelic exclusion
$\mu\mu$ membrane exons	An early failure of B cell development and a lack of allelic exclusion
Transcription factors	
Bcl-6	Normal B cell development, failure to generate germinal centers
BSAP	A failure of B cell development with an arrest at stage B. DJ but no VDJ rearrangements
E2A	An early failure of B cell development probably occurs prior to BSAP expression as no DJ rearrangements are detected
EBF	A failure of B cell development with only very early B cell progenitors present. No Ig rearrangements
Ets-1	A marked expansion of IgM plasma cells
Ikaros	A complete lack of B cell progenitors
Oca-B	Reduction in the number of mature recirculating B cells. Poor response to TD and TI antigens, a lack of germinal center formation
Oct-2	Normal development, impaired response to LPS, and impaired Ig secretion
p50	B cell development normal, impaired response to LPS and decreased serum Ig levels and impaired switching to IgG3, IgE, and IgA
PU.1	A lack of B cell progenitors, transcription and rearrangement of Ig blocked
RelB	Normal B cell development, mild reduction in B220$^+$ cells in spleen, no germinal center formation during TD responses
Sox-4	Partial block in B cell development, Stages A–C intact, reduced number of C′ and stage D cells in the bone marrow
Protein kinases	
BTK	Reduction in B2 cells and a severe deficiency in B1 cells, decreased IgM and IgG3, defective response to TI-2 antigens
c-Abl	Reduction in the number of mature B cells, reduction in LPS response and Ig response following SRBC immunization
Lyn	Reduced number of recirculating B cells, elevated levels of serum IgM, presence of autoantibodies implicating lyn in establishing B cell tolerance
Syk	Markedly impaired B cell development likely due to an impaired signaling from the pre-B cell receptor, thereby preventing clonal expansion
Cell survival proteins	
Bcl-2	Normal B cell development, collapse of peripheral immune system by massive apoptosis
Bcl-x	Markedly impaired B cell development, absence of mature B cells
Bax	B cell hyperplasia

Table 2 Continued

Targeted gene	Phenotype
Miscellaneous	
Igκ intronic	Greatly impaired VJ rearrangements, normal levels of κ expression, κ:λ enhancer ratio of 1:1 rather than 1:10
Igκ 3′ enhancer	Reduction in the number of κ-bearing B cells, reduced number of rearrangements at the κ locus
J_H	Mice cannot assemble a μ heavy chain, they lack sIg$^+$ B cells and B cell development is blocked at large, CD43$^+$ stage (C)
RAG-1	No Ig rearrangements and an arrest of B cell development at stage B, C
SDF-1	Failure of B cell development, reduced precursors in fetal liver and bone marrow
TdT	Lack of N-terminal additions in the adult repertoire, no obvious B cell phenotype
Vav	Normal B2 B cell development but a lack of B1 cells. Mature B cells hyporeactive to antigen signaling

They may reactivate the recombinase machinery and rearrange another light chain, generating a new antigen receptor with a different specificity, a process termed receptor editing. Finally, an immature B cell acquires IgD and passes into the periphery.

B cell differentiation in peripheral lymphoid tissues

B cell differentiation in the peripheral lymphoid tissues is predominantly antigen driven. B cell antigens can be broadly divided into thymus dependent (TD) and thymus independent (TI). TD antigens are usually soluble protein antigens that require major histocompatibility complex (MHC) class II-restricted T cell help for antibody production while TI antigens do not require such help, and are often multivalent and poorly degraded *in vivo*. Good examples of TI antigens are bacterial polysaccharides. In general, TI responses generate poor immunological memory, induce minimal germinal center formation, and trigger IgG2 secretion. The B cells responding to TI antigens have a distinct phenotype (IgM$^+$, IgD$^-$, CD21^{high}) and localize in the marginal zone in the spleen. The dependence upon these cells for responses to TI antigens may account for the poor responses to polysaccharide antigens seen in splenectomized individuals and human infants (the marginal zone B cells don't mature until ~2 years of age). Coupling polysaccharides to a carrier protein results in an effective infant vaccine since the conjugate triggers a TD response.

Exposure to a TD antigen triggers two pathways of B cell differentiation, the extrafollicular pathway, which leads to early antibody production, and the germinal center pathway, which leads to germinal center formation, immunological memory, and the generation of plasma cell precursors. In the spleen, the antigen-activated B cells migrate to T cell-rich zones in the periarteriolar lymphoid sheath searching for T cell help. Failure to find it likely results in sub-

sequent unresponsiveness or anergy, however, successful T–B cell collaboration produces short-lived oligoclonal proliferative foci (each derived from several B cells). Many of the B cells in these foci secrete IgM and undergo isotype switching (a DNA splicing event that exchanges IgH constant region). These events depend upon costimulatory signals, CD40 and CD40L interactions (see below), and cytokines such as IL-2, IL-4, IL-6, IL-10 and transforming growth factor β (TGFβ). Some B cells migrate from these foci into primary follicles to enter the germinal center pathway. Within a primary follicle an oligoclonal expansion of B cells forms the dark zone of the germinal center. There somatic mutations are introduced into the variable regions of Ig genes that may alter the B cell antigen receptor specificity or affinity. Eventually these cells migrate into the light zone of the germinal center region where they interact with helper T cells and follicular dendritic cells that have trapped antigen localized on their surfaces. Here, B cells with high-affinity antigen receptors are selected to survive, while those that lack such receptors die or perhaps re-enter the dark zone for another round of somatic mutations. B cells that acquire an autoreactive antigen receptor are also eliminated. Rescue signals such as the engagement of CD40 (a member of the TNFα receptor family expressed on B cells) induce Bcl-x and Bcl-2, resulting in the survival of selected cells. CD40, CD40L (a member of the TNFα family expressed on activated T cells), B7-1, CD21, TNFαR and CD19 all have critical roles in germinal center formation. Individuals with the X-linked hyper-IgM syndrome underscore the importance of CD40L, as they do not express functional CD40L following T cell activation and do not form germinal centers.

Passage through the germinal center leads to the formation of memory B cells or plasma cell precursors (there are few antibody-secreting cells within the germinal center). Cytokines and CD40L influence this decision. IL-2, IL-10 and IL-6 promote differentiation toward plasma cells while CD40/CD40L interactions promote memory cell formation and inhibit plasma cell generation. Cytokines also contribute to isotype switching. IL-4 enhances switching to IgE and IgG4; IL-10 toward IgG1, IgG3, and IgA; and TGFβ toward IgA. While plasma cells secrete large amounts of Ig, they are short-lived cells that need to be replenished to sustain high antibody levels. Plasma cells lose their membrane Ig and many of the markers used to identify B cells although they express high levels of CD38. Memory B cells are long-lived cells that contain somatically mutated V genes and are morphologically distinct from naive B cells. They can be rapidly restimulated to generate a secondary antibody response. Together the extra follicular and germinal center pathways of B cell differentiation lead to a coordinated humoral response providing the very rapid production of low-affinity antibodies, the subsequent production of high-affinity antibodies, and the potential for a rapid amnestic response. The failure of B cell differentiation at any of the many steps may result in a crippled immune system incapable of protecting an individual against many potentially pathogenic organisms or in an autoreactive immune system capable of inflicting damage upon self tissues.

See also: **Antigens, T dependent and independent; B lymphocyte activation; B lymphocyte repertoire; B lymphocytes; Bone marrow and hematopoiesis; Bursa of Fabricius; CD22; CD40 and its ligand; CD45 (the leukocyte common antigen); Cytokines; Diversity, generation of; Humoral immunity; Immunoglobulin, cell surface; Immunoglobulin class switching; Lymphocyte trafficking; Lymphocytes; Microenvironment; Ontogeny of the immune response; Somatic mutation.**

Further reading

Goodnow CC, Cyster JG, Hartley SB *et al* (1995) Self-tolerance checkpoints in B lymphocyte development. *Advances in Immunology* 59: 279–368.

Henderson AJ and Calame KL (1998) Transcriptional regulation during B-cell development. *Annual Review of Immunology* 16: 163–200.

Loffert D, Schaal S, Ehlich A *et al* (1994) Early B-cell development in the mouse: Insights from mutations introduced by gene targeting. *Immunological Reviews* 137: 135–153.

MacLennan ICM (1994) Germinal centers. *Annual Review of Immunology* 12: 117–139.

Opstelten D (1996) B lymphocyte development and transcription regulation *in vivo*. *Advances in Immunology* 63: 197–268.

Rajewsky K (1996) Clonal selection and learning in the antibody system. *Nature* 381: 751–758.

B LYMPHOCYTE REPERTOIRE

Phyllis-Jean Linton, Department of Immunology, The Scripps Research Institute, California, USA

Over the years two experimental approaches have been used to assess antigen-specific B cell populations at the clonal level. These use antigenic or polyclonal mitogenic stimulation of B cells in limiting dilution. Since polyclonal stimulation encompasses a broad range of B cell responsiveness, assays for antibody production discriminate between the various antigen reactivities. In contrast, antigen stimulation is more selective in the B cells that respond, thus enabling analyses for positive antibody production. The advent of hybridoma technology not only allowed for ease in experimental execution but also made feasible the analyses of the molecular events involved. With advances in molecular biology technology, e.g. polymerase chain reaction (PCR) and reverse transcriptase-PCR, sequences could be obtained from single cells without any form of selection.

Among the early major findings are that B cell antigen receptors are clonally distributed, each B cell expresses a single immunoglobulin specificity and each stimulated primary B cell gives rise to a clone of antibody-forming cells (AFCs) whose antibody replicates the variable region clonotype of the antigen receptor of the original stimulated B cell. Although the primary B cell clonotype repertoire is extremely diverse, individuals of the same murine strain tend to express similar repertoires. Many studies have led to the conclusion that the B cell clonotype repertoire of a given mouse strain as well as the individual mice is highly restricted during late fetal and early neonatal development, and is acquired in a highly patterned and reproducible fashion. Among the more recent findings are the elucidation of the molecular events involved in the diversity of B cell repertoire expression, the mechanisms by which each B cell obtains a single specificity, and the mechanisms that underlie the gradual acquisition of B cell repertoire during neonatal development.

Molecular basis for repertoire expression

Diversity in the primary B cell repertoire can be generated at three levels: 1) combinatorial association of V_H, D_H and J_H and of V_L and J_L gene segments; 2) junctional diversity due to imprecise joining, P- or N-nucleotide additions; and 3) combination of heavy and light chains. Given all these sources of diversity, the potential for variable region diversity in the primary B cell repertoire of mice can be estimated to be at least 10^7–10^8 specificities. Although antibody specificity of a given B cell is determined by the genome of that cell, random somatic events as well as evolutionarily selective forces contribute to V region expression. Among those processes that exemplify stochastic somatic events is somatic mutation. Somatic mutations can occur throughout the V region but antigen selection appears to favor those mutations leading to amino acid replacements in the hypervariable regions. The studies of Berek, Milstein, Manser, Rajewsky and Siekevitz suggest that although the process of somatic mutation which occurs during the generation of a secondary immune response is responsible for an almost limitless number of new selectable specificities, it plays no major role in the diversification of the primary B cell repertoire.

Junctional diversity appears to be less random than originally thought. This is supported by the reproducible occurrence of major clonotypes in all mice of a given strain, such as the cross-reactive idiotype (CRI) found in the A strain of mice after immunization with arsonate (ARS). In addition, junctional diversity may be greatly influenced by particular D region haplotypes.

V gene segment combinations and selection are not simply a random assortment of functional V gene elements. For example, the occurrence of predominant clonotypes, such as T15, is due to a disproportionate selection of variable region gene segments from within the V region pool. In addition, Press, Fernandez, Cancro, Denis, Fung, Kearney, Klinman and Teale have shown that repertoire expression during late fetal and early neonatal B cell development is severely restricted, representing less than 1% of the total potential repertoire of an adult individual. Repertoire expression in neonates is also reproducibly and sequentially expressed among individuals of the same strain, such that the V_H region gene segments utilized during early development are clustered toward the D proximal end of the V_H gene segment

complex. Reproducible differences in repertoire are found not only in neonates versus adults but, as Zharhary, Riley and others have shown, also in aged individuals. Together these findings may be interpreted as the consequence of an evolutionarily predetermined repertoire acquisition. A V_H gene may be over-represented due to a number of possibilities, including chromosomal location, copy number and accessibility to recombinases, as well as through environmental influences such as positive or negative selection.

Environmental influences on repertoire expression

Clonal selection begins to exert its influence on the B cell at the time of surface heavy chain acquisition in B cell development. Recently, several stages of pro- and pre-B cell development have been defined and in some of these stages cell division and potentially selection may occur. Following precedents in the T cell lineage, Schwartz and Stollar have suggested that the immature μ^+/κ^- or μ^+/λ^- B cell dies if its surface μ variable region binds with high affinity to a self antigen. At the μ^+/κ^+ or μ^+/λ^+ stage of differentiation, it is possible that a B cell with a high-affinity antiself receptor could avoid deletion by undergoing a second V_L (or V_H) gene rearrangement ('receptor editing'). The ability of unmutated natural autoantibodies to bind both to autoantigens and bacterial antigens raises the possibility that, in adults, pre-B cells could be selected positively or negatively by either self antigens or microbial antigens.

The expressed B cell repertoire appears to arise from the interplay of environmental influences acting upon an extremely diverse repertoire of clonally distributed specificities that are determined by the aforementioned molecular events. The environment may up- or downregulate the pre-existing specificities. To assess the effects of environmental regulation on B cell repertoire expression, the repertoire expressed in the mature B cell population is compared to that in cells directly derived from the sIg⁻ population of bone marrow cells because these developing B cells cannot be influenced by antigenic or anti-idiotypic mechanisms requiring sIg interactions. Upon comparison, the frequency of newly generated bone marrow B cell responses to various antigens (such as BALB/c responses to 2,4-dinitrophenyl (DNP), (3-hydroxy-4-nitrophenyl) acetyl (NP), phosphorylcholine (PC), α1,3 dextran (Dex), and influenza A/PR/8 hemagglutinin (HA)) appears to be the same as that of mature B cell responses. Importantly, examination of B cell responsiveness to HA variants revealed similar reactivity patterns in the two B cell populations.

Thus, the environment does not appear to impact upon the diversification of the primary B cell repertoire.

Similarly, environmental influences appear to play little or no role in the establishment of the predominant clonotypes or clonotype families expressed in the primary B cell repertoire, e.g. the T15$^+$ clonotype in PC responses, the λ-bearing antibodies to α1,3-Dex in Igh^a mice and the λNP^b responses. The frequency with which these clonotypes are expressed in the spleen is entirely reflective of the frequency with which they emanate from the generative cell pool. Therefore, environmental upregulation cannot explain the occurrence of dominant clonotypes.

The major environmental influences that affect primary B cell repertoire expression are through clonotype elimination during B cell maturation. During development, B cells pass through a phase during which they are susceptible to inactivation. Although the mechanisms for the downregulation of particular clonotypes are believed to involve tolerance induction and anti-idiotypic regulation, formal proof of the latter's existence *in vivo* awaits. Nonetheless, substantive evidence exists for the downregulation of the expression of certain B cell clonotypes. Examples of downregulation include responses to antigens such as murine cytochrome *c* (cyt *c*), PC, NP and α1,3-Dex.

Experimentally induced anti-idiotypic suppression has been shown by Kearney, Kelsoe, Kohler, Accolla, Cerny and others to affect the expression of the primary B cell repertoire. Among the more convincing data for anti-idiotypic immunoregulation is the finding by Froscher and Klinman examining the λ-bearing, α1,3-Dex specific response. The representation of this phenotype in Igh^b mice is low compared with that in Igh^a mice, and the responsiveness in the precursor versus mature B cell pool appears normal. Interestingly, if the Igh^b sIg$^-$ B cell precursors are allowed to mature and respond in an allogeneic environment, the frequency of responsiveness is significantly increased. Because of the Igh haplotype specificity of this phenomenon, the elimination of the λ-bearing, α1,3-Dex-specific B cells in Igh^b mice is thought to be the result of naturally occurring idiotype specific downregulation.

In some of the aforementioned antigen systems, clonotype elimination during B cell development is presumed to occur by tolerance induction, although the responsible self antigen has not been definitively identified. Teale, Klinman, Metcalf, Riley, Nossal, Chiller and others have experimentally induced B cell tolerance. Recently, using immunoglobulin transgenic mice, Nemazee, Weigert, Goodnow and others have demonstrated B cell tolerance *in vivo*. The tolerance trigger has been demonstrated as an active process requiring metabolic energy and protein synthesis by the B cell as well as surface receptor interlinkage in the form of multivalent antigen or multivalent antigen presentation. In addition, the affinity threshold to tolerize B cells as they mature through the tolerance gauntlet is higher than that required to trigger these cells once they have fully matured. Thus, B cells whose affinity for self antigen are low may escape tolerance induction; once fully mature their affinity could be sufficient to permit triggering. This phenomenon could serve to preserve repertoire diversity but at the expense of the persistence of B cells in the primary repertoire with low affinity antiself reactivities.

Repertoire expression in B cell subpopulations

The secondary B cell repertoire can be divided into three broad categories. The first category contains those secondary responses whose predominant clonotype or clonotype families are the same as those found in the primary response (i.e. total overlap in V gene usage), although the secondary antibodies have accumulated somatic mutations. Examples of these responses include the T15 clonotype, the λ-bearing antibodies to α1,3-Dex and to some extent the λNP^b clonotype. In the last example, the secondary response to NP in Igh^b mice is ultimately dominated by other clonotype families. The second category includes those responses whose specificities constitute a minority of the primary response but dominate the secondary response. Examples include the response to PR8-HA and the CRI in response to ARS in strain A mice. This phenotype can be explained by the preferential selection by antigen of those somatic mutants which could increase affinity. Finally, responses to 2-phenyl-5-oxazalone (phOX) by BALB/c mice, NP by C57BL/6, horse cyt *c* and *Salmonella typhimurium* by BALB/c are examples which display almost total disparities between primary and secondary responses. One possible explanation is that secondary B cells and their progenitors express variable region gene combinations that are not used by primary B cells and their precursors.

The secondary B cell repertoire, unlike the primary B cell repertoire, appears to be highly dependent upon environmental influences for its generation and regulation. Since antigenic stimulation and continued antigen selection is necessary for the establishment of secondary B cells, the secondary repertoire of individual mice within a strain can vary considerably, as seen with responses to PR8-HA and tobacco mosaic virus protein. Although still controversial, Linton and Klinman have shown the splenic progenitors to memory B cells to be separable from the precursors to primary AFCs. These secondary B cell progenitors are stimulated by lower affinity interactions than those that are required for stimulation of precursors to primary AFCs. Moreover, as shown by Linton and Klinman *in vitro*, and later by Nossal and Goodnow *in vivo*, the progenitors to memory B cells pass through a tolerance susceptible phase. *In toto*, secondary B cell specificity appears to be derived from a broad spectrum of potentially responsive cells which are stimulated in a much less specific fashion. These specificities can somatically mutate and continue to be selected upon positively by antigen or negatively through tolerance induction of antiself reactivities.

Another small subpopulation of murine B cells has been defined by their expression of the cell surface marker Ly-1 (CD5 in humans). Because the names applied to this subset are misleading (since CD5 clearly can be induced on 'conventional' B cells and there is a subset of cells in mice that shares many features with Ly-1 B cells (i.e. 'sister' population)), these cells are now referred to as B1 cells. The B1 cells show a variety of novel features: a novel anatomical localization (enrichment in the peritoneal cavity); early appearance in ontogeny; secretion of particular autoreactive antibodies (notably antibody to a cryptic determinant on mouse red blood cells revealed by proteolytic treatment with the enzyme bromelain (BrMRBC)); extensive capacity for self-renewal; increased frequency in autoimmune mouse strains; repetitive usage of particular germline immunoglobulin variable genes; and an apparent predisposition for unregulated growth.

Since B1 cells represent a sizable portion of neonatal splenic B cells, and fetal/neonatal-derived B cells have been shown to lack non-templated nucleotide (N) region additions found at the VDJ junctions, it was thought that all B1 cells lacked N additions. This restriction in repertoire size has been attributed to terminal deoxynucleotidyl transferase, TdT, the enzyme which adds N nucleotides and becomes active during the first week after birth. A comparison of heavy chain sequences from B1 cells isolated at different stages of development revealed some N additions in the B1 cells of the adult population. The increased N-region diversity is found in the 'sister' population of B1 cells.

Since B1 cells develop early in ontogeny, repertoire differences may, at least in part, reflect selection by different endogenous antigens. For instance, the enrichment of B1 cells with N additions in adults may be the consequence of a selective advantage. In addition, analysis of cells responding to BrMRBC has shown that the antigen receptor is encoded by novel V_H genes (V_H11 and V_H12), and the significant increased frequency of V_H11 usage in B1 cells is largely restricted to V_H11–J_H1 rearrangements. There appears to be no general overuse of particular V genes, rather such genes are used in distinctive V_H–V_L combinations to encode selected autoreactive antibodies. Moreover, B1 cells show a preference for using J_H1 gene segments which is not observed in the conventional B cell population, and while most murine pre-B and B cells preferentially use the DSP and DFL D_H gene segments in a given reading frame (RF1), cells in the 'sister' population frequently express D_H genes in another reading frame (RF2).

See also: **Affinity maturation; Antibodies, specificity; B lymphocyte differentiation; CD5; Clonal selection; Diversity, generation of; Hybridomas, B cell; Idiotype network; Immunoglobulin genes; Maturation of immune responses; Memory, immunological; Neonatal immune response; Polyclonal activators; Somatic mutation; Tolerance, peripheral.**

Further reading

Hardy RR (1992) Variable gene usage, physiology and development of Ly-1+ (CD5+) B cells. *Current Opinion in Immunology* 4, 181–185.

Casali P and Silberstein LE (eds) (1995) Immunoglubulin gene expression in development and disease. *Annals of the New York Academy of Sciences* 764.

Klinman NR and Linton PJ (1988) The clonotype repertoire of B cell subpopulations. *Advances in Immunology* 42: 1–93.

Klinman NR and Linton PJ (1990) The generation of a B cell memory: a working hypothesis. *Current Topics in Microbiology and Immunology* 159: 19–35.

Loffert D, Schaal S, Ehlich A *et al* (1994) Early B-cell development in the mouse: insights from mutations introduced by gene targeting. *Immunological Reviews* 137: 135–153.

Möller, G (ed) (1990) Concepts in immunology. *Immunological Reviews* 115.

Rolink A, Karasuyama H, Haasner D *et al* (1994) Two pathways of B lymphocyte development in mouse bone marrow and the roles of surrogate L chain in this development. *Immunological Reviews* 137: 185–201.

Schwartz RS and Stollar BD (1994) Heavy-chain directed B-cell maturation: continuous clonal selection beginning at the pre-B cell stage. *Immunology Today* 15: 27–32.

Wu G (ed) (1994) Mechanisms of V(D)J rearrangement. *Seminars in Immunology* 6: 3.

B LYMPHOCYTES

B David Stollar, Tufts University School of Medicine, Boston, Massachusetts, USA

B lymphocytes are the antibody-forming cells of the immune system. B cells were so named in 1965, when they were shown to develop in the bursa of Fabricius (an outpouching of the gut) of chickens and were distinguished from T cells, which develop in the thymus. Physical separation allowed identification of separate functions of B cells (antibody production) and T cells (cell-mediated responses and regulatory processes). Mammals do not have a bursa of Fabricius, but their B cells arise in the bone marrow, so the original initial-based name is still applicable.

B lymphocytes are found in blood, lymph nodes, spleen and tonsil and other mucosal tissues. About 5–25% of all human blood lymphocytes, which number 1000–2000 cells mm³, are B lymphocytes. B cells comprise a majority of the bone marrow lymphocytes, one-third to one-half of lymph node and spleen lymphocytes, but less than 1% of those in thymus. Nonactivated B cells circulate through lymph nodes and spleen, in which they are clustered in follicles and marginal zones around the follicles. Circulating B cells may interact with and be activated by T cells at extrafollicular sites, where T cells occur around small blood vessels in association with antigen-presenting dendritic cells. Appropriately activated B cells enter the follicles, where they proliferate and displace resting cells, forming germinal centers. There they differentiate into plasma cells specialized for antibody production and long-lived memory B cells.

Each B cell produces many copies of its unique antibody molecule, which it may anchor on its cell membrane or secrete into tissue fluid and blood. The membrane antibodies form a major part of antigen-binding receptors, which may initiate cell proliferation and antibody production or processing of antigen for presentation to T cells. Secreted antibodies bind antigen in blood or tissues and initiate reactions that lead to elimination of antigen from the body. Thus B lymphocytes function both in afferent and effector phases of antibody-producing immune responses.

Intracellular features of B cells

A defining feature of B lymphocytes is that they are the only cells that rearrange chromosomal DNA in the loci that code for antibodies (immunoglobulins). Other intracellular features help to identify B cells but are not as exclusively characteristic as is gene rearrangement. Proteins associated with the rearrangement include the RAG-1 and RAG-2 recombination proteins and the enzyme terminal deoxynucleotidyl transferase (TdT). Proteins related to immunoglobulin gene expression include the transcription factors Oct-2, dimeric E2A, Bob-1 and Pu.1. Certain protein kinases that mediate signals from the antigen receptor are also characteristic of B cells.

Cell surface features of B cells

The unique B cell surface feature is the antigen receptor, formed in part by membrane immunoglobulin. Receptor assemblies of newly formed mature B cells contain immunoglobulin M (IgM) and/or IgD. B cells appropriately stimulated by interaction with T helper cells and their interleukin products may switch to production of other Ig classes, and the B cell antigen receptors then contain IgG, IgA or IgE, but not IgM or IgD. The H chain of receptor immunoglobulin is anchored in the membrane, in association with proteins Ig-α (CD79a) and Ig-β (CD79b). The intracellular domains of Ig-α and Ig-β participate in generating a receptor-mediated signal within the cell, transmitted through activation of protein kinases. Lyn (Src family) and Syk (Syk/Zap70 family) are protein kinases that associate with the resting B cell receptor and, along with additional kinases, participate in B cell activation pathways.

Other B cell membrane proteins regulate the intensity of responses that follow antigen binding (**Table 1**). Cross-linking of a B cell-specific complement-binding assembly (proteins CD19, CD21, CD81 and Leu-13) to the antigen receptor dramatically lowers the antigen concentration required for B cell activation. CD45, a positive regulator (perhaps an initiator) of signaling, is a transmembrane protein with a cytoplasmic tail that has essential phosphatase activity. Other phosphatases (e.g. SHP-I) are attenuating, and some membrane molecules (e.g. CD22, FcγR) increase the effect of attenuating phosphatases.

Additional B cell surface molecules have diverse functions, serving to present processed antigen fragments and costimulatory signals to T cells, mediate adhesion between B and T cells, or as receptors for cytokines produced by T cells (**Table 2**). B cell activation and class switching can be stimulated through

Table 1 B cell receptors and associated membrane proteins

Receptor complex	Protein	Family	Function
B cell antigen receptor (BCR)	IgM, IgD, IgG, IgA or IgE	Ig	Receptor-mediated signaling
	Ig-α (CD79a)	Ig	Receptor-mediated signaling
	Ig-β, Ig-γ (CD79b)	Ig	Receptor-mediated signaling
Pre-B cell receptor	Ig-μ H chain	Ig	Signaling for maturation progression
	Vpre-B	Ig	Component of surrogate L chain
	14.1 (human)	Ig	Component of surrogate L chain
	λ5 (mouse)	Ig	
Complement receptor complex	CD19	Ig	Costimulates BCR signaling when cross-linked to BCR. Forms a complex with CD21, TAPA-1 and Leu-13
	CD21	Selectin, C-R	EBV receptor gp350/220; complement receptor, binds iC3b, CD23, IFNα
	TAPA-1 (CD81)	Tetraspan	
	Leu-13	16 kDa membrane protein	
Modulators of receptor signaling	CD45	Tyr phosphatase	Increases BCR signaling
	CD22 (CR2)	Ig	Inhibits BCR signaling; mediates adhesion; binds to SHP-1, Syk, PLCγ1
	FcγRII	Ig	Low-affinity IgG receptor Inhibits BCR signaling
	CD23	Lectin	Low-affinity FcεR2; regulates IgE production

B cell CD40, a receptor for a ligand, CD40L (also called gp39), produced by T cells. B cell apoptosis follows engagement of the cell surface protein Fas (CD95) by specific Fas ligand, which is produced by activated T cells, dendritic cells and cells of many tissues in which apoptosis occurs. Some of these surface proteins, such as CD19, are nearly unique to B cells; others, such as major histocompatibility complex (MHC) class II molecules and Fas, occur on cells of several tissues.

B cell development

B cells are generated from hematopoietic stem cells. In birds, new B cells are produced in the bursa of Fabricius in both embryonic and adult life. In mammals, B lymphocytes are produced mainly in liver and spleen in fetal life, but in bone marrow after birth. Multipotential hematopoietic stem cells can develop into lymphoid cells or myeloid cells (granulocytes, erythrocytes and platelets). Along the lymphocyte differentiation pathway there is an intermediate lymphoid precursor for both B and T cells. The earliest precursors committed only to B cell development, pro-B cells, have not yet rearranged their V region genes, but can be identified by their ability to grow in culture in the presence of bone marrow stromal cells, kit-ligand and IL-7; their cell surface CD19 and CD43; and their intracellular terminal deoxynucleotidyl transferase, RAG-1 and RAG-2. Somewhat more differentiated (pre-B I) cells have begun to rearrange H chain V region genes but do not synthesize H chain protein. When rearrangement of H chain but not L chain gene segments is completed, developing cells synthesize and express μH chain on the cell surface in association with a surrogate L chain (**Table 1**). Membrane expression of this complex is essential for progression from the pre-B I to the pre-B II stage, at which L chain rearrangement begins. L chain synthesis and Ig assembly occur in immature B cells. The unmodified term 'B cell' is applied to small lymphocytes that have completed V gene rearrangements, synthesize both chains and express cell surface Ig. Most B cells express only one rearranged H and one L chain; this process, known as allelic exclusion, ensures that a B cell will make only one antibody. The progressive stages of V gene rearrangement are accompanied by characteristic expression of cell surface proteins that are also used as markers of these stages.

At birth, before exposure to foreign antigens, new IgM+IgD+ B cells comprise a 'primary repertoire' of

Table 2 B cell membrane proteins that interact with T lymphocytes and cytokines produced by T lymphocytes

B cell protein	Nature/family	Interacting T cell surface molecule	Function
MHC class II	Ig	TCR, CD4	Presentation of processed antigen to TCR
B7-1 (CD80) and B7-2 (CD86)	Ig Ig	CD28, CTL4	Costimulatory signal in antigen presentation to TCR
CD40	TNFR	CD40L (gp39)	Germinal follicle formation, class switching
ICAM-1	Ig	LFA-1	Adhesion
LFA-1	Integrin	ICAM-1	Adhesion
LFA-3	Ig	CD2	Adhesion
Fas (CD95)	TNFR	FasL	Apoptosis signal
		Soluble T cell product	Effect on B cells
IL-2R	HCR type I	IL-2	Growth, activation, Ig secretion
TNFαR	TNFR family	TNFα	Costimulation of proliferation, Ig secretion
IFNγR	HCR type II	IFNγ	Class switch to IgG2a; enhanced MHC class II expression
IL-4R	HCR type I	IL-4	Class switch to IgE, IgG1; stimulation of MHC class II and CD23 expression
IL-5R	HCR type I	IL-5	Enhanced growth, differentiation, Ig secretion by activated B cells
IL-6R	HCR type I	IL-6	Growth, differentiation, Ig secretion
IL-10R	Related to IFN receptors	IL-10	Increased MHC class II expression (mouse); proliferation, differentiation, Ig secretion (human)
TGFβR	Protein kinase	TGFβ	Inhibition of growth; class switch to IgA, IgG2b

HCR, hematopoietic cytokine receptor; ICAM, intercellular adhesion molecule; IFN, interferon; Ig, immunoglobulin; IL, interleukin; LFA, leukocyte function antigen; MHC, major histocompatibility complex; TCR, T cell receptor; TGF, transforming growth factor; TNF, tumor necrosis factor.

cells producing diverse Ig products. Diversity of the primary repertoire is generated in various ways: rearrangement of numerous Ig V gene segments without somatic mutations (fetal mice); similar rearrangements plus the addition of untemplated nucleotides at the junction of H gene segments (humans, postnatal mice); gene conversion with a smaller number of functional genes (rabbit, chicken); or mutation of functional genes (sheep ileal Peyer's patches). By the time the B cells emerge from the bursa or bone marrow, or shortly thereafter, the great potential diversity has been narrowed by elimination of cells making strongly autoreactive antibodies and by the short lifespan of cells that encounter no antigen. About 1.5×10^7 B cells are produced in adult mouse bone

marrow daily; 10–15% of them survive to enter the total B cell pool, which totals about 5×10^8 cells. A significant fraction of neonatal IgM reacts both with bacterial antigens and, weakly, with autoantigens, as do IgM products of newly formed B cells through adult life. Normal regulatory processes, however, prevent the expansion of B cells that would produce large amounts of high-affinity autoantibodies of other Ig classes. When that regulation fails, autoantibody production is often associated with autoimmune disease.

In humans and mice a small subset of B cells expresses CD5 (Ly-1), a protein present on all T cells. CD5+ B cells are prominent in fetal and neonatal mice, in the peritoneum of adult mice, and among human fetal B cells and adult B cells that make natural autoantibodies. CD5 expression may be a reflection of how antigen stimulation occurs or a marker for a particular B cell lineage.

B cell activation

When activated by either T-independent antigens or by interactions with T helper cells, small resting B cells are converted to large lymphoblasts and then either to plasma cells, specialized for antibody production, or long-lasting small memory cells. Within germinal centers, B cells are converted to large replicating centroblasts and then to nonreplicating centrocytes. Additional intermediate stages in the activation process are defined by cell surface protein expression and localization within the germinal center. Striking features of the germinal center activation process are the generation of frequent mutations in the Ig V regions and the switch from IgM to IgG, IgA or IgE production. Mutation greatly increases the diversity of antigen-binding sites. If mutation eliminates antigen binding, the cell has a short life, dying by apoptosis. The few cells in which mutation yields an Ig product with high affinity for the antigen are selected for survival. Antigen-selected cells may differentiate terminally into plasma cells, which then secrete a large amount of the antibody, or into small, long-lived, memory B cells that are distributed in blood and lymphoid tissues. These cells no longer express surface IgD.

B cell deficiency diseases

The physiological importance of B cell function is revealed by diseases that result from selective B cell deficiencies and consequent lack of antibodies (agammaglobulinemia). Bruton's agammaglobulinemia (XLA) is an X-linked defect in B cell maturation in humans, with arrest at the Pre-B I stage and a resulting deficiency in all immunoglobulin classes. A corresponding B cell maturation defect, the Xid mutation, also occurs in CBA/N mice. In male children with XLA, the maturation block results from deficiency of a B cell-specific protein tyrosine kinase, btk. With a profound lack of mature B cells but normal T cells, these children are particularly susceptible to infections by bacteria, mycoplasma, hepatitis virus and enteroviruses. They have recurrent middle ear infection, pneumonia, sinusitis and tonsillitis caused by *Pneumococcus*, *Streptococcous* and *Hemophilus*. Problems with infection begin several months after birth, when the pool of protective maternal antibody decreases. XLA children are not unusually susceptible to most virus or fungal infections, for which T cell responses provide sufficient protection. In contrast, subjects with profound defects of both B cells and T cells (severe combined immunodeficiency, SCID), are threatened by all infectious agents; they survive only in a germ-free environment unless the deficiency can be treated.

Immunodeficiency with elevated IgM but very low IgG or IgA levels results from a failure in the signaling that instructs B cells to switch from production of IgM to other classes of Ig. The signals come in part from T cells, and in most subjects the basic defect is in the T cell even though it is expressed through B cell dysfunction. An X-linked type of this disease is due to a mutation in the gene for CD40L, the T cell ligand for B cell CD40. High levels of IgM in this disease are associated with autoimmunity. A non-X-linked immunodeficiency, in which there is a selective lack of IgA-producing B cells, leads to bacterial infections primarily in the respiratory, gastrointestinal and urogenital tracts.

B cell malignancies

B cells may undergo malignant transformation at various stages of development or activation. Some human acute lymphocytic leukemia cells express features of early B cells, such as expression of TdT or only cytoplasmic H chain. Infection of mouse B cell precursors with Abelson virus generates a variety of leukemic B cells frozen in development at the pre-B cell stage. Epstein–Barr virus (EBV) activates human B cells to become lymphoblasts and, occasionally, to undergo transformation to malignancy. Mature B cells occur in some acute lymphocytic leukemias and in B cell lymphomas, hairy cell leukemia, and chronic lymphocytic leukemia. Some leukemic B cells produce IgM with properties of natural autoantibodies.

Multiple myeloma is a malignant clonal expansion of a differentiated plasma cell, with production of a large amount of a single Ig molecule or Ig chain (myeloma protein). Some spontaneous myeloma proteins have identifiable antigen-binding activity, and analyses of myeloma proteins provided important keys to understanding antibody structure. Mutated myeloma cells of mice also serve as partners for fusion with specific antibody-producing cells, forming hybridomas that produce monoclonal antibodies. Overproducing cells that lack malignant properties but yield a large amount of Ig product occur in Waldenström's macroglobulinemia and primary amyloidosis.

See also: **Antibodies, synthesis; Antigen presentation via MHC class II molecules; Autoimmunity; B lymphocyte activation; B lymphocyte, antigen processing** and presentation; B lymphocyte repertoire; B lymphocyte differentiation; Bruton's agammaglobulinemia; CD antigens; CD5; CD22; CD40 and its ligand; CD45 (the leukocyte common antigen); Cell surface molecules, immunoprecipitation of; Clonal selection; Cytokines; Dendritic cells; Diversity, generation of; Epstein-Barr virus, infection and immunity; Fas (CD95) and fas ligand; Fc receptors; Gene conversion; Germinal center; Heavy chain diseases; Humoral immunity; Hybridomas, B cell; Hypergammaglobulinemia; Hyper-IgM syndrome; Immunodeficiency, primary; Immunoglobulin genes; Leukemia; Lymphocytes; Mucosal immunity; Natural antibodies; Polyclonal activators; Second signals for lymphocyte activation; Somatic mutation; Tolerance, peripheral.

Further reading

Cambier JC, Pleiman CM and Clark MR (1994) Signal transduction by the B cell antigen receptor and its co-receptors. *Annual Review of Immunology* **12**: 457–486.

Goodnow CC (1998) Positive versus negative signaling by lymphocyte antigen receptors. *Annual Review of Immunology* **16**.

Herzenberg LA and Haughton G (eds) (1992) CD5 B cells in development and disease. *Annals of the New York Academy of Sciences* **651**: 1–601.

Karasuyama H, Rolink AG and Melchers F (1996) Surrogate light chains B cell development. *Advances in Immunology* **63**: 1–41.

Kehry MR (1996) CD40-mediated signaling in B cells. Balancing cell survival, growth, and death. *Journal of Immunology* **156**: 2345–2348.

Kincade PW and Gimble JM (1993) B Lymphocytes. In: Paul WE (ed) *Fundamental Immunology*, 3rd edn, pp 43–73. New York: Raven Press.

Liu Y-J and Banchereau J (1996) The paths and molecular controls of peripheral B-cell development. *The Immunologist* **4**: 55.

Möller G (ed) (1994) B-cell differentiation. *Immunological Reviews* **137**: 5–229.

Osmond DG (1986) Population dynamics of bone marrow B lymphocytes. *Immunological Reviews* **93**: 103–124.

Rajewsky K (1996) Clonal selection and learning in the antibody system. *Nature* **381**: 751–758.

Snow EC (ed) (1994) *Handbook of B and T Lymphocytes*. San Diego: Academic Press.

β₂-MICROGLOBULIN

Rho H Seong, Institute for Molecular Biology and Genetics and Department of Molecular Biology, Seoul National University, Seoul, Korea

Jane R Parnes, Division of Immunology and Rheumatology, Department of Medicine, Stanford University Medical Center, Stanford, California, USA

β₂-Microglobulin (β₂M) is a protein of approximately 12 kDa and is found in serum and on the surface of most mammalian cells. It was first isolated from the urine of patients whose renal tubules were damaged by chronic cadmium poisoning. The protein is referred to as β₂-microglobulin because of its low molecular weight and its localization in the β₂ region of globulins when blood plasma is subject to moving-boundary electrophoresis.

β₂M is noncovalently associated with several transmembrane proteins, including the heavy chain of class I major histocompatibility complex (MHC) proteins encoded by the mouse H-2 K, D and L and Qa/Tla loci and the human HLA-A, -B, and -C. loci. β₂M is also found in noncovalent association with an immunoglobulin G (IgG) receptor (Fc receptor) of neonatal gut cells and with CD1 glycoproteins. β₂M is encoded by a single gene on human chromosome 15 and mouse chromosome 2.

Biochemical nature and evolution

β₂M consists of a single, nonglycosylated, 99 amino acid polypeptide chain. Homologs of β₂M have been described and sequenced for a number of mammalian species. Comparison of amino acid sequences indicates a high degree of evolutionary conservation of this protein. The overall sequence identity among the various mammalian β₂Ms is approximately 70%, except for mouse and rat β₂M, which, as might be expected, show greater identity (86%). The high degree of structural conservation of β₂M among species is further indicated by the observation that β₂M of different species can functionally substitute for each other. Since β₂M is located entirely outside the cell with no direct attachment to the cell membrane, and since the association between β₂M and the class I heavy chain is noncovalent, β₂M on the cell surface can exchange with free β₂M present in serum used to grow cultured cells. Mammalian β₂M contains two cysteine residues at positions 25 and 80, and these are involved in a disulfide bond. Because of sequence similarity of β_2M to Ig molecules and because of the presence of a disulfide loop with a predicted tertiary structure similar to that of Ig domains, β_2M has been considered a member of the Ig gene superfamily. The primary structural identity between β_2M and the Ig constant region domain is about 30%. The similarity between them is more significant considering matches of specific key amino acids. The placement of β_2M in the Ig gene superfamily has been confirmed by crystal structure studies discussed below. The heavy chain of class I MHC proteins is also a member of Ig superfamily.

Polymorphism

Within a species β_2M is virtually invariant. Although a few variants have been found in many species, only in the mouse could the difference be attributed to a change in an encoded amino acid. In guinea pig, the structural difference between two variants has been shown to involve the presence or absence of a lysine residue at the C-terminus of the molecule, and it is postulated that this variation results from posttranslational modification, but not from genetic polymorphism. Three alleles of β_2M have been defined among laboratory strains of mice. Amino acid sequence analysis of the β_2M protein obtained from Balb/c (β_2Mᵃ) and C57BL/6 (β_2Mᵇ) mouse strains revealed a substitution of aspartic acid for alanine at position 85 as the only difference between the two forms. A third variant has been identified by sequence analysis of cDNA from the mouse strain B10.pa-H-3ᵉaᵗ/Sn. All three alleles among laboratory strains differ by a single base substitution at exactly the same base postion: the second nucleotide of codon 85. β_2Mᵃ (e.g. Balb/c) has GCC (alanine), β_2Mᵇ (C57BL/6) GAC (aspartic acid) and β_2Mᶜ (B10.pa-H-3ᵉaᵗ/Sn) GTC (valine).

Structure of β_2M

Primary sequence comparisons and physicochemical data suggested that β_2M strongly resembles Ig constant domains in polypeptide chain folding and overall tertiary structure. The structure of β_2M in the class I heterodimeric protein was also shown to be very similar to that determined for the free β_2M monomer from bovine serum. The crystal structure of the human class I MHC protein HLA-A2 was determined, and these data confirmed the expectation that β_2M is very similar in tertiary structure to the $\alpha3$ domain of class I heavy chains and to Ig

constant domains (**Figure 1**). Both the $\alpha3$ and β_2M domains in the class I MHC molecule are β-sandwich structures composed of two antiparallel β-pleated sheets, one with four β strands and one with three β strands, connected by a disulfide bond. The residues in contact across the $\alpha3$-β_2M interface are in the four-stranded β sheets. The crystal structure also shows how β_2M binds to the heavy chain of class I protein; β_2M is positioned upward apparently supporting the $\alpha1/\alpha2$ peptide-binding platform (**Figure 1A**). This interaction results in minimal contact between the heavy chain $\alpha3$ domain and $\alpha1/\alpha2$ domains, while β_2M contacts all three domains of the heavy chain. The interaction between β_2M and the $\alpha1/\alpha2$ domains extends across the entire β-pleated platform and one long stretch of β_2M fits into a pleat on the underside of the $\alpha1/\alpha2$ β-pleated sheet (**Figure 1C**). These interactions appear to stabilize the $\alpha1/\alpha2$ conformation and therefore the peptide binding site on the class I protein.

Expression of β_2M

Mouse β_2M is encoded by a single gene per haploid genome, indicating that the same β_2M gene encodes the light chain of the various class I proteins, CD1 and intestinal Fc receptors. The β_2M gene consists of four exons, with the majority of the protein-coding sequence (amino acids 3–95), within a single exon (exon II). All types of interferon (IFN) (α, β and γ), of which IFNγ is usually the most potent, and tumor necrosis factor α (TNFα) have been shown to induce or increase expression of both chains of class I molecules in a wide variety of cell types. For β_2M this is thought to occur by both transcriptional and post-transcriptional events. The expression of the β_2M gene has been thought to be related to that of the class I heavy chain by sharing common regulatory mechanisms. However, the expression of these genes follows a different time course during embryogenesis; the synthesis of β_2M is first detectable at the two-cell stage, while class I heavy chain mRNA is detectable after the midsomite stage on gestation day 9 in the mouse embryo. This suggests that expression of these genes is not always coordinately regulated. It has been shown in some embryonic carcinoma cell lines that expression of class I MHC proteins can be induced by driving the cells from an undifferentiated state to a differentiated state, and that transcription of both the β_2M and class I heavy chain genes is activated by this induction. A transcriptional enhancer activity has been found in the 5′ flanking sequence of the mouse β_2M gene. This enhancer may have at least two important regions, one of which shows sequence similarity to the H-2 enhancer (class I regu-

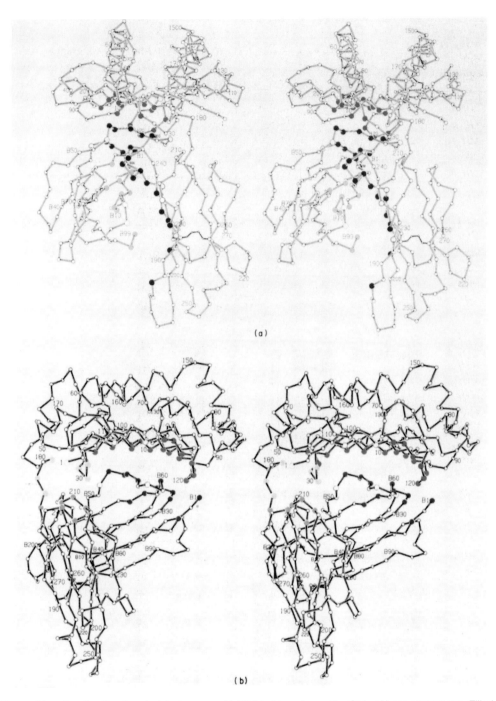

Figure 1 The residues forming the domain interfaces are highlighted in color on the C^{α} backbone stereogram. Filled and colored C^{α} atoms make contacts ≤ 4 Å. Red, α_1, α_2 residues in interface with β_2M; green, β_2M residues in interface with $\alpha_1\alpha_2$; blue α_3 residues in interface with β_2M; yellow, β_2M residues in interface α_3; pink, $\alpha_1\alpha_2$ residues in interface with α_3; orange, α_3 residues in interface with $\alpha_1\alpha_2$. (A) A view perpendicular to $\alpha_1\alpha_2$ pseudodyad with the binding cleft viewed end-on ($\alpha_1\alpha_2$–α_3 interface not shown). (B) A side view with the molecule rotated $90°$ about the pseudodyad (α_3–β_2M interface not shown). (C) A drawing of the β_2M residues (blue) interacting underneath the $\alpha_1\alpha_2$ β sheet. $\alpha_1\alpha_2$ Residues in β_2M interface are in red; those in α_3 interface with small green labels. Hatched region highlights the pleat under which β_2M side-chains Phe-B56 and Trp-B60 make van der Waals' contacts with $\alpha_1\alpha_2$. (Reprinted with permission from Saper MA, Bjorkman PJ and Wiley DC (1991) Refined structure of the human histocompatibility antigen HIA-A2 at 2.6 Å resolution. *Journal of Molecular Biology* **219**: 277–319.) (See also color **Plate 9**.)

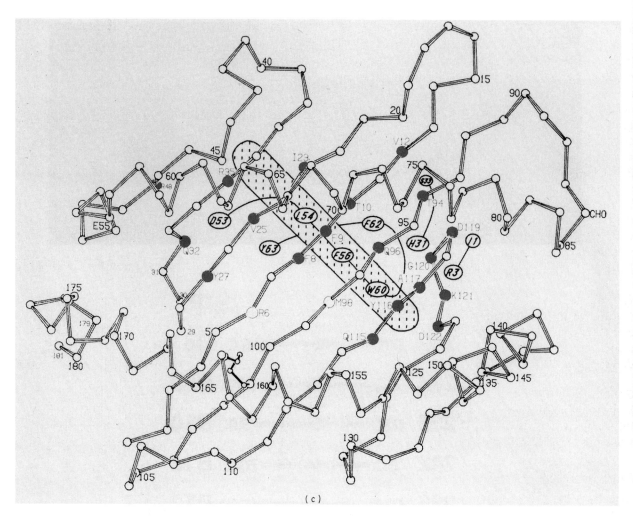

Figure 1 Continued.

latory element, CRE) region 1. Both this β₂M sequence and region I of the H-2 enhancer bind the nuclear factors KBF1 and H2TF1.

Function of β₂M

Although the precise role of β₂M is not known, a number of studies suggest possible roles for it. It serves to stabilize the tertiary structure of class I heavy chains. Circular dichroism studies show that isolated heavy chains lose some of their β-pleated structure and assume more of a random coil configuration in the absence of β₂M. Other studies have shown that when β₂M is dissociated from the HLA heavy chain, HLA alloantisera are less able to recognize the protein, and antigenic activity can be restored if the heavy chain–β₂M complex is carefully renatured. Cytoplasmic HLA molecules lack β₂M in Daudi cells and are not recognized by alloantisera, but can be recognized by xenoantisera raised against denatured HLA heavy chains. In addition to stabiliz-

ing the tertiary structure of class I heavy chains, β₂M seems to be required for the expression of these chains on the cell surface. This conclusion has been based on studies of the human Daudi cell line and of mutants of the mouse R1 cell line. In both systems mutations in the β₂M gene are accompanied by lack of expression of β₂M protein and lack of cell surface class I molecules. Cell surface expression of class I proteins was shown to be restored in each of these mutant cell lines after fusion to cells that express normal β₂M protein. Furthermore, transfection of the β₂M gene into these cell lines rescued cell surface expression of class I proteins. It has been shown that peptide binding is also required for the cell surface expression of class I proteins. Using a mutant cell line deficient in β₂M which transports low amounts of nonpeptide-associated heavy chains to the cell surface, it has also been shown that only after association with β₂M could heavy chain stably bind peptide. An approach using purified class I proteins also strongly suggested that peptide binding to yield active antigenic class I MHC complexes can occur after β_2M binding to heavy chain occurred. Thus, β_2M association with the class I heavy chain is required for optimal peptide ligand binding to form the antigenic complex recognized by T cells. β_2M-deficient mice were produced by disrupting the β_2M gene by homologous recombination. In these mice, cell surface expression and function of the entire array of class I molecules were eliminated. Neonatal β_2M-deficient mice also lacked the intestinal cell transepithelial transport of IgG from mother's milk by the β_2M-associated Fc receptor, suggesting that the Fc receptor heavy chain in mouse must associate with β_2M for functional expression on the cell surface. Furthermore, most CD4⁻CD8⁺ cytotoxic T cells failed to develop in these mice because of the lack of cell surface class I MHC proteins. Interestingly, the fact that these mice were born and appeared normal (except for the cellular alterations mentioned above and their consequences) demonstrates that no β_2M-associated proteins are critical during mouse development.

See also: **CD1; Fc receptors; H2 class I; HLA class I; Immunoglobulin gene superfamily; Interferon α; Interferon β; Interferon γ; MHC restriction; MHC, evolution of; MHC, functions of.**

Further reading

Brutkiewicz RR, Bennink JR, Yewdell JW and Bendelac A (1995) TAP-independent, β_2-microglobulin-dependent surface expression of functional mouse CD1.1. *Journal of Experimental Medicine* 182: 1913–1919.
Israel EJ, Patel VK, Taylor SF, Marshak-Rothstein A and Simister NE (1995) Requirement for a β_2-microglobulin-associated Fc receptor for acquisition of maternal IgG by fetal and neonatal mice. *Journal of Immunology* 154: 6246–6251.
Kane KP, Sherman LA and Mescher MF (1991) Exogenous β_2-microglobulin is required for antigenic peptide binding to isolated class I major histocompatibility complex molecules. *European Journal of Immunology* 21: 2289–2292.
Koller BH, Marrack P, Kappler JW and Smithies O (1990) Normal development of mice deficient in β_2M, MHC class I proteins, and CD8⁺ T cells. *Science* 248: 1227–1230.
Maloy WL and Coligan JE (1985) Is β_2-microglobulin required for MHC class I heavy chain expression? *Immunology Today* 6: 263–264.
Parnes JR and Seidman JG (1982) Structure of wild-type and mutant mouse β_2-microglobulin genes. *Cell* 29: 661–669.
Raulet DH (1994) MHC class I-deficient mice. *Advances in Immunology* 55: 381–421.
Restifo NP, Marincola FM, Kawakami Y, Taubenberger J, Yannelli JR and Rosenberg SA (1996) Loss of functional β_2-microglobulin in metastatic melanomas from five patients receiving immunotherapy. *Journal of the National Cancer Institute* 88: 100–108.
Saper MA, Bjorkman PJ and Wiley DC (1991) Refined structure of the human histocompatibility antigen HLA-A2 at 2.6 Å resolution. *Journal of Molecular Biology* 219: 277–319.
Vitiello A, Potter TA and Sherman LA (1990) The role of β_2-microglobulin in peptide binding by class I molecules. *Science* 250: 1423–1426.
Zijlstra M, Bix M, Simister NE, Loring JM, Raulet DH and Jaenisch R (1990) β_2-Microglobulin deficient mice lack CD4⁻CD8⁺ cytotoxic T cells. *Nature* 344: 742–746.

bm MUTANTS

Roger W Melvold, Department of Microbiology–Immunology, Northwestern University Medical School, Chicago, Illinois, USA

Background

The H-2 complex (the major histocompatibility complex of the mouse) consists of a series of genes which are intimately involved in regulation of many functions of the immune system. Of particular relevance here are the class I and class II genes within the H-2 complex. The products of these highly polymorphic genes are particularly crucial to the various activities carried out by lymphocytes, particularly T lymphocytes. Mutations of these loci have been extremely useful in dissecting the relationships between the fine structure and function of these genes/gene products. H-2 gene mutations have been recovered from many different genetic strains of mice, but the best known and most widely utilized have been those which occurred in the *H-2ᵇ* haplotype (the set of H-2 genes found in strains such as C57BL/6 and C57BL/10). The mutants were typically identified because they resulted in unexpected graft rejections between animals presumed to be genetically identical, and therefore expected to be completely histocompatible.

H-2 mutants are designated by the letter of the haplotype from which they were derived (in this case, '*b*'), the letter '*m*' (for 'mutant') and an arabic numeral which designates the chronological sequence in which the mutants were found – thus the mutations of $H-2^b$ are collectively known as the '*bm*' mutants. Prior to recent methods developed for site-directed mutagenesis, exon shuffling and transgene insertion, H-2 mutants provided the only available means for evaluating the effects of such small discrete changes in the class I and II genes expressed in the $H-2^b$ haplotype. The current listing of mapped *bm* mutants is shown in **Table 1**.

Frequency and sources of *bm* mutants

The fact that *bm* mutants are more frequent than those derived from other haplotypes is not due to a more intensive screening of mice bearing $H-2^b$, but to the fact that one of its genes (K^b, the $H-2^b$ allele at the $H-2K$ locus) mutates spontaneously at the unusually high rate of approximately 2×10^{-4} per locus per gamete. As a result, over 80% of all H-2 mutants recovered are derived from the K^b gene.

One of the most interesting features of class I and class II H-2 genes is their high polymorphism, i.e. a large number of alleles per locus in the population, and it is assumed that this unusually high diversity is an important part of their biological role(s). The *bm* mutants display three characteristics which bear on the source of this variability: 1) the unusually high mutation rates, 1–2 orders of magnitude above those for average mammalian genes; 2) the recurrence of identical amino acid changes in several independently arising mutations; and 3) multiple (but not necessarily adjacent) amino acid changes resulting from single mutational events. It has been shown that these genes engage in exchanges of DNA sequences between homologous, but non-allelic, genes. This process (referred to as gene conversion, microconversion or microrecombination) can occur during either meiosis or mitosis, and the details of its mechanism are still unknown. Analysis of H-2 mutations derived from the $H-2^d$, $H-2^f$ and $H-2^k$ haplotypes indicate that these mutations can also be attributed to microrecombination, although their frequency is far below that of K^b.

Functional consequences of *bm* mutations

Class I H-2 molecules are crucial in directing the function of CD8⁺ cytotoxic T lymphocytes. As they progress toward the cell surface during their synthesis, they bind to peptide fragments, which they ultimately 'display' on the cell surface. They thus present to CD8⁺ T lymphocytes a sampling of intracellular peptides, including those derived from infectious organisms growing within the cell.

The T cell receptors of each CD8⁺ T lymphocyte

Table 1   Known and mapped *bm* mutations

Locus	MHC class	Mutation	Type	Amino acid change[a]
H-2K	I	$H-2^{bm1}$	GL	152 Glu → Ala 154 Arg → Tyr 156 Leu → Tyr
	I	$H-2^{bm2}$	GL	Unknown
	I	$H-2^{bm3}$	GL	77 Asp → Ser 89 Lys → Glu
	I	$H-2^{bm4}$	GL	173 Lys → Glu 174 Asn → Leu
	I	$H-2^{bm5}$	GL	116 Tyr → Phe
	I	$H-2^{bm6}$	GL	116 Tyr → Phe 121 Cys → Arg
	I	$H-2^{bm7}$	GL	116 Tyr → Phe 121 Cys → Arg
	I	$H-2^{bm8}$	GL	22 Thr → Phe 23 Met → Ile 24 Glu → Ser 30 Asp → Asn
	I	$H-2^{bm9}$	GL	116 Tyr → Phe 121 Cys → Arg
	I	$H-2^{bm10}$	GL	163 Thr → Phe 165 Val → Met 173 Lys → Glu 174 Arg → Leu
	I	$H-2^{bm11}$	GL	77 Asp → Ser 80 Thr → Asn
	I	$H-2^{bm15}$	L	Unknown
	I	$H-2^{bm16}$	GL	116 Tyr → Phe
	I	$H-2^{bm17}$	GL	116 Tyr → Phe 121 Cys → Arg
	I	$H-2^{bm18}$	GL	Unknown
	I	$H-2^{bm19}$	GL	Unknown
	I	$H-2^{bm20}$	GL	Unknown
	I	$H-2^{bm21}$	GL	Unknown
	I	$H-2^{bm22}$	GL	Unknown
	I	$H-2^{bm23}$	GL	75 Arg → His 77 Asp → Ser
	I	$H-2^{bm29}$	GL	89 Lys → Arg
	I	KB-98	GL	116 Tyr → Phe
I-A$_\beta$	II	$H-2^{bm12}$	GL	67 Ile → Phe 70 Phe → Tyr 71 Thr → Lys
H-2D	I	$H-2^{bm13}$	GL	114 Leu → Gln 116 Phe → Tyr 118 Silent 119 Glu → Asp
	I	$H-2^{bm14}$	GL	70 Gln → His

Table 1 Continued

Locus	MHC class	Mutation	Type	Amino acid change[a]
I	H-2^{bm24}	GL	63 Silent
				70 Gln → Asn
				73 Trp → Ser
				77 Ser → Asp
				80 Asn → Thr
I	H-2^{bm28}	GL	97 Gln → Trp
				99 Ser → Tyr
				103 Silent

GL, simultaneous gain and loss of antigenic determinants; L, loss of antigenic determinants.

[a]*References*: McIntyre KR and Seidman JG (1984) *Nature* **308**: 551–553; Nathenson SG, Geliebter J, Pfaffenbach GM and Zeff RA (1986) *Annual Review of Immunology* **4**: 471–502; Hemmi S, Geliebter J, Zeff RA, Melvold RW and Nathenson SG (1988) *Journal of Experimental Medicine* **168**: 2319–2335; Pfaffenbach GM, Melvold RW and Nathenson SG (1990) *Biochemical Genetics* **28**: 433–411; Pease LR, Horton RM, Pullen JK and Cai Z (1991) *Critical Reviews in Immunology* **11**: 1–32; Horton RM, Loveland BE, Parwani A, Pease LR and Fischer Lindahl K (1991) *Journal of Immunology* **147**: 3180–3184; Pease LR, Horton RM, Pullen JK and Yun TJ (1993) *Molecular and Cellular Biology* **13**: 4374–4381; Yun TJ, Melvold RW and Pease LR (in press; for *bm28*).

are specialized so that they bind only to a specific combination of [antigen + class I molecule] on a cell surface. The amino acid sequence of the peptide-binding region(s) of a major histocompatibility complex (MHC) class I molecule imparts an affinity for preferential binding of particular peptides. Thus changes in the amino acid sequence of a class I molecule can alter the subset of peptides which are displayed on the cell surface, and this in turn determines which subset(s) of CD8+ T cells are able to bind and become activated. Therefore, changes in MHC class I molecules can alter the immune repertoire. The *bm* mutations, by altering only one or a few amino acids at various sites in the *H-2K* and *H-2D* gene products have been crucial in identifying which portions of these molecules are important sites for the associations between class I molecule and peptide and between class I molecule and T cell receptor. Small changes, even only a single amino acid, can completely alter the ability of some individuals to respond to particular antigens. While all of the class I *bm* mutants affect cell-mediated functions, their effects on serologic functions are somewhat less consistent and dramatic, and many of them fail to stimulate antibody production when mutant and parental mice are immunized against one another.

Only a single spontaneous *in vivo* mutation of an H-2 class II gene has been recovered, and it too is a *bm* mutant (*H-2^{bm12}*). CD4+ T lymphocytes recognize combinations of [peptide + class II molecule] on cell surfaces. The *bm12* mutation, which involves a change in only three amino acids, has profound effects on the immunobiology of the mutant animal by altering the way in which the class II molecule interacts with antigenic peptide or with T cell receptors on CD4+ lymphocytes. For example, the mutant is unable to respond to some antigens to which the parental strain responds well. On the other hand, the mutant has gained the ability to respond to certain antigens to which the parental strain is unable to respond. The mutation is also able to confer resistance to the development of an autoimmune disease, experimental myasthenia gravis, to which the parental strain is susceptible.

In summary, the *bm* mutants have provided exquisitely subtle genetic tools for the fine-detail analysis of H-2 gene structure and the relationship of that structure to the function of the resultant gene products, and are particularly valuable where whole, intact animals are required to study a particular process. They have been instrumental in the assignment of diverse biological and immunologic functions to single H-2 genes, and have even been shown to influence mating preferences, in that mice can distinguish parental animals from those carrying *bm* mutations by urine-associated odors. The *bm* mutations, and those derived from other haplotypes as well, will undoubtedly continue to demonstrate their value in immunogenetic research.

See also: **Cell-mediated immunity; Congenic mice; Cytotoxic T lymphocytes; Gene conversion; H2 class I; H2 class II; Immune response (Ir) genes; Inbred strains; Mouse inbred strains.**

Further reading

Melvold RW and Kohn HI (1990) Spontaneous frequency of H-2 mutations. In: Egorov I and David C (eds) *Transgenic Mice and Mutants in Major Histocompatibility Complex Research*, pp 3–13. New York: Springer-Verlag.

Pease LR, Horton RM, Pullen JK and Cai Z (1991) Structure and diversity of class I antigen presenting molecules in the mouse. *Critical Reviews in Immunology* **11**: 1–32.

Pfaffenbach GM, Uehara H, Geliebter J, Nathenson SG and Schulze DH (1991) Analysis of the H-2K^{bm8} mutant: correlation of structure with function. *Molecular Immunology* **28**: 697–701.

Shepherd SE, Sun R, Nathenson SG and Sheil JM (1992) Selective reactivity of CD8-independent T lymphocytes to a cytotoxic T lymphocyte-selected H-2K^b mutant altered at position 222 in the alpha 3 domain. *European Journal of Immunology* **22**: 647–653.

Young AC, Zhang W, Sacchettini JC and Nathenson SG (1994) The three-dimensional structure of H-2D^b at 2.4 Å resolution: implications for antigen-determinant selection. *Cell* **76**: 39–50.

BONE MARROW AND HEMATOPOIESIS

David C Linch, Department of Haematology, University College
London Medical School, London, UK

Ontogeny

During human development hematopoiesis passes through several distinct phases. In the embryo, large megaloblastoid nucleated red cells are produced in the extraembryonic membranes, from where they enter circulation. These cells synthesize the embryonic hemoglobins Hb Gower 1, Hb Gower 2 and the relatively minor hemoglobin Hb Portland. From 6 weeks gestation, erythropoiesis transfers to the fetal liver. At this time there is a switch in Hb production from the embryonic Hbs to fetal Hb ($\alpha_2\gamma_2$). This switch is time rather than site dependent, with residual erythroid cells in the extra-amniotic membranes at this stage also producing fetal Hb. Bone marrow hematopoiesis is established between the 11th and 22nd week of gestation and probably arises by stem cell migration into appropriate marrow stroma. In mid-gestation there are high levels of circulating hematopoietic progenitor cells which decline progressively until birth. At about 40 weeks gestation the synthesis of fetal Hb is replaced by adult Hb ($\alpha_2\beta_2$) and this event is related not to birth but to the time of gestation. The Hb switching involves the serial expression of the α-like globin chains on chromosome 16 and the β-like globin chains on chromosome 11 in a 5' to 3' direction. The precise mechanism of the switch is not understood.

The fetal liver contains both myeloid and erythroid progenitor cells and yet few phagocytes are produced until the end of gestation. This indicates that in aseptic fetal life there is inadequate environmental stimulus to induce the proliferation and differentiation of myeloid progenitor cells. Around the time of birth there is a pronounced rise in the peripheral blood neutrophil and monocyte levels. Lymphocytes appear in the blood by 8 weeks gestation and by the second trimester the T cells have a mature but generally naive phenotype. Full functional competence is not gained until after birth. The fetal blood contains relatively high numbers of circulating stem and progenitor cells and although these levels fall throughout gestation, cord blood levels are still sufficiently high to allow the use of cord blood for allogeneic hematopoietic stem cell transplantation.

Stem cell origin of hematopoiesis

There is definitive evidence that multipotential stem cells give rise to cells of all the myeloid and lymphoid elements. In chronic myeloid leukemia the clonal expansion involves not only the red cell, platelet and phagocyte series but also B lymphocytes. Transplantation experiments in mice using stem cells marked by retroviral insertions indicate that T cells are also derived from a common lymphohematopoietic stem cell.

In the adult the large majority of hematopoietic stem cells are noncycling. These cells can be assessed in mice by competitive repopulation assays into irradiated recipients. The enumeration of cells capable of forming day 12 spleen colonies (CFU-S) in irradiated mice (assay developed by Till and McCulloch in the early 1960s) allows a simpler quantitation of primitive cells, but the most primitive repopulating stem cells are at an earlier stage in the developmental pathway than the average CFU-S. There is obviously no direct human equivalent of the CFU-S assay but stem cells can be grafted into immunodeficient mice, and such studies are providing important information about human stem cell biology. Assays of cells capable of forming 'cobblestone areas' on preformed stroma also provide an assessment of very primitive cells. When appropriately stimulated these cells proliferate and either undergo a process of self-renewal or differentiate ultimately to mature cells. A single stem cell can almost totally repopulate a mouse, although in the steady state a very large number of stem cells are available. The morphological appearance of the most primitive stem cells is probably similar to a small lymphocyte. As it proliferates and differentiates it assumes a blastic appearance. The majority of cell divisions arise in this blast cell pool, and the recognizable precursor cells in the bone marrow are the outcome of only the terminal six or seven divisions. As stem cells pass down the differentiation pathway, there is progressive commitment to a given lineage and the stem cell progeny lose the potential for self-renewal. The process of commitment has a stochastic (random) element but is sensitive to environmental modulation. Cells intermediate between the stem cells and the more mature precursor cells are known as progenitor cells and can be quantitated by *in vitro* colony forming assays. These assays were developed in the murine system by Pluznik and Sachs and by Bradley and Metcalf in the mid-1960s. In these assays, immobilized suspensions of hematopoietic cells are induced to form colonies in the presence of 'colony stimulating factors'. The cells giving rise to colonies are capable of many cell divisions and may have either restricted or multiple lineage potential. They are not, however, capable of self-renewal. The colonies and cells giving rise to them are named after the mature progeny that they produce: G-CFC, M-CFC, GM-CFC, Eo-CFC and Mega-CFC give rise to granulocytes, monocytes, both granulocytes and monocytes (and also eosinophils), eosinophils and megakaryocytes, respectively. Relatively late erythroid colony forming cells are referred to as colony forming units – erythroid (CFU-E), and the early erythroid progenitor cells as burst forming units – erythroid (BFU-E) because of the multiple cluster appearance of these colonies. CFC-mix give rise to cells of multiple lineages. There is some evidence that T cells may be derived from these CFC-mix progenitors, but this has not been widely confirmed.

Myelopoiesis

Hematopoietic growth factors

Myelopoiesis is regulated at least in part by a series of glycoproteins referred to as hematopoietic growth factors (HGFs). Erythropoietin, produced in response to hypoxia by the peritubular adventitial cells of the kidney, is a true hormone, and G-CSF is similar in so far as the circulating levels are inversely related to the neutrophil count. Interleukin 6 (IL-6) levels also rise in neutropenic and infective states. Thrombopoietin, which regulattes megakaryocyte production, is of particular interest as the serum levels are largely regulated by end-organ (platelet) sequestration, and more thrombopoietin becomes available when the platelet count falls. Several other HGFs such as GM-CSF and IL-3 cannot be readily measured in the plasma and probably act in a paracrine manner.

From *in vitro* and *in vivo* studies, the HGFs can be grouped into three broad categories. Firstly, there are the late-acting factors which are relatively lineage restricted and stimulate the terminal divisions of the maturation pathway with associated differentiation to mature cells (**Table 1**). These include erythropoietin, G-CSF, M-CSF, Eo-CSF, known as IL-5, and thrombopoietin (TPO). The proliferation of more primitive cells in the pathway is regulated by the multi-CSFs IL-3 and GM-CSF. Both of these factors stimulate the early divisions of several cell lineages, including granulocytes, monocytes, eosinophils, megakaryocytes and red cells; IL-3 also stimulates mast cell progenitors and some early lymphoid cells. It is probably active at an earlier stage in the myeloid differentiation pathway than GM-CSF but probably has little effect on the most primitive stem cells. More primitive stem cells are influenced by a range of factors including stem cell factor (SCF), Flt-3 ligand, IL-6, IL-11, and leukemia inhibitory factor (LIF). These factors render very primitive cells susceptible to the later-acting factors and are thus often referred to as 'synergistic factors'. The categorization of the HGFs into three groups is undoubtedly an oversimplification and G-CSF and M-CSF, for instance, have some effects on primitive progenitor cells.

The most primitive of all stem cells appear not to be responsive to known soluble factors and the additional signals required for proliferation of these cells is poorly understood.

Finally, the activity of the HGFs is not restricted to immature cells. G-CSF enhances many of the functional activities of mature neutrophils; GM-CSF enhances neutrophil, monocyte and eosinophil function; and M-CSF and IL-3 prime some monocyte functions – the latter also modulating eosinophil and mast cell function.

The central importance of erythropoietin in red cell production is apparent from the profound anemia that occurs in anephric individuals. Similarly, mice with knockouts of the G-CSF or thrombopoietin genes have severe neutropenia and thrombocytopenia, respectively. Knockout mice without a functional GM-CSF gene have normal blood counts but do develop a pulmonary condition secondary to poor alveolar macrophage function, in line with the view that many of the earlier-acting factors exhibit considerable redundancy with regard to hematopoiesis and that a major role for GM-CSF is as an inflammatory mediator. The Steel mouse however, which is unable to produce SCF, develops a macrocytic anemia, mast cell deficiency and albinism which in some strains can be lethal.

Hematopoietic growth factor receptors

Each HGF has a specific receptor or receptors, these being expressed at low levels, generally in the range

Table 1 Growth factors in hematopoiesis

Stem cells		Mature myeloid cells
SCF	IL-3	Erythropoietin
Flt-3 ligand	GM-CSF	Thrombopoietin
IL-6		G-CSF
IL-11		IL-5
LIF		(M-CSF)

of 10^2–10^3 receptors per cell. These receptors can be considered as two categories. Firstly the M-CSFR, which is the cellular homolog of v-fms and the SCFR which is the cellular homolog of v-kit are tyrosine kinase receptors similar to the PDGF receptor. Ligand occupation causes autophosphorylation and dimerization of the receptor chains followed by a cascade of signaling events mediated largely by cytoplasmic enzymes binding to phosphorylated tyrosine residues in the intracytoplasmic domains of the receptor. The EpoR, G-CSFR, GM-CSFR, TPOR, IL-3R, IL-4R, IL-5R, IL-6R, IL-7R, IL-11R, IL-13R and IL-15R are all members of the cytokine receptor family. The EpoRs, TPORs and G-CSFRs appear to consist of a single chain which dimerizes on activation by ligand. Other members of the family appear to be composed of two components. The GM-CSFR has an α chain which binds to GM-CSF with low affinity and a β chain which, although unable to bind GM-CSF when expressed alone, when complexed to an α chain produces a high affinity GM-CSF receptor. This β chain is common to the IL-3R and the IL-5R, and is largely responsible for signal transduction, which accounts in part for the similarity of action of these factors in cells which express more than one of the relevant α chains. Other receptors are even more complex, with at least three heterologous components: α, β and γ. The receptors for IL-2, IL-4, IL-7, IL-13 and IL-15 all share a common γ chain. The cytokine receptor chains do not contain a tyrosine kinase but they are able to bind and activate members of the Janus family of tyrosine kinases (JAKs). Activation of these kinases leads to activation of a family of transcription factors known as STATS, the c-myc pathway and the ras-MAP kinase pathway. The latter pathway is also stimulated by the shc binding directly to the activated receptor with subsequent activation of ras.

Bone marrow microenvironment

The specialized environment provided by the bone marrow stromal tissue is essential for effective hematopoiesis, particularly for the survival, self-renewal and proliferation of stem cells. The microenvironment is often considered to provide a 'stem cell niche', but this terminology is not particularly illuminating and, although it is now over 15 years since Dexter and colleagues established bone marrow stromal cultures which could support stem cell and thus long-term hematopoiesis *in vitro*, a limited amount is known about the precise function of the stromal tissue. Adhesion of certain categories of stem cells to the stroma is probably essential for proliferation and it is also likely that the stroma can provide negative regulatory signals to other stem cells, helping to maintain them in the relatively protected G_0 state. A large range of adhesion molecules has been described on primitive hematopoietic cells, including the integrins VLA-2, -4, -5 and LFA-1, members of the immunoglobulin superfamily such as ICAM-1 and -3, PECAM-1, Thy-1 and LFA-3, the selectin L-selectin, the ligands for P-selectin and L-selectin and a number of sialomucins and other ligands, including CD6, CD34, CD43 and CD44.

The bone marrow stromal cells undoubtedly produce SCF. SCF contains a highly hydrophobic region so that, unlike the other HGFs, a large amount remains cell associated rather than being secreted as a soluble factor. It is likely that there are other stromal associated factors of this type. M-CSF, IL-6 and IL-7 are also produced constitutively but it has proved difficult to show that stromal cells produce other HGFs. This may be because only very small quantities are required in the context of intimate cell-to-cell contact. Furthermore, it has been shown that components of the stromal matrix avidly bind a range of HGFs, and this may serve to present a local stimulus to a stem cell or progenitor cell without releasing HGF into the surrounding milieu.

Lymphopoiesis

Primitive hematopoietic stem cells migrate from the bone marrow to the specialized environment of the thymus which is the site of T cell development. B cells by contrast, or at least immature B cells, are produced in the bone marrow, with only the later stages of B cell maturation and selection ocurring in the peripheral lymphoid tissues. The bone marrow stages of B cell development have been designated as stem cell, early pro-B cell, late pro-B cell, pre-B cell and immature B cell on the basis of sequential immunoglobulin gene rearrangements and the expression of surface immunoglobulin. The earliest B cell precursors appear to be dependent on adhesion to the bone marrow stroma and VCAM-1, VLA-4 and CD44 have been particularly implicated in B cell development. The multipotent stem cells can be regulated by a number of early-acting cytokines as discussed above, but at the late pro-B cell stage a requirement develops for the presence of IL-7, which is produced in small quantities by the stromal cells.

See also: **Colony stimulating factors; Granulocyte colony stimulating factor (G-CSF); Granulocyte-macrophage colony stimulating factor (GM-CSF); Interleukin 1 and its receptors; Interleukin 3; Interleukin 4; Interleukin 5 and its receptor; Interleukin 6; Macrophage colony stimulating factor (CSF-1); Microenvironment.**

Further reading

Ihle JN and Kerr IM (1995) Jaks and Stats in signaling by the cytokine receptor superfamily. *Trends in Genetics* **11**: 69–214.

Janeway CA and Travers P (1997) B cell development. In: *Immunobiology*, 3rd edn. New York: Garland.

Keleman E, Calvo W and Fliedner TM (1979) *Atlas of Human Hemopoietic Development*. New York: Springer.

Metcalf D and Nicola N (1995) *Colony Stimulating Factors*. Cambridge: Cambridge University Press.

Miyajima A, Mui A L-F, Ogorochi T and Sakamaki K (1993) Receptors of granulocyte-macrophage colony-stimulating factor, interleukin-3 and interleukin-5. *Blood* **82**: 1960–1974.

BORDETELLA, INFECTION AND IMMUNITY

Gwendolyn E Wood and **Richard L Friedman**, Department of Microbiology and Immunology, University of Arizona College of Medicine, Tucson, Arizona, USA

Bordetella pertussis is a strict human pathogen which causes the respiratory disease whooping cough or pertussis. The other *Bordetella* species (*B. parapertussis, B. bronchiseptica, B. avium* and *B. hinzii*) are primarily animal pathogens but can, at times, cause disease in humans.

It is estimated that over 60 million cases of pertussis occur worldwide each year, resulting in 700 000 deaths. Clinically, pertussis has three phases. The disease begins with the catarrhal phase which may last from 7 to 21 days and is typified by symptoms similar to a common cold. The paroxysmal phase begins with severe, violent coughing spells and an inspiratory 'whoop' typical of the disease. This intense coughing lasts 2–4 weeks and can result in cyanosis, vomiting, severe exhaustion and death in infants. During the final or convalescent phase, cough paroxysms gradually decrease over 3–4 weeks. Although pertussis is considered a childhood disease, recent studies have demonstrated a high incidence of pertussis in adults.

Characteristics of the organism and its antigens

B. pertussis is a strictly aerobic, gram-negative coccobacillus which oxidizes amino acids as energy and carbon sources. Diagnosis of pertussis involves culture of the organism from nasopharyngeal swabs on Bordet–Gengou or Regan–Lowe agar (charcoal agar) and specific identification by direct immunofluorescence. Growth of *B. pertussis* on all media (at 35–37°C) is slow, requiring 2–6 days for the appearance of tiny, pearl-like colonies.

B. pertussis produces a large number of antigens, including adhesins and toxins that play a role in disease. The bacterium adheres specifically to the ciliated respiratory epithelium and remains localized in the airways. Attachment factors include filamentous hemagglutinin (FHA), fimbriae and pertactin (PRN). FHA is a secreted and surface-associated filament-like protein composed of numerous monomeric 220 kDa subunits which agglutinate erythrocytes from several different species *in vivo*. *B. pertussis* produces two serologically distinct fimbriae (types 2 and 3) which appear to facilitate adherence to the upper respiratory tract. PRN is a nonfimbrial, 69 kDa outer membrane protein that also plays a role in attachment. Both PRN and FHA contain the amino acid sequence Arg-Gly-Asp (RGD) that mediates attachment to mammalian cells.

B. pertussis produces several toxins including pertussis toxin (PT), adenylate cyclase toxin (ACT), tracheal cytotoxin (TCT), and dermonecrotic toxin (DNT). Pertussis toxin (PT) is the most studied and has many biological activities *in vivo* including leukocytosis, histamine sensitization, stimulation of insulin secretion, and mitogenicity. Pertussis toxin is a classic A-B type toxin. After binding a specific host cell receptor via the B subunit, the toxin is internalized, and the A subunit catalyzes the adenosine 5′-diphosphate ribosylation of a group of guanine nucleotide regulatory proteins. This leads to increased host cell adenylate cyclase activity.

Host cell cAMP levels are also increased by the action of ACT. ACT enters mammalian cells where it is activated by calmodulin and converts host ATP to cAMP. As a consequence of its ability to insert into eukaryotic membranes, ACT is also responsible for the organisms's hemolytic activity on blood-containing culture media. ACT is a member of the RTX family of bacterial toxins which have in common a series of nonameric amino acid repeats in the C-terminus of the protein.

TCT is a 1,6-anhydromuramic acid-containing disaccharide-tetrapeptide fragment of peptidoglycan released by growing bordetellae. In humans, TCT causes extrusion of ciliated cells, increases the frequency of sparsely ciliated cells and is toxic for other cells at epithelial surfaces. These changes cause a profound disruption of mucociliary clearance, leaving coughing as the only means to clear mucus and debris from the airways.

DNT is a heat-labile toxin that produces vasoconstriction and subsequent necrosis when injected subdermally in mice. Its specific role in disease progression is not understood.

B. pertussis lipopolysaccharide (LPS) is highly immunogenic with the properties typical of an endotoxin. It has a lipid A moiety linked via keto-deoxy-octulosonic acid to a branched-chain oligosaccharide domain containing heptoses and hexoses. The role of LPS in the pathogenesis of pertussis has not been well studied. The recent cloning and sequencing of the LPS operon should allow a specific determination of its contribution to virulence.

All *B. pertussis* virulence factors (except TCT and LPS) are regulated by the BvgAS system which belongs to the two-component family of bacterial transcriptional regulators. BvgS senses changes in the environment and phosphorylates BvgA; phosphorylated BvgA then activates transcription of the virulence factor genes. While the *in vivo* signals are not known, the Bvg system can be activated *in vitro* by increasing the temperature from 25°C to 37°C or by decreasing the concentration of $MgSO_4$ and nicotinic acid in the culture medium. This system presumably prevents wasteful synthesis of virulence factors not needed until the organism encounters a suitable host. The Bvg$^+$ phase is required for full virulence of *B. pertussis*. The Bvg$^-$ phase may be important in establishment of infection, persistence, transmission and/or survival in an unidentified environmental reservoir.

Immune response of the host

Humoral and cell-mediated immune (CMI) responses to pertussis are poorly understood. Neutralizing antibodies are considered to be a major protective mechanism against infection with *B. pertussis*. Recent vaccine trials demonstrated that antibody levels to *B. pertussis* antigens including PT, FHA, PRN and fimbriae correlate with protection against pertussis. In addition, a nonlethal pertussis infection provides long-term immunity to subsequent pertussis, and recovered patients produce anti-*B. pertussis* immunoglobulin A (IgA) in serum and saliva, suggesting the importance of mucosal antibodies.

However, CMI may also be important since *B. pertussis* specific T_H1 cells are found in humans following vaccination or infection. In mice, high anti-*B. pertussis* IgG correlates with rapid clearance of the bacteria in a respiratory infection model but a pertussis-specific CMI response is required for complete elimination of the organisms from lungs. *B. pertussis* survives in human monocytes and other mammalian cells *in vitro*, and a CMI reponse may be necessary for eliminating this potential intracellular reservoir of bacteria. In humans, natural immunity induced by infection may prevent respiratory colonization whereas immunity generated by vaccination may protect against toxin-mediated disease.

Evasive strategies by the organism

Many of the antigens produced and secreted by *B. pertussis* have been demonstrated to suppress the normal responses of the host to pertussis *in vitro* and *in vivo*. TCT, by destruction of ciliated epithelial cells, impedes clearance of bacteria, mucus and debris from airways. Mucociliary clearance is an important first line of defense and its destruction predisposes the patient to the secondary bacterial infections that commonly occur in pertussis.

Both ACT and PT have been demonstrated to inhibit immune cell function via induction of increased intracellular cAMP levels. PT and ACT reduce the migratory, chemotactic and phagocytic capabilities of polymorphonuclear leukocytes, blood monocytes, alveolar macrophages and lymphocytes. A synergistic effect between ACT and PT may occur locally in the respiratory tract to suppress the immune response to the infection and allow the organism to survive and persist in the host.

Variation of fimbrial type occurs readily in pertussis infections. *B. pertussis* may produce one, both or neither type of fimbriae and this may represent a means of avoiding fimbrial type-specific immune responses.

Vaccines

A whole-cell vaccine was in extensive use by the 1950s but, while the vaccine is effective at reducing the incidence of pertussis in vaccinees, it is reactogenic, fails to confer lasting immunity and is poor at protecting infants less than 6 months old. The whole-cell vaccine is composed of killed whole virulent *B. pertussis* combined with diphtheria and tetanus toxoids (DT) in the DTP vaccine. In the USA, infants are immunized beginning at 2 months of age and given three primary injections, followed by two boosters at 4–6 years of age. The US whole-cell vaccine is efficacious when all doses are given, with 80–95% protection levels reported. However, adverse effects including local pain, redness, swelling and fever occur in 30–70% of vaccine recipients. Inconsolable crying, excessive somnolensce and febrile seizures have been reported in rare cases with no permanent neurological damage.

Concerns about adverse effects associated with the vaccine led to loss of public confidence in the vaccine and decreased use, with a resultant increase in pertussis cases. This prompted efforts to produce an acellular vaccine, which was first developed in Japan and shown to be safe and effective. Various acellular pertussis vaccines contain 2–5 purified components which may include pertussis toxoid, FHA, PRN, and fimbriae types 2 and 3. The results of initial field trials led to the approval in the US of an acellular vaccine for boosters (fourth or fifth dose) when the whole-cell preparation is used for primary immunization.

Recent studies in Sweden and Italy compared DT alone and DT combined with either acellular or whole-cell pertussis vaccines for primary immunization. In both trials, the acellular preparations produced fewer and milder side-effects than the whole-cell vaccine and were more effective at inducing serum antibody responses and protection from pertussis. In 1996, acellular pertussis vaccines were approved for use in primary immunization against pertussis by the US government.

See also: **Adjuvants; Toxins; Vaccines; Vaccines, adverse reactions to.**

Further reading

Greco D, Salmaso S, Mastrantonio P *et al* and the Pregetto Pertosse Working Group (1996) A controlled trial of two acellular vaccines and one whole-cell vaccine against pertussis. *New England Journal of Medicine* 334: 341–348.

Gustafsson L, Hallander HO, Olin P, Reizenstein E and Storsaeter J (1996) A controlled trial of a two-component acellular, a five-component acellular, and a whole-cell pertussis vaccine. *New England Journal of Medicine* 334: 349–355.

Hewlett EL (1995) *Bordetella* species. In: Mandell GL, Bennett JE and Dolin R (eds) *Principles and Practice of Infectious Diseases*, 4th edn, pp 2078–2084. New York: Churchill Livingstone.

Locht C, Bertin P, Menozzi FK and Renauld G (1993) The filamentous haemagglutinin, a multifaceted adhesion produced by virulent *Bordetella* spp. *Molecular Microbiology* 9: 653–660.

Scarlato V, Arico B, Domenighini M and Rappuoli R (1993) Environmental regulation of virulence factors in *Bordetella* species. *BioEssays* 15: 99–104.

Uhl MA and Miller JF (1995) *Bordetella pertussis* BvgAS virulence control system. In: Hoch JA and Silhavy TJ (eds) *Two Component Signal Transduction*, pp 333–349. Washington, DC: American Society for Microbiology.

Wintermeyer SM, Nahata MC and Kyllonen KS (1994) Whole-cell and acellular pertussis vaccines. *Annals of Pharmacotherapy* 28: 925–939.

BORRELIA, INFECTION AND IMMUNITY

Ronald F Schell and **Steven M Callister**, Department of Medical Microbiology and Immunology, University of Wisconsin Medical School, Washington, USA

Although the clinical presentation of borreliosis, especially relapsing fever, has fascinated physicians for centuries, the mainstream of immunologic research bypassed the disease for many years. The advent of penicillin and DDT discouraged researchers anxious to study the immunology of borreliosis. After World War II, except for a few devotees whose laboratories continued to work on some problems related to the microbiology and immunology of relapsing fever, research on *Borreliae* was ignored. Scientific publications plunged from 50 a year in the 1950s to approximately 10 a year in the 1980s.

The increased recognition of Lyme disease renewed interest in the *Borreliae*. Lyme disease was first recognized in Europe during the early 1900s. However, this illness was not reported in the USA until 1969, when a grouse hunter from Wisconsin contracted the first reported case of Lyme disease in North America. Subsequently, additional cases of Lyme disease were reported from the upper Atlantic Coastal states and the upper midwest of the USA. Human cases have since become increasingly recognized throughout the world. Lyme disease is the most common tick-associated illness in the USA.

During the 1980s, the spirochetal bacterium *Borrelia burgdorferi* was implicated as the causative agent of Lyme disease. Since that time, molecular characterization studies have demonstrated at least several *Borrelia* subsp. capable of causing Lyme disease. The three most common are *B. burgdorferi* sensu stricto, *B. afzelii* and *B. garinii*. To date, only *B. burgdorferi* sensu stricto spirochetes have been detected in the USA, while these three genospecies are found throughout Europe.

Borreliae are entirely host-associated. Spirochetes have been found only in arthropods or host vertebrates that the arthropods have fed upon. *B. burgdorferi* sensu lato spirochetes are transmitted to human hosts by ixodid ticks of the *Ixodes ricinus* complex. Lyme disease is a multisystem disorder which usually begins with localized infection of the skin manifested by an expanding skin lesion, erythema migrans (EM), and constitutional symptoms such as fatigue, headache, mild stiff neck, arthralgia, myalgia and fever. Subsequent dissemination of the spirochete can cause more severe clinical manifestations, including secondary annular skin lesions, meningitis, Bell's palsy, radiculoneuritis and atrioventricular heart blockage. Arthritis or nervous system manifestations are hallmarks of chronic Lyme disease. An additional late manifestation, acrodermatitis chronica atrophicans, is seen primarily in Europe. Differences among the genospecies of *B. burgdorferi* sensu lato may account for geographic and regional variations in the clinical presentations.

In contrast to Lyme disease, relapsing fever caused by *B. hermsii* confirms that this illness is primarily a result of infection in the bloodstream. The clinical presentation is characterized by periods of fever lasting several days, separated by week-long intervals of normal temperatures. Diseases caused by *Borreliae* are curable with antimicrobial agents and are rarely fatal.

Spirochetes are not closely related to either gram-negative or gram-positive bacteria. *B. burgdorferi* sensu lato spirochetes are 0.2–0.3 by 20–30 μm. These organisms are highly flexible, left-handed (rotate in counterclockwise direction) helical cells, composed of 3–10 loose coils. They are susceptible to drying, but can survive for several months in medium at 4°C. The Lyme spirochete is composed of an outer cell membrane (outer sheath), protoplasmic cylinder and numerous flagella.

Some *Borreliae* are also surrounded *in vivo* by an amorphous slime layer. The slime layer, likely composed of host components, is weakly attached to the spirochete and is lost upon washing. The presence of host proteins in the slime layer may explain the inability of humans or animals to eliminate the Lyme disease spirochete despite a vigorous immune response. Thus, the spirochete may evade direct cell killing, antibody-dependent phagocytosis or anti-body-mediated lysis with a coating of protective 'self molecules' that prevent immune recognition.

A similar outer envelope exists on *Treponema pallidum*. Treatment of treponemes with detergents to remove this outer envelope is required to achieve high reactivity in immunologic assays. The polysaccharide 'capsular' material appears to prevent phagocytosis. Similarly, there is evidence that carbohydrates are present in the slime layer of *B. burgdorferi* sensu lato, which may also influence the destruction of spirochetes by host factors.

The outer cytoplasmic membrane of Lyme disease spirochetes has a trilaminar organization of 45–62% protein, 23–50% lipid and 3–4% carbohydrate. The fluid membrane can be easily separated from the underlying protoplasmic cylinder with dilute solutions of sodium dodecyl sulfate or nonionic detergents. The outer membrane can move to one end of the spirochete by a phenomenon called 'patching' or 'capping'. The outer envelope layers also form blebs when *B. burgdorferi* sensu lato are incubated with specific antibody and complement. Bleb formation is a prelude to cell death.

The major surface proteins are located in the outer cell membrane of *Borreliae*. To date, outer surface proteins (Osp), designated A, B, C, D, E and F, have been demonstrated in *B. burgdorferi* sensu lato organisms; however, their functions remain unknown. These proteins are heterogeneous, especially among European isolates. Initial investigations demonstrated that the Osp A of USA isolates was homogeneous; however, more recent investigations have confirmed significant heterogeneity. The genes for Osp A and Osp B are located on a 40 kb double-stranded linear plasmid. Linear plasmids also encode the variable major proteins (VMP) of *B. hermsii*, which undergo antigenic variation. These antigenic changes allow survival of spirochetes in the human host for extended periods of time. Lyme disease spirochetes also appear to upregulate or downregulate individual Osps, especially Osp A and Osp C, during infection of humans.

A variety of other antigens can also be detected in the outer membrane of *B. burgdorferi* sensu lato. These include proteins with molecular weights of 16, 27, 55, 60, 66 and 83 kDa. Antibodies against these proteins are readily detectable in chronic and complicated cases of Lyme disease. However, their relationship to the chronic nature of the disease and development of autoimmune immunologic reactions has not been elucidated. No single or combination of polypeptides has been directly associated with the different clinical manifestations of Lyme disease. The development of persistent or chronic Lyme arthritis that is not responsive to antimicrobial therapy has been associated with an immune response to Osp A and Osp B and class II major histocompatibility complex molecules HLA-DR4 and HLA-DR2.

The flagella, responsible for motility, are located within the outer membrane and are generally not exposed to the surface. Between 7 and 11 flagella are inserted subterminally and bipolarly to the protoplasmic cylinder of *B. burgdorferi* sensu lato. Numbers of flagella vary among other *Borreliae*. The flagella run parallel to the long axis and overlap in the middle of the spirochete. Flagellin, with a molecular weight of 41 kDa, is the predominant flagellar protein. An antibody response to flagellin is a consistent feature in all stages of Lyme disease. Despite the presence of high concentrations of flagellar antibodies, Lyme disease continues to progress, suggesting that flagellin does not induce a protective immune response.

The structure and importance of the protoplasmic cylinder remains undefined. The cell wall contains muramic acid and ornithine as part of the peptidoglycan. Another component may be lipopolysaccharide. The Jarisch–Herxheimer reaction (characterized by a transient high fever), which can occur in Lyme disease patients after treatment with antibiotics, may be due to the sudden release of lipopolysaccharide from lysed organisms. Many patients have experienced a Jarisch–Herxheimer reaction following antimicrobial therapy.

Borreliae can be cultivated in artificial medium; however, the bacteria multiply slowly. Generation times range from 8 to 15 h (*B. burgdorferi*) to 26 h (*B. recurrentis*). Continuous passage of *Borreliae* in artificial medium alters the antigenic structure and renders the bacteria noninfectious.

The clinical presentation alone is usually sufficient to diagnose relapsing fever. In contrast, diagnosis of Lyme disease is often difficult because of the variety of symptoms that can develop. Visualization of *B. burgdorferi* sensu lato in blood has not been successful because Lyme disease spirochetes rapidly disseminate into tissues. Silver staining has been used to demonstrate spirochetal forms in both biopsy and autopsy tissues; however, spirochetes cannot be positively identified.

Lyme disease spirochetes have been successfully cultured *in vitro* from blood, cerebrospinal fluid and synovial fluid but only a small number of these cultures have yielded organisms. In contrast, recovery of *B. burgdorferi* sensu lato from EM skin lesions has been more successful. Polymerase chain reaction (PCR) technology has also been used to directly detect Lyme disease spirochetes in patients. To date, PCR testing appears to be useful for recovery of *B. burgdorferi* sensu lato DNA from atypical EM lesions, cerebrospinal fluid and synovial fluid, provided the laboratory has sufficient expertise with the technology.

In many cases, serologic evidence of infection with Lyme disease spirochetes is the only option available to clinicians. Unfortunately, gross inaccuracies caused by the lack of specificity of conventional diagnostic assays and their subjectivity have made misdiagnosis and overdiagnosis common. These factors have contributed to confuse the general public and make many clinicians distrust serologic testing. During the past several years, however, diagnostic assays have been greatly improved. Unfortunately, there is currently no single assay that offers sufficient sensitivity and specificity to become the 'gold standard' of Lyme disease testing, although detection of borreliacidal antibodies in Lyme disease patients offers promise. A flow cytometric borreliacidal antibody test that measures the killing of live spirochetes after they were inoculated in the patient's serum and complement showed a sensitivity of 72% and more than 98% specificity. Regardless, quality laboratory procedures are available, provided results are obtained from experienced laboratories and interpreted correctly and the clinician understands the advantages and disadvantages of each laboratory procedure.

In early studies of the pathogenesis of Lyme disease, a major obstacle was the lack of suitable animal models. Rabbits and guinea pigs infected with *B. burgdorferi* develop skin lesions which histologically resemble human EM. These lesions, however, are not consistently induced and are the only clinical manifestations detected. Disseminated infection occurs in mature hamsters, rats and mice but clinical manifestations similar to those seen in human Lyme disease do not occur, despite persistence of spirochetes in the tissues. The hallmark of chronic *B. burgdorferi* sensu lato infection in humans, Lyme arthritis, appears to be observable in rodent models only when the immune system is immature or compromised. Rhesus monkeys have been shown to develop clinical signs and symptoms similar to localized and disseminated human infection; however, development of clinical arthritis only occurred in a small percentage of infected animals. In addition, the high costs associated with these animals has precluded widespread use of this Lyme disease model.

Despite these imperfections, animals models have been used extensively to elucidate pathogenic mechanisms of *B. burgdorferi* sensu lato. Lyme disease spirochetes have been shown to stimulate various inflammatory cytokines, including interleukin 1 (IL-1), IL-6 and tumor necrosis factor α (TNFα), and several autoimmune mechanisms which appear to play a role in pathogenesis.

Animal models also continue to play a vital role in efforts to develop an effective Lyme disease vaccine. The role of cell-mediated immunity remains largely unknown; however, an important role for antibody-mediated immunity after vaccination has been established. The induction of antibodies, termed borreliacidal, that can specifically kill *B. burgdorferi* sensu lato are often responsible for anti-body-mediated protection. Vaccination of animals with several individual Osps, including Osp A, Osp B, Osp C, and a 39 kDa protein have provided protection against Lyme disease spirochetes. Concomitantly, borreliacidal antibodies against Osp A, Osp B and the 39 kDa protein have been detected *in vitro*.

Osp A has emerged as the leading Lyme disease vaccine candidate and the efficacy of several recombinant Osp A vaccines is being investigated in animals and humans. Clinical trials have demonstrated safety in human volunteers; however, several significant obstacles must be overcome before induction of long-term comprehensive protection can be demonstrated. Most importantly, the success of Osp A vaccination appears to be dependent on the induction and long-term maintenance of high concentrations of borreliacidal antibodies. The present formulations of the Osp A vaccine have not maintained and sustained high concentrations of borreliacidal antibodies.

An anamnestic response will likely occur too slowly to prevent infection. Shortly after infection with *B. burgdorferi* sensu lato, the spirochetes become refractory to killing by borreliacidal antibodies. High levels of borreliacidal antibodies are detectable in sera from humans with all stages of Lyme disease; however, spirochetes are not eliminated. A recently developed flow cytometric test for detecting these highly specific borreliacidal antibodies is useful for confirming a Lyme disease diagnosis, and widespread availability of this test should greatly improve Lyme disease testing. However, induction of protective levels of anti-Osp A borreliacidal antibodies for extended periods of time has been difficult, even after vaccination of animals with high concentrations of Osp A in combination with adjuvants.

In addition, experimental Osp A vaccines comprise a single protein, despite the fact that Osp A is antigenically polymorphic. Thus, vaccination provides little or no protection against heterologous *B. burgdorferi* sensu lato isolates. Significant frequencies of anti-Osp A escape mutants have also been observed in animals after vaccination with a single Osp A protein. More recently, researchers demonstrated downregulation of Osp A expression and upregulation of other Osps shortly after infection of the vertebrate host. Thus, the incorporation of multiple Osp A proteins and other *B. burgdorferi* sensu lato Osps, especially Osp C, appears necessary for comprehensive protection against the Lyme disease spirochete.

See also: **Antigenic variation; Bacterial cell walls; Endotoxin (lipopolysaccharide (LPS)); Rheumatological disorders.**

Further reading

Barbour AG (1986) Biology of *Borrelia* species. *Microbiological Reviews* 50: 381–400.

Callister SM, Schell RF, Lim LCL *et al* (1994) Detection of borreliacidal antibodies by flow cytometry: an accurate, highly specific serodiagnostic test for Lyme disease. *Archives of Internal Medicine* 154: 1625–1632.

Callister SM, Schell RF, Lovrich SD and Jobe DA (1994) Lyme disease: laboratory diagnosis and serologic testing. *Endeavor* 18: 80–84.

Callister SM, Jobe DA, Schell RF *et al* (1996) Sensitivity and specificity of the borreliacidal-antibody test during early Lyme disease: a "Gold standard"? *Clinical and Diagnostic Laboratory Immunology* 3: 399–402.

Lovrich SD, Callister SM, DuChateau BK *et al* (1995) Abilities of Osp A proteins from different seroprotective groups of *Borrelia burgdorferi* to protect hamsters from infection. *Infection and Immunity* 63: 2113–2119.

Philipp MT and Johnson BJB (1994) Animal models of Lyme disease: pathogenesis and immunoprophylaxis. *Trends in Microbiology* 2: 431–437.

Steere AC (1989) Lyme disease. *New England Journal of Medicine* 321: 586–696.

Stevenson B, Schwan TG and Rosa PH (1995) Temperature-related differential expression of antigens in the Lyme disease spirochete, *Borrelia burgdorferi*. *Infection and Immunity* 63: 4535–4539.

BRUCELLA, INFECTION AND IMMUNITY

Christina Cheers, Department of Microbiology, University of Melbourne, Parkville, Victoria, Australia

Brucellae are gram-negative coccobacilli, which lack capsules or flagellae. They establish persistent intracellular infections in mammals (**Table 1**). In animals, brucellosis typically affects the reproductive organs, and abortion is usually the only outward sign of the disorder. Human brucellosis is either an acute febrile disease or a chronic disease with a wide variety of symptoms, often difficult to diagnose. It is not associated with abortion. It is a true zoonosis, in that virtually all human infections are acquired from animals (**Figure 1**). Typically, brucellae may infect handlers of infected livestock or carcasses, and people consuming unpasteurized milk products. Aerosol transmission is a hazard in abattoirs. Diagnosis of brucellosis often rests on serology, but the protective immune response is cell mediated.

Characteristics of the organisms and their antigens

Species of *Brucella* were originally classified according to the reservoir hosts (**Table 1**). The species are differentiated in the laboratory by colony morphology, growth requirements, various biochemical tests and lysis by bacteriophages. Nevertheless, DNA hybridization studies suggest they are so closely related that they should be classified as a single species.

Fresh isolates of most *Brucella* spp. are smooth, but dissociation occurs readily into rough or mucoid colonies. *B. ovis* and *B. canis* are normally rough or mucoid and lack the O chains of lipopolysaccharide (LPS). *Brucella* LPS is less toxic, less pyrogenic and less effective as a polyclonal activator than that of most gram negatives. Nevertheless, it appears to be the main virulence factor of *Brucella* species.

Two different O chains occur on *Brucella* LPS: A, generally associated with *B. abortus*, and M, with *B. melitensis*. However, some *B. abortus* biovars carry M antigens, and some common *B. melitensis* carry A antigen. Both are linear polymers of an unusual amino sugar, perosamine (4,6-dideoxy-4-formamido-D-mannopyranose). They differ in that the A chain sugar molecules are always linked 2–1, whereas the M chain has a 3–1 linkage at every fifth junction. They can be distinguished by monoclonal antibodies, or by polyclonal serum rendered specific by cross-absorption. Cross-absorption is needed because the core structure of LPS is common to all species.

Other cell envelope antigens include the outer membrane proteins (MPS) which fall into two molecular weight ranges, 25–27 kDa and 36–38 kDa. The latter act as porins. In addition there are more than 30 internal antigens identified by western blotting or immunoelectrophoresis.

Table 1 Host ranges of the genus *Brucella*

Species	Colony type[a]	Predominant hosts	Occasional hosts[b]
B. melitensis (3 biovars)	S	Sheep, goats	Cattle, humans
B. abortus (7 biovars)	S	Cattle	Sheep, goats, horses, other domestic and wild ungulates, dogs, humans
B. suis (5 biovars)	S	Biovar 1: pigs	Humans
		Biovar 2: hares	Pigs
		Biovar 3: pigs	Humans
		Biovar 4: reindeer	Humans
		Biovar 5: wild rodents	
B. neotomac	S	Desert wood rat[c]	Not reported
B. ovis	R	Rams	Ewes
B. canis	R	Dogs	Humans

[a] Wild-type on isolation. S, smooth; R, rough. Avirulent R mutants of S strains are readily obtained on laboratory media.
[b] Not a complete list – examples only.
[c] *Neotoma lepida*.

B. abortus

B. melitensis

B. suis

B. canis

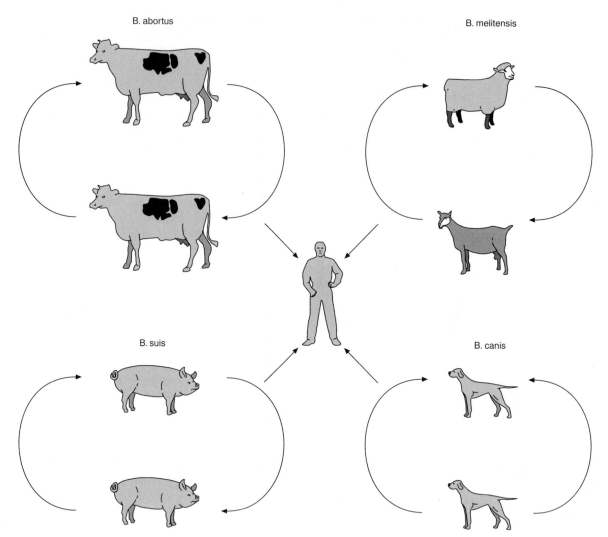

Figure 1 Brucellosis is a true zoonosis with different bacterial species infecting different animal species, and only incidentally infecting humans, often as a result of occupational hazard or drinking unpasteurised milk.

Immune responses of the host

Protective immunity

The primary antibody response to *Brucella* infection in humans involves early immunoglobulin M (IgM) production followed by a switch to IgG and IgA. IgE can also be detected by radioimmunoassay. IgM persists for an unusually long period into the late stages of the disease and in subclinical infection. It is interesting to speculate that this might relate to the T cell-independent nature of the major antigen, LPS, acting on B cells without causing class switching. Notwithstanding the importance of antibody in serodiagnosis of brucellosis, the role of antibody in protection is probably confined to pre-existing mucosal antibody reducing the likelihood of initial infection.

As facultative intracellular bacteria, brucellae are controlled by the activation of macrophages and the formation of granulomas to localize the infection. In experimental infection of mice, it has been shown that both CD4$^+$ and CD8$^+$ T lymphocytes are involved. The function of the CD8$^+$ T cells is apparently to lyse ineffective macrophages and non-professional phagocytes to release the bacteria for phagocytosis by activated macrophages. The function of CD4$^+$ T cells is to produce interferon γ (IFNγ) and other cytokines to activate and attract macrophages.

Depletion of IFNγ from infected mice by injection of monoclonal antibody specific for IFNγ increases bacterial numbers and suppresses the attraction of macrophages to the infected tissues. Even more dramatic are the effects of depleting interleukin 12 (IL-12), the cytokine which controls the differentiation of T cells and natural killer (NK) cells to produce IFNγ. Injection of antibody to IL-12 prevents IFNγ production by the T cells, prevents the influx of cells which causes splenomegaly, and grossly exacerbates bacterial numbers over a prolonged period of time. Other cytokines produced during experimental infection include IL-1, tumor necrosis factor α (TNFα), IL-6, macrophage colony-stimulating factor (M-CSF), granulocyte colony-stimulating factor (G-CSF). TNFα is important early in infection, either directly activating macrophages or stimulating the NK cells to produce IFNγ. Its depletion also increases early bacterial numbers and suppresses splenomegaly but, in contrast to the effect of IL-12 depletion, the mice develop IFNγ-producing T cells and recover.

In humans, the tissue lesions produced by *Brucella* sp. consist of minute granulomata, comprising epitheloid cells, neutrophils, mononuclear leukocytes and some giant cells. Necrosis is not common, and abscesses do not form, except in *B. suis* infection. Hepatosplenomegaly is a common clinical manifestation, a symptom shared by experimental mice. As with experimentally and naturally infected animals, human patients develop delayed-type hypersensitivity (DTH), a correlate of the cell-mediated resistance to infection, but also a cause for immunopathology.

Immunopathology

Immunopathology is a major factor in the disease. The granulomata which form at the foci of infection provide the main histopathologic signs. A pathogenic role for immune complexes has been suggested but there is no correlation between their levels and severity of disease. In people who have been sensitized by previous infection, albeit subclinical, needlestick injury can be followed within 24–48 h by a severe, generalized DTH response which resembles many aspects of the infection itself. The ability of components of brucellae to induce polyclonal activation of B lymphocytes could explain the high incidence of autoantibodies in acute infection. Alternatively, the presence of stress proteins which have been conserved across species and cross-react with mammalian proteins have been implicated in autoimmune sequelae of other infections, and may be important in brucellosis also.

Serology

Because of the nonspecific nature of the symptoms of human brucellosis, and the difficulty of isolating the causative organisms, diagnosis often must be made serologically. Most of the antibody detected is directed towards the LPS, with some specific for protein antigens. A variety of tests have been used, including agglutination, complement fixation, precipitation, radioimmunoassay, indirect fluorescence antibody assays and ELISA. To date, the agglutination assay remains the most widely used,

although this is likely to be replaced by ELISA when better standardization is achieved. A feature of the agglutination assay has been the prozone, seen in high-titer sera, and blocking antibodies. The majority of studies suggest that these are IgA, although some have found blocking antibody amongst IgG. The problems of prozone or blocking antibody can be overcome by further dilution of the serum or the use of an indirect agglutination assay. Where it is necessary to distinguish IgM and IgG antibodies, 2-mercaptoethanol is used to inactivate IgM agglutination, leaving 2-mercaptoethanol-resistant IgG.

In domestic animals intradermal testing for DTH is the most convenient way of establishing the presence of infection in the herd. Nevertheless serology is the best way of detecting infected individual animals.

Evasive strategies by the organism

These bacteria can survive within the phagocytic cells of the host. Extracts of *B. abortus* have been reported to inhibit phagosome–lysosome fusion in macrophages, degranulation of neutrophils and the oxygen-dependent antibacterial system of bovine neutrophils. The organisms may spread from the initial site of infection either within these cells or free in the bloodstream. They localize in certain target organs, such as lymph nodes, spleen, liver, bone marrow and, especially in animals, reproductive organs. The presence of mesoerythritol in the testes and placentae of ruminants and pigs stimulates enormous multiplication of brucellae in those tissues, leading to infertility and abortion. However, erythritol is absent in humans.

Vaccines

While LPS is the target of antibodies, there is a spectrum of proteins which can stimulate T cells. A number have been identified. Some were found to be stress proteins. Nevertheless, a defined vaccine is some time away, since, as with other intracellular bacteria, live attenuated vaccines are the only ones so far shown to be effective in the induction of cell-mediated resistance.

B. abortus strain 19 is used to immunize cattle, while *B. melitensis* strain Rev 1 is used in sheep and goats. However, vaccination of humans has not been widely used outside Russia due to the questionable safety of these strains. Accidental infection with vaccines is a hazard for veterinarians exposed to needlestick injuries or splashes on to the conjunctiva.

The preferred approach to prevention of human infection is the pasteurization of milk products and

386 BRUTON'S AGAMMAGLOBULINEMIA

the ultimate eradication of infected herds. Once infection in domestic animals is reduced by vaccination, vaccination is replaced by testing followed by slaughter of infected animals. At this stage, vaccination of the herds only leads to confusion, since neither the serological tests used nor DTH screening can distinguish between infected and vaccinated animals. Although vaccination of very young animals usually results in antibody dropping to undetectable levels by the time surveillance of the herd is undertaken, remaining positives lead to confusion as to whether or not they are infected.

See also: **Cell-mediated immunity; Cytotoxic T lymphocytes; Delayed-type hypersensitivity; Granuloma; Immunoglobulin class switching; Interferon γ; Interleukin 12 and its receptor; *Listeria*, infection and immunity; Macrophage activation; *Mycobacteria*, infection and immunity; T cell vaccination; Tumor necrosis factor α.**

Further reading

Alton GG, Jones LM, Angus RD *et al* (1988) *Techniques for the Brucellosis Laboratory.* Paris: INRA.
Baldwin CL and Winter AJ (1994) Macrophages and brucella. *Immunology Series* 60: 363–380.
Hall WH, Mannion RE and Zinneman HH (1971) Block-ing serum lysis of *Brucella abortus* by hyperimmune rabbit immunoglobulin A. *Journal of Immunology* 107: 41–46.
Neilsen KH, Kelly L, Gall D, Nicoletti P and Kelly W (1995) Improved competitive enzyme immunoassay for the diagnosis of bovine brucellosis. *Veterinary Immunology and Immunopathology* 46: 285–291.
Oliviera SC and Splitter GA (1995) CD8+ type 1 CD44hi CD45 RBlo T lymphocytes control intracellular *Brucella abortus* infection as demonstrated in major histocompatibility complex class I and class II deficient mice. *European Journal of Immunology* 25: 2551–2557.
Pavlov H, Hogarth M, McKenzie IFC and Cheers C (1982) *In vivo* and *in vitro* effects of monoclonal antibody to Ly antigens on immunity to infection. *Cellular Immunology* 71: 127–138.
Verger JM, Grimont F, Grimont PAD and Crayon M (1985) *Brucella*, a nonspecific genus as shown by deoxyribonucleic acid hybridization. *International Journal of Systematic Bacteriology* 3: 292–295.
Young EJ (1995) An overview of human brucellosis. *Clinical Infectious Diseases* 21: 283–290.
Young EJ and Corbel MJ (eds) (1989) *Brucellosis: Clinical and Laboratory Aspects.* Boca Raton, FL: CRC Press.
Zhan YF and Cheers C (1995) Endogenous interleukin-12 (IL-12) is involved in the resistance to *Brucella abortus* infection. *Infection and Immunity* 63: 1387–1390.
Zhan Y, Liu Z and Cheers C (1996) TNF-α and IL-12 contribute to resistance to the intracellular bacterium *Brucella abortus* by different mechanisms. *Infection and Immunity* 64: 2782–2786.

BRUTON'S AGAMMAGLOBULINEMIA

Mary Ellen Conley, Department of Pediatrics, University of Tennessee, and St Jude Children's Research Hospital, Memphis, Tennessee, USA

Historical background

In 1952 Colonel Ogden C Bruton reported the case of an 8-year-old boy with a 4 year history of recurrent bacterial sepsis, osteomyelitis and otitis. This child failed to make antibodies to pneumococcus after repeated antigenic challenge. In a seminal observation, Bruton noted that the patient's serum lacked the gamma globulin fraction by electrophoretic analysis but was otherwise normal. This was the first case in which an abnormal result in a laboratory study explained the clinical problems and dictated the therapy for an immunodeficient patient. The patient was treated with gamma globulin and had a marked decrease in the incidence of infection. In the next 5 years many similar patients were reported.

Most of these patients could be divided into one of two groups. The first group consisted of adults who had the onset of recurrent or persistent infections after early childhood. Males and females appeared to be equally affected and the disorder could not be accounted for by a single gene defect by mendelian inheritance. This disorder came to be called acquired hypogammaglobulinemia or common variable immunodeficiency. The patients in the second group were boys who had the onset of their disease in the first 2 years of life. Many of these children had similarly affected brothers, maternal uncles or cousins. This disorder is now referred to as X-linked agammaglobulinemia (XLA), congenital agammaglobulinemia or Bruton's agammaglobulinemia.

Studies performed in the 1970s showed that patients with XLA had markedly reduced numbers of B cells in the peripheral circulation; however, pre-B cells could be found in their bone marrow, suggesting that stem cells could enter the B cell lineage but they could not progress through normal B cell differentiation. In 1986, preliminary linkage studies mapped the XLA defect to the midportion of the long arm of the X chromosome. The same year, X chromosome inactivation studies performed on the B cells of carriers of XLA, the mothers of affected boys, showed that the XLA gene product was expressed in B cells and it was not transportable between cells. In 1993, two groups, using positional cloning or analysis of a candidate gene, independently showed that XLA was due to mutations in the gene encoding a cytoplasmic tyrosine kinase which is now called Btk (Bruton tyrosine kinase) (**Table 1**).

Clinical characteristics

Most patients with XLA are healthy at birth and remain well for the first few months of life. Recurrent infections, particularly otitis and pneumonia, usually develop sometime during the second 6 months of life, after the loss of maternally acquired antibody. The majority of patients with XLA are evaluated for immunodeficiency before 3 years of age. However, 20–30% of patients present later; some of these patients have higher concentrations of serum immunoglobulins and/or more B cells than are typical for XLA. A helpful clinical clue to the diagnosis of XLA is unusually small peripheral lymph nodes and tonsils. Germinal follicles, which constitute a considerable proportion of the volume of lymph nodes, are largely made up of B cells. In the absence of B cells, lymph nodes are quite small. Except for signs of past infection, there are no other striking physical findings. By the time of diagnosis approximately 80% of patients have experienced recurrent upper and/or lower respiratory tract infections. Diarrhea and pyoderma are also frequently seen before diagnosis and initiation of therapy. Between

20 and 30% of patients have experienced sepsis, meningitis, arthritis or failure to thrive. Profound neutropenia is present at the time of diagnosis in about 25% of patients. Overwhelming bacterial sepsis with rapid demise is not unusual. The most frequent infecting organisms in patients with XLA, and in all other patients with hypogammaglobulinemia, are *Haemophilus influenzae*, *Streptococcus pneumoniae* and *Staphylococcus aureus*.

After diagnosis and initiation of gamma globulin replacement therapy, upper and lower respiratory tract infections may continue to be a problem, particularly if the patient has developed chronic pulmonary changes prior to diagnosis. Diarrhea due to Giardia is not uncommon in patients with XLA but is usually easily treated. Mycoplasma or ureoplasma infections can cause persistent arthritis, pneumonitis or urologic problems. Between 5 and 10% of patients with XLA have chronic enteroviral infections resulting in meningitis/encephalitis, arthritis or a dermatomyositis-like syndrome. These infections are often slowly progressive and fatal. Although echovirus is the most common organism, vaccine-associated polio and Coxsackie have also been isolated.

High-dose gamma globulin therapy is expected to decrease the incidence of chronic lung disease and enteroviral or mycoplasma infections in patients with XLA; however, it has been the source of hepatitis C infection in some patients. At the present time, the majority of adolescents with XLA have intermittent or chronic mild sinusitis or bronchitis but are otherwise completely well with normal growth and development.

Laboratory characteristics

The hallmarks of XLA are markedly decreased concentrations of serum immunoglobulins and an almost complete absence of B cells in the peripheral circulation. The serum immunoglobulin G (IgG) is usually less than 2 mg ml^{-1}, and the IgM and IgA are less than 0.1 mg ml^{-1}. B cells, which constitute 5–18% of the peripheral blood lymphocytes in the normal individual, cannot be detected using standard techniques; however, a small number (0.005–0.1% of peripheral blood lymphocytes) are uniformly present. As evaluated with antibodies to surface markers, these B cells have an immature phenotype that is similar to that seen in B cells from X-linked immunodeficient (xid) mice. Epstein–Barr virus (EBV)-transformed B cell lines, produced from the blood of patients with XLA, make normal immunoglobulins with correct rearrangements of V, D and J gene segments. A disproportionate number of the

Table 1 Characteristics of Bruton's agammaglobulinemia

X-linked recessive (occurs only in males)

Onset in the first 3 years of life

Recurrent infections with encapsulated bacteria

Sinusitis, otitis, bronchitis and pneumonia

Increased susceptibility to mycoplasma, enterovirus and hepatitis C

Marked decrease in serum IgG, IgM and IgA

Profoundly reduced numbers of B cells

Pre-B cells present in the bone marrow

Treatment with gamma globulin and antibiotics

Mutations in the gene for Bruton's tyrosine kinase (Btk)

pre-B cells found in the bone marrow of patients with XLA are at the earliest stage of development and a reduced percentage of them are in the S phase of the cell cycle.

Abnormalities in cell lineages other than B cells have been reported; however, these abnormalities may be secondary to the marked reduction in B cell numbers or the hypogammaglobulinemia rather than a direct effect of the genetic defect.

Bruton tyrosine kinase

Bruton tyrosine kinase (Btk) is a 659 amino acid member of a recently identified subfamily of src-related cytoplasmic tyrosine kinases (**Figure 1**). It is expressed throughout B cell and myeloid development but it is not expressed in nonhematopoietic cells. Like src, Btk has a carboxy-terminal catalytic domain adjacent to SH2 and SH3 (src homology 2 and 3) domains. However, unlike src but similar to the other members of its subfamily, which include Tec, Itk and Bmx, Btk has an amino-terminal PH (pleckstrin homology) domain followed by a proline-rich region. Although the substrates phosphorylated by Btk have not yet been identified, like other tyrosine kinases, Btk is thought to function in signal transduction. This view is supported by the observation that the protein–protein interaction domains of Btk bind to other molecules known to be involved in signal transduction, including src family members, the $\beta\gamma$ subunit of G proteins, protein kinase C and cbl.

Btk is phosphorylated and its kinase activity is increased by stimulation of a variety of cell surface receptors, including, and perhaps most importantly, the B cell receptor complex (BCR). After cross-linking of cell surface IgM, src family members phosphorylate Btk, which then increases its catalytic activity by autophosphorylation. This process is associated with movement of Btk to the inner surface of the cell membrane.

The well-characterized murine immunodeficiency, xid, is caused by an amino acid substitution in the PH domain of Btk. The phenotype of the xid defect appears to be milder than the XLA defect. Mice with either the spontaneous Btk mutation or a null mutation in Btk induced by homologous recombination have reduced concentrations of serum IgM and IgG3 and they lack a mature population of B cells; however, they do have an antibody response to T cell-dependent antigens and they have relatively normal concentrations of serum IgG1, IgG2a and IgG2b. The phenotype of the xid mice suggests that Btk is required not only at the transition from pre-B cell to B cell but also at later stages of differentiation.

Genetics

Brutons agammaglobulinemia occurs in all racial groups, with a prevalence of between 2 and 8 per 1 000 000. As is true with all X-linked disorders that are lethal without medical intervention, the disorder is maintained in the population by the occurrence of new mutations. This has two important consequences. First, approximately half of the patients with the clinical and laboratory characteristics of XLA have no family history of the disorder because they are the first manifestation in their family of a new mutation. Second, the mutations in Btk that cause XLA are independently derived and highly variable.

The gene for Btk consists of 19 exons spread over 37 kb at Xq22. Human Btk has over 95% homology to murine Btk and 58% homology to a drosophila kinase, Dsrc28C. Over 100 different mutations in Btk have been identified. Although deletions that are detectable by Southern blot analysis do occur, they constitute less than 10% of the mutations in this gene. About one-third of the mutations result in amino acid substitutions, the majority of which are in the kinase domain; however, amino acid substitutions in the PH domain and the SH2 domain have also been seen. The remaining mutations are almost equally divided between single base pair substi-

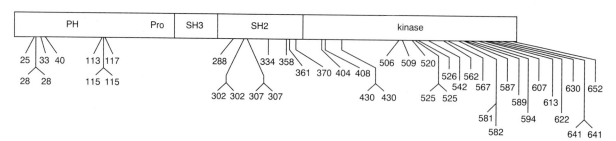

Figure 1 Structure of the 659 amino acid cytoplasmic tyrosine kinase, Btk. The amino-terminal pleckstrin homology domain (PH) is followed by a proline rich region (Pro), and SH2 and SH3 domains and the catalytic domain. The mutations causing amino acid substitutions in patients with XLA and the codons affected by those mutations are shown. Some codons have been altered by two different mutations; xid mice have an amino acid substitution in codon 28 in the PH domain.

tutions that cause premature stop codons, small insertions or deletions that result in frameshift mutations and splice defects. These mutations are spread almost evenly throughout the Btk gene. Studies done on EBV-transformed cell lines or myeloid cells from patients with XLA indicate that this last group of mutations (stop codons, frameshifts and splice defects) usually result in poor accumulation of the Btk mRNA in the cytoplasm. Thus, these mutations are functionally equivalent.

Attempts to correlate the severity of the clinical manifestations of XLA with specific mutations in Btk suggest that the site or type of mutation may influence the phenotype. Amino acid substitutions in the SH2 domain or noncritical regions of the catalytic domain are sometimes seen in patients with milder disease. However, additional factors, including other genes, past infections and therapy, may also influence the phenotype of patients with XLA.

Differential diagnosis

X-linked agammaglobulinemia should be distinguished from two other X-linked disorders that result in hypogammaglobulinemia in infant males. X-linked severe combined immunodeficiency (SCID), which is due to mutations in the common γ chain of cytokine receptors, is associated with the onset of persistent fungal and viral, as well as bacterial, infections in the first 6 months of life. Laboratory studies show normal or increased proportions of B cells but markedly decreased numbers of T cells, and absent proliferation in response to T cell mitogens. Mutations in the gene for CD40 ligand cause X-linked hyper-IgM syndrome, a disorder in which serum concentrations of IgG and IgA are markedly decreased but the level of IgM, while not always strikingly elevated in infancy, is higher than that usually seen in XLA. Patients with X-linked hyper-IgM syndrome have normal numbers of peripheral blood B cells and T cells. Patients with common variable immunodeficiency can be distinguished from patients with XLA in that they usually have somewhat higher concentrations of serum immunoglobulins and normal or near normal numbers of B cells in the peripheral circulation. T cell number and function may be abnormal in patients with common variable immunodeficiency. A small number of girls in whom both the clinical and laboratory findings are indistinguishable from XLA have been reported, suggesting that there is one or more autosomal recessive disorder(s) phenotypically identical to XLA.

Therapy

Patients with XLA are treated with gamma globulin replacement therapy and liberal use of antibiotics. All live viral vaccines should be avoided. Although the identification of Btk as the defective gene in XLA sets the stage for gene therapy, a better understanding of the regulation and function of Btk, as well as improved technology of gene transfer, will be required before this goal can be achieved.

See also: **B lymphocyte differentiation; CD40 and its ligand; Common variable immunodeficiency; Gammaglobulin; Humoral immunity; Immunodeficiency, animal models; Immunodeficiency, primary; Immunoglobulin, cell surface; Protein kinases; Severe combined immunodeficiency.**

Further reading

Bruton OC (1952) Agammaglobulinemia. *Pediatrics* **9**: 722–728.

Conley ME, Brown P, Pickard AR *et al* (1986) Expression of the gene defect in X-linked agammaglobulinemia. *New England Journal of Medicine* **315**: 564–567.

Conley ME, Fitch-Hilgenberg ME, Cleveland JL, Parolini O and Rohrer J (1994) Screening of genomic DNA to identify mutations in the gene for Bruton's tyrosine kinase. *Human Molecular Genetics* **3**: 1751–1756.

Kwan SP, Kunkel L, Bruns G, Wedgwood RJ, Latt S and Rosen FS (1986) Mapping of the X-linked agammaglobulinemia locus by use of restriction fragment-length polymorphism. *Journal of Clinical Investigation* **77**: 649–652.

Lederman HM and Winkelstein JA (1985) X-linked agammaglobulinemia: an analysis of 96 patients. *Medicine* **64**: 145–156.

Ochs HD and Winkelstein J (1996) Disorders of the B-cell system. In: Stiehm ER (ed) *Immunologic Disorders in Infants and Children*, pp 296–338. Philadelphia: WB Saunders.

Pearl ER, Vogler LB, Okos AJ, Crist WM, Lawton AR and Cooper MD (1978) B lymphocyte precursors in human bone marrow: an analysis of normal individuals and patients with antibody-deficiency states. *Journal of Immunology* **120**: 1169–1175.

Rawlings DJ, Saffran DC, Tsukada S *et al* (1993) Mutation of unique region of Bruton's tyrosine kinase in immunodeficient XID mice. *Science* **261**: 358–361.

Rawlings DJ, Scharenberg AM, Park H *et al* (1996) Activation of BTK by a phosphorylation mechanism initiated by SRC family kinases. *Science* **271**: 822–825.

Sideras P and Smith CIE (1995) Molecular and cellular aspects of X-linked agammaglobulinemia. *Advances in Immunology* **59**: 135–223.

Touhara K, Inglese J, Pitcher JA, Shaw G and Lefkowitz RJ (1994) Binding of G Protein $\beta\gamma$-subunits to pleckstrin homology domains. *Journal of Biological Chemistry* **269**: 10217–10220.

Tsukada S, Saffran DC, Rawlings DJ *et al* (1993) Deficient expression of a B cell cytoplasmic tyrosine kinase in human X-linked agammaglobulinemia. *Cell* **72**: 279–290.

Vetrie D, Vorechovsky I, Sideras P *et al* (1993) The gene involved in X-linked agammaglobulinemia is a member of the src family of protein-tyrosine kinases. *Nature* **361**: 226–233.

Vihinen M (1996) BTK base: XLA-mutation registry. *Immunology Today* **17**: 502–506.

BUNYAVIRIDAE, INFECTION AND IMMUNITY

James S Porterfield, formerly of the Sir William Dunn School of Pathology, University of Oxford, Oxford, UK

In 1943 a virus was isolated from a pool of wild-caught *Aedes* mosquitoes collected in an uninhabited area of Semliki Forest in western Uganda known as Bunyamwera. The virus was unrelated to yellow fever virus, or to any of the 20 or so arthropod-borne viruses or 'arboviruses' then known, and it was named Bunyamwera virus. Although antibodies against Bunyamwera virus were detected in some residents of nearby villages, no disease association was apparent, and the virus appeared to be little more than a virological curiosity. By 1960 about a dozen arboviruses isolated in North and South America, Europe, Africa and Asia had been shown to be serologically related to Bunyamwera virus, and this number increased over the next decades. More than 50 years after its isolation, Bunyamwera virus remains an unimportant virus in terms of human disease, causing at the most a mild fever with a rash, but it has been intensively studied as the type species both of the genus *Bunyavirus* and of the large and diverse family Bunyaviridae which now contains more than 300 members placed in five different genera, *Bunyavirus*, *Hantavirus*, *Nairovirus*, *Phlebovirus* and *Tospovirus* (**Table 1**).

Although the majority of Bunyaviridae resemble the type species in being of minor medical importance, the family does contain a number of major pathogens of humans and/or animals. Most bunyaviruses are transmitted by mosquitoes or by *Culicoides*, most phleboviruses by *Phlebotomines*, and all nairoviruses by ticks, whereas hantaviruses are not arthropod-borne, but are zoonotic agents capable of infecting humans after close contact with infected animals, mainly rodents and voles. Tospoviruses are thrip-transmitted plant viruses such as tomato spotted wilt and related viruses. They are of no medical or veterinary interest, but are included in the Bunyaviridae on the basis of their close physical, biochemical and genetic similarities to viruses in the other genera. They illustrate the great genetic diversity shown by members of this substantial family.

Characteristics of the Bunyaviridae

Bunyaviridae are enveloped RNA viruses about 100 nm in diameter containing a tripartite, single-stranded RNA genome of negative polarity (**Figure 1**). Virions contain three main proteins, namely the envelope glycoproteins G1 and G2, and the nucleocapsid protein N, together with a minor large protein L. The three viral RNA species are designated as small (S), medium (M) and large (L), of which the S RNA encodes the N protein, the M RNA encodes the two envelope glycoproteins G1 and G2 and the L RNA encodes the large, virion-associated polymerase protein L. Three different expression strategies are used to generate the nonstructural proteins of the S

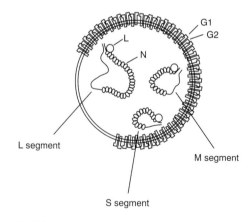

Figure 1   Schematic representation of a bunyavirus particle, showing the two virion spike glycoproteins, G1 and G2, and the three RNA genome segments L, M and S encapsidated by the N (nucleocapsid) protein and associated with the L (RNA-dependent RNA polymerase) protein. From J.F. Simons, PhD Thesis, Stockholm, 1992.

Table 1 Pathogenic Bunyaviridae

Genus	Vector	Serogroup	Pathogenic viruses
Bunyavirus (over 150)	Mosquito	Anopheles A (12)	Tacaiuma
		Anopheles B (2)	—
		Bakau (5)	—
		Bunyamwera (32)	Bunyamwera, Cache Valley[a], Calovo, Germiston, Guaroa, Ilesha, Maguari, Tensaw, Wyeomyia
		Bwamba (2)	Bwamba
		C group (14)	Apeu, Caraparu, Itaqui, Madrid, Marituba, Murutucu, Oriboca, Ossa, Restan
		California (14)	*California encephalitis*, *La Crosse*, Inkoo, Jamestown Canyon, snowshoe hare, Tahyna, trivittatus
		Capim (10)	—
		Gamboa (8)	—
		Guama (12)	Catu, Guama
		Koongol (2)	—
		Minatitlan (2)	—
		Nyando (2)	—
		Olifanstsvlei (5)	—
		Patois (7)	—
		Simbu (24)	Aino[a], Akabane[a], *Oropouche*, Shuni
		Tete (6)	—
		Turlock (5)	—
		Ungrouped (4)	—
Hantavirus (>8)	None	Hantaan (>8)	*Bayou, Black Creek Canal, Dobrava, Hantaan, Muerto Canyon, Puumala, Seoul, Sin Nombre*
Nairovirus (34)	Tick	Crimean–Congo (3)	*Crimean–Congo hemorrhagic fever*, Hazara
		Dera Ghazi Khan (6)	—
		Hughes (10)	Soldado
		Nairobi SD (3)	Dugbe, Ganjam[a], Nairobi Sheep Disease[a]
		Qalyub (3)	—
		Sakhalin (7)	Avalon
		Thiafora (2)	—
Phlebovirus (57)	Sandfly	Phlebotomus (44)	Alenquer, Candiru, Chagres, *Sandfly fever*, Naples & Sicilian, Punta Toro, *Rift Valley Fever*[b], Toscana
	Tick	Uukuniemi (13)	Uukuniemi, Zalev-Terpeniya
Unassigned (53)	Mosquito		Bangui, Kasokero, Tataguine
	Tick		Bhanja, Keterah, Tamdy, Wanowrie
Tospovirus (>3)	Thrip	Tomato spotted wilt	

The approximate number of viruses in the genus or serogroup is given in parentheses.
[a]Viruses causing important animal diseases.
[b]Mosquito vector for Rift Valley fever virus.
Viruses in italics are responsible for important human diseases.

segment, and two different strategies are found for the M segment. Viral replication occurs in the cytoplasm of infected cells, using a Golgi-associated morphogenesis with budding into intracytoplasmic vacuoles.

The most important bunyavirus disease of man is probably California encephalitis, which occurs in North America and affects mainly children. Most infections are due to La Crosse, snowshoe hare or Keystone viruses rather than to California encephalitis virus itself. These viruses are maintained in nature in small rodents and are transmitted to man by mosquito bites, *Aedes triseriatus* being the principal vector. Aino and Akabane are two Simbu serogroup

bunyaviruses which are causes of congenital malformations (arthrogryposis, hydranecephaly and anencephaly) in sheep, goats and cattle in Japan, Australia, East and South Africa, Cyprus and Israel. Oropouche virus is another Simbu serogroup bunyavirus which has caused thousands of human infections in Brazil, many involving the central nervous system, although fatalities are very rare.

Hantaan virus and related hantaviruses cause Korean hemorrhagic fever, otherwise known as hemorrhagic fever with renal syndrome (HFRS), a severe and often fatal infection that occurs across Asia from China into Europe. In Scandinavia, Puumala and related viruses cause a much milder clinical syndrome known as nephropathia epidemica. In 1993 a new and severe illness known as Hantavirus pulmonary syndrome (HPS) was recognized in the southwestern USA, and by 1996 similar infections had been identified in Canada, Brazil, Paraguay and Argentina, associated with three different hanta-viruses, Sin Nombre, Black Creek Canal and Bayou viruses. The overall mortality in 128 confirmed cases of HPS in the USA to February 1996 was 50%, with a peak incidence in June and July. Most cases have been in rural residents. Rodent association with human disease is indicated in **Table 2**.

Crimean–Congo hemorrhagic fever, which occurs in countries of the former USSR, the Middle East and Africa, as far south as the Cape, is the most important *Nairovirus* infection, having a mortality of around 20%. Deaths have occurred in hospital staff following surgical intervention in patients who have presented with severe intestinal bleeding.

Phlebotomus fever occurs in the Mediterranean and Middle East regions as a mild, but troublesome erythematous fever, but the most important *Phle-*

Table 2 Taxonomic relationship between rodents and their related hantaviruses (associated human diseases in parentheses)

Order Rodentia	
Suborder Sciurognathi	Genus *Hantavirus* (family Bunyaviridae)
Family Muridae	
Subfamily Arvicolinae	
Genus *Clethrionomys*	
Species *glareolus*	Puumala (Nephropathia epidemica/HFRS)
Microtus	
pennsylvanicus	Prospect Hill
californicus	Isla Vista
Sigmodontinae	
Peromyscus	
maniculatus	Sin Nombre (HPS)
leucopus	New York 1 (HPS)
Oryzomys	
palustris	Bayou (HPS)
Reithrodontomys	
megalotis	El Moro Canyon virus
mexicanus	Rio Segundo virus
Sigmodon	
hispidus	Black Creek Canal (HPS)
Oligoryzomys	
microtis	Rio Mamore virus
Murinae	
Apodemus	
agrarius	Hantaan (HFRS)
flavicollis	Dobrava/Belgrade (HFRS)
Rattus	
norvegicus	Seoul (HFRS)

Reproduced with permission from Khan *et al* (1996).

bovirus is Rift Valley fever virus, transmitted by mosquitoes rather than phebotomines. Rift Valley fever is enzootic in sub-Saharan Africa and produced a major human epidemic with some 600 deaths in Egypt in 1977; a decade later another epidemic occurred in Mauritania, and there have been many smaller outbreaks in humans and animals.

Immune responses of the host

Bunyaviridae are highly immunogenic, inducing neutralizing antibodies which are type specific but show limited cross-reactivity within the genus. Recovery is normally followed by solid protection against reinfection. In some infections the immune response occurs too late to prevent invasion of the central nervous system or the liver. Thus animal infection with Rift Valley fever virus can produce overwhelming infection, with liver necrosis and high mortality. Some American hantaviruses target the lungs, rather than the liver, kidneys or central nervous system, resulting in hantavirus pulmonary syndrome. The intense inflammatory response in these infections leads to the release of mediators followed by increased vascular permeability throughout the lungs, and consequent clinical disease.

Antibodies against the G1 glycoprotein neutralize viral infectivity, and inhibit hemagglutination. The nucleocapsid protein is the dominant antigen in complement fixation tests. There have been few studies of cell-mediated immunity, but mice infected with Tahyna *Bunyavirus*, which normally recover following a subclinical infection, die when immunosuppressed with cyclophosphamide. Circulating immune complexes have been reported in nephropathia epidemica.

Evasive strategies by the organism

The possession of a segmented genome allows the possibility of genetic reassortment, which has been demonstrated in the laboratory and also occurs in nature.

Vaccines

Formalin-inactivated veterinary vaccines against Rift Valley fever and Nairobi sheep disease have been available for a number of years, but vaccines for use in humans are still experimental. Laboratory workers immunized with inactivated Rift Valley fever virus vaccines develop high levels of neutralizing antibodies and remain free from infection. Attenuated strains of Rift Valley fever virus have been developed with a view to their possible use as live viral vaccines. Hantavirus vaccines are being developed: one prepared using brains of newborn mice has been used in South Korea with no significant adverse reactions.

See also: **Attenuated organisms as vaccines; Vaccines; Viruses, immunity to.**

Further reading

Calisher CH and Nathanson N (1995) *Bunyavirus* infections. In: Porterfield JS (ed) *Exotic Viral Infections*, pp 247–260. London: Chapman & Hall.

Gonzalez-Scarano F and Nathanson N (1996) *Bunyaviridae*. In: Fields BN, Knipe DM, Howley PM *et al* (eds) *Fields Virology*, 3rd edn, pp 1473–1504. Philadelphia: Lippincott-Raven.

Khan AS, Ksiazek TG and Peters CJ (1996) Hantavirus pulmonary syndrome. *Lancet* **347**: 739–741.

LeDuc JW (1995) *Hantavirus* infections. In: Porterfield JS (ed) *Exotic Viral Infections*, pp 261–284. London: Chapman & Hall.

Peters CJ and Johnson KM (1995) California encephalitis virus, hantaviruses, and other Bunyaviridae. In: Mandell GL, Bennett JE and Dolin R (eds) *Principles and Practice of Infectious Diseases*, 4th edn, pp 1567–1572. New York: Churchill Livingstone.

Schmaljohn CS (1996) Bunyaviridae: the viruses and their replication. In: Fields BN, Knipe DM, Howley PM *et al* (eds) *Fields Virology*, 3rd edn, pp 1447–1472. Philadelphia: Lippincott-Raven.

Smithburn KC, Haddow AJ and Mahaffy AF (1946) A neurotropic virus isolated from *Aedes* mosquitoes caught in the Semliki Forest. *American Journal of Tropical Medicine and Hygiene* **26**: 189–208.

Swanepoel R (1995) *Nairovirus* infections. In: Porterfield JS (ed) *Exotic Viral Infections*, pp 285–293. London: Chapman & Hall.

Verani P and Nicoletti L (1995) *Phlebovirus* infections. In: Porterfield JS (ed) *Exotic Viral Infections*, pp 295–317. London: Chapman & Hall.

BURSA OF FABRICIUS

Paavo Toivanen, Department of Medical Microbiology, Turku University, Turku, Finland

The bursa of Fabricius is a sac-like lymphatic organ present only in birds and situated dorsal to the cloaca. It was first described by Hieronymus Fabricius, Professor of Anatomy and Surgery at Padua University in 1565–1610. Fabricius erroneously proposed the bursa to be a female organ into which the cockbird delivers semen, so that it may be stored. It was William Harvey, the most famous of the many students of Fabricius, who pointed out that the organ was present in both sexes and could not serve the function assumed by Fabricius. Thereafter it took more than three centuries until a serendipitous experiment by Bruce Glick in 1955 revealed the central role of the bursa of Fabricius in antibody production. Glick was involved in a demonstration for students, of antibody production against *Salmonella*. The only animals available were from an experiment where the birds had had the bursa of Fabricius removed soon after hatching. These birds failed to produce the antibody.

Development and structure

The bursal anlage is first observed in the chicken embryo at 4 days of incubation as an epithelial bud in the cloacal region. While enlarging, the bud becomes increasingly vacuolized, the coalescence of the vacuoles giving rise to the bursal lumen. Epithelial longitudinal folds are formed on the inner surface of the sac, and the columnal epithelium, covering the plicae, proliferates and forms outgrowths into the underlying lamina propria. Formation of these epithelial buds is dependent on interaction between the mesenchymal and epithelial tissues. Each epithelial bud is colonized by one or two prebursal stem cells. They proliferate vigorously, leading to formation of the medulla of the bursal follicles, which start to appear on day 12 of incubation in the chicken embryo. Prebursal stem cells originate in the intra-embryonic mesenchyme. On arrival at the bursa they have the germ-line immunogloublin (Ig) genes rearranged, being already committed to development along the B cell lineage. The period of prebursal stem cell arrival in the chicken bursa extends from day 8 to day 14 of incubation. Cells bearing IgM on the surface appear in the bursa on day 12 of embryogenesis. At the time of hatching, about 90% of the bursal cells carry surface IgM and <1% IgG or IgA.

The epithelial anlage of the bursa of Fabricius is decisive in providing differentiation signals to the arriving prebursal stem cells and to their descendants, the bursal stem cells. How the signals are mediated remains unknown, as no definitive evidence, e.g. for existence of a specific bursal hormone, is available.

Epithelial cells within the medulla form a loose cellular network with desmosome connections, and they are secretory in morphological structure. In addition to epithelial cells, the fully developed bursal medulla contains small lymphocytes, plasma cells and phagocytic histiocytic cells. Less than 1% of the bursal cells are T cells. They are mostly located in a diffusely infiltrated area of lymphoid cells, dorsal to the bursal duct opening to the cloaca. At the time of hatching lymphoid cells also appear in the mesenchymal tissue surrounding each follicular medulla, and a follicular cortex develops. The medulla and cortex are separated by a basement membrane.

At the plical surface against the bursal lumen the epithelial cells differentiate into a follicle-associated epithelium, with a specific function to phagocytose and transport antigenic material from the bursal lumen into the follicular medulla. The epithelial cells in the follicle-associated epithelium and within the bursal medulla are different in their phagocytic capacity and enzyme activities. Structural organization of the bursa is presented in **Figure 1**.

At the time of hatching the chick bursa of Fabricius weight 30–40 mg and reaches a maximum of 3–4 g at the age of 2–4 months. Thereafter, with the beginning of sexual maturation, it involutes, and both the lymphoid and epithelial structures have completely disappeared at the age of 6–12 months.

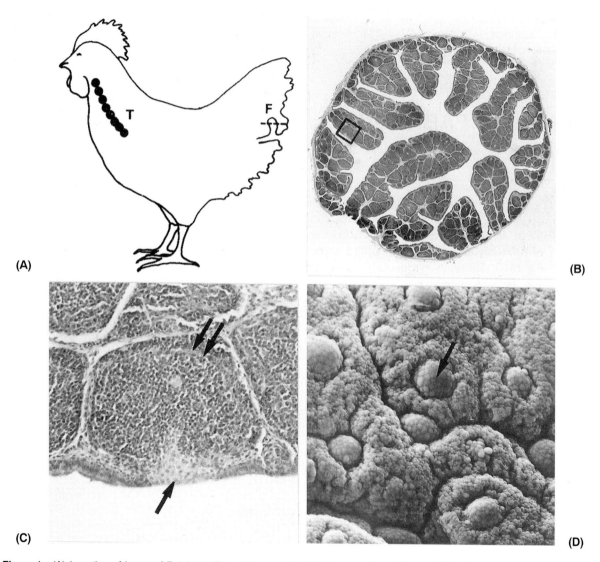

(A)   (B)   (C)   (D)

Figure 1   (A) Location of bursa of Fabricius (F) and thymus (T). (B) Cross-section of bursa of Fabricius at the level indicated by a broken line in Figure 1A. The plicae are longitudinal in dorsoventral direction, with a bursal lumen opening ventrally to the cloaca; 4-day-old chick. H & E; magnification × 10. (C) A bursal follicle from the area marked with a square in Figure 1B. The cortex and medulla are separated by a basement membrane (double arrows). The interfollicular epithelium against the bursal lumen is broken by the follicle-associated epithelium (arrow). H & E; magnification × 250. (D) Scanning electron micrograph of plical surface against the bursal lumen. The phagocytosing follicle-associated epithelium appears as clearly distinguishable areas (arrow). Magnification × 200.

Bursectomy

Experiments on birds with the bursal tissue removed have proved crucial in revealing the function of the bursa. Surgical bursectomy in the newly hatched period is not sufficient to prevent migration of B cells into the periphery because the cellular outflow starts during the embryonic period. The same holds true if the surgical bursectomy is carried out during late embryogenesis. More complete results have been obtained when the surgical bursectomy has been combined with *in ovo* treatment with antibodies against the heavy chain of IgM. Surgical removal of the bursal anlage can also be performed before the bursa is populated by prebursal stem cells. However, even in such animals, operated on days 2–5 of incubation, some plasma cells and antibodies with extremely limited antibody repertoire are found, indicating restricted extrabursal B cell maturation.

Other methods of bursectomy include treatment with testosterone or cyclophosphamide. Testosterone given *in ovo* also destroys the epithelial compartment of the bursa, whereas cyclophosphamide leaves it intact, allowing experimental repopulation by prebursal or bursal stem cells.

Central function

The bursa of Fabricius functions as a central lymphoid organ, required for development of the antigen-specific B cell repertoire. It is necessary for the differentiation of prebursal stem cells into bursal stem cells present in the bursa until the 5th week after hatching. These cells are capable of reconstituting the bursal morphology and specific antibody production when transferred into birds with the bursal lymphoid structures destroyed with cyclophosphamide in the newly hatched period. They comprise a clearly defined stage in the stepwise maturation of the avian antibody-producing cells.

The bursa of Fabricius is necessary for the development of the postbursal B cell population, including the mature antigen-specific B cells and the self-renewing postbursal stem cells. Neither of these populations is capable of homing, in contrast to the

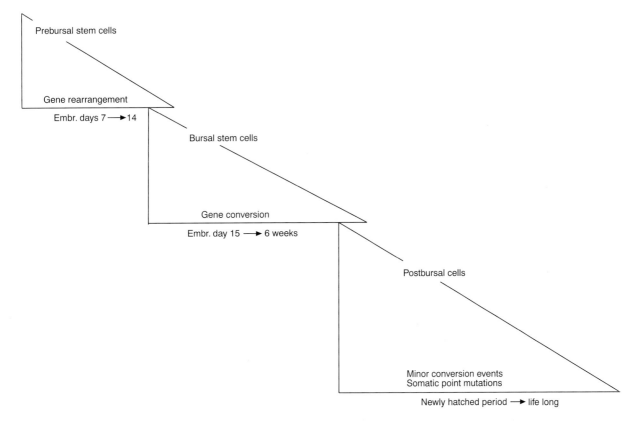

Figure 2 The bursa of Fabricius is necessary for the development of the antigen-specific B cell repertoire. Prebursal stem cells with germ line immunoglobulin genes rearranged are found in the intraembryonic mesenchyme from embryonic (Embr.) day 7 onwards. After arrival in the bursa of Fabricius they become bursal stem cells undergoing extensive, high rate gene conversion, which leads to diversification of the germ line repertoire; these cells need the bursal microenvironment for further maturation. Postbursal cells, present both in the bursa and periphery, include mature antigen-specific B cells and self-renewing postbursal stem cells, capable of further maturation without bursal influence.

prebursal or bursal stem cells, to the cyclophosphamide-treated bursal reticulum, even though they are capable of reconstituting antibody production. In other words, the postbursal cells have passed the stage of bursal development once and for all.

The bursa of Fabricius is necessary for the diversification of the antibody repertoire by providing a site for extensive, high rate gene conversion, which occurs between only one functional V gene (V_{H1} or V_{L1}) and a group of V pseudogenes. The bursal microenvironment selects and promotes for further differentiation bursal stem cells undergoing productive gene conversions, whereas all the others (>90%), probably with unproductive conversion events, die within the bursa. Only minor gene conversion events and somatic point mutations may occur outside the bursa. Molecular events in avian B cell development, as related to the central function of the bursa of Fabricius, are summarized in **Figure 2**.

Peripheral function

At the time of hatching the bursal lumen opens to the cloaca, allowing environmental antigens to enter the bursal space. The antigens arrive in the cloaca after digestion in the gastrointestinal tract and, with the help of anal sucking movements in the newly hatched period, also through the caudal end of the cloaca. The bursal follicles in turn have contact with the bursal lumen through the phagocytosing follicle-associated epithelium.

A peripheral function of the bursa of Fabricius in the uptake of environmental antigens has an important role in enforcing the expansion of specifically reacting B cell clones which lead to formation of plasma cells and memory cells.

Mammalian equivalent

In the mammalian species the basic, preimmune repertoire of antibody diversity is created in the fetal liver and bone marrow; the role of intestinal lymphoid tissue is negligible, as it is only weakly developed during the fetal period. In the postnatal expansion and selection of the antibody repertoire the intestinal lymphoid tissue also has an important function in the mammalian species. Peyer's patches play a key role here and have a similar follicular structure as in the bursa of Fabricius. In sheep, Peyer's patches may even have a central function similar to that of the bursa of Fabricius.

Mammalian species generate the antibody repertoire by use of multiple functional V (V_H and V_L) genes when compared to the few functional ones in the avian species. Therefore, by relying on gene rearrangement and other types of somatic diversification, mammals are able to create an extensive antibody repertoire without having an organ particularly specialized for this purpose.

See also: **Avian immune system; B lymphocyte differentiation; Diversity, generation of; Gene conversion; Humoral immunity; Immunodeficiency, animal models.**

Further reading

Mansikka A, Sandberg M, Lassila O and Toivanen P (1990) Rearrangement of immunoglobulin light chain genes in the chicken occurs prior to colonization of the embryonic bursa of Fabricius. *Proceedings of the National Academy of Sciences of the USA* 87: 9416–9420.

Masteller EL, Pharr GT, Funk PE et al (1997) Avian B cell development. *International Review of Immunology* 15: 185–206.

Payne LN and Powell PC (1984) The lymphoid system. In: Freeman BM (ed) *Physiology and Biochemistry of the Domestic Fowl*, pp 277–321. London: Academic Press.

Toivanen A and Toivanen P (eds) (1987) *Avian Immunology, Basis and Practice*, vol I. Boca Raton: CRC Press.

Weill J-C and Reynaud C-A (1996) Rearrangement/ hypermutation/gene conversion: when, where and why? *Immunology Today* 17: 92–97.

BYSTANDER EFFECTS

Jacques Thèze, Immunogenetique Cellulaire, Institut Pasteur, Paris, France

The fine specificity of effector cells and molecules for an eliciting antigen is usually considered the most important feature of an immune response. However, each immune response can in fact be viewed as being composed of two parts: 1) direct, antigen-specific interactions between cells, resulting in the specific response towards the antigen; and 2) indirect, non-antigen-specific phenomena, termed 'bystander' effects, resulting in polyclonal responses. Both aspects of the response occur simultaneously and account for the overall response, which comprises both specific and nonspecific events.

Bystander effects, as opposed to antigen-specific interactions, can therefore be defined as the result of cellular interactions occurring without antigen recognition or under conditions where antigen and receptors for antigen are not involved. However, bystander effects are described as phenomena linked to the specific immune response, in that they do not happen on their own but only in connection with a specific response. Cells that are not directly involved in the antigen-specific responses are then 'trans-stimulated' or 'carried along' in the response.

Experimental evidence for bystander effects

The existence of bystander phenomena involving T cell as well as B cell responses has been demonstrated in several *in vitro* experimental models.

T helper cell responses

Specific T cell proliferative responses are elicited by recognition through the T cell antigen receptor of the specific antigenic complex presented by specialized cells. Antigen-specific primed T cells proliferate when challenged *in vitro* with their specific antigen. However, in addition to antigen-specific T cells, the proliferative response can also affect neighboring T lymphocytes with unrelated T cell receptors. Proliferation of bystander T cells occurs independently of antigen recognition on antigen-presenting cells but simultaneously with a specific T cell proliferative response.

B cell responses

One of the most studied bystander phenomena concerns the T cell-dependent B cell response. B cell proliferation and antibody production in response to most soluble proteins requires the participation of T helper cells. This antigen specific T–B cooperation involves linked recognition of the antigen: the epitopes recognized by T and B cells need not be identical but need to be linked. This effect is known as the hapten-carrier effect. The interaction between T and B cells is termed cognate interaction and leads to the secretion by B cells of specific antibodies directed towards the eliciting antigen.

However, several *in vitro* experimental situations suggest that B cell responses can also be elicited under conditions of 'unlinked' recognition, where the antigens recognized by T helper cells and B cells are not covalently linked (bystander help).

When cultured in the presence of naive B cells and antigen, preactivated T cells, or T cell lines specific for a given antigen, elicit a specific B cell response

and antibody production (linked or cognate response). In addition, if another, unrelated antigen is added to the culture, antibody production against this unrelated antigen can also be observed in the culture (unlinked or bystander response). For example, sheep red blood cell (SRBC)-specific T cells induce SRBC-specific antibody production by B cells if SRBC but no horse red blood cells (HRBC) are present in the culture (specific response). However, when SRBC and HRBC are added together, simultaneous production of antibodies to SRBC and to HRBC is observed (specific and bystander response).

Other systems involving the bystander proliferation of B cells in response to specific T cells and antigens have been described. In response to cognate T–B cell interaction syngeneic B cells proliferate but proliferation of allogeneic B cell can also be observed in the culture. In this case, allogeneic B cells do not bear the appropriate major histocompatibility complex (MHC) class II antigens to be recognized by the T cell receptor but they are stimulated by nonspecific signals and/or interactions.

CTL responses

Cytotoxic T cells (CTLs) are differentiated effector T lymphocytes that specifically kill target cells bearing an appropriate antigenic complex (peptide–MHC) recognized by their T cell receptor. However, during this process, nonspecific lysis of unrelated bystander target cells can be observed in the culture. The unrelated target cells do not exhibit the appropriate antigenic complex on their surface and therefore cannot be recognized by the T cell receptor. This phenomenon can be detected *in vitro* using cytotoxic T cell lines of defined specificity and mixing together target cells bearing the appropriate or unrelated antigenic complex.

Possible mechanisms controlling bystander effects

Trans-stimulation of spectator T or B lymphocytes and killing of unrelated target cells imply that a signal can be transmitted to these cells independently of the structures involved in specific antigen recognition. Several explanations have been proposed but the exact mechanism controlling this phenomenon is still a matter of debate. In fact, whether there is an essential difference between specific and bystander effects is not clear and, apart from the process of antigen recognition, mechanisms involved in specific cellular responses could also be responsible for bystander responses.

Cytokines

The most accepted explanation for the existence of such nonspecific effects is the secretion of soluble factors – cytokines – by activated T lymphocytes. During the course of an antigen-specific T cell response, activated T lymphocytes release various lymphokines and, in particular, interleukin 2 (IL-2), IL-4, interferon γ (IFNγ) and tumor necrosis factor β (TNFβ; lymphotoxin). These lymphokines exhibit nonantigen specific, pleiotropic effects. They could act on any other cell present at the site of the immune response. These cells could be T or B lymphocytes, macrophages or target cells for CTLs, provided they are competent to respond to lymphokines (i.e. they express functional surface receptors for these factors). Local effects of such nonspecific factors on neighboring cells not directly involved in the antigen-specific response could explain the involvement of these cells in the overall response: for example, IL-2 could induce the proliferation of T cells and CTLs; IL-4 could transmit activation signals to naive B cells; and IFNγ and TNFβ could prepare target cells for CTL lysis.

Stage of lymphocyte activation

Bystander responses could be restricted to particular subpopulations of T or B lymphocytes that would be more susceptible to nonspecific signals. Of particular interest is the question of whether bystander effects involve cells in a particular stage of activation. Since cytokines are likely to be responsible for bystander effects, expression of cytokine receptors by the reacting cell may be an important key in this phenomenon.

Cell surface antigens

Cell-to-cell contact through specific and nonspecific cell surface molecules is obviously an important feature of antigen-specific responses. Similarly, nonantigen-specific cell-to-cell contact could occur during bystander responses. This could involve nonpolymorphic surface molecules, conserved regions of polymorphic cell surface molecules (including MHC molecules), or molecules induced after stimulation.

Polyclonal B lymphocytes can be stimulated in cultures containing T cells and a T cell mitogen or polyclonal activator (such as anti-CD3 or anti-T cell receptor monoclonal antibodies). Under these conditions, polyclonal B cell proliferation and antibody production are observed. Therefore, when efficient T cell stimulation is obtained, induction of a B cell response without any added antigen can be observed. In this case, bystander B cell stimulation is thought to be dependent upon T–B cell contact and probably involves recognition of B cell surface molecules by T cells (e.g. CD28/B7 interactions).

Similarly for CTL responses nonspecific attachment of any target cell to a specific cytotoxic T lymphocyte by means of lectins causes the lysis of the target cell independently of antigen recognition.

In vivo significance of bystander effects

Although bystander antibody production has been observed for primary responses in the mouse, bystander effects are more readily observed *in vitro* than *in vivo* and their physiological significance has been questioned. Nevertheless, it is known that a polyclonal, nonspecific response frequently accompanies any specific immune response *in vivo*. In particular, B cell responses to a given antigen generally consist of antibodies recognizing the initial antigen, together with a significant production of nonspecific immunoglobulins.

Bystander effects have been evoked to explain the onset of autoimmune responses, as self antigens could be present at the site of the immune response elicited by a foreign antigen. *In vitro* bystander responses can be obtained towards self antigens or normally tolerated antigens.

Finally, bystander phenomena might not have a precise role in the effector phase of the immune response and might simply reflect the existence of a network of connections between the different cellular elements of the immune system. These connections could be maintained by the cytokine network or cell surface molecule interactions. Altogether these interactions may participate in the homeostasis of the immune system.

See also: **Cooperation, mechanisms of cellular; Cytokines; Enhancement, immunological; Proliferation, lymphocyte; Specificity.**

Further reading

Nicos A (ed) (1994) *Guidebook to Cytokines and their Receptors*. Oxford: Oxford University Press.
Thèze J (1994) Cytokine receptors: a combinative family of molecules. *European Cytokine Network* 5: 353–368.
Thomson A (1994) *The Cytokine Handbook*. 2nd edn. London: Academic Press.

CALICIVIRUS, INFECTION AND IMMUNITY

Michael J Carter, School of Biological Sciences, University of Surrey, Guildford, UK

W David Cubitt, Institute of Child Health, Virology, Camelia Botnar Laboratories, Hospital for Children, Great Ormond Street, London, UK

Characteristics of the organism and its antigens

General features

The caliciviruses (**Table 1**) comprise a monogeneric family of 34 nm, nonenveloped viruses (**Figure 1**) with characteristic morphology; the surface is covered with cup-shaped depressions (L. *calix*, cup). In some caliciviruses (insect, rabbit) smooth particles are formed, possibly by partial proteolysis. These lack surface projections and are composed of smaller proteins. The calicivirus genome is single-stranded, positive-sense RNA and genes are arranged in two basic patterns.

Table 1 Probable and confirmed caliciviruses

Virus	Serotypes	Infection
San Miguel sea lion virus	16 or more	Vesicular
Vesicular exanthema of swine	13	FMDV-like
Feline calicivirus	1	URTI, stomatitis, limping syndrome
Rabbit hemorrhagic disease virus	1	Hemorrhagic hepatitis
European brown hare syndrome virus	1	Hemorrhagic hepatitis
Human calicivirus	5 or more 'typical' HuCV; 4–9 SRSV	Enteric infections
Hepatitis E virus	1	Hepatitis
Canine calicivirus	At least 2	1 Enteric; 1 vesicular
Infectious stunting calicivirus of chickens	?	Enteric infections
Newbury agent of cattle	2?	Enteric infections
Porcine enteric calicivirus	?	Enteric infections

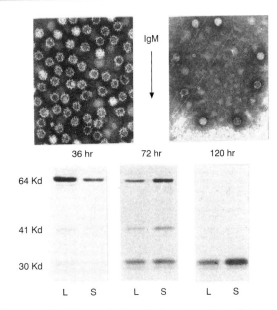

Figure 1 Particle morphology. Calicivirus particles (34 nm) are built from a single species of capsid protein which gives a characteristic morphology, unique among animal viruses; the structural proteins are linked by arch-like protuberances which ring the points of five- and threefold symmetry, giving the impression of cup-like depressions on the surface of the virus. Partial proteolysis occurring around 72hr pi may degrade the capsid protein forming smooth particles. Figures courtesy of Dr Lorenzo, Instituto Zooprofilattico Sperimentale, Brescia, Italy.

Feline calicivirus, some human caliciviruses, vesicular exanthema and San Miguel sea lion virus possess a genome that contains three sequential open reading frames (ORFs). ORF 1 encodes nonstructural proteins and ORF 2 the capsid protein. ORF 3 is of unknown function but known to be used. This basic structure appears to be flexible and in some viruses ORFs 1 and 2 are fused (e.g. rabbit hemorrhagic disease virus, European brown hare syndrome virus and some human caliciviruses). All viruses appear to synthesize two separate mRNAs, the first to direct the manufacture of ORF 1 proteins, and the second for proteins from both ORFs 2 and 3. Additional open reading frames have been reported in some of these viruses but there is no evidence that these are functional.

Hepatitis E virus (HEV), also possesses three ORFs but there are significant differences in the sequence of the genes. There is no protein equivalent of ORF 3 in the former viruses; the third ORF of HEV differs in position, sequence and probably in manner of expression. These differences have led to calls for the subdivision of the family. Multiple genera will certainly be required to account for these differences and HEV may be removed to a subfamily or possibly a different family entirely.

Best characterized members

HEV is endemic in parts of eastern Europe, Asia, Africa and South America. Symptoms and transmission are similar to hepatitis A and both infections are more severe in adults. Pregnant women are particularly vulnerable and can develop fulminant hepatitis (20–40% mortality).

Human caliciviruses were recognised as a cause of gastric illness in the 1970s; symptoms include diarrhea, vomiting, pyrexia, anorexia, abdominal pains, aching joints and nausea. Historically, human caliciviruses have been divided according to the clarity of their morphology: those with obvious calicivirus appearance were designated 'typical caliciviruses' (HuCV), e.g. HuCV/Sapporo; those in which the cup structure was indistinct were termed 'small round structured viruses' (SRSV), e.g. Norwalk virus (NV) and Hawaii virus (HV). However, underlying particle architecture and genome organization were similar in both cases and all are now termed human caliciviruses (HuCV); any subdivisions are best made according to RNA sequence. HuCV infect all age groups, although reportedly some occur more often in children (e.g. HuCV/Sapporo) and others in older individuals (NV, HV), but age distribution of infection varies geographically. When infections occur in hosts of the same age the clinical features are indistinguishable. Spread is through contaminated water or food, and especially consumption of shellfish from contaminated waters.

San Miguel sea lion virus (SMSV) is a common cause of death in neonatal pinnipeds and causes abortions in California sea lions. Vesicles or wart-like lesions occur on the tail and flippers.

Vesicular exanthema of swine virus (VESV) was identified in 1932 and is clinically indistinguishable from foot-and-mouth disease in pigs. High fever is often accompanied by severe diarrhea; vesicular lesions form on the tongue, lips and snout and between the toes. Strains vary in severity and some carry a high risk of piglet mortality. VESV is closely related to SMSV and may have originated as a cross-species infection, transmitted to pigs through uncooked sea lion meat in swill.

Feline calicivirus (FCV) is a major cause of upper respiratory tract infection (URTI) in Felidae but symptoms also include conjunctivitis, stomatitis and sometimes diarrhea. Some strains also cause polyarthritis (limping syndrome). Virulence is variable; mortality may reach 33% in kittens. Recovery is commonly accompanied by virus clearance, but persistent infections can be established in which apparently healthy animals continue to shed virus.

Rabbit hemorrhagic disease virus (RHDV) was described in China (1984), and is now widespread. Adult mortality is 40–90%, but younger animals (<2 months) often survive; this is not due to maternal antibody. RHDV is of major economic and ecologic importance, killing 64 million farmed rabbits in Italy in 1989, and drastically diminishing wild populations. Infection causes high fever and hemorrhagic viremia, and virus reaches high titer in many organs. Retrospective serology shows that a related (presumably nonpathogenic) virus predated the emergence of this condition.

European brown hare syndrome virus (EBHSV) is related to RHDV and has occurred throughout Europe since the 1980s. Clinical signs are similar, with high adult mortality (90–100%); however, the viruses do not cross host species and spread independently.

Antigen structure of the viruses

Many caliciviruses (especially human viruses) cannot be grown in culture, and conventional serotyping is impossible. Noncultivable viruses have been typed by ELISA, immunoelectron microscopy (IEM) or solid phase IEM (SPIEM) and both type-specific and common epitopes exist. However, reagents have been limited and independent classification schemes have been devised. These should be unified now that recombinant antigens are available.

FCV and RHDV/EBHSV are the best understood. The single structural protein is the major antigen for all viruses. In FCV neutralizing antibodies bind to a highly variable region of the capsid protein in the C-terminal half of the protein, which is presumably exposed on the virus surface. This region is bisected by a conserved sequence of 20 amino acids which may contribute to the cell-binding site, and antibodies binding here may prevent attachment; variability in this region could allow FCV to evade immune control. Nonneutralizing antibodies bind elsewhere. RHDV and EBHSV strains are well conserved and so potentially variable regions cannot be identified. However, most monoclonal antibodies (including those which are protective) also recognize the C terminal half of the protein. Such antibodies tend to be specific for RHDV or EBHSV and react poorly with smooth particles which lack the surface projections. Conversely, antibodies recognizing smooth particles tend not be protective and react with both RHDV and EBHSV. Thus the antigenically distinctive surface structure of the virus is probably formed by the C-terminal of the protein, while underlying structures are similar.

Immune responses of the host

Feline calicivirus

FCV infection causes transient lymphopenia and neutrophilia, but cats may also be infected with feline immunodeficiency virus (FIV), which also decreases lymphocyte number and immune response. Thus coinfection with FCV and FIV increases the clinical severity of infection. However, FIV has no effect on the period of FCV shedding and is not important in the establishment of persistent infections.

Persistently infected cats mount both cell-mediated and humoral immune responses but fail to clear the virus promptly. The reasons for this are unknown. The tonsils are the major site of persistence but tonsillectomy does not cure the infection and other lymphoid tissue may be involved; feline T lymphoblastoid cell lines have been persistently infected with FCV. Persistence may be lifelong but some studies imply a half-life of approximately 75 days, with animals spontaneously eliminating the virus.

Human caliciviruses

Seroprevalence studies still reflect the previous distinction between the typical caliciviruses and SRSVs (above). Exposure to one of these forms (SRSVs in particular) may induce antibody which cross-reacts with other viruses of the same form (i.e. other SRSVs). These cross-reactions may be one-way (presumably because the immunogenicity of certain epitopes is sometimes functionally masked). Thus a fourfold rise in antibody titer is not sufficient for diagnostic purposes, and an eightfold rise may be preferable; alternatively IgA is more type specific.

Reinfection by NV is believed to be common; surprisingly, pre-existing antibody (secretory or serum) has been correlated with susceptibility to illness. Recovery was associated with an antibody rise, but many volunteers were soon susceptible, becoming ill again on rechallenge. Thus adults may differ in susceptibility to NV – sensitive individuals being protected only by high titers acquired after several infections; however, other studies have not confirmed this correlation.

In Scandinavian countries, infection occurs early in childhood but adults are protected. Thus age at first exposure could be relevant to protection in adults. Swedish children soon develop immunoglobulin G1 (IgG1) responses to NV, but persons over 21 years old also showed NV-specific immunoglobulin G4 (IgG4), indicating repeated exposure, but it is not known how often this was associated with illness. Immunity to these agents thus requires more investigation.

In contrast, antibody to the morphologically typical HuCV is protective and mainly type specific. Antibodies to HuCV/Sapporo were detected in 65% of Japanese children aged 2–5 years and in 90% of those aged 6–12 years. A second virus, UK1, also circulates in Japan and 69% of children aged 6–12 years had antibodies to both viruses. Both viruses are probably distributed worldwide.

Evasive strategies of the virus

The FCV capsid protein is known to be variable (above). FCV comprises a single serotype but variation is such that sequential infection by antigenic variants is possible. During infection (persistent or acute), the antigenic profile of the virus may drift; virus isolated later in infection may be more vaccine resistant. This drift may allow the virus to resist herd immunity. It may also affect pathology by influencing host tissue range; for example, enteric forms of FCV resist bile salts, while respiratory forms do not. However, bile-resistant variants can be selected from bile-sensitive populations. Monoclonal antibodies may differentiate between strains associated with different clinical presentations, implying that some determinants of pathology may be close to antigenic regions.

Vaccines

Vaccines are available for FCV and RHDV. The FCV vaccine is based on a live virus, using a single strain (F9), chosen for low pathogenicity and cross-reactivity; it induces neutralizing antibody to approximately 50% of field strains. Protection is probably wider, as non-neutralizing antibody can protect *in vivo*. Recently FCV field strains have changed; this may reflect natural variation, but the effects of widespread vaccination with a strain of restricted antigenicity cannot be ruled out. These changes have not yet undermined the usefulness of F9 as a vaccine. Vaccine 'failure' is probably due to inadvertent vaccination of cats already incubating the virus after natural infection. Isolates obtained from postvaccination complications are not normally vaccine related, but are usually wild-type strains, susceptible to neutralization by vaccine-induced antibody. Multivalent vaccines may be required in future because low levels of antibodies to different strains give better neutralization than high levels of antibody to just one. Vaccination neither prevents nor cures a persistent infection.

The RHDV vaccine is made from virulent virus grown in rabbits and inactivated; it is effective but difficult to manufacture. The recently characterized nonpathogenic form of RHDV may be a suitable live vaccine if cultivation problems can be solved. Recently, recombinant virus-like particles (VLPs) have been developed for RHDV and are effective immunogens. VLPs have also been made for some of the human caliciviruses (e.g. NV and HV) but these have yet to be proven as vaccines.

See also: **Antigenic variation; Epitopes; Fascioliasis; Gastrointestinal tract infections; Immunoassays; Vaccines; Viruses, immunity to; Viruses, infection of immune cells by.**

Further reading

Ando T, Mulders MN, Lewis DC *et al* (1994) Comparison of the polymerase region of small round structured virus strains previously classified in three antigenic types by solid phase immune electron microscopy. *Archives of Virology* 135: 217–226.

Bradley DW (1990) Enterically-transmitted non-A, non-B hepatitis. *British Medical Bulletin* 46: 442–461.

Carter MJ and Cubitt WD (1995) Norwalk and related viruses. *Current Opinion in Infectious Diseases* 8: 403–409.

Carter MJ, Milton ID and Madeley CR (1991) Caliciviruses. *Reviews of Medical Virology* 1: 177–186.

Cubitt WD (1989) Diagnosis, occurrence and clinical significance of the human candidate caliciviruses. *Progress in Medical Virology* 36: 103–119.

Cubitt WD (1995) Caliciviruses. In: Kapikian AZ (ed) *Viral infections of the Gastrointestinal Tract*, pp 549–568. New York: Marcel Dekker.

Gaskell RM and Dawson S (1994) Viral-induced upper respiratory tract disease. In: Chandler EA, Gaskell CJ and Gaskell RM (eds) *Feline Medicine and Therapeutics*, 2nd edn, pp 453–472. Oxford: Blackwell Scientific.

Graham DY, Jiang X, Tanaka T *et al* (1994) Norwalk virus infection of volunteers: new insights based on improved assays. *Journal of Infectious Diseases* 170: 34–43.

Gray JJ, Cunliffe C, Ball J *et al* (1994) Detection of immunoglobulin M (IgM), IgA and IgG Norwalk virus-specific antibodies by indirect enzyme-linked immunosorbent assay with baculovirus-associated Norwalk virus capsid antigen in adult volunteers challenged with Norwalk virus. *Journal of Clinical Microbiology* 32: 3059–3063.

Johnson RP (1992) Antigenic change in feline calicivirus during persistent infection. *Canadian Journal of Veterinary Research* 56: 326–330.

Kapikian AZ, Estes MK and Chanock RM (1996) Norwalk group of viruses. In: Fields BN, Kneipe PM, Howley PM *et al* (eds) *Fields Virology* (3rd edn), pp 783–810. Philadelphia: Lippincott-Raven.

Lambden PR, Caul EO, Ashley CR *et al* (1994) Human enteric caliciviruses are genetically distinct from small round structured viruses. *Lancet* 343: 666–667.

Neill JD, Meyer RF and Seal BS (1995) Genetic relatedness of the caliciviruses – San Miguel sealion and vesicular exanthema of swine viruses constitute a single genotype within the caliciviridae. *Journal of Virology* 69: 4484–4488.

Parrino TA, Schrieber DS, Trier JS *et al* (1977) Clinical immunity in acute gastroenteritis caused by Norwalk agent. *New England Journal of Medicine* 96: 756–761.

Prasad BV, Rothnagel R, Jiang X *et al* (1994) Three-dimensional structure of baculovirus-expressed Norwalk virus capsids. *Journal of Virology* 68: 5117–5125.

Seal BS (1994) Analysis of capsid protein gene variation among divergent isolates of feline calicivirus. *Virus Research* 33: 39–53.

CAMPATH-1 ANTIGEN (CD52)

Geoff Hale, Sir William Dunn School of Pathology, University of Oxford, Oxford, UK

The CD52 antigen of human lymphocytes was first defined with monoclonal antibodies isolated in the Department of Pathology, University of Cambridge. It is a lipid-anchored glycoprotein, unusual in having an extremely small peptide component. CD52 antibodies are remarkably lytic, killing cells *in vitro* with human complement, and also *in vivo*, probably by other mechanisms. They have many possible applications for therapy, for example in treatment of leukemia, bone marrow transplantation, organ transplantation, rheumatoid arthritis, vasculitis and multiple sclerosis.

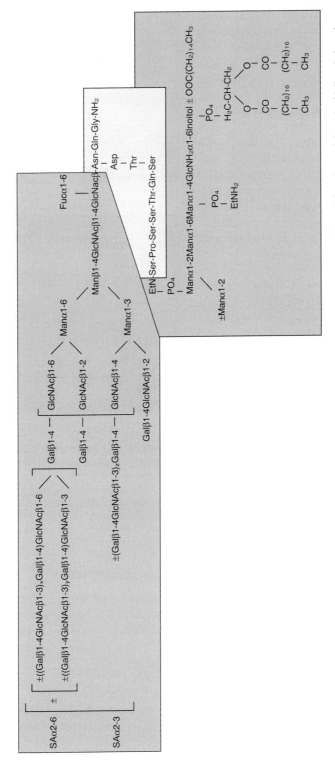

Figure 1 Primary structure of the CD52 antigen, showing the large *N*-linked carbohydrate, the small peptide and the glycosylphosphatidylinositol anchor. (Reproduced with permission from Treumann *et al.* (1995).)

Monoclonal antibodies

Many CD52 antibodies have been generated including different rat isotypes (e.g. CAMPATH-1M, rat immunoglobulin M (IgM) and CAMPATH-1G, rat IgG2b), matched sets of chimeric human/rat IgG and a variety of mutants. These have been used to demonstrate the role of IgG isotype for complement activation and Fc receptor binding, showing that rat IgG2b and human IgG1 are among the best subclasses for activating human effector systems. However, even human IgG4 (previously thought to be inert) was able to deplete human lymphocytes *in vivo*. CAMPATH-1H (human IgG1) was the first fully humanized monoclonal antibody. It was created by transplantation of the complementarity-determining regions of CAMPATH-1G into human heavy and light chain genes. Initial binding affinity was diminished, but this was corrected by small modifications to framework residues. Administration of the humanized antibody to patients has greatly reduced the possible antiglobulin response, compared with the original rat antibody. Following this experience, most other therapeutic antibodies are likely to be humanized.

Antigen structure

The CD52 antigen is well defined at a genetic and structural level, but its function is currently unknown. Encoded by a single gene on chromosome 1, it is a remarkably small glycoprotein, having only 12 amino acids (**Figure 1**). Attached to Asn3 is a complex carbohydrate consisting of sialylated polylactosamine units with a tetra-antennary fucosylated mannose core. At the C-terminus is a glycosylphosphatidylinositol (GPI) anchor. The CAMPATH-1 epitope includes the C-terminal amino acids and part of the GPI anchor. This implies that the antibodies bind close to the cell membrane, which explains why they are so good for cell lysis. Other antigens with a similar structure to CD52 include CD24 and its mouse homologue J5 (heat-stable antigen).

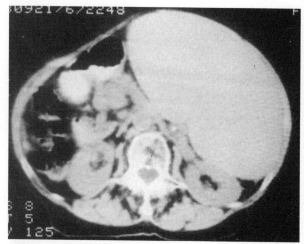

(A)

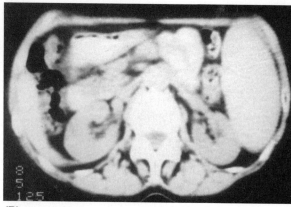

(B)

Figure 3 Treatment of prolymphocytic leukemia with CAMPATH-1H. Complete clearance of tumor cells from blood and bone marrow was achieved, together with substantial reduction in the mass of tumor in the spleen, as shown by these computed tomograms taken (A) before and (B) after therapy. In total it was estimated that approx 4 kg of tumor was cleared by 126 mg of antibody. (Reproduced with permission from Hale *et al.* (1988).)

Tissue distribution

The distribution of the CD52 antigen is one of its most distinctive features. In humans the antigen is abundantly expressed on virtually all lymphocytes at most stages of differentiation (except plasma cells)

Human	GQ − − − − − NDTS− − − − − − − − − − − − − − − QTSSPS
Monkey	SQ − − − − − NATS− − − − − − − − − − − − − − − Q-SSPS
Mouse	GQATTAASGTNKNSTS− − − − − − − − − − − − − − − TKKTPLKS
Rat	GQ − − − − − NSTAVTTPANKAATTAAATTKAAATTATKTTTAVRKTPGKPPKA
Dog	G − − − − − −NST − − − − − − − − − − PRMTTKKVKSATPA

Figure 2 Comparison of CD52 protein sequences from different species showing the diversity of the mature sequences. Signal peptides (not shown) are much more similar. The human peptide has a single *N*-linked oligosaccharide. The rat peptide (SMemG) probably has, in addition, up to 14 *O*-linked oligosaccharides attached to the various Thr residues.

and also on monocytes, macrophages and eosinophils. T cells have approximately 450 000 molecules per cell. The antigen is not found on any other tissues except the male reproductive tract, where it is expressed very strongly on epithelial cells lining the epididymis, vas deferens and seminal vesicle. Antigen is shed from these cells in large quantities into seminal plasma, where it exists in small micellar particles and in larger membrane-bound structures called prostasomes. From these, it can be transferred to other cells, particularly spermatozoa. The CD52 antigen, along with other GPI-anchored antigens such as CD55 and CD59, is a major membrane protein of sperm, acquired during maturation. It is a matter of speculation whether transfer of GPI-anchored molecules from one cell to another is of more general physiological significance. Genes homologous to human CD52 have been described in monkey, dog, rat and mouse. They are all expressed in the male reproductive tissues and (where tested) in lymphocytes. Although the genes have substantial homology in the nontranslated regions and signal peptides, the short mature peptides are quite different (**Figure 2**).

Antibodies in therapy

CAMPATH-1 antibodies have been used in a variety of clinical trials. The IgM antibody, CAMPATH-1M, was developed for prevention of graft-versus-host disease by depletion of donor T cells from bone marrow. This was very effective, but resulted in an increased risk of graft rejection and of leukemia relapse. Now CAMPATH-1G or CAMPATH-1H are being tested for simultaneous control of both donor and host T cells, with a proportion of donor T cells being kept for later administration in the event of leukemia recurrence. CAMPATH-1H has been used for treatment of lymphoid malignancies and was very effective in patients with certain leukemias (T cell prolymphocytic leukemia and B chronic lymphocytic leukemia), but less so in patients with solid tumor masses (**Figure 3**). It has also been used as an immunosuppressive agent for treatment of transplant rejection and autoimmune diseases, including rheumatoid arthritis, vasculitis and multiple sclerosis (**Figure 4**). Treatment resulted in longlasting lymphopenia, particularly of CD4$^+$ cells, which may not

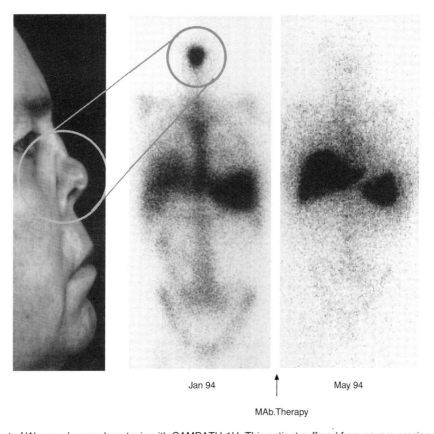

Jan 94   ↑   May 94

MAb.Therapy

Figure 4 Treatment of Wegener's granulomatosis with CAMPATH-1H. This patient suffered from severe erosion of sinus passages due to leukocyte infiltration, as shown by whole body scanning after injection of ^{111}In-labeled leukocytes (area circled). Antibody treatment depleted the T cells which were driving the inflammatory process and this resulted in a normal leukocyte scan and disease stabilization for at least 12 months. (Reproduced with permission from Reuter *et al.* (1995).)

return to normal blood levels for several years. The immunological significance of this is not obvious as few, if any, of the patients appear to suffer any long-term immunodeficiency. The majority of patients experienced an improvement in symptoms (in the case of multiple sclerosis, a decline in the frequency of new lesions) which lasted from 2 months to over a year. In the event of relapse, retreatment was possible and only infrequently limited by an anti-idiotype response.

In a minority of patients, the first lymphocytes to regenerate lacked GPI-anchored proteins. This is characteristic of cells in paroxysmal nocturnal hemoglobinuria (PNH) and probably results from a somatic mutation in the X-linked PIG-A gene which codes for a critical step in GPI biosynthesis. Considering the frequency and time course of appearance of these cells, it seems unlikely that a mutation was induced by therapy, rather that it selected GPI-deficient cells already present at low numbers. So far, these cells appear to have normal functions and may even mediate graft rejection. Patients do not appear to suffer any adverse effect and in due course they are replaced by normal lymphocytes.

Conclusion

The CD52 antigen is an unusual molecule which provides a model for studying the role of carbohydrate and GPI anchors in immune and reproductive systems. The lytic ability of CD52 antibodies *in vivo* raises many possibilities for therapy and for study of the role of lymphocytes in different diseases.

See also: **Antilymphocyte serum; Autoimmune diseases; Complement, classical pathway; Glycosylation of immune system molecules; Graft-versus-host reaction; Idiotype; Immunosuppression; Leukemia; Monoclonal antibodies (mAbs); Multiple sclerosis; Rheumatoid arthritis, human; Transplantation.**

Further reading

Dyer MJS, Hale G, Hayhoe FGJ and Waldmann H (1989) Effects of CAMPATH-1 antibodies *in vivo* in patients with lymphoid malignancies: influence of antibody isotype. *Blood* **73**: 1431–1439.

Friend PJ, Rebello P, Oliveira D *et al* (1995) Successful treatment of renal allograft rejection with a humanized antilymphocyte monoclonal antibody. *Transplantation Proceedings* **27**: 869–870.

Hale G and Phillips JM (1995) Clinical trials with CAMPATH-1 and other monoclonal antibodies. *Biochemical Society Transactions* **23**: 1057–1063.

Hale G and Waldmann H (1994) CAMPATH-1 monoclonal antibodies in bone marrow transplantation. *Hematotherapy* **3**: 15–31.

Hale G, Dyer MJS, Clark MR *et al* (1988) Remission induction in non-Hodgkin lymphoma with reshaped human monoclonal antibody CAMPATH-1H. *Lancet* **ii**: 1394–1399.

Hale G, Rye PD, Warford A, Lauder I and Brito-Babapulle A (1993) The GPI-anchored lymphocyte antigen CDw52 is associated with the epididymal maturation of human spermatozoa. *Journal of Reproductive Immunology* **23**: 189–205.

Isaacs JD, Watts RA, Hazleman BL *et al* (1992) Humanised monoclonal antibody therapy for rheumatoid arthritis. *Lancet* **340**: 748–752.

Kirchhoff C and Hale G (1996) Cell to cell transfer of glycosylphosphatidylinositol-anchored membrane proteins during sperm maturation. *Molecular Human Reproduction* **2**: 177–184.

Kirchhoff C, Krull N, Pera I and Ivell R (1992) A major mRNA of the human epididymal principal cells, HE5, encodes the leucocyte differentiation CDw52 antigen peptide backbone. *Molecular Reproduction and Development* **34**: 11–15.

Lockwood CM, Thiru S, Isaacs JD, Hale G and Waldmann H (1993) Humanised monoclonal antibody treatment for intractable systemic vasculitis. *Lancet* **341**: 1620–1622.

Mehta J, Powles R, Treleaven J *et al* (1997) Autologous transplantation with CD52 monoclonal antibody-purged marrow for acute lymphoblastic leukemia: long-term follow-up. *Leukemia Lymphoma* **25**: 479–486.

Moreau T, Thorpe J, Miller D *et al* (1994) Preliminary evidence from magnetic resonance imaging for reduction in disease activity after lymphocyte depletion in multiple sclerosis. *Lancet* **344**: 298–301.

Osterborg A, Dyer MJ, Bunjes D *et al* (1997) Phase II multicenter study of human CD52 antibody in previously treated chronic lymphocytic leukemia. European Study Group of CAMPATH-1H Treatment in Chronic Lymphocytic Leukemia. *Journal of Clinical Oncology* **15**: 1567–1574.

Osterborg A, Fassas AS, Anagnostopoulos A, Dyer MJ, Catovsky D and Mellstedt H (1996) Humanized CD52 monoclonal antibody Campath-1H as first-line treatment in chronic lymphocytic leukemia. *British Journal of Hematology* **93**: 151–153.

Reuter H, Wraight EP, Qasim FJ and Lockwood CM (1995) Management of vasculitis: the contribution of scintigraphic imaging to the evaluation of disease activity and classification. *Quarterly Journal of Medicine* **88**: 509–516.

Riechmann L, Clark M, Waldmann H and Winter G (1988) Reshaping human antibodies for therapy. *Nature* **332**: 323–327.

Treumann A, Lifely R, Schneider P and Ferguson MAJ (1995) Primary structure of CD52. *Journal of Biological Chemistry* **270**: 6088–6099.

Xia M-Q, Hale G, Lifely MR *et al* (1993) Structure of the CAMPATH-1 antigen, a GPI-anchored glycoprotein which is an exceptionally good target for complement lysis. *Biochemical Journal* **29**: 633–640.

CAMPYLOBACTER, INFECTION AND IMMUNITY

Diane G Newell, Central Veterinary Laboratory, Weybridge, UK

Characteristics of the organism and its antigens

The *Campylobacter* genus comprises several species of gram-negative, highly motile, bacteria with an S-shaped morphology and microaerobic growth requirements. Clinically the most important *Campylobacter* species are the thermophilic organisms, *C. jejuni* and *C. coli*, which colonize and invade the small intestine and colon and are the most common cause of human acute bacterial enteritis. Asymptomatic infection is common in underdeveloped countries but in susceptible patients diarrhea occurs, usually 3 days after infection, and lasts 2–3 days, although excretion may continue for several weeks. The mechanisms by which these campylobacters cause enteritis are, as yet, unknown but may involve adherence, invasion and/or toxin production. Several other *Campylobacter* species, including *C. lari*, *C. hyointestinalis*, *C. concisus* and *C. upsaliensis* have also been implicated as causative agents of enteritis. All these enteric campylobacters may also cause blood and systemic infections. *C. fetus* subsp. *fetus* usually causes opportunistic septicemic infections in humans. Campylobacteriosis is generally self-limiting but arthritis and glomerulonephritis are not uncommon reactive complications and about 50% of cases of Guillain–Barré syndrome are thought to be associated with a prior *C. jejuni* infection.

In the following text the term 'campylobacter' will refer to the *C. jejuni/coli* group of organisms unless otherwise stated. The strains in this group are diverse and two serotyping schemes have been developed for use in epidemiologic tracing. The Lior serotyping scheme is based on heat-labile antigens and utilizes slide agglutination of live bacteria with serotype-specific rabbit antisera preabsorbed with homologous heated and heterologous unheated cross-reactive antigens. Flagellin is considered to be one of the antigens involved in this serotyping scheme. The Penner serotyping scheme is based on heat-stable antigens and involves the passive hemagglutination of erythrocytes, sensitized with boiled saline bacterial extracts, by serotype-specific rabbit sera. Lipopolysaccharides (LPSs) are though to be the dominant heat-stable antigen involved in this scheme.

Several surface protein antigens of the campylobacters have been described. The most well characterized antigens are the flagellins. The campylobacters have single, bipolar flagella. In animal models using isogenic mutants fully active flagella are essential virulence factors. There are two flagellin genes (*flaA* and *flaB*) in tandem in all strains, although only one of these genes may be expressed. The flagellins have a molecular weight of approximately 62 kDa and are the major protein surface antigen. The antigenicity of campylobacter flagellin is complex and epitopic analysis indicates that common as well as serotype-specific linear epitopes are expressed. The common epitopes are antigenically cross-reactive with flagellins from most *Campylobacter* species, including *C. fetus fetus*, *C. lari* and *Helicobacter pylori* (formerly *C. pylori*). Antigenic variations occur between these flagellins, and a microheterogeneity in charge properties due to post-translational modification, probably glycosylation, also demonstrates some antigenic variation. Additionally there is a reversible transition between flagellated and aflagellated variants.

There are several other conserved groups of protein antigens. The variable molecular weight (42–47 kDa) major outer membrane protein (MOMP) is surface exposed. The antigenicity of this protein mainly relies on its native conformation and it is antigenically cross-reactive with similar proteins in *C. coli* and *C. lari* but not other *Campylobacter* species. A group of surface extractable antigens (26–32 kDa), called the PEB proteins (PEB 1–4), have been isolated and partly characterized. PEB 1 has been cloned and sequenced and may have adherence properties. Some of the campylobacters produce detectable toxins, one of which has some antigenic cross-reactivity with cholera toxin, but is structurally different, comprising a 66 kDa polypeptide, probably a holotoxin, and a series of antigenically related subunits. Recently the expression of pili on *C. jejuni* has been described but the role of these structures in pathogenicity has yet to be determined.

Immune response of the host

Patients with campylobacter enteritis produce a rapid circulating antibody response. These antibodies have complement fixing, bactericidal and agglutinating properties. The initial specific immunoglobulin M (IgM) response is produced by the 8th day of infection and is relatively short lived. This is followed by a rapid serum polymeric and monomeric IgA response, which peaks at about 2 weeks after onset of symptoms but disappears by the 5th week. The IgG antibodies are detectable within 10 days of the illness and persist for several months. The short illness generally associated with campylobacter enteritis suggests that these antibodies are effective at limiting infection. The antibody responses form the basis of a serologic test for the retrospective diagnosis of infection using ELISA, with an acid-extractable surface antigen which primarily comprises flagellin.

Analysis of the antigenic specificity of the host immune responses shows that the immunodominant surface antigen is flagellin. Antibodies directed against this polypeptide are produced early in infection and may be protective. The MOMP is also immunogenic, during infection, in most patients. When present all these antibodies react against homologous and heterologous strains. LPSs appear to induce inconsistent antibody responses, which when present may be serotype specific.

Guillian–Barré syndrome is characterized by acute motor neuropathy, which appears to be a sequela of campylobacter enteritis in about 50% of cases. Many patients with this disease have increased circulating IgG and IgM antibodies binding to GM1 and GD1 ganglioside epitopes and which cross-react with LPS of certain serotypes of *C. jejuni*, especially types O:19 and O:4.

To date, T cell responses to the campylobacters have been poorly investigated.

Evasive strategies by the organism

No mechanism by which *C. jejuni/coli* evade the host immune response has been identified; however, in some experimental models virulence is associated with persistence in the bloodstream, survival in extraintestinal organs and resistance to macrophage ingestion. One potential mechanism for bacterial avoidance of host immune responses could be antigenic variation of the flagellin proteins.

C. fetus fetus has a well-defined microcapsule, comprising surface array proteins (S-layer proteins), which is responsible for resistance to the complement-mediated bactericidal activity of normal human serum and phagocytosis by polymorphonuclear cells. These S-layer proteins, which form a crystalline subunit structure on the outer surface of the bacterium, have a range of molecular weights (97–149 kDa) and are encoded by about eight homo-

logs of the *sapA* gene. The S-layer proteins are highly immunogenic during infection. There is significant antigenic variation between each of these proteins, and antigenic switching occurs throughout infection, apparently enabling the persistence of this organism in host tissues.

Vaccines

The evidence suggesting that protective immune responses can be produced after campylobacter infection includes: a progressive decrease in the illness:infection ratio in children from underdeveloped countries with endemic infections; high antibody levels and asymptomatic infections after multiple exposures to campylobacter-contaminated foodstuffs; and the development of protective immunity to rechallenge in experimentally infected volunteers and nonhuman primates. Passive immunization may also be effective as campylobacter-specific sIgA antibodies in breast milk apparently protects infants from disease. These sIgA antibodies are primarily directed against flagellin. Epidemiologic evidence suggests that protective immunity controls the symptoms of disease but does not necessarily prevent intestinal colonization.

Vaccines against campylobacter enteritis are currently under development. A killed whole-cell vaccine induces protection in a mouse model using the heat-labile toxin of *Escherichia coli* (LT) as the mucosal adjuvant. The same vaccine has been successfully tested for safety and immunogenicity in nonhuman primates. Potential candidates for subunit vaccines include the flagellins and other surface acid-extractable proteins.

See also: **Bacteria, immunity to; Bacterial cell walls; Endotoxin (lipopolysaccharide (LPS)); Neurological autoimmune diseases; Opportunistic infections; Toxins.**

Further reading

Hartug HP, Pollard JD, Harvey GK and Toyka KV (1995) Immunopathogenesis and treatment of the Guillain–Barré syndrome – Part I. *Muscle and Nerve* 18: 137–153.

Nachamkin I, Blaser MJ, Tompkins LS (eds) (1992) Campylobacter jejuni: *Current Status and Future Trends.* Washington DC: ASM Press.

Newell DG, Ketley J and Feldman RA (eds) (1996) *Campylobacters, Helicobacters and Related Organisms.* New York: Plenum Press.

CANDIDA, INFECTION AND IMMUNITY

David K Wagner and **Peter G Sohnle**, VA Medical Center, Milwaukee, Wisconsin, USA

Characteristics of the organism and its antigens

Infections due to organisms in the genus *Candida* are relatively common, with a variety of different manifestations of disease in both humans and animals. These organisms all grow as yeast and most of the individual species also have filamentous forms, which are either pseudohyphae or true hyphae. There are over 150 species of *Candida*, but only 10 are significant pathogens for humans. These species include: *C. albicans, C. glabrata* (formerly *Torulopsis glabrata*), *C. parapsilosis, C. krusei, C. guillermondii, C. Stellatoidea* (now considered *C. albicans*), *C. tropicalis, C. pseudotropicalis, C. lusitaniae* and *C. rugosa*. Of these, *C. albicans* is the primary pathogen for humans.

Candida can produce a wide variety of human infections that can be generally divided into superficial and deep infections. Superficial *Candida* infections involve skin, nails or mucous membranes of the mouth and vagina. Deep *Candida* infections include candidemia, localized infections of various deep tissues, and disseminated candidiasis in immunosuppressed patients. This classification is significant because the host defense mechanisms involved in the two groups of infections may be different. In particular, cell-mediated immunity is a primary host defense in superficial candidiasis, while neutrophils (and possibly macrophages) are important in deep candidiasis. Hence, patients with the acquired immune deficiency syndrome (AIDS) and its prominent T cell immune defect commonly have oral thrush, but usually do not have deep *Candida* infections. On the other hand, patients with hematologic and other malignancies who become neutropenic during chemotherapy are more at risk for deep *Candida* infections.

The antigens of these organisms are complex, and infected patients often respond to a number of cell wall, cell membrane or cytoplasmic components. The major cell surface antigen of *Candida* is mannin, a part of the cell wall. *C. albicans* isolates have been serotyped into two groups, A and B, by antigenic differences in their mannins. Cytoplasmic antigens of this organism have also been extensively studied for use in the diagnosis of *Candida* infections. Humoral immunity to a cytoplasmic antigen of approximately 50 kDa in patients with deep candidiasis has been described by a number of investigators. Unfortunately, immunosuppressed patients at the highest risk of serious disease may not have an appropriate antibody response, and often have false-negative antibody levels. Also, because some patients with superficial *Candida* infections may develop a significant antibody response, the assays for humoral immunity to *Candida* antigens have not proven to be useful diagnostically. However, because an early clinical diagnosis of systemic *Candida* infection is frequently difficult, there is interest in other serologic tests. Testing for the presence of *Candida* cytoplasmic antigens has been described by multiple investigators. Unfortunately, this test has a high incidence of false negative results. It has been suggested that the antigen does not circulate or may not circulate in a detectable form. Other diagnostic tests more recently studied include amplification of *Candida* DNA by polymerase chain reaction (PCR). This assay can detect as few as 15 cells of *Candida* in clinical specimens, but its clinical utility remains to be determined.

Immune responses of the host

Candida species are found commonly in the environment, and can be recovered from the soil. They are normal flora in the human gastrointestinal tract, and can often be found at other mucosal sites and on diseased skin. The initial host defenses are the nonspecific barriers including intact skin and mucosal epithelium, as well as the indigenous bacterial flora that competes for binding sites. Breakdown of these barrier functions, (e.g. from burns or indwelling intravascular devices) allows for invasive *Candida* infections. Once the organisms invade past the nonspecific defenses, the major cellular mechanism against *Candida* infections is through neutrophils. These cells are capable of phagocytosing *Candida* spores as well as damaging the pseudohyphae. Intracellular killing appears to be primarily through oxidative mechanisms. Other cells of the immune system (monocytes and eosinophils) are also able to phagocytose and kill *Candida* organisms. Even so, the initial response in the tissues is predominantly by neutrophils, frequently with the formation of microabscesses in infected tissues. This response may be reduced in patients with significant impairment of host defenses, particularly in neutropenic patients or those on pharmacologic doses of corticosteroids. With more chronic infections the inflammatory response usually becomes mononuclear. In cutaneous candidiasis, the organsisms are generally confined to the stratum corneum; the resulting inflammatory response may be an epidermal accumulation of neutrophils in acute infections, or a dermal mononuclear cell response in more chronic infections. Both yeast and pseudohyphae are seen in infected tissues of both deep and superficial sites, although the filamentous forms are generally felt to be more characteristic of tissue invasion.

Because *C. albicans* is part of the normal gastrointestinal flora, the majority of normal human subjects will show evidence of prior sensitization to the antigens of this organism. Most people will have low levels of antibodies to *Candida* mannin. In infected patients, elevated levels of *Candida*-specific antibodies have been found, representing the IgG, IgM and IgA immunoglobulin classes. Elevated salivary IgA levels have also been demonstrated in response to *Candida* stomatitis, and IgA levels against this organism have been found in vaginal secretions. In addition, patients with either allergic respiratory diseases or the hyper IgE syndrome have been demonstrated to have elevated levels of IgE antibodies specific for *Candida*. Whereas antibody titers to *Candida* are usually elevated in infected patients, the humoral immune response does not appear to play a major role in host defense against *Candida*. It has been shown, for instance, that serum and plasma alone (containing antibodies and complement) are not able to kill *Candida* organisms.

In addition to making antibodies, most people will also demonstrate delayed hypersensitivity to *Candida* antigens when subjected to skin testing with extracts of this organism. As described above, patients with defects in cell-mediated immunity are at higher risk for superficial *Candida* infections. This finding is especially apparent in conditions such as AIDS and in the condition known as chronic mucocutaneous candidiasis. AIDS patients are commonly afflicted with recurrent oral *Candida* infections. Patients with chronic mucocutaneous candidiasis have long-lasting and often disfiguring superficial candidiasis without obvious predisposing causes. Endocrinopathies, thymomas, vitiligo, alopecia, and a tendency to develop other types of infections are found in some of these patients. A variety of immunologic abnormalities have been described in this condition, but of these, defective cell-mediated immunity to *Candida* antigens, as manifested by negative delayed hypersensitivity skin tests and abnormal *in vitro* assays of lymphocyte function, have been found most consistently. In contrast, patients at risk for deep candidiasis usually have other types of predisposing factors such as neutro-

penia, steroid therapy, indwelling vascular devices, broad-spectrum antibiotic therapy, and the like. Some of these factors may also enhance the patient's susceptibility to superficial candidiasis as well.

Evasive strategies by the organism

Adhesion is an important initial step in infection of epithelial or mucosal sites. In this regard, *Candida* organisms have been shown to express three types of adhesion molecules. After adhesion of the organisms, other potentially important virulence factors of *Candida* which may assist in promoting invasive disease include lytic enzymes, hyphal formation, and contact sensing. One lytic enzyme, an aspartyl proteinase, may assist penetration into the stratum corneum. Another enzyme, a keratinase, allows invading organisms to use keratin as a source of nutrients. Hyphal formation appears to be useful both in establishing colonization of surfaces and in tissue invasion but may not be absolutely essential for invasion. Contact sensing (also called thigmotropism), may also be a possible mechanism by which *Candida* organisms distribute and align themselves in order to penetrate surfaces.

Infection of superficial sites such as the skin, mucous membranes and nails may also be a method by which *Candida* organisms can avoid a vigorous inflammatory response. In acute infection, neutrophils do seem to be able to reach the site in the stratum corneum where the organisms reside; however, in chronic mucocutaneous candidiasis this infiltrate is generally not present, and the mononuclear infiltrate which does occur is usually confined to the dermis and is therefore not directly in contact with the organisms.

As discussed above, neutrophils appear to be a very important component of the host's defense against *Candida* invasion into deep tissues. These cells are capable of ingesting and killing *C. albicans* yeast cells *in vitro*; however, unkilled yeast cells have also been observed to germinate within neutrophils and perforate through the cell membrane to the outside of the cell. More virulent strains of *C. albicans* have been demonstrated in one study to be relatively resistant to intracellular killing by human or mouse neutrophils, perhaps because they form germ tubes more rapidly than do less virulent strains. Therefore, germination to the filamentous hyphal or pseudohyphal forms may be a mechanism by which this organism can avoid killing by phagocytic cells. In addition, the filamentous forms of *C. albicans* have been shown to release a soluble product which inhibits chemotaxis, adherence, iodination of ingested particles, and superoxide production.

Vaccines

Studies with experimental animals have shown that vaccination with *C. albicans* preparations containing cell surface antigens can be protective when the animals were challenged with *Candida* organisms. However, as described above, most normal human subjects show both humoral and cell-mediated immunity to *Candida* antigens in the absence of preceding vaccination or known infection. Because lack of exposure to the organism does not appear to be involved in the susceptibility of humans to *Candida* infections (i.e. *Candida* is an opportunistic pathogen) vaccination is unlikely to be an effective method for preventing these infections.

See also: **Acquired immune deficiency syndrome (AIDS); Fungi, immunity to; Macrophage migration inhibitory factor (MIF); Polyendocrine autoimmunity.**

Further reading

Bodey GP (ed) (1993) *Candidiasis*, 2nd edn. New York: Raven Press.

Cannon RD, Holmes AR, Mason AB and Monk BC (1995) Oral candida: clearance, colonization, or candidiasis? *Journal of Dental Research* 74: 1152–1161.

Domer JE and Carrow EW (1989) Candidiasis. In: Cox RA (ed), *Immunology of the Fungal Diseases* pp 57–92. Boca Raton, FL: CRC Press.

Edwards JE, Jr (1995) Candida species. In: Mandell GL, Douglas RG, Jr. and Bennett JE (eds) *Principals and Practice of Infectious Diseases*, pp 2289–2306. New York: Churchill Livingstone.

Han Y and Cutler JE (1995) Antibody response that protects against disseminated candidiasis. *Infection and Immunity* 63: 2714–2719.

Hopfer RL, Walden P, Setterquist S and Highsmith WE (1993) Detection and differentiation of fungi in clinical specimens using polymerase chain reaction (PCR) amplification and restriction enzyme analysis. *Journal of Medical Veterinary Mycology* 31: 65–75.

Kirkpatrick CH (1994) Chronic mucocutaneous candidiasis. *Journal of American Academy of Dermatology* 31: S14–S17.

Kirkpatrick CH and Sohnle PG (1981) Chronic mucocutaneous candidiasis. In: Safai B and Good RA (eds) *Immunodermatology*, pp 495–613. New York: Plenum Press.

Odds FC (1994) pathogenesis of candida infections. *Journal of the American Academy of Dermatology* 31: S2–S5.

Seyfarth M, Neumann I, Simm R and Kaben U (1994) Analysis of candida-specific antibodies in saliva. *Immunitat und Infektion* 22: 152–153.

CANINE IMMUNE SYSTEM

Tom R Phillips, Department of Neuropharmacology, The Scripps Research Institute, La Jolla, CA, USA

The canine immune system is just as impressive in its complexity and diversity as are the more thoroughly studied murine and human immune systems. Relative to most species, a large body of knowledge has accumulated about the canine immune system. This knowledge has arisen largely because of the importance of the dog as both a companion animal and transplantation model. Although this entry will primarily concentrate on the differences between the canine immune system and the immune systems of the more thoroughly studied species, it is important to note that the overall structural and functional organization of the canine immune system closely resembles its murine and human counterparts and that there are more similarities than there are differences.

Ontogeny

The gestation period of the dog is approximately 63 days. As with other animals, the stem cells of the immune system are believed to originate in the yolk sac. After a few weeks of gestation, the fetal liver and later the bone marrow become the primary source of these undifferentiated cells. The fetal thymus is apparent by the 28th day of gestation. However, it is not until 35 days postconception that precursor T cells are found in this organ. The ability to reject skin allografts first develops on day 40 of gestation, whereas antibody responses to sheep red blood cells cannot be elicited until the 48th day. Splenic lymphocytes first respond to phytohemagglutinin (PHA) on day 45. However, thymocytes do not develop this ability until gestation day 48. It is not until the second day after birth that peripheral blood lymphocytes respond effectively to PHA. Furthermore, this response does not peak until the puppy is at least 6 weeks old. Thus, the canine immune system develops late and is not fully mature at birth. This, in part, explains the importance of maternal immunity.

Maternal immunity

Maternal immunity, a form of passive immunity, plays a vital role for the neonate. It helps to protect the neonate during the critical transition from the protected uterine environment of the fetus to the hostile external environment of the newborn. Not only does this transition occur at a time when the neonate's immune system is not fully developed but also at a time when the neonate's immune system is naive to virtually all pathogens. Without the acquisition of maternal immunity, the survival of the neonate is greatly reduced. However, maternal immunity is not without its negative effects. It often interferes with active immunization, and is the most common cause of vaccine failure in the dog.

Rodents and primates obtain most of their maternal immunity by placental transfer, whereas dogs obtain the majority of their maternal immunity via colostral transfer. Dogs have an endotheliochorial placenta. With this type of placenta, the fetal and maternal circulation are separated by four tissue layers: 1) the maternal capillary endothelium, 2) the chorionic epithelium, 3) the fetal connective tissue, and 4) the fetal capillary endothelium. In the hemochorial placenta, the placenta of primates and rodents, the maternal capillary endothelial layer is not present. With this latter type of placenta, the maternal blood actually bathes the fetal placental tissues. Because of the close approximation of the maternal and fetal circulation in the hemochorial placenta, maternal immunoglobulin G (IgG) is efficiently transferred to the fetus. Thus, approximately 75% of the primate and rodent maternal immunity is conveyed by placental transfer. In contrast, in the dog only 25% of the maternal immunity is transferred by this process, the additional placental layer being largely responsible for the decreased placental transfer of IgG.

The ingestion of colostrum during the first 24 h of life is responsible for the transfer of the remaining maternal immunity. Colostrum is the first secretion of the mammary gland after parturition and contains a high concentration of immunoglobulins. Within the first 24 h of life, the gastrointestinal system of the neonate is not fully functional. During this time, protein digestion does not occur. Thus, the immunoglobulins within the colostrum are not digested and remain intact as they pass through the digestive tract of the neonate. Additionally, the intestinal epithelial cells at this time are actively transporting proteins, including the intact colostral immunoglobulins, through the intestinal wall of the neonate. Once the immunoglobulins are transported through the intestinal epithelium, they are taken up by the lymph system and eventually reach the general circulation. Colostral intake is particularly important to the dog, since 75% of its maternal immunity is derived via this route. The degree and duration of the dog's maternal immunity is largely dependent on the following factors: the amount of colostrum produced, immunoglobulin content of the colostrum, the amount of colostrum ingested, the age of the neonate at the time of colostral ingestion, and the size and growth rate of the neonate.

Natural resistance

The dog, like most multicellular organisms, has a vast array of defense mechanisms. Some of the most effective defense mechanisms are not part of the immune system but are classified as natural resistance. Natural resistance is defined as defense mechanisms which prevent or combat disease-causing agents by nonimmunologic means (without memory or specificity). Examples of canine natural resistance are barriers (skin, mucous membranes), commensal organisms (normal bacterial and viral flora), mechanical action (mucociliary tree, coughing, and desquamation), flushing action (urine, saliva, tears, milk and diarrhea), chemical and enzymatic action (gastric acid, digestive enzymes, lysozyme, and complement), nonspecific phagocytosis (macrophages and polymorphonuclear neutrophils), hormonal (α and β interferon), iron-chelating agents (lactoferrin), and natural killer cells. Although the dog does not have unique natural resistance mechanisms, it is important to understand the role of natural resistance in aiding the canine immune system. Natural resistance is the first line of defense against disease. Without natural resistance, the immune system would be overwhelmed and the dog or any other organism could not survive. It is only when natural resistance fails to prevent or eliminate disease-causing agents that the immune system has a role in disease control.

Humoral immunity

The immunoglobulin composition of the dog consists of the isotypes IgM, IgG, IgA, and IgE. Each of the canine isotypes serves the same basic function as the corresponding murine and human isotype. In a primary antibody response, IgM is the first and the most abundant immunoglobulin isotype produced. IgM is a pentameric molecule and, on a molar basis, is the most efficient isotype in complement fixation, opsonization and agglutination reactions.

The immunoglobulin isotype with the highest concentration in blood is IgG, which has a higher affinity for antigen than does IgM. IgG, a monomeric molecule, can also participate in complement fixation, opsonization and agglutination reactions, although relative to IgM more molecules of IgG are required. Canine IgG has four subtypes, identified as IgG1, IgG2, IgG3, IgG4.

Usually found as a dimer, IgA is the most important isotype in canine mucosal immunity. IgA is often produced by submucosal lymphocytes and transported to mucosal surfaces by epithelial lining cells. As it is transported through the epithelial cell, the IgA molecule acquires a secretory piece. This secretory piece, which is produced by the epithelial cell, protects the IgA molecule from proteolytic enzymes that are frequently found on mucosal surfaces. Although IgA is the second most common isotype in human sera, it is only a minor component of canine sera. IgA agglutinates antigens but does not fix complement nor does it act as an opsonin. A major function of IgA is to prevent potential pathogens from adhering to or being absorbed by the various mucosal surfaces.

The canine serum concentration of free IgE is very low, the majority of IgE being bound to mast cells and basophils. Immediate hypersensitivity and systemic anaphylaxis reactions are mediated by vasoactive amines that are released when antigen crosslinks mast cell-bound IgE. The most frequent form of immediate hypersensitivity in the dog is inhalant dermatitis, whereas immediate hypersensitivity usually involves the respiratory system in man. Another difference between the human and canine immune systems is the major anaphylaxis shock organ. In the dog, the shock organ is the liver; while in people it is the lung.

Cell-mediated immunity

Cell-mediated immunity in the dog, as in other species, is genetically restricted to class I and class II histocompatibility antigens. The major histocompatibility complex (MHC) of the dog, known as the dog leukocyte antigens (DLA), is less well characterized than the human or murine MHC. Three class I loci have thus far been identified in the dog: DLA-A (8 alleles), DLA-B (5 alleles), and DLA-C (4 alleles). For the canine class II loci, DRB, DQB and DPB genes have been identified. The class III MHC loci for the canine C4 has been identified. This locus codes for the fourth complement component of the dog.

Positive identification of the various canine T cell subtypes has been hampered by the lack of appropriate reagents. However, recently two developments have helped to rectify this situation: 1) the production of monoclonal antibodies with reactivity to various canine T cell subtypes and 2) the recognition that some murine and human reagents cross-react with their canine homologs.

Canine cell-mediated immunity does not differ greatly from the murine and human systems. Antigen-processing cells, usually macrophage or dendritic cells, ingest the antigen, secrete interleukin 1 (IL-1) and present the various antigenic determinants on its surface in the contexts of the dog's MHC (class I or class II antigens). T helper cells, that have encountered IL-1 and recognize antigenic determinants complexed with the class II MHC, clonally expand and secrete various interleukins (e.g. IL-2, IL-4 and IL-5). Interleukins 2, 4 and 5 enable antigen-stimulated B cells to clonally expand and differentiate into plasma and memory cells. Additionally, IL-2 facilitates the differentiation and clonal expansion of cytotoxic T cells which have recognized antigenic determinants complexed primarily with class I MHC.

Natural killer (NK) cells, killer (K) cells, and T suppressor cells have also been identified in the dog. The NK cell of the dog is a large granular lymphocyte that directly kills viral-infected and cancerous cells in a nonimmune manner, without prior exposure to the antigen. In contrast, K cells kill their targets through antibody-dependent cellular cytotoxicity (ADCC). Macrophages, polymorphonuclear neutrophils, and some of the null (non-T non-B) lymphocytes can function as K cells. Genetically restricted T suppressor cells help to limit and control the canine immune response.

Pathologic alterations

There are numerous examples of inherited canine immunodeficiencies, which, not surprisingly, are often associated with a particular breed of dog. Canine cyclic hematopoiesis (gray collie syndrome) has been described in gray collies, pomeranians and cocker spaniels. With this condition, there is a cyclic fluctuation in the number of peripheral blood neutrophils, which, in turn, is associated with periodic bouts of bacterial infections. Although not a true immunodeficiency, Kartagener's syndrome, an absence of ciliary defense mechanisms, has been recognized in puppies with chronic respiratory disease. A selective IgA deficiency has been reported in beagles, doberman pinschers, German shepherd dogs, and shar-peis. A condition in weimaraners and bull terriers has been described, where the puppies have an atrophied thymus, grow at a reduced rate and have a severely depressed lymphocyte response to mitogen. Severe combined immunodeficiency (SCID) in bassett hounds and Cardigan Welsh corgis has been identified. Also, in Brittany spaniels, a C3 deficiency is associated with an increase in the number and severity of bacterial infections.

Acquired immunodeficiencies occur in a variety of conditions ranging from vitamin and mineral deficiencies (vitamin E and selenium) to viral and bacterial infections (neonatal canine distemper virus infection and severe staphylococcal pyoderma).

A variety of autoimmune conditions occur in the dog. These include but are not limited to autoimmune hemolytic anemia, thrombocytopenia, pemphigus, immune-complex glomerulonephritis, autoimmune thyroiditis, Sjögren's syndrome, rheumatoid arthritis and systemic lupus erythematosus. Antinuclear antibodies have been associated with the MHC gene DLA-12; and systemic lupus erythematosus is associated with MHC DLA-A7. An association with diabetes mellitus with DLA-B4 as well as DLA-A3, A7, and A10 has also been reported.

Evaluation of immunologic responsiveness

From the discussion of the canine immune system, it is clear that many similarities to the murine and human immune system are found. However, it is vital to realize that critical differences between these systems exist. It is tempting to directly apply a human or murine function test to assess the canine immune system. This direct application could yield erroneous results or interpretations. Often, all that is required is a minor alteration of the assay or its interpretation to make the assay applicable to the canine immune system. Since it is beyond the scope of this entry to discuss each assay and their potential alterations, the reader is referred to the Further reading section for more information.

See also: **Autoimmune disease, spontaneous experimental models; Innate immunity; Maternal antibodies; Ontogeny of the immune response.**

Further reading

Andreu G, Boccaccio C, Klaren J et al (1992) The role of UV radiation in the prevention of human leukocyte antigen alloimmunization. *Transfusion Medicine Revues* 6: 212–224.

Colgrove GS and Shirine M (1980) Canine immunology: current status. In: Shirine M and Wilson FD (ed) *The Canine as a Biomedical Research Model: Immunological, Hematological, and Oncological Aspects*, pp 43–66. Washington, DC: Technical Information Center, US Department of Energy.

Day MJ and Penhale WJ (1987) A review of major histocompatibility complex-disease associations in man and dog. *Veterinary Research Communications* 11: 119–132.

Felsburg PJ (1994) Overview of the immune system and immunodeficiency diseases. *Veterinary Clinics of North America. Small Animal Practice* 24: 629–653.

Felsburg PJ, Somberg RL and Perryman LE (1992) Domestic animal models of severe combined immunodeficiency: canine X-linked severe combined immunodeficiency annd severe combined immunodeficiency in horses. *Immunodeficiency Reviews* 3: 277–303.

Schultz RD and Adams LS (1978) Immunologic methods for the detection of humoral and cellular immunity. In: Schultz RD (ed) *Symposium on Practical Immunology. Veterinary Clinics of North America* 8: 721–753.

Tizard IR (1996) *Veterinary Immunology An Introduction*, 5th edn. Philadelphia: WB Saunders.

CAPPING, CLUSTERING, MEMBRANE MICRODOMAINS AND CELL SURFACE DYNAMICS

Francis Loor, Pharmacological and Biotechnological Research Center, University of Strasbourg, Illkirch, France

The discovery of membrane component mobility and redistribution (capping and clustering), by immunologists, some 25 years ago was a major breakthrough in cell surface science. It has also been a major step in the development of our understanding of how the cell surface may have evolved and how it may work to transmit messages which are more complex than those mediated by the simple binding of a ligand to a receptor molecule. By contrast, cell-to-cell recognition is a phenomenon involving a coordinated sequence of interactions of several different ligands and recognition elements on each cell partner. To fully achieve antigen presentation by one cell and antigen recognition by the other cell, there is a need for a reciprocal recognition of two-dimensional glycoprotein *patterns* which can be created only by the precise *topographical* rearrangements of membrane components within given *microdomains* of the plasma membranes of both interacting cells.

Capping

Capping phenomena have been described for a variety of membrane components in a variety of cell types. The basic model remains the polar capping of membrane immunoglobulins (mIg) on B lymphocytes by anti-immunoglobulin antibody. When different membrane components are successively capped, they migrate to the same cell pole. This pole is assigned to the cell by the zone of contact of its membrane either with another cell or with a substratum. The general characteristics of the capping phenomenon, particularly the energy requirements, temperature dependence, inhibition or reversion by microfilament-directed drugs (cytochalasins), and the accumulation of microfilaments under the cap, have led to the suggestion that capping is probably an active cellular contractile phenomenon. Early cell adhesion studies also suggested that the expression, distribution and dynamics of ligand recognizing domains might be controled by the microfilamentous network of the cell. Ligand recognition may be followed by cell motility changes and by increased adhesion to a substratum or to other cells. As early as 1973, expression of adhesive sites by lymphocytes was also found to be an active cellular process, its linkage to microfilament dynamics being shown later. It is unclear, however, whether adhesion and capping may be mechanistically related to each other.

For capping to occur, contractile microfilaments drag *anchored* patches of *aggregated* membrane components into an area of the cell where they can be endocytosed and digested, or shed from the surface. As microtubules do not appear to enhance microfilament mobility but rather to inhibit it, their role in the capping phenomenon is more complex. When microtubules are depolymerized by exposing the cells to specific drugs (e.g. colchicine, *Vinca* alkaloids) or to a chilling shock, the capping occurs on the uropod of the cell. Shedding or endocytosis may, however, occur on the whole cell surface when microtubules interfere with the polar redistribution of clustered ligands and membrane components. Capping of any membrane component would occur as a consequence of entrapment of microfilament-associated membrane anchors within the lattices or clusters formed on the plasma membrane. These microfilament-driven anchors would then sweep any aggregated membrane components or adsorbed material toward the cap area, a zone of high endocytotic activity. Both the membrane sites involved in intercellular adhesion and the membrane anchors involved in capping might be proteins of the integrin and cadherin families.

Clustering

Monomeric antigens, monovalent lectins and monovalent antibody to mIg or any other membrane component do not cap on the cell surface, nor do they form large clusters (spots or patches). Like capping, clustering requires multivalent ligand binding, but unlike capping it is a passive redistribution process: spotting/patching does not require the cell to be alive or metabolically active. It is actually best to observe clustering on cells whose capping machinery is inhibited either by specific drugs or as a consequence of a general inhibition of cellular metabolism. In the context of the original postulate of Singer and Nicolson for cell membrane organization as a 'fluid mosaic of proteins and lipids', the clustering of membrane components may be viewed as an immunoprecipitin reaction or a lectin-mediated aggregation occurring in a two-dimensional pattern at the level of the plasma membrane. Clustering should therefore be affected not only by all the factors that commonly control such phenomena occurring in a three-dimensional fluid aqueous phase (e.g. 'antigen' or 'antibody' excess in a precipitin reaction), but also by the physicochemical properties of the plasma membrane. Besides factors intrinsic to the lipid-bilayered membrane itself, the outcome of the cluster formation should also be influenced by physiological interactions between the membrane proteins themselves. While intermediate filaments, actin filaments and microtubules constitute the main skeleton of the cell and control its overall 'long-range' shape, a variety of both integral and peripheral membrane components may constitute a distinct but interacting skeleton in the submembranous peripheral cell cortex which would sustend the plasma membrane and may cause a 'mid-range' modulation of membrane component topography.

Colocalization

A method of 'differential redistribution' of membrane components into patches and caps has been broadly used to probe the possible interactions between various plasma membrane components, or between the cell membrane and cytoplasmic structures. If two components A and B were stably associated in the membrane, the clustering and capping of A should always copatch and cocap B. If on the contrary, A and B were never associated, the clustering of one should not affect the distribution of the other. Obviously, since mIg epitopes and major histocompatibility complex (MHC) epitopes were not cocapped, it could be concluded that these were different and independent molecules. Similarly the myosin involvement in the contractile processing and removal of the aggregates from the cell surface was supported by it being found concentrated in the cytoplasmic cortex of the cell just beneath patches of membrane components aggregated by an external ligand.

A number of membrane and cytosolic components were studied in this way and showed 'colocalization'. This led to the discovery of a host of membrane skeletal proteins which may create complex networks of interacting components on and between both faces of the membrane. Similarly, interactions of antigen receptor complexes with proximally recruited CD membrane components in the plasma membrane plane eventually lead to three-dimensional scaffolds of cytosolic protein tyrosine kinases and phosphatases and adaptor proteins as transducer units.

Such differential redistribution studies have a variety of potential pitfalls. Indeed, besides the two aforementioned, simple cases, there were a variety of alternate forms of incomplete and/or unidirectional interactions, three of which are suggested hereafter. 1) Although A and B are molecularly independent, ligand binding might cause conformational changes in A, which then allows binding of A to B, so that capping of A may lead to cocapping of B, whereas the interaction of B with its ligand would not bring A in the cap ('syn-capping'). 2) If there is a large excess of one membrane component over another, a massive aggregation and capping of the major component might entrap the minor one and bring it into the cap, even though the two types of components never showed any affinity for each other during this 'mass effect'. 3) Ligand binding might also trigger a complement-like 'cascade reaction' on the cell surface which may involve several membrane components, both integral proteins and peripheral membrane components in the glycocalix and in the cytosolic membrane skeleton.

Although such colocalization studies may show that a variety of integral and peripheral membrane components do easily interact with each other, they may not always indicate whether there was *prior colocalization* or whether there has been *recruitment*. They say little about the natural status of distribution of such components in a 'resting' cell. To evaluate membrane component interactions, e.g. to determine whether various membrane components constitute homodimers, heteropolymers or large complexes of several different molecules, instantaneous ('pulse') nearest-neighbor-type biochemical studies of the membrane of cells, both resting and in different activated status, are more suitable than patching and capping.

In addition to these restrictions, the possible isomeric forms of some membrane proteins should also be taken into account; the most representative cases are those of proteins which may exist as two widely different membrane forms, either with a classical transmembrane polypeptide anchor ('TM proteins') or with a glycosylphosphatidylinositol anchor (GPI proteins'), and which may show different physicochemical and/or physiological relationships with other molecular partners in *cis* on the membrane. Moreover, the hypothesis has been formulated that not only ligand-clustered components but rather whole *microdomains* of plasma membrane (including unliganded components) might be brought into the cap. This concept puts severe restrictions on the use of capping as a means of *selective* removal of given membrane components from the plasma membrane.

Finally, it is unclear whether any membrane component may be capped by clustering ligands, and there is also no evidence that all types of membrane component redistributions reported as 'caps' actually proceed through a unique mechanism. Even though the caps were made on the same cell pole and mediated by actin filaments, capping may involve anchorage through integrins for some membrane components, but through cadherins for some others, whereas some 'caps' may actually represent a polar redistribution of microvilli, or a passive recruitment of all clusters into a single one. If whole membrane microdomains rather than individual components show polar redistribution, cocapping may simply reflect the fact that the capped components belong to the same type of domain, whereas independent capping would show they are in different domains, and further conclusions on physical interactions of components with each other are probably speculative.

Capping as a sign of leukocyte polarization?

A misinterpretation of the Singer–Nicolson model of biological membranes would be that the entire cell surface was organized as a continuous fluid mosaic of proteins and lipids without any short-, mid- or long-range order. Obviously, this could not hold true for highly polarized cells. The epithelial cell represents the most straightforward case for a *segregation* of the whole cell surface as large domains, the apical membrane and the basolateral membranes not only showing widely different protein, lipid and carbohydrate compositions but also being sustained by different types of submembranous skeletons and controled by different sets of deeper cytoskeletal networks.

Of greater concern in immunology are the domains with the ligand recognition-coupled transduction signals. Would the plasma membrane of the round and resting leukocyte also show segregation of its components as multiple microdomains? Would their polarized redistribution on the leukocyte, when it develops a prominent uropod, possibly mimic the epithelial cell model? Effective triggering through ligand-recognizing domains is usually coupled to changes in cell motility. Moreover, one of the most prominent responses of lymphocytes to recognition of their ligands is an increased adhesion, through tangles of microvilli, either distributed all over the cell surface or redistributed to the uropod, such as observed when various types of killer cells bind to their targets, when lymphocytes interact with macrophages, when leukocytes bind to vascular endothelium for migrating into tissues, when T cells form rosettes with red cells, and when lymphocytes form aggregates either spontaneous or induced by ligands or mitogens.

Membrane component freedom

Most *functional antigen-receptor units* on the lymphoid cell surface are 'receptor complexes' which are constituted by several interacting subunits, some endowed with a recognition function (ligand binding), some responsible for effector function (cytoplasmic signaling) and some having a conveying function (linker, transducer). Thus, in 'resting', i.e. non-activated conditions, a cell surface may show the existence of discrete microdomains, with a short- to mid-range order organization of selected membrane components. Most such receptor complexes might not be under the 'permanently assembled' form, however – nature would not have missed such a key regulatory mechanism and a good occasion to create a host of variants. Rather, components of receptor complexes must be in a continuous equilibrium of association and dissociation, being regulated both by the intracellular, physiological status of the cell and by its extracellular, environmental context. Such regulation of receptor complex assembly needs not to be exclusively occurring at the level of the integral elements which are directly anchored within the lipid

bilayer itself; it may also be mediated by peripheral membrane elements which belong to the outer cell surface, such as components of the glycocalix, and to the inner cell surface, such as components of the membrane skeleton.

If they do not permanently form covalent or non-covalent complexes, the dissociated elements of the receptor complexes must find each other. Membrane fluidity would be a disadvantage if such elements which need to interact reversibly with each other could diffuse on the whole cell surface. Therefore, lateral diffusion of the membrane proteins should be restricted in fluid membranes in order to allow the coupling in a two-dimensional space of spatially organized receptor units whose function requires vectorial interactions.

Membrane microdomains

So long as spatial order of the fluid membrane is maintained, fluidity will actually increase the rate of coupling of independent molecules. It may be worth recalling here that the surface representation of antigen receptors on B and T cells would be very low, were such B and T cell receptors uniformly distributed over the entire cell surface, and that restriction of their distribution to selected domains of the lymphocyte surface might favor both their clustering by polymeric antigens and their recognition by membranous and cytosolic adaptor and transducer molecules. For instance, assuming it is a smooth sphere, a small B lymphocyte with a mean diameter of 8 μm would have a surface of about 200 μm^2, but there must be an at least equivalent (if not much higher) amount of surface membrane stored (e.g. for cell division) under the form of various membrane ruffles and pseudopodia or microprojections. Thus, assuming a near-maximal expression of 40 000 mIg molecules for at least 400 μm^2 B cell surface, one reaches the fairly low surface density of $\leq$100 mIg molecules per μm^2. While this is a maximal estimate, it is interesting to consider that this corresponds to only one single mIg molecule per patch of 100 nm $\times$ 100 nm, which is about the size reported for some membrane microdomains! For comparison, the diameter of the membranous IgM stem (stalk) is in the range of 4 nm only, and the distance between its two Fv domains is about 12 nm. Because of such a low surface density of antigen receptors, cross-linking of two individual IgM molecules by an antigen would require much mobility, were they distributed at random.

Similarly, there would be a rather poor efficacy of coupling between recognition by the extracellular antigen/ligand-binding elements, and transduction and signaling by the CD3 complex(-like) elements of the membranous receptor complexes, were they randomly distributed over the whole cell surface. Moreover, the antigen receptor complexes themselves should be in close proximity to their stoichiometrically associated, membrane-anchored and function-controlling elements such as specific protein kinases and protein phosphatases, as well as to the variety of CD coreceptors which are regulating the signal levels. Therefore, there is a high probability for such receptor–operator units to function within specialized membrane microdomains. The latter might not exist as such in the resting cells, and the fully functional signaling unit would probably proceed through *recruitment* of some key elements of the receptor–operator unit. Possibly, only a few of these units are functional at any given time, but a first successful coupling of recognitive elements with effector elements might cause something I would call 'membrane stressing'. This might be acting like a catalyst for further unit assembly, e.g. the activation of a phospholipase whose primordial membrane effects would be to favor the further segregation of the membrane into microdomains, which would much enhance the chances of encounters of relevant elements.

Proximity and promiscuity

Besides the *covalent* interactions of membrane elements such as the various polypeptide chains which constitute the TCR, BCR and MHC antigen receptors, and a number of oligomeric CD coreceptor components which are involved in coupling ligand adhesion to signal transduction, two major mechanisms may favor the selective encounters of membrane components: proximity and promiscuity. The differences between these two terms may look subtle or semantic, but they may be large in terms of mechanisms and consequences.

Promiscuity would refer to membrane components, both integral and peripheral ones, which are loosely held close to each other by *low affinity interactions* such as those taking place between elements of the 20 nm thick glycocalix (e.g. weak lectin-like interactions in a microenvironment where local carbohydrate concentrations may be in 0.1 M range) and those occurring between the array of membrane-stabilizing proteins constituting the endoskeleton. Moreover, promiscuity may also be created within the membrane by lipid domains showing hydrophobicity features which may be more or less favorable for the preferential localization of integral proteins with a TM anchor (TM proteins) or with a GPI anchor (GPI proteins), of cytosolic proteins with a myristoyl anchor, and also more or less suitable for the association of some glycolipids, such as gangliosides, endowed with an innate tendency for self-association and microdomain formation with the membrane phospholipids. Molecular promiscuity may have a coordinated biosynthetic origin, most interacting elements being synthesized and organized as a membrane patch before the membrane vesicle reaches the cell surface.

Proximity would rather refer to a higher occurrence of membrane components within a microdomain, which would only be favored by the existence of *molecular boundaries* in the membrane, in the absence of specific molecular interactions, even of low affinity, between the components of the microdomain. Such domain boundaries might be constituted by protein fences both within the lipid bilayer (integral proteins) and on both of its faces by peripheral proteins, some of which constitute a subplasmalemmal skeleton (membranous endoskeleton) and some others participating to the cell glycocalix (membranous exoskeleton). Within such boundaries of the microdomain, the membrane components would thus be kept in close proximity to each other.

Specialized membrane microdomains defined by submembranous protein networks

In addition to those which may be defined by TM protein- or glycocalix-based fences and others which may depend on particular lipid clusters (caveolae), other membrane microdomains may be defined by the subplasmalemmal assembly of various types of protein skeletons. These endoskeletal networks may recruit a selection of peripheral and cytosolic proteins, with the eventual connection of a membrane patch to the actin microfilaments. At least four types of microdomains may be defined, the first one being mostly an endoskeleton, the next two involving TM proteins with intercellular adhesion sites, and the last one concerning microvilli and possibly ligand recognition.

In erythrocytes, a spectrin-based filamentous network is apposed to the inner face of the lipid bilayer, conferring mechanical support to the membrane. Several members of the *spectrin family* occur as endoskeletal components of nonerythroid cells (ankyrin, fodrin, TW260/240, dystrophin, dystrophin-related protein, α-actinin). These proteins constitute membrane skeletons with a fixed stoichiometry but a flexible morphology (due to the properties of spectrin). They help to organize and stabilize microdomains which are enriched in some integral membrane proteins. None of these skeletal proteins is a TM protein, i.e. they cannot be directly in touch with the cell outside, but one of them (often ankyrin) can link the assembly to a TM protein (often a channel or transporter). Moreover, most of these proteins bind to actin, providing specific attachment sites for cytoskeletal components; the latter may thus define the topographical distribution and cell surface dynamics of such microdomains whose occurrence in leukocytes remains unknown.

Integrin-mediated adhesion to the extracellular matrix reveals the colocalization of two submembranous skeleton proteins, α-actinin and talin; these actin-binding proteins connect the cytosolic domains of integrins to a matrix of actin microfilaments and other actin-binding proteins, including vinculin, paxillin, tensin and zyxin. *Cadherin-mediated adhesion* similarly results in the localized recruitment to their cytosolic domain of several cytosolic proteins (β-catenin, plakoglobin, p120) which bind to α-catenin (homologous to vinculin), itself binding to fodrin and actin, with α-actinin joining the complex. In both the integrin and the cadherin cases, the networks of interacting submembranous skeletal proteins strengthen cell adhesion and provide protein scaffolds for signaling networks, which involve kinases, phosphatases, GTP-binding proteins and adaptor proteins.

Another actin-based cytoskeleton characterizes the noncontacting surface of epithelial cells, i.e. its apical surface which expresses numerous *microvilli*. Each microvillus is sustented by a bundle of actin filaments, cross-linked by villin and fimbrin, coupled laterally to the membrane by myosin I, and anchored into the cortical actin filament network by fodrin. In the case of epithelial/endothelial borders, the microvilli are found on the apical surfaces of the cells, thus facing the 'not self' in the lumen. Would adhesion through the integrin- and cadherin-based domains be rather involved in recognition of self, whereas microvillus-based recognition would be devoted to the not self? In the case of lymphoid cells, microvilli tend to redistribute to the area of contact with the target cell, possibly showing their direct involvement as an early recognition step. Assuming the analogy to epithelial cells goes further, lymphocyte microvilli might not mediate adhesion, but only be involved in signaling ligand recognition.

Another case for specialized membrane microdomains is found on the apical surface of epithelial cells: these are the *caveolae* which are 50–100 nm invaginations found at the bases of the apical microvilli. These membrane protein–lipid microdomains are remarkably resistant to detergent (e.g. Triton-X100)-mediated solubilization. They are coated with caveolin, a TM protein which is a v-Src substrate, and they contain G protein-coupled receptors; in caveolae, caveolin exists as a hetero-oligomeric complex with integral proteins and known cytosolic signaling molecules, suggesting the involvement of caveolae in transmembrane signaling. Moreover, caveolae would recruit and 'cluster' GPI proteins (in a 'promiscuity' sense), such as the folate-binding protein (showing their important physiological role). In T cells, GPI proteins (e.g. Thy-1 or DAF[CD55]) may play a role in signal transduction, particularly through an activation of submembranous protein tyrosine kinases (e.g. Fyn or Lck), which are proteins anchored to the inner leaflet of the lipid bilayer by N-terminal myristoylation. It is assumed that the connection (as found by coimmunoprecipitation) of the latter proteins to the extracellular GPI proteins (whose anchor is restricted to the outer leaflet of the lipid bilayer) might be done by the TM protein caveolin.

Finally, the topography of the various microdomains might be determined on the cell surface by anchorage of the various scaffolds to the *microtubular cytoskeleton*. As suggested for the epithelial cell model, microtubule organization might confer a polarity to the lymphocyte for microdomain redistribution to the cap/uropod area.

Adhesion or recognition, but not both?

Does the cell segregate adhesion molecules and recognition-coupled effector molecules into separate microdomains? An *ad hoc* argument was made that molecules endowed with recognition of the non self, such as antigen receptors, might be naturally expressed on microvilli. Microvilli were indeed reported to express mIg at higher cell surface density than the rest of the B cell surface. Whether this is true for the TCR was not examined, but one may also assume that T cell microvilli might have the function of recognizing target cell-presented antigens. A microvillus redistribution to the intercellular contact area would also bring the caveolae to the same pole, if these two microdomains are topographically associated on lymphocytes, as they are on the apical surface of epithelial cells.

Since microvilli are labile structures which may grow or retract quickly, whereas caveolae may be structurally stable structures occurring (and possibly forming boundaries) at the microvillus bases, the high expansion and contraction of microvillus membrane might be explained if the fluid lipid bilayers would percolate between the caveolae: the lipids may rapidly flow through the caveolae network and go back and forward between the bulk of the plasma membrane and the microvillus membrane domains. Selected membrane components, including proteins, would cross the caveolae network boundaries much more slowly.

Once recognition has occurred, microvilli could retract, bringing the lymphocyte closer to the other cell. At the membrane level, a fast microvillus retraction after ligand encounter might thus markedly increase the surface density of selected components of the 'recognition domain'. For instance, assuming a 1 µm long microvillus with a 0.1 µm diameter, its 0.16 µm^2 surface would be converted into a flat 0.008 µ^2 patch on the cell membrane, possibly causing a 20-fold increased density of selective TM proteins, GPI proteins and myristoylated proteins and other microvillus membrane components whose diffusion was delayed by the caveolae network. This mechanism would thus provide a higher occurrence for interactions of the receptor, adaptor and effector elements of the recognition units displayed on the former microvillus membrane, as well as higher chances of interactions of such initiating complexes with other effector components of the caveolae at the boundaries.

Clustering *for* cell activation, but capping *against* it?

How ligand binding results in a signal to differentiate or to divide is a complex sequence of events. Although the actual consequences of capping for the physiology of the cell remain poorly understood, it seems that clustering rather than capping actually initiates cell triggering. It is generally admitted that the very first signal is the clustering of receptors by interaction with a cross-linking ligand (e.g. polyvalent antigen, lectin, antibody). Capping itself may not be perceived by the cell as a triggering signal, although it may be used as a *scavenging* mechanism for the efficient removal of bound ligands and engaged cellular receptors. One could, however, speculate that a more efficient capping of antigen–mIg complexes on a B cell surface might lead to an earlier and/or more efficient endocytosis, processing and antigen presentation.

There is tremendous support for the generalization that clustering of plasma membrane components is a prerequisite for triggering. In all cases where a ligand is mitogenic, it is found to be bi- or polyvalent, and its monovalent derivatives are no longer mitogenic. Even more conclusive is the fact that monovalent, nonmitogenic ligands can be made mitogenic by polymerization. Thus, the cross-linking of membrane sites is required for triggering. Yet

attempts to establish a closer link between clustering and triggering are not easy, as the clustering of antigen receptors by itself does not appear to trigger the whole activation cycle. This first signal is obviously necessary but not sufficient to activate the cell.

Whether lymphocyte activation may involve more subtle and specific consequences of antigen receptor clustering, such as increased frequency of encounters between given elements of the B cell or T cell receptor complexes, is a matter for ongoing research. The essential fact is that mIg clustering, like patching of any other membrane component by its cognate ligand, creates patches of membrane with a *selective* component composition which might initiate cellular activation but which are normally removed by capping. Thus, capping rather appears as a mechanism which limits the *duration* of the signaling period. By limiting the persistence of patches of selected membrane components on the cell surface, capping may regulate cell activation by up- or down-modulating the overall signal delivered by clustered receptor units. The early changes in the physicochemical properties of the membrane normally last for a few minutes only, as does the normal persistence of the mIg clusters on the B cell surface (at least *in vitro*).

Too rapid a removal of clustered mIg by capping may actually impair triggering, this being due to insufficient first signal hits delivered to the cell, and thus resulting in a failure to reach a hypothetical threshold level for stimulation. Conversely, in the case of very delayed capping, the long persistence of large clusters of receptors would deliver excess signals which might lead either to cell paralysis and inactivation or to terminal differentiation, both of which pathways ultimately result in deletion of the cell concerned. Thus, the rate of capping-mediated removal of clustered receptors from a cell surface may be crucial to position the signal levels within a triggering window where cell activation to mitosis and clonal expansion will occur, a window defined by a minimum threshold level below which the signals are not perceived as activating and a maximum threshold above which the signals are inactivating the cell, potentially leading to 'clonal deletion'. The microdomain concept brings a novel dimension to the problem: in T cells, for instance, it may be crucial to know whether TCR/CD3-containing receptor–effector complexes, which if stimulated alone would lead to anergy, occur in the same or different microdomains as the CD28-operated units, whose involvement is needed for stimulation.

Abnormalities of capping

Various alterations of capping are found in cases of immunodeficiency and/or autoimmunity, or following cell treatment with pharmacological agents known to show immunomodulatory properties. Various agents or conditions, which may be physiological, pharmacological or genetic factors and are known to modulate the immune responsiveness, are also found to alter the rate of capping. Thus, capping of B cell mIg occurs at different rates for mice of different strains and shows different susceptibilities to pharmacological agents; immature, fetal or neonatal B cells cap faster than mature, adult B cells; peripheral blood lymphocytes from elderly human beings show decreased capping rates in comparison with young adults; and cyclosporine-treated B cells show a faster capping.

Within identical genetic contexts, single mutations, which do not seem to directly target components of the capping machinery, can affect the capping rate found for B cell mIg, such as the xid, nu, lpr, gld and me^v mutations. Presumably, such mutations lead to the selective development of some particular B cell subsets which may be minor components of the wild mouse B cell population. However, some mutations may directly touch the capped or associated components. Thus in the mouse, the bg mutation (a mouse model of the Chédiak–Higashi syndrome) targets a gene encoding a coiled-coil phosphoprotein 'Lyst' which may act on the microtubular network as a relay integrating cellular signal response coupling; the Lyst deficiency accelerates mIg capping and even allows capping of some lectins in the absence of treatments which weaken the microtubular restraints on membrane mobility. Similarly, the sph mutation (α-spectrin deficiency causing hereditary hemolytic anemia) accelerates the lectin or antibody-induced capping of membrane glycoproteins on erythroleukemia cells, suggesting that spectrin may limit the lateral mobility of integral membrane proteins in cells with a fluid membrane (i.e. other than the erythrocytes). Similarly, in human beings, several cases of abnormalities of leukocyte function and of capping and/or adhesion have been reported, such as in Duchenne muscular dystrophy (an abnormality of dystrophin, a member of the spectrin family of membrane skeleton proteins) and in leukocyte adhesion deficiency (deficiency of the β$_2$-integrins).

See also: **Adhesion molecules; Antigen-presenting cells; Antigen presentation via MHC class I molecules; Antigen presentation via MHC class II molecules; Antigens, cell surface; B lymphocyte activation; B lymphocytes; CD antigens; Cytotoxicity, mechanisms of; Erythrocytes; High endothelial venules; Immunoglobulin, cell surface; Integrins; Lectins; Lymphocyte trafficking; Membrane-associated cytoskeleton: role in regulating immune cell function; Rosetting techniques; T lymphocyte activation.**

Further reading

Ager A (1994) Lymphocyte recirculation and homing: roles of adhesion molecules and chemoattractants. *Trends in Cell Biology* 4: 326–333.

Brown DA (1992) Interactions between GPI-anchored proteins and membrane lipids. *Trends in Cell Biology* 2: 338–343.

Drubin DG and Nelson WJ (1996) Origins of cell polarity. *Cell* 84: 335–344.

Edidin M (1992) Patches, posts and fences: proteins and plasma membrane domains. *Trends in Cell Biology* 2: 376–380.

Lisanti MP, Scherer PE, Tang Z and Sargiacomo M (1994) Caveolae, caveolin and caveolin-rich membrane domains: a signalling hypothesis. *Trends in Cell Biology* 4: 231–235.

Loor F (1977) Structure and dynamics of the lymphocyte surface, in relation to differentiation, recognition and activation. *Progress in Allergy* 23: 1–153.

Loor F (1980) Plasma membrane and cell cortex interactions in lymphocyte functions. *Advances in Immunology* 30: 1–120.

Loor F (1984) Ligand-induced patching and capping of surface immunoglobulins. *Methods in Enzymology* 108: 371–385.

Pumplin DW and Bloch RJ (1993) The membrane skeleton. *Trends in Cell Biology* 3: 113–117.

Schaller MD and Parsons JT (1993) Focal adhesion kinase: an integrin-linked protein tyrosine kinase. *Trends in Cell Biology* 3: 258–262.

Schwartz MA (1992) Transmembrane signalling by integrins. *Trends in Cell Biology* 2: 304–308.

CARBOHYDRATE ANTIGENS

Cornelis PJ Glaudemans, Chief, Section on Carbohydrates, National Institute of Diabetes and Digestive and Kidney Diseases, National Institutes of Health, Bethesda, Maryland, USA

Carbohydrates, containing n asymmetric carbon atoms, can exist in 2^n stereoisomeric forms. A common hexose possesses *a priori* four asymmetric carbon atoms (C-2, -3, -4 and -5) and thus can exist in 16 stereoisomeric forms (i.e. D-glucose, L-glucose, D-mannose, L-mannose, etc.). Each of these isomers can occur in either a six-membered (pyranose) or five-membered (furanose) ring form. When a hexose is in the ring form, the C-1 aldehyde function also becomes asymmetric, and the 1-hydroxyl group can assume either the α or the β configuration, thereby doubling the number of possible isomers. In total, a hexose can thus occur in an oligo- or polysaccharide in 64 different ways. This enormous capability for diversity makes carbohydrates very versatile as nature's alphabet for recognition in biological events, including immunology. Bacteria, viruses and mammalian cells nearly always have polysaccharides as capsular or cell wall material, and/or have glycolipids and glycoproteins on, or in, their walls, and these wall components or capsules often dictate the ensuing cascade of biological events in which they participate.

Structure of polysaccharides and the saccharides of glycoproteins and glycolipids

Polysaccharides, and the saccharide epitopes of glycoproteins and glycolipids, are secondary gene products. Thus, glycosyl transferases are encoded at the genetic level, and these in turn catalyze the formation of oligo- or polysaccharides or the glycosylation of proteins and lipids. One of the consequences for polysaccharides is that they have no uniform, sharply defined molecular weight but instead possess a molecular weight distribution. Linkages between monosaccharides in the polysaccharide chain are acetal linkages; they involve a carbon atom bearing two oxygen atoms: the ring oxygen and the intersaccharidic oxygen. Acetals are susceptible to acid-catalyzed hydrolytic cleavage, as well as enzymic cleavage, since both operate by the same chemistry.

Sugar residues in an oligo- or polysaccharide chain frequently carry substituents such as (acyl)amino-, carboxyl-, acetoxyl, pyruvoyl-, phosphorylcholine-, or can be esterified with long-chain fatty acids. This additional diversification can profoundly affect the immunogenicity or biological activity of the entire molecule.

Naturally occurring carbohydrate antigens can be divided into two main categories, which can again be subdivided:

1. Polysaccharides
   Bacterial, capsular polysaccharides
   Bacterial cell wall polysaccharides
   Bacterial lipopolysaccharides
   Plant polysaccharides (e.g. cellulose, etc.)
   Storage polysaccharides (e.g. glycogen, etc.).
   The last two classes of polysaccharides will not be discussed here.
2. Carbohydrates borne on other (macro)molecules
   Glycoproteins
   Glycolipids.

Concerning (1), capsular polysaccharides of bacteria exist on the outside of the cell wall. The loss of capsular material does not lead to autolysis, but it does often lead to loss of virulence. By and large, bacterial capsular polysaccharides are made up of small, linear or branched units (of from one to several sugar residues). These are repeated with great regularity to make up the extended, polymeric chain. Most of these polysaccharides possessed by bacteria within a given species (e.g. within the gram-positive species *Streptococcus pneumoniae* there are more than 80 types) show pronounced immunologic specificity. However, if capsular polysaccharides share certain features between them that are structurally akin, they may cross-react with each other's immune sera. If the structural similarity is extensive, infection with one could even confer cross-reactive protection towards the other. For instance, the capsular polysaccharide from *S. pneumoniae* type III is a high molecular weight, linear heteroglycan (= a polysaccharide containing differing sugars) made up of D-glucuronic acid (in the six-membered ring, or pyranose form: Glc_pA) whose acetal carbon-1 is linked to the 4-hydroxyl group of D-glucose (also in the pyranose form) by a β linkage, and these disaccharide units are repeated by being linked to each other by β(1→3) linkages to make up the extended polymeric chain (I).

$$\rightarrow 3[\beta\text{-D-Glc}_p\text{A}(q \rightarrow 4)\text{-}\beta\text{-D-Glc}_p]_n 1 \rightarrow$$

I

The high molecular weight capsular polysaccharide from *S. pneumoniae* type VIII has a tetrasaccharide repeating unit, the disaccharide part of which is identical to the one above. In addition it has a 4-linked glucose that is linked $\alpha(1\rightarrow4)$ to a galactose residue. The tetrasaccharide repeating units are connected by $\alpha(1\rightarrow4)$ linkages (II).

$$\rightarrow4[\beta\text{-}D\text{-}Glc_pA(1\rightarrow4)\text{-}\beta\text{-}D\text{-}Glc_p(1\rightarrow4)\text{-}\alpha\text{-}D\text{-}Glc_p(1\rightarrow4)\text{-}\alpha\text{-}D\text{-}Gal_p]_n1\rightarrow$$

II

These two polysaccharide antigens – having 50% of their structure in common – show extensive cross-reaction with one another's serum antibodies.

Several gram-negative bacteria can produce extracellular polysaccharides. When these surround the organism, i.e. when they become a capsular polysaccharide, they also dictate the immunologic specificity of the organism. Those polysaccharides are often acidic. They can have intracatenary phosphoric diester groups, substituents such as pyruvic acid acetalated with certain sugar residues, or they can carry simple uronic acids. An example is the capsular antigen of *Escherichia coli* K100, possessing intracatenary diester groups (III).

$$[\rightarrow3)\text{-}\beta\text{-}D\text{-}Rib_f\text{-}(1\rightarrow2)\text{-}D\text{-}ribitol\text{-}5(\text{-}O\text{-}P\text{-}O\text{-}]_n \quad \text{E. coli K100}$$

(where Rib_f stands for ribofuranosyl).

III

Differing species can show cross-reactivity as well, and these can be biologically significant. For instance the antigen of *Hemophilus influenzae* type b (Hib) shows near structural identity (IV) with the capsule of *E. coli* K100 (see above) and protective antibodies towards Hib are believed to result from the presence of that *E. coli*.

$$[\rightarrow3)\text{-}\beta\text{-}D\text{-}Rib_f\text{-}(1\rightarrow1)\text{-}D\text{-}ribitol\text{-}5(\text{-}O\text{-}P\text{-}O\text{-}]_n$$

H. influenzae type b (Hib)

IV

Cryptococcus neoformans is the only *fungal* species of unarguable pathogenicity that possesses capsular polysaccharides, whose most abundant components are glucurono-xylo-mannans. There also, the capsule may be a factor in virulence. Returning to bacteria: compromise of the underlying bacterial cell wall, for instance through interference of the biosynthesis of the wall's peptidoglycan (see below)

by penicillin, causes autolysis, as the wall's integrity arises mostly from a high molecular weight, cross-linked and 'net-like' peptidoglycan polymer. That substance is composed of two components. The first is a polysaccharide of alternating N-acetyl-D-glucosamine (D-GlcNAc), linked $\beta(1\rightarrow4)$ to N-acetyl muramic acid (NAM = D-GlcNAc carrying a lactic acid substituent at its O-3). The carboxyl group of the lactic acid in NAM is attached to a short peptide chain, which, in *Staphylococcus aureus* consists of L-alanine, D-γ-glutamic acid, L-lysine and D-alanine. The D-alanine's carboxyl end is connected by a pentaglycine to the ϵ-amino group of the lysine of another tetrapeptide. Further bridging is probably achieved to make this giant molecule three dimensional. The peptides vary in differing bacterial species, but the intricate, resulting network of cross-linked polysaccharide/polypeptide is very similar (V).

Teichoic acids, composed of sugar residues, some of which are linked by phosphodiester- rather than acetal-linkages, may be attached to some of the GlcNAc residues by a phosphate linkage. Peptidoglycans occur in both gram-positive and gram-negative organisms, where they have similar, albeit not identical, structures.

Gram-negative bacteria possess a lipopolysaccharide (LPS), also called endotoxin. It is made up of three distinct segments.

First, the *lipid A*, which consists in most cases of two residues of N-acyl D-glucosamine, linked $\beta(1\rightarrow6)$. This disaccharide fragment is phosphorylated at positions 1 and 4', and each residue is extensively esterified, as well as N-acylated, with long-chain fatty acids. The lethal toxicity the LPS can exhibit in animals (and humans) resides in the lipid A segment.

Second, the so-called *core region* is covalently attached to the 6' position of lipid A. It is a fairly short oligosaccharidic segment (usually less than 15 sugars) consisting of one or more residues of keto-deoxy-octulosonic acid (forming the linkage with the lipid A), heptoses, various sugars, ethanolamine (EtAm) and phosphate (P) substituents. It is similarly but not identically structured in most Gram-negative bacteria.

Third, the so called *O-polysaccharide* (O-PS) can possess up to roughly 100 sugar residues, made up of distinct repeating units, linear or branched, that can involve (from one to) several sugars. It is covalently linked to the core region.

The lipid A segment is inserted – and anchored through the hydrophobic interaction of its fatty acid chains with the cell wall lipids – into the fluid lipid bilayer of the bacterium's wall. The entire LPS is oriented so that its O-polysaccharide projects out

```
                                          etc.
                                           |
                                         L-Ala
                                           |
                                        D-γ-Glu
                                           |
                        ---Gly₅---L-Lys         D-Ala---Gly₅---
                                   |                 |
                              D-Ala---Gly₅---L-Lys
                                                 |
                                              D-γ-Glu
                                                 |
                                               L-Ala
                                                 |
→4)-β-D-GlcNAc(1→4)-β-D-NAM(1→4)-β-D-GlcNAc(1→4)-β-D-NAM(1→
                             |
                           L-Ala
                             |
                          D-γ-Glu
                             |
          ---Gly₅---L-Lys         D-Ala---Gly₅---
                     |                 |
                D-Ala---Gly₅---L-Lys
                                   |
                                D-γ-Glu
                                   |
                                 L-Ala
                                   |
→4)-β-D-GlcNAc(1→4)-β-D-NAM(1→4)-β-D-GlcNAc(1→4)-β-D-NAM(1→
                                                      |
                                                    L-Ala
                                                      |
                                                    etc.
```

V

from the bacterial wall into the surroundings. Consequently, the O-polysaccharide often dictates the immunodeterminant behaviour of the organism, and it differs for each type within a species. Most wild-type bacteria carry O-polysaccharide and are then said to be in the smooth- or S-form. Bacteria not carrying O-polysaccharide, but only possessing the lipid A/core combination are said to be of the rough- or R-form. These terms are descriptive of their respective colony morphology. The presence of O-polysaccharide cannot be regarded as a necessary factor for pathogenicity, since R-type LPS is observed in some wild-type bacteria that are highly pathogenic in humans (e.g. *Bordetella pertussis*, *Neisseria gonorrhoeae*, and others). Below are two examples of an LPS. The first is for *Salmonella*, the second for *Legionella pneumophila*. Note that although the core regions are quite different, both are short saccharidic stretches situated between the lipid A and the O-chain. Note also that KDO is the sugar residue linked to the lipid A portion (VI):

where GlcNAc = *N*-acetyl D-glucosamine, Gal = galactose, Hep = Heptose, KDO = keto-deoxy-octulosonic acid, EtAm = 2-aminoethyl, P = phosphate, FE = fatty acid ester. The lipid A is indicated on the right, while the O-polysaccharide is indicated on the left. The location of the phosphates or 2-aminophosphates, or the branch-terminating KDO, remains tentative (VII).

In the case of systemic infection by gram-negative organisms, the overwhelming amount of solubilized endotoxin produced by bacterial lysis can cause shock and even death. It is interesting to note that affinity-purified rabbit anti-LPS immunoglobulin M (IgM) and IgG protects rats lethally challenged with *Pseudomonas aeruginosa*.

Concerning (2), in addition to the polysaccharide antigens, such as discussed above, many mammalian or viral cell walls carry glycoproteins and/or glycolipids on or in them, and these can define their antigenicity. Glycoproteins are proteins that are naturally substituted by short and/or medium length

```
                              P     EtAm-P-P
                              |       |
(O-PS)(1→4)-α-D-Glc(1→2)-α-D-Gal(1→3)-α-D-Glc(1→3)-α-Hep(1→3)-α-Hep(1→5)-α-KDO→LipidA
              2                      6        7                              4
              ↑                      ↑        ↑                              ↑
              1                      1        1                              2
         α-D-GlcNAc              α-D-Gal   α-Hep      α-KDO(2→4)-α-KDO
                                                              |
                                                           EtAm-P
```

Salmonella core region

```
                                        GlcNAc
                                          1
                                          ↓
                                          6
(O-PS)(1→3)-α-L-Rha(1→3)-α-L-Rha(1→3)-α-D-QuiNAc(1→4)-β-D-GlcNAc(1→4)-α-D-Man(1→5)-KDO →LipidA
         2                 2              4              3                        4
        OAc               OAc            OAc            OAc                       ↑
                                                                                 2
              Legionella pneumophila core region                                KDO
```

VII

oligosaccharide substituents, whose internal linkages are purely of the acetal type. The linkage between protein and carbohydrate can be of the O-linkage type (C-1 of the sugar is glycosidically linked to the hydroxyl of a serine or threonine residue, thus forming a regular glycosidic linkage), or of the N-linkage type (C-1 of the sugar is linked to the NH$_2$ of an asparagine residue of the protein, forming an N-glycosidic linkage). Two examples are given below, one is human gastric mucin and the other is one of the many glycoforms of an oligosaccharide chain that occurs on human IgG at asparagine (Asn)-297 of the heavy chain of the immunoglobulin (Ga1NAc stands for N-acetyl galactosamine) as in VIII.

The term 'neoglycoprotein' indicates a glycoprotein that arises through synthetic glycosylation of a protein. Several 'conjugate' vaccines are in fact neoglycoproteins where the saccharide part is the desired immunodeterminant that is linked synthetically to a carrier protein.

Glycolipids consist of an oligosaccharidic fragment linked to, for instance, ceramide. They are frequently of fairly low molecular weight, and the carbohydrate moiety is the immunodeterminant. Below is shown a typical glycolipid (GM1 ganglioside) where NeuAcid stands for neuraminic (= sialic) acid (IX).

Hakmori and associates have shown that glycolipids can seat their lipid moiety in cell wall membranes, projecting their carbohydrate antigenic grouping into the environment outside the cell. Human blood-group specificity is a function of oligosaccharidic determinants carried on erythrocyte surfaces as glycolipids or glycoproteins. Transfusion into individuals possessing differing blood groups causes an antibody response in the host due to the immunogenicity of the carbohydrate determinant, or causes the transfused antigen to cross-react with pre-existing antibodies already present in the host. Both of these substances, glycoproteins and glycolipids, can occur as oncodevelopmental antigens. These are antigens which appear and disappear during successive stages of embryogenesis. They may reappear in adult life as tumor antigens, but are not necessarily unique to cancer cells *per se*, as they can occur at low levels in most normal adult cells.

Viruses, including the human immunodeficiency virus (HIV), are usually not capable of encoding for glycosylation enzymes. This means that the glycoprotein-120 on the surface of the HIV virus has its carbohydrates (making up some 50% of the gp120) attached by enzymes and substrates defined by the cells the virus has infected. The various glycosyl transferases or substrates may be modified by the infection, and thus the expressed virus can possess differing glycan structures. The diversity amongst N-glycans in gp120 is very great – there is more diversity than there are glycosylation sites – indicating structural heterogeneity. Since the glycans are attached by the mechanism of the host cell, they may

```
                                                           protein
                                                             |
β-D-Gal(1→3)-β-D-GlcNAc(1→3)-β-D-Gal(1→3)-α-D-GalNAc 1→Serine (or Threonine)
                                                             |
                                                           protein
                                                             |
                                                                    Gastric mucin oligoglycan

β-D-Gal(1→4)-β-D-GlcNAc(1→2)-α-D-Man 1
                                        ↘
                                         3                          |
                                                                 protein
              β-D-Man(1→4)-β-D-GlcNAc(1→4)-β-D-GlcNAc 1→Asn         |
                                         6                       protein
                                        ↗                           |
         β-D-GlcNAc(1→2)-α-D-Man 1
                                                                 Oligoglycan occuring on human IgG
```

VIII

$$\text{β-D-Gal(1→3)-β-D-GalNAc(1→4)-[α-(2→3)-NeuAcid]-β-D-Gal(1→4)-β-D-Glc 1}$$

$$CH_3\text{-}(CH_2)_{12}CH=CH\text{-}CH(OH)\text{-}CH\text{-}CH_2O$$

GM1 ganglioside

$$NH$$

$$CH_3(CH_2)_{16}C=O$$

IX

present an image of 'self' to the host, and thus escape immune surveillance. Nevertheless, some monoclonal antibodies showing specificity for rare carbohydrate structures can neutralize a broad range of HIV-1 and -2 isolates, as well as block syncytia, even by virus taken directly from patients with the acquired immune deficiency syndrome (AIDS).

Conformation in solution

Polysaccharides as well as the oligosaccharide components of glycoproteins and glycopeptides and glycolipids may be linear or branched, homo- or heteropolymer, neutral or charged. These oligo- and polysaccharides can assume tertiary (globular) structure, and in some cases the particular spacial presentation of a carbohydrate becomes critical in dictating the immunologic specificity. For instance, Jennings and associates have evidence that the capsular polysaccharide of group B streptococcus assumes a conformation in which short, sialic acid-terminated sidechains each form a hydrogen bond with an intrachain GlcNAc nearby. That results in an immunologically specific conformation. This, even though the sialic acid itself is not a (contact) immunodeterminant, and apparently only functions as the vector in creating the correct conformational rigidity. However, it must be kept in mind that for carbohydrates, conformational changes on the polymeric level are easier to achieve (i.e. have lower energy barriers) than they are for proteins. Indeed, various conformational possibilities are probably populated in proportion to the energy differences between them. Critically important requirements such as in the example above do not (yet?) appear ubiquitous for carbohydrate antigens. It should be realized that, for proteins, loss of tertiary structure (i.e. denaturation), once it occurs, is often hard to reverse, even when conditions are changed, while denaturation of polysaccharides is unknown, or rare at best. Polysaccharides are quite heat stable – although autohydrolysis can occur if they are acidic polysaccharides – and their solution structure is less influenced by changes in electrolyte concentration unless they carry charged groupings.

Immune response to carbohydrates

The early discovery that the 'soluble-specific substance', the capsular material of *Streptococcus pneumoniae*, is immunogenic in humans prompted immunizations with purified polysaccharide in the early 1940s. The contemporary and subsequent great success of the treatment of pneumonia with antibiotics rapidly diminished the initial interest in vaccines. However, the continued frequency of serious diseases such as pneumococcal meningitis, and the appearance of bacterial strains showing resistance to antibiotics, including *S. pneumoniae*, has rekindled an intense interest in immunization with polysaccharide-based vaccines. Unfortunately, polysaccharides themselves are often poor immunogens, particularly in infants and in immunocompromised individuals. In addition, for pneumococci, the existence of 84 distinct serotypes has complicated the issue. For this organism, penicillin resistance is concentrated amongst the (pediatric) serotypes 6, 14, 15, 19 and 23, while types 1, 2, 3 and 4 are still largely penicillin sensitive at this time. Polysaccharides are conveniently termed 'T cell independent' (TI) immunogens, and they do not induce immunologic memory, which is required for booster responses. Often only a limited number of B cell clones are activated, resulting in restricted – albeit polyclonal – heterogeneity. Most polysaccharides can induce a state of unresponsiveness, or tolerance, and also do not elicit delayed-type hypersensitivity. In addition, the immunogenicity of polysaccharides increases with molecular weight, and when that is less than 50 kDa the polysaccharide is nonimmunogenic. For all these reasons, immunization with purified polysaccharides has been only partially successful. Frequently, covalent linkage of the carbohydrate determinant epitope, or the entire polysaccharide, to a protein carrier to give a so-called 'conjugate vaccine' allows enhancement of immunogenicity in animals and humans, and instates immunologic memory. The resulting antibodies are protective, and show binding to the parent capsular polysaccharide from which they were derived. Some such immunogens, i.e. Hib polysaccharide linked to tetanus toxoid, have been licensed as human vaccines, and have become very successful in the immunization of infants. The length of an oligosaccharide, to be attached to proteins to form a suitable conjugate vaccine, must vary. In cases where there is a distinct tertiary structure (see above) of the saccharidic immunodeterminant in the natural, bacterial or viral product, that tertiary structure must undoubtedly be mimicked by the (synthetic or derived) saccharide to be conjugated. The resulting antibodies generated by the immune response would then be able to recognize readily the natural immunogen.

Interaction of carbohydrate antigens with antibodies

In the 1960s Kabat showed that polyclonal antidextran antibodies bound maximally to about five sequentially linked sugar residues of the antigen. Modern work on monoclonal antibodies and sharply defined carbohydrate immunodeterminants have since shown that the determinant in an antigenic polysaccharide can be 2–4 sugars long. Affinity constants for the entire immunodeterminant can range from 10^3 to 10^6 M^{-1}. These values suffice for the initiation of an immune response. Antibodies elicited by polysaccharides can be directed against either the interior segments or the terminal segment of the antigenic chain, and the antibody can bind the polysaccharide chain on its surface, or inside cavities. In the case of a monoclonal antibody to $\alpha(1\rightarrow6)$-dextran it was shown that one group of monoclonal antibodies could bind the dextran all along its chain. Another set of monoclonal antibodies could bind only to a stretch of residues of the dextran that had to include the single chain-end glucose residue of the dextran. The latter was held inside a pronounced cavity, while its three sequential sugars were held near the surface of the immunoglobulin. It was found that an antibody combining area was thus made up of a set of subsites, and these could be mapped. Each one could

accommodate a single sugar residue of the polysaccharide. All together these subsites can bind the entire immunodeterminant of four sugar residues. Generally, the major subsite shows an affinity of 10^2–10^3 M^{-1} for its single carbohydrate residue, while the other subsites often possess far less affinity for their particular sugar residues. In the case of a comprehensively studied monoclonal antibody to a homopolysaccharide (galactan), it was found that the immunoglobulin could also maximally bind four sugar residues. Here the monoclonal immunoglobulin could access and bind these repetitively occurring four galactosyl residues in the interior of the polysaccharide chain. All four subsites of the immunoglobulin were on the protein surface, and the subsite with the major affinity was located *within* the sequence of four. In yet another study, a monoclonal anti-*Shigella dysenteriae* type 1 antibody could also bind interiorly located repeating determinants of the bacterium's O-specific heteropolysaccharide.

See also: **ABO blood group system; Affinity; Antibody-antigen intermolecular forces; Antigen-binding site; Antigens; Bacterial cell walls; Lectins; Tumor antigens; Vaccines.**

Further reading

Aspinal GO (ed) (1982–1985) *The Polysaccharides*, 3 volumes. New York: Academic Press.

Dabelsteen E and Clausen H (eds) (1992) Carbohydrate pathology. *APMIS Supplementum 27* **100**.

Frontiers in Medicine: Vaccines (1994) *Sciences* **265**: 1371–1404.

Glaudemans CPJ, Kováč P and Nashed EM (1994) Mapping of hydrogen-bonding between saccharides and proteins in solution. *Methods in Enzymology* **247**: 305–322.

Jennings HJ and Sood RK (1994) In: Lee YC and Lee HT (eds) *Neoglycoconjugates, Preparation and Applications*, pp 325–371. New York: Academic Press.

CARBOHYDRATES, IMMUNE STIMULATING

Ian R Tizard and **Yawei Ni**, Department of Veterinary Pathology, The Texas Veterinary Medical Center, Texas A&M University, and Carrington Laboratories Inc., Texas, USA

Recent developments in glycobiology have shown that carbohydrates play an important part in diverse immunological processes such as opsonization and phagocytosis of microorganisms, and cell activation and differentiation (**Table 1**). Carbohydrates exert

their functions through interacting with carbohydrate-binding proteins or lectins which are widely distributed in mammalian tissues including those of the immune system. Those with immune-stimulating effects are usually large polymers of glucose (glucans

Table 1 Immunostimulating carbohydrates and their structures

Carbohydrates	Structures
β-Glucans	β1 → 3 Glucose
Lentinan	β1 → 3 Glucose with β1,6-glucose branches
Mannan (plant)	β1 → 4 Mannose
Mannan (yeast)	α2 → 6 Mannose with α1,3-mannose branches
Acemannan	β1 → 4 Acetylated mannose
Pectin	Mainly polygalactose
Inulin	β2 → 1 Fructofuranosyl-α-glucose
Levan	β2 → 6 Fructose
Xylan	β1 → 4 Xylose
Lichenan	β1 → 4 and β1 → 3 Glucose

and lentinans), mannose (mannans), xylose (hemicelluloses), fructose (levans) or mixtures of these sugars.

Immune stimulation

Complex carbohydrates act as immune stimulators through two distinct mechanisms. Some, such as the fungal glycans, activate macrophages while others, such as lentinan, are T cell stimulators. Other carbohydrates, such as acemannan, derived from the pulp of the *Aloe vera* plant, act on both macrophages and T cells, and as a result, may influence both cellular and humoral immunity.

Intravenous injection of purified glucan in rodents results in an increase in liver and spleen weight attributed to increased macrophage activity. Clearance of colloidal carbon is significantly enhanced in glucan-treated animals. Macrophages from glucan-treated mice are larger than controls and attach and spread more rapidly on glass. These same macrophages show augmentation of their chemotactic activity. Spleen cells from glucan-treated mice elicit a much more severe graft-versus-host reaction in recipient animals than do cells from normal mice. Administration of glucan to irradiated mice prior to bone marrow transplantation has no effect on syngeneic bone marrow grafts but may prevent acceptance of allogeneic or xenogeneic bone marrow. Depending on the injection protocol, glucan administration to mice may either enhance or depress the *in vitro* response of isolated spleen lymphocytes to concanavalin A and *Escherichia coli* endotoxin.

Lentinan has an adjuvant effect on the response of mice to sheep red cells having a greater effect on the immunoglobulin G (IgG) response than on the IgM response and it enhances antibody-dependent cellular cytotoxicity (ADCC) reactions. Inulin, a polysaccharide consisting of fructose and glucose, also has adjuvant properties. It increases the mouse IgG response to keyhole limpet hemocyanin as well as delayed-type hypersensitivity (DTH) reactions to sheep red blood cells. Levan causes macrophage spreading and swelling and stimulates their acid phosphatase and peroxidase activities. β-Glucan and inulin exist in insoluble or microparticulate forms. The microparticulate carbohydrates are better adjuvants because of enhancement of antigen phagocytosis. Targeting antigens into the phagocytic pathway is required for inducing a strong cell-mediated response, a key element for viral and tumor vaccines.

Interaction with lectins on immune cells and the consequent changes in cellular functions is most likely an important underlying mechanism for the observed immunostimulation and adjuvant effect of these polysaccharides. Macrophages play a central role in initiating the immune response. There are several different lectins on macrophages, including the mannose receptor. The receptor on macrophages for β-glucan is Mac-1 (CD11b/CD18).

Antimicrobial effects

Because glucans activate macrophages and stimulate their lysosomal and phagocytic activity, they stimulate immunity to bacterial diseases. Thus, glucan has a protective effect against experimental footpad inoculation of *Mycobacterium leprae*. It reduces the concentration of both viable and dead bacilli in the lesion. Mannan, in contrast, has only a brief protective effect while lentinan is inactive in this system. Intraperitoneal glucan therapy also enhances survival in mice challenged intraperitoneally with virulent *E. coli*. This is probably due to enhanced macrophage phagocytosis and accelerated blood clearance of bacteria.

Attachment to cell or tissue surfaces is often the first step in microbial invasion. This process is mediated by adhesins on the surface of bacteria, many of which are lectins. Thus, blockage of the interaction between bacterial lectin-like adhesins and cell surface oligosaccharides can be a mechanism for the antimicrobial effect of these polysaccharides. That is, these polysaccharides act as structural analogs of the cell surface carbohydrate receptors, binding to bacterial adhesins and therefore preventing them from attaching to cell surfaces. Sugars or oligosaccharides that are known to interact with lectin-like adhesins of a specific bacteria have been shown to inhibit its infection in animal models.

Effects on tumors

The practical importance of complex carbohydrate therapy may rest on their use as immune stimulants in humans or animals suffering from neoplastic conditions.

Glucans

Although common polysaccharides such as starch ($\alpha1 \rightarrow 6$ glucan), and inulin (fructan) do not have antitumor activity, there is abundant evidence that some mannans and glucans are very potent anticancer agents. The factors that determine this are unclear. The soluble D-glucans have antitumor activity if they are mainly linear, without excessively long branches, and provided they are relatively resistant to degradation by glucanases. Thus glycogen, starch and dextrans are inactive while compounds with long stretches of $\beta1 \rightarrow 3$ linkages are effective. Dextrans may be made active if derivatized with diethylaminoethyl groups. Studies on synthetic, $\beta1 \rightarrow 6$ linked celluloses suggest that antitumor activity against sarcoma-180 in mice is greatest in molecules with a high degree of polymerization and homogeneous distribution of side-chains.

Intravenous glucan inhibits the growth of a murine allogenic adenocarcinoma and increases tumor macrophage populations. The glucan decreases the number of hepatic metastases as well as the size of the primary tumor. Enhanced Kupffer cell antitumor activity is correlated with this increased resistance to hepatic metastases. Intravenous administration of soluble glucans also results in a significant reduction in the growth of syngeneic murine mammary carcinoma and melanoma B16. Glucan from *Saccharomyces cerevisiae* has been reported to reduce the size of malignant melanomas and adenocarcinomas in patients with advanced neoplastic disease when administered in and around selected lesions. This reduction in size is associated with necrosis, abscessation and liquefaction of the tumor and a monocytic infiltrate. Water-soluble glucan administered in combination with lymphokine-activated killer (LAK) cells to mice, significantly suppresses the growth and metastasis of a reticulum cell sarcoma. This therapy increased splenic natural killer (NK) cell activity as well as Kupffer cell tumoricidal activity.

Other investigators have failed to substantiate the antitumor activity of glucans in syngeneic systems. Thus when *Saccharomyces* glucan was tested in a guinea pig hepatoma, two murine fibrosarcomas, a murine melanoma and a murine adenocarcinoma and compared with BCG vaccine, no effect was noted. Intralesional, intraperitoneal or intravenous administration of glucan was also found to be inef-

fective in the murine system. The glucan had no significant effect on tumor size, tumor incidence or host survival. It was concluded that the effects of glucan, although impressive in allogeneic systems (such as the sarcoma-180 system), are much less effective in syngeneic tumor systems.

Saccharomyces glucan probably exerts its antitumor effects by activating macrophages. Its activity appears not to be T cell mediated since administration of glucan severely inhibits the growth of melanoma B16 cells in nude mice. This antitumor activity in nude mice was associated with enhanced macrophage phagocytosis. The glucan probably stimulates macrophages to produce cytokines such as interleukin 1 and tumor necrosis factors. Thus macrophages from glucan-treated animals have been shown to release factors cytotoxic for tumor cells. Glucan also increases serum lysozyme levels, suggesting increased macrophage function and stimulated *in vivo* and *in vitro* secretion of interleukin 1 (IL-1). IL-2 production by splenic lymphocytes is enhanced 6 h after glucan administration and remains elevated for 9 days, presumably in response to the IL-1. Peak plasma IL-1 and IL-2 activities are found 9 and 12 days, respectively, following glucan administration. Given the very short half-life of these interleukins, this sustained elevation of IL-1 and IL-2 suggests that there is a very high rate of production.

Lentinans

Lentinan is a glucan derived from *Lentinus edodes*, a common edible mushroom. It has been shown to be active against several different allogeneic and syngeneic tumors. Lentinan, like other glucans has no direct cytotoxicity on tumor cells. Nevertheless it shows an optimal dose for antitumor action. The antitumor activity of lentinan varies between mouse strains which may be classified as either high or low responders. In strong responder mice, lentinan will completely regress 3-methylcholanthrene-induced transplantable fibrosarcomas. Lentinan is very effective against mouse methylcholanthrene-induced primary tumors in combination with cyclophosphamide. When administered to cancer patients in phase I and II trials, encouraging results have been obtained.

The antitumor activity of lentinan, unlike that of glucan, does not occur in neonatally thymectomized mice or in mice treated with antilymphocytic serum or by whole-body irradiation. It does not increase phagocytosis but it can stimulate macrophage cytotoxic activity *in vivo*. As a result, the antitumor effect of lentinan may be blocked by antimacrophage agents such as carrageenan or silica. Lentinan does not accelerate antibody formation, nor does it cause an increase in blood lymphocytes, accelerate allograft rejection or influence delayed-hypersensitivity reactions.

Mannans

Mannans with significant antitumor activity have been isolated from several species of yeast. They have been tested for activity against sarcoma-180 in Swiss albino mice. There appears to be no relationship between the amount of glucose in these mannans and their activity. The mannan from *C. utilis* that contains an α-linked glucose is poorly inhibitory while the mannan from *C. albicans* that contains a β-glucan component is highly active. Mannans from *S. cerevisiae* and from *Candida utilis* inhibit the growth, not only of sarcoma-180 but also of 3-methylcholanthrene-induced tumors, Ehrlich carcinoma and NF sarcoma. None of these mannans appear to be active against the ascites form of sarcoma-180.

When mannoglucan prepared from *Magnaporthe grisea* is administered intravenously to C3H mice bearing the solid MH134 hepatoma, the blood flow to the tumor is inhibited within 6 h and tumor growth retarded within 3 days. If the tumor mass is excised and extracted at various intervals after administration of mannan, a soluble cytotoxic factor is detectable in the tumor homogenate. This factor is probably a form of tumor necrosis factor (TNF) since its activity is inhibited by anti-TNF serum, it has the same molecular weight range as TNF (70–80 kDa) and the dose dependencies of the cytotoxin and TNF are similar.

Acemannan (polyacetylated mannan) obtained from *Aloe vera* stimulated a tenfold release of ^{51}Cr from labeled tumor cells in the presence of macrophages. When injected intraperitoneally into female CFW mice subcutaneously implanted with murine sarcoma cells, acemannan reduces mortality from 100% of the control animals to 60–65% mortality in treated animals. Acemannan-treated animals exhibit characteristics of *in vivo* tumor necrosis, including development of concave liquefied areas on the tumor mass, and show visible evidence of necrotic toxemia. Necrotic tumors are found to exhibit central necrosing foci with hemorrhage and peripheral fibrosis. Similar effects have been observed in cats and dogs with spontaneous fibrosarcomas treated with acemannan.

Levans

The antitumor activity of levans, unlike that of the other polysaccharides described above, is a result of its ability to stimulate not only macrophages, but also B cells and T cells. For example, levan is a B cell mitogen and can therefore stimulate a polyclonal B cell response. Inhibition of growth of Lewis lung carcinoma (3LL) by levan in mice is probably due primarily to macrophage activation. The site and timing of treatment with high molecular weight levan (2×10^4 kDa) significantly affects its activity against transplanted AKR lymphoma. Thus tumor growth is best inhibited by inoculation of levan directly into the primary tumor soon after tumor inoculation. It is ineffective if administered more than 2 days later. However, metastases are most effectively inhibited by intraperitoneal inoculation, suggesting that macrophage activation may be required for antitumor activity.

Pectin

Pectin, a galactose-rich carbohydate abundant in citrus, is also known to have an antitumor effect. Inhibition by pectin of the metastasis of prostate cancer cells has been shown in a rat model. It has been suggested that pectin blocks galectin-3, a galactose-specific lectin, on cancer cells so that they cannot interact with the cellular matrix and therefore cannot emigrate.

In conclusion, it is clear that many complex carbohydrates have immunostimulating activity which may be of use for the treatment of malignancies. However, all complex carbohydrates clearly do not have the same mode of action, but act on different components of the immune system. Further studies are clearly required to determine the optimal conditions for their use in humans and animals. Recent developments in understanding carbohydrate–lectin interactions in the mammalian system will certainly add to these efforts.

See also: **Carbohydrate antigens; Immunopotentiation; Tumors, immune response to.**

Further reading

Chihara G (1992) Recent progress in immunopharmacology and therapeutic effects of polysaccharides. *Developments in Biological Standardization* **77**: 191–197.

Dennert G and Tucker D (1973) Antitumor polysaccharide Lentinan-A T cell adjuvant. *Journal of the National Cancer Institute* **51**: 1727–1729.

DiLuzio NR (1983) Immunopharmacology of glucan: a broad spectrum enhancer of host defense mechanisms. *Trends in Pharmacological Sciences* **4**: 344–347.

Drickamer K (1994) Molecular structure of animal lectins. In: Fukuda M and Hindsgaul O (eds). *Frontiers in Molecular Biology*, pp 53–87. Oxford: IRL Press.

Karlsson KA (1995) Microbial recognition of target-cell glycoconjugates. *Current Opinion in Structural Biology* **5**: 622–635.

Pienta KJ, Naik H, Akhtar A *et al* (1995) Inhibition of spontaneous metastasis in a rat prostate cancer model by oral administration of modified citrus pectin. *Journal of the National Cancer Institute* 87: 348–352.

Whistler RL, Bushway AA, Singh PB, Nakahara W and Tokuzen R (1976) Noncytotoxic, antitumour polysaccharides. *Advances in Carbohydrate Chemistry and Biochemistry* 32: 235–275.

Womble D and Helderman JH (1988) Enhancement of allo-responsiveness of human lymphocytes by acemannan. *International Journal of Immunopharmacology* 10: 967–974.

CARDIAC DISEASE, AUTOIMMUNE

John B Zabriskie, The Rockefeller University, New York, USA

Allan Gibofsky, The Hospital for Special Surgery, New York, USA

In contrast to the extensive experimental and clinical knowledge that has accumulated concerning immunological and autoimmune mechanisms in the pathogenesis of tissue injury and dysfunction, notably the kidney, the concept that autoimmunity might play an important role in cardiac disease is just beginning to emerge. The slow progress in this area is, in part, due to the lack of good experimental models of autoimmune heart disease and also perhaps because of the difficulty of direct accessibility to the target organ itself. With the advent of the endocardial biopsy and other technological advances in cardiology, the ability to study cardiac tissue 'in situ' has improved considerably and should provide the investigator with reasonable amounts of material for study similar to that seen since the advent of the renal biopsy.

These drawbacks notwithstanding, knowledge supporting the idea of autoimmune mechanisms in human heart disease has evolved greatly over the last two decades.

Microbe-induced cardiac autoimmunity

Rheumatic fever

The 'grand-daddy' of all microbial-induced autoimmune heart disease is rheumatic fever (RF). The concept of autoimmunity playing a role in this disease was introduced over 50 years ago by a number of investigators when antibodies to heart were noted in the sera of patients with acute rheumatic fever (ARF) and/or rheumatic heart disease (RHD). The origin of these antibodies was better defined when Kaplan and colleagues noted that immunization of rabbits with group A streptococci induced antibodies that bound to human heart in a manner strikingly similar to that observed with human patient sera. Further experiments revealed that the cross-reacting antigen being identified was similar to (but not identical with) M protein and was also present in a limited number of group A streptococcal strains. Fischetti and colleagues identified the complete chemical structure of the M protein and demonstrated a close homology of the M protein moiety with cardiac cytoskeletal proteins. Further studies by Sargent and coworkers have clearly demonstrated that the M protein moiety contains numerous epitopes cross-reactive with certain cardiac proteins (e.g. tropomyosin and myosin) including those unrelated to the cytoskeletal proteins.

Similar studies in our own laboratory demonstrated the presence of a second cross-reactive antigen residing in the streptococcal membrane unrelated to M protein. This antigen was present in all streptococcal throat stains tested, and has been purified to a series of four peptides ranging in molecular weight from 23 to 22 kDa. An important feature of this protein was the demonstration by van de Rijn that the heart-reactive staining pattern of ARF sera was completely abolished by preabsorption of the sera with these closely spaced peptides. Further studies on lymphocytes by Zabriskie from ARF patients revealed enhanced cellular reactivity to this membrane antigen but not the cell wall antigen. This reactivity was confined to membrane preparations from streptococcal throat strains and not strains isolated from skin-associated streptococcal infections.

Autoimmune mechanisms are also thought to play a role in another major clinical manifestation of ARF, namely rheumatic chorea. Through the work of Husby and Williams, it was clear that the sera of patients with active chorea contained an antibody which bound to the cytoplasm of the cells of the caudate nuclei and was specific for these cells. The presence of the antibody correlated with the clinical activity of the disease and could be absorbed by streptococcal antigens. Further, the antibody was detected in the cerebrospinal fluid of five patients with active chorea.

The nature and reactivity of lymphocytes from the RF valvular lesions is an area of active investigation in our laboratory. For example, using a panel of monoclonal antibodies specific for various cell surface markers, Dr Kemeny demonstrated that valvular lesions contained equal numbers of macrophages and T cells. Helper T cells predominated in the more active cardiac lesions; the T helper/T suppressor ratio in chronic carditis closely resembled that seen in normal peripheral blood. Recently, Dr Yoshinaga extended these experiments one step further and was able to isolate and clone T cell lines from these valvular specimens. When these T cell clones were stimulated with various streptococcal antigens, only streptococcal membrane antigens isolated from rheumatic fever-associated strains elicited a reaction in proliferation assays. Antigens isolated from nephritogenic strains or antigens from other groups of streptococci were nonreactive. One unanticipated and therefore surprising finding was that none of these T cell clones reacted against cardiac antigens or a variety of purified M protein antigens. In contrast to these findings Guilherme and colleagues have isolated individual T cell clones from RF valvular specimens which reacted both with streptococcal antigens and mammalian cytoskeletal proteins. The exact nature of these reactive antigens is under investigation.

The question of whether or not these heart-reactive antibodies or activated T cells isolated from patients are actually cytotoxic for the relevant tissue antigens has been difficult to prove. The experiments of Yang and colleagues clearly demonstrated that guinea pigs sensitized to streptococcal membranes produced activated T cells specifically cytotoxic for guinea pig neonatal myofibers but not for other tissues, whereas immunization with cell walls did not. However, the addition of heart-reactive antibodies obtained from the sera of these animals did not enhance the cytotoxicity, indicating that the observed cytotoxicity was antibody independent. The few experiments performed to date with cells obtained from 'inactive' rheumatic fever patients also show increased cytotoxicity for human atrial myofibers. Once again, the addition of heart-reactive antibody from the sera of these patients did not enhance the cytotoxicity. These results would suggest that cellular autoreactivity by activated T cells may play a more important role in the rheumatic cardiac lesion than previously thought.

In this context, recent observations by Cunningham and her coworkers are worth mentioning and may correlate with observations made by Rose and colleagues in an experimental model of cardio-myopathy (see below). Using streptococcal-induced monoclonal antibodies that cross-react with M protein and human cardiac myosin, they could neutralize coxsackieviruses B3 and B4. The viral-neutralizing antibodies were also cytotoxic for heart and fibroblast cell lines and reacted with viral capside proteins on western blots.

Given the evidence of an abnormal host immune response to streptococcal antigens cross-reactive with relevant target antigens, the tantalizing and as yet unresolved question is whether there is a genetic basis for this response in rheumatic fever patients. Beginning with Cheadle's work 100 years ago, numerous investigators have presented evidence for and against this concept. Recent articles have suggested that susceptibility to ARF following streptococcal infection might be related to alleles of the human major histocompatibility complex (MHC) but the association with a given phenotype has been either controversial or inconclusive.

To date the strongest association of a cell marker with rheumatic fever has been the identification of a B cell marker apparently unrelated to the MHC by Patarroyo in Colombia and our group in New York. The relative risk of contracting the disease if one bears the marker was 12.9. Because of the limited supply of the original alloantiserum used to identify the marker, we embarked on a series of studies attempting to reproduce this marker using hybridoma technology and immunization of mice with B cells isolated from rheumatics. Of a number of monoclonal antibodies, we have recently isolated one called D8/17 which identifies all rheumatics tested in a number of widely differing geographic areas of the world. The antibody is also not related to the MHC, and family studies indicate this marker is inherited in an autosomal recessive fashion. The exact nature of the antigen is as yet unknown but our experiments suggest it is not present on other lymphoid cells. The antigen is, however, also expressed on other tissues, most notably the heart and smooth muscle cells. What role this antigen plays in the disease process is unknown at present but its expression on B cells from all rheumatics strongly suggests its direct involvement in the etiopathogenesis of rheumatic fever.

Chagas disease

Although rarely seen in more temperate climates this disease is endemic in many parts of the world, most notably in South America where an estimated 11 million people or more are infected with *Trypanosoma cruzi*. The acute disease is the result of multiplication of the organism in the reticuloendothelial system followed by direct invasion of muscle tissue, liver and occasionally the meninges. In contrast, in chronic Chagas' cardiomyopathy, the organism is absent but there is a progressive inflammatory cardiac myofibrillar degeneration with necrosis. An important clue to the etiology of the chronic form of disease was provided by Cossio and coworkers who noted that the sera from a high percentage of these patients contained antibodies reactive against components of cardiac sarcolemma as well as with the valvular endothelial cells. A causal role for this antibody in disease pathogenesis was suggested when cardiac biopsies from Chagas patients demonstrated immunoglobulin bound to cardiac myofibers. Eluted antibody from this tissue bound to myofibers of unaffected heart tissue in a pattern similar to that seen in the patient.

In addition to the presence of immunoglobulin in these biopsies, numerous investigators have also commented on the presence of chronic lymphocytic infiltrates in these tissues, suggesting that abnormalities in cellular reactivity might also be involved in the initiation and/or perpetuation of target organ damage. Santos-Buch and colleagues examined cellular immunity in a mouse model of Chagas' disease and noted that sensitized cells from these animals exhibited cytotoxic activity for mouse heart cells in culture. As with rheumatic fever (see above) the addition of heart-reactive antibody from these animals did not enhance the cytotoxicity, again suggesting that cellular autoimmunity to heart antigens might play the primary role in this disease.

As with chorea of rheumatic fever, a new chapter is being written on the relationship of the *T. cruzi* antigens to structures of the parasympathetic nervous system causing the neurological manifestations of the disease. Several investigators have now reported antigenic cross-reactions between *T. cruzi* and neuronal and glial antigens. Using cloning techniques and recombinant technology, Voorhis and Eigen have shown that a 160 kDa *T. cruzi* flagellar protein cross-reacts with a 48 kDa human neuronal antigen. Immunoperoxidase studies of brain sections revealed that at least part of the reaction is related to a neuronal protein of the mysenteric plexus (also found in the neurons in the ileum) perhaps explaining the observed megacolon and megaesophagus so often seen in Chagas patients. Interestingly, this cross-reaction was also localized to the Purkinje fibers of the brain.

In summary, autoimmune phenomena have been reported and implicated in the etiology of progressive cardiac damage in both experimentally infected animals and chronic Chagas disease in humans (Cossio and colleagues and Gazzinelli and colleagues). It has been suggested that both changes in the T cell reper-

toire (Miniprio and coworkers) and also molecular mimicry (Van Voorhis and colleagues) might be implicated in the pathogenesis of the autoimmune phenomena seen following *T. cruzi* infection. Yet another intriguing possibility is a chronic immune response to local parasites that may persist in cardiac tissue during the chronic stage of the disease (Jones and coworkers). D'Imperio Lima and colleagues have described persistent B cell activation and immunoglobulin production in the murine model of *T. cruzi* infection, even when injected parasites are no longer detected in the blood. Finnegan and colleagues have reported that autoreactive CD4$^+$ T cell clones are capable of polyclonal activation of immunoglobulin production of B cells in both MHC-restricted and non-cognate fashions.

Recently, Freire-de-Lima and colleagues have reported that splenic CD4$^+$ T cells from chronically infected mice have markedly enhanced autoreactivity towards normal syngeneic but not allogeneic resting B cells. This suggests that enhanced CD4$^+$ T cell autoreactivity can be a potential cause of persistent B cell activation and autoantibody production in chronic Chagas' disease.

Cardiomyopathies

It has long been known that numerous microbes, parasites and viruses can cause acute myocarditis. In these clinical syndromes the organism can be readily demonstrated in the tissues of the individual. In contrast, there is an ill-defined group of cardiomyopathies in which the offending organism that caused the acute inflammation is no longer present, yet the cardiomyopathy continues to progress. These cases are distinguished by the presence of lymphocytic infiltrations and, in a majority of cases, increased titers of heart-reactive antibodies. Among the agents considered to be important causal agents in this group of cardiomyopathies have been the group B coxsackieviruses. These agents frequently cause acute cardiac inflammation in humans, and 10–12% of patients go on to develop a more chronic phase of the disease. Because chronic and progressive myocarditis is restricted to a small number of patients, it has also been suggested that there might be a genetic basis for the disease.

This concept has been greatly strengthened by the elegant work of Rose and his colleagues, working with an animal model of coxsackie B3 virally induced myocarditis. Using genetically different strains of mice, they could induce a chronic myocarditis primarily in H-2 congenic strains bearing an A background (i.e. ACA, ASW) whereas C57BL/10 H-2 mice were resistant. A key finding in these studies was that only those mice with heart-reactive antibodies in their sera went on to develop chronic cardiomyopathy; these antibodies were primarily directed against the cardiac isoform of myosin. A causal role for myosin in the etiology of this cardiomyopathy was shown when injection of myosin alone was able to induce severe immunologically mediated myocarditis in certain genetic strains of mice.

Hoping to demonstrate that myosin and the coxsackie B virus shared common antigen determinants, Rose and colleagues were disappointed in their inability to show that heart-reactive antibodies in their coxsackie B3-induced cardiomyopathy cross-reacted with viral antigens. Saegusa and coworkers however, in preparing a series of different monoclonal antibodies against coxsackie B4 virus identified one which both neutralized the coxsackie B4 virus and also bound to rabbit and mouse heart tissue. An important observation was that this antibody did not bind to human heart tissue, suggesting that both the strain of virus and the myosin of a given species may be crucial for the induction of cardiac disease. Whether or not viruses other than coxsackie B are involved in chronic human cardiomyopathies and whether this progression is on a genetic basis, though unknown at present, is a particularly fertile field for future study.

Postpericardiotomy syndrome

The possible pathogenetic role of heart-reactive antibodies in the postpericardiotomy syndrome (PPS) has been investigated over a number of years by Dr Engle and her colleagues. In both adults and children the syndrome appears 10–14 days after surgery, and is characterized clinically by fever, chest pain, pericardial and plural effusions. Long thought to be related to rheumatic fever, it is clearly a separate syndrome. One common feature, however, is the presence of high-titer heart-reactive antibodies in the sera of patients with these conditions.

An interesting and as yet not entirely explained observation for the induction of postpericardiotomy syndrome is that while the syndrome can be induced by damage to cardiac muscle and the surrounding pericardium, it is almost never seen in operations such as those involving repair of coarctation of the aorta or closure of a patent ductus. Furthermore, the degree of trauma to cardiac muscle often defines the severity of the syndrome. For example, excision of ventricular muscle (such as repair of tetralogy of Fallot) results in the highest incidence of the syndrome.

The question of whether or not a microbe is responsible for the induction of the autoimmunity in this syndrome is unresolved. Engle noted that approximately 70% of her PPS patients had a rise in antiviral titers to one or more of eight common viruses tested (e.g. coxsackie, megalovirus, adenovirus, etc.). The heightened antibody response to a given virus was not constant however, and seemed to vary with viruses common in the community that year. Preliminary experiments attempting to identify viral presence or isolate whole virus from the excised tissues of these patients have been uniformly unrewarding.

In vitro cytotoxic studies do, however, suggest that the heart-specific antibody in the sera of these patients does play a direct role in the disease pathogenesis. The addition of heart-reactive antibody from these patients to cultured beating heart cells *in vitro* was not cytotoxic, yet caused a marked decrease in contractility. The questions of whether or not susceptibility may be mediated via alleles of the human MHC and the role of sensitized lymphocytes in disease pathogenesis have not been answered.

Significance

It is now clear that many microbes share antigenic determinants not only with other microbes but also with a variety of human tissues. Cross-reactions between streptococci and heart tissue, E. coli antigens and colonic antigens, HLA-B27 and shigella antigens, gram-negative bacteria and blood groups are but a few examples of these cross-reactions seen in nature. The majority of these cross-reactions are generally harmless and may serve the purpose of protecting humans against a wide variety of microbes which might be pathogenic. However the combination of the right microbe infecting the genetically susceptible host may result in serious autoimmune consequences.

As indicated above, perhaps the two best examples of microbially induced autoimmune cardiomyopathies are RF and Chagas disease. Here the cross-reactions between host and relevant target organs have been well defined; there is an abnormal host cellular and humoral response to tissue and microbial antigens. Further, in RF, there appears to be a genetic predisposition to the disease. Whether this genetic predisposition allows for breakage of tolerance on the part of the host, an abnormal response to the specific cross-reactive determinant or production of anti-idiotypic antibodies bearing the cross-reactive epitopes is unknown and will require further investigation.

In terms of the immune response of the host, it is becoming increasingly apparent that the cellular response to cross-reactive antigens may play a more significant role in the observed pathological damage then previously thought. In both rheumatic fever and Chagas disease, T cells are specifically cytotoxic for the target organ and the addition of antibody does not enhance the cytotoxicity, suggesting a more crucial role for cellular immunity in the disease process. Similar studies of experimental models of autoimmune heart disease point to the same conclusion. To date, these studies have not been done in either the PPS syndrome of the idiopathic cardiomyopathies.

In more general terms, what is the significance of heart-reactive antibodies in these disease states? It is well-known that organ-specific antibodies increase with age; appear in a variety of other disease states (e.g. systemic lupus erythematosus, RA) and in many instances do not appear to cause damage. Even for rheumatic fever and Chagas disease, is it a question of the 'chicken or the egg'?

In other words, are these cross-reactive antibodies directly involved in the disease process or are they merely a reflection of prior heart damage and a fortuitous cross-reaction with a given microbe? The evidence in rheumatic fever suggests the latter concept is not true since these heart-reactive antibodies are absorbed by both streptococcal and cardiac antigens while heart-reactive antibodies in PPS are absorbed only by cardiac tissue. Thus in RF the heart-specific antibody appears to relate to the infection whereas in PPS the antibody appears to relate to tissue damage.

Whether or not these heart-reactive antibodies (from whatever origin) play a direct role in the disease process is difficult to ascertain with certainty. They do correlate with the disease state and disappear during convalescence; they are seen in the pathological tissue specimens but they do not apparently kill target organ cells or enhance specific cellular cytotoxicity *in vitro*. Perhaps complement activation and/or other factors are needed *in situ* to produce the observed immunoglobulin staining seen in the lesions of several cardiomyopathies. To our knowledge, these experiments have not been attempted *in vitro*.

What is becoming increasingly clear, not only in cardiac autoimmunity but also in other autoimmune diseases such as rheumatic arthritis, is that cellular activation specific for a given target tissue appears to be important in the pathogenesis of disease. Cytotoxic T cells specific for cardiac myofibers are seen in both rheumatic fever and Chagas' disease, and it is our impression they may be important in the pathogenesis of other cardiomyopathies as well. Obviously, it will be important to define the exact nature of the cross-reactive epitopes recognized by these active cells and their role in causing cytotoxicity to human tissue.

Finally, the specific mechanisms operating in the interaction between host genetic factors and environment resulting in the induction of autoimmune disease of the heart is still not clear. In rheumatic fever there appears to be a marker called D8/17 which is inherited in an autosomal fashion and is preferentially increased in the B cells of rheumatic fever patients. However it is well-known that not all strains of group A streptococci cause rheumatic fever, even in the genetically susceptible individual. The most plausible explanation for this discrepancy is that only certain strains exhibit the epitopes that activate the immune system to produce tissue cross-reactive antibodies and activated T cells. Then, only in the context of the immune response (a heightened response, break in tolerance, etc.) will the disease occur. A similar mechanism can be postulated for the other cardiomyopathies, as it appears that only select individuals will develop progressive autoimmune disease following active infection. Future studies of each of the cardiopathies mentioned above should concentrate not only on the immune response of the host to a given cross-reactive antigen (either in the microbe or host) but should examine more carefully whether or not a particular microbe exhibits a specific epitope.

Obviously the field is ripe for applying the modern tools of molecular biology to the study of these intriguing host–microbial relationships in cardiac disease.

See also: **Autoimmune diseases; Autoimmunity; Chagas' disease; Circulatory system infections; Molecular mimicry; *Streptococcus*, infection and immunity; Trypanosomiasis, African.**

Further reading

Cossio PM, Diez C, Szarfman A, Kreutzer E, Candiolo B and Arana RM (1974) Chagasic cardiomyopathy: demonstration of a serum gamma globulin factor which reacts with endocardium and vascular structures. *Circulation* 49: 1302–1305.

Cunningham MW, Antone SM, Gulizia JM, McManus BM, Fischetti VA and Cauntt CJ (1992) Cytotoxin and viral neutralizing antibodies cross react with streptococcal M protein, enteroviruses and human cardiac myosin. *Proceedings of the National Academy of Sciences of the USA* 89: 1320–1324.

Engle MA, Gay WA, Zabriskie JB and Senterfit LB (1984) The post-pericardiotomy syndrome: 25 years' experience. *Journal of Cardiovascular Medicine* April: 321–332.

Fischetti VA (1989) Streptococcal M protein: molecular design and biological behavior. *Clinical Microbiology Reviews* 2: 285–314.

Friere-de-Lima C, Pecanha LMT and does Reis GA (1996)

Chronic experimental Chagas disease: Functional syngeneic T-B-cell cooperation *in vitro* in the absence of exogenous stimuli. *Infection and Immunity* **64**: 2861–2866.

Guilherme L, Cunha-Neto E, Coelho V *et al* (1995) Human heart-infiltrating T-cell clones from rheumatic heart disease patients recognize both streptococcal and cardiac proteins. *Circulation* **92**: 415–420.

Husby G, Van de Rijn I, Zabriskie JB, Abdin ZH and Williams Jr RC (1976) Antibodies reacting with cytoplasm of sulthalmic and caudate nuclei neurons in chorea and acute rheumatic fever. *Journal of Experimental Medicine* **144**: 1094–1110.

Jones EM, Colley DG, Tostes SJ, Lopes ER, Vnencak-Jones CL and McCurley TL (1993) *T. cruzi* DNA sequences in human inflammatory cardiac lesion. *American Journal of Tropical Medicine and Hygiene* **48**: 348–357.

Kemeny E, Husby G, William Jr RC and Zabriskie JB (1994) Tissue distribution of antigen(s) defined by monoclonal antibody D8/17 reacting with B lymphocytes of patients with rheumatic heart disease. *Clinical Immunology and Immunopathology* **72**: 35–43.

Malkiel S, Kuan AP and Diamond B (1996) Autoimmunity in heart disease: mechanisms and genetic susceptibility. *Molecular Medicine Today* **2**: 336–342.

Rose NR, Beisel KW, Herskowitz A *et al* (1987) Cardiac myosin and autoimmune myocarditis. In: Everet D (ed) *Autoimmunity and Autoimmune Disease, CIBA Foundation Symposium*, **29**: 3–24. Chichester: John Wiley.

Sargent SJ, Beachey EH, Corbett CE and Dale JB (1987) Sequence of protective epitopes of streptococcal M proteins shared with cardiac sarcolemmal membranes. *Journal of Immunology* **139**: 1285–1290.

Takle GB and Hudson L (1989) Autoimmunity and Chagas' disease. In: Oldstone MBA (ed) *Current Topics in Microbiology and Immunology*, **145**: 79–92. Berlin: Springer-Verlag.

Yoshinaga M, Figueroa F, Wahid MR, Marcus RH, Suh E and Zabriskie JB (1995) Antigenic specificity of lymphocytes isolated from valvular specimens of rheumatic fever patients. *Journal of Autoimmunity* **8**: 601–613.

Zabriskie JB (1985) Rheumatic fever: the interplay between host, genetics and the microbe. *Circulation* **71**: 1027–1086.

CARRIER

Huw Davies, Division of Life Sciences, King's College, London, UK

Our current understanding of antibody production by B lymphocytes, and the underlying cooperation between T and B lymphocytes, owes much to the early use of hapten–carrier conjugates in immunologic studies. It had been known from the work of Landsteiner and of Pauling in the 1940s that haptens, small antigenic determinants such as dinitrophenol (DNP), were insufficient by themselves to elicit specific antibody, but would bind to antibody once it was produced. The problem of how to generate hapten-specific antibodies was resolved by physical coupling of the hapten to a larger 'carrier' molecule. Proteins that have proved to be suitable carriers include bovine serum albumin, bovine gammaglobulin and ovalbumin.

We now understand that an efficient carrier is an immunogenic antigen that elicits a response from helper T lymphocytes. These cells will provide the necessary signals to enable B lymphocytes to generate hapten-specific antibodies. The following recapitulates the evidence for this. The first evidence that the carrier molecule itself was also recognized during an immune response to the hapten was provided by Ovary and Benacerraf in 1963. Animals primed with hapten A coupled to carrier B developed a secondary,

anamnestic antihapten (and anticarrier) antibody response after boosting with the original A–B conjugate. However, no antibodies to A were seen if the mice were challenged with hapten A coupled to an unrelated carrier such as carrier C. This curious phenomenon was termed the 'carrier effect'.

The mid-1960s was an exciting period that saw the emergence of the small circulating lymphocyte, hitherto regarded as uninteresting, as a primary component of the immune system. This apparently homogeneous population of cells was soon split into two functionally different, but cooperative subsets. The pioneering work of Gowans, in which the immune system could be severely compromised by depletion of circulating lymphocytes, demonstrated the fundamental importance of this cell. A functional dichotomy was revealed by extirpation experiments by both Glick and Cooper, using chickens, and in mice by Miller. Their findings, that depletion of B lymphocytes by bursectomy abolished antibody production without affecting cell-mediated immunity, and that depletion of T lymphocytes by neonatal thymectomy ablated both antibody and cellular immune responses, laid the foundations of modern cellular immunology. A series of influential studies then followed (Claman; Davies; Mitchell and Miller) which dealt with establishing that an antibody response required both T and B lymphocyte subsets. In essence, B cells which were shown to be responsible for the generation of antibodies, and T cells which helped by providing regulatory signals, both had to interact with each other before a specific antibody response could be elicited.

The next problem was to explain how the antigen fitted into this interaction between helper T cells and B cells. Hapten–carrier conjugates provided a powerful tool in addressing this question. It was already known that some proteins were better carriers than others. Immunization with hapten–carrier conjugates only induced hapten-specific antibody responses when the carrier to which the hapten was attached was itself 'immunogenic', that is if the carrier was a T cell (or thymus) dependent antigen. Nonimmunogenic molecules served as poor carriers for haptens. This, and the 'carrier effect', indicated that separate recognition systems existed for the hapten and carrier, presumably mediated by B lymphocytes and T lymphocytes, respectively. The first direct evidence that cooperating T and B lymphocytes responded to different determinants on the same antigen molecule was provided by Mitchison (1971) using hapten–carrier conjugates. An adoptive transfer system, originally developed by Playfair and colleagues was used, in which lymphocytes were transferred from donor mice to a syngeneic recipient which had been rendered immunoincompetent by sublethal irradiation. T and B lymphocytes primed previously to different determinants were tested for their ability to cooperate within the recipient host (as manifested by the production of hapten-specific antibodies) in response to challenge with the determinants complexed on the same molecule. Mitchison observed that adoptively transferred spleen cells primed to hapten A conjugated to carrier B responded to challenge with A–B but not A–C (the carrier effect). However, if spleen cells from A–B primed mice were transferred together with cells primed to carrier C, an excellent response to challenge with A–C occurred. Moreover, hapten A and carrier C had to be physically linked.

These data, which have been confirmed in many experimental systems since, established that recognition of hapten and carrier is performed by different populations of cells that can cooperate to produce hapten-specific antibody, provided that the hapten and carrier are part of the same molecule. Formal proof that T lymphocytes recognized carrier determinants came from Raff in 1970. Employing the adoptive transfer system, depletion of Thy-1$^+$ lymphocytes (T cells) from the carrier-primed population using Thy-1-specific antibody plus complement abolished the adoptive antihapten response. Elimination of T lymphocytes from the hapten-primed population had no effect.

These experiments using defined B lymphocyte determinants coupled to carrier proteins revealed the importance of cognate T and B lymphocyte interactions in antibody synthesis and the recognition of spatially disparate determinants within the antigen by the cells participating in the response. A macromolecular antigen can thus be regarded as a complex of carrier and haptenic determinants, or, more precisely, T helper and B lymphocyte epitopes.

Recent interest in carriers has been revived by the potential use of synthetic polypeptides which contain antigenic determinants for use as vaccines. The efficient generation of antibody responses to peptides usually requires the peptide to be coupled to an immunogenic carrier as a source of helper T cell determinants. In order that an appropriate anamnestic response is mounted upon subsequent pathogenic infection, the carrier must possess helper T cell determinants derived from the same pathogen as those recognized by the antibodies, thereby ensuring that T and B cells capable of cognate interaction in response to the pathogen will be present in the memory pool. Studies in inbred animals have shown that the helper T cell determinants above, in the form of synthetic peptides, can be used in place of the carrier molecule – thereby raising the prospect of vaccines comprising no more than arrays of contiguous T and B cell epitopes.

See also: **CD40 and its ligand; B7 (CD80 & CD86); Cooperation, mechanisms of cellular; Cytokines; Epitopes; Hapten; Helper T lymphocytes; Vaccines**

Further reading

Claman HN, Chapteron EA and Triplett RF (1966) Thymus-marrow cell combinations. Synergism in antibody production. *Proceedings of the Society for Experimental Biology and Medicine* 122: 1167–1171.

Cooper MD, Raymond DA, Peterson RD *et al* (1966) The functions of the thymus and bursa system in the chicken. *Journal of Experimental Medicine* 123: 75–102.

Davies AJS, Leuchars E, Wallis V, Marchant R and Elliott EV (1967) The failure of thymus-derived cells to produce antibody. *Transplantation* 5: 222–231.

Glick B, Chang TS and Jaap RG (1956) The bursa of Fabricius and antibody production. *Poultry Science* 35: 224–225.

Gowans JL and Knight EJ (1964) The route of recirculation of lymphocytes in the rat. *Proceedings of the Royal Society of London. Series B: Biological Sciences* 159: 257–282.

Miller JFAP (1961) Immunological function of the thymus. *Lancet* ii: 748–749.

Miller JFAP (1962) Effect of neonatal thymectomy on the immunological responsiveness of the mouse. *Proceedings of the Royal Society of London. Series B: Biological Sciences* **156**: 415–428.

Mitchell GF and Miller JFAP (1968) Cell to cell interaction in the immune response. II. The source of hemolysin-forming cells in irradiated mice given bone marrow and thymus of thoracic duct lymphocytes. *Journal of Experimental Medicine* **128**: 821–837.

Mitchison NA (1971) The carrier effect in the secondary response to hapten–protein conjugates. II. Cellular cooperation. *European Journal of Immunology* **1**: 18–27.

Ovary Z and Benacerraf B (1963) Immunological specificity of the secondary response with dinitrophenylated proteins. *Proceedings of the Society for Experimental Biology and Medicine* **114**: 72–76.

Playfair JH, Papermaster BW and Cole LJ (1965) Focal antibody production by transferred spleen cells in irradiated mice. *Science* **149**: 998–1000.

Raff MC (1970) Role of thymus-derived lymphocytes in the secondary humoral immune response in mice. *Nature* **226**: 1257–1258.

CATALYTIC ANTIBODIES

Irene Lee and **Stephen J Benkovic**, Department of Chemistry, The Pennsylvania State University, University Park, Pennsylvania, USA

The concept of inducing antibodies that would possess, in addition to their exquisite ligand specificity, catalytic potential has its roots in the seminal contributions of Pauling. His proposal, that the ability of an enzyme to speed up a chemical reaction stemmed from the 'complementarity of the enzyme's active site structure to the activated complex', shifted the research focus from concerns about substrate–enzyme fit to a means for defining the structural requirements for binding the transition state. Since a transition state by definition has a negligible lifetime, evidence was sought for transition state stabilization in the tighter binding of inhibitors whose structures mimicked those of the presumed transition state relative to the weaker binding of substrate. Many examples of such high-affinity transition state inhibitors are now documented. However, stabilization of the transition state alone is necessary but not sufficient to give catalysis, which requires differential binding of substrate and transition state. The use of transition state analogs to induce catalytic antibodies successfully stems not only from this differential binding but other factors such as the introduction of catalytic residues. Nevertheless, it was apparent that such inhibitors would furnish a convenient starting point for creating catalytic antibodies which would owe their catalytic properties to their ability to bind the transition state of the reaction. Earlier attempts, however, were thwarted by the use of polyclonal rather than monoclonal antibodies, and by the need for better transition state mimics. In some cases, optimum haptens cannot be obtained owing to difficulties in the synthesis of precise mimics.

Reaction types catalyzed by antibodies

There are now approximately 100 reactions that have been catalyzed by antibodies. Representative examples include: pericyclic processes (Diels–Alder condensation, Claisen rearrangement, oxy-Cope rearrangement); elimination reactions (E2 elimination of benzisoxazole, syn elimination of hydrogen fluoride from fluoroketones, dehydration, decarboxylation); various hydrolyses (carbonate esters, amides, esters, lactones, enol ethers); several types of bond-forming reactions (lactonization, peptide synthesis, cationic cyclization, aldol condensation) and redox processes (sulfide oxidation, reduction of ketones, epoxidation). Specific cases are given in **Figures 1–**

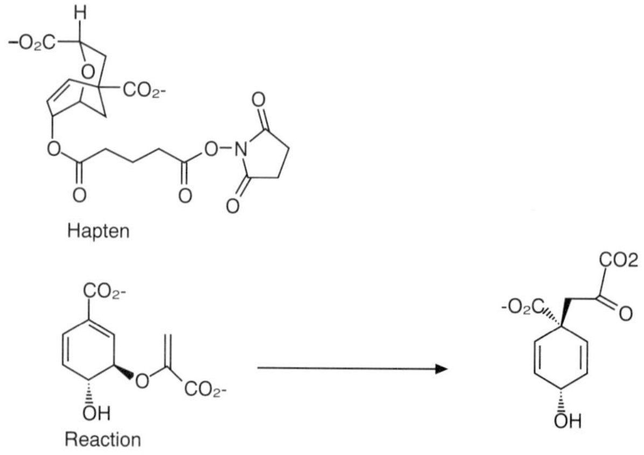

Figure 1 Claisen rearrangement. (Reproduced with permission from Benkovic SJ. Catalytic antibodies. *Annual Review of Biochemistry* **61**: 29–54, © 1992, by Annual Reviews Inc.)

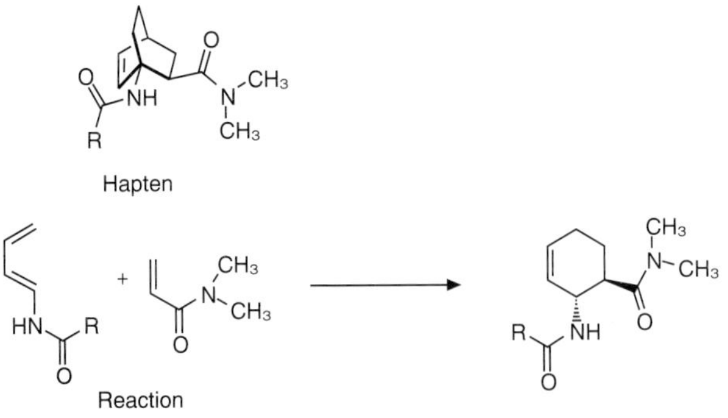

Hapten

Reaction

Figure 2 Disfavored exo Diels–Alder reaction. (Modified from Benkovic SJ. Catalytic antibodies. *Annual Review of Biochemistry* **61**: 29–54, © 1992, by Annual Reviews Inc.)

Hapten

Reaction

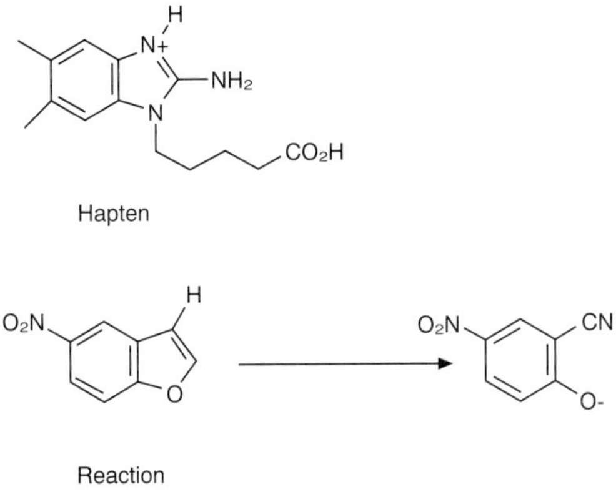

Figure 3 E2 Elimination. (Modified from Benkovic SJ. Catalytic antibodies. *Annual Review of Biochemistry* **61**: 29–54, © 1992, by Annual Reviews Inc.)

11. The chosen reactions illustrate the more significant features of antibody catalysis. The majority of antibody-catalyzed reactions are highly stereospecific; the Diels–Alder condensation (**Figure 2**) is an example of enantioselectivity in which the normally disfavored exo product is generated over the inherent

Hapten

a) R$_1$=H, R$_2$=NO$_2$, X=F
b) R$_1$=NO$_2$, R$_2$=H, X=H (inhibitor)

R$_1$=H, R$_2$=NO$_2$

Reaction

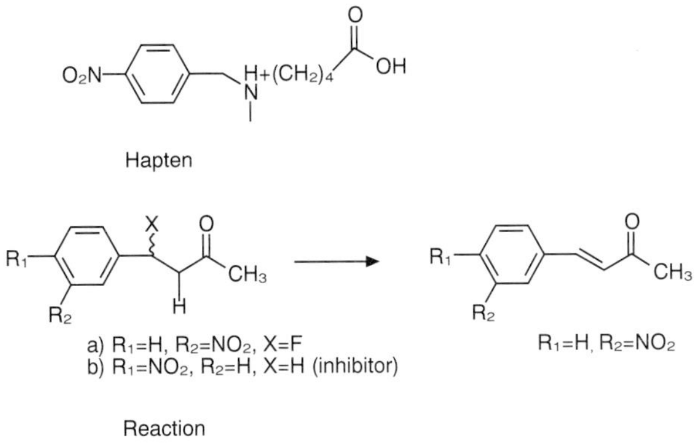

Figure 4 β-Elimination. (Reproduced with permission from Benkovic SJ. Catalytic antibodies. *Annual Review of Biochemistry* **61**: 29–54, © 1992, by Annual Reviews Inc.)

Hapten

+ CO$_2$

Reaction

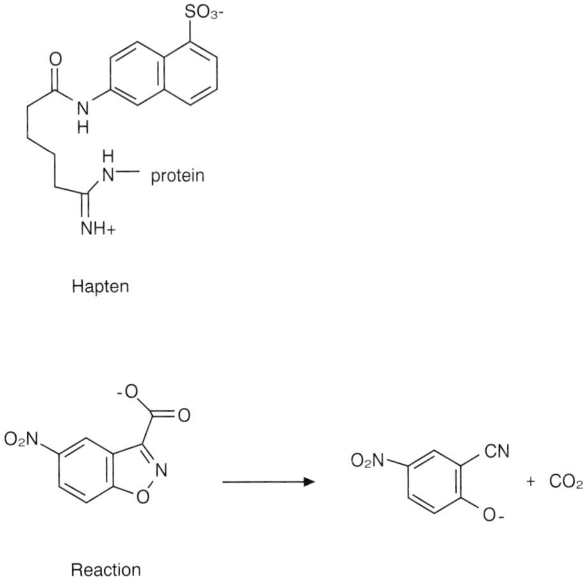

Figure 5 Decarboxylation. (Reproduced with permission from Benkovic SJ. Catalytic antibodies. *Annual Review of Biochemistry* **61**: 29–54, © 1992, by Annual Reviews Inc.)

endo specificity of the Diels–Alder reaction. Similarly the antibody catalyzed cyclization (**Figure 7**), in which racemic starting material is resolved kinetically, represents a case in which one major product is generated under solvolytic conditions that generally yield a mixture. The stereo- and regiospecificity of antibody catalysis, particularly for transformations for which there is no comparable enzymic process, has the potential to be useful in commercial synthetic and medical applications such as the formation of pharmaceuticals and prodrug activation.

For efficient catalysis, strategies are needed for the introduction of catalytic functions within the antibody-combining site correctly juxtaposed to the substrate. Charge complimentarity to induce a catalytic base for promoting the elimination of hydrogen fluoride is shown in **Figure 4**. A catalytic base also is operative in the E2 elimination illustrated in **Figure 3**. The use of a reactive diketone hapten (**Figure 11**) to elicit antibodies with a combining-site amine provided catalysts capable of forming an active-site enamine. The latter forms an aldol product (the α-hydroxyketone) upon reaction with a substrate aldehyde followed by hydrolysis. Alternatively, the reactive reagent could be provided externally, as in the case of the periodate (**Figure 10**).

Nature of the combining site

There is a small repertoire of main-chain conformations, 'canonical structures', for at least five of the six hypervariable regions of antibodies whose

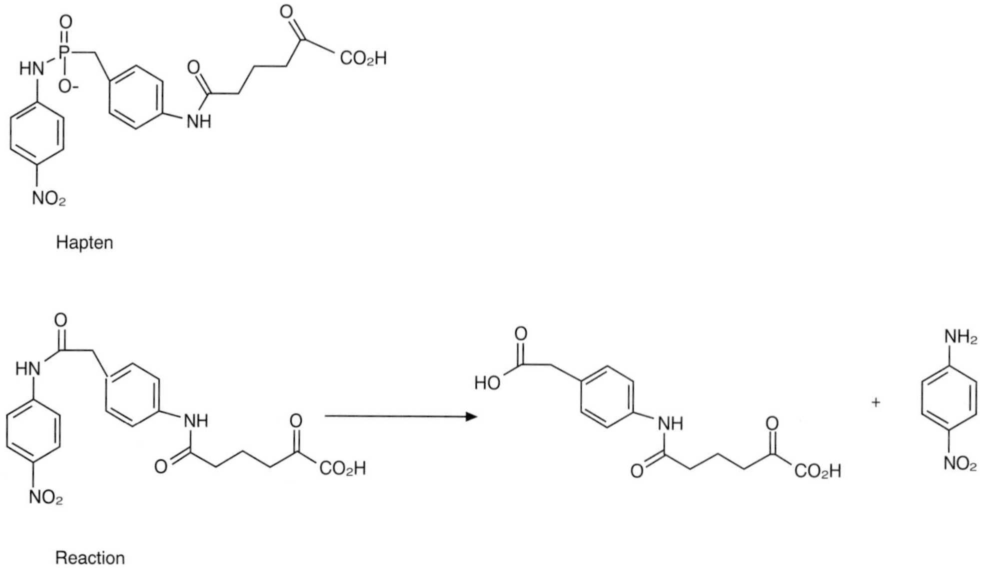

Figure 6 Amide hydrolysis. (Reproduced with permission from Benkovic SJ. Catalytic antibodies. *Annual Review of Biochemistry* **61**: 29–54, © 1992, by Annual Reviews Inc.)

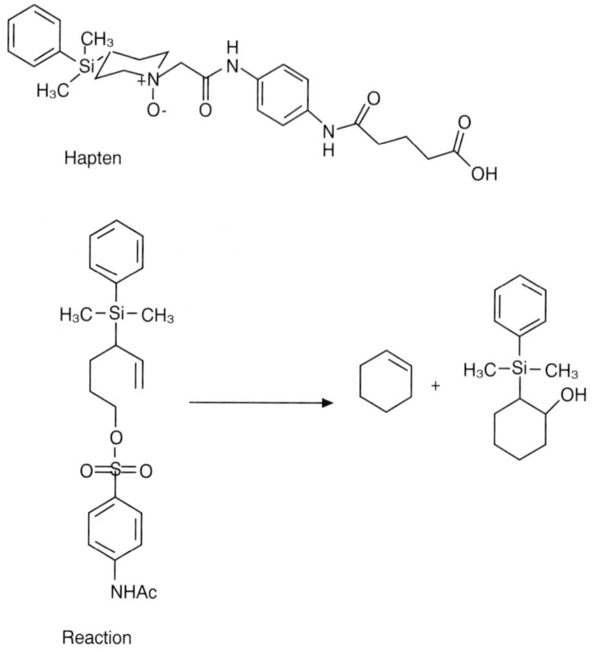

Figure 7 Cationic cyclization. (Modified from Schultz PG and Lerner RA (1995) Molecular diversity to catalysis: lessons from the immune system. *Science* **269**: 1835–1842.)

are in excess of 600Å^3. For small organic molecules the dissociation constant of the antibody–antigen complex ranges from 10^{-4} to 10^{-10} M, which if totally coupled to drive a chemical transformation would provide a free energy change up to 15 kcal M^{-1}, sufficient to promote most reactions in aqueous solution. The binding of antigen does not result in a global conformational change in the antibody. Rather, the union is accommodated by conformational adjustments in the specific amino acid side-chains that improve the initial binding interactions of hydrogen bonds, van der Waals and electrostatic forces. For a series of catalytic antibodies that were induced by phosphonate haptens (**Figure 6**) and hydrolyze esters, the active site structures are surprisingly congruent, suggesting the immunological response despite its diversity is tightly programmed by the chemical nature of the hapten. In general the crystallographic studies of catalytic antibodies show the bound hapten has induced antibodies that provide a three-dimensional arrangement of critical residues which resemble that found in enzymes of analogous activity. Although specific transition state binding is a feature of any enzyme or catalytic antibody, there is no assurance that the combining site has side residues suitable for efficient catalysis. From crystallographic studies of both the catalytic antibody and enzyme that catalyze the Claisen rearrangement of chorismate to prephenate, the active sites of both provide environments that complement the bound transition state analog (**Figure 12**). The 10^4 difference in catalytic efficiency may be more a matter of degree, as the enzyme apparently provides

conformation is determined by a few key residues. The area of interaction between the antigen and antibody may be relatively flat and extensive for protein antigen binding to an antibody (700–750 Å^2), whereas in the case of small organic molecules the binding may occur by way of clefts whose volumes

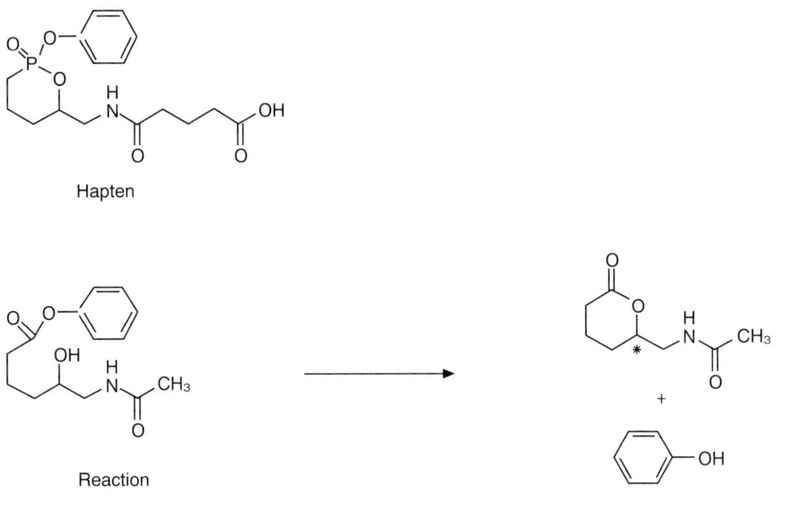

Hapten

Reaction

Figure 8 Lactonization. (Reproduced with permission from Benkovic SJ. Catalytic antibodies. *Annual Review of Biochemistry* **61**: 29–54, © 1992, by Annual Reviews Inc.)

Hapten

Reaction

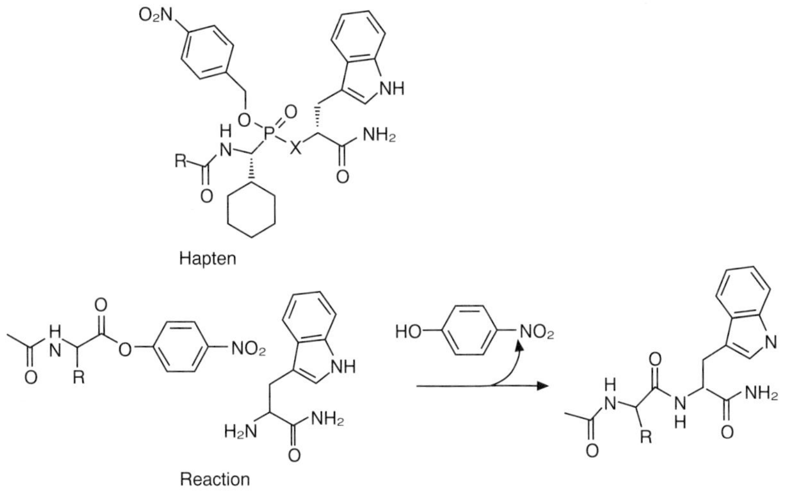

Figure 9 Peptide synthesis. (Reproduced with permission from Hirschmann R *et al* (1994) Peptide synthesis catalyzed by an antibody containing a binding site for variable amino acids. *Science* **265**: 234–237.)

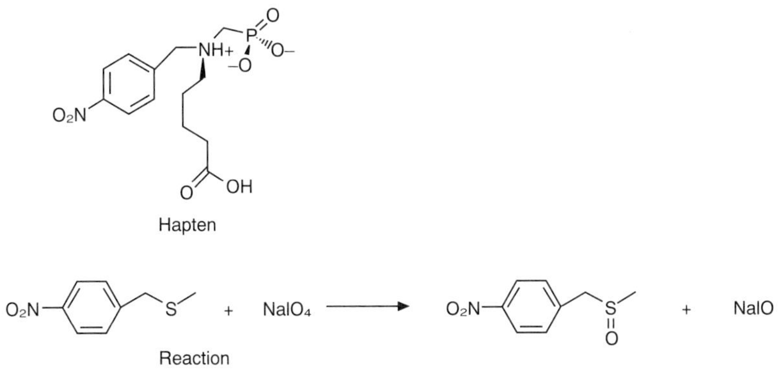

Hapten

Reaction

Figure 10 Periodate-dependent oxidation. (Modified with permission from Benkovic SJ. Catalytic antibodies. *Annual Review of Biochemistry* **61**: 29–54, © 1992, by Annual Reviews Inc.)

more extensive electrostatic and hydrogen binding interactions than the antibody (**Figure 12**).

Nature of catalysis

Catalytic antibodies (abzymes) like enzymes process their substrates through a Michaelis complex in which the chemical transformation occurs, followed by product dissociation. There are two general indices based on steady-state kinetic analyses that are used to assess the catalytic efficiency of an antibody: k_{cat}/k_{uncat} and k_{cat}/K_M. The steady-state kinetics for all abzymes obey the Michaelis–Menten rate expression for both K_M (the concentration of sub-

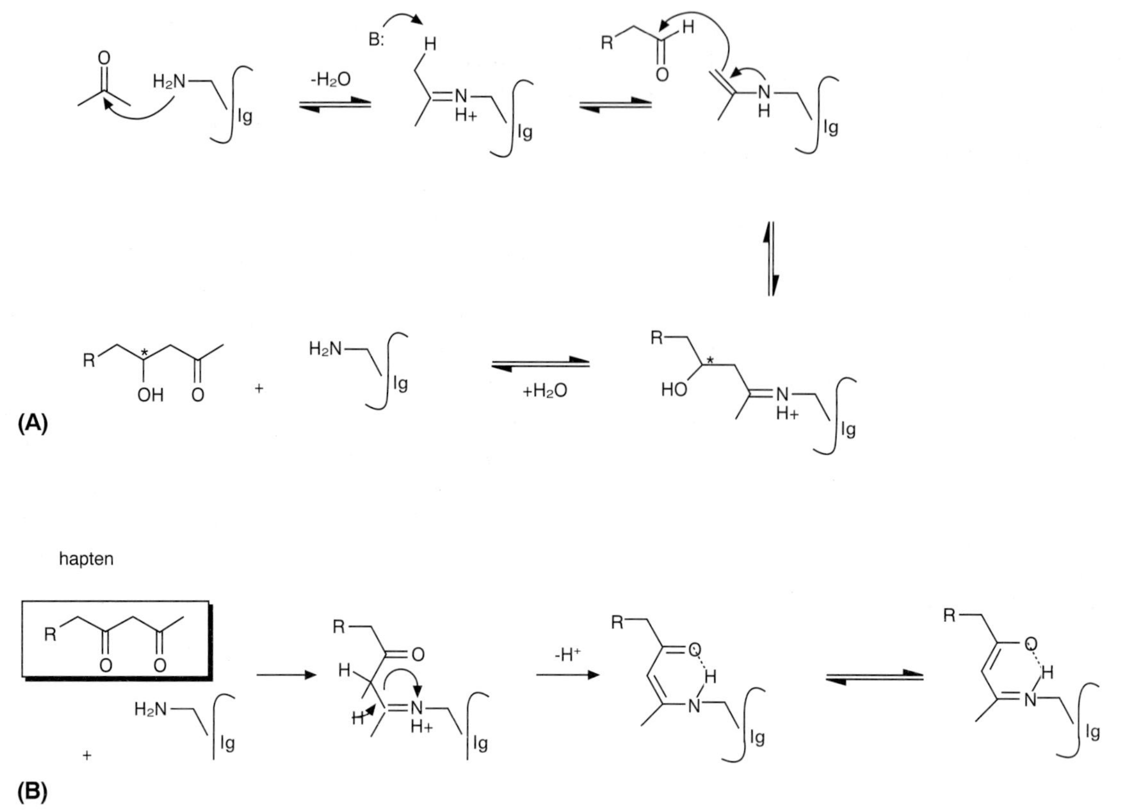

(A)

(B)

Figure 11   (A) Mechanism-base screen for an active site lysine residue. (B) Antibody-catalyzed aldol condensation via Schiff-base formation. (Reproduced with permission from Jacobsen JR and Schultz PG (1995) The scope of Antibody Catalysis. *Current Opinion in Structural Biology* **5**: 818–824.)

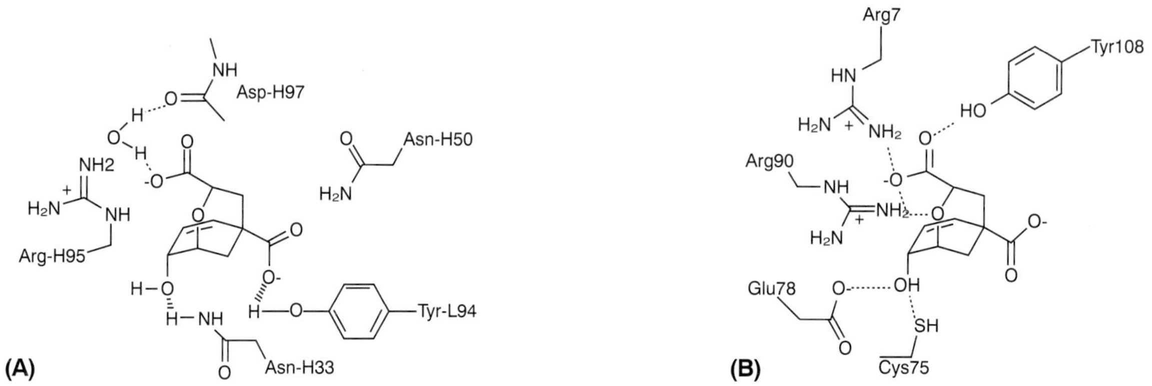

(A)   **(B)**

Figure 12   Comparison of the transition state analog binding between antibody 1F7 (A) and *Bacillus subtilis* chorismate mutase (B). (Reproduced with permission from Haynes MR *et al* (1994) Routes to catalysis: structure of a catalytic antibody and comparison with its natural counterpart. *Science* **263**: 646–652.)

strate that produces one-half the maximal catalytic rate) and k_{cat} (the rate constant for product formation under conditions when the antibody is saturated with substrate). Note that the K_M parameter also represents an approximate measure for the dissociation of the abzyme–substrate complex. The meaning of the first index k_{cat}/k_{uncat}, where k_{uncat} is the rate constant for the same chemical process in

the absence of antibody, is obvious and for enzymes often exceeds 10^{10}. (For hydrolytic reactions both k_{cat} and k_{uncat} have the same units, as the activity of water is set equal to unity.) The second index of efficiency, the ratio k_{cat}/K_M, represents a measure of the kinetic barrier encountered, commencing with the combination of antibody and substrate and proceeding along the reaction coordinate to the transition state of the highest energy. This ratio has a limit of approximately $10^7 \, \text{M}^{-1} \, \text{s}^{-1}$ when the reaction is limited by diffusion together of the substrate and antibody.

The values of k_{cat}/k_{uncat} for catalytic antibodies generally span a range from 10 to 10^6. Likewise, the values of k_{cat}/K_M are below that of a diffusion-controlled process. Both lines of evidence are consistent with the chemical step of a particular transformation as being rate limiting. For the majority of abzyme-catalyzed reactions there is a fair proportionality of the k_{cat}/k_{uncat} ratio with the affinity of the antibody for its inducing hapten, although the coupling is generally not complete.

This observation is in accord with a view that antibodies catalyze their reactions primarily through restrictions which the active site cavity imposes on the translational and rotational movements of the bound substrate and to a lesser extent through active

site acid/base or nucleophilic catalysis. The latter apparently are not optimized like the situation with enzymes.

The few, unequivocal examples of covalent catalysis (in **Figure 13** the reaction proceeds through an acyl histidine) rank near the upper end of the kinetic indices, although overall flux here may be limited by the buildup of product inhibition. The energy profile of this antibody-catalyzed reaction recapitulates a number of characteristics expected of an enzyme whose later evolution reduces the free energy barriers for the chemical and product release step. Therefore this catalytic antibody can be viewed as a primitive form of its enzyme counterpart. At present the success of this technology is greatly influenced by the serendipitous selection and placement of functional catalytic active site residues, particularly if the reaction is mechanistically complex.

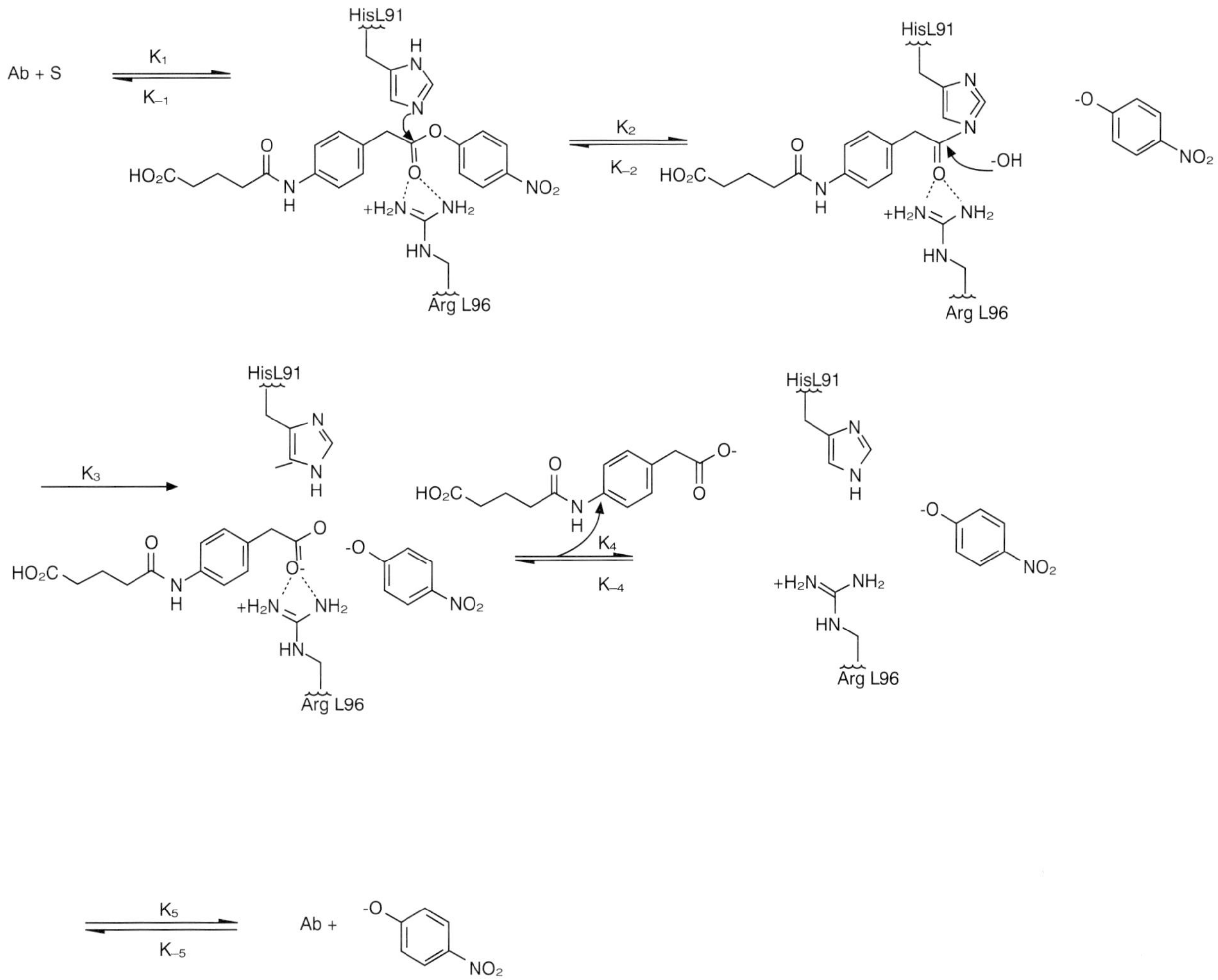

Figure 13 Covalent catalysis exhibited by antibody 43C9. (Reproduced with permission from Stewart JD et al (1994) Site-directed mutagenesis of a catalytic antibody: an arginine and histidine residue play key roles. *Biochemistry* **33**: 1994–2003.)

Screening for catalysis

To date the majority of catalytic antibodies were derived from monoclonals, in most cases fewer than 100 were screened for activity. Recent developments include the adaptation of phage expression systems displaying single chain or Fab antibody fragments, permitting screening of larger numbers ($>10^6$) for catalytic activity. Given the often low activity of catalytic antibodies, several methods have been developed to identify an active fragment. Cat ELISA is based on screening for catalytic activity by using an amplification system in which the expected product is specifically bound by another antibody which recognizes the product as antigen. A second method depends on the catalytic release of a reactive species that can be trapped via covalent modification of bacteriophage-displayed antibody fragments, thus permitting the capture of the parent phage and the encoding DNA for the active abzyme. A third procedure is one of selection: antibodies that complement yeast or bacterial auxotrophs are identified by sustaining growth of the organism under minimal reaction conditions. The host organism, however, may also impose an addition selection on the catalytic antibody that can be recovered from an antibody library, as the host generally will not survive expressing an antibody with high toxicity. The latter two methods are particularly powerful because they reveal directly active species in large libraries. It is evident that screening large libraries resulting from primarily immunization or secondarily from a shuffled library of heavy and light chain fragments is the next critical step in the evolution of this technology for practical applications, which often require higher catalytic flux than generally found by limited screening.

See also: **Affinity; Antibodies, specificity; Antibody-antigen intermolecular forces; Antigen-binding site; Phage display of antibodies; Antibody-antigen complexes, three-dimensional structures.**

Further reading

Benkovic SJ (1992) Catalytic antibodies. *Annual Review of Biochemistry* 61: 29–54.

Charbonnier JB, Golinelli-Pimpaneau B, Gigant B et al (1997) Structural convergence in the active sites of a family of catalytic antibodies. *Science* 275: 1140–1142.

Haynes MR, Stura EA, Hilvert D and Wilson IA (1994) Routes to catalysis: structure of a catalytic antibody and comparison with its natural counterpart. *Science* 263: 646–652.

Hirschmann R, Smith AB III, Taylor CM et al (1994) Peptide synthesis catalyzed by an antibody containing a binding site for variable amino acids. *Science* 265: 234–237.

Janda KD, Lo L-C, Lo C-HL et al (1997) Chemical selection for catalysis in combinatorial antibody libraries. *Science* 275: 945–948.

MacBeath G and Hilvert D (1996) Hydrolytic antibodies: variations on a theme. *Chemistry & Biology* 3: 433–445.

Smiley JA and Benkovic SJ (1994) Selection of catalytic antibodies for a biosynthetic reaction from a combinatorial cDNA library by complementation of an auxotrophic *Escherichia coli*: antibodies for orotate decarboxylation. *Proceedings of the National Academy of Sciences of the USA* 91: 8319–8323.

Steward JD, Krebs JF, Siuzdak G, Berdis AJ, Smithrud DB and Benkovic SJ (1994) Dissection of an antibody-catalyzed reaction. *Proceedings of the National Academy of Sciences of the USA* 91: 7404–7409.

Tang Y, Hicks JB and Hilvert D (1991) *In vivo* catalysis of a metabolically essential reaction by an antibody. *Proceedings of the National Academy of Sciences of the USA* 88: 8784–8786.

Tawfik DS, Green BS, Chap R, Sela M and Eshhar Z (1993) catELISA: a facile general route to catalytic antibodies. *Proceedings of the National Academy of Sciences of the USA* 90: 373–377.

Ulrich HD, Mundorff E, Santarsiero BD et al (1997) The interplay between binding energy and catalysis in the evolution of a catalytic antibody. *Nature* 389: 271–275.

CD ANTIGENS

Hannes Stockinger, Otto Majdic and **Walter Knapp**, Institute of Immunology, University of Vienna, Vienna, Austria

Recognition of signals from outside and mediation of appropriate responses are key functions of immune cells. In particular, these processes are mediated by cell surface molecules which have the capacity to receive and transmit signals from the environment and to execute effector functions. Therefore, a better knowledge and understanding of immune cell surface molecules has been a dream of immunologists since the formulation of Ehrlich's side-chain theory.

For several decades, however, progress in this field has been hampered by technical difficulties. The turning point was clearly the introduction of the monoclonal antibody (mAb)-producing hybridoma technology by George Köhler and César Milstein in 1975. This technique allowed workers for the first time to reproducibly demonstrate, purify and characterize minute amounts of distinct molecules on the surface of immune cells, the leukocytes, by specific mAbs.

The introduction of this technology into leukocyte biology quickly led to the identification of a vast array of single mAb-defined, but otherwise ill-characterized cell surface molecules by individual laboratories. In 1981, at the leukemia marker conference held in Vienna many of these new mAb-defined molecules were presented and discussed. There it became clear that intense international collaboration and gathering of the expertise available in the various laboratories is a prerequisite for optimal progress in this field.

Laurence Boumsell and Alain Bernard were the pioneers to initiate this international collaboration and to gather a group of scientists (J. Dausset, R.L. Evans, J.A. Hansen, B.F. Haynes, W. Knapp, A.J. McMichael, C. Milstein, E.L. Reinherz, S.F. Schlossman) willing to collaborate in this approach. The still valid basic rules of this cooperation were set up by this council, and Laurence Boumsell and Alain Bernard then organized in 1981/82 the First International Workshop on Human Leukocyte Differentiation Antigens with the final conference being held in Paris in 1982. Everybody working in the field was invited to join and to submit mAbs for evaluation and/or to offer analytical skills for characterizing these mAbs.

The specific reactivity of an mAb with certain cell types and/or differentiation stages and the molecular weight of the recognized antigen (molecule) were at that time the main features which allowed distinction of different and clustering of similar mAb specificity. This explains the now historical terms used in the nomenclature (CD for cluster of differentiation) and in the title of the workshop and conference series (Leukocyte Differentiation Antigens rather than Leukocyte Surface Molecules).

So far, six international workshops and conferences have been held. Each workshop collects data over a period of approximately 2 years and meets in a conference which results in a well-documented proceedings volume: Ist Conference – Paris November 1982, IInd Conference – Boston September 1984, IIIrd Conference – Oxford September 1986, IVth Conference – Vienna February 1989, Vth Conference – Boston November 1993, VIth Conference –

Kobe November 1996. The organization of the VIIth Workshop is led by David Mason (Oxford), and the Conference is planned for June 2000 in Harrogate, UK, http://phoenix.jr2.ox.ac.uk/HLDA7

The principal organization of the workshops has not changed dramatically since the Ist Workshop in Paris. However, new technologies have been integrated into the evaluation process rapidly, and have profoundly influenced the overall design and philosophy of the series. This has not only maintained the nomenclature authority of the workshop series but also strengthened its role as a creative international instrument with a substantial impact on modern immunological research.

In essence, international investigators are invited to submit interesting mAbs to the workshop organizers, who group the mAbs in coded or open panels on the basis of the information provided. The panels are then distributed to investigators who can offer informative and innovative studies on these reagents. The generated data have to be returned to the organizers who are responsible for joint evaluation and publication. For example, at the VIth Workshop, within 2 years, 1152 mAbs directed to more than 200 leukocyte cell surface molecules were evaluated by more than 500 laboratories. This resulted in 42 new CD entities, the redefinition of several previously established, mainly provisional clusters, and a considerable advancement in understanding the structure and function of leukocyte surface molecules in general. The database of the VIth Workshop including the individual reaction patterns of the mAbs is available at the Internet address: <http://immunol.mcb.osaka-u.ac.jp/>.

Originally and still as a rule, the CD designation describes a cluster of mAbs (e.g. CD2 mAbs) all of which show identical cellular reaction patterns and identify the same molecular species. Consequently, the term 'anti-CD...' would mean anti-idiotypes and, therefore, should not be used to name CD mAbs. Later, the CD designation was used to describe the recognized molecule, but it had to be clarified by using the terms antigen or molecule (e.g. CD2 molecule). Meanwhile, the CD nomenclature without the additive is used by most people to designate the leukocyte surface molecules, the characterization for which the CD mAbs have been established.

So far, 202 CD entities have been assigned to the 166 main CDs delinated in **Table 1**. Provisional clusters are designated as CDw. Further information on the CDs is available in the proceedings of the individual workshops and the Protein Reviews on the Web (PROW) database. PROW has been established based on a concept developed by Stephen Shaw and aims to organize and synthesize information on all

Table 1 Human leukocyte CD molecules

	Other name (s)	Main reactivity of mAbs	Short characteristic of the CD molecule	Molecular weight reduced (kDa)
CD1a	T6	Thy, LHC, DC	Noncovalently associated with β_2M. Structural similarity with MHC-class I molecules (see CD1b and CD1c)	49
CD1b		Thy, DC	Noncovalently associated with β_2M (see also CD1a). Potential lipid antigen-presenting molecule	45
CD1c		Thy, LHC, DC, B sub	Noncovalently associated with β_2M (see also CD1a). Potential lipid antigen-presenting molecule	43
CD2	T11; Tp50; sheep red blood cell (SRBC) receptor; LFA-2	T, NK	Cytoadhesion molecule binding to CD58 molecule (LFA-3), CD48 molecule and probably also to CD59 molecule	50
CD2R	CD2 epitopes restricted to activated T cells	T act	Same molecule as CD2 molecule, CD2R antibodies recognize CD2 epitopes expressed on activated T cells	50
CD3	CD3 complex	T	Multigene cell surface complex that is part of the T cell antigen receptor	16, 20, 22, 25, 28
CD4	T4	T sub	Coreceptor of the T cell antigen receptor; binds to MHC class II molecules. Also, receptor for interleukin 16, and for human immunodeficiency virus	55–59
CD5	Tp67	T, B sub	Member of the scavenger receptor family (see CD6). Possible CD72 counter-receptor	67
CD6	T12	T, B sub	Member of the scavenger receptor family. Counter-receptor of CD166	110
CD7		T sub	Type I integral membrane glycoprotein	40
CD8	T8	T sub	Two-chain complex expressed as disulfide-linked α/α homodimers or α/β (see CD8beta) heterodimers. Coreceptor of the T cell antigen receptor; binds to MHC class I molecules	32–38
CD8beta	T8	T sub	β chain of CD8	30–34
CD9	p24	Pre-B, T act, Plt, Eo, EC	Member of the tetraspans gene molecules that contain four transmembrane domains and have both the N- and C-termini on the cytoplasmic side (see CD37, CD53, CD63, CD81, CD82, CD151)	24
CD10	Neutral endopeptidase; gp100; common acute lymphatic leukemia antigen (CALLA)	Lymphoid Prog, cALL, Germ Ctr. B, G	Type II transmembrane glycoprotein, which is a neutral endopeptidase (enkephalinase)	100
CD11a	α chain of: leukocyte function associated antigen 1 (LFA-1), gp180/95	Leukocytes broad	β_2-integrin member (see CD11b, CD11c, CD18). The CD11a/CD18 (LFA-1) complex has binding capacity to CD54 molecules (ICAM-1), CD102 molecules (ICAM-2), CD50 molecules (ICAM-3), Laisolsteiner-Wiener antigen (ICAM-4), telencephalin (ICAM-5)	180
CD11b	α chain of: C3bi receptor, complement receptor type 3 (CR3), gp155/95, Mac-1, Mo1	M, G, NK, T sub	β_2-integrin member (see CD11a, CD11c, CD18). The CD11b/CD18 complex (CR3) binds C3bi, lipid IVa in LPS, kininogen, coagulation factor X, CD54 molecules, the neutrophil inhibition factor of the hookworm *Ancyclostoma caninum*, oligonucleotides	170
CD11c	α chain of: complement receptor type 4 (CR4); gp150/95	M, G, NK, B sub, T sub	β_2-integrin member (see CD11a, CD11b, CD18). The CD11c/CD18 complex (CR4) binds C3bi, fibrinogen and CD54 molecules	150
CDw12		M, G, Plt		90–120
CD13	Aminopeptidase N; gp150;	M, G	Type II transmembrane glycoprotein, identical to the proteolytic enzyme aminopeptidase N	150

Table 1 Continued

	Other name (s)	Main reactivity of mAbs	Short characteristic of the CD molecule	Molecular weight reduced (kDa)
CD14	gp55; lipopolysaccharide (LPS) receptor	M, G	Receptor for the LPS/LPS binding protein (LBP) complex	55
CD15	Lewis^x (Le^x); 3-fucosyl-*N*-acetyllactosamine (3-FAL); X-Hapten; lacto-*N*-fucopentaose III; SSEA	G, some antibodies also M	CD15 antibodies recognize the trisaccharide 3-FAL (Gal1–4 (Fuc1–3) GlcNac) which is also recognized by CD62P molecules	shared by a vareity of proteins and lipids
CD15s	Sialyl Lewis^x (sLe^x)	Broad	Sialyated form of CD15. It is recognized by CD62E, CD62L and CD62P molecules	shared by a variety of proteins and lipids
CD16	Fcγ receptor type IIIa (FcγRIIIa); gp50-65	NK, G, Mac	Low-affinity receptor for complexed IgG	50–65
CD16b	Fcγ receptor type IIIb (FγRIIIb);	G	Glycosylphosphatidylinositol-anchored form of the CD16 molecule expressed on granulocytes	48–60
CDw17	Lactosylceramide	G, M, Plt	Lactosylceramide (Gal-Glc-Cer type 2 chain)	
CD18	Integrin β_2 βchain	Leukocytes broad	Noncovalently linked to either CD11a, CD11b or CD11c molecules (α chains) Defect in CD18 results in leukocyte adhesion deficiency (LAD)	95
CD19	Bgp95, B4	B	Part of the B cell antigen receptor complex	95
CD20	B1; Bgp35	B	Phosphoprotein expressed on B cells in three forms (37 and 35 and 33 kDa) as a result of different phosphorylation. This molecule has four membrane-spanning regions	33, 35, 37
CD21	C3d receptor (CR2); gp140	B sub	Member of the regulator of complement activation (RCA) gene family (see CD35, CD46, CD55). Molecule functions as C3d receptor (CR2) and serves also as receptor for Epstein–Barr virus	140
CD22	Bgp135; BL-CAM	Cytoplasm: pan B; surface: B sub	Functions as an adhesion molecule with a sialic acid binding capacity for carbohydrates which were found e.g. on CD45RO, CDw75 and CDw76 molecules	135, 140
CD23	Low-affinity Fcϵ-receptor; FcϵRII; gp50-45; Blast-2	B, M	The extracellular region contains a C-type lectin domain (see CD69, CD72, CD94, CD161)	45–50
CD24	Heat stable antigen homolog; BA-1	B, G, EPC	Glycophosphoinositol-linked, extremely glycosylated protein. Possible counter-receptor for CD62P	42
CD25	Interleukin (IL)-2 receptor α chain; Tac-antigen	T act, B act, M act	Has low-affinity IL-2 binding capacity. By noncovalently associating with the CDw122 molecule and the CD132 (common to CD124 and CD127) molecule, it forms the high-affinity IL-2 receptor complex	60
CD26	Dipeptidylpeptidase IV; gp120; Ta1	T act, B, Mac, NK	Has also collagen binding properties. Associated with adenosine deaminase and CD45 molecules	110
CD27	T14	T sub	Member of the tumor necrosis factor (TNF)/nerve growth factor (NGF) receptor family (see CD30, CD40, CD95, CD120a, CD120b, CD134, CDw137). Counter-receptor for CD70	55
CD28	Tp44;	T sub	Counterreceptor for CD80, CD86 and B7-3 molecules	44
CD29	Integrin β_1 chain; platelet GPIIa; VLA (CD49) β chain	Broad	β chain of the VLA protein family (CD49 molecule family), however, can also associate with other integrin α chains (see CD51)	130
CD30	Ki-1 antigen	T act, B act, Reed Sternberg cells, Hodgkin cells	Member of the TNF/NGF receptor family (see CD27, CD40, CD95, CD120a, CD120b, CD134, CDw137). Counter-receptor for CD153	105

Table 1 Cintinued

	Other name (s)	Main reactivity of mAbs	Short characteristic of the CD molecule	Molecular weight reduced (kDa)
CD31	PECAM-1; platelet GPIIa[1]; endocam	Plt, M, G, B, T sub	Adhesion molecule involved in migration of leukocytes and regulation of the T cell response	140
CD32	Fcγ receptor type II (FcγRII), gp40	M, G, B, Eo	Six isoforms are known which originate from alternative splicing of three genes on chromosome 1 (FcγRIIA, -B and -C)	40
CD33	My9	M, normal and malignant myeloid progenitor cells	Related to myelin-associated glycoprotein and CD22 molecules	67
CD34	My10	Prog, EC	Sialomucin-like (see CD43, CD68, CD164) transmembrane glycophosphoprotein. Potential cytoadhesion molecule probably interacting with CD62E and CD62L molecules	105–120
CD35	C3b/C4b receptor; complement receptor type 1 (CR1)	G, M, B, some T/NK	Has binding capacity for C3b, iC3b, C3c and C4b complement fragments. Mediates erythrocyte clearance of immune complexes, involved in inhibition of complement activation by blocking C3 convertase formation	190, 220, 250, 280
CD36	Platelet GPIV, GPIIIb, OKM-5 antigen	M, Plt, (B)	Functions as receptor for Plasmodium falciparum-infected erythrocytes. Binding affinity for thrombospondin (thrombospondin receptor), collagen I and IV and oxidized low-density lipoprotein has been shown	90
CD37	gp40-52	B, (T), (M), (G)	Member of the tetraspans family (see CD9)	36–52
CD38	T10; gp45	PC, Thy, T act	Has NAD$^+$ glycohydrolase, ADP ribosylcylase and cyclic ADP-ribose hydrolase activity	45
CD39	gp80	B sub		80
CD40		B, DC	Member of the TNF/NGF receptor family (see CD27, CD30, CD95, CD120a, CD120b, CD134, CDw137). Counter-receptor of CD154	44, 48
CD41	Platelet glycoprotein GPIIb	Plt	Heterodimeric 140 kDa transmembrane glycoprotein (posttranslationally cleaved into a disulfide linked 120 kDa α chain and a 22 kDa β chain) also known as platelet glycoprotein GPIIb, which forms a calcium-dependent complex with platelet glycoprotein GPIIIa (CD61 molecule)	120, 22 (GPIIb), 110 (GPIIIa)
CD42a	Platelet glycoprotein GPIX	Plt	Forms a noncovalent complex (CD42 complex) with platelet glycoprotein GPIb and GPV (see CD42b, CD42c and CD42d). Complex functions as receptor for von Willebrand factor and as von Willebrand factor-dependent adhesion receptor	23
CD42b	Platelet glycoprotein GPIb-α	Plt	135 kDa protein (α chain) that forms with the CD42c molecule (β chain) a disulfide-linked 160 kDa membrane protein known as platelet glycoprotein GPIb (subunit of the CD42 complex, see CD42a)	135(α), 22(β)
CD42c	Platelet glycoprotein GPIb-β	Plt	See CD42b	135(α), 22(β)
CD42d	Platelet glycoprotein GPV	Plt	See CD42a	85
CD43	Leukosialin; gp95; sialophorin; leukocyte sialoglycoprotein; gp115	T, G, M, NK, Plt	Member of the 'cell surface mucin' family (see CD34, CD68, CD164). Suggested to function as adhesion molecule interacting with MHC class I, CD54 and CD62P molecules, or (controversial) as antiadhesion protein	95–135

Table 1 Continued

	Other name (s)	Main reactivity of mAbs	Short characteristic of the CD molecule	Molecular weight reduced (kDa)
CD44	Pgp-1; gp80-95; In (Lu)-related p80, Hermes antigen, ECMR-III and HUTCH-I	T, B, G, M	Receptor for hyaluronate and involved in lymphocyte homing	80–95
CD44R	CD44 variant; CD44v9	T act, carcinoma cells	CD44R (CD44v9) may be a marker for cell transformation	130, 190, 250, 300
CD45	T200; leukocyte common antigen (LCA); EC3.1.3.4	Leukocytes	Transmembrane glycoprotein consisting of 4 isoforms, which result from differential splicing. The CD45 molecule has intrinsic cytoplasmic protein tyrosine phosphatase activity	220, 205, 190, 180
CD45R0	Restricted T200; gp180	T sub, G, M	Isoform of the CD45 molecule family, this isoform does not contain exon A, B, or C sequences. Interacts via carbohydrate residues with the CD22 molecule	180
CD45RA	Restricted T200; gp220; isoform of leukocyte common antigen	T sub, B, G sub, M	Isoform determinant of CD45 sharing exon A sequences. Expressed on resting/naive T cells	220
CD45RB	Restricted T200; isoform of leukocyte common antigen	T sub, B, G, M	Isoform determinant of CD45 sharing exon B sequences	220, 205, 190
CD45RC	Restricted T200; isoform of leukocyte common antigen	T sub, B, NK	Isoform determinant of CD45 sharing exon C sequences within CD4 cells expressed on long living memory cells	220, 205
CD46	Membrane cofactor protein (MCP); gp45-70	Leukocytes broad	Member of the RCA gene family (see CD21, CD35, CD55). Inhibits complement activation by inhibition of C3 convertase formation. Receptor for measles virus	51–58/59–68
CD47	Integrin associated protein; OA3; 1D8	Extremely broad	Physically and functionally associated with the vitronectin receptor (CD51/CD61)	47–52
CD48	gp41; BLAST-1	Leukocytes	Glycophosphatidylinositol-linked glycoprotein. Counter-receptor for CD2	41
CD49a	VLA-1 α chain	T cultured	Associates with the CD29 molecule to form the VLA-1 (integrin $\alpha_1\beta_1$) complex. VLA-1 mediates cell adhesion to collagens and laminin	210
CD49b	VLA-2 α chain platelet glycoprotein GPIa	Plt, T cultured	Associates with CD29 molecules to form the VLA-2 (integrin $\alpha_2\beta_1$) complex. Functions as collagen receptor or collagen/laminin receptor, receptor for echovirus 1	170
CD49c	VLA-3 α chain	Adherent cell lines	Associates with CD29 molecule to form the VLA-3 (integrin $\alpha_3\beta_1$) complex. VLA-3 mediates cell adhesion to fibrinogen, laminin, collagens and epiligrin/kalinin, VLA-2	125, 30
CD49d	VLA-4 α chain	M, T, B, (LHC), Thy	Associates with CD29 molecules in VLA-4 (integrin $\alpha_4\beta_1$) which binds fibronectin, thrombospondin, invasin and CD106 molecules. Upon noncovalent association with the integrin β_7 subunit the integrin $\alpha_4\beta_7$ complex is formed, which binds fibronectin, MadCAM and CD106 molecules	150
CD49e	VLA-5 α chain	T, M, Plt	Associates with CD29 molecules to form the VLA-5 (integrin $\alpha_5\beta_1$) complex, which is a receptor for fibronectin	135, 25
CD49f	VLA-6 α chain	Plt (T)	Associates with CD29 molecules in VLA-6 (integrin $\alpha_6\beta_1$). This complex has been shown to be a laminin receptor. The CD49f molecule can also associate with CD104 molecules to form the $\alpha_6\beta_4$ laminin receptor	120, 130
CD50	Intercellular adhesion molecule 3 (ICAM-3)	Broad, not on EC	Functions as counter-receptor for LFA-1 (CD11a/CD18)	130

Table 1 Continued

	Other name (s)	Main reactivity of mAbs	Short characteristic of the CD molecule	Molecular weight reduced (kDa)
CD51	Vitronectin receptor (VNR) α chain; integrin α_v	(Plt), EC, Fibroblasts	Can noncovalently associate with β_1 (CD29), β_3 (CD61), β_5, β_6 or β_8 integrins. The $\alpha_v\beta_1$ complex was found to bind vitronectin, fibronectin and collagen I. The $\alpha_v\beta_3$ complex binds vitronectin, fibronectin, fibrinogen, von Willebrand factor, thrombospondin, osteopontin and collagen, $\alpha_v\beta_5$ binds to vitronectin, and $\alpha_v\beta_6$ to fibronectin	125, 25
CD52	Campath-1; gp21–28	Leukocytes	Good target for complement-mediated cell lysis	21–28
CD53		Exclusively leukocytes	Member of the tetraspans family (see CD9)	32–40
CD54	Intercellular adhesion molecule 1 (ICAM-1)	Broad	Counter-receptor of LFA-1 (CD11a/CD18) and CR3 (CD11b/CD18). Also serves as major group rhinovirus receptor	90
CD55	Decay-accelerating factor (DAF)	Broad	Glycophosphatidylinositol-linked membrane glycoprotein. Molecule prevents the formation and causes dissociation of C4b2a and C3bBb, the amplification convertases of the complement cascade. Counter-receptor of the CD97 molecule, receptor for echoviruses and enterovirus	80
CD56	NKH1; isoform of neuronal cell adhesion molecule (N-CAM)	NK, T act	Homotypic adhesion molecule	175–185
CD57	HNK1; gp110	NK, T, B sub, brain	Carbohydrate structure, probably attached to several proteins and lipids	
CD58	Leukocyte function-associated antigen 3 (LFA-3)	Leukocytes, EC, EPC, fibroblasts	Counterreceptor of CD2	40–65
CD59	gp18-20; Ly6 analogous; homologous restriction factor 20 (HRF-20); Protectin	Broad	Glycophosphatidylinositol-linked glycoprotein. Mediates inhibition of the complement membrane attack complex by binding to C8 on C5b678 and thereby preventing accumulated binding of C9	18–20
CDw60		T sub, Plt	Acetylated disialosyl group (NeuAc-NeuAc-Gal) predominantly found on ganglioside GD3	
CD61	Integrin β_3 chain, platelet glycoprotein GPIIIa	Plt	Forms a complex with CD41. The CD61 molecule can also associate with integrin α_v (CD51 molecule) forming the $\alpha_v\beta_3$ vitronectin receptor	90
CD62E	E-selectin; ELAM-1; LECAM-2	EC act	Related to CD62L and CD62P molecules (selectin family). Recognizes carbohydrate ligands (e.g. CD15s) on various molecules including GlyCAM1, CD34, CD162, ESL1	115
CD62L	L-selectin; LAM-1; Leu-8; TQ1; LECAM-1	G, M, T, B sub, NK	Recognizes carbohydrate ligands (e.g. CD15s) on various molecules including GlyCAM-1, MadCAM, CD162, CD34 as well as sulfated glycolipids	75
CD62P	P-selectin; gmp140; PADGEM	Plt act, EC act	Recognizes carbohydrate ligands (e.g. CD15 and CD15s) on various molecules including CD162	150
CD63	Platelet 53 kDa activation antigen; LIMP; ME491	Plt act, M, (G, T, B)	Member of the tetraspans family (see CD9)	30–60
CD64	Fcγ receptor type I (FcγRI); high-affinity Fc-IgG receptor	M, G act	Encoded by three genes. Associates with the γ chain of Fcϵ receptor type I	75

Table 1 Continued

	Other name (s)	Main reactivity of mAbs	Short characteristic of the CD molecule	Molecular weight reduced (kDa)
CD65	Desialylated form of CD65s	G	Fucoganglioside (Gal-GlcNAc-Gal-GlcNAc(Fuc)-Gal-Gl cNAc-Gal-GlcNAc-Gal-Glc-Cer) based on a type II chain. Desialylated form of CD65	
CD65s	Ceramide-dodecasaccharide 4c, VIM2 Antigen	M, G, AML blasts	Fucoganglioside (NeuAc-Gal-GlcNAc-Gal-GlcNAc(Fuc)-Gal-Gl cNAc-Gal-GlcNAc-Gal-Glc-Cer). Carried by various glycolipids and glycoproteins. Potential ligand for CD62E and CD62L	
CD66a	Biliary glycoprotein (BGP); nonspecific cross-reacting antigen (NCA) 160	G, EPC	Member of the carcinoembryonic antigen (CEA) gene family. Adhesion molecule, has bacterial binding property, in particular, for Opa-proteins of pathogenic *Neisseria*	160–180
CD66abce		G	Antibodies recognizing CD66a, CD66b, CD66c, CD66e molecules	
CD66acd		G	Antibodies recognizing CD66a, CD66c, CD66d molecules	
CD66acde		G	Antibodies recognizing CD66a, CD66c, CD66d, CD66e molecules	
CD66ace		G	Antibodies recognizing CD66a, CD66c, CD66e molecules	
CD66ade		G	Antibodies recognizing CD66a, CD66d, CD66e molecules	
CD66ae		G	Antibodies recognizing CD66a, CD66e molecules	
CD66b	CD67; p100; CGM6; nonspecific cross-reacting antigen (NCA) 95	G	Glycophosphatidylinositol-anchored glycoprotein. Member of the carcinoembryonic antigen (CEA) gene family. Adhesion molecule	95–100
CD66be		G	Antibodies recognizing CD66b, CD66e molecules	
CD66c	nonspecific cross-reacting antigen (NCA) 50, NCA 90 or TEX	G	Glycophosphatidylinositol-anchored glycoprotein. Member of the carcinoembryonic antigen (CEA) gene family. Recognizes type 1 fimbriae from *E. coli* and Opa-proteins of pathogenic *Neisseria*	90–95
CD66ce		G	Antibodies recognizing CD66c, CD66e molecules	
CD66d	CGM1	G	Member of the carcinoembyronic antigen (CEA) gene family. Recognizes Opa-proteins of pathogenic *Neisseria*	30
CD66de		G	Antibodies recognizing CD66d, CD66e molecules	
CD66e	Carcinoembryonic antigen (CEA)	EPC	Prototype of the carcinoembryonic antigen (CEA) gene family. Glycophosphatidylinositol-anchored. Adhesion molecule, binds to CD66a and CD66c molecules and Opa-proteins of pathogenic *Neisseria*	180–200
CD66f	Pregnancy-specific glycoprotein (PSG), SP-1	Myeloid cells, placenta, fetal liver	Secreted molecule. Member of the carcinoembryonic antigen (CEA) gene family. Low blood level predicts spontaneous abortion	54–72
CD67	Deleted, now CD66b			
CD68	gp110, Macrosialin	M, Mac	Mucin-like molecule (other members CD34, CD43, CD164, GlyCAM-1) and lysosomal/plasma membrane shuttling protein (see CD107a, CD107b). Recognizes oxidized low-density lipoprotein	110
CD69	Activation inducer molecule (AIM); EA1; MLR; Leu23; BL-AC/p26	B and T early act, Mac act	Member of the Ca^{2+}-dependent (C-type) lectin superfamily of type II transmembrane receptors (see CD23, CD72, CD94, CD161)	28, 34
CD70	Ki-24	T, B-EBV, pre-BLL act	Member of the TNF family (see CD153, CD154, CD95L). Counter-receptor for CD27	50
CD71	Transferrin receptor; T9 antigen	T and B act, Mac, proliferating cells	Mediates cellular iron uptake via internalization and recycling of transferrin	95

Table 1 Continued

	Other name (s)	Main reactivity of mAbs	Short characteristic of the CD molecule	Molecular weight reduced (kDa)
CD72	Lyb-2	B	Member of the Ca^{2+}-dependent (C-type) lectin superfamily of type II transmembrane receptors (see CD23, CD69, CD94, CD161). Possible counter-receptor for the CD5 molecule	39, 43
CD73	ecto-5'-nucleotidase (ecto-5'-NT), EC.3.1.3.5.	B sub, T sub, EC	Glycophosphatidylinositol-linked membrane glycoprotein. Catalyses the dephosphorylation of purine and pyrimidine ribo- and deoxyribonucleoside	69
CD74	MHC class II-associated invariant chain (Ii)	B, M, T act, EC act, EPC act	Involved in intracellular transport and surface expression of MHC class II proteins	33, 35, 41, 42
CDw75		Mature B	Carbohydrate, suggested to be recognized by CD22 molecules	
CDw76		B, T sub, EC	Carbohydrate of the sialylated type 2 glycosphingolipids. May be recognized by CD22 molecules	
CD77	Globotriaosylceramide (Gb3); P^k blood group antigen; Burkitts lymphoma-associated antigen (BLA), ceramide trihexoside (CTH)	B sub	Neutral glycosphingolipid of the globo series (Galα1–4 Galβ1–4 Glc1–1 Cer). Interacts with CD19 molecules on B cells and seems to be involved in CD19 signaling	
CDw78	Ba	B	Not fully characterized	
CD79a	mb-1; Igα	B	Forms with the CD79b molecule a disulfide-linked heterodimer which functions as a coupling module of the B cell antigen receptor	47
CD79b	B29; Igβ	B	Forms with the CD79a molecule a disulfide-linked heterodimer which functions as a coupling module of the B cell antigen receptor	37
CD80	B7-1; BB1	B, B act, M, DC, T act	Counter-receptor of the T cell accessory molecules CD28 and CD152	60
CD81	Target of an antiproliferative antibody (TAPA-1); M38	Broad	Member of the tetraspans family (see CD9)	26
CD82	R2; 4F9; C33; IA4	M, B, B act, T act, LGL	Member of the tetraspans family (see CD9)	40–60
CD83	HB15	LHC, DC, reticulum cells (T and B act)	Dendritic cell marker	45
CD84	p75	B, M, Plt, Mac.	Not fully characterized	74
CD85	VMP-55; GH1/75	PC, Mac, hairy cells	Not fully characterized	83
CD86	B7-2; B70	B act, M, DC	Structurally related to the CD80 molecule, and functions as counter-receptor for the T cell accessory molecules CD28 and CD152	75
CD87	Urokinase plasminogen activator-receptor (uPA-R)	M, G, EC	Glycophosphatidylinositol-anchored glycoprotein involved in cell migration. Serves also as receptor for vitronectin	45–55
CD88	C5α receptor	G, M, DC, smooth muscle cells	Member of the rhodopsin superfamily that contain seven transmembrane domains	
CD89	Fcα receptor	G, M, B sub, T sub	Binds serum and secretory IgA1 or IgA2	55–70
CD90	Thy-1	Prog sub, EC, neurons	Glycophosphatidylinositol-anchored protein	25–35
CD91	α_2-macroglobulin receptor; low-density lipoprotein receptor-related protein	M	Receptor for a variety of ligands including α_2-macroglobulin–proteinase complex, plasminogen activators (urokinase and tissue) in complex with type 1 inhibitors, chylomicron remnants, lipoprotein lipase, *Pseudomonas* exotoxin A	85, 515
CDw92	p70	G, M		70

Table 1 Continued

	Other name (s)	Main reactivity of mAbs	Short characteristic of the CD molecule	Molecular weight reduced (kDa)
CD93	p120	M, EC		120
CD94		NK, T sub	Member of the Ca^{2+}-dependent (C-type) lectin superfamily of type II transmembrane receptors (see CD23, CD69, CD72, CD161). The CD94 molecule forms a disulfide linked heterodimer with NKG2A. This complex functions as receptor for certain HLA-A, B, C alleles and HLA-G, and is involved in the downregulation of NK cell activity. In contrary, upon interaction with a less-defined 39 kDa protein, CD94 seems to form an activatory NK cell receptor	30
CD95	Apo-1; Fas	T act, M act, B act	Member of the TNF/NGF receptor family (see CD27, CD30, CD40, CD120a, CD120b, CD134, CDw137)	43
CD96	Tactile	T, T act		160
CD97	p74/80/89	G, M, T act, B act	Seven-span transmembrane protein belonging to the secretin receptor superfamily. Counter-receptor for the CD55 molecule	74, 80, 89
CD98	4F2	T, B, Plt	Disulfide-linked heterodimer	40, 80
CD99	E2; MIC2	Broad	The extracellular domain contains five G-X-Y repeats that are found in collagen and collagen-like proteins	32
CD99R	Restricted CD99	T sub	CD99 epitopes, the expression of which is restricted to T cell subpopulations	
CD100	p150	Broad	The extracellular region consists of a semaphorin domain and an Ig-like domain. Modifies CD40-CD40L B cell signaling by augmenting B cell aggregation and survival	150
CD101	P140; V7	G, M, T sub, DC	The extracellular domain consists of 7 IgV-like domains. Some mAb modify T cell activation	140
CD102	Intercellular adhesion molecule 2 (ICAM-2)	M, Plt	Functions as counter-receptor for the CD11a/CD18 (LFA-1) complex	55–65
CD103	α chain of HML-1, $\alpha_E\beta_7$ integrin; integrin α_E	Intestinal intraepithelial lymphocytes, hairy cells	Post-translationally cleaved into two disulfide-linked units of 25 kDa and 150 kDa. Noncovalently associates with the 105 kDa integrin β_7 chain to form the human mucosal lymphocyte 1 (HML-1) antigen	25, 150
CD104	Integrin β_4 chain		Associates with CD49f molecule (integrin α_6 chain) to form the integrin $\alpha_6\beta_4$ laminin receptor. This complex also binds epiligrin	220
CD105	Endoglin	EC, M act	Binds in association with TGFβ receptor I and II, TGFβ$_1$ and TGFβ$_3$	95
CD106	Vascular cell adhesion molecule 1 (VCAM-1); INCAM110	EC act	Binds to CD49d/CD29 (VLA-4, integrin $\alpha_4\beta_1$) and CD49d/integrin β_7 (integrin $\alpha_4\beta_7$) complexes	95, 100
CD107a	Lysosomal-associated membrane protein (LAMP)-1	Plt act, EC act, G act	Together with the 60% homologs CD107b molecule, the major sialoglycoprotein of lysosomal membranes	110
CD107b	Lysosomal-associated membrane protein (LAMP)-2	Plt act, EC act, G act	Together with the 60% homologous CD107a molecule, the major sialoglycoprotein of lysosomal membranes	120
CDw108	GPI-gp80, JMH blood group antigen	HPB-ALL (T cell line)	Glycosylphosphatidylinositol-anchored cell membrane glycoprotein	75
CD109		EC, T act, Plt, stromal cells	Glycosylphosphatidylinositol-anchored cell membrane glycoprotein. Sialomucin	120–165, 170
CD114	G-CSF receptor	G, M	Member of the cytokine receptor family	130

Table 1   Continued

	Other name (s)	Main reactivity of mAbs	Short characteristic of the CD molecule	Molecular weight reduced (kDa)
CD115	Colony-stimulating factor (CSF)-1 receptor; macro-phage CSF receptor, c-*fms* proto-oncogene	M, Mac	Belongs to the Ig and receptor tyrosine kinase family (see CD117, CD135, CD140a, CD140b). The cytoplasmic region contains a protein tyrosine kinase domain	150
CD116	Granulocyte-macrophage colony-stimulating factor (GM-CSF) receptor α chain	M, G	Member of the cytokine receptor (hematopoietin) superfamily. Upon association with CDw131 (common to CDw123 and CDw125), it forms the high-affinity GM-CSF receptor	75–85
CD117	Stem cell factor receptor; steel factor receptor; c-*kit*	Mast cells, myeloid Prog	Belongs to the Ig and receptor tyrosine kinase family (see CD115, CD135, CD140a, CD140b)	145
CDw119	Interferon γ receptor	M, G	Related to the interferon α/β receptor and the CD142 molecule	90–100
CD120a	55 kDa tumor necrosis factor receptor	(M)	Member of the TNF/NGF receptor family (see CD27, CD30, CD40, CD95, CD120b, CD134, CDw137). It binds both TNFα and β with high affinity	50–60
CD120b	75 kDa tumor necrosis factor receptor	M, G	Member of the TNF/NGF receptor family (see CD27, CD30, CD40, CD95, CD120a, CD134, CDw137). It binds both TNFα and β with high affinity	75–85
CD121a	Interleukin 1 receptor type I	T, B, M, G, NK, EC	Binds both IL-1α and IL-1β with high affinity, as well as the IL-1 receptor antagonist	80
CDw121b	Interleukin 1 receptor type II	G, T, B, M	Binds both IL-1α and IL-1β with high affinity, as well as the IL-1 receptor antagonist	60–70
CDw122	Interleukin 2 receptor β chain	T, NK, B, M	Member of the cytokine receptor (hematopoietin) superfamily. Binds IL-2 with low affinity. Noncovalently associates with the CD25 molecule and the CD132 molecule (common to CD124 and CD127 molecules) to the high-affinity IL-2 receptor complex. Also part of the IL-15 receptor complex	75
CDw123	Interleukin 3 receptor α chain	M	Associates with CDw131 (common to CD116 and CDw125) to form the functional IL-3 receptor	70
CD124	Interleukin 4 receptor	(Broad)	Receptor subunit for IL-4 and IL-13 by noncovalently associating with the CD132 molecule or the IL-13 receptor, respectively	140
CDw125	Interleukin 5 receptor α chain	Eo, B act, basophils	Associates with CDw131 (common to CD116 and CDw123) to form the functional IL-5 receptor	60
CD126	Interleukin 6 receptor	T, B act, M	Binds IL-6 with low affinity. Noncovalently associates with the CD130 molecule to form the functional high-affinity IL-6 receptor	80
CD127	Interleukin 7 receptor	T	Associates with the CD132 molecule, which results in augmentation of binding affinity and internalization of IL-7	75
CDw128	Interleukin 8 receptor	G	The two identified forms are members of the rhodopsin superfamily that contain seven transmembrane domains and couple to GTP-binding proteins	58–67
CD130	gp130	(Broad)	Binds oncostatin M (OSM) with low affinity. Noncovalently associates with the CD126 molecule to form the high-affinity receptor for IL-6. Signal transducing component of the IL-11 receptor. Upon association with the leukemia inhibitory factor (LIF) receptor, the high-affinity receptor for LIF, OSM and cardiotrophin-1 is generated. This functional LIF/OSM receptor is probably converted to the ciliary neurotrophic factor (CNTF) receptor upon association with the CNTF binding protein	130

Table 1 Continued

	Other name (s)	Main reactivity of mAbs	Short characteristic of the CD molecule	Molecular weight reduced (kDa)
CDw131	Common β chain	Myeloid cells, pre B	Associates either with the CDw123, the CDw125, or the CD16 molecule to form the appropriate functional receptor	120
CD132	Common γ chain	Broad	γ chain of the receptors for IL-2 (see CD25 and CDw122), IL-4 (see CD124), IL-7 (see CD127), IL-9, and IL-15. Mutation causes x-linked severe combined immunodeficiency	64
CD134	OX40	T act sub	Member of the TNF/NGF receptor family (see CD27, CD30, CD40, CD95, CD120a, CD120b, CDw137). Costimulatory molecule of T cells. Involved in T-B and T-EC interactions by binding to the OX40 ligand	48–50
CD135	flt3/flk2; STK-1	Prog sub, pre B	Belongs to the Ig and receptor tyrosine kinase family (see CD115, CD117, CD140a, CD140b). Receptor for flt3 ligand. Important receptor/ligand system for hematopoietic cell proliferation and differentiation	155
CDw136	Macrophage-stimulating protein receptor (MSPR), RON	M, G, EPC	Member of the receptor tyrosine kinase family. The mature protein is organized as a disulfide-linked α/β dimer, which is derived from a single chain pro RON. Involved in the regulation of production of blood cells, and in the development of epithelial tissue	150, 35
CDw137	4-1BB	T act	Member of the TNF/NGF receptor family (see CD27, CD30, CD40, CD95, CD120a, CD120b, CD134). Receptor for 4-1BB ligand. Seems to be important for T cell survival	30
CD138	Syndecan-1, B-B4	PC, EPC	The extracellular domain bears heparan sulfate glycosaminoglycans through which it binds both growth factors and extracellular matrix constituents. The cytoplasmic domain interacts with cytoskeletal components. Proposed to have roles in growth factor action, extracellular matrix adhesion and cytoskeletal organization that controls cell morphology	80–160
CD139		B, M, G	Not fully characterized	220+250
CD140a	α-platelet-derived growth factor (PDGF) receptor	Undetectably expressed	Belongs to the Ig supergene and receptor tyrosine kinase family (see CD115, CD117, CD135, CD140b). PDGF binding induces either homodimerization or heterodimerization with the CD140b molecule. Binds both PDGF-A and PDGF-B chains. Induces a mitogenic response	180
CD140b	β-platelet-derived growth factor (PDGF) receptor	Focal EC, stromal cell lines	Belongs to the Ig supergene and receptor tyrosine kinase family (see CD115, CD117, CD135, CD140a). PDGF binding induces either homodimerization or heterodimerization with the CD140a molecule. Binds PDGF-B chains. Induces a mitogenic response, actin reorganization and chemotaxis	180
CD141	Thrombomodulin	Myeloid cells, EC, Plt	Receptor for thrombin. Involved in regulation of coagulation	100
CD142	Tissue factor, thromboplastin, coagulation factor III	M act, EC act, EPC	Related to the IFNα receptor and the CDw119 molecule. High-affinity receptor for factor VII, and it is the essential cofactor for factor VII. Forms a ternary complex with factor VII and X to induce the extrinsic pathway of the coagulation cascade	45

Table 1 Continued

	Other name (s)	Main reactivity of mAbs	Short characteristic of the CD molecule	Molecular weight reduced (kDa)
CD143	Angiotensin-converting enzyme (ACE), peptidyl dipeptidase A, EC3.4.15.1	EC, EPC	Somatic form of ACE. Zinc metallopeptidase with specificity for the vasoactive peptides angiotensin I and bradykinin. Differentially expressed along the vascular tree. EC of arterioles, small arteries, capillaries in organs such as lung are positive. EC of large arteries and veins are mostly negative	170
CD144	Vascular endothelial cell cadherin (VE-cadherin), cadherin 5, 7B4	EC	Ca^{2+} dependent homophilic cell adhesion molecule. It interacts with catenins which link CD144 to the cytoskeleton; this complex is crucial for the regulation of cell adhesion	130
CDw145		EC	Defined by the mAbs 7E9 and P7A5. Not fully characterized	25
CD146	Muc18/S-endo, MCAM, Mel-CAM	EC, T act sub, smooth muscle cells, melanoma cells	Member of the Ig supergene family. Potential cell adhesion molecule	130
CD147	Neurothelin, basigin, M6, EMMPRIN	Leukocytes broad, EC, Plt, red blood cells	Member of the Ig supergene family. Potential cell adhesion molecule	50–60
CD148	p260, HPTPη/DEP1	Leukocytes broad, Plt	Density enhanced protein tyrosine phosphatase-1 (DEP-1). Type III protein tyrosine phosphatase	200–260
CDw149	MEM-133	Lymph, M	Not fully characterized. Defined by mAbs MEM-120 and MEM-133	120
CDw150	Signaling lymphocyte activation molecule (SLAM), IP0-3	T sub, B sub, Thy	Member of the Ig supergene family. It is a homotypic adhesion molecule involved in T/T, T/B, B/B interaction, and thereby in the regulation of T cell and B cell activation	70
CD151	Platelet-endothelial tetra-span antigen (PETA)-3	Plt, EC, stromal cells	Member of the tetraspans family (see CD9)	27
CD152	Cytotoxic T lymphocyte antigen (CTLA)-4	T act	Receptor for CD80 and CD86. Functions as a regulator of the T cell activation	44
CD153	CD30 ligand	T act	Member of the TNF family (see CD70, CD95L, CD154). Counter-receptor for CD30	40
CD154	gp39; TRAP-1; CD40 ligand	T act, mast cells	Member of the TNF family (see CD70, CD95L, CD153). Essential for germinal center formation and for Ig class switching	39
CD155	Poliovirus receptor	M, CD34$^+$ cells	Member of the Ig supergene family	80–90
CD156	MS2, ADAM-8	M, G	Belongs to the ADAM (a disintegrin and metalloproteinase domain) family. The extracellular region consists of a disintegrin-, metalloproteinase-, cysteine rich and EGF domain. Probably involved in loosening of cell–cell, cell–matrix contacts	69
CD157	Bst-1, Mo5	M, G, bone marrow stromal	Glycosylphosphatidylinositol-linked, CD38-like protein having both ADP-ribosyl cyclase activity and cyclic ADP-ribose (cADPR) hydrolase activity	42–50
CD158a	p58.1/p50.1	NK Sub, T sub	Receptor for HLA CW2, CW4, CW5, CW6. Killer cell inhibitory receptor (KIR) family member. p58.1 is the inhibiting form, p50.1 is the activating form; the difference is in the truncation of the cytoplasmic domain in p50.1	58.50

Table 1 Continued

	Other name (s)	Main reactivity of mAbs	Short characteristic of the CD molecule	Molecular weight reduced (kDa)
CD158b	p58.2/p50.2	NK	Receptor for HLA CW1, CW3, CW7, CW8. Killer cell inhibitory receptor (KIR) family member p58.2 is the inhibiting form, p50.2 is the activating form; the difference is in the truncation of the cytoplasmic domain in p50.2	58.50
CD161	NKR-P1A	NK, M, T sub, Thy precursors	Member of the Ca^{2+}-dependent (C-type) lectin superfamily of type II transmembrane receptors (see CD23, CD69, CD72, CD94)	30
CD162	PSGL-1, CD62 ligand	M, G, T	Counter-receptor of CD62E, CD62L and CD62P. Involved in leukocyte rolling	110
CD163	KiM8, M130, GHI/61	M	The CD163 molecule is a type I transmembrane molecule. The extracellular domain consists of nine scavenger-like repeating elements	130
CD164	MGC-24, MUC-24	T, M, G, epithelial cells, stroma cells, bone marrow cells	Sialomucin-like glycoprotein (see CD34, CD43, CD68). Involved in adhesion of hematopoietic cells to stroma cells	80
CD165	AD2/GP37	Plt, NK sub, T sub	Not fully characterized. Defined by mAbs AD2 and SN2	42
CD166	Activated leukocyte-cell adhesion molecule (ALCAM), CD6 ligand	M act, T act, Thy epithelium, neurons	Counter-receptor for CD6	100

Abbreviations: B, B-cells; act, activated; DC, dendritic cells; EC, endothelial cells; Eo, eosinophils; EPC, epithelial cells; G, granulocytes; LHC, epidermal Langerhans cells; M, monocytes; Mac, macrophages; NK, natural killer cells; PC, plasma cells; Plt, platelets; Prog, progenitor cells; sub, subpopulation; T, T cells; Thy, thymocytes. Cell types in brackets indicate weak reactivity or heterogeneous expression.

human proteins/genes. Within this database the CDs form a subgroup. The individual CD guides of PROW are written and reviewed by different experts and will be updated permanently. Links to other resources including Entrez, MEDLINE and sequence databases are available. There is free access to PROW via the Internet address <http://www.ncbi.nlm.nih.gov/prow/>.

See also: **Adhesion molecules; Campath-1 antigen (CD52); CD1; CD2; CD3; CD4; CD5; CD8; CD22; CD28; CD40 and its ligand; CD44; CD45 (the leukocyte common antigen); CD46 (membrane cofactor protein, MCP); CD59; Cell surface molecules, immunoprecipitation of; Lewis^x/sialyl-Lewis^x (CD15/CD15s); Complement receptors; Cytokine receptors; Decay-accelerating factor (CD55); Fas (CD95) and fas ligand; Fc receptors; Ig α/β (CD79a/CD79b); Integrins; Intercellular adhesion molecules: ICAM-1, ICAM-2 and ICAM-3; Interferon γ receptor; Invariant chain (Ii); Lymphocyte function-associated antigen 1 (LFA-1); Lymphocyte function-associated antigen 3 (LFA-3); Selectins (CD62-E/L/P); Thy-1; Transferring receptor (CD71); TNF receptors; Cell surface receptors and adhesion molecules, three-dimensional structures**

Further reading

Bernard A, Boumsell L, Dausset J, Milstein C and Schlossman SF (eds) (1984) *Leucocyte Typing*. Berlin: Springer-Verlag.

Boumsell L (1996) The international workshops and conferences on human leukocyte differentiation antigens – birth, current status and future. *Tissue Antigens* **48**: 238–241.

Ehrlich P (1900) Croonian lecture on Immunity. *Proceedings of the Royal Society, London* **66**: 424.

Kishimoto T, Goyert S, Kikutani H et al (eds) (1997) *Leucocyte Typing VI*. New York: Garland Publishers.

Köhler G and Milstein C (1975) Continuous cultures of fused cells secreting antibody of predefined specificity. *Nature* **256**: 495–497.

Knapp W (ed) (1981) *Leukemia Markers*. New York: Academic Press.

Knapp W, Dörken B, Gilks WR et al (eds) (1989) *Leucocyte Typing IV*. Oxford: Oxford University Press.

McMichael AJ, Beverly PC, Cobbold S et al (eds) (1987) *Leucocyte Typing III*. Oxford: Oxford University Press.

Reinherz EL, Haynes BF, Nadler LM and Bernstein ID (eds) (1986) *Leucocyte Typing II*. Berlin: Springer-Verlag.

Schlossman SF, Boumsell L, Gilks W et al (eds) (1995) *Leucocyte Typing V*. Oxford: Oxford University Press.

CD1

Said M Shawar, R & D Department, SA Scientific, San Antonio, Texas, USA

The CD1 family of cell surface glycoproteins is a well-defined group of non-major histocompatibility complex (MHC) encoded molecules. This nonpolymorphic cluster is the best understood of the MHC-unlinked antigen-presenting molecules. Five CD1 genes (CD1a, b, c, d and e) have been identified in humans and two genes (mCD1.1 and mCD1.2) in the mouse. However, CD1 genes and their products are evolutionarily conserved in mammals as they were identified in rats, rabbits, guinea pigs, cows and sheep.

Apparently, CD1 molecules represent a third and distinct lineage of antigen-presenting molecules that differ from MHC class I and class II molecules. Whereas CD1 molecules are structurally similar to MHC class I molecules and are associated with β_2-microglobulin (β_2m), their expression at the cell surface requires an endocytic compartment similar to MHC class II molecules.

CD1a was fortuitously discovered in 1979 as the first human leukocyte antigen (HLA) recognized by a monoclonal antibody. Nevertheless, the most remarkable discovery regarding these molecules was reported only a few years ago when human CD1b was shown to present a nonpeptide antigen to T cells. Indeed, CD1 proteins are capable of presenting nonpeptide antigens such as microbial lipids and glycolipids as well as peptide antigens. Such novel bio-chemical properties may reflect a specialized role for CD1 in the immune system and the potential to exploit it in vaccine development.

CD1 genes and CD1 protein structure

CD1 genes are MHC-unlinked, i.e. the human CD1 genes are encoded on chromosome 1, while HLA genes are encoded on chromosome 6. Similarly, the mouse CD1 genes are encoded on chromosome 3, whereas MHC genes are mapped to chromosome 17. The intron–exon structure of CD1 genes is similar to that of the MHC class I genes (**Figure 1**).

At least four human CD1 proteins (the CD1a, b c and d isoforms) are expressed on the surface of cells in association with β_2m. The protein products of these genes have been loosely classified into two groups according to their structure and tissue distribution (**Table 1**). The first group includes human CD1a, CD1b and CD1c, which are abundantly expressed on professional antigen-presenting cells such as Langerhans cells, dermal and lymph node cells, dendritic cells, mantle zone B cells and cytokine-activated monocytes. The second group includes human CD1d, and mouse CD1.1 and CD1.1, which are strongly expressed on the intestinal epithelium.

Amino acid homology of CD1 proteins and MHC class I and II molecules is minimal in the α1 domain

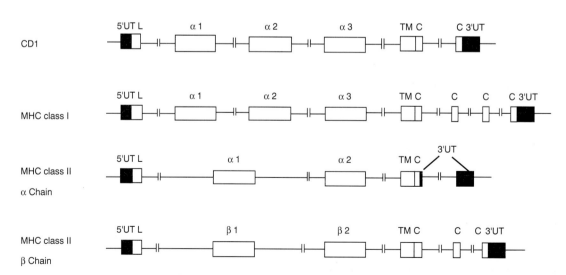

Figure 1 Intron–exon organization of CD1 and MHC class I and II genes. Open boxes are coding for exons. 5′ UT, 5′ untranslated region; L, leader sequence; TM, transmembrane domain; C, cytoplasmic domain; 3′ UT, 3′ untranslated region. (Reproduced with permission from Porcelli (1995).)

Table 1 CD1 molecules are classified into two groups according to their structure and tissue distribution

CD1 group	Known members	Tissue distribution
Group 1	Human CD1a, CD1b, CD1c and CD1e Sheep CD1b	Professional antigen-presenting cells such as Langerhans cells, dendritic cells, dermal and lymph node cells, mantle zone B cells and cytokine-activated monocytes
Group 2	Human CD1d Mouse CD1.1 and CD1.2 Rabbit CD1d	Intestinal epithelium, cortical and medullary thymocytes, circulating and splenic B cells, and hepatocytes

and is very limited in the α2 domain (especially with respect to class I proteins) (**Figure 2**). In the α3 domain, detectable homology is seen between CD1 and both MHC class I and class II proteins. The highest similarity scores in this region are with HLA-F (34%), HLA-A2 (27.8%), and HLA-DRβ (25.8%). Indeed, the α3 domain of CD1 proteins falls within the C1 group of immunoglobulin (Ig) superfamily members.

Antigen processing and presentation

The majority of antigens presented by MHC class I molecules are generated in the cytosol after proteolysis of endogenous proteins by proteasomes. Short peptides are then transferred into the endoplasmic reticulum (ER) by the transporter associated with antigen processing (TAP), and after binding to newly assembled MHC class I molecules, are transported to the plasma membrane. Similar to MHC class I, class II molecules assemble in the ER. However, class II molcules bind antigenic peptides in endosomal structures. MHC class II antigen processing and presentation can be blocked by reagents that raise endosomal pH (such as ammonium chloride, concanamycin A or chloroquine). In the ER, MHC class II molecules associate with the invariant chain (Ii); this association is required for efficient release of MHC class II from the ER. The signals that target the class II–Ii complex to the endosomal compartment are located in the cytoplasmic tail of Ii. Upon arrival in the endosomes, Ii is degraded, allowing the peptide-binding groove of MHC class II to be exposed for loading of the antigenic peptide. Two MHC class II-like structures, HLA-DMA and HLA-DMB, play an essential supporting role in processing of antigens presented by MHC class II molecules. Class II molecules on cells with specific deletions in HLA-DM

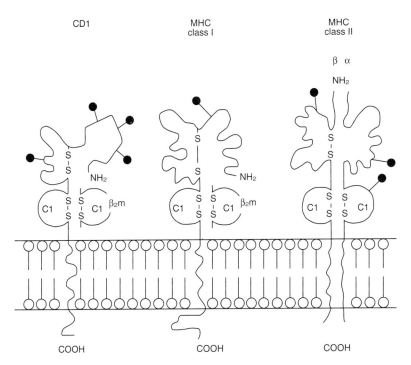

Figure 2 A proposed domain organization of CD1 proteins in comparison to MHC class I and II proteins. ●—, N-linked glycosylation; C1, immunoglobulin C1-like domain; S–S, intradomain disulfide bonds. (Reproduced with permission from Porcelli (1995).)

genes fail to present most but not all antigens and their MHC molecules contained mostly an Ii-derived fragment designated CLIP (class II-associated Ii peptide). Recently it has been demonstrated that HLA-DM molecules facilitate the release of CLIP and the subsequent binding of other peptides to MHC class II molecules. Although not all MHC class II molecules depend on HLA-DM for antigenic loading, HLA-DM proteins appear to function as chaperones that help in the last step of MHC class II folding and antigenic peptide loading.

Despite association with β_2m, the antigen processing pathway employed by CD1 molecules is closer to that of MHC class II than to that of class I. CD1 antigen presentation is independent of TAP-1 and TAP-2. Using cells from TAP-deficient patients (TAP$^{-/-}$), recent studies demonstrated that CD1a and CD1c are normally expressed on the surface of epidermal Langerhans cells. In addition, normal expression of CD1a, b and c was seen on dendritic cells differentiated *in vitro* from monocytes from the same patients. Furthermore, these studies showed that CD1a molecules on the surface of the TAP$^{-/-}$ dendritic cells were functional. Thus, this implies that either cell surface CD1 molecules are empty, or that CD1 molecules present TAP-independent antigens.

Although antigen presentation by CD1 does not require the MHC class II-like dimer, HLA-DMA/B, it is inhibitable by chloroquine and concanamycin A. In addition, recent studies demonstrate that nonpeptide antigens are processed in endocytic compartments. CD1b molecules appear to arrive at the endosomal compartment through at least two distinct routes: 1) a major recycling pathway, where CD1b molecules are endoctyosed at the plasma membrane and subsequently delivered to the MHC class II compartment (also called MIIC); this pathway is mediated by the cytoplasmic domain of CD1b molecules; and 2) a pathway comparable to MHC class II–Ii targeting to the endosomes; however, the signals that target CD1 molecules to MIIC appear to be a tyrosine-based motif in its cytoplasmic tail.

CD1-restricted antigens

Among the most unique features of the CD1 family members is the ability of certain CD1 molecules to present nonpeptide antigens to T cells. At least three classes of antigens have been shown to be presented by CD1 molecules, i.e. a lipid moiety, a lipoglycan and peptide antigens were recognized by CD1-restricted T cells.

In 1994, a group of scientists at Harvard University described the first CD1-restricted antigen as a protease-resistant moiety that copurified with the lipid fraction of the mycobacterial extract. Biochemical analysis of this antigen showed that it is a member of the mycobacterial family of mycolic acids (**Figure 3**). The fact that mycolic acid is found in the cell wall of several bacterial species such as *Nocardia* and *Corynebacterium* spp. suggests that CD1 molecules may present antigens derived from bacterial pathogens other than mycobacteria. A year later, these findings were extended by describing two *Mycobacterium leprae*-specific CD1b-restricted human T cell lines that recognize lipoarabinomannan (LAM), a glycolipid from the mycobacterial cell wall, and do not cross-react with mycolic acid. This molecule belongs to the lipoglycan family and is com-

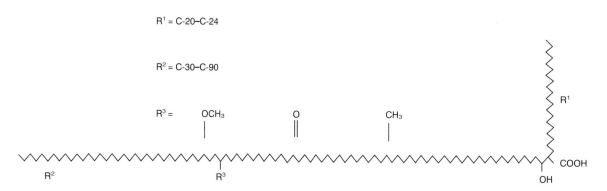

Figure 3 Mycolic acids are high molecular weight α-branched, β-hydroxy fatty acids that are components of the cell wall of all mycobacteria. All known mycolic acids have the basic structure R²CH(OH)CHR¹COOH where R¹ is a C-20–C-24 linear alkane and R² is a more complex structure of 30–90 carbon atoms that may contain various numbers of carbon–carbon double bonds and/or cyclosporane rings, methyl branches and oxygen function groups such as C = O, CH3OCH = COOH. Three principal categories of mycolic acid are known, i.e. corynomycolic acids (C-28–C-40), nocardomycolic acid (C-40–C-60) and mycobacterial mycolic acids (C-60–C-90), produced by strains of *Corynebacterium*, *Nocardia* and *Mycobacterium*, respectively.

NH₂XXXX1XX4XX7XXXCOOH
F I W
W L
M

Figure 4 Mouse CD1 binds peptides with a sequence motif comprising aromatic, bulky and hydrophobic amino acids with an overhanging NH₂-terminus. The majority of these long peptides include aromatic residues at positions 1 and 7 and an aliphatic residue in position 4. F, Phenylalanine; W, tryptophan; L, leucine; I, isoleucine; M, methionine; X, any amino acid.

posed of a hydrophobic lipid-containing phosphatidyl inositol group attached to a large and complex hydrophilic heteropolysaccharide. Further studies using chemically modified LAM and related compounds showed that both carbohydrate and lipid components of the antigen were required for presentation and/or T cell recognition. In addition, these two T cell lines differed in their ability to recognize LAM purified from different species of mycobacteria, suggesting a significant level of specificity in CD1-restricted T cell responses. This distinct recognition may arise from subtle variations in the lipid and carbohydrate moieties of LAM.

The previous examples suggest that CD1 proteins could have evolved to present nonpeptide lipid antigens to T cells. However, using random peptide phage displayed libraries, mouse CD1 was shown to bind peptides with a sequence motif comprising aromatic, bulky and hydrophobic amino acids with an overhanging NH₂-terminus (**Figure 4**). The study identified several dozen peptides which appear to be of immunological relevance as they can elicit specific CD1-restricted CD8⁺ cytotoxic T lymphocytes (CTLs). The length of these peptide antigens was not critical; however, the majority of these peptides include aromatic residues at positions 1 and 7 and an aliphatic residue in position 4. The characteristics of the mouse CD1–peptide interactions are similar to the interactions of MHC class II molecules with its ligands. For example, in common with class II ligands, mouse CD1 appears to prefer long peptides with hydrophobic and bulky amino acids at certain positions. In addition, the affinity of interaction of these peptides is similar to that of naturally processed peptides copurified with class II molecules.

Although mouse CD1 has been shown to bind peptides, it is not known if mycolic acid and the other lipoglycans directly bind to CD1b. In addition, it is not yet known whether CD1b presents one or more members of the mycolic acid families to T cells as a processed or intact molecule, or as part of a modified epitope.

Interestingly, the amino acid sequence of all known CD1 molecules from various mammalian species, as well as another MHC-unlinked molecule, neonatal Fc-receptor (FcRn), share a proline at position 162 in the α2 helix. Recent crystallographic studies of FcRn showed that Proline 162 induces a kink that closes the peptide-binding groove, thus preventing peptide binding. If this kink is found in CD1 molecules, then it is possible that the interaction between CD1 molecules and their ligands is different from that known for conventional MHC class I molecules. Also, it may resemble that of MHC class II–superantigen association. In addition, the full range of antigens presented by the CD1 molecules is not yet known and the natural ligands remain to be defined. However, studies from several laboratories support the hypothesis that CD1 molecules contain a hydrophobic pocket between the α1 and α2 domains capable of accommodating lipids, glycolipids or

Table 2 Comparison between CD1, MHC class I and MHC class II molecules

	CD1 Molecules	MHC class I	MHC class II
Antigen processing and presentation			
TAP-1/TAP-2 requirement	No	Yes for the majority	No
HLA-DMA/B requirement	No	No	Yes for the majority
Chloroquine sensitivity	Yes	No	Yes
Invariant chain (Ii) requirement	No	No	Yes
Endosomal compartment passage	Yes	No	Yes
ER to endosome targeting	Signal in the cytoplasmic tail	Not applicable	Signal in the Ii
β₂m association	Yes	Yes	No
T cell recognition	CD4⁻/CD8⁻, CD8⁺, CD4⁺	Mostly CD8⁺	CD4⁺
Nature of antigens presented	Lipid, glycolipid and long hydrophobic peptides	Mostly peptides, 8–10 amino acids long	Mostly peptides, 8–20 amino acids long

hydrophobic peptides. It is clear that further biochemical studies and the determination of the crystal structures of both mouse and human CD1 are needed to elucidate these issues.

Role of CD1 in the immune system

The initial reports implicating CD1 in T cell function demonstrated that human T cell clones expressing either α/β or γ/δ T cell receptors (TCRs) recognized tumor cells expressing specific isoforms of human CD1. These CD1-restricted T cells were phenotypically CD4$^-$CD8$^-$ or double negative (DN) T cells. CD1b-restricted proliferative and cytotoxic responses of human DN-α/β$^+$ and DN-γ/δ$^+$ lymphocytes specific for *M. tuberculosis* and *M. leprae* were seen in cells isolated from blood of normal humans. Also, CD1-restricted T cells specific for mycobacterial antigens have been found among CD8$^+$ TCR-αβ$^+$ T cells. In addition, mouse NK1$^+$ TCR-αβ$^+$ T cells, which appear to be entirely CD1 restricted, were isolated recently. These T cells were either DN or CD4$^+$. Thus, it is now accepted that CD1 recognition is broadly distributed among T cell subsets. The different biochemical features of the various members of the CD1 family and the wide spectrum of recognition by T cell subsets indicate that CD1 molecules may subserve several specialized functions in the immune system, such as presentation of hydrophobic ligands (lipids or peptides) and/or regulation of the classes of immune responses.

The mouse MHC class I molecule, H2-M3, was the first definitive example of a specialized molecule in antigen presentation. H2-M3 preferentially binds hydrophobic *N*-formylated peptides, which make it suited to the presentation of antigens derived from intracellular pathogens. CD1 and H2-M3 molecules share a common feature, i.e. both bind and present hydrophobic antigens of bacterial origin. While both CD1 and H2-M3 may have evolved to combat microbes, each of these molecules seem to use different antimicrobial strategies. The antigens presented by H2-M3 are from the NH$_2$-terminus of prokaryotic proteins and appear to be intracellular in nature. In contrast, CD1 molecules seem to bind bacterial cell wall lipids that come from the extracellular milieu. Interestingly, H2-M3 has not been found in species other than rodents (including humans). Thus, human group I CD1 molecules, may accomplish the role assigned to H2-M3 in the mouse.

Autoreactive CD1-restricted T cells (NK1$^+$) have been identified in normal unimmunized mice. Although this rare T cell population includes the DN phenotype, the majority are CD4$^+$ cells. A prominent subset of these CD1-specific cells uses an invariant TCRα chain in conjunction with a restricted set of TCR Vβ families. During their differentiation in the thymus, these cells acquire several unique properties, i.e. they express natural killer cell receptors, and they display unusual cytokine secretion functions. In particular, the CD4$^+$ subset secretes large amounts of interleukin 4 (IL-4) upon primary stimulation, within an hour of TCR engagement. Several studies indicated that NK1$^+$ T cells could potentially influence the TH$_1$/T$_H$2 profile of the immune response, and thus could act as natural suppressors of graft-versus-host disease, mediate acute graft rejection, or regulate autoimmune symptoms in lupus and diabetes. As yet, however, there is no physiological phenomenon that these T cell subsets are associated with.

CD1b is abundantly expressed in the lesions of patients with the self-healing form of leprosy (where interferon γ secreting T$_H$1 CD4$^+$ cells are recruited) but not with the lepromatous form (where T$_H$2 CD4$^+$ cells predominate). Thus, it is suggested that CD1b expression may determine the T$_H$1/T$_H$2 set of specialized cytokines produced in response to *M. leprae*. Mycobacterial lipids are an ideal foreign target; indeed, mycolic acid is an active component of one of the most powerful adjuvants (Freund's complete adjuvant). Therefore, it is postulated that early production of cytokines by CD1b-restricted, mycobacterial-specific T cells may jump-start the immune response or may determine its T$_H$1 differentiation. The possible roles of CD1-expressing cells and NK1$^+$ T cells in influencing the T$_H$1/T$_H$2 differentiation and development pathway remains to be fully understood.

The oligomorphic CD1 proteins are a third and distinct group of antigen-presenting molecules (**Table 2**) that are conserved in all mammalian species tested. Monomorphic and oligomorphic antigen-presenting molecules may be more effective in inducing a protective immune response, and for potential vaccine design, than their polymorphic counterparts. Whereas the latter group might bind tens of antigens with different sequences, the former binds a single or very limited number of antigens. A single peptide or a microbial lipid, in the case of CD1 proteins, might be sufficient to induce this protective response in all recipients. Thus, CD1 proteins are definitive candidates for antigen-presenting molecules in vaccination strategies intended to induce a universal CTL response.

See also: **Antigen presentation via MHC class I molecules; Antigen presentation via MHC class II molecules; β$_2$-microglobulin; Effector lymphocytes; Fc receptors; MHC, functions of;** *Mycobacteria,* **infection and immunity.**

Further reading

Bauer A, Huttinger R, Staffler G et al (1997) Analysis of the requirement for beta 2-microglobulin for expression and formation of human CD1 antigens. *European Journal of Immunology* 27: 1366–1373.

Beckman EM and Brenner MB (1995) MHC class I-like, class II-like and CD1 molecules: distinct roles in immunity. *Immunology Today* 16: 349–352.

Beckman EM, Porcelli SA, Morita CT, Behar SM, Furlong ST and Brenner MB (1994) Recognition of a lipid antigen by CD1-restricted αβ+ T cells. *Nature* 372: 691–694.

Behar SM and Porcelli SA (1995) Mechanisms of autoimmune disease induction: the role of the immune response to microbial pathogens. *Arthritis and Rheumatism* 38: 458–476.

Bendelac A (1995) Mouse NK1+ T cells. *Current Opinion in Immunology* 7: 367–374.

Bendelac A (1995) CD1: presenting unusual antigens to unusual T lymphocytes. *Science* 269: 185–186.

Bendelac A, Rivera MN, Park SH et al (1997) Mouse CD1-specific NK1 T cells: development, specificity, and function. *Annual Review of Immunology* 15: 535–562.

Calabi F, Yu CY, Bilsland CAG and Milstein C (1991) CD1: from structure to function. In: Srivastava R, Ram BP and Tyle P (eds) *Immunogenetics of Major Histocompatibility Complex*, pp 215–243. New York: VHC.

Castano AR, Tangri S, Miller JE et al (1995) Peptide binding and presentation by mouse CD1. *Science* 269: 223–226.

Porcelli SA (1995) The CD1 family: a third lineage of antigen presenting molecules. *Advances in Immunology* 59: 1–98.

Porcelli SA, Morita CT and Brenner MB (1992) CD1b restricts the response of human CD4-8- T lymphocytes to a microbial antigen. *Nature* 360: 593–597.

Shawar SM, Vyas JM, Rodgers JR and Rich RR (1994) Antigen presentation by major histocompatibility complex class I-b molecules: *Annual Review of Immunology* 12: 839–880.

Teitell M, Holcombe HR, Brossay L et al (1997) Nonclassical behavior of the mouse CD1 class I-like molecule. *Journal of Immunology* 158: 2143–2149.

CD2

Stefan C Meuer, Ruprechts-Karls-Universität, Heidelberg, Germany

CD2 is a glycoprotein of 50 kDa expressed by the vast majority of non-B lymphocytes in humans. In the mouse, unlike in humans, CD2 is also present on B lymphocytes and, in the rat, on splenic macrophages. CD2 appears at the earliest level of T lineage ontogeny and demonstrates a remarkable structural conservation among species. Several differentially glycosylated forms have been found on the cell surface of human non-B lymphocytes. In the mouse, two distinct isotypic forms of CD2 exist in different strains.

Structure

The CD2 gene maps to the human chromosome 1. Analysis of CD2 cDNA clones indicates a cleaved signal peptide of 24 amino acids, an extracellular segment of 185 residues, a transmembrane domain of 26 residues and a cytoplasmic region of 116 residues. Restriction analysis and sequencing of genomic DNA shows that the gene is divided into five exons, one encoding the signal peptide, two encoding the two extracellular domains, one encoding the transmembrane domain, and one encoding the intracellular domain. On the basis of significant primary sequence homology, a relationship of CD2 to the Ig superfamily has been proposed. Secondary structure predictions reveal a mix of α helical and β sheet structures.

Ligands

Employing transfection of cells with mutagenized plasmids or human CD2 chimeric and mutant proteins, distinct CD2 epitopes are defined by monoclonal antibodies and mapped to one of the Ig-like domains of the CD2 ectodomain. CD2 binds to the ubiquitously expressed cell surface glycoprotein, CD58, which is present on many human cell types including antigen-presenting cells and endothelial cells. A sheep homolog of CD58 exists which binds to human CD2, providing the molecular explanation for the fortuitous observation that human T lymphocytes and sheep blood cells spontaneously form rosettes. A second structurally related ligand, CD48, binds to CD2 but with an affinity two orders of magnitude weaker than that of the CD2/CD58 interaction. CD59 is also thought to bind to CD2.

Interactions of CD2 with its ligands are mediated through the N-terminal membrane distal Ig-like domain. The precise role of the second or membrane-proximal Ig domain has not been elucidated in depth, although activation of T cells in response to paired mitogenic combinations of CD2-specific monoclonal antibodies requires that one monoclonal antibody is directed against an epitope (CD2R) within or closely related to this region.

Role of CD2

Expression of CD2 on resting versus activated human T cells not only differs from a quantitative point of view (CD2 on resting T cells: approximately 30 000 molecules per cell; CD2 on activated T cells: approximately 200 000 molecules per cell) but also with regard to expression of the CD2R epitope, which is only found on activated T cells and exposed as a consequence of ligand-induced conformational changes within the CD2 ectodomain.

The involvement of CD2 in T lymphocyte adhesion and activation is well documented. In addition to providing accessory signals for T cell receptor-mediated activation of lymphocytes, *in vitro* activation in the absence of direct stimulation through the T cell receptor using mitogenic combinations of CD2-specific monoclonal antibodies has been described. CD2 has been shown to play a role in potentiating T cell responses to the cytokines interleukin 1 (IL-1), IL-6 and IL-12 and to be involved in the regulation of T cell anergy. In this regard, perturbation of particular regions of CD2 can inhibit T cells and this inhibition is independent of the disruption of the adhesion function of CD2 with its ligands. Rather, polyclonal T cell hypo-responsiveness which persists long after the recovery of CD2 cell surface expression may be due to an inhibitory signal which is delivered to T cells through CD2. T cell anergy correlates with a loss of the CD2R epitope expression but not CD2 expression. Reversal of anergy following culture with IL-2 is induced when challenged with antigen and CD58 and this coincides with the reappearance of the CD2R epitope. Among the accessory T cell molecules examined so far, CD2 appears to be unique in its ability to participate in the reversal of anergy.

Signaling

CD2 itself has no enzymatic activity but transmits signals in part via the T cell receptor/CD3/ζ complex through its interaction with the ζ chain and CD3 ϵ and also through other unknown pathways as suggested by the tyrosine phosphorylation of distinct intracellular substrates and the serine dephosphorylation and nuclear translocation of cofilin, a cyclosporine-insensitive event. Of particular interest is the interaction of CD2 with the tyrosine phosphatase CD45. CD2 also interacts with the tyrosine kinases p56[lck], p59[fyn] and the ζ subunit of the T cell receptor/CD3/ζ complex, each of which have been shown to be targets for CD45 phosphatase activity. Indeed it is possible that CD2 regulates T cell activation by bringing CD45 into the proximity of these molecules.

Perturbation of CD2 and/or its associated signaling molecules provides a means for positively and negatively regulating T cell responses and may turn out to represent a central component of therapeutic efforts to regulate tolerance.

See also: **Adhesion molecules; CD45 (the leukocyte common antigen); Cell-mediated lysis; Lymphocyte function-associated antigen 3 (LFA-3); T lymphocyte activation; T lymphocyte differentiation.**

Further reading

Bell GM and Imboden JB (1995) CD2 and the regulation of T cell anergy. *Journal of Immunology* 155: 2805–2807.

Beyers AD, Spruyt LL and Williams AF (1992) Molecular associations between the T-lymphocyte antigen receptor complex and the surface antigens CD2, CD4, or CD8 and CD5. *Proceedings of the National Academy of Sciences of the USA* 89: 2945–2949.

Boussiotis VA, Freeman GJ, Griffin JD, Gray GS, Gribben JG and Nadler LM (1994) CD2 is involved in maintenance and reversal of human alloantigen-specific clonal anergy. *Journal of Experimental Medicine* 180: 1665–1673.

Gückel G, Berek C, Lutz M, Altevogt P, Schirrmacher V and Kyewski BA (1991) Anti-CD2 antibodies induce T cell unresponsiveness in vivo. *Journal of Experimental Medicine* 174: 957–967.

Holter W, Schwarz M, Cerwenka A et al (1996) The role of CD2 as a regulator of human T-cell cytokine production. *Immunological Reviews* 153: 107–122.

Hünig T, Tiefenthaler G, Meyer zum Büschenfelde KH and Meuer SC (1987) Alternative pathway activation of T cells by binding of CD2 to its cell-surface ligand. *Nature* 325: 298–301.

Meuer SC, Hussey RE, Fabbi M et al (1984) An alternative pathway of T-cell activation: a functional role for the 50 kD T11 sheep erythrocyte receptor protein. *Cell* 36: 897–907.

Moingeon P, Chang H-C, Sayre PH et al (1989) The structural biology of CD2. *Immunological Reviews* 111: 111–144.

Samstag Y, Eckerskorn S, Wesselborg S, Henning S, Wallich R and Meuer SC (1994) Costimulatory signals for human T-cell activation induce nuclear translocation of pp19/cofilin. *Proceedings of the National Academy of Sciences of the USA* **91**: 4494–4499.

Schlossman SF, Boumsell L, Gilks W *et al* (eds) (1995) *Leukocyte Typing V* Oxford: Oxford University Press.

Schraven B, Samstag Y, Altoevogt P and Meuer SC (1990) Association of CD2 and CD45 on human T lymphocytes. *Nature* **345**: 71–74.

Schraven B, Wild M, Kirchgessner H *et al* (1993) Alterations of CD2 association with T cell receptor signalling molecules in 'CD2 unresponsive' human T lymphocytes. *European Journal of Immunology* **23**: 119–123.

Seed B and Aruffo A (1987) Molecular cloning of the CD2 antigen, the T-cell erythrocyte receptor, by a rapid immunoselection procedure. *Proceedings of the National Academy of Sciences of the USA* **84**: 3365–3369.

Verhagen AM, Schraven B, Wild M, Wallich R and Meuer SC (1996) Differential interaction of the CD2 extracellular and intracellular domains with the tyrosine phosphatase CD45 and the ζ-chain of the TCR/CD3/ζ complex. *European Journal of Immunology* **26**: 2841–2849.

CD3

Alan Tunnacliffe, Anglia Research Foundation, Cambridge, UK

Originally known as T3, CD3 was identified by Kung and colleagues in 1979 and was one of the first groups of human T lymphocyte surface antigens identified using monoclonal antibodies. It was subsequently shown that antibodies against CD3 could, depending on the conditions used, either stimulate T cells to divide or inhibit the development of effector functions such as cytotoxicity. Therefore, it was apparent early on that CD3 had an important role in T cell function. Initially, CD3 was thought to consist of a single polypeptide, but later analysis demonstrated its three-chain nature (CD3γ, δ and ε) and its close association with T cell antigen receptor (TCR) heterodimers. This established the CD3 molecules, together with other invariant subunits (ζ and η), as part of the core TCR. Although the TCRαβ or γδ heterodimers govern the antigen recognition capability of the TCR, signal transduction and the regulation of TCR function are mediated through the invariant subunits.

Structure and assembly of TCR invariant subunits

Investigation of the structure of the TCR has been an area of intense activity, since such studies should provide insight into the molecular details of receptor function, but much remains to be learned. The current picture is of an elaborate structure comprising at least four invariant polypeptides forming a complex with the antigen-binding heterodimer. The most common form of the αβ-type core receptor is likely to have the stoichiometry $\alpha\beta\gamma\delta\epsilon_2\zeta_2$, where the γ, δ and ε chains are the CD3 subunits proper, being specific to the TCR, and ζ is the most prevalent member

of a family of similar molecules which include η and the γ chain of some Fc receptors. The structural characteristics of the most important of these molecules are given in **Table 1**.

The cDNAs for the three CD3 molecules were cloned in the mid-1980s and examination of the predicted amino acid sequences suggested that they form a small family of homologous integral membrane proteins, with γ and δ showing a particularly high degree of relatedness to each other. Close linkage of the CD3 genes is consistent with their evolution from a common ancestral gene. The extracellular domain of each chain possesses some sequence similarity with immunoglobulin (Ig) and the potential to arrange stretches of β sheet as a partial Ig fold. The CD3 proteins, therefore, like TCRαβ and TCRγδ, are members of the Ig superfamily. The transmembrane regions of the CD3 molecules each contain an acidic amino acid within the stretch of hydrophobic residues, an unusual feature which is probably significant given the presence of corresponding basic residues in the transmembrane regions of TCR heterodimers. Although it is unlikely that full ionization of acidic and basic side-chains takes place in the hydrophobic environment of the plasma membrane, interactions between the transmembrane sequences of heterodimers and the CD3 subunits may help to stabilize the TCR complex. The sequences of the cytoplasmic domains of the CD3 subunits show little relatedness to other known proteins, but all contain the tyrosine-containing Reth motif implicated in signal transduction, which is also found three times in the ζ cytoplasmic domain and in other receptor-associated polypeptides including the surface IgM-associated Ig-α and Ig-β proteins, and the β and γ subunits of FcεRI.

Table 1 Structural data on TCR invariant subunits

Subunit	Molecular weight (kDa)		Ig superfamily?	Glycosylated?
	Human	Mouse		
CD3γ	25	21	Yes	Yes
CD3δ	20	28	Yes	Yes
CD3ε	19	25	Yes	No
ζ	16	16	No	No
η	Not encoded	22	No	No

In mouse, the vast majority (80–90%) of the ζ chain exists as a disulfide-linked homodimer, but can also form heterodimers with the related η, γ and (possibly) θ chains. This leads to the formation of several isoforms of the mature TCR complex within a single T cell, with the potential for functional variation between forms. Cloning and sequencing predict a structure for ζ which is markedly different from that of the CD3 proteins. One feature which ζ does share with CD3 subunits is the acidic residue in its transmembrane region. Otherwise, it has a minimal extracellular domain, consisting of only nine amino acids including the cysteine responsible for disulfide linkage, and an intracellular domain with a consensus sequence for ATP binding and multiple (six in mice; seven in humans) tyrosines, whose phosphorylation results in a dramatic apparent increase in M_r to 21 kDa. Intriguingly, η and θ derive from the same gene as ζ, by alternative mRNA processing, although γ is encoded by a separate, though linked, gene. The significance of the η, γ and θ chains is unclear, however, given that η has been demonstrated to be absent from human T cells.

Study of the assembly of a multisubunit complex such as the TCR is hindered by a number of problems. First, the receptor is built up of several transmembrane proteins and requires translocation of subunits across a membrane for its formation. Therefore, it is difficult to study interactions of purified proteins in solution. Furthermore, all TCR components (excepting η) may need to be present for efficient complex formation. However, the combination of several approaches including the examination of immature T cells and T cell lines, together with the analysis of partial receptor complexes, has provided considerable information.

Thymocytes express CD3γ, δ and ε at an early stage in their development, before the TCRα and β genes have completed their rearrangements: between days 14 and 16 of mouse fetal thymus development, and from week 10.5 in human fetal thymus. In humans, there is also evidence for expression of the CD3 genes from week 7 in fetal liver, prior to colonization of the thymus. Thus, the CD3 genes are among the earliest T cell lineage genes to be expressed. Without the antigen-binding heterodimer proteins, immature thymocytes do not express significant levels of surface CD3. Cell lines lacking either TCRα or β also fail to deliver CD3 to the cell surface, or do so inefficiently. Mutant cell lines defective in ζ production express only 5% of normal cell surface receptor levels. Cumulatively, these data indicate that a $ζ_2$-type receptor requires most, and possibly all, subunits for efficient transport to the plasma membrane.

During assembly of the TCR complex, the individual components form partial complexes, a situation which can be mimicked experimentally when genes for the individual subunits are transfected in various combinations into heterologous cells. Such partial complexes are largely unstable and most are rapidly degraded within the cell before reaching the mid-Golgi, but they can be studied to reveal likely subunit interactions within the mature TCR complex. Thus, observed isolated pairwise combinations are CD3γε, CD3δε, but not CD3γδ, which is interpreted as evidence against close contact between the CD3γ and δ chains. Intracellular TCR complex assembly may be aided by the molecular chaperone proteins TRAP and calnexin, which are thought to mediate correct subunit interactions. Whether the TCRα and β chains dimerize before association with CD3 molecules may depend on which cells are examined, but in immature double-positive thymocytes this is thought not to occur. Instead, trimeric complexes, αδε and βγε, form first which then combine via αβ dimerization and finally associate with the $ζ_2$ dimer giving a stoichiometry of $αβγδε_2ζ_2$. This is supported by transgenic mouse experiments which indicate one TCRα, one TCRβ and two CD3ε chains per complex. A model structure for the core receptor based on these data is shown in **Figure 1**.

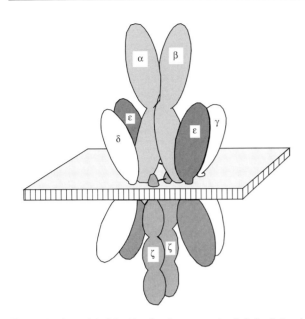

Figure 1 A model of the T cell antigen receptor ($\alpha\beta\gamma\delta\epsilon_2\zeta_2$-type) showing an arrangement of subunits compatible with current data. A transverse section through the plasma membrane is shown. Disulfide bonds between α and β, and between ζ subunits, are shown as solid lines.

Function of TCR invariant subunits

A critical early finding was that monoclonal antibodies to CD3, most of which recognize the CD3ϵ chain, were able to activate resting T cells in the presence of monocytes bearing appropriate Fc receptors. Antibodies directed to the $\alpha\beta$ heterodimer can behave similarly. Thus, a T cell bridged to an antigen-presenting cell via TCR/mAb/FcR reacts in a manner analogous to the physiological situation, where the link is TCR/Ag/MHC (major histocompatibility complex). For signaling through the TCR, therefore, some form of cross-linking or partial immobilization of the receptor is necessary, which need not be dependent on specific antigen recognition. This signaling process takes place through the invariant subunits of the TCR, since the heterodimeric antigen-binding chains themselves have very small cytoplasmic domains which are unlikely to have more than an anchoring function. In peripheral T cells, full activation also requires signaling through the costimulatory CD28 molecule by the B7-1/B7-2 antigen on B cells and macrophages. Signaling through the TCR alone results in the functionally unresponsive state known as anergy.

T lymphocyte activation involves multiple intracellular events, all leading to transition from the quiescent G_0 phase of the cell cycle into G_1 and induction of interleukin 2 (IL-2) secretion and IL-2 receptor expression. T cell growth, involving progression from G_1 to S phase and mitosis, is then controlled by IL-2 binding to the IL-2 receptor. At least two signaling pathways are thought to result from TCR occupancy, the first routing through the G protein $p21^{ras}$, and the second through phospholipase C. Both pathways act synergistically with CD28-derived signals to effect action of the transcription factor NF-AT1 (nuclear factor of activated T cells) on, for example, the IL-2 gene.

During antigen recognition by the TCR on a CD4$^+$ helper T cell, the coreceptor molecule CD4 is recruited into the receptor complex, having associated with monomorphic sites on the MHC class II molecule of the antigen-presenting cell. The Src family protein tyrosine kinase $p56^{lck}$ associates with CD4 and, in one model of the molecular consequences of antigen binding, $p56^{lck}$ phosphorylates the CD3 and ζ chains on the tyrosine residues within their Reth activation domains. This promotes association of the TCR with the T cell-specific protein tyrosine kinase ZAP-70 through its SH2 domains, when ZAP-70 itself becomes phosphorylated and provides a signal to both $p21^{ras}$ and phospholipase C pathways via intermediate protein species.

The structure of the TCR thus reflects its two major functions of antigen recognition and signal transduction, with the latter role being governed by the invariant chains. The CD3 proteins, together with the ζ chain, must interact with other cell surface molecules, including CD4 and CD8, and several intracellular proteins such as $p56^{lck}$ and ZAP-70, as well as other tyrosine and serine/threonine kinases. It is now apparent that the complexity of the TCR is not unique, with other receptors governing cellular activation, such as the B cell antigen receptor (surface IgM), the Fc receptors and the IL-2 receptor, also having oligomeric structures commensurate with their complex function.

See also: **CD4; CD8; CD28; CD45 (the leukocyte common antigen); Fc receptors; IgM; Interleukin 2; Interleukin 2 receptor; Protein kinases; T cell receptor, $\alpha\beta$; T cell receptor, $\gamma\delta$; T cell receptor, recognition by; T lymphocyte activation; T lymphocyte differentiation.**

Further reading

Huppa JB and Ploegh HL (1997) *In vitro* translation and assembly of a complete T cell receptor-CD3 complex. *Journal of Experimental Medicine* **186**: 393–403.

Kearse KP, Roberts JP, Wiest DL and Singer A (1995) Developmental regulation of $\alpha\beta$ T cell antigen receptor assembly in immature CD4$^+$CD8$^+$ thymocytes. *Bio-Essays* **17**: 1049–1054.

Maniolos N (1995) Hierarchy of T cell antigen receptor assembly. *Immunology and Cell Biology* 73: 544–548.

Pastor MI, Reif K and Cantrell D (1995) The regulation and function of p21^{ras} during T-cell activation and growth. *Immunology Today* 16: 159–164.

Tanaka Y, Ardouin L, Gillet A *et al* (1995) Early T-cell development in CD3-deficient mice. *Immunological Reviews* 148: 171–199.

Weiss A and Littman DR (1994) Signal transduction by lymphocyte antigen receptors. *Cell* 76: 263–274.

CD4

Rafick Pierre Sekaly and **Ronald Rooke**, Montreal Institute of Clinical Research, Immunology Laboratory, Montreal, Canada

The cell surface glycoprotein CD4 is expressed on a subpopulation of mature T lymphocytes, where its presence is tightly correlated with recognition of major histocompatibility complex (MHC) class II antigens. It is also present on various other cell types.

Structure

The CD4 molecule is an elongated (125 Å × 25–30 Å) cell surface glycoprotein that is conserved among various primates and rodents, e.g. 79% amino acid identity between mouse and human (**Table 1**). It is made up of four extracellular domains (D1–D4). The N-terminal, outermost domain (D1) consists of nine β strands disposed in the topology of variable immunoglobulin domains. Crystallography of the D1–D2 fragment has confirmed that the last strand of D1 runs directly into the first strand of D2, which brings both domains in close contact and confers rigidity to this part of the molecule (**Figure 1**). Crystallographic and proteolytic studies have shown that a short, hinge-like region bridges the D1–D2 fragment of CD4 to the D3–D4 part. The membrane proximal fragment, comprising the D3–D4 domains, is referred to as a connecting peptide. It is made up of two additional, degenerate, v-like domains that also make up a rigid structure. Recently, the four extracellular domains of the human CD4 molecule have been crystallized. This work has confirmed the presence of the hinge region between D2 and D3. More interestingly, in all crystals obtained, the CD4 appears as a dimer (H. Wu and W. Hendryckson, personal communication). The highly basic cytoplasmic tail is the most conserved domain in the molecule. Three serine residues may serve as regulatory phosphorylation sites. The D1 domain is encoded by two exons, while D2–D4 are encoded by individual exons. The human gene is made up of nine exons and eight introns and spans 33 kb, while the murine gene includes ten exons covering 26 kb.

Expression

The full length 3.7 kb CD4 transcript, along with the expression of the protein on the cell surface, was identified initially in thymocytes and mature T lymphocytes in mice and humans. However, CD4 is also seen on human macrophages, Langerhans cells, neuronal and glial cells and some Epstein–Barr virus-transformed human B cell lines. CD4 is found as a monomer on the cell surface. The presence of a smaller 2.7 kb transcript has been described in the mouse forebrain, cortex and striatum. The predicted protein from this smaller mRNA would be a truncated form of mouse CD4 beginning at amino acid 214 (within the connecting peptide) and continuing through the normal cytoplasmic tail. This smaller transcript has also been seen in human brain tissue. The significance and function of this truncated CD4

Table 1 Comparison between human and murine CD4 genes and molecules

	MW (kDa)	Protein (AA)	Leader (AA)	Extracellular (AA)	Transmembrane (AA)	Cytoplasmic (AA)	Cysteines	Glycosylation (sites)	Chromosome	Gene size (kb)
Mouse	54	457	26	368	25	38	13	4	6	26
Human	55	458	25	372	23	38	12	2	12	33

AA, amino acids; MW, molecular weight.

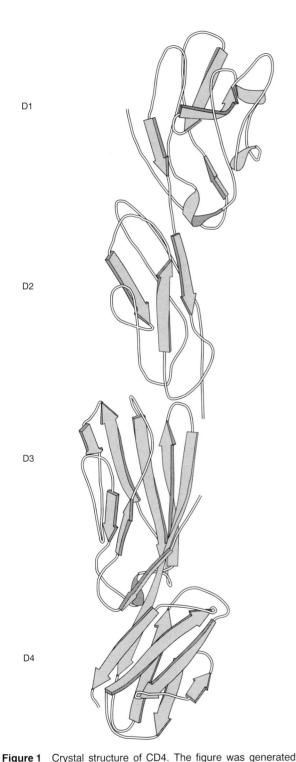

Figure 1 Crystal structure of CD4. The figure was generated using Molscript (Kraulis PJ (1991) *Journal of Crystallography* **24**: 946–950) according to X-ray diffraction coordinates published by Rye SE *et al* (1994) *Structure* **2**: 59–74 for D1 and D2, and by Brady RL *et al* (1993) *Science* **260**: 979–983 for D3 and D4. Domains 1 and 2 are from the human molecule while domains 3 and 4 are from the rat molecule. The hinge region is not shown.

D1

D2

D3

D4

mRNA are not known. Littman and coworkers have identified and characterized a T cell-specific enhancer located 13 kb upstream of the transcriptional initiation site of the mouse and human CD4 genes. They also have demonstrated the existence of an intronic regulatory region located between the first and second exons of the murine gene. The element is orientation and position independent. This negative regulatory region functions in combination with heterologous *cis*-acting regulatory elements, indicating that it is a developmentally regulated transcriptional silencer.

Interactions

Early studies suggested that CD4 might have signal transduction as well as ligand-binding capabilities. The advent of transgenic and knockout animals has confirmed and significantly extended these results, showing that the CD4 molecule is involved in a number of crucial steps during the lifespan of T cells. It is obvious that to play such a central role in the choices made by T cells, the CD4 molecule must interact with many other molecules.

MHC class II molecule

Doyle and Strominger provided the first strong evidence for physical binding between CD4 and class II MHC molecules. This was done with the use of transfected cells, which also indicated that this adhesion can take place in the absence of the T cell receptor (TCR). By using a class I (D^d) specific, $CD4^+$ T cell hybridoma, Gay and coworkers investigated the role of CD4 in T cell activation. These experiments correlated the interaction of CD4 and class II MHC with an enhanced T cell activation. More recently, mutagenesis studies indicated CD4 affinity changes when residues 110, 137, 140, 141 and 142 of the solvent-exposed loop of the $\beta2$ domain of class II were altered. Moreover, peptides with the sequence of the $\beta2$ domain residues 134–148 (less so for 138–152) can bind CD4. From these studies and the fact that no natural polymorphic variant of MHC class II proteins have been identified that fail to bind CD4, it has been assumed that CD4 interacts with a relatively invariant part of the $\beta2$ domain of class II. This idea has recently been challenged by Fleury and coworkers, who associated crystallographic and functional data obtained from class II molecules with varying affinities for CD4. They mapped polymorphic residues between positions $\beta180$ and $\beta189$ that can exert a dramatic influence on the interaction with CD4; this could contribute to the predominance of certain DR alleles or isotypes in antigen-restricted responses.

Moreover, König and coworkers have also added to our view of the interaction between CD4 and MHC class II by demonstrating that a second surface-exposed segment in the α2 domain of class II is also critical for the function of CD4. Both these reports are in accordance with the crystallographic data and suggest that in order for the CD4 molecule to contribute efficiently to signal transduction, it has to dimerize or oligomerize.

On the other hand, the class II contact residues on the CD4 remain controversial and will only be solved by cocrystallization of CD4 and class II. Different regions throughout D1, D2 and D3 domains have been suggested. A recent study making use of alanine-scan mutants showed that residues from both lateral faces of D1 and from one loop of D2 are involved in the interaction. This suggests an extended region of contact with the membrane-proximal lateral face of the class II molecule. These results are also consistent with an oligomerization event during the interaction.

The efficacy of interspecies interactions of human and murine CD4 with murine or human class II MHC molecules has also been a matter of debate. Sequence comparisons among human (hCD4), murine (mCD4) and rat CD4 show that residues that are implicated in the overall conformation are conserved, suggesting they will adopt similar three-dimensional structures. It was found that hCD4 and mCD4 can function to a comparable extent with at least five different class II MHC and four different mouse class II MHC molecules. Moreover, this work indicates that the structural features of this cross-species interaction are strongly conserved. These data confirm previous experiments which used transgenic animals that express various HLA class II proteins and showed that the interaction between HLA class II and mouse CD4 molecules is sufficient in provoking peptide-specific, HLA class II restricted T cell responses.

T cell receptor

Various approaches have led to the conclusion that the CD4 molecule can also physically associate with the TCR. The first evidence came from the observation that under certain circumstances, CD4-specific antibody can inhibit T cell responses. Other groups have shown that cocapping and comodulation of CD4 and TCR/CD3 at the cell surface can be induced with CD3-specific antibodies. Energy transfer experiments suggest that one TCR molecule associates with more than one CD4 in a single receptor complex. This association results in an enhanced avidity of the TCR complex for recognition of antigen–MHC class II complex and increased T cell

responsiveness. However, the molecular nature of the TCR–CD4 interaction remains poorly understood, although it is presumed to involve the membrane-proximal D3 and D4 parts of CD4.

p56^{lck}

The availability of monoclonal antibodies directed against CD4 and the TCR/CD3 complex provided strong evidence for a role of these molecules in the T cell antigen recognition and effector function. While the TCR itself does not have intrinsic protein tyrosine kinase (PTK) or phosphatase functions, an src-related PTK, Lck, is physically associated with a distinct sequence in the cytoplasmic domain of CD4. A region towards the amino-terminal end of p56^{lck} containing a stretch rich in negatively charged amino acids is believed to form ionic bonds with basic residues found within a conserved consensus sequence in the cytoplasmic domain of CD4. Moreover, p56^{lck} gains kinase activity when aggregated on the cell surface. p56^{lck} is anchored to the cytoplasmic face of the plasma membrane through a myristylated amino-terminal glycine. In lymph node cells, 75–95% of cellular Lck is associated with CD4. Conversely, 30–40% of membrane CD4 is bound to Lck. This kinase is activated by receptor cross-linking, which in turn induces phosphorylation of numerous targets. p56^{lck} serves to phosphorylate TCRζ and possibly CD3 γ,δ,ε chains. By acting on TCRζ, p56^{lck} initiates an activation cascade by enabling the receptor to recruit downstream molecules. Also, it has been proposed that CD4-associated p56^{lck} anchors CD4 and the stimulated TCR/CD3/ζ complex to the same MHC molecule.

HIV-1 proteins

The CD4 molecule also plays an important functional role in the course of human immunodeficiency virus 1 (HIV-1) infection. Recent reports have demonstrated that the CD4 protein is not only the cellular receptor for HIV-1 but also participates actively in postbinding events important for infection and cell fusion. Mutagenesis and monoclonal antibody studies have shown that the region spanning amino acids 40–60 of the D1 domain of CD4 is the part of the molecule directly in contact with the viral gp120 for all isolates examined, with residues Phe43 and Arg59 being particularly important. However, the gp120–CD4 combining site is not universally conserved in its molecular details. A 15–100-fold range in affinities for CD4 have been reported. This reflects a complex situation that can depend on glycosylation, oligomerization of receptors, sequence variations and/or involvement of other cellular components, which ultimately contributes to viral tropism and cytopathicity. It has also been shown that mutants in D3 can abrogate the binding of gp120. Moreover, Healey and colleagues reported that by blocking viral access to Gln425 and Gln428 they could block steps subsequent to the viral binding without affecting binding of the virus. It has been speculated that the hinge region in CD4 may be necessary to bring gp41 close to the target membrane. To test this hypothesis, a panel of point mutations and small deletions spanning the hinge region of CD4 were generated, transferred into a CD4$^-$, HIV-1 susceptible T cell line, and their individual capacity to render this cell line infectable by HIV-1 assessed. Syncytia formation was also examined. This study clearly demonstrated that the hinge region of CD4 is necessary for HIV-1-induced cell fusion but not for infection. This confirmed the data from a number of groups that movement of this region is required for fusion. A region of the D1 domain of human CD4 has also been shown to participate in these events. This stems from the observation that although they share the same affinity for gp120 and susceptibility to HIV-1 infection, unlike their human homolog, the CD4 molecules from chimpanzee and rhesus monkey do not support syncytia formation. Complementary sequence exchange mapped the fusion determinant to Glu87 of the human CD4. At least three other HIV-1 proteins interact with the CD4 present at the cell surface and have been shown to be involved in its downmodulation. In HIV-1 infected cells, newly synthesized CD4 molecules are retained in the endoplasmic reticulum by a phenomenon termed receptor interference. This is the result of the formation of a complex between new CD4 and the viral gp160-env protein in the endoplasmic reticulum. The retained molecules of CD4 are degraded in this compartment by a mechanism induced by another HIV-1 protein, vpu. Another viral protein interacting with CD4 is nef. HIV-1-nef is a 206 amino acid, cytoplasmic protein that is nonessential for viral replication and associates with the plasma membrane through an N-terminal myristic acid. It is responsible for the loss of CD4 from the cell surface by inducing its endocytosis and ultimately resulting in its lysosomal degradation. This phenomenon was shown to occur early in the course of the infection, before gp160-induced receptor interference. It is mediated by a dileucine motif similar to endocytosis and lysosomal degradation signals, contained in the membrane-proximal 20, residues of the CD4 cytoplasmic tail.

have circumvented this problem by making use of coreceptors. In the case of a T cell that expresses a TCR recognizing antigenic peptides in the groove of a class II MHC molecule, this coreceptor function is fulfilled by CD4. If the TCR recognizes a class I MHC molecule, the coreceptor is CD8. By acting synergistically with the TCR, the coreceptors induce signal transduction events at low levels of receptor occupancy. T cells that go through maturation steps in the thymus are bipotential and can differentiate either along the CD4$^+$ (helper) pathway or the CD8$^+$ (cytotoxic) pathway.

Early work addressing the role of the CD4 coreceptor in thymocyte differentiation made use of monoclonal antibodies specifically directed towards CD4. Although most of these experiments were instrumental in describing the coreceptor and/or cosignaling functions of CD4, they are at odds with more contemporary data using mouse lines containing either disrupted genes or transgenes. Indeed, the latter models have generated good evidence that thymocyte commitment is a stochastic event. It follows that no distinct TCR-mediated signals are required in this choice. This is consistent with experiments in which a mutated molecule of CD4 (tailless), incapable of binding p56^{lck}, can rescue T helper development in a CD4$^{-/-}$ mouse line. Therefore, in the context of thymic selection, the role of CD4 in the coreceptor-mediated TCR signaling is one of stabilization of the TCR–MHC interaction. In mice deficient for CD4 coreceptor expression, 90% of peripheral $\alpha\beta$TCR$^+$ T cells are CD8$^+$. These CD4$^{-/-}$ mice have been used to show that the human CD4 molecule can substitute for its murine counterpart. Interestingly, the requirement for CD4 in superantigen-mediated negative selection of specific Vβ seems to be differential and inversely proportional to the avidity of some Vβ for Mls. That is, Mls1^{A+}–CD4$^{-/-}$ animals, thymocytes expressing Vβ6, Vβ8.1 and Vβ9 are deleted as in normal animals, while Vβ7$^+$ thymocytes are not, reflecting the low avidity of Vβ7 for Mls1^A. These cells might require CD4 coreceptor-mediated stabilization of binding or signaling for clonal deletion. T helper activity and most class II-restricted T cell responses are also virtually absent in the periphery of these animals. For example, antibody titers are diminished 100-fold when these animals are immunized with T cell-dependent antigens. Moreover, these animals fail to mount an alloresponse.

Function

It is believed that the encounter between a TCR and its antigen involves a low-affinity interaction. T cells

See also: **CD3; CD8; CD45 (the leukocyte common antigen); Thymic epithelium: potential role in regulatory T cell tolerance; H2 class II; HLA class II; T cell**

receptor, $\alpha\beta$; T cell receptor, $\gamma\delta$; T lymphocyte activation; T lymphocyte differentiation.

Further reading

Aiken C, Konver J, Landau NR, Lenburg ME and Trono D (1994) Nef induces CD4 endocytosis: requirement for a critical dileucine motif in the membrane proximal CD4 cytoplasmic domain. *Cell* 76: 853–864.

Cammarota G, Scheirle A, Takacs B *et al* (1992) Identification of a CD4 binding site on the $\beta2$ domain of HLA-DR molecules. *Nature* 356: 799–801.

Eiden LE and Lifson JD (1992) HIV interaction with CD4: a continuum of conformation and consequences. *Immunology Today* 13: 201–201.

Fleury S, Thibodeau J, Croteau G *et al* (1995) HLA-DR polymorphism affects the interaction with CD4. *Journal of Experimental Medicine* 182: 733–741.

Fleury S, Huang B, Zerbib A, Croteau G, Long EO and Sekaly RP (1996) Mutations in human CD4 impair the functional interaction with different human and mouse class II isotypes and alleles. *Journal of Immunology* 156: 1848–1855.

Janeway CA (1992) The T cell receptor as a multicomponent signalling machine: CD4/CD8 coreceptors and CD45 in T cell activation. *Annual Review of Immunology* 10: 487–512.

Julius M, Maroun CR and Haughn L (1993) Distinct roles for CD4 and CD8 as co-receptors in antigen receptor signaling. *Immunology Today* 14: 177–184.

Konig R, Fleury S and Germain RN (1996) The structural basis of CD4–MHC class II interactions: coreceptor contributions to T cell receptor antigen recognition and oligomerization-dependent signal transduction. *Current Topics in Microbiology and Immunology* 205: 19–46.

Pantaleo G and Fauci AS (1995) New concepts in the immunopathogenesis of HIV infection. *Annual Review of Immunology* 13: 487–512.

Parnes JR (1989) Biology and function of CD4 and CD8. *Advances in Immunology* 44: 265–311.

Rudd CE, Jannsson O, Cai YC, da Silva AJ, Raab M and Prasad KVS (1994) Two-step TCRζ/CD3-CD4 and CD28 signaling in T cells: SH2/SH3 domains, protein-tyrosine and lipid kinase. *Immunology Today* 15: 225–234.

Sawada S, Scarborough JD, Killeen N and Littman DR (1994) A lineage-specific transcriptional silencer regulates CD4 gene expression during T cell development. *Cell* 77: 917–929.

Sweet RW, Truneh A and Hendrickson WA (1991) CD4: its structure, role and immune function in AIDS pathogenesis, and potential pharmacological targets. *Current Opinion in Biotechnology* 2: 622–633.

CD5

PM Lydyard, Department of Immunology, University College, London, UK

C Jamin and **PY Youinou**, Brest University Medical School, France

CD5 was initially detected as an alloantigen called Ly-1 on murine T cells and together with the alloantigen Ly-2,3 (now CD8) they were the first 'markers' to be used to identify functional T cell subpopulations. Ly-1 identified a helper T cell population while Ly-2,3 was present on a cytotoxic-suppressor subset. With more sensitive analysis it was shown that the Ly-2,3$^+$ T cells also expressed low levels of surface Ly-1 in their membranes, thus indicating that the majority, if not all, T cells expressed Ly-1. A few years later, a pan-T cell marker of similar molecular mass was identified on human lymphocytes by a variety of monoclonal antibodies and termed CD5. Subsequent studies showed that this molecule was homologous at the DNA level with Ly-1.

Structure of the molecule

CD5 is a type 1 transmembrane glycoprotein with a molecular mass of 67 kDa. It comprises a single polypeptide of around 470 amino acids as deduced from the nucleotide sequence. The first 25 amino acids form the signal peptide. The external portion of the molecule contains 22 cysteines. The outer of the three external domains shows the greatest homology with the immunoglobulin supergene family of molecules with an intrachain disulfide bridge. All three outer domains show homology with a protein, Pap D, which is a chaperone protein mediating assembly of P pili of *E. coli*. In addition, there is strong homology of the extracellular domain(s) with the scavenger receptor on macrophages. CD5 has a transmembrane sequence of 29 residues and an intracytoplasmic tail of 92 amino acids with four phosphorylation sites – consistent with the function of this molecule being one of signal transduction (see later). Approximately 25% of the CD5 molecule is composed of *N*- and *O*-linked oligosaccharides.

Cellular distribution of CD5

CD5 is expressed on the surface of all T cells bearing the $\alpha\beta$ heterodimer T cell receptor (around

50 000 molecules per cell) but is absent or at lower density on the γδ T cell subset.

It is present but at lower density (2–10 000 molecules per cell) on a minor population of murine and human B cells. More sensitive techniques are therefore required to detect CD5 on B than on T cells. CD5$^+$ B cells, now termed B1 cells, represent a significant proportion of murine thymic and peritoneal B cells. They are the first B cells to colonize lymphoid tissues during early development in humans and are present at very high frequency in the blood of newborns, diminishing through childhood, adulthood and up to old age. Interestingly, all B cells in mature rabbits are CD5 positive.

CD5 has been found on many murine B cell lymphomas, some human B cell lymphomas and on the majority of human chronic lymphocytic leukemia (CLL) cells.

Other cells which have been shown to express CD5 are endothelial cells of blood vessels in the pregnant sheep uterus but the significance of this isolated example of nonlymphoid cell expression of CD5 is at present unknown.

Ligands for CD5

To date, three ligands for CD5 have been identified: 1) CD72 on B cells (mouse and human) is thought to act as a costimulatory molecule during cognate interaction with T cells (see later); 2) immunoglobulin $V_{H\alpha}2$ framework sequences in the rabbit bind to CD5; and 3) a molecule of around 32 kDa on activated murine spleen cells binds to CD5. The significance of the latter two ligands is at present unclear but might be involved in selection processes.

Role of CD5 on T cells

As indicated above, CD5 is found on thymocytes and the majority of peripheral T cells. Increased expression of CD5 by a number of protein kinase C activators has suggested that this molecule is important in the activation process of T cells (and probably B1 cells). CD5 is associated with the TCR ζ chain and the cytoplasmic domain of CD5 is phosphorylated on tyrosines on activation via the TCR. This is thought to bind SH2 domain-containing proteins. Studies on peripheral T cell activation *in vitro* have shown a costimulatory role for CD5 on TCR-mediated proliferative responses. Thus, cross-linking of CD5 on T cells by monoclonal antibodies results in a rise in intracellular Ca^{2+} derived from an extracellular source (via Ca^{2+} channels) and generation of cyclic GMP. Furthermore, solid-phase immobilization of CD5 antibodies alone provides a stimulus for interleukin 2 (IL-2) receptor induction and responsiveness to IL-2. It is thought that, along with other costimulatory interactions of molecules on T and B cells, CD5 on T cells binds to CD72 on B cells which enhances T cell and B cell activation. In contrast, in CD5 knockout mice, unlike peripheral T cells, thymocytes are hyper-responsive to stimulation through the TCR. In addition, selection of T cells expressing transgenic TCRs were abnormal in these mice indicating that CD5 plays a role as a negative regulator of TCR mediated activation during T cell development.

B cells and CD5

Unlike T cells, CD5 is present on only some B cells and there is now strong evidence that this is a marker which identifies a normal B cell subpopulation (B1 cells), the size of which is genetically regulated. This population is different in origin, and can be distinguished from, conventional B cells responsible for most of the antibodies specific for exogenous antigens. In mice, B1 cells are self-renewing.

Both murine and human studies have indicated that B1 cells have minimal mutation of their rearranged immunoglobulin genes. They are responsible for the production of polyreactive and autoreactive antibodies and give rise to the so-called 'natural antibodies' present in normal serum. In this regard, elevated levels of CD5$^+$ B cells have been described in a plethora of autoimmune diseases in man including rheumatoid arthritis, primary Sjögren's syndrome, systemic lupus erythematous, Graves' disease, diabetes and many more. The significance of this is at present unclear. The presence of CD5 on human CLL cells and the polyreactive nature of antibodies programmed by these cells indicates that these malignant B cell tumors, are derived from this particular B cell subpopulation.

It is likely that normal B1 cells can act as 'antigen-presenting cells', using their polyreactive receptors to take in antigens for processing and presentation with surface major histocompatibility complex (MHC) class II molecules.

Identification of CD5 as a lineage marker has recently been challenged in experiments with murine and human cells. Expression of CD5 can be induced on murine splenic B cells (mostly B2 cells) following activation. In humans, B cells activated by phorbol ester treatment express CD5, and IL-4 has been shown to downregulate this molecule on the surface of these cells.

Taking these data together, it is possible that classical B1 cells prominent in early life are antigen-presenting cells and are a separate lineage representing germline encoded antibodies, many of which are activated through recognition of self antigen *in vivo*. Other B cells (B2 cells) appear to be capable of being induced to express CD5. The function of CD5 on these two B cell types may be different. The function of CD5 molecules on B cells has recently been addressed and there is now substantial evidence for its role in regulating B cell activity. CD5 is part of the B cell receptor complex as shown by capping and co-capping studies. Cross-linking of CD5 on B cells by monoclonal antibodies has a profound effect on stimulation of B cells through the antigen-specific immunoglobulin M (IgM) receptor. In mice, stimulation of peritoneal B1 cells with anti-IgM results in apoptosis. This is inhibited in CD5-deficient (CD5 knockout) mice. Cross-linking of CD5 in normal wild-type mice rescues the cells from anti-IgM-induced apoptosis and leads to proliferation of these cells. A similar effect is seen with human tonsillar CD5$^+$ B cells in the presence of IL-2. Direct stimulation of CD5 on human tonsillar B cells alone can also stimulate apoptosis but different biochemical pathways appear to be used compared with induction of apoptosis via anti-IgM. The physiological relevance of these latter observations is currently unknown.

Recent data have suggested that in mice, one of the signal transduction activators of transcription (STAT3) is constitutively activated in B1 cells but not in unmanipulated B2 cells. This may play a role in B cell antigen-specific signaling and its constitutive activation, associated with the intrinsic proliferative nature of this population.

CD5 as a target for therapy

Since CD5 is a pan-T cell marker it is used as a target for depletion of normal T cells in the clinical setting for transplantation and human therapy. It has an advantage over anti-CD3 treatment since it does not result in activation of cytokine production which gives rise to transient 'flu-like' symptoms after injection. Monoclonal antibodies coupled to ricin (immunotoxin) are used in the treatment, *ex vivo*, of allogeneic bone marrow for prevention of graft-versus-host disease following ablation therapy for transplantation. These antibodies have also been used successfully with additional therapy in the treatment of CLL tumors.

See also: **Autoimmune diseases; Autoimmunity; B lymphocyte repertoire; B lymphocytes; IgM; Leuke-**mia; **Natural antibodies; Neonatal immune response; Nude (athymic) mice.**

Further reading

Agostini C and Semenzato G (1996) The CD5/CD72 receptor system is coexpressed with several functionally relevant counterstructures on human B cells and delivers a critical signaling activity. *Journal of Immunology* 157: 1854–1862.

Biancone L, Bowen MA, Lim A, Aruffo A, Andres G and Stamenkovic I (1996) Identification of a novel inducible cell-surface ligand of CD5 on activated lymphocytes. *Journal of Experimental Medicine* 184: 811–819.

Bikah G, Carey J, Ciallella JR, Tarakhovsky A and Bondada S (1996) CD5-mediated negative regulation of antigen receptor-induced growth signals in B-1 B cells. *Science* 274: 1906–1909.

Borrello MA and Phipps RP (1996) The B/macrophage cell: an elusive link between CD5$^+$ B lymphocytes and macrophages. *Immunology Today* 17: 471–475.

Chen X, Matsuura Y and Kearney JF (1995) CD5 transgenic mice. *Current Topics in Microbiology and Immunology* 194: 209–217.

Hardy RR and Kayakawa K (1994) CD5 B cells, a fetal B cell lineage. *Advances in Immunology* 55: 297–339.

Hardy RR, Li YS and Hayakawa K (1996) Distinctive origins and specificities of the CD5$^+$ B-cell subset. *Seminars in Immunology* 8: 37–44.

Hashimoto S, Dono M, Wakai M et al (1995) Somatic diversification and selection of immunoglobulin heavy and light chain variable region genes in IgG$^+$ CD5$^+$ chronic lymphocytic leukemia B cells. *Journal of Experimental Medicine* 181: 1507–1517.

Huang CA, Henry C, Iacomini J, Imanishi-Kari T and Wortis HH (1996) Adult bone marrow contains precursors for CD5$^+$ B cells. *European Journal of Immunology* 26: 2537–2540.

Jamin C, Le Corre R, Lydyard PM and Youinou P (1996) Anti-CD5 extends the proliferative response of human CD5$^+$ B cells activated with anti-IgM and interleukin-2. *European Journal of Immunology* 26: 57–62.

Jamin C, Le Corre R, Pers JO et al (1997) Modulation of CD72 by ligation of B cell receptor complex molecules on CD5$^+$ B cells. *International Immunology* 9: 1001–1009.

Kearney JF (1993) CD5$^+$ B-cell networks. *Current Opinion in Immunology* 5: 223–226.

Lankester AC, van Schijndel GM, Cordell JL, Van Noesel CJ and van Lier RA (1994) CD5 is associated with the human B cell antigen receptor complex. *European Journal of Immunology* 24: 812–816.

Martin PJ, Nelson BJ, Appelbaum FR et al (1996) Evaluation of CD5-specific immunotoxin for treatment of acute graft-versus-host disease after allogeneic marrow transplantation. *Blood* 88: 824–830.

Olsen NJ, Brooks RH, Cush JJ et al (1996) A double-blind, placebo-controlled study of anti-CD5 immunoconjugate in patients with rheumatoid arthritis. The Xoma RA Investigator Group. *Arthritis and Rheumatism* 39: 1102–1108.

Pospisil R, Fitts MG and Mage RG (1996) CD5 is a potential selecting ligand for B cell surface immunoglobulin framework region sequences. *Journal of Experimental Medicine* 184: 1279–1284.

Tarakhovsky A, Kanner SB, Hombach J et al (1995) A role for CD5 in TCR-mediated signal transduction and thymocyte selection. *Science* 269: 535–537.

CD8

Georg F Weber and **Harvey Cantor**, Harvard Medical School and Laboratory of Immunopathology, Dana-Farber Cancer Institute, Boston, MA, USA

Definition of T cell subsets

CD8 represents the first cell surface glycoprotein used to define T cell subsets. Studies into the cellular basis of the immune response had shown that T lymphocytes mediated a wide variety of immunological functions. These cells generated cytotoxic responses to alloantigens, exerted helper and suppressor effects on the production of antibodies by B cells and initiated both delayed-type inflammatory responses and graft-versus-host responses. These findings could be explained by one of two alternative hypotheses. A single mature T lymphocyte, after activation by antigen, could give rise to cells capable of mediating the complete range of T cell responses. Alternatively, each T cell function might be mediated by a subset of T cells programmed during differentiation to express a limited range of immunological functions.

A direct approach to this question made use of alloantibodies that defined cell surface differentiation antigens, called Ly antigens, found on mouse thymocytes and a fraction of peripheral lymphocytes. Since these alloantigens had not yet been detected on the surface of nonlymphoid cells, it was hoped that they might represent components expressed exclusively on the surface of lymphocytes undergoing thymus-dependent differentiation. Lyt-2, since renamed CD8, and Lyt-3 represent cell surface antigens encoded by two closely linked genes. Lyt-2^+3^+ cells accounted for approximately half of peripheral T cells and included those cells required for generation of cytotoxic activity and excluded T cells that mediated helper activity. Additional studies of the major histocompatibility complex (MHC) specificity of $CD8^+$ and $CD8^-$ subclasses of T cells revealed that thymus-dependent differentiation gave rise to at least two separate sublines of mature T cells. The $CD8^-$ subset was programmed to amplify a number of immune responses and was preferentially activated by class II MHC products in association with antigenic peptides. The $CD8^+$ subset was programmed for the development of cytotoxic T lymphocyte (CTL) activity and responded preferentially to class I MHC products in association with antigenic peptides. These studies showed that thymus-dependent differentiation resulted in two lineages of T cells, $CD8^+$ and $CD8^-$, equipped to recognize and respond to products of the MHC that were foreign by virtue of polymorphic variation (alloantigen) or because they had been modified by association with nonself peptides. Selective engagement of either screening system by foreign or altered class I or class II MHC region products activated a series of immune reactions already programmed in one or another activated T cell subset.

Structure of CD8

CD8 exists as a disulfide-linked dimer of either α and β chain or two α chains. The crystal structure of the N-terminal 113 amino acids of human CD8 revealed homology to immunoglobulin (Ig) variable domains with nine β strands divided into two β sheets, one of four and the other of five strands. An Ig-like intersheet disulfide bridge from the B strand to the F strand is present in CD8α. Another disulfide bond may be formed between cysteines in the B strand and the C strand. The hinge region connecting the amino-terminal Ig-like domain to the transmembrane segment consists of 50 residues in the α chain and 30 residues in the β chain, both of which are likely to be glycosylated and sialylated. The level of sialylation on the β chain hinge region varies with the activation state of the T cell and may have functional implications for CD8 (**Figure 1**).

Class I MHC recognition

It has become apparent that the CD8 molecule directly contributes to the development of cytotoxic activity by $CD8^+$ cells. Antibodies to CD8 block the

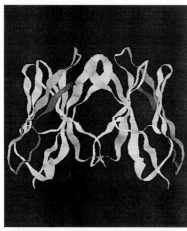

(A)

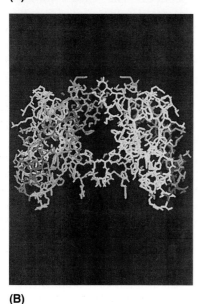

(B)

Figure 1 Three-dimensional molecular model of the N-terminal region of a CD8 homodimer consisting of two α chains; (A) ribbon presentation, (B) stick presentation. The structural data for the N-terminal 113 amino acids are based on crystallography (protein data base: 1CD8). The three-dimensional model for each monomer was generated with RasMol version 2.5 (Roger Sayle, Greenford, Middlesex, UK), and the two monomers were combined as described (Leahy *et al.* (1992) *Cell* **68**: 1145). The color coding represents groups; blue corresponds to the CDR1-like loop, light blue to the CDR2-like loop, and lime to the CDR3-like loop. The monomers are distinguished in brightness of color. (See also color **Plate 10**.)

generation and effector phases of the CTL response specific for class I MHC antigens without regard to function. Functional and cell-binding studies have shown that the ligands for the CD8 receptor are encoded by MHC class I genes. A role for CD8 in the interaction with class I molecules was demonstrated from the ability of CHO cells transfected with the

CD8 gene to form conjugates with class I-positive but not class I-negative cells. Similar to the interaction between CD4 and MHC class II, CD8 binds with weak affinity to MHC class I and contributes to cell adhesion. CDR-like loops (homologous to the complementarity-determining region 2 loop of antibodies) in the N-terminal end of CD8α are the most likely binding site for MHC class I as judged by mutational analyses, crystal structure and orientation in the cell membrane. In addition, an A/B strand surface may interact with a region on the α2 domain of MHC class I. The primary binding site on MHC class I is the α3 loop, a nonpolymorphic region in the membrane proximal domain and distant to the antigen-binding cleft. Furthermore, the structures of CD8 and MHC class I make it possible that one CD8 dimer could simultaneously bind two MHC class I molecules.

Biochemistry and genetics

Lyt-2 and Lyt-3 (murine CD8) are both transmembrane glycoproteins which are encoded by two closely linked genes on murine chromosome 6. Except for a subset of natural killer cells, the expression of murine Lyt-2/3 appears to be restricted to T cells. The molecule is a 70 kDa homo- or heterodimer composed of two covalently linked chains: an α chain (32–38 kDa), which expresses epitopes detected by Lyt-2-specific antibodies, and a β chain (30–34 kDa), which expresses Lyt-3 epitopes. The Lyt-2 chain is the homolog of the CD8 chain in humans, which consists of homodimers and multimers of this chain. Recently, human CD8β genes have been identified that encode a CD8 monomer corresponding to murine Lyt-3.

The Lyt-2 gene contains five exons. The first encodes a signal peptide and an N-terminal region which shows close homology with IgV κ light chain regions, including a cysteine-mediated intrachain disulfide bond. Exons 2–5 encode the spacer region, the transmembrane region and two cytoplasmic regions, C1 and C2, respectively. Although there is only a single Lyt-2 gene segment there are two types of Lyt-2 chains, α and α′, of slightly different size. The 34 kDa α′ chain, found only in mice and expressed preferentially in the thymus, is a truncated form of the α chain resulting from alternative splicing of exons encoding the C-terminal cytoplasmic domain including the p56[lck] binding site.

There is uneven homology between human and murine CD8 molecules. Human CD8 α and β chains are encoded on chromosome 2p12. The most substantial degree of genetic conservation is found in the transmembrane and cytoplasmic domains, while the least is in the external V gene-like domain. Since there is 70% identity of the class I MHC external domain residues between mouse and human, this degree of divergence in the putative binding regions of CD8 is somewhat surprising. On the other hand, conservation of the C-terminal domain may reflect a requirement for this region to interact with intracellular T cell proteins involved in transmembrane signaling. A comparison of rodent CD8 chains with the α and β chains of the T cell receptor (TCR) suggests evolution of these three receptor genes from a common ancestor. Divergence between them may be reflected in the acquisition of intervening sequences between V and J by the TCR genes, resulting eventually in the capacity to rearrange multiple V genes during development. The CD8 gene has lost regions encoding C-region domains but, like TCR, has acquired the capacity to recognize MHC molecules at some point in evolution (**Figure 2**).

T cell activation

Studies have shown that CD8 may function as a coreceptor with the α/β TCR in recognition of adjacent epitopes on the same class I molecule. These findings support the concept that T cell activation involves formation of a ternary complex composed of CD8 and TCR on the T cell and class I MHC molecules on the target cell. Indeed, ligation of CD8 with the TCR complex elicits much more vigorous T cell responses than ligation of either receptor molecule alone, indicating that CD8 plays a decisive role in augmenting TCR-dependent activation, either by increasing the avidity of binding to MHC class I or

by amplification of signal transduction. High-avidity interaction between T cells and antigen-presenting cells is heavily dependent on CD8 expression, which is more important for primary proliferative responses than for CTL activity. While stimulation of T cells by anti-TCR antibodies results in coordinate localization of TCR and CD8, it is not yet clear whether the TCR α/β chain directly contacts the CD8 molecule in the lipid bilayer of a cell membrane. However, the ability of the two cell surface molecules to interact with distinct but adjacent regions of class I MHC products places CD8 and the TCR in close proximity to one another.

A potential molecular basis for the role of CD8 in T cell activation comes from studies showing that CD8 is closely associated with the tyrosine kinase p56^{lck}, an src-related tyrosine kinase expressed mainly in T lymphocytes. p56^{lck} is a cytoplasmic protein that, unlike other growth factor receptors, is found on the inner leaflet of the plasma membrane where it associates with a highly conserved cytoplasmic domain of CD8. Site-directed mutagenesis of CD8 defines a motif of CD8α which may bind to the N-terminal region of p56^{lck}: +-+-x-cys-x-cys-(pro) where x denotes a nonconserved residue and + a basic residue. It is currently thought that engagement of CD8 leads to enhanced activity of the associated p56^{lck} enzyme which phosphorylates the ζ chain of the CD3 complex leading to signal transduction. In mature T cells, CD4 and CD8 may associate with equal amounts of p56^{lck}; however, kinase activity after cross-linking of CD8 is much lower than after cross-linking of CD4. On the other hand, protein kinase C appears to be activated much more strongly after ligation of CD8 than after ligation of CD4. The cytoplasmic segment of CD8α also has two serine residues which are likely to be phosphorylated in signaling. T cells with targeted mutations of the cytoplasmic serine residues are insignificantly impaired in their response to antigen, whereas cells with substitutions in both cytoplasmic cysteine residues display deficient responses. Surprisingly, transgenic mice whose CD8 lacks the p56^{lck} binding site show no impairment of T cell function.

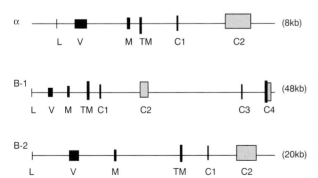

Figure 2 Exon intron organization of the human CD8 genes. The CD8α gene is comprised of six exons which span about 8 kb. There are two genes encoding CD8β, CD8B-1 contains eight exons and is spread over approximately 48 kb, whereas the CD8B-2 gene consists of six exons and has a length of 20 kb. L = leader peptide, V = IgV-like sequence, M = membrane proximal region, TM = transmembrane domain, C = cytoplasmic domains.

T cell selection

The ability to trace T cell clones according to their TCR α/β chain expression has led to the demonstration of MHC-dependent negative and positive selection in the thymus. These studies also provide strong evidence for the involvement of the CD8 molecule in class I-mediated positive selection. Although the precise role of CD8 in this process is not known, there is good evidence that the generation of single-positive CD8 cells from double-positive (CD4$^+$8$^+$) precursors in the thymus is associated with class I MHC recognition. Possibly, coordinate ligation of TCR and CD8 with class I MHC at the CD4$^+$8$^+$ precursor stage induces the cell to shut off CD4 expression. Alternatively, CD4 or CD8 might be eliminated on a random basis at the double-positive stage, allowing the formation of single-positive CD8 cells or CD4 cells. The former CD8$^+$4$^-$ population would be equipped to be selected by class I MHC, while the latter (CD8$^-$4$^+$) cells would display a TCR specific for class II and would die in the thymus. CD8 may also contribute to negative selection, as highly elevated levels of CD8α block thymocyte maturation. Immature CD4$^+$CD8$^+$ thymocytes express CD8 at levels fourfold higher than CD4; nevertheless, activation of p56^{lck} is mostly seen after ligation of CD4 but not CD8, as a minority of surface CD8 molecules are associated with p56^{lck}. It has been shown that negative selection does not require increased CD8-dependent signaling through p56^{lck}. A critical question that remains to be answered involves the role of CD8 in the differentiation of cytotoxic cells. Possibly, a signal mediated by CD8 results in the differentiation of a thymic precursor cell to a prekiller and killer cell. An alternative explanation is that CD8 represents part of the mature cytolytic cell program. In either case, a critical feature of CD8 expression is restriction of cytolytic responses to T cells that recognize class I but not class II MHC products. This feature of the CD8 genetic program may prevent cytolytic cells from reacting to and eliminating class II-bearing B cells and macrophages that display relevant peptide antigens.

Analysis of CD8 by gene-targeting techniques

Models with manipulated CD8 genes have become available. Disruption of the CD8α gene prevents expression of CD8 protein on the cell surface and impedes generation of cells which express receptors specific for MHC class I. Disruption of the CD8β gene, or removal of its cytoplasmic tail, has a less dramatic effect on MHC class I restricted cells. Mutant mice contain 20–30% of the normal number

of CD8 cells and those may have a restricted set of TCRs. These results are similar to the effects of eliminating the CD8 ligand: a deficiency of MHC class I gene products also prevents maturation of CD4$^-$8$^+$ cells. Introduction of a CD8 transgene with a mutated binding site for p56^{lck} into CD8$\alpha^{-/-}$ mice leads to reduction of mature CD8 cells by half but no apparent restrictions of the TCR repertoire. In contrast, introduction of a tailless CD8α transgene into CD8$^{-/-}$ mice leads to a more dramatic reduction in CD8 cell numbers, reduced capacity to mount cytotoxic T lymphocyte responses, and restrictions in the TCR repertoire.

See also: **CD4; Cytotoxic T lymphocytes; H2 class I; HLA class I; T lymphocyte activation; T lymphocyte differentiation; T lymphocytes.**

Further reading

Boyse EA, Miyazawa M, Aoki T and Old LJ (1968) Ly-A and Ly-B: two systems of lymphocyte isoantigens in the mouse. *Proceedings of the Royal Society of London. Series B* 170: 175–193.

Cantor H and Boyse EA (1975) Functional subclasses of T lymphocytes bearing different Ly antigens. I. Generation of functionally distinct T-cell subclasses is a differentiative process independent of antigen. *Journal of Experimental Medicine* 141: 1376–1389.

Connolly JM, Hansen TH, Ingold AL and Potter TA (1990) Recognition by CD8 on cytotoxic T lymphocytes is ablated by several substitutions in the class I alpha3 domain: CD8 and the T cell repertoire recognize the same class I molecule. *Proceedings of the National Academy of Sciences of the USA* 87: 2137–2141.

Fung-Leung W-P, Schillham MW, Rahemtulla A *et al* (1991) CD8 is needed for development of cytotoxic T cells but not helper T cells. *Cell* 63: 443–449.

Littman DR (1987) The structure of the CD4 and CD8 genes. *Annual Review of Immunology* 5: 561–584.

Leahy DJ (1995) A structural view of CD4 and CD8. *FASEB Journal* 9: 17–25.

Turner JM, Brodsky MH, Irving BA, Levin SD, Perlmutter RM and Littman DR (1990) Interaction of the unique N-terminal region of tyrosine kinase p56^{lck} with cytoplasmic domains of CD4 and CD8 is mediated by cysteine motifs. *Cell* 60: 755–765.

Zamoyska R (1994) The CD8 coreceptor revisited: one chain good, two chains better. *Immunity* 1: 243–246.

CD22

Dennis Sgroi and **Ivan Stamenkovic**, Department of Pathology, Harvard Medical School, and Pathology Research, Massachusetts General Hospital, Boston, Massachusetts, USA

CD22 expression and cDNA cloning

CD22 is a B cell lineage, restricted cell surface phosphoglycoprotein of 130–150 kDa which demonstrates a unique developmental pattern of expression closely paralleling that of immunoglobulin D (IgD). Cytoplasmic expression of CD22 can be detected in pro-B and pre-B cells, whereas surface expression is first identified in immature B cells. B cell activation results in a transient increase in surface CD22 expression, which is followed by progressive down-regulation as activated B cells differentiate into plasma cells.

Two cDNA clones encoding human CD22 have been isolated and shown to predict an integral membrane polypeptide and a member of the Ig superfamily. The smaller isoform, CD22α, possesses an extracellular domain composed of five Ig-like subdomains, while the larger isoform, CD22β, is identical to CD22α with the exception of two additional Ig-like extracellular subdomains (subdomains 3 and 4) positioned between subdomains 2 and 3 of the smaller isoform. The predominant isoform of human CD22 expressed in B cells is CD22β and is henceforth called CD22 unless otherwise specified. A murine CD22 cDNA clone has been isolated and displays 62% amino acid identity to the human form, with the closest relatedness being located between the seventh Ig domain and the cytoplasmic tail, and the greatest divergence observed within Ig domains 1 and 2. The extracellular domains of CD22 are highly related to several known adhesion molecules, which include myelin-associated glycoprotein (MAG), Schwann cell myelin protein (SMP), CD33, sialoadhesin, neural cell adhesion molecule (NCAM), and the vascular adhesion molecule VCAM/InCAM110. Interestingly, the first Ig-like domain of CD22, like CD33, MAG, SMP and sialoadhesin, is a V-set domain which contains an unusual intradomain disulfide bond between the predicted B and E β strands rather than the B and F β strands ordinarily found in immunoglobulins.

B cell adhesion molecule CD22 is a sialic acid-binding lectin

COS cells expressing both human CD22 isoforms promote sialic acid-dependent leukocyte rosetting, but transfectants expressing CD22β promote leukocyte rosetting more strongly than COS cells expressing CD22α. The sialic acid binding domain of CD22 has been demonstrated to be situated on the GFCC′C″ β sheet of the V-set Ig domain centered on an arginine residue in the F strand. Furthermore, the second N-linked glycosylation site within the V-set Ig domain of CD22 has been demonstrated to play an important role in the regulation of CD22-mediated adhesion. While the binding domain of CD22 is localized to the first Ig-like domain, the second and third Ig-like domains as well as the second N-linked glycosylation site, play an important role in generating the optimal binding conformation.

Several studies using a soluble recombinant CD22–Ig fusion protein, CD22Rg, have shown that CD22 binds a variety of cell surface and soluble sialoglycoproteins and that the observed adhesion is dependent upon the presence of ligand-associated N-linked oligosaccharides containing α2,6-linked sialic acid. The role of sialic acid in CD22 recognition is further supported by the observation that mild periodate oxidation of B and T cells, which selectively removes the C-7–C-9 exocyclic side-chain of sialic acid, results in the abrogation of CD22-mediated binding. The minimal oligosaccharide motif specifically recognized by CD22 is Neu5Acα2–6Galβ1–4Glc(NAc). The apparent affinity of this interaction is low ($K_d \sim 30$ μM), suggesting that in common with most lectins the functional avidity of CD22 may be attained through multivalent binding. Further detailed analysis of N-linked oligosaccharides isolated from CD22 glycoprotein ligands has demonstrated that high-affinity recognition by CD22 is determined by the number of sialic acid residues associated with a glycoprotein ligand and by appropriate sialic acid presentation by the underlying ligand polypeptide backbone. These observations demonstrate that although CD22 is structurally related to the Ig superfamily of adhesion molecules, it has the functional properties of a sialic acid-binding lectin. The structurally related molecules CD33, MAG, SMP and sialoadhesin have been demonstrated to mediate α2,3-linked sialic acid-dependent adhesion and, together with CD22, constitute a family of mammalian lectins, designated I-type lectins.

Regulation of CD22-mediated adhesion

CD22-expressing COS cells adhere to multiple subsets of leukocytes *in vitro*, yet CD22-bearing B cells do not demonstrate appreciable cell–cell adhesion *in vivo*. This suggests that B cells which constitutively express CD22 might possess regulatory mechanisms to avert undesired CD22-mediated aggregation. Interestingly, CD22 expressed in B cells possesses N-linked oligosaccharides that are sialylated exclusively in an α2,6 linkage. Since α2,6-linked sialic acid provides a natural CD22 ligand, this observation raises the possibility that α2,6-linked sialic acid on CD22 itself might play a role in regulating CD22–ligand interactions. Recent studies have shown that α2,6-specific sialylation of CD22 itself abrogates CD22-mediated adhesion. Additional studies *in vivo* have demonstrated that regulation of CD22-mediated adhesion may also occur at the level of the glycoprotein ligands. More specifically, 9-O-acetylation of the sialic acid side-chain of splenic, thymic and lymph node lymphocytes and macrophages has been demonstrated to negatively regulate CD22-mediated adhesion. Thus, regulation of CD22-mediated adhesion occurs at the level of reciprocal α2,6 sialylation and sialic acid side-chain modification of both receptor and ligand. CD22 is the first known example of an Ig superfamily member whose function is under the control of two specific glycosyltransferases, α2,6 sialyltransferase and O-acetyltransferase.

Role of CD22 in lymphocyte signal transduction

Multiple T and B cell surface glycoproteins have been immunoprecipitated using a soluble recombinant CD22–Ig fusion protein, CD22Rg. Several of these putative T and B cell ligands appear to have an identical molecular mass, and may represent the same polypeptides expressed on both T and B cells. The first of the CD22 T cell ligands to be identified was CD45. Subsequent *in vitro* experiments demonstrated that cross-linking of CD3 and CD22 T cell ligands with anti-CD3 monoclonal antibody (mAb) and CD22Rg on the surface of the T cell line CEM results in the inhibition of calcium flux and tyrosine phosphorylation of phospholipase Cγ1 (PLCγ1) generated by cross-linking CD3 alone. However, the presence of multiple unknown CD22-binding glycoproteins on the surface of T cells, in addition to CD45, precluded the conclusion that the observed modulation of early T cell activation events was due exclusively to CD22–CD45 interactions. Through the use of several Jurkat cell lines, including a CD45-deficient variant which was reconstituted with a recombinant fusion protein composed of the intracellular domain of CD45 and the extracellular and transmembrane domains of major histocompatibility complex (MHC) class I molecule HLA-A2, it was demonstrated that a direct physical interaction between CD22 and CD45 resulted in modulation of early signal transduction events. These experiments suggest that the interaction of CD22 on the surface of B cells with CD45 on adjacent T cells may play a role in regulating an immune response during T cell–B cell interactions.

The pattern of CD22 cell surface expression, coinciding with the acquisition of B cell responsiveness to antigen, suggests that CD22 may also play a role in early B cell activation events. Two early studies supported this notion. First, cross-linking of surface CD22 with anti-CD22 mAbs resulted in augmentation of anti-IgM-induced B cell activation signals. Second, anti-Ig responsiveness was demonstrated to be restricted to B cells which express surface CD22. Subsequent work has further supported the notion that CD22 plays a role in B cell signal transduction. CD22 has been demonstrated to be associated with surface Ig (sIg) and to be rapidly phosphorylated upon cross-linking of sIg. Furthermore, these phosphorylated intracellular tyrosine residues have been demonstrated to be arranged in one or perhaps two intracellular tyrosine-based activation motifs (ITAMs), one of which associates with p72^{syk}, p53/56^{lyn} and phosphatidylinositol 3-kinase during B cell activation. Most recently, intracellular tyrosine phosphorylation of CD22 has been shown to bind and activate protein tyrosine phosphatase 1-C (PTP1-C), which negatively regulates signaling through sIg. This suggests that ligation of sIg induces tyrosine phosphorylation of CD22, which in turn localizes and activates PTP1-C at the intracellular site of the signaling complex and thereby results in an inhibitory feedback effect on the activation of B cells. Additional experiments have shown that engagement and sequestration of CD22 from sIg with anti-CD22 mAb-coated protein A-sepharose lowered the threshold of B cell activation in a phosphotyrosine-dependent manner. Thus, overall these studies suggest that the absence or presence of CD22 in the sIg complex may serve to upregulate or downregulate B cell activation, respectively.

The functional relationship between the extracellular and the intracellular domains of CD22 is relatively unexplored; however, at least one line of evidence suggests that engagement of the extracellular domain of CD22 may, in turn, influence the function of the intracellular domain. Previous studies with the CD22 mAbs HD6 and HD39 have shown that these antibodies could costimulate B cell proliferation with anti-IgM, but they were unable to directly stimulate B cell proliferation. Engagement of CD22 with the anti-CD22 mAb, HB22.23, which blocks the binding of CD22 to its ligands, results in rapid phosphorylation of CD22, increased association with Src and non-Src family kinases, and proliferation of B cells. These results taken together suggest that engagement of different epitopes of the extracellular domain of CD22 has different functional sequelae. It is rather interesting to note that the anti-CD22 mAb which could stimulate B cells directly was also an antibody which blocks the interaction of CD22 with its ligands; this raises the possibility that this particular mAb may recognize the same structural element which is required for CD22-mediated adhesion. If this is in fact the case, then engagement of CD22 by one of its ligands may result in direct modulation of B cell signal transduction events independent of sIg.

See also: **B lymphocyte activation; B lymphocyte differentiation; CD antigens; CD45 (the leukocyte common antigen); Lectins.**

Further reading

Crocker PR, Mucklow S, Bouckson V *et al.* (1994) Sialoadhesion, a macrophage sialic acid binding receptor for haemopoietic cells with 17 immunoglobulin-like domains. *EMBO Journal* **13**: 4490–4503.

Cyster JG and Goodnow CC (1997) Tuning antigen receptor signaling by CD22: integrating cues from antigens and the microenvironment. *Immunity* **6**: 509–517.

Doody GM, Dempsey PW and Fearon DT (1996) Activation of B lymphocytes: integrating signals from CD19, CD22 and Fcγ RIIb1. *Current Opinion of Immunology* **8**: 378–382.

Doody GM, Justement LB, Delibrias CC *et al.* (1995) A role in B cell activation for CD22 and the protein tyrosine phosphatase SHP. *Science* **269**: 242–244.

Dorken B, Moldenhauer G, Pezzutto A *et al.* (1986) HD39 (B3), a B lineage-restricted antigen whose cell surface expression is limited to resting and activated human B lymphocytes. *Journal of Immunology* **136**: 4470–4479.

Law CL, Craxton A, Otipoby KL *et al.* (1996) Regulation of signalling through B-lymphocyte antigen receptors by cell-cell interaction molecules. *Immunological Reviews* **153**: 123–154.

Law CL, Sidorenko SP, Chandran KA *et al.* (1996) CD22 associates with protein tyrosine phosphatase 1C, Syk, and phospholipase C-γ1 upon B cell activation. *Journal of Experimental Medicine* **183**: 547–560.

Nitschke L, Carsetti R, Ocker B *et al.* (1997) CD22 is a negative regulator of B-cell receptor signalling. *Current Biology* **7**: 133–143.

Otipoby KL, Andersson KB, Draves KE *et al.* (1996) CD22 regulates thymus-independent responses and the lifespan of B cells. *Nature* **384**: 634–637.

O'Keefe TL, Williams GT, Davies SL *et al.* (1996) Hyperresponsive B cells in CD22-deficient mice. *Science* **274**: 798–801.

Powell LD and Varki A (1995) I-type lectins. *Journal of Biological Chemistry* **270**: 14243–14246.

Powell LD, Jain RK, Matta KL, Sabesan S and Varki A (1995) Characterization of sialyloligosaccharide binding by recombinant and native cell-associated CD22. *Journal of Biological Chemistry* **270**: 7523–7532.

Sgroi D, Koretzky GA and Stamenkovic I (1995) Regulation of CD45 engagement by the B cell receptor CD22. *Proceedings of the National Academy of Sciences of the USA* **92**: 4026–4030.

Sgroi D, Nocks A and Stamenkovic I (1996) A single N-linked glycosylation site is implicated in the regulation of ligand recognition by the I-type lectins CD22 and CD33. *Journal of Biological Chemistry* **271**: 18803–18809.

Sjoberg ER, Powell LD, Klein A *et al.* (1994) Natural ligands of the B cell adhesion molecule CD22β can be masked by 9-O-acetylation of sialic acids. *Journal of Cell Biology* **126**: 549–562.

Stamenkovic I and Seed B (1990) The B cell antigen CD22 mediates monocyte and erythrocyte adhesion. *Nature* **344**: 74–77.

Tedder TF, Tuscano J, Sato S *et al.* (1997) CD22, a B lymphocyte-specific adhesion molecule that regulates antigen receptor signaling. *Annual Review of Immunology* **15**: 481–504.

Torres RM, Law CL, Santos-Argumedo L *et al.* (1992) Identification and characterization of the mouse homologue of CD22, a B lymphocyte restricted adhesion molecule. *Journal of Immunology* **149**: 2641–2649.

Tuscano JM, Engel P, Tedder TF, Agarwal A and Kehrl JH (1996) Involvement of p72syk kinase, p53/56lyn kinase and phosphotidyl inositol-3 kinase in signal transduction via the human B lymphocyte antigen CD22. *European Journal of Immunology* **26**, 1246–1252.

van der Merwe VM, Crocker PR, Vinson M, Barclay AN, Schauer R and Kelm S (1996) Localization of the putative sialic-acid binding site on the immunoglobulin superfamily cell-surface molecule CD22. *Journal of Biological Chemistry* **271**: 9273–9280.

CD28

Jeffrey A Ledbetter and **Peter S Linsley**, Bristol-Myers Squibb Pharmaceutical Research Institute, Seattle, Washington, USA

CD28 is a receptor on T cells that is activated by engagement with ligands CD80 (B7-1) and CD86 (B7-2) that are expressed on the surface of activated antigen-presenting cells (APCs). CD28 delivers signals to the T cell that increase expression of the high-affinity interleukin 2 (IL-2) receptor (CD25) and enhance the synthesis of multiple cytokines, including IL-2. Thus CD28 regulates T cell responsiveness to antigen during T cell contact with APCs. CD28 is referred to as a costimulatory receptor because the signals it provides are synergistic with signals provided by the T cell antigen receptor (TCR/CD3) in driving T cell activation and proliferation. In the absence of a signal from TCR/CD3, signals from CD28 can stimulate only minimal proliferation of T cells, and may result in T cell unresponsiveness. Although CD28 and TCR/CD3 work together, CD28 signals are at least partly independent of TCR/CD3, as, unlike TCR/CD3, CD28 signals are resistant to inhibition by cyclosporine.

CD28 Structure and expression

CD28 was first detected and characterized with a monoclonal antibody (mAb) (9.3) made by Paul Martin and John Hansen at the Fred Hutchinson Cancer Research Center in 1981. Studies with this mAb showed that CD28 is a differentiation antigen expressed on thymocytes and most mature T cells, including all CD4 T cells and CD8 T cells with cytolytic activity. A subpopulation of CD8 T cells with suppressor activity are CD28 negative. The CD28 molecule was shown to be a homodimeric glycoprotein composed of a disulfide-bonded 44 kDa subunit. The cloning and expression of a CD28 cDNA by Aruffo and Seed showed that each CD28 monomer contains 134 extracellular amino acids with a single transmembrane domain and a short cytoplasmic tail. The extracellular domain of CD28 shows homology with immunoglobulin variable region domains. The CD28 gene contains four exons, with each exon defining a functional domain of the protein. CD28 shares amino acid sequence homology with CTLA-4, a receptor expressed by activated T cells. CD28 and CTLA-4 genes are closely linked on human chromosome 2, bands q33–q34 (**Figure 1**).

CD28 Receptor function

The potent costimulatory activity of anti-CD28 mAbs was first recognized by Gmunder and Lesslauer and was later confirmed and studied by many others. Identification of CD80 and CD86 molecules as CD28 ligands has allowed a comparison of CD28 signaling through anti-CD28 mAbs versus the natural ligands. These studies show that CD28 clustering on the cell surface during cell–cell adhesion results in optimal stimulation, whereas soluble CD80-Ig or CD86-Ig fusion proteins are not effective. CD28 mAbs have activity in solution when they are bivalent or multivalent, but are less effective than CD80- or CD86-positive cells in activating the CD28 receptor. Optimal stimulation of the CD28 receptor therefore requires a high degree of receptor cross-linking or oligomerization.

CD28 signals depend on the activation of intracellular protein tyrosine kinases, including *lck* and *itk*, resulting in direct phosphorylation of CD28 on tyrosine residues. After activation, CD28 associates with phosphatidylinositol 3-kinase (PI3K) by an SH_2 interaction with phosphorylated Tyr170. However, the association with PI3K is not essential for CD28 costimulatory function, and Tyr188 plays a more important role. However, it is not yet clear how the CD28 cytoplasmic tail delivers costimulatory signals.

CD28-deficient mice have been generated and found to have an impaired immune system, with reduced responses to T cell mitogens and reduced ability to mount antibody responses to T-dependent antigens. In contrast, CTLA-4 deficient mice die at an early age of lymphoproliferative disease, demonstrating that CTLA-4 delivers inhibitory signals for T cell activation. CTLA-4 has been reported to associate with a tyrosine phosphatase, SYP, that is thought to inhibit the activation of tyrosine kinases or tyrosine kinase substrates during CD28 cross-linking.

CTLA4-Ig

Soluble CD28-Ig and CTLA-4-Ig fusion proteins have been expressed and found to bind their shared ligands with different affinities. CTLA-4-Ig binds more than 100-fold better than CD28-Ig to both CD80 and CD86, and CTLA-4-Ig inhibits the ability of CD80 or CD86 to stimulate CD28 responses.

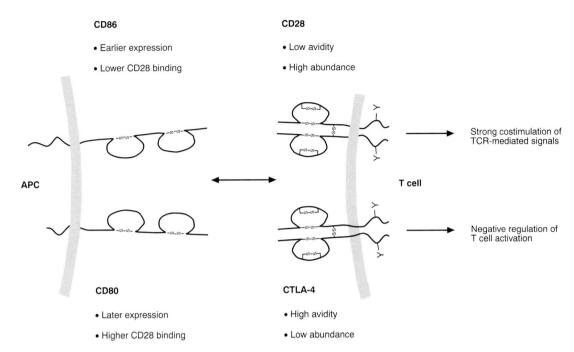

Figure 1 The CD28 receptor system. CD28 and CTLA-4 are stimulated by CD80 and CD86 ligands on activated APCs. Signals from CD28 are required for T cell activation and cytokine secretion, while signals from CTLA-4 inhibit T cell activation.

CTLA-4-Ig has been tested in numerous animal models of autoimmune disease and transplantation, and is currently in a phase I clinical trial in patients with refractory psoriasis, CTLA-4-Ig offers significant promise as a selective, nontoxic molecule for improved immunosuppressive therapy.

See also: **CD antigens; B7 (CD80 & CD86); Cyclosporine; Cytokine genes, regulation of; Immunotherapy of tumors; Interleukin 2; Second signals for lymphocyte activation; T lymphocyte activation; T lymphocytes; Tolerance, peripheral; Tumors, immune response to.**

Further reading

Green JM, Noel PJ, Sperling AI *et al* (1994) Absence of B7-dependent responses in CD28 deficient mice. *Immunity* **1**: 501–508.

June CH, Bluestone JA, Nadler LM and Thompson CB (1994) The B7 and CD28 receptor families. *Immunology Today* **15**: 321–332.

Krummel MF and Allison JP (1995) CD28 and CTLA-4 have opposing effects on the response of T cells to stimulation. *Journal of Experimental Medicine* **182**, 459–465.

Lenschow DJ, Walunas TL and Bluestone JA (1996) CD28/B7 system of T cell costimulation. *Annual Review of Immunology* **14**: 233–258.

Linsley PS and Ledbetter JA (1993) The role of the CD28 receptor during T cell responses to antigen. *Annual Review of Immunology* **11**: 191–211.

Linsley PS, Brady W, Urnes M, Grosmaire LS, Damle NK and Ledbetter JA (1991) CTLA-4 is a second receptor for the B cell activation antigen B7. *Journal of Experimental Medicine* **174**: 561–569.

Lucas PJ, Negishi I, Nakayama K, Fields LE and Loh DH (1995) Naive CD28-deficient T cells can initiate but not sustain an *in vitro* antigen-specific immune response. *Journal of Immunology* **154**: 5757–5768.

Marengere LEM, Waterhouse P, Duncan GS, Mittrucker H-W, Feng G-S and Mak TW (1996) Regulation of T cell receptor signaling by tyrosine phosphatase SYP association with CTLA-4. *Science* **272**: 1170–1173.

Shahinian A, Pfeffer K, Lee KP *et al.* (1993) Differential T cell costimulatory requirements in CD28-deficient mice. *Science* **261**: 609–612.

Sperling AI and Bluestone JA (1996) The complexities of T-cell co-stimulation: CD28 and beyond. *Immunological Reviews* **153**: 155–182.

Truitt KE, Nagel T, Suen LF and Imboden JB (1996) Structural requirements for CD28-mediated costimulation of IL-2 production in Jurkat T cells. *Journal of Immunology* **156**; 4539–4541.

Walunus TL, Lenschow DJ, Bakker CY *et al* (1994) CTLA-4 can function as a negative regulator of T cell activation. *Immunity* **1**: 405–413.

Waterhouse P, Penninger JM, Timms E *et al* (1995) Lymphoproliferative disorders with early lethality in mice deficient in CTLA-4. *Science* **270**: 985–988.

CD40 AND ITS LIGAND

Jacques Banchereau, Baylor Institute of Immunology Research, Dallas, Texas, USA

Francine Brière, Schering-Plough, Laboratory for Immunological Research, Dardilly, France

The CD40 antigen was identified in the mid-1980s from monoclonal antibodies that react with carcinomas and B cells and show costimulatory effects for B lymphocyte proliferation. In the early 1990s, the CD40 ligand (CD40-L) was identified on activated T cells and its genetic alteration was found to lead to the X-linked immunodeficiency referred to as the hyper IgM syndrome.

Structure and expression of CD40 and its ligand

The CD40 antigen, a 45–50 kDa glycoprotein of 277 amino acids, is a member of the tumor necrosis factor receptor family. The 193 amino acid extracellular domain is composed of four imperfect repeats of approximately 40 residues, anchored by a superimposable pattern of six cysteines. This organization is found in the other members of the superfamily including: the p75 low-affinity nerve growth factor receptor; the p55/CD120a and p75/CD120b receptors for tumor necrosis factor; the receptor (TNF-R rp) for the lymphotoxin α/lymphotoxin β membrane complex; CD27 and CD30; OX40; 4-1-BB/ILA; Fas/CD95; and two viral homologs of the TNF receptors. The X-ray crystal structure of the complex formed by soluble binding domains of p55 TNF-R and a lymphotoxin α trimer suggests that CD40 looks like a slightly bent rod. Three CD40 subunits are likely to engage the CD40-L trimer and scrupulously avoid contact between each other. The mouse CD40 gene, composed of nine exons that span 16.3 kb of genomic DNA, is located on the distal region of chromosome 2, which is syntenic to human chromosome 20q11–q13, where the human CD40 gene is located. CD40 is expressed by multiple cell types. In the hematopoietic system, it is expressed on $CD34^+$ hematopoietic progenitors, B cell progenitors, mature B lymphocytes, plasma cells, monocytes, dendritic cells and on some T lymphocytes. CD40 is also expressed on nonhematopoietic cells such as endothelial cells, fibroblasts and epithelial cells. In 1992, expression cloning using a CD40-Fc fusion protein allowed the isolation of a CD40-L from activated T cells. The human CD40-L is a polypeptide of 261 amino acids, including a 215 amino acid extracellular domain with five cysteines. CD40-L is a member of the tumor necrosis factor (TNF) family that includes TNFα, LTα, LTβ, CD27-L/CD70, CD30-L, 4-1BB-L, OX40-L, Fas-L and TRAIL. The gene for CD40-L is located on the X-chromosome position q26.3–q23.1. It spans over 12–13 kb and consists of five exons. CD40-L is readily expressed on $CD4^+$ and $CD8^+$ T cells after activation through pathways that are inhibited by cyclosporine. Basophils, eosinophils and activated B lymphocytes have also been reported as expressing CD40-L.

CD40 signal transduction

While the TNF-R family members display structural homologies in their extracellular ligand-binding domains, no obvious homologies can be detected in their intracellular domains. In particular, CD40 has no kinase domain and no known consensus sequence for binding to kinases. Yet, CD40 ligation activates protein-tyrosine kinases, including *lyn* and *syk* and induces the tyrosine phosphorylation of multiple substrates including phosphatidylinositol 3-kinase and phospholipase Cγ2. The phosphorylation of the latter is consistent with the anti-CD40 induced IP_3 production. The inhibitory effects of protein-tyrosine kinase inhibitors and of CD45 cross-linking demonstrate the functional relevance of the CD40-induced tyrosine phosphorylation. CD40 ligation also appears to activate the serine-threonine protein kinases and, most particularly, the stress-activated protein kinases (SAPK, also known as JNK for c-jun NH_2-terminal kinase). Finally, these different activation pathways result in the activation of various transcription factors including NF-kB, NF-kB-like molecules (such as p50, p65 (rel A), c-Rel), c-jun and NF-AT.

Through their intracytoplasmic domains, the members of the TNF-R family bind to a family of intracellular molecules, the TRAF proteins for (TNF-R)-associated factors. $CRAF_1/TRAF_3$, a 62 kDa intracellular protein, binds to the cytoplasmic domain of CD40 and to the EBV (Epstein–Barr virus)-transforming gene product LMP-1 (latent infection membrane protein 1) but not to TNF-RI, TNF-RII or Fas. $CRAF_1/TRAF_3$ appears to be essential for CD40 signaling inasmuch as a mutant CD40 with a point mutation Thr-234 to Ala does not bind $CRAF_1/TRAF_3$ and is functionally inactive. In addition to recruiting $TRAF_3$, CD40 utilized $TRAF_2$, a 56 kDa intracellular protein that is also used by the 75 kDa TNF-R.

Functions of CD40 *in vitro* (Figure 1)

B lymphocytes

CD40 ligation activates resting B cells as shown by increase in size and expression of new surface molecules involved in homotypic and heterotypic aggregation (CD23, VLA-4), T cell costimulation (CD80/CD86) as well as cell death (Fas). Importantly, dual triggering of resting B lymphocytes through their CD40 and antigen receptor induces a phenotype characteristic of cells from germinal centers, the anatomical site where B cells become memory cells. Furthermore, CD40-activated B cells secrete a panel of cytokines which may act as autocrine and paracrine growth and differentiation factors. CD40-activated B cells also enter into proliferation which is further stimulated by addition of cytokines such as interleukin 4 (IL-4), IL-13 or IL-10 and their combination. Cytokines can also induce CD40-activated B cells to secrete immunoglobulins, with IL-10 inducing the secretion of large quantities of immunoglobulins (Igs) as a consequence of induced plasma cell differentiation. In addition to being a differentiation factor, IL-10 acts as a factor inducing switch towards IgG1 and IgG3, as well as IgA when combined with transforming growth factor β (TGFβ) IL-4/IL-13 induce CD40-activated B cells to switch towards IgG4 and IgE. Prolonged triggering of CD40 skews the maturation of B cells into memory cells, while interruption of CD40 signaling allows plasma cell differentiation.

While progenitor B lymphocytes proliferate in response to CD40 engagement, plasma cells appear unresponsive. Regarding B cell malignancies, chronic lymphocytic leukemias, acute lymphoblastic leukemias, B cell lymphomas, hairy cell leukemias and multiple myelomas proliferate in response to CD40 engagement. In contrast, CD40 ligation appears to inhibit the proliferation of diffuse B cell lymphomas, thus illustrating a possible negative role of CD40 on cell proliferation.

Monocytes and dendritic cells

The low spontaneous expression of CD40 on monocytes can be upregulated by cytokines such as granulocyte-macrophage colony-stimulating factor (GM-CSF), IL-3 and interferon γ (IFNγ). In contrast,

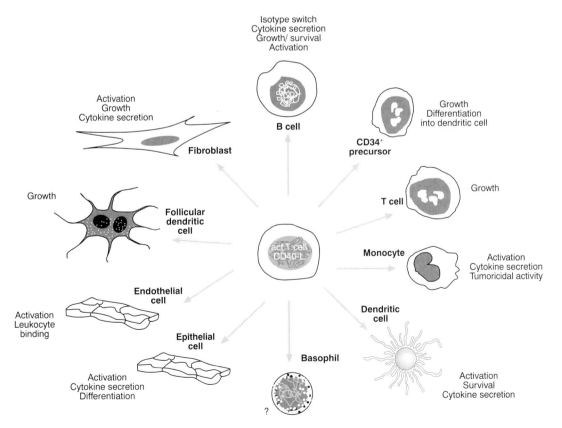

Figure 1 Functional consequences of CD40 triggering on different cell types. Activation includes increase in cell size and alteration of phenotype. (Reproduced with permission from van Kooten C and Banchereau J (1996) CD40 and its ligand. *Advances in Immunology* 61: 1–77.)

CD40 is expressed at high levels on dendritic cells isolated from different tissues or generated *in vitro* by culturing hematopoietic progenitors. CD40 ligation of monocytes and dendritic cells results in the secretion of multiple cytokines, including IL-1, IL-6, IL-8, IL-10, IL-12, TNFα and MiP1α. Importantly, the secretion of IL-12 allows a skewing of T cell maturation towards the T_H1 pathway. CD40 ligation considerably alters the phenotype of these antigen-presenting cells (APCs) by upregulating the expression of costimulatory molecules such as CD54 (ICAM-1), CD58(LFA-3), CD80(B7-1), CD86(B7-2). Interrupting CD40/CD40-L interactions during T cell/dendritic cell cocultures results in reduced T cell proliferation. This observation is likely to be the consequence of both altered CD40 signaling to the APCs (reduced expression of costimulatory membrane molecules and cytokines) and altered CD40-L signaling to the T cells. Indeed, it was clearly demonstrated that CD40-L-dependent activation of T cells occurs through signaling of CD40 in the antigen-presenting cell to enhance requisite costimulatory pathways including B7. CD40 ligation turns on monocyte tumoricidal activity as well as nitric oxide synthesis. In response to CD40 ligation, $CD34^+$ hematopoietic progenitors proliferate and differentiate into cells with prominent dendritic cell attributes. Such dendritic cells are not only capable of inducing primary T cell activation but also interact with activated B cells enhancing their proliferation and differentiation.

Endothelial cells, epithelial cells and fibroblasts

Immunohistology performed on various tissue sections shows that CD40-L-specific antibodies stain vascular endothelium, epidermal basal membrane, scattered fibroblasts, thymic epithelium and follicular dendritic cells. Consistently, primary lines of endothelial cells, thymic and kidney tubular epithelial cells, keratinocytes, skin and synovial fibroblasts as well as follicular dendritic cells express CD40 at relatively low density. Yet, these adherent cells express a functional CD40 whose ligation induces phenotypic alterations, cytokine secretion as well as stimulation or inhibition of proliferation. In particular, endothelial cells display marked upregulation of CD54(ICAM-1), CD106(VCAM-1) and CD62E(E-selectin), thus resulting in increased ability to bind leukocytes. Interestingly, while fibroblasts and follicular dendritic cell lines are induced to proliferate following CD40 ligation, keratinocyte lines cease proliferating to terminally differentiate.

In vivo functions of CD40(CD40-L) interactions

Hyper IgM syndrome in humans

The first demonstration of the critical role of CD40(CD40-L) interactions *in vivo* came from the discovery that the hyper IgM syndrome, an X-linked immunodeficiency, is due to a genetic alteration of the CD40-L. This disease is characterized by a severe impairment of T cell dependent antibody responses with no B cell memory, no circulating IgG, IgA and IgE and no somatic hypermutation, as a consequence of the lack of germinal centers within secondary lymphoid organs. Enhanced susceptibility of patients to opportunistic infections, such as *Pneumocystis carinii* pneumonia and *Cryptosporidium* diarrhea, also indicates a role for CD40–CD40-L interactions in cell-mediated immune responses. Interruption of CD40 (CD40-L) interactions *in vivo* in mice impairs B cell memory as well as T cell priming. Initial experiments performed with antagonists to CD40(CD40-L) interactions, such as antibodies to CD40-L or CD40-Fc fusion proteins, demonstrated impairment of B cell memory. The generation of CD40 and CD40-L knockout (KO) mice confirmed and further extended these observations and revealed a phenotype comparable to that of the patients suffering from the hyper IgM syndrome. In particular, these mice display decreased IgM responses to thymus-dependent antigens, no antigen-specific IgG1, IgA and IgE and no germinal centers but normal T and B lymphocyte numbers. As expected, these mice respond normally to thymus-independent antigens with increased IgM and IgG3 levels. CD40-L KO mice display a considerable impairment of antigen-specific T cell priming and appear particularly susceptible to *Leishmania* infection. This is the result of a defective T_H1 response which is related to an impaired production of IL-12 by antigen-presenting cells. As observed in patients, CD40 KO mice show decreased reactive granulopoiesis in response to infections. Studies with a CD40-Fc fusion protein have highlighted the important role of T cell signaling through CD40 ligand in the development of helper function. In particular, administration of soluble CD40 *in vivo* to CD40 KO mice initiates germinal center formation, and T cells primed in the absence of CD40 are unable to help normal B cells to class switch and to form germinal centers. In this context, ligating CD40 ligand of human activated T cells considerably enhances their production of IL-4.

Interruption of CD40–CD40-L interactions as a treatment of autoimmunity

Administration of antibodies to CD40-L has been

shown to prevent the establishment of autoimmune symptoms in various murine models including: 1) collagen type II-induced arthritis, a model for human rheumatoid arthritis; 2) lupus nephritis in lupus-prone mice that represent models of systemic lupus erythematosus; 3) proteolipoprotein-induced experimental encephalomyelitis, a model of human multiple sclerosis. Importantly, in this last case, the antibody could induce a substantial reduction of the disease even when administered after onset. Consistently, activated helper T cells expressing CD40-L surface protein are detected in multiple sclerosis patient brain sections where CD40-bearing APCs can be found.

Interruption of CD40–CD40-L interactions as a way of inducing transplantation tolerance

Administration of CD40-L-specific antibodies prevents the development of graft-versus-host disease (GVHD) that occurs as a major complication of allogeneic bone marrow transplantation. This treatment affects both the acute GVHD, essentially mediated by cytotoxic T cells, and the chronic GVHD, mainly due to the polyclonal B cell activation and the production of self reactive antibodies. Antibodies against CD40-L markedly prolong the survival of cardiac allografts in both naive and sensitized hosts when administered at the time of transplantation. Finally, a combination of allogeneic B cells and CD40-L-specific antibody considerably decreases host reactivity of both CD4$^+$ and CD8$^+$ T lymphocytes, thereby allowing efficient transplantation of allogeneic pancreatic β islet cells. The addition of CD40-L-specific antibody appears to considerably enhance the tolerogenic effect of B cells.

Thus, multiple pathologic states appear to be improved by interruption of CD40–CD40-L interactions. While this is presently accomplished by preventing the association of the receptor with its ligand, using antibodies or soluble receptor, small synthetic chemical agents preventing this interaction may eventually be identified. However, it is likely that pharmacologic agents may be found that will block the intracellular pathways turned on after ligation of either CD40 or CD40-L.

See also: **B lymphocyte activation; Dendritic cells; Germinal center; Hyper-IgM syndrome; TNF receptors.**

Further reading

Baker SJ and Reddy EP (1996) Transducers of life and death: TNF receptor superfamily and associated proteins. *Oncogene* **12**: 1–9.

Banchereau J, Bazan F, Blanchard D *et al* (1994) The CD40 antigen and its Ligand. *Annual Review of Immunology* **12**: 881–922.

Dubois B, Vanbervliet B, Fayette J, Massacrier C, van Kooten C, Brière F *et al* (1997) Dendritic cells enhance growth and differentiation of CD40-activated B lymphocytes. *Journal of Experimental Medicine* **185**: 941–951.

Foy TM, Aruffo A, Bajorath J, Buhlmann JE and Noelle RJ (1996) Immune regulation by CD40 and its ligand gp39. *Annual Review of Immunology* **14**: 591–617.

Grewal IS, Foellmer HG, Grewal KD, Xu J, Hardardottir F, Baron JL *et al* (1996) Requirement for CD40 ligand in costimulation induction, T-cell activation and experimental allergic encephalomyelitis. *Science* **273**: 1864–1867.

Gruss HJ and Dower SK (1995) Tumor necrosis factor ligand superfamily: involvement in the pathology of malignant lymphomas. *Blood* **85**: 3378–3404.

Hollenbaugh D, Ochs HD, Noelle RJ, Ledbetter JA and Aruffo A (1994) The role of CD40 and its ligand in the regulation of the immune response. *Immunological Reviews* **138**: 23–37.

Kroczek RA, Graf D, Brugnoni D *et al* (1994) Defective expression of CD40 ligand on T cells causes 'X-linked immunodeficiency with hyper-IgM (HIGM1)'. *Immunological Reviews* **138**: 39–59.

van Kooten C and Bancherau J (1996) CD40–CD40 ligand, a multifunctional receptor–ligand pair. *Advances in Immunology* **61**: 1–77.

van Kooten C and Bancherau J (1997) Functions of CD40 on B cells, dendritic cells and other cells. *Current Opinion in Immunology* **9**: 330–337.

Yang Y and Wilson JM (1996) CD40 ligand-dependent T-cell activation: requirement of B7-CD28 signaling through CD40. *Science* **273**: 1862–1864.

CD44

David Naor, The Lautenberg Center for General and Tumor Immunology, The Hebrew University–Hadassah Medical School, Jerusalem, Israel

CD44 is a ubiquitous multistructural and multifunctional cell surface glycoprotein involved in adhesive cell–cell and cell–matrix interactions, as well as in cell migration and cell homing. Its principal ligand is hyaluronic acid (HA, hyaluronate, hyaluronan). The glycoprotein was accorded various functional names which merged to an established single name only after molecular sequencing. The CD44 cluster assigned by the Third International Workshop on Leukocyte Typing includes the following earlier synonyms: GP90[Hermes], extracellular matrix receptor III (ECMRIII), homing cell adhesion molecule (HCAM), phagocytic glycoprotein 1 (Pgp-1), glycoprotein 85 (gp85), Ly-24, hyaluronate receptor, HUTCH-1 and ln (Lu)-related-p80 glycoprotein.

Structure

CD44 is encoded by a single gene located on human chromosome 11 and mouse chromosome 2. The genomic organization of the CD44 gene involves 20 exons in both mouse and humans (**Figure 1b**). The first five exons coding for the extracellular domain are constant, whereas the next ten exons are subjected to differential alternative splicing, resulting in the generation of the variable region. Note that exon 6 (or V1) is not expressed in humans. Constant exons 16 and 17, together with part of exon 15, encode the membrane-proximal region; constant exon 18 encodes the transmembrane domain. Differential utilization of exons 19 and 20 generates the short version (3 amino acids) and the long version (70 amino acids) of the cytoplasmic tail, respectively.

Standard CD44 (CD44s), which lacks the entire variable region (**Figure 1c**), is preferentially expressed on hematopoietic cells, and is therefore also designated CD44H. Northern blot analysis of RNA isolated from CD44 of different hematopoietic cells revealed three major transcripts in humans (~1.6, 2.2 and 4.8 kb) and mice (~1.6, 3.3 and 4.6 kb). Human CD44s mRNA is translated into 361 (mouse 363) amino acids. The predicted size of the core protein is 37–38 kDa. Post-translational modification doubles the molecular size of human and mouse primary protein, bringing it to 80–95 kDa. The mature CD44s is a single-chain molecule composed of a distal extracellular domain, a membrane-proximal region (together containing 248 amino acids in humans and 250 amino acids in the mouse),

a transmembrane-spanning domain (23 amino acids), and a short (3 amino acids) or longer (70 amino acids), and much more abundant, cytoplasmic tail. The N-terminal domain contains six cysteine residues, which are possibly used to form one or more globular domains. This region, which includes the ligand (HA) binding sites of the molecule, displays ~30% homology with cartilage link protein and proteoglycan core protein, which also both bind HA. The N-terminus, transmembrane domain and cytoplasmic tail, but not the membrane-proximal region, exhibit high (~80–90%) interspecies homology. The cytoplasmic tail contains several optional phosphorylation sites (**Figure 1a**).

Differential utilization of the variable region exons yields at least 20 different CD44 isoforms; those expressing alternatively spliced exons are designated CD44v (v stands for variant) (**Figure 1c**). The CD44s and CD44v repertoire is further enriched by N- and O-glycosylation and glycosaminoglycanation (by heparan sulfate and chondroitin sulfate). The multistructural nature of CD44 (its molecular weight ranging from 85 to 230 kDa) may extend the ligand inventory of this molecule and further increase its optional functions.

Distribution

Standard CD44 (**Figure 1**) is a ubiquitous molecule expressed on many types of cells of lymphohematopoietic origin, including erythrocytes, T and B lymphocytes, natural killer cells, macrophages, Kupffer cells, dendritic cells and granulocytes. However, CD44s is also expressed on other cells, such as fibroblasts and cells of the central nervous system. After immunologic activation, T lymphocytes and other leukocytes transiently upregulate CD44v, particularly those containing V6 exon products. A CD44 variant, expressing exons V8 to V10 (CD44V8–10, also known as epithelial CD44 or CD44E), is preferentially expressed on epithelial cells. The longest CD44 isoform, CD44V3–10, was detected in keratinocytes (**Figure 1c**).

Function

Hyaluronic acid, the principal extracellular matrix (ECM) ligand of CD44, is a ubiquitous polysaccharide (glycosaminoglycan) with a high molecular mass

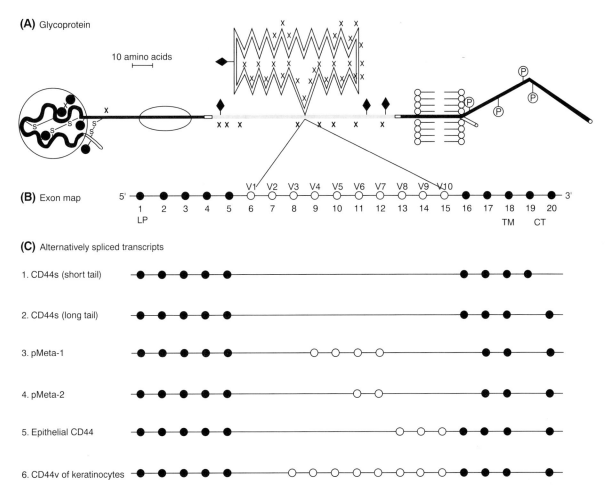

Figure 1 The CD44 glycoprotein, its exon map and examples of six alternatively spliced transcripts. (A) *Protein structure*. Using disulfide bonds, the amino terminus of the molecule forms a globular domain, or three globular subdomains. The circle and the 'downstream' ellipse represent areas that influence hyaluronate binding. The black track inside the circle refers to a region displaying ~30% homology with cartilage link protein and proteoglycan core protein, both showing HA-binding ability. The black track at the amino terminus (inside and outside the circle), transmembrane-spanning domain and cytoplasmic tail represent regions with ~80–90% interspecies homology. The alternatively spliced short cytoplasmic domain is nonproportionately represented by a small bar. The hatched track in the center indicates the nonconserved membrane-proximal region with ~35–45% interspecies homology. The variable region, containing various combinations of alternatively spliced exon products (see Part C), is inserted between amino acids 201 and 202 (mature protein) and marked by a zigzag track. ●, Potential *N*-linked glycosylation sites (only those of standard CD44 are shown); ×, areas rich in serine/threonine, possible sites for *O*-linked glycosylation (those of the variable region are depicted arbitrarily); ◆, potential sites for glycosaminoglycans (chondroitin sulfate or heparan sulfate) incorporation; Ⓟ, potential sites for phosphorylation (only part of the sites are described). The symbols on the standard part of the molecule mostly refer to mouse CD44, whereas those of the variable region are based on information taken from both mouse and humans. (B) *Exon map*. The filled circles represent the exons of the constant regions. Empty circles represent exons that can be inserted by alternative splicing, resulting in the generation of the variable region. Note that exon V1 is not expressed in the human CD44. LP, leader peptide-encoding exon; TM, transmembrane-encoding exon; CT, cytoplasmic tail-encoding exons. (C) *Examples of alternatively spliced transcripts*. 1 and 2, standard CD44 with short and long cytoplasmic tails, respectively, which lack the entire variable region. 3, pMeta-1 (CD44V4–7). Exons V4, V5, V6 and V7 are inserted in tandem between exons 5 and 17. 4, pMeta-2 (CD44V6,7). Exons V6 and V7 are inserted between exons 5 and 17. pMeta-1 and pMeta-2 are known as 'metastatic' CD44, as their cDNA confers, upon transfection, metastatic potential on nonmetastatic rat tumor cells. Note that exon 16 is not expressed in both pMeta-1 and pMeta-2. 5, epithelial CD44 (CD44V8–10), expressed preferentially on epithelial cells. Exons V8, V9 and V10 are inserted between exons 5 and 16. 6, keratinocyte CD44 (CD44V3–10), one of the largest CD44 molecules known. Exons V3 through V10 are inserted between exons 5 and 16. (Reproduced from Naor *et al* (1997). © Academic Press.)

(10^6–10^7 Da), consisting of a linear polymer of the disaccharide (D-glucuronic acid [1-β-3] N-acetyl-D-glucosamine [1-β-4])$_n$. However, CD44 (or its chondroitin-sulfated version) also interacts with other ligands of the ECM, such as collagen, fibronectin and laminin. Mucosal addressin, serglycin, osteopontin and class II invariant chain (Ii) are additional, ECM-unrelated, ligands of CD44. In many, but not in all, cases CD44 does not bind HA unless it is stimulated by phorbol esters, activated by agonistic CD44-specific monoclonal antibody (mAb) or deglycosylated (e.g. by tunicamycin). Apparently, cytoskeleton-dependent receptor aggregation is required for HA binding, although cytoskeletal involvement can be bypassed by external cross-linking of cell surface CD44 molecules (e.g. with agonistic CD44-specific mAb or immobilized HA).

CD44 is a multifunctional receptor involved in cell–cell and cell–ECM interactions, cell traffic on endothelium or ECM, lymph node homing via binding to high endothelial venules, presentation of chemokines or growth factors to migrating cells, and transmission of growth signals, either independently or in association with other cell surface molecules. CD44 also participates in the uptake and intracellular degradation of HA, as well as in the transmission of signals mediating lymphohematopoiesis and prevention of apoptosis. Marked accumulation of CD44 (both standard and variant), and in some cases also of HA, is detected in areas of intensive cell migration and proliferation, as in wound healing, tissue remodeling, morphogenesis, inflammation and carcinogenesis.

Pathological aspects

Many cancer cell types, as well as their metastases, express high levels of CD44. Whereas some tumors, such as gliomas, exclusively display CD44s, other neoplasms, including brain metastases, gastrointestinal cancer, pancreatic adenocarcinoma, bladder cancer, uterine cervical cancer, breast cancer and non-Hodgkin's lymphomas, additionally and sometimes preferentially express CD44 variants. Hence, CD44, particularly its variants, may be used as diagnostic or prognostic markers of at least some human malignant diseases. Furthermore, it has been demonstrated in animal models that upon transfection with CD44s, or CD44v cDNA, nonmetastatic tumor cells acquire metastatic potential. In addition, injection of reagents interfering with CD44-ligand interaction (e.g. CD44s- or CD44v-specific mAb) inhibit local tumor growth and metastatic spread in murine species. In this context, CD44 may confer a growth advantage on some neoplastic cells, and consequently could be used as a target for cancer therapy. The functional significance of CD44 in malignant, autoimmune and infectious diseases, as well as in allergy, transplant rejection and graft-versus-host reaction, is yet to be established.

See also: **Adhesion molecules; Glycosylation of immune system molecules; High endothelial venules;** **Immunotherapy of tumors; Lymphocyte trafficking; Motility of immune cells.**

Further reading

Aruffo A, Stamenkovic I, Melnick M, Underhill CB and Seed B (1990) CD44 is the principal cell surface receptor for hyaluronate. *Cell* **61**: 1303–1313.

Bourguignon LYW, Lokeshwar VB, Chen X and Kerrick WGL (1993) Hyaluronic acid-induced lymphocyte signal transduction and HA receptor (GP85/CD44)–cytoskeleton interaction. *Journal of Immunology* **151**: 6634–6644.

Günthert U (1993) CD44: A multitude of isoforms with diverse functions. *Current Topics in Microbiology and Immunology* **184**: 47–63.

Günthert U, Hofmann M, Rudy W et al (1991) A new variant of glycoprotein CD44 confers metastatic potential to rat carcinoma cells. *Cell* **65**: 13–24.

Lesley J, Hyman R and Kincade PW (1993) CD44 and its interaction with extracellular matrix. *Advances in Immunology* **54**: 271–335.

Lesley J, English N, Perschl A, Gregoroff J and Hyman R (1995) Variant cell lines selected for alterations in the function of the hyaluronan receptor CD44 show differences in glycosylation. *Journal of Experimental Medicine* **182**: 431–437.

Moll J, Schmidt A, van der Putten H et al (1996) Accelerated immune response in transgenic mice expressing rat CD44V4-V7 on T cells. *Journal of Immunology* **156**: 2085–2094.

Naor D, Vogt Sionov R and Ish-Shalom D (1997) CD44: structure, function and association with the malignant process. *Advances in Cancer Research* **71**: 241–319.

Peach RJ, Hollenbaugh D, Stamenkovic I and Aruffo A (1993) Identification of hyaluronic acid binding sites in the extracellular domain of CD44. *Journal of Cell Biology* **122**: 257–264.

Screaton GR, Bell MV, Jackson DG et al (1992) Genomic structure of DNA encoding the lymphocyte homing receptor CD44 reveals at least 12 alternatively spliced exons. *Proceedings of the National Academy of Sciences of the USA* **89**: 12160–12164.

Screaton GR, Bell MV, Bell JI and Jackson DG (1993) The identification of a new alternative exon with highly restricted tissue expression in transcripts encoding the mouse Pgp-1 (CD44) homing receptor. Comparison of all 10 variable exons between mouse, human, and rat. *Journal of Biological Chemistry* **268**: 12235–12238.

Seiter S, Arch R, Reber S et al (1993) Prevention of tumor metastasis formation by anti-variant CD44. *Journal of Experimental Medicine* **177**: 443–455.

Tarin D and Matsumura Y (1993) Deranged activity of the CD44 gene and other loci as biomarkers for progression to metastatic malignancy. *Journal of Cellular Biochemistry. Supplement* **17G**: 173–185.

Zahalka MA, Okon E, Gosslar U, Holzmann B and Naor D (1995) Lymph node (but not spleen) invasion by murine lymphoma is both CD44- and hyaluronate-dependent. *Journal of Immunology* **154**: 5345–5355.

Zheng Z, Katoh S, He Q *et al* (1995) Monoclonal antibodies to CD44 and their influence on hyaluronan recognition. *Journal of Cell Biology* **130**: 485–495.

Zhou DFH, Ding JF, Picker LJ *et al* (1989) Molecular cloning and expression of Pgp-1. The mouse homologue of the human H-CAM (Hermes) lymphocyte homing receptor. *Journal of Immunology* **143**: 3390–3395.

CD45

John Seavitt and **Matthew L Thomas**, Howard Hughes Medical Institute, Center for Immunology and Department of Pathology, Washington University School of Medicine, St Louis, Missouri, USA

CD45 is an abundant transmembrane protein-tyrosine phosphatase (PTPase) expressed uniquely by all nucleated cells of hematopoietic origin. With regard to lymphocytes, CD45 functions to activate Src-family members involved in antigen receptor signaling. Recent studies have demonstrated that several transmembrane PTPases, including CD45, are involved in regulating adhesion and this may be a common theme to their function.

Structure

CD45 contains a large extracellular domain, a single transmembrane region, and two cytoplasmic PTPase domains (**Figure 1**). cDNAs have been isolated from human, rat, mouse, chicken and shark and comparison of the predicted protein sequences indicates a conservation of domain structure. The extracellular domain of CD45 consists of three distinguishable regions: an O-linked carbohydrate domain, a cysteine-containing domain and a domain containing three fibronectin type III repeats (which also contain several cysteines). Electron microscopy analysis of the extracellular domain demonstrates that the O-linked carbohydrate region which is most membrane distal has an extended rod conformation. Multiple isoforms of CD45 exist, ranging in molecular weight from 180 to 220 kDa. The basis for the different isoforms is alternative splicing of exons that encode part of the O-linked carbohydrate region. Since this region has an extended conformation, the length of the extracellular domain is dramatically altered (28 nm for the low molecular weight isoform and 51 nm for the high molecular weight isoform) (**Figure 2**). The O-linked carbohydrate region is encoded by exons 3–8. cDNA cloning shows that exons 4, 5 and 6 (also named A, B and C) are spliced in a variety of combinations to give rise to eight distinct protein products. In addition, a ninth isoform is predicted to exist that is the product of a splice between exons 3 and 8. The proposed nomenclature for the different CD45 isoforms is shown in **Table 1**.

The extracellular domain contains numerous sites for N-linked carbohydrate addition. Indeed, CD45 is 25% carbohydrate by weight. Owing to the high level of expression on lymphocytes, 100 000 molecules per cell, and its large size, CD45 occupies approximately 10% of the lymphocyte cell surface and bears much of the carbohydrate of these cells. Further diversification of CD45 species is generated with the addition of carbohydrate groups by cell type-specific and developmentally regulated glycosyltransferases. The existence of specific modifications on CD45 has been demonstrated using monoclonal antibodies that recognize distinct carbohydrate groups.

The cytoplasmic domain of CD45 contains two tandemly arranged tyrosine phosphatase domains. Mutational analysis suggests the first, membrane proximal, domain is both necessary and sufficient for biological responses and contains most if not all the catalytic activity. This is consistent with the observation that the sequence of the second domain contains changes at critical amino acids in the active site signature motif 'HCSAGXGRTG'. Nonetheless, it is possible that the second domain does possess intrinsic phosphatase activity. Alternatively, the second domain may function to regulate substrate availability.

Expression patterns of CD45 isoforms

CD45 isoform expression is dynamically controlled in both leukocyte differentiation and cellular activation. Isoform expression by a given population has been characterized by both amplification of this region of the mRNA by reverse transcription–polymerase chain reaction analysis and by a large assortment of monoclonal antibodies that recognize epitopes affected by the use of the alternative exons. The antibodies that recognize epitopes encoded by the alternatively spliced exons 4, 5 and 6 have been termed CD45RA, B and C, respectively. For humans, an antibody termed CD45RO exists that recognizes

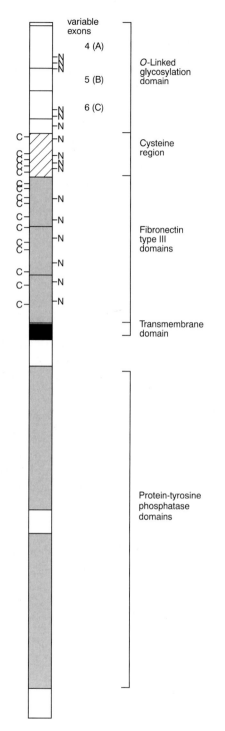

Figure 1   Human CD45. The variable exons 4, 5 and 6 are indicated. N represents site of potential *N*-linked glycosylation. C represents the location of cysteine residues in the extracellular domain.

the junction between exon 3 and 7; this is specific for the CD45θ isoform. A similar reagent does not exist for mouse or rat CD45. Unlike CD45R0, however, the remaining CD45R antibodies are all capable of recognizing multiple isoforms (**Table 1**). This

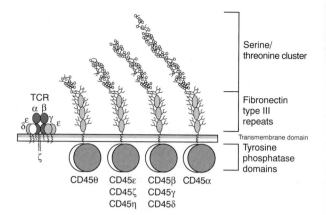

Figure 2   Representation of the sizes of different CD45 isoforms compared to the T cell receptor (TCR). Estimates are based on either electromicroscopy data or inferred from crystal structures.

complicates the characterization of isoform expression with these reagents. In addition, many of the CD45R antibodies are sensitive to carbohydrate modifications and some are specific for carbohydrate epitopes, not all of which are dependent on the presence of the alternatively spliced exons. While the CD45R antibodies provide only a limited insight into the specific patterns of isoform expression, they have proved a powerful tool in demonstrating that CD45 isoform expression is exquisitely regulated by different leukocyte populations.

T cell lineages express distinct CD45 isoforms depending on compartment and activation state. Most thymocytes express the CD45θ isoform, however there is increased expression of the higher molecular weight isoforms during thymocyte development. Of interest, very early thymocyte precursors that do not express TCR, CD4 or CD8 also stain for CD45R isoforms. This may indicate that thymocyte maturation is accompanied by cyclical expression of

Table 1   CD45 isoforms

Isoform	CD45R antibody recognition	Alternative exon usage					
CD45α	A, B, C	3	4	5	6	7	8
CD45β	A, B	3	4	5		7	8
CD45γ	A, C	3	4		6	7	8
CD45δ	B, C	3		5	6	7	8
CD45ε	A	3	4			7	8
CD45ζ	B	3		5		7	8
CD45η	C	3			6	7	8
CD45θ	O	3				7	8
CD45τ		3					8

CD45 splice isoforms depending on maturation stage.

Naive mature T cells express CD45R epitopes, and activation shifts isoform usage towards the CD45θ form. Furthermore, functionally distinct T cell subsets have characteristic patterns of CD45 isoforms. CD8⁺ cytolytic T cells express higher levels of CD45RA, and distinct CD45R staining patterns on T helper subsets are observed. Carbohydrate specific monoclonals also reveal distinct compartmental and activation state epitopes on T cell CD45. Therefore, T cell CD45 isoform usage is dynamic and likely reflects a complex regulatory program.

B cells normally express the high molecular weight CD45α isoform (also termed B220). However, cytokine treatment and viral transformation induce a change in staining pattern of the CD45R antibodies, including an increase in the expression of lower molecular weight isoforms. B cells also express carbohydrate epitopes on CD45 distinct from other cell lineages.

Monocytes express primarily the CD45θ isoform. Similar to the effects in T and B lineages, activation events induce the appearance of CD45RA epitopes, suggesting the expression of higher molecular weight isoforms.

Thus, the polypeptide and carbohydrate composition of the CD45 extracellular domain is highly regulated in a cell type-specific, developmentally regulated and activation state-dependent manner.

CD45 ligands

As yet it is not clear how the extracellular domain regulates the defined biology of CD45. While a number of candidate ligands have emerged, it has been difficult to identify specific interactions that modulate the biological function of CD45. Due to its extensive modification with carbohydrate, it is likely that lectins will be important CD45 ligands.

CD22 is a cell surface cation-independent lectin with a specificity for α2,6-linked sialic acid moieties and is expressed specifically on mature naive B cells. It is a member of the immunoglobulin (Ig) superfamily, with two alternatively spliced isoforms that contain five or seven Ig domains, respectively. Upon activation, CD22 is tyrosine phosphorylated and associates with the protein-tyrosine kinase p72^{syk} and the protein-tyrosine phosphatase SHP-1. Initially studied as a cell–cell adhesion molecule, recombinant CD22 interacts with a number of T cell surface proteins, among them CD45. However, the interaction is dependent upon the expression of α2,6-sialyltransferase, which is only expressed by some leukocytes. CD45 cross-linking with CD22 augments early

T cell activation events. Nonetheless, it is unclear whether in an immune response CD22 and CD45 represent a cognate pair in which binding results in a change in signal transduction through either protein.

Galectin 1 is a widely expressed β-galactoside binding protein family member. It is a dimer of 14 kDa subunits, each with a separate carbohydrate binding site. A number of primary T cell populations and T leukemic cell lines undergo apoptosis upon treatment with galectin 1. This effect requires CD45 N-linked carbohydrates, although it may be negatively regulated by increased O-linked glycosylation on higher molecular weight isoforms of CD45. Interestingly, in the thymus, galectin 1 expression occurs in areas where apoptosis is thought to occur. The very high level of CD45 protein expression in the thymus makes it difficult to conclude that interaction of CD45 with galectin 1 results in thymic apoptosis, although the development of galectin 1-deficient mice may clarify this issue.

Other carbohydrate-binding proteins may serve as CD45 ligands. Serum mannan-binding protein (S-MBP) is reported to interact specifically with the CD45θ isoform. S-MBP is a cation-dependent lectin that binds mannose and N-acetylglucosamine. Originally studied as a serum opsonin, S-MBP inhibits antigen receptor-induced T cell apoptosis. Although these results remain to be examined in greater detail, they suggest the extracellular domain of CD45 will have a role in regulating its biological function.

CD45 function

Genetic analysis using CD45-deficient cell lines and mice has been instrumental in delineating CD45 functions. CD45 is an important regulator of T and B lymphocyte antigen receptors and natural killer cell activation. With regard to T cells, CD45 functions to dephosphorylate and activate src-family member protein tyrosine kinases p56^{lck} and p59^{fyn}, a necessary first step for signaling through the T cell antigen receptor.

CD45 is expressed by leukocytes that do not express antigen receptors. Although analysis is not complete, this may be explained by a role for CD45 in cell–cell adhesion events and coordinate regulation of the cytoskeleton. Monoclonal antibodies to CD45 induce or inhibit aggregation of primary and transformed lymphocyte cell lines. This latter inhibition is also correlated with reduced levels of tyrosine phosphorylation on ICAM-3 and LFA-1. Immobilized CD45-specific monoclonal antibodies promote the adherence to plastic of T cell lines in conjunction with an increase of cellular phosphotyrosine. Cell adhesion events involve the cytoskeleton, and CD45 interacts with the cytoskeletal component fodrin (non-erythroid spectrin). Association with the cytoskeleton via fodrin or other molecules may control the ability of CD45 to interact with its substrates. Whether there are distinct mechanisms by which CD45 regulates antigen receptor signaling and adhesion is not clear. However, it is of interest to note that in lymphocytes CD45 associates with the lymphocyte-specific protein termed CD45-associated protein (CD45AP). CD45AP contains a short extracellular domain, a single transmembrane region, and a 146 amino acid cytoplasmic domain that contains a putative WW domain (a protein-binding module containing two conserved tryptophans [W]) and an acidic domain. CD45 associates with CD45AP through the transmembrane domain, and thus the WW domain and the acidic domain may associate with other proteins. The possibility exists that CD45AP may affect the substrates that CD45 interacts with and, as such, may regulate the ability of CD45 to function in antigen receptor signaling and/or adhesion.

The ability of the CD45 extracellular domain to regulate function has been pursued either by expressing in CD45-deficient cells chimeric proteins containing a different extracellular domain or by expressing distinct CD45 isoforms. Reconstitution of CD45-deficient cells, in which the extracellular domain has been deleted or exchanged, partially reconstitutes antigen receptor signaling. Interestingly, while expression of a chimeric protein with the epidermal growth factor (EGF) receptor extracellular and transmembrane domains and the CD45 cytoplasmic domain does reconstitute some antigen receptor signals, the addition of EGF ablates the response immediately, presumably as a result of receptor dimerization. This is consistent with the inhibitory effects on T cell activation seen with some monoclonal antibodies against CD45. However, it is not known whether these experimental systems mimic a physiologically relevant mode of CD45 regulation.

Expression of distinct CD45 isoforms in either transgenic mice or CD45-deficient cell lines suggests that the extracellular domain is important in regulating function. Specific expression of CD45α but not CD45θ in transgenic animals results in an augmented proliferative response. Furthermore, it has been suggested that the lower molecular weight CD45θ isoform more readily associates with the TCR complex to increase signaling capacity. Therefore, the extracellular domain appears to have the capacity to regulate CD45 function, although the

mechanism is unknown. Characterization of CD45 ligands and their ability to modulate CD45 function will help clarify this issue.

See also: **CD antigens; CD22; Membrane-associated cytoskeleton: role in regulating immune cell function; Memory, immunological; T lymphocyte activation.**

Further reading

Barondes SH, Castronovo V, Cooper DNW et al (1994) Galectins: a family of animal β-galactoside-binding lectins. *Cell* 76: 597–598.

Clark EA (1993) CD22, a B cell-specific receptor, mediates adhesion and signal transduction. *Journal of Immunology* 150: 4715–4718.

Cyster JG, Healy JI, Kishihara K, Mak TW, Thomas ML and Goodnow CC (1996) Regulation of B-lymphocyte negative and positive selection by tyrosine phosphatase CD45. *Nature* 381: 325–328.

Desai DM, Sap J, Schlessinger J and Weiss A (1993) Ligand-mediated negative regulation of a chimeric transmembrane receptor tyrosine phosphatase. *Cell* 73: 541–554.

Kishihara K, Penninger J, Wallace VA et al (1993) Normal B lymphocyte development but impaired T cell maturation in CD45-exon 6 protein tyrosine phosphatase-deficient mice. *Cell* 74: 143–156.

McKenney DW, Onodera H, Gorman L, Mimura T and Rothstein DM (1995) Distinct isoforms of the CD45 protein-tyrosine phosphatase differentially regulate interleukin 2 secretion and activation signal pathways involving Vav in T cells. *Journal of Biological Chemistry* 270: 24949–24954.

Perillo NL, Pace KE, Seilhamer JJ and Baum LG (1995) Apoptosis of T cells mediated by galectin-1. *Nature* 378: 736–739.

Sgroi D, Koretzky G and Stamenkovic I (1995) Regulation of CD45 engagement by the B-cell receptor CD22. *Proceedings of the National Academy of Sciences of the USA* 92: 4026–4030.

Suchard SJ and Bourguignon LYW (1987) Further characterization of a fodrin-containing transmembrane complex from mouse T-lymphoma cells. *Biochimica et Biophysica Acta* 896: 35–46.

Thomas ML (1989) The leukocyte common antigen family. *Annual Review of Immunology* 7: 339–369.

Trowbridge IS and Thomas ML (1994) CD45: an emerging role as a protein tyrosine phosphatase required for lymphocyte activation and development. *Annual Review of Immunology* 12: 85–116.

van der Merwe PA, Crocker PR, Vinson M, Barclay AN, Schauer R and Kelm S (1996) Localization of the putative sialic acid-binding site on the immunoglobulin superfamily cell-surface molecule CD22. *Journal of Biological Chemistry* 271: 9273–9280.

CD46 (MEMBRANE COFACTOR PROTEIN, MCP)

M Kathryn Liszewski and **John P Atkinson**, Department of Internal Medicine, Washington University School of Medicine, St Louis, Missouri, USA

The complement system consists of a group of sequentially interacting proteins that promote the inflammatory response and facilitate the destruction of microorganisms. The system must be tightly regulated to prevent activation in the fluid phase (i.e. no target) and on host tissue (i.e. inappropriate target). Nearly half of the complement proteins serve in regulation. One such inhibitory protein is CD46, membrane cofactor protein (MCP). This regulator is a type one transmembrane protein that serves as a cofactor for the factor I-mediated proteolytic cleavage and inactivation of C3b and C4b deposited on self tissue. CD46 performs this role intrinsically in that it protects the cell on which it is expressed, not neighboring cells. CD46 is also the measles virus receptor and is involved in the adherence of *Streptococcus pyogenes* (group A streptococcus) to epithelial cells. CD46 belongs to a group of structurally, functionally and genetically related proteins called the regulators of complement activation (RCA) that includes decay-accelerating factor (DAF; CD55), complement receptors 1 (CR1; CD35) and 2 (CR2; CD21), and the plasma proteins factor H and C4-binding protein.

Structural characteristics

CD46 possesses an unusual electrophoretic pattern in that it consists of two rather heterogeneous protein species of 51–58 kDa ('lower' band) and 59–68 kDa ('upper' band). This variability is inherited as three phenotypic patterns consisting of upper band predominance in 65% of the population, equivalence of both bands in 29% and predominance of the lower band in 6%. This heterogeneity represents a size polymorphism and relates to CD46 being expressed as a family of at least four isoforms that arise by alternative splicing of a single gene (**Figure 1**). A dominating characteristic of CD46 is the presence of four of the repeating motifs called complement control protein repeats (CCPRs) (also called short consensus repeats). These are the building blocks of RCA proteins that contain the binding sites for C3b and C4b. Sites for N-linked glycosylation are found in CCPR-1, -2 and -4. Following the CCPRs is an area enriched in serines, threonines and prolines (STP) that is extensively O-glycosylated.

This domain consists of 14 or 29 amino acids depending on whether the STP exon B (15 amino acids) is spliced out. The presence of STP-B produces the higher molecular weight protein isoforms (possessing more sialic acid) while its absence generates the lower molecular weight forms. Following this is a tract of 12 amino acids of unknown significance, a transmembrane region, intracytoplasmic anchor and one of two alternatively spliced cytoplasmic tails (CYT-1 of 16 amino acids or CYT-2 of 23 amino acids). The CD46 gene consists of 14 exons and 13 introns with a minimum length of 43 kb and resides in the RCA cluster on the long arm of chromosome one (1q3.2). A partial duplicate of CD46 is also present in this cluster but no mRNA for this species has been identified.

Functional role

Host cells must be protected from inadvertent complement activation at sites of inflammation and from the continuous, natural 'tickover' of C3. A biochemical mechanism to regulate C3b/C4b is termed 'cofactor' activity. In this process, CD46 interacts with C3b or C4b to promote their limited enzymatic cleavage by factor I, a plasma serine protease. CD46 possesses 'intrinsic' cofactor activity, i.e. it protects the cell on which it is anchored, not bystander cells.

The reason for the expression of four isoforms in a given cell or tissue is only partially understood. For example, the cytoplasmic tails of CD46 mediate the differential processing of CD46 precursors. Isoforms bearing tail 1 (CYT-1) processed into their mature forms four times faster than isoforms with tail 2 (CYT-2). Additionally, the BC isoforms provide enhanced cytoprotection against the classical pathway as compared to C isoforms. The presence of distinct consensus phosphorylation signals on the cytoplasmic tails suggests roles in cell signaling.

The CCPRs are the sites of functional activity for CD46 and other RCA proteins. C4b-binding and cofactor activity map to CCPRs 2, 3 and 4. To regulate C3b, the third and fourth CCPRs are necessary for binding while 2, 3 and 4 are needed for cofactor activity.

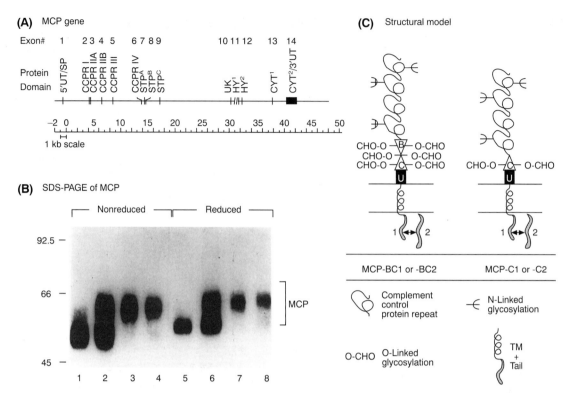

Figure 1   Genetics and structure of membrane cofactor protein (MCP; CD46). (A) the genomic organization of the alternatively spliced CD46 reveals 14 exons and 13 introns for a minimum length of 43 kb. 5'UT/SP, 5' untranslated region/signal peptide; CCPR, complement control protein repeat; STP^A, STP^B, STP^C are the segments enriched in serines, threonines and prolines; UK, region of unknown functional significance; HY^1 and HY^2 are hydrophobic regions 1 and 2; CYT^1, cytoplasmic tail 1; CYT^2/3'UT, cytoplasmic tail 2 and 3' untranslated region. (B) The electrophoretic profile of the protein shows three phenotypic patterns: lower band predominant, equal banding, and upper band predominant. The apparent molecular weight of all species increases with reduction. (C) Structural model shows the four primary isoforms of CD46–note the alternatively spliced STP and cytoplasmic tail regions.

Tissue distribution

CD46 is widely expressed on host tissue, a logical consequence of the critical role it plays in self-protection. Although most cells express CD44, erythrocytes are an interesting exception. Soluble forms are present in low concentrations in plasma, tears, saliva and seminal fluid and are increased in plasma in the presence of certain malignancies.

As mentioned, CD46 is expressed as a family of isoforms. While most cells in a given individual express the same ratio of the four isoforms, a predominance of certain species has been noted in brain, salivary gland, kidney and fetal heart. Different molecular weights resulting from variable glycosylation have been noted on granulocytes and spermatotozoa. Tissues including kidney, skin, reproductive, eye, thyroid, liver and synovium differ in the relative expression and distribution pattern of CD46. Additionally, malignant and transformed cells tend to express high amounts of CD46.

Homologous proteins of other species

CD46 has been identified in primates, pigs, guinea pigs and rabbits. A functional homolog has been characterized in the mouse (Crry/p65) and rat (5I2 antigen). However, these resemble the human complement receptor CR1 in that they possess both cofactor activity and decay-accelerating activity. However, human CR1 has limited tissue distribution.

CD46 in other biological areas

Since the identification of CD46 as a C3b-binding protein more than a decade ago, its biologic and pathophysiologic role has expanded. CD46 is the receptor for measles virus. Additionally, CD46 is involved in the adherence of *Streptococcus pyogenes* (group A streptococcus). Recently, it was found that human immunodeficiency virus 1 (HIV-1) can incorporate complement control proteins CD46, CD55 and CD59 as common surface constituents in order to promote resistance against complement.

CD46 also is of interest in transplant biology. Acute rejection of the organs of other species is in part mediated by the complement system. To overcome this, complement regulators are being engineered to produce transgenic pigs whose organs will be used in xenotransplantation.

In reproductive biology, CD46 is abundantly expressed at the maternal–fetal interface, on fetal tissue and on the inner acrosomal membrane of spermatozoa. Alterations in function or expression of CD46 may play a role in habitual abortion or infertility. The surprising acrosomal site for CD46 expression may be part of the egg–sperm attachment mechanism and/or protect against C3b deposition during penetration by spermatozoa.

See also: **Complement, alternative pathway; Complement, classical pathway; Complement deficiencies; Complement fixation test; Complement, genetics; Complement, membrane attack pathway; Complement receptors; Decay-accelerating factor (CD55); Paramyxoviruses, infection and immunity; *Streptococcus*, infection and immunity; Xenotransplantation.**

Further reading

Barlow P, Norman DG, Baron M and Campbell ID (1991) The secondary structure of a complement control protein module by two-dimensional 1H NMR. *Biochemistry* 30: 997–1004.

Campbell ID and Baron M (1991) The structure and function of protein modules. *Philosophical Transactions of the Royal Society of London. Series B: Biological Sciences* 332: 165–170.

Dorig RE, Marcil A and Richardson CD (1994) CD46, a primate-specific receptor for measles virus. *Trends in Microbiology* 2: 312–318.

Hourcade D, Holers VM and Atkinson JP (1989) The regulators of complement activation (RCA) gene cluster. *Advances in Immunology* 45: 381–416.

Liszewski MK and Atkinson JP (1993) The complement system. In: Paul WE (ed) *Fundamental Immunology*, pp 917–939. New York: Raven Press.

Liszewski MK and Atkinson JP (1996) Membrane cofactor protein (CD46) and decay accelerating factor (CD55). In: Hansch M, Till G and Rother K (eds) *The Complement System*. New York: Springer-Verlag.

Liszewski MK, Farries TC, Lublin DM, Rooney IA and Atkinson JP (1996) Control of the complement system. *Advances in Immunology* 61: 201–283.

McCurry KR, Kooyman DL, Alvarado CG *et al* (1995) Human complement regulatory proteins protect swine-to-primate cardiac xenografts from humoral injury. *Nature Medicine* 1: 423–427.

Morgan BP (1995) Complement regulatory molecules: application to therapy and transplantation. *Immunology Today* 16: 257–259.

Platt JL (1994) A perspective on xenograft rejection and accommodation. *Immunological Reviews* 141: 127–149.

Rooney IA, Liszewski MK and Atkinson JP (1993) Using membrane-bound complement regulatory proteins to inhibit rejection. *Xeno* 1: 29–35.

Rooney IA, Oglesby TJ and Atkinson JP (1993) Complement in human reproduction: activation and control. *Immunologic Research* 12: 276–294.

CD59

Alexandra Davies and **Peter Lachmann**, Department of Medicine, University of Cambridge, Medical Research Council Centre, Cambridge, UK

CD59 is an 18 kDa membrane glycoprotein whose primary function is to regulate the activity of the complement membrane attack complex (MAC). Alternative names for CD59 include protectin, membrane inhibitor of reactive lysis (MIRL), homologous restriction factor 20 (HRF20) and membrane attack complex inhibitory factor (MACIF). CD59 is attached to the outer layer of the membrane by a glycosylphosphatidylinositol (GPI) anchor and is very widely distributed (**Table 1**). It has also been detected in a number of body fluids, but often in association with lipoproteins or small membrane vesicles, and has probably been shed from cell surfaces with its anchor intact or released enzymatically (**Table 1**). There is no evidence for a secreted form of the protein. The molecule is now extremely well-characterized and species homologs are known in a variety of primates as well as the rat, sheep, pig and mouse. Functionally analogous proteins have also been described in some microorganisms.

CD59 inhibits the formation of the MAC by binding to sites on C8 and C9, thus blocking the uptake and incorporation of multiple C9 molecules into the complex. CD59 from any given species interacts with C8 and C9 from heterologous species with variable efficiency, working best with homologous proteins.

Table 1   Cells and tissues expressing CD59

Liver	*Pancreas*
Bile canaliculi	Ductal epithelium
Bile duct	*Peripheral nervous system*
Lung	Schwann cells
Bronchi and bronchioles	Endothelial cells
Kidney	Neurons
Glomerular capillaries	*Eye*
Glomerular epithelial cells	Lacrimial gland
Distal tubules	Acinar cells
Collecting ducts	Retinal pigment epithelium
Central nervous system	Cornea and conjunctiva
Myelin	*Body fluids*
Microglia	Serum (low levels)
Neurons	Urine
Oligodendrocytes	Milk
Astrocytes	Seminal plasma
Neoplastic cells	Cerebrospinal fluid
Melanoma	Saliva
Malignant glioma	*Other*
Colonic adenocarcinoma	Hematopoietic cells
Thyroid carcinomas	Vascular endothelium
Reproductive system	Prostatic epithelium
Unfertilized oocytes	Nasal epithelium
Preimplantation embryos	Chrondocytes
Amniotic epithelium	Salivary duct
Syncytiotrophoblast	Thyroid follicular cells

This forms the basis for the phenomenon of 'homologous restriction' of lysis, a term used to describe the relative inefficiency with which complement lyses homologous cells. The physiological importance of the complement inhibitory role of CD59 is demonstrated in the acquired hemolytic disease paroxysmal nocturnal hemoglobinuria (PNH; see below), in which affected cells are deficient in CD59 and other complement regulatory proteins and are extremely sensitive to lysis. Roles for CD59 in T cell adhesion and activation have also been proposed but not firmly established.

Protein and gene structure

cDNAs for CD59 have been isolated by several independent groups. The nucleotide sequence encodes a precursor polypeptide of 128 amino acids in length, the first 25 residues constituting a signal peptide. The sequence contains one site for N-linked glycosylation at Asn18, and the carbohydrate attached here is a common biantennary structure accounting for approximately 25% of the molecular weight of CD59. At the C-terminus there is a hydrophobic stretch of residues characteristic of proteins which are processed to carry a GPI anchor. The presence of such an anchor in the case of CD59 was originally confirmed by release of the protein from various cell surfaces by phosphatidylinositol-specific phospholipase C. Subsequently, protein sequencing of tryptic fragments and nuclear magnetic resonance (NMR) studies of the protein purified from human urine have indicated that the GPI anchor is attached to Asn77. The protein contains a total of 10 cysteine residues which form disulfide bonds as follows: Cys3-26, Cys6-13, Cys19-39, Cys45-63, Cys64-69.

CD59 is unique in the complement control protein superfamily in that it bears no structural or immunologic relationship with other member proteins, although these are distinctly related to one another and encoded by genes which are situated together in the RCA (regulators of complement activation) region on chromosome 1. The gene for CD59 is in contrast located on the short arm of chromosome 11, distributed throughout over 27 kb of genomic DNA. Although initial studies identified four exons, a fifth alternately spliced exon has recently been discovered between what were originally considered to be exons 1 and 2. The transcriptional start site for both forms of mRNA is the same. Since the newly identified exon occurs within the 5′ untranslated region of the CD59 transcript there is still no evidence as yet to suggest that there are alternative forms of the mature protein. Both types of transcript are expressed concordantly in all the cell types analyzed so far, and their expression appears to be regulated similarly. The purpose of the alternately spliced exon is therefore not known.

The structure of the CD59 gene is similar to that of the murine Ly-6 antigens and of the human urokinase plasminogen activator receptor (HUPAR). These and other proteins such as the mouse thymocyte and B cell antigen ThB, and the squid glycoprotein SGP2, constitute a separate family of proteins which share some sequence homology (in particular, conserved cysteine residues) and therefore some structural similarity. CD59 has on occasion been proposed as the human homolog of the murine Ly-6 antigens, despite only 25% sequence identity between the two, and differences in the pattern and regulation of gene expression. However, the recent cloning of mouse CD59 clearly demonstrates that CD59 and Ly-6 are distinct proteins.

Inhibition of complement lysis
Mechanism of action

CD59 is the major cell surface inhibitor of the complement membrane attack complex (MAC), a multimolecular assembly of complement components C5 to C9 which forms as a consequence of complement activation. At the C5b-7 stage of assembly, a labile binding site is exposed on C7 which allows the growing MAC to bind cell membranes; then as C8 and multiple copies of C9 are incorporated, the complex inserts further into the membrane and finally forms a functional pore through the bilayer, leading to cell lysis. CD59 prevents lysis by interfering with the assembly of a fully functional MAC, binding to C8 in the C5b-8 complex and thereby blocking the uptake and polymerization of C9 (**Figure 1**). Binding sites for CD59 are located on the α subunit of C8 and on the C9b fragment (the putative membrane-binding domain) of C9. However, the regions on CD59 which are involved in this interaction have not yet been fully elucidated. Studies using proteolytic fragments of the protein implicate sites in the N-terminal region. Some early observations that deglycosylated CD59 did not inhibit cell lysis suggested that the carbohydrate moiety was also important for function, although paradoxically the deglycosylated CD59 retained its ability to bind to isolated C8 and C9 immobilized on plastic. One possible explanation for this is that the presence of the carbohydrate moiety somehow influenced the orientation of CD59 on the cell surface and thereby influenced its interaction with the MAC, without being directly involved in the binding of C8 and C9. Subsequent studies in which the site of N-linked glycosylation was removed from the CD59 cDNA by site-directed mutagenesis have demonstrated that the carbohydrate is not necessary for complement inhibitory activity.

CD59 deficiency and paroxysmal nocturnal hemoglobinuria

Paroxysmal noctural hemoglobinuria (PNH) is an acquired hemolytic disease characterized by bouts of intravascular hemolysis. The disease is caused by somatic mutation in a pluripotent stem cell of the hematopoietic system, leading to the appearance in the circulation of a clone of cells exhibiting increased sensitivity to complement lysis. Depending upon the point in the lineage at which mutation occurs, erythrocytes, granulocytes, monocytes, platelets and lymphocytes may all be affected. Cells in the affected clone are abnormally sensitive to complement because they fail to express GPI-anchored proteins on their surfaces and therefore lack CD59 and decay accelerating factor (DAF), another complement regulatory protein. The defect in PNH arises from mutation of the PIG-A gene whose product is an enzyme involved in the biosynthesis of the GPI anchor. Various mutations in PIG-A have been identified, and since PIG-A is carried on the X chromosome, loss of function in the single active allele is sufficient for disease to be manifest. There is an isolated case of CD59 deficiency due to a mutation in

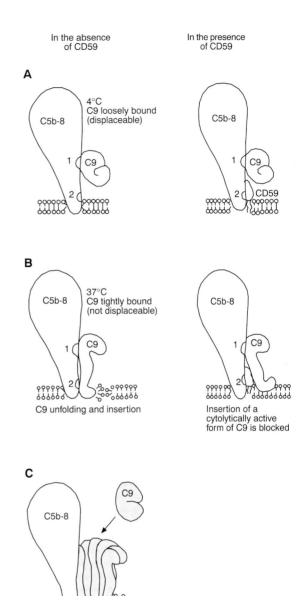

Figure 1 Model for the mechanism of action of CD59. Two putative binding sites on C5b-8 for C9 are shown. C9 binds loosely in its globular form at site 1 and at this stage may be displaced by other C9 molecules; this may be demonstrated experimentally by holding the temperature at 4°C (A). However, at 37°C C9 normally unfolds and interacts with site 2 on the C5b-8 complex (B), begins to penetrate the cell membrane, and exposes sites for interaction with additional C9 molecules which polymerise to form a transmembrane pore (C). In the presence of CD59, the initial interaction of C9 with C5b-8 occurs, but the binding of CD59 to C8 prevents the C5b-8 catalyzed unfolding and insertion of multiple C9 molecules into the membrane, and thereby blocks cell lysis. (Reproduced with permission of Blackwell Science Ltd, from Meri S, Morgan BP, Davies A *et al* (1990) Human protection (CD59), an 18,000–20,000 MW complement lysis restricting factor, inhibits C5b-8 catalyzed insertion of C9 into lipid layers. *Immunology* **71**: 1–9).

the CD59 gene. Despite having all the other GPI-anchored proteins, including DAF, the patient with CD59 deficiency suffers from a PNH-like condition characterized by hemolysis. This underlines the importance of CD59 as the major factor for regulation of complement lysis on erythrocytes.

Role in T cell activation

Antibody cross-linking of CD59 on the surface of human T cells induces a rise in intracellular calcium, inositol phosphate production, release of cytokines and cell proliferation. These phenomena occur when any GPI-anchored proteins are cross-linked in the membrane, and the mechanisms by which their assembly in the *outer* layer of the membrane can transmit signals to the *interior* of the cell are currently under investigation. Whether or not the observed effects of experimentally cross-linking CD59 using antibody have any real significance depends upon there being a physiological ligand for CD59. There have been several claims that like CD58 (LFA-3) and CD48, CD59 is a ligand for CD2, a molecule involved in T cell activation, but an equal number of reports dispute this. As yet the role of CD59 in the processes of T cell activation remains equivocal.

Microbial counterparts of CD59

It has been to the advantage of many microbial pathogens to acquire mechanisms for immune evasion. For example, an open reading frame encoding a sequence highly homologous to that of human and various monkey species of CD59 has been identified in the genome of herpesvirus saimiri (HVS), whose natural host is the squirrel monkey. It appears highly likely that the virus has captured this sequence from its host during the course of evolution. Preliminary studies indicate that the sequence does indeed encode a functional protein, so expression of this sequence by HVS could be considered as a virulence factor in aiding the virus to evade the detrimental effects of complement activation. Complement-inhibiting proteins that appear to have some antigenic relationship to CD59 have also been described in *Entamoeba histolytica* and *Schistosoma mansoni*. The *E. histolytica* protein is an integrin-like molecule consisting of two subunits, one of which shares very limited sequence homology with CD59. A cDNA for the *S. mansoni* protein has not yet been isolated. Since many pathogens are adept at avoiding destruction by the complement system, it is highly likely that other microbial proteins will emerge that are functionally, if not structurally, related to CD59 or the other human complement control proteins.

CD59 transgenics and xenotransplantation

The shortage of suitable donor organs for transplant surgery has led to the proposal that animal organs be used instead. A major problem with this is that of hyperacute rejection, whereby discordant xenografts come under attack within minutes, and are destroyed by complement that has been activated by naturally occurring antibodies in the host that recognize carbohydrate epitopes in the xenograft. A major strategy now being researched to overcome this is the production of transgenic animals (mainly pigs) that carry the genes for human complement control proteins, including CD59. These human proteins are expressed in a wide range of tissues in the transgenic animals, sometimes at very high levels, and have been shown to confer increased protection upon endothelial and other cell types against human complement. Although these results seem very promising, a major drawback to the use of xenotransplantation is the possibility that xenografts may harbor viruses or other microbes that could be extremely harmful to a human host, and this is currently the main objection to proceeding with clinical trials.

See also: **CD antigens; CD2; Complement, membrane attack pathway; Decay-accelerating factor (CD55); Xenotransplantation.**

Further reading

Albrecht JCJ, Nicholas J, Cameron KR *et al* (1992) Herpesvirus saimiri has a gene specifying a homolog of the cellular membrane glycoprotein CD59. *Virology* 190: 527–530.

Davies A and Lachmann PJ (1993) Membrane defence against complement lysis: the structure and biological properties of CD59. *Immunologic Research* 12: 258–275.

Diamond LE, McCurry KR, Martin MJ *et al* (1996) Characterization of transgenic pigs expressing functionally active human CD59 on cardiac endothelium. *Transplantation* 61: 1241–1249.

Fletcher CM, Harrison RA, Lachmann PJ *et al* (1994) Structure of a soluble, glycosylated form of the human complement regulatory protein CD59. *Structure* 2: 185–199.

Holguin MH, Martin CB *et al* (1996) Analysis of the gene that encodes the complement regulatory protein, membrane inhibitor of reactive lysis (CD59). *Journal of Immunology* 157: 1659–1668.

CELL-MEDIATED IMMUNITY

Frank W Fitch, The Ben May Institute, Division of Biological Sciences, The University of Chicago, Chicago, USA

Cell-mediated immunity is mediated by T lymphocytes; humoral immunity, by antibodies. These distinctions are based on observations that delayed-type hypersensitivity (DTH) and other manifestations of cell-mediated immunity can be adoptively transferred by lymphoid cells but not by serum from sensitized animals, while other manifestations of immunity can be passively transferred by serum from immune animals. Cell-mediated and humoral immunity can exist in isolation: some chemicals induce contact sensitivity, a manifestation of cell-mediated immunity, but do not induce production of antibodies, and some antigens can stimulate antibody production in the apparent absence of T lymphocytes. However, cell-mediated and humoral immunity usually develop concurrently *in vivo*, and the two responses often act synergistically. For example, although DTH can be adoptively transferred with T lymphocytes, the intensity of the reaction is usually greater if antibody is also passively administered. There also are conceptual difficulties inherent in these definitions: antibodies are produced by cells, and cells participate in many of the protective reactions mediated by antibodies. Also, T lymphocytes carry out many of their functions through soluble products which they secrete following stimulation with antigen.

In the early 1880s, Elie Metchnikoff proposed that inflammation had a protective role in responses to pathogens, and that phagocytic cells, rather than being harmful, constituted the primary line of defense through their ability to ingest and digest invading organisms. However, the contrary view, that humoral antibody played the dominant role, was furthered by the demonstration of bactericidal properties of immune serum and the protective effects of antibodies against bacterial exotoxins. Although in the early 1900s the phenomenon of DTH was shown to be unrelated to circulating antibody, it proved difficult to determine with certainty the relative contributions of humoral and cell-mediated immunity until the central involvement of lymphocytes in immune responses was established finally in the late 1950s. In the early 1960s, several serendipitous observations led to the identification of two separate lymphocyte lineages, based on their development pathways: B lymphocytes, which originate in the bursa of Fabricius in birds and in the bone marrow of mammals; and T lymphocytes, which develop within the thymus from precursors originating initially in the yolk sac and later in the bone marrow.

These two developmentally distinct sets of lymphocytes were soon shown to have different functions: B cells display and secrete antibody molecules which react with intact antigen molecules; T cells react with processed antigen fragments which are associated with molecules of the major histocompatibility complex (MHC). T lymphocytes carry out some functions, such as the lysis of target cells that express the appropriate antigens, through direct cell-to-cell contact, but they exert many of their effector functions through secreted hormone-like proteins, called cytokines, which modulate the activities of various cells, including lymphocytes and phagocytes.

Although the classical manifestations of cell-mediated immunity are phenomena which can be observed only *in vivo*, it is difficult to dissect the cellular and biochemical processes involved in these reactions in animals. Therefore, a variety of responses by antigen-stimulated T lymphocytes have been used as surrogate cell-mediated responses *in vitro*. It is generally assumed that these responses – which include T lymphocyte proliferation, cytolytic activity, 'helper' functions, and/or secretion of cytokines – relate to manifestations of cell-mediated immunity observed *in vivo*. However, none of the phenomena of cell-mediated immunity observed in sensitized animals have been characterized fully in cellular and biochemical terms.

Recognition of antigens by T lymphocytes

T and B lymphocytes recognize antigens in fundamentally different ways. Both T and B lymphocytes have extensive antigen-specific receptor repertoires and can react with a very large number of different antigens, each being able to distinguish among more than 10^7 distinct antigenic determinants. However, entirely different genes which are located on different chromosomes are used to construct their cell surface receptors for specific antigens. Nevertheless, they use similar mechanisms to produce their antigen receptors, employing a limited number of gene segments which are combined in many different ways to construct a very large number of conformationally distinct polypeptides. The T cell receptor (TCR) for antigen consists of a heterodimeric structure, which in most T cells consists of α and β chains. However, a minority of peripheral T cells (approximately 5%) employ a TCR composed of structurally related but distinct γ and δ polypeptides. Such T cells are the dominant population in most surface epithelia in mice. There is generally allelic exclusion in the expression of genes encoding TCR peptides so that a given T lymphocyte expresses only one functional α and one β gene or one γ and one δ gene. The use of α and β or γ and δ chain polypeptides in various heterodimeric combinations contributes to the very large repertoire. Somatic mutation, which contributes to the affinity maturation of antibodies, does not appear to take place in T lymphocytes.

T lymphocytes react with antigen fragments associated with molecules of the MHC expressed by the individual in which the T lymphocytes arose. During the course of maturation in the thymus, T lymphocytes appear to be positively selected for the ability to recognize self antigens, but those T lymphocytes which react too strongly with self antigens appear to be negatively selected and deleted. The vast majority of cells which enter the thymus fail to survive these selection processes and die; probably less than 5% of thymocytes find their way to peripheral lymphoid tissues as mature T lymphocytes.

In addition to rearrangements of genes encoding the TCR and subsequent selection events, maturation of T lymphocytes in the thymus also involves sequential expression of a number of lineage-specific molecules, including CD4 and CD8 which distinguish different T lymphocyte subsets. The most immature cells in the thymus express neither of these cell surface structures and have not rearranged their TCR genes. The TCR is expressed first in cells which express both CD4 and CD8; CD4$^+$ and CD8$^+$ subsets of T lymphocytes develop from this 'double-positive' population. Expression of CD4 is associated conventionally with 'helper' cell functions and CD8 expression with cytolytic activity, but these distinctions are by no means absolute. Many CD4$^+$ T cells have cytolytic capabilities, and at least some CD8$^+$ T cells can carry out helper functions. The mutually exclusive expression of CD4 or CD8 correlates better with the class of MHC antigen which serves as the restriction element for antigen recognition than it does with function: CD4$^+$ T cells usually recognize antigenic peptides associated with class II MHC molecules, while CD8$^+$ T cells are usually restricted to recognition of peptides associated with class I MHC molecules. Both CD4 and CD8 have 'coreceptor' function, probably by bringing the protein tyrosine kinase *lck* into the TCR–antigen complex.

Full activation of CD4$^+$ T cells requires two signals: one delivered through TCR, and a second 'co-stimulatory' signal which is not antigen specific. Stimulation of the TCR alone induces anergy, defined as the long-lived inability to secrete interleukin 2 (IL-2) and proliferate in response to antigenic stimulation. CD28 has been identified as the dominant costimulatory molecule expressed by T cells. While stimulation through CD28 alone has little effect, interaction of CD28 with B7 on antigen-presenting cells (APCs) in conjunction with TCR engagement augments significantly the secretion of multiple cytokines. A full understanding of the phenomenon of costimulation is complicated by the fact that these counterreceptor families have multiple members: CTLA-4, which is structurally similar to CD28, also binds to B7-1 and B7-2, which also are related structurally. These B7 family members are not expressed concordantly on all cell types, and their expression is differentially regulated. While most resting T cells express CD28, CTLA-4 is expressed only on activated T cells. An attractive model proposes that interactions between CD28 and B7-2 provide costimulation for T cell activation, while interactions between CTLA-4 and B7-1, both of which are expressed later in immune responses, terminate ongoing responses.

Several other cell surface molecules are involved in the interaction between T lymphocytes and APCs. CD2, expressed on all human thymocytes and peripheral T cells, interacts with LFA-3, a broadly distributed glycoprotein. The T lymphocyte integrin, LFA-1, interacts with ICAM-1, a heavily glycosylated and widely expressed molecule, and with ICAM-2. There are probably additional cell surface structures which are important in interactions of T lymphocytes with other cells. While these structures enhance cell-to-cell contact, many of them also appear to be involved in cell activation, either participating directly in signaling events or indirectly by modulating, either positively or negatively, signals induced through the TCR.

Manifestations of cell-mediated immunity *in vivo*

Allograft rejection, DTH, and graft-versus-host disease are manifestations of T cell-mediated immunity *in vivo*. In addition, much of the protective immunity to viral and some bacterial infections is also dependent upon cell-mediated immunity. A subset of murine CD4$^+$ T cells designated T$_H$1 appears to mediate DTH, while the T$_H$2 subset does not. Since these subsets differ in the array of cytokines they secrete, it is likely that DTH is mediated by particular cytokines. The pathophysiological processes that lead to organ allograft rejection are not well characterized, but it is likely that cytokines play a major role here as well. Mechanisms of allograft rejection depend on the nature of the antigens being recognized as well as the type of graft involved. Antibodies also are produced in response to allografts, and antibody-mediated vascular lesions often are prominent. T lymphocytes presumably can injure allografts of dispersed cells (bone marrow or lymphoid cells) by direct effector mechanisms such as cytolysis. T cells can also act indirectly through secreted cytokines (lymphotoxin or tumor necrosis factor) which can themselves directly injure target cells or through effects of cytokines (interferon γ, IFNγ) on macrophages to increase their killing and other activities. Vascularized allografts (kidney, heart and liver) can be rejected through effects on blood vessels rather than through primary injury to the parenchymal cells in these organs. Other tissue grafts can be rejected by mechanisms which interfere with revascularization. Although it is clear that T lymphocytes mediate these reactions, details of the cellular and biochemical processes that are involved remain obscure.

Manifestations of cell-mediated immunity *in vitro*

A number of model systems have been studied *in vitro* to evaluate the molecular mechanisms controlling T cell responses; these include proliferation, induction of cytolytic activity, expression of helper functions for antibody production, secretion of cytokines and biochemical signaling events. Clonal populations of T lymphocytes which retain normal phenotypic characteristics and monoclonal antibodies reactive with different T cell surface structures have greatly facilitated the detailed analysis of these correlates of cell-mediated immunity *in vitro*. Monoclonal antibodies, which react with the TCRs, can serve as surrogate antigens, making it possible to distinguish the effects initiated by stimulation of the TCR from those involving other cell surface structures.

Many of the biological effects of T cells are mediated by secreted cytokines which affect the activities of different kinds of target cells. Different arrays of cytokines are produced by different T cell subsets following stimulation, and regulatory mechanisms that control which cytokines a particular T cell will secrete are beginning to be defined. It is clear that the array of cytokines secreted is of major functional significance. More than 15 different cytokines have been identified and their genes cloned. Their properties have been defined unequivocally, using products obtained by recombinant DNA technology. Most cytokines act on several different cell types.

Most if not all T lymphocyte proliferation is due to growth factors secreted by T cells. T lymphocytes stimulated with antigen are induced to express receptors for transferrin and for T cell growth factors, and they undergo cell division in response to cytokines having T cell growth factor activity. IL-2 was first identified on the basis of its ability to stimulate proliferation of T cells, and was thought initially to be the only T cell growth factor. Subsequently, however, IL-2 was found to stimulate proliferation of B cells as well. IL-4 is an additional T cell growth factor; it was first identified as a stimulatory factor for B cells. Both IL-2 and IL-4 serve as autocrine growth factors for the T cells which secrete them, and as paracrine growth factors for T cells which do not. IL-4 favors the development of cells that produce IL-4, IL-15, produced preferentially by nonlymphoid cells, also stimulates T cell growth. Uncontrolled growth of T cells that would occur through the autocrine pathway is prevented by regulatory processes which include desensitization of the T cell receptor for antigen, limitation of the period of time that cytokines are secreted, and modulation of the level of expression of growth factor receptors.

Much of the 'help' provided by T lymphocytes for antibody production is mediated by secreted cytokines. However, resting B cells require interactions with cell surface molecules expressed by T cells. The interaction of CD40, expressed constitutively by B cells, with CD40 ligand, expressed by T cells only upon activation, renders B cells responsive to IL-4 and other cytokines. This interaction stimulates the T cell as well. The most efficient help for B cells is provided by the T cell subset designated T_H2, which secretes IL-4 and IL-5. These cytokines provide optimal B cell proliferation and differentiation. The T_H1 subset, which secretes IL-2 and IFN-γ but not IL-4 or IL-5, also may be able to provide help for B cells. Cytokines influence which antibody isotype is produced: IL-4 is required for immunoglobulin E (IgE) responses, and IFN-γ and perhaps other factors from T_H1 cells favor IgG2a production. In addition to their effects on antibody production by B cells, cytokines secreted by $CD4^+$ helper T cells enhance generation of $CD8^+$ cytolytic T cells. Thus, both T_H1 and T_H2 cells appear to be able to serve as helper cells, although they may function in different situations and promote qualitatively different immune responses.

In addition to the antiviral effects that led to its designation, IFN-γ causes increased expression of both class I and class II MHC antigens by macrophages and activation of macrophages for greater killing of ingested microorganisms. However, IFN-γ also inhibits the effects of IL-4 on B cells and inhibits proliferation of bone marrow cells induced by several other T cell cytokines. IL-6, which is secreted by some nonlymphoid cells, acts as a B cell stimulation and differentiation factor and stimulates the release of acute-phase reactants from liver cells; IL-3 stimulates pluripotential bone marrow stem cells and mast cells. IL-10 inhibits the ability of macrophages to stimulate T_H1 cells. IL-12 increases production of IFN-γ by naive T cells. Granulocyte-macrophage colony-stimulating factor (GM-CSF) stimulates granulocyte and monocyte precursors. Tumor necrosis factor α (TNF-α) is produced by macrophages as well as T cells; it causes leukocytosis, fever, weight loss and necrosis of some tumors. Lymphotoxin also kills target cells; its gene is closely linked to that for TNF-α, and there is 30% homology in the sequence of amino acids for these two proteins. Most major cytokines have probably been identified. These and other interactions among cytokines are important in the regulation of immune responses.

Although cytolytic activity has usually been associated with CD8+ T cells, many CD4+ T cells also have cytolytic potential. There are several distinct cytolytic mechanisms. Perforin, a complement-like molecule, is found in intracellular granules in cytolytic T cells and natural killer (NK) cells. Interaction between surface-bound Fas ligand, expressed by activated T cells, with Fas, expressed by some target cells, can also mediate cytotoxicity. Cytokines, such as lymphotoxin or TNF, can kill some target cells. The killing process is unidirectional, and the T cell is not injured by the cytolytic events. NK cells appear to use similar killing mechanisms as CD8+ cytolytic T cells. Most NK cells, at least in the human, appear not to be of the T cell lineage; the receptors that NK cells use to interact with target cells have not been well characterized. Also, NK cells can mediate antibody-dependent cytotoxicity (ADCC); this involves interactions of Fc receptors on NK cells with antibody bound to target cells.

Conclusion

Different T cell subsets have different roles in the various features of cell-mediated immunity, although these roles have not been fully characterized. In several experimental infections, the patterns of disease indicate preferential involvement of one or another T cell subset. Factors which influence the development of the several T lymphocyte subsets are beginning to be understood, and the mechanisms that selectively regulate their responses have been partially defined.

See also: **Antibody-dependent cellular cytotoxicity; Helper T lymphocytes; Contrasuppression; Cytokines; Cytotoxic T lymphocytes; Delayed-type hypersensitivity; Effector lymphocytes; Graft rejection; Graft-versus-host reaction; Mononuclear phagocyte system; Natural killer (NK) cells; Perforin; Suppressor T lymphocytes; T lymphocytes.**

Further reading

Fitch FW, McKisic MD, Lancki DW and Gajewski TF (1993) Differential regulation of murine T lymphocyte subsets. *Annual Review of Immunology* **11**: 29–48.

Henkart PA (1994) Lymphocyte-mediated cytotoxicity: two pathways and multiple effector molecules. *Immunity* **1**: 343–346.

Lenschow DJ, Walunas TL and Bluestone JA (1996) CD28/B7 system of T cell costimulation. *Annual Review of Immunology* **14**: 233–258.

CELL-MEDIATED LYSIS

David W Lancki, Frank W Fitch Monoclonal Antibody Facility, The Gwen Knapp Center, Chicago, Illinois, USA

Cell-mediated lysis (CML) of antigen-bearing target cells was first demonstrated in 1960, when it was shown that thoracic lymphocytes sensitized *in vivo* towards allogeneic kidney cells could, *in vitro*, lyse target cells expressing the appropriate alloantigens. This lytic activity of lymphoid cells from sensitized individuals is believed to be the correlate *in vitro* of corresponding effector functions of lymphoid cells *in vivo*. The destructive potential of lymphocytes from immunized animals was confirmed subsequently by other investigators. Close cell-to-cell contact was found to be required between the lymphocytes and the target cells. Lysis was shown to be a rapid event which progressed as a linear function of time and depended on the concentration of effector cells. The observations suggested that a 'single hit' was required for inactivation of target cells, i.e. a single effector cell was able to destroy a target cell. These remarkable early observations were made using model systems that involved relatively difficult and time-consuming methods of surveying target cell death.

The quantification of the lytic potential of lymphocytes was greatly facilitated by the development of convenient and sensitive assays for the measurement of target cell death, using radioactive isotopes to label target cells. One such well-defined system involved the measurement of release of radioactivity from ^{51}Cr-labeled cells lysed by immune lymphocytes. Improved culture systems made possible the detailed investigation of CML. By 1970, it was possible to generate cytotoxic murine and human lymphocytes in unidirectional mixed lymphocyte reaction (MLR). This was achieved by culturing normal lymphocytes with allogeneic lymphoid cells that had been rendered unable to divide by treatment with X-rays or mitomycin C. The reproducible populations of effector cells generated in MLR greatly facilitated the analysis of the genetic basis of CML and the investigation of the mechanism(s) of lysis. In addition, the MLR provided the fundamental techniques that enabled the derivation of clonal populations of effector lymphocytes. Homogeneous populations of lymphocytes allow specific functions to be associated with a particular cell type, providing the means to study the molecular basis for CML specificity, cell adhesion events, activation, and lytic mechanisms.

Effector cells capable of mediating lysis

With reproducible methods of generating effector cell populations and assessing target cell death, thymus-derived (T) lymphocytes were identified as the principal effector cells involved in antigen-specific CML. T lymphocytes have been divided functionally into helper T lymphocytes (T_H) or cytolytic T lymphocytes (CTLs) based on the apparent predominant function of these cells. However, recent studies indicate that there is considerable functional overlap among these populations. The capacity to demonstrate the lytic potential of a given lymphocyte population depends in part on the nature of the target cells used. Other T cell populations, whose recognition mechanisms are less well characterized than those of $CD4^+$ T_H and $CD8^+$ CTL, are also capable of mediating lysis. These include the CD4/CD8 double negative $\alpha\beta$ TCR-positive T cells and the $\gamma\delta$ TCR-positive T cells.

Lymphoid cells other than T lymphocytes can also display lytic activity against certain target cells. Natural killer (NK) cells are lymphoid cells that have the capacity to lyse certain transformed target cells such as K562 (human) or YAC-1 (murine) by a process that does not involve MHC restriction. NK activity occurs in cells having the morphology of large granular lymphocytes (LGLs); these cells express distinctive cell surface markers but they are not well defined with respect to their lineage. Natural killer lysis involves events similar to those that have been identified in antigen-specific lysis by CTLs, and may involve similar mechanisms. NK cells bear receptors for the Fc portion of immunoglobulin G (IgG); these receptors allow NK cells to lyse antibody-coated target cells by a process referred to as antibody-dependent cellular cytotoxicity (ADCC). Cells having properties that are distinguishable from those of NK cells and CTLs, termed killer (K) cells, also function as effector cells in ADCC. Finally, lytic activity can be induced in lymphoid cells in culture by exposure to supraoptimal concentrations of interleukin 2 (IL-2), which leads to the induction of lymphokine-activated killer (LAK) cells.

Properties of cell-mediated lysis

The process of CML involves the close interaction of cytotoxic lymphocytes with appropriate 'target' cells in a way that results in the unidirectional lysis of the target cell. It has been divided into several discrete stages: 1) recognition of the target cell by the effector cell, and the formation of a magnesium-dependent strong adhesion between the effector and target cells; 2) the 'programming for lysis' or 'delivery of the lethal hit'; 3) target cell lysis which does not require the continued presence of the effector cell; and 4) recycling of the effector cell.

CML is best characterized in systems involving antigen-specific T lymphocytes and, to a lesser extent, NK or ADCC effector cells. Initial cell contact between lymphocytes and target cells appears to be a random event. Once this has occurred, effector cells can form a close association or conjugate with target cells. Several cell surface structures have been implicated as mediating or contributing to cell adhesion, based on the capacity of specific antibodies to inhibit effector–target conjugation or lysis. CD11a/CD18 (LFA-1) and CD2 (LFA-2), which are expressed on lymphocytes, and CD54 (ICAM-1) and CD58 (LFA-3), which are expressed on target cells, represent adhesion molecules involved in interactions between immune cells and their targets. Other structures, including CD8 and CD4, may contribute to cell adhesion between T cells and target cells bearing class I or class II major histocompatibility complex (MHC) molecules, respectively. However, CD4, CD8 and CD11a/CD18 also may be involved in the regulation of signaling through the T cell receptor (TCR).

A similar role has been postulated for CD2 which reacts with CD58 expressed on target cells. Other receptor–ligand interactions are involved in the generation of CTLs from nonlytic precursors. Interactions between CD28 or the related CTLA-4 molecule on small resting T cells with CD80 (B7 or BB1) or CD86 (B70 or B7-2) on the antigen-presenting cell provide costimulatory signals for activation through the antigen receptor complex. However, CD28 costimulation does not appear to be essential for the effector phase of CTL function.

The recognitive events associated with CTL–target cell interaction is mediated through the clonally distributed TCR. In both the human and the mouse, the predominant TCR structure is that of an αβ heterodimer, which has variable regions similar to but distinct from those of Ig molecules. Cells expressing the alternative, γδ TCR structure have also been shown to function as lytic effector cells. The precise mechanism by which the lethal hit is triggered is not known. The TCR is physically associated on the cell surface with the CD3 complex, which has been identified as the primary structure involved in transmembrane signaling. The role of the TCR–CD3 complex in triggering the lethal hit comes from studies showing that soluble anti-TCR–CD3 monoclonal antibodies (mAbs) can inhibit lysis, while anti-TCR–CD3 mAb immobilized on the surface of target cells can induce lysis of those targets. The combination of calcium ionophore and phorbol esters (capable of activating protein kinase C) can mimic the activation via the TCR–CD3 complex. This treatment induces the release of CTL granule-associated molecules and triggers lysis of target cells nonspecifically.

Mechanisms of target cell destruction

No single mechanism seems to account for all of the events associated with target cell destruction observed in short term cell-mediated lytic assays. Membrane damage, through a process which requires extracellular calcium, has been implicated as an effector mechanism in nearly every form of CML, but the lysis of nucleated target cells also involves apoptosis. Two cell-mediated cytolytic pathways have been identified and molecularly defined. One pathway involves membrane damage inflicted on the target cell by the regulated release of pore-forming proteins by the killer lymphocyte, leading directly to the death of the target cell. A second pathway involves interaction of membrane proteins on the effector cell and the target cell which provides a signal leading to apoptosis in the target cell.

Membrane damage (perforin/exocytosis) pathway of lysis

Evidence that membrane damage may play a role in the lysis of target cells came initially from morphological studies which indicated that target cells swell and burst after contact with lymphoid cells. These observations led to the proposal that death resulted from 'colloid osmotic' forces due to the influx of water through the lesions. Direct evidence for the formation of 'pores' was provided by electron microscopy of erythrocyte ghosts following lysis by lymphocytes in an ADCC reaction, and these findings were extended to cloned CTL and NK cells. Enucleated target cells are susceptible to CML events including the release of ^{51}Cr, and anucleate erythrocytes coated with anti-TCR-CD3 mAb can be lysed by conventional CTL. Collectively, these and other data suggest that membrane damage can occur as a result of the interaction between at least some cytotoxic lymphocytes and target cells during CML. A complement component C9-like molecule, perforin, is present in the granules of CTL and NK cells. Stimuli that trigger lysis by CTL also trigger the exocytosis of granule-associated serine esterase activity. A model has been proposed in which TCR cross-linking induces the activation of protein kinase C and increased intracellular levels of calcium, which in turn leads to CTL granule exocytosis. Calcium appears to be required for exocytosis and is absolutely required for the perforin pathway. However, certain target cells can be lysed by CTL in the apparent absence of extracellular calcium or exocytosis of granular material. These findings suggested that the perforin/exocytosis pathway was not the sole mechanism of CML.

Internal disintegration (Fas) pathway of lysis

CTLs induce rapid DNA damage in target cells that is not observed in complement-mediated or perforin-mediated lysis of cells. Based on this observation, an 'internal disintegration' model has been proposed in which CTLs induce target cell endonucleases which digest DNA, yielding 150–180 base pair units. This process can occur in the absence of extracellular calcium.

Perforin-deficient mice have been generated using gene targeting techniques. They provide a direct assessment of the role of perforin *in vivo*. Lymphocyte development is unaffected in mice lacking perforin. Perforin-dependant cytotoxicity appears to be required to clear at least some pathogens *in vivo*. Perforin-deficient mice are unable to clear lymphocytic choriomeningitis virus, but were able to control vaccinia virus infection, although both induce strong primary CTL responses. CTLs generated *in vivo* or *in vitro* in response to these stimuli are highly lytic toward antigen-bearing target cells that express the Fas antigen (CD95), but not against target cells which do not express Fas antigen. Studies using perforin-deficient mice have provided direct evidence for Fas-mediated pathway of lysis, which requires the expression of Fas antigen on the target cell, and involves DNA damage in target cells. The Fas ligand (FasL), is expressed on CTLs. It is currently thought that Fas-dependent cell-mediated cytotoxicity requires the interaction of the FasL on the effector cell and Fas on the target cell (perhaps inducing Fas trimerization) which triggers an, as yet poorly defined, cell death signal pathway. T cell activation can induce FasL expression, but the regulation of FasL expression is incompletely understood.

CD4$^+$ as well as CD8$^+$ T cells can lyse target cells bearing relevant antigen; however, not all T cells use the same lytic mechanisms. The perforin/exocytosis pathway is generally expressed by CD8$^+$ CTLs and some CD4$^+$ T$_H$2 cells, but not by CD4$^+$ T cells having properties of T$_H$1 cells. The Fas pathway of lysis appears to be expressed by both CD4$^+$ and CD8$^+$ T cells.

Although perforin/exocytosis and Fas pathways seem to account for most, if not all, CML observed in short-term assays, lymphocytes produce several factors that are cytotoxic. Tumor necrosis factor α (TNFα), lymphotoxin (LT) and TNFα/LT-like molecules such as NK cytotoxic factor (NKCF) are potential effector molecules. In susceptible target cells, LT-containing supernatants produced by CTLs can induce DNA fragmentation, and LT-like molecules have been found to be associated with granules; LT-like molecules are produced by CTLs and NK, T$_H$ and mast cells. Proteolytic enzymes have also

been implicated in the lytic activity of CTLs and NK cells and in ADCC, based on the observation that various protease inhibitors inhibit lytic activity. CTLs from mutant mice lacking the neutral serine protease, granzyme B, are able to induce ^{51}Cr release from target cells with reduced efficiency, but are profoundly deficient in their ability to induce rapid DNA fragmentation. The role of these enzymes in lysis is not clear; however, they may be cosecreted with other granule-related molecules to induce or enhance DNA fragmentation.

Conclusion

Cell-mediated lysis is clearly a complex phenomenon that involves distinct mediators, which are either released through the process of exocytosis or are expressed on the cell surface. Those mediators which are critical to a particular form of lymphocyte-mediated lysis may depend on the type of effector cell involved and also on properties of the target cell. The identification of specific molecular mechanisms of cell mediated lysis *in vitro* should facilitate the assessment of their *in vivo* relevance.

See also: **Adhesion molecules; Antibody-dependent cellular cytotoxicity; Cytotoxic T lymphocytes; Cytotoxicity, assays for; Cytotoxicity, mechanisms of; Lymphokine-activated killer (LAK) cells; Mixed lymphocyte reaction (MLR); Natural killer (NK) cells; Perforin; Tumor necrosis factor α; Lymphotoxin.**

Further reading

Griffiths GM and Tschopp J (eds) (1995) Pathways for cytolysis. *Current Topics in Microbiology and Immunology* 198: 1–217.

Moller G (ed) (1995) Molecular basis of T-cell cytotoxicity. *Immunological Reviews* 146: 1–266.

CELL SEPARATION TECHNIQUES

Silvano Ferrini and **Lorenzo Moretta**, Istituto Nazionale per la Ricerca sul Cancro, Genoa, Italy

The past three decades have witnessed major progress in the development of methods allowing the identification and separation of various cell populations. This has had a major impact upon the precise dissection of the immune system and the definition of the cellular basis of the immune response. The combined use of newly identified cell surface markers and cell separation techniques has been fundamental

for the precise assignment of given functional properties to well-defined cell subsets.

The first cell separation techniques, which were developed in the early 1960s, were based on physical differences such as cell size and density. The limitation of these methods is mostly related to the low degree of physical heterogeneity existing among lymphocytes. However, this approach may be particularly useful when combined with techniques which make use of phenotypic markers to tag the cells so that they can be separated by physical means (e.g. rosetting techniques). Major advances in cell separation techniques were made possible by the identification of membrane receptors or surface antigens which are differently expressed by lymphocyte subsets. For example, the identification of immunoglobulin (Ig) molecules on the surface of B lymphocytes and of receptors for sheep erythrocytes on human T cells allowed the identification and the separation of B and T lymphocytes, respectively. More recently, the development of monoclonal antibody (mAb) technology has provided a potent tool to precisely and reproducibly identify lymphocyte subsets expressing given antigens. Most of the mAb-defined surface leukocyte antigens have been classified into a still growing list of 'cluster of differentiation' (CD) antigens. Therefore, at present, the most widely applied lymphocyte separation techniques are represented by immunoselection procedures based on the use of mAbs. Among immunoselection techniques, the use of mAbs and complement (immunotoxicity) allows the selective depletion ('negative selection') of cells expressing a given surface antigen. Other immunoselection techniques, however, allow both 'negative' and 'positive' selection. Most of these techniques are based on the attachment of antibodies to different substrates or carriers, including plastic surfaces, erythrocytes or magnetic beads. Cells that are recognized by these mAbs and thus bind to these substrates can be subsequently separated by adherence, density gradients or magnetic fields, respectively. There is little doubt that the most precise and objective tool for the separation of cells stained with fluorochrome-labeled mAbs is represented by the fluorescence-activated cell sorter (FACS). A major advantage of FACS fractionation over the other immunoselection procedures is represented by the possibility of precisely defining the density of a given surface antigen and, therefore, the threshold values for cell separation. In addition, the FACS allows simultaneously analysis of several parameters and the separation of cells accordingly. In spite of these major advantages, a limitation of the FACS is related to the relatively low numbers of cells that can be processed per unit of time.

When approaching a problem of lymphoid cell separation, the choice of the technique to be applied should take into account a number of parameters, including cell numbers, purity and yield. In most instances, cell purity is inversely related to the yield. Less purity should also be expected when the cells of interest represent a minor fraction of the initial population. In addition, the possible consequences of

cell manipulations on sterility, cell viability and function should be carefully considered. In some instances it may be convenient to combine two methods, for example a rosetting technique (which allows the processing of large numbers of cells) followed by FACS sorting (to obtain a high degree of purity).

The principal methods of lymphoid cell separation are listed in **Table 1** and are described below.

Techniques based on physical properties of the cells

The two procedures that have been most widely applied for lymphocyte separation based on physical differences are sedimentation separation and density gradient separation.

In *sedimentation separation* (or velocity sedimentation), cell suspensions are stratified in a thin layer on top of a fluid column contained in appropriate sedimentation chambers. Cells are allowed to sediment through the fluid under the action of gravitational forces ($1g$ sedimentation). Alternatively, to speed up the procedure, larger forces can be applied by the use of centrifugation. To this end, a special device has been developed, the centrifugal elutriator, which allows the purification of larger numbers of cells within a short time. In sedimentation separation, cells are fractionated primarily on the basis of differences in size, while the cell density has a minor influence on the sedimentation rate. After appropriate time intervals cell fractions can be collected through the bottom of the sedimentation chambers. Clearly, cells collected first are those of a larger size.

Techniques based on *density gradient separation* are widely employed and many different procedures have been developed. These techniques are based on the preparation of gradients of appropriate density which may be either discontinuous or continuous. In principle, the material composing the gradient should be nontoxic for the cells. In the case of continuous gradients, cells are usually layered on top of the gradient (in some instances, however, it may be convenient to load cells on the bottom, or disperse them within the gradient). The range of densities of the gradient should cover the densities expected for the cells of interest. The gradient is centrifuged for a time sufficient to allow cells to reach an equilibrium in the portion of the gradient corresponding to their density. Cells of density greater than that of the gradient will sediment at the bottom of the tube. For lymphoid cell separation it should be noted that the differences in density among cell subsets are small, ranging between 1.05 and 1.10 g ml^{-1}. The materials originally employed for continuous density gradients

Table 1 Principal methods of cell separation

Principal	Method	Applications
Physical differences	Sedimentation	Cell separation according to size
	Density gradient centrifugation	Cell separation according to density
Functional properties	Adhesion to plastic	Positive or negative selection of
	Adhesion on nylon wool columns	macrophages
	Phagocytosis of iron particles	Isolation of T lymphocytes
	'Hot' thymidine pulse	Depletion of macrophages
	Selective cell stimulation and growth	Depletion of proliferating cells
		Enrichment of proliferating cells
Expression of surface receptors	E (erythrocyte) rosettes	Positive or negative selection of T cells:
	EA (erythrocyte–antibody) rosettes	Fcγ-receptor$^+$ cells
	EAC (erythrocyte–antibody–complement) rosettes	Complement receptor$^+$ cells
Expression of surface antigens (immunoselection)	Immunotoxicity (complement depletion)	Depletion of cells expressing a given surface antigen
	Immunoaffinity columns	
	Immunoadherence (panning)	Negative or positive selection of cells expressing a given surface antigen
	Rosetting with antibody-coated erythrocytes	
	Immunomagnetic beads	
	Immunofluorescence and FACS fractionation	

included bovine serum albumin (BSA) and, more recently, colloidal silica. In discontinuous density gradients, which may be either single or multiple step, cell suspensions are layered on the top of the gradient and centrifuged until equilibrium is reached. Cells will not move into the portion of the gradient having a higher density than that of the cells and will thus accumulate at the interface. The most widely used materials for discontinuous gradients are Ficoll-Hypaque, BSA or colloidal silica. The Ficoll-Hypaque solution used for human lymphocyte separation is an isotonic solution of sodium metrizoate and Ficoll with a density of $1.077\,\mathrm{g\,ml^{-1}}$. Ficoll-Hypaque gradients are primarily used for the isolation of mononuclear cells (lymphocytes and monocytes) from blood and for the isolation of lymphocytes forming rosettes with erythrocytes. Diluted blood (1:2–1:4) is layered on the top of Ficoll-Hypaque and then spun on a centrifuge. After a suitable time interval, mononuclear cells can be collected at the interface, while erythrocytes and neutrophils are found at the bottom of the tube. Percoll is a commercially available solution composed of colloidal silica coated with polyvinylpyrrolidone in order to render the material nontoxic for cells. Percoll is characterized by high density (1.130) and low osmolarity; as a consequence, for the preparation of Percoll density gradients for cell separation, the osmolarity is adjusted to physiological values by mixing 9 parts of Percoll solution with 1 part of 10$\times$ saline. Percoll solutions with different densities can be easily obtained by appropriate dilutions in isotonic medium, thus allowing the preparation of multiple step discontinuous gradients; these are particularly useful for the isolation of different subsets of lymphocytes characterized by density differences (e.g. isolation of 'large granular lymphocytes' (LGL) from a lymphoid suspension or isolation of activated blasts from resting lymphocytes).

Techniques based on functional properties of the cells

Adhesive or phagocytic properties

Certain mononuclear cell types have the property of adhering to plastic surfaces and/or to nylon wool. Thus, cells of the monocyte/macrophage lineage rapidly (30–60 min) adhere to plastic when incubated at 37°C. This property has been widely exploited for both positive and negative selection of monocytes from peripheral blood-derived mononuclear cells. The preferential ability of monocytes and B lymphocytes to adhere to nylon wool columns has been frequently applied to remove these cells from mononuclear cell suspensions and, thus, to enrich for T lymphocytes. The demonstration that subsets of interleukin 2 (IL-2)-activated effector cells capable of lysing fresh tumor cells (i.e. lymphokine-activated killer (LAK) cells) display the ability to adhere to plastic (adherent LAK) has provided a useful tool for enriching for these cells. Another method frequently employed for removal of monocytes is based on the fact that monocytes display phagocytic properties:

cells that have ingested iron particles (carbonyl iron) are removed by application of a magnetic field.

Selective depletion of cells undergoing proliferation

Lymphocytes undergoing proliferation induced by antigens or mitogens actively incorporate ^{3}H-thymidine [^{3}H]TdR and their DNA. Beside the conventional measurement of cell proliferation, [^{3}H]TdR with a higher specific activity can be used to induce selective killing of proliferating cells. If the amount of [^{3}H]TdR incorporated in the cDNA is sufficiently high, intranuclear irradiation due to β-particle emission will result in cell death. The addition of cold TdR will prevent further incorporation of [^{3}H]TdR. This technique allows, for example, the selective elimination of T cells proliferating in response to soluble antigens or alloantigens. An alternative procedure is based on the use of 5-bromodeoxyuridine (BrdU) followed by exposure of cells to ultraviolet (UV) light. When activated by UV light the BrdU incorporated into the DNA of proliferating cells will cause breaks in the DNA, resulting in cell death.

Selective cell stimulation and growth

Another approach to the selection of given lymphocyte populations is based on the ability of these cells to respond selectively to appropriate mitogenic stimuli in culture. For example, superantigens or mAbs specific for a given TCR-V$_\beta$ will induce a selective activation and proliferation of T cells expressing the appropriate V$_\beta$. In addition, the use of recombinant cytokines acting as growth/differentiation factors may induce the preferential expansion of given subsets. For example, IL-4 will induce a preferential growth/differentiation towards T$_H$2 cells. On the other hand, peripheral mononuclear cells, in the presence of both IL-4 and granulocyte-macrophage colony-stimulating factor (GM-CSF) will lead to proliferation and differentiation of immature dendritic cells, which can be induced to a more mature phenotype by subsequent addition of, for example, tumor necrosis factor α.

Rosetting techniques

Rosetting techniques are widely employed in immunology for the detection or purification of cells expressing a given surface 'receptor' of antigen. The principle of this separation technique is the formation of cell agglutinates (rosettes) with a consequent change in size or density of the rosetting cells with respect to nonrosetting cells. A common approach is the use of erythrocytes which spontaneously bind to certain lymphocyte subsets (e.g. sheep erythrocytes binding to human T cells via CD2 surface molecules). Other erythrocytes which do not spontaneously bind to human lymphocytes can be coated with appropriate ligands or mAbs which allow binding to specific receptors or surface antigens. Whatever the rosetting technique employed, the cell suspension containing rosetting cells can be subjected to either sedimentation or, more frequently, density gradient separation. Rosettes formed with erythrocytes can be easily separated from nonrosetting cells by Ficoll-Hypaque gradients and recovered from the bottom of the gradient. Rosetting cells can be freed from erythrocytes by lysis in appropriate buffers containing ammonium chloride or using distilled water.

Immunoselection techniques

These techniques make use of antibodies (either polyclonal antisera or preferably mAbs) directed to surface antigens expressed by given lymphocyte subsets. Both direct and indirect immunoselection procedures have been applied. Direct methods require a single step (i.e. only the antibody directed to a relevant antigen is needed), while indirect methods require a second reagent (i.e. an antiserum directed to the first antibody). The advantages of direct methods include a greater speed and a better specificity, since possible reactions of the second (anti-Ig) reagent with cell surface antigens are avoided. However, indirect methods may be preferable due to their sensitivity (amplification given by the second antibody) and the use of less reagent (e.g. mAbs). In addition, indirect procedures may be more convenient when several different first-step antibodies requiring a common second reagent are used.

Immunotoxicity

In these procedures, antibodies are used as a means to induce selective cytolysis of cells expressing a given antigen at the cell surface. This can be achieved either by coupling mAbs to cytotoxic reagents (immunotoxins) or by the addition of complement. These procedures (particularly the complement depletion that has been widely applied in both basic and clinical immunology) have the major advantage that large numbers of cells can be processed. For example, complement depletion has been used in *in vitro* studies aimed at establishing whether a given function is associated with a phenotypically defined cell subset. It should be noted that the inhibition of a cell function following depletion of a lymphocyte subset may be consequent either to the elimination of cells directly responsible for that function or to removal of cells with a regulatory role on the function itself. An important clinical application of complement depletion has been the removal of T lymphocytes from bone marrow prior to allogeneic transplantation. Both polyclonal antisera and mAbs can be used as a source of antibody to be used in complement depletion. However, not all antibody isotypes are capable of complement fixation and this should be taken into account when using mAbs: only murine IgM, IgG2a and IgG2b work in this procedure. Regarding the source of complement, rabbit or guinea pig serum is routinely used, either fresh, lyophilized or stored at −80°C. It should be stressed that sera may contain 'natural' antibodies reacting with the cells of interest, thus leading to complement activation and cell lysis even in the absence of test antibody. This problem must be avoided by carefully selecting sera on the basis of low 'natural' antibody titers. In addition, natural antibodies (e.g. antihuman) can be removed by adsorbing sera with appropriate cells (e.g. human erythrocytes) at 4°C. The procedure for complement depletion involves a first step in which cell suspensions are incubated for 30–60 min at 4°C with an appropriate dilution of the relevant antibody. Subsequently, cells are washed and, after the addition of appropriate amounts of complement, they are incubated at 37°C for at least 1 h. The first step (binding of antibody to cells) must be carried out at low temperature in order to avoid antibody-mediated surface antigen capping and modulation, which would prevent optimal complement fixation and cell lysis. An approximate estimation of the efficiency of cell lysis can be obtained by dye-exclusion viability tests (e.g. trypan blue). Dead cells can be further removed by density gradient separation.

Immunoadhesion

In these procedures, antibodies directed to cell surface antigens are bound to a solid support, so that cells expressing the relevant antigen can be easily separated by adherence to the support itself. The solid support is represented by either plastic surfaces (e.g. Petri dishes) or beads. The latter have been used to prepare immunoaffinity columns for cell separation. These columns have been primarily employed for negative selection of cell populations, as the recovery of cells sticking to the columns is difficult and results in poor cell yield and viability. In contrast, immunoadherence to plastic surfaces (panning) allows both positive and negative cell selection. Attachment of the antibody to the solid support can be achieved either by a chemical covalent link or by physical adsorption on appropriate hydrophobic plastic surfaces. In the case of panning, the antibody (5–50 μg ml^{-1}) can be easily attached to untreated

polystyrene Petri dishes by adsorption using alkaline buffers (e.g. 50 mM TRIS pH 9.5). After overnight incubation the unbound antibody is washed out and free adsorption sites of the plastic are saturated by incubation with a protein solution (e.g. BSA or fetal calf serum, FCS). For lymphocyte fractionation, cell suspensions are layered in a small volume on Petri dishes and incubated at 4°C in the presence of low protein concentration (e.g. 2% FCS) for 1 h. Incubation at low temperature is required in order to prevent nonspecific binding of cells to the plastic. The occurrence of cell adherence to Petri dishes during the procedure can be conveniently checked by microscopic examination. At the end of the incubation period, the nonadherent cells are gently removed by pipette, followed by washing. The adherent cells, expressing the relevant antigen, are recovered after vigorous pipetting or by scraping with a 'rubber policeman' (a rubber-covered glass rod).

Immunomagnetic beads

In this immunoselection technique, antibodies are attached to iron-containing microspheres (2–5 μm diameter). Polystyrene microspheres obtained by polymerization in the presence of colloidal iron are now widely employed. The antibody is attached to the beads either by physical adsorption or by chemical covalent links. Either antibodies directed to relevant cell surface antigens or anti-Ig (second) antibodies can be linked to the beads for direct or indirect separation techniques, respectively. In the first approach, the cell suspension is allowed to interact directly with the microspheres; in the indirect approach, lymphocytes are first stained with the relevant mAb and subsequently mixed with the anti-Ig covered beads. In both cases, antigen-positive cells will form rosettes with the beads. Rosetting cells can be easily separated from other cells by applying a magnetic field for a short time (1–2 min). Both negatively and positively selected cells can be utilized for further analysis or cell culture. In general the magnetic bead:lymphocyte ratio should be higher in the case of negative selection. Release of magnetic beads from rosetting cells can be achieved by 24–48 h incubation of cells at 37°C or by the addition of an excess of soluble antibody, displacing the beads-bound antibody. Free beads can then be removed by magnetic separation. Magnetic beads have been successfully used both for fractionation of lymphoid subsets and for 'purging' bone marrow to remove tumor cells or T lymphocytes prior to transplantation.

Magnetic cell sorting

Magnetic cell sorting represents an interesting evolution of immunomagnetic separation techniques. The principle is based on the use of mAbs or other ligands (e.g. lectins) which specifically bind to surface antigen/receptor expressed by a given cell subset. These reagents are labeled with microbeads (5×10^2-fold smaller than eukaryotic cells). The cell suspension treated with the magnetically-labeled mAbs are passed through a separation column which is placed in a potent magnetic field. Unlabeled cells pass through the column and can be collected at the bottom, while labeled cells are retained on the column. In order to recover the labeled subset of cells the column is removed from the magnetic field, thus permitting the labeled cells to be eluted from the column. Both direct or indirect labeling can be used with this technique and it is possible to separate a relatively large number of cells in a short time.

Separation by fluorescence-activated cell sorter (FACS)

Flow cytofluorimetry has provided a precise and objective means of quantifying both the number of cells expressing a given surface marker and the extent to which the marker is expressed. By combining this technology with mAbs directed to lymphocyte surface antigens it is now possible to define and purify lymphocyte subpopulations with a precision that was not possible using other methodologies.

Lymphocytes to be analyzed and/or separated by FACS must be labeled with fluorochrome-conjugated antibodies using either direct or indirect immunofluorescence techniques. The FACS allows purification of both antigen-positive/negative subsets and also allows the definition and separation of subsets on the basis of multiple parameters.

See also: **Antigen-specific cells, enrichment and isolation; Hematopoietic stem cell transplantation; CD antigens; CD2; Complement, membrane attack pathway; Cytotoxicity, assays for; Flow cytometry; Immune response *in vitro*; Lymphocytes; Lymphokine-activated killer (LAK) cells; Monoclonal antibodies (mAbs); Phagocytosis; Proliferation, lymphocyte; Rosetting techniques; Viability, methods of assessing leukocyte.**

Further reading

Abts H, Emmerich M, Miltenyi S, Radbruch A and Tesch H (1989) CD20 positive human B lymphocytes separated with the magnetic cell sorter (MACS) can be induced to proliferation and antibody secretion *in vitro*. *Journal of Immunological Methods* **125**: 19–28.

Battye FL and Shortman K (1991) Flow cytometry and cell separation procedures. *Current Opinion in Immunology* **3**: 238–241.

Feucht HE, Hadam MR, Frank FR and Riethmuller G (1980) Efficient separation of human T lymphocytes from venous blood using PVP-coated colloidal silica particles (Percoll). *Journal of Immunological Methods* **38**: 43–51.

Herzenberg LA, Weir DM, Herzenberg LA and Blackwell C (eds) (1997) *Handbook of Experimental Immunology* 5th edn. Blackwell Science, Oxford.

Knapp W, Rieber P, Dorken B, Schmidt RE, Stein H and Borne AEG (1989) Towards a better definition of human leukocyte surface molecules. *Immunology Today* **10**: 253–258.

Lea T, Verdtal F, Davies C and Ugelstad J (1985) Magnetic monosized polymer particles for fast and specific fractionation of human mononuclear cells. *Scandinavian Journal of Immunology* **22**: 207–216.

Manyonda IT, Soltys AJ and Hay FC (1992) A critical evaluation of the magnetic cell sorter and its use in the positive and negative selection of CD45RO$^+$ cells. *Journal of Immunological Methods* **149**: 1–10.

Miller RG, Gorkynski RM, Lafleur L, MacDonald HR and Phillips RA (1975) Cell separation analysis of B and T lymphocyte differentiation. *Transplantation Reviews* **25**: 59–97.

Mishell RI and Shiigi SM (eds) (1980) *Selected Methods in Cellular Immunology*. San Francisco: WH Freeman.

Shortman K (1972) Physical procedures for the separation of animal cells. *Annual Review of Biophysics and Bioengineering* **1**: 93–130.

Timonen T, Reynolds CW, Ortaldo JR and Herberman RB (1982) Isolation of human and rat natural killer cells. *Journal of Immunological Methods* **51**: 269–277.

Wysoki LJ and Sato WL (1978) 'Panning' for lymphocytes: a method for cell selection. *Proceedings of the National Academy of Sciences of the USA* **75**: 2844–2848.

CELL SURFACE MOLECULES, IMMUNOPRECIPITATION OF

Frank AW Verreck and **Frits Koning**, Department of Immunohepatology and bloodbank, University Hospital Leiden, Leiden, The Netherlands

Immunoprecipitation of cell surface molecules is a quick and reliable method that allows the analysis of cell surface expressed molecules recognized by monoclonal antibodies and by antisera. In addition, using proper solubilization techniques, interactions between cell surface expressed molecules can be defined that give insight into subunit interactions in multichain receptor complexes. Usually lysates of cell surface iodinated cells are used. The principle of immunoprecipitation is based on 1) solubilization of membrane proteins by the use of nonionic detergents, 2) subsequent interaction of specific antibody with the solubilized membrane antigen, and 3) recovery of the antibody–antigen complexes by binding to an insoluble support, thereby allowing washing procedures to remove unbound molecules. Analysis of such immunoprecipitates usually takes place by SDS-PAGE or isoelectric focusing (IEF).

Solubilization of membrane molecules

The most widely used detergents for membrane solubilization are the nonionic detergents Triton X-100 and NP40 that have almost identical properties. Typically, $1–10 \times 10^7$ cells are resuspended in 0.5–1 ml of the following buffer: 50 mM Tris-HCl, 150 mM NaCl, 5 mM EDTA, 10 mM iodoacetamide, pH 8, containing either 0.5–1% Triton X-100 or NP40 and the following protease inhibitors: leupeptin, antipain, chymostatin, pepstatin (all $1 \, \mu g \, ml^{-1}$) and 0.1 mM 4-(2-aminoethyl)-benzenesulfonylfluoride (AEBSF), and lysed at 0°C for 30 min. Insoluble material is subsequently removed by centrifugation at 13 000 g for 15 min.

As an alternative to NP40 and Triton X-100 the nonionic detergents CHAPS (5 mM final concentration) or digitonin (1% final concentration) can be used in the lysis buffers. CHAPS and digitonin share the property that, in contrast to NP40 and Triton X-100, they do not, or hardly, disrupt subunit interactions within multichain receptor complexes like the T cell receptor, thereby allowing the recovery of more intact receptor complexes.

Immunoprecipitation

For immunoprecipitation, the antibodies used to detect the antigens must be bound to an insoluble ligand either before or after binding to their target antigen in order to facilitate washing procedures. For this purpose there are a number of alternatives: either the antibodies are covalently coupled to Sepharose beads or they are bound to Sepharose beads that have been coated with protein A or anti-immunoglobulin (Ig) antisera. It is also possible to use fixed *Staphylococcus aureus* bacteria, that express the protein A on their cell surface. Since at pH 8 protein A binds to the large majority of mouse, rabbit and human derived Ig types (not IgM), Sepharose protein A is a very convenient reagent to immobilize many antibodies used for immunoprecipitation. Before specific immunoprecipitations are carried out, the lysates are precleared to remove nonspecifically binding material by adding 100 μl Sepharose protein A beads and 75 μl normal rabbit serum to 1 ml lysate, followed by gently shaking at room temperature for 2 h. After removal of the beads, specific immunoprecipitations are carried out by mixing 1–10 μl monoclonal antibody or antiserum and 100 μl lysate for 60 min, either at room temperature or at 4°C, followed by the addition of 10 μl Sepharose protein A beads. After an additional 60 min, the beads are spun down (30 s, 13 000 g) and washed four times with 0.5 ml lysis buffer before analysis. This methodology can be easily modified for the use of immobilizing reagents other than Ig.

Sequential immunoprecipitation

Many cell surface expressed antigens are multichain complexes in which the chains may or may not be held together by disulfide bridges. The question may arise as to which chain in such complexes is actually recognized by the antibody or antiserum studied. Depending on the presence or absence of a disulfide bridge, one of the following procedures may be used to answer this question. Absence of a disulfide bridge: a normal immunoprecipitate is resuspended in 0.5% SDS and boiled for 3 min. This treatment leads to the dissociation of the individual chains and to the destruction of the antibody used as immunoprecipitating reagent. Subsequently, the SDS is neutralized by the addition of three volumes of lysis buffer containing 1.5% NP40. This preparation is now used for immunoprecipitation with the antibody of interest. Part of the preparation can be analyzed directly. Comparison of the bands present in the original and in the reprecipitated material indicates which molecule is actually recognized by the antibody. Presence of a disulfide bridge: the immunoprecipitate is resuspended in a 0.5% SDS solution containing 2 mM DTT and boiled for 3 min to reduce the disulfide bridge and dissociate the individual chains. Subsequently the material is alkylated by the addition of 10 mM Iodoacetamide. The remaining procedure is as described above.

Cross-linking

Biochemical cross-linkers are available that are reactive with lysine residues and, as these cross-linkers have two reactive groups, they can generate covalent, thiol-cleavable bonds between cell surface molecules that are in close vicinity to each other (<13 Å). They can thus be used to study the spatial relationship between cell surface expressed molecules. The most commonly used cross-linker is DSP (dithiobis (succinimidyl propionate)). For cross-linking, cells are resuspended in 0.5 ml PBS containing 1 mM $MgCl_2$, 0.02% NaN_3. Subsequently 50–100 μg DSP is added (5–10 μl of 10 mg DSP per ml DMSO) and the mixture is incubated on a shaker at room temperature for 30 min. Then the cells are washed twice with PBS and lysed. Subsequently immunoprecipitates can be obtained from these lysates as described above. Analysis of such immunoprecipitates under both reducing and nonreducing conditions by SDS-PAGE indicates which molecules are cross-linked by the DSP treatment.

Bulk purification of molecules of the major histocompatibility complex

Since the recent insight into the molecular basis of peptide presentation by molecules of the major histocompatibility complex (MHC), the bulk purification of peptide–MHC complexes has become established as a standard technique. It is now widely used in order to identify natural peptide ligands or peptide-binding characteristics of particular MHC specificities. In principle, this purification method can be considered as a large-scale immunoprecipitation procedure, which can be adapted for the bulk purification of any cell surface molecule.

The isolation of MHC-bound peptides

The MHC–peptide complexes are purified from cells of which pellets are collected at $-70°C$. A lysate (of 10^{10} cells or more) is made by thawing and resuspending the cell pellet at a concentration of 2×10^8 cells ml^{-1} in NP40-containing lysis buffer (described above). The lysate is precleared by incubation with Sepharose CL-4B beads (10 ml beads per 50 ml lysate; Pharmacia). This incubation can be done batchwise in 50 ml tubes under quiet agitation for 2 h at room temperature. After the incubation the Sepharose beads are removed from the lysate using a glass filter that is placed over a vacuum. The precleared lysate is subsequently incubated batch-wise for 16 h at 4°C with CNBr-activated Sepharose CL-4B beads to which antibody specific for the MHC molecule of interest has been covalently coupled (according to manufacturer's guidelines; Pharmacia). Then the affinity beads are washed on a glass filter (placed over a vacuum), taking care not to disturb the homogenous gel bed on the filter or letting the bed run dry. First, the beads are washed with minimally 5 bed volumes of a buffer containing 50 mM TRIS, 150 mM NaCl, pH 8.0, to which 0.5% NP40 (v/v; HPLC grade) has been added and subsequently with minimally 10 bed volumes of the TRIS/NaCl buffer without NP40. Then washing proceeds with 10 bed volumes 10 mM TRIS buffer, pH 8.0, and the beads are transferred and packed into a disposable column. The MHC–peptide complexes are eluted from the affinity beads with 3 bed volumes 10% acetic acid or 0.1% trifluoroacetic acid. The high molecular weight chains of the MHC molecules are removed from the eluate by ultracentrifugation over a membrane filter with a 10 kDa cut-off (Centriprep 10, Amicon). The ultimate peptide sample is concentrated by evaporation under vacuum and is ready for further processing.

The isolation of MHC molecules

In order to isolate intact MHC molecules for the purpose of (peptide) binding analyses, the procedure to follow is identical to that described for the isolation of MHC-bound peptides, except for the use of different buffers in the washing procedure and the elution of MHC under basic rather than acidic conditions. Briefly, the affinity beads that have been incubated with the precleared lysate are washed on a glass filter using the following buffers: minimally 5 bed volumes of TRIS/NaCl buffer (see above) with 0.5% NP40, 10 bed volumes of TRIS/NaCl buffer without NP40 and minimally 10 bed volumes of TRIS/NaCl with 0.4% (w/v) n-octylglucoside. In the latter buffer the beads are transferred to a disposable column and the

MHC complexes are eluted with 3 bed volumes of 50 mM diethylamine, 150 mM NaCl, 0.4% (w/v) *n*-octylglucoside, pH 11.5. The eluate can be neutralized using a 2M glycine solution (pH 2.5) and the high molecular weight MHC complexes in the eluate can be retained in a small volume after ultracentrifugation over a membrane filter (10 kDa cut-off).

See also: **Affinity chromatography; Antibodies, specificity; Isoelectric focusing; Radiolabeling; SDS-polyacrylamide gel electrophoresis (SDS-PAGE).**

Further reading

Findlay JBC (1989) Purification of membrane proteins. In: Harris ELV and Angel S (eds) *Protein Purification Applications: A Practical Approach.* Oxford: IRL Press.

Williams AF and Barclay AN (1986) Glycoprotein antigens of the lymphocyte surface and their purification by antibody affinity chromatography. In: Weir DM, Herzenberg LA, Blackwell C and Herzenberg LA (eds) *Handbook of Experimental Immunology,* 4th edn, chap 22. Oxford: Blackwell Scientific.

CELL SURFACE RECEPTORS AND ADHESION MOLECULES, THREE-DIMENSIONAL STRUCTURES

Jürgen Bajorath, Bristol-Myers Squibb Pharmaceutical Research Institute, Seattle, Washington, USA

The extracellular regions of immune cell surface proteins consist of one or more protein domains. These domains are often independent folding units which can be expressed in soluble form and subjected to structural analysis. Since 1990, more than 30 three-dimensional structures of immune cell surface proteins have been determined. These include single or multiple domains of adhesion molecules, receptors, and a few receptor–ligand complexes. The studies have provided structural prototypes of cell surface protein superfamilies. The structural basis of cell adhesion, specific receptor–ligand interactions, and ligand-induced receptor oligomerization is beginning to be understood.

Cell surface proteins of the immune system

In recent years, significant progress has been made in understanding the three-dimensional structures of proteins which are expressed on the surface of immune cells. **Table 1** lists 35 structures of such proteins (major histocompatibility complex molecules are not discussed here). Smaller domains have often been studied using nuclear magnetic resonance (NMR) methods. The larger and more complex structures have been determined by X-ray crystallography.

A large number of immune cell surface proteins include a single transmembrane region, and their extracellular binding domains are relatively independent from the membrane. Thus, soluble extracellular fragments suitable for structural studies can be obtained in many cases. This is in contrast to, for example, G protein-coupled receptors of the nervous system. These receptors traverse the membrane seven times, and the ligand binding sites are more intimately associated with transmembrane segments and difficult to isolate.

Modular arrangement of extracellular regions and protein superfamilies

The extracellular regions of immune cell surface proteins include distinct domains which are often connected to the transmembrane domain by a linker or stalk region. Only one or two domains may have specific binding functions. Others may trigger oligomerization or ensure that binding domains are sufficiently distant from the membrane. Many extracellular protein modules belong to superfamilies. By definition, members of protein superfamilies share limited sequence similarity, often 30% or less, but similar three-dimensional structures. **Table 1** includes structural prototypes of superfamilies determined to date. Some small domains found in different cell surface proteins consist of β sheets or hairpins which may be arranged sandwich-like and stabilized by disulfide bonds.

Table 1 Three-dimensional structures of immune cell surface receptors and adhesion molecules

EGF[a,b]	Cooke et al (1987) Nature **327**: 339
FN type I[a,b]	Baron et al (1990) Nature **345**: 642
FN type II[a,b]	Constantine et al (1992) J Mol Biol **223**: 281
CD4 (domains 1 + 2)[c]	Rye et al (1990) Nature **348**: 419
	Wang et al (1990) Nature **348**: 411
CD4 (domains 3 + 4)[c]	Brady et al (1993) Science **260**: 979
CD8α[c]	Leahy et al (1992) Cell **68**: 1145
CD2 (domain 1)[c]	Driscoll et al (1991) Nature **353**: 762
CD2 (domains 1 + 2)[c]	Jones et al (1992) Nature **360**: 232
CD2 (domain 1, glycosylated)[a]	Whitka et al (1993) Structure **1**: 69
FN type III[a,b,d]	Main et al (1992) Cell **71**: 671
FN type III	Leahy et al (1992) Science **258**: 987
FN type III (domains 7–10)	Leahy et al (1996) Cell **84**: 155
hGH/hGHR[d] complex	De Vos et al (1992) Science **255**: 306
hGH/hPRLR[d] complex	Somers et al (1994) Nature **372**: 478
CCP (two domains)[a,b]	Barlow et al (1993) J Mol Biol **232**: 268
TNFR/TNFβ complex	Banner et al (1993) Cell **73**: 431
TNFR	Naismith et al (1995) J Biol Chem **270**: 13303
NFcR	Burmeister et al (1994) Nature **372**: 336
NFcR/Fc complex	Burmeister et al (1994) Nature **372**: 379
E-selectin (C-type lectin + EGF domains)	Graves et al (1994) Nature **367**: 532
CD59 (glycosylated)[a]	Fletcher et al (1994) Structure **2**: 185
Tissue factor[d]	Harlos et al (1994) Nature **370**: 662
Tissue factor/FVIIa complex	Banner et al (1996) Nature **380**: 41
VCAM-1 (domains 1 + 2)[c]	Jones et al (1995) Nature **373**: 539
Integrin CD11b/CD18 (A domain, Mg^{2+} form)	Lee et al (1995) Cell **80**: 631
Integrin CD11b/CD18 (A domain, Mn^{2+} form)	Lee et al (1995) Structure **3**: 1333
cbEGF[a,b]	Rao et al (1995) Cell **82**: 131
cbEGF (two domains)	Downing et al (1996) Cell **85**: 597
TCR (V$_β$ + C$_β$ domains)[c]	Bentley et al (1995) Science **267**: 1984
TCR (V$_α$ domain)[c]	Fields et al (1995) Science **270**: 1821
IFNγ/IFNγRα complex[d]	Walter et al (1995) Nature **376**: 230
E-Cadherin (domain 1)[a,d]	Overduin et al (1995) Science **267**: 386
N-Cadherin (domain 1)[d]	Shapiro et al (1995) Nature **374**: 327
E-Cadherin (domains 1 + 2)[d]	Nagar et al (1996) Nature **380**: 360
LM-EGF (three domains)[b]	Stetefeld et al (1996) J Mol Biol **257**: 644
TCR/MHC class I complex[c]	Garcia et al (1996) Science **274**: 209
TCR/MHC class I complex[c]	Garboczi et al (1996) Nature **384**: 134
EPOR/peptide complex[d]	Livnah et al (1996) Science **273**: 464
Link domain[a]	Kohda et al (1996) Cell **86**: 767
NCAM (domain 1)[a,c]	Thomsen et al (1996) Nature Struct Biol **3**: 581
ICAM-2 (domains 1 + 2)[c]	Casanovas et al (1997) Nature **387**: 312
IL-1R/IL-1β complex[c]	Vigers et al (1997) Nature **386**: 190
IL-1R/IL-1RA complex[c]	Schreuder et al (1997) Nature **386**: 194
CD4 (domains 1–4)	Wu et al (1997) Nature **387**: 527
CD8α/MHC class I complex	Gao et al (1997) Nature **387**: 630

C, constant; CCP, complement control protein; C-type, calcium-dependent; EGF, epidermal growth factor; cbEGF, calcium-binding epidermal growth factor; EOPR, Erythropoietin receptor; FVIIa, blood coagulation factor VIIa; Fc, antibody constant fragment; FN, fibronectin; hGH, human growth hormone; hGHR, human growth hormone receptor; hPRLR, human prolactin receptor; ICAM, intercellular adhesion molecule; IL-1R, interleukin-1 receptor; IL-1RA, interleukin-1 receptor antagonist; IFN, interferon; IFNγRα, high-affinity interferon γ receptor; LM-EGF, laminin-type EGF-like; NCAM, neural cell adhesion molecule; NFcR, neonatal Fc receptor; TCR, T cell receptor; TNF, tumor necrosis factor; TNFR, tumor necrosis factor receptor; V, variable; VCAM-1, vascular cell adhesion molecule 1.
[a] Structures determined by NMR.
[b] Small domains which occur in many cell surface or extracellular matrix proteins.
[c] Immunoglobulin superfamily (IgSF) members.
[d] Structurally similar to IgSF domains.

The immunoglobulin superfamily (IgSF): variations of a common fold

Many of the leukocyte-specific cell surface proteins characterized to date include immunoglobulin (Ig) domains or closely related structures. The Ig fold, as seen in antibody structures, is a tightly packed sandwich of two antiparallel β sheets of four and three (constant, C) or four and five strands (variable, V), respectively, which are connected following conserved topology. In V domains, the sheets are formed by strands ABED and GFCC'C", respectively. In C domains, the C' and C" strands are absent. A canonical disulfide bond covalently links the sheets. The N- and C-termini are on opposite sides of the domain, thereby permitting Ig domains to form linear arrays.

Structural studies on Ig-like domains have revealed variations of the Ig fold. For example, the length of β strands and the spatial positions of strands at the edges of the sheets vary. The N-terminal (A) strand is often split into A and A' strands which hydrogen bond to different sheets. Strands may completely switch from one sheet to the other and thereby change the topology of the structure. Furthermore, the length and conformations of loops connecting the sheets are variable. The canonical disulfide bond is absent in some structures and other disulfide bonds may be present. On the basis of sequence and structure comparison, IgSF domains have been classified as, for example, V, C1 or C2 (related by a strand switch), I (intermediate between V and C), or A (V variant where the C" strand switches the sheet)

domains. V domains often include (part of) the binding site in IgSF cell surface proteins. Only a few examples of V domain-mediated interactions have been studied in detail. The (A')GFCC'C" face appears to be the center of interactions studied so far, irrespective of the molecular nature of the ligand.

Structures of IgSF cell surface receptors and related proteins

Figure 1A shows examples of IgSF cell surface receptor structures. The extracellular region of CD8 includes a single V domain which dimerizes like the variable light and heavy chains of an antibody. The structure of a CD8/MHC class I complex shows that residues in Complementarity Determining Region (CDR)-like loops and β-strands of the CD8 homodimer contact the α2-, α3-, and β2-microglobulin domains of MHC class I. The extracellular regions of CD4 and CD2 are stable as monomers and include four and two IgSF domains, respectively. In both structures, an N-terminal V-like domain is followed by a C2 domain. In CD4, a continuous β strand connects the first and second domain which form an extensive and rigid interface. This structure is very similar to the structure including the third and fourth domain of CD4. Structures of CD4 including all four extracellular domains in different crystal lattices reveals that domains 2 and 3 are more flexibly connected. In CD2, the two domains are connected by a linker and the interface is less extensive. Despite

(A)

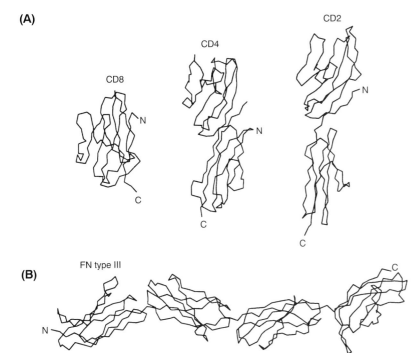

(B)

Figure 1 Cell surface proteins of the IgSF and related molecules. Structures are represented as Cα traces. N- and C-termini are labeled. (A) Three IgSF members: CD8, CD4 and CD2. (B) Structure of a four-domain fragment of fibronectin. The three-dimensional structure of FN type III is similar to IgSF C domains.

these differences, the relative orientation of the two domains is similar in CD4 and CD2.

Structures of a V_α domain and β chain of different TCRs, a complete mouse TCR (and its preliminary complex with MHC class I), and a human TCR/ MHC class I complex have been reported. These structures confirm the structural similarity of antibodies and TCRs. In the V_α domain, which forms a tetramer of homodimers, the C" strand switches the sheet, a departure from V domain structure (see above). The β chain includes a V and a C domain which form an extensive interface (two to four times larger than in antibody structures). Overall, the mouse and human TCR structures are similar. In the mouse TCR structure, the Cα domain, which is disordered in the human TCR, substantially departs from known IgSF structure types. In the structure of the complex with peptide-bound MHC class I, the TCR binds with its CDR-like loops diagonally across the composite MHC/peptide surface. The orientation is such that the Vα CDR loop 1 contacts the N-terminal and the Vβ CDR loop 3 the C-terminal region of the peptide.

In **Figure 1B**, a structure consisting of four fibronectin (FN) type III domains is shown. FN type III domains are structurally similar to C2 domains, but are not included in the IgSF. Their structure is a sandwich of a four-stranded and a three-stranded β sheet. The domain lacks the Ig disulfide bond, and the packing of its hydrophobic core is distinct from the IgSF. FN type III domains are found in extracellular matrix proteins and in cytokine receptors. Domain 10 of fibronectin includes an RGD sequence in a loop and is therefore an integrin ligand and

implicated in cell adhesion. Although the structures of single FN type III domains are very similar, their domain interfaces are not conserved. The two central domains display a relative orientation similar to CD4 and CD2.

Cadherins, also distantly related to the IgSF, are homophilic and calcium-dependent adhesion molecules. Like fibronectin, cadherins may include ten or more extracellular domains. The interfaces between domains are stabilized by calcium binding which also supports dimerization of cadherin domains. Crystal packing has suggested different ways in which cadherins interact. On the basis of crystal lattice interactions, models have been proposed for the formation of network-like multivalent cellular adhesion interfaces.

Structures of leukocyte and endothelial cell adhesion molecules

In the course of an inflammatory response, leukocytes are recruited to activated vascular endothelium by adhesion interactions of increasing strength. Selectins are responsible for the initial low avidity (protein/carbohydrate) interactions. Firm adhesion is achieved by high avidity (protein/protein) interactions between leukocyte integrins and their endothelial ligands. Structures of binding domains of key molecules have been determined and are shown in **Figure 2**.

The X-ray structure of E-selectin includes an N-terminal calcium-dependent (C-type) lectin domain which is followed by an EGF-like domain. The C-type lectin fold, first observed in the structure of rat

E-selectin   Mac-1   VCAM-1

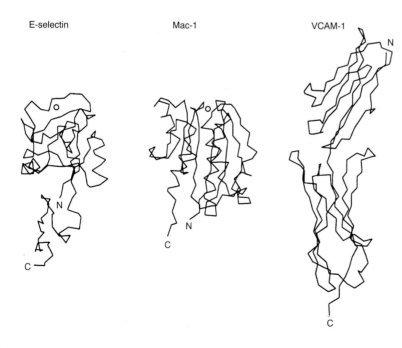

Figure 2 Binding domains of adhesion proteins. Structures are represented as Cα traces, and the N- and C-termini are labeled. E-Selectin includes two (C-type lectin and EGF-like) domains. The circle indicates the position of a conserved calcium ion. The I domain of Mac-1, a β_2-integrin, is shown. The circle indicates the position of the MIDAS motif (see text). The structure of VCAM-1, a β_2-integrin ligand, includes two Ig domains (see also **Figure 1**).

mannose-binding protein, includes extended regions of unusual secondary structure in the vicinity of a highly conserved calcium-binding site. In the mannose-binding protein, this calcium is directly involved in carbohydrate binding. A similar role has been proposed for the conserved calcium in E-selectin, but the structure of a complex between E-selectin and its carbohydrate ligand remains to be determined.

The ligand binding domain of the β_2-integrin Mac-1 (CD11b/CD18) adopts a dinucleotide-binding (Rossmann) fold which consists of a hydrophobic parallel β sheet covered by amphipathic α helices on both sides. The Mac-1 structure includes an Mg^{2+}-binding site which topologically corresponds to the active site in dinucleotide cofactor-binding enzymes. The cation coordination sphere is open and, in the crystal, completed by a negatively charged residue from a neighboring molecule. This site has been termed the metal ion-dependent adhesion site (MIDAS motif) and is thought to be directly involved in ligand binding. Structural analysis of an Mn^{2+}-bound form of Mac-1 has revealed conformational changes, compared to the original structure.

The structure of ICAM-1, the Mac-1 ligand, is unknown, but the structure of the related VCAM-1 has been determined. This structure includes two of seven IgSF domains which form VCAM-1's extracellular region. A terminal IgSF I domain is followed by a C2 domain, and the domain interface is reminiscent of CD2. The conserved integrin-binding sequence (QIDSPL) resides in the CD loop of the I domain. The aspartic acid is thought to complement the MIDAS motif. The interaction involves surface regions proximal to the shared cation-binding site.

Structures of cell surface receptor–ligand complexes

The structures of several receptor–ligand complexes have also been reported (see **Table 1**). For immune cell surface receptors, ligand-induced receptor oligomerization is a major determinant of signal transduction. **Figure 3** compares the structures of the complexes involving human growth hormone (hGH) receptor (hGHR) and the 55 kDa tumor necrosis factor (TNF) receptor (TNFR).

The prototypic fold of the TNFR/nerve growth factor receptor superfamily (**Figure 3A**) consists of stacked elongated domains. These domains have a very limited hydrophobic core and are stabilized by conserved disulfide bonds in a ladder-like arrangement. TNFR includes four domains, but only domains 2 and 3, which contact ligand, are well ordered in the X-ray structure. In contrast, the TNF fold consists of an antiparallel β sandwich with jelly-roll topology. Three monomers form a threefold symmetrical trimer. Three symmetry-related receptor-binding sites are formed at the interfaces between the TNF monomers. The receptor binds roughly parallel to the threefold axis, and the bound receptors do not contact each other. Thus, ligand binding leads to TNFR trimerization. Structures of free TNF and TNFR have shown that neither ligand nor receptor undergo significant conformational changes upon binding. In the crystal of uncomplexed TNFR,

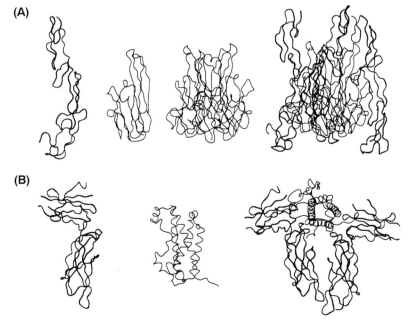

(A)

(B)

Figure 3 Cell surface receptor–ligand complexes. Structures are represented as backbone traces (receptors, thick lines; ligands, thin lines). (A) The TNFβ/TNFR complex. From left to right: TNFR, a TNF subunit, trimeric TNF, and the TNF/TNFR complex. (B) hGH/hGHR. From left to right: hGHR, consisting of two FN type III-like domains (see also **Figure 1**), hGH, and the hGH/hGHR complex.

dimeric forms were observed which, if present on the cell surface, may stabilize an inactive state of TNFR in the absence of ligand.

Figure 3B shows the structure of the hGH/hGHR complex. The receptor consists of two FN type III domains, and the ligand displays a four helix bundle fold. The hGHR architecture is shared by other cytokine receptors including the human prolactin receptor (hPRLR), the interferon γ receptor (IFNγRα) and tissue factor (TF), but the relative orientations of the FN type III domains differ. Binding of hGH to its receptor leads to receptor dimerization. In contrast to TNF/TNFR, the binding sites in the hGH/hGHR complex are not equivalent, and the bound receptors contact each other. The hGH/hGHR interaction is asymmetrical in the sense that the receptors bind to different sites of the ligand. The complex forms sequentially. First, a high affinity 1:1 complex is formed, then a second receptor is engaged in the interaction. The binding of the second receptor is stabilized by receptor–receptor interactions. hGH also binds to hPRLR, and the structure of a 1:1 (high-affinity) hGH/hPRLR complex has been determined. This interaction is made possible in part by changes in the relative domain orientation of hPRLR compared to hGHR.

The erythropoietin (EPO) receptor is also structurally similar to hGHR but dimerizes in a somewhat different orientation when complexed with an agonist peptide. In contrast to hGH, IFNγ is an intertwined helix bundle homodimer. Two equivalent receptor-binding sites are presented which correspond to the high-affinity site in hGH. In the structure of the complex, receptors are bound at twofold symmetry-related sites and are separated by ~27 Å. Tissue factor binds a structurally distinct ligand, blood coagulation factor VIIAa, in a 1:1 complex. The TF region involved in binding differs topologically from the binding sites in hGHR. The interleukin (IL)-1 receptor consists of three extracellular Ig-like domains and binds IL-1β (and an antagonist) involving regions not corresponding to those in other cytokine receptors.

The structure of the rat neonatal Fc receptor (NFcR), responsible for binding maternal IgG, is very similar to MHC class I. However, the helices corresponding to the MHC peptide-binding site move together and essentially close the groove. A low-resolution structure of NFcR in complex with an Fc fragment has shown that the Fc-binding site does not correspond to the MHC peptide-binding site. Rather, the Fc fragment binds to the side of the receptor. The NFcR/Fc complex provides an instructive example of how similar structures can mediate distinct binding functions.

See also: **Adhesion molecules; Antigens, cell surface; CD antigens; Cytokine receptors; Domains, immunoglobulin-type; Immunoglobulin gene superfamily; Specificity; Antibody-antigen complexes, three-dimensional structures.**

Further reading

Barclay AN, Brown MH, Law SKA *et al.* (1997) *The Leucocyte Antigen FactsBook.* 2nd edn. London: Academic Press.

Beutler B and van Huffel C (1994) Unraveling function in the TNF ligand and receptor families. *Science* **264**: 667–668.

Bork P, Holm L and Sander C (1994) The immunoglobulin fold. Structural classification, sequence patterns and common core. *Journal of Molecular Biology* **242**: 309–320.

Campbell ID and Spitzfaden C (1994) Building proteins with fibronectin type III modules. *Structure* **2**: 233–237.

Harpaz Y and Chothia C (1994) Many of the immunoglobulin superfamily domains in cell adhesion molecules and surface receptors belong to a new structural set which is close to that containing variable domains. *Journal of Molecular Biology* **238**: 528–539.

Heldin C-H (1995) Dimerization of cell surface receptors in signal transduction. *Cell* **80**: 213–223.

Orengo CA, Jones DT and Thornton JM (1994) Protein superfamilies and domain superfolds. *Nature* **372**: 631–634.

Pigott R and Power C (1993) *The Adhesion Molecule FactsBook.* London: Academic Press.

Sprang SR and Bazan JF (1993) Cytokine structural taxonomy and mechanisms of receptor engagement. *Current Opinion in Structural Biology* **3**: 815–827.

Stuart DI and Jones EY (1995) Recognition at the cell surface: recent structural insights. *Current Opinion in Structural Biology* **5**: 735–743.

Wagner W and Wyss DF (1994) Cell surface adhesion receptors. *Current Opinion in Structural Biology* **4**: 841–851.

Williams AF and Barclay AN (1988) The immunoglobulin superfamily – domains for cell surface recognition. *Annual Review of Immunology* **6**: 381–406.

CHAGAS' DISEASE

Martín E Rottenberg and **Anders Örn**, Microbiology and Tumorbiology Center, Karolinska Institute, Stockholm, Sweden

Characteristics of the organism and its antigens

Life cycle of *Trypanosoma cruzi*

T. cruzi, the causative agent of Chagas' disease in humans, infects 16–20 million people in Central and South America and constitutes a prominent health problem. The parasite is a kinetoplastid protozoan whose life cycle alternates between an insect belonging to the family Reduviidae, and a mammalian host. Transmission is initiated by insect vectors which after a blood meal defecate and release infective metacyclic trypomastigotes near the bite wound. These infective stages differentiate from epimastigotes, the noninfective replicative form that live in the insect gut. Both forms are flagellated and highly motile. In contrast to the African trypanosomes, the vertebrate stages of *T. cruzi* are obligate intracellular pathogens and must enter host cells to replicate. After disruption of the membrane-bounded vacuole, parasites escape to the cytoplasm and differentiate into amastigotes, less motile with a very short flagellum and spherical body (**Figure 1**). After a 24 h lag period, amastigotes start dividing by binary fission, which occurs 7–10 times. After 5–7 days, more than 500 parasites have accumulated in the cytoplasm. When the replicative period is completed, amastigotes differentiate into trypomastigotes, the host cell ruptures and parasites are released into the bloodstream; thus, infection disseminates to other tissues. These released forms, equivalent to the metacyclic trypomastigotes, are called bloodstream trypomastigotes and are able to invade nearly every kind of nucleated cell (**Figure 2**). The *T. cruzi* life cycle (**Figure 3**) is completed when trypomastigotes are ingested by blood-sucking insect vectors. Amastigotes released from ruptured cells are also able to invade new host cells, probably involving different receptors from those used by trypomastigotes.

Invasion of the mammalian cell

Several antigens from the trypomastigote as well as host cell receptors are involved in sequential processes leading to invasion. The ability of *T. cruzi* to invade almost every nucleated cell from any mammalian species indicates the presence of ubiquitous and conserved receptor(s) on the host cell. Among the parasite molecules involved in binding to the host cell, a relevant role has been attributed to trypomastigote stage-specific molecules of a large family that includes trans-sialidases/sialidases. Sialic acid on the surface of host cells influences the invasion process. *T. cruzi* parasites do not synthesize sialic acid, but make use of transialidases that transfer mammalian sialic acid to highly glycosylated mucin-like acceptors (35–50 kDa) on the parasite surface. Treatment with antibodies to both trans-sialidase or the mucin acceptors, desialylation of parasites or treatment with tunicamycin (which blocks glycosylation) inhibit infection, and mutants defective in sialic acid are more resistant to infection. Moreover, trans-sialidase released inside the phagolysosome desialylates lysosomal proteins, allowing activity of a parasite-encoded acidic pore-forming molecule (Tc-TOX or

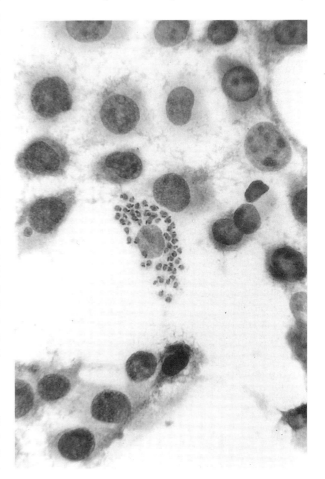

Figure 1 Photomicrograph of *T. cruzi* amastigotes in the cytoplasm of mouse peritoneal macrophages (316 × magnification).

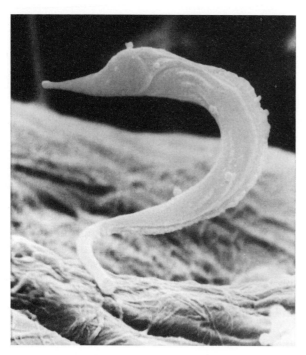

Figure 2 Scanning electron micrograph of a *T. cruzi* trypomastigote invading a fibroblast cell (L-929) (25000 × magnification). (Courtesy of Dr L Nilsson and D Sunnemark.)

hemolysin) immunologically related to the C9 component of complement, and probably involved in escape into the cytosol. Penetrin, a 60 kDa trypomastigote-specific heparin-binding protein, has also been implicated in attachment to host cells. On the host surface, receptors binding fibronectin (as β_1-integrins) and collagen play a role in the invasion process.

T. cruzi does not bind well to the host plasma cell membranes at 4°C, suggesting the need for energy-dependent mechanisms. In particular, those depending on parasite energy appear to play a key role in invasion. *T. cruzi* trypomastigotes invade the mammalian cell through a unique mechanism, distinct from phagocytosis, and without the need of pseudopodia formation and actin polymerization. Clusters of lysosomes gather in close proximity to the host plasma cell membrane at regions in contact with trypomastigotes. The parasite slides gradually into the host cell and fusion of lysosomes probably provides the membrane required for the formation of a vacuole that surrounds the parasite (**Figure 4**). Such an interaction is accompanied by, and probably depends on, alterations of cellular homeostasis, involving signal transduction events such as an increase in the intracellular concentration of free Ca^{2+} transients, both in the host cell and the infecting parasite. Ca^{2+} elevation in the cell is mediated by a parasite soluble factor that mediates its activity

through activation of host cell phospholipase C, at least in some cellular populations. Buffering or depleting intracellular Ca^{2+} results in inhibition of *T. cruzi* entry, indicating a physiologic role for such ions in the infection. *T. cruzi* invasion also directly activates the transforming growth factor β (TGFβ) signaling pathway which is in turn required for parasite entry into the mammalian cells. Cruzipain, a cysteine protease from *T. cruzi*, is also thought to be involved in differentiation between amastigotes and trypomastigotes.

Immune responses of the host

Outcome of infection with *T. cruzi in vivo*

Following initial infection, the acute phase of Chagas' disease ensues. This phase is characterized by high blood parasitemia and extensive tissue parasitism. In a high proportion of Chagas' cases the acute phase is asymptomatic but, especially in children, fever, hepatosplenomegaly, adenopathy and myocarditis may occur. Parasitemia subsides after 1–2 months, coincident with the development of a specific immune response, and the patients enter a chronic stage of infection, without showing symptoms of disease. The asymptomatic phase of infection lasts for an unspecified period (up to 10–30 years), and is followed in 30–40% of cases by a clinical chronic disease, usually focused in the heart or the digestive tract. Chronic chagasic cardiac pathology may include arrhythmia, conduction abnormalities, apical aneurysm, myositis and infarction with fibroadipose replacement of the myocardium. In a final stage the most significant clinical manifestations of Chagas' cardiomyopathy include congestive heart failure, thromboembolic phenomena, severe arrythmias and sudden death. Less frequent abnormalities in the digestive system involve hypertrophy of the esophagus or colon.

All mammalian species are susceptible to infection; however, the relative susceptibility of animals varies not only between, but also within, species. The genetic basis for this susceptibility is unclear. Genes both within and outside the major histocompatibility complex (MHC) loci have been implicated, as well as the genetic background of different strains of the parasite.

Immune response

Polyclonal activation and immunosuppression *T. cruzi* infection elicits both specific immune responses and several non-specific alterations in the homeostasis of the immune system in humans and experimental animals. The immune response is both humoral and cell mediated and has been associated both with protection and pathogenesis.

A polyclonal activation of B cells (in particular Ly-1+ [CD5]), and CD4+ and CD8+ T cells, follows early after infection with *T. cruzi*. The majority of the responding clones are not directed against parasite antigens. Although the parasite does not seem to possess any T cell-specific superantigens, an octapeptide from an 85 kDa parasite antigen has been shown to generate nonspecific B cell polyclonal activation. Elevated levels of type I interferons, interleukin 12 (IL-12) and IL-2, are found early after infection. These cytokines might be responsible for elevated cytolytic activity and secretion of interferon γ (IFNγ) by natural killer (NK) cells during early infection, and are probably involved in protection. An immunodepression stage characterizes the infection later during the acute phase. This immunosuppression is transient, although partially depressed responses have also been documented during the chronic stage of human and experimental infections. It is currently thought that the immunodepression undermines the defences against the establishment

and dissemination of the invading parasite in the host. During the acute stage of infection, T and B cells have an impaired ability to proliferate in response to mitogens as well as to specific or heterologous antigens. The unresponsive state has been associated with an impaired capacity to produce IL-2 and a downregulation of IL-2 receptor expression, and to an apoptotic death of CD4+ T cells. Additionally, the activation of suppressor T cells, macrophages secreting nitric oxide (NO) or prostaglandin E and the downregulation of CD28 on T cells have all been proposed to explain the unresponsive state. Parasite molecules or soluble factors released by *T. cruzi* (proteins as well as a glycosylinositol phospholipid) mediate different features of the immunodepression *in vitro* and *in vivo* in a parasite dose-dependent way. *In vivo*, the immunodepression phase is also accompanied by an extensive thymic destruction and splenomegaly, whereas lymph nodes appear not to be affected to similar levels. High levels of IFNγ, released by CD4−CD8− T cells, and specific antibodies are detectable during this phase, indicating the presence of active immune responses during

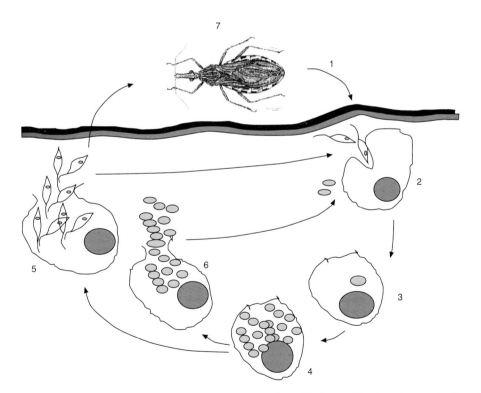

Figure 3 The life cycle of *T. cruzi*. (1) Metacyclic trypomastigotes are released in feces of the insect and enter the vertebrate host through the bite wound. (2) Trypomastigotes invade mammalian cells (see Figure 4). (3) After 30–120 min trypomastigotes escape from the vacuole and transform into replicative amastigotes. (4) Amastigotes multiply in the cytoplasm. (5) After a number of cycles amastigotes differentiate into trypomastigotes, which will rupture the host cell. (6) Amastigotes may also lyse infected cells before differentiation into trypomastigotes, and are thereby released into circulation, invade macrophages, survive, divide and further differentiate into trypomastigotes. (7) With a blood meal, the insect vector ingests bloodstream trypomastigotes, which in the insect midgut differentiate into noninfective and replicating epimastigotes. Epimastigotes further differentiate into metacyclic trypomastigotes in the hindgut of the vector, completing the life cycle.

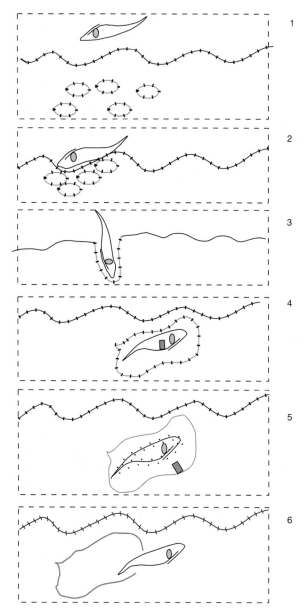

Figure 4 *T. cruzi* invasion into a mammalian cell. (1) *T. cruzi* trypomastigotes attach to the cell surface. (2) Host cell lysosomes (○) migrate to the attachment site. (3) Lysosomes fuse with the plasma membrane at the attachment site and start to form an intracellular vacuole around the parasite. (4) The intracellular vacuole is formed. (5) Lysosomal glycoproteins are desialylated by the *T. cruzi* trans-sialidase and sialic acid (black dots) is transferred to parasite acceptors. *T. cruzi* Tc-TOX (▨) anchors in the lysosome membrane. (6) The vacuolar membrane is disrupted. The parasite escape into the cytoplasm, where they will differentiate into amastigotes.

a stage of general dysregulation. In summary, the relevance of both polyclonal activation and immunodepression in the biology of the infection and outcome of disease is unknown. It is believed that the immunomodulation events occurring in the acute phase influence alterations later during the infection by modifying the quality of the specific immune responses.

Protective immune responses   The immune response controls the high parasite load in the acute phase to produce virtually undectable parasitemia in the chronic phase. However, sterile immunity and complete parasite clearance and cure are unknown in humans and in experimental models of infection. Rather than achieving a cure, the immune response maintains a host–parasite balance which lasts for the lifetime of the infected individual.

NK cells, macrophages, B cells and both CD4[+] and CD8[+] T cells play important roles in resistance of mice infected with *T. cruzi*. Such diversity of cellular populations is reflected in manifold humoral and cellular immune effector mechanisms of destruction of both intracellular amastigotes and bloodstream trypomastigotes. Antibodies can lyse the parasite through activation of the classical or alternative pathways of complement. Antibodies might also lyse trypomastigotes through antibody-dependent cell-mediated cytotoxocity. Eosinophils, neutrophils, mononuclear cells and platelets have been shown to lyse the trypomastigotes when coated with specific antibodies. T cells can regulate production of such antibodies, lyse infected target cells or release cytokines (**Table 1**) that modulate different trypanocidal mechanisms of phagocytes. Whether they influence the physiology of infection in nonphagocytic cells is not known. Macrophage activation by tumor necrosis factor α (TNFα) IL-3, IFNα, IFNβ, IFNγ or granulocyte-macrophage colony-stimulating factor (GM-CSF) leads to inhibition of the replication or killing of the intracellular forms of *T. cruzi*. Of these cytokines, IFNγ has been most closely associated with host resistance. Conversely, cytokines such as IL-4, IL-10 and TGFβ counteract the effects of IFNγ during *T. cruzi* infection *in vitro* and *in vivo*. However, *T. cruzi* infection appears not to be a model for T_H1/T_H2 dichotomy, as in infection with *Leishmania major*. Cytokines belonging to both T_H1 and T_H2 are simultaneously produced during infection in a variety of mice, but the balance between cytokines belonging to either pattern appears to influence the outcome of infection. Such cytokine balance regulates the transcriptional rate and mRNA stability of inducible nitric oxide synthase (iNOS) by macrophages, mediating high output of NO. Macrophages produce reactive oxygen species (ROS) and NO and show induction of iNOS during the course of *T. cruzi* infection *in vivo*. Both NO and ROS are toxic for the parasite *in vitro*, and some trypanocidal drugs, such as nifurtimox or crystal violet, act by generating such species. In addition, the superoxide anion and

Table 1 Role of cytokines in the outcome of infection with *T. cruzi in vivo* and *in vitro*

Cytokine	Effect on T. cruzi *infection*
IFNγ	Reduces parasitemia and mortality. Activates trypanocidal activity of macrophages, mainly through induction of inducible NO synthase. The peak of production coincides with the high parasite load during the acute phase of infection
TNFα	Inhibits intracellular multiplication. Synergizes with and mediates IFNγ trypanocidal activity. It has been shown both to aggravate and protect *in vivo*. Produced by macrophages after *in vitro* infection with parasites
TGFβ	Inhibits IFNγ-mediated trypanocidal activation of macrophages. Is involved in parasite penetration and intracellular multiplication. Increases susceptibility to infection *in vivo*
IL-1	Released by infected macrophages and endothelial cells. Probably associated with microcirculatory alterations, and thereby heart dysfunction
IL-2	Spontaneously released early after infection, its production is markedly suppressed during the acute phase of infection
IL-3	Activates a trypanostatic activity of macrophages
IL-4	Inhibits IFNγ-mediated macrophage activation and NO release. Its levels are increased in the chronic phase of infection, especially in susceptible hosts. Increases susceptibility to infection with at least some *T. cruzi* strains
IL-6	Decreases cumulative mortality *in vivo*. Released by endothelial cells after *in vitro* infection with *T. cruzi*
IL-10	Inhibits IFNγ-mediated macrophage activation. Increases susceptibility to infection. Increased in susceptible as compared with resistant strains of mammalian hosts
IL-12	Reduces parasitemia and mortality, through IFNγ- and possibly TNFα-mediated mechanism of resistance

NO might react with each other to form peroxynitrite, a stronger trypanocidal molecule than its precursors. Whereas the relevance of ROS is still controversial, NO is necessary for control of the parasite load both in *in vitro* activated macrophages and during *in vivo* infection with *T. cruzi*.

Pathogenesis and immunopathology   Different mechanisms have been proposed to participate in the pathogenesis of chagasic cardiopathy, and probably all have some degree of involvement in such a process. Microvascular changes, as manifested by platelet aggregates, increased levels of P-selectin, thrombus formation and histochemical evidence of myocardial hypoxia in humans and experimental models, might cause focal necrosis. Conversely, the

reduction of parasympathetic ganglion cells in the heart and gut of chronic Chagas' patients has prompted suggestions for a role for denervation in pathogenesis. Vagal and myenteric plexus denervation could induce an increased sympathetic tone that may have a direct effect in heart arrythmogenesis or gut megasyndrome. There is by now convincing evidence that immune responses are involved in pathogenesis. Chronic inflammatory reactions depend on a persistent antigenic stimulation by parasite antigens. Although a chronically infected host displays undetectable parasitemia and very rarely tissue amastigotes, parasite antigens have been detected in inflammatory infiltrates and such lesions correlate with the severity of the disease. Autoantibodies or autoreactive cellular responses generated through polyclonal activation or by parasite antigens cross-react with mammalian neurons, lymphoid cells, laminin, ribosomal proteins, sarcolemma, myocardial β receptors and myosin. The levels of some of these antibodies correlate with the clinical status (myosin for example), and some antibodies mediate physiologic alterations in the target cells. For example, parasite cross-reactive antibodies trigger neurotransmitter–receptor interactions in myocytes and thereby alter the physiology of normal myocardium. Tissue destruction by inflammatory cells is probably facilitated by the presence of parasite antigens and ectopic expression of adhesion molecules and histocompatibility antigens on the surface of infected or noninfected cells during infection. CD8+ T cells have been shown to dominate the inflammatory infiltrate; however, the pathogenic role for CD8+ T cells is not clear. In contrast, CD4+ cells from chronically infected mice comprise only 5–10% of the inflammatory infiltrate but have been shown to play a role in pathogenesis, as they are involved in the rejection of grafted syngeneic heart tissue. Hypothetically, almost every immunologic mechanism described as participating in protection might also be involved in tissue pathology. Whatever the damaging mechanism, no data presented as yet can explain the prolonged latent period between the initial infection and the pathologic changes 5–40 years later in human infection.

Escape mechanisms

As with all microorganisms, *T. cruzi* has developed stage-specific strategies to circumvent host defence mechanisms before, during and after entry into host cells. The major evasion method employed by *T. cruzi* is its promiscuity, in other words the ability to invade all nucleated cells, thereby hiding from the immune response. Although antigenic variation of surface antigens has not been described in *T. cruzi*, many of the surface genes including those coding for enzymes necessary for invasion (trans-sialidase for example) are expressed as multigenic families. Expression of such antigens might be modulated by the parasite to present a constantly changing face to the host immune system. As an alternative escape mechanism, some of the components of these multigenic families do not possess enzymatic activity but have extensive cross-reactivities with their enzymatic relatives. Moreover, the active sites of such enzymes are not immunodominant, and are thereby protected from neutralizing immune responses. As a protective back-up, *T. cruzi* displays several molecules involved in invasion, but none of them appears to be an absolute requirement for invasion and inactivation of any of them rarely renders a complete inhibition. Soluble molecules shed or secreted by *T. cruzi* bind non-infected cells, and if correctly presented to the immune response they will divert it. Moreover, this phenomenon, and the presence of cross-reactive antigens, can convert a potent and sterilizing immune response into a detrimental one as it might also harm noninfected tissue. Once inside the lysosome Tc-TOX and trans-sialidase cooperate in *T. cruzi* liberation into the cytosol, thereby avoiding the toxic millieu in the phagolysosome. Extracellular trypomastigotes have also developed evasion mechanisms and are protected from activation of the alternative complement pathway by complement regulatory molecules displaying genetic and functional similarities to decay-accelerating factor (DAF).

Vaccines

Vaccination studies have been undertaken in a number of different animal species by using a variety of different antigens, including whole lysed parasites, subcellular fractions and purified/recombinant antigens. The results generally show that many of these antigen preparations reduce parasitemias during the acute phase of the disease and convert lethal to non-lethal infections. However, no vaccination study has achieved complete protection and the vaccinated animals become infected. Reduction of parasitemia might reduce the incidence and severity of the chronic phase of the disease, and might constitute a goal for immunoprophylactic studies. In any case, alternative measures, such as eradication of the insect vector, control of the parasite in blood banks and chemotherapy of congenital and acute cases, have rendered considerable positive results in the battle against Chagas' disease during the last 10–20 years.

See also: **Cardiac disease, autoimmune; Contraception, immunological; Decay-accelerating factor (CD55); Parasites, immunity to; Trypanosomiasis, African.**

Further reading

Brener Z (1980) Immunity to *Trypanosoma cruzi*. *Advances Parasitology* 18: 247–292.

Burleigh B and Andrews N (1995) The mechanisms of *Trypanosoma cruzi* invasion of mammalian cells. *Annual Review of Microbiology* 49: 175–200.

Hall B and Joiner K (1993) Developmentally regulated virulence factors of *Trypanosoma cruzi* and their relationship to evasion of host defences. *Journal of Eukaryotic Microbiology* 40: 207–213.

Rossi MA and Bestetti RB (1995) The challenge of chagasic cardiomyopathy. *Cardiology* 86: 1–7.

Takle GB and Snary D (1993) South American trypanosomiasis. In: Warren KS (ed) *Immunology and Molecular Biology of Parasitic Infections*, 3rd edn, pp. 213–236. Boston: Blackwell Scientific.

Tanowitz H, Kirchhoff L, Simon D, Morris S, Weiss L and Wittner M (1992) Chagas' disease. *Microbiology Reviews* 5: 400–414.

Tarleton R (1993) Pathology of American trypanosomiasis. In: Warren KS (ed) *Immunology and Molecular Biology of Parasitic Infections*, 3rd edn, p. 64–70. Boston: Blackwell Scientific.

CHÉDIAK–HIGASHI SYNDROME

Charles M Perou and **Jerry Kaplan**, Division of Cell Biology and Immunology, Department of Pathology, University of Utah, Salt Lake City, Utah, USA

Chédiak–Higashi syndrome (CHS) is an autosomal recessive disorder of humans that results in the formation of 'giant' intracellular vesicles. The formation of these large vesicles results in impaired function, which often compromises cellular activities. Many of the granule types affected in this disorder are required for proper immune cell function, and hence cause a severe immunodeficiency in afflicted individuals.

This rare human disorder has numerous phenotypically similar disorders in other species including beige mice, Aleutian minks, cats, cattle, and even killer whales. The beige mouse has been used as a model organism for the study of CHS for many decades, and much of what is known about CHS has been obtained through the study of these mice. Somatic cell fusion studies have suggested that beige mice, Aleutian minks and CHS patients have defects within homologous genes, therefore providing genetic evidence which supports the hypothesis that beige and CHS are genetically similar disorders.

CHS/beige primarily affects four classes of intracellular vesicles: lysosomes, melanosomes, platelet-dense granules and cytolytic granules (**Figure 1**). It is thought that the formation of these 'giant' vesicles is due to a malregulation of either vesicle fusion or fission. The net result of this single gene defect is a reduction in the number of vesicles and an increase in their average size. The mouse beige gene has recently been identified and will be discussed below.

The clinical phenotypes in CHS/beige are the formation of giant vesicles, pigment dilution, a bleeding tendency and a severe immunodeficiency. Giant lysosomes are found in almost every cell of the body. This defect causes impaired lysosome function, which is tolerated by many cell types but which may ultimately kill others (e.g. neurons). The formation of giant melanosomes causes a pigment dilution that results in a near albino appearance of most CHS patients. In these individuals, the hair, eyes, skin, or any combination of the three, are the sites of pigment alterations. In mice and other mammals this defect results in an alteration in coat color. Platelet-dense granules also form anomalous large structures that result in a platelet storage pool deficiency. Due to this deficiency, CHS patients and beige mice have decreased platelet aggregation and a bleeding tendency.

It is within the immune system that the CHS/beige defect exerts its most profound and deadly effects. The cell types known to show the CHS defect of enlarged granules include CD8$^+$ T cells, eosinophils, basophils, neutrophils, mast cells, macrophages, megakaryocytes, B cells and natural killer (NK) cells. Each of these cell types contains large lysosomes as well as enlarged specialized granules; for example, neutrophils often contain large granules derived from the fusion of azurophilic and specific granules. Neutrophils from affected individuals also show defective chemotaxis; they have normal bacterial phagocytosis but impaired intracellular killing of bacteria. It has been demonstrated for neutrophils and macrophages that the newly formed phagosomes often fail to fuse with lysosomes, thereby allowing the internalized bacteria to survive longer and to multiply.

A second cell type profoundly affected by the CHS/beige defect is the NK cell. The numbers of NK cells and their target specificity and binding appear normal, but these cells are unable to kill their targets. The beige mouse is often used as a NK cell-deficient animal in order to study the role of NK cells in various immune responses. It is believed that defective NK cell activity is due to impaired exocytosis of cytolytic granules. A very similar defect is also observed

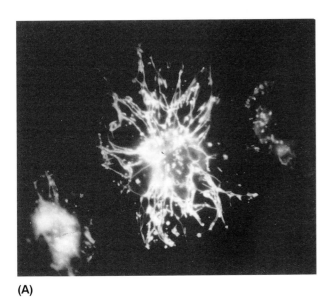

(A)

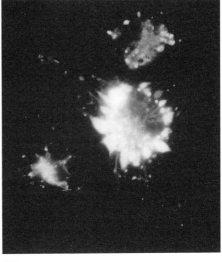

(B)

Figure 1 Bone marrow macrophages from (A) a C57BL/6J mouse and (B) a C57BL/6J-bg/bg mouse (100 × magnification). Note the 'giant' lysosomes clustered near the nucleus in (B). (Reproduced with permission of Company of Biologists Ltd from Perou CM and Kaplan J (1993) Chédiak-Higashi-syndrome is not due to a defect in microtubule-based lysosome mobility. *Journal of Cell Science* **106**: 99–107.)

in CD8[+] T cells. The decreased activity of these cell types can be overcome *in vitro* by chronic stimulation with exogenously added cytokines and longer incubation times. Unfortunately, these results cannot be replicated *in vivo*. Other cell types of the immune system show the CHS defect (e.g. B cells, eosinophils, basophils and mast cells), but their function does not appear to be significantly compromised. For example, CHS patients and beige mice are capable of making antibodies against invading organisms.

Until the advent of antibiotics, infections killed most CHS patients. Today, the most deadly effect of the CHS mutation is the 'accelerated phase'. The accelerated phase is a mononuclear lymphoma-like cellular infiltrate that invades the major organs of the body. This infiltrate, along with the bleeding tendency, causes major organ failure, hemorrhage and the death of the afflicted individual. It is thought that the accelerated phase is triggered by a viral infection but the precise virus or even the cellular origin of this lymphoma, is not known.

The only cure for CHS is to prevent the accelerated phase. This can be done by whole body irradiation to kill the endogenous bone marrow that gives rise to the lymphoma, followed by allogeneic bone marrow transplantation. This treatment has worked in many cases, and has prevented the accelerated phase from recurring for up to 13 years in one patient. As these CHS patients age, however, other problems may arise, such as neurologic defects due to the loss of neurons. CHS is a candidate for gene replacement in hematopoetic stem cells, which would cure the immunodeficiency and prevent the accelerated phase, while also circumventing the problem of graft-versus-host disease.

The mouse beige gene has recently been identified using a Yeast Artificial Chromosome complementation approach. The human homolog of the beige gene was then isolated and shown to contain mutations within CHS patients. These data demonstrate that beige and CHS are due to mutations within orthologous genes. The Beige/CHS protein is approximately 3800 amino acids in length and contains a protein–protein interaction motif (WD40 repeats) and a highly conserved domain of unknown function. This conserved domain identifies homologs in *Saccharomyces cerevisiae* and *Caenorhabditis elegans*, demonstrating that this protein is conserved throughout evolution. The overall sequence of the Beige/CHS protein is novel and gives few clues as to its biochemical function.

See also: **Exocytosis; Hematopoietic stem cell transplantation; Immunodeficiency, animal models; Natural killer (NK) cells; Phagocytosis.**

Further reading

Baetz K, Isaaz S and Griffiths GM (1995) Loss of cytotoxic T lymphocyte function in Chédiak–Higashi syndrome arises from a secretory defect that prevents lytic granule exocytosis. *Journal of Immunology* **154**: 6122–6131.

Barak Y and Nir E (1987) Chédiak–Higashi syndrome. *American Journal of Pediatric Hematology/Oncology* **9**: 42–55.

Barbosa MDFS, Nguyen QA, Tchernev VT *et al* (1996) Identification of the homologous beige and Chédiak–Higashi syndrome genes. *Nature* **382**: 262–265.

Burkhardt JK, Weibel FA, Hester S and Argon Y (1993) The giant organelles in *Beige* and Chédiak–Higashi fibroblasts are derived from late endosomes and mature lysosomes. *Journal of Experimental Medicine* **178**: 1845–1856.

Haddad E, Le Deist F, Blanche S *et al* (1995) Treatment of Chédiak–Higashi syndrome by allogenic bone marrow transplantation: report of 10 cases. *Blood* **85**: 3328–3333.

Lutzner MA, Teirney JH and Benditt EP (1966) Giant granules and widespread cytoplasmic inclusions in a genetic syndrome of Aleutian mink. *Laboratory Investigation* **14**: 2063–2079.

Nagle DJ, Karim MA, Wolf EA *et al* (1996) Identification and mutation analysis of the complete gene for Chédiak–Higashi syndrome. *Nature Genetics* **14**: 307–311.

Novak EK, Hui S-W and Swank RT (1983) Platelet storage pool deficiency in mouse pigment mutations associated with seven distinct genetic loci. *Blood* **63**: 536–544.

Perou CM and Kaplan J (1993) Complementation analysis of Chédiak–Higashi syndrome: the same gene may be reponsible for the defect in all patients and species. *Somatic Cell and Molecular Genetics* **19**: 459–468.

Perou CM, Moore KJ, Nagle DL *et al* (1996) Identification of the murine *beige* gene by YAC complementation and positional cloning. *Nature Genetics* **13**: 303–308.

Root RK, Rosenthal AS and Balestra DJ (1972) Abnormal bactericidal, metabolic, and lysosomal functions of Chédiak–Higashi syndrome leukocytes. *Journal of Clinical Investigation* **51**: 649–665.

Witkop CJ, Quevedo WC and Fitzpatrick TB (1990) Albinism and other disorders of pigment metabolism. In Laufer RS, Warren E and McIvor D (eds): *The Metabolic Basis of Inherited Disease*, 5th edn. New York: McGraw-Hill. Chapter 15.

CHEMOKINES

Dennis D Taub, Clinical Services Program, National Cancer Institute – Frederick
Cancer Research and Development Center, Frederick, Maryland, USA

The salient feature in a number of inflammatory conditions, such as infection, hypersensitivity reactions or autoimmune diseases, is the presence of infiltrating leukocytes. The extravasating leukocytes are critical for host defense, leading to clearance of the inciting factors such as infectious agents and particulate antigens. However, it should be appreciated that leukocyte recruitment may also contribute to the pathogenesis of an underlying disease. The maintenance of leukocyte recruitment during inflammation requires communication between infiltrating leukocytes and and the endothelium as well as various extravascular cells. These signals are mediated via the generation of early response cytokines, the expression of surface adhesion molecules and the production of chemotactic molecules. While many cytokines modulate cellular adhesion and promote leukocyte recruitment, few have been shown to directly affect integrin avidity. Recent studies have identified a superfamily of small, soluble, structurally-related cytokines called 'chemokines' (chemotactic cytokines) that appear to be excellent, physiologically relevant candidates for the rapid triggering of integrin-mediated adhesion and selectively induce the directional migration of various leukocyte subsets both *in vivo* and *in vitro* (**Figure 1** and **2**). These molecules and their receptors play critical roles in hematopoiesis, angiogenesis, cellular activation, cytotoxicity and wound healing, as well as in a variety of acute and chronic inflammatory disease states.

Characteristics of chemokines

Over 30 unique human and mouse cytokines have been identified as members of the chemokine superfamily (**Table 1**). Based on the presence or absence of an intervening amino acid residue located between the first two of the four conserved cysteine residues, the chemokine superfamily can be separated into two distinct subfamilies called the α (or C-X-C) and the β (or C-C) subfamilies. As the chemokines are secreted molecules, their cDNAs code for a precursor protein which contains a leader sequence (20–25 amino acids), which presumably enables the chemokines to

be produced, cleaved and secreted to yield a mature form at the cell membrane by a wide variety of cell types. Chemokines share many other similarities, including their high basic nature as well as their ability to bind heparin through heparin-binding domains. At the amino acid level these molecules exhibit between 24–80% homology. Chemokines in

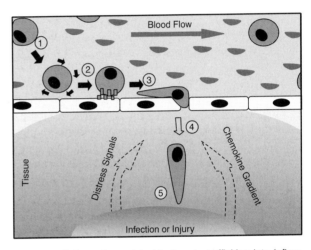

Figure 1 Schematic model of leukocyte trafficking into inflammatory tissues. Many of the models describing leukocyte entry into inflammatory sites depend on at least three distinct molecular interactions: selectin-carbohydrate, chemokine-receptor, and intergrin-CAM. As leukocytes circulate in the blood and lymph (1), they constantly survey the surrounding endothelial barrier for the presence of distress signals alerting them to problem areas. Once alerted, a sequential series of signals is required to mediate leukocyte entry into the extravascular tissues. With the release of distress mediators such as IL-1, TNF, LPS, or histamine, various selectin ligands are rapidly expressed and mobilized to the membrane of the activated endothelial cells within the tissue environment. The selectins mediate the initial tethering and rolling of responding leukocytes to the blood vessel wall slowing their transit through the circulation (2). Upon interacting with proadhesive signals (3), most likely provided by heparan proteoglycan- or extracellular matrix-bound chemokines, the integrin molecules on the leukocyte surface are altered from a conformationally inactive complex to a high avidity state permitting leukocyte binding to the expressed cell adhesion molecules (such as ICAM-1, VCAM-1, etc.) present on inflamed endothelial cell surface (3). At this point, leukocyte rolling stops and firm adhesion begins. These adherent leukocytes are then permitted to spread out along the activated endothelial barrier and migrate (with the assistance of various proteinases) through the vascular endothelial barrier and basement membrane into the extravascular tissue space (5). Once through, soluble as well as extracellular matrix- and heparan proteoglycan-bound chemokines derived from the inflammatory lesion form a concentration gradient promoting the directional migration of leukocytes from areas of low chemokine levels toward the areas of chemokine production.

Table 1 Members of the α, β and γ chemokine superfamily

Subfamily	α Chemokines		β Chemokines		γ Chemokines	
Structure	---C-X-C-----C---C---		---C-C------C---C---		---C-------------C---	
Species	Human	Mouse	Human	Mouse	Human	Mouse
Chromosome	4q12–q21	—	17q11–q21	11	—	1
Members	IL-8/NAP-1 GCP-1	—	MCP-1/MCAF	JE	Ltn	Ltn
	GROα/MGSA	KC	MCP-2	HC14	—	ATAC
	GROβ/MIP-2α	MIP-2	MCP-3	fic/MARC		
	GROγ/MIP-2β	—	RANTES	RANTES		
	ENA-78	ENA-78	MIP-1α/LD78	MIP-1α		
	NAP-2	—	MIP-1β/ACT2 pAT744	MIP-1β		
	—	KC	I-309	TCA-3/p500		
	NAP-4	—	—	C10/MRP-1		
	GCP-2	—	—	MRP-2		
	PF-4	—	HCC-1	—		
	IP-10	IP-10/C7 CRG-2	—	—		
	MIG	MIG	—	—		

The C-X-C and C-C subfamilies possess a conserved four-cysteine motif distinguished by the presence or absence of an intervening amino acid between the first two cysteines, while the C branch of the chemokine family lacks the first and third cysteines in the motif but still possess cysteines 2 and 4 as well as other chemokine features. The C-X-C chemokines include interleukin 8 (IL-8) (also called neutrophil-activating peptide 1 (NAP-1)), growth-related peptide α (GROα) (also called melanoma growth stimulatory activity (MGSA)), GROβ, GROγ, NAP-2, epithelial derived neutrophil attractant 78 (ENA-78), granulocyte chemotactic protein 2 (GCP-2), platelet factor 4 (PF-4), platelet basic protein (PBP), β-thromboglobulin (β-TG), connective tissue activating protein III (CTAP-III), stromal cell derived factor 1α (SDF-1α), SDF-1β, interferon-inducible protein 10 (IP-10) and monokine induced by interferon γ (MIG). The C-C chemokine subfamily members include macrophage inflammatory protein 1α (MIP-1α), MIP-1β, regulated-upon-activation, normally T cell expressed and secreted (RANTES), macrophage chemotactic protein 1 (MCP-1), MCP-2, MCP-3, C10, I-309 (also called T cell-activation gene-3 (TCA-3) in mice), HCC-1, and eotaxin. The C chemokine subfamily members include lymphotactin (Ltn) and probably activation-induced, T cell-derived and chemokine-related molecule (ATAC). A number of additional names and homologs from other species exist and are described in greater detail in the supplied reading list.

their monomeric form range from 7 to 14 kDa and are active at concentrations ranging from 10^{-8} to 10^{-10} M. However, many of the chemokines form dimers, trimers and tetramers upon secretion. While chemokine dimer formation has been shown to be necessary for optimal ligand interaction with chemokine receptors by some investigators, this requirement is rather controversial as chemokine monomers have also been shown to be biologically active. Chemokine subfamily members are also coclustered on the same chromosomes. α Chemokines are clustered on human chromosome 4q12–q21, while β chemokines cluster on human chromosome 17q11–q21 and mouse chromosome 11. Lymphotactin (Ltn), a member of the 'C' subfamily (γ chemokines) lacking two of the typical four cysteine residues, is located on human chromosome 1. Many of the α chemokines possessing -ELR- residues at position 4–6 near the N-terminus have been shown to be potent mediators of neutrophil chemotaxis both in vitro and in vivo and have the capacity to bind the shared interleukin 8 (IL-8) receptor type II. All α chemokines which lack the -ELR- motif fail to chemoattract neutrophils or bind the shared IL-8 type II receptor.

Chemokines are not typically expressed in unstimulated cells, tissues or cell lines but are rapidly induced (usually within 1–2 h post stimulation) in response to either endogenous or exogenous stimuli. Typically, agents which enhance inflammation (e.g. lipopolysaccharide (LPS), IL-1, tumor necrosis factor α (TNFα), injurious stimuli and infectious agents) or immune activation (e.g. lectins, antigenic stimulation, mitogens, immunoglobulin E (IgE) antigen and phorbol esters) also promote chemokine production. Chemokine mRNA can comprise up to 1% of the total mRNA content of a stimulated cell. Chemokine production appears to be ubiquitous, in that almost every cell and tissue type in the body has been shown to produce chemokines upon stimulation. It is believed that chemokines produced within a given tissue, rather than remaining in solution, are preferentially immobilized through low-affinity binding to heparin-bearing proteoglycans (HP) on the vascular endothelial cell barrier or to extracellular matrix proteins within the extravascular tissues (**Figure 1** and **2**). As chemokines possess GAG-binding sites and bind heparin through their carboxyl-termini, this binding may be important in cytokine localization and immobilization on endothelial cells and matrix proteins as well as their biological activity.

Biological activities

The chemokine subfamilies can be distinguished from one another by their apparent leukocyte specificity in mediating cell migration and adhesion. Typically, ELR$^+$ α chemokines induce neutrophil but not

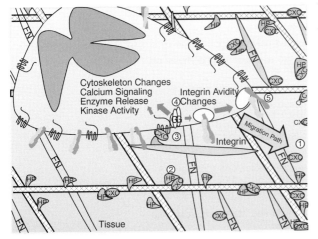

Figure 2 Leukocyte entry and migration within an inflammatory environment. Once across the vascular barrier, leukocytes directionally adhere and migrate along the various extracellular matrix proteins and CAMs within the tissue toward the sites of chemokine production (1). The chemotactic gradients are believed to be maintained via chemokine binding to extracellular matrix proteins (e.g. fibronectin (FN), collagen (CN), etc.) and heparan proteoglycans (HP) found within the tissues (2). The migrating leukocytes directionally move from regions of low levels of chemoattractants to regions containing higher concentrations. As leukocytes infiltrate sites of increased chemokine concentrations, chemokine receptor desensitization may inhibit further migration in response to a given chemokine gradient. In addition, it seems quite possible that the expression of various matrix- and proteoglycan-degrading enzymes may also serve to regulate leukocyte entry and departure from inflammatory sites by the cleavage of chemokine presenting molecules. The presentation of a chemokine to a specific cell surface chemokine receptor (CXCR or CCR) induces a complex series of intracellular signals that facilitate cell adhesion and migration (3, 4). As chemokine receptors are associated with a heterotrimeric G protein complex (with each receptor possessing its own unique G protein profile), signaling through these molecules is believed to transduce a signal(s) necessary to activate integrin adhesiveness (5). Both chemokine receptors and integrin molecules mobilize to the leading edge of the migrating leukocyte, optimizing ligand recognition and promoting directional migration. Signals induced by these receptors also induce an increase in integrin expression and the release of various metalloproteases/TIMPs may assist in transversing the various layers of the basement membrane and tissue environment. Furthermore, it seems most likely that only certain integrin molecules are activated by chemokine receptor interactions (depending on the receptor and its G-protein association) possibly by regulating leukocyte adhesion to specific extracellular matrix proteins (5). A greater definition of the interplay between chemokines, adhesion molecules, and enzyme release may further elucidate the true mechanisms required for leukocyte transmigration through the vascular barrier and basement membrane.

monocyte migration, while β chemokines predominantly act on monocytes and macrophages with no activity on neutrophils. Besides neutrophils and monocytes, both α and β family members are active on a number of cell types (**Table 2**). In addition to the subtype of leukocyte being examined, the chemokine responsiveness of a cell may depend on its activation state. In addition, stimulation of certain cell populations with cytokines or activation stimuli appears to enhance their chemokine responsiveness. Chemokine activities are not only restricted to chemotaxis and adhesion, multiple other proinflammatory effects have been described. These include the induction of superoxide anion, nitric oxide, metalloproteinases, intracellular granules and cell adhesion molecules (**Table 2**). Many of these biological properties are believed to contribute not only to their immunological roles in inflammation but also to their physiological roles in tissue repair and cellular growth/differentiation.

Chemokine receptors

Chemokine receptors are members of the rhodopsin or serpentine receptor superfamily and have the characteristic G protein-coupled seven hydrophobic transmembrane spanning regions. These receptors also exhibit varying degrees of homology, particularly within their transmembrane spanning regions. Studies have revealed a number of human chemokine receptors with various chemokine binding characteristics (**Table 3**). Chemokine ligand–receptor interactions initiate a characteristic pattern of responses, including shape change, integrin activation, chemotaxis, degranulation, enzyme secretion and respiratory burst. Depending on the chemokine and leukocyte subtype, receptor ligation has been shown to activate a number of signaling pathways, including phosphoinositol hydrolysis, arachidonic acid metabolism, the activation of various kinases, and the rapid elevation of diacylglycerol and cytosolic Ca^{2+} levels. In addition, all chemokine receptors contain one or more of the consensus sequences for G_i protein activation which is believed to be essential for the high-affinity binding of chemokines and their adhesion/migration activities.

Pathological disease states

Many chemokines have been shown to be present in numerous inflammatory and noninflammatory disease states, including sepsis, atherosclerosis, arthritis, cystic fibrosis and asthma. In many of the inflamed lesions the presence of chemokines is highly correlated with the level of leukocyte infiltration within

Table 2 *In vitro* effects of α and β chemokine family members

Chemokine	Target cell	Biological effects on various target cells
α Chemokines		
IL-8, GROα, GROβ, GROγ, NAP-2	Neutrophils	Chemotaxis; shape change; increased degranulation; increased respiratory burst; increased cytosolic Ca^{2+}; increased adhesion to endothelial cells, fibrinogen and extracellular matrix proteins; increased *Candida albicans* growth inhibition; increased expression of CD11a, CD11b, CD11c and CD18; increased lysosomal enzyme release; decreased L-selectin expression
PF-4	Neutrophils	Chemotaxis; superoxide release
IL-8, GROα	T cells	Chemotaxis; stimulated polyphosphoinositide hydrolysis
IP-10	T cells	Chemotaxis; increased adhesion to endothelial cells and extracellular matrix proteins
IL-8	B cells	Inhibits IL-4-induced IgE production; inhibits B cell proliferation
IP-10, IL-8	NK cells	Chemotaxis; increased killing of tumor targets
IP-10	Monocytes	Chemotaxis
IL-8	Basophils	Chemotaxis; inhibits histamine release; increased leukotriene release
IL-8, IP-10	Keratinocytes	Increased proliferation
IL-8	Endothelial cells	Increased blood vessel proliferation (angiogenic)
PF-4	Endothelial cells	Increased ICAM-1 expression; decreased blood vessel proliferation (angiostatic)
IL-8, GROα	Melanomas	Increased adhesiveness and haptotactic response
IL-8	Smooth muscle	Chemotaxis
PF-4, CTAP-III, β-TG, NAP-2	Fibroblasts	Chemotaxis; increased proliferation
β Chemokines		
MCP-1, MCP-2, MCP-3, MIP-1α, MIP-1β, RANTES, C10	Monocytes	Chemotaxis; increased superoxide anion release; increased cytosolic Ca^{2+}; increased adhesion to endothelial cells and extracellular matrix proteins; increased *N*-acetyl-β-glucuronaminidase; increased cytostatic augmenting activity; increased intracellular calcium; induced arachidonic acid release
MCP-1, MIP-1α, MIP-1β, RANTES, MCP-3, C10	T cells	Chemotaxis; increased adhesion to extracellular matrix proteins and cytokine-activated endothelial cell monolayers; increased metalloprotease and TIMP release; increased CTL killing of tumor cell targets; degranulation; costimulation
MCP-1, MIP-1α, RANTES	Mast cells	Chemotaxis; histamine release
MCP-1, MCP-3, MIP-1α, RANTES	Basophils	Chemotaxis; increased histamine release; increased intracellular calcium; increased leukotriene release; increased adhesion
MIP-1α, MCP-1, RANTES, MCP-3	B cells	Chemotaxis; increased proliferation; increased IgE and IgG4 production
MIP-1α, MIP-1β, RANTES, MCP-1	NK cells	Chemotaxis; increased killing of tumor targets; increased adhesion to extracellular matrix proteins
MIP-1α, RANTES, eotaxin, MCP-3	Eosinophils	Chemotaxis; induces cationic protein release; increased intracellular calcium; increased cell surface integrins
MIP-1α, MCP-3	Neutrophils	Weak increases in intracellular calcium; increased shape change

CTL, cytotoxic T lymphocyte; ICAM, intercellular cell adhesion molecule; NK, natural killer; TIMP, tissue inhibitor of metalloproteinase.

the diseased tissue. Under some conditions the chemokines facilitate leukocyte adhesion and transmigration into compromised tissues, resulting in the phagocytosis and killing of microbes or allogeneic cells (host resistance), while in other states aberrant chemokine production contributes to the induction and progression of disease pathology (**Figure 1** and **2**). Several chemokine receptors act as human immunodeficiency virus 1 (HIV-1) coreceptors. T cell tropism is associated with CXCR4 expression whereas macrophage-tropic strains bind to CCR5. A

greater understanding of the complexities of the chemokines that mediate cell adhesion and transmigration may assist in the orchestration, regulation and control of various pathological disease states.

See also: **Acute inflammatory reaction; Adhesion molecules; Autoimmune diseases; Autoimmunity; Chemotaxis; Cytokines; Endothelium; Human immunodeficiency viruses; Hypersensitivity reactions; Integrins; Interleukin 8 and its receptor.**

Table 3 Chemokine receptors

Chemokine receptor	Ligands
CXCR1 (IL-8RI)	IL-8, GCP-2
CXCR2 (IL-8RII)	IL-8, GCP-2, GRO-α, -β, -γ, ENA-78, NAP-2, LIX
CXCR3	IP-10, MIG, I-TAC
CXCR4	SDF-1
CCR1	MIP-1α, RANTES, MCP-3, -4
CCR2	MCP-1, -2, -3, -4, -5
CCR3	Eotaxin-1, -2, RANTES, MCP-3, -4
CCR4	TARC
CCR5	MIP-1α, MIP-1β, RANTES
CCR6	MIP-3α
CCR7	MIP-3β
CCR8	I-309
Duffy receptor	All α and β chemokines except MIP-1α, MIP-1β and IP-10

See **Table 1** for explanation of abbreviations.

Further reading

Bacon KB and Schall TJ (1996) Chemokines as mediators of allergic inflammation. *International Archives of Allergy and Immunology* 109: 97–109.

Baggiolini M and Dahinden CA (1994) CC chemokines in allergic inflammation. *Immunology Today* 15: 127–133.

Baggiolini M, Dewald B and Moser B (1994) Interleukin-8 and related chemotactic cytokines – CXC and CC chemokines. *Advances in Immunology* 55: 97–179.

Baggiolini M, Dewald B, Moser B (1997) Human chemokines: an update. *Annual Review of Immunology* 15: 675–705.

Luster AD (1998) Chemokines—chemotactic cytokines that mediate inflammation. *The New England Journal of Medicine* 338: 436–445.

Oppenheim JJ, Zachariae COC, Mukaida N and Matsushima K (1991) Properties of the novel proinflammatory supergene 'intercrine' cytokine family. *Annual Review of Immunology* 9: 617–648.

Rollins BJ (1997) Chemokines. *Blood* 90: 909–928.

Schall TJ and Bacon KB (1994) Chemokines, leukocyte trafficking, and inflammation. *Current Opinion in Immunology* 6: 865–873.

Strieter RM, Standiford TJ, Huffnagle GB, Colletti LM, Lukacs NW and Kunkel SL (1996) The good the bad, and the ugly. The role of chemokines in models of human disease. *Journal of Immunology* 156: 3583–3586.

Taub DD and Oppenheim JJ (1994) Chemokines, inflammation and the immune system. *Therapeutic Immunology* 1: 229–242.

CHEMOTAXIS

Peter C Wilkinson, Department of Immunology, University of Glasgow, Glasgow, UK

Chemotaxis, the directional locomotion of cells towards a source of a chemical gradient, was first described in bracken fern spermatozoa by Pfeffer in 1884. Shortly afterwards (1888) Leber described a similar phenomenon in mammalian leukocytes responding to a focus of injury. Since then, chemotaxis has been accepted as an important mechanism for mobilizing phagocytic and immune cells at sites of infection, tissue injury, and immune reactions. However, it is only recently that something has been learnt about the sensory mechanisms by which cells detect attractants and about the motor which provides the power for their locomotion, and knowledge of both is still very incomplete. Chemotaxis is simply a special form of locomotion, and a brief preliminary description of leukocyte locomotor behavior will help understand its mechanism.

Morphological events of leukocyte locomotion

Leukocytes which are unstimulated are spherical and immotile. This is their morphology both in the bloodstream and after careful *in vitro* preparation. Following stimulation with a chemoattractant, the cells change shape within a minute or so by extending a pseudopod, or lamellipodium, at one pole. Slow contraction waves may then pass anteroposteriorly down the cell from this point. The cell thus adopts a typical, tapered, locomotor morphology (**Figure 1**). The ruffled anterior lamellipodium is initially hyaline and is rich in actin and actin-associated proteins but lacking in organelles. Behind it is the organelle-rich cell body with a posterior tail (uropod) which forms after the complete passage of a contraction from front to back. All these changes occur whether the cell is in suspension or on a surface. Surfaces, either two-dimensional or three-

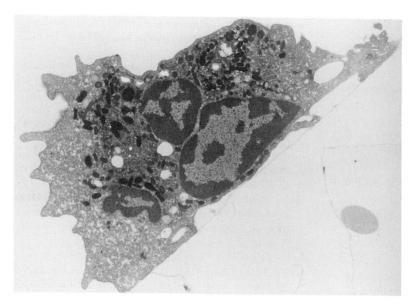

Figure 1 A neutrophil migrating on a surface. Note the broad, ruffled anterior lamellipodium which is free of organelles. Behind this is the cell body containing the nucleus and cytoplasmic organelles. The cell is 'waisted' about a third of the way down. Observation of moving cells shows that this is due to a constriction which passes from front to back as the cell moves forward. A posterior tail is also seen. Special techniques reveal that the anterior lamellipodium is rich in actin and actin-associated protein and that cell surface receptors are frequently concentrated at this pole (not shown in this picture). (Photography by courtesy of Dr Wendy Haston).

dimensional (such as collagen or fibrin gels) give purchase for locomotion. Similar changes are seen in neutrophils, macrophages, lymphocytes and eosinophils. They are initiated by binding of 'chemotactic' factors to cell surface receptors, and all of these cells show chemotaxis, though the neutrophil is the best studied. The term chemotactic factor is imprecise since such factors also activate chemokinesis (below) and other functions such as adhesion, oxidative metabolism, secretion, etc.

Definitions of locomotor reactions

Random and directional locomotion

The paths of moving cells may be directional or random. In random locomotion, the different cells of a population move in directions that are random in relation to one another and to the environment, but the individual cells may persist in their initial direction of locomotion for several minutes. This is called a 'persistent random walk'. When observed over long periods, the cells turn so that, over long periods (>5 min), mean square displacement is proportional to time. In directional locomotion the cells show preference for a particular direction, and their morphological axis is oriented in that direction.

Locomotor responses to physical or chemical cues

The environment of the cell may determine both directional and random locomotion. Chemical cues determine reactions as follows.

Chemokinesis Chemokinesis has two forms: orthokinesis and klinokinesis. In orthokinesis, the speed or frequency of locomotion is determined by the magnitude of the stimulus, i.e. the attractant concentration.

In klinokinesis the amount of turning the cell does is determined by the magnitude of the stimulus. Orthokinesis is thus a straightforward acceleration or deceleration of cells in response to stimuli. It is certainly important in leukocytes. Klinokinesis is of uncertain importance in leukocytes, though, in bacteria such as *Escherichia coli*, chemicals determine whether the organisms 'tumble' or show straight runs. In the rest of this article, the term 'chemokinesis' will be used synonymously with 'orthokinesis' as defined above.

Chemotaxis Chemotaxis is a reaction by which the direction of locomotion is determined by the direction and magnitude of a chemical stimulus. The stimulus is usually in the form of a concentration gradient. In leukocytes, chemotaxis is always positive, i.e. towards a gradient source. Negative chemotaxis away from a source may exist in other organisms.

Contact guidance Chemotaxis is not the only cue that causes cells to move directionally. Contact guidance is a reaction by which the direction of locomotion is determined by the shape or curvature of the substratum on which the cell moves, i.e. by physical rather than chemical properties of the environment. For example, in aligned matrices of collagen or fibrin, neutrophils and lymphocytes prefer to move in the axis of the aligned fibers rather than across them. Cells are equally free to move in both directions in that axis, i.e. this is not a unidirectional locomotion, like chemotaxis. It is likely to be an important determinant of the ability of leukocytes to accumulate, particularly in tissues with complex patterning.

Locomotor capacity Leukocytes only show the capacity for locomotion at certain stages of their development. Thus myeloid precursors in bone marrow are nonmotile, and lack chemotaxis receptors, but they acquire these as they develop, so that virtually all blood neutrophils and monocytes have a capacity for locomotion and chemotaxis. T lymphocyte precursors may be attracted chemotactically into the thymus, though as they mature, they may lose locomotor capacity. Many lymphocytes in blood and peripheral lymphoid tissues are not motile in the G_0 stage of growth, but develop locomotor capacity when the enter the G_1 phase of cell cycle if cultured in the presence of mitogen or antigen. Obviously locomotor capacity is an essential prerequisite for chemotaxis, chemokinesis, etc.

Haptotaxis The term haptotaxis was introduced by Carter in 1967 to describe directional locomotion on a surface bearing a gradient of changing adhesiveness. It is now used in a different sense to describe chemotaxis on gradients of surface-bound attractants. This is postulated to be important for transmigration of leukocytes across vascular endothelium and through connective tissue matrices towards sites of inflammation. Leukocyte migration requires contact with a surface but is not always dependent on adhesion since all the morphological changes described above occur when chemoattractants are added to cells in suspension. Moreover cells are capable of migrating through three-dimensional matrices without adhering since they can gain purchase by using the meshwork of fibres like a climbing frame. Nevertheless on two-dimensional surfaces, migration must be dependent on adhesion and there is now much evidence that, in sites of inflammation, the adhesion of both leukocytes and vascular endothelial cells is greatly increased.

How do leukocytes perceive chemotactic gradients?

Various explanations have been proposed for how a cell exposed to a gradient knows that the concentration on one side is higher than on the other and how it translates this information into locomotion in the direction of the highest concentration. Leukocytes can detect differences of as little as 1% in concentration across their lengths. Various ideas are as follows.

Spatial detection of a gradient

Stationary leukocytes exposed to a gradient put out a pseudopod in the direction of the gradient source before the cell has moved, possibly because receptor occupancy by ligand on the side facing the gradient source is higher than receptor occupancy on the other side. The cell response occurs where receptor

occupancy is highest. There are difficulties with this idea. The difference in receptor occupancy between the two sides may be very small and there is no easily imagined biochemical mechanism for the cell to perform the complex computations involved in spatial sensing and converting them into a polarized response.

Temporal detection of a gradient

Bacteria are small and fast-moving and it is believed that they move from point to point, sample the attractant concentration as they move, and act on the information thus received. Thus they detect the gradient in time. This requires a simple memory, the biochemistry of which is simpler than for spatial sensing. However, leukocytes detect gradients without moving. It has therefore been suggested that temporal sensing is determined not by movement of the cell but by movement of receptors on the cell surface. Receptors moving forward on the front of the cell experience increased ligand binding, which would determine increased cytoskeletal activity and motion at this region. At the cell's rear the opposite would be the case.

Chemotaxis may be a stochastic process

Neither spatial nor temporal mechanisms explain why leukocytes assume a front-tail polarity (**Figure 1**) in uniform concentrations of attractant. Under these conditions the cells ought to respond uniformly all over if the response resulted from a simple ligand–receptor interaction linked to the cytoskeleton. One possibility is that the cellular response is determined by the position on the cell surface at which the first signal is received. This requires the attractant concentration to be low enough to allow a cell to distinguish a first signal from subsequent signals. At low attractant concentrations, cells appear to be able to do this, but at higher concentrations, they show irregular morphologies when stimulated and take a few minutes to adopt a head–tail polarity. Possibly one pole becomes dominant due to chance fluctuations in receptor occupancy or signal transduction in different parts of the cell. In gradients, most cells will polarize up-gradient because most cells will receive their first signals on the side facing the gradient source. Both in gradients and in uniform concentrations, polarization is stabilized by redistribution of receptors to the head of the cell so that subsequent ligand–receptor interactions are most likely to occur there. If the stochastic model is correct, the molecular mechanisms for chemotaxis and chemokinesis are identical, and the path of locomotion of the cell, random or directional, is determined by the topographical distribution of attractant molecules rather than

Table 1 Chemokine attractants for leukocytes

	Neutrophils	Monocytes/ macrophages	T lymphocytes	Eosinophils	Basophils
α *Chemokines*					
IL-8	++	−	+		
NAP-2	+	−			
GRO	+	−			
IP-10	−	−	(+)		
ENA-78	+	−			
MIP-2	+	−			
GCP-2	+	−			
β *Chemokines*					
MIP-1α	−	++	(+)	+	
MIP-1β	−	++	(+)	−	+
MCP-1	−	++	+	−	+
MCP-2	−	++	+		
MCP-3	−	++	+	+	
MCP-4	−	++	+	+	
RANTES	−	++	±	+	+
Eotaxin	−	−		+	
Other Chemokines					
SDF-1	−	+	++		

Receptors for chemokines

α Chemokines	CXCR1 (previously IL-8RA): specific for IL-8
	CXCR2 (previously IL-8RB): broad specificity
	CXCR3: binds IP-10
	CXCR4: binds SDF-1
β Chemokines:	CCR1: binds MIP-1α and β, MCP-3, RANTES
	CCR2A: and B bind MCP-1 and 3
	CCR3: binds eotaxin, RANTES, MCP-1
	CCR4: binds MIP-1α, MCP-1, RANTES
	CCR5: binds MIP-1α and β, RANTES

Note: The list of both chemokines and their receptors is incomplete. Parentheses indicate activity for a T cell subset. SDF-1 attracts resting T cells. Other chemokines attract only activated T cells.

by different cellular mechanisms for locomotion in gradients or in isotropic attractant concentrations.

Chemotactic factors

The term chemotactic factor is used of molecules which stimulate the directional locomotion of cells in gradients. In many cases a formal demonstration of directional locomotion has not been made and the less specific term chemoattractant is often used instead. There is a vast literature documenting such activity of many molecules for different classes of leukocyte. Recent interest has centered on the chemokine family of cytokines, different members of which are specific attractants for particular leukocytes, and which are believed to play a central role in inflammation. It is not possible to discuss all of these here but **Table 1** lists some of the important chemokines and **Table 2** lists some of the better-known nonchemokine attractants. Chemokines bind to serpentine seven membrane-spanning domain receptors of the rhodopsin superfamily (type III transmembrane proteins) which are linked to trimeric GTP-binding proteins of the $G\alpha_1$ class. Many of the nonchemokine attractants bind to receptors of this family as well, e.g. formyl peptides, C5a, but other attractants, e.g. interleukin 2 (IL-2), IL-15, transforming growth factor β (TGFβ), tumor necrosis factor α (TNFα), stimulate chemotaxis through other types of receptor, so no generalizations can be made about the structure of chemotaxis receptors. The responsiveness of lymphocytes to chemoattractants is more complex than these tables would suggest, since there are many classes of lymphocyte, and, for example, neither B cells nor natural killer (NK) cells are included in the tables although there is literature describing attractants for both.

Importance of chemotaxis and chemokinesis *in vivo*

These reactions have been defined in *in vitro* studies,

Table 2 Nonchemokine attractants for leukocytes

	Cell type				
	Neutrophils	Monocytes/ macrophages	T lymphocytes	Eosinophils	Basophils
Formyl peptides	++	++	−	±	
C5a; C5a des Arg	++	++	−	+	
Leukotriene B$_4$	+	+	−		
PAF	±	±	−	+	
Thrombin		+			
Cytokines (nonchemokine)					
TGFβ		++			
TNFα	+	+			
GM-CSF	++	++	−		
M-CSF (CSF-1)		+			
IL-2	−	−	++		
IL-15	−	−	++		
IL-16			+		

Note: Partial list. A large number of other chemoattractants have been documented.

and are difficult to study with precision *in vivo*. Buckley, in 1963, made small burns in tissues with a microelectrode and observed leukocytes migrating directionally to the injured site. This is similar to the reaction of 'necrotaxis' described by Bessis in which individual red cells are damaged with a laser, and in which nearby neutrophils migrate in and ingest the damaged red cell, but only immediately after the burn. Chemotactic gradients *in vivo* may be easily disturbed. However, if chemotactic factors are also all chemokinetic factors, it is possible that leukocytes leaving a vessel will move around at speed even in the absence of a gradient. Those that get closest to the lesion, where gradients are likely to be sharpest, will then pick up the gradient and move directionally to the lesion site.

Methods

There are two basically different types of assay in use to study chemotaxis. The first is to film, with a camera or videotape, the detailed movements of cells and to measure speed, direction, etc. in different absolute concentrations and different concentration gradients of attractant. This gives precise information about the reactions defined above, but requires fairly specialized equipment. The second is to measure the distribution of a cell population at a fixed time-point after exposure to an attractant in uniform concentration, gradients, etc. This is the basis of the widely used filter assays, agarose assays, etc. and the methodology and measurement are simple. However, these assays only give indirect measures of the reactions defined above and it is difficult to dis-

tinguish chemotaxis from chemokinesis using them. This has resulted in much confusion, and, for example, many workers equate directional locomotion with chemotaxis, and random locomotion with chemokinesis. These are not synonymous as the definitions above make clear.

See also: **Motility of immune cells; Phagocytosis; Chemotaxis of macrophages and monocytes; Chemotaxis of neutrophils; Chemotaxis of lymphocytes.**

Further reading

Baggiolini M and Dahinden CA (1994) CC chemokines in allergic inflammation. *Immunology Today* **15**: 127–133.

Devreotes PN and Zigmond SH (1988) Chemotaxis in eukaryotic cells. *Annual Review of Cell Biology* **4**: 649–686.

Dunn GA (1981) Chemotaxis as a form of directed cell behaviour. In: Lackie JM and Wilkinson PC (eds) *Biology of the Chemotactic Response*, pp. 1–26. Cambridge: Cambridge University Press.

Horuk R (1994) The interleukin-8 receptor family: from chemokines to malaria. *Immunology Today* **15**: 169–174.

Keller HU, Wilkinson PC, Abercrombie M *et al* (1977) A proposal for the definition of terms related to locomotion of leucocytes and other cells. *Clinical and Experimental Immunology* **27**: 377–380.

Murphy PM (1994) The molecular biology of leukocyte chemoattractant receptors. *Annual Review of Immunology* **12**: 593–633.

Wilkinson PC (1982) *Chemotaxis and Inflammation*, 2nd edn. Edinburgh: Churchill Livingstone.

CHEMOTAXIS OF LYMPHOCYTES

Peter C Wilkinson, Department of Immunology, University
of Glasgow (Western Infirmary), Glasgow, UK

Lymphocytes have long been known to be motile cells, but study of their locomotion has lagged behind that of monocytes and neutrophils, partly because of the heterogeneity of lymphocytes and their migratory behavior. Under normal circumstances there is continuous recirculation of both T and B cells between the blood and the lymphoid tissues. The recirculating population consists of naive small lymphocytes which are not in cell cycle. When lymphocytes recognize antigen, their migratory behavior alters. These cells enter the cell cycle and leave the recirculatory pool. Their adhesion phenotype changes, since they lose L-selectin and lose their affinity for the high endothelial venule (HEV) cells of lymphoid tissue. At the same time, they show increased expression and activity of many other adhesion molecules which allow them to attach to inflammatory endothelia, to cluster round antigen-presenting cells, and to bind to target cells for cytotoxicity. Thus the lymphocyte changes from a cell monitoring the environment for antigen to a cell that is focused on to effector functions. As would be expected, there are changes in locomotor properties between resting and activated lymphocytes which reflect these changes in function.

Small recirculating lymphocytes

Most of the lymphocytes in blood are recirculating cells. These cells give poor responses to most cytokines which have been reported to be lymphocyte chemotactic factors. It is difficult to induce more than 5–10% of blood lymphocytes to respond to any of these agents. However, small lymphocytes show a rapid change from a spherical to a polarized shape on contact with cultured HEV cell monolayers. Many of the cells transmigrate rapidly across to the undersurface of the monolayer where they continue to show active locomotion. It is likely that locomotion is activated by contact between specific surface molecules on the lymphocyte and the HEV. The chemokine, stromal cell-derived factor 1 (SDF-1) has recently been shown to attract resting T cells and is therefore likely to be a signal for lymphocyte recirculation.

Locomotion and chemotaxis of T cells: the role of activation

The capacity of lymphocytes from blood or lymphoid tissues to respond to chemoattractants is considerably enhanced by a period of 12–48 h of culture in the presence of activating agents. Polyclonal activators such as CD3-specific antibody, phytohemagglutinin (PHA), concanavalin A (con A), or even fetal calf serum will increase the proportion of locomotor cells from 10% to 30–70%. Antigens such as purified protein derivative of *Mycobacterium tuberculosis* (PPD) or superantigens such as staphylococcal enterotoxin B (SEB) have a similar effect. These are not direct chemoattractant effects. If the cultured cells are washed and resuspended in the presence of a fresh preparation of the activator, they may show no response, but if they are resuspended in their own supernatant medium, they do respond, suggesting that chemotactic cytokines are released during culture. Both lymphocyte activation and the release of attractants into the supernatant are dependent on the presence of accessory cells and highly purified T cells fail to become activated.

Following culture in the presence of accessory cells, the activated T lymphocytes can be purified and will then show chemotactic responses to pure cytokines (see tables 1 and 2 of the 'Chemotaxis' article). Interleukin 2 (IL-2) and IL-15 are both good chemotactic factors for these cells. The shared β chain (and probably also the γc chain) of the IL-2 and the IL-15 receptor are essential for this activity. The chemotactic activity of IL-15 probably plays a major role in recruitment of T cells into the lesions of rheumatoid arthritis. IL-16 also is a T cell attractant with a selective activity for CD4$^+$ cells. Several chemokines also have activity. They include the α (C-X-C) chemokines, IL-8, and IP-10 (induced by IFNγ), and the β (C-C) chemokines, MIP-1α and β, MCP-1, -2, -3 and -4, and RANTES. During activation with PPD, SEB or anti-CD3, as detailed above, sufficiently large quantities of IL-8 are released by monocytes to stimulate locomotion of T lymphocytes. β Chemokines have very little activity for T lymphocytes cultured for 24–48 h with the above-mentioned activators, but, during a week of culture with IL-2, the lymphocytes acquire chemokine receptors and show stronger locomotor responses to MIP-1α and RANTES. The list of presently known attractant cytokines is certainly incomplete. The profusion of lymphocyte attractant factors suggests that each may have specific roles in different types of lesion, but this is conjecture at present.

B cells

B cells, like T cells, recirculate and their first encounter with antigen may be in the T cell zone of lymphoid tissue where they meet antigen in clusters with interdigitating cells and T cells. Antigen-reactive B cells then migrate to the follicles to form a germinal center where a second encounter with antigen, in the form of immune complexes on the surfaces of follicular dendritic cells (FDCs), takes place. Further development to antibody-forming or memory cells also requires contact with CD40 ligand (CD40L)-positive germinal center T cells. All of these processes require active locomotion by B cells. Like T cells, B cells respond much better to attractants once they are activated.

Resting (G_0) B cells acquire locomotor activity during culture *in vitro* with T cell products, IL-4 and anti-CD40 (which mimics CD40L), and the motile cells are in the G_1 phase of growth. After a few hours of culture with these factors, the B cells are capable of locomotor and chemotactic responses to antiimmunoglobulin (anti-IgM and anti-IgD). Germinal center B cells die rapidly in culture unless they receive rescue signals, and anti-CD40 provides such a signal. Germinal center cells not only survive but become motile in culture in anti-CD40+IL-4. These cells, again, are attracted by anti-immunoglobulin and, since they have switched isotypes, they are capable of recognizing anti-IgA and anti-IgG as locomotor signals. This suggests that antigen may be a natural chemoattractant for B cells. It is possible, but has not been investigated, that germinal center cells migrate in antigen gradients towards FDCs. Immune complexes activate complement and it has been reported that germinal center B cells cultured with FDCs respond to C5a as a chemotactic factor. This could also form a gradient which would bring B cells into contact with FDCs.

Natural killer (NK) cells

There is little information on NK cell locomotion, though time-lapse films of these cells attached to target cells show vigorous locomotion of the attached cytotoxic cells, which then become released once the target cell dies. Reports suggest that NK cells,

especially after activation with IL-2, can respond to chemoattractants including the chemokines MIP-1α, MCP-1, RANTES and IL-8, as well as IL-2 itself and C5a.

See also: **Adhesion molecules; B lymphocytes; Chemokines; Chemotaxis; Endothelium; High endothelial venules; Interleukin 2; Interleukin 15 and its receptor; Lymphocyte trafficking; Lymphocytes; Natural killer (NK) cells; T lymphocytes.**

Further reading

Bleul CC, Fuhlbrigge RC, Casanovas JM *et al* (1996) A highly efficacious lymphocyte chemoattractant, stromal cell-derived factor 1 (SDF-1). *Journal of Experimental Medicine* 184: 1101–1109.

Burton GF, Kupp LI, McNalley EC and Tew JG (1995) Follicular dendritic cells and B cell chemotaxis. *European Journal of Immunology* 25: 1105–1108.

Gesser B, Lund M, Lohse N *et al* (1996) IL-8 induces T cell chemotaxis, suppresses IL-4, and up-regulates IL-8 production by CD4$^+$ T cells. *Journal of Leukocyte Biology* 59: 407–411.

Jinquan T, Frydenberg J, Mukaida N *et al* (1995) Recombinant human growth-regulated oncogene-α induces T lymphocyte chemotaxis. A process regulated via IL-8 receptor by IFN-γ, TNF-α, IL-4, IL-10, and IL-13. *Journal of Immunology* 155: 5359–5368.

Komai-Koma M, Leiw FY and Wilkinson PC (1995) Interactions between IL-4, anti-CD40 and anti-immunoglobulin as activators of locomotion of human B cells. *Journal of Immunology* 155: 1110–1116.

Loetscher P, Seitz M, Clark-Lewis I, Baggiolini M and Moser B (1996) Activation of NK cells by CC chemokines. Chemotaxis, Ca^{2+} mobilization and enzyme release. *Journal of Immunology* 156: 322–327.

Roth SJ, Carr MW, Rose SS and Springer TA (1995) Characterization of transendothelial chemotaxis of T lymphocytes. *Journal of Immunological Methods* 188: 97–116.

Tan J and Thestrup-Pedersen K (1995) T Lymphocyte chemotaxis and skin diseases. *Experimental Dermatology* 4: 281–290.

Taub DD, Key ML, Clark D and Turcovski-Corrales SM (1995) Chemotaxis of T lymphocytes on extracellular matrix proteins. Analysis of the in vitro method to quantitate chemotaxis of human T cells. *Journal of Immunological Methods* 184: 187–198.

Wilkinson PC and Liew FY (1995) Chemoattraction of human blood T lymphocytes by interleukin-15. *Journal of Experimental Medicine* 181: 1255–1259.

Wilkinson PC, Komai-Koma M and Newman I (1997) Locomotion and chemotaxis of lymphocytes. *Autoimmunity* 26: 55–72.

CHEMOTAXIS OF MACROPHAGES AND MONOCYTES

Peter C Wilkinson, Department of Immunology, University of Glasgow (Western Infirmary), Glasgow, UK

The locomotor behavior of monocytes and macrophages, and their behavior in response to attractants, are as described in the article 'Chemotaxis'. Like neutrophils, they show chemotactic and chemokinetic responses under appropriate conditions and the direction of their locomotion also shows guidance in relation to aligned fibrous matrices. Monocytes and macrophages are quite strongly adherent cells and spread rapidly on substrata *in vitro*. As a consequence, their rate of locomotion on such substrata is slower than that of neutrophils, but is faster than that of fibroblasts which are even more adherent.

Locomotor capacity and macrophage heterogeneity

The locomotor capacity of mononuclear phagocytes is determined by their differentiation status. Marrow precursor cells (as those for neutrophils) are non-motile and motility is acquired as these cells develop into monocytes. This is illustrated by the behavior of monoblast lines such as U937 which develop locomotor capacity only on addition of agents such as dibutyryl cyclic AMP or cytokines which drive differentiation into monocyte morphology. These differentiated monocytes are polarized, motile, and have chemotactic receptors not found on their unstimulated precursors. Most blood monocytes are also motile and respond to a range of attractants (see below). Once monocytes leave the blood and become macrophages, they may differentiate into many forms depending on the nature and site of stimulation, and these heterogeneous macrophages vary widely in locomotor activity. This can be studied well using peritoneal exudate macrophages, e.g. from mice. Following an inflammatory stimulus such as thioglycollate, many highly motile macrophages enter the peritoneum, newly recruited from blood monocytes. However, following an immunological stimulus such as *Corynebacterium parvum* or BCG, a more mixed exudate is found with many lymphocytes as well as macrophages. These macrophages also are motile, but less so than those found in thioglycollate exudates. In immunologically stimulated exudates, the lymphocytes are very motile, and these activated lymphocytes show chemotactic responses.

Locomotion and chemotaxis contribute to interactions between macrophages and lymphocytes (see below). Macrophages in culture may slowly lose their motile behavior, especially when they become adherent and sessile and resident peritoneal macrophages usually show little locomotor behavior and respond poorly to attractants. A similar state of affairs may exist in the pulmonary alveoli in which cells newly recruited in response to inflammation are more motile than the resident macrophage population. Macrophages in other tissues may form tight adhesions with neighboring tissue cells. Presumably, macrophages such as hepatic Kupffer cells have little requirement for locomotor activity, since agents needing removal are brought to them by blood flow, though this is difficult to study since methods for isolation may damage surface receptors on such cells.

Chemotactic responses

Like neutrophils, monocytes and macrophages show accurate chemotactic responses to microorganisms, and respond to factors such as formyl-Met-Leu-Phe, C5a, C5a des Arg, leukotriene B_4, platelet-activating factor, thrombin and denatured proteins or breakdown products of proteins such as elastin, and these responses are probably important both for the microbicidal role and the scavenger role of macrophages. In the latter role, alveolar macrophages are reported to be attracted to, and to ingest, surfactant lipoprotein, presumably in degraded form.

These factors are not monocyte or macrophage specific and may attract neutrophils or other leukocytes strongly. Monocytes also respond to many of the C-C (β) chemokines. These chemokines (MIP-1α and β, MCP-1, -2, -3 and -4, and RANTES) attract blood monocytes but not neutrophils. This allows selective attraction of monocytes into lesions containing these molecules, though the attraction is not completely specific, since the same chemokines may also attract T lymphocytes or eosinophils (see Table 1 of 'Chemotaxis' article). Cell specificity is determined by the possession by different cells of receptors for β chemokines (CCR1–8). Of these receptors CCR1 (which binds MIP-1α, MCP-3, MCP-4 and RANTES) is the most strongly represented on human monocytes. Other cytokines that attract mononuclear phagocytes are transforming growth factor β

(TGFβ), granulocyte-macrophage colony-stimulating factor (GM-CSF), macrophage colony-stimulating factor (M-CSF), tumor necrosis factor α (TNFα) and lymphotoxin (TNFβ).

Attraction of other leukocytes by products of macrophages

Macrophages are important generators of attractants for other cell types and there is an extensive literature describing such factors. For example, many of the chemokines are made and secreted by monocytes or macrophages. These include neutrophil attractants such as interleukin 8 (IL-8). IL-15 is a molecule with functions similar to IL-2 but made by macrophages (and other cells) rather than by T cells. It is an effective attractant for T lymphocytes and is found in large amounts in the lesions of rheumatoid arthritis together with several of the chemokines. Murine macrophages from *C. parvum*-stimulated peritoneal exudates do not attract nearby lymphocytes unless they are given a phagocytic stimulus. However, immediately after phagocytosis, the macrophages release a brief pulse of an as yet unidentified attractant which causes nearby lymphocytes to migrate in by chemotaxis and to cluster round the macrophage. This may be a mechanism for focusing lymphocytes round a macrophage that is presenting newly processed antigen.

Clinical abnormalities

The most interesting of these is probably the observation that both patients with certain tumors (melanoma, certain carcinomas) and tumor-bearing experimental animals may have monocytes or macrophages which migrate poorly in chemotaxis assays. This is due to an inhibitor released by tumor cells and is reversed by removal of the tumor.

See also: **Chemokines; Chemotaxis; Chemotaxis of neutrophils; Macrophage activation; Monocytes; Mononuclear phagocyte system; Neutrophils.**

Further reading

Baggiolini M and Dahinden CA (1994) CC chemokines in allergic inflammation. *Immunology Today* **15**: 127–133.

McInnes IB, Leung BP, Sturrock RD *et al* (1997) Interleukin-15 mediates T cell-dependent regulation of tumour necrosis factor-α production in rheumatoid arthritis. *Nature Medicine* **3**: 189–195.

Murphy PM (1994) The molecular biology of leukocyte chemoattractant receptors. *Annual Review of Immunology* **12**: 593–633.

Premack BA and Schall TJ (1996) Chemokine receptors: gateways to inflammation and infection. *Nature Medicine* **2**: 1174–1178.

Wilkinson PC (1982) *Chemotaxis and Inflammation*, 2nd edn. Edinburgh: Churchill Livingstone.

CHEMOTAXIS OF NEUTROPHILS

Peter C Wilkinson, Department of Immunology, University of Glasgow, Glasgow, UK

Neutrophil locomotion in inflammation

Neutrophils, the most numerous of the white blood cells, are the classical cells of acute inflammation and appear at inflammatory sites within a few hours of tissue injury. This mobilization from the bloodstream requires two events, each with its own molecular recognition mechanisms, the first being adhesion to vascular endothelium at the inflamed site, and the second, migration from the vessels in response to signals generated in the damaged tissue. These events occur in concert. In sites of inflammation, vascular endothelial cells rapidly become more adhesive due to rapid increased expression of P-selectin induced by thrombin or histamine, and later expression of E-selectin and ICAM-1 induced by lipopolysaccharide (LPS), interleukin 1 (IL-1), tumor necrosis factor (TNF) and probably other stimuli. Chemotactic factors cause transient increases in adhesion on contact with neutrophils due to increased expression of β$_2$-integrins, chiefly CD11b/CD18 (MAC-1). Since any chemotactic factors diffusing from the inflammatory site which cross the vascular endothelium and reach the blood are likely to be swept rapidly downstream, it is postulated that chemotactic factors must become attached to the luminal surface of endothelial cells at least transiently in order to do this. By these means, both surfaces, that of the endothelium and that of the neutrophil, increase their adherence to one another. Adherence is followed by transmigration across the endothelium and detachment from it by mechanisms which are still not entirely clear. This is followed by migration through the tissues to the site of injury by a combination of chemotaxis, chemokinesis and contact guidance, as discussed in the article on chemotaxis. *In vitro*, neutrophils respond best (both by chemotaxis and chemokinesis) to many chemotactic factors at nanomolar concentrations or lower, but at higher (micromolar) concentrations locomotion is much slower. Thus cells at some distance from the injured site are fast moving and, as they reach the center of the gradient, they become slowed at the center of the lesion. Moreover, deposition of immune complexes, which bind to Fc receptors at the site of the lesion, also slows the cells by acting as an 'adhesive trap'. Also at micromolar concentrations of chemotactic factors, neutrophils are stimulated optimally to produce an oxidative metabolic burst, to secrete hydrolases and to ingest microorganisms. Thus the dose optima for locomotion and phagocytic events are arranged so that the cells perform these functions in sequence.

Chemotactic factors

Lists of chemotactic factors are given in Tables 1 and 2 under the Chemotaxis article, although there are many others which are not included. Many act on both neutrophils and monocytes/macrophages but not on lymphocytes. These include well-known factors such as C5a, formyl peptides and leukotriene B₄. More recently, studies of the chemokine family have shown that α-chemokines such as IL-8 are neutrophil specific, whereas β-chemokines are monocyte specific, thus providing a mechanism for the specificity of influx of inflammatory cells into different types of lesion.

It is important to emphasize that the term 'chemotactic factor' is inadequate to describe the actions of these factors. In locomotion assays their prime effect is always to stimulate locomotion, and the form the locomotion takes, i.e. whether it is directed or random, depends on whether a gradient is present or not. But as well as effects on locomotion, these factors stimulate various metabolic and microbicidal activities of the cell (**Table 1**).

Formyl peptides are probably the most widely studied of all chemotactic factors. Formyl-met-leu-phe (FMLP) is the best-studied example but many related peptides have similar actions. They are putative representatives of release products from bacteria. Prokaryotic cells commence protein synthesis with a formyl-methionyl starter sequence which is later cleaved and may be recognized as a leukocyte attractant. There are probably many other prokaryotic chemoattractants which have not been defined, as most work has been concentrated on endogenously-derived attractants. The first of the latter to be defined was C5a, a peptide generated by complement activation which probably plays a major role in many inflammatory situations. Leukotriene B₄ (LTB₄) is generated by neutrophils themselves upon activation, and is likely to act as an amplifying device calling cells into sites of activation. Interest has centered recently on IL-8 and related chemokines, which are present at active concentrations in many inflammatory lesions, including those of rheumatoid arthritis and inflammatory lung disease, and which are produced by macrophages and other types of cells, including epithelial cells and vascular endothelial cells, usually following stimulation of these cells. Other cytokines such as TNFα and granulocyte-macrophage colony-stimulating factor (GM-CSF) also have chemoattractant activity for neutrophils. These are just as active as chemokines.

Chemotactic receptors and transduction systems

Receptors for formyl peptides, for C5a and for the chemokines all belong to the same family of serpentine, seven-membrane-spanning domain molecules, related to rhodopsin. These are linked to pertussis

---

Table 1

(a) Functions activated in neutrophils by chemotactic factors	
Locomotion:	chemotaxis; chemokinesis
Secretion:	release of products of specific, azurophil, and other granules
Changes in cell adhesion:	transient homotypic aggregation; longer term increase in adhesion to endothelium or to artificial surfaces
Increased microbicidal activity	

(b) Effector biochemical events activated in neutrophils by chemotactic factors	
Chemotaxis receptors:	receptor redistribution to leading edge of cell; changes in receptor numbers or concentration-dependent changes in receptor affinity
Other events:	increase in LFA-1 family surface receptors; increased actin polymerization; increased f-actin at leading edge; increased myosin-1 at leading edge; increased generation of superoxide (H_2O_2)

toxin-sensitive trimeric GTP-binding proteins containing a $G\alpha_1$ chain. Following ligand binding, these G proteins activate a phospholipase C, leading in turn to hydrolysis of phosphatidylinositol polyphosphates to form the second messengers, inositol triphosphate (IP_3) which, when released into the cytoplasm mobilizes calcium from internal stores, and diacylglycerol (DAG) which activates protein kinase C.

It is known that these are essential events for the activation of neutrophils by chemotactic factors, but a difficulty arises from the fact that these factors activate multiple functions in neutrophils. Most workers on signaling measure chemoattractant-induced metabolic activation or secretory events which are easier to quantify than locomotion, but which occur at higher ligand concentrations than those optimal for locomotion. Different signaling systems may be engaged at different ligand concentrations, and it seems probable that the different functions of neutrophils are signaled through different pathways. Locomotion can occur in the absence of calcium, either extracellular or intracytoplasmic, but this may simply reflect the possibility that there are back-up mechanisms for signaling. The essential requirements is to link the signal generated at the cell surface to actin polymerization so that a microfilament network can be formed which generates contractility and thus motility of the cell. It is likely that small G proteins such as p21 Rac as well as tyrosine kinases are involved downstream of the initial signal. It is also true that chemotaxis is signaled by cytokines which bind to receptors other than the serpentine receptors and these may use different signaling systems from the trimeric G proteins.

The polarity of the locomotor response should be emphasized. The response is polar in the sense that the cell does not behave as a unit but that different events are happening at the front of the cell, where recognition and response to chemotactic factors occurs, from those happening in the cell body. This is illustrated by experiments where the leading edge of a polarized neutrophil was detached from the cell body. These leading edge fragments contained cell surface receptors and actin filaments but lacked organelles or a nucleus. Such cell fragments continued to migrate and to detect chemotactic gradients. Conversely they lacked microbicidal activity, which depends on organelles which remain in the body of the cell. In neutrophils, polarization is initiated by events occurring at the leading edge of the cell, and many receptors, probably including chemotactic receptors, become selectively concen-

trated there. This edge of the cell is also rich in filamentous actin. As the cell moves forward, i.e. as a contraction wave moves from front to back, these events may sequentially involve the rest of the cell. A signaling system for an all-or-none event such as metabolic activation or secretion may be straightforward, but for locomotion over long distances in varying attractant concentrations it is probably more complex than we realize.

Clinical defects of neutrophil locomotion

Locomotor defects in neutrophils are rarely seen and poorly defined. The 'lazy leukocyte syndrome', described some years ago, is not a discrete clinical entity. Patients with leukocyte adhesion deficiency (LAD), due to a defect in the integrin β_2 chain and consequent defective adhesive function of β_2-integrins, have neutrophils that show poor locomotion under circumstances where adhesion is required (e.g. on two-dimensional surfaces of in filters) but not where locomotion is adhesion independent (e.g. through collagen gels). LAD cells can polarize normally, which means that they recognize chemotactic factors normally. Neutrophils from Chédiak–Higashi syndrome have a chemotactic defect whose cause is unknown. A chemotaxis defect has also been reported in neutrophils with specific granule deficiency. In other reported abnormalities, the neutrophils are normal, but the patients have either circulating inhibitors of locomotion or are unable to generate endogenous chemotactic factors normally.

See also: **Chemokines; Chemotaxis; Interleukin 8 and its receptor; Chemotaxis of macrophages and monocytes; Chemotaxis of lymphocytes.**

Further reading

Devreotes PN and Zigmond SH (1988) Chemotaxis in eukaryotic cells. *Annual Review of Cell Biology* **4**: 649–686.

Edwards SW (1994) *Biochemistry and Physiology of the Neutrophil,* Cambridge: Cambridge University Press.

Horuk R (1994) The interleukin-8 receptor family: from chemokines to malaria. *Immunology Today* **15**: 169–174.

McKay DA, Kusel JA and Wilkinson PC (1991) Studies of chemotactic factor-induced polarity in human neutrophils. *Journal of Cell Science* **100**: 473–479.

Murphy PM (1994) The molecular biology of leukocyte chemoattractant receptors. *Annual Review of Immunology* **12**: 593–633.

Wilkinson PC (1982) *Chemotaxis and Inflammation,* 2nd edn. Edinburgh: Churchill Livingstone.

CHIMERISM, HEMATOPOIETIC

Yair Reisner, Department of Immunology, Weizmann Institute of Science, Rehovot, Israel

The ancient Greek chimera, that awesome monster composed of different animals, has in modern times been tamed, and now represents a most desirable clinical status in recipients of organ transplants in general, and bone marrow transplants in particular. Thus, the term chimerism has come to represent a clinical status in which a graft of an organ from one individual is accepted and tolerated by the immune system of another. While acceptance of solid organs, such as kidney, heart or liver, is largely dependent on adequate suppression of the recipient's immune system, as well as on the degree of matching between donor and recipient histocompatibility antigens, bone marrow transplantation is unique in that, in most instances, incomplete or mixed hematopoietic chimeras are generated, and both host-type and donor-type blood cells can be detected in the recipient. Furthermore, while immune reactivity against donor type cells is an obstacle to bone marrow engraftment in all transplants, bone marrow transplantation is uniquely complicated by a second immune barrier, known as graft-versus-host disease (GVHD), mediated by donor type T cells reactive to host antigens.

A successful bone marrow transplant results in a state of hematological and/or immunological chimerism in which donor-type blood cells coexist permanently with host-type tissues, without manifesting alloreactivity to each other. If such a state of tolerance is achieved, subsequent organ grafts from the original bone marrow donor will be accepted without the need to further suppress the recipient's immune system. For this reason, investigation of the mechanisms of tolerance, as well as new and safer approaches for its induction, have challenged immunologists for over three decades.

Currently, bone marrow transplantation is mainly used as a rescue therapy following lethal radio-chemotherapy in patients with leukemia and other forms of cancer, but it can also be beneficial in the treatment of several nonmalignant hematological disorders and enzyme deficiencies.

The first demonstration that a bone marrow transplant could protect lethally irradiated animals from death came from the pioneering studies of Jacobson and colleagues and Lorenz and colleagues towards the beginning of the 1950s. However, it was only in 1956 that several laboratories independently confirmed that a cellular component of the transplanted bone marrow protected recipient mice from the lethal effects of radiation, by its ability to generate new donor-type blood cells for prolonged periods of time.

A better understanding of the bone marrow cellular identity involved in radioprotection was achieved by Till and McCuloch, who discovered a correlation between the presence of spleen colonies in transplanted mice 8–12 days after bone marrow transplantation and the capacity of a given bone marrow cell suspension to protect lethally irradiated mice. This finding helped Trentin and Fohlberg to demonstrate that the entire repertoire of the hematopoietic system could be generated from a single spleen colony. By 1963, Becker and coworkers were able to use chromosome markers to demonstrate the clonal nature of spleen colonies. The existence of a pluripotent stem cell, and its importance in the protection of lethally irradiated mice, thus came to be postulated.

To this day, the characterization of the pluripotent hematopoietic stem cell has been the subject of intense research. With the identification of new cell surface markers, great progress has recently been made. However, since these cells have not been purified to a homogeneous state, they cannot be unequivocally identified in a bone marrow cell suspension.

Knowledge of the radioprotective properties associated with bone marrow transplantation found dramatic application in 1955, when five victims of the radiation accident in Vinca, Yugoslavia were flown to Paris and treated by Mathe and colleagues with bone marrow transplants. Due to technical problems in analyzing the origin of blood cells in these patients, interpretation of results was controversial, but it was agreed that, at best, some transient engraftment occurred, and could have helped the patients to survive, even though their own blood cells returned to normal levels. Fortunately for these patients, they did not suffer from GVHD, as the transplanted bone marrow did not engraft for a substantial period of time.

In the late 1960s, encouraged by the development of histocompatibility antigen (HLA) typing, it was felt that it might be possible to contain the severity of GVHD by transplanting bone marrow from matched sibling donors into patients with severe combined immune deficiency (investigated by Good and colleagues) and leukemia (investigated by Thomas and colleagues). Both groups experienced many frustrating setbacks in their attempts to achieve stable chimerism, but it is primarily due to their perseverance that bone marrow transplantation has now become an integral part of the curative protocol used to treat such patients.

The duel between host-versus-graft activity and GVHD following bone marrow transplantation

The growing experience with transplantation of solid organs, such as kidney and heart, has clearly shown that it is possible to overcome graft rejection, and establish stable donor-type chimerism, when donors and recipients are appropriately matched for histocompatibility antigens and when adequate long-term immune suppression is maintained. Compared with other transplantable organs, however, cells in the bone marrow are highly antigenic, and recipients must first undergo a drastic immunosuppressive regimen of supralethal radiochemotherapy if the transplant is to succeed. In patients suffering from leukemia, as well as from other forms of cancer, this extreme conditioning serves to suppress adequately the recipient's immune system, as well as to eradicate pathological cells. However, despite the use of such intensive radiochemotherapy, administered in doses as high as the human body can tolerate, rejection of the bone marrow may still occur, in particular when poorly matched marrow is used for transplantation.

A second major immunological problem associated with bone marrow transplantation is the complication of GVHD, initiated by donor-type T cells capable of mounting an immune response against host-type antigens. In general, this reaction is directed against the skin, liver and gut, and is lethal in 10–15% of HLA-identical marrow recipients, as well as in over 40% of HLA-nonidentical marrow recipients.

During the 1970s, different laboratories demonstrated that removal of T cells from mouse or rat bone marrow by physical methods, by differential agglutination with lectins or by specific anti-T cell monoclonal antibodies, could effectively prevent the development of GVHD following transplantation of bone marrow allografts. In 1980, T cell-depleted mismatched parental bone marrow was successfully used for the first time to reconstitute the immune systems of infants suffering from severe combined immune deficiency (SCID). The growing international experience, with more than 100 such 'bubble children' to date, has shown that the use of this approach can allow successful bone marrow trans-

plantation across major histocompatibility barriers, thereby effectively curing this otherwise fatal disease. These cured patients have become 'split chimeras'. Their red cells, myeloid cells and platelets are generally of host origin, while their lymphocytes bear the donor type HLA phenotype. Moreover, since many SCID patients lack only T cells, the majority of B cells in these patients also remain of host origin. SCID patients are unique in that their immune response to donor cells is minimal. In these patients, therefore, the graft-versus-host (GVH) activity of T cell-depleted bone marrow can be studied with minimal interference from a host-versus-graft (HVG) reaction.

When T cell-depleted bone marrow was used to treat leukemia patients, however, results were disappointing, as residual immune cells and pathological cells which survived the intense conditioning regimen led to a markedly enhanced rate of graft rejection, as well as to a higher incidence of leukemia relapse in some types of the disease. Results from primate studies, later confirmed by analysis of peripheral blood lymphocytes (PBLs) from transplanted human leukemia patients, suggest that residual clonable T cells ($1–10 \times 10^6$ cells in the entire blood system) remain after completion of the supralethal conditioning protocol. Such cells more easily reject T cell-depleted bone marrow than unseparated bone marrow, as the latter contains about 1×10^9 donor-type T cells, an amount capable of outnumbering and destroying residual host T cells as well as leukemia cells. Thus, GVHD, which can be fatal, may also be beneficial, not only by paving the way for the engraftment of donor-type stem cells but also in its antileukemia effect (generally referred to as graft-versus-leukemia, GVL).

Altogether, although GVHD can be completely prevented in leukemia patients, the use of T cell-depleted bone marrow did not lead to an improvement in the overall long-term survival rate. Alternative methods, by which donor type T cells are partially suppressed by immunosuppressive drugs, such as cyclosporine A and methotrexate, seem to reduce the severity of GVHD and lower the risk of graft rejection and leukemia relapse. Thus, it may be possible to improve the therapeutic management of the 25–40% of patients for whom HLA-identical siblings are available. However, such methods cannot offer a solution for those patients who lack a matched sibling donor in the family.

Very recently, a novel approach to overcome the HLA barrier, employing megadose hematopoietic transplants, has been attempted successfully by Aversa and colleagues in mismatched leukemia patients. To achieve these megadose transplants, we supplemented the conventional T cell-depleted bone marrow inoculum with CD34 peripheral blood progenitor cells obtained from the donor after the administration of recombinant human granulocyte colony-stimulating factor (G-CSF). The potent enhancement of engraftment which was experienced in these leukemia patients indicates that the massive number of infused stem cells may be capable of suppressing residual host cells which otherwise would mediate graft rejection. However, because only very miniscule numbers of T cells could be spared in these transplants, due to the marked GVHD risk associated with their HLA disparity, the T cell reconstitution in the engrafted patients is relatively slow.

Clearly, the question of whether the usefulness of T cells in promoting bone marrow engraftment and in conferring post-transplant immunity, as well as GVL effect, can be separated from their harmful GVH activity, has become a critical issue in bone marrow transplantation today.

Two independent studies have focused on this problem. The group of Tourain and our group showed that a transplant of non-GVHD-producing T cells from (donor × host) F1 mice could enhance long-term engraftment of allogeneic fetal liver cells or T cell-deficient 'nude' bone marrow cells, respectively. These results clearly suggest that T cells can enhance bone marrow engraftment in the absence of GVHD.

Although it is not yet known whether the T cell subpopulation responsible for this positive effect is separable from the T cell subpopulation which causes GVHD, recent studies have demonstrated that alloreactive T cells can be specifically contained *in vivo* by coblockade of the LFA-1:ICAM and CD28/CTLA-4:B7 pathways. Blazar and colleagues showed that hCTLA-4-Ig (inhibitor of the CD28/CLTA-4:B7 costimulatory pathway) plus LFA-1-specific antibody is highly effective in preventing GVHD induced lethality. Alternatively, Cavazzana and coworkers showed that specific elimination of interleukin 2 (IL-2) receptor-positive T cells, after allostimulation *in vitro*, can lead to attenuation of GVHD while maintaining a marked number of relatively nonalloreactive T cells. Both these promising approaches are being investigated in clinical trials.

Human–mouse hematopoietic chimeras

Successful xenogeneic bone marrow transplants between close species such as rat and mouse have in the past been demonstrated. Could human bone marrow cells be engrafted in lethally irradiated mice? This question is of particular relevance to acquired immune deficiency syndrome (AIDS) research, as human immunodeficiency virus (HIV) does not cause AIDS in any other species except in humans, and it is believed that the presence of human CD4$^+$ helper T cells is a reprequisite to infection. If such human–mouse chimeras could be created, they could provide a novel means by which to investigate the development of AIDS and leukemia, as well as for studies of human hematopoiesis.

The poor cross-reactivity between several human and mouse cytokines, as well as between other molecules involved in cellular recognition, was for many years believed to negate the possibility of producing human–mouse chimeras. In 1988, however, two independent studies involving the transplantation of human pluripotent stem cells into genetically determined immune deficient mice, such as the SCID mouse or the Bg/Nu/Xid mouse, documented for the first time the achievement of a transient split hematopoietic chimerism. Moreover, this xenogeneic chimerism was achieved without the apparent development of GVHD.

McCune and colleagues transplanted SCID mice with human fetal liver cells as a source of pluripotent stem cells void of GVHD, along with an additional grafting of human thymic epithelium under the kidney capsule. Thus, they were able to provide a human microenvironment sufficient for the development of human T lymphocytes bearing normal phenotypes. Such T cells remained in the peripheral blood of engrafted mice for 4–8 weeks, during which time they could be infected with HIV.

Kamel-Reid and Dick were able to engender transient myeloid engraftment in Bg/Nu/Xid immunodeficient mice by transplanting them with human bone marrow. Nine weeks after transplant, *in vitro* culture of bone marrow cells from these mice revealed the presence of human genetic material in early myeloid progenitors, suggesting that differentiation of human myeloid precursors can take place in such mice. Subsequently, this same murine model enabled the engraftment in Bg/Nu/Xid mice of pathological cells from human acute lymphocytic leukemia patients. More recently, Lapidot and colleagues identified a new human acute myeloid leukemia (AML)-initiating cell, which is less mature than colony-forming cells, by transplantation into SCID mice. These cells, which are CD34$^+$ CD38$^-$, home to the bone marrow and proliferate extensively in response to *in vivo* cytokine treatment.

Mosier's group further demonstrated that stable mixed lymphoid human–mouse chimerism could be established simply by intraperitoneal injection of human PBLs into SCID mice. Recently, they showed that donor T and B lymphocytes could be detected in the peripheral blood of recipient mice several weeks later, without having caused GVHD. Such human–mouse chimeras could be infected with HIV. Several studies have shown that the engrafted human T cells in these chimera become anergic, unresponsive to stimulation with anti-CD3 or mitogens, and that the human T cell repertoire is limited to xeno-reactive clones.

Recently, Lubin and colleagues described a new approach enabling engraftment of human PBMC in normal strains of mice and rats, following split-dose lethal irradiation. Irradiated animals are initially converted into SCID-like animals by means of bone marrow transplantation from SCID donors and subsequently are infused with human PBMC. These chimeric animals allow an effective and rapid engraftment of human cells, enabling their functional study early after transplant. Moreover, a marked human primary and secondary humoral response, as well as vigorous antiallogeneic human cytotoxic T lymphocyte (CTL) response, could be generated in the human–BALB/c radiation chimera by immunizing them with foreign antigens and allogeneic cells, respectively. In addition, the marked immuno-deficiency induced in these radiation chimera has recently enabled us to transplant human liver fragments under the kidney capsule in such mice and to induce hepatitis C viremia, so as to provide a new murine model for the study of hepatitis B and C infection.

More recently, engraftment of human cells was also enhanced in SCID mice within the first few weeks after transplant, by conditioning of the recipient mice and by using a large inoculum of human cells. Although these preparative regimens were associated with marked lethality, engrafted human lymphocytes exhibited human antibody production and T cell responses similar to those found in BALB/c radiation chimera.

Mixed lymphoid chimerism and organ transplantation

Mixed chimerism, in which both host and donor lymphocytes coexist in significant numbers, rarely develops following bone marrow transplantation. Generally, one cell type is overtly dominant, due to its increased potential to eliminate or to compete with the other cell type. However, stable, long-term mixed lymphoid chimerism can spontaneously occur in nature, as when stem cells from one of two dizygotic twins penetrate the bone marrow of the other twin by placental vascular anastomoses. With the development of DNA analysis, it is now known that following bone marrow transplantation in leukemia patients, normal host lymphocytes can be detected in most transplanted patients even many months after the transplant. It is believed that in such long-term, stable chimeras, host and donor lymphocytes are not reactive towards each other.

Likewise it has been suggested recently that resident 'passenger' leukocytes of hematolymphoid origin that migrate from whole organ grafts subsequently establish systematic microchimerism that is essential for graft acceptance and for the induction of donor specific nonreactivity. This hypothesis has been based primarily on observations in organ transplant recipients in whom transplantation was under postoperative immunosuppression with FK506 and prednisone. More recently, attempts to enhance hematopoietic chimerism in recipients of organ transplants by using bone marrow transplantation from the organ donor under postoperative immunosuppression led to some improvement of solid organ acceptance. Nevertheless, enhancement of chimerism was still very limited and not sufficient to afford acceptance of organs in about 50% of the patients, even though they were treated with immunosuppressive drugs. Clearly, if post-transplant immunosuppression had been omitted in these patients, the results are likely to have been even less successful.

Though the mechanisms underlying the development of mutual tolerance have been studied for more than a decade, they are not yet completely understood, although great progress has recently been made in the molecular characterization of the T cell receptor structure, and the selection of its repertoire during thymic differentiation. It is interesting to note that once stable and substantial mixed lymphoid chimerism is established, transplantation of any other organ from the same donor will be accepted without further need for immunosuppression.

Since the early 1970s, many studies have involved attempts to achieve mixed lymphoid chimeras under conditions less severe than those employed in bone marrow transplantation of leukemia patients. Attempts to induce classical transplantation tolerance in sublethally conditioned animals have generally made use of donor bone marrow cells. Traditionally, in these studies more attention was dedicated to achieving lymphoid chimerism than a complete donor-type hematopoiesis. Pierce and colleagues have demonstrated that infusion of unseparated bone marrow cells, comprising GVHD-producing T cells, into sublethally irradiated allogeneic recipients results in mixed lymphoid chimera which were tolerant to donor-type skin grafts. This approach, shown to be mediated by Thy-1[+] cells, is not only associated with a potential risk of GVHD, but is also limited to the lymphoid lineage due to the insufficient myeloablation associated with the conditioning (3 × 2.5 Gy) regimen used. Further progress has been made by Cobbold and colleagues, who were able to induce, with T cell-depleted bone marrow, lymphoid chimerism in sublethally irradiated recipients conditioned with a nonmyeloablative regimen, including 6 Gy total body irradiation (TBI) and *in vivo* treatment with anti-CD4 plus anti-CD8. Likewise, Sharabi and Sachs demonstrated that transplantation tolerance can be induced after a very low dose of TBI (3 Gy) if the conditioning is supplemented with booster irradiation of the thymus with 7 Gy and with anti-T cell therapy, similar to that employed by Cobbold and coworkers. Again, mixed chimerism was only documented in the peripheral blood and was based on monitoring of donor-type cells within the Thy-1 positive and negative cells, whereas analysis of chimerism in the myeloid compartment in bone marrow or spleen is missing.

Very recently, Bachar and colleagues attempted to broaden the 'megadose' approach and to test whether large inocula of T cell-depleted mismatched bone marrow transplants can induce stable donor-type chimerism in sublethally irradiated mice. We addressed this goal, which represents a difficult challenge due to the marked number of host-type lymphocytes surviving the sublethal irradiation, by investigating whether escalation of the bone marrow cell dose can effectively promote the establishment of complete donor-type hematopoietic chimerism across full MHC barriers. Our results demonstrated that full donor-type hematopoietic chimera, which are stable for over 6 months in both the myeloid and the lymphoid lineages, can be produced by this approach in the bone marrow and in the spleen without any post-transplant immune suppression and in the absence of GVHD. Furthermore, anti-host antibody therapy, which was found to be necessary in previous studies, is not required and the marked numbers of residual host-type lymphocytes which survive 6.5 Gy TBI, are probably overwhelmed and paralyzed by the megadose transplant.

Future directions

Despite the importance of allogeneic bone marrow transplantation in humans, its use presently remains restricted to the treatment of fatal disorders such as cancer, SCID and aplastic anemia. A wider use of this curative approach is limited by the occurrence of GVHD if T cell purging is not used, and by the graft rejection associated with T cell depletion.

However, two major approaches to overcome these barriers, namely the use of B7–CD28 blockade or the use of megadose T cell-depleted transplants,

which have been proven successful in sublethally irradiated mice, lend the hope that the use of allogeneic hematopoietic stem cells will become safer in the near future, thereby expanding its use to the treatment of genetic disorders other than SCID, which are less acute but which can, nevertheless, be lethal over the course of years.

In addition, it is hoped that by the same approach, using nonlethal preparative regimens, induction of specific immunological tolerance towards donor-type antigens, as a prelude for transplantation of solid organs from the same donor, will also become possible.

Meanwhile, an alternative approach has captured the interest and imagination of both scientists and the public at large. Experiments in mice have shown that it is possible to insert a particular gene into the hematopoietic stem cell pool by means of retroviral vectors. It is hypothesized that a diseased bone marrow could be corrected *in vitro* by such 'gene therapy', and then reinfused successfully into the patient. By employing such an approach, the problems of GVHD or graft rejection could be entirely avoided. However, due to the low frequency of pluripotent stem cells in the marrow preparations, and the difficulty in stimulating self renewal of such cells *in vitro*, this new approach is still in the embryonic stages of development. If successful, we may have to define a new chimerism status in which transplanted cells differ from the host cells by a very minute piece of DNA.

An alternative approach to achieving hematologic chimerism involves replacing the bone marrow or peripheral blood stem cells with cord blood hematopoietic stem cells. In 1990, Gluckman and colleagues demonstrated for the first time that cord blood can correct Fanconi anemia in a matched sibling. Both the HLA and the disease-free status of the embryo were established by prenatal testing, and transplantation could be planned for before birth. Thus, the potential number of matched sibling donors in the family could be increased. Moreover, if large numbers of cord blood preparations could be collected and cryopreserved, it could potentially increase the availability of matched unrelated donors. While this possibility is gaining increasing enthusiasm worldwide, it is still hampered by a marked incidence of engraftment failure, associated with the limited number of hematopoietic stem cells which can be collected in cord blood. Clearly, the potential of this approach could be greatly enhanced if it were possible to expand the pluripotential stem cells *ex vivo*. Results in animal models regarding the self renewal capacity of expanded stem cell populations are encouraging but still controversial.

Finally, studies in animals have clearly demonstrated that hematopoietic chimerism can be achieved before birth by *in utero* transplantation of allogeneic stem cells. The success of this approach is based on the relative ease by which tolerance can be induced in the embryonic state, compared with in adults. In the future, it is hoped genetic diseases may be corrected *in utero*, thus eliminating the need for intensive conditioning protocols required for transplantation in adult recipients.

See also: **Alloantigens; Bone marrow and hematopoiesis; Hematopoietic stem cell transplantation; Cell separation techniques; Graft-versus-host reaction; Immunodeficiency, primary; Radiation, effects on immune system; Tissue typing; Transplantation.**

Further reading

Bachar-Lustig E, Rachamim N, Li HW, Lan F and Reisner Y (1995) Megadose of T-cell-depleted bone marrow overcomes MHC barriers in sublethally irradiated mice. *Nature Medicine* 1: 1268–1273.

Blazar BR, Taylor PA, Linsley PS and Vallera DA (1994) *In vivo* blockade of CD28/CTLA4: B7/BB1 interaction with CTLA4-Ig reduces lethal murine graft-versus-host disease across the major histocompatibility complex barrier in mice. *Blood* 83: 3815–3825.

Cavazzana Calvo M, Stephan JL, Sarnacki S *et al* (1994) Attenuation of graft-versus-host disease and graft rejection by *ex vivo* immunotoxin elimination of alloreactive T cells in an H-2 haplotype disparate mouse combination. *Blood* 83: 288–298.

Cobbold SP, Martin G, Qin S and Waldmann H (1986) Monoclonal antibodies to promote marrow engraftment and tissue graft tolerance. *Nature* 323: 164–166.

Dick JE (1996) Normal and leukemic human stem cells assayed in SCID mice. *Seminars in Immunology* 8: 197–206.

Gale RP and Reisner Y (1986) Graft rejection and graft-versus-host-disease: mirror images. *Lancet* 1: 1468–1470.

Gribben JG, Guinan EC, Boussiotis VA *et al* (1996) Complete blockade of B7 family-mediated costimulation is necessary to induce human alloantigen-specific anergy: a method to ameliorate graft-versus-host disease and extend the donor pool. *Blood* 87: 4887–4893.

Korngold R and Sprent J (1978) Lethal graft-versus-host disease after bone marrow transplantation across minor histocompatibility barriers in mice. *Journal of Experimental Medicine* 148: 1687–1698.

Lubin I, Segall H, Marcus H *et al* (1994) Engraftment of human peripheral blood lymphocytes in normal strains of mice. *Blood* 83: 2368–2381.

Marcus H, David M, Canaan A *et al* (1995) Human/mouse radiation chimera are capable of mounting a human primary humoral response. *Blood* 86: 398–406.

McCune JM (1996) Development and applications of the SCID-hu mouse model. *Seminars in Immunology* 8: 187–196.

Mosier DE (1996) Viral pathogenesis in hu-PBL-SCID mice. *Seminars in Immunology* 8: 255–262.

O'Reilly RJ, Keever CA, Small TN and Brochstein J (1989) The use of HLA-non-identical T-cell-depleted marrow transplants for correction of severe combined immunodeficiency disease. *Immunodeficiency Review* 1: 273–309.

Reisner Y and Martelli MF (1995) Bone marrow transplantation across HLA barriers by increasing the number of transplanted cells. *Immunology Today* 16: 437–440.

Ricordi C, Karatzas T, Selvaggi G *et al* (1995) Multiple bone marrow infusions to enhance acceptance of allografts from the same donor. *Annals of the New York Academy of Science* 770: 345–350.

Segall H, Lubin I, Marcus H, Canaan A and Reisner Y (1996) Generation of primary antigen-specific human cytotoxic T lymphocytes in human/mouse radiation chimera. *Blood* 88: 721–730.

Sharabi Y and Sachs DH (1989) Mixed chimerism and permanent specific transplantation tolerance induced by a nonlethal preparative regimen. *Journal of Experimental Medicine* 169: 493–502.

Starzl TE, Demetris AJ, Murase N *et al* (1996) The lost chord: microchimerism and allograft survival. *Immunology Today* 17: 577–584.

CHLAMYDIA, INFECTION AND IMMUNITY

Roger G Rank, Department of Microbiology and Immunology, University of Arkansas for Medical Sciences, Little Rock, Arkansas, USA

Characteristics of the organism and its antigens

The genus *Chlamydia* of the order Chlamydiales consists of four species: *C. trachomatis*, *C. pneumoniae*, *C. psittaci* and *C. pecorum*. *C. trachomatis* is comprised of three biovars, two of which are natural parasites of humans and the remaining biovar a pathogen solely for mice. The two human biovars are subdivided into 12 oculogenital serovars which are responsible for trachoma (serovars A, B, Ba and C) and genital infections (serovars D, E, F, G, H, I, J and K). Genital infections result in urethritis in males and cervicitis, endometritis and salpingitis, potentially leading to tubal obstruction, in females. The remaining three serovars (LGV 1–3) are responsible for lymphogranuloma venereum, a more aggressive and systemic genital infection. *C. pneumoniae* has recently been found to be a major cause of community-acquired pneumonia. Of even greater interest, *C. pneumoniae* has been found in association with atherosclerotic plaques in coronary artery disease. Whether this organism actually causes coronary artery disease has not been confirmed. *C. psittaci* and *C. pecorum* are diseases of veterinary importance although *C. psittaci* may cause a serious and potentially lethal zoonotic infection in humans. Phenotypic and genotypic differences are recognized among the *C. psittaci* but the taxonomic differentiation has not been clearly defined. A wide variety of animals, including but not limited to birds, ruminants, cats, and guinea pigs are infected with different biovars. *C. pecorum* is primarily a pathogen of swine although koalas have also been found to be infected.

Chlamydiae are obligate intracellular parasites and as such are incapable of replicating outside of a host cell, apparently depending upon the host pools for growth. They are able to infect a variety of host cells both *in vivo* and *in vitro* and survive intracellularly by preventing phagosome–lysosome fusion. Chlamydiae are unique among pathogenic bacteria in that they undergo a developmental growth cycle which consists of two stages. The elementary body (0.3 μm) is metabolically inert and is the infectious form of the organism. It attaches to the host cell via a mechanism(s) which is not yet clearly defined. Potential adhesins including the major outer membrane protein (MOMP) ($\approx$40 kDa), a cysteine-rich 60 kDa protein (Omp2), and the 70 kDa protein have been suggested although binding via heparan sulfate and surface glycoproteins has also been proposed. After internalization within an inclusion vacuole, the elementary body differentiates into a reticulate body (1 μm) which is metabolically active and divides via binary fission. By 25–30 h after infection, reticulate bodies begin to differentiate back to elementary bodies. Ultimately, the host cell dies with the release of the elementary bodies which go on to infect other cells, the complete cycle taking approximately 40 h.

The major structural component of the chlamydial outer membrane is the MOMP, comprising about 60% of the outer membrane proteins. Rigidity is provided by extensive intramolecular disulfide bonds and the protein is folded so that four segments, termed variable domains, are surface-exposed. These domains vary among different serovars of *C. trachomatis*, while the remaining regions are conserved among the serovars. MOMP contains genus-, species- and serovar-specific epitopes. Chlamydiae produce a lipopolysaccharide (LPS) which is also associated with the outer membrane and contains a genus-specific antigen. The LPS is immunologically and chemically related to the 'deep rough' (Re) mutant LPS of enteric bacteria. Also highly immunogenic are the Omp2 protein and the 57 kDa heat shock protein.

Immune responses of the host

Because chlamydiae infect a wide array of animal species as well as different anatomical species, it is difficult to define a single pattern of host response. There are undoubtedly similarities in the effector mechanisms involved in eliminating the organism, but the critical effector mechanisms appear to vary with the site of the infection, the host species, the particular strain of a host species, and even the infecting strain or serovar of the chlamydiae. The majority of our information regarding immune responses to chlamydial infections has been derived from *in vitro* studies and from genital, respiratory and ocular animal models of infection which can basically be divided into protective host responses and pathologic host responses.

In virtually all chlamydial infections, the initial host response is an acute inflammatory reaction consisting of polymorphonuclear leukocytes (PMNs) which can be chlamydicidal but also may be responsible for tissue pathology. The mechanism by which PMNs are attracted to the local site is not clear, but recent data have shown that by infecting epithelial cells, chlamydiae effect the release of interleukin 1 (IL-1) and IL-8, the latter being a powerful chemoattractant for PMNs. Infection of macrophages by chlamydiae results in the lipopolysaccharide triggering the production of tumor necrosis factor α (TNFα), IL-1 and IL-6. Chlamydiae have also been shown to activate the alternative complement pathway. Thus, IL-8, TNFα, and complement can potentially mediate the chemotaxis of PMNs to the local site either directly or by upregulating the expression of ICAM-1. In studies in the murine model of genital tract infection, ICAM-1, VCAM-1 and MAdCAM-1, have been found to be expressed early in the infection and could be addressins which are responsible for the extravasation of PMNs and other inflammatory cells at the site of infection.

In both genital tract and respiratory murine models, natural killer (NK) cells have been found to appear at the local site very early in infection, as early as 24 h after infection in the genital tract. The NK cells are the source of interferon γ (IFNγ) which has also been detected early in the infection and could play a role in the control of the infection until the acquired immune response develops. IFNγ has been shown to be chlamydiostatic *in vitro* and to drive the organisms into a nonreplicating state. TNFα has also been observed *in vitro* to inhibit the growth of chlamydiae. Some data suggest that IFNγ produced by NK cells may be important in the ultimate induction of a T_H1 response.

Both humoral and cell-mediated immune responses are elicited by chlamydial infection. In some models, it appears that antibody is important for the resolution of the infection. It has been well-documented that antibody can neutralize chlamydial elementary bodies *in vitro*. Passive immunization with antibody has met with varied success but at least in the *Chlamydia psittaci* strain GPIC:guinea pig model, serum immunoglobulin G (IgG) was actually able to reduce the level of genital infection. Specific IgA is commonly found at local mucosal sites in association with the development of infection and could play a role in the protective response, especially in chlamydial ocular infections. Cell-mediated immunity (CMI) has been found to be important in both murine and guinea pig models. In the mouse, CMI is solely responsible for the resolution of the infection, since B cell-deficient mice are able to recover normally from the infection, while nude mice and CD4 knockout mice do not resolve their infections. The majority of the evidence indicates that CD4 cells are the primary subset responsible for protective cell-mediated immunity. Adoptive transfer of CD4 cells, CD4-enriched lines and a CD4 T_H1 clone are effective in resolving chlamydial genital infections. Nevertheless, adoptive transfer of CD8 cells, CD8 cell lines and a CD8 clone can also resolve infections, albeit not as effectively as CD4 cells. In genital infections, the dominant CD4 subtype is the T_H1 cell, resulting in high levels of IFNγ and minimal levels of IL-4. IFNγ produced by CD4 and CD8 cells most likely plays a major protective role in the acquired immune response. While cytotoxic T lymphocyte (CTL) activity of CD8 cells has been described, their *in vivo* function has not been confirmed. Interestingly, in the primate models of eye and genital infection, equivalent numbers of CD4 and CD8 cells have been reported at the local site, while in the murine genital tract, the dominant cell type is CD4.

Immunity to chlamydial infections is short-lived in humans as well as animal models. In trachoma, the number of organisms isolated is reduced upon subsequent infections, but pathology persists. There is evidence in the murine and guinea pig genital tract models that susceptibility to reinfection is associated with the loss of T cells in the genital tract. However, it also appears from studies in the guinea pig that reduction in the level of a challenge infection may be associated with the antibody response.

While animal models indicate that CMI is important in the resolution of and resistance to infection, it may also be a critical factor in the development of immunopathology. Trachoma has been clearly defined as a disease caused by repeated antigenic challenge and production of a delayed-type hypersensitivity response, even when few organisms can be isolated. Several animal models have also implicated a similar mechanism in fallopian tube damage resulting from multiple chlamydial genital infections. Of importance has been the observations by several groups that the course of infection may vary in different strains of mice and that different serovars of *C. trachomatis* may produce infections of differing severity. The reasons for the differing response among strains has not been clearly defined.

Evasive strategies by the organism

A key feature of chlamydiae is their unique replication cycle and their ability to replicate inside host cells. Obviously, growth intracellularly protects the organism to some extent from antibody although the elementary body is susceptible to neutralization. In order to survive in the host cell, the organisms have developed a mechanism for preventing phagosome–lysosome fusion. Nevertheless, the prevention of phagosome–lysosome fusion is overcome when chlamydial elementary bodies are opsonized by antibody. A potentially significant mechanism of host immune response invasion may be associated with the apparent ability of chlamydiae to remain in a persistent or latent infection state. Evidence for such a form has been provided by the detection of chlamydial DNA, RNA and antigen in the absence of organisms which could be isolated by standard technology. A variety of other data suggest that a latent form may be present. While the mechanism for latency or persistence has not been defined, it is interesting to note that IFNγ is bacteriostatic *in vitro* for chlamydiae, in that it prevents the organism from dividing. However, upon removal of the IFNγ, the organism again begins to replicate and to complete its growth cycle. It is tempting to speculate that the presence of IFNγ from NK or T cells drives the organism into a nonreplicating form until the cellular source of IFNγ leaves the local site and thus brings about a decrease in IFNγ and its control of the infection.

Vaccines

Currently, there is no effective vaccine for chlamydial infections in humans, but a whole-organism vaccine has been available to the veterinary industry for years against the *C. psittaci* feline conjunctivitis organism and ovine abortion agent. An inactivated whole-organism vaccine against trachoma was tested in humans in the 1960s and was to some extent effective. However, the trials were discontinued when some individuals developed more severe disease. These data were supported by primate studies.

Recently, the thrust of vaccine design for chlamydiae has been aimed at determining the protective antigen. The major target for immunization because of its surface exposure and potential involvement in adherence has been the MOMP. The MOMP has been shown to have epitopes which elicit neutralizing antibodies, although to date, subunit vaccines have not been able to elicit protective immunity in animal models. It is important to note that purified MOMP has been found to be protective in animal models, but only if the protein retains its native conformation. Denatured or recombinant MOMP has not been found to be protective. Thus, it appears that with regard to the humoral response, protective antibodies are directed against conformational epitopes on MOMP. While MOMP appears to be the best target to date, there are other chlamydial components which may also be useful targets for a vaccine. Because *in vivo* data indicate an important role for cell-mediated immunity, it will be important to develop a vaccine which also elicits a protective T cell response. Nevertheless, a major consideration in the development of a vaccine needs to be the possibility that the vaccine may actually elicit more severe pathology or that the vaccine may expedite the development of persistence. Thus, a successful vaccine for chlamydial infections may be one that prevents pathology, although it would be ideal to have a vaccine which prevents infection altogether.

See also: **Bacteria, immunity to; Bacterial cell walls; Cytokines; T lymphocytes.**

Further reading

Barron AL (1988) *Microbiology of Chlamydia.* Boca Raton, FL: CRC Press.

Bavoil PM, Hsia RC and Rank RG (1996) Prospects for a vaccine against *Chlamydia* genital disease. 1. Microbiology and pathogenesis. *Bulletin of the Institut Pasteur* 94: 5–54.

Rank RG and Bavoil PM (1996) Prospects for a vaccine against *Chlamydia* genital disease. 2. Immunity and vaccine development. *Bulletin of the Institut Pasteur* 94: 55–82.

Storz J and Krauss H (1985) Chlamydial infections and diseases of animals. In: Blobel H and Schliesser T (ed) *Handbook on Bacterial Infections in Animals*, vol 5, pp 477–531. Jena, Germany: Gustav Fisher.

Ward ME (1995) The immunobiology and immunopathology of chlamydial infections. *APMIS* 103: 769–796.

CHROMOSOME TRANSLOCATIONS OF IMMUNE GENES

Kishor Bhatia and **Marina I Gutiérrez**, Lymphoma Biology Section, Pediatric Branch, National Cancer Institute, NIH, Bethesda, Maryland, USA

The uniqueness of the immune system lies in the immense diversity of the reactive proteins that the immune cells can synthesize. The immune genes, as we know now, are one exception to the notion that DNA is immutable. Indeed, the cutting and repasting of DNA segments in lymphocytes is necessary to provide the immune system the varied repertoire to discriminate between the vast array of antigenic moieties that an organism encounters. The reconfiguration of the 'germline' immune genes is achieved by the action of a normal recombination machinery that allows this process to be restricted to developing lymphocytes. This recombination program relies upon nucleotide sequences in the recombining substrates to provide regional specificity to the cutting and repasting. The process of recombination is influenced by several other factors, including the regional organization of chromatin, the coordinated expression of the recombinase enzymes and the components in the nuclear matrix.

Although the recombinational program that provides for the DNA breakage and rejoining is monitored to prevent errors, some baseline of error-prone recombination may ensue. The probability that this instability will occur at a higher frequency is greater in cell lineages that are prone to such recombination.

It is easy to see how this error-prone recombination could juxtapose regions that are not meant to be ordinarily recombined. The consequences of such illegitimate recombination could range from none to severe depending upon the kind of substrates that recombine. For example, the accidental fusion of sequences that enhance transcription to genes that control proliferation, could result in uncontrolled growth. Thus, the occurrence of error-prone recombination, mediated either because of errors in selecting the sequences that need to be cut and ligated or because of errors in the configuration of the chromatin, is of significant consideration in both leukemogenesis and in lymphomagenesis.

Immune genes as substrates for recombination

The unrearranged immune receptor genes (immunoglobulin and T cell receptor) share the same basic organization – the genes are discontiguous. The chains of the immunoglobulin and T cell receptor (TCR) molecules are encoded as small segments (V, D, J and C) that must associate with each other to provide the complete coding sequence. The genes for the immunoglobulin heavy chain and for the light chains κ and λ are located on chromosomal bands 14q32, 2p12 and 22q11, respectively. The TCR genes are encoded on 7p11 (TCRγ), 7q34 (TCRβ) and 14q11 (TCRα and TCRδ).

Recombinational pathway in the rearrangement of immune genes

During the process of generating a functional heavy chain, the intervening genomic DNA between the randomly selected D (diversity) and J (joining) segments is excised, bringing together the D_H and the J_H segments. This process is thought to occur simultaneously on both alleles. Following this rearrangement, a V (variable) region on one of the alleles is approximated to the DJ region to form the VDJ exon. The coupling of the VDJ regions is an imprecise mechanism which includes the insertion of a few extra nucleotides (N) and may result in an 'out-of-frame' rearranged gene. If so, the V region on the second allele is allowed to recombine to give the B cell a second chance to generate a productive allele, before undergoing apoptosis. The light chain and the TCR genes go through a similar VJ/VDJ rearrangement.

Normally, the mechanism of recombination necessary for the production of an immunoglobulin or a T cell receptor molecule allows intralocus recombination to assemble the VDJ regions of the immune genes. In B cells an additional recombination pathway, which again is intralocus, carries out the juxtaposition of the various constant regions to the rearranged VDJ region, allowing the Ig molecule to switch from IgM to any other class. A third pathway that provides additional diversity to the immune molecules is the hypermutation pathway.

Several factors subscribe to the catalysis of these recombination mechanisms. The recombinase machinery interacts with signal sequences on the two segments that need to be cut and pasted, which consist of a heptamer, defined by the consensus sequence CACAGTG, and a nonamer (GGTTTTGT) present on each site. It seems reasonable that the substrates for the recombination should be accessible to the recombinase enzymes, thus it is likely that structural features, e.g. the chromatin structure, will mechanistically influence the recombination pathway.

Error-prone recombination: cause of chromosomal aberrations

Given the high frequency of all recombinational events in the lifetime of an organism it is likely that in some instances errors in the recombinase machinery will lead to interlocus rather than intralocus

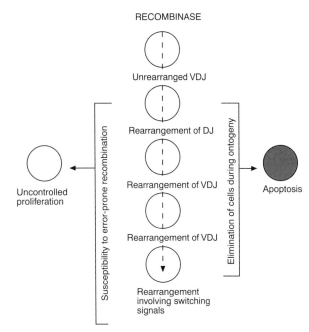

Figure 1 The generation of a productive immune receptor gene is linked to the activity of the recombinase complex. The multi-step rearrangements of the immune locus that takes place during maturation of lymphocytes provides the 'window' during which error-prone recombination may result in a translocation that will allow the clonal proliferation of the cell that has undergone such a translocation. It is possible that normal monitors of the differentiation process that determine the suitability of the lymphocyte at each step also need to be neutralized in the cell with an immune gene translocation in order to resist apoptosis.

recombination. The time window of such errors would, of necessity, mirror the time window in the cell lineages where recombinase machinery is active (**Figure 1**). The recombinational events that are more likely to result in such mistakes include the juxta-position of the D to the J regions, the recombination of the V and the rearranged DJ region and the switch recombinations.

The occurrence of interlocus recombination within the same chromosome but involving relatively distant sites has been documented for the inversions of chromosome 14, between the immunoglobulin heavy chain and the TCRα genes, and of chromosome 7, involving the TCRβ and γ genes. Interlocus recombination that involves two chromosomes has also been documented for the translocations that involve chromosomes 7 and 14 where there is a VDJ recombination that juxtaposes V_γ to DJ_δ or VD_δ to J_γ. It has been suggested that this interchromosomal event may occur at a frequency as high as 1×10^{-3}.

The possibility that the presence of a heptamer sequence alone may in some circumstances catalyze the locus to act as a substrate of recombinase albeit at a low frequency, increases the likelihood of recombination involving immune genes and nonimmune partners.

Chromosomal translocations in hematological malignancies

In several neoplastic entities, the development of a malignant phenotype has been intimately related to the gain of abnormal chromosomal patterns. Chronic myelogenous leukemia is the first disease in which an association with a consistent chromosomal abnormality (chromosome Philadelphia) was established. This results from a reciprocal translocation involving chromosomes 9 and 22. Subsequently, this translocation was also shown to occur in acute lymphoblastic leukemia (ALL) and acute myelogenous leukemia (AML) at low frequencies. The consequence of this t(9;22) is the expression of a chimeric protein that contains sequences from both the partner genes c-ABL (9) and BCR (22).

As can be seen in **Table 1**, the list of nonrandom chromosomal abnormalities in hematological malignancies has grown significantly. Several points can be made from cytogenetic correlations. In most cases there is a high specificity between the morphological classification and the presence of a given abnormality, e.g. the t(14;18) is specifically observed in follicular lymphomas. A more impressive correlation is the restricted involvement of chromosomal loci that harbor immune genes: 2p12, 7q34, 14q11, 14q32 and 22q11 in tumors of lymphoid lineage rather than

Table 1 The most frequent nonrandom chromosomal translocations in hematological neoplasms

Translocation	Genes involved	Neoplasms
t(1;7)(p32;q34)	SCL; TCRβ	T-ALL
t(1;7)(p34;q34)	LCK; TCRβ	T-ALL
t(1;11)(p32;q23)	AF-1P; MLL	Pre-B ALL, AML
t(1;14)(p32;q11)	SCL; TCRδ	T-ALL
t(1;19)(q23;p13)	PBX-1; E2A	Pre-B ALL
t(2;3)(p12;q27)	Ig-κ; Bcl-6	B-NHL
t(2;5)(p23;q35)	ALK; NPM	NHL – anaplastic large cell
t(2;8)(p12;q24)	Ig-κ; MYC	B-ALL, BL
t(2;18)(p12;q21)	Ig-κ; Bcl-2	CLL; B-NHL
t(3;3)(q21;q26)	EVI-1; ?	AML-M6
t(3;5)(q25;q34)	MLF1; NPM	AML
t(3;14)(q27;q32)	Bcl-6; IgH	B-NHL
t(3;21)(q26;q22)	EVI-1; AML-1	CML-bc, t-AML
t(3;22)(q27;q11)	Bcl-6; Ig-λ	B-NHL diffuse
t(4;11)(q21;923)	AF-4/FEL; MLL	Early B precursor ALL; AML
t(5;12)(q33;p13)	PDGFRβ; TEL	CMML
t(5;14)(q31;q32)	IL-3; IgH	B-ALL
t(5;17)(q32;q21)	NPM; RARα	AML-M3
t(6;9)(p23;q34)	DEK;CAN	AML-M2,4
t(6;11)(q27;q23)	AF-6; MLL	AML-M5; pre-B ALL
t(7;9)(q34;q32)	TCRβ; TAL-2	T-ALL
t(7;9)(q34;q34)	TCRβ; TAN-1	T-ALL; T-NHL
t(7;10)(q34;q24)	TCRβ; HOX-11	T-ALL
t(7;11)(q34;p13)	TCRβ; RBTN-2	T-ALL
t(7;19)(q34;p13)	TCRβ; LYL-1	T-ALL
t(8;14)(q24;q11)	MYC; TCRα	T-ALL, T-CLL
t(8;14)(q24;q32)	MYC; IgH	B-ALL, BL
t(8;21)(q22;q22)	ETO; AML-1	AML-M2
t(8;22)(q24;q11)	MYC; Ig-λ	B-ALL, BL
t(9;11)(p21;q23)	AF-9; MLL	AML-M4,5, ALL
t(9;22)(q34;q11)	ABL; BCR	CML, AML-M1,2,4, B-ALL
t(10;11)(p12;q23)	AF-10; MLL	AML-M4,5
t(10;14)(q24;q11)	HOX-11; TCRδ	T-ALL
t(10;14)(q24;q32)	LYT-10; IgH	B-NHL
t(11;14)(p13;q11)	RBTN-2; TCRδ	T-ALL
t(11;14)(p15;q11)	RBTN-1; TCRδ	T-ALL
t(11;14)(q13;q32)	BCL-1; IgH	B-NHL – mantle cell, B-CLL, MM
t(11;14)(q23;q32)	MLL: IgH	B-NHL
t(11;17)(q23;q21)	MLL; AF-17	AML
t(11;17)(q23;q21)	PLZF; RARα	AML-M3
t(11;19)(q23;p13)	MLL; ENL	AML-M4,5, pre-B ALL
t(11;22)(q13;q11)	Bcl-1, Ig-λ	B-NHL
t(14;14)(q11;q32)	TCRα; TCL-1	T-ALL, T-NHL
t(14;18)(q32;q21)	IgH; Bcl-2	B-NHL – follicular
t(14;19)(q32;q13)	IgH; Bcl-3	B-CLL, PLL
t(15;17)(q22;q11)	PML; RARα	AML-M3
t(16;16)(p13;q22)	MYH11; CBFB	AML-M4
t(16;21)(p11;q22)	TLS; ERG	AML-M4; CML
t(17;19)(q22;p13)	HLF; E2A	Pre-B ALL
t(18;22)(q21;q11)	Bcl-2; Ig-λ	B-NHL
t(X;11)(q13;q23)	AFX1; MLL	T-ALL

ALL, acute lymphoblastic leukemia; AML, acute myelogenous leukemia; NHL, non-Hodgkin lymphoma; BL, Burkitt's lymphoma; CLL, chronic lymphocytic leukemia; CML, chronic myelocytic leukemia; CMML, chronic myelomonocytic leukemia; PLL, prolymphocytic leukemia; MM, multiple myeloma; CML-bc, CML in blast crisis; t-AML, AML secondary to therapy.

Table 2 Translocations involving immune loci in T cell neoplasms

Neoplasia	Immune locus	Partner locus	Gene involved	Deregulated oncogenic function/domain
ALL	7q34	1p34	LCK	Signal transduction/Tyrosine kinase
ALL	7q34	1p32	SCL	Transcriptional/bHLH
ALL	7q34	9q32	TAL-2	Transcriptional/bHLH
ALL, NHL	7q34	9q34	TAN-1	Signal transduction/'Notch'-like protein
ALL	7q34	19p13	LYL-1	Transcriptional/bHLH
ALL	7q34	10q24	HOX-11	Transcriptional/Homeobox
ALL	7q34	11p13	RBTN-2	Transcriptional/LIM
ALL	14q11	10q24	HOX-11	Transcriptional/Homeobox
ALL	14q11	1p32	SCL	Transcriptional/bHLH
ALL, NHL	14q11	8q24	MYC	Transcriptional/bHLH-LZ
ALL	14q11	10q24	HOX-11	Transcriptional/Homeodomain
ALL	14q11	11p15	RBTN-1	Transcriptional/LIM
ALL	14q11	11p13	RBTN-2 (LMO-2)	Transcriptional/LIM
ALL, NHL	14q11	14q32	TCL-1	?
ALL, NHL	14q11	Xq28	MTCP-1	?

in tumors of myeloid origin. Furthermore, there is a lineage dependency even among lymphoid malignancies for the immune loci involved. Thus, translocations involving 7q34 and 14q11 are restricted to T cell malignancies (**Table 2**) whereas translocations that involve 2p12, 14q32 and 22q11 are specifically associated with B cell neoplasms (**Table 3**). Since loci 7q34 and 14q11 harbor the TCR genes and in T cells these genomic loci undergo rearrangements, errors in recombination that allow interchromosomal translocations are targeted to these regions in T cells. A similar conclusion can be derived about translocations associated with the immunoglobulin genes in B cells. It is also significant that these immune loci contain powerful transcriptional regulatory sequences. The major function of a mature immune cell is to synthesize immune molecules – immunoglobulin or T cell receptors – thus, recombinase-mediated rearrangements that will erroneously juxtapose genes that are normally silent in these cells will result in the forced expression of such genes. Depending upon the nature of the gene translocated, this deregulated expression of the rearranged gene could result in various phenotypic changes. If the phenotype conferred by the deregulated expression is survival advantage, it will cause a clonal expansion of the lymphoid cells with this particular rearrangement and provide a pool of cells that are prone to

Table 3 Translocations involving immune loci in B cell neoplasms

Neoplasia	Immune locus	Partner locus	Gene involved	Deregulated oncogenic function/domain
CLL, MM, NHL – mantle cell	14q32	11q13	Bcl-1	Cyclin
NHL – follicular	14q32	18q21	Bcl-2	Inhibitor of apoptosis
CLL, PLL	14q32	19q13	Bcl-3	Transcriptional/REL/NFκB
NHL	14q32	3q27	Bcl-6	Transcriptional/Zinc finger
BL, ALL-L3	14q32	8q24	c-myc	Transcriptional/bHLH-LZ
pre-B ALL	14q32	5q31	IL-3	Cytokine
NHL	14q32	10q24	LYT-10	Transcriptional/REL/NFκB
NHL	14q32	11q23	RCK	Helicase
NHL, CLL	2p12	18q21	Bcl-2	Inhibitor of apoptosis
NHL	2p12	3q27	Bcl-6	Transcriptional/Zinc finger
BL, ALL-L3	2p12	8q24	c-myc	Transcriptional/bHLH-LZ
NHL	22q11	11q13	Bcl-1	Cyclin
NHL, CLL	22q11	18q21	Bcl-2	Inhibitor of apoptosis
NHL	22q11	3q27	Bcl-6	Transcriptional/Zinc finger
BL, ALL-L3	22q11	8q24	c-myc	Transcriptional/bHLH-LZ

MM, multiple myeloma

additional genetic insults, eventually leading to transformation.

There are two types of interlocus abnormalities that can be mediated by the VDJ recombinase: one that involves an immune loci as a partner and one that allows recombination between two nonimmune loci. Examples of the latter include translocations involving the MLL locus on chromosome 11q23 and an interstitial deletion on chromosome 1 which involves two independent transcription units, SIL and SCL, and allows the expression of SCL to be promoted by SIL regulatory sequences. In both these recombinations, it has been proposed that the regions of breakage and rejoining contain cryptic recombinase signal sequences and extra nucleotides, supporting the idea that these translocations are mediated by the recombinase machinery.

Chromosomal translocations that do not involve immune loci frequently result in the formation of novel chimeric fusion products and are not usually a result of recombinase errors. Examples of such translocations include the BCR-ABL and the ALK-NPM fusion products resulting from the t(9;22) and the t(2;5) respectively. The hybrid proteins may have unique biochemical properties that are not derived from their respective normal partner gene products, thus the chimeric genes result in a gain of function lesion that promotes leukemogenesis/lymphomagenesis. Thus, recombinational errors resulting in translocations could either promote malignancy via gene activation or via structural alteration, as depicted in **Figure 2**. When immune loci are involved, the mechanism of tumorigenesis is likely to be of a quantitative nature and is limited to gene activation.

Pathogenetic mechanisms: contribution of translocations involving immune genes

A common theme in the molecular pathology of neoplasia is that tumor-associated genetic abnormalities provide the neoplastic cell with the ability to overcome the normal controls of homeostasis. There are three basic pathogenetic mechanisms: the abnormal expression of genes that result in cell proliferation, the silencing of growth inhibitory genes, or the loss of the ability of cells to self-destruct through programmed cell death (apoptosis). Frankly neoplastic cells accumulate more than one abnormality since multiple lesions allow the tumor cell to avoid or pass through the checkpoints present in normal cells that regulate such intricately balanced events as cell cycle, cell differentiation, cell migration and apoptosis. Cells which are lacking some essential attributes are diverted at these checkpoints for repair or self-destruction.

Translocations involving immune genes result in the abnormal expression of proteins either with respect to the cell lineage or the particular stage during differentiation or even with respect to the amount of protein synthesized. This deregulated expression may result from a positive influence – because of the juxtaposition of strong transcriptional regulators like

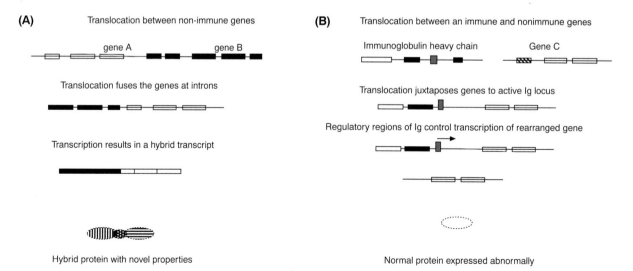

Figure 2 The recombinase machinery, which normally allows only intralocus recombination, is error prone and may cut and paste either two nonimmune genes (A), or juxtapose an immune locus with a nonimmune locus (B), by utilizing sequences present within these loci that serve as signal. If the recombinant product provides a survival advantage, the translocation will often be detected as a marker of clonal proliferation. The mechanisms by which the juxtaposition of an immune locus with a nonimmune locus or of two nonimmune loci provide a survival advantage are discrete. The former translocation often results in the formation of a fusion protein which carries some properties of both the partner proteins so that it acts as a novel protein. The latter translocation very often does not alter the expressed protein but nonetheless results in the inappropriate expression of this protein.

the enhancer elements present in the immune receptor genes, such as that which occurs in juxtaposition of c-MYC to IgH – or may result from loss of negative elements, e.g. the rhombotin 2 on 11p13 loses an upstream regulatory region during translocation with the TCR locus on 14q11.

The pathogenetic contribution of many, if not all, the translocations is the provision of a dominant genetic lesion. None of the translocations examined so far have resulted in the silencing of a growth-inhibitory or a tumor-suppressor gene product. The ultimate mechanism of lymphomagenesis or leukemogenesis is dependent upon the specific partner gene(s) involves in the translocation. The contribution of the immune genes appears mainly to be that of a switch to turn on the expression of the 'oncogenic' gene partners. As seen in **Tables 2** and **3** four major classes of partner genes have been recognized: 1) genes that are master regulators of the expression of other genes (transcriptional factors); 2) genes that affect signal transduction mechanisms; 3) genes that

directly influence cell cycling and proliferation; 4) genes that affect cell survival.

Translocations that deregulate transcription factors
Among the various lesions that are a hallmark of oncogenic events, deregulation of those genes that themselves coordinate the expression of other genes are by far the most common of all lesions.

Transcription factors are versatile proteins that are essentially DNA-binding proteins. A common feature of these proteins is their modular structure which allows two unique domains to be independently defined, the DNA-binding domain and the transcriptional activation domain (**Figure 3**). The DNA-binding domain allows these proteins to specifically bind regulatory elements, through which they modulate gene transcription. Several classes of transcription factors have been identified as partners in translocations involving immune genes, these include the basic helix-loop-helix (bHLH) proteins, exemplified by SCL; proteins that contain zinc fingers (e.g. BCL-6), proteins with a cysteine-rich LIM domain like the rhombotin proteins (which also include a zinc finger-like structure), and proteins with specific leucine repeats termed as a leucine zipper, a domain that is found in the c-MYC protein; the c-MYC protein also contains a bHLH motif.

In translocations that involve immune genes and a transcription factor, the expression of these master regulators is deregulated. Since these genes themselves may control the expression of a set of genes that determine cell differentiation and proliferation, it is not surprising that such genetic lesions are oncogenic (**Figure 3**). In those translocations where the transcription factors are not juxtaposed to immune receptor genes, the deregulation of the transcription factor is often achieved by the formation of novel hybrid proteins where there is an exchange, for example, of the DNA binding domain conferring upon the hybrid protein an altered specificity of transcriptional regulation.

There appears to be a remarkable correlation between the specific type of transcription factor involved in the translocation and the progenitor cell lineage in which it occurs, suggesting strongly that these lesions disrupt regulatory cascades that control cellular differentiation programs. Thus, translocations involving TCRβ and LYL-1 are confined to pro-T ALL while those involving HOX-11 are often seen in pre-T ALL.

In several cases these rearrangements have been directly correlated to mistakes in VDJ recombination. The 'smoking gun' for such mistakes include the presence of nucleotides inserted at the breakpoint junction and the identification of target heptamer-

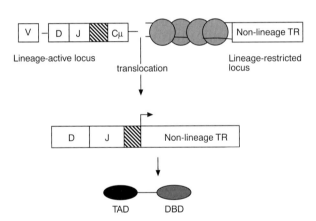

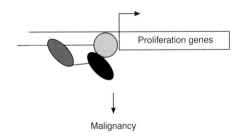

Figure 3 Schema of a possible translocation in a pro-B cell. The translocation juxtaposes a powerful transcriptional regulator (TR), not otherwise expressed in this cell lineage, and an immune gene that is normally active in this cell lineage. As a result of the translocation the TR gains a powerful enhancer from the immune locus and is no longer subjected to lineage restriction. The out-of-lineage expression of the transcriptional regulator provides the switch to turn on other target genes initiating a cascade of events that leads to immortalization of this cell and eventually to neoplasia.

like sequences in the breakpoint region. Thus, recombinase errors have been demonstrated in translocations involving HOX-11 and SCL. One of the most common rearrangement involving SCL (1p interstitial deletions) occurs in as much as a quarter of all pediatric T-ALL and although it does not involve the immune genes, it is nonetheless presumed to be mediated by recombinases. This presumption is again based upon sequencing data that demonstrate the presence of extra nucleotides at the breakpoint junctions. The regions of chromosome 1 that are 'stitched' together also harbor heptamer-like recognition sequences, which catalyze erroneous recombination processes.

Translocations that induce an aberrant signal transduction pathway When the extracellular environment is conducive to proliferation, the cell orchestrates various sets of events that result in growth. This communication from the cell surface, which senses the environment through specific receptors, to the nucleus is transduced by pathways specific for a given signal(s). If the molecular switches within these pathways are locked in the 'on' position, the cell will play out all the downstream events and proliferate even in the absence of a signal.

Translocations that involve the immune genes and thereby dysregulate the signal transduction mechanisms include the t(7;9) (q34;q34) present in about 5% of T-ALL and resulting in a rearrangement of the TCRβ locus with TAN-1, and the less frequent t(1;7) (p34;q34) which juxtaposes the LCK gene to the TCRβ locus. The LCK gene product, which is a receptor tyrosine kinase homologous to the SRC protein, is predominantly expressed in lymphoid cells. TAN-1 is homologous to the *Drosophila* 'notch' protein which is thought to affect development and cellular differentiation. Unlike LCK, however, the expression of TAN-1 is not preferentially lymphoid. In addition to relocating TAN-1 under the transcriptional control of TCRβ, this translocation results in decapitation of the gene, such that the 5' portion of TAN-1 is lost, permitting the redistribution of the protein from its normal location in the plasma membrane to the nucleus.

Translocations that cause a constitutively 'on' cell cycle switch The commitment to enter the cell cycle is an active process initiated by signals received from the extracellular environment. The cell can develop lesions within the cell cycle commitment program, such that it is induced to proliferate even in the absence of upstream signals. A critical phase of the cell cycle commitment occurs in G_1. Following commitment to cycle, several proteins are expressed early

in the G_1 phase. These include c-MYC, c-MYB, c-FOS, c-JUN and PCNA. The critical role these proteins play is highlighted by the observations that when expressed inappropriately, a large number of them promote cell transformation. Deregulation of the proto-oncogene c-*myc* by juxtaposition to an immune gene is seen in both B and T cell lymphomas. In B cell lymphomas, typically in Burkitt's lymphoma, this deregulation in most cases results from transposition of one allele of c-*myc* – normally present on chromosome 8 – into the Ig heavy-chain locus on chromosome 14. Breakpoint locations vary with respect to geography, thus endemic Burkitt's lymphomas very frequently have breakpoints far upstream of the c-*myc* gene, whereas sporadic Burkitt's tumors often carry breakpoints within the transcriptional unit of c-*myc*. It is possible that these breakpoints may be influenced by other factors like the presence of the Epstein–Barr virus, which in certain circumstances may actually influence error-prone recombinations involving the immune genes. Less frequently, the light-chain genes on chromosomes 2 and 22 are involved in deregulation of the expression of c-*myc* in B cell lymphomagenesis. In these cases the light chain genes are juxtaposed to a site downstream of the c-*myc* gene. In T cell lymphomas the deregulation of c-*myc* is achieved by juxtaposition with TCRα.

Among the several proteins that act in concert in allowing the normal progression of the cell cycle, the cyclins play a critical role. Cyclins are expressed transiently during specific phases in the cell cycle and then degraded. Key cyclins mediating G_1 transition are cyclins D1, D2, D3 and E. One error during DJ rearrangement may occur in precursor B cells, leading to a t(11;14) that gives rise to a low-grade B cell lymphoma classified as mantle cell lymphoma. The partner locus on chromosome 11, known as Bcl-1 or PRAD1, has homology to cyclin D1 which associates with CDK-4 and CDK-6. Following activation of the cyclin D/CDK complex, RB is phosphorylated leading to the release of E2F which is now available to transactivate genes like c-*myc*, c-*myb*, thymidylate kinase and thymidine synthetase that are essential for the G_1–S transition.

Death-defying translocations A reciprocal translocation between chromosomes 14 and 18 was found to occur frequently in follicular lymphomas. Molecular analysis indicated that the heavy-chain J segments were juxtaposed to a novel locus designated Bcl-2. The majority of breakpoints on chromosome 18 cluster in a short span of about 300 nucleotides termed as 'major breakpoint region' (MBR). Subsequently, another less frequent cluster of breakpoints was identified 30 kb from the MBR and was designated as 'minor cluster region' (mcr). The translocation did not compromise the integrity of the open reading frame of the major transcript from the Bcl-2 locus. Detailed sequence analysis of the recombinational sites revealed the presence of extra nucleotides at the junctions of the derivative chromosomes suggesting an error mediated by recombinases. However, the actual recombination in this translocation may be catalyzed by chi-like sequence elements. Thus, the t(14;18)(q32;q21) may involve homologous recombination and errors in the action of the recombinases.

Functional analyses to elucidate the pathogenic contribution of the Bcl-2 gene provided insights into a fundamentally novel pathway in tumorigenesis. Aggressive uncontrolled proliferation of cells is one aspect of tumorigenesis, and accumulation resulting from a loss of susceptibility to dying is another pathway to neoplasia. Normal architecture is usually maintained within organs from early in embryogenesis, because all normal cells are subject to homeostasis. An important mechanism that contributes to this regulation is an inherent ability to selectively deplete cells. This ability is derived from the capacity of cells to activate pathways that result in suicide. These pathways are referred to as apoptosis. It is now apparent how the aberrant loss of this program in a cell in multicellular organisms can lead to neoplasia. The involvement of Bcl-2 in overcoming apoptosis suggested that the deregulation of this death-defying gene interfered with normal B cell ontogeny and prevented the otherwise normal loss of B cells due to programmed cell death. It now appears that resistance to death in several normal lymphoid cells relates to overexpression of Bcl-2. Recently, several other proteins with homology to Bcl-2 have been described. Although none of these members have been associated with chromosomal translocations, it is clear that several members of the Bcl-2 family interact with each other in orchestrating the cell death program.

Immune gene translocations associated with DNA repair deficiency

The cutting and repasting of DNA segments during the process of legitimate immune gene rearrangements must surely involve some components of the normal DNA repair machinery. Increased frequency of chromosomal aberrations are indeed observed in normal cells following severe DNA damage and in lymphocytes of individuals with a DNA repair deficiency. Several DNA repair deficiencies are also characterized by an increased risk of malignancies. Patients with ataxia telangiectasia (AT), for example,

are significantly prone to accumulating chromosomal aberrations and 10% of these patients demonstrate an abnormal karyotype in their peripheral blood lymphocytes. In a large proportion of these lymphocytes, the chromosomal aberrations are nonrandom and are often limited to breakpoints on 14q11, 14q32 and 7q34, loci that harbor immune receptor genes.

Molecular analyses have implicated TCRα, TCRβ and IgH to be intimately involved in the recombinational processes that generate these aberrations. Translocations and inversions affecting chromosome 14 are the most frequent clonal rearrangements in AT lymphocytes. Some cases of AT clonal T cell expansion have been reported to progress to T cell leukemias. Interestingly, AT inversions that give rise to chimeric TCR are not associated with leukemogenesis, whereas the t(14;14)(q11;q32) or the inv-(14)(q11;q32) clonal proliferations, both of which involve the TCL-1 locus, can progress to malignancy. In addition, some cases of T cell leukemias in AT patients carry a t(X;14)(q28;q11) which involves a locus termed as MTCP-1 and possibly the J region of TCRα.

Translocations involving immune genes in 'normal' cells

Several of the interlocus recombinations that involve immune receptor genes have also been observed in a small fraction of lymphocytes of healthy individuals. These recombinations include those that form hybrid immune receptor complexes by stitching together VDJ regions between different immune receptors genes. Our ability to detect these rearrangements suggests that they may be positively selected for. The finding that the hybrid receptors frequently recombine to be in-frame is in support of this argument. The analyses of these rearrangements (translocations or inversions) also suggest that they are mediated by the VDJ recombinases at a frequency of about 10^{-4} and predominantly involve chromosomes 7 and 14. It has been demonstrated that the frequency increases following exposure to pesticides. This increase is intermittent and reversible. Exposure to pesticides may also increase the risk of developing lymphoid malignancy. These observations, coupled with the increase of such rearrangements in AT patients, indicate that rearrangements involving immune receptor loci are subject to both exogenous and endogenous influences on DNA stability and that some of these rearrangements, for example the frequency of hybrid receptors, may serve as monitors of error-prone recombinase activity.

The functional consequences of these interlocus

rearrangements are not clear. At least one of the translocations described in lymphomas, the t(14;18) which juxtaposes the Bcl-2 locus within the transcriptional influence of the immunoglobulin heavy chain gene, has also been shown to occur in lymphocytes of healthy individuals, and also bears the 'signature' of recombinase activity. The frequency of this translocation increases with age and parallels the age-dependent incidence of follicular lymphomas. Whether this particular rearrangement is affected by exogenous influences such as exposure to pesticides is not known. However, its frequency is not increased in lymphocytes of AT patients. It is entirely possible that an error in recombinase will promote illegitimate recombination between interlocus immune genes more readily than between an immune and a nonimmune locus.

Summary

The principal function of T and B lymphocytes is to support the immune defense mechanisms of the organism. To do this effectively, these cells have acquired the capability of recognizing and neutralizing a diverse array of 'nonself' antigenic epitopes. This diversity is inherent in the germline structure of the immune genes, which contain several different regions. These discrete regions of the immune genes undergo several recombinational steps and reassortment of multiple segments to express the primary immune protein products.

The reassortment of the immune regions is achieved via a cutting and pasting mechanism that draws its specificity from the presence of specific nucleotide signal sequences, modulation of the accessibility of the genomic regions necessary for recombination, developmentally regulated expression of enzymes that will catalyze the recombination and possibly monitoring mechanisms that will prevent nonlegitimate substrates from recombining. In order to ensure the fidelity of the reaction, all productive recombinational processes are limited to be intralocus. Nonetheless there is a baseline error rate in the recombination process and some interlocus recombinations are also catalyzed. When these recombinations are catalyzed between immune and nonimmune partners, the expression of the nonimmune gene is deregulated. If the nonimmune partner is a growth-stimulatory protein, the recombinational

event can lead to a clonal expansion and eventually transformation of a lymphoid cell. As an extreme, these errors may also involve two nonimmune genes that contain nucleotide sequences that are similar to the recombinase signal sequences. Mistaken recombination of such partner genes may also be transforming if the two genes form a novel product with growth-stimulatory properties or if the expression of one of the growth-supporting partner genes is rendered lymphoid specific by the rearrangement. It is possible that the error-prone mechanisms by which these lymphoid-specific transformation events occur may also overlap with errors in other mechanisms that cause genetic instability and promote transformation of nonlymphoid tumors.

See also: **Apoptosis; B lymphocyte repertoire; B lymphocyte differentiation; B lymphocytes; Bone marrow and hematopoiesis; Diversity, generation of; Genetic analysis at the molecular level; Immunoglobulin class switching; Immunoglobulin genes; Immunoglobulin structure; Leukemia; Lymphocytes; Lymphoma; T lymphocytes.**

Further reading

Drexler HG, Borkhardt A and Janssen JWG (1995) Detection of chromosomal translocations in leukemia-lymphoma cells by polymerase chain reaction. *Leukemia and Lymphoma* 19: 359–380.

Gaidano G and Dalla-Favera R (1993) Biological and molecular characterization of non-Hodgkin's lymphoma. *Current Opinion in Oncology* 5: 776–784.

Gauwerky CE and Croce CM (1993) Chromosomal translocations in leukemia. *Seminars in Cancer Biology* 4: 333–340.

Griesser H and Mak TW (1994) The T-cell receptor – structure, function and clinical application. *Hematology and Pathology* 8: 1–23.

Hwang L-Y and Baer RJ (1995) The role of chromosome translocations in T cell acute leukemia. *Current Opinion in Immunology* 7: 659–664.

Kirsch IR (1993) *The Causes and Consequences of Chromosomal Aberrations.* Boca Raton, FL: CRC Press.

Klein G (1995) B-cell neoplasia in a developmental framework. *International Journal of Developmental Biology* 39: 713–718.

Knowles DM (1992) *Neoplastic Hematopathology.* Baltimore, MD: Williams & Wilkins.

Magrath IT (1997) *The Non-Hodgkin's Lymphomas,* 2nd edn. London: Edward Arnold.

CHRONIC ACTIVE AND AUTOIMMUNE HEPATITIS

Ian R Mackay, Centre for Molecular Biology and Medicine, Monash University, Melbourne, Victoria, Australia

Early descriptions

Autoimmune hepatitis (AH) is now the preferred name for the disease originally described as chronic active hepatitis (CAH) in the 1940s in reference to a protracted viral hepatitis among military personnel. However, CAH, as later understood, emerged from descriptions in the 1950s of a relapsing or progressive and usually fatal liver disease of young women of no ascertainable cause, but perhaps the result of subclinical viral hepatitis. Emphasis was given to endocrine abnormality, amenorrhea, striae and acne due to the diseased liver failing to metabolize steroid hormones, and to hyperglobulinemia with reversal of the albumin–globulin ratio in serum, a then popular liver functional index. Autoimmunity was later implicated because of findings of lupus erythematosus (LE) cells in the blood, and a positive serum complement fixation test with human tissue homogenates as antigen. Clinical and serological resemblances between CAH and systemic lupus erythematosus (SLE) led to the name lupoid hepatitis, but the full expression of SLE was seldom seen, and the LE cell test was usually weaker and more transiently positive. Immunofluorescence testing in the 1960s for antinuclear antibody (ANA) replaced the LE cell test. Later, a serological reaction with smooth muscle was recognized as another identifying marker.

Heterogeneity of CAH

It was realized in the early 1970s that 'chronic active hepatitis' was a generic term for a liver disease with a variable expression and etiology. The hepatitis B surface antigen (HBsAg) had been identified as a marker of infection with hepatitis B virus (HBV), so that some cases of CAH could be characterized as HBV-associated CAH, in addition to autoimmunity and other causes.

Several categories of CAH can now be listed, as follows: 1) The archetypic CAH described in the 1950s as lupoid hepatitis, and now identifiable by autoimmune serological markers; 2) CAH due to persistence of hepatitis B virus (HBV) in the liver, marked (usually) by the presence of HBsAg in serum; 3) CAH due to persistence in the liver of hepatitis C virus (HCV); 4) CAH due to persisting immune-mediated hepatitic reactions to a drug; 5) histological CAH in accompaniment with liver diseases of known toxic, genetic or metabolic cause; 6) a category with neither autoimmune nor viral markers, nor any identifiable cause, referred to as 'cryptogenic'. The relative frequency among populations of these categories of CAH varies. Chronic active hepatitis due to virus infection (HBV, HCV) is now numerically more frequent overall than the autoimmune type and, in some localities, virus-related CAH is seen almost exclusively.

General features of CAH

Chronic hepatitis ranges from an asymptomatic disease recognized only by biochemical abnormalities to one that is severe and progressively cirrhotogenic. Some cases of autoimmune hepatitis can have a long asymptomatic preclinical course, as pertains for other autoimmune disorders. Likewise, an insidious onset and clinical latency is usual for CAH associated with infection with HCV and, in many instances, with HBV. Cases of chronic active hepatitis will have some common general features related to liver dysfunction or cirrhosis, whatever the cause, and other features related to the individual etiological agent or process.

The general features include symptoms of hepatitis, including nausea, anorexia, jaundice, hepatosplenomegaly, and biochemical evidence of liver parenchymal damage, in particular high levels of transaminase enzymes in serum. The biopsy of the liver may show either of two histological lesions, named as chronic *persistent* hepatitis which is indolent and nondestructive, or chronic active hepatitis in which the main morphological feature is the disruption of the peripheral limiting plate of the liver lobule, with a periportal 'spillover' of the inflammatory exudate into the liver parenchyma: 'piecemeal necrosis' (**Figure 1**). This lesion generates scarring and eventually macronodular cirrhosis (**Figure 2**). Hepatocellular carcinoma is a frequent late sequel in CAH due to chronic virus infection but is seldom seen in autoimmune hepatitis. There are features unique to each of the individual categories, as indicated below.

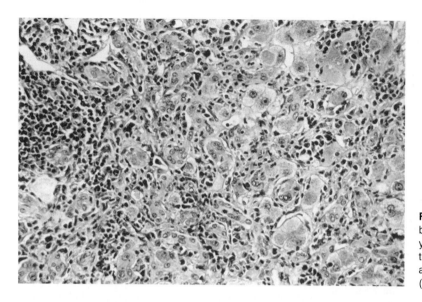

Figure 1 Histological appearance of liver biopsy specimen from a female aged 65 years with recent-onset autoimmune hepatitis, showing periportal and lobular hepatitis and extensive hepatocellular necrosis (HE × 200).

Figure 2 Liver from a female aged 45 years with autoimmune hepatitis, showing scarring and a coarse macronodular cirrhosis.

Features of specific types of CAH

Autoimmune hepatitis

Diagnostic criteria are currently being developed for autoimmune hepatitis. Characteristics that provide a 'disease profile' are: seronegativity for viral markers; female sex; northern Caucasian ethnic origin; multi-system disease expression (arthritis, rashes, thyroiditis, hemolytic anemia, ulcerative colitis); histologically large areas of periportal necrosis and prominence of plasma cells; pronounced hypergammaglobulinemia, >30 g l^{-1}; serum autoantibodies; HLA-B8, -DR3 and -DR4; rapid response to, and dependency on, corticosteroid drugs; and 'resistance' to hepatocellular carcinoma compared with other types of chronic hepatitis or cirrhosis. Most weight attaches to the autoantibody markers, which are predominantly to antigens of nuclei and smooth muscle

(Figure 3). The multiple nuclear antigenic reactants include DNA (rarely), histones and lamins, and the smooth muscle reactant is the cytoskeletal filament, F-actin. Autoantibody to neutrophil cytoplasmic antigen (ANCA) is also seen. In a variant now called autoimmune hepatitis type 2, the marker antigen is enriched in liver and kidney microsomes (LKM). The LKM antigen has been identified as a particular cytochrome P450 isoform, CYP450 2D6. There is suspected to be a liver-specific autoantigen, perhaps membrane-associated, and one candidate is the asialoglycoprotein receptor (ASGP-R); however this to a degree lacks fine disease specificity for association with autoimmune hepatitis. Long-term treatment with prednisolone, combined with azathioprine, is highly effective.

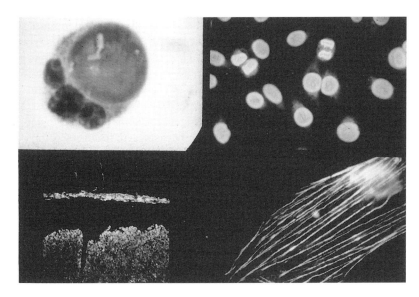

Figure 3 Serological reactions in type 1 autoimmune hepatitis. Top left, lupus erythematosus (LE) cell as the former marker of antinuclear antibody (ANA); top right, homogeneously reactive ANA by immunofluorescence on Hep2 cells; bottom left, smooth muscle antibody (SMA) by immunofluorescence on mouse stomach; bottom right, F-actin specificity of SMA on cultured fibroblast showing staining of cytoplasmic microfilaments.

HBV-associated CAH (CAH-B)

HBV is a DNA virus that is parenterally transmitted. The frequency of chronic infection is higher in males and in localities in which HBV infection is endemic. Infection with HBV is acquired neonatally from infected mothers in high endemicity regions, and sporadically as a parenteral infection in low endemicity regions. The diagnosis of HBV-associated CAH (CAH-B) depends on detecting antigens of HBV in serum, the surface 's' antigen (HBsAg), and in early cases the 'e' antigen (HBeAg). In liver cells, HBV as the core antigen (HBcAg) is demonstrable immunohistochemically or by nucleic acid hybridization. CAH-B has a variable clinical expression and, although often indolent, undergoes progression to cirrhosis, and there is a clear predisposition to supervening hepatocellular carcinoma. Treatment with type 1 interferons may eliminate the virus and arrest the disease.

HCV-associated CAH (CAH-C)

HCV-associated CAH, which accounts for most examples of previously called non-A, non-B viral hepatitis, is due to an RNA virus which is transmitted parenterally. Formerly transmission was mainly by blood transfusion or treatment of hemophilia by blood products; currently the main routes are contaminated equipment of intravenous drug abusers, or close intrafamilial contact. Persisting infection with HCV is frequent after an acute infection. HCV-associated CAH (CAH-C) usually progresses silently to cirrhosis, and primary hepatocellular carcinoma is a risk in the later stages. Cirrhosis and hepatocellular carcinoma appear to be potentiated by coexisting alcoholic liver disease. Many cases formerly specified as cryptogenic CAH

(see below) will probably be attributable to infection with HCV. The diagnosis depends on serologic demonstration of antibody to antigens of HCV, or amplification of viral sequences in blood or liver tissue by the polymerase chain reaction. Treatment with type 1 interferons arrests infection in a proportion of cases. Some instances of CAH-C are associated with low-titer anti-LKM reactions, but this reactivity is not regarded as signifying that autoimmunity plays any role in their pathogenesis.

Drug-associated CAH

Various drugs, of which well-known examples include halothane and chlorpromazine, induce (infrequently) acute idiosyncratic hypersensitivity reactions affecting the liver, with hepatitic or cholestatic expressions. As an accompaniment of these reactions, there may be demonstrable serum autoantibodies of the type usually seen in autoimmune liver diseases, directed to antigens of nuclei (ANA), smooth muscle (SMA), mitochondria (AMA) or liver microsomes (anti-CYP450 2D6). In cases with a protracted course, the histopathology of the liver resembles that of autoimmune CAH. However, characteristically, the disease resolves when the offending drug is withdrawn, and cirrhosis seldom eventuates. The immunopathogenesis of drug-induced CAH is uncertain.

'Toxic-metabolic' CAH

Histologically evident CAH may be seen in cases of chronic liver disease with a defined metabolic cause including alcohol abuse, or effects of inborn genetic errors including α_1-antitrypsin deficiency, Wilson's disease or hemochromatosis. This category is relatively unimportant in terms of immunology, and features of the associated disease are dominant.

Cryptogenic CAH

This term is used for cases of CAH that are negative for markers of autoimmunity or infection with HBV or HCV and for which no other cause is ascertainable. Some cases may be attributable to infection with hepatitis viruses of which markers are absent from serum, to infection with as yet unidentified hepatitis viruses, or to autoimmunity wherein autoantibodies are no longer demonstrable.

Experimental models of CAH

Animal models of CAH of varying fidelity are recognized. HBV-associated CAH has the best models, represented by natural infections of animals in the wild, e.g. wood-chucks or ducks, with a 'hepadna' virus similar to human HBV. Models of autoimmune hepatitis have been induced by neonatal thymectomy and/or immunization with liver preparations, or by other techniques, but none so far has entirely simulated the naturally occurring human disease.

Liver-specific autoantigen

A liver-specific autoantigen as the target for immune-mediated damage in autoimmune hepatitis has not yet been identified. Crude preparations of liver cells and liver cell membrane preparations have been examined in various ways for reactivity with serum or peripheral blood T cells from patients with autoimmune hepatitis with promising but not unequivocal results. No liver-specific autoantigen has yet been identified by techniques applied successfully in other autoimmune disease, namely immunoblotting on electrophoretically separated liver cell membrane preparations, or probing gene expression libraries, using serum from cases of autoimmune hepatitis. Claims for ASGP-R as a liver-specific autoantigen relevant to autoimmune hepatitis need more substantiation.

Mechanisms of hepatocellular damage

The mechanisms of hepatocellular damage in chronic active hepatitis will vary according to the particular cause. In CAH-B there are two likely processes, a specific immune deficiency to critical antigens of the virus, probably the surface antigen, that allows a state of tolerated infection to occur, and a noneliminative attack by cytotoxic T cells on epitopes of the core antigen (HBcAg) expressed with class I major histocompatibility complex (MHC) molecules on the liver cell membrane. In CAH-C, the cytotoxic T cell attack would be on epitopes of HCV expressed with class I MHC molecules on the liver cell membrane. In autoimmune hepatitis the suspected but as yet unknown processes include a T cell-dependent cytotoxicity due to cytokines released from CD4 T cells or cytotoxic effects of CD8 T cells, and an immunoregulatory failure permitting responses to tolerated hepatocellular autoantigens. Whether any pathogenetic connotations can be ascribed to the serologic reactivities, ANA, SMA, anti-LKM, that serve as disease markers is uncertain. It is intriguing that LKM autoantibodies in type 2 autoimmune hepatitis are highly focused towards one particular isotype (2D6) of CYP450, and that there have been identified linear autoepitopes on this enzyme, with the main site (WDPAQPPRD) at residues 262–270; also, a conformational epitope is suggested by the capacity of anti-LKM to inhibit CYP450 enzyme activity. Pathogenicity of the autoantibodies could depend on their cellular penetration, or the cell surface expression of the autoantigens, which remain under debate.

A final common immunocytotoxic pathway in CAH

The occurrence of autoantibody to various liver cell constituents, together with histological appearances of CAH in diseases that are not primarily attributable to an autoimmune process, has led to the idea that an immune-mediated attack on liver cells can supervene as a 'final common immunocytotoxic pathway' in liver diseases with different initiating causes. Whilst this may indeed occur, the features of this postulated 'secondary' autoimmune hepatitis do not really simulate those of the primary disease. Accordingly it is recommended that autoimmune hepatitis be regarded as an entity *sui generis* for which the nature should be better understood if and when a disease-specific and tissue (liver)-specific autoantigen is identifiable.

See also: **Autoantibodies, tests for; Autoimmune diseases; Autoimmunity; Systemic lupus erythematosus (SLE), human; Primary biliary cirrhosis.**

Further reading

Czaja AJ and Dickson ER (eds) (1986) *Chronic Active Hepatitis: The Mayo Clinic Experience*. New York: Marcel Dekker.

Durazzo M, Philipp T, Van Pelt NAM *et al* (1995) Heterogeneity of liver-kidney microsomal autoantibodies in chronic hepatitis C and D infection. *Gastroenterology* 108: 455–462.

Gershwin M, Manns MP and Mackay IR (1992) Molecular aspects of cytoplasmic autoantigens in liver disease.

In: Rose NR and Mackay IR (eds) *The Autoimmune Diseases II*, pp 213–233. Orlando: Academic Press.

Johnson PJ and McFarlane IG (1993) Meeting report: International Autoimmune Hepatitis Group. *Hepatology* **18**: 998–1005.

Krawitt EL (1996) Autoimmune hepatitis. *New England Journal of Medicine* **334**: 897–903.

Mackay IR (1991) Pathogenesis of autoimmune hepatitis. In: Krawitt EI and Wiesner RH (eds) *Autoimmune Liver Diseases*, pp 21–42. New York: Raven Press.

Meyer zum Büschenfelde K-H (ed) (1991) Autoimmune hepatitis. *Seminars in Liver Disease* **11**: 183–262.

Meyer zum Büschenfelde K-H, Hoofnagle JH and Manns M (eds) (1993) *Immunology and Liver: Falk Symposium 70*. Dordrecht: Kluwer.

Nishioka M, Toda G and Zeniya M (eds) (1994) *Autoimmune Hepatitis*. Amsterdam: Elsevier.

Schaffner F (1986) Autoimmune chronic active hepatitis: three decades of progress. *Progress in Liver Disease* **VIII**: 485–503.

Treichel U, McFarlane BM, Seki T *et al* (1994) Demographics of anti-asialoglycoprotein receptor autoantibodies in autoimmune hepatitis. *Gastroenterology* **107**: 799–804.

CHRONIC GRANULOMATOUS DISEASE

Anthony W Segal, Department of Medicine, University College London, Rayne Institute, London, UK

Chronic granulomatous disease (CGD) is a syndrome, the uniting features of which are a predisposition to infection, often with otherwise relatively nonpathogenic organisms, a granulomatous tissue reaction and impaired activity of the 'respiratory burst' of phagocytic cells. Although relatively rare, this syndrome has been the focus of intense investigation because it provides an excellent model for the examination of the mechanisms by which phagocytic cells kill and digest microbes, and has been central to our understanding of the structure and function of the NADPH oxidase electron transport chain, components of which are defective in the different subtypes of the disease.

NADPH oxidase of phagocytic cells

The uniting feature of CGD is an absence of the NADPH oxidase activity of professional phagocytic cells. When these cells engulf particles or are activated by a variety of stimuli, including the tetrapeptide formyl leucyl methionyl phenylalanine or the protein kinase C activator, phorbol myristate acetate (PMA), an intense burst of oxygen consumption is observed. This respiration is not mitochondrial, and is not required for the engulfment of microbes, but is important for the efficient killing of a variety of bacteria and fungi, both those classified as pathogenic, and normal commensals. In classical CGD this respiratory burst is completely defective, whereas in a few very rare cases, termed 'variant CGD' a small amount of oxidase activity can be detected.

Composition of the NADPH oxidase

The oxidase system is an electron transport chain that shuttles electrons from NADPH, generated by the hexose monophosphate shunt from glucose, to oxygen in the phagocytic vacuole. The only functionally defined component of the system is a very unusual flavocytochrome b, flavocytochrome $b558$. The flavin part of the molecule binds the NADPH and has strong homology with the FNR family of reductases. There are two hemes, which are unusual by virtue of their very low redox potential ($E_m = -225$ mV and -265 mV). It is composed of a 22 kDa subunit (α subunit, or p22^{phox}) and a 76–92 kDa heavily glycosylated subunit (β subunit, or gp91^{phox}). gp91^{phox} is the location of the FAD and NADPH binding sites and most probably both of the hemes. This cytochrome is located in the plasma membrane and membrane of the specific granules, and moves into the wall of the phagocytic vacuole as this forms.

A number of components of the oxidase have been identified; 40 kDa (p40^{phox}), 47 kDa (p47^{phox}) and a 67 kDa (p67^{phox}) proteins are located in the cytosol of the cell and move into association with the cytochrome in the membrane upon activation of the system. A small GTP-binding protein, p21^{rac} seems to be important for activation. The function of these molecules remains to be determined.

Molecular pathology

Chronic granulomatous disease is a syndrome in which the uniting feature is the complete absence of NADPH oxidase activity. The molecular pathology varies, but most cases fall into two main groups.

Approximately 70% have an X-linked pattern of inheritance and 30% are autosomal recessive.

X-linked

In almost all these patients flavocytochrome $b558$ is missing from their cells and the lesion is in the gene coding for gp91^{phox}.

Autosomal recessive

The cytochrome is normal in these patients but they are unable to transport electrons on to it from NADPH. Their lesion has been shown generally to involve the p47^{phox}, which is undetectable in their phagocytes. p22^{phox} and p67^{phox} are missing in a minority of patients with this pattern of inheritance. No lesions involving p40^{phox} have been described.

Variant CGD

Unusual subjects have been described in whom a variable but small (less than 20% of normal) amount of oxidase acitivity can be detected. They are largely X-linked and have reduced expression of the large subunit of the cytochrome.

Clinical features

The respiratory burst of phagocytes is required for the optimal killing of a wide variety of bacteria and fungi. In its absence the microbes are engulfed but killing is impaired. This manifests in the patients in an increased frequency of infection, predominantly in the reticulo endothelial system. The most common sites include cervical lymph nodes, lungs, bone marrow (leading to osteomyelitis), liver and skin. *Staphylococcus aureus* is by far the most common infecting pathogen, although a wide variety of otherwise relatively avirulent organisms, for example *Serratia marcescens* can cause serious infections in these subjects. CGD must be excluded in children presenting with cervical or inguinal adenitis, liver abscesses, or aspergillus or nocardia pneumonia.

The defective function of phagocytes from these patients is not limited to their failure to kill microbes. Digestion by these cells is also grossly defective. This results in the diffuse development in the tissues of the granulomas that have lent their name to this syndrome. Granulomas in biopsies from these patients often result in an incorrect diagnosis of tuberculosis being made. Abnormal digestion and the granulomatous response result in poor healing, with the breakdown of wounds and chronic sinus formation. Exuberant attempts at healing can result in narrowing and obstruction of hollow muscular organs like the duodenum and urinary system. Chronic inflammation of the gut may mimic inflammatory bowel disease, particularly Crohn's disease, where bowel disease is associated with the presence of granulomas in histological sections.

Diagnosis

The simplest and most rapid test for CGD is the NBT (nitroblue tetrazolium) test. Neutrophils from a small sample of peripheral blood are activated to produce superoxide which is detected by the NBT, which is converted from a yellow water-soluble compound to a dark-blue insoluble formazan that can be clearly detected microscopically. This slide test can be useful for detecting the X-linked type of disease in which the carrier mothers have a mosaic of normal and abnormal cells in their circulation. The respiratory burst can be accurately quantitated by measuring oxygen consumption with an oxygen electrode or superoxide generation by the reduction of cytochrome c in the presence and absence of superoxide dismutase. Immunological and molecular biological reagents are becoming available for the characterization of the nature of the defect in terms of the proteins and genes that are defective in each case.

Treatment

The prophylactic use of antimicrobial agents, in particular co-trimoxazole (a compound of trimethoprim and sulphamethoxazole) has transformed the natural history of this condition from one of frequent, life-threatening infections to that resulting in an almost normal life.

Infections that do occur must be treated aggressively with antimicrobial agents. Infusions of neutrophils should be used in addition in severe or systemic infection.

See also: **Granuloma; Macrophage activation; Microbicidal mechanisms, oxygen-dependent; Neutrophils; Phagocytosis; *Staphylococcus*, infection and immunity.**

Further reading

Jackson SH, Gallin JI and Holland SM (1995) The p47phox mouse knock-out model of chronic granulomatous disease. *Journal of Experimental Medicine* 182: 751–758.

Liese JG, Jendrossek V, Jansson A *et al* (1996) Chronic granulomatous disease in adults. *Lancet* 347: 220–223.

Pollock JD, Williams DA, Gifford MA *et al* (1995) Mouse model of X-linked chronic granulomatous disease, an inherited defect in phagocyte superoxide production. *Nature Genetics* 9: 202–209.

Porter CD, Parkar MH, Collins MK, Levinsky RJ and Kinnon C (1996) Efficient retroviral transduction of human bone marrow progenitor and long-term culture-initiating cells: partial reconstitution of cells from patients with X-linked chronic granulomatous disease by gp91-phox expression. *Blood* **87**: 3722–3730.

Roos D, de-Boer M, Kuribayashi F *et al* (1996) Mutations in the X-linked and autosomal recessive forms of chronic granulomatous disease. *Blood* **87**: 1663–1681.

Sokolic RA, Sekhsaria S, Sugimoto Y *et al* (1996) A bicistronic retrovirus vector containing a picornavirus internal ribosome entry site allows for correction of X-linked CGD by selection for MDR1 expression. *Blood* **87**: 42–50.

Thrasher AJ, Keep NH, Wientjes F and Segal AW (1994) Chronic granulomatous disease. *Biochimica Biophysica Acta* **1227**: 1–24.

CIRCULATORY SYSTEM INFECTIONS

James P Burnie, University of Manchester, Manchester, UK

The most important infection involving the circulatory system with immunologic sequelae is infective endocarditis. The annual incidence in the USA and the UK is approximately 6 per 100 000 inhabitants, with an overall mortality of 15–30%. In acute endocarditis, most commonly due to *Staphylococcus aureus*, there is a high fever and, if untreated, a fatal rapid destruction of the heart valves. In subacute endocarditis there is a more indolent course and it is here that the immunologic complications occur. These may in part be due to emboli breaking off from the infected heart valve. Clinically these include splinter hemorrhages. Osler's nodes, Janeway's macules, glomerulonephritis, conjunctival hemorrhages (Roth spots) and clubbing of the fingers.

The major causative group of microorganisms is the streptococci. These can be subdivided into the relatively antibiotic-sensitive viridans streptococci and the more antibiotic-resistant enterococci. The viridans streptococci originate in the mouth and are defined by producing partial hemolysis on blood agar plates. They include *Streptococcus sanguis*, *S. mutans* and *S. salivarius*. The enterococci originate in the bowel and include *Enterococcus faecalis*, *E. faecium* and *S. bovis*. The last is associated with underlying bowel pathology.

Immunologic studies

The definitive diagnosis of endocarditis is dependent on the demonstration of vegetations on a heart valve at surgery or necropsy, or a peripheral embolus. Recently this has been augmented by a secondary set of clinical criteria. This consists of major criteria (positive echocardiogram and typical blood culture) and minor criteria (predisposition, fever, vascular phenomena, hematological phenomena, suggestive echocardiogram and suggestive microbiology). In addition to this there is increasing literature showing that antibody levels, as measured by immunoblotting, are very high in enterococcal or streptococcal endocarditis and that these are species specific. For example, there is a strong immunoglubin M (IgM) and IgG response in patients with *E. faecalis* endocarditis to an 88–90 kDa band identified as a homolog of heat shock protein 90. In *S. mutans* endocarditis there is an endocarditis-specific pattern of IgM, including antibody against a 190 kDa homolog of the PAc protein of *S. mutans* and the Spa protein of *S. sobrinus*. *S. mutans* antigen I/II (PAc homolog) has been implicated in the bacteria's adherence to teeth surfaces. Furthermore, monkeys immunized with the protein were protected against dental caries. The viridans streptococci have recently been demonstrated as being not only a cause of endocarditis but also a cause of septicemia in cancer patients. There have been changes in the taxonomy which have led to the emergence and description of *S. oralis* both as an important pathogen in neutropenic cancer patients and in infective endocarditis. Studies of the antibody in these diseases have defined two antigens as immunodominant. One of these has been cloned and demonstrated to be a homolog of the Pac protein of *S. mutans* and the Spa protein precursor of *S. sobrinus*. The protein has been further epitope mapped, demonstrating areas to which antibody was seen only in patients with endocarditis due to *S. oralis*. Human recombinant antibodies have been raised against these epitopes and shown to have some therapeutic activity in an animal model of infection. The second immunodominant endocarditis-specific antigen identified was an hsp90 homolog with an apparent molecular weight of 85 kDa. Similar specific antibody patterns have been shown in *Candida albicans* endocarditis, *Corynebacterium jeikeium* endocarditis and endocarditis due to *S. lactis*. In contrast, in patients with staphylococcal endocarditis the level and pattern of antibody, as measured by immuno-blotting, could not distinguish between cases and controls.

In all of the above the antibody patterns were specific to patients with endocarditis and the level of IgM correlated with disease. The resolution of infection by appropriate antibiotic therapy saw a rapid reduction in IgM levels when samples were measured weekly. The description of these patterns has led to a further study in which they were used as a way of diagnosing culture-negative endocarditis. This is a syndrome in which the patient has proven endocarditis but consistently negative blood cultures. Negative serology was found in 28 patients where the diagnosis of endocarditis was rejected or, if proven, staphylococcal, yeast, gram-negative, systemic lupus erythematosus, due to Q fever or *Chlamydia psittaci* or nonbacterial thrombotic. Positive serology was found in 27 of the 34 patients where the response to antibiotics suggested streptococcal or enterococcal infections. In 22 of these there was objective evidence of endocarditis. Positive serology was also found in three out of four further patients with vegetations at necropsy.

In summary, the diagnosis of endocarditis, both positive and negative, has been helped by the study of antibody levels. Individual antigens are now being identified and their role in the pathogenesis of infection characterized.

See also: **Molecular mimicry; Oral immunity; Respiratory and cardiac infections; Specificity; *Staphylococcus*, infection and immunity; *Streptococcus*, infection and immunity; Western blotting.**

Further reading

Aitchison EJ, Lambert PA and Farrell ID (1986) Antigenic composition of an endocarditis-associated isolate of *Streptococcus faecalis* and identification of its glycoprotein antigens by ligand blotting with lectins. *Journal of Medical Microbiology* 21: 161–167.

Bansal RC (1995) Infective endocarditis. *Medical Clinics of North America* 79: 1205–1240.

Brooks W and Burnie JP (1994) Cloning and sequencing the endocarditis immunodominant antigen of *Streptococcus sobrinus* strain MUCOB 26. *Journal of Medical Microbiology* 40: 330–337.

Burnette-Curley D, Wells V, Viscount H *et al* (1995) FimA, a major virulence factor associated with *Streptococcus parasanguis* endocarditis. *Infection and Immunity* 63: 4669–4674.

Burnie JP and Clark I (1995) Immunoblotting in the diagnosis of culture negative endocarditis caused by streptococci and enterococci. *Journal of Clinical Pathology* 48: 1130–1136.

Burnie JP, Holland M, Matthews RC and Lee W (1987) Role of immunoblotting in the diagnosis of culture negative and enterococcal endocarditis. *Journal of Clinical Pathology* 40: 1149–1158.

Burnie JP, Brooks W, Donohoe M, Hodgetts S, Al-Ghamdi A and Matthews RC (1996) Defining antibody targets in *Streptococcus oralis* infection. *Infection and Immunity* 64: 1600–1608.

Durack DT, Lukes AS and Bright DK (1994) New criteria for diagnosis of infective endocarditis: utilization of specific echocardiogram findings. *American Journal of Medicine* 96: 200–209.

Kaye D (1996) Treatment of infective endocarditis. *Annals of Internal Medicine* 124: 606–608.

Russell ME, Wu HY, White PL, Kilian M and Henrichsen J (1992) Serum antibody responses to *Streptococcus mutans* antigens in humans systemically infected with oral streptococci. *Oral Microbiology and Immunology* 7: 321–325.

Various authors (1995) Infective endocarditis: recent perspectives. *European Heart Journal* 16 (suppl B): 1–131.

Wilson WR, Karchmer AW, Dajani AS *et al* (1995) Antibiotic treatment of adults with infective endocarditis due to streptococci, enterococci, staphylococci, and HACEK microorganisms. *JAMA* 274: 1706–1713.

CLONAL DELETION

John H Russell, Department of Molecular Biology and Pharmacology, Washington University School of Medicine, St Louis, Missouri, USA

Clonal deletion refers to the process of eliminating unwanted clones of cells by death of the progenitors. At different points in development, the process eliminates lymphocyte (B and T cell) progenitors either through the stimulation or failure to stimulate their clonally unique, membrane-bound antigen receptors. Clonal deletion is an important, general mechanism to limit the development and expansion of autoreactive lymphocyte populations that would cause autoimmune disease (**Figure 1**). Clonal deletion may also play an important role in limiting the organism's response to tumors.

Our early understanding of the interaction between pathogens and lymphocytes relied on the 'selective' expansion of appropriate lymphocyte clones in response to antigenic challenge. This allowed the maintenance of a pool of precursor lymphocytes to a broad range of pathogens that could be expanded through proliferation of the most appropriate clones for a specific pathogenic challenge. The lymphocyte clones with the highest affinity for pathogenic antigens would be selected for expansion because their receptor stimulation was the most effective. The paradoxical notions that antigen receptor stimulation could lead to nonresponsiveness through death (clonal deletion) or anergy as well as expansion of the progenitor has changed our fundamental understanding of lymphocyte biology. The antigen receptor can no longer be modeled as a digital on/off switch. Rather, the context in which the antigen is presented as well as the differentiation/activation state of the responding lymphocyte determines the lymphocyte's functional response.

Clonal deletion in thymus-derived lymphocytes (T cells)

An important distinction between T cells and B cells is that T cells can only recognize cell-bound (antigen-presenting cell, APC) antigenic peptides in the context of major histocompatibility complex (MHC) proteins. T cells are involved in surveillance of the peptides bound to MHC molecules in their environment from the earliest period of their development.

Thymus

The primary site for development of T cells is in the thymus. The process begins *in utero* as T cell progenitors migrate from their mesenchymal origin in the yolk sac and fetal liver and continues to a lesser extent after birth with progenitors from the bone marrow. These cells migrate to the thymus and begin to rearrange the genes encoding the heterodimeric T cell receptor (TCR). From this point forward the cells can be selected for complete maturation and export to the peripheral lymphoid organs (lymph nodes and spleen) or they are clonally deleted either because they fail to produce a functional TCR or because their TCR would be self-reactive in a functional, mature lymphocyte and cause autoimmune disease.

One reason T cells may fail to reach full maturity is because they are unable to complete the random rearrangement of the TCR genes. A second reason is that they successfully rearrange their genes and produce a functional TCR on the cell surface, but that protein with its CD4 or CD8 coreceptors does not recognize environmental MHC–peptide complexes sufficiently for completion of maturation. In a sense this failure of clones to be selected for further maturation is because they do not produce TCRs of sufficient affinity to be useful (**Figure 2**). The molecular basis of this arrested differentiation and subsequent cell death is not well understood, but is often referred to as deletion by 'neglect'. It is clear that the expression of anti-apoptotic proteins such as Bcl-2 in these cells can prolong their life, but does not ultimately rescue them for further differentiation.

Production of rearranged TCR gene products that alone, or in association with the CD4 and CD8 coreceptors, react strongly with MHC–peptide complexes results in the rapid death of the T cell progenitor (**Figure 3**). The death (active deletion) of these cells takes place at the double positive (CD4$^+$CD8$^+$) stage of T cell development, shortly after expression of a functional TCR. There appear to be no special APC requirements to induce deletion, but rather deletion is a function of peptide density on the APC and the affinity of the TCR for the MHC–peptide complex. Deletion can take place on any appropriate MHC$^+$ cell in the thymus (MHC class I to delete CD8 cells and MHC class II to delete CD4 cells) but is generally thought to occur at the corticomedullary junction.

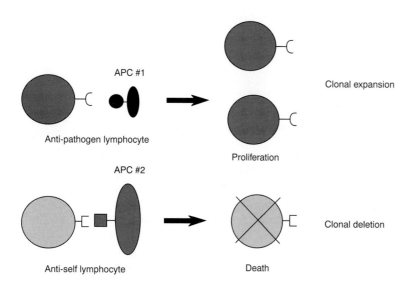

Clonal deletion

Figure 1 Depending on the activation state of the lymphocyte and the APC, antigen receptor engagement can result in either the selection and expansion of the clone or the death of the lymphocyte.

The molecular details of active deletion are incompletely understood. Evidence suggests that the time the TCR remains bound (k_{off}) to the MHC–peptide complex is the most important kinetic parameter determining the functional outcome. There is evidence from T cell hybridomas and from transgenic mice that nur77, an orphan member of the nuclear hormone receptor superfamily, may be involved in clonal deletion. However, animals with a null mutation in the gene for nur77 demonstrate normal T cell development and function. Thus, nur77's signaling function may be redundant. Some other member of the superfamily may be primarily involved and nur77's physiological involvement is secondary to other pathways leading to T cell progenitor death.

Mature T cells

Antigen-stimulated death of mature T cells was not recognized until the early 1990s. Shortly thereafter, it was recognized that the process was defective in two mouse mutant strains associated with lymphoproliferative disease and autoimmunity (lpr and gld). At the same time, Nagata and colleagues determined that the molecular bases for the mutations are in a receptor–ligand pair. The lpr mutation functionally eliminates the expression of Fas (CD95/Apo-1) and the gld mutation is an inactivating, point mutation in Fas ligand (FasL) (**Figure 4**). The Fas (Apo-1) protein had previously been identified as a member of the tumor necrosis factor receptor (TNFR) family of proteins and produced apoptosis in sensitive cells when stimulated with agonist antibodies. The recognition of the importance of Fas in the animal models has led to the discovery that defective Fas expression is associated wth lymphoproliferative disease and autoimmunity in some human patients.

Fas ligand is a member of the TNF family of proteins that act as membrane-bound or soluble homotrimers to aggregate their receptors into functional signaling units. Yeast two-hybrid analyses have revealed that both Fas and TNFR signal through a series of protein–protein interaction ('death') domains that result in the activation of a unique series of proteases cascading into 'programmed' cell death or apoptosis.

T cells from animals carrying the lpr mutation are defective both in culture and *in vivo* in dying in response to chronic exposure to high-dose antigen. It appears that Fas does not regulate most acute responses, but rather is important in limiting the expansion of lymphocyte populations to high doses and/or chronic exposure to antigen. This can be important both in limiting autoimmunity and in limiting the long-term response to immunogenic tumors. There is recent data that the related TNF system also

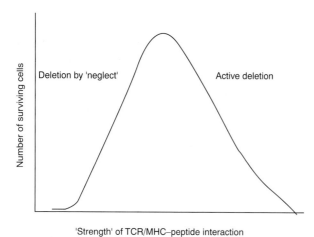

Figure 2 The 'strength' of the interaction, determined by MHC–peptide density and TCR affinity, determines whether the developing thymocyte is clonally deleted or allowed to mature.

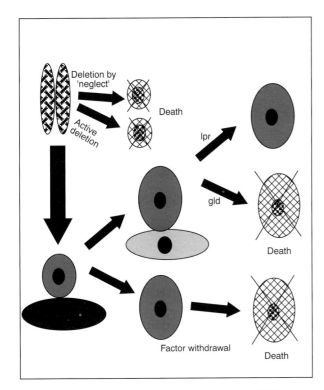

Figure 3 At various stages in T cell development, TCR stimulation or lack of stimulation results in death of those progenitors. Deletion can take place in the thymus by 'neglect' or by active deletion and in the periphery deletion can occur depending on the strength of the TCR/MHC–peptide interaction and on signals from costimulators.

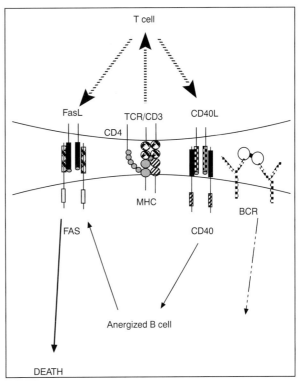

Figure 4 Chronic stimulation of the BCR creates an anergized B cell that increases Fas expression when stimulated by T cell CD40 ligand. It then dies in response to Fas stimulation by T cell Fas ligand. (Adapted from Rathmell *et al.*, 1996.)

plays an important role in the process of culture and *in vivo*. However, unlike animals with defective Fas or Fas ligand expression, the TNF role in lymphoproliferative disease or autoimmunity is not apparent when there are defects in TNF or its receptors alone, but rather appears to exacerbate the disease in animals with defective Fas or Fas ligand. It is likely that other members of this family will be identified that also contribute to lymphocyte hemostasis.

Fas is expressed at low levels on naive T cells and both its expression and sensitivity to signaling are increased after activation. In contrast, Fas ligand is transiently expressed upon TCR stimulation. The expressed ligand can act as a membrane-bound molecule to kill other cells (murder) or be released from the surface by metalloproteases as functional trimer. This soluble form of Fas ligand is important for the autocrine death (suicide) of the stimulated cell. There appear to be significant species differences in the stability of the soluble trimer. In addition, there appear to be soluble forms of Fas released from cells that neutralize the soluble Fas ligand. Thus under physiological conditions, soluble Fas ligand has a short functional range. Fas and Fas ligand do not

appear to play a significant role in clonal deletion of thymic T cells.

Clonal deletion in antibody-producing B cells

Deletion of self-reactive clones of B cells is also an important part of antibody repertoire development. Like T cells, each clone of B cells produces a unique, antigen-specific membrane receptor. For B cells this is a membrane-bound form (BCR, B cell receptor) of the antibody produced and secreted by that cell. The BCR arises by alternative splicing of the antibody mRNA to include a membrane anchoring domain. Like the TCR, the BCR is associated with other proteins involved in transmitting signals into the cell upon stimulation. Unlike the TCR, the BCR binds protein, nucleic acids, carbohydrate and lipid sequences (antigenic determinants) independently of their association with MHC proteins. Thus B cells can be stimulated by both cell-bound and soluble antigens.

Progenitors for B cells develop from mesenchymal tissue in the yolk sac and fetal liver like T cell progenitors. However, there is a nearly continuous influx of new B cell progenitors for most of the lifetime of the animal, in contrast to T cells progenitor production that is largely restricted to embryonic and neonatal life. In avian species the B cell progenitors develop in the bursa of Fabricius (they were first discovered here and thus the term B cell), an appendix-like evagination of the avian gut. The bone marrow is the major source of B cell progenitors in other vertebrate adults. During B cell maturation there are several checkpoints where the developing clone can die either as a result of a negative signal from the BCR or from the lack of a positive signal from either the BCR or its environment (in this case a helper T cell).

Deletion of B cell clones prior to germinal center formation

Much of our understanding of the checkpoints in B cell development resulting in deletion has come from the analysis of BCR transgenic mice (mice carrying genes for a specific, rearranged BCR inserted into their genome and therefore expressed in virtually all developing B cells) by the laboratories of Goodnow, Weigart and Nemanzee. BCR transgenic animals were crossed to animals carrying their antigen as a transgene in various compartments and levels of expression. Antigenic determinants present as highly expressed membrane components cause the apoptotic death of the earliest progenitor with a functional BCR. This process is analogous to clonal deletion of autoreactive T cells in the thymus but the molecular basis is currently unknown.

Clones of developing B cells that fail to successfully rearrange their BCR or whose BCR is not stimulated within 1–3 days after export to the primary lymphoid organs (lymph node and spleen) also die. Death of the newly developed B cell also occurs if it is stimulated by antigen, but does not promptly receive a helper signal (helper T cell cytokines or surface molecules such as CD40 ligand). Cells that are chronically stimulated by soluble antigen (e.g. B cells that react to serum proteins) from their earliest stages of development become anergic. That is restimulation by antigen and helper cells fails to produce normal proliferation and maturation into antibody-secreting cells. These anergized but potentially autoreactive cells are exported to the primary lymphoid organs, but are eliminated in two ways: 1) they remain in the periarteriolar zones and do not compete with normal B cells for space in follicles and germinal centers where continued expansion and maturation occurs; or 2) they are killed by activated T cells.

The lysis of the anergic B cells by T cells is dependent on the Fas/Fas ligand pathway and in lpr animals lacking Fas, autoreactive B cells accumulate in the T cell-rich, periarteriolar sheath. Adoptive transfer studies have indicated that elimination of these anergic B cells requires functional Fas on the B cell and functional Fas ligand on the T cell. In addition, it requires cooperation with other members of the TNF family. In this case CD40 on the B cell and CD40 ligand on the T cell. Stimulation of CD40 on the B cell induces the expression of Fas on that cell and stimulation of B cell Fas by Fas ligand on the T cell causes the death of that anergic B cell (**Figure 4**). Interestingly, the same sequence of events with normal B cells after acute antigen stimulation is required for B cell proliferation and maturation. Thus the activation state of the B cell (chronic versus acute) determines the functional outcome (death versus expansion and maturation) of the T/B cell interaction.

Deletion of B cells after primary activation

Thus far we have discussed elimination of B cells during the maturation of progenitors. However, mature B cells, unlike mature T cells, can undergo somatic mutation of their BCR after antigenic stimulation. This property allows affinity maturation of the response in germinal centers to produce higher affinity antibodies for a given challenge, but also creates a new risk of autoantibody development. One mechanism for solving the problem is analogous to the costimulator strategy in T cells. In this case the 'costimulator' CD19 dramatically lowers the number of BCRs needed to be occupied for maximal proliferation by allowing synergistic signaling between the complement receptor CD21 and the BCR. Cells stimulated by antigen in the context of complement (e.g. on the surface of a bacterium) or complement on the surface of a specialized antigen-presenting cell (follicular dendritic cell, FDS) do not undergo apoptosis. The FDC can also provide a similar function through CD23 on its surface. Stimulation of the germinal center B cell (centrocyte) by antigen in the absence of complement or CD23 stimulation results in deletion of those clones. This type of clonal deletion of mature B cells is independent of the Fas system. Rather, complement or FDC stimulation of the B cell regulates the expression of antiapoptotic molecules such as Bcl-2 and deletion of the cells not receiving signals from both the BCR and the costimulator are deleted by a pathway more analogous to the 'neglect' pathway of thymocytes.

Summary

Regulated survival of clonal progenitors is a primary mechanism of determining the lymphoid repertoire. Clones that are unwanted either because they do not express useful antigen receptors or express receptors that would cause autoimmune disease are deleted through a death process. There appear to be two general strategies to eliminate these cells. In some instances (e.g. through Fas and Fas ligand) a clear receptor–ligand interaction actively initiates a death response. In other circumstances such as in the thymus or in germinal center B cells it appears that death is a 'default' step in the differentiation pathway that occurs unless there is active intervention by signals from other cell surface molecules that rescue them from death by regulating the expression of anti-apoptotic molecules like Bcl-2.

See also: **Antigen-presenting cells; MHC peptide-binding specificity; Apoptosis; Anergy, T cell; Clonal selection; Thymic epithelium: potential role in regulatory T cell tolerance; MHC restriction.**

Further reading

Calnan BJ, Szychowski S, Chan FK, Cado D and Winoto A (1995) A role for the orphan steroid receptor Nur77 in apoptosis accompanying antigen-induced negative selection. *Immunity* 3: 273–282.

Chen C, Nagy Z, Radic MZ *et al* (1995) The site and stage of anti-DNA B-cell deletion. *Nature* 373: 252–255.

Cyster JG and Goodnow CC (1995) Antigen-induced exclusion from follicles and anergy are separate and complementary process that influence peripheral B cell fate. *Immunity* 3: 691–701.

Dhein J, Walczak H, Baumler C, Debatin KM and Krammer PH (1995) Autocrine T-cell suicide mediated by APO-1/(Fas/CD95). *Nature* 373: 438–441.

Goodnow CC (1996) Balancing immunity and tolerance: Deleting and tuning lymphocyte repertoires. *Proceedings of the National Academy of Sciences of the USA* 93: 2264–2271.

Jacobson BA, Panka DJ, Nguyen KA, Erikson J, Abbas AK and Marshak-Rothstein A (1995). Anatomy of auto-antibody production: dominant localization of antibody-producing cells to T cell zones in Fas-deficient mice. *Immunity* 3: 509–519.

Murphy KM, Heimberger AB and Loh DY (1990) Induction by antigen of intrathymic apoptosis of CD4+CD8+TCR[lo] thymocytes *in vivo*. *Science* 250: 1720–1723.

Nagata S and Golstein P (1995) The Fas death factor. *Science* 267: 1449–1456.

Nemanzee DA and Bürki K (1989) Clonal deletion of B lymphocytes in a transgenic mouse bearing anti-MHC class I antibody genes. *Nature* 337: 562–566.

Rathmell JC, Townsend SE, Xu JC, Flavell RA and Goodnow CC (1996) Expansion or elimination of B cells *in vivo*: Dual roles for CD40- and Fas (CD95)-ligands modulated by the B cell antigen receptor. *Cell* 87: 319–329.

Russell JH (1995) Activation-induced death of mature T cells in the regulation of immune responses. *Current Opinion in Immunology* 7: 382–388.

Russell JH, Rush B, Weaver C and Wang R (1993) Mature T cells of autoimmune *lpr/lpr* mice have a defect in antigen-stimulated suicide. *Proceedings of the National Academy of Sciences of the USA* 90: 4409–4413.

Singer GG and Abbas AK (1994) The Fas antigen is involved in peripheral but not thymic deletion of T lymphocytes in T cell receptor transgenic mice. *Immunity* 1: 365–371.

Takashi R, Tanaka M, Brannan CI *et al* (1994) Generalized lymphoproliferative disease in mice caused by a point mutation in the Fas ligand. *Cell* 76: 969–976.

van Meerwijk JP, Marguerat S, Lees RK *et al* (1997) Quantitative impact of thymic clonal deletion on the T cell repertoire. *Journal of Experimental Medicine* 185: 377–383.

CLONAL SELECTION

Norman R Klinman, The Scripps Research Institute, California, USA

By the mid-1950s numerous theories had been proposed to account for the remarkable capacity of the immune system to respond specifically to the myriad of foreign antigenic determinants. One group of theories, championed by Alexander, Mudd, Haurowitz, Pauling and Karush, relied on the entry of antigen into antibody-forming cells to serve as a template for the synthesis of complementary antibodies, and, as such, were considered 'instructional'. A novel 'natural selection theory', put forward by Jerne in 1955, suggested that all potential antibodies pre-existed as 'natural antibodies' and

appropriate cells, internalizing antigen complexed to a given antibody, would duplicate the internalized antibody. In 1957, Talmage suggested that cells might express their potential antibody as a cell surface receptor, and in 1958 Macfarlane Burnet fully elaborated the 'clonal selection theory'. This theory, like Jerne's theory, proposed that appropriate antibodies pre-existed in the absence of antigen 'instruction' but that the diverse array of antibodies was the product of multiple cell clones, each capable of expressing a single antibody product. The major tenets of the hypothesis were as follows (all quotations excerpted from Burnet (1959), see Further reading):

1. 'in the animal there exist clones of mesenchymal cells each carrying immunologically reactive sites corresponding in appropriate complementary fashion to one (or possibly a small number of) potential antigenic determinants'.

2. These clones provide 'a population of cells which, when an appropriate stage of development has been reached, are capable of producing the population of globulin molecules which collectively provide the normal antibodies'.

3. In order that antigen–antibody complexes localize to 'cells, which are genetically determined to produce the corresponding type of antibody molecule – it would simplify matters a great deal if the antigen were in a position to react with natural antibody or a pattern equivalent thereto on the surface of the cell which produced it'.

4. 'When an antigen is introduced it will make contact with a cell of the corresponding clone, presumably a lymphocyte, and by so doing stimulate it to produce in one way or another more globulin molecules of the cell's characteristic type.'

5. That this 'stimulation initiates proliferation'.

6. 'that active sites on cell surface or globulin molecule can be modified to a wider reactivity by somatic mutation, provides the chief agent to allow change in antibody character as immunization proceeds.'

7. 'Self–not-self recognition means simply that all those clones which would recognize (that is, produce antibody against) a self-component have been eliminated in embryonic life. All the rest are retained.'

8. The secondary response is accounted for thus: 'on the simplest form of the hypothesis – the primary stimulus finds only a few examples of the appropriate clones; by the time of the secondary stimulus, many more individuals of the selected clones are accessible'.

Over the past 30 years each of these postulates has to a considerable extent been validated by experimental observation. Although other elements of Burnet's thesis are not as prescient as the above, it should be noted that prior to 1960 neither the molecular basis for antibody formation nor the T cell–B cell dichotomy and cell–cell collaboration were understood.

Unipotentiality of lymphoid cells

The most fundamental tenet of the clonal selection hypothesis, and that which distinguished it from all others, was 'the *existence of multiple clones of globulin-producing cells*, each responsible for one genetically determined type of antibody globulin'. Indeed, in discussing the implication of the theory, Burnet stated 'the clonal selection hypothesis would be completely validated if it could be shown that single cells from a non-immune animal gave rise to clones, each cell of which under proper physiological conditions contained, or could liberate, antibody-type globulin of a single pattern or at most of a uniform small range of patterns'. Early efforts to test this postulate were hardly supportive. Attardi, Horabita, Lennox and Cohn concluded, from single-cell studies of phage-specific antibodies, that single cells were multipotential. Studies from a variety of laboratories, including those of Cunningham, Liacoupoulus, Hiramoto and Sercarz, appeared to demonstrate multiple antibodies per single cell. Additionally, Burnet's own experiments, using a tissue reactivity test devised by Simonsen, were incompatible with a highly diverse repertoire of unipotential cells. However, in retrospect, each of these anomalous findings has been attributable to experimental artifact, the capacity of certain antibodies to bind numerous antigens (multispecificity), or, as in the case of the Simonsen assay, an inordinately high frequency of T cell responses to any given major histocompatibility complex (MHC) alloantigen.

In addition, the numerous examples of the homogeneity of immunoglobulins produced by multiple myeloma cells and the existence of restricted antibody responses to certain antigens, such as Krause's demonstration of restricted antibodies in rabbits responding to A-carbohydrate, implied that the product of single antibody-forming cell clones was homogeneous. A similar conclusion was drawn from findings of numerous laboratories, including those of Nossal, Mäkelä and Biozzi, that single cells bound only one antigen. Using the splenic focus assay, where single antigen-specific precursor cells were isolated in cultures of splenic fragments, Klinman demonstrated, in 1969, the homogeneity of the antibody product of the clonal progeny of a single stimulated precursor cell (**Figure 1**). These studies demonstrated, by the homogeneity of antigen binding as well as heavy (H) and light (L) chain recombination analyses, that the product of antibody-forming cell clones was homogeneous and displayed binding characteristics that, in composite, could account for the affinity and heterogeneity characteristics of

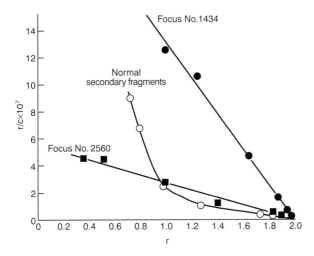

Figure 1 Hapten binding curves constructed from equilibrium dialysis at 7°C with a) antibody from two antibody forming cell clones (foci) generated in splenic fragments, focus No. 1434 (●) and focus No. 2560 (■); and b) pooled antibody from the clonal progeny of numerous secondary B cells (○). r represents the moles of α, N-(^{3}H)-acetyl-δ-DNP lysine bound per mole of antibody at the equilibrium free hapten concentration, c. Antibody concentrations were determined at each point by radioimmunoassay and points represent duplicate samples which agreed to within 5%.

serum antibodies. Although these particular studies used B cells from previously immunized mice, subsequent studies extended these findings to B cells from nonimmune mice, thus fulfilling Burnet's requirements. The only exception to the homogeneity of the antibody produced by single clones was the production of multiple isotypes by most clones; however, Gearhart and Klinman demonstrated that antibodies of different isotypes generated from the same clone shared variable regions. In recent years, the molecular mechanisms that account for the sorting of unique specificities to individual lymphocytes have become well documented and are discussed elsewhere in this volume.

Immunoglobulin receptor on B cells

Essential to 'clonal selection' is the availability of a mechanism to focus the antigen to the appropriate B cells and, in so doing, enable the stimulation of those B cells. In 1967 Mitchison and his coworkers indirectly demonstrated that the fine specificity of antibody produced by B cells could be influenced by selectively stimulating these cells with a crossreactive hapten. This indirect demonstration of a correlation between the B cell's surface receptor and secreted antibody product was later extended by Klinman, who demonstrated that clonal precursors whose potential antibody product was of high affinity could be selectively stimulated with low antigen

concentrations. That B cells bore surface immunoglobulin was demonstrated by numerous investigators including Naor, Sulitzeanu, Wigzell, Vitetta, Uhr and Marchalonis, and the mobility of these receptors on the cell surface was shown by Raff and Taylor. However, the identity between the B cell's potential antibody product and its surface immunoglobulin receptor awaited the demonstration by Köhler and Cosenza that they shared idiotype.

Tolerance and memory

In part, the clonal selection hypothesis was necessitated by the need to account for two fundamental hallmarks of the immune response: the capacity to respond to nonself or foreign antigens while not responding to self antigens; and the long-term retention of the capacity to mount accelerated and vigorous responses to previously encountered antigens. As anticipated by the theory, numerous studies have demonstrated the inactivation of developing B and T cells by antigens present in their environment, thus validating negative clonal selection as the basis for self tolerance. Although most B cells in an unimmunized animal have the capacity only to generate antibody-forming cell clones and not memory B cells, Linton, Decker and Klinman have identified a subpopulation of precursor cells that do give rise to memory B cells and that fulfill, in detail, Burnet's predictions: 1) 'that a first contact with antigen sets some sort of tooling-up process in train, while secondary contact is needed to evoke actual antibody liberation into the circulation'; and 2) that 'the combination of frequent minor mutation and a highly effective selective process would rapidly improve the accuracy of the complementary relationship to new antigenic determinations'. The process of somatic mutation and antigen selection of these mutations has been described by numerous investigators including Tonegawa, Weigert, Gefter, Rajewsky, Berek and Milstein.

Conclusion

Since its first elaboration, the clonal selection hypothesis has served as the take-off point for experiments, not only to test the theory itself, but also to extend our knowledge of the mechanism of immune responsiveness. While many of the speculations with which Burnet decorated this theory have not stood the test of time, the fundamental aspects of the theory remain and constitute the foundation of our current understanding of the immune response.

See also: **B lymphocyte differentiation; B lymphocyte**

repertoire; Clonal deletion; Immunoglobulin, cell surface; Memory, immunological; Natural antibodies; Proliferation, lymphocyte; Somatic mutation; Specificity; T lymphocyte clonal expansion; Tolerance, peripheral.

Further reading

Burnet M (1959) *The Clonal Selection Theory of Acquired Immunity*. Nashville: Vanderbilt University Press.

Casson LP and Manser T (1995) Evaluation of loss and change of specificity resulting from random mutagenesis of an antibody VH region. *Journal of Immunology* 155: 5647–5654.

Forsdyke DR (1995) The origins of the clonal selection theory of immunity as a case study for evaluation in science. *FASEB Journal* 9: 164–166.

Kelsoe G (1996) Life and death in germinal centers (Redux). *Immunity* 4: 107–111.

Linton P-J, Decker DJ and Klinman NR (1989) Primary antibody forming cells and secondary B cells are generated from separate precursor cell subpopulations. *Cell* 59: 1049–1059.

Möller G (ed) (1993) Positive T-cell selection in the thymus. *Immunological Reviews* 135: 183–214.

Schwartz RS and Stollar BD (1994) Heavy-chain directed B-cell maturation: continuous clonal selection beginning at the pre-B cell stage. *Immunology Today* 15: 27–32.

Sigal NH and Klinman NR (1978) The B cell clonotype repertoire. *Advances in Immunology* 26: 255–337.

CLOSTRIDIUM, INFECTION AND IMMUNITY

Charalabos Pothoulakis, Beth Israel Deaconess Medical Center, Division of Gastroenterology, Harvard Medical School, Cambridge, Massachusetts, USA

Characteristics of the organisms and their antigens

The clostridia are spore-forming rod-shaped gram-positive bacteria that usually grow under anaerobic conditions. An important characteristic of these microorganisms is their ability to survive in high numbers for long periods of time in feces and soil, an ability related to the formation of spores which can be very resistant to temperature and pH extremes. Clostridia are potent pathogens in animals and humans because of their ability to release various exotoxins. Furthermore, many clostridia species release more than one toxin and each toxin is immunologically distinct. For example, eight types of *Clostridium botulinum* and five types of *Clostridium perfringens* have been identified and each type elaborates different toxins. Many similarities exist among clostridial toxins. Amino acid homology and immunologic cross-reactivity exist between *C. difficile* toxins and *C. sordellii* lethal toxins and between tetanus toxins and botulinum B toxin, and these toxins have similar mechanisms of action. In addition, many clostridia produce a variety of enzymes, including collagenases, proteinases, deoxyribonucleases, and neuraminidases, which compromise the host and increase the pathogenicity of these microorganisms.

Although most of the clostridia toxins are large protein exotoxins with distinct biochemical properties and immunological characteristics, classification of these toxins based on their pharmacologic properties and cellular targets is far from complete. For the purpose of this review clostridia toxins will be categorized according to the diseases they produce into four groups: 1) neurotoxins, represented primarily by *C. tetani* and *C. botulinum* which are associated with tetanus and botulism in humans; 2) enterotoxins, represented by *C. perfringens* enterotoxin produced by some strains of *C. perfringens* type A which mediate acute food poisoning, *C. perfringens* ε and ι toxins causing entertoxemia in sheep, calves, lambs and guinea pigs, and *C. sordellii* hemorrhagic toxin which is associated with diarrhea in cattle and sheep; 3) histotoxins or cytolytic toxins, represented by some of the *C. perfringens* toxins that are associated with gas gangrene and anaerobic cellulitis, and *C. sordellii* lethal toxin (LT), one of the causes of gas gangrene; and 4) cytoskeleton-altering toxins, represented by *C. difficile* toxins A and B, that mediate antibiotic-associated colitis and diarrhea following antibiotic intake in animals and humans, and *C. botulinum* C2 toxin. All cytoskeleton-altering toxins disrupt filamentous (F) actin in target cells. It should be emphasized, however, that many of these toxins have several other biological activities other than the ones listed above. For example, toxin A of *C. difficile* is also a potent enterotoxin that induces fluid secretion when injected into rabbit and rat intestinal loops.

An interesting topic of pathogenicity associated with clostridial toxins is the molecular mechanism by which these toxins modify properties of cellular proteins and, by altering their function, cause human disease (**Table 1**). Toxins are enzymes which can biochemically modify specific molecules on the plasma membrane or cytosol of target cells. Some of the *C. perfringens* toxins are very good examples of toxins which act on plasma membranes of cells. *C. perfringens* α toxin, a phospholipase C or lecithinase, cleaves lecithin in cell membranes into diglyceride and phosphorylcholine as well as hydrolyzes cephalin and sphingomyelin. *C. perfringens* κ toxin is a collagenase, whereas the μ toxin is a hyaluronidase.

A major breakthrough in our understanding of the pathogenesis of tetanus and botulism has been the recent identification of the molecular mechanism by which *C. tetanus* and *C. botulinum* B toxins cause paralysis. Botulinum neurotoxins act on peripheral motor nerves to block acetylcholine release at neuromuscular junctions, thereby causing muscle paralysis (flaccid paralysis). On the other hand tetanus neurotoxin acts on the central nervous system by blocking neurotransmitter release from inhibitory neurons causing muscle spasms (spastic paralysis). Although these two diseases have different clinical symptoms it is now known that botulinum B and tetanus neurotoxins have identical mechanism in intoxicating

nerve cells. Both toxins are zinc endopeptidases that require a zinc atom for their activity and both have a similar protein structure with a receptor binding B domain and a catalytic A domain. The mechanism of action of these toxins initially involves binding to cell surface receptors and internalization into the cytosol. Once into the cell the toxins are then cleaved by proteases into active fragments which possess catalytic action. The cellular target of botulinum B and tetanus toxin is synaptobrevin, a membrane protein which is important in neurotransmitter release and associated with small synaptic vesicles. The active forms of botulinum and tetanus toxin inactivate synaptobrevin by cleaving it at a specific peptide site.

Another important recent discovery in the field of clostridial toxins is the cellular mode of action of large clostridial toxins including *C. difficile* toxins A and B, and *C. sordellii* and *C. novii* toxins. The common characteristic of these toxins is their large molecular weight (>250 kDa), amino acid similarity, absence of subunits, and their similar cytopathogenic (rounding) effect on cultured cells. These toxins exert their cytopathogenic effect by modifying specific small GTP-binding proteins of the Ras superfamily that regulate cellular actin. Studies with *C. difficile* toxins showed that these toxins bind to specific cell receptors and are then internalized into the cytosol

Table 1 Mechanisms of some clostridial toxins

Organism	Disease	Major lethal toxins	Mechanism of toxicity
C. perfringens type A	Gas gangrene	α toxin	Cytotoxic, calcium-dependent phospholipase C
	Food poisoning	Enterotoxin	Changes permeability of cells.
C. perfringens type C	Gas gangrene	α toxin	Calcium-dependent phospholipase
	Enteritis necroticans	β toxin	Cytotoxin, pore-forming?
C. septicum	Gas gangrene	α toxin	Hemolysin, cytolytic, pore formation
C. novyi type A	Gas gangrene	α toxin	Cytotoxin, actin cytoskeleton breakdown, glucosylation of Rho, Rac, Cdc-42.
C. sordellii	Gas gangrene	Lethal toxin (LT)	Cytotoxin, disruption of actin microfilaments, glucosylation of Ras, Rap and Rac
	Hemorrhagic diarrhea	Hemorrhagic toxin (HT)	Cytotoxin, enterotoxin, glucosyltransferase
C. tetani	Tetanus	Tetanospasmin	Neurotoxin, cleavage of synaptobrevin
C. botulinum types A, B, C1, D, E, F, G	Botulism	Botulinum neurotoxin	Neurotoxin, cleavage of synaptobrevin
C. botulinum type C2	Unknown	C2 or binary toxin	Cytotoxin, inhibition of actin polymerization, ADP-ribosylation of actin
C. difficile	Antibiotic-associated diarrhea and pseudomembranous colitis	Toxin A Toxin B	Cytotoxins, disruption of actin microfilaments, glucosylation of Rho, Rac, Cdc-42

via coated pits. Once into the cytosol these toxins monoglucosylate the small GTP-binding proteins Rho, Rac and Cdc-42 at position Thr37. As a result, these small GTP-binding proteins are unable to regulate actin polymerization thus leading to actin filament breakdown and cell rounding. *C. sordellii* lethal toxin, which also rounds up cells and causes disruption of actin fibers, also glucosylates the small GTP-binding proteins Ras, Rap and Rac, that regulate actin filament formation. These recent discoveries on the molecular mechanism of clostridial toxins not only increase our understanding of their cellular actions, but may also help to design rational prevention or treatment of diseases associated with these toxins.

Evasive strategies by the organism

Clostridia have devised many ways to enter the host and cause disease. In the case of gas gangrene and wound infections *C. perfringens* enters the host through traumatic or surgical wound often taking advantage of poor blood supply in the wound area. Once clostridia grow they release their toxins and cause disease. In *C. difficile*-associated colitis the bacteria multiply when the normal bowel flora is disrupted by antibiotics. *C. difficile* then releases its toxins which target intestinal epithelial cells and cause diarrhea and colonic inflammation. In the case of botulism, however, the organism does not grow in the host but the disease is caused by ingestion of *C. botulinum* toxins present in contaminated food.

Immune responses of the host and vaccines

For most clostridial-mediated diseases, there is no immunity following the experience of the first episode. The reasons for absence of prophylaxis following exposure of patients to clostridia and their toxins is not clear but could involve the small amount of toxins required to produce disease, which may be inadequate to produce an immunogenic response. Despite the absence of systemic immunity following disease, toxoid immunization against tetanus provides immunity for up to 5 years. Passive immunization with tetanus immunoglobulin is also of great value in suspected cases. An antibotulinum toxin antibody has also been available for laboratory workers, and intravenous treatment with gamma globulin preparations containing a high-titer antibody to *C. difficile* toxin was effective in treating patients with relapsing *C. difficile* diarrhea.

See also: **Bacteria, immunity to; Toxins; Vaccines.**

Further reading

Domenighini M, Pizza M and Rappuoli R (1995) Bacterial ADP-ribosyltransferases. In: Moss J, Iglewski B, Vaughan M and Tu AT (eds) *Bacterial Toxins and Virulence Factors in Disease*. New York: Marcel Dekker.

Eichel-Streiber CV, Boquet P, Sauerborn M and Theleastam M (1996) Large clostridial cytotoxins – a family of glucosyltransferases modifying small GTP-binding proteins. *Trends in Microbiology* 4: 375–381.

Hall A (1994) Small GTP-binding proteins and the actin cytoskeleton. *Annual Review of Cell Biology* 10: 31–54.

Montecucco C and Schiavo G (1993) Tetanus and botulism neurotoxins: a new group of zinc proteases. *Trends in Microbiology* 18: 324–329.

Sears CL, Guerrant RL and Kaper JB (1995) Enteric bacterial toxins. In: Blaser MJ, Smith PD, Ravdin JI, Greenberg HB and Guerrant RL (eds) *Infections of the Gastrointestinal Tract*. New York: Raven Press.

Swartz MN (1990) Anaerobic spore-forming bacilli: the clostridia. In: Davis BD, Dulbecco R, Eisen HN and Ginsberg H (eds) *Microbiology*, 4th edn. San Francisco: JB Lippincott.

Wells CL and Wilkins TD (1986) In: Baron Samuel (ed) *Clostridia. Medical Microbiology*, 2nd edn. New York: Addison-Wesley.

CLOTTING SYSTEM

Arthur S Brecher, Department of Chemistry, Bowling Green State University, Bowling Green, Ohio, USA

The clotting system consists of a mixture of components including cells, fragments thereof, zymogens, their activation products and naturally occurring inhibitors, adhesive and structural proteins, phospholipids, lipids, cyclic and noncyclic nucleotides, hormones and inorganic cations, all of which are normally maintained in a state conducive to blood flow. Upon damage to the vascular wall with disruption of the monocellular layer of endothelial cells, exposing the subendothelial layer, and also permitting bleeding, a series of events is initiated designed to produce clot formation. These homeostatic reactions lead to the generation of the primary platelet plug, followed by a clot principally containing cross-linked fibrin (secondary hemostasis). Subsequently, the blood vessel is repaired and the clot is dissolved by a mechanism which includes fibrinolysis.

Local vasoconstriction

A number of physiologically derived compounds appear to induce vasoconstriction of a transient nature at the site of vascular injury. These include participation of endothelin, a very potent vasoconstrictor which is synthesized by endothelial cells, thromboxane A_2 (TXA_2), serotonin and the α-adrenergic system. Thrombin, interleukin 1 (IL-1), transforming growth factor β (TGFβ), angiotensin II and epinephrine promote the expression of endothelin mRNA, whereas shear stress, atrial natriuretic peptides (ANP) and brain natriuretic peptides negatively modulate its expression. Endothelial-derived relaxing factor (EDRF), an inhibitor of platelet function, inhibits the release of endothelin. The lung clears endothelin from the circulation. Angiotensin II, also a vasoconstrictor, is synthesized locally, as renin and angiotensinogen are generated within the endothelial cell (EC), and angiotensin-converting enzyme (ACE) is found on the surface of the EC membrane. As a counterbalance to constriction, ECs secrete such vasodilators as adenosine, prostacyclin and EDRF. Nitric oxide (NO) exhibits similar effects as EDRF. However, S-nitrosocysteine appears to behave more akin to EDRF. The final identity of EDRF, is, as yet, unresolved. The ECs also can degrade serotonin.

Platelet components and function

Disk-shaped platelets circulate in the blood, being quite unreactive with the intact vascular wall. Upon injury to the vascular wall, however, components from the platelets, ECs and damaged subendothelial cells (SECs) (SEC matrix), other vascular tissue constituents and circulating plasma components contribute to the formation of a primary platelet plug. The sequence of reactions in response to injury is as follows: initial activation and adhesion of platelets to the damaged SECs, contributing to activation of circulating platelets, and aggregation of platelets to one another at the site of injury, followed by stabilization of the platelet plug by extensive cross-linking of polymeric fibrin molecules. Platelet membrane proteins include numerous receptors for adhesion proteins such as collagen, fibrinogen, fibronectin, von Willebrand factor (vWF), thrombin receptor, and

others. Dense granule constituents in platelets include ATP, ADP, Ca^{2+} and serotonin, while α granule components of platelets include platelet factor 4 (PF4), β-thromboglobulins, fibrinogen, vWF, fibronectin, thrombospondin, coagulation factors V, XI and protein S (PS), α_2-antiplasmin (α_2-AP) and plasminogen activator inhibitor 1 (PAI-1). Cytoplasmic proteins which are secreted by platelets are represented by protease nexin I, protease nexin II, tissue factor pathway inhibitor (TFPI), factor XIII, α_1-antitrypsin (α_1-AT), C1-inhibitor, α_2-macroglobulin (α_2-MG), high molecular kininogen (HMWK) and IL-Iβ). Endothelial cells release prostacyclin (PGI$_2$), an inhibitor of platelet aggregation, as well as platelet activating factor (PAF) and vWF, which contribute to platelet adhesion, in addition to fibrinolytic components, tissue plasminogen activator (t-PA) and PAI-1. The mechanisms for release of these compounds is not yet understood. Thrombomodulin (TM), tissue factor (TF), ACE and binding sites for factors Va, Xa, and XIa are observed on EC membrane surfaces. However, TF is expressed only upon injury to tissue. The subendothelial tissue damage exposes such adhesive proteins as collagen (types IV, V and VI), vWF, fibrinogen and vitronectin, while the damaged media exposes collagen (types I and III), and damaged adventitia exposes collagen and TF.

Flow rate of blood affects adhesion of platelets to the damaged SECs. In areas of low blood flow, collagen and fibronectin play a greater role as adhesive proteins linking the platelets to the SEC. With higher flow areas, however, vWF appears to play a more significant role as an adhesive protein. Upon vascular injury, multimers of circulating vWF bind to platelet receptor glycoprotein GPIb/IX. Subsequently, GPIIb/IIIa receptors are activated. The complex then binds to exposed collagen and fibronectin on the SEC matrix. Additionally, newly exposed SEC matrix-bound vWF binds to circulating platelets. GPIa/IIa receptors on the platelet surface also permit direct binding of platelets to the exposed collagen from the SEC matrix. Additionally, collagen binds fibrinogen, fibronectin and vWF, thereby stimulating further binding with GPIIb/IIIa, GPIc/II and GPIb/IX receptors on the platelet surface.

The activation of platelets is stimulated by strong and weak agonists. Thrombin, which may be locally generated at the site of injury, and collagen have been identified as strong agonists while ADP, epinephrine, TXA_2, serotonin, PAF and vasopressin (Vp) have been relegated as weaker agonists. The consequences of platelet activation are: alteration of platelet shape from discoid to globular, with pseudopods; increased cytosolic Ca^{2+}; alteration of the GPIIb/IIIa receptor to a high-affinity receptor in order to effectively bind vWF and/or fibrinogen for adhesion/aggregation; biosynthesis of TXA_2, a vasoconstrictor, and other eicosanoids from arachidonic acid (AA); phosphorylation of platelet proteins; induction of platelet coagulation activity; release of dense granule constituents (ADP, ATP, Ca^{2+}, serotonin, pyrophosphate); release of α granule constituents (platelet-specific proteins such as PF4, which interacts with heparin and lowers its anticoagulant activity; β-thromboglobulin, and adhesive glycoproteins such as fibrinogen, vWF, and fibronectin); release of lysosomal constituents, expression to the cell surface of dense and α granule membrane proteins, factors V and XI and PS; inhibitors of fibrinolysis ($α_2$-AP, PAI-1); platelet-derived growth factor (PDGF).

Platelet activation involves the mobilization of two enzyme systems in response to agonists. Phospholipase A_2 (PLA_2) and phospholipase C (PLC) act upon platelet membrane phospholipid (PL) substrates. PLA_2 cleaves AA from phospholipids. (Linoleic acid may also serve as a metabolic precursor to AA in mammals.) Upon subsequent successive action on AA by a cyclo-oxygenase and a peroxidase, prostaglandin H_2 (PGH_2) is formed. PGH_2 serves as the precursor to TXA_2 (mediated by TXA_2 synthase) and PGI_2 (mediated by PGI_2 synthase). The EC is a major source of TXA_2. TXA_2 then alters platelet shape and stimulates platelet aggregation. It also promotes the platelet secretion and expression of the fibrinogen receptor. (PGI_2 inhibits platelet aggregation.) The alternative activation pathway involves hydrolysis of membrane PL by PLC to produce diacylglycerol (DAG), inositol triphosphate (IP_3) and some AA. The AA is metabolized by the cyclo-oxygenase and peroxidase in the above described manner. In addition, IP_3 promotes an increase in cystolic Ca^{2+}, which stimulates an alteration in platelet shape, platelet secretion and fibrinogen expression. DAG affects identical changes in platelet shape and function.

A number of factors act counter to the activation of platelets. These include PGI_2, EDRF, NO and ecto-ADPases, derived from ECs which degrade the platelet activator ADP into adenosine, a platelet function inhibitor. Furthermore, substances which negatively modulate the activity of thrombin, the strong agonist for platelet activation, contribute to antiplatelet activation controls. These include antithrombin III (AT III), $α_2$-MG, heparin cofactor II (HC II), and activated protein C inhibitor I (APCI). Additionally, 13-hydroxyoctadecadienoic acid (13-HODE), produced in the ECs, inhibits adhesion and aggregation of platelets and TXA_2 synthesis, and promotes the synthesis of PGI_2.

Subsequent to platelet adhesion and activation, additional circulating platelets aggregate to the platelet monolayer. Aggregation involves the participation of fibrinogen which binds to the GPIIb/IIIa receptor site of the platelet membranes and forms a bridge to another platelet, thereby expanding the platelet plug. There are two binding sites for the GPIIb/IIIa receptor on each fibrinogen molecule.

Secretion of the platelet granule components as well as cytosolic proteins (protease nexin I and II, TFPI, factor XIII, $α_1$-AT, C1-inhibitor, HMWK, $α_2$-MG, vascular permeability factor and IL-1β) adds components for positively or negatively affecting coagulation in the blood vessel at the site of vascular injury.

As part of the activation process, a rearrangement of phospholipids occurs whereby phosphatidylserine and phosphatidylinositol position themselves from the inner surface of the platelet membrane to the outer surface as a means of presenting a negative charge to coagulation factors for binding purposes.

Contraction of the clot and secretion of granule proteins are believed to incorporate the use of the contractile protein, actinomyosin.

Coagulation and its modulation

A veritable cascade of limited proteolytic reactions are encompassed in the coagulation process. A series of inactive proteins, namely, zymogens, are sequentially activated by limited proteolysis, culminating

Figure 1 Pathways of coagulation and fibrinolysis. II, Prothrombin, factor II; IIa, thrombin, factor IIa; V, factor V; Va, factor Va; VII, factor VII; VIIa, factor VIIa; VIII, factor VIII; VIIIa, factor VIIIa; IX, factor IX; IXa, factor IXa; X, factor X; Xa, factor Xa; XI, factor XI; XIa, factor XIa; XII, factor XII; XIIa, factor XIIa; XIII, factor XIII; XIIIa, factor XIIIa; $α_1$-AT, $α_1$-antitrypsin; $α_2$-MG, $α_2$-macroglobulin; C1-Inhib., C1-inhibitor; APCI, activated protein C inhibitor; HMWK, high molecular weight kininogen; P, plasmin; K, kallikrein; PK, prekallikrein; M, membrane; ATIII, antithrombin III; Fg, fibrinogen; H, heparin; MPL, membrane phospholipid; TF, tissue factor, thromboplastin; TF-VII, tissue factor–factor VII complex; TF-VIIa, tissue factor–factor VIIa complex; TFPI, tissue factor pathway inhibitor; Xa–TFPI, factor Xa-tissue factor pathway inhibitor complex; ATIII-H, antithrombin III–heparin complex; vWF, vonWillebrand factor; spont., spontaneously; DP, degradation products; PC, protein C; APC, activated protein C; PS, protein S; APC–PS, activated protein C–protein S complex; C4bBP, C4b binding protein; PS–C4bBP, protein S–C4bBP complex; HCII, heparin cofactor II; F, fibrin; TM, thrombomodulin; IIa–TM–Ca–M, thrombin–thrombomodulin–calcium–membrane complex; X-linked F, cross-linked fibrin; Pg, plasminogen; $α_2$-AP, $α_2$-antiplasmin; His-rich GP, histidine-rich glycoprotein; 1c-u-PA, one-chain urinary plasminogen activator; 2c-u-PA, two-chain urinary plasminogen activator; 1-c-t-PA, one-chain tissue plasminogen activator; 2-c-t-PA, two-chain tissue plasminogen activator; PAI-1, plasminogen activator inhibitor 1; PAI-2, plasminogen activator inhibitor 2.

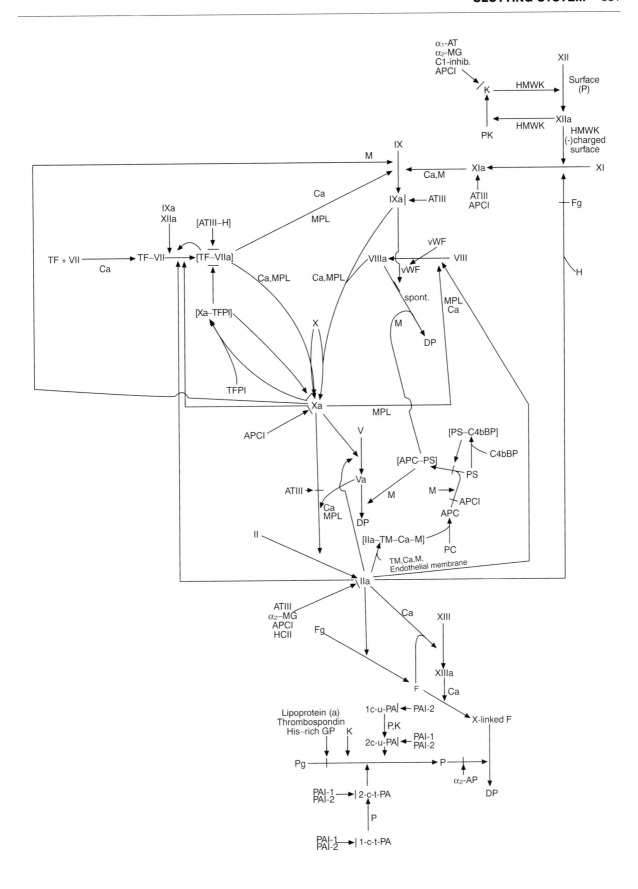

ultimately in the formation of the stable, insoluble fibrin clot. Many of the activated zymogens are serine proteases, descended from the same evolutionary tree as the digestive enzymes, trypsin, chymotrypsin and elastase. They contain the catalytic triad consisting of histidine, aspartic acid and serine. These include kallikrein, thrombin, factors VIIa, IXa, Xa, XIa and XIIa from the coagulation cascade and plasmin, t-PA, and urinary-plasminogen activator (u-PA) from the fibrinolytic enzyme system. This hemostatic process was historically conceived to meld an *intrinsic* pathway with an *extrinsic* pathway at a juncture resulting in the activation of factor X to factor Xa, whereupon a common pathway concluded with the formation of the fibrin clot. The clotting cascade including the *extrinsic* and the 'historic' intrinsic pathways, together with the fibrinolytic system for dissolution of the clot, is depicted in **Figure 1**. Activation of the historic *intrinsic* pathway could be accomplished upon contact of factor XII with a negatively charged surface to yield the activated factor XIIa. It was observed that factor XIIa could activate two zymogens, prekallikrein (PK) and factor XI, each in the presence of HMWK. Activation of PK yields the protease kallikrein (K). K, in turn, activates factor XII in the presence of HMWK to produce additional factor XIIa, a positive feedback step as the *intrinsic* cascade is initiated. (K activity is inhibited by α_1-AT, α_2-MG, C1-inhibitor and APCI.) The activation of factor XI by factor XIIa yields factor XIa. Factor XI is also activated by factors XIa and IIa (thrombin), the latter activation requiring heparin as a cofactor. The activation of factor XIa by thrombin is inhibited by fibrinogen. (Antithrombin III (AT III) and APCI inhibit the subsequent proteolytic activity of factor XIa).

All subsequent steps involving the *intrinsic* system factors occur on membrane surfaces such as the platelet membrane. Endothelial cell membranes also bind coagulation factors. PL is required, serving as the negatively charged surface. The localization of PL in the membrane permits the formation of ternary and quaternary complexes as necessary, for the accomplishment of the clotting steps. Factor XIa activates factor IX in the presence of Ca^{2+}. (AT III inhibits the proteolytic activity of factor IXa.) Factor IXa, in the presence of factor VIIIa and Ca^{2+}, activates factor X to factor Xa. The activation of factor VIIIa will be dealt with below. Factor Xa then activates prothrombin (factor II) to yield thrombin (factor IIa). This occurs with the mediation of factor Va in the presence of Ca^{2+}. Thrombin subsequently acts upon circulating or locally entrapped fibrinogen to generate the initial fibrin gel which is then cross-linked with the assistance of a transglutaminase, factor XIIIa, in the presence of Ca^{2+}. Fibrinogen is a protein containing six polypeptide chains, two Aα, two Bβ and two γ chains, appropriately linked via disulfide bridges. Initial activation of fibrinogen by thrombin causes the release of fibrinopeptide A from the α chain in a relatively rapid reaction, permitting polymerization of the remaining protein. A rate-limiting cleavage of fibrinopeptide B from the Bβ chain subsequently occurs. The resultant fibrin molecules may then be cross-linked longitudinally and transversely by factor XIIIa. Factor XIIIa is activated by thrombin from its inactive precursor, factor XIII, in the presence of Ca^{2+}. Factor XIIIa also functions in the presence of Ca^{2+}. The transglutaminase excises the amide groups of select glutamines in the carboxyl terminal region of γ chains and links the resultant glutamic acids with select ϵ-amino groups of lysines in the carboxyl terminal region of the γ chains. It also acts similarly with the α chains. Longitudinal cross-links are established with γ-γ as well as α-α chains, whereas transverse links are formed only with α-α chains. The resultant polymeric product is increasingly insoluble and more resistant to proteolysis. Factor XIIIa cross-links other localized proteins in addition to fibrin, such as fibronectin, thrombospondin, collagen, actin, vWF and α_2-AP, in forming a tight mesh. Hence, components related to coagulation and fibronolytic mechanisms may be effectively entrapped at the coagulation site. As will be discussed below in the fibrinolytic section, plasminogen is incorporated in the fibrin clot. Furthermore, t-PA binds to fibrin.

Factor Xa and thrombin have multiple roles in the clotting system. Thrombin activates the inactive factor XIII to the active factor XIIIa in the presence of Ca^{2+}. The initial fibrin gel appears to promote this step. In addition to activating factors XI and XIII, thrombin activates factor V to factor Va, factor VIII to factor VIIIa in the presence of Ca^{2+}, and the tissue factor–VII (TF–VII) complex to its active form, TF–VIIa.

TF is considered as part of the extrinsic blood clotting pathway (to be described shortly, after further discussions of factors Va, VIIIa, IIa and Xa). Factor Xa also catalyzes the activation of factor V, as does thrombin. The activation of factor VIII by thrombin is more complex. Factor VIII circulates in blood as a complex with vWF. In the process of activation of factor VIII by thrombin, vWF dissociates from the complex, thereby availing itself of the opportunity to complex with more circulating factor VIII. vWF stabilizes factor VIII, thereby prolonging its circulating half-life. Factor VIIIa can apparently be degraded to degradation products spontaneously. This degradation occurs at a reduced rate in the presence of high concentrations of factor IXa. Factor Xa also activates factor VIII to factor VIIIa. The activation of factors Va and VIIIa by thrombin and factor Xa serve as additional examples of positive feedback.

Factors Va and VIIIa, which participate in the coagulation system as cofactors of factor Xa and IXa, respectively, are also subject to enzymic degradation. Both factors Va and VIIIa are degraded by a complex of activated protein C (APC) with protein S (PS), APC–PS. The formation of the APC–PS complex occurs on the membrane surface, as do all the reactions in the clotting cascade from the functioning of factor XIa to the activation of prothrombin. The series of reactions begins with the initial formation of a complex comprising thrombin, thrombomodulin (an EC membrane protein) and Ca^{2+} on the membrane. This complex catalyzes the transformation of protein C (PC) to APC. The APC interacts with PS to yield the APC–PS complex in which the APC contains the catalytic degradative potential to fragment factors Va and VIIIa. Under such circumstances, the catalytic functions of factors IXa and Xa are depressed, thereby reducing the generation of thrombin from prothrombin. Hence, thrombin can act not only as a positive modulator (positive feedback) in activating factors Va and VIIIa, but also as a negative modulator by initiating the formation of APC–PS which degrades factors Va and VIIIa, limiting thrombin production. An inhibitor of APC (APCI) has been identified which inhibits the formation of the APC–PS complex from its APC and PS components. It further inhibits the functioning of factor XIa. It therefore functions overall to promote clotting at the Va and VIIIa steps by 'lowering' their 'inactivation' rate. Its effect on factor XIa may be of questionable impact, as discussed below. Another protein, a plasma component, C4b-binding protein (C4b-BP), also negatively modulates the degradation of factors Va and VIIIa by forming a complex with PS, the PS–C4b-BP complex which competitively blocks the formation of the APC–PS complex.

Thrombin activity is inhibited by four naturally occurring proteins: antithrombin III (ATIII), α_2-MG, HCII, and APCI. The APCI also inhibits factor Xa. ATIII, HCII and APCI are *serpins* (serine protease inhibitors). ATIII is a glycoprotein which is capable of forming a stable tetrahedral complex with thrombin thereby inactivating it. ATIII also inhibits factors IXa, Xa, XIa and XIIa. ATIII contains two domains for binding heparin. Both domains are rich in basic amino acids. Hence they readily bind to the negatively charged sulfate esters in heparin. They also bind to heparan sulfate, a proteoglycan which is synthesized by ECs and expressed to their surface. Heparin is synthesized by mast cells and is detected in granules of these cells beneath endothelial tissue. When ATIII binds to heparin to form an ATIII–heparin complex, the conformation of the ATIII is presumably altered, significantly enhancing reaction with thrombin. Following formation of the ATIII–thrombin complex, heparin is released, thereby permitting it to react with free ATIII molecules. The heparan sulfate–ATIII complex is also a powerful inhibitor of thrombin. HCII inactivates thrombin. Its inactivation of thrombin can be accelerated 1000-fold by complexing with dermatan sulfate, a mucopolysaacharide component of the vascular wall.

As may be seen in **Figure 1**, factor Xa exerts multiple roles in coagulation, as does thrombin. It activates factors II, V and VIII, thereby promoting the clotting process. It also activates factors IX on a membrane surface, a positive feedback step, thereby stimulating its own activation from factor X, and is further involved in the activation of factor IX by activating the TF–VII complex of the *extrinsic* clotting system. Lastly, it is a component of a negative feedback system whereby it complexes with tissue factor pathway inhibitor (TFPI) to form the Xa–TFPI complex which inhibits factor Xa function as well as TF–VIIa function (Factor Xa is also inhibited by ATIII and by APCI.)

The significance of the contact system for the initial activation of blood clotting in the intrinsic clotting pathway has been questioned as a functional pathway *in vivo* as a deficiency in factor XII does not lead to a clotting abnormality. In addition, a deficiency in factor XI leads to a mild clotting abnormality, if at all. Hence, current views accept the proposal that the exposure of damaged vascular tissue initiates the clotting cascade in what historically was considered as the *extrinsic* clotting system. Damaged vascular tissue causes an immediate response with the induction of mRNA for TF. TF is a glycoprotein which is associated with the membrane of medial smooth muscle cells and adventitia. It has not been observed in the EC. However, it is inducible in the EC upon vascular injury, and exposure to thrombin. Other factors inducing enhancement of TF are platelets, granulocytes, macrophages, IL-1, and tumor necrosis factor α. Exposed TF binds to factor VII to form the TF–VII complex, a mostly inactive complex. It is activated by thrombin, which may be present in small amounts at the initial site of damage, as well as factor Xa. The TF–VII complex can also be activated by factors IXa and XIIa, and by its product, TF–VIIa, the latter being a positive feedback step. The TF–VIIa complex reacts with factor X on the membrane surface to transform factor X to the active factor Xa. Subsequently factor Xa activates

Table 1 Inhibitors of thrombotic and fibrinolytic enzymes

Coagulation/ fibrinolytic enzyme	ATIII	ATIII–H	α₂-MG	HCII	TFPI	TFPI–Xa	α₁-AT	Fg	α₂-AP	PAI-1	PAI-2	C1 inhibitor	Heparan sulfate-ATIII	Protein C inhibitor
TF														
TF-VIIa						X								
IIa	X	X	X	X			X	X	X				X	X
VIIa		X						X	X	X			X	
IXa	X	X												
Xa	X	X	X		X	X	X		X				X	X
XIa		X					X		X			X		X
XIIa		X										X		
XIIIa														
Kallikrein			X				X			X		X		X
Plasmin	X		X				X		X	X		X		
APC			X				X		X	X				X
One-chain t-PA										X	X			
Two-chain t-PA										X	X			
One-chain u-PA											X			
Two-chain u-PA										X	X			

TF, tissue factor; APC, activated protein C; t-PA, tissue plasminogen activator; u-PA, urinary plasminogen activator; ATIII, antithrombin III; H, heparin; α₂-MG, α₂-macroglobulin; HCII, heparin cofactor II; TFPI, tissue factor pathway inhibitor; α₁-AT, α₁-antitrypsin; Fg, fibrinogen; α₂-AP, α₂-antiplasmin; PAI-1, plasminogen activator inhibitor 1; PAI-2, plasminogen activator inhibitor 2; C1 inhibitor, complement protein 1 inhibitor.

prothrombin into thrombin with the mediation of factor Va. (The TF–VIIa complex is inhibited by ATIII–heparin and by the Xa–TFPI complex.) The TF–VIIa complex has the capacity to activate factor IX to factor IXa.

Since TF–VIIa is capable of activating factor X, the necessity for the utilization of factor IX in the clotting system has been raised and addressed. However, individuals with deficiencies of factors VIII and IX do exhibit abnormal clotting times and clinical bleeding. Therefore, current beliefs suggest that the TF–VIIa complex activates both factors IX and X, and that factor IXa, in conjunction with factor VIIIa, activates factor X as the need arises in order for normal coagulation times to be experienced.

Fibrinolysis and its modulation

The fibrinolytic system is a process which modulates the degradation of the clot as the organism repairs and replaces damaged vascular tissue. This process encompasses the degradation of the fibrin clot and its cellular components to soluble degradation products. Many of the constituent zymogens, activators and enzyme inhibitors are either intimately located within the clot or within the adjacent endothelial tissue associated with the clot. t-PA is a secretory product of the EC whose secretion is promoted by thrombin. Its inhibitor, PAI-1 is also observed in ECs, as well as in platelets, plasma and the EC matrix. (PAI-2 has only been seen in extracts of placental tissue in the third trimester of pregnancy.) Plasminogen, the inactive zymogen for the fibrinolytic plasmin, is readily bound by thrombospondin, a glycoprotein produced by platelets and expressed to the membrane surface upon activation. Thrombospondin acts to inhibit interaction of plasminogen with fibrin, as well as the activation of the plasminogen-fibrin complex. Plasminogen is entrapped in the clot and acts locally upon appropriate activation. α_2-AP is a component of the α granules of platelets. Accordingly, all the components necessary for fibrinolysis and its control are strategically placed at the site of the clot. Circulating α_2-AP, for example, is not believed to penetrate the clot and affect fibrinolysis, whereas α_2-AP in the entrapped platelet (granules) can be released upon activation of the platelets. Likewise, fibrinolysis occurs only within the clot, and not systemically. Hence, the postulated pathway for fibrinolysis and its modulation envisions the degradation of fibrin into soluble degradation products by plasmin. (Plasmic activity may be inhibited by α_2-AP.) Plasmin is activated from the inactive plasminogen by two-chain t-PA. It may also be activated by two-chain u-PA and by kal-

likrein. The two-chain t-PA and two-chain u-PA are both generated from their one-chain precursors by plasmin. Kallikrein transforms the one-chain u-PA into its two-chain metabolite. PAI-1 and PAI-2 inhibit the catalytic activity of one-chain t-PA, two-chain t-PA and u-PA. Only PAI-2 inhibits one-chain u-PA. The activation of plasminogen to plasmin is also inhibited by lipoprotein(a), thrombospondin and histidine-rich glycoprotein (His-rich-GP).

A summary of the active proteases associated with coagulation and fibrinolysis, together with their naturally occurring inhibitors, is given in **Table 1**.

See also: **Erythrocytes; Fibronectin; Macrophage activation; Plasma; Platelet-activating factor (PAF); Platelets; Prostaglandins.**

Further reading

Bauer KA and Rosenberg RD (1995) Control of coagulation reactions. In: Beutler E, Lichtman MA, Coller BS and Kipps TJ (eds) *Williams Hematology*, 5th edn, pp 1239–1252. New York: McGraw-Hill.

Boon GD (1993) An overview of hemostasis. *Toxicologic Pathology* 21: 170–179.

Coller BS (1992) Platelets in cardiovascular thrombosis and thrombolysis. In: Fozzard HA, Haber E, Jennings RB, Katz AM and Morgan HE (eds) *The Heart and Cardiovascular System*, 2nd edn, pp 219–273. New York: Raven Press.

Cox DW (1989) α1-Antitrypsin deficiency. In: Scriver CR, Beaudet AL, Sly WS *et al* (eds) *The Metabolic Basis of Inherited Disease*, 6th edn, pp 2409–2437. New York: McGraw-Hill.

Francis CW and Marder VJ (1995) Mechanisms of Fibrinolysis. In: Beutler E, Lichtman MA, Coller BS and Kipps TJ (eds) *Williams Hematology*, 5th edn, pp 1252–1260. New York: McGraw-Hill.

Garrett RH and Grisham CM (1995) *Biochemistry*, pp 757–802. Fort Worth: Saunders.

Jaffe EA (1995) Vascular function in hemostasis. In: Beutler E, Lichtman MA, Coller BS and Kipps TJ (eds) *Williams Hematology*, 5th edn, pp 1261–1276. New York: McGraw-Hill.

Jesty J and Nemerson Y (1995) The pathways of blood coagulation. In: Beutler E, Lichtman MA, Coller BS and Kipps TJ (eds) *Williams Hematology*, 5th edn, pp 1227–1238. New York: McGraw-Hill.

Majerus PW, Broze GJ Jr, Miletich JP and Tollefsen DM (1990) Anticoagulant, thrombolytic, and antiplatelet drugs. In: Gilman AG, Rall TW, Nies AS and Taylor P (eds) *Goodman & Gilman's the Pharmacological Basis of Therapeutics*, pp 1311–1331. New York: Pergamon Press.

Mann KG and Lorand L (1993) Introduction: Blood coagulation. *Methods in Enzymology* 222: 1–10.

Mann KG, Gaffney D and Bovill EG (1995) Molecular

biology, biochemistry, and lifespan of plasma coagulation factors. In: Beutler E, Lichtman MA, Coller BS and Kipps TJ (eds) *Williams Hematology*, 5th edn, pp 1206–1226. New York: McGraw-Hill.

Mosher D (1992) Disorders of blood coagulation. In: Wyngaarden JB, Smith LH Jr and Bennett JC (eds) *Cecil Textbook of Medicine*, 19th edn, pp 999–1017. Philadelphia: WB Saunders.

Silverstein RL (1995) Drugs affecting hemostasis. In: Muson PL (ed) *Principles of Pharmacology*, pp 1123–1143. New York: Chapman and Hall.

Suzuki K (1993) Protein C inhibitor. *Methods in Enzymology* 222: 385–399.

Travis J and Salvesen GS (1983) Human plasma proteinase inhibitors. *Annual Review of Biochemistry* 52: 655–709.

Were JA and Coller BS (1995) Platelet morphology, biochemistry, and function. In: Beutler E, Lichtman MA, Coller BS and Kipps TJ (eds) *Williams Hematology*, 5th edn, pp 1161–1201. New York: McGraw-Hill.

Zubay GL, Parson WW and Vance DE (1995) *Principles of Biochemistry*, pp 411–457. Dubuque: Wm C Brown.

COBRA VENOM FACTOR

Carl-Wilhelm Vogel, Department of Biochemistry and Molecular Biology, University of Hamburg, Hamburg, Germany

Cobra venom factor (CVF) is a constituent of cobra venom that specifically interacts with the serum complement system, causing its continuous activation. Whereas numerous studies on the effect of cobra venom on blood and blood components, including complement, were performed during the early part of this century, CVF was not purified until the late 1960s. The molecular interaction of CVF with the complement system became understood in subsequent years, simultaneously revealing the reaction sequence of the alternative complement pathway, and CVF has been extensively biochemically characterized. The molecule is a structural and functional analog of complement component C3. CVF is also often used to decomplement laboratory animals in order to investigate biological functions of complement. The decomplementing activity of CVF has recently been exploited in animal models of xenotransplantation where it has been shown that complement is a major contributor to the hyperacute rejection of the transplanted organ. Another application of CVF is its use in antibody conjugates to introduce cytotoxic activity to monoclonal antibodies, e.g. as a concept for experimental immunotherapy.

Structure of CVF

Cobra venom factor has been isolated from the Asian cobra (*Naja naja*, including several subspecies: *N.n. naja, N.n kaouthia, N.n. atra*) and the Egyptian cobra (*Naja haje*). The isolated proteins have been biochemically characterized and found to exhibit only minor structural differences. CVF is a three-chain glycoprotein with a molecular weight of ~136 kDa, as determined by equilibrium sedimentation. SDS polyacrylamide gel electrophoresis yields a molecular weight of ~149 kDa as the sum of the α chain (~68.5 kDa), β chain (~48.5 kDa), and γ chain (~32 kDa). The γ chain of CVF shows size heterogeneity, with usually 3–5 bands being detectable. The oligosaccharide portion of the molecule represents ~7.4% (w/w). The major oligosaccharide was found to be a fucosylated symmetric N-linked chain of the complex type with an unusual α-galactosyl residue at the nonreducing end. Circular dichroism spectroscopy revealed a secondary structure of CVF of 11% α helix and 47% β sheet. The molecule is an irregular and somewhat elongated ellipsoid structure with dimensions of 137×82 Å, as revealed by transmission electron microscopy.

More recently, the molecular cloning of CVF was accomplished using a cDNA library from cobra venom glands. The CVF mRNA contains a single open reading frame of 4926 nucleotides, coding for a single-chain preproprotein of 1642 amino acid residues. The mature three-chain protein is derived from the single-chain prepro-CVF by removal of a 22 residue signal peptide, an 83 amino acid peptide consisting of four arginine residues and a 79 amino acid peptide resembling a C3a anaphylatoxin generating the C-terminus of the CVF α chain and the N-terminus of the CVF γ chain, and of an approximately 279 residue peptide resembling the C3d domain of C3, yielding the C-terminus of the CVF γ chain and the N-terminus of the CVF β chain (**Figure 1**).

Several methods have been reported to purify CVF. Phospholipase A₂ has been identified as a common contaminant of CVF preparations. Certain uses of CVF require the removal of the contaminating

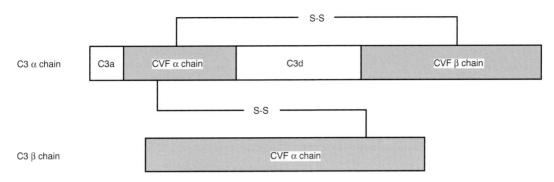

Figure 1 The two-chain structure of human C3 and the three-chain structure of CVF, indicating regions of homology (see text for further details).

phospholipase A_2; and several methods have been reported for that purpose.

The molecule is immunogenic, and antisera can easily be raised in several species of laboratory animals. These antisera can be used in antibody-based immunoassays for the detection and quantification of CVF. A simple hemolytic assay has been devised to determine the activity of CVF.

Molecular interaction of CVF with complement

When CVF is added to human or mammalian serum it activates complement and leads to complement consumption. It binds to factor B of the alternative pathway. When factor B is in complex with CVF, factor B is cleaved by factor D into Ba, the activation peptide, which is released, and Bb, which remains bound to CVF. The bimolecular complex CVF,Bb is a C3 convertase which cleaves C3 into C3a and C3b (**Figure 2**). CVF,Bb generated with CVF from *N. naja*, but not from *N. haje*, is also a C5 convertase, cleaving C5 into C5a and C5b. The generated C5b will consume the terminal complement components in plasma by formation of the membrane attack complex. In conclusion, through the formation of the CVF,Bb enzyme CVF will consume C3, C5 and the

terminal complement components, leading to the depletion of complement activity in serum.

Functional and structural similarity of CVF and C3

The formation and function of the CVF-dependent C3 convertase is analogous to the formation and function of the C3b-dependent C3 convertase which is formed during activation of the alternative pathway of complement (**Figure 2**). Both enzymes, CVF,Bb and C3b,Bb are C3/C5 convertases, consisting of a structural subunit (CVF or C3b) and the identical active site-bearing subunit Bb. Despite this similarity, the two enzymes exhibit several functional differences. The C3b,Bb enzyme is very short lived with a half-life of decay into the two inactive subunits of 1.5 min, while the CVF-Bb enzyme is rather stable, with a decay half-life of 7 h. In addition, the C3b,Bb enzyme is subject to rapid and efficient regulation by the complement components factor H and I. Factor H dissociates C3b,Bb and serves as cofactor for the proteolytic inactivation of C3b by factor I. In contrast, the CVF,Bb enzyme and CVF are completely resistant to the regulatory actions of factors H and I. Due to these two properties, the CVF,Bb enzyme is stable and present in plasma for prolonged periods of time. This is the basis for its ability to activate efficiently, and thereby consume, complement in serum.

Extensive structural homology has been found between CVF and mammalian C3. The structural homology includes immunologic cross-reactivity, similar amino acid compositions, similar secondary structures, and a similar shape and dimension under the electron microscope. The N-termini of the three chains of CVF show sequence homology with human C3, leading to the conclusion that the CVF α chain and the C3 β chain are homologous structures, and

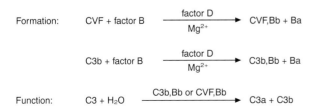

Figure 2 Formation and enzymatic activity of alternative pathway C3 for convertases, CVF,Bb and C3b,Bb.

that the CVF β and γ chains are derived from a C3 α chain (**Figure 1**). Molecular cloning has recently confirmed the chain relationships and structural homology of CVF and C3.

Both C3 and CVF code for single-chain precursor molecules which are then processed to yield the mature two-chain C3 or three-chain CVF, respectively. The sequence identity between pre-pro-CVF and mammalian pre-pro-C3 molecules on the protein level is ~51% and increases to ~70% if one allows for conservative amino acid replacements. In the case of pre-pro-C3 from cobra the similarity at the protein level is 91.6%, corresponding to a sequence identity on the DNA level of 93.3%. These results strongly suggest that the gene for CVF was generated by gene duplication from a C3 gene.

Use of CVF as an experimental tool to study the biological functions of complement

Cobra venom factor can be safely administered to laboratory animals. With the exception of an acute and transient reaction due to massive complement activation at high dosages, no toxic effects of CVF are known. Injection of CVF causes consumption of complement components *in vivo* and depletes complement activity in the plasma of treated animals. The complement activity will remain low for 1 to several days, and resynthesis of consumed complement components will restore normal complement activity within 5–10 days. Accordingly, temporary suppression of complement activity by CVF has become a widely used experimental tool for studying the biological functions of complement by comparing normal with complement-depleted animals. Questions addressed include the role of complement in the generation of an immune response, in host defense against infections and in the pathophysiology of disease.

Antibody conjugates with CVF

The property of the CVF,Bb enzyme to activate complement exhaustively has been exploited for the selective killing of tumor cells by coupling of CVF to monoclonal antibodies with specificity for surface antigens of tumor cells. Antibody conjugates with CVF will target CVF to the cell surface where the CVF,Bb enzyme forms from complement factors B and D of the host complement system. The antibody-bound and therefore cell surface-bound CVF,Bb enzyme will continuously activate C3 and C5 and

elicit complement-dependent target cell killing through the formation of membrane attack complexes. Antibody conjugates with CVF have been shown to kill human melanoma cells, human lymphocytes and leukemia cells, and human neuroblastoma cells. The concept of coupling CVF to monoclonal antibodies seems particularly promising in light of the fact that many monoclonal antibodies against tumors bind with good specificity but do not activate biological effector mechanisms such as complement. The coupling of CVF to monoclonal antibodies therefore introduces a biological effector function to the antibody.

Outlook

As CVF is a structural analog of C3, it may be possible to engineer a human C3 derivative that has the property of CVF to form a stable C3/C5 convertase. Such a 'human CVF' can be expected to be significantly less immunogenic. A 'human CVF' might be a useful therapeutic agent for modulating the complement activity in certain diseases where complement is known to be involved in the pathogenesis. One particular application of a 'human CVF' might be the depletion of complement in patients prior to xenotransplantation. 'Human CVF' could also be used in antibody conjugates as an immunotherapeutic agent in cancer patients.

See also: **Complement, alternative pathway; Complement, classical pathway; Complement deficiencies; Complement fixation test; Complement, membrane attack pathway; Immunotherapy of tumors; Venoms; Xenotransplantation.**

Further reading

Eggertsen G, Lind P and Sjöquist J (1981) Molecular characterization of the complement activating protein in the venom of the Indian cobra. *Molecular Immunology* 18: 125–133.
Fritzinger DC, Bredehorst R and Vogel C-W (1994) Molecular cloning and derived primary structure of cobra venom factor. *Proceedings of the National Academy of Sciences of the USA* 91: 12775–12779.
Vogel C-W (ed) (1987) *Immunoconjugates. Antibody Conjugates in Radioimaging and Therapy of Cancer.* New York: Oxford University Press.
Vogel C-W (1991) Cobra venom factor: the complement-activating protein of cobra venom. In: Tu AT (ed) *Handbook of Natural Toxins*, vol 5: *Reptile Venoms and Toxins*, pp 147–188. New York: Marcel Dekker.
Vogel C-W and Müller-Eberhard HJ (1984) Cobra venom factor: improved method for purification and biochemi-

cal characterization. *Journal of Immunological Methods* 73: 203–220.

Vogel C-W, Bredehorst R, Fritzinger DC *et al* (1996) Structure and function of cobra venom factor, the complement-activating protein in cobra venom. In: Singh R and Tu AT (eds) *Natural Toxins II: Structure,*

Mechanism of Action and Detection, pp 97–114. New York: Plenum Publishing.

Vogt W (1990) Snake venom constituents affecting the complememt system. In: Stocker KF (ed) *Medical Use of Snake Venom Proteins*, pp 79–96. Boca Raton: CRC Press.

COCCIDIOIDES, INFECTION AND IMMUNITY

Jon E Lutz, **David W Denning** and **David A Stevens**, Department of Medicine, Division of Infectious Diseases, Santa Clara Valley Medical Center, California, USA

Coccidioidomycosis is a fungal disease of humans and animals caused by the dimorphic fungus *Coccidioides immitis*. It is acquired by inhalation of arthroconidia in the southwestern USA and Central and South America. After exposure, most infected persons (60%) are asymptomatic and some 40% will develop a primary illness, usually pneumonic. Most of these resolve without sequelae. Up to 8% of infected individuals will have prolonged or later emergence of disease with, usually, pulmonary nodules or cavities (5%), but occasionally (1%) meningitis, osteomyelitis, cutaneous, lymph node, urogenital and other disease sites affected. Men, pregnant women, immunocompromised hosts, Blacks and persons of Filipino ancestry (dissemination 175 times more common than Whites) tend to have a higher frequency of dissemination and more severe disease. Disseminated and chronic forms of the disease require therapy. The mortality of coccidioidal meningitis is reduced by treatment from 100 to 30%. Pathologically, the spherule (the tissue phase of the fungus), which may contain many endospores, is surrounded by varying degrees of granulomatous reaction with or without caseation.

Antigens

At least 15 antigens can be found on immunoblots of SDS-PAGE gels from both soluble mycelial and spherular extracellular preparations. These include the tube precipitating antigen (detected by immunoglobulin M (IgM) antibody) which is a mycelial phase glycoprotein containing about 20% protein and the sugars 3-O-methylmannose (unique to *C. immitis* among pathogenic fungi), mannose and glucose, and the antigen recognized by complement fixing IgG antibody, a 110 kDa protein which runs at 48 kDa in a denaturing gel. IgM and IgG antibodies can also react in immunodiffusion with these two specific antigens. These two antigens are present in both fungal phases. Recently, a 33 kDa protein antigen has been purified, its gene cloned and expressed in bacteria. It is distinct from the antigens used in conventional complement fixation, tube precipitin and immunodiffusion procedures. It has been localized to the inner conidial wall of arthroconidia, within the cell wall and septa of spherules and on the wall surface and interconnecting glycocalyx of endospores.

Cellular and cytokine responses

T lymphocyte responses to *C. immitis* are critical for host defense. Thymectomy in rodents leads to severe disease. Immunity can be transferred to naive mice by infusions of T cells from immune mice. Patients infected with human immunodeficiency virus (HIV) who develop coccidioidomycosis have low CD4 T cell counts, median <150 cells per cubic millimeter. Macrophage killing of arthroconidida by enhanced phagosome–lysome fusion only proceeds (in mice) in the presence of antigen-stimulated T lymphocytes or soluble mediators produced by these T cells. Natural killer cells are able to kill endospores and spherules *in vitro*.

DBA/2 mice are relatively resistant to *C. immitis*; BALB/c mice are highly susceptible. The lungs of infected DBA/2 mice have relatively increased interleukin 6 (IL-6) and interferon γ (IFNγ) and their splenocytes produce greater amounts of tumor necrosis factor α (TNFα), IL-6 and IL-1α in response to stimulation with formalin-killed spherules *in vitro*. Treatment of the DBA/2 mice with an IFNγ-specific monoclonal antibody (mAb) increases their susceptibility. Infected BALB/c mice have increased levels of IL-4 in the lungs. Treatment of BALB/c mice with an IL-4-specific mAb provides significant protection. Treatment of susceptible BALB/c mice with recombinant IFNγ provides significant protection. *In vitro*, treatment of murine peritoneal or alveolar macrophages with rIFNγ augments anti-*Coccidioides* activity.

Independent of the immune status of the donor, human peripheral blood monocytes phagocytose arthroconidia and inhibit growth of the fungus and kill it. Monocytes may therefore play a role in limiting infection before a specific immune response develops. Peripheral blood mononuclear cells from skin test-positive individuals display increased lymphocyte transformation, IL-2 production and IFNγ production in response to spherule antigen. Spherules and arthroconidia elicit production of TNFα from human monocytes *in vitro.* TNFα alone or in combination with IFNγ enhances killing of spherules by human monocytes *in vitro.* The cytokine responses of a small number of patients with overwhelming infection with *C. immitis* have been studied. IL-1 and IL-2 were undetectable but levels of TNFα and IL-6 were elevated. T Lymphocyte coccidioidal-specific responses are suppressed in some patients and various lines of evidence suggest that antigen overload, specific suppressor T lymphocyte activity, circulating humoral suppressive substances and spherule-produced suppressive substances may all be involved.

A positive skin test is a marker of previous infection, and remains positive for life in the absence of severe immunosuppression such as the acquired immune deficiency syndrome (AIDS). Spherule-phase antigens may be more sensitive in eliciting cell-mediated responses. Cell-mediated responses *in vitro* are mirrored by intradermal skin testing which correlates reasonably well with clinical outcome – persons with disseminated disease are often anergic and those who are anergic are more likely to have a poor outcome.

Arthroconidia, endospores and particularly spherules are ordinarily quite resistant to killing by neutrophils or products of oxidative metabolism. A residual hyphal wall layer on arthroconidia and an extracellular matrix (acidic glycoproteins which are both carboxylated and sulfated) surrounding spherules and endospores appear to protect the fungus from phagocytosis and killing. Neutrophils comprise part of the initial response to arthroconidia in the lower airways and inhibit the growth of arthroconidia. Phagocytosis of arthroconidia and endospores is augmented by immune serum. Neutrophils fail to kill any phase of *C. immitis* unless immunologically activated, such as by IFNγ, in which instance they are capable of killing endospores but not arthroconidia. There appears to be some strain-to-strain variation in intrinsic susceptibility to neutrophil activity.

Humoral responses

Both asymptomatic infection and disease are marked in over 90% of all infected persons by an antibody response to *C. immitis.* Mycelial phase antigens are most useful in serodiagnosis. IgM is detected earliest by precipitation, latex agglutination or immunodiffusion in 75% of infected individuals. Detectable IgM usually disappears within 6 months of infection. In identifying progression of disease, IgG is useful: elevated titers indicate dissemination, and titers will fall with successful therapy in serum and in cerebrospinal fluid (CSF) in patients with meningitis. Antibody to the 33 kDa antigen can be detected in the CSF of patients with *Coccidioides* meningitis, including about half of those without detectable coccidioidal complement-fixing (CF) antibody. The antibody against the antigen appears to persist longer than detectable CF antibody. For patients who were failing therapy, a significant increase in antibody to the 33 kDa antigen was demonstrated over time; for patients responding to therapy, a significant decrease. Circulating immune complexes are found in up to 70% of patients with active, disseminated disease. Circulating free antigen has also been detected in patients with active disease. Total serum hemolytic complement activity is depressed early in primary infection in some patients but later recovers. Both classic and alternate pathways are probably activated.

Hypersensitivity

Erythema nodosum may occur during the primary infection and is a marker of hypersensitivity to coccidioidal antigens. Serum IgE is elevated in patients with active disease and tissue eosinophilia (or eosinophilic pleocytosis in CSF) may accompany severe disseminated disease.

Immunosuppression

Solid organ transplantation, corticosteroid therapy and AIDS may lead to severe, often fatal, disease, due to either recent infection or reactivation. The serologic response in compromised hosts is usually, but not always, at least qualitatively intact.

Vaccines

Formalin-killed spherule vaccine is highly effective in a murine model. Unfortunately, a recent trial of formalin-killed spherules in humans failed to demonstrate a significant protective effect. Work is proceeding to identify protein immunogens as potential vaccines.

See also: **Avian immune system; Fungi, immunity to.**

Further reading

Ampel NM (1992) *In vitro* assessment of cellular immunity in human coccidioidomycosis: relationship between dermal hypersensitivity, lymphocyte transformation, and lymphocyte production by peripheral blood mononuclear cells from healthy adults. *Journal of Infectious Diseases* 165: 710–715.

Ampel NM and Galgiani JN (1991) Interaction of human peripheral blood mononuclear cells with *Coccidioides immitis* arthroconidia. *Cellular Immunology* 133: 253–262.

Ampel NM, Bejarano GC, Salas SD and Galgiani JN (1994) *In vitro* production of tumor necrosis factor-alpha by adherent human peripheral blood mononuclear cells incubated with killed coccidioidal arthroconidia and spherules. *Cellular Immunology* 153: 248–255.

Beaman L (1991) Effects of recombinant gamma interferon and tumor necrosis factor on *in vitro* interactions of human mononuclear phagocytes with *Coccidioides immitis*. *Infection and Immunity* 59: 4227–4229.

Cox RA and Magee DM (1995) Production of tumor necrosis factor alpha, interleukin-1-alpha, and interleukin-6 during murine coccidioidomycosis. *Infection and Immunity* 63: 4178–4180.

Galgiani JN and Ampel NM (1990) Coccidioidomycosis in human immunodeficiency virus-infected patients. *Journal of Infectious Diseases* 162: 1165–1169.

Galgiani JN and the National Institute of Allergy and Infectious Diseases Mycoses Study Group (1996) Cerebrospinal fluid antibodies detected by ELISA against a 33-kDa antigen from spherules of *Coccidioides immitis* in patients with coccidioidal meningitis. *Journal of Infectious Diseases* 173: 499–502.

Magee DM and Cox RA (1995) Roles of gamma interferon and interleukin-4 in genetically determined resistance to *Coccidioides immitis*. *Infection and Immunity* 63: 3514–3519.

Pappagianis D and the Valley Fever Vaccine Study Group (1993) Evaluation of the protective efficacy of the killed *Coccidioides immitis* spherule vaccine in humans. *American Review of Respiratory Diseases* 148: 656–660.

Stevens DA (1980) Immunology of coccidioidomycosis. In: Stevens DA (ed) *Coccidioidomycosis, A Text*, pp 87–95. New York: Plenum Press.

Stevens DA (1993) Do dimorphic fungi more easily escape host defenses and treatment? *Coccidioides immitis* as a model. In: van den Bossche H (ed) *Dimorphic Fungi in Biology and Medicine*, pp 313–316. New York: Plenum Press.

Stevens DA (1995) *Coccidioides immitis*. In: Mandell GL, Bennett JE and Dolan R (eds) *Principles and Practice of Infectious Diseases*, 4th edn, pp 2365–2375. New York: Churchill Livingstone.

Stevens DA (1995) Coccidioidomycosis. *New England Journal of Medicine* 332: 1077–1082.

Zhu Y, Tyron V, Magee DM *et al* (1997) Identification of a coccidioides immitis antigen 2 domain that expresses B cell reactive epitopes. *Infection and Immunity* 65: 3376–3380.

COCCIDIOSIS

David A Stevens, Santa Clara Valley Medical Center, San Jose, California, USA

Coccidiosis is the generic term given to the disease caused by infection of domestic animals with *Eimeria* species. These are apicomplexan protozoa that parasitize mainly epithelial cells, principally those of the intestinal tract. They exhibit a high degree of host and site specificity and it is usual for a given species of animal to be host to several different *Eimeria* spp., each with its distinct location in the gut. Because of the self-limiting nature of the life cycle and the potential of the host to develop resistance to reinfection, coccidiosis is rarely a problem in nature but may be important in highly intensive systems of animal husbandry. In modern poultry production, where it is estimated to cause annual losses of $US1.5 billion, most flocks are prophylactically medicated. In humans, closely related organisms (*Isospora* spp.) cause a similar, but rarely significant, condition.

Characteristics of the organism and its antigens

The complex life cycle is monoxenous and sporozoan. Within the host, a period of asexual replication (schizogony) is followed by a sexual phase (gametogony). The number of cycles of schizogony, usually fixed, varies with the species but is commonly three or four, the last being followed by the formation of gametes (**Figure 1**). After fertilization, the zygote, protected within a resistant shell (oocyst), is voided in the feces. A period of maturation outside the host (sporogony), including a meiotic nuclear division, is necessary for the oocyst to become infective. Transmission is fecal–oral.

Infection causes enteritis of varying severity, depending upon the number and the biology of the

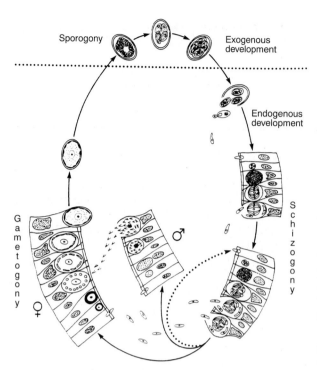

Figure 1 Life cycle of *Eimeria* species. (Reproduced with permission of Springer-Verlag GmbH & Co. KG from Rose ME (1985) The *Eimeria*. In: Parkhouse RME (ed) *Parasite antigens in protection, diagnosis and escape. Current Topics in Microbiology and Immunology* **120**: 7–17.

Eimeria spp. ingested. Those that develop in crypt epithelium, resulting in hemorrhage, are highly pathogenic and may cause serious mortality. Anorexia and stunted growth are common consequences of infection.

The various developmental stages of the parasite are morphologically distinct and possess both stage-specific and common antigens. Some of these have been purified and characterized, mostly those from species parasitizing the domestic fowl, such as *E. tenella* and *E. maxima*. The emphasis has been on the initial infective stage, the easily accessible sporozoite; this is a major target for immune inhibition and, once development has been initiated, is capable of inducing immunity.

Sporozoite antigens of current interest are those associated with some of the organelles, i.e. the refractile globule and those forming the apical complex (rhoptries, dense granules and micronemes) and presumably involved in invasion of the host cell. Treatment with a refractile body antigen of 26–28 kDa has been reported to protect chickens against challenge infections with four different *Eimeria* spp.; similar antigens are present in sporozoites of *E. bovis* (infecting cattle), becoming distributed within the cytoplasm of the invaded host cell. Rhoptry polypeptides migrate in the 45–65 kDa range and differ anti-

genically between species, paralleling the species-specificity of immunity induced by infection. A merozoite protein from *E. maxima* of 230 kDa has been reported to induce maternally transmissible immunity (to homologous and heterologous challenge), as have gametocyte-derived 56, 82 and 230 kDa antigens of the same species.

Immune responses of the host

Species of *Eimeria* differ widely in the degree of resistance to challenge induced by infection, even within the same species of host. Immunity induced in this way is species- and, in some cases, strain-specific but other methods of immunization, e.g. injection of purified antigens (above), may produce heterologous protection. The specificity, or otherwise, of immunity to the different developmental stages is not known.

Immunity is T cell mediated, apparently with little involvement of natural killer cell activity or reactive oxygen/nitrogen intermediates. Both humoral and cell-mediated immune responses participate in resistance but the latter is the more important. Antibodies are probably most effective against extracellular parasites, thereby reducing invasion. Experimentation in mice has shown that CD4+ T lymphocytes, which play the major role in controlling primary infections, are able to do so without the participation of inflammatory cells, and that CD8+ lymphocytes appear to be more important in the later stages of infection. The cytokine-release profile of responding lymphocytes does not indicate any correlation between T_H1 and T_H2 type responses and resistance/susceptibility. Although IFNγ, acting via the host cell, is very effective in halting the development of the parasite, it does not seem to mediate the prompt suppression seen in immunized animals. Work in chickens indicates that this may be due to the action of CD8+ lymphocytes in preventing sporozoites from reaching their developmental site in crypt enterocytes.

Evasive strategies by the organism

Eimerian coccidia are not known to use mechanisms for avoiding the immune response of the host. The brevity and finite nature of the life cycles, coupled with antigenic differences between the developmental stages, probably accounts for the ability of the parasite to complete its cycle, relatively unhindered, in the naive host; however, in a few (unusual) species additional asexual cycling occurs in immunocompromised hosts.

Some *Eimeria* spp. isolated from chickens in geographically distinct areas may show intraspecific variation, demonstrable by incomplete cross-protection, but their antigens have not been studied. Variation of this type has not been induced experimentally, nor has it emerged over time in any one site.

Vaccines

Vaccination, as a means of controlling coccidiosis, is an attractive alternative to prophylactic medication which is, inevitably, accompanied by the emergence of drug-resistant strains of the parasite. Until recently the only type of 'vaccine' commercially available (for chickens) consisted of wild-type, fully virulent organisms. Now there are two vaccines whose constituents have been attenuated by selection for abbreviated developmental cycles, or by adaptation to growth in developing chicken embryos. These are being successfully used in various types of flocks but, in view of their cost, are likely to be most useful for breeders and layers. The possibility of deriving live, attenuated strains suitable for vaccinating rabbits or sheep is being pursued.

Although live vaccines are effective, for reasons of cost, convenience (e.g. shelf-life) and safety, the ultimate goal of immunoprophylaxis for coccidiosis must be the availability of subunit vaccines, produced by recombinant DNA technology. Crude parasite extracts (primarily of sporozoites), given parenterally or orally, are capable of inducing protection against subsequent homologous challenge infection, but the results are influenced by the resistance phenotype of the host. Various purified candidate peptide antigens have afforded partial protection, either when given directly or via the hen (above).

See also: **Avian immune system; Parasites, immunity to.**

Further reading

Coombs GH, Denton H *et al* (1997) Biochemistry of the coccidia. *Advances in Parasitology* **39**: 141–226.
Lillehoj HS and Trout JM (1993) Coccidia: a review of recent advances on immunity and vaccine development. *Avian Pathology* **22**: 3–31.
Lillehoj HS and Trout JM (1994) CD8+ T cell–coccidia interactions. *Parasitology Today* **10**: 10–14.
Ovington KS, Alleva LM and Kerr EA (1995) Cytokines and immunological control of *Eimeria* spp. *International Journal for Parasitology* **25**: 1331–1351.
Rose ME (1996) Immunity to coccidia. In: Davison TF, Payne LN and Morris TR (eds) *World's Poultry Science Association Symposium No. 24: Poultry Immunology*, pp 265–299. Abingdon, Oxon, UK: Carfax Publishing.
Tenter AM and Johnson AM (1997) Phylogeny of the tissue cyst-forming coccidia. *Advances in Parasitology* **39**: 69–139.
Wakelin D and Rose ME (1990) Immunity to coccidiosis. In: Long PL (ed) *Coccidiosis of Man and Animals*, pp 281–306. Raton: CRC Press.
Wallach M, Smith NC, Braun R and Eckert J (1995) Potential control of chicken coccidiosis by maternal immunization. *Parasitology Today* **11**: 262–265.

COLD AGGLUTININS

Ten Feizi, Glycosciences Laboratory, Imperial College School of Medicine, Northwick Park Hospital, Harrow, UK

Cold agglutinins are autoantibodies of low affinity which agglutinate erythrocytes at temperatures below 37°C, and optimally at 4°C. Sera of the majority of healthy adults contain harmless cold autoagglutinins at low titers (1 : 2 to 1 : 32). Sera of newborns usually do not contain cold agglutinins; they become detectable during the first year of life. The majority of these naturally occurring autoantibodies are directed at the I or i antigens. Raised levels of cold agglutinins occur a) transiently following certain infections, for example with *Mycoplasma pneumoniae* and Epstein–Barr virus (anti-i), and b) persistently in a chronic relatively benign lymphoproliferative disorder termed chronic cold agglutinin disease. Raised levels of cold agglutinins may go unnoticed, and are frequently detected incidentally during blood cross-matching or other hematological investigations. The antibodies of certain individuals however, cause clinical symptoms: cyanosis (blueness) with impaired circulation at the extremities upon exposure to the cold resulting from erythrocyte autoagglutination, or an autoimmune hemolytic disorder associated with a positive Coombs' (antiglobulin) test resulting from coating of erythrocytes with the complement components C3 and C4. The severity of the symptoms does not necessarily correlate with the cold agglutinin titers measured at 4°C, rather it is thought to be a reflection of the relatively high binding affinities of the antibodies in certain patients.

Restricted clonality and cross-reactive idiotypes

Cold agglutinins have been the subject of considerable interest since the late 1950s when it was realized that they are usually monoclonal or oligoclonal antibodies. Those occurring in chronic cold agglutinin disease are almost always monoclonal, but even the transiently occurring, postinfective cold agglutinins, when isolated with care to avoid contamination with serum immunoglobulins, have been found to be monoclonal or oligoclonal antibodies. Cold agglutinins with anti-I and anti-i specificities are almost always of the IgM class; the majority have κ light chains, and only a minority, λ. Cold agglutinins with other specificities, designated anti-Pr, anti-Gd, anti-Fl etc. occur less commonly. The majority of these are also of the IgM class but several monoclonal IgA and IgG have been described.

There is a predominance of κ light chains among monoclonal anti-I, whereas λ chains are not uncommon among anti-i and other types of cold agglutinin. Cold agglutinins were the first antibodies among which cross-reactive idiotypes were demonstrated. Two distinct idiotypic systems have been described: one found among anti-I and anti-i, and a second among anti-Pr antibodies; the latter included proteins of the IgM and IgA classes. The first demonstration of idiotypic antigens on blood lymphocytes corresponding to those serum antibodies in the same individuals was made in patients with cold agglutinin disease. The idiotypic antigens among anti-I and anti-i are located predominantly on the variable regions of their heavy chains. Restricted V_H and V_L subgroups are represented among these antibodies, and the cross-reactive idiotypes are almost certainly associated with the framework rather than the complementarity determining regions, since an occasional myeloma protein lacking erythrocyte cold agglutinin activity also has been found to express the same idiotypic determinants.

Combining specificities towards carbohydrates

The I and i antigens are expressed in a developmentally regulated manner on human erythrocytes. In neonates i predominates, and in adults I. The level of i decreases on erythrocytes in the course of the first year of life while I increases. These antigens were the first among developmentally regulated antigens to have been characterized at the molecular level. They are carbohydrate structures: i is expressed on a linear hexasaccharide sequence (structure 1, **Figure 1**) consisting of alternating galactose and N-acetyl-

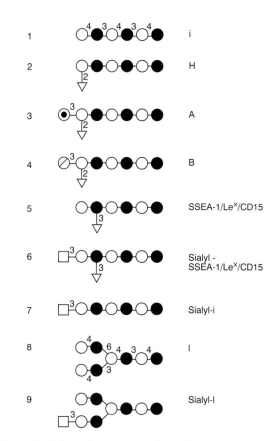

Figure 1 Schematic representation of oligosaccharide sequences which express the i and I antigens and are the most common targets of cold agglutinins. These sequences occur as the backbone domains of oligosaccharides that are O- or N-linked to proteins, or linked to lipids. Also shown are examples of several related oligosaccharides which are based on the i and I backbones and express the major blood group antigen A, B and H, or carbohydrate differentiation antigens SSEA-1 (also designated Le^x or CD15) and sialyl-SSEA-1. The latter two structures are among ligands for leukocyte to endothelium adhesion molecules, the selectins. *Mycoplasma pneumoniae* binds to oligosaccharide structures 7 and 9, but with a stronger affinity for the latter. Symbols for monosaccharides: ○, galactose-β; ∅, galactose-α; ●, N-acetylglucosamine-β; ∇, fucose-α; ⊙, N-acetylgalactosamine-α; □, N-acetylneuraminic acid-α. The numbers over the glycosidic bonds indicate the positions of linkage of the monosaccharides.

glucosamine residues, and I on the related branched octasaccharide (structure 8). Each monoclonal antibody recognizes a particular domain on these oligosaccharide sequences. These sequences occur not only on glycoproteins but also on glycolipids. They are not confined to erythrocytes, but have differing patterns of expression in various tissues of the body. They occur not only as accessible structures but also as internal structures (backbone structures) of the major blood group antigens A, B and H. As illustrated for the i sequence, fucosylation at galactose masks the i antigen activity but gives rise to the blood group H antigen (structure 2). In blood group A persons there occurs addition of an *N*-acetylgalactosamine residue to the H antigen structure to form blood group A (structure 3), and in B individuals there is a galactose residue instead of *N*-acetylgalactosamine (structure 4). Less detailed information is available on the target antigens of cold agglutinins anti-Pr, Gd, etc. The majority of these are directed at various sialo-oligosaccharide sequences on glycoproteins or glycolipids. For example anti-Gd binds to structure 7 on glycolipids.

Clues to pathogenesis

What triggers the production of cold agglutinins? Why are they monoclonal? The precise details are not yet known. The transient cold agglutinin syndrome that follows *M. pneumoniae* infection offers a unique opportunity to study aspects of the mechanism of stimulation of anti-I production. Negligible amounts of I antigen can be detected on cultured *M. pneumoniae*, and there is evidence that this represents passively adsorbed material, probably in association with other lipids and glycolipids, from the serum. As autoantibodies to other glycolipids in the serum, e.g. those with blood group A, B, H, and Lewis activities, do not prevail in this infection, it is unlikely that the anti-I are directed against this passively adsorbed form of the I antigen. On the other hand, the receptors on host cells to which the mycoplasma adheres are sialo-oligosaccharide sequences such as structures 7 and 9, that are based on backbones of Ii type, the highest affinity binding being to the branched I type, structure 9. It seems likely that the selective production of high titer anti-I (i.e. 'antireceptor' antibodies) following *M. pneumoniae* infection is somehow related to these interactions. Possibly the lipid rich mycoplasma serves as an adjuvant overcoming tolerance to self-antigen I. It should be noted that the sialo oligosaccharide receptor sequences occur not only on erythrocytes but also on B and T lymphocytes as well as monocytes, for example. Thus there remains considerable scope for dissection of the macromolecular interactions that culminate in the production of auto-anti-I.

Clues to the biological importance of the target antigens of cold agglutinins and related carbohydrate structures

More recent work with hybridoma-derived monoclonal antibodies that were raised to differentiation antigens of human leukocytes and other cell types, and to various tumor-associated antigens of epithelial tissues has shown that the I and i sequences constitute backbone structures of an array of differentiation antigens and tumor-associated antigens in addition to the blood group antigens discussed above. For example, fucosylation of the penultimate *N*-acetylglucosamine as in structure 5 forms the antigen that has been variously designated SSEA-1, Le^x or CD15. This antigen is a stage-specific embryonic antigen (SSEA-1) in the mouse; it is a distinctive marker of granulocytes (CD15) in the human, while the corresponding sialylated structure which occurs on monocytes as well as granulocytes is also a tumor-associated antigen in certain epithelial malignancies.

Much progress is being made in the cloning of the glycosyltransferases that give rise to this family of oligosaccharides. There is much current interest in the fucosylated and sialylated oligosaccharides in this series (e.g. structures 5 and 6) as ligands for the endothelium to leukocyte adhesion molecules, the selectins which have important roles in leukocyte recruitment to sites of inflammation.

Conclusions

Cold agglutinin syndrome on the one hand presents excellent opportunities for studying mechanisms that operate in the generation of an autoimmune response in humans. On the other hand, the carbohydrate sequence-specific monoclonal autoantibodies in this disorder have served as remarkable reagents, and work with these antibodies opened the way to a whole new field of carbohydrate onco-developmental antigens, a field that expanded rapidly with the advent of the hybridoma technology and advanced further with the demonstration of roles for oligosaccharides as ligands in biological recognition.

See also: **Antiglobulin (Coombs') test; Autoimmune diseases; Autoimmunity; Carbohydrate antigens; Lewis^x/sialyl-Lewis^x (CD15/CD15s); Idiotype:** *Mycoplasma***, infection and immunity.**

Further reading

Feizi T (1981) The blood group Ii system: a carbohydrate antigen system defined by naturally monoclonal or oligoclonal autoantibodies of man. *Immunological Communications* 10: 127–156.

Feizi T (1981) Carbohydrate differentiation antigens. *Trends in Biochemical Sciences* 6: 333–335.

Crocker PR and Fcizi T (1996) Carbohydrate recognition systems: functional triads in cell–cell interactions. *Current Opinion in Structural Biology* 6: 679–691.

Feizi T and Childs RA (1987) Carbohydrates as antigenic determinants of glycoproteins. *Biochemical Journal* 245: 1–11.

Feizi T and Hadler NM (1983) Autoantibodies and disease. In: Elkeles RS and Tavill AS (eds) *Biochemical*

Aspects of Human Disease, pp 656–692. Oxford: Blackwell Scientific.

Feizi T and Loveless RW (1996) Carbohydrate recognition by *Mycoplasma pneumoniae* and pathologic consequences. *American Journal of Respiratory and Critical Care Medicine* 154: S133–S136.

Frank MM, Atkinson JP and Gadek J (1977) Cold aggluti-

nins and cold-agglutinin disease. *Annual Review of Medicine* 28: 291–298.

Pruzanski W and Shumak KH (1977) Biological activity of coldreacting auto-antibodies. (Second of two parts). *New England Journal of Medicine* 297: 583–589.

Roelcke D (1989) Cold agglutination. *Transfusion Medicine Review* 3: 140–166.

COLONY-STIMULATING FACTORS

John W Schrader, The Biomedical Research Centre, UBC, Vancouver, Canada

Colony-stimulating factor (CSF) is the operational term for a class of molecules that stimulate hematopoietic progenitor cells to divide and generate colonies of differentiated progeny such as neutrophils or macrophages. Colony-stimulating factors were originally detected and assayed by culturing a source of hematopoietic progenitor cells, such as a cell suspension derived from the bone marrow, in medium that has been jellified by the addition of a substance such as agar or methyl cellulose. Provided a CSF or a source of a CSF is present, hematopoietic progenitors survive and grow, and over a period of a week or so, give rise to colonies of 100–10 000 differentiated cells. The number of colonies and the extent to which a preparation can be diluted and still retain activity, can be used to quantitate the CSFs in that preparation. Moreover the morphology of the differentiated cells in the colonies can be determined by picking off and staining the colonies or by staining the whole culture.

Colony assays were developed in the 1960s by Pluznik and Sacks and Bradley and Metcalf, and have in large part provided the data that have generated our current picture of the molecular regulation of hematopoiesis and of the cellular steps in the differentiation of hematopoietic cells. Colony assays also have allowed the identification of different types of committed progenitor cells and determination of their physical and antigenic characteristics.

All CSFs share three basic properties:

1 they support the survival of hematopoietic progenitor cells and mature cells such as neutrophils by suppressing apoptosis;
2 they stimulate growth of stem/progenitor cells and in some cases of mature cells, e.g. mast cells or macrophages;
3 they regulate the function of cells, for example activating mature granulocytes.

Nomenclature

Originally, CSFs were given names that reflected in some measure their function. Thus a preparation that stimulated progenitor cells and generated colonies containing both neutrophils and macrophages was said to contain granulocyte-macrophage CSF (GM-CSF); one that stimulated the growth of colonies containing only neutrophils was said to contain granulocyte CSF (G-CSF). The various CSFs are now recognized as members of a large family of cytokines and hormones united by a common evolutionary origin and similarities in their three-dimensional structure (discussed below). Both GM-CSF and G-CSF have gained wide acceptance as names of two, well-characterized molecules that have been produced in large quantities by recombinant DNA techniques and are now in clinical use. It should be noted, however, that activities of these molecules can be broader than implied by their name or by their action in one particular species. Thus whereas in the mouse, GM-CSF generates colonies containing neutrophils and macrophages, in the human it also generates colonies of eosinophils. Likewise, not only does G-CSF stimulate the growth of progenitors of neutrophils, but it also affects more primitive cells. Interleukin 3 (IL-3) acts as a CSF with a broad target range and the capacity to stimulate progenitors of megakaryocytes, mast cells, eosinophils, macrophages, neutrophils, basophils and erythroid cells, as well as those multipotent progenitors generating colonies containing various mixtures of these cell types. Because of these properties IL-3 has also been termed 'multi-CSF'. A fourth CSF, widely called CSF-1, stimulates colonies of macrophages and has also been termed macrophage CSF (M-CSF). As noted below CSF-1 differs slightly from the GM-CSF, G-CSF and IL-3 in its overall molecular structure and greatly in the type of cell surface receptors that it stimulates. It also differs from the other CSFs in that it occurs in the bloodstream in normal animals and in that it has targets outside the lymphohematopoietic system, in the female reproductive tract.

It should be noted that operationally a number of different CSFs can stimulate one type of hematopoietic cell (**Table 1**). For example, a colony of macrophages can develop from a macrophage progenitor that has been stimulated by GM-CSF or by IL-3, or by CSF-1. Thus, in the earlier literature, prior to the molecular characterization of CSFs and the subsequent development of specific neutralizing antibodies, an activity that was referred to operationally as 'GM-CSF' may in fact have reflected the presence, not of the molecule now defined as GM-CSF, but instead of another molecule such as IL-3 that could also stimulate the development of colonies containing neutrophils and macrophages. Likewise, in earlier studies, the reader will encounter terms such as 'eosinophil CSF' or 'megakaryocyte CSF'. No distinct molecular species that specifically stimulate the development of large colonies of eosinophils or megakaryocytes have yet been characterized. Many of the earlier studies of eosinophil CSF or megakaryocyte CSF were assaying the ability of IL-3 to stimulate colonies of these cells.

Other molecules are able to stimulate progenitor cells and act operationally as CSFs. In the human, but not the mouse, IL-5 can stimulate the growth of small colonies of eosinophils although its major action appears to be to enhance differentiation of eosinophils. Under some circumstances, IL-6 can give rise to small colonies. Steel locus factor (SLF) or stem cell factor, which is the ligand of the c-kit protein, can stimulate the growth of small colonies of mast cells and of neutrophils.

An important principle is that mixtures of factors often exert synergistic effects on colony formation.

Interleukin 3 and CSF-1, for example, in the human strongly synergize in the production of macrophage colonies. Other peptide regulatory factors such as SLF, IL-1, IL-6 and IL-4 all have been reported to have synergistic activity in colony formation in various situations. IL-11 and thrombopoietin synergize with other cytokines in generating colonies of various hematopoietic lineages, but have a particular propensity to stimulate the generation of megakaryocytes and platelets.

Sources

The colony-stimulating factors are made in many cell types, including epithelial cells, endothelial cells, fibroblasts, smooth muscle cells and cells of the hematopoietic system, in particular T lymphocytes. In general, CSFs are only produced in response to stress, for example infection, although there are exceptions such as SLF or CSF-1, which are produced in the body under normal conditions. Microbial products such as endotoxin or nucleic acids are potent stimuli for CSF production. Other peptide regulatory factors such as IL-1 can induce the production of colony-stimulating factors, for example GM-CSF, from cells such as endothelial cells or fibroblasts. The antigen-activated T lymphocyte is a source of two CSFs: GM-CSF and IL-3. Macrophages can produce GM-CSF, G-CSF and CSF-1. When stimulated by LPS B lymphocytes produce small amounts of GM-CSF. Mast cells and eosinophils produce small quantities of IL-3, IL-5 and GM-CSF when activated by cross-linking the Fc receptor for immunoglobulins.

Table 1 Stimulation of proliferation and differentiation of hematopoietic cells by colony-stimulating factors

Target cells acted on in bone marrow	Multi-CSF (IL-3)	GM-CSF	G-CSF	M-CSF (CSF-1)
Pluripotent stem cell	+	(+)	(−)	(−)
Granulocyte-monocyte progenitor	+	+	+	(+)
Monocyte progenitor	+	+	−	+
Neutrophil progenitor	+	+	+	−
Eosinophil progenitor	+	+	−	−
Basophil progenitor	+	+	−	−
Mast cell	+	−	−	−
Megakaryocyte	+	−	−	−
Erythroid progenitor	+	+/−	−	−
Lymphoid				
B progenitor	+	−	−	−
T progenitor (thymus)	−	−	−	−

Physiological role of CSF

Physiologically, the CSFs can be regarded as part of a larger family of peptide regulatory factors or cytokines that play a major role in regulating the body's response to infection or injury. A general characteristic of the CSFs is that they stimulate not only the growth of progenitor cells leading to production of various differentiated progeny, but also the effector functions of the mature differentiated cells. Thus GM-CSF can prime for a respiratory burst in neutrophils, and GM-CSF and IL-3 can enhance phagocytosis by macrophages.

Some of the CSFs have been shown to enhance immune responses. Both GM-CSF and IL-3 have these effects which probably are mediated via actions on accessory cells. For example, IL-3 induces the release of substances such as IL-1 from macrophages and upregulates the expression of class II major histocompatibility complex antigens. GM-CSF, with IL-4, promotes the differentiation of monocytes to dendritic cells.

A minority of CSFs have a role in the normal development of the hematopoietic system as opposed to its activation during stress. Mice with mutations blocking production of CSF-1 exhibit defects in the development of macrophages and osteoclasts. Genetic lesions in SLF or its receptor leads to defects in the development of erythrocytes and mast cells as well as in nonhematopoietic tissues. In the absence of GM-CSF, a lung disease called alveolar proteinosis occurs.

Structure of the CSFs

The CSFs are small polypeptides of M_r around 15 000 which are heavily and variably modified by glycosylation, although the functional significance of this carbohydrate has not been established. IL-3, IL-5, GM-CSF, G-CSF erythropoietin, thrombopoietin and IL-11 are monomers, whereas CSF-1 and SLF are homodimers, linked by disulfide bonds. As discussed below, CSF-1 and SLF also differ from the other CSFs in binding to a different structural class of cell surface receptors. Although there are few similarities in the amino acid sequences of different CSFs, analysis of their three-dimensional structures has revealed that they all belong to one structural family of proteins, characterized by four α helices, bundled in a particular way. This family also includes most interleukins, as well as hormones such as growth hormone, thrombopoietin, erythropoietin and leptin.

IL-3, GM-CSF and G-CSF bind to members of a structural family of receptors termed the cytokine receptor superfamily, members of which also bind IL-2, erythropoietin, IL-4, IL-5, IL-6 and IL-7, as well as other cytokines such as LIF, CNTF and leptin.

GM-CSF and IL-3 each bind with low affinity to specific receptor α chains belonging to this cytokine receptor family. High-affinity binding and signal transduction, however, depends upon interaction with a second β receptor chain, which is also a member of the cytokine receptor family and is a common component of the receptors for IL-3, GM-CSF and IL-5. Ligand-binding induces or stabilizes dimerization of α and β chains leading to activation of cytoplasmic tyrosine kinases that associate with the intracytoplasmic portions of these chains. Activation of these tyrosine kinases, which include members of the JAK and Src families of kinases, triggers a cascade of intracellular events that regulate cellular growth, survival and differentiation.

The receptors for CSF-1 and SLF do not belong to the cytokine receptor family, but instead to a distinct family of receptors that are characterized by immunoglobulin-like domains in the extracellular portion of the molecule, and a tyrosine kinase domain in the intracytoplasmic part of the molecule. These receptors resemble those for platelet-derived growth factor and, more distantly, insulin. Ligand-induced dimerization of the CSF-1 and SLF receptors leads to activation of the intrinsic kinase activity of the receptors themselves. Despite these differences in the two major families of receptors used by CSFs, ligand binding in both cases triggers activation of the same intracellular paths that regulate cellular growth and apoptosis. Much more is known about the similarities of the intracellular signals activated by CSFs than their differences.

Clinical use

G-CSF and GM-CSF are already at a relatively advanced stage of their clinical evaluation. They have proven their value in accelerating the recovery of white blood cell counts following myelotoxic procedures such as bone marrow transplantation or chemotherapy. Further indications, for example in the treatment of infections, are being explored. Given the role of colony-stimulating factors in inflammatory processes, it is possible in the future that small molecules that antagonize their action will find use as modulators in diseases in which inflammation plays a role. Thrombopoietin (TPO) – also known as megakaryocyte growth and differention factor or megapoietin – is a new member of the four-helix bundle cytokine family that is able to stimulate increases in levels of platelets in normal animals. In myelosuppressed animals TPO also stimulated recovery of neutrophils, probably reflecting the synergistic effects of combinations of TPO and other hematopoietins on the *in vitro* proliferation of hematopoietic progenitors of multiple lineages. Administration of IL-11 also accelerates recovery of platelet levels in myelosuppressed animals and, like TPO, also accelerates the regeneration of neutrophils.

See also: **Bone marrow and hematopoiesis; Cytokine assays; Granulocyte colony stimulating factor (G-CSF); Granulocyte-macrophage colony stimulating factor (GM-CSF); Interleukin 3; Macrophage colony stimulating factor (CSF-1); Organ culture of lymphoid cells.**

Further reading

Estey EH (1994) Use of colony-stimulating factors in the treatment of acute myeloid leukemia. *Blood* **83:** 2015–2019.

Freifeld A and Pizzo P (1995) Colony-stimulating factors and neutropenia: intersection of data and clinical relevance. *Journal of the National Cancer Institute* **87:** 781–782.

Hamilton JA (1993) Colony stimulating factors, cytokines and monocyte-macrophages – some controversies. *Immunology Today* **14:** 18–24.

Metcalf D (1995) The granulocyte-macrophage regulators: reappraisal by gene inactivation. *Experimental Hematology* **23:** 569–572.

Metcalf D and Nicola NA (1995) *The Hemopoietic Colony-Stimulating Factors: From Biology to Clinical Applications.* Cambridge: Cambridge University Press.

Petersdorf SH and Dale DC (1995) The biology and clinical applications of erythropoietin and the colony-stimulating factors. *Advances in Internal Medicine* **40:** 395–428.

Steward WP (1993) Granulocyte and granulocyte-macrophage colony-stimulating factors. *Lancet* **342:** 153–157.

COMMON VARIABLE IMMUNODEFICIENCY

Thomas A Selvaggi, Laboratory of Clinical Investigation, National Institute of Allergy and Infectious Diseases, National Institutes of Health. Bethesda, Maryland, USA

Michael C Sneller, Laboratory of Immunoregulation, National Institute of Allergy and Infectious Diseases, National Institutes of Health, Bethesda, Maryland, USA

Common variable immunodeficiency (CVI) is a heterogeneous syndrome characterized by hypogammaglobulinemia and recurrent bacterial infections. This rare syndrome has an estimated prevalence ranging from 1:50 000 to 1:200 000. Although classified as a primary antibody deficiency syndrome, CVI represents a generalized state of immune dysregulation characterized by functional abnormalities of both T and B cells. Clinically, this is reflected in the susceptibility of these patients to a variety of conditions not easily explained on the basis of an isolated humoral immune defect.

Clinical features (Table 1)

Patients with CVI present with recurrent bacterial infections of the respiratory tract, such as sinusitis, otitis media, bronchitis and pneumonia. The most common etiologic agents are encapsulated bacteria such as *Streptococcus pneumoniae* and *Haemophilus influenzae*. The onset of these abnormally frequent infections may occur at any age but most patients do not come to medical attention until the second or third decade. This is in contrast to X-linked agammaglobulinemia, where recurrent infections develop in the first 2 years of life. The recurrent bacterial infections in CVI are a direct result of the deficiency in antibody production (specifically immunoglobulin G, IgG) that is the hallmark of this syndrome. If CVI goes undiagnosed (and hence untreated), recurrent pulmonary infections can lead to irreversible chronic lung disease with bronchiectasis. Septicemia and recurrent infections of the skin, urinary tract, joints or central nervous system also occur in patients with CVI, but are less frequent. In rare instances, patients with CVI can become infected with a variety of opportunistic fungi, mycobacteria and *Pneumocystis carinii*. An unusual syndrome of severe enteroviral meningoencephalitis is seen in patients with primary antibody-deficiency syndromes. This type of infection is most commonly associated with X-linked agammaglobulinemia, but several well-documented cases have occurred in patients with CVI. Other viral infections that can occur with increased frequency in CVI include recurrent attacks of herpes simplex and herpes zoster.

Patients with CVI suffer from a variety of infectious and noninfectious gastrointestinal disorders. The protozoan *Giardia lamblia* is a common cause of infectious diarrhea in these patients. Malabsorption, of unknown etiology, leading to severe weight loss and diarrhea, is another major gastrointestinal

Table 1 Clinical features of common variable immunodeficiency

Relative frequency	Recurrent infections		Autoimmune disease	Other
	Manifestation	Pathogens		
Most common	Sinusitis, otitis media, pneumonia	Streptococcus pneumoniae Haemophilus influenzae	Hemolytic anemia Neutropenia, thrombocytopenia	Lymphadenopathy Splenomegaly Nodular lymphoid hyperplasia
	Infectious diarrhea	Giardia lamblia Salmonella spp. Campylobacter spp. Cryptosporidium Dysgonic fermentor-3	Pernicious anemia Autoimmune thyroid disease Rheumatoid arthritis Juvenile rheumatoid arthritis	Bronchiectasis
Less common	Septic arthritis	Staphylococcus aureus Mycoplasma spp. Haemophilus influenzae	Systemic lupus erythematosus Sjögren's syndrome Ulcerative colitis Crohn disease	Malignancy Cholelithiasis Idiopathic malabsorption Sarcoid-like granulomatous disease
	Meningitis	Streptococcus pneumoniae Haemophilus influenzae Neisseria meningitidis		
	Encephalitis	Enteroviruses		
	Pneumonia	Pneumocystis carinii		

manifestation of CVI. Small bowel biopsy reveals flattening of the villi with a lymphocytic infiltration in the lamina propria. Neoplasms of the gastrointestinal tract (specifically, adenocarcinoma of the stomach and intestinal lymphomas) appear to occur with increased frequency in CVI.

Approximately 25% of patients with CVI will develop one or more autoimmune diseases, indicating that CVI is a disease of abnormal immune regulation as well as immunodeficiency. Autoimmune (Coombs'-positive) hemolytic anemia and idiopathic thrombocytopenic purpura (ITP) are the two most common autoimmune diseases seen. Neutropenia is also seen in a significant number of patients with CVI, and in some cases antigranulocyte antibodies have been demonstrated. A variety of other autoimmune diseases can occur in association with CVI (**Table 1**).

Patients with CVI frequently develop lymphoproliferative disorders, which can take several forms. Malignant lymphoma occurs with increased frequency in these patients, although the exact magnitude of this increase is unclear. This high incidence of lymphomas (and cancers in general) is an indication that some patients with CVI may have clinically important defects in cell-mediated as well as humoral immunity. More common than malignant lymphoma is the occurrence of benign lymphoid hyperplasia manifested by one or more of the following: splenomegaly; diffuse lymphadenopathy; or nodular lymphoid hyperplasia of the intestinal tract.

Immunogenetics

Evidence for a genetic influence was noted very early in the study of CVI, when family studies disclosed that a significant number of patients had first-degree relatives with other immunologic diseases such as isolated IgA deficiency and various autoimmune diseases. Recent studies have found an association of CVI and IgA deficiency with certain major histocompatibility complex (MHC) haplotypes. These results suggest that CVI and IgA deficiency are related disorders, susceptibility to which is determined by a gene or genes in or near the MHC region.

Immunologic features

The hallmark of CVI is a marked decrease in serum IgG, which is usually associated with significant depression of serum IgM and IgA levels. Despite this panhypogammaglobulinemia, the majority of patients with CVI have normal numbers of B cells in the circulation and peripheral lymphoid tissues. However, the numbers of surface IgG$^+$ and IgA$^+$ B cells are often reduced, suggesting an impaired ability of CVI B cells to undergo immunoglobulin class switching.

Although the exact nature of the immunologic defect(s) that give rise to CVI are unknown, a number of *in vitro* immunologic abnormalities have been identified in these patients. In early studies, peripheral blood lymphocytes from patients with CVI were stimulated *in vitro* with the lectin pokeweed mitogen, and culture supernatants were assayed for immunoglobulin production. A consistent finding in this type of study was the inability of peripheral blood lymphocytes from patients with CVI to secrete normal amounts of immunoglobulin. Since pokeweed mitogen-induced immunoglobulin secretion is strictly dependent on the presence of functional helper T cells, it was unclear whether this decreased immunoglobulin production by patient B cells was due to an abnormality intrinsic to the B cell or secondary to a T cell abnormality. In subsequent studies partially purified T cells and B cells of patients were separately analyzed in pokeweed mitogen-driven cultures containing allogeneic normal T cells and B cells. This approach showed that most patients with CVI appeared to have a B cell defect, in that coculture of their B cells with normal allogeneic T cells did not correct the defect in immunoglobulin production, and T cells from most patients were able to support immunoglobulin production by normal B cells. Occasional patients whose T cells were capable of suppressing normal B cell immunoglobulin production were identified, but in most patients shown to have excessive suppressor T cell activity, coculture of their B cells with normal T cells failed to rescue B cell function, thereby indicating that these patients also had a B cell defect.

More recent *in vitro* studies indicate that B cells from patients with CVI can be induced to proliferate and secrete immunoglobulin if appropriately stimulated. Studies using combinations of B cell mitogens or monoclonal antibodies (anti-CD40, anti-IgM) and various cytokines have shown that the severity of the defect in B cell immunoglobulin secretion varies among patients. In most cases B cells from patients with CVI can be induced to secrete at least some immunoglobulin; however, only a minority of patients produce normal amounts of all immunoglobulin isotypes. The *in vitro* defect in immunoglobulin secretion seen in CVI tends to be hierarchical, with IgM secretion affected least, IgG secretion affected to an intermediate degree, and IgA secretion reduced to the greatest extent. These results indicate that the B cell defect in CVI is not absolute and suggest that B cells from a subset of patients with CVI may only require the appropriate stimuli (which are presumably lacking *in vivo*) to mature into immunoglobulin-secreting plasma cells.

In addition to abnormalities of B cell function, many patients with CVI also exhibit *in vitro* abnormalities of T cell function. In about half of CVI patients, a selective abnormality of T cell activation can be demonstrated; it appears to arise from a signaling defect and is manifest as reduced expression of genes directing the synthesis of interleukin 2 (IL-2), IL-4 and IL-5. In addition, T cells from a subset of CVI patients fail to express normal levels of CD40 ligand following activation. Since both CD40 ligand and lymphokines are essential ways by which T cells provide help to B cells for antibody secretion, the fundamental immunologic abnormality in some patients with CVI may be a defect in T cell help.

While most patients with CVI have a normal CD4:CD8 T cell ratio, approximately one-third of patients exhibit a reduced CD4:CD8 T cell ratio due to elevation in the absolute number of CD8 cells, most of which also express CD57 and HLA-DR. The expanded population of CD8 T cells in these patients have phenotypic and functional properties that are characteristic of activated cytotoxic T lymphocytes. The origin and functional significance of the expanded population of CD8 T cells in this subgroup of CVI patients is unclear.

Treatment

Standard therapy of CVI currently consists of intravenously administered immunoglobulin, which is less painful and more effective at preventing infections than intramuscular immunoglobulin. Vigorous treatment of infections and readiness to promptly evaluate and treat any unusual complications are also important aspects of managing these patients. Treatment of noninfectious complications is the same as in nonimmunodeficient patients.

See also: **Gammaglobulin; Immunodeficiency, primary.**

Further reading

Cunningham-Rundles C (1989) Clinical and immunologic analyses of 103 patients with common variable immunodeficiency. *Journal of Clinical Immunology* 9: 22–33.
De La Concha EG, Oldham G, Webster ADB, Asherson GL and Platts-Mills TAE (1977) Quantitative measurements of T- and B-cell function in 'variable' primary hypogammaglobulinaemia: evidence for a consistent B-cell defect. *Clinical and Experimental Immunology* 27: 208–215.
Eisenstein EM, Chua K and Strober W (1994) B cell differentiation defects in common variable immunodeficiency are ameliorated after stimulation with anti-CD40 antibody and IL-10. *Journal of Immunology* 152: 5957–5868.

Farrington M, Grosmaire LS, Nonoyama S *et al* (1994) CD40 ligand expression is defective in a subset of patients with common variable immunodeficiency. *Proceedings of the National Academy of Sciences of the USA* **91**: 1099–1103.

Jaffe JS, Strober W and Sneller MC (1993) Functional abnormalities of CD8⁺ T cells define a unique subset of patients with common variable immunodeficiency. *Blood* **82**: 192–201.

Lawton AR and Hummell DS (1996) Primary antibody deficiencies. In: Rich RR (ed) *Clinical Immunology: Principles and Practice*, pp 621–636. St Louis: Mosby-Year Book.

Rosen FS, Cooper MD and Wedgewood RJP (1995) The primary immunodeficiencies. *New England Journal of Medicine* **333**: 431–440.

Sander CA, Medeiros LJ, Weiss LM, Yano T, Sneller MC and Jaffe ES (1992) Lymphoproliferative lesions in patients with common variable immunodeficiency syndrome. *American Journal of Surgical Pathology* **16**: 1170–1182.

Schaffer FM, Palermos J, Zhu ZB, Barger BO, Cooper MD and Volanakis JE (1989) Individuals with IgA deficiency and common variable immunodeficiency share polymorphisms of major histocompatibility complex class III genes. *Proceedings of the National Academy of Sciences of the USA* **86**: 8015–8019.

Sneller MC, Strober W, Eisenstein EM, Jaffe JS and Cunningham-Rundles C (1993) New insights into common variable immunodeficiency. *Annals of Internal Medicine* **118**: 720–730.

Spickett GP, Farrant J, North ME *et al* (1997) Common variable immunodeficiency: how many diseases? *Immunology Today* **18**: 325–328.

Spickett GP, Webster ADB and Farrant J (1990) Cellular abnormalities in common variable immunodeficiency. *Immunodeficiency Reviews* **2**: 199–219.

COMPLEMENT, ALTERNATIVE PATHWAY

Peter J Lachmann, University of Cambridge, SmithKline Beecham Microbial Immunology Laboratory, Centre for Veterinary Science, Cambridge, UK

The term 'alternative pathway of complement activation' is used to describe the activation pathway that is alternative to the so-called 'classical' pathway of activation which was the model of complement activity used to characterize the system. The classical pathway is the reaction sequence by which antibody-sensitized sheep erythrocytes are lysed by human or guinea pig complement. It was already inherent in the original description of the third component of complement, by Coca in 1914, that there must be a separate pathway of complement activation used by yeast cell walls which depleted complement activity without depleting either C1 or C2. It was not until the 1950s, however, that Pillemer and his colleagues recognized that there was a novel pathway of complement activation which they described as the 'properdin pathway'. This pathway did not require antibody for its initiation and they postulated it to be a major mediating pathway for nonspecific immunity. They described a new protein – 'properdin' – which they ascribed the central role in this pathway and major importance in resistance to infection and tumors. Towards the end of the 1950s this group also described the existence of other new factors that were needed for the inactivation of C3 by zymosan. Although much of this work later turned out to be essentially correct, it was much contested at the time, largely by RA Nelson (in 1958), and the existence of the alternative pathway was not fully accepted until the discovery of sera genetically deficient in C2 and C4 in the 1960s. It was also at this time that the complement components were first isolated as proteins and as antigens so that the biochemistry of their interactions could be worked out. It was not until the 1970s, however, that the biochemistry and reaction pathway of the alternative pathway was clarified after a period of considerable confusion.

At the heart of the alternative pathway is the C3 feedback cycle (**Figure 1**). The primary large cleavage product of C3 is C3b, which combines in the presence of magnesium ions with factor B – the C2-like protein of the alternative pathway – to form a bimolecular complex, C3b,B. This acts as a substrate for factor D – the C1 analog of the alternative pathway – which cleaves a bond in factor B splitting off a fragment, Ba, and leaving the complex C3b,Bb. This is the 'C3'convertase' of the alternative pathway and is the homologous enzyme to C4b,2b; the C3-convertase of the classical pathway. Generating a C3 cleaving enzyme from C3b provides a positive feedback amplification loop, generating more C3b and consuming more factor B until one or other of these components is exhausted. Factor D is a single domain serum protease occurring in plasma in active form. It was a great surprise when it was recently discovered, following the cloning of the molecule,

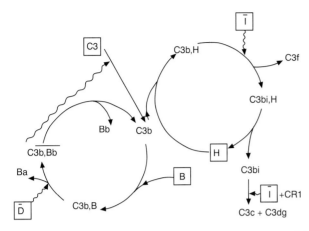

Figure 1 C3b feedback and breakdown. (From Lachmann PJ and Hughes-Jones NC (1984) *Seminars in Immunopathology* **7**: 143–162.)

that factor D is identical to a serine protease known as 'adipsin' which occurs in fat tissue and in nerves. The function of adipsin is unknown, but its levels are strikingly reduced in certain genetic forms of obesity and of diabetes.

The C3b feedback cycle is subject to homeostatic control by an analogous reaction cycle where C3b combines with another normal serum protein – factor H – to give a complex C3b,H which is cleaved by another serine protease present in active form in plasma – factor I. Factor I cleaves two bonds in C3b, cleaving out a small fragment – C3f – and leaving the large fragment iC3b which still has important functions as an inflammatory mediator but is no longer capable of combining with factor B or giving rise to a C3 convertase. The rate of C3 activation by the alternative pathway is controlled by the relative velocities of the C3b feedback cycle on the one hand and the C3b breakdown cycle on the other.

The alternative pathway is therefore fired by any mechanism which either increases the rate of C3b production or reduces the rate of C3b breakdown. Mechanisms that increase C3b production include:

1. *The generation of extrinsic enzymes that cleave C3.* The principal of these is the C3-convertase of the classical complement pathway, C4b,2b. Kallikrein and plasmin also split C3 as does elastase and a number of proteases from phagocytic cells or from bacteria. At inflammatory sites a number of these enzymatic systems may be active.

2. *Mechanisms that stabilize the alternative pathway C3 convertase.* Physiologically this enzyme is stabilized by properdin which binds to it. This is the part that properdin plays in the alternative pathway – not at all what the Pillemer group had envisaged. Although properdin levels have not

been found of great diagnostic value, the total absence of properdin leads to (usually severe) immunodeficiency. A more complete stabilization of C3b,Bb is produced by autoantibodies that react with it. Such autoantibodies are called 'nephritic factors' since they were first described in mesangiocapillary glomerulonephritis. However, the renal disease follows the formation of the nephritic factors rather than causing it and the mechanisms underlying the formation of the nephritic factor remain unknown.

An artefactual way of producing a stable C3-convertase is the use of cobra venom factor. This is a reptilian analog of a C3 breakdown product that functionally resembles C3b and has the curious property that it combines with mammalian factor B but is not dissociated by mammalian factor H and therefore produces a stable C3-convertase not susceptible to homeostatic control which causes the C3b feedback cycle to run to exhaustion.

The principal mechanism that decreases the rate of C3b breakdown is the 'protected surface' phenomenon; C3b bound on certain surfaces is relatively poorly reactive with factor H and therefore resistant to breakdown whilst supporting the C3b feedback cycle by reaction with factor B. Such protected surfaces include particulate polysaccharides (for example zymosan and particulate inulin); the surfaces of most parasites and of many virus-infected and some tumor cells; and certain immunoglobulin aggregates particularly those of IgA. More dramatic failure of C3b breakdown occurs in the genetic deficiencies of factor I or of factor H. A further mechanism of reducing C3b breakdown is provided by local removal of factor H. This was first described for 'sulfated sephadex' and has been seen also with an intestinal glycoprotein and a myeloma light chain dimer. The physiological or pathophysiological relevance of this mechanism is still unclear.

The view that the alternative pathway is essentially governed by the velocity of competing reactions requires that there is a minimal level of C3b (or of a C3b-like protein) always available. This is the essential feature of the 'tickover' model of the alternative pathway. It was originally proposed that the tickover was maintained by minimal levels of proteolysis of C3 by any of the enzymes that can cleave it and indeed this is likely to be the case. However, another mechanism has been suggested: namely that the hydrolysis by water of the internal thioester bond generates a C3b-like molecule and that this spontaneous hydrolysis of C3 may be sufficient to keep the tickover working. The levels of C3b or C3b-like proteins that are required for the maintenance of the tickover are so low that it has not so far been possible to define critically the relative roles of proteolysis and thioester hydrolysis in maintaining the tickover *in vivo*.

See also: **Immunoconglutinins; Complement, alternative pathway; Clotting system; Cobra venom factor; Complement, classical pathway; Complement deficiencies; Complement, genetics; Complement receptors.**

Further reading

Coca AF (1914) A study of the anticomplementary action of yeast, of certain bacteria and of cobra venom. *Zeitschrift für Immunitatsforschung Experimentale Therapie* 21: 604.

Lachmann PJ (1979) An evolutionary view of the complement system. *Behring Institute Mitteilungen* 63: 25–37.

Lachmann PJ and Hughes-Jones NC (1984) Initiation of complement activation. *Seminars in Immunopathology* 7: 143–162.

Nelson RA Jr (1958) An alternative mechanism for the properdin system. *Journal of Experimental Medicine* 108: 515–535.

Pangburn MK and Muller-Eberhard HJ (1984) The alternative pathway of complement. *Seminars in Immunopathology* 7: 163–192.

Pillemer L, Blum L, Lepow H *et al* (1954) The properdin system and immunity. I Demonstration and isolation of a new serum protein, properdin, and its role in immune phenomena. *Science* 120: 279–285.

Ratnoff WD (1980) A war with the molecules: Louis Pillemer and the history of properdin. *Perspectives in Biology and Medicine* 23: 638–655.

Rosen BS, Cook KS, Yaglom J *et al* (1989) Adipsin and complement factor D activity: an immune-related defect in obesity. *Science* 244: 1483–1487.

COMPLEMENT, CLASSICAL PATHWAY

Robert B Sim, MRC Immunochemistry Unit and Department of Biochemistry, University of Oxford, Oxford, UK

The complement system consists in total of about 20 soluble proteins in plasma and other body fluids, and a similar number of cell surface receptors and control proteins, present on blood cells and other tissues. Complement has a major role in controlling the uptake and removal, by phagocytosis, of materials such as immune complexes, microorganisms or host cell breakdown products, which are recognized by, and activate the system. Complement proteins, and their fragments generated during activation, also have roles in regulating cellular immune responses. Individual complement proteins serve the functions of recognizing and binding to target material. Recognition is followed by activation of serine proteases of the complement system (**Figure 1**), which assemble on the surface of the target. One such protease is termed C3 convertase and is capable of cleaving the most abundant soluble complement protein, C3. C3 is then cleaved and activated, and a major fragment of C3, called C3b, binds covalently to the target. Covalent binding occurs by direct nucleophilic attack of surface hydroxyl or amine groups of the target on an activated thiolester within C3b. Surface-bound molecules of C3b, or of its proteolytic breakdown product iC3b, serve as ligands for C3 receptors on phagocytic cells, and so act as labels for phagocytosis of the target. Surface-bound C3b also forms part of the binding site for C5, which is cleaved by the same protease which cleaved C3. The proteolytic fragment C5b binds to C6, C7, C8 and C9 to form the membrane attack complex, which, if the target material contains a lipid bilayer, associates with the membrane and may cause cell lysis.

The activation of the complement system occurs by either or both of two distinct routes (**Figure 1**). The first route for which the sequence of reactions was elucidated was termed the *classical pathway*, which consists of the proteins (or 'components') C1, C2, C4 and C3 (named in order of their sequence of action, which by historical accident, differs from numerical order). C1 is a large complex made up of three distinct proteins (or 'subcomponents') called C1q, C1r and C1s. A more recently elucidated route is called the *alternative pathway*, and consists of the proteins factor B, factor D and C3, together with the regulator proteins factor H, factor I and properdin.

Both pathways contain a target recognition mechanism, and both pathways lead to assembly of proteases which cleave C3 and C5. Cleavage of C5 by either pathway results in activation of the lytic pathway (components C5–C9). In the last few years, it has been shown that another protein similar in shape

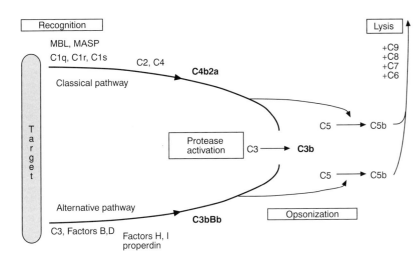

Figure 1 Pathways of the complement system. The major stages of target recognition, protease activation, opsonization by deposition of C3b, and cell lysis are shown. Interactions of the classical pathway components are discussed in the text. The 'C3 convertase enzymes', C4b2a and C3bBb are shown prominently.

to C1q can also participate in classical pathway activation. This is mannose-binding lectin (MBL), a member of the collectin protein family. MBL appears to be associated with two proteases, named MASP-1 and MASP-2, which are homologous to C1r and C1s, and appear to have similar function. In some publications, activation of complement via MBL is regarded as a third, separate pathway (the lectin pathway), but it is discussed here as a 'branch' of the classical pathway. Discussion of the classical pathway thus is limited to the interactions of C1, C2, C4 and C3, MBL and the MASPs, together with 1) the soluble regulatory proteins C1-inhibitor, C4b-binding protein (C4bp) and factor I, which control activation of this part of the complement system, and 2) the cell surface receptors or regulatory proteins which interact with classical pathway components. These include complement receptor type 1 (CR1), membrane cofactor protein (MCP), decay-accelerating factor (DAF) and C1q receptor (C1q-R).

Distinction between classical and alternative pathways

In experimental work, the two pathways of activation can be readily distinguished, in that both pathways require Mg^{2+}, but only the classical pathway requires Ca^{2+} ions: if these are chelated by EGTA (ethyleneglycol-bis-(β-amino-ethylether) tetra-acetic acid) and Mg^{2+} ions are added in excess, only the alternative pathway will function. Further, the activation of the alternative pathway is prevented by dilution of human serum beyond about ten-fold, and is generally considerably impaired after 2–3 days storage of human serum at 4°C: the classical pathway, via C1q, operates at lower concentrations of serum and is stabler on storage. The stability of

activation occurring via MBL has not been extensively examined.

The proteins of the classical pathway and their mechanisms of action

C1

C1 is a multimeric protein consisting of two molecules each of the serine protease proenzymes C1r and C1s bound to a single molecule of C1q. The associations of C1q, C1r and C1s are the Ca^{2+} ion-dependent stages of the pathway. C1q itself consists of 18 polypeptide chains, of three different types, A, B and C, which are encoded by separate, closely linked genes on the short arm of human chromosome 1. The A, B and C chains are each about 225 amino acids long, and are homologous to each other. Each consists of a short N-terminal region containing a cysteine residue, followed by a stretch of 81 amino acids of collagenous sequence (i.e. repeating triplets of sequence Gly-X-Y, where Y is often a hydroxylated proline or lysine residue). The rest of the sequence is noncollagenous. The collagenous regions of one A, one B and one C chain align to form a short stretch of collagen triple helix structure, and the rest of the three chains fold to form a globular head, which consists of three lobes, one derived from each of the A, B and C chains (**Figure 2**). The collagenous stalk is bent in the middle, because of irregularities in the collagenous sequences. Fully assembled C1q (**Figure 2**) has a single cylindrical core, made up of the N-terminal ends of the six collagen triple helices: at the bend in the middle of the helices, they splay apart, forming six stalks, which join the six globular heads to the core. The overall appearance of C1q is likened to a bunch of six tulips. The globular head regions of C1q are responsible for recognition and binding to most classical pathway activators,

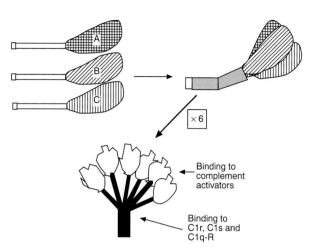

Figure 2 The assembly of C1q from three types of polypeptide chains. The assembly is discussed in the text. MBL has similar structure and assembly, but only one type of polypeptide chain.

while the collagenous regions interact with the next complement proteins in the pathway, C1r and C1s.

C1r and C1s are serine protease proenzymes, encoded by closely linked genes on human chromosome 12p13. Each monomer consists of a single polypeptide chain of about 700 amino acids: the C-terminal approximately 250 amino acids in each is a serine protease domain, homologous to trypsin or chymotrypsin. Like most complement proteins, they are mosaic proteins, i.e. segments of the primary sequence can be recognized as being homologous to segments of many other proteins, and are likely to represent independently folding domains or modules. The approximately 450 N-terminal amino acids of C1r and C1s are homologous to each other, and are made up of five domains (see **Figure 3**). Each con-

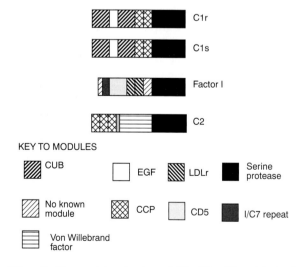

KEY TO MODULES

CUB

No known module

Von Willebrand factor

EGF

CCP

LDLr

CD5

Serine protease

I/C7 repeat

Figure 3 The modular structure of C1r, C1s, C2 and factor I. MASP-1 and MASP-2 have the same modules as C1r and C1s. (This diagram is adapted from the work of Dr A. J. Day.)

tains an EGF (epidermal growth factor) module, which is the Ca^{2+}-binding site. Each also contains two internal repeats of about 100 amino acids, known as CUB (C1r/C1s, Uefg, Bmp1) modules, and two CCP (complement control protein) modules, each about 60 amino acids long. CCP molecules are found in many complement proteins, and are a particular feature of the proteins which interact with C3 and C4 turnover, such as factor H, C4bp, CR1, MCP and DAF. The CUB domains are likely to be involved in binding to C1q.

The overall structure of each C1r or C1s monomer is a dumb-bell shape, with two globular regions of unequal size connected by a short strand. Isolated C1r exists as an elongated dimer, with the dumbbells joined end-to-end. Two molecules of C1s bind, one to each end of the C1r dimer, in the presence of Ca^{2+} ions. This forms the very elongated $C1r_2C1s_2$ tetramer, which binds to the collagenous regions of C1q. The structure of the large C1 complex is not clearly established, but several models which indicate how $C1r_2C1s_2$ might interact with C1q have been proposed (see Colomb *et al*, 1989 for review).

Activation of C1 occurs when two or more globular heads of C1q bind to a complement activator: movement of the heads is transmitted by the collagenous stalks to the core region and thence to C1r. A conformational change is induced in C1r, which causes the C1r molecules to cleave and activate each other: these then cleave and activate the C1s molecules. During this process, each C1r and C1s monomer is cleaved at the N-terminal end of the serine protease domain, forming a structure with two disulfide-linked polypeptide chains of approximately 56 and 28 kDa. The activated forms have very restricted proteolytic activity: activated C1r will cleave only proenzymic C1s, and activated C1s will cleave only C2 and C4. Both proteases have arginyl specificity. Both also have a low level of esterase activity towards esters of basic (C1r) or basic and hydrophobic (C1s) amino acids. In older literature, activated C1s is often described as C1 esterase, and the nomenclature C1r, C1s, and occasionally $\overline{C1r}$, $\overline{C1s}$ denoting the activated forms, is also frequently encountered.

C4

Once C1s has been activated, it will cleave and activate C4. C4 is a 205 kDa protein, synthesized as a single polypeptide chain, but processed on secretion into a form with three disulfide-linked polypeptides, named α, β and γ (97, 75 and 33 kDa). C4 is homologous to C3 and C5, and also to the family of protease inhibitors related to $α_2$-macroglobulin. This group of proteins do not have an obvious mosaic structure, and little can be predicted of their tertiary structure. Low-resolution analysis, by S.J. Perkins and colleagues, of the structure of C4 or C3 in solution, show that they are flat, ellipsoid molecules, about 18 nm long and 10 nm wide. C4, like C3, contains an internal thiolester in the α chain, formed between the Cys and Gln residues of a sequence Gly-Cys-Gly-Glu-Gln.

Activated C1s cleaves a 9 kDa fragment, C4a, from the N-terminus of the α chain of C4. C4a has weak anaphylatoxin activity. The rest of the molecule, C4b, contains the thiolester, which becomes exposed on proteolytic cleavage. The thiolester is very reactive, and will be attacked by any nucleophilic (electron-donating) species in the vicinity. Since C4 is normally activated by C1s which is within C1 bound to a complement activator, the reactive C4b (often called nascent C4b) is generated close to the surface of the activator, and can react with surface OH, NH_2 or SH groups. These form ester or amide linkages to the carbonyl group of the thiolester, and the carbon–sulfur bond in the thiolester is broken, forming a free SH group on the C4b (**Figure 4**). In this way, C4b becomes covalently bound to the surface of the complement activator. Much of the nascent C4b generated, however, simply reacts with the most abundant nucleophile present, water, and does not become surface-bound. This species, in which the thiolester is hydrolysed, plays no further part in complement activation.

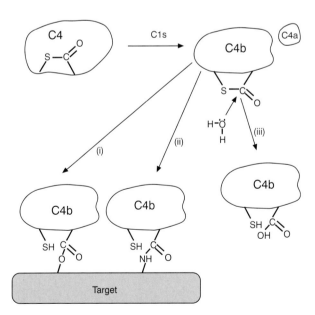

Figure 4 The activation of C4, and covalent binding of C4b. C4 contains an internal thiolester which becomes exposed on cleaveage of C4 by activated C1s. The exposed thiolester may react with OH or NH_2 groups on the surface of the complement activator ((i) and (ii)) or may simply react with water (iii). The activation and binding of C3 occurs in the same way.

The major histocompatibility complex (MHC) class III region of chromosome 6 contains two functional genes for C4: these encode the C4A and C4B isotypes of C4. The sequences of C4A and C4B differ by less than 1%, and both function as C4 in the complement system. They have differences, however, in their covalent binding reaction: activated C4B binds with similar efficiency to hydroxyl and amino groups, while C4A reacts much more readily with amino groups. In a standard assay of complement activity, in which erythrocytes are lysed by complement, C4B is more active than C4A, probably because C4B binds more readily to the carbohydrate-rich red cell surface than does C4A. In contrast, C4A binds better than does C4B to immunoglobulin G (IgG) immune complexes containing nonglycosylated protein antigen.

The selectivity of covalent binding of C4A and C4B appears to be controlled mainly by an Asp (C4A) to His (C4B) amino acid interchange at position 1106 in the sequence. These residues, although not adjacent to the thiolester in the primary sequence, are close in the tertiary structure, and affect polarization of nucleophilic groups approaching the thiolester.

The C4A (acidic) and C4B (basic) nomenclature is based on electrophoretic mobility and corresponds to the older terms 'fast' and 'slow' (C4F, C4S). Each isotype of C4 has many allotypes, distinguishable by agarose electrophoresis, which are designated C4A1, C4A2, C4B1, C4B2, etc. Null alleles (termed C4AQO or C4BQO) at either C4 locus are relatively common. The A and B nomenclature must be carefully distinguished from the a and b nomenclature used to designate proteolytic fragments: terms such as C4Aa, C4Ab, used to denote the proteolytic fragments of the A isotype, are also encountered. C4 fragments bound to erythrocytes carry the Chido/Rodgers blood group. In general C4A allotypes carry the Rodgers blood group, while C4B carries Chido determinants.

C2

C2 is a serine protease proenzyme, which is highly homologous to factor B of the alternative pathway. Both proteins are encoded by genes in the MHC class III region of human chromosome 6, closely linked to the C4A and C4B genes. C2 and factor B are, like C1r and C1s, mosaic proteins (see **Figure 3**). The N-terminal portion of C2 is made up of three CCP modules, followed by a segment of about 200 amino acids which is homologous to structures in von Willebrand Factor (and also in complement receptor type 3, CR3), and is referred to as a vWF-A domain. This is followed by a serine protease domain. C2 is cleaved by activated C1s at an arginyl bond situated between the third CCP module and the vWF domain. This creates two nondisulfide-linked fragments, C2b (34 kDa, from the N-terminus) and C2a (74 kDa, C-terminal). There is some confusion in C2 fragment nomenclature, and the term C2a was sometimes used for the smaller fragment. Although C2 can be cleaved by isolated, activated C1s in solution, the C2 fragments produced have no proteolytic activity. To be active, C2 must form a complex with C4b before it is activated. During normal complement activation, C1s, within C1, bound to an activator, will cleave several molecules of C4, some of which will bind covalently to the activator. These can then bind C2, but in only a very few of the C4b–C2 complexes will the C2 be in an appropriate position to be activated by the surface-bound C1s. This may occur, for example, when C1 is fixed to the IgG Fc in an immune complex, and the C4b is fixed to the Fab arms. C2 associates first with C4b via the CCP-domain region at the N-terminus: this is Mg^{2+}-dependent. Cleavage of C2 by C1s then occurs, and the C2a portion remains bound to C4b by a secondary non-Mg^{2+}-dependent interaction, probably through the vWF-A domain. The complex C4b–C2a (generally written C4b2a) is proteolytically active, and is the C3 convertase enzyme of the classical pathway. The proteolytic active site is the serine protease domain of C2a. Proteolytic specificity is restricted to cleavage of single arginyl bonds in C3 and C5, Activated C2, whether free in solution or bound to C4b, has a very low level of esterolytic and amidolytic activity.

C3

C3, as noted above, is homologous to C4: it is a major component of the alternative, as well as the classical pathway. C3 is synthesized as a single polypeptide chain, and processed on secretion into two disulfide-linked chains, α (110 kDa) and β (75 kDa). C3 is cleaved and activated by C4b2a (or by the alternative pathway C3 convertase, C3bBb). Cleavage releases the anaphylatoxic fragment C3a (77 amino acids) from the N-terminus of the α chain. The rest of the molecule, C3b, has like C4b (**Figure 4**), an exposed reactive thiolester, and will react with surface hydroxyl or amine groups on the complement activator, or with water. Covalent binding to an activator is called the 'acceptor binding reaction' of C3b to distinguish it from noncovalent binding to specific receptors. Again only about 10% of the 'nascent' C3b generated binds to the activator: the rest reacts with water and diffuses away. The half-life of the reactive thiolester is <100 μs, and so nascent C3b can diffuse only a short distance before

it reacts with a nucleophile. The suface-bound C3b is therefore clustered around the site of proteolytic activation: such clusters are likely to be important in promoting adhesion to C3 receptors. Among the C3b molecules which become activated, one may become bound to the C4b portion of the activating enzyme. This forms a C4b2a3b complex. The covalently associated C4b and C3b molecules form a binding site for C5, which orients C5 for cleavage by the protease domain of C2a, thus initiating the lytic phase of the complement system. C4b2a3b is referred to as the C5 convertase of the classical pathway.

The lectin pathway

Recent work has shown that a protein similar in structure to C1q, mannan- or mannose-binding lectin (MBL), can substitute for C1q in the activation of complement. MBL was formerly called mannose- or mannan-binding protein (MBP) or Ra-reactive factor (RaRF). MBL is made up of 18 identical polypeptide chains, which like those of C1q, contain an N-terminal collagenous segment, and a C-terminal noncollagenous region. The chains associate in groups of three to form collagen triple helices, and six of these groups associate to form the whole molecule (as shown for C1q in **Figure 2**). MBL, like C1q, has a collagenous core and stalks, and three-lobed globular heads. The major difference from C1q is that the MBL globular heads are lectins, and bind to carbohydrate in the presence of calcium ions. MBL binds mainly to mannose-rich structures, such as yeast mannan. MBL is thought to occur in forms with three, four, or five globular heads instead of six, but this may be an artefact of purification. *In vitro*, MBL bound to a target such as mannan binds and activates $C1r_2C1s_2$, and so activates the complement classical pathway. Other evidence strongly suggests however that *in vivo* MBL is associated with other proteases. One of these, MASP (MBL-associated serine protease) or MASP-1 is known to form a complex with MBL, and is highly homologous to C1r and C1s. Another highly homologous protease MASP-2 has been characterized by cDNA sequencing, and appears also to be involved in complex formation with MBL. The activities of MASP-1, and particularly MASP-2 are not yet known in detail. However MASPs can cleave and activate C2 and C4, and are thought also to cleave C3 at a low rate. MBL therefore probably mediates activation of the classical pathway via the MASPs. In density-gradient centrifugation of plasma, MBL sediments as a 19S complex, of the same size as the C1 ($C1qr_2s_2$) complex. C1q or MBL which are not associated with proteases migrate as 11S proteins. This indicates that MBL forms a complex like C1 in plasma. This is probably an MBL–MASP complex, although formation of MBL–C1r$_2$s$_2$ complexes might also be possible. This MBL complex has previously been characterized under another name, Ra-reactive factor (RaRF) which has been identified in sera from several vertebrates, particularly rodents. RaRF was detected by its binding to the Ra polysaccharide found on enterobacteria, e.g. *Salmonella*, and was shown to consist of MBL and a serine protease (presumably corresponding to MASP-1, or possibly MASP-1 and -2) which activates C2 and C4.

Activators of the classical pathway

The classical pathway is activated, via C1q or MBL, by a wide range of materials. Both C1q and MBL mediate antibody-dependent and nonantibody-dependent activation. These are summarized in **Table 1.** For C1q, activators include immune complexes containing IgG or IgM, or *in vitro*, aggregated IgG. Human subclasses IgG3 and IgG1 are more efficient activators than IgG2 and IgG4. Interaction with IgG is via the C$_\gamma$2 domain, and protein engineering studies by Winter and Duncan indicate that charged residues Glu318, Lys320 and Lys322 in IgG are of major importance in C1q binding. In IgM, the C$_\mu$3 domain is implicated in C1q binding. MBL binds to glycosylation variants of IgG (IgG lacking terminal galactose residues on the Fc oligosaccharides), and activates complement. MBL also interacts with high-mannose oligosaccharides on IgM, although it is not known whether this interaction does lead to complement activation.

A wide range of gram-negative bacteria have been reported to bind C1q directly, and activate C1, without need for antibody. Mycoplasma species may also activate C1, as do some viruses, including Epstein–Barr virus and Rauscher leukemia virus, and some parasites, such as *Entamoeba*. Many bacteria, viruses and single-cell or multicellular parasites activate complement without need for antibody: alternative pathway activation is the commoner mechanism, but in many cases the contribution of the classical pathway has not been fully studied. Yeasts activate the classical pathway via MBL, as well as activating the alternative pathway. MBL also binds to saccharides on a wide range of bacteria, viruses and fungi, but complement activation via MBL has not generally been examined in these sytems.

Tissue-damage products, such as mitochondrial and other subcellular membranes, cytoplasmic filaments, polynucleotides and components of myelin have also been reported to activate C1. The acute phase protein CRP (C-reactive protein), when bound to phosphorylcholine-containing phospholipids, binds and activates C1. Since C1q recognizes a very wide range of targets, mostly via its globular heads,

---

Table 1 Classical pathway activators

The classical pathway is mainly involved in recognizing charge groupings. This is the case for C1q and CRP, but not for MBL which recognizes neutral sugars. Charges may be on proteins, like IgG, or on complex charged carbohydrates found on surfaces of microorganisms, or on nucleic acid–protein complexes, or on lipids and glycolipids. Sialic acid on cell surfaces tends to promote activation of the classical pathway, but to inhibit activation of the alternative pathway.
Classical pathway activation occurs via:

C1q:	C1q binds to: Fc portions of antigen-fixed IgG and IgM Nucleic acid and chromatin Cytoplasmic intermediate filaments (vimentin-type) Mitochondrial membranes possibly via cardiolipin or via mitochondrial proteins Some viruses, e.g. MuLV Gram-positive bacteria, e.g. some pneumococci, streptococci, via capsular polysaccharide (neuraminidase treatment reduces activating capacity) Gram-negative bacteria via the lipid A component of the lipopolysaccharide of the cell wall
CRP + C1q:	CRP (C-reactive protein) recognizes phosphate groups in choline phosphate of pneumococcal C-type polysaccharide, and also binds to phosphocholine (PC)-containing and non-PC-containing microbial polysaccharides and lipids, polyanion/polycation complexes, and chromatin. It is also reported to bind to galactans. Bound CRP interacts with C1q, and activates the classical pathway
Mannose-binding lectin (MBL):	MBL binds to high mannose and other polysaccharides and oligosaccharides on yeasts, bacteria and viruses, and activates the classical pathway. It also binds to carbohydrate on glycosylation variants of IgG (IgG-Go). MBL probably acts, *in vivo*, via the proteases known as MASPs, but *in vitro* it can act via C1r and C1s. RaRF, formerly reported as being a specific factor mediating classical pathway activation by *Salmonella* Ra polysaccharide, is the same as MBL.

it is likely that the three homologous 'lobes' of each head have different binding specificities, but this has not yet been proved.

The quantitative significance of complement activation via MBL is not yet clear. MBL and the MASPs are at very low concentration in plasma relative to C1q, C1r and C1s (see **Table 2**).

Control mechanisms

The activation of the classical pathway has multiple control mechanisms. The proteolytic activity of activated C1 is controlled by C1-inh, which irreversibly activates C1r and C1s. It is also a physiological inhibitor of kallikrein and activated factors XII and XI. C1-inh is a 100–110 kDa single polypeptide chain protein, containing about 50% carbohydrate. It is homologous to other serpins, such as antithrombin III. It acts as a pseudosubstrate for the proteases which it inhibits: these cleave an Arg–Thr bond 34 residues from the C-terminus of C1-inh, but C1-inh remains covalently bound to the protease, probably by an ester bond formed by the arginine carbonyl and the active-site serine of the protease. C1-inh attacks activated C1 by first reacting with C1s, then with C1r: the $C1r_2C1s_2$ complex dissociates to form two C1inh–C1r–C1s–C1inh complexes, which no longer bind to C1q. C1q, still bound to the complement activator, can now bind to C1q receptor, or can participate in a further slow cycle of binding, activation and inactivation of $C1r_2C1s_2$. MASP-1 is also inhibited by C1-inh, but this has not been investigated for MASP-2.

The C3 and C5 convertase enzymes are also subject to control: one aspect of control is the inefficiency of binding of nascent C4b and C3b to appropriate sites to form the convertases. Once formed, the convertases are unstable: C2a dissociates from C4b or C4b3b with a half-life of 2–5 min. Once C2a has dissociated, more C2 can bind to C4b, but the adjacent C1 molecule required to cleave the C2 may already have been inactivated. The stability of the convertases is further decreased by a group of control proteins which includes the plasma proteins factor H and C4bp, and the membrane proteins CR1, MCP and DAF. These proteins, together with CR2, are composed mainly, or only of CCP domains, and are all encoded by genes in the RCA (regulation of complement activation) cluster on human chromosome 1q31–32.

CR1, DAF and C4bp bind to C4b2a or C4b2a3b and cause C2 to dissociate: they also compete with C2 for the initial binding to C4b. CR1 and C4bp, and also MCP, once bound to C4b, render C4b susceptible to attack by the control serine protease, factor I, which cleaves at two sites in the α chain of C4b, forming C4c (145 kDa) and C4d (45 kDa), which no longer participate in convertase formation. CR1 and MCP also act as cofactors for the factor I-mediated cleavage of C3b to form iC3b, as does factor H. In the alternative pathway, CR1, DAF and factor H accelerate the decay of the C3 convertase,

Table 2 Properties of classical pathway proteins

Protein	Mol. wt (kDa)	Chromosomal localization of gene	Plasma concentration ($\mu g \ ml^{-1}$)
Components			
C1q	462	1	80
C1r	83	12	50
C1s	83	12	50
C4	205	6	600
C2	102	6	20
C3	185	19	1300
MBL	500	10	<1
MASPs	80–90	?	<1
Regulatory proteins			
C1-inh	110	11	200
C4bp	540	1	250
Factor I	88	4	35
Membrane proteins			
			Distribution on blood cells
CR1	160–250	1	Erythrocytes, polymorphs, monocytes, B lymphocytes
MCP	45–70	1	B and T lymphcoytes, monocytes, polymorphs
DAF	70	1	Erythrocytes, leukocytes and many other tissues
C1q-R	60	?	B and T lymphocytes, monocytes, polymorphs

C3bBb, by displacing Bb, and by competing with factor B for binding to C3b.

Receptors and classical pathway components

C3b and its breakdown products, iC3b, C3dg and C3d, bind to several receptors, including CR1, CR2 and CR3: these are discussed in more detail elsewhere. C4b binds to CR1, and immune adherence to erythrocytes can be mediated by a CR1–C4b interaction, rather than by CR1–C3b. During normal complement activation, much more C3b is fixed than C4b, and it is unlikely that C4b has an important role in receptor-mediated adhesion or ingestion mechanisms. C1q also binds, via its collagenous region, to a receptor, a widely distributed 60 kDa species (C1q-R). C1q-R also binds other ligands (collectins) which are structurally similar to C1q: these include MBL, lung surfactant protein A and conglutinin. All of these ligands are reported to function as opsonins, and a major role of C1q-R may be a phagocytic uptake.

Pathological alterations of the classical pathway

The functioning of the classical pathway is disrupted in many circumstances. These include genetic deficiencies of single components: complete deficiencies of C1q, C1r, C1s, C4, C2, C3, factors H and I have been reported. These are associated with susceptibility to infection and/or inappropriate deposition of immune complexes. Low concentrations of MBL are associated with poor opsonization of yeast and some bacteria, and with recurrent infection in infants. Diminished synthesis of C1-inh, or synthesis of inactive C1-inh mutants is the cause of hereditary angioedema, and causes secondary consumption of C2 and C4. Autoantibodies to C1-inh have been reported, which destabilize the C1-inh-protease complex releasing free active protease: these give rise to autoimmune angioedema. Autoantibodies to C3 convertases, termed nephritic factors, occur in membranoproliferative glomerulonephritis. These generally recognize C3bBb, but a few reports indicate reactivity against C4b2a. They stabilize convertases, leading to excessive consumption of C3. Autoantibodies against bound C1q occur in systemic lupus erythematosus (SLE), but it is not clear to what extent they affect the function of C1q.

Further effects on the classical pathway arise from the presence of reactive thiolesters in C3 and C4: the thiolesters can be cleaved by low molecular weight nucelophiles without the need for proteolytic activation of C3 or C4: this occurs at a low rate with water, causing hydrolysis of the thiolester and generating species named $C4(H_2O)$, C4u or C4b-like C4 (and similarly for C3). Ammonia production in ischemic tissue, or during kidney malfunction, may cause extensive formation of these species. C3b-like C3 can bind factor B, and cause alternative pathway activation; formation of C4b-like C4 does not cause further complement activation.

Activated (nascent) C4b and C3b, as well as reacting with water or binding to complement activator surfaces, will react with any strong nucleophile present; any such species will inhibit the binding of C3b and C4b to its real target, the complement activator. A number of drugs which are nucleophilic or have nucleophilic metabolites induce SLE as a toxic side-effect, and these may act by inhibiting C4b and C3b binding, diminishing the opsonization of immune complexes.

See also: **Acute phase proteins; Anaphylatoxins; Bacteria, immunity to; Immunoconglutinins; Complement, alternative pathway; Clotting system; Complement deficiencies; Complement, genetics; Complement, membrane attack pathway; Complement receptors; Decay-accelerating factor (CD55); HLA class III region; Immune complexes; Immunoglobulin, functions; Neisseria, infection and immunity; Phagocytosis; Systemic lupus erythematosus (SLE), human.**

Further reading

Campbell RD, Law SKA, Reid KBM and Sim RB (1988) Structure, organisation and regulation of the complement genes. *Annual Review of Immunology* 6: 161–195.

Colomb MG, Loos M and Reid KBM (eds) (1989) *C1, the First Component of Complement.* Behring Institute Mitteilungen vol 84. Marburg: Medizinische Verlagsgesellschaft.

Law SKA and Reid KBM (1995) *Complement,* 2nd edn. Oxford: IRL Press.

Malhotra R, Thiel S, Reid KBM and Sim RB (1990) Human leukocyte C1q receptor binds other soluble proteins with collagen domains. *Journal of Experimental Medicine* 172: 955–959.

Malhotra R, Wormald MR, Rudd PM, Fischer PB, Dwek RA and Sim RB (1995) Agalactosyl IgG activates complement via mannose-binding protein. *Nature medicine* 1: 237–243.

Matsushita M and Fujita T (1992) Activation of the classical complement pathway by mannose-binding protein in association with a novel C1s-like serine protease. *Journal of Experimental Medicine* 176: 1497–1502.

Perkins SJ, Nealis A and Sim RB (1990) Molecular modelling of human complement component C4 and its fragments by X-ray and neutron scattering. *Biochemistry* 29: 1167—1175.

Reid KBM and Day AJ (1989) Structure–function relationships of the complement components. *Immunology Today* 10: 177–180.

Sim E (1989) Drug-induced immune complex disease. *Complement and Inflammation* 6: 119–126.

Sim RB (ed) (1993) *Activators and Inhibitors of Complement.* Dordrecht: Kluwer Academic.

Sim RB and Malhotra R (1994) Interactions of carbohydrates and lectins with complement. *Biochemistry Society Transactions* 22: 106–111.

Super M, Thiel S, Lu J, Levinsky RJ and Turner MW (1989) Association of low levels of mannan-binding protein with a common defect of opsonisation. *Lancet* ii: 1236–1239.

Takada F, Takayama Y, Hatsuse H and Kawakami M (1993) A new member of the C1s family of complement proteins found in a bactericidal factor, Ra-reactive factor, in human serum. *Biochemical and Biophysical Research Communications* 128: 1009–1013.

Thiel S, Vorup-Jensen T, Stover CM *et al* (1997) A second serine protease associated with mannan-binding lectin that activates complement. *Nature* 386: 506–510.

Whaley K (ed) (1987) *Complement in Health and Disease.* Lancaster: MTP Press.

Whaley K, Sim RB and He S (1996) Autoimmune C1-inhibitor deficiency. *Clinical and Experimental Immunology* 106: 423–426.

COMPLEMENT DEFICIENCIES

Klaus O Rother and **Ursula A Rother**, Institute of Immunology, University of Heidelberg, Germany

Inherited deficiencies of all known complement (C) components, of most regulator proteins and of the respective receptors have been found in humans. **Table 1** is a compilation of the defects. Although acquired deficiencies – be they by consumption or otherwise – may also cause clinical conditions comparable to those listed in **Table 1**, they will not be specifically addressed in this entry.

Inherited deficiencies are rare. Since complement is not routinely measured in healthy persons, the incidence is difficult to determine and so is the disease incidence in a given component deficiency. In a Japanese study of healthy blood donors, C5, C6, C7 and C8 have each been found missing in about 3 per 100 000. C9 was absent in 3 per 1000. The prevalence of deficiencies of the late-acting components together was calculated at approximately 12 per 100 000. Some combined deficiencies – total or subtotal – of two or more components were reported when the terminal complex was afflicted. Deficiency in C7 in some cases was combined with the additional absence of C4 (C4a and/or C4b).

Considering the many biological activities associated with complement activation (**Figure 1**), it initially came as a surprise that clinical symptoms were absent in many cases of missing components. However, experimentation with defective animals clarified the situation by showing that redundant pathways are operative to assure complement-dependent life-preserving functions. Thus, a missing link in one pathway may cause defect symptoms only if other pathways are also affected, or if control of a given condition requires mobilization of all reserves.

By and large, the syndromes expected in complement-deficient states may be subdivided into three groups.

1. Recurrent and/or persistent infections

Bacteria may cause life-threatening conditions in the absence of C3 or factor I or any part of the alternative pathway. Since absence of factor I results in total consumption of C3, the outcome in functional terms is identical with a primary lack of C3. Opsonization and phagocytosis are drastically diminished in these conditions. A contributory factor in combined deficiencies may be a defective immune response, as shown in C4-, C2- and C3-deficient states.

Deficiencies of the later reacting components C5, C6, C7 or C8 are often associated with infections, almost exclusively with meningococci or gonococci, suggesting that the normal defense against these strains rests mainly with the bactericidal (membrane attack) function of complement. In this light, the apparent health of the C9-deficient individuals may be explained with the intact membrane attack function of C5b678 in the absence of C9, although proceeding somewhat more slowly.

2. Connective tissue or immune complex diseases

Most striking is the association of unclear nature of systemic lupus or other autoimmune conditions with C1qrs, C4 or C2 defects alone or in combination with other factor defects. It is surmised that the pathophysiology in these disease states is a defect in

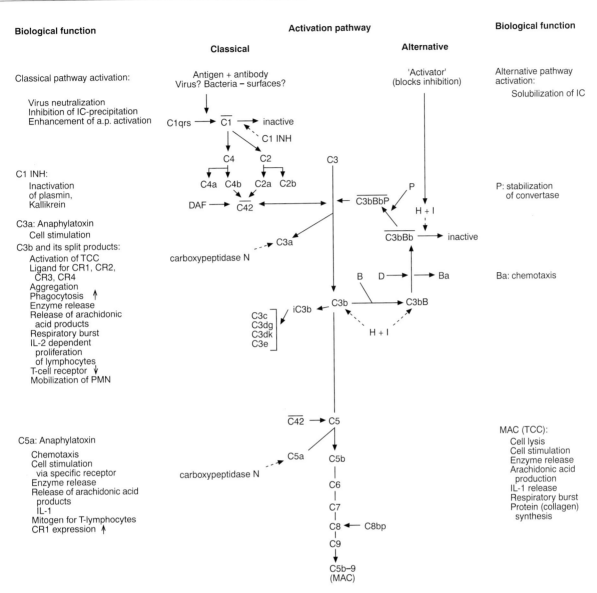

Figure 1 Reaction pathways of complement and biological activities. ----▶, Inhibition; a.p., alternative pathway; C1 INH, C1 inhibitor; IC, immune complexes; B, factor B; D, factor D; H, factor H; I, factor I: DAF, decay-accelerating factor; MAC, membrane attack complex; P, properdin; TCC, terminal complement complex (see article entitled Complement, Classical Pathway for further clarification).

complement-dependent clearance or solubilization of immune complexes due to a failure to enhance the feedback loop in alternative pathway activation.

One of the most common abnormalities involves the C1 inactivator which regulates the classical pathway as well as the kinin and clotting systems. It is this threefold intervention that has so far prevented a clear-cut opinion on whether the symptoms of hereditary angioedema (HANE) are causally related to the complement or to the other two systems. The defect is, so far, the only one in which the infusion of the missing factor ameliorates the clinical condition.

Little is known of receptor deficiencies, except for a decreased expression of receptor molecules such as

CR1 – whether inherited or acquired – in certain immune complex diseases. It seems reasonable to predict a pathogenic role for the lack of the receptors, as CR1 not only serves as a cofactor for factor I (**Figure 1**) but is also the main receptor molecule on the surface of erythrocytes used to transport immune complexes. A deficiency of CR3 has been described in a boy with severe infections.

Another cell surface constituent involved in complement regulation is the C8 binding protein (C8bp). It controls lysis of homologous cells. Along with other similar factors, C8bp (**Table 1**) is missing in paroxysmal nocturnal hemoglobinuria (PNH) cells, which are therefore abnormally sensitive to lysis by

Table 1 Inherited complement deficiencies in humans

Component	Inheritance	Remarks	Observed clinical condition	Laboratory findings
C1q	Autos. codom.	Three types: 1) partial, 2) complete, 3) inactive protein: combined with immunoglobulin deficiency	Infections, SLE	CH50 = 0; Bactericidal activity = 0; C1r↓ C1s↑
C1r, C1s	Autos. codom. not MHC linked	Mostly combined C1r + C1s	Infections (meningitis); Collagen diseases	CH50 = 0; C1 NH↑
C4	Autos. codom. (4 genes) MHC linked	Degree dependent on number of 'null' alleles	Collagen diseases; some combined with IgA disorders	CH50 = 0; Bactericidal activity = 0; Chemotaxis↓ Opsonization↓: no IgM → IgG switch; MLC↓
C2	Autos. codom. MHC (A25, B18, DR2) linked	30–70% activity in heterozygotes	Often none; Infections when combined with low factor B; SLE; juvenile rheumatoid arthritis	CH50 = 0 Bactericidal activity = 0 Phagocytosis↓
C3	Autos. codom. not MHC linked		Severe infections; collagen diseases; nephritis	C3 < 0.1% CH50 = 0; bactericidal activity = 0; immune adherence = 0; opsonization↓ Mobilization of PMN↓ Factor B cleavage = 0 Chemotaxis↓
C5	Autos. codom. not MHC linked (regulatory gene?)	13–65% activity in heterozygotes	Collagen diseases; Infections with meningococci, gonococci	CH50 = 0; bactericidal activity = 0; chemotaxis = 0 Platelet aggregation = 0 Opsonization normal (staphylococci)
C6	Autos. codom. not MHC linked; linked to C7 and C9 on chromosome 5		Gonococcal and meningococcal infections; streptococcal meningitis; chronic meningococcemia	CH50 = 0 Bactericidal activity = 0 Chemotaxis normal Opsonization and intracellular killing = normal Subtotal deficiency: truncated proteins hemolytically functional
C7	Autos. codom. not MHC linked		Some healthy: 50% Neisseria infections: 12% connective tissue disorders	CH50 = 0; Reactive lysis positive; sera activatable up to C5,6
C8	Autos. codom. not MHC linked; C8αγ and C8β controlled by two independent loci	C8αγ or C8β missing; can be reconstituted with missing part; dysfunctional C8β chain?	Meningococcal infections (often uncommon serogroups)	CH50 = 0
C9	Autos. codom. not MHC linked		None	Normal lysis and bactericidal activity at reduced rate (erythrocytes and Escherichia coli)

C1 NH	Autos. codom. structural gene	Three types: I) synthesis deficiency II) inactive protein III) C1 NH complexed to albumin (acquired deficiency sometimes by autoantibodies)	Angioedema following trauma or stress. Therapy: danazol, C1 NH infusion	C1 NH function↓ C1 NH protein↓/normal C4↓C2↓ C1↓ in acquired form
Factor I	?		Pyogenic infections, meningitis. Therapy: plasma infusion	CH50↓ C3↓ C3b↑ Factor B↓ properdin↓ Factor H↓ Bactericidal activity↓ Chemotaxis↓; phagocytosis↓
Factor H	Autos. recessive? codom.?	Low levels present	Hemolytic uremic syndrome; dense deposit disease; lupus nephritis	CH50↓ C3↓ factor B↓ C3d present on erythrocytes C5–C9 normal
Properdin	X-linked	1) Complete, or 2) partial	Meningococcal meningitis; septicemia None (?)	CH50 = normal Properdin = protein↓/0 apH50↓ Opsonization↓
Anaphylatoxin inactivator (carboxypeptidase N)	Autos. recessive	Low titers present	Chronic idiopathic urticaria/angioedema	CH50 normal during attacks: Histamine↑; C3a↑ C4↓; C3↓; Factor B cleavage
CR3 (CD18 deficiency)	Autos. codom.	Three proteins missing; relative contribution unclear	Recurrent infections, LAD	Proteins missing on leukocytes; zymosan response of monocytes↓
CR1	? Acquired?		Immune complex disease	Diminished CR1 on erythrocytes. Defective immune clearance
C8bp ('HRF')	Acquired	Reduced in PNH	Intravascular lysis	Acid lysis
C59 (p18, 'MIRL' or 'HRF20')	Acquired	Reduced in PNH	Intravascular lysis	Acid lysis
DAF	Acquired	Reduced in PNH	Intravascular lysis	Acid lysis

apH50, Hemolytic test for alternative pathway activity; Autos. codom., autosomal codominant; CH50, hemolytic test for classical pathway activity; DAF, decay-accelerating factor; HRF, homologous restriction factor; Ig, immunoglobulin; LAD, leukocyte adhesion deficiency syndrome; MHC, major histocompatibility complex; MIRL, membrane inhibitor of reactive lysis; MLC, mixed lymphocyte culture; PNH, paroxysmal nocturnal hemoglobinuria.

homologous complement. Intravascular lysis is the clinical syndrome.

One of the enzymes regulating split-product activity of the effector phase is the anaphylatoxin (C5a) inactivator (carboxypeptidase N). It cleaves the terminal arginine off the C5a peptide, resulting in the $C5a_{desarg}$ form. *In vitro* $C5a_{desarg}$ has lost its spasmogenic and basophil-stimulating activities, as well as a large part of its chemotactic activities. *In vivo*, however, the chemotactic activity is not diminished by the loss of the arginine. The clinical role of the regulator defect is doubtful. One family with anaphylatoxin inactivator deficiency and HANE symptoms has been described.

With a few exceptions (see above) the therapy in complement-deficient conditions is symptomatic. A more direct approach such as gene therapy is untried.

3. Immune response

Antibody production following administration of limited amounts of antigen to mice was drastically reduced in the cobra venom factor-induced absence of C3 and this was true for both T cell dependent and T cell independent antigens. Both primary and secondary immune responses were affected by the treatment. Similarly, guinea pigs genetically deficient in C3 were poor responders in the primary phase and later failed in the switch to IgG. Analogous observations were made in C2-deficient guinea pigs or C4-defective mice. In mice with an inherited absence of C4, a fully functional immune response could be elicited following administration of C4. A boy deficient in C4 was analyzed for antibody production with similar results. Since C5-deficient mice were normal immune responders the impaired functions must be dependent on C3. This was further supported by studies on the role of the CR1 or CR2 receptors for C3 split products. Experimental blockade *in vivo* by monoclonal antibodies resulted in markedly reduced primary and secondary antibody responses to low concentrations of antigen. Memory formation was also diminished but T helper cells were not affected. As far as tested in these studies, larger amounts of antigen elicited undiminished responses. It is thus postulated that as yet unidentified enhancing functions are associated with C3 split products in the antigen-presenting pathways and that large-dose immunization does not need the enhancement.

Animal experimentation was the key tool in analyzing the biological functions of complement (**Figure 1**). While decomplementation (inactivation) of components by various means was helpful, the advent of strains with hereditary deficiencies provided more clearly defined conditions. Presently available are strains with a deficiency in C2 (guinea pigs), C4 (guinea pigs, including a coisogenic +/− colony), C3 (guinea pigs, dogs), C3a receptor (guinea pigs), C5 (mice, including a coisogenic +/− colony) or C6 (rats, pigs, rabbits). Genetic engineering to delete production of defined components is in progress. So far gene knockout mice with no C3 or factor B have been constructed. Further advances are expected from the production of recombinant species-compatible fluid phase inhibitors such as, for example, the CR1 receptor for C3. The trans-species genetic transfection of cell surface control factors may help in circumventing the otherwise effective complement attack against xenografts.

See also: **Anaphylatoxins; Complement, alternative pathway; Clotting system; Complement, classical pathway; Complement fixation test; Complement, genetics; Complement, membrane attack pathway; Complement receptors; Decay-accelerating factor (CD55); Kallikrein-Kinin system; Systemic lupus erythematosus (SLE), human.**

Further reading

Alvarez V, Coto E, Setien F, Spath PJ and Lopez-Larrea C (1995) Genetic detection of the silent allele (QO) in hereditary deficiencies of the human complement C6, C7 and C9 components. *American Journal of Medical Genetics* 55: 408–413.

Frank MM (1995) Animal models for complement deficiencies. *Journal of Clinical Immunology* 15 (suppl): 113–121.

Mollness TE and Lachmann PJ (1988) Regulation of complement. *Scandinavian Journal of Immunology* 27: 127–142.

Morgan BP (1995) Physiology and pathophysiology of complement: progress and trends. *Critical Reviews in Clinical Laboratory Sciences* 32: 265–298.

Rother K and Rother U (eds) (1986) Hereditary and acquired complement deficiencies in animals and man. *Progress in Allergy* 39.

Rother K, Till GO and Hänsch G (eds) (1997) *The Complement System*, 3rd edn. Berlin: Springer.

COMPLEMENT FIXATION TEST

Seppo Meri, Department of Bacteriology and Immunology, Haartman Institute, University of Helsinki, Helsinki, Finland

Carl-Henrik von Bonsdorff, Department of Virology, Haartman Institute, University of Helsinki, Helsinki, Finland

The complement fixation (CF) test has traditionally been used for the determination of antimicrobial (viral, bacterial, parasitic and fungal) antibodies in patient sera. In a broader sense, CF refers to any technique that exploits the binding and activation of complement components as a reporter system for antigen–antibody reactions. Potential applications thus include: 1) direct measurement of complement activity using antibody-sensitized erythrocytes; 2) indirect complement consumption assay to detect antibody or antigen; and 3) determination of complement-activating ('fixing') autoantibodies (such as islet cell antibodies in diabetes). Although the CF test could be considered as a piece of history of immunology transferred to the modern world, it still has a significant role in diagnostics and research in human and veterinary medicine. Despite the fact that the method represents a multicomponent biological assay with many easily disturbed components, it works well in professional hands. The method is thoroughly known, reliable, inexpensive in material costs and especially well suited for screening purposes. On the negative side are the long time it takes to obtain results and the labor intensity of the assay.

Principle of the test

The CF test is based on the ability of patient serum antibodies to form complement-activating immune complexes upon binding to their antigens. In immune complexes the complement component C1q binds to neighbouring Fc regions of antibody molecules with at least two of its six globular heads. In subsequent reactions some of the early complement components (C1s, C4, C2 and C3) are consumed in sequential proteolytic cleavages. The antibody assay (**Figure 1**) is performed in two stages: first, a dilution series of antibody (the serum to be studied) is mixed with a standard amount of antigen and complement (guinea pig serum is usually used as a source of complement components); second, a detection system for unconsumed complement (rabbit antibody-coated sheep erythrocytes, EA) is added. Lack of hemolysis in the detection system indicates the presence of antibodies. The test is quantitative and the result is usually given as the highest titer of patient serum that still prevents lysis of the indicator cells. Critical components in the assay are the complement (fresh frozen or lyophilized guinea pig serum) and the sheep red blood cells (E). The latter requires the use of cells from a single or a couple of selected animals. The amount of antibody on E needs to be optimized to a saturating, but subagglutinating, level so that the assay is sensitive to changes in complement activity. The amount of complement is titrated to a level that typically corresponds to twice the amount of the 50% hemolytic dose (CH_{50}) under the test conditions. The amount of complement should be just enough to lyse the indicator cells. Controls for the viability of the detection system (EA + complement), background lysis (no complement) and 100% lysis (lysis by water) need to be included. Reproducibility of the CF assay requires that the ionic strength, pH, Ca^{2+} and Mg^{2+} content remain constant. Chelators (EDTA, EGTA) should not be used in the test samples because they directly block complement activity. As the test sera must be void of their own complement, they are heat-inactivated before the assay. For most applications the method utilizes 96-well microtiter plates; it can be automated. A detailed description of the standardization and procedure can be found from the further reading listed below.

Application and interpretation of the assay

The CF test is often used for the screening of antibodies against a variety of possible pathogenic microbes (especially viruses); for this a pool of 15–20 different antigens can be used. Most antigens are commercially available and reasonably priced. Relatively crude antigens (infected cell lysates) are mostly sufficient for the test. Test sera need to be screened in at least two dilutions because in high titer sera an excess of antibody may fail to generate complement-activating immune complexes (the "prozone' effect).

The test is relatively simple to perform and easy to interpret. The CF test broadly measures the humoral immune response (immunoglobulin M (IgM) and IgG class antibodies) against specific microbial antigens. A diagnosis of an acute infection can be made by demonstrating a significant increase in the anti-

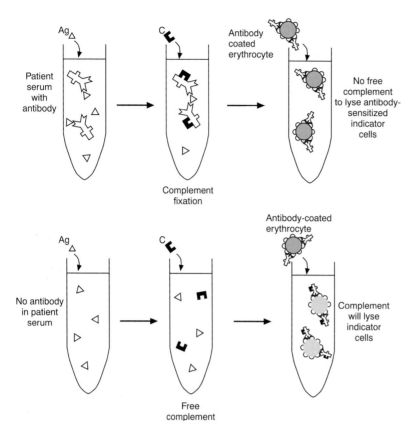

Figure 1 Principle of the complement fixation test.

body titer against a given microbe in paired patient serum samples (generally taken 7–10 days apart from one another). A minimum of a fourfold increase (or sometimes decrease) in antibody level is diagnostic. In screening, a practical way of testing is to analyze the second serum sample at low dilutions (e.g. 1:8 and 1:16) with all the antigens in use and subsequently to test both sera at higher dilutions for the antigens which are positive. A high titer in a single serum sample can be indicative of the state of immunity against the microbe. A declining titer may be the sign of a somewhat older infection. Because of its relatively low sensitivity the complement fixation test may not be applicable for the demonstration of protective immunity acquired a long time ago. Other tests, such as ELISA, are more suitable for this purpose.

The use of the CF test is hindered if the patient serum sample turns out to be 'anticomplementary', i.e. it consumes complement from the test mixture without addition of antigen. The anticomplementarity is usually due to the presence of pre-existing complement-activating factors in the patient sera. These include immune complexes and other immune aggregates, cryoglobulins, contaminating bacteria or bacterial products such as endotoxin. For example, acute sera from patients with a parvovirus B19 infection often contain immune complexes and are anti-

complementary. Polyclonal B cell activation in patients with an Epstein–Barr virus infection may generate, for example, antibodies against sheep erythrocytes that also can give a false (positive) result in the assay. An additional control to exclude direct anticomplementarity of the test serum (test mixture in the absence of antigen) is thus essential.

See also: **Antibodies, detection of; Antigens; Complement, classical pathway; Humoral immunity; IgG; IgM; Immune complexes; Immunoassays; Viruses, immunity to.**

Further reading

Bengali ZH, Das SR and Levine PH (1980) A large scale radiometric micro-quantitative complement fixation test for serum antibody titration. *Journal of Immunological Methods* 33: 63–77.

Bordet J and Gengou O (1901) *Annales de l'Institut Pasteur Paris* 15: 289.

Department of Health, Education and Welfare (1962) *Standard Diagnostic Complement Fixation Method and Adaptation to Micro Test*, Public Health Monograph 74. Hyattsville, MD: Public Health Service, Health Resources Administration.

Hardy RR (1986) Complement fixation by monoclonal antibody–antigen complexes. In: Weir DM (ed) *Handbook of Experimental Immunology*, vol 1: *Immuno-*

chemistry, 4th edn. pp 40.1–40.12. Oxford: Blackwell Scientific.

Lennette DA (1995) General principles for laboratory diagnosis of viral, rickettsial and chlamydial infections. In: Lennette EH, Lennette DA and Lennette ET (eds) *Diagnostic Procedures for Viral, Rickettsial and Chlamydial Infections*, 7th edn, pp 3–26, New York: American Public Health Association.

COMPLEMENT, GENETICS

C Rittner and **PM Schneider**, Institute for Legal Medicine of Johannes Gutenberg, Universitaet Mainz, Mainz, Germany

In 1919, Moore discovered a strain of guinea pigs that was complement deficient; for example, serum of these animals did not mediate antibody-dependent cytolysis. Since that time substitution of a component either artificially depleted from or genetically deficient in sera of individuals of a given species has been a major tool of complement research. In humans, a number of autoimmune diseases have been associated with complement deficiencies of the classical pathway. Additionally, fulminant or recurrent bacterial infections are directly correlated with genetic deficiencies of early and late complement components, respectively. The first polymorphism of a complement component was found by Alper and Propp for the third component in humans in 1968. Subsequently, knowledge about deficiencies and polymorphisms in different species at the phenotypic and genotypic level has continuously accumulated.

Definition of genetics

Polymorphism was defined by Ford as 'the occurrence together in the same habitat of two or more discontinuous forms, or "phases", of a species in such portions that the rarest of them cannot be maintained by recurrent mutations'. Polymorphism of complement components can be studied at four different levels:

1. by allotyping of native complement components in serum (the phenotypic level);
2. by defining their subunit composition (the sub-phenotypic level);
3. by establishing the population and formal genetics (frequency of allotypes, and frequency and segregation of the respective genes/alleles);
4. by gene mapping and DNA sequencing to reveal the gene structure and define sequence variants (the genotypic level).

For this purpose, a complex methodology including electrophoretic and isofocusing techniques with functional or immunologic detection of individual components, serology, quantitation, Southern blot and restriction fragment length polymorphism (RFLP) analysis, polymerase chain reaction (PCR) amplification and sequencing of DNA is applied (**Table 1**). By these means, insights into the evolution of polymorphisms and deficiencies and structure–function relationships, as well as into genetically determined disease susceptibilities, are gained. The analysis of complement polymorphisms at the DNA level has provided an even more complex picture by revealing further variants, which subdivide alleles defined at the protein level. DNA sequence analysis of protein allotypes of a number of complement components has demonstrated that most sequence variations are not confined to short stretches of genomic DNA, but rather are scattered throughout the entire gene; therefore it appears to be technically difficult completely to replace protein typing methods by direct DNA typing using the PCR methodology. A combination of typing methods, both at the protein and the DNA level, should be applied to obtain complete analysis for complement component polymorphisms, as well as for the detection of complement deficiencies.

Gene clusters of complement components and their function

In humans, most genes coding for complement components and related proteins have been cloned, partially or completely sequenced and assigned to chromosomal locations, providing further insight into the evolutionary origin of the large variety of complement components (**Table 2**). This is also reflected by their genomic location and gene structure, as a number of structurally and/or functionally closely related components are organized in major gene clusters in the human genome. These findings support assumptions, based on homology studies at the protein level, that the majority of complement components have evolved by duplication from only a small number of precursor genes.

Table 1 Summary of polymorphisms and deficiency of complement components in humans and animals

Complement component	Typing technique	Total no. of known alleles	Deficiency	Polymorphism in other species	Disease associations
C1q	Imm/Funct	—	Yes	—	Yes
C1r	IEF+WB	>10	Yes	—	Yes
C1s	IEF+WB	2	Yes	—	Yes
C2	IEF+WB RFLP/PCR	<10	Yes	Ch,Rh,Gp,Hm	Yes
C3	HVAGE+IFX RFLP/PCR	>30	Yes	Ch,Rh,Ba,Mc,Hl, Ms,Rb,D	Yes
C4	HVAGE+IFX/WB HVAGE+HOV MAB SDS-PAGE (α/β chains) HAI (Rodgers/Chido) RFLP/PCR	>30	Yes	Ch,Mc,D,Ms,Gp,Xl	Yes
C5	IEF+WB	2	Yes	—	Yes
C6	IEF+WB	>20	Yes	Ch,Rh,Rb,Ms	Yes
C7	IEF+WB/HOV MAB	>10	Yes	—	Yes
C8	IEF+WB/HOV SDS-PAGE RFLP/PCR	<10	Yes	Ch	Yes
Factor B	HVAGE+IFX/HOV IEF RFLP/PCR	>20	Partial	Ch,Rh,Hl,Ba, Gp,Ms	No
Factor I	IEF+WB RFLP/PCR	<5	Yes	—	Yes
Factor H	IEF+WB	<5	Yes	—	Yes
P	Imm/Funct	—	Yes	—	Yes
C4BP	IEF+WB/IFX	<5	No	—	No
CR1	SDS-PAGE EXP RFLP/PCR	<5	Yes	—	Yes
CR2	SDS-PAGE RFLP/PCR	<2	No	—	No
CR3	SDS-PAGE	—	Yes	—	Yes
DAF	Imm (Cromer blood group antigen) RFLP/PCR	<2	Yes	—	Yes
MCP	EXP	<2	No	—	No
MBL	RFLP/PCR	3	No	—	Yes

Typing techniques: EXP, expression polymorphism (number of membrane-associated molecules per cell); Funct, Functional assay; HAI, Hemagglutination inhibition with human alloantisera; HOV, Complement component-dependent hemolytic overlay; HVAGE, High-voltage agarose gel electrophoresis; IEF, Isoelectric focusing; IFX, Immunofixation; Imm, Immunologic detection with specific antisera; MAB, Monoclonal antibodies; RFLP/PCR, DNA restriction fragment length polymorphism detected by Southern blot or polymerase chain reaction analysis; SDS-PAGE, SDS polyacrylamide gel electrophoresis; WB, western blot.
Animal species: Ba, Baboon; Ch, Chimpanzee; D, dog; Gp, guinea pig; Hm, hamster; Hl, Hanuman langur monkey; Mc, Macaque; Ms, mouse; Rb, rabbit; Rh, Rhesus monkey; Xl, *Xenopus laevis*.

Regulators of complement activation (RCA) gene cluster on human chromosome 1

This cluster includes genes for complement receptors CR1 and CR2, the decay-accelerating factor (DAF), the membrane cofactor protein (MCP), factor H (HF), and the C4-binding protein (C4BP). All six proteins share common sequence motifs called short consensus repeats (SCR) of about 60 amino acids in length. In addition, multiple RNA transcripts due to alternative splicing have been described for most members of this cluster. Since this tightly-linked gene family controls the activity of the complement system, it is hard to escape the conclusion that genetic linkage is the evolutionary concept for the maintenance of closely related functions.

Table 2 Chromosomal assignments of complement components and related proteins

Component (or subunit)	Gene symbol	Chromosomal location
C1q: α chain	C1QA	1p34.1–p36.3
C1q: β chain	C1QB	1p34.1–p36.3
C1q: γ chain	C1QG	1p34.1–p36.3
C8: α chain	C8A	1p32
C8: β chain	C8B	1p32
C4-binding protein: α chain	C4BPA	1q32[a]
C4-binding protein: β chain	C4BPB	1q32[a]
Complement receptor 1 (CD 35)	CR1	1q32[a]
Complement receptor 2 (CD 21)	CR2	1q32[a]
Decay-accelerating factor (CD 55)	DAF	1q32[a]
Membrane cofactor protein (CD 46)	MCP	1q32[a]
Factor H	HF	1q32[a]
Factor I	IF	4q25
C6	C6	5p13[b]
C7	C7	5p13[b]
C9	C9	5p13[b]
C2	C2	6p21.3[c]
Factor B	BF	6p21.3[c]
C4A (isotype)	C4A	6p21.3[c]
C4B (isotype)	C4B	6p21.3[c]
C8: γ chain	C8G	9q22.3–q32
C5	C5	9q33
Perforin	PRF1	10q22
Mannose-binding protein (lectin)	MBL	10q11.2–q21
Surfactant protein A (SP-A)	SFTP1	10q22–q23[d]
Surfactant protein D (SP-D)	SFTP4	10q22–q23[d]
Membrane inhibitor of reactive lysis (MIRL, CD59)	CD59	11p13
C1 Inhibitor	C1NH	11q12–q13.1
C1r	C1R	12p13
C1s	C1S	12p13
Complement receptor 3: α chain	CR3A	16p11.2[e]
Vitronectin (S-protein)	VTN	17q11
C3	C3	19p13.3–p13.2
C5a receptor 1	C5R1	19q13.3–q13.4
Leukocyte adhesion molecule: β chain (CD18)	ITGB2	21q22.3[f]
Properdin	PFC	Xp11.4–p11.2

[a]Regulators of complement activation (RCA) gene cluster.
[b]Membrane attack complex (MAC) gene cluster.
[c]MHC class III gene region.
[d]Surfactant protein (SP) gene cluster.
[e]Leukocyte adhesion α (LAA) gene cluster.
[f]Common β chain for the cell adhesion molecules CR3, LFA-1, and gp150,95.
No map assignment: C1q receptor (C1QR, collectin receptor), factor D (DF), factor J (JF), C8-binding protein (C8BP, HRF).

Membrane attack complex (MAC) components C6, C7 and C9 on human chromosome 5

Another gene cluster of complement components was assigned recently to chromosome 5. It has been known for some time that C6 and C7 of the terminal complex are genetically linked, evidence of which was mainly derived from a case of combined C6/C7 deficiency. Whereas the C6 and C7 genes are closely linked (only about 160 kb apart), the C9 gene is located at a distance of >2.5 mb. These three genes share a number of common structural features with those of the C8 α and β chains (C8A and C8B) on chromosome 1: a central cysteine-poor region flanked by several thrombospondin, epidermal growth factor (EGF) precursor and low-density lipoprotein (LDL) receptor repeats. The genes of the MAC may have evolved by duplication and translocation from an ancestral precursor functionally related to perforin, a pore-forming protein of cytotoxic T cells.

C2, factor B and C4 as class III components of the major histocompatibility complex (MHC) on human chromosome 6

These central components of the classical and alternative pathway are encoded in a 120 kb stretch of DNA flanked by the genes of class I and II MHC antigens, HLA-A, -B, -C and -DR, -DQ and -DP, respectively. Although the C2 and BF genes differ significantly in size, they share extensive homology in the coding sequence (both are precursors of functional serine proteases) and have arisen by gene duplication. No homozygous factor B deficiency has yet been reported. Homozygous C4 deficiency is a rare condition and regularly associated with autoimmune or immune complex disease (e.g. systemic lupus erythematosus (SLE) or SLE-like disease). In contrast, about two-thirds of homozygous C2-deficient individuals appear to be healthy, although cases with SLE-like disease or bacterial infections have been described. Whereas there is only a limited polymorphism of C2 and BF, the fourth component of humans is encoded by two closely linked loci – C4A and C4B – exhibiting an extensive polymorphism with a total of more than 30 alleles. Two duplicated and functionally active C4 loci are found only in higher primates and humans. In all mammals (except for the rabbit), as well as in amphibians, the class III complement genes are located in the MHC.

Complexity of the fourth component of human complement with regard to molecular basis, functions and disease associations

For a number of reasons, human C4 is unique among all complement components with regard to its genetic basis, the subtle functional differences of isotypes and allotypes as well as its potential role in the pathogenesis of disease:

1. Human C4 has the most complex molecular basis: the C4A and C4B genes encode proteins with 99% sequence homology but clearly different functions. The two isotypes differ only in a single serologic determinant defined by amino acid residues of the α-chain. A single amino acid substitution from Lys to Pro at position 1101 is responsible for an apparent molecular weight change of 2 kDa on SDS-PAGE; the change from Asp to His at position 1106 alters the hemolytic activity by three- to fourfold. Further, both loci contain so-called 'null' alleles C4Q0 (= quantitative zero), which express no detectable gene product, at remarkable high frequencies (10–20%). These 'silent' alleles are due to: deletions of an entire C4 gene including one of the adjacent genes of steroid 21-hydroxylase, CYP21 (such as C4AQ0 in the most common Caucasoid HLA haplotype A1-Cw7-B8-C2C-BFS-C4AQ0B1-DR3), gene conversion from one C4 isotype to the other (e.g. in the HLA haplotype B44-C2C-BFS-C4A3BQ0-DR4), or non-expression of structural genes due to individual point mutations (e.g. in the HLA haplotype B60-C2C-BFS-C4AQ0B2-DR6). In addition, a number of haplotypes with structurally duplicated C4 genes have been found.

2. Different functions have been ascribed to the thiolester bond of nascent C4b: C4A preferentially transacylates on to amino group nucleophiles, whereas C4B prefers hydroxyl groups for ester formation. Furthermore, C4A is 1.7-fold more efficient at inhibiting immune precipitation than C4B. Complete C4-deficient serum has almost no neutralizing activity in a mumps virus neutralization assay; purified C4A enhances the reaction about tenfold compared with C4B. Immunization experiments with complement-deficient guinea pigs have provided evidence that both C4 isotypes play distinct roles in the induction and amplification of the T cell-dependent immune response.

3. There is a steadily growing list of associations (of variable confidence) of C4 deficiency with a wide variety of diseases such as SLE, rheumatoid arthritis, systemic sclerosis, subacute sclerosing panencephalitis (SSPE), primary biliary cirrhosis, chronic polyarthritis, multiple sclerosis, visceral leishmaniasis, chronic glomerulonephritis, leprosy, Brazilian paracoccidioidomycosis, common variable immunodeficiency, immunoglobulin A deficiency, insulin-dependent diabetes mellitus, Chagas disease and the acquired immune deficiency syndrome (AIDS). A number of autoimmune diseases are associated with the HLA haplotype A1-Cw7-B8-C4AQ0B1-DR3.

Possible mechanisms of complement and disease associations

Since only some, but not all, complement-deficient individuals show disease manifestations, it appears legitimate to conclude that the deficiency is the common genetic basis, not the primary cause in the pathogenesis of a given disease. Also, there is no direct evidence for a role of single genetic variants of a given component in the pathogenesis of autoimmune or infectious diseases. However, there are several lines of evidence suggesting an important physiologic role of complement in immune defense:

1. It has been shown that the intact classical pathway is needed to prevent formation of insoluble immune complexes (ICs); the components of the classical pathway play an important role in this function. In cases of deficiency, ICs may not be cleared by the reticuloendothelial system and therefore recirculate until being deposited at capillary or basal membranes, leading eventually to tissue damage. This mechanism could be envisaged in some forms of vasculitis and glomerulonephritis, as well as autoimmune disease in the presence of nuclear antibodies.

2. In the case of viral antigens, small ICs may escape from CR1-mediated clearance by erythrocytes if the individual is C4-deficient. Circulating ICs may even, after years, be deposited in the brain, having passed the blood–cerebrospinal fluid barrier, contributing to cytotoxic effects in the central nervous system, as seen in diseases such as SSPE and AIDS.

3. Deficiency of MAC components may render these individuals more susceptible to recurrent infections with bacteria such as *Neisseria*. On the other hand, the lack of complement-dependent bacterial lysis protects the patient from massive levels of bacterial endotoxin, leading to a milder course of disease. Depending upon the structural components of the bacterial membranes, some strains appear to be more resistant to complement-mediated lysis than others.

Concluding remarks

A deep insight into the complex genetic structure of most complement components and their evolution has been gained in the last decade. A number of genetic abnormalities of complement components have been observed in association with disease. It is, however, still premature to bridge the variation or loss of *in vitro* functions to a given *in vivo* situation. It will be an important task to replace the statistical relationship of a disease association by the elucidation of causal factors in the pathogenesis of complement-related diseases, as well as to establish evidence for a functional relevance of polymorphic complement allotypes in the natural selection process.

See also: **Complement, alternative pathway; Complement, classical pathway; Complement deficiencies; Complement receptors; Decay-accelerating factor (CD55); H2 class III; HLA class III region; Systemic lupus erythematosus (SLE), human.**

Further reading

Alper CA and Propp RP (1968) Genetic polymorphism of the third component of human complement (C′3). *Journal of Clinical Investigation* **47**: 2181–2191.

Farries TC and Atkinson JP (1991) Evolution of the complement system. *Immunology Today* **12**: 295–300.

Figueroa JE and Densen P (1991) Infectious diseases associated with complement deficiencies. *Clinical Microbiology Reviews* **4**: 359–395.

Hobart MJ, Fernie BA and DiScipio RG (1995) Structure of the human C7 gene and comparison with the C6, C8A, C8B and C9 genes. *Journal of Immunology* **154**: 5188–5194.

Hourcade D, Post TW, Holers M, Lublin D and Atkinson JP (1990) Polymorphisms of the regulators of complement activation gene cluster. *Complement and Inflammation* **7**: 302–314.

Morgan BP and Walport MJ (1991) Complement deficiency and disease. *Immunology Today* **12**: 301–306.

Porter RR (1983) Complement polymorphism, the major histocompatibility complex and associated disease: a speculation. *Molecular Biology and Medicine* **1**: 161–168.

Reid KBM and Day AJ (1989) Structure–function relationships of the complement components. *Immunology Today* **10**: 177–180.

Rittner C and Schneider PM (1988) Genetics and polymorphism of the complement components. In: Rother K and Till GO (eds) *The Complement System*, pp 80–135. Berlin: Springer-Verlag.

Rittner C, Hauptmann G, Mauff G and Schneider PM (eds) (1990) Proceedings of the VIth Complement Genetics Workshop and Conference, Mainz, FRG, 1989. In: *Complement and Inflammation*, vol 7, pp 173–314. Basel: Karger.

Rother K and Rother U (eds) (1986) Hereditary and acquired complement deficiencies in animals and man. In: *Progress in Allergy*, vol 39. Basel: Karger.

Schneider PM and Rittner C (1997) Complement genetics, In: Dodds A and Sim B (eds) *Complement – A Practical Approach*. Oxford: Oxford University Press.

Trowsdale J (1995) 'Both man & bird & beast': comparative organization of the MHC genes. *Immunogenetics* **41**: 1–17.

COMPLEMENT, MEMBRANE ATTACK PATHWAY

Agustin P Dalmasso, Department of Laboratory Medicine and Pathology, VA Medical Center and University of Minnesota, Minneapolis, USA

The membrane attack pathway represents a common effector mechanism of the classical and alternative pathways of complement activation. Activation of the membrane attack pathway constitutes the last stage of complement activation and results in assembly of a multiprotein complex known as the membrane attack complex (MAC). The MAC is comprised of the complement components C5b, C6, C7, C8 and C9 (**Table 1**). Assembly of the MAC on the surface of a cell may have two major consequences. First, the MAC may activate a series of cellular processes that result in MAC elimination as well as cellular responses that are mostly proinflammatory. Second, if sufficient MAC attaches to a cell membrane, cell death may ensue. The name MAC derives from this latter property as the complex can damage a cell membrane independently of the binding of earlier complement components to that cell.

Assembly, structure and control of the MAC

The first step in assembly of the MAC is the generation of C5b from C5. This is accomplished through cleavage of C5 into C5a and C5b by the C5 convertases of the classical pathway (C4b2a3b) or the alternative pathway (C3bBbC3b) (**Figure 1**). C5 binds to C3b which serves both as an assembly site and a cofactor for the enzyme site in the C5 convertases that cleave the α chain of C5, generating C5a and C5b. Then C5b interacts with the terminal complement proteins in a nonenzymatic sequential association, resulting in assembly of the MAC (**Table 1** and **Figure 1**). As each protein incorporates into the complex a conformational rearrangement produces a binding site for the next component. After generation C5b exposes a binding site for C6 with a half-life of 2.3 min at 37°C. Binding of C6 to the

Table 1 Properties of the proteins, complexes and inhibitors of the MAC

	Molecular weight (kDa)	Binding sites for
Individual proteins[a]		
C5	α Chain: 115 β Chain: 75	C3b, C6, C7, C8
C5b	α′ Chain: 104 β Chain: 75	C6, C7
C6	Single chain: 120	C5, C5b
C7	Single chain: 110	C5, C5b
C8	α Chain: 64 β Chain: 64 γ Chain: 22	C5, C9 C5b–7
C9	Single chain: 71	C5b–8, C5b–9
Protein complexes		
C5b6	328	C7
C5b–7	430	Lipid bilayer, C8, vitronectin, clusterin
C5b–8	589	C9, control proteins
C5b–9	660–1850	C9, control proteins
Control proteins		
Vitronectin[a]	Single chain: 83	C5b–7, C5b–8, C5b–9
Clusterin[a]	α Chain: 40 β Chain: 40	C5b–7, C5b–8, C5b–9
CD59	Single chain: 20	C5b–8, C5b–9
HRF	Single chain: 65	C5b–8, C5b–9

[a] Serum concentrations are 50–70 μg ml⁻¹ for each of the MAC precursor proteins, 500 μg ml⁻¹ for vitronectin and 50 μg ml⁻¹ for clusterin.

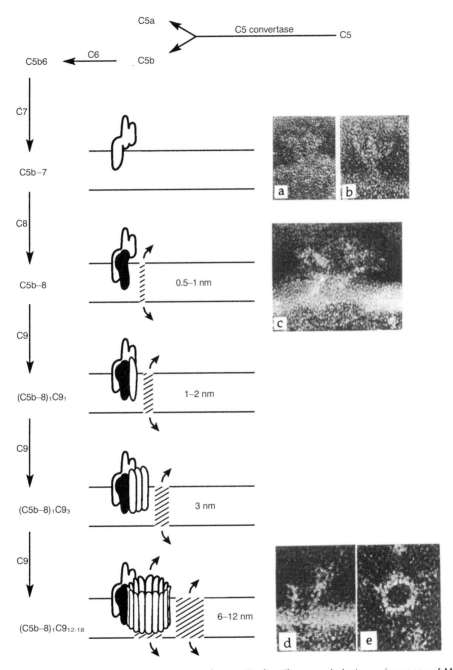

Figure 1 Diagrammatic illustration of the complement membrane attack pathway and electron microscopy of MAC protein complexes. Reaction sequence from activation of C5 through assembly of the complete MAC is shown. Interaction of complexes with a cell membrane is illustrated, with C8 depicted in black. Stippled areas indicate membrane pores of progressively larger size that develop in parallel with progression of MAC assembly. Arrows indicate loss of permeability barrier. Also shown are electron micrographs of membranes bearing C5b–7 (panels a and b), C5b–8 (panel c) and the fully assembled MAC (panel d, lateral view, and panel e, top view). (Electron micrographs are reproduced from RR Dourmashkin (1978), The structural events associated with the attachment of complement components to cell membranes in reactive lysis, *Immunology* **38**: 205–212, with permission from the publisher.)

transient site is facilitated by the weak association of C5 and C6 in solution. The resultant C5b6 is stable and has a binding site for C7. C5b6 can remain loosely associated with C3b, which assists in directing C5b–7 to the adjacent membrane, or detach to the fluid phase. Once C7 incorporates into the complex a metastable binding site with a high affinity for phospholipids is produced. This site is very short-lived, less than 10 ms, and allows the C5b–7 complex, after detachment from C3b, to anchor in the external surface of the lipid bilayer, primarily through C7. The electron microscopic appearance of membrane-bound C5b–7 is that of a foliaceous particle (**Figure 1**). Assembly of the complex can also continue in the fluid phase; however, competition for the lipophilic binding site precludes attachment to a cell membrane. Vitronectin, clusterin, lipoproteins and C8 can all bind to fluid phase C5b–7 and prevent further association with membrane phospholipids.

Membrane-associated C5b–7 binds one molecule of C8, forming the C5b–8 complex, which then may bind multiple molecules of C9. The C5b–7 complex in the membrane bilayer binds a C8 molecule by interaction of the C8 β chain with C5b; possibly a second binding site on C7 promotes a conformational rearrangement in C8 resulting in the C8 α chain penetrating the lipid bilayer. Bound C5b–8 appears as a particle with a variable number of arms (**Figure 1**), with C5b and C8β most distal from the membrane. The resultant C5b–8 complex has a greater affinity for phospholipids than C5b–7, penetrates more deeply into the membrane and disrupts membrane integrity to produce small transient ion-permeable channels. C9 binds to the C8 α chain in the C5b–8 complex and undergoes a conformational change that allows C9 to insert through the bilayer and expose additional binding sites for C9 polymerization. The C5b–9 complex has a greater affinity for phospholipids than C5b–8 and the membrane channel becomes more stable. The channels are formed by the disruption of the bilayer structure as membrane phospholipids attach to the complex. Additional molecules of C9 incorporate into the complex in a circular configuration and the size of the channel continues to increase (**Figure 1**). Incorporation of 12–18 molecules of C9 results in formation of the closed ring, tubular polyC9 structure, which may function as a protein-walled channel. The ultrastructure of this complex on top view corresponds to a ring with an internal diameter of 10 nm and an external diameter of 21 nm. On a lateral view there is a pedicle attached to polyC9 that represents the majority of the C5b–8 complex and extends 16 nm beyond the ring which has a height of 15 nm. Penetration of a membrane by the C5b–9 complex results in loss of membrane phospholipids and a reduction in membrane fluidity. Phospholipids and cholesterol in red cell membranes that have been exposed to the MAC are resistant to dissociation by caotropic agents.

MAC assembly is controlled by several regulatory mechanisms that protect tissues from damage by physiologic activation of autologous complement. Inhibition of early events of complement activation reduces formation of C5 convertases and thus prevents generation of C5b and MAC. Even after C5b has been produced there are mechanisms that control MAC assembly. Intrinsic control is provided by the lability of the exposed binding sites in C5b and C5b–7. There are also membrane-bound and plasma inhibitors that prevent further assembly of complement proteins into the complex. The membrane-associated inhibitors are homologous restriction factor (HRF) and CD59 (also called protectin, MAC inhibitory factor or HRF20) and they are more effective to protect a cell from lysis by complement of the same species than by complement from other species (homologous restriction). CD59 and HRF inhibit formation of the MAC through interaction with membrane-bound C5b–8 to impair the binding of C9 and with C5b–9 to block additional binding and polymerization of C9. These inhibitors are expressed on most cells that are in contact with blood or other biological fluids containing complement. These proteins as well as the inhibitor of the C3 and C5 convertases decay-accelerating factor (DAF) are anchored to the membrane through a glycosyl phosphatidylinositol moiety, although in certain cells they may also exist as transmembrane proteins. There are also plasma proteins that control MAC formation. Vitronectin (S protein) and clusterin (SP-40,40) are multifunctional proteins that interact with late-acting complement components as complexes assemble in plasma, and inhibit binding of the protein complex to cell membranes. In addition, apolipoproteins A-I and A-II may inhibit MAC formation by interfering with polymerization of C9.

Physiologic and pathologic significance of the MAC

The MAC is endowed with the potential to inflict damage on cell membranes that may result in cell death and to induce cellular responses that are generally proinflammatory. These activities may participate significantly in varied physiologic and pathologic processes. Induction of cell damage is a consequence of the ability of the MAC to generate ion-permeable channels in the cell membrane. Membrane-bound C5b–8 can lyse red cells at a low rate but this process is enhanced by C9. Because of the strong affinity of C5b–8 for phospholipids, the membrane bilayer is disrupted, causing increased permeability, which is further enhanced by larger channels formed by addition of C9. Addition of one C9 molecule per C5b–8 is sufficient for rapid lysis of red cells. The permeability changes may cause osmotic swelling and lysis of red cells. Red cells are able to offer some resistance to osmotic swelling by means of a Ca^{2+}-activated K^+ channel and may repair lesions through a Ca^{2+}-dependent vesiculation process. Killing of nucleated cells by the MAC is independent of permeability changes and is associated with an increase in cellular Ca^{2+} and intracellular lipid metabolism, mitochondrial swelling, and hydrolysis of membrane lipids. Nucleated cells are capable of defending themselves from the cytotoxic effect of the MAC and, consequently, lysis is achieved only when large numbers of MAC with multiple C9 are deposited on the plasma membrane. Sublytic amounts of MAC induce activation of the target cell, which, among other effects, results in energy-dependent elimination of membrane-bound MAC by endocytosis or exocytosis. This process requires extracellular Ca^{2+}, with participation of protein kinase C (PKC) and cAMP. Cells with increased levels of cAMP are resistant to MAC-mediated killing. Conversely, inhibition of protein synthesis or lipid metabolism increases susceptibility to MAC-mediated killing.

The MAC plays a role in host defense processes through its ability to kill certain microorganisms and to promote inflammation. The function of the MAC in protection against infections is best demonstrated in individuals with homozygous deficiency of a MAC protein. These individuals have increased susceptibility to develop disseminated disease when infected with the gram-negative organism *Neisseria gonorrhoeae* or *N. meningitidis*. Thus killing by the MAC must be essential to maintain localization and prevent dissemination of neisserial infections. Other gram-negative bacteria, but not gram-positive bacteria, may be killed by the MAC; however, susceptibility is variable. In general smooth strains, but not rough strains, are resistant to killing because they are protected from the MAC by long-chain lipopolysaccharides. For bactericidal activity the deposits of MAC on the bacterial surface must contain at least three molecules of C9 per C5b–8. Enveloped viruses and parasites may also be susceptible to the cytotoxic effect of the MAC. The poor susceptibility to MAC-mediated killing of many microorganisms is due to their defense mechanisms against complement, including certain surface proteins that are homologous to human complement inhibitors.

In vitro studies have shown that formation of sublytic amounts of MAC on the surface of nucleated cells may trigger certain transduction pathways that may result in generation of mediators of inflammation. Even the C5b–7 complex, which binds to membranes but does not form a channel, is able to induce in certain cells an increment in cAMP, diacylglycerol (DAG) and ceramide. C5b–8 and C5b–9 in sublytic amounts can activate several transduction pathways mainly through the participation of Ca^{2+} which first enters the cell through the MAC pore and then triggers the release of Ca^{2+} from intracellular organelles. Transduction pathways that are Ca^{2+}-independent may also be activated. The MAC can induce activation of PKC and stimulate phosphoinositide metabolism, with increased production of IP_1, IP_2 and IP_3, and increase the intracellular concentration of sn-1,2-diacylglycerol. The MAC can also interact with pertussis toxin-sensitive guanine nucleotide-binding proteins (G proteins). C5b–9 causes arachidonic acid release, which in part requires external Ca^{2+}, resulting in production of DAG, which may activate PKC and thus stimulate phospholipase A_2. The MAC may induce cell cycle in oligodendrocytes, which involves c-*jun* activation, and can also cause hydrolysis of myelin basic protein.

Through these and possibly other cell activation mechanisms, the MAC may induce the synthesis of soluble and membrane-associated inflammatory mediators. Thus, it may stimulate the conversion of arachidonic acid into various metabolic products, including prostaglandins, thromboxanes and leukotrienes, and facilitate the production of interleukin 1 (IL-1), tumor necrosis factor α (TNFα) and oxygen-derived free radicals. In endothelial cells, the MAC stimulates the secretion of IL-8 and monocyte chemoattractant protein 1, and inhibits endothelial cell-dependent relaxation, and C5b–7 causes endothelial cell retraction. The MAC may also modify the expression of adhesion molecules in endothelial cells, resulting in upregulation of P-selectin and secretion of von Willebrand factor. In endothelial cells that have been pretreated with TNFα, the MAC enhances the expression of E-selectin and ICAM-1. The MAC is able to directly stimulate mitogenesis in target cells and may also induce the release of mitogenic substances from endothelial cells. In addition to causing cell activation and production of several inflammatory substances, molecules such as cAMP may exit the cell through the C5b–9 channel and modulate the function of neighboring cells.

The MAC plays an important pathophysiologic role in several autoimmune and inflammatory diseases. In some cases this may be due to its cytotoxic effect, as in several immune hematologic diseases. In many instances, however, the pathophysiologic participation of the MAC is more likely related to its ability to elicit cell activation when present in sublytic amounts. The MAC has been implicated in renal diseases such as acute poststreptococcal glomerulonephritis, membranous and membranoproliferative type III nephropathy and lupus nephritis, in neurological diseases such as multiple sclerosis, Guillain–Barré syndrome and myasthenia gravis, in rheumatoid arthritis and immune-complex vasculitis, and in the extension of myocardial infarction lesions and ischemia-reperfusion injury. The MAC also plays a major role in hyperacute rejection of allografts and xenografts. In xenografts this rejection is in part due to the fact that the complement inhibitors are inhibitory to homologous complement but have little inhibitory capacity upon complement from a different species. For this reason transgenic donor pigs that express human complement inhibitors such as CD59 and DAF have been prepared and are being tested in nonhuman primates. The complement-mediated xenogeneic tissue injury is less severe in pig organs that express the human inhibitors than in organs from control pigs.

The biological importance of the inhibitors CD59 and DAF in protection of host cells against physiologic activation of autologous complement is highlighted by the disease paroxysmal nocturnal hemoglobinuria. This condition is caused by an acquired mutation in a gene for one of the enzymes that participates in the synthesis of the glycan phosphatidylinositol moiety shared by the complement inhibitors and certain other membrane proteins. As a consequence the peripheral blood cells derived from the mutant stem cell have low or absent expression of CD59 and DAF and are highly susceptible to complement mediated lysis. A role for the membrane-associated complement inhibitors, including CD59, in resistance of cancer cells to complement-mediated control has been proposed. However, human malignancies that express little or no complement inhibitors do not appear to have a better course than malignancies that express large amounts of inhibitors.

See also: **CD59; Complement, alternative pathway; Complement, classical pathway; Complement deficiencies; Complement, genetics; Cytotoxicity, mechanisms of; Immunopathology; Xenotransplantation.**

Further reading

Bhakdi S and Tranum-Jensen J (1987) Damage to mammalian cells by proteins that form transmembrane pores. *Reviews of Physiology, Biochemistry and Pharmacology* 107: 147–223.

Dalmasso AP (1996) The role of complement in xenograft rejection. In: Cooper DKC *et al* (eds) *Xenotransplantation*. Berlin: Springer-Verlag.

Esser AF (1994) The membrane attack complex of complement. Assembly, structure and cytotoxic activity. *Toxicology* 87: 229–247.

Falk RJ, Dalmasso AP, Kim Y *et al* (1983) Neoantigen of the polymerized ninth component of complement. Characterization of a monoclonal antibody and immunohistochemical localization in renal disease. *Journal of Clinical Investigation* 72: 560.

Mathey D, Schofer J, Schafer HJ *et al* (1994) Early accumulation of the terminal complement-complex in the ischaemic myocardium after reperfusion. *European Heart Journal* 15: 418–423.

Meri S (1994) Protectin (CD59). Complement lysis inhibitor and prototype domain in a new protein superfamily. *The Immunologist* 2: 149–155.

Müller-Eberhard HJ (1984) The membrane attack complex. *Springer Seminars in Immunopathology* 7: 93–141.

Müller-Eberhard HJ (1988) Molecular organization and function of the complement system. *Annual Review of Biochemistry* 57: 321–347.

Nicholson-Weller A and Halperin JA (1993) Membrane signaling by complement C5b-9, the membrane attack complex. *Immunology Research* 12: 244–257.

Niehans GA, Cherwitz DL, Staley NA, Knapp DJ and Dalmasso AP (1996) Human carcinomas variably express the complement inhibitory proteins CD46 (membrane cofactor protein), CD55 (decay accelerating factor), and CD59 (protectin). *American Journal of Pathology* 149: 129–142.

Podack ER (1988) Assembly and structure of the membrane attack complex (MAC) of complement. In: Podack ER (ed) *Cytolytic Lymphocytes and Complement: Effectors of the Immune System*, pp 173–184. Boca Raton, FL: CRC Press.

Rus HG, Niculescu F, Shin ML (1996) Sublytic complement attack induces cell cycle in oligodendrocytes. *Journal of Immunology* 156: 4892–4900.

Sims PJ, Wiedmer T (1995) Induction of cellular procoagulant activity by the membrane attack complex of complement. *Cell Biology* 6: 275–282.

COMPLEMENT RECEPTORS

Gordon D Ross, Division of Experimental Immunology and Immunopathology, Department of Pathology, University of Louisville, Louisville, Kentucky, USA

Complement (C) receptors were first reported by Levaditi and Inmann, in 1905, who found that phagocytic cells exhibited enhanced ability to ingest bacteria after treatment with fresh antisera that served as a source of complement as well as antibacterial antibody. This process, termed opsonization, was subsequently shown to involve the coating of bacteria with C3 molecules that facilitated attachment of the bacteria to membrane C3 receptors expressed on the phagocytes (i.e. neutrophils or monocyte/macrophages). Later, in 1930, Duke and Wallace observed that complement-opsonized trypanosomes bound to primate red blood cells, producing the phenomenon that was named immune adherence by Robert Nelson in 1953. Nelson was the first to demonstrate that immune adherence with red blood cells or neutrophils required only the activation of C3, and not the terminal lytic complement components. The immune adherence receptor of erythrocytes and neutrophils was subsequently named complement receptor type 1 (CR1) when the existence of other types of C3 receptors was appreciated (**Table 1**). Four additional types of C3 receptors have been named according to their order of discovery. CR2 (1973), CR3 (1979), CR4 (1984) and CR5 (1984). Four receptors for other complement components and for C3a have been named according to their ligand specificity: C1q-R (C1q receptor, 1975), C5a-R (C5a receptor, 1978), C3a-R (C3a receptor, 1979), fH-R (factor H receptor, 1980). In addition, several of the complement receptors have been recognized as leukocyte CD antigens by the International Leukocyte Antigen Workshop: CR1 is CD35, CR2 is CD21, CR3 is CD11b, CR4 is CD11c, and C5a-R is CD88. Complement receptors have a wide range of functions that include, in addition to phagocytosis, enhancement of B cell antigen recognition, removal of immune complexes from the blood, release of histamine from mast cells, and chemotaxis of phagocytic cells to sites of inflammation.

Structure, specificity and cellular distribution of complement receptors

Complement receptor type 1 (CR1)

CR1 (CD35) binds to C3b, and with lower affinity to C4b and iC3b. Proteolysis of iC3b into C3dg destroys CR1 activity. Several cell types express CR1, including erythrocytes, phagocytic cells, lymphocytes (B cells and some T cells), kidney podocytes and peripheral nerves. CR1 along with CR3, CR4 and immunoglobulin G (IgG) Fc receptors are the major opsonin receptors on phagocytic cells. The CR1 of erythrocytes has two important functions in the clearance of circulating immune complexes. First, immune complexes and particles that activate complement are bound rapidly to erythrocytes via CR1. Erythrocytes then serve as a vehicle that transports the complexes to the liver and splenic macrophages. Second, erythrocyte CR1 function as the obligate cofactor for factor I cleavage of complex-bound iC3b into bound C3dg and fluid-phase C3c. B cell CR1 forms a membrane complex with CR2 that functions to promote the uptake of protein antigens that are coated with C3b or iC3b via natural antibodies and the classical pathway of complement activation. Antigen complexes that are bound to the CR1 portion of this B cell membrane complex via C3b are transferred to CR2 following proteolysis of the C3b into iC3b and C3dg. T cell CR1 may have a similar antigen-trapping function, but only small subsets of $CD4^+$ and $CD8^+$ T cells express CR1, and the amount of CR1 expressed per cell is $\leq 10\%$ of that expressed by B cells.

CR1 is a member of a family of proteins known as the 'regulators of C activation' (RCA) that are encoded by chromosome 1 in humans. Other RCA members include CR2, factor H, decay accelerating factor (DAF, CD55), membrane cofactor protein (MCP, CD46), and C4-binding protein or C4-BP. CR1 exists in four allotypic forms that vary in size from 160 kDa to 250 kDa. Analysis of CR1 cDNA has demonstrated that CR1 consists of 3–5 linked protein segments that exhibit a high degree of internal sequence homology and are termed 'long homologous repeats' (LHRs). Allotypic variation in the number of LHRs per CR1 explains the large size variation in the CR1 from different individuals. Each LHR consists of seven short (60–70 amino acid) repeating sequence motifs ('short consensus repeats', SCRs). These SCR motifs are the common feature of the RCA proteins that apparently explain their C3b- and C4b-binding activity. Variations in SCR sequence determine binding activity, and distinct SCR sequences in CR1 confer either C3b- or C4b-binding activity.

Table 1 Structure, specificity and cellular distribution of complement receptors

Receptor type	Specificity	Structure	Cell type distribution
CR1 (CD35)	C3b > C4b > iC3b	Four allotypes that vary in size from 160 kDa to 250 kDa due to different numbers of repeating sequence motif units	Monocytes, neutrophils: high expression Tissue macrophages: low expression B cells, eosinophils: high expression Kidney podocytes: high expression T cells (~20%): low expression Peripheral nerves: low expression
CR2 (CD21)	iC3b = C3dg > C3d > C3b, Epstein–Barr virus, CD23	Made up of repeating sequence motif units similar to CR1; 140 kDa	B lymphocytes: high expression Lymph node follicular dendritic cells: very high expression Thymocytes, pharyngeal epithelial cells: low expression
CR3 (CD11b; Mac-1; $\alpha_M\beta_2$-integrin)	iC3b, C3dg, C3d, β-glucan, ICAM-1, fibrinogen, factor X, collagen, heparan sulfate, CD14, CD16, CD87	Two noncovalently linked glycoprotein chains: 165 kDa α_M chain (CD11b), 95 kDa β_2 chain (CD18)	Neutrophils, monocytes: high expression Tissue macrophages: low expression Activated cytotoxic T cells, NK cells, eosinophils: high expression
CR4 (CD11c; p150,95; $\alpha_X\beta_2$-integrin)	iC3b, C3dg, fibrinogen	Two noncovalently linked glycoprotein chains: 150 kDa α_X chain (CD11c), 95 kDa β_2 chain (CD18)	Neutrophils, monocytes: low expression Tissue macrophages: high expression Activated B cells: high expression Activated cytotoxic T cells, NK cells, eosinophils: low expression
CR5	C3d portion of fluid-phase iC3b, C3dg, C3d	Unknown; 95 kDa candidate molecule expressed by platelets	Neutrophils: low expression Platelets: low expression
gC1q-R	C1q globular 'head', as well as vitronectin and high molecular weight kininogen	33 kDa glycoprotein	All leukocyte types: variable expression Platelets: high expression Endothelial cells: high expression
cC1q-R	C1q collagen 'tail'	60 kDa glycoprotein; homologous to calreticulin	All leukocyte types: variable expression
C1q-R$_p$	C1q collagen-like fragment, mannose-binding protein, lung surfactant protein A	126 kDa glycoprotein	Neutrophils: high expression Monocytes: high expression
C3a-R	C3a, C4a	Guinea pig platelet: 95–105 kDa Human mast cell: 57 kDa and 97 kDa Human leukocyte: 482 amino acids, ~54 kDa, seven membrane-spanning domains	Mast cells: high expression Eosinophils, basophils: high expression Neutrophils, monocytes: low expression Guinea pig platelets: high expression
C5a-R (CD88)	C5a, C5a$_{des\ Arg}$	47 kDa glycoprotein binding unit with seven membrane-spanning domains expressed as an oligomer of 150–200 kDa	Mast cells, neutrophils: high expression Monocytes and tissue macrophages: high expression Eosinophils: high expression Hepatocytes, astrocytes, endothelial cells: high expression

In the mouse there is a closer relationship between CR1 and CR2, and the two membrane glycoproteins are derived from a single gene by alternative splicing of mRNA. As a result, the larger 190 kDa murine CR1 molecule contains the entire 140 kDa CR2 sequence as part of its structure. Monoclonal antibodies to CR2 are therefore equally reactive with CR1 and unable to distinguish the two types of C3 receptors. Murine CR1 appears to be restricted to B cells, and is not expressed on neutrophils or macrophages for phagocytosis, nor is it expressed on erythrocytes or platelets where it could function in immune complex clearance. Murine neutrophils and platelets express instead distinct C3b/C4b-binding molecules that appear structurally unrelated to CR1 or CR2.

Complement receptor type 2 (CR2)

CR2 (CD21) is expressed by B lymphocytes, lymph node follicular dendritic cells, pharyngeal epithelial cells and thymocytes. Only minor subsets of T lymphocytes express CR2, and the amount per cell is only 10% of the amount expressed by B cells. CR2 is not only a receptor for C3 fragments but also functions as the cellular attachment site for Epstein–Barr virus (EBV) and the counterligand for CD23. CR2 is specific for the C3d portion of iC3b, C3dg or C3d, and has only a low affinity for C3b. B cell CR2 has been shown to play a major role in primary and secondary antibody responses to protein antigens. In a primary response, natural antibodies form immune complexes with protein antigens, resulting in activation of the classical complement pathway and covalent fixation on to the antigen of C3b that is rapidly degraded by factor I into iC3b and C3dg. This bound C3 promotes efficient antigen uptake by B cells via CR2, and the resulting CR2 stimulation of the B cell lowers the antigen concentration threshold required for antigen recognition by specific surface Ig on the B cell. CR2 signaling results from a B cell membrane complex of glycoproteins that includes CR2, CD19 and TAPA-1 in which transmembrane signaling occurs via the CD19 portion of the complex. This pathway for use of complement and CR2 for antigen recognition was initially demonstrated with blocking antibodies to C3 or to CR2, and then later with gene knockout mice deficient in either C3, C4 or B cell CR2. Although an immune response could be generated in these mice with greatly increased antigen doses as compared with those required in normal mice, antibody levels were abnormally low, isotype switching did not occur, and there was no immunologic memory. This pathway for humoral immunity to protein antigens represents an important link between the innate and specific immune systems.

B cell isotype switching to IgE production also involves CR2 and its ability to form membrane complexes with the IgE receptor CD23. However, in a subversion of its normal function, CR2 is utilized by EBV to gain entry into B cells, permitting virus infection (infectious mononucleosis) or a malignant transformation of B cells or epithelial cells (Burkitt's lymphoma or nasopharyngeal carcinoma, respectively).

CR2 consists of a single polypeptide chain of 140 kDa with the same type of SCR structure as CR1. The CR2 gene is closely linked to the CR1 gene, and, in the mouse, a single gene transcribes both receptor proteins via alternative RNA splicing.

Complement receptor type 3 (CR3)

CR3 (also known as CD11b/CD18, Mac-1, or $\alpha_M\beta_2$-integrin) is a multifunctional membrane protein that serves as both a membrane receptor to trigger phagocyte and natural killer (NK) cell cytotoxic events and as an adhesion molecule used by leukocytes for diapedesis across the endothelium (via attachment to ICAM-1) or the extracellular matrix (via attachment to heparan sulfate or fibrin). The I domain of CD11b binds with high avidity to opsonizing iC3b attached to microorganisms, and with lower avidity to opsonizing C3dg or C3d. However, its receptor function is complex, because CR3 not only recognizes exogenous target cell-associated ligands directly but also extends its effective ligand specificity by coupling itself to certain other endogenous leukocyte membrane receptors that utilize CR3 for their transmembrane signaling function. Critical to both forms of receptor activity is a lectin site located C-terminal to the I domain of CD11b and involved in recognition of either microbial cell wall polysaccharides or the leukocyte membrane glycoproteins that couple to CR3 for transmembrane signaling. Bacteria or yeast that bear opsonizing iC3b trigger CR3 activation because of simultaneous recognition of microbial cell wall polysaccharides via the CR3 lectin site and bound iC3b via the I domain. Potential target particles that bear fixed iC3b but lack specific polysaccharides recognized by this lectin site of CR3 do not stimulate cellular activation, despite avid adhesion of the particles to CR3 via the fixed iC3b. Ligation of polysaccharides to the lectin site of CD11b induces a tyrosine kinase- and magnesium divalent cation-dependent conformational change in CD11b that is associated with generation of a primed state of CR3 capable of stimulating cellular cytotoxic activation events (e.g. phagocytosis, degranulation) when CR3 subsequently attaches to target cell-bound iC3b via its I domain-localized binding site. Three neutrophil membrane receptors that are attached to membranes via surface phosphatidylinositol glycolipid (PIG) bridges acquire transmembrane signaling function by forming lectin site-dependent complexes with the transmembrane CR3 molecule: 1) the IgG Fc receptor FcγRIIIA (CD16), 2) the urokinase plasminogen activator receptor (uPAR or CD87), and 3) the lipopolysaccharide (LPS) receptor (CD14).

Unlike C-type (calcium-dependent) lectins, the polysaccharide-binding site of CR3 does not require divalent cations and has a relatively broad reactivity with certain polysaccharides containing mannose or N-acetyl-glucosamine, as well as glucose (β1,3-glucans).

Unstimulated phagocytes express small amounts of membrane CR3 and retain large stores of CR3 in cytoplasmic granules. Following stimulation with C5a or a variety of cytokines, much of the initial membrane surface CR3 becomes linked to the actin cytoskeleton in a way that renders it capable of mediating phagocytosis or extracellular adhesion to ICAM-1. Simultaneously, specific granules come to the cell surface, where their membranes fuse with the outer cell membrane, greatly increasing the expression of membrane surface CR3. However, this granule-derived CR3 is not linked to the cytoskeleton and is thus incapable of mediating firm cellular adhesions or phagocytosis. This more abundant but loosely associated CR3 is very mobile within the membrane and functions to promote phagocyte attachment to iC3b-coated target cells, allowing their subsequent phagocytic recognition by the less mobile but cytoskeleton-bound CR3 (or CR4).

CR3 consists of two noncovalently associated glycoprotein chains known as α_M or CD11b (165 kDa) and β_2 or CD18 (95 kDa). CR3 is one of four members of the leukocyte β_2-integrins that share the common β_2-integrin structure linked to a distinct α-chain type. The other three leukocyte β_2-integrins are LFA-1 (CD11a/CD18), CR4 (CD11c/CD18 or p150,95) and CD11d/CD18.

Complement receptor type 4 (CR4)

CR4 (CD11c/CD18 or p150,95), the third member of the leukocyte β_2-integrins, is closely related to CR3. The CR4 α chain (CD11c, 150 kDa) is ~87% homologous in sequence to CD11b, and recognizes similar ligands including iC3b, fibrinogen and, according to some reports, even ICAM-1. CR4 is expressed preferentially on tissue macrophages that bear only small amounts of CR1 and CR3. Phagocyte CR3 and CR4 differ in cytoplasmic domain structure and attachment to the actin cytoskeleton, and this is thought to provide a mechanism for differential regulation of cellular adhesion or phagocytosis. The relative importance of CR4 as a receptor for iC3b is unclear, as most of the iC3b receptor function of leukocytes, including tissue macrophages, is blocked by use of antibodies to CR3 alone.

Complement receptor type 5 (CR5)

CR5 appears to be specific for the C3d portion of iC3b, C3dg and C3d, but reacts only with these fragments in the fluid phase and not when they are fixed via their normal covalent site. CR5 activity has been defined with fluid-phase dimers of C3dg labeled with [125]I. Neutrophil uptake of ^{125}I-C3dg dimers was blocked by competing unlabeled iC3b, C3dg and C3d, but not by C3b. At one time it was believed that the C3dg dimer receptor might be the same as the receptor for erythrocyte C3dg rosette formation, and so both receptor activities were designated CR4. Later, however, the receptor activity responsible for rosette formation was shown to have several properties that distinguished it from the C3dg dimer receptor, and so the C3dg dimer receptor was named CR5. The binding of CR4 to fixed iC3b was prevented by ethylene diamine tetraacetic acid (EDTA), whereas EDTA had no effect on the uptake of ^{125}I-C3dg dimers. Although CR5 activity has been identified on neutrophils and platelets, it is unknown whether the same molecule is responsible for this activity on both cell types. A platelet membrane glycoprotein of 95 kDa identified by affinity labeling techniques has been shown to function as a C3dg receptor. In the absence of sequence data established from a molecular clone, the existence of CR5 as a distinct entity is less certain than the other C3 receptors.

C1q receptors (C1q-R)

Three distinct types of C1q-R have been described: one that binds to the globular 'head' portion and two that react with the collagen 'tail'. All three of the receptors have been shown to react with other molecules in addition to C1q, such as vitronectin, kininogen and mannose-binding protein. A 33 kDa glycoprotein with affinity for the C1q globular head, 'gC1q-R', and a 60 kDa glycoprotein that reacts with the collagen tail, 'cC1q-R', were first identified on Raji B lymphoblastoid cells. Antibodies to these two molecules have now shown a wider cell type distribution, and gC1q-R is particularly expressed on platelets and endothelial cells, as well as eosinophils. A second type of receptor for the collagen portion of C1q is a 126 kDa monocyte and neutrophil membrane glycoprotein that has been termed C1q-R$_p$ because of its ability to enhance phagocytosis mediated via CR1. The cDNAs for all three of these molecules have been cloned, and gC1q-R has been expressed as a recombinant molecule that retains C1q-binding activity. Although the two have novel sequences, the 60 kDa cC1q-R has considerable homology with calreticulin and may represent a membrane surface variant of this cytoplasmic protein. The 33 kDa gC1q-R is the product of a single gene localized to chromosome 17 and has a specificity similar to the Fc region of Ig. By contrast, cC1q-R and C1q-R$_p$ do not compete with Ig Fc, and thus can promote cellular uptake of immune complexes bearing C1q linked to Ig. These latter types of C1q-R bind immune complex-associated C1q preferentially, because single C1q molecules have a low affinity for cC1q-R or C1q-R$_p$, and the C1q binding site in native C1 is masked by C1r and C1s. The collagen binding site in C1q is exposed by C1 inhibitor that complexes with activated C1r and C1s, separating them away from C1q.

Factor H receptor (fH-R)

A fH-R activity has been detected on B lymphocytes, monocytes and neutrophils, but no structural comparison of the fH-R on these cell types has been carried out and the molecular entity representing fH-R has not been identified. Since plasma did not block cellular uptake of radiolabeled factor H, it was proposed that fH-R were unreactive with 'native' plasma factor H, and that either purification procedures or immune complex attachment might alter factor H in a way that exposed a binding site for fH-R. Subsequently, purified factor H preparations were shown to contain two species of factor H, designated ϕ_1 and ϕ_2, that could be separated by phenyl-Sepharose hydrophobic affinity chromatography. Only the ϕ_2 form of factor H bound specifically to lymphoid cells, but it is unknown whether this ϕ_2 form of factor H exists in plasma or if it is generated by H interaction with immune complexes. The first attempt at isolation of the fH-R from lymphoblastoid cells used either antifactor H idiotypic antibody or factor H-Sepharose and identified a protein complex of ≥ 150 M_r with 100 kDa and 50 kDa components. A second study using factor H agarose affinity chromatography detected a single protein species of 170 kDa on the surface of B lymphoblastoid cells and tonsil B cells. This 170 kDa protein bound specifically to factor H agarose, and in soluble form, prevented rosettes with factor H-coated erythrocytes. B cells have been shown to release endogenous stores of factor I in response to fluid-phase or immune complex-associated factor H, and purified H has been reported to serve as a growth factor for the maintenance of B cell lines.

C5a receptor (C5a-R)

The inflammatory functions of C5a are mediated via specific C5a-R (CD88) expressed on a variety of cell types including mast cells, phagocytes, bronchial and alveolar epithelial cells, hepatocytes, astrocytes and vascular endothelial cells. The action of C5a is regulated both by serum carboxypeptidase N (SCPN), which removes the C-terminal arginine (forming C5a$_{des\ Arg}$), and by neutrophil catabolism of C5a following specific uptake by C5a-R. Although C5a$_{des\ Arg}$ has reduced binding affinity as compared with C5a, it is a major ligand for C5a-R *in vivo* because of the

serum protein ('cochemotaxin') that combines with the C5a$_{des\ Arg}$ and enhances its action with C5a-R. Cochemotaxin is identical to GC globulin or vitamin D-binding protein. The ~47 kDa C5a-R glycoprotein is a member of the family of related G protein-linked chemokine receptors that have seven membrane-spanning domains. A two-site model has been suggested in which part of the N-terminal extracellular domain of the receptor recognizes the N-terminal and disulfide-linked core of C5a. This is then thought to be followed by interaction of the C-terminus of C5a with a second region of the receptor that is linked to G protein and responsible for the activating signal. Both the contractile responses of smooth muscle cells and the increased vascular permeability produced by C5a are thought to result from histamine release by mast cells or basophils that express the same C5a-R structure. C5a-R mediate a wide range of leukocyte responses, including chemotaxis, homotypic aggregation (clumping), activation of CR3 to expose its high-affinity binding site for ICAM-1 (thus promoting leukocyte adhesion to endothelium), and upregulation of the number of CR1, CR3 and CR4 exposed on external membrane surfaces. Larger doses of C5a cause degranulation and a respiratory burst. Because of the importance of C5a in mediating inflammatory responses, C5a-R antagonist drugs have been widely sought as therapeutic agents for autoimmune and inflammatory disease syndromes.

Receptor for C3a and C4a (C3a-R)

A single type of receptor is believed to be responsible for responses to C3a or C4a. This receptor activity was first characterized on mast cells, and later a similar C3a-R was demonstrated on basophils, eosinophils, neutrophils and guinea pig platelets. The first successful molecular cloning of the C3a-R was reported with cDNA libraries generated from differentiated HL-60 cells or U-937 cells. As with C5a, smooth muscle spasmogenic responses occur with nanomolar concentrations of C3a or C4a that stimulate mast cell secretion of histamine. Although disputed for many years, the chemotactic activity of C3a has now been shown with eosinophils and is likely to occur also with neutrophils or monocytes that express C3a-R. As with C5a, SCPN removes a C-terminal arginine from both C3a and C4a, greatly reducing, if not totally eliminating, the ability of these anaphylatoxins to stimulate cellular responses. Not only are all spasmogenic and leukocyte-associated activities of C3a and C4a absent in C3a$_{des\ Arg}$ and C4a$_{des\ Arg}$, but also no cochemotaxin-like serum factor has been identified that restores C3a/C4a$_{des\ Arg}$ activity in the same way as has been shown for C5a$_{des\ Arg}$. Attempts to identify a C3a-R with

[125]I-C3a coupled to heterobifunctional cross-linking reagents identified a putative C3a-R only on guinea pig platelets and failed to identify a C3a-R on human platelets and neutrophils; however, similar methods were successful with a human mast cell line, HMC-1. These studies identified two putative guinea pig platelet C3a-R candidate molecules of 95 kDa and 105 kDa, and two human mast cell C3a-R species of 57 kDa and 97 kDa. Sequence homology with both the C5a-R (37% at the nucleotide level) and the fMLP-receptor allowed molecular cloning of the C3a-R. Cells expressing recombinant C3a-R exhibited the same reactivity with C3a as the native receptor, including the failure to bind C5a. Northern blotting with the 4.3 kb cDNA for C3a-R demonstrated transcripts of both 2.3 kb and 3.9 kb, perhaps explaining the two different sized receptors noted in cross-linking experiments. Based on the 2.3 kb transcript, a polypeptide of 482 residues was predicted with the typical seven membrane-spanning domains of the G protein-linked receptor family.

See also: **Adhesion molecules; Anaphylatoxins; Complement, alternative pathway; Chemokines; Complement, classical pathway; Complement, genetics; Epstein-Barr virus, infection and immunity; Immune adherence; Integrins; Opsonization; Phagocytosis; Viruses, infection of immune cells by.**

Further reading

Birmingham DJ (1995) Erythrocyte complement receptors. *Critical Reviews in Immunology* 15: 133–154.

Crass T, Raffetseder U, Martin U *et al* (1996) Expression cloning of the human C3a anaphylatoxin receptor (C3aR) from differentiated U-937 cells. *European Journal of Immunology* 26: 1944–1950.

Croix DA, Ahearn JM, Rosengard AM *et al* (1996) Antibody response to a T-dependent antigen requires B cell expression of complement receptors. *Journal of Experimental Medicine* 183: 1857–1864.

Fearon DT and Carter RH (1995) The CD19/CR2/TAPA-1 complex of B lymphocytes: linking natural to acquired immunity. *Annual Review of Immunology* 13: 127–149.

Ghebrehiwet B, Lu PD, Zhang W *et al* (1996) Identification of functional domains on gC1Q-R, a cell surface protein that binds to the globular 'heads' of C1Q, using monoclonal antibodies and synthetic peptides. *Hybridoma* 15: 333–342.

Guan E, Robinson SL, Goodman EB and Tenner AJ (1994) Cell-surface protein identified on phagocytic cells modulates the C1q-mediated enhancement of phagocytosis. *Journal of Immunology* 152: 4005–4016.

Holmskov U, Malhotra R, Sim RB and Jensenius JC (1994) Collectins: collagenous C-type lectins of the innate immune defense system. *Immunology Today* 15: 67–74.

Molina H, Kinoshita T, Webster CB and Holers VM (1994) Analysis of C3b/C3d binding sites and factor I cofactor regions within mouse complement receptors 1 and 2. *Journal of Immunology* 153: 789–795.

Petty HR and Todd RF III (1993) Receptor–receptor interactions of complement receptor type 3 in neutrophil membranes. *Journal of Leukocyte Biology* 54: 492–494.

Quigg RJ and Holers VM (1995) Characterization of rat complement receptors and regulatory proteins: CR2 and Crry are conserved, and the C3b receptor of neutrophils and platelets is distinct from CR1. *Journal of Immunology* 155: 1481–1488.

Thornton BP, Větvička V, Pitman M, Goldman RC and Ross GD (1996) Analysis of the sugar specificity and molecular location of the β-glucan-binding lectin site of complement receptor type 3 (CD11b/CD18). *Journal of Immunology* 156: 1235–1246.

Větvička V, Thornton BP and Ross GD (1996) Soluble β-glucan polysaccharide binding to the lectin site of neutrophil or NK cell complement receptor type 3 (CD11b/CD18) generates a primed state of the receptor capable of mediating cytotoxicity of iC3b-opsonized target cells. *Journal of Clinical Investigation* 98: 50–61.

Wetsel RA (1995) Structure, function and cellular expression of complement anaphylatoxin receptors. *Current Opinion in Immunology* 7: 48–53.

CONGENIC MICE

M Viviana Bozón and **Edmond J Yunis**, Division of Immunogenetics, Harvard Medical School, Boston, Massachusetts, USA

Inbreeding is the mating of individuals more closely related than mates chosen at random from a population. An inbred strain is a population that is almost genetically identical. Two animals (lines) that are genetically identical save for a difference at one locus are called coisogenic (L. *co*, together; Gr. *iso*, identical).

When George D. Snell, working at the Jackson Laboratory, realized that rejection of a graft between two mice was affected by multiple genes, he developed the concept of 'congenic mice', by transferring resistance genes from one mouse to another from a different genetic background. He produced lines by genetic backcrossing, and calculated that 12 generations were needed to obtain a line that differed from the original at one chromosomal region carrying an identified marker. While working on this breeding, Snell noticed that not only was there a locus intimately related to the rejection of tumor grafts, but another gene seemed to be retained from the donor strain, the Fu locus, a marker for a deformity of the tail. He named it the histocompatibility locus. During the development of the first congenic lines, Snell observed that some of the mice retained not only the tumor resistance but also marker genes of the donor strain. For example, the congenic line ACA, was produced from the inbred strain A and an outbred stock CA carrying the mutation fused tail (Fu). This not only carried the resistance to A strain tumors but also had the shortened tails caused by the Fu gene. This was the first demonstration of genetic linkage in mammals and the first genetic marker for the major histocompatibility complex later to be found by serology as H2.

At the same time, Peter Gorer in England discovered a hemagglutinating antibody associated with the rejection of transplantation of tumors. It appeared that a cytotoxic antibody responsible for this rejection was associated with blood group antigens. This was not considered a general rule for rejection, but the gene encoding this antigen was indeed located at the named 'H' locus. Gorer named the antigen 'antigen II'. In 1948, Gorer and Snell, working together, discovered that the H locus was linked to the tail marker (Fu) and was associated with rejection. Using congenic strains they found that skin grafts were rejected from the mice at different periods after the transplant. Experiments with different congenic strains produced support to the concept that some genes were associated with different degrees of influence in the rejection of allografts.

The H2 genes were identified as major genes and later were located in a single region at chromosome 17 named the major histocompatibility complex (MHC).

Congenic mice are useful tools for the analysis of the genetics of tissue and bone marrow transplantation, the genetics of the immune response including cellular interactions and the role of genes of the MHC in autoimmunity and longevity.

Production of congenic strains

Coisogenic strains are produced when an inbred mouse becomes genetically identical to another, except with a difference at a single locus produced by mutation. This can be achieved by crossing mice in order to bear or introduce a small dominant region of one donor into a common genetic background. Therefore, congenic mice are two strains that are identical except for a short chromosomal segment. Coisogenic strains differ in one locus and congenic differ in a small variable region of a chromosome including several loci.

Backcrossing

The backcrossing procedure is applicable to the introduction of an autosomal dominant or codominant allele. The original pair, one inbred strain which donates the genetic background (first parent or inbred partner) and one donor strain which donates the chromosomal segment (second parent), are crossed. The F1 progeny are backcrossed to the inbred partner. For the next generation, a donor that poses the desired allele is selected. After 12 generations heterozygote siblings are mated, originating the desired genotype. At this point of the backcrossing, the offspring will be the progenitors of the desired congenic strain, which will be perpetuated by standard sibling mating (intercross) or by further backcrossing to the inbred parent.

The production of congenic strains of mice is based on the introduction of a short chromosomal segment into a second strain. The resulting strain is congenic. Molecular techniques are required to identify the marker gene of the genetic region that will be introduced into a common genetic background. Most of the existing congenic strains were named congenic resistant to indicate the introduction of genes that induced resistance to an incompatible tumor originating from a parent of the donor strain involved in the backcrossing. They differed from their inbred part at the histocompatibility locus. However, they can be produced for any genetic marker. The production of the strain B10.D2 is given as an example (**Figure 1**). In this example the genetic background is given by the B10 (C57BL/10SN) strain which is H2-b and the donor of H2-d of the strain DBQ/2J. The diagram shows that by a number of backcrosses, usually 10–15, it produces strains that differ from their inbred partner by a chromosomal segment 12–20 centimorgans (cM) long. In the case of the H2 (2 cM long) it would require at least 30 backcrosses to produce strains differing at less than 10 cM.

Essentially the backcrosses are tested for H2 markers (usually antibodies specific for MHC gene products). In the example of the figure, the homozygotic H2-b are discarded. The backcrosses are always between a b/d and the B10 inbred. It is important

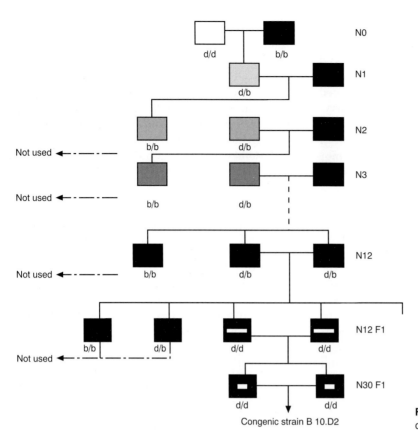

Figure. 1 Breeding system for producing congenic mice.

that the coisogenic strains differ only by a point mutation. When they are produced the level of probability is defined by the equation:

$$P_n = 1 - (1 - c)^{n-1}$$

where p = probability, n = number of generations and c = recombination frequency.

The higher the number of backcrosses the smaller the length of the differential chromosomal segment.

Genetics of the donor strains in congenic mice

The majority of the congenic mice were produced in the C57BL6 of C57BL10 mice (**Table 1** gives examples of congenic and A mice background).

Symbols

The H2 complex occupies a segment of the chromosome 17 at a distance of some 15 cM from the centromere. The segment is between 0.1 and 1.5 cM long and contains a minimum of 10–15 loci. (The length of the segment and the number of loci in it depend on which loci one counts as belonging to the H2 complex.) To understand the designation of the congenic lines, **Table 1** illustrates the strains (background partners) from which they originated

with the locations. These are some of the congenic strains that are available today at the Jackson Laboratory in Bar Harbor, Maine.

Congenic strains can be named by the symbols of the parents' strains used in the original mating. They are separated by a period, i.e. B10.D2; this means that B10 originated from C57BL/10SN and D2 from DBA/2J. They can also be designated by using the name of the inbred partner followed by a hyphen and then the name of the differential allele contributed by the donor strain as described.

Numbers and letters in parenthesis are used when several different strains are derived from one initial cross.

There are also symbols that originated for laboratory purposes only but subsequently were used in the literature, i.e. (5M), (HW80), (HW19).

For designation of substrains, the addition of an abbreviation of the laboratory where they originated from is used, e.g.: Sn for Snell and By for Bailey.

When congenic strains differ at nonhistocompatibility loci, designations are used to distinguish the differential loci; e.g. Ea for erythrocyte antigen, Ly for lymphocyte, Thy for thymocyte and Tla for thymus-leukemia antigen.

See also: **Allelic exclusion; Genetic analysis at the phenotypic level; H2 class I; Inbred strains; Linkage**

Table 1 Examples of congenic strains

Strain	Genotype*	Donor strain
Congenic strains with differential locus in the H2 complex		
A.BY/Sn	H2^b Tla$^?$	Non-inbred
A.CA/Sn	H2^f Tla^a	Non-inbred
A.SW/Sn	H2^s Tla^b	Non-inbred
B6.AKR-H-2^h/FlaEg	H2^k	AKR/JBy
B6.C-H-2^d/aBy (HW19)	H2^d	BALB/cBy
B10.A/SgSn	H2^a Tla^a	A/WySn
B10.AKM/Sn	H2^m Tla^k	AKR.M/oSn
B10.Br/SgSn	H2^k Tla^a	C57BR/cdJ
B10.D2/nSn	H2^d Tla^c Hc^l	DBA/2
B10.HTG/2Cy	H2^g	HTG/GoSfSn
C3H.HTG/Sn	H2^g Tla$^{b?}$	HTG/Sn
C3H.NB/Sn	H2^p Tla$^{c?}$	Non-inbred
C3H.SW/Sn	H2^b Tla$^{b?}$	Non-inbred
Congenic strains with differential locus at H loci other than H2		
B6.H-1^b/By (HW80)	H-1^b, c, Hbb^d	BALB/cBy
B6.C-H-7^b/By (HW23)	H-7^b, Mod-1^a	BALB/cBy
B6.C-H-8^c/By (HW96)	H-8^c	BALB/cBy
B6.C-H-15^c/By (HW13J)	H-15^c	BALB/cBY
Congenic strains with differential locus that determines nonhistocompatibility cell membrane alloantigens		
B6.RIII(76NS)/Sn	Ea-2^a	RIII
B6.PL-Ly-2^{a}Ly-3^a/Cy	Ly-2^a Ly-3^a	PL/J
B6.PL-Thy-1^a/Cy	Thy-1^a	PL/J
BALB/c-Igh^b/Smn (C.B-17) Igh^b		C57BL/Ka
BALB/c-Igh^d/Smn (C.B-20) Igh^d		AL/N
C57BL/6-Igh^a (B6.C20)	Igh^a	BALB/cAn

*The genotypes listed are from The International Committee on Standardized Genetic Nomenclature for Mice. Genetic mutations of each gene are identified by superscript numbers or letters. For example, H2^b is a specific mutation of the histocompatibility locus 2 (H2) gene.

disequilibrium; Mouse inbred strains; Mouse inbred strains, origins of; Transgenic animals.

Further reading

Federation of American Societies for Experimental Biology (1979) Inbred animals. In: Altman PL and Dittmer D (eds) *Inbred and Genetically Defined Strains of Laboratory Animals*, Part 1: *Mouse and Rat*, pp 1–4. Bethesda, MD: Biological Handbooks.

Flaherty L (1981) Congenic strains. In: Foster HL, Small JD and Fox JG (eds) *The Mouse in Biomedical Research*, vol I, pp 215–222. London: Academic Press.

Green MC and Witham BA (1991) Histocompatibility and other cell membrane alloantigens. In: Green MC and Witham BA (eds) *Handbook of Genetically Standardized Jax Mice*, 4th edn, pp 4.1–4.13. Bar Harbor ME: Jackson Laboratory.

Klein J (ed) (1982) The experimental animal. In: *Immunology: The Science of Self–Nonself Discrimination*, pp 41–53. New York: Wiley.

Klein J (ed) (1996) The Story. In: *Natural History of the Major Histocompatibility Complex*, pp 2–12. New York: Wiley.

Klein J (1989) Congenic mice and segregating inbred strains. In: Lyon MF and Searle AG (eds) *Genetic Variants and Strains of the Laboratory Mouse*, 2nd edn, pp 707–825. New York: Oxford University Press.

Lyon MF (1989) Rules and Guidelines for gene nomenclature. In: Lyon MF and Searle AG (eds) *Genetic Variants and Strains of the Laboratory Mouse*, 2nd edn, pp 1–11. New York: Oxford University Press.

Morse H (1981) The laboratory mouse – a historical perspective. In: Foster HL, Small JD and Fox JG (eds) *The Mouse in Biomedical Research*, vol I, pp 1–16. London: Academic Press.

Silverstein AM (1989) Transplantation and immunogenetics. In: *A History of Immunology*, pp 275–304. San Diego: Academic Press.

Snell GD and Stimpfling JH (1966) Genetics of tissue transplantation. In: Green EL (ed) *Biology of the Laboratory Mouse*, pp 457–591. New York: McGraw Hill.

CONTACT HYPERSENSITIVITY

PS Friedmann, Department of Dermatology, Liverpool University, Liverpool, UK

Contact hypersensitivity is a form of delayed-type or cell-mediated hypersensitivity expressed in the skin. It is initiated by agents/antigens that penetrate through the outer epidermal barrier (stratum corneum) and reach the viable layers of the epidermis. Once the immune system has been activated via the epicutaneous route, topical re-exposure to the relevant antigen elicits an inflammatory response, characterized by edema formation, which reaches a maximum 48–72 h later. In humans, immunological memory to contact antigens is long-lived, whereas in mice it is usually reported as being transient, lasting only a few weeks.

Functional significance

Contact hypersensitivity is probably important for protective immunity against tumors and microbes, such as viruses, fungi and parasites (ticks and mites), that invade the skin; however, there is also a response to environmental substances that enter the skin, causing the clinical condition of allergic contact eczema/dermatitis.

Immunobiology

Activation of the immune system via the epicutaneous contact route is dependent upon several factors.

Antigen potency

Some antigens, such as 2,4-dinitrochlorobenzene (DNCB), pentadecylcatechol (urushiol of poison ivy) and diphenylcyclopropenone (diphencyprone) are potent and can sensitize all subjects. Many organic compounds and inorganic salts of metals such as nickel, cobalt and chromium are weak antigens and appear only to sensitize some subjects.

Genetic factors

In experimental animals there are clearly genetic controls of immune reponsiveness. Thus, inbred guinea pigs of strain XIII can be sensitized with mercury but not chromate or beryllium, whereas animals of strain II can be sensitized with chromate and beryllium but not with mercury. Evidence in humans is less clearcut. With regard to a strong antigen (DNCB), it seems that everyone can become sensitive but there is a normal distribution of the degree of sensitivity. Family studies have indicated that 'high responder' characteristics are transmitted to children. Studies of HLA linkage in subjects with the propensity to form numerous allergic sensitivities to environmental substances have not found positive evidence of genetic control.

Intact lymphatic drainage

Guinea pigs cannot be sensitized if antigen is applied to islands of skin lacking lymphatic drainage. This is because the early stages of the induction process involve circulation of antigen-bearing cells via the lymphatics to the draining lymph nodes.

Antigen-presenting cells

The epidermis is populated with Langerhans cells. These are leukocytes whose function is presentation of antigens to the appropriate CD4$^+$ T lymphocytes. They have long dendritic processes ramifying between the epidermal cells, forming a network likely to be encountered by any organism or antigen which penetrates through the stratum corneum barrier. They are characterized by a formalin-resistant membrane ATPase, a specific cytoplasmic organelle,

the Birbeck granule, membrane antigens including CD1a (T6), class II major histocompatibility complex (MHC) antigens and costimulatory molecules B7-1 and B7-2. Langerhans cells also express various adhesion molecules including E-cadherin, probably necessary for maintaining position in the epidermis, and ICAM-1 and LFA-1, necessary for their migration to the regional lymph node and interaction with T cells.

Induction of contact sensitivity

When epicutaneously applied antigen reaches the Langerhans cells they exhibit signs of activation, as shown by formation of coated pits, appearance of Birbeck granules and loss of surface ATPase activity. During the next 1–4 h antigen-bearing Langerhans cells emigrate from the epidermis and are found in the superficial dermis. They are observed in the lymphatics leaving the site and by 24 h they have reached the draining lymph node. This is the site of interaction with the appropriate antigen-specific CD4$^+$ T lymphocytes, which are activated to proliferate. Langerhans cell migration is dependent upon expression of ICAM-1 and LFA-1; mice treated with antibodies against these adhesion molecules fail to develop contact sensitivity and antigen-bearing Langerhans cells fail to reach the regional lymph nodes. Also, evidence suggests that tumor necrosis factor α (TNFα) is an important mediator in stimulation of Langerhans cell migration. The interaction between Langerhans and T cells is via the T cell receptor and antigen–MHC complex and also includes LFA-1/ICAM-1, LFA-3/CD2 and B7-1/CD28 recognition. Additional cytokine signals including interleukin 1β (IL-1β) and possibly IL-12 result in differentiation of T cells of the T_H1 type. It is not known to what extent Langerhans cells have to 'process' the antigen. It seems likely that small molecules (haptens), such as DNCB or nickel, may not be processed as they could bind directly to the MHC class II epitopes important for recognition by the T cell receptor. However, evidence is emerging that even small molecules may require metabolic conversion from the prohapten to the immunogenic hapten.

The sequence of events in which Langerhans cells become activated and leave the epidermis *en route* for the regional lymph nodes appears to be determined at least in part by the antigen. Thus, in contrast to DNCB, a potent antigen, 2,4-dichloronitrobenzene (DCNB), a nonsensitizer, does not induce emigration of Langerhans cells, although it is absorbed through the epidermis equally, and has equal protein-binding properties. It would be interesting to know if DCNB can bind directly to the MHC class II determinants.

Dose–response relationships

As for other physiological systems, the immune system obeys a variety of dose–response relationships. These have been studied in mice and humans using experimental contact sensitivity. Firstly, increasing the concentration of antigen per unit area leads to an increase in the proportion of reactive subjects. Thus, using a 3 cm diameter circle on the forearm, application of 62.5 μg DNCB sensitized 8%, 116 μg sensitized 50% and 500 μg sensitized 100% of experimental volunteers. Not only are more subjects sensitized by increased concentrations of antigen, but also their degree of sensitivity increases linearly with the log of sensitizing dose. By contrast, when concentration is kept constant then, over a wide range, changes of total dose and area of application have relatively little effect. These observations imply that, although the number of Langerhans cells reaching the lymph node is important, it is actually the number of antigen molecules per Langerhans cell that is the major determinant in the activation of specific T cells and their subsequent clonal expansion. Of course, at small areas (less than 1 cm diameter) this ceases to be true and the number of Langerhans cells also becomes critical.

Expression of contact hypersensitivity

When a sensitized animal or person re-encounters an antigen, a series of events occurs which results in the clinically recognizable response of contact hypersensitivity. The response is characterized by vasodilation (erythema), edema of both dermis and epidermis, fibrin deposition and the accumulation of an inflammatory infiltrate of monocyte/macrophages and lymphocytes. Detectable sensitivity reflects the presence of specifically committed CD4+ lymphocytes circulating and trafficking through the tissues. Their numbers presumably determine the magnitude of the reaction to antigenic challenge; thus, in fact, subclinical sensitization could be present if the clone of T cells had not expanded sufficiently to leave the lymph node, although 'memory' would have been established. There is clear evidence that such subclinical sensitization can occur. The extent of the clonal proliferation appears to be proportional to the 'drive' from antigen-bearing Langerhans cells, reflected in the increasing degree of reactivity induced by increasing sensitizing doses of antigen.

One of the unanswered questions is whether Langerhans cells have to participate in the secondary presentation of antigen to passing T cells to initiate the response. It seems probable that they are required.

The normal traffic of T cells through the tissues is light and hence the likelihood of the appropriately committed T cell passing by and encountering a few antigen-bearing Langerhans cells in the superficial dermis must be so low that the efficiency and reliability of the system as one of protection would be quite hopeless; therefore there must be initial processes, independent of the physical presence of T cells, which can increase cellular traffic. In rodents, mast cells have been implicated as providing such a mechanism. In humans, the evidence is against the involvement of mast cells. However, the skin 'senses' physical or chemical perturbation, whether by irritant or antigen, by activation of a range of mechanisms aimed at increasing the speed and efficiency of T cell traffic and hence immune surveillance. The mechanisms activated include production of cytokines, upregulation of adhesion molecules on endothelial cells and translocation of Langerhans cells from the epidermis to the superficial dermis.

Cytokines

Within 15 min of application of a contact sensitizer to mouse skin, IL-1β gene transcription is activated in Langerhans cells. Other cytokines including IL-1α, TNFα and chemokines IP-10 and MIP-2 are also upregulated within a few hours. In mice, macrophage migration inhibition factor is also expressed. Some evidence suggests that keratinocytes rather than Langerhans cells are the source of these, and that they are induced by contact sensitizers but not by irritants.

Adhesion molecule expression

Dermal microvascular endothelial cells show upregulation of expression of E-selectin, first observable, 2 h after application of provoking chemicals. ICAM-1 and VCAM-1 increase from 4–6 h onwards and reach a maximum by 24 h. The upregulation of adhesion molecules is seen with both irritants and antigens, and whether individuals are sensitive or 'naive'. These events precede any cellular infiltration. Lymphocyte infiltration is first detectable by 8 h. In individuals sensitive to the provoking substance, a few activated T cells expressing CD25 (IL-2 receptor α chain) are seen at 8 h. After this the reaction builds into a full 'positive response' with heavy infiltration of mononuclear cells. In nonsensitive subjects the various features all subside over the next 12–24 h. Thus, the tissue elements in skin respond to perturbation by activating mechanisms designed to increase the traffic of T cells through the tissues. If an appropriate T cell encounters its target antigen on a Langerhans cell, it is activated to release interferon γ (IFNγ), and a general and nonspecific recruitment of other lymphocytes occurs. This continued accumulation of cells appears to be mediated in large part by IFNγ, as inoculation of rats with a monoclonal antibody to IFNγ reduced by 50–90% the migration of lymphocytes into reaction sites.

Dose–response relationships

As for the induction component of the immune response, so the expression component also exhibits predictable dose–response relationships. Application of a graded series of challenge doses to sensitized subjects elicits a graded series of inflammatory responses. There are several methods for quantifying responses, including measurement of thickness of the edema with calipers or ultrasound, measurement of the redness with reflectance instruments, measurement of the blood flow with a laser Doppler flowmeter, and in experimental animals accumulation of radiolabeled cells can be determined. None of the methods are perfect and various caveats apply to them all. The main one is that at large responses, when edema formation is great enough to cause blistering, all the methods, with the possible exception of   radio-labeled cell accumulation, break down.

The mechanisms by which the inflammatory reaction of contact hypersensitivity resolves are not clear. Postulated mechanisms include induction of immunosuppressive cytokines, such as IL-10, or apoptosis of the effector T cell.

See also: **Antigen, entry into the body; Antigen-presenting cells; Antigen presentation via MHC class II molecules; Mast cells; Cell-mediated immunity; Delayed-type hypersensitivity; Eczema; Hapten;** **Macrophage migration inhibitory factor (MIF); Skin, contribution to immunity.**

Further reading

Enk AH and Katz SI (1992) Early molecular events in the induction phase of contact sensitivity. *Proceedings of the National Academy of Sciences of the USA* 89: 1398–1402.

Friedmann PS (1989) Contact hypersensitivity. *Current Opinion in Immunology* 1: 690–693.

Friedmann PS (1989) The immunology of allergic contact dermatitis: the DNCB story. In: Dahl MV (ed) *Advances in Dermatology*, 5th edn, pp 175–195. Chicago: Year Book-Medical.

Friedmann PS (1991) Graded continuity, or all or none – studies of the human immune response. *Clinical Experimental Dermatology* 16: 79–84.

Friedmann PS and Moss C (1985) Quantification of contact hypersensitivity in man. In: Maibach HI and Lowe NJ (eds) *Models in Dermatology*, pp 275–281. Basle: Karger.

Friedmann PS, Moss C, Shuster S and Simpson JM (1983) Quantitative relationships between sensitising dose of DNCB and reactivity in normal subjects. *Clinical and Experimental Immunology* 53: 709–711.

Friedmann PS, Strickland I, Memon AA and Johnson PM (1993) Early time course of recruitment of immune surveillance in human skin after chemical provocation. *Clinical and Experimental Immunology* 91: 351–356.

Macatonia SE, Edwards AJ and Knight SC (1986) Dendritic cells and the initiation of contact sensitivity to fluorescein isothiocyanate. *Immunology* 59: 509–514.

Polak L, Barnes JM and Turk JL (1968) The genetic control of contact sensitisation to inorganic metal compounds in guinea pigs. *Immunology* 14: 707–711.

Walker FB, Smith PO and Maibach HI (1967) Genetic factors in human allergic contact dermatitis. *International Archives of Allergy and Applied Immunology* 32: 453–462.

CONTRACEPTION, IMMUNOLOGICAL

GP Talwar, International Centre for Genetic Engineering and Biotechnology, New Delhi, India

A major technological advance in the twentieth century was the development of a number of methods to prevent an unwanted pregnancy. Amongst newer methods currently under development are those which employ immunological approaches. Vaccines inducing appropriate immune response have been made, with demonstrated ability to control fertility in experimental animals, including subhuman primates. Extensive safety and toxicology studies have shown the safety and reversibility of some of these vaccines, and these, with due approval of the drugs regulatory authorities and institutional ethics committees, have undergone clinical trials in humans. Six vaccines have completed phase I clinical trials documenting their safety and reversibility – three vaccines in women and three in men. One vaccine has also successfully completed the phase II trials in women, providing evidence for its efficacy in preventing pregnancy. These trials have established the titers of antibodies and other characteristics (avidity, immunodominant epitopes, bioneutralization capacity) to achieve efficacy. Of interest is the application of some of these vaccines in hormone-dependent cancers (carcinoma of the prostate) and lung cancers secreting human chorionic gonadotropin (hCG).

Principle

The rationale behind birth control vaccines is the generation of antibodies and/or cell-mediated immune responses (CMIs) against either a hormone or gamete antigen(s) important for the success of reproduction. The production of the gametes in both males and females is critically regulated by hormones. A cascade of hormones is involved, starting from the gonadotropin-releasing hormone (GnRH or LHRH) secreted by the hypothalamus. This decapeptide hormone, common to both males and females, stimulates the production and secretion of the two gonadotropins follicle stimulating hormone (FSH) and luteinizing hormone (LH) by the pituitary. These act in concert on the gonads to generate eggs or sperm from the ovaries or the testes, respectively (**Figure 1**).

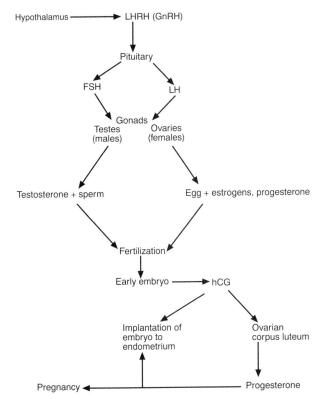

Figure 1 Hormones involved in the production of gametes and sex steroids. Antibodies inactivating one or more of these hormones would block fertility. hCG secretion from the embryo starts at the preimplantation stage. It has a role in nidation (initiation of pregnancy) and in its sustenance for 7 weeks by production of progesterone from ovaries.

The fertilized egg also makes the hormone hCG, secretion of which by the preimplantation human embryo is detectable in culture following *in vitro* fertilization prior to transfer to the uterus. Evidence points to a crucial role of this hormone in implantation, and antibodies inactivating hCG intercept implantation. Following implantation, the amount of hCG secreted increases sharply until 7–9 weeks of pregnancy, after which it declines to a lower level and stays so throughout pregnancy in humans. A second important biological role of hCG is in sustenance of the ovarian corpus luteum and in continued production of progesterone for the first 7–9 weeks, after which the placenta takes over the production of progesterone. hCG thus has a dual role, in establishment of pregnancy (implantation of the embryo into the endometrium) and in its sustenance for at least 7–9 weeks. Antibodies against hCG can prevent the establishment of the pregnancy if these are pre-existing in the circulation by virtue of active immunization. Antibodies given passively at the postimplantation stage but during the first 7 weeks of pregnancy have been shown, in baboons, to terminate pregnancy and thus act as an abortifacient.

Vaccines under development

Antibodies inactivating any one or more of the hormones depicted in **Figure 1** would theoretically result in impairment of fertility. However, intervention in the action of LHRH would also block the production of sex steroids. This may be desirable for the control of fertility of animals (dogs, cats, animals raised for meat) but not acceptable for contraception in humans. It should be noted, however, that LHRH secretion remains suppressed during lactational amenorrhea. Family planning advocates recommended spacing of children by breast-feeding, which in ancient societies was a 'natural' method of stopping ovulation. But to keep LHRH, and thereby ovulation, suppressed, the breast suction must take place frequently during the day and the night, a *modus vivendi* not easily practicable for modern women. An alternative would be to inactivate LHRH by circulating antibodies by immunization with the LHRH vaccine to prolong lactational amenorrhea and interchild interval. LHRH vaccine is thus conceivable as a postpartum vaccine and can have a special niche in the contraceptive array. Fraser and colleagues have reported the block of ovulation in breast-feeding women for 9–11 months by using an LHRH agonist.

Blocking ovulation has been the principal strategy for contraception in oral pills and contraceptive steroids delivered as injections. Most of them inhibit the production of the normal sex steroids by the woman, and their deficiency is made good by the synthetic hormonal analogs administered. It will be counter-productive to have a vaccine which would also demand synthetic hormones as implants for retention of libido and other metabolic functions. Hence an LHRH vaccine will not in general be suitable for contraception, other than in the period following delivery of the child and during lactation where physiologically LHRH secretion remains inhibited.

In contrast, if immunological interception is tar-geted at hCG, the normal hormonal cascade would stay intact. The woman would ovulate and produce normal levels of sex steroids. The intervention occurs only following fertilization at the preimplantation stage. These were amongst the considerations that led to hCG being the preferred target for the first type of birth control vaccines devised.

Tables 1 and **2** summarize the many vaccines being made. It will be noted that the most advanced vaccines are those directed against hormones. Four vaccines are directed against hCG, two against LHRH and one against FSH.

A large number of vaccines are being made against sperm and egg antigens; the nature and status of these are summarized in **Table 2**. Additionally, one vaccine aims to block the uptake of an essential vitamin for embryo development.

Antibody response to 'self' hormones – need for carriers

βhCG or LHRH used as vaccines in humans would not by themselves induce appreciable antibody responses, especially when employing permissible but relatively weak adjuvants such as alum. Their immunogenicity is substantially enhanced, however, by linkage with an immunogenic carrier. Tetanus toxoid (TT), diphtheria toxoid (DT) and cholera toxin chain B (CTB) have been used for this purpose with successful results. They increase the immune response against the hormone and at the same time they generate antibodies against the carrier, which

Table 1 Birth control vaccines reaching clinical trial

Target	Vaccine	Destined use	Status	Principal investigator(s)
hCG	HSD-TT/DT	Women for reversible fertility control	Phase I safety and Phase II efficacy trials completed; prevents pregnancy at >50 ng ml^{-1} titers; no significant side-effects; ovulation maintained with regularity of menstrual cycles	G.P. Talwar and colleagues
hCG	βhCG-TT	Women for reversible fertility control	Phase I trials completed in India, Sweden, Finland, Brazil and Chile	G.P. Talwar and ICCR of Population Council
	βhCG-TT	Women for reversible fertility control	Phase I trials determining hormone profiles which remained normal	Horatio Croxatto Vivian Brache Rose Marie Thau
hCG	CTP-DT	Women for reversible fertility control	Phase I clinical trials conducted in Australia	V. Stevens Warren Jones
hCG	Vaccinia-βhCG anchored	Men and women, lung cancer-secreting hCG	Experimental efficacy *in vitro* and *in vivo* in nude mice on Chago cells; preliminary clinical trials in three lung cancer patients in Mexico	G.P. Talwar Debajit Biswas Carlos Gual
LHRH	LHRH-6 DLys-DT	Men, carcinoma of prostate	Phase I/phase II trials conducted in India and Austria on advanced stage patients with carcinoma of the prostate	G.P. Talwar S.N. Wadhwa S. Sharma J. Frick
LHRH	LHRH-1-TT	Men for fertility control with androgen supplement, and for carcinoma of the prostate	Experimental studies completed; phase I trials initiated in USA	Rose Marie Thau, Y. Tsong and colleagues
FSH	FSH	Men for fertility regulation without loss of libido and decline in testosterone	Phase I trials initiated in India	N.R. Moudgal

Table 2 Birth control vaccines under development at the experimental stage

Target	Vaccine	Destined use	Status	Principal investigator(s)
Riboflavin carrier protein (RCP)	Chicken RCP, CTP and RCP-DT	Pregnancy interception in females; renders males subfertile	Tested in rodents and primates. Immunodominant epitopes determined	P.R. Adiga
Sperm	LDH-C$_4$	Female fertility control	Immunodominant epitopes identified; protection studies in rabbits and baboons with partial success	E. Goldberg
Sperm	RSA	Male fertility control	Inhibition of sperm–egg interaction by monoclonal antibodies	M.G. O'Rand
Sperm	PH-20	Males and females	Fully effective in guinea pigs	P. Primakoff
Sperm	SP-10	Females	Intra-acrosomal protein. Vaccine trials in baboons caused reduction of fertility	John C. Herr
Sperm	HSA-63	Females	Antibodies inhibit human sperm penetration. Cross-reactive with SP-10	M.S. Liu
Sperm	FA-1	Females	Conserved across species Antibodies prevent human sperm penetration. Present in infertile patients; functional epitope identified	R.K. Naz
Sperm	FA-2	Females	Antibodies block human sperm penetration	R.K. Naz
Sperm	CS-1	Females	Antibodies inhibit first cleavage of pronuclear stage zygotes; antibodies present in infertile patients	R.K. Naz
Oocyte	Rabbit recombinant 55 and 75 kDa	Females	Immunization of cynomolgus monkey with 55 kDa protein leads to infertility without effecting ovarian function; 75 kDa protein causes ovarian dysgenesis	B.S. Dunbar
Oocyte	Human/cynomolgus macaque ZP3 peptide	Females	Immunization of cynomolgus macaques leads to infertility with normal ovarian functions	C.A. Mahi-Brown
Oocyte	Recombinant human ZP3/porcine ZP3	Females	Immunization of marmoset monkey leads to infertility associated with ovarian dysfunction characterized by suppression of folliculogenesis and depletion of the primordial follicle pool	R.J. Aitken
Oocyte	Pig zona pellucida	Females	Demonstrated effect of immunization for control of wild-life population	J.F. Kirkpatrick
Oocyte	Synthetic peptide corresponding to mouse ZP3	Females	Efficacy to block fertility in female mice without concomitant autoimmune oophoritis	K.S.K. Tung
Oocyte	Recombinant pig ZP1 and synthetic peptides	Females	Mapped the epitope for a monoclonal antibody inhibiting binding of pig and human sperm–egg interaction	K. Koyama

Table 2 Continued

Target	Vaccine	Destined use	Status	Principal investigator(s)
Oocyte	Porcine ZP3	Females	Immunization of bonnet monkey with porcine ZP3 along with permissible adjuvants leads to reversible block of fertility	S.K. Gupta
Oocyte	Bonnet monkey ZP1/ZP2/ZP3; synthetic peptides	Females	Cloning, sequencing and expression of bonnet monkey ZP1, ZP2 and ZP3. Active immunization with ZP3 and its synthetic peptides corresponding to monoclonal antibody identified epitopes	S.K. Gupta
Oocyte	Mouse ZP3 sythetic peptide KLH conjugate	Females	Immunization of Swiss mice leads to reversible block of fertility	J. Dean
Oocyte	Dog, cat, cow, pig, cynomolgus monkey and human ZPA/ZPB/ZPC	Females	Cloning, sequencing and expression of the various zona proteins. Testing efficacy to block fertility	Zonagen Inc.
Oocyte	Porcine ZP3 cynomolgus deglycosylated form	Females	Demonstrated contraceptive efficacy in squirrel monkeys and rabbits	A.G. Sacco

brings in an immunoprophylactic benefit to nonimmunized individuals. TT and DT are good carriers. However, repeated immunization with conjugates containing these carriers can cause hyper-responsiveness to the carrier, shutting off the immune response to the attached hormone. In humans, about 11–15% of subjects developed carrier-induced immunosuppression upon repeated use of TT-containing conjugates. The suppression could, however, be overcome by presenting the ligand on an alternative carrier, such as CTB. As has been shown by Eli Sercarz and colleagues, a protein such as lysozyme has both stimulating and inhibitory determinants. Proteins have epitopes stimulating T and B cells. A number of T helper determinants have been mapped in viral, bacterial and parasite coat proteins. Their judicious choice can enable communication with the entire major histocompatibility complex (MHC) spectrum, so that vaccines constructed using these peptides as carriers can elicit immune responses in individuals of different genetic background. Experimentally it has been found that the heterospecies dimer (HSD) hCG vaccine linked to peptides containing three different T cell epitopes induces as good, if not higher, antibody responses than TT or DT conjugates in mice of different genetic strains.

Vaccines in clinical trial and their current status

The hCG vaccines

Three vaccines have been developed against hCG for use as antifertility agents. One of them employs the carboxy-terminal 37 amino acid peptide (CTP) of the β subunit of hCG, another the entire βhCG, and the third hCG vaccine is an HSD composed of the β-hCG associated noncovalently with the α subunit of ovine LH. The ability of the subunits to combine is conserved across species. In fact, the HSD has a higher steroidogenic potency than the homospecies dimer hCG. The α peptide of another species would be expected to enhance immunogenicity of the vaccine in humans. Data in **Table 3** summarize the highest antibody titers attained in humans using the three types of hCG vaccine which have undergone phase I clinical trials. HSD is indeed the most immunogenic of the three constructs. Another feature of this vaccine is the higher bioneutralization capacity of the antibodies that it generates. Different epitopes in a macromolecular hormone antigen induce antibodies with variable capacities for inactivating the hormone. High titers of antibodies (as determined by radioimmunoassay) obtained against the CTPs of

Table 3 Characteristics of the antibodies generated by the three hCG vaccines during phase I clinical trials

	CTP37-DT[b] (Squalene + MDP + Arlacel A)[a]	βhCG-TT[c] (Alum)[a]	HSD-TT/DT[d] (Alum + SPLPS)[a]
Peak titers (ng ml^{-1})	36–127	120–1800	222–6000
Avidity (M^{-1})[e]	10^8	10^{10}	10^{10}
B/I index[f]	?	52	61
Cross-reaction with:			
hTSH and hFSH	–	–	–
hLH	–	+	+
Pancreatic cells	+[g]	–	–

[a]Adjuvant used.
[b]Jones et al (1988).
[c]Thau et al (1989).
[d]Om Singh et al (1989).
[e]Avidity data from collaborative studies.
[f]B/I bioneutralization index data from Talwar et al (1988).
[g]Data from Rose et al (1988).

βTSH or βhCG using strong adjuvants such as Freund's complete adjuvant do not always inactivate the bioactivity of the parent hormone, possibly due to the poor avidity of these antibodies. The affinity of hCG for its ovarian receptors is of the order of 10^9. Antibodies ten times less avid may not be able to prevent hCG binding to its receptors.

The lead work on the βhCG CTP vaccine was carried out by Vernon Stevens in Ohio. Phase I clinical trials of this vaccine were conducted by Warren Jones in Australia with the support of the WHO. The vaccine was employed at different doses in 20 women who had elective tubal ligation, another ten women served as vehicle controls. No significant side-effects ascribable to immunization were reported by the investigators. However, this vaccine could not proceed to phase II efficacy trials because it produced unacceptable side-effects in the first seven subjects enrolled in Sweden. Its efficacy in humans thus remains untested. Dirnhofer and colleagues have cast serious doubts on the efficacy of this vaccine.

The βhCG-TT vaccine was initially conceived and developed by Talwar and coworkers in New Delhi. Its early phase I trials were conducted in India. The same vaccine was taken up by the International Committee on Contraception Research of the Population Council and two series of phase I clinical trials were carried out, the first in Finland (Tapani Luukkainen), Sweden (Elof Johansson), Brazil (Elsimar Coutinho) and Chile (Horacio B. Croxatto), and the second in the Dominican Republic (Vivian Brache), Finland (Pekka Latheenmaki) and Chile (Horacio Croxatto). Both the trials in India and in other countries demonstrated the safety of the vaccine and lack of side-effects. Sequential bleeds provided data on the levels of FSH, LH, estradiol and progesterone, which remained normal with ovulatory cycles. In all centers the antibodies declined to near zero levels in the course of time in the absence of boosters, thus indicating the reversibility of the vaccine.

The HSD vaccine was made by Talwar and colleagues with the aim of further improving the immunogenicity of the βhCG-TT vaccine (**Table 3**). After confirming its safety, lack of side-effects and noninterference in ovulation and regularity of menstrual cycles, phase II efficacy trials were conducted with this vaccine in 148 women of proven fertility (at least 2 children) who were sexually active; 119 of them (80%) made antibodies above 50 ng ml^{-1} bioneutralization capacity, a threshold fixed for determining the effective titers. Women had the option of leaving the trial or taking booster injections as and when antibody titers declined towards or below 50 ng ml^{-1}. Only one pregnancy occurred in 1224 cycles, showing the high efficacy of the vaccine in preventing pregnancy as long as the titers remained above 50 ng ml^{-1}. The ability of antibodies to deter pregnancy was also confirmed by postcoital tests. The block of fertility was reversible. On decline of antibody titers below 35 ng ml^{-1} conceptions readily occurred (**Figure 2**). Those desirous of having another child, after a gap with the use of the vaccine, have carried pregnancy to term and have given birth to normal babies.

Optimization of the HSD   The HSD-hCG vaccine has provided the scientific foundations of a birth control vaccine which prevents pregnancy without impairing ovulation or deranging menstrual regularity. Its characteristics render it usable at all stages of reproductive life. It is, however, not yet ready as a product. Further optimization of the vaccine is

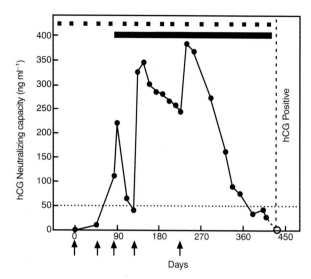

Figure 2 A representative subject showing the kinetics of anti-hCG titers (●--●), menstrual events (top squares) and the period of protection from pregnancy (solid line). This lady of 30 years of age with two live children and one elective termination of pregnancy was among the 119 subjects on which the efficacy of the HSD vaccine was determined in phase II trials. The graph also shows the reversibility of the vaccine with return of fertility in the cycle when her antibody titers declined to less than 5 ng ml^{-1} bioneutralization capacity. (Reproduced from Talwar et al (1994).)

necessary to enhance the percentage of high responders making antibodies above 50 ng ml^{-1}. The present vaccine is adsorbed on Alhydrogel. As more potent adjuvants get regulatory approval, their use may facilitate the enhancement of antibody titers. Another strategy will be the substitution of the DT/TT by T cell determinants communicating with the entire MHC spectrum.

We have determined the joint ability of three T cell epitope peptides derived from circumsporozoite protein of *Plasmodium falciparum*, respiratory syncitial virus and purified protein derivative (*Mycobacterium tuberculosis*) to generate higher titers of antibodies in seven genetic strains of mice than those obtained with DT as a carrier for the HSD. Encapsulation of the vaccine in biodegradable microspheres can also add to the immunogenicity and at the same time enable the delivery of multiple doses of the vaccine at a single contact point. To make the vaccine at low cost and in a reproducible manner on a large scale, it will be necessary to use recombinant DNA technology. βhCG has been expressed with and without fusion proteins in vaccinia as a naturally glycosylated peptide, in baculovirus with higher yield but somewhat different glycosylation, and in *Escherichia coli* and *Vibrio cholerae* with still higher yield unglycosylated. Live recombinant vaccines employing attenuated pox viruses,

adenoviruses, salmonella or BCG as vectors may offer very low cost vaccines generating a protective immune response over long periods. Ivan Roitt and colleagues have employed recombinant technology to make a mutant of βhCG lacking in reactivity with a panel of anti-hLH antibodies but preserving the immunoreactivity with monoclonal antibodies recognizing hCG.

Applications of the hCG vaccine in hCG-synthesizing lung cancers Although hCG is known mainly as a trophoblast product and its increased levels in serum or urine are employed as a diagnostic test for pregnancy, its synthesis and secretion has also been reported in about 30 different types of cancers. The function, if any, of hCG or its subunits made by tumor cells is unknown. Debajit Biswas and coworkers at Harvard Medical School observed that Chago cells derived from a human lung cancer produced hCG α chain, which promoted the growth of these tumor cells. Antibodies reacting with the hCG subunit, or antisense RNA, caused inhibition of cell proliferation. Cell clones derived from lung cancer make either isolated α or β chains or whole hCG. Antihormonal subunit antibodies given passively to nude mice bearing tumors formed from Chago cell implants have been shown to cause necrosis of the tumor. When tumor cells were exposed to antibodies from the time of implantation, growth was inhibited in a dose-dependent manner, with total absence of tumor growth at high doses of antibody.

Given that no effective chemotherapy is at present available for hCG-synthesizing lung cancers, regulatory permission was given in Mexico to carry out clinical trials with the hCG vaccine in three patients characterized on the basis of clinical manifestations backed by radiography, histopathology and serum βhCG levels. All three patients tolerated immunization with the vaccine well. The serum βhCG declined to near zero levels after immunization. No further metastasis occurred during 2.5 years of follow up and the Karnofsky index improved for one of the patients. These studies clearly need to be extended to a larger number of individuals in order to draw any conclusions regarding the efficacy of the hCG vaccine in such patients.

LHRH vaccines

Two vaccines against LHRH are in clinical trials in carcinoma prostate patients. The vaccine made by Rose Marie Thau, Y. Tsong and colleagues at the Population Council in New York has TT tagged at the N-terminus of the decapeptide, whereas the vaccine developed by Talwar and coworkers in New Delhi employs a modified LHRH with the glycine at position 6 replaced by D-lysine. This is linked through a spacer to DT.

The rationale employed in the New Delhi vaccine is to preserve the natural conformation of the LHRH, where N- and C-terminal amino acids are proximal to each other with a bend in the middle of the molecule. Substitution of glycine at position 6 by D-lysine stabilizes this conformation and also slows the catabolic degradation of LHRH by the enzyme cleaving at glycine 6.

Both vaccines are immunogenic in rodents, have passed through toxicology studies, and are in clinical trials. The Population Council vaccine (LHRH-1-TT) was tried in four orchiectomized men to determine the immunogenicity of the vaccine, its reversibility and immediate and delayed side-effects. These studies have shown that the vaccine was well tolerated and that although there was a large variability in antibody titers between the four subjects, they all made antibodies to LHRH. In order potentially to use this vaccine for male fertility control, these investigators have also carried out studies in rodents to assess the dose of androgens required to restore libido without reversing the inhibition of spermatogenesis.

The New Delhi LHRH vaccine (LHRH-6D-Lys-DT) has undergone phase I/phase II clinical trials in advanced stage patients with metastatic carcinoma of the prostate. In one study 24 patients received either 200 or 400 μg LHRH equivalent per injection. No ill-effects of immunization were reported in any of the studies despite the advanced age of the patients and their low health status. All the subjects made antibodies against LHRH and many, but not all, produced sufficiently high titers to cause depression of testosterone to castration levels. Prostatic-specific antigen serum levels declined significantly. Ultrasonography showed shrinkage of prostatic mass. These studies indicate the potential of this vaccine in prostatic hypertrophy as an inexpensive alternative to the LHRH synthetic analogs. Immunotherapeutic use could extend to endometriosis and precocious puberty, however clinical trials remain to be undertaken in these conditions.

The LHRH vaccine, with stronger adjuvants, also has applications for reversible fertility control of domestic pets. Given that this decapeptide hormone is identical in males and females, the same vaccine could be used in male and female animals.

FSH vaccine

This vaccine was conceived by Moudgal and colleagues for male fertility control on the basis of the requirement of FSH for spermatogenesis in primates. Passively administered antibodies to FSH caused a significant reduction of bonnet monkey sperm count without affecting testosterone. Ovine FSH was chosen as the antigen, which induced in monkeys both monkey and human FSH cross-reactive antibodies of high affinity. Immunization caused a reduction in sperm count and the fertilizing capacity of the remaining sperm was significantly reduced. A study conducted in three laboratories demonstrated that 25 out of 27 monkeys immunized with ovine FSH became infertile. Fertility was regained on decline of antibodies.

After toxicology studies and regulatory ethical approval, a phase I study with this vaccine was initiated in 19 adult human males in three centers in India. Antibodies were made by all of the subjects but the titers of antibodies reactive with human FSH were low. The mean avidity of the antibodies was also an order of magnitude lower than in the previous studies in primates. Vaccination was, however, well tolerated. There were variations in the levels of pituitary hormone such as prolactin in some subjects. No significant effect of immunization on sperm count was noted, presumably owing to the low titers of antibodies or an insufficient duration of the study. Repeat phase I trials are planned with the vaccine employed at different doses.

See also: **Autoimmunity; Infertility, immunological causes of; Neutralization of biological reactions by antibodies; Sex hormones and immunity; Vaccines.**

Further reading

Bronson RA, Alexander N, Anderson D, Ware Branch D and Kutteh WH (eds) (1996) *Reproductive Immunology*. Oxford: Blackwell.

Dirnhofer S, Klieber R, deLeeuw R *et al* (1993) Functional and immunological relevance of the carboxy terminal extension of human chorionic gonadotropin beta: implication for the WHO birth control vaccine. *FASEB Journal* 7: 1381–1385.

Dondero F and Johnson PM (eds) (1993) *Reproductive Immunology*, Serono Symposium vol 97. New York: Raven Press.

Gaur A, Arunan K, Singh Om *et al* (1990) Bypass by an alternate carrier of acquired unresponsiveness to hCG upon repeated immunization with tetanus conjugated vaccine. *International Immunology* 2: 151–155.

Gupta SK and Doberska C (eds) (1996) Zona pellucida glycoproteins and immunocontraception. *Journal of Reproduction and Fertility* 50 (suppl).

Jackson AM, Klonisch T, Lapthorn AJ *et al* (1996) Identification and selective destruction of shared epitopes in human chorionic gonadotropin beta subunit. *Journal of Reproductive Immunology* 31: 21–26.

Jones WR, Bradley J, Judd SJ *et al* (1988) Phase I clinical trial of a World Health Organization birth control vaccine. *Lancet* i: 1295–1298.

Kumar S, Talwar GP and Biswas DK (1991) Necrosis and inhibition of growth of human lung tumour by anti-αhCG antibodies. *Journal of the National Cancer Institute* **84**: 42–47.

Kurpisz M and Fernandez N (eds) (1995) *Immunology of Reproduction*. Oxford: Bios.

Om Singh, Rao LV, Gaur A, Sharma NC, Alam A and Talwar GP (1989) Antibody response and characteristics of antibodies in women immunized with three contraceptive vaccines inducing antibodies against human chorionic gonadotropin. *Fertility and Sterility* **52**: 739–744.

Rose NR, Burek CL and Smith JP (1988) Safety evaluation of hCG vaccine in primates: autoantibody production. In: Talwar GP (ed) *Contraception Research for Today and the Nineties*, pp 231–239, New York: Springer.

Talwar GP and Raghupathy R (eds) (1995) *Birth Control Vaccines*. Austin TX: RG Landes.

Talwar GP, Om Singh and Rao LV (1988) An improved immunogen for anti-human chorionic gonadotropin vaccine eliciting antibodies reactive with a conformation native to the hormone without crossreaction with human follicle stimulating hormone and human thyroid stimulating hormone. *Journal of Reproductive Immunology* **14**: 203–212.

Talwar GP, Rao KVS and Chauhan V (eds) (1994) *Recombinant and Synthetic Vaccines*. New Delhi: Narosa.

Talwar GP, Singh Om, Pal R *et al* (1994) A vaccine that prevents pregnancy in women. *Proceedings of the National Academy of Sciences of the USA* **91**: 8532–8536.

Thau R, Croxatto H, Luukkainen T *et al* (1989) Advances in the development of an antifertility vaccine. In: Mettler L and Billington WD (eds) *Reproductive Immunology*, pp 237–244. Amsterdam: Elsevier.

CONTRASUPPRESSION

Douglas R Green and **Patrick M Flood**, La Jolla Institute for Allergy and Immunology, La Jolla, California, USA

Contrasuppression refers to any immunoregulatory activity that facilitates immune responses by interfering with suppressive influences, without otherwise helping or augmenting the response. While this is the original definition given by RK Gershon who coined the term, it came to refer more specifically to a regulatory T cell activity, i.e. the function of T contrasuppressor cells. As is true for other regulatory T cells (e.g. suppressor T cells), the existence of contrasuppressor T cells as a discrete functional population is controversial.

In this brief overview, the concept of contrasuppression is reviewed from two perspectives. The first is an uncritical view of the original literature on the phenomenon; the second is from the standpoint of current thinking on the functions of T cells. From the outset, however, the reader should be aware that while most of the observations on contrasuppression have eluded biochemical and molecular characterization, they were described from a number of laboratories and continue to be reproduced. Although this state of affairs demands that all of the conclusions regarding contrasuppression be treated with caution, this regulatory phenomenon exists. Questions concerning whether or not contrasuppression is *important* are discussed in more detail below.

Background

The study of immunoregulatory T cells began in 1970, with the experiments of Gershon and Kondo, showing that T cells can adoptively transfer some forms of immunological tolerance. Work from a large number of laboratories focused on such suppressor T cells and their soluble mediators ('suppressor factors'). During the 1970s, complex regulatory pathways were described in which different T cell subpopulations induce, transduce and effect antigen specific suppression of immune responses. Intensive study of the regulatory cells and factors implicated their involvement in a range of immunologic phenomena.

Based on the idea that tolerance is due to active suppression of immunity and on the observation that cross-reactive antigens can sometimes break tolerance, in 1974 Gershon predicted that there is an immunoregulatory activity that functions to interfere with suppression. In 1981 his laboratory published a series of papers describing such an activity, and since then T cells with contrasuppressive activity have been identified in a number of different systems. In all cases, contrasuppression allows immune responses to proceed in the presence of demonstrable, active suppression.

Research on suppressor and contrasuppressor T

cells suddenly slowed in the mid- to late-1980s for several reasons. Most significantly, efforts to fully characterize antigen specific regulatory T cell factors uniformly failed, despite encouraging results early on. A second confounding problem was I-J, a marker that was associated with many regulatory T cells (including T contrasuppressor cells). Molecular analysis of the region of the major histocompatibility complex (MHC) to which I-J was mapped revealed an absence of any structural MHC gene encoding the molecule. These and other problems cast the study of regulatory T cells in a poor light. Nevertheless, several groups continue to successfully study these regulatory phenomena with interesting results, and therefore an open-minded outlook is warranted.

Characteristics of cells with contrasuppressive activity

The single discriminating characteristic of contrasuppressor T cells is their function: the ability to interfere with immune suppression *without* providing active help. Depending upon the system studied, this functional activity may appear to be antigen specific or nonspecific. Contrasuppressor cells act prior to suppressor cells, i.e. contrasuppressor cells do not restore responsiveness to previously suppressed cells, but rather interfere with inhibition. In some systems, contrasuppression has been shown to render target cells (helper T cells or B cells) resistant to subsequent suppressive influences. However, this does not rule out the possibility that some contrasuppressive effects are mediated by direct inhibition of suppressor functions in some systems.

In general most murine cells with contrasuppressive activity are Thy-1$^+$ and where examined, human and rodent contrasuppressor cells have also been found to be CD3ϵ^+. The cells are therefore likely to bear T cell receptors. In addition, most contrasuppressor cells are bound by the *Vicia villosa* lectin, but while this trait distinguishes them from other functional T cells (such as helper T cells) it does not provide a unique marker. It is important to note therefore, that binding of this N-acetyl-D-galactosamine-specific lectin does not *define* contrasuppressor cells, but rather provides a convenient means of enriching cells with functional contrasuppressive activity.

Contrasuppressive T cells are phenotypically heterogeneous with respect to CD4 and CD8. Functional contrasuppressor cells may be CD4$^+$, CD8$^+$, or CD4$^-$8$^-$, depending upon the system studied and the cellular interactions involved. Where examined, CD8$^+$ T contrasuppressor cells require the presence of a population of CD4$^-$, CD5^{hi}, CD8$^+$ T cells in order to mediate contrasuppression. Therefore, such

CD8$^+$ cells have been designated as inducer cells, or Tcsi. In contrast, where examined, CD4$^+$ T contrasuppressor cells have been found to act without a requirement for an intermediary (or 'transducer') population, and have therefore been designated as effector cells, or Tcse. The relationships between Tcsi and Tcse have not been rigorously explored.

Little is known about the T cell receptors of contrasuppressor cells. In one series of studies, a population of CD3$^+$, CD8 intraepithelial cells from murine intestine were found to have contrasuppressive activity *in vitro* and *in vivo*. Immunoprecipitation from the cell surface suggests that this population of T cells express the $\gamma\delta$ T cell receptor (TCR). Other contrasuppressor cells are likely to express the $\alpha\beta$ TCR, as has been observed in a T cell hybridoma with contrasuppressive activity.

One marker that has been associated with contrasuppressor T cells is 'I-J'. As mentioned above, the nature of I-J is controversial. Nevertheless, antisera and monoclonal antibodies with anti-I-J activity have been shown to remove cells with contrasuppressive activity in many different systems.

It is important to note that since contrasuppression is defined by function and not by cell phenotype, there is little evidence to suggest that contrasuppressor T cells represent a discrete T cell population. Although this remains a possibility, it is equally likely that contrasuppression represents a functional property of many T cells that may have other functions as well.

Experimental studies of contrasuppression

In order to study contrasuppressive effects, it is necessary (by definition) to employ a system involving active suppression of a measurable immune response. This necessarily complex situation is one source of the problems associated with this phenomenon (see below). Nevertheless, contrasuppression has been demonstrated in a number of different systems, both *in vitro* and *in vivo*.

In vivo studies of contrasuppression often take advantage of protocols for the induction of antigen-specific tolerance. For example, antigen-coupled spleen or peritoneal exudate cells, injected intravenously, induce an active state of tolerance that is blocked by the administration of T cells with contrasuppressive function. Such contrasuppressor cells may act either antigen specifically or nonspecifically, depending upon the source of the cells. Tolerance induced by oral administration of xenogeneic red blood cells is similarly blocked by contrasuppressor T cells derived from gut-associated lymphoid tissue.

In this system the contrasuppressive effect favors immunoglobulin A (IgA) responses, and the contrasuppressor cells appear to bear γδ T cell receptors (as determined by immunoprecipitation of the receptor on the enriched functional population).

Studies of the regulation of the adoptive transfer of contact hypersensitivity have also demonstrated the effects of contrasuppression *in vivo*. T Cells from tolerized animals inhibit the ability to T cells from immune animals to adoptively transfer immunity into naive recipients, and contrasuppressor T cells block this inhibitory effect. These hapten-specific contrasuppressor T cells have been generated by injection of haptenated Langerhans cells, haptenated murine IgG, or haptenated peritoneal exudate cells treated with antihapten antibody of the IgM, IgG1, or IgG3 subclasses. In each case *V. villosa* lectin-adherent T cells from the treated animals were found to be incapable of adoptively transferring immunity, but capable of blocking suppression of immune T cells. Further, these contrasuppressor T cells were found to release a cell-free factor that renders immune T cells resistant to suppression, either by inhibitory T cells or by the environment of a tolerized recipient.

A murine model of autoimmune nephritis has implicated contrasuppression in the development of autoimmunity. In the nephritis-prone kdkd mutant, T cells capable of contrasuppressing delayed-type hypersensitivity to renal tubule antigen appear with onset of autoimmunity. When these *V. villosa* lectin-adherent T cells were mixed with wild-type spleen cells and injected into kidney capsules, destruction of tubules and mononuclear infiltration followed. This was not observed with either population alone, nor with spleen cells plus lectin-nonadherent (and noncontrasuppressive) T cells. One interpretation of these results is that antitubule immunity is normally suppressed by an active mechanism, and that contrasuppressor cells from the autoimmune mice are capable of interfering with this suppression.

Another series of studies suggest that contrasuppressor T cells may be important in some forms of tumor immunity. Two fibrosarcoma cell lines, one regressive and one progressive, have strikingly different effects when haptenated and injected into animals. The haptenated progressor line was observed to induce T cells capable of suppressor hapten-specific responses *in vivo*, while the haptenated regressor line instead induced hapten-specific contrasuppressor cells. These effects were studied using the contact hypersensitivity systems mentioned above. The contrasuppressor T cells induced by the regressor line displayed markers common to such cells, and released a cell-free, hapten-specific, contrasuppress-

ive factor. The cells were used to generate a T cell hybridoma that constitutively produces this factor. Injection of hapten-immune mice with either the *in vivo* generated contrasuppressor cells or with the hybridoma-derived factor rendered these animals immune to haptenated progressor tumor cells (that otherwise grow in and eventually kill naive or hapten-immune animals).

A number of studies have characterized contrasuppression *in vitro*, including human contrasuppressor cells. As in the murine system, human contrasuppressor T cells were found to be adherent to the *V. villosa* lectin and to interfere with active, T cell-mediated inhibition of immune responses. The induction of these cells was found to be dependent upon antigen dose (the optimum dose depending upon HLA-DR type) and they have been shown to block suppression of both antibody responses and T cell proliferation *in vitro*.

Problems with contrasuppression

As mentioned above, the phenomenon of contrasuppression is controversial for a number of reasons. One of the most important reasons lies in the fact that contrasuppression is defined by its effects on suppression. However, the mechanisms of suppression (let alone contrasuppression) are unknown.

Regulatory cells are by their nature a property of the immune *system* whose activity can only be measured as a function of the immune activity of other cells. This complexity carries special problems of completely characterizing the activity of even a single component of these interactions. On the other hand, the demonstration of this functional activity *in vivo*, and the common features of the cells responsible for contrasuppressive function, suggest that this may be an important, if poorly understood phenomenon.

No known lymphokine or other well-defined molecule, either alone or in combination with other molecules, can fully account for the phenomenon of contrasuppression. The suggestion that at least some contrasuppressor cells release antigen-specific contrasuppressor factors presents additional problems, since no such facto (suppressor or contrasuppressor) has been well characterized. The alternative, that some contrasuppressor T cells act via the release of one or more lymphokines has not been fully explored. Thus the molecular basis of contrasuppression in any system is unknown.

It is unlikely that the problems associated with the study of contrasuppression will be solved in the near future. It *is* likely, however, that the phenomenon will return in a different guise as we learn more about the workings of the immune system as a whole.

[This article is reproduced from the first edition (1992)]

See also: **CD3; CD4; CD5; CD8; I-J; Lectins; Suppressor T lymphocytes; T cell receptor, αβ; T cell receptor, γδ; Thy-1.**

Further reading

Diele F, Colonna-Romana G, Zingone D and Salerno A (1992) Impairment of contrasuppressor activity in mice infected with the paramyxovirus of Newcastle disease. *Immunology* 75: 245–249.

Flood PM and Cruse JM (eds) (1988) Contrasuppression, symposium. *Immunological Research* 7: 1–92.

Ikemoto K, Kobayashi M, Fukumoto T, Morimatsu M, Pollard RB and Suzuki F (1996) 2-Carboxyethylgerm-anium sesquioxide, a synthetic organogermanium compound, as an inducer of contrasuppressor T cells. *Experientia* 52: 159–166.

Paliwal V, Friedman AM, Ptak W and Askenase PW (1994) Monoclonal, antigen-specific, T cell contrasuppressor factor expresses determinants of TCR alpha-chain (not necessarily TCR beta-chain), having a molecular mass of about 40 kDa. *Journal of Immunology* 152: 2811–2820.

Pecquet SS, Zazulak J, Simpson SD and Ernst PB (1992) Reconstruction of xid mice with donor cells enriched for CD5$^+$ B cells restores contrasuppression. *Annals of the New York Academy of Sciences* 651: 173–175.

Ptak W, Bryniarski K, Szczepanik M, Ptak M and Plewska A (1992) Regulation of contact sensitivity: contrasuppressor T cells and contrasuppressor factor downregulate efferent T suppressor cells. *Cellular Immunology* 144: 95–104.

Simpson SD and Ernst PB (1995) Mice with the xid mutation lack the regulatory antibodies that are necessary for the induction of contrasuppression. *Cellular Immunology* 164: 126–132.

COOPERATION, MECHANISMS OF CELLULAR

Theodore J Yun, Department of Microbiology, University of Washington, Seattle, Washington, USA

Edward A Clark, Departments of Microbiology and Immunology, University of Washington, Seattle, Washington, USA

Various pathogens, ranging from viruses to helminths, can invade the host by a number of pathways, and usually the pathogen is cleared through an orchestrated immune response. Moreover, protection from a repeat infection is provided by a memory response, which, relative to the primary response, is rapid and highly specific. This coordination of multiple effector cells relies on communication between cells of the immune system and cells in their environment. Many of the components involved in cellular cooperation are molecules that are produced by the cells which bind to receptors on other cells. We can roughly divide these components into two major categories: membrane-bound and secreted. This discussion will focus on certain membrane-bound molecules and their influence on the immune response.

The immune response has many examples of cellular cooperation. Tissues secreting chemokines alert the immune response to areas of damage and potential pathogen invasion. Adhesion molecules, such as selectins and integrins, present on cells of the tissues and leukocytes mediate cellular homing, margination and migration. Once these cells are in the site of damage, membrane-bound receptors in conjunction with secreted cytokines activate immune cells and enable them to develop a potent effector reaction. As a prototypical example of cellular cooperation in the immune response, we will focus on germinal center (GC) development in the response to T cell dependent antigens. Consider the formation and maintenance of GCs developed during primary immune responses. This entire process relies upon communication between multiple cells, including T cells, B cells, interdigitating dendritic cells (IDCs), germinal center dendritic cells (GCDCs) and follicular dendritic cells (FDCs). Resting T cells interact with activated IDCs presenting antigen initially captured from local sites of damage, such as mucosal or epidermal tissues. B cells, also activated through antigen encounter, are further helped along their maturation pathway by interaction with the T cells. The activated B cells undergo affinity maturation by interaction with antigen bound on FDCs. Early in this process, somatic hypermutation of B cell antigen receptors (BCRs) generates novel specificities, some of which have greater affinity for antigen. Antigen uptake mediated by the BCRs, followed by processing and presentation in class II major histocompatibility complex (MHC) molecules to the cognate T cells results in T cell help that propagates the B cell. B cells bearing novel specificities which have lost affinity to antigen, or have acquired affinity to another antigen, must be eliminated. Through types of receptor-mediated 'reciprocal dialogues' in the GC, lymphocytes can be induced to proliferate and differentiate, or, equally as important, can be instructed to undergo programmed cell death.

Membrane-bound molecules are critical for lymphocyte activation

Lymphocyte activation by a foreign antigen is the initial step in the humoral response against T-dependent antigens. We generally regard activation of a resting B or T cell as a multistage process involving multiple signals transduced through membrane receptors. This model is based on the historic two-signal model initially proposed by Bretscher and Cohn. For example, a T cell requires costimulation in addition to the signal it receives from its antigen receptor binding to its cognate MHC/foreign antigen complex. If the T cell fails to receive costimulatory signals, the model proposes that the cells cannot be activated. Similarly, multiple signals are required to activate B cells. Some studies have suggested that resting lymphocytes which receive one signal are rendered unresponsive, or anergic. Characterization of single molecules which synergize with antigen receptor signals to activate lymphocytes has remained elusive. This fact emphasizes the dialogue of multiple receptor signals between cells during lymphocyte activation. The following discussion will focus primarily on the recent body of evidence dealing with specific membrane-bound coreceptors that appear to be necessary for activating or downregulating T cells or B cells. Two receptor/counter-receptor families will be discussed: members of the immunoglobulin superfamily (IgSF), and members of the tumor necrosis factor receptor (TNF-R) and tumor necrosis factor (TNF) family. The IgSF molecules, CD80/CD86 (B7-1/B7-2) interact with two distinct counter-receptors, CD28 and CD152 (CTLA-4), which either activate or downregulate T cells, respectively. Currently, novel members of the TNF-R/TNF family are rapidly being characterized. Functionally, these molecules appear to have an important role in determining cell fate, as exemplified by CD40 and CD95 (Fas).

CD80/CD86: CD28/CD152 interactions have dual roles in regulating lymphocytes

CD80 and CD86 are members of the IgSF. They are approximately 60 kDa in size. Both bear similar overall structure, with two extracellular Ig-like domains, a transmembrane domain and cytoplasmic tail; however, at the amino acid level they have only 25% homology to each other. Interestingly, the cytoplasmic domains of CD80 and CD86 barely resemble each other, which suggests different signaling functions.

Consistent with their role as critical costimulatory molecules in the initial steps of T cell activation, CD80/86 are expressed on antigen-presenting cells (APCs), such as IDCs, GCDCs, Langerhans cells and activated monocytes. The expression of these molecules can be induced upon activation of other APCs. In particular, CD80/86 are upregulated on B cells by cytokines, such as interleukin 4 (IL-4), or by receptor cross-linking of the BCR, MHC class II or CD40. There are differences in expression between CD80 and CD86, although the functional relevance of this is unclear. For example, during activation of B cells, CD86 is expressed more rapidly than CD80.

While CD80 and CD86 have both been demonstrated to bind their counter-receptors CD28 and CD152, there is suggestive evidence that CD80 and CD86 may have different biologic functions. This variance may, in part, be due to differences in ligation of receptor – such as variation in binding kinetics and avidity – and in induction and expression of CD80 and CD86. For example, in the GC, expression of CD80 and CD86 differs between B cell centroblasts and centrocytes. Ectopic over-expression of CD86 results in deletion of B cells by CD28[+] T cells which can be prevented by introduction of hen egg lysozyme (HEL)-specific B cells, T cells and the HEL antigen. This suggests that CD86 can play a role in elimination of nonspecifically activated B cells. Comparing immune responses of mice which are CD80[-/-]CD86[+/+], CD80[+/+]CD86[-/-] or CD80[-/-]CD86[-/-] suggests that either molecule is required to mount a humoral response, depending on the route of antigen administration. Either CD80 or CD86 is sufficient for immune responses to soluble antigen inoculated intradermally. However, CD86, but not CD80, is required for antigens inoculated intravenously.

CD28 costimulates T cells

CD28, one of the two known ligands for CD80/86, is also a member of the IgSF. It is expressed on the surface as a 90 kDa, disulfide-linked homodimer. CD28 is mainly expressed on T lineage cells, including thymocytes, but may also be found on plasmablasts. The level of expression varies, depending on the lineage and the activation state. Upon activation of a mature T cell, either by mitogen or by cross-linking of the TCR, the expression of CD28 increases. However, following this upregulation, ligation of CD28 by its counter-receptors apparently induces a transient negative feedback to downregulate expression and render the cells unresponsive to CD28 signaling.

CD28 usually transduces a positive signal that promotes proliferation of TCR-stimulated T cells. Studies demonstrating its importance in the initial steps of T cell activation include *in vivo* blockade of its counter-receptors, CD80 and CD86, and genetic deletion of CD28 expression. In addition to its costimulatory role, CD28 ligation can enhance the production of various cytokines, such as IL-2, IL-4 and IL-10. CD28$^{-/-}$ mice have reduced IgG responses to T-dependent antigens and reduced GC formation. Taken together, these observations suggest that CD28 is critical for T cell-dependent antibody responses. Responses generally attributed to T_H1 cells remain. In some experimental systems, CD28 ligation rescues T cells from anergy. CD28 may also play a role in prolonging an activated T cell's fate and initiating its differentiation into the memory phenotype. In the absence of CD28 signaling, activated T cells do not survive as long. CD28 costimulation can upregulate the expression of Bcl-xL, a protein that prevents CD95-induced apoptosis.

CD152 downregulates T cells

In addition to their role of providing costimulation to T cells, CD80 and CD86 may also play a role in downregulating the immune response. A second counter-receptor, CD152, binds to both CD80 and CD86 with approximately 20-fold higher affinity than CD28. This molecule has significant sequence identity to CD28. The *cd152* and *cd28* loci are located on the same chromosome and share similar intron/exon structure. They probably arose from a gene duplication. CD152 is also a member of the IgSF of molecules.

CD152 is expressed on most activated T cells. Its cell surface expression pattern is unusual in that it appears to be regulated post-translationally. At the mRNA level, CD152 transcription is detectable hours after T cell stimulation; however, the protein is retained intracellularly. Truncation or replacement of the cytoplasmic region of CD152 increases its cell surface expression. Temporally, the expression of CD152 is upregulated during a period of transient downregulation of the CD28 molecule expression.

CD152 can function as a negative regulator of the immune response. Antibody blockade of this receptor enhances T lymphocyte proliferation and delays apoptosis, suggesting a negative regulatory function for CD152. The generation of CD152-deficient mice has confirmed this. These mice have massive lympho-

proliferation defects and multiorgan destruction. This lymphoproliferation in CD152$^{-/-}$ mice appears to be antigen driven. An accumulation of lymphocytes in secondary lymphoid organs is noticeable about 1 week after birth. By 4 weeks, the number of lymphocytes in these organs is up to five times the number found in wild-type controls. Also by this time, most organs are infiltrated by lymphocytes. These observations, taken together, suggest that CD152 plays a critical role in the regulation of autoreactive T cells, as well as in the downregulation of activated T cells.

TNF/TNF-R receptor/counterreceptors influence cell fate

CD154:CD40 ligation costimulates B cells

CD154 (CD40L, gp39 or T-BAM) is a member of the TNF gene family, which includes TNF, CD30L, FasL and TRAIL. Similar to other members of this family, it is a type II membrane protein of 30 kDa in size. CD154 can be detected on activated T cells, monocytes, natural killer (NK) cells, human mast cells, basophils, some DCs and some CD8 T cells. CD154 is not detectable on resting T cells. Upon ligation of the TCR, CD154 becomes transiently expressed. The expression of CD154 on T cells is consistent with its importance of providing help to B cells during a humoral response to T-dependent (TD) antigens. CD154 expression on DCs can also promote B cell maturation. The function of CD154 on other cell types is currently unknown.

Trimeric CD154 binds to and cross-links CD40. CD40 is expressed on all APCs, such as DCs, Langerhans cells, macrophages and B cells. It is also found on basal epithelial cells, FDCs, endothelium and thymic epithelium. CD40 is approximately 45–50 kDa in size and is a member of the TNF-R family, which includes CD95, TNF-RI, TNF-RII, CD30, CD27, TRAIL-R, NGF and 41-BB. These proteins are characterized by a cysteine-rich extracellular domain and a unique cytoplasmic domain. Currently, it is generally believed that regions in the cytoplasmic domain mediate the receptor's association with other proteins that transduce signals from the receptor. One molecule with which CD40 has been shown to associate is termed TRAF3. This protein has a number of putative DNA-binding motifs; however, its function is currently unknown. It may mediate activation of MAP kinase family members, because stimulation of CD40 causes activation of NF-κB, SAPK (JNK) and p38 MAP kinase pathways.

The importance of the CD154/CD40 interaction in the generation of a humoral response is highlighted by a naturally occurring congenital defect of

CD154 in humans, and is paralleled by the CD154-deficient mouse. The human disease, X-linked hyper-IgM syndrome, is signified by lack of IgG, IgA and IgE isotypes, GC formation and memory B cells in patients. Consequently, these patients have severe immune system defects and are susceptible to numerous immune system disorders and to opportunistic infections.

The transduced signal through CD40 has different effects, depending on the cell type studied. Generally, ligation of CD40 by T cells expressing the counter-receptor results in activation of the cell. In terms of APCs, this leads to the expression of cytokines that stimulate cells in a paracrine or autocrine manner. CD40 also upregulates cell surface proteins, such as the costimulatory molecules, CD80 and CD86 and other adhesion molecules. Notably, this interplay between costimulatory molecules CD154:CD40 and CD80/86:CD28 forms the basis of reciprocal dialogue between T cells, B cells and other APCs (**Figure 1**).

For the humoral response to T-dependent antigens, the CD40 signaling pathway apparently complements signals from the BCR that are necessary to promote proliferation. Wheeler and colleagues demonstrated that the signal generated through CD40 effectively lowers the threshold for activation through the BCR. Mice that are genetically deficient for CD40 clearly have abnormal B cell responses to TD antigens, and part of this defect lies in the inability of T cells to stimulate CD40$^{-/-}$ B cells.

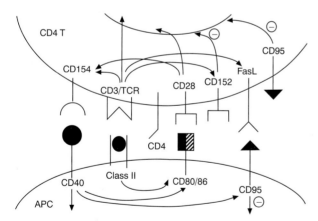

Figure 1 Receptor-mediated reciprocal dialog between a T cell and an antigen-presenting cell. Activation of T cells and APCs cause upregulation of costimulatory molecules and their counter-receptors. These molecules enhance the activation process and can lead to proliferation of lymphocytes. Downregulatory molecules such as CD95 and CD152 are important for eliminating lymphocytes after they have served their function. The APC in this figure represents a class of cells, including dendritic cells, macrophages and activated B cells. Not shown in this figure are other surface molecules and secreted compounds which also play an important role in the communication process.

In addition to its costimulatory role, these synergistic signals between CD40 and the BCR may play an integral role in the positive selection of highly antigen-specific B cells during the GC response. As the B cells undergo hypermutation of their antigen receptor, novel specificities are generated. Positive selection of B cells bearing high-affinity receptors is mediated through ligation of the BCR, presumably by interacting with FDC-bound antigen, and ligation of CD40, provided by helper T cells bearing CD154. In studies where *ex vivo* GC B cells are isolated, in the absence of T cell help, these cells eventually undergo programmed cell death. These cells can be rescued via engagement of CD40 with or without BCR ligation. Consistent with this observation is the fact that signaling through CD40 can increase the expression of Bcl-xL, a negative regulator of apoptosis.

CD40 has also been implicated in B cell differentiation. GC B cells which have been positively selected for their high-affinity antigen receptors differentiate by switching of Ig isotype and maturing into long-lasting memory B cells or terminally differentiating into Ig-secreting plasma cells. Cytokines influence the differentiation pathways, especially in the process of isotype switching. There is evidence from *in vitro* systems that demonstrate specific cytokine profiles that result in the development of certain Ig isotypes. The role that CD40 plays in any of the differentiation steps is currently unknown. CD40 activates expression of IL-12 in DCs, which can promote a T_H1 response, yet CD40 can also promote IgE class switch, typical of a T_H2 response.

In addition to the severe defects in humoral immunity, X-linked hyper-IgM syndrome patients appear to have defects in the T cell compartment. They are susceptible to diseases that are typically associated with T cell immunodeficiency. Whether this defect is due to a direct effect from the lack of CD154 signaling on the T cell, or an indirect effect from the lack of CD40-induced activation of the APC, is not clear. There is evidence that CD154 can transduce a signal to T cells. Alternatively, CD154-mediated stimulation of APCs has been shown to be critical in their ability to counterstimulate the T cell.

FasL/CD95 interactions downregulate the immune response

CD95 (Fas, APO-1) is also a member of the TNF-R family. As previously mentioned, TNF-R family members are distinguished by a cysteine-rich extracellular domain. In the cytoplasmic region, some family members contain a 'death domain' which is important for initiating programmed cell death. The death domain mediates binding of the receptor to intracellular proteins that also contain death domains. These cytoplasmic proteins operating in conjunction with members of a specialized protease family, the caspases, are important in transducing the apoptotic signal.

The expression of CD95 is broadly distributed. It can be detected on the surface of myeloid, stromal and lymphoid cells. High expression of CD95 is observed upon activation of B cells and T cells. Also, experiments with cell lines suggest that expression of CD95 can be upregulated if cells are treated with interferon γ (IFNγ) alone, or in combination with TNFα.

The ligand for CD95, FasL, is a member of the TNF family, and, like the other characterized family members, is a type II membrane protein. FasL can also be secreted, similar to other members such as TNF and LT. The expression of FasL appears to be limited, in contrast to the broader expression pattern of CD95. FasL can be detected on the surface of DCs, activated, mature T lymphocytes and on NK cells. This is consistent with its suspected role in immunoregulatory or killer function. Interestingly, the other tissues which FasL has been detected are small intestine, eye, lung and mouse or rat (but not human) testes. The function of FasL in these tissues is not known but it might protect some tissues, such as eye and testes, from infiltration by activated T cells. Another proposed function for FasL is in T cell deletion by DCs following an immune response. One of the possible sites of activated T cell deletion is believed to be the gut. One particular paradox with the expression of FasL concerns the thymus: FasL expression is not detectable there, despite the fact that thymocytes express high levels of CD95. There is considerable controversy about whether CD95 plays a role in thymocyte selection.

In numerous experimental systems, antibody or soluble FasL ligation of CD95 induces a cell death program. CD95 plays a role in CD8$^+$ T cell and NK cell-mediated cytotoxic function. In this context, cytotoxic cells expressing the counter-receptor to CD95 ligate CD95 present on the target cells.

Another interesting role of CD95 is in the regulation of T and B cell maturation. As previously mentioned, activation of mature T or B lymphocytes increases the expression of CD95. This renders the activated cell susceptible to CD95-mediated cell death. Thus, CD95 offers an attractive explanation for how activated lymphocytes are eliminated after they have served their function. For example, during the GC response, CD95 expression is increased on activated B cells which are undergoing the process of somatic hypermutation. CD95 renders them susceptible to FasL-mediated death, unless the B cell is stimulated effectively through the BCR and CD40. According to this model, anergic B cells may be deleted, as their BCR signaling pathway is inoperative, thereby preventing BCR-mediated rescue from death.

Activated T cells also need to be downregulated, especially following an effective immune response. A possible mechanism by which the expression of CD95 and its counter-receptor on activated, responding T cells could cause apoptosis is by an autocrine or paracrine mechanism. One possibility is that after an effective immune response and the number of target cells becomes limiting, FasL on the surface of the activated killer cell will begin to ligate CD95 on itself or on neighbouring cells. This mechanism is a form of self-limiting effector function.

The importance of CD95-mediated downregulation of the immune response is underscored by the phenotype of mice with naturally occurring lpr and gld mutations which have genetic disruption of either CD95 or FasL, respectively. The phenotypes are generally similar in either mutant strain: they display an accumulation of lymphocytes in the peripheral lymphoid organs that resembles a lymphoproliferative disorder. While the immune response to antigen is apparently normal, the elimination of the responding cells is impaired in these mice. In the B cell compartment, a defect in the elimination of activated and maturing B cells is reflected by a high production of IgG and IgM antibodies. In lpr or gld mice that have been bred on to the MRL background (MRL/lpr and MRL/gld mice), the inability to control autoreactive cells in the periphery is apparent. These mice develop an autoimmune disease resembling that of systemic lupus erythematosus (SLE) in humans. This is marked by the production of autoreactive antibodies such as anti-DNA and rheumatoid factor.

Conclusions

By describing the function of certain IgSF and TNF/TNF-R family of molecules as 'stimulatory' or 'downregulatory', we have presented them in a conventional manner. However, as these molecules become further defined, their function in the process of cellular cooperation must be considered in the context of a cell's activation state and its location. In considering their relevance to the biology of the entire immune response, we have metaphorically compared them to words used by cells to communicate. Depending on the context, these words can effect a different meaning to a message. An example of this is recent evidence suggesting that CD95 may actually have a costimulatory function. Much remains to be learned, not only about the range of definitions that receptor 'words' may have, but also of the syntax and semantics of this intercellular language.

To conceptualize the cellular communication process, we have described only a small fraction of molecules that are involved. Our intent is to highlight key molecules that function during the discrete steps of the immune response: activation, differentiation and elimination. However, at each step, there are clearly other molecules that have a role in modifying the signals. For example, the CD19/CD21 complex, CD22 and CD45 have been shown to regulate signals through the BCR. At the time of this writing, there are over 160 molecules with a cluster of differentiation (CD) designation. Many of these play important roles in intercellular communication during immune responses. In addition, secreted compounds also play a role in enhancing or modifying cellular fate. Cytokines secreted by APCs and T cells are crucial in determining the type of immune response to a particular antigen. Again, the number of characterized secreted compounds is growing. The challenge that immunologists face is to decipher the multiple signals these molecules provide to a cell during a given maturation step, with the hope of eventually being able to comprehend the intricate language by which cells of the immune system communicate.

See also: **Adhesion molecules; Antigen-presenting cells; Apoptosis; B lymphocyte activation; B lymphocyte, antigen processing and presentation; B lymphocyte differentiation; B7 (CD80 & CD86); CD2; CD22; CD28; CD40 and its ligand; CD45 (the leukocyte common antigen); Chemokines; Chemotaxis; Cytokines; Dendritic cells; Fas (CD95) and fas ligand; Germinal center; Hyper-IgM syndrome; Integrins; Intercellular adhesion molecules: ICAM-1, ICAM-2 and ICAM-3; Langerhans cells; Lymphocyte function-associated antigen 1 (LFA-1); Lymphocyte function-associated antigen 3 (LFA-3); Microenvironment; Second signals for lymphocyte activation; Selectins (CD62-E/L/P); T lymphocyte activation; TNF receptors.**

Further reading

Abbas A, Murphy KM and Sher A (1996) Functional diversity of helper T lymphocytes. *Nature* 383: 787–793.

Borriello F, Sethna MP, Boyd SD *et al* (1997) B7-1 and B7-2 have overlapping, critical roles in immunoglobulin class switching and germinal center formation. *Immunity* 6: 303–313.

Boussiotis VA, Freeman GJ, Gribben JG and Nadler LM (1996) The role of B7-1/B7-2:CD28/CTLA-4 pathways in the prevention of anergy. *Immunological Reviews* 153: 5–26.

Bretscher P and Cohn M (1970) A theory of self–nonself discrimination. *Science* 169: 1042–1049.

Clark EA (1997) Regulation of B lymphocytes by dendritic cells. *Journal of Experimental Medicine* 185: 801–803.

Clark EA and Ledbetter JA (1994) How B and T cells talk to each other. *Nature* 367: 425–428.

Foy TM, Aruffo A, Bajorath J, Buhlmann JE and Noelle RJ (1996) Immune regulation by CD40 and its ligand gp39. *Annual Review of Immunology* 14: 591–617.

Grewal IS and Flavell RA (1996) The role of CD40 ligand in costimulation and T-cell activation. *Immunological Reviews* 153: 85–106.

Henkart PA (1994) Lymphocyte-mediated cytotoxicity: two pathways and multiple effector molecules. *Immunity* 1: 343–346.

Jenkins MK and Schwartz RH (1987) Antigen presentation by chemically modified splenocytes induces antigen-specific T cell unresponsiveness *in vitro* and *in vivo*. *Journal of Experimental Medicine* 165: 302–319.

Law C-L, Craxton A, Otipoby KL, Sidorenko SP, Klaus SJ and Clark EA (1996) Regulation of signalling through B-lymphocyte antigen receptors by cell–cell interaction molecules. *Immunological Reviews* 153: 123–154.

Lenschow DJ, Walunas TL and Bluestone JA (1996) CD28/B7 system of T cell costimulation. *Annual Review of Immunology* 14: 233–258.

MacLennan ICM (1994) Germinal centers. *Annual Review of Immunology* 12: 117–139.

Nagata S (1997) Apoptosis by death factor. *Cell* 88: 355–365.

Nagata S and Golstein P (1995) The Fas death factor. *Science* 267: 1449–1456.

Parker DC (1993) T cell-dependent B cell activation. *Annual Review of Immunology* 11: 331–360.

Rathmell JC, Townsend SE, Xu JC, Flavell RA and Goodnow CC (1996) Expansion or elimination of B cells *in vivo*: dual roles for CD40- and Fas (CD95)-ligands modulated by the B cell antigen receptor. *Cell* 87: 319–329.

Shahinian A, Pfeffer K, Lee KP *et al* (1993) Differential T cell costimulatory requirements in CD28-deficient mice. *Science* 261: 609–612.

Tedder TF, Inaoki M and Sato S (1997) The CD19–CD21 complex regulates signal transduction thresholds governing humoral immunity and autoimmunity. *Immunity* 6: 107–118.

Xu J, Foy TM, Laman JD *et al* (1994) Mice deficient for the CD40 ligand. *Immunity* 1: 423–431.

GLOSSARY

The glossary of terms is reproduced with permission from *Essential Immunology (9e)* (1997) by Ivan M Roitt and publishers Blackwell Science, Oxford, UK.

acquired immune response: Immunity mediated by lymphocytes and characterized by antigen-specificity and memory.

acute phase proteins: Serum proteins, mostly produced in the liver, which rapidly change in concentration (some increase, some decrease) during the initiation of an inflammatory response.

adjuvant: Any substance which nonspecifically enhances the immune response to antigen.

affinity (intrinsic affinity): The strength of binding (affinity constant) between a receptor (e.g one antigen-binding site on an antibody) and a ligand (e.g. epitope on an antigen).

allele: Variants of a polymorphic gene at a given genetic locus.

allelic exclusion: The phenomenon whereby, following successful rearrangement of one allele of an antigen receptor gene, rearrangement of the other parental allele is suppressed, thereby ensuring each lymphocyte expresses only a single specificity of antigen receptor.

allergen: An antigen which causes allergy.

allergy: IgE-mediated hypersensitivity, e.g. asthma, eczema, hayfever and food allergy.

allogeneic: Refers to the genetic differences between individuals of the same species.

allograft: Tissue or organ graft between allogeneic individuals.

allotype: An allelic variant of an antigen which, because it is not present in all individuals, may be immunogenic in members of the same species which have a different version of the allele.

alternative pathway (of complement activation): Activation pathway involving complement components C3, Factor B, Factor D, and Properdin which, in the presence of a stabilizing activator surface such as microbial polysaccharide, generates the alternative pathway C3 convertase $\overline{\text{C3bBb}}$.

anaphylatoxin: A substance (e.g. C3a, C4a or C5a) capable of directly triggering mast cell degranulation.

anaphylaxis: An often fatal hypersensitivity reaction, triggered by IgE or anaphylatoxin-mediated mast cell degranulation, leading to anaphylactic shock due to vasodilation and smooth muscle contraction.

anergy: Potentially reversible specific immunological tolerance in which the lymphocyte becomes functionally nonresponsive.

antibody-dependent cellular cytotoxicity (ADCC): A cytotoxic reaction in which an antibody-coated target cell is directly killed by an Fc-receptor-bearing leukocyte, e.g. NK cell, macrophage or neutrophil.

antigen: Any molecule capable of being recognized by an antibody or T cell receptor.

antigen-presenting cell (APC): A term most commonly used when referring to cells that present processed antigenic peptide and MHC class II molecules to the T cell receptor on CD4$^+$ T cells, e.g. macrophages, dendritic cells, B cells. Note, however, that most types of cell are able to present antigenic peptides with MHC class I to CD8$^+$ T cells, e.g. as occurs with virally infected cells.

antigenic determinant: A cluster of epitopes (*see* epitope).

apoptosis: A form of programmed cell death, characterized by endonuclease digestion of DNA.

atopic allergy: IgE-mediated hypersensitivity, i.e. asthma, eczema, hayfever and food allergy.

autologous: From the same individual.

avidity (functional affinity): The binding strength between two molecules (e.g. antibody and antigen) taking into account the valency of the interaction. Thus the avidity will always be equal to or greater than the intrinsic affinity (*see* affinity).

β_2-microglobulin: A 12 kDa protein, not itself encoded within the MHC, but forming part of the structure of MHC class I-encoded molecules.

B-1/B-2 cells: The two major subpopulations of B lymphocytes. B-1 cells are Mac-1$^+$, CD23$^-$ and most express the cell surface antigen CD5; they are self-renewing, and frequently secrete high levels of antibody which binds to a range of antigens ('polyspecificity') with a relatively low affinity. The majority of B cells, however, are B-2 which do not express CD5 and are Mac-1$^-$, CD23$^+$; they are directly generated from precursors in the bone marrow, and secrete highly specific antibody.

basophil: A type of granulocyte found in the blood and resembling the tissue mast cell.

BCG (bacille Calmette–Guérin): Attenuated *Myco-*

bacterium tuberculosis used both as a specific vaccine for tuberculosis and as an adjuvant.

biolistics: The use of small particles, e.g. colloidal gold, as a vehicle for carrying agents (drugs, nucleic acid, etc) into a cell. Following coating with the desired agent(s), the particles are fired into the dermis of the recipient using a helium-powered gun.

bispecific antibody: An artificially produced hybrid antibody in which each of the two antigen-binding arms is specific for a different antigenic epitope. Such antibodies, which can be produced either by chemical cross-linkage or by recombinant DNA techniques, can be used to link together two different antigens or cells, e.g. a cytotoxic T cell and a tumor cell.

bursa of Fabricius: A primary lymphoid organ in avian species, located at the cloacal-hind gut junction; it is the site of B cell maturation.

capping: An active process whereby cross-linking of cell surface molecules (e.g. by antibody) leads to aggregation and subsequent migration of the molecules to one pole of the cell.

carrier: Any molecule which when conjugated to a non-immunogenic molecule (e.g. a hapten) makes the latter immunogenic by providing epitopes for helper T cells which the hapten lacks.

CD antigen: Cluster of differentiation designation assigned to leukocyte cell surface molecules which are identified by a given group of monoclonal antibodies.

CD3: A trimeric complex of γ, δ and ϵ chains which together with a $\zeta\zeta$ homodimer or $\zeta\eta$ heterodimer acts as a signal transducing unit for the T cell receptor.

CD4: Cell surface glycoprotein, usually on helper T cells, that recognizes MHC class II molecules on antigen-presenting cells.

CD8: Cell surface glycoprotein, usually on cytotoxic T cells, that recognizes MHC class I molecules on target cells.

cell-mediated immunity (CMI): Refers to T cell mediated immune responses.

chemokines: A family of structurally-related cytokines which selectively induce chemotaxis and activation of phagocytic cells and lymphocytes. They are also able to rapidly trigger integrin-mediated leukocyte adhesion.

chemotaxis: Movement of cells up a concentration gradient of chemotactic factors.

chimeric: Composite of genetically distinct individuals, e.g. following an allogeneic bone marrow graft.

class switching: The process by which a B cell changes the class but not specificity of a given antibody it produces, e.g. switching from an IgM to an IgG antibody.

classical pathway (of complement activation): Activation pathway involving complement components C1, C2 and C4 which, following fixation of C1q, e.g. by antigen–antibody complexes, produces the classical pathway C3 convertase C4b2b.

clonal deletion: A process by which contact with antigen (e.g. self antigen) at an early stage of lymphocyte differentiation leads to cell death by apoptosis.

clonal selection: The selection and activation by antigen of a lymphocyte bearing a complementary receptor, which then proliferates to form an expanded clone.

clone: Identical cells derived from a single progenitor.

colony stimulating factors (CSF): Factors that permit the proliferation and differentiation of hematopoietic cells.

complement: A group of serum proteins, some of which act in an enzymatic cascade, producing effector molecules involved in inflammation (C3a, C5a), phagocytosis (C3b) and cell lysis (C5b-9).

complementarity determining regions (CDR): The hypervariable amino acid sequences within antibody and T cell receptor variable regions which interact with complementary amino acids on the antigen or peptide-MHC complex.

conA (concanavalin A): A T cell mitogen.

congenic: Animals which only differ at a single genetic locus.

conjugate: Covalently-linked complex of two or more molecules (e.g. fluorescein conjugated to antibody).

Coombs' test: Diagnostic test using anti-immunoglobulin to agglutinate antibody-coated erythrocytes.

cortex: Outer (peripheral) layer of an organ.

c-reactive protein: An acute phase protein which is able to bind to the surface of microorganisms where it functions as a stimulator of the classical pathway of complement activation, and as an opsonin for phagocytosis.

cyclophosphamide: Cytotoxic drug used as an immunosuppressive.

cyclosporine: A T cell specific immunosuppressive drug used to prevent graft rejection.

cytokines: Low molecular weight proteins that stimulate or inhibit the differentiation, proliferation or function of immune cells.

cytophilic: Binds to cells.

cytotoxic: Kills cells.

cytotoxic T lymphocyte (CTL): T cells (usually

CD8$^+$) which kill target cells following recognition of foreign peptide-MHC molecules on the target cell membrane.

delayed-type hypersensitivity (DTH): A hypersensitivity reaction occurring within 48–72 hours and mediated by cytokine release from sensitized T cells.

differentiation antigen: A cell surface molecule expressed at a particular stage of development or on cells of a given lineage.

DiGeorge syndrome: Immunodeficiency caused by a congenital failure in thymic development resulting in a lack of mature functional T cells.

diversity (D) gene segments: Found in the immunoglobulin heavy chain gene and T cell receptor β and δ gene loci between the V and J gene segments. Encode part of the third hypervariable region in these antigen receptor chains.

edema: Swelling caused by accumulation of fluid in the tissues.

effector cells: Cells which carry out an immune function, e.g. cytokine release, cytotoxicity.

ELISA (enzyme-linked immunosorbent assay): Assay for detection or quantitation of an antibody or antigen using a ligand (e.g. an anti-immunoglobulin) conjugated to an enzyme which changes the color of a substrate.

endocytosis: Cellular ingestion of macromolecules by invagination of plasma membrane to produce an intracellular vesicle which encloses the ingested material.

endogenous: From within.

endosomes: Intracellular smooth surfaced vesicles in which endocytosed material passes on its way to the lysosomes.

endotoxin: Pathogenic cell wall-associated lipopolysacharides of Gram-negative bacteria.

eosinophil: A class of granulocyte, the granules of which contain toxic cationic proteins.

epitope: That part of an antigen recognized by an antigen receptor (*see* antigenic determinant).

Epstein–Barr virus (EBV): The virus responsible for infectious mononucleosis and Burkitt's lymphoma. Used to immortalize human B cells *in vitro*.

equivalence: The ratio of antibody to antigen at which immunoprecipitation of the reactants is virtually complete.

erythema: The redness produced during inflammation due to erythrocytes entering tissue spaces.

erythropoiesis: Erythrocyte production.

exotoxin: Pathogenic protein secreted by bacteria.

exudate: The extravascular fluid (containing proteins and cellular debris) which accumulates during inflammation.

Fab: Monovalent antigen-binding fragment obtained following papain digestion of immunoglobulin. Consists of an intact light chain and the N-terminal V$_H$ and C$_H$1 domains of the heavy chain.

F(ab′)$_2$: Bivalent antigen-binding fragment obtained following pepsin digestion of immunoglobulin. Consists of both light chains and the N-terminal part of both heavy chains linked by disulfide bonds.

Fas: A member of the TNF receptor gene family. Engagement of Fas (CD95) on the surface of the cell by the Fas ligand present on cytotoxic cells can trigger apoptosis in the Fas-bearing target cell.

Fc: Crystallizable, non-antigen-binding fragment of an immunoglobulin molecule obtained following papain digestion. Consists of the C-terminal portion of both heavy chains which is responsible for binding to Fc receptors and C1q.

Fc receptors: Cell surface receptors which bind the Fc portion of particular immunoglobulin classes.

fibroblast: Connective tissue cell which produces collagen and plays an important part in wound healing.

fluorescein isothiocyanate (FITC): Green fluorescent dye used to 'tag' antibodies for use in immunofluorescence.

fluorescent antibody: An antibody conjugated to a fluorescent dye such as FITC.

follicular dendritic cell: MHC class II-negative Fc receptor-positive dendritic cells which bear immune complexes on their surface and are probably involved in the generation of antibody-secreting cells and maintenance of B cell memory in germinal centres. (N.B. a different cell type to interdigitating dendritic cells).

framework regions: The relatively conserved amino acid sequences which flank the hypervariable regions in immunoglobulin and T cell receptor variable regions and maintain a common overall structure for all V-region domains.

Freund's adjuvant: Complete Freund's adjuvant is an emulsion of aqueous antigen in mineral oil that contains heat-killed *Mycobacteria*. Incomplete Freund's adjuvant lacks the *Mycobacteria*.

gammaglobulin: The serum proteins, mostly immunoglobulins, which have the greatest mobility towards the cathode during electrophoresis.

germ line: The arrangement of the genetic material as transmitted through the gametes.

germinal center: Discrete areas within lymph node and spleen where B cell maturation and memory development occur.

giant cell: Large multinucleate cell derived from

fused macrophages and often present in granulomas.

glomerulonephritis: Inflammation of renal glomerular capillary loops, often resulting from immune complex deposition.

graft versus host (gvh.) reaction: Reaction occurring when T lymphocytes present in a graft recognize and attack host cells.

granulocyte: Myeloid cells containing cytoplasmic granules (i.e. neutrophils, eosinophils and basophils).

granuloma: A tissue nodule containing proliferating lymphocytes, fibroblasts, and giant cells and epithelioid cells (both derived from activated macrophages), which forms due to inflammation in response to chronic infection or persistence of antigen in the tissues.

granzymes: Serine esterases present in the granules of cytotoxic T lymphocytes and NK cells. They induce apoptosis in the target cell which they enter through perforin channels inserted into the target cell membrane by the cytotoxic lymphocyte.

gut-associated lymphoid tissue (GALT): Includes Peyer's patches, appendix, and solitary lymphoid nodules in the submucosa.

H2: The mouse major histocompatibility complex (MHC).

haplotype: The set of allelic variants present at a given genetic region.

hapten: A low molecular weight molecule that is recognized by preformed antibody but is not itself immunogenic unless conjugated to a 'carrier' molecule which provides epitopes recognized by helper T cells.

helper T lymphocyte (TH): A subclass of T cells which provide help (in the form of cytokines and/or cognate interactions) necessary for the expression of effector function by other cells in the immune system.

hemagglutinin: Any molecule which agglutinates erythrocytes.

hematopoiesis: The production of erythrocytes and leukocytes.

high endothelial venule (HEV): Capillary venule composed of specialized endothelial cells allowing migration of lymphocytes into lymphoid organs.

hinge region: Amino acids between the Fab and Fc regions of immunoglobulin which permit flexibility of the molecule.

histamine: Vasoactive amine present in basophil and mast cell granules which, following degranulation, causes increased vascular permeability and smooth muscle contraction.

HLA (human leukocyte antigen): The human major histocompatibility complex (MHC).

humoral: Pertaining to extracellular fluid such as plasma and lymph. The term humoral immunity is used to denote antibody-mediated immune responses.

hybridoma: Hybrid cell line obtained by fusing a lymphoid tumor cell with a lymphocyte which then has both the immortality of the tumor cell and the effector function (e.g. monoclonal antibody secretion) of the lymphocyte.

hypersensitivity: Excessive immune response which leads to undesirable consequences, e.g. tissue or organ damage.

hypervariable regions: Those amino acid sequences within the immunoglobulin and T cell receptor variable regions which show the greatest variability and contribute most to the antigen or peptide-MHC binding site.

idiotope: An epitope made up of amino acids within the variable region of an antibody or T cell receptor which reacts with an anti-idiotope.

idiotype: The complete set of idiotopes in the variable region of an antibody or T cell receptor which react with an anti-idiotypic serum.

idiotype network: A regulatory network based on interactions of idiotypes and anti-idiotypes present on antibodies and T cell receptors.

immune complex: Complex of antibody bound to antigen which may also contain complement components.

immunoadsorption: Method for removal of antibody or antigen by allowing it to bind to solid phase antigen or antibody.

immunofluorescence: Technique for detection of cell or tissue-associated antigens by the use of a fluorescently-tagged ligand (e.g. an anti-immunoglobulin conjugated to fluorescein isothiocyanate).

immunogen: Any substance which elicits an immune response. Whilst all immunogens are antigens, not all antigens are immunogens (*see* hapten).

immunoglobulin superfamily: Large family of proteins characterized by possession of 'immunoglobulin-type' domains of approximately 110 amino acids folded into two β-pleated sheets. Members include immunoglobulins, T cell receptors and MHC molecules.

inflammation: The tissue response to trauma, characterized by increased blood flow and entry of leukocytes into the tissues, resulting in swelling, redness, elevated temperature and pain.

innate immunity: Immunity which is not intrinsically affected by prior contact with antigen, i.e. all aspects of immunity not directly mediated by lymphocytes.

interdigitating dendritic cell: MHC class II-positive, Fc receptor-negative, antigen-presenting dendritic cell found in T cell areas of lymph nodes and spleen. (N.B. a different cell type to follicular dendritic cells).

interferons (IFN): IFNα is derived from various leukocytes, IFNβ from fibroblasts and IFNγ from T lymphocytes. All three types induce an anti-viral state in cells and IFNγ acts as a cytokine in the regulation of immune responses.

interleukins (IL): Designation for some of the cytokines secreted by leukocytes.

internal image: An epitope on an anti-idiotype which binds in a way that structurally and functionally mimics the antigen.

invariant chain: A polypeptide which binds MHC class II molecules in the endoplasmic reticulum, directs them to the late endosomal compartment and prevents premature association with self peptides.

Ir (immune response) **genes:** The genes, including those within the MHC, that together determine the overall level of immune response to a given antigen.

isotype: An antibody constant region structure present in all normal individuals, i.e. antibody class or subclass.

ITAM: Immunoreceptor Tyrosine-based Activation Motifs are consensus sequences for src-family tyrosine kinases. These motifs are found in the cytoplasmic domains of several signaling molecules including the signal transduction units of lymphocyte antigen receptors and of Fc receptors.

J chain: A molecule which forms part of the structure of pentameric IgM and dimeric IgA.

joining (J) gene segments: Found in the immunoglobulin and T cell receptor gene loci and, upon gene rearrangement, encode part of the third hypervariable region of the antigen receptors.

K (killer) cell: Large granular lymphocyte which mediates antibody-dependent cellular cytotoxicity (ADCC), is Fc receptor positive, but does not rearrange or express either immunoglobulin or T cell receptor genes.

kinins: A family of polypeptides released during inflammatory responses and which increase vascular permeability and smooth muscle contraction.

knockout: The use of homologous genetic recombination in embryonal stem cells to replace a functional gene with a defective copy of the gene. The animals that are produced by this technique can be bred to homozygosity, thus allowing the generation of a null phenotype for that gene product.

Kuppfer cells: Fixed tissue macrophages lining the blood sinuses in the liver.

Langerhans cell: Fc receptor and MHC class II-positive antigen-presenting dendritic cell found in the skin.

large granular lymphocyte (LGL): Large lymphocytes which contain cytoplasmic granules and function as natural killer (NK) and killer (K) cells. Activated CD8$^+$ cytotoxic T lymphocytes (CTL) also assume an LGL morphology.

lectins: A family of proteins, mostly of plant origin, which bind specific sugars on glycoproteins and glycolipids. Some lectins are also mitogenic (e.g. PHA, conA).

leukotrienes: Metabolic products of arachidonic acid which promote inflammatory processes (e.g. chemotaxis, increased vascular permeability) and are produced by a variety of cell types including mast cells, basophils and macrophages.

ligand: General term for a molecule recognized by a binding structure such as a receptor.

linkage disequilibrium: The occurrence of two alleles being inherited together at a greater frequency than that expected from the product of their individual frequencies.

lipopolysaccharide (LPS): Endotoxin derived from Gram-negative bacterial cell walls which has inflammatory and mitogenic actions.

Ly markers: A nomenclature based on the genetics of murine lymphocyte cell surface antigens. Nowadays largely replaced by the monoclonal antibody-based CD nomenclature as originally developed for human cell surface antigens.

lymph: The tissue fluid which drains into and through the lymphatic system.

lymphadenopathy: Enlarged lymph nodes.

lymphokine: Cytokine produced by lymphocytes.

lymphokine-activated killer cells (LAK): Killer (K) and natural killer (NK) cells activated *in vitro* by IL-2 to give enhanced killing of target cells.

lymphotoxin: Synonym for tumor necrosis factor-β (TNFβ).

lysosomes: Cytoplasmic granules containing hydrolytic enzymes involved in the digestion of phagocytosed material.

lysozyme: Anti-bacterial enzyme present in phagocytic cell granules, tears and saliva, which digests peptidoglycans in bacterial cell walls.

macrophage: Large phagocytic cell, derived from the blood monocyte, which also functions as an antigen-presenting cell and can mediate ADCC.

mannose binding protein: A member of the collectin family of calcium-dependent lectins, and an acute phase protein. It functions as a stimulator of the classical pathway of complement activation, and as an opsonin for phagocytosis by binding to mannose, a sugar residue usually found in an exposed form only on the surface of microorganisms.

marginal zone: The outer area of the splenic peri-arteriolar lymphoid sheath (PALS) which is rich in B cells, particularly those responding to thymus-independent antigens.

margination: Leukocyte adhesion to the endothelium of blood vessels in the early phase of an acute inflammatory reaction.

mast cell: A tissue cell with abundant granules which resembles the blood basophil. Both these cell types bear Fc receptors for IgE, which when crosslinked by IgE and antigen cause degranulation and the release of a number of mediators including histamine and leukotrienes.

medulla: Inner (central) region of an organ.

megakaryocyte: A bone marrow precursor of platelets.

membrane attack complex (MAC): Complex of complement components C5b–C9 which inserts as a pore into the membrane of target cells leading to cell lysis.

memory (immunological): A characteristic of the acquired immune response of lymphocytes whereby a second encounter with a given antigen produces a secondary immune response; faster, greater and longer lasting than the primary immune response.

memory cells: Clonally expanded T and B cells produced during a primary immune response and which are 'primed' to mediate a secondary immune response to the original antigen.

MHC (major histocompatibility complex): A genetic region encoding molecules involved in antigen presentation to T cells. Class I MHC molecules are present on virtually all nucleated cells and are encoded mainly by the H2K, D, and L loci in mice and by HLA-A, B, and C in man, whilst class II MHC molecules are expressed on antigen-presenting cells (primarily macrophages, B cells and interdigitating dendritic cells) and are encoded by H2A and E in mice and HLA-DR, DQ, and DP in man. Allelic differences can be associated with intense graft rejection within a species.

MHC restriction: The necessity that T cells recognize processed antigen only when presented by MHC molecules of the original haplotype associated with T cell priming.

minor histocompatibility antigens: Non-MHC-encoded cell surface processed peptides which, in association with MHC-encoded molecules, contribute to graft rejection, albeit not usually as severe as that due to MHC mismatch.

mitogen: A substance which non-specifically induces lymphocyte proliferation.

mixed lymphocyte reaction (MLR): A T cell proliferative response induced by cells expressing allogeneic MHC.

monoclonal antibody: Homogeneous antibody derived from a single B cell clone and therefore all bearing identical antigen-binding sites and isotype.

monocyte: Mononuclear phagocyte found in blood and which is the precursor of the tissue macrophage.

mononuclear phagocyte system: A system comprising blood monocytes and tissue macrophages.

mucosal-associated lymphoid tissue (MALT): Lymphoid tissue present in the surface mucosa of the respiratory, gastrointestinal and genitourinary tracts.

multiple myeloma: Plasma cell malignancy resulting in high levels of monoclonal immunoglobulin in serum and of free light chains (Bence-Jones protein) in urine.

murine: Pertaining to mice.

myeloma protein: Monoclonal antibody secreted by myeloma cells.

negative selection: Deletion by apoptosis in the thymus of T cells which recognize self peptides presented by self MHC molecules, thus preventing the development of autoimmune T cells. Negative selection of developing B cells is also thought to occur if they encounter high levels of self antigen in the bone marrow.

neutrophil: The major circulating phagocytic polymorphonuclear granulocyte. Enters tissues early in an inflammatory response and is also able to mediate antibody-dependent cellular cytotoxicity (ADCC).

NK (natural killer) cell: Large granular lymphocyte which does not rearrange nor express either immunoglobulin or T cell receptor genes but is able to recognize and destroy certain tumor and virally-infected cells in an MHC and antibody-independent manner.

nude mouse: Mouse which is T cell deficient due to a homozygous gene defect (*nu/nu*) resulting in the absence of a thymus (and also lack of body hair).

oncofetal antigen: Antigen whose expression is normally restricted to the fetus but which may be expressed during malignancy in adults.

opsonin: Substance, e.g. antibody or C3b, which enhances phagocytosis by promoting adhesion of the antigen to the phagocyte.

opsonization: Coating of antigen with opsonin to enhance phagocytosis.

PAF (platelet activating factor): An alkyl phospholipid released by a variety of cell types including mast cells and basophils, which has immunoregulatory effects on lymphocytes and monocytes/macrophages as well as causing platelet aggregation and degranulation.

paracortex: The part of an organ (e.g. lymph node) which lies between the cortex and the medulla.

perforin: Molecule produced by cytotoxic T cells and NK cells which, like complement component C9, polymerizes to form a pore in the membrane of the target cell leading to cell death.

periarteriolar lymphoid sheath (PALS): The lymphoid tissue which forms the white pulp of the spleen.

Peyer's patches: Part of the gut associated lymphoid tissue (GALT) and found as distinct lymphoid nodules mainly in the small intestine.

PHA (phytohemagglutinin): A plant lectin which acts as a T cell mitogen.

phage antibody library: A collection of cloned antibody variable region gene sequences which can be expressed as Fab or scFv fusion proteins with bacteriophage coat proteins. These can be displayed on the surface of the phages. The gene encoding a monoclonal recombinant antibody is enclosed in the phage particle and can be selected from the library by binding of the phage to specific antigen.

phagocyte: Cells, including monocytes/macrophages and neutrophils, which are specialized for the engulfment of cellular and particulate matter.

phagolysosome: Intracellular vacuole where killing and digestion of phagocytosed material occurs following the fusion of a phagosome with a lysosome.

phagosome: Intracellular vacuole produced following invagination of the cell membrane around phagocytosed material.

phorbol myristate acetate (PMA): A mitogenic phorbol ester which directly stimulates protein kinase C and acts as a tumor promoter.

plaque forming cell (PFC): Antibody-secreting plasma cell detected *in vitro* by its ability to produce a 'plaque' of lysed antigen-sensitized erythrocytes in the presence of complement.

plasma cell: Terminally differentiated B lymphocyte which actively secretes large amounts of antibody.

pokeweed mitogen (PWM): A plant lectin which is a T cell dependent B cell mitogen.

polyclonal: Many different clones, or the product of many different clones, e.g. polyclonal antiserum.

poly-Ig receptor: A receptor molecule which specifically binds J-chain-containing polymeric Ig, i.e. dimeric secretory IgA and pentameric IgM, and transports it across mucosal epithelium.

positive selection: The selection of those developing T cells in the thymus which are able to recognize self MHC molecules. This occurs by preventing apoptosis in these cells.

precipitin: Precipitate of antibody and multivalent antigen due to the formation of high molecular weight complexes.

primary immune response: The relatively weak immune response which occurs upon the first encounter of naive lymphocytes with a given antigen.

primary lymphoid organs: The sites at which immunocompetent lymphocytes develop, i.e. bone marrow and thymus in mammals.

prime: The process of giving an initial sensitization to antigen.

prostaglandins: Acidic lipids derived from arachidonic acid which are able to increase vascular permeability, mediate fever, and can both stimulate and inhibit immunological responses.

proteasome: Cytoplasmic proteolytic enzyme complex involved in antigen processing for association with MHC.

protein A: *Staphylococcus aureus* cell wall protein which binds to the Fc region of IgG.

protein tyrosine kinases: Enzymes which are able to phosphorylate proteins on tyrosines, and often act in a cascade-like fashion in the signal transduction systems of cells.

prozone effect: The loss of immune precipitation or agglutination which occurs when antibody concentration is increased to an extent that the antibody is in such excess that it is no longer able to effectively cross-link the antigen. A similar phenomenon may occur in antigen excess.

Qa antigens: 'Non-classical' MHC class I molecules of mice.

respiratory burst: The increased oxidative metabolism which occurs in phagocytic cells following activation.

reticuloendothelial system (RES): A rather old term for the network of phagocytes and endothelial cells throughout the body.

rheumatoid factor: IgM, IgG and IgA autoantibodies to IgG, particularly the Fc region.

rosette: Particles or cells bound to the surface of a lymphocyte (e.g. sheep erythrocytes around a human T cell).

scFv: A single chain molecule composed of the variable regions of an antibody heavy and light chain joined together by a flexible linker.

SCID (severe combined immunodeficiency): Immunodeficiency affecting both T and B lymphocytes.

secondary immune response: The qualitatively and quantitatively improved immune response which occurs upon the second encounter of primed lymphocytes with a given antigen.

secretory component: Proteolytic cleavage product of

the poly-Ig receptor which remains associated with dimeric IgA in sero-mucus secretions.

secretory IgA: Dimeric IgA found in sero-mucus secretions.

somatic hypermutation: The enhanced rate of point mutation in the immunoglobulin variable region genes which occurs following antigenic stimulation and acts as a mechanism for increasing antibody diversity and affinity.

stem cell: Multipotential cell from which differentiated cells derive.

superantigen: An antigen which reacts with all the T cells belonging to a particular T cell receptor V region family, and which therefore stimulates (or deletes) a much larger number of cells than does conventional antigen.

surface plasmon resonance: A technique based upon changes in the angle of reflected light which occur upon ligand binding to an immobilized target molecule on a biosensor chip. This permits the observation of protein–protein interactions (such as antibody binding to an antigen) in 'real-time', i.e. by continuous monitoring of the association and dissociation of the reversible reaction.

switch sequences: Highly conserved repetitive sequences which mediate class switching in the immunoglobulin heavy chain gene locus.

syngeneic: Genetically identical, e.g. a fully inbred strain of mice.

TAP: The Transporters associated with Antigen Processing (TAP-1 and TAP-2) are molecules which carry antigenic peptides from the cytoplasm into the lumen of the endoplasmic reticulum for incorporation into MHC class I molecules.

T cell receptor (TCR): The heterodimeric antigen receptor of the T lymphocyte exists in two alternative forms, consisting of α and β chains, or γ and δ chains. The αβ TCR recognizes peptide frag-

ments of protein antigens presented by MHC molecules on cell surfaces. The function of the γδ TCR is less clearly defined but it can recognize native proteins on the cell surface.

T-dependent antigen: An antigen which requires helper T cells in order to elicit an antibody response.

T-independent antigen: An antigen which is able to elicit an antibody response in the absence of T cells.

thymocyte: Developing T cell in the thymus.

titer: Measure of the relative 'strength' (a combination of amount and avidity) of an antibody or antiserum, usually given as the highest dilution which is still operationally detectable in, for example, an agglutination assay.

tolerance: Specific immunological unresponsiveness.

tolerogen: An antigen used to induce tolerance. Often depends more on the circumstances of administration (e.g. route and concentration) than on any inherent property of the molecule.

toxoid: Chemically or physically modified toxin that is no longer harmful but retains immunogenicity.

tumor necrosis factors (TNFα and TNFβ): Two related cytokines originally named for their cytotoxic effects on certain tumor cells but which also have immunoregulatory functions.

variable (V) gene segments: Genes that rearrange together with D (diversity) and J (joining) gene segments in order to encode the variable region amino acid sequences of immunoglobulins and T cell receptors.

vasoactive amines: Substances including histamine and 5-hydroxytryptamine which increase vascular permeability and smooth muscle contraction.

xenogeneic: Genetic differences between species.

xenograft: A tissue or organ graft between individuals of different species.

INDEX

NOTE

Cross-reference terms in *italics* are either general cross-references, or refer to subentry terms within the same main entry (the main entry is not repeated in order to save space).
Readers are also advised to refer to the end of each article for additional cross-references – not all of these cross-references have been included in the index cross-references.

This index is in letter-by-letter order, whereby hyphens and spaces within index headings are ignored in the alphabetization. Terms in parentheses are excluded from the initial alphabetization.

Abbreviations used in subentries without explanation:

ADCC	Antibody-dependent cellular cytotoxicity	Ig	Immunoglobulin
APCs	Antigen-presenting cells	ITP	Idiopathic thrombocytopenic purpura
CMV	Cytomegalovirus	LAK	Lymphokine activated killer cells
CSF	Colony-stimulating factor	LPS	Lipopolysaccharide
CTL	Cytoxic T lymphocytes	mAb	Monoclonal antibody
CVID	Common variable immunodeficiency	MIF	Macrophage migration inhibition factor
EAE	Experimental autoimmune encephalomyelitis	NK	Natural killer cells
EBV	Epstein–Barr virus	PAF	Platelet-activating factor
G-CSF	Granulocyte colony-stimulating factor	PUFA	Polyunsaturated fatty acids
GM-CSF	Granulocyte-macrophage colony-stimulating factor	SCID	Severe combined immunodeficiency
GVHD	Graft-versus-host disease	SLE	Systemic lupus erythematosus
HBV	Hepatitis B virus	TCR	T cell receptor
HCV	Hepatitis C virus	TfR	Transferrin receptor
HEVs	High endothelial venules	TGF	Transforming growth factor
HIV	Human immunodeficiency virus	TNF	Tumor necrosis factor
HPV	Human papillomavirus	UVB	Ultraviolet light B
HSV	Herpes simplex virus	VIP	Vasoactive intestinal peptide
IDDM	Insulin-dependent diabetes mellitus		

A

A4 protein (amyloid β protein) 85–86
A33 antigen 2428
A23187 calcium ionophore 253
Ab1 clones 1186, 1190, 1191
Ab2 clones, *see* Anti-idiotype antibodies;
  under Idiotype(s)
ABA-1 (allergen) 241, 242(Fig)
Abelson murine leukemia virus 1564
  transformed pre-B cell lines 63
ABH antigens 5

ABH antigens (*continued*)
  amphibia and reptiles 4
  ontogeny 4
  see also ABO blood group, group H
ABO blood group 1–5, 1174
  A-/B- transferases 2, 4
  agglutination tests 1, 1(Table), 115, 136,
    141
  alloantigenic diversity 70–71
  antibodies 4–5, 347
    age-related changes in titers 5
    loss 5
    naturally-occurring 347
  antigens 2

ABO blood group (*continued*)
  antigens (*continued*)
    blood transfusion 2400
    cold agglutinins 4, 594, 595
    see also Blood group antigens
  cross-reactions with *Toxocara canis* 2380
  detection
    monoclonal antibody use 76, 1746–
      1747
    see also Blood typing
  discovery 1
  distribution 4, 71
  'ECO' (enzymically converted group O)
    4

ABO blood group (*continued*)
environmental antigens 4
epitopes 2–4
fetus 4, 5
frequency of groups 1
genetics 1–2
genotype 2
glycosidase modification of expression 4
group A
  A_1 and A_2 subgroups 1
  antibodies 4
  differences between A_1 and A_2 2
  pernicious anemia association 104–105
  streptococcal antigen mimicry in
    rheumatic fever 1737
group B 1737
  antibodies 4
  subgroups 1
group H 2, 4, 1737
  antigens 2
  urinary tract infections 2453
  see also ABH antigens
group O 1–2
  alleles 2
  antibodies 4–5
as histocompatibility antigens 4
incompatibility, hemolytic disease of
  newborn (HDN) 1070–1071, 1072,
  1674
nucleotide sequences 2
number of sites on red cells 4
ontogeny 4
phylogeny 4
'secretor' locus 4
subgroups 1
synthesis 2, 3(Fig), 4, 1737
urinary tract infections 2453
see also Blood groups; Blood
  transfusion(s)
ABO hemolytic transfusion reactions, see
  Blood transfusion reactions
Abortion
habitual 497
leptospirosis in animals 1552
Listeria monocytogenes causing 1592
recurrent spontaneous, maternal immune
  response 900
spontaneous, in SLE 2257
ABO transferases 2, 4
Abscess
amebic liver, see Amebic liver abscess
Bacteroides inducing 328–329
renal 2066
subcutaneous, Fusobacterium causing
  962
Absolute risk 1698
Abzymes, see Catalytic antibodies
Acanthocyte 834
Acanthocytosis 837
Acantholysis 2188
Accessory cells, see Antigen presenting cells
  (APCs)
Accessory cholera enterotoxin (ACE) 2372,
  2477
'Accommodation', xenograft survival
  prolongation 2510
Acemannan 430
Acetaminophen, prostaglandin synthesis
  inhibition 118
Acetic acid-induced colitis 1384
Acetylcholine (ACh)
antibodies 1341
gastric acid secretion control 1103
release 1834, 1849
Acetylcholine receptor (AChR) 1847–1848
administration, experimental myasthenia
  gravis treatment 1897
antibodies 264, 1675, 1834, 1847–1848
  detection/titer 1835
  experimental autoimmune myasthenia
    gravis 1849
  experimental models 273

Acetylcholine receptor (AChR) (*continued*)
antibodies (*continued*)
  half-life 1675
  heterogeneity 1848
  measurement 1848
  production rates 1848
  α subunits 1834, 1847
cross-reactive protein in thymoma 1848
experimental autoimmune disease
  induction 273, 1849
extrajunctional form 1834, 1835
fetal 801, 1848
junctional form 1834
loss of function 1847–1848
'main immunogenic region' 1834, 1848
on myoid cells 2235
see also Myasthenia gravis
Acetylcholinesterase
hookworms secreting 1122b
Toxocara canis secreting 2381
N-Acetylgalactosaminyl transferase 2
N-Acetyl-D-glucosamine, blood group A
  1737
N-Acetyl-D-glucosamine 321
N-Acetyllactosamine 1373
N-Acetylmuramic acid (NAM) 321, 423
Acetylsalicylic acid, see Aspirin
O-Acetyltransferase, CD22 regulation 480
Acid phosphatase 1388
Acid–base interactions, hydrogen bonds
  164
Acinetobacter, elastase effect 1723
Acne 662
immune response 662
Acoelomates, immune response 1499
Aconitase 236
Acquired immune deficiency syndrome, see
  AIDS
Acquired immune response 3–15
characteristics 14
historical background 14
mechanisms 14–15
medical indications, see Vaccination
see also Cell-mediated immunity;
  Humoral immune response
Acrodermatitis chronica atrophica 380
Acrodermatitis enteropathica 1284, 2516
Acrylamide 2043
gel electrophoresis of DNA 2195
polymerization 2043
ACTH, see Corticotropin (ACTH)
Actin
LFA-1 activation mechanism 1612
polymerization, chemoattractant-
  stimulated leukocytes 1760
α-Actinin 419, 1612
Actinobacillus actinomycetemcomitans
  1890
antibodies 1890
Actinomycin D, T cell hybridoma selection
  1153–1154
Activated leukocyte-cell adhesion molecule
  (ALCAM; CD166) 457(Table)
Activated partial thromboplastin time
  (APTT) 1519
Activated protein C (APC) 583
inhibitor 583
Activation-induced cell death (AICD) 877
defects in murine lupus 2252
Fas/FasL role 2332
IL-2 role 1438
mechanism 2332
negative regulation of T cell expansion
  2332
Acute inflammatory demyelinating
  polyneuropathy (AIDP) 1836–1837
diagnosis 1837
IgM and IgG 1837
management 1837
model 1836–1837
pathology/clinical features 1836, 1837

Acute inflammatory reaction, see
  Inflammatory reaction
Acute motor axonal neuropathy (AMAN)
  1837–1838
Acute necrotizing hemorrhagic
  leukoencephalitis 1841
Acute phase proteins 18–20
in bacterial infections 315
biological/clinical importance 20
concentration 19
definition 19
disorders with minimal levels 19
diversity 19–20
interspecies differences 19
invertebrates 1500
'negative' 18, 85
as opsonins 1886–1887
structure 19
synthesis 18–19
see also C-reactive protein (CRP); Serum
  amyloid A (SAA) protein
Acute phase response 18, 663
absence in IL-6 knockout mice 18
effect on zinc distribution 2516
IL-1 role 1830
IL-6 role 1459, 1830
induction, leukemia inhibitory factor
  (LIF) 1561
monitoring 20
see also Acute phase proteins
Acute respiratory distress syndrome
  (ARDS), see Adult respiratory distress
  syndrome (ARDS)
Acute sensori-motor axonal neuropathy
  (ASMAN) 1838
Acyclovir, in EBV infection 833
ADAM-8 (CD156) 456(Table)
ADCC, see Antibody-dependent cellular
  cytotoxicity (ADCC)
Addison's disease 39, 40(Table), 996
animal models 42
autoantibodies 41–42
autoimmune diseases associated 42
autoimmune polyendocrinopathy–
  candidiasis–ectodermal dystrophy
  1984, 1985
autoimmune polyglandular syndrome
  type II 1985
autoimmune thyroid disease 1986, 2313
cellular autoimmune response 42
etiology 43
humoral autoimmune response 41–42
immunogenetics 42
immunopathology 40–41, 41(Fig)
MHC class II expression 41, 43
molecular mimicry 43
pathogenesis 42–43
pathology 39–41, 40(Fig)
sporadic 39
Addressins 1778, 2060
antibodies 1094
expression 1095, 1099, 2060
development 1098–1099
homing receptors 1097, 1618
see also Homing receptors
mucosal 1096(Fig), 1097, 1097–1098
development of expression 1098
in lamina propria 1099
peripheral 1094, 1096(Fig), 1097, 1097–
  1098, 1249, 1618, 1778
development of expression 1098
role in lymphocyte adhesion 1097–1098,
  1249
see also High endothelial venules (HEV)
Adducin, in red cell membrane 835,
  838(Table)
Adenocarcinoma, antitumor effects of
  glucans 429
Adenoids 1775
Adenosine deaminase (ADA) 749
deficiency 1278, 2170, 2172–2173
enzyme replacement 2174

Adenosine deaminase (ADA) (*continued*)
deficiency (*continued*)
gene therapy 978, 979(Table), 2174
mutation, SCID mice 1268
see also Severe combined
immunodeficiency (SCID)
Adenoviruses (Ad) 21–26
antibodies 23
antibody-mediated inhibition 23
antigens 21–23
changes 24
cell death genes in 25
characteristics 21–23
classification and subgroups 21
detection 23
discovery and isolation 21
E1A and E1B regions 25
E3/19K glycoprotein 22
antigen presentation inhibition 193
E3 region 22, 23
in gene delivery 24
early (E) nonstructural proteins 21, 22
genome 21, 22
host immune response 21, 23–24
infection, *see* Adenoviruses (Ad) infection
(*below*)
major late promotor (MLP) 25
oncogenic 21
serotypes 21
recombination between 24
structural proteins 22–23
structure 21–23, 22(Fig)
SV40 hybrid viruses 24
VA-1 protein 22
vaccines 21, 24
administration route 2455
SV40 in 21, 24
as vectors for gene delivery 24–25
Adenoviruses (Ad) infection 21
animal models 23
eye 872
immunocompromised hosts 23
respiratory tract 21, 24
therapy 25
Adenylate cyclase-hemolysin, *Bordetella
pertussis* 2377
Adhesins
Escherichia coli 844, 2066
urinary tract infections 2452, 2453
Forssman antigen as receptor 954
Mycoplasma 1799
uroepithelial cell 2041
Yersinia 2514
Adhesion, cell
cadherin-mediated 419
CD antigens involved 73
CD44 role 488, 490
CD45 role 493
to fibronectin 910
galectins role 1538–1539
integrin-mediated 419
mechanisms 2059–2061
recognition *vs* 419–420
see also Adhesion molecules; Cadherins;
Integrins; *specific cell types*
Adhesion molecules 26–33
CD4⁺ cell interaction with APCs 195
CD44 488
clinical importance and diseases 31–32
cytokine-induced expression 30
definition 26, 31
domains 515
endothelial cells 803–805
see also Addressins
experimental autoimmune thyroiditis
2310
expression 30
contact hypersensitivity 639–640
fibroblasts 907
germinal centers 992, 993(Fig)
membrane attack complex role 627
mice lacking 32

Adhesion molecules (*continued*)
expression (*continued*)
modulation in tumors 32
regulation 30–31
function, regulation 30–31
hematopoietic cells 376
inhibitors, prostaglandins 119
intercellular, *see* ICAM-1; ICAM-2;
ICAM-3
invertebrates 1500
in vivo importance 32
leukocyte recruitment 2059–2060
knockout mice 2060, 2062(Table)
listing and characteristics 27(Table)-
28(Table)
monocytes 1753–1754, 1753(Table),
1754
neutrophil migration, *see under*
Neutrophil(s)
NSAIDs action 119
phagocyte rolling 2059–2060
see also Leukocyte(s); Neutrophil(s)
porcine 1993
rheumatoid arthritis 2114
role in immune regulation 29–30
segregation from recognition effectors
419–420
signal transduction 31
soluble 30
structural families 26, 27(Table), 515
T cell activation/proliferation 2145–2146
three-dimensional structure 515–520,
516(Table), 518–519
thymocyte migration 2236
see also Cadherins; Cell surface antigens;
Immunoglobulin (Ig) superfamily;
Integrins; Mucins; Selectins
Adhesive properties of cells, separation
based on 509–510
'Adhesive trap' 542
Adipsin 603
Adjuvant(s) 36–39, 36(Table), 220
alum 36, 220, 2454, 2455
aluminium compounds 36–37
antigen combinations 38
of bacterial origin 37–38
see also Lipopolysaccharide (LPS);
Muramyl dipeptide (MDP)
biodegradable delivery systems 38
combinations 38
cytokines acting as 38
definition 36, 2455
emulsions 37
in experimental autoimmune uveoretinitis
(EAU) 868
formulations used/under trial
2456(Table)
functions 2455
future prospects 38–39
hydrophobic compounds 37
immunomodulators of biological origin
38, 1345
ISCOMs 37
action 1507–1508
lipopolysaccharides 37
liposomes 37
role 1590, 1591
living organisms as 38
mechanism of action 1980, 1980–1981
muramyl dipeptide activity, *see* Muramyl
dipeptide (MDP)
properties 36
Quil A 37
saponin 37
surfactants 37
toxicity 36
in vaccination/vaccines 36, 2455–2456
parenteral administration 2454
see also Freund's adjuvant
Adjuvant arthritis (AA) 33–35, 335
clinical expression 33–34
determinant spreading 755

Adjuvant arthritis (AA) (*continued*)
factors influencing 33
features and comparisons 2106(Table)
hsp60 role 34, 2231
hsp65 and 34–35
induction 33–34, 34
pathogenesis theories 33
prevention by hsp65 34
regulation 34–35
resistance 33
severity and duration 33
suppression/inhibition 34–35
transfer by T cell clone 34
treatment by collagen type I 1897
Adoptive transfer
activated lymphocytes 1344–1345
Chlamydia infections 551
CMV immunity 723, 729
contact hypersensitivity,
contrasuppression effect 650
CTLs, in EBV infection 833
experimental autoimmune uveoretinitis
(EAU) 869
hapten carrier systems 437
influenza virus studies 1386
lymphocytes, tumor immunotherapy
2441, 2442
nonspecific immunopotentiation 1348
obese strain of chickens 281, 282
reovirus infection studies 2070
T cells role in graft rejection 1012
ADP-ribosyl transferases, toxins 2369
Adrenal atrophy
Addison's disease 39, 40(Fig)
idiopathic 39
Adrenal autoantibodies 41, 262(Table),
263, 1985, 1986
Adrenal autoantigens 1986
Adrenal autoimmunity 39–43
diseases 40(Table)
see also Addison's disease; Adrenal
autoantibodies
Adrenal cells, autoantibodies to 41
Adrenal cortex
cell loss in Addison's disease 39
steroid hormones 996
see also Glucocorticoids;
Mineralocorticoids
Adrenalectomy 1827, 2224
effects of IL-1 moderated by 1435
Adrenal hyperplasia/hypertrophy 40
Adrenaline, *see* Epinephrine
Adrenalitis, experimental 42
α-Adrenergic receptors, exercise-induced
stimulation 846
β-Adrenergic receptors 2224
agonists in asthma 246(Table)
blockers 279
exercise-induced effects 847
Adrenocorticotropic hormone (ACTH), *see*
Corticotropin (ACTH)
Adult respiratory distress syndrome
(ARDS) 86, 319
IL-8 levels 1470
MIF role 1656
neutrophils 1858
P-selectin 2159
Adult T cell leukemia/lymphoma (ATLL)
1559, 1564–1565, 1632, 1633, 2096,
2097
causative agent 1633, 2096, 2097
see also Human T lymphotropic virus
type I (HTLV-I)
Advanced glycation end-products (AGE)
1046, 1115
lysozyme binding 1723
receptor, *see* RAGE
role in aging 1115
Adventitial reticular cells 2236
Aerobic spore-forming bacilli (ASB) 311
Affinity (K_A) 43–47, 50
definition 44, 219

Affinity (K$_A$) (*continued*)
  immobilization effect 44–45
  importance 46
  measurement methods 45
    competition ELISA 45–46
  monoclonal antibodies 44, 45, 45(Fig),
    1745–1746
  in solution 44, 45
  theory 44–45
  see also under Antibodies
Affinity chromatography 47–49, 2038
  anti-idiotypic antibodies 48
  high-pressure liquid chromatography
    (HPLC) 48
  historical perspective 47–48
  principle 47
  procedure 48–49
    hydrophobic columns 48, 49
    ligand selection/preparation 47, 48
    metal chelate columns 49
  protein separation 48, 2038
  purification success 47
  uses and advantages 47
  see also Antibody-antigen intermolecular
    forces
Affinity cross-linking 51
Affinity electrophoretic method 1296
Affinity labeling 50–52
  antibody combining site 50–51
  applications 51
  criteria for good labels 50
  definition and principle 50
  results obtained 51
Affinity matrices, B cell adsorption 179
Affinity maturation 14, 52–54, 153, 292,
    1145–1146, 1325, 1678
  apoptosis role 226
  autoimmunity pathogenesis 289
  cellular cooperation 651
  definition 52
  germinal center microenvironment 1728
  models 53(Fig)
  as process of somatic evolution 53–54
  see also Somatic hypermutation
Affinity purification
  antibodies, Western blotting 2506
  by SDS-PAGE 2144, 2144(Fig)
  transfer factors 2385
African swine fever (ASF) 54–56
African swine fever (ASF)-like viruses
    (family) 54
African swine fever (ASF) virus
  antigens 54–55
  characteristics 54–55
  evasive strategies 55–56
  genome 56
  hemadsorption (HAD) of erythrocytes 54
  host immune response 55
  infection process 54–55
  vaccines 56
African trypanosomiasis, *see*
    Trypanosomiasis, African
Agammaglobulinemia 366
  Bruton's, *see* Bruton's
    agammaglobulinemia
  Swiss type 1277
    see also Severe combined
      immunodeficiency (SCID)
  X-linked (XLA) 216, 1279–1280
  see also Immunodeficiency, primary
Agarose 1250
  affinity chromatography 48
  antibody coupling methods 1250–1251
  isoelectric focusing 1512
  plaque-forming cell (PFC) assays 1961
  single radial immunodiffusion 1289
Agarose gel electrophoresis
  DNA 2195
  Northern blotting 1864, 1864–1865
  Southern blotting 2195
  Western blotting 2504
AGE

AGE (*continued*)
  see Advanced glycosylation end-products
    (AGE)
  autoimmune disease pathogenesis 61,
    279
  HIV infection progression and 8
Age-related changes 59–61
  advanced glycosylation end-products
    (AGE) 1115
  autoimmunity increase 61, 279
  B cells 61
  calorie restriction effect on disease 884
  cell-mediated immunity 135
  disease increase, PUFA causing 884
  factors determining progression of aging
    59
  heterogeneity of population 60
  IgG glycosylation variations 1002
  immune response decline 60, 1870–1871
  immune response increase 60
  immune system 59–61
  immunodeficiency 1285
  interleukin formation 60
  LAK cells 60
  NK cells 60–61, 61
  oxidative stress 135
  polymorphism of 60
  stem cells 59, 61
  suppressor capacity for cellular immunity
    60
  suppressor capacity for humoral
    immunity 60
  T helper cells 60
  thymus 60
  see also Elderly
Agglutination 56–59, 141–142
  antibody detection 56, 141–142
  applications 56, 58
  autoantibody detection 260
  automated reading/processing of results
    58
  brucellosis diagnosis 385
  carrier molecules 141
  classification of reactions 57
  definition 57
  direct 57
  factors influencing 57
  historical background 57
  in immunoassays 1253
  inhibition 57
    applications 58
  'lattice' theory 57
  mechanisms 57–58
  microplate techniques 58
  nonspecific, theory 57
  passive 57
  protective mechanism in infections 58–59
  quantitation 58
  rapid testing in ultrasonic standing wave
    58
  red blood cells 1, 1(Table), 57, 115, 136
    see also Coombs' test;
      Hemagglutination
  specific 57
  viruses by antibody 2481
Agglutination reactions
  definition 57
  see also Agglutination
Aggrecan 864
  structure 864(Fig)
Aggressins, *Pasteurella multocida* 1928
Aging and immune system 59–61
  factors determining progression 59
  see also Age-related changes
Agouti locus 1272
Agriculture, transgenic technology 2407
AICD, *see* Activation-induced cell death
    (AICD)
AIDP, *see* Acute inflammatory
    demyelinating polyneuropathy (AIDP)
AIDS 6–13, 1130
  adenovirus infections 23

AIDS (*continued*)
  animal models 1268, 1274, 2005
  B cell lymphoma, HHV-8 association
    1090
  Candida infections 409, 410
  case number and spread 6
  clinical features 8
  cryptococcosis 672, 673
  discovery 6
  EBV-associated tumors 832
  epidemiology 6–7
  feline immunodeficiency virus similarities
    895
  HIV causing 2096
  human/mouse chimeras use 546
  IL-12 role 1487
  immune complexes in 1225, 2096
  immunopathogenesis 10–11
    CD8$^+$ cells and role of FACS study 938
    germinal center microenvironment role
      1728–1729
  Kaposi's sarcoma in 1360
  leishmaniasis and 1920–1921
  lifespan prediction, CD38/glutathione
    measurement 941
  lymphocyte-specific antibodies 124
  lymphomas 7, 8, 1090, 1635, 1884
  microsporidians 1921
  Mycoplasma as cofactor 1801
  natural history 8–9
  opportunistic infections 7, 8, 1884
  opportunistic tumors 7, 8
    see also AIDS, lymphomas; Kaposi's
      sarcoma
  parvovirus B19 infection 1924, 1924–
    1925, 1926
  Pneumocystis carinii infection 1977
  polyclonal hypergammaglobulinemia in
    1163
  progression, *see under* HIV infection
  resistance, CCR-5 mutation 712
  respiratory tract infections 2081–2082
  Strongyloides stercoralis hyperinfection
    1921
  syphilis in 2417
  therapy 1138
    combination therapy 12
    gene therapy 978, 979(Table)
    GM-CSF use 1022
    IL-2 1438
    interferon α combined therapy 1416
    strategies 11–12
    thymic hormones 1346
    transfer factor 2388
    zidovudine monotherapy 12
    see also HIV, vaccines
  toxoplasmic encephalitis 2384
  vaccines, *see* HIV, vaccines
  see also HIV infection
AIDS dementia complex 7, 11
Air pollution 1368
  allergic rhinitis 2123
Airway hyperresponsiveness 243
  TNFα role 2439–2440
Airway inflammation 244
AITD, *see* Thyroid autoimmunity
A/J mice 1763
  immunology 1763
  infectious agents susceptibility/resistance
    1763
  Legionella pneumophila infection 1544–
    1545, 1545
  origin/characteristics 1763
AKR/J mice 1764
  immunology 1764
  infectious agents susceptibility/resistance
    1764
  origin/characteristics 1764
  streaker (nu^{str}) mutation 1866
  Thy-1 discovery 2290
Albumin 1964–1965

Albumin (*continued*)
  equilibration time 1599
  preparation 1967
  synthesis, after plasmapheresis 1970
  tolerance breakdown 2308
  see also Bovine serum albumin (BSA)
Alcohol abuse, chronic active hepatitis 563
Aldosterone 996
Aleppo button 1547
Alkaline phosphatase 260
  antibody detection methods 143
  calf intestine 814
  ELISA 818
  immunohistochemistry 143, 1263
  probe labeling in Northern blotting 1865
Alkaline phosphatase–antialkaline
    phosphatase (APAAP) complex 1259,
    1263
ALK-NPM chromosomal translocations
    556
Alkylating agents, autoimmune hemolytic
    anemia (AIHA) 97
Alleles 986, 987
  codominant expression 987
  dominant/recessive 987
  multiple, disease association 1699, 2065
Allele-specific amplification 1693
Allelic exclusion 61–64, 146, 155, 356,
    364
  definition 62
  regulated model 63–64
  V gene assembly 62–64
  see also Immunoglobulin gene(s), V genes
Allelism 74
Allergens 64–70, 206
  avoidance 69, 2125
    asthma 245
  bronchoconstriction due to 1103
  cat 2122
  clinical significance 69
  cross-reactions with inhaled/ingested
    allergens 950
  definition 251, 1170, 1171
  food, *see* Food allergens
  history 64, 65(Table)
  identification 66
  immune response 68–69
    T cells role 69
  immunotherapy, *see* Immunotherapy, of
    allergic disease
  indoor 69
    exposure measurement 69
  inhalant 67(Table)
    features 66
    IgE response 65
    immunotherapy 1354
  injections, atopy treatment 255
  insect venom 2471(Table)
  molecular biology 66–68
    cDNA libraries 66
    cloning/sequencing 66
    modeling and tertiary structure 68
    protein families and functions 66–68
  nomenclature 65–66, 251
    IUIS subcommittee 65, 66(Table)
  properties 65–66
  recombinant 65
    expression/activity 68
    immunotherapy 1355
  seasonal allergic rhinitis 2123
  uptake, atopic allergy 252
  vaccines 69
  see also Allergic reactions; Atopic allergy;
    Atopy; Food allergy; Hypersensitivity
Allergic asthma, *see* Asthma, allergic
Allergic contact dermatitis 787, 1365
  compounds associated 787
  Langerhans cells 1530
  mercury causing 1689
  pathogenic mechanism 1531
Allergic disease
  chronic 254

Allergic disease (*continued*)
  IL-3 antagonists role 1444
  immunotherapy, *see* Immunotherapy, of
    allergic disease
  incidence 252
  lung disease 1365
    see also Asthma, allergic
  rhinitis, *see* Allergic rhinitis
  see also Allergy; Atopy
Allergic inflammation, C3a action 89
Allergic reactions 1170
  to drugs, *see* Drug allergy
  histamine 1101–1102
  IgE role, *see under* Immunoglobulin E
    (IgE)
  to insect bites/stings 680, 2471
  to marine animal venom 2473
  plasma-containing products causing 1967
  to snake venom 2472
  see also Allergens; allergy; Cutaneous
    hypersensitivity; Hypersensitivity, type
    I; Urticaria
Allergic rhinitis 252, 2121–2126
  causes 2122–2123
  chronic symptoms 2123, 2124(Fig)
  clinical appearance 2122
  food inducing 948
  histamine release 2123, 2124
  immediate symptoms 2123, 2124(Fig)
  immune response 2123
  immunotherapy 1354, 2125
  mechanism 2123–2124, 2124(Fig)
  mediators 2123–2124
  nasal blood flow and 2124–2125
  perennial 2122
  provocation tests 2124
  seasonal (hayfever) 252, 2121, 2123
    IgG to pollen allergens 69
    increases and reasons 2123
  treatments 2125
    cetirizine 2124
Allergic vasculitis, foods inducing 949
Allergy 1170
  castor beans 2122
  cats 2122
  definition 25
  drug, *see* Drug allergy
  food, *see* Food allergy
  latex 67(Table), 681, 2122
  tests 1172–1174
  toxic agents causing 1365
  see also Allergens; Allergic reactions;
    Atopy
Alloaggression, invertebrates 1499
Alloantibodies 346
  allotype detection 76
  red cell 347
Alloantigenic responses, development 70
Alloantigens 70–74
  biochemistry 73–74
  major systems 70–72
    see also Blood group antigens; CD
      antigens; MHC
  molecular biology 73–74
  polymorphisms, reasons for 70
  x-ray crystallography 74
Allogeneic diversity 70, 208
Allograft, *see* Transplantation
Allograft rejection, *see* Graft rejection
Alloimmunization 70
  recurrent spontaneous abortion and 900
Allophycocyanins (APCs) 945
Allotope 74
Allotypes 62, 72–73, 74–77, 137, 204
  applications 76
  definition 62, 74, 137
  detection/assays 76
  disease associations 76
  genes, nomenclature 75
  haplotypes 75–76, 75(Table)
  human 75(Table)
  matching of monoclonal antibodies 76

Allotypes (*continued*)
  mouse and rabbit 75(Table)
  nomenclature 74–75
  rabbit 2047
  rat inbred strains 2057
  see also Immunoglobulin
All-*trans*-retinoic acid 1559
Alphafetoprotein (AFP) 799, 799–800,
    1361
  in ataxia telangiectasia (AT) 247
  elevated
    amniotic fluid 799
    congenital abnormalities associated
      799, 800(Table)
    primary liver cancer 799–800
  genes 799
  as immunosuppressive factor 800
  plasma levels 799
  in pregnancy 799
  structure 799
  synthesis 799, 799(Fig), 800
α granules
  proteinase 3 264
  see also under Platelet(s)
Alphaviruses 2350(Table)
  envelope proteins 2351
Alport syndrome 1007–1008
Altered peptide ligands (APL) 1357
  tolerance induction 2355
Altered self hypothesis 1625
Alternative splicing
  CD44 1680
  cytokine receptors 714
  FcεRII (low-affinity; CD23) 891
  glycoproteins 861
  Goodpasture antigen 1010
  IL-4 receptor 1454
  IL-13 1489
Alum adjuvant, *see* Adjuvant(s), alum
Aluminium compounds, as adjuvants 36–
    37
Aluminium hydroxide, as adjuvant 37, 38
Alveolar macrophage
  antigen uptake 191
  chemotactic response 540
  cytokines synthesized, LTB_4 inducing 231
  lipids 1389
  migration 191
  in pigs 1994
  pulmonary intravascular macrophage
    differences 1994
  sarcoidosis 2136
Alzheimer's disease 1046
  HLA class III association 1120
  senile plaques, amyloid β protein 85–86
Amalgam fillings 1686
Ambystoma mexicanum 79
  see also Axolotl
Amebae, *Legionella pneumophila* ingestion
    1542
Amebiasis 77–79, 968
  clinical features 77
  definition 77
  evasive strategies of *Entamoeba* 78–79
  immune response 77–78
    animal models 78
    antibody 77–78
    cell-mediated 78
    complement role 78
  mortality 77
  pathology 77
  prevalence 77
  vaccines 79
  see also Entamoeba histolytica
Amebic dysentery (AD) 77
Amebic liver abscess 77
  model 78
  vaccines for 79
Amebocytes 1499
Ameboma 78
Amenorrhea, lactational 641

Amide hydrolysis, catalytic antibodies 440(Fig)
Amine intolerance 952
Amino acid polymers, antigenic 205
Amino acids
  dietary deficiency 1870
  immunoglobulins 1337
  substitutions and phenotypic variation 987
Aminoacyl-transfer RNA synthetases, antibodies 2118
3-Amino-9-ethylcarbizol method 1263
Aminophospholipid translocase ('flippase') 834
Aminopterin, in hybridoma selection 1149
Ammonia 611
Ammonium chloride, toxicity 669
Amniotic fluid, elevated α-fetoprotein 799
Amphibian immune system 79–83
  ABH antigens 4
  B cells 80, 82
  heavy chain genes 1307
  immunobiology 81–82
  lymphocyte antigen-specific receptors 80–81
    B cell receptors 81
    T cell receptors 80–81
  lymphocytes 80
  lymphoid organs 80
  major histocompatibility system 81
  T cells 80, 82
  tumors 82–83
Amphibians
  evolution 79
  venom 2472–2473
Amphipathic molecules, liposomes 1588
Amphiphysin, antibodies 1842
'Ampholines' 1511
Amphotericin B 2410
Amplification refractory mutation system (ARMS) 1693
Amyloid 84–86
  AA protein 85
    SAA as precursor 19
  AL 85, 341, 1165
  AP component 85
  β2M 85
  β protein 85–86
  classification 84(Table)
  deposits, see Amyloidosis
  historical perspectives 84
  localized deposits 84
  types 85–86
β Amyloid 85–86
β Amyloid protein precursor (AβPP) 86
Amyloid enhancing factor (AEF) 85
Amyloidosis
  AA-type 19, 20
  definition 84–85
  hemodialysis association 84, 85
  hereditary (familial) 84
  multiple myeloma association 84, 85
  pathogenesis 85–86
  primary (idiopathic; AL) 84, 1165
  secondary (reactive; AA) 84
Analytical ultracentrifuge 2447
Anaphylactic shock, see Anaphylaxis
Anaphylactoid reactions 678
Anaphylatoxin(s) 86–90
  activities outside immune system 90
  bioactivity 89–90
  C3a, C4a, C5a 86
    see also C3a; C4a; C5a
  cytokine expression 90
  definition 86
  detection 781
  generation 86–87
  immunoregulation 90
  receptors 88–89
  structure 87
Anaphylatoxin inactivator

Anaphylatoxin inactivator
  (carboxypeptidase N), deficiency (continued)
    (carboxypeptidase N), deficiency 615(Table), 616
Anaphylaxis 86, 254, 678, 1170
  clinical features 1102
  cutaneous, see Cutaneous anaphylaxis
  diagnosis 781
  in dogs 413
  emergency self-treatment kits 685
  food inducing 950
    treatment 953
  histamine release 1102
  IgE role 1207
  localized 1170, 1207
  plasma-containing products causing 1967
  systemic 1170
  treatment 684–685
  see also Hypersensitivity, type I
ANCA, see Antineutrophil cytoplasmic autoantibodies (ANCAs)
ANCOVA (analysis of covariance) 2212
Ancylostoma caninum 1121, 1123, 1125
  vaccines 1921
Ancylostoma ceylanicum 1121, 1123
Ancylostoma duodenale 1121, 1122
Androgen, receptors 2176
Anemia
  aplastic, see Aplastic anemia
  autoimmune hemolytic, see Autoimmune hemolytic anemia (AIHA)
  congenital, parvovirus B19 infection 1925
  hemolytic, see Hemolytic anemia
  in idiopathic thrombocytopenic purpura 1975–1976
  iron-deficiency 1505
  megaloblastic 2490
  pernicious, see Pernicious anemia
  in persistent parvovirus B19 infection 1925
  sickle-cell 988, 1286, 1924
  in theilerosis 2288
  transient aplastic crisis 1924
Anergy 1228, 2362, 2363
  definition 108, 109, 569
  by immunosuppressive agents 1350
  mortality association 135
  myelin basic protein inducing 859
  signals 2366
  tolerance induction
    experimental model 2361
    oral 1894, 1894(Fig)
    see also Tolerance
  tumors 2444
Anergy , B cell 105–108, 358
  cell death 107, 108
  induction 572
    doses effect 106
    early models 106
    non membrane-bound antigen 107
  lifespan 107
  loss, tolerance breakdown 276
  mechanism 2364
  non self-reactive B cells differences 107
  recirculation abnormality 107
  reversal by CD40 and IL-4 107, 108
    reasons for 108
  surface IgM downregulation 107, 2364
  surface markers 107
  T cell-induced lysis 572
  tolerance induction 2361
  transgenic models 106–107
  see also Tolerance
Anergy , T cell 109–111, 202, 1436, 2262, 2328, 2365
  CD2R epitope loss 464
  function 110
  hu-SCID mice 1126
  IL-10 role 110, 2263
  induction 109–110, 502

Anergy , T cell (continued)
  induction (continued)
    by altered peptide ligands 110
    cross-reactive self-antigens 2332–2333
    mechanism 2328
    by superantigens 110
  in vivo 110
  LFA-3–CD2 interaction/role 1614
  loss 275
  one signal activation 1436, 2332
  partial inactivation 109
  prevention 109, 109–110
  reversal 110–111
  T_H1 cells 2332
  T_H2 cells 2332
  transgenic mice 110
Angioedema 678
  acquired 684–685
  C1 components crossed immunoelectrophoresis 1293, 1293(Fig)
  hereditary, see Hereditary angioedema
Angiogenesis
  cytokines inducing 805–806
  rheumatoid arthritis 2116
  tumor antigens 2429–2430
Angioimmunoblastic lymphadenopathy with dysproteinemia (AILD) 1162
Angiotenin-converting enzyme (ACE; CD143) 456(Table)
Angiotensin II 579
Animal models
  acetylcholine receptor (AChR) antibodies 273
  Addison's disease 42
  adjuvant arthritis, see Adjuvant arthritis (AA)
  arthritis, see Arthritis; Collagen-induced arthritis (CIA)
  autoimmune disease, see Autoimmune disease
  autoimmune disease of eye 867, 868(Table)
    see also Experimental autoimmune uveoretinitis (EAU)
  autoimmune gastritis 104
  autoimmune hemolytic anemia (AIHA) 91–93
    see also Autoimmune hemolytic anemia (AIHA)
  autoimmune polyglandular syndromes (APS) 1986
  borreliosis 381–382
  Chédiak–Higashi syndrome 527
  Chlamydia infections 551
  chronic active hepatitis (CAH) 564
  congenital rubella 2352
  copper insufficiency 657
  diabetes, see Diabetes mellitus, insulin-dependent (IDDM); NOD mouse
  flaviviruses 929
  gene therapy 978–979
  Guillain–Barré syndrome 1836
  H2 class II and disease association 1044
  Hashimoto's thyroiditis 104
  HIV infection 1268, 1274, 2005
  immunodeficiency, see Immunodeficiency, animal models
  immunotherapy with LAK cells 1629–1630
  inflammation induced by gene disruption 1382–1383
  inflammatory bowel disease, see under Inflammatory bowel disease
  insulin-dependent diabetes mellitus, see Diabetes mellitus, insulin-dependent (IDDM)
  kallikrein–kinin system 1520
  Klebsiella pneumoniae infection 1522
  leukocyte adhesion deficiency (LAD) 1566
  lipopolysaccharide tolerance 808

Animal models (*continued*)
  Lyme disease 381–382
  lymphatic filariasis 914, 915
  mucosal immune system 1785
  multiple sclerosis (MS), *see* Multiple
    sclerosis (MS)
  myasthenia gravis 1835
    see also Experimental autoimmune
      myasthenia gravis (EAMG)
  Mycoplasma infections 1799
  onchocerciasis 1874
  oral tolerance 1896–1897, 1897(Table)
  primates 2004, 2005
  reovirus infections 2068–2069
  rheumatoid arthritis (RA), *see*
    Rheumatoid arthritis (RA)
  scleroderma 283–284, 283–285
  serum sickness, *see* Serum sickness
  Sjögren's syndrome (SS) 2183
  SLE, *see* Murine lupus; Systemic lupus
    erythematosus (SLE)
  thyroid autoimmunity, *see* Thyroid
    autoimmunity, experimental models
  tolerance, *see* Tolerance
  tumor growth, exercise and 848
  type III hypersensitivity 1177
  vitiligo 2502
Animals
  immune systems, *see specific types of*
    animals
  phylogeny 1946–1947, 1947(Fig)
Anions, 'ping-pong' exchange 840
A-NK cells, *see under* Natural killer (NK)
  cells
ANK repeat 1118, 1119
Ankylosing spondylitis 1737–1741
  clinical features 2120
  HLA-B27 association 1737, 2121, 2513
  molecular mimicry 1737–1741
    antigen structures 1738(Fig)
    collagen and pulA protein 1738(Fig),
      1739
    HLA-B27 and nitrogenase 1738(Fig),
      1739, 1741
    HLA-B27 and pulD protein 1738(Fig),
      1739
    Klebsiella pneumoniae 1522, 1696
  pathology 1739–1741
  receptor theory 1737
  in twins and concordance rate 1737
Ankyrin
  binding to IP$_3$ receptor 1681
  CD44 complex 1680
  in red cell membrane 835, 838(Table)
  ryanodine receptor association 1681
Annexin I 112–113, 113, 115
Annexin II 112–113, 113
  dimer 113
  DNA replication regulation 115
Annexin V 114
Annexin VI 112
Annexin VII 114
Annexins (lipocortins) 111–115,
    852(Table)
  antibodies 113, 114
  anti-inflammatory actions 111, 112, 113
  binding proteins 113
  biological actions 111, 113–115,
    114(Table)
  cDNA clones 112
  genes 113
  glycosylation and acylation 114
  historical background 111–112
  localization 114
  mechanism of action 113
  origin of term 112
  phospholipid binding 113
  phosphorylation 115
  physiological roles 113–115
  receptors 114
  recombinant 113
  structure and properties 112–113, 113

Annexins (lipocortins) (*continued*)
  types and terminology 112–113,
    112(Table)
ANO2 antibody 159
Anogenital squamous cell carcinoma 1360
Anorexia, postoperative 1561
ANOVA (analysis of variance) 2212
Anterior chamber (eye)
  ocular antigens escaping 870
  privileged site 2013
Anterior chamber-associated immune
  deviation (ACAID) 870
Anterior uveitic disease 867
Anthrax 311, 312
  horse antiserum 314
  host resistance 312–313
  immune response 314
  pathogenesis 312–313
  toxin, *see under Bacillus anthracis*
  vaccine development 314
  see also Bacillus anthracis
Anthropological studies, tissue typing
  application 2322
Anti-allotype reagents 76
Anti-allotypic antisera 62
Anti-antibodies (AAs) 136–138
  to altered antibody molecules 137
    see also Rheumatoid factor (RF)
  development in xenogeneic antibody
    therapy 1345
  to native antibodies 136–137
    see also Allotypes; Idiotype(s)
Antibasement membrane antibodies 1341
  glomerular (anti-GBM) 1005, 1008–1009
    see also Goodpasture's syndrome
Antibiotics
  Bacillus producing 311
  classification 2013
  effect on opsonization 1887
  false food allergy 952
  mammalian (defensins) 317
    see also Defensins
  resistance
    Pseudomonas aeruginosa 2042
    retroviral vector marker 2087
Antibodies 1144
  affinity 43, 219, 2466
    protein-energy malnutrition 1869
    range 43
    specificity relationship 2200–2201
    see also Affinity (K$_A$)
  affinity maturation, *see* Affinity
    maturation
  altered during reactions with antigens
    137
  amino acid composition 1337
  antigen combining sites, *see* Antibody
    combining sites
  antigenicity 136–138
    see also Allotypes; Anti-antibodies
      (AAs); Anti-idiotype antibodies
  assay, *see* Antibody detection methods
  avidity 148, 219
    ELISA limitation 819
    immunocytochemistry 1260
    thymulin and thymopentin effect 2301
  binding sites, *see* Antibody combining
    sites
  biological activity, affinity importance 46
  bispecific (bifunctional), *see* Bispecific
    antibodies
  as bivalent molecules 2466
  blocking (incomplete) 57, 115
    removal on protein A-coated columns
      1348
    Rh disease 1071
    schistosomiasis 2141
    Taenia solium infections 692
  borreliacidal 382
  'capture' 1254–1255
  to carbohydrate antigens 427
  catalytic, *see* Catalytic antibodies

Antibodies (*continued*)
  chimeric, *see* Chimeric antibodies
  combinatorial libraries 985
  'connectivity' 1819
  cross-reactivity 2202
    functional (energetic) epitopes 2203–
      2205
    induced fit hypothesis and 2202
  crystal structure 152
  C terminal sequences, 'retention signals'
    144
  decreased, in iron deficiency 1506
  deficiency 1279–1281
    common variable immunodeficiency
      599, 600–601
    see also Agammaglobulinemia;
      Hypogammaglobulinemia;
      Immunodeficiency
  definition 218
  detection, *see* Antibody detection
    methods
  diversity, *see* Diversity generation;
    Immunoglobulin gene rearrangements;
    Somatic hypermutation
  donor-specific immunosuppression
    induced by 810
  enhancing, avoidance in HIV vaccine
    development 1137
  enzyme labeling, *see* Enzyme labeling
  epitope 'conformation' recognition 150
  fluorochrome labeling, *see* Fluorochrome
    labeling
  formation 1227
    clonal selection theory 1338
    histamine suppression 1105
    instructive-type theory 1337
    natural selection theory 573, 1338
    selection theories 1337
    template theory 1337, 1338
    see also Antibody synthesis; Clonal
      selection theory
  function 1227
  heterophile, *see* Heterophile antibodies
  high-affinity 2466
    phage display technology 1932
    role 1678
    selection 52–53, 153, 214
  homocytotrophic 64
    in ungulates 2449
  humanized, *see* Humanized antibodies
  idiotypic determinant recognition, in
    neonates 1819
  in immunocytochemistry, *see*
    Immunocytochemistry (ICC)
  incomplete, *see* Antibodies, blocking
  induced fit hypothesis 2201–2203
  induction 1677
  in influenza virus infections 1385, 1386
  labeling 2053
    immunocytochemistry 1258
    Western blotting 2505–2506, 2506–
      2506
    see also Enzyme labeling;
      Fluorochrome labeling; Radiolabeling
  lectin differences 1535
  maternal, *see* Maternal antibodies
  monomeric 148
  natural, *see* Natural antibodies
  neutralization of hormones 1851, 1852–
    1853
  neutralizing
    adenovirus detection 23
    Bordetella pertussis 378
    cross-reactive in poxvirus infections
      1996
    parvovirus B19 infection 1924
    poxviruses 1996
    selective pressure for antigenic variants
      200
    viruses 2481
  non-neutralizing, to viruses 2482, 2483
  N-terminal signal sequence 144, 145(Fig)

Antibodies (*continued*)
parallel sets 1184
paratopes, *see* Antibody combining sites;
Paratopes
passive enhancement 811–812
phage display, *see* Phage display of
antibodies
polyclonal 2199
affinity 46
induction by Fc subfragments 1318
see also Polyclonal antisera
polyreactive, *see* Natural antibodies
to polysaccharides 427
production, *see* Antibody synthesis
quantitation, ELISA 817
radiolabeled 2053
see also Radiolabeling
'reaginic' 64
in ungulates 2449
regulation, radiation as tool 2051
replacement by gammaglobulin 966
response, *see* Humoral immune response
restricted repertoire, neonates 1819
second, in antibody detection methods
142
secretion, *see* Antibody secretion
side-chain theory 1337
signal (leader) sequence 144
single domain 1256
as soluble receptors 714
specificity, *see* Antibody specificity
'spectrotypes' 1513
spontaneously produced, *see* Natural
antibodies
structure 154, 1140, 1227
structure–function relationship, affinity
labeling use 50–51
synthesis, *see* Antibody synthesis
to therapeutic monoclonal antibodies
122, 123(Fig)
titers, statistical analysis 2211–2212
valency 2465, 2467
determination 166
veneered 1143
virus-specific 2481
in Western blotting 2505, 2506
xenogeneic, therapy 1345
see also Immunoglobulin
Antibody-antigen interactions
affinity 43
agglutination 57
see also Agglutination
anti-idiotype complexes 161–162
chemical nature 159–161
conformational change at 161, 162(Fig)
energetics 166, 2199–2200, 2203
measurement 167
see also Energy
equilibrium 44
heterogeneous phase system, affinity 44
intermolecular forces, *see* Antibody-
antigen intermolecular forces
law of mass action 165–166
long-range 164, 164–165
precipitation reaction, *see* Precipitin
(precipitation) reaction
Protein Data Bank 160(Table)
rate of decay with distance 165
residues involved 159
surface plasmon resonance (SRP)
measurements 2249(Fig)
thermodynamics 2199–2200
three-dimensional structures 159–163,
1220, 2199, 2201(Fig)
future directions of study 162
interface of antibody/antigen 159
see also Antibody combining sites;
Epitopes; Immune complexes
Antibody-antigen intermolecular forces
163–167, 172
catalytic antibodies 440
electrostatic interactions 164, 2200

Antibody-antigen intermolecular forces
(*continued*)
hybrid forces 165
hydrogen bonds (polar forces) 164, 172,
2200
long-range attraction of epitope/paratope
164, 164–165
measurement of interaction energy 167
primary/secondary bonds 165
rate of decay with distance 165
thermodynamics 165–167, 2199–2200
energetics 166, 2199–2200, 2203
temperature effects 166–167
types and nature 163–165
van der Waals, *see* van der Waals forces
see also Affinity chromatography;
Hydrogen bonding/bonds;
Immunodiffusion
Antibody-antigen reactions, *see* Antibody-
antigen interactions
Antibody combining sites 62, 62(Fig), 171–
174, 202, 219, 2201
affinity labeling 50–51
allelic exclusion 62
amino acid residues in 172
antisera to 137–138
avidity 148–149
see also Antibodies, avidity
canonical structures 152, 153, 174
catalytic antibodies 439–440
carbohydrate antigens 150, 427
catalytic antibodies 439–441
CDR loops 152–153
concave surfaces 2201
contacting surface 152, 172, 440
discontinuous conformational epitope
150
'diverse sequence-similar site' 151
Fab and Fab-hapten complexes 171
genetic engineering 174
groove- and cavity-type 150, 159
hybridomas 171
light and heavy chains in 51, 153, 171,
1329
molecular modeling 173–174
nature of interaction, *see* Antibody–
antigen interactions
numbers (avidity) 148–149
protein antigens 150, 172
side-chains orientation 174
size measurement 150
structural diversity 151
structures 171–174, 1331–1332
types 150
valency 2465
X-ray crystallography 152
see also Complementarity determining
regions (CDR); Paratopes
Antibody-dependent cellular cytotoxicity
(ADCC) 168–171, 1146
Addison's disease 42
African swine fever (ASF) virus 55
avian 302
cutaneous lupus erythematosus 2187
cytolysis, mechanism 510
definition 168
enhanced by lentinan 428
FcγR role 889
flavivirus infections 929
IFNγ role 1424
IgE in 169
induction, metabolic requirements 169
infections 168, 169, 2459
parasitic 1918
viral, *see* viruses (below)
macrophage 169
mechanisms 168, 169–170, 1175(Fig)
models 168, 169
modulation 170
170; 1019
monocytes 169
nature of effector cells 168–169

Antibody-dependent cellular cytotoxicity
(ADCC) (*continued*)
NK cells 168–169, 505
parasitic infections 1918
phagocytes 169
see also NK cells (*above*)
porcine 1993
reactive oxygen intermediates role 169
role 169
schistosomiasis 1920, 2141, 2141(Fig)
specificity 168
T and B cells 169
tumor antigens 2442
viruses 929, 2481, 2486
Antibody-dependent cytotoxic
hypersensitivity, *see* Hypersensitivity,
type II
Antibody detection methods 141–144
agglutination, *see* Agglutination
blotting techniques 142
see also Northern blotting; Southern
blotting; Western blotting
complement-dependent assays 142
ELISA 796
ELISPOT assay 796
future advances 143
immunohistochemistry 142–143
immunopathology investigation 1340
immunoprecipitation 141
increasing sensitivity 143
labeled anti-immunoglobulin reagents
142
see also ELISA; *individual methods*
Antibody-directed enzyme prodrug therapy
(ADEPT) 1363
Antibody microspot arrays 1256
Antibody response, *see* Antibodies;
Humoral immune response;
Immunoglobulin
Antibody-secreting cells, detection, *see*
Immunoglobulin-secreting cells (ISCs)
Antibody secretion 144–148, 158
defects 147
during B cell differentiation 145–146,
158
fully assembled immunoglobulins 146
glycosylation and 144, 146–147
IgM 145, 158
developmental control 146
intracellular degradation of newly
synthesized Ig 147
as model for protein secretion 144–145
by nonlymphoid cells 147–148
pathological conditions association 147
'positive' sorting 144
'retention' signals 144
secretory immunoglobulins 148
transcription and 158
see also Antibody synthesis
Antibody specificity 148–154, 172, 2198–
2205
antibody affinity 2200–2201
autoantibodies 91–92
CDR segments determining 153
definition 2198
'diverse sequence-similar site' 151
functional epitopes and cross-reactivity
2203–2205
historical background 2198–2199
induced fit hypothesis 2201–2203
cross-reactivity 2202
investigations 149
low-/high-affinity antibodies 2201
physical origins 2200
noncovalent forces 2200
theoretical concepts 2199–2200
see also Antibody combining sites; B
cell(s), specificity; Complementarity
determining regions (CDRs)
Antibody synthesis 154–158, 764–765
B cell development, *see* B cell(s)
B cell repertoire, *see* B cell(s), repertoire

Antibody synthesis (*continued*)
  class switching, see Immunoglobulin class
    switching
  in fetus 1673
  helper T cell-dependent stimulation 156–
    157
  IL-6 role 1458
  inflammatory bowel disease 1378
  inhibition by ACTH 1828, 1829(Fig)
  intracellular transport and 158
  lymphocyte transformation test 1624
  pokeweed mitogen effect 1978, 1979
  radiation-induced decrease 2051–2052
  suppression in in chronic lymphocytic
    leukemia 1283
  T cell-independent B cell stimulation
    157–158
  TGFβ inhibiting 2396
  theories, see Antibodies, formation
  see also Antibody secretion;
    Immunoglobulin gene rearrangements
Anticardiolipin antibodies (aCL) 2119
  function and induction 2119
  see also Antiphospholipid antibodies
    (aPL)
Anti-CD3 antibodies, see OKT3 (anti-
  CD3)
Anti-CD4 antibodies
  autoantibodies 122, 124
  autoimmune disease therapy 1358
  therapeutic use 1352
Anti-CD5 antibodies 1358
Anti-CD7 antibodies 1358
Anti-CD25 antibodies, therapeutic use
  1352
Anticentromere antibodies 131
α1 Antichymotrypsin (ACT) 86
Anticoagulants, hookworms secreting
  1122–1123
Anticonvulsants, adverse reactions 1052
Anti-D gammaglobulin 1070, 1072, 1147,
  1344
Antidigoxin, antibody binding site
  2203(Fig)
Anti-DNA antibodies 2182
  assays 129, 129(Table)
    avidity index 130
    screening 130
  cross-reactions 2258
  detection and clinical significance 128–
    129
  dsDNA 2182
  fate of immune complexes with 184
  high-avidity 130
  interaction with heparan sulfate 130
  SLE 2257, 2258
    pathogenesis 130
Anti-DNAase B antibodies, *Streptococcus*
  2218
Anti-DNP antibodies, in *Xenopus* 82
Antigen 201–207
  acquired immunity not produced 15
  adherence to erythrocytes 1219
  antibody reaction, see Antibody-antigen
    interactions
    bivalent 216, 2466
  blood groups, see ABO blood group;
    Blood group antigens
  cell surface, see Cell surface antigen
  clearance, see Antigen clearance (*below*)
  complex 206–207
  concentration, for T cell tolerance
    induction 2355
  concentration determination,
    immunodiffusion 1288–1289
  definition 201, 266, 1290, 1297
  detection, enzyme cytochemical staining
    (immunoblotting) 813, 815
  donor-specific immunosuppression
    induced by 810
  drugs as 779–780
  entry, see Antigen uptake

Antigen (*continued*)
  environmental, type III hypersensitivity
    1176
  enzyme labeling, see Enzyme labeling
  heterophile 953, 1092
    see also Forssman antigen
  immune-associated (Ia), see Ia antigens
  for immune response *in vitro* 1233
    primary response 1240
    secondary response 1241
  immunogenicity improvements 219
    by 'carrier' molecules 38
  immunoglobulin as, see also Anti-
    antibodies (AAs); Anti-idiotype
    antibodies
  immunoglobulins as 204
  ingested 1774
  inhaled/intranasal 1774
  internalization into vesicles 196, 827
  ISCOM complexes, see ISCOM
    (immuno-stimulating complex)
  lipid 203, 204
  liposomes as carriers, see Liposomes
  macromolecules 203–204
  monovalent 216, 2465, 2466
  multivalent 216, 2465, 2466
  nucleic acid 204
  oral
    inflammation suppression by 1895
    processing 1893
    see also Gut-associated lymphoid tissue
    (GALT); Oral tolerance; Vaccines,
    oral
  persistence
    delayed-type hypersensitivity 739, 741
    memory T cells maintenance 15
    SLE and murine lupus etiology 2258
    tolerance development 2293
  polysaccharide 203, 203–204
  potency, contact hypersensitivity 638
  presentation, see Antigen presentation
    (*below*)
  processing, see Antigen processing
    (*below*)
  protein 203
    antibody combining sites for 150
    globular 205
    spatial folding 205
    structure and antigenicity 203
  quantitation, ELISA 816–817
  radiolabeled 2053
  receptors, see B cell(s); T cell(s)
  sequestered
    tolerance induction 2013, 2359, 2363
    see also Immune privilege
  'suicide' 178
  synthetic 204–206
    chemical modifications 205
    size 205
  T-dependent, see T cell-dependent
    antigens
  T-independent (TI), see T cell-
    independent (TI) antigens
  tissue, localization
    (immunocytochemistry) 815
  transfer factors interactions 2386
  transport, in lymph 1602, 1726
  tumor, see Tumor antigens
  uptake/sampling mechanism, see Antigen
    uptake (*below*)
  valency 163, 216, 2465, 2466–2467
  viruses 2480
Antigen-antibody complexes, see Immune
  complexes
Antigen-antibody interactions, see
  Antibody-antigen interactions
Antigen arthritis, features and comparisons
  2106(Table)
Antigen-binding site, see Antibody
  combining sites
Antigen clearance 182–188

Antigen clearance (*continued*)
  adaptive/innate immune systems 182–
    187, 186(Fig)
  autoantigens 184–185
  in cold agglutinin disease 184–185
  by IgA 1198
  by immune complex formation 182–185
    animals 183–184
    humans, models 184
    see also Immune complexes
  nonclonal receptors 185–187
    CD14 186–187
    mannose-binding protein/lectin
     186(Fig), 187
    mannose receptors 187
    scavenger receptors 185–186
  sites, *in vivo* studies in animals 183
Antigenic competition 203
Antigenic determinants, see Epitopes
Antigenic drift
  influenza viruses 200, 1385, 1386
  paramyxoviruses 1915
  vaccine development 258
Antigenicity
  antibodies, see under Antibodies
  definition 1290, 2203
  theories 2205
Antigenic shift, influenza viruses 200, 1386
Antigenic site, see Epitopes
Antigenic specificity, definition 201, 1297
Antigenic variation 199–201
  HIV 1134–1135
  immunity and 202
  influenza A virus 199, 200
  lentiviruses 199, 200–201
  Neisseria 1817
  Neisseria gonorrhoeae 2072
  outer membrane proteins (OMPs) 322
  protozoa 199, 199–200
  trypanosomes, see under Trypanosomes
  viruses 2482
Antigen presentation 174–175, 1236(Fig),
    1677
  to B cells 756
  by CD1, see CD1
  to cytotoxic T lymphocytes 726,
    727(Fig), 1236(Fig)
  in delayed-type hypersensitivity 739, 740
  by dendritic cells, see Dendritic cells
  enhancement, by IFNγ 1424
  in fish 923
  H2 class II molecules role 1040, 1044
  H2-M3 role 462
  HLA-G role 1110
  hydrostatic pressure effect 1155
  IgE role 1171
  for immune response *in vitro*
    primary response 1239–1240,
     1239(Fig)
    secondary response 1241
  mode, T cell tolerance induction 2355
  nonpeptide, by CD1, see CD1
  peptide binding, class I MHC molecules
    193–194
  stress proteins role 2231–2232
  to T cells, see T cell(s); under B cell(s)
  tonsils 1775
  vaccines 2455
  via MHC class I, see MHC class I
  via MHC class II, see MHC class II
Antigen-presenting cells (APCs) 174–178,
    194, 1248, 1709
  antigen stimulation of 175
  B7-1 and B7-2 expression 305, 652
  B cells, see B cell(s)
  CD2 expression and clustering 1614
  CD4⁺ cell interaction 195
    see also T cell(s)
  contact hypersensitivity 638, 740
  culture 194
  dendritic cells, see Dendritic cells
  differentiation 175

Antigen-presenting cells (APCs) (*continued*)
dogs 413
endothelial cell interactions 1237(Fig)
enrichment 1237(Fig), 1239, 1241
in fungal infections 960
hematopoietic cell function 2338
historical aspects 1626
HLA class II expression 1112
in IDDM 1402
immune response *in vitro* 1233,
1237(Fig), 1239, 1241
Langerhans cells 750, 1530–1531,
1531(Fig)
LFA-3 expression 1613
in lymph nodes 1604
macrophage as 175, 1826, 1826(Fig)
memory B cells as 14
MHC class II dimers 2283
mixed lymphocyte reaction (MLR) 1736
neurosecretory mediators acting on 1826,
1826(Fig)
parasitic infections 1918
in Peyer's patches 1777, 1781
properties 175
response to liposome-associated antigens
1590
sheep 1905
stimulation, antigen-ISCOM complexes
1509
T cell anergy induction 109
T cell cytotoxicity against 2242
T cell interaction 175, 175(Table), 177
T cell requirements for 175
T cell tolerance induction 2355
TCR γδ interaction 2277
tolerance induction 2355, 2360
tonsils 1775
see also B cell(s); Dendritic cells;
Macrophage
Antigen processing 14, 195–196, 1677
allergens 1171
B cells, *see* B cell(s)
dendritic cells 746
for immune response *in vitro*
primary response 1239–1240,
1239(Fig)
secondary response 1241
in lymphoid follicles 1728
via class I MHC 192
via class II MHC molecules 195–197,
1112
Antigen recognition activation motif
(ARAM), *see* ITAMs (immunoreceptor
tyrosine-based activation motifs)
Antigen-specific cells
enrichment and isolation 178–182
see also B cell(s); T cell(s)
'Antigen suicide' 178
Antigen uptake 188–191
alveolar macrophage 191
gut 189–190
mucosal surfaces 189, 252, 1776, 1781
nonspecific by APCs 1626
Peyer's patches 1776, 1781
respiratory tract 190–191
skin 188–189
specific by B cells 1626
Antiglobulin reagents 116
Antiglobulin serum 116, 136
Antiglobulin test, *see* Coombs' test
Anti-glomerular basement membrane
antibodies 1005, 1008–1009
Antihistamines 1101
allergic rhinitis 2124, 2125
cetirizine 2124
H1, *see* H$_1$ antihistamines
H2, *see* H$_2$ antihistamines
tumor growth 1104
Antihistone antibodies 131
Antihuman globulin 1967
Anti-idiotopes (Ab2) 1190
see also Idiotype(s)

Anti-idiotype antibodies 138, 151, 161,
1183, 1184, 1186
affinity chromatography 48
to autoantibodies 277, 291, 294
autoimmune disease pathogenesis 291,
293, 294
experimental autoimmunity 273
donor-specific immunosuppression
mechanism 810
I-J 1218
immunoregulation of B cell repertoire
361
internal image of idiotypes 1187
maternal 1192–1193
networks 2285–2286
sequential activation of clones 1878
stimulatory role 1189
tumor therapy 1189
in two-site immunoassays 1255
see also Idiotype network; Idiotype(s)
Anti-idiotypic networks, *see* Idiotype
network
Anti-immunoglobulin reagents, labeled 142
Anti-immunoglobulins
development in xenogeneic antibody
therapy 1345
see also Anti-antibodies (AAs)
Anti-insulin antibodies 273, 294
Anti-Jo1 antibodies 132
Anti-Ku antibodies 131
Anti-La antibodies, *see under* La antigen
Anti-lymphocyte globulin (ALG) 121, 136
in transplantation 2414
Anti-lymphocyte serum (ALS) 121–124,
1351
aplastic anemia treatment 121, 123
bone marrow disorder treatment 121
experimental use 124
as immunosuppressive agent 121
mechanism of action 123–124
monitoring use 123–124
monoclonal antibodies 122
natural antibodies 124
preparations 121
side-effects 122–123
therapeutic uses 122
Antimetatype response 1679
Antimicrobial agents 2013
see also Antibiotics
Antineutrophil cytoplasmic autoantibodies
(ANCAs) 264
cytoplasmic (C-ANCA) 264, 2120
perinuclear (P-ANCA) 131, 264, 2120
Anti-nuclear antibodies (ANAs) 125–133,
264–265
clinical significance 127–132
to cytoplasmic antigens 126–127
detection/assays 125, 125(Table), 127–
132, 264–265
IFT 127–128
in dogs 414
frequencies in autoimmune diseases
128(Table)
induction, T cell role 132
to nuclear antigens 125–126
sequencing and somatic mutations 133
Sjögren's syndrome (SS) 2184
SLE 2257
UCD 200 chicken strain 284–285
see also Cytoplasmic antigens; Nuclear
antigens; *specific antibodies*
Antinucleolar antibodies, mercury inducing
1688
Antinucleosome antibodies 130–131, 133
Antioxidant micronutrients 133–136
Antioxidants 133
assessment of status 134
deficiency, effects 134
diabetes prevention in animal models
1397
essential micronutrients as 133–134
hookworms secreting 1122, 1124

Antioxidants (*continued*)
immune cell function and 134
clinical examples 134–126
vitamin C 2491, 2493
vitamin E 2500, 2501
Anti-PCNA antibodies 131, 264, 2120
Antiphosphocholine antibodies,
Streptococcus pneumoniae 2219
Antiphospholipid antibodies (aPL) 1843,
2118–2119
function and induction 2119
heterogeneity 2119
IgG subclasses 2119
isotypes 2119
SLE 2257
specificity and affinity 2119
stroke, epilepsy and migraine associated
1843
see also Anticardiolipin antibodies; Lupus
anticoagulant
Antiphospholipid syndrome 265, 2118–
2120
antibodies 2119
clinical features 2119
experimental 2119
primary/secondary 2118
thromboembolism 2119, 2120
Antiproteinases, inactivated by neutrophils
17
Anti-RA-33 131
Antiretroviral therapy, in HIV infection
11–12
Antirheumatic drugs 2112
Anti-Rh gammaglobulin 1070, 1072, 1147,
1344
Anti-Ri antibodies 1843
Anti-Ro antibodies, *see* Ro antigen,
antibodies
Anti-rRNP 132
Anti-scRNP antibodies 132
Antiserum 218–220
affinity 219
definition 218
high titer 219
immunogenicity of antigens 219
polyclonal, *see* Polyclonal antiserum
preparation 219
species choice 219
specificity 218, 2465
uses 220
Anti-Sm antibodies 131
lupus mice 2252
SLE 2257
Anti-snake venom, valency 2465
Anti-snRNP antibodies 131
Anti-SS-A antibodies, *see under* Ro antigen
Anti-SS-B antibodies, *see under* La antigen
Antistreptolysin antibodies (ASO) 2218
Anti-Tac antibodies 1144
Antithrombin III (ATIII) 583, 1520
Antithymocyte globulin (ATG) 121, 1351
serum sickness due to 2169
Antithymocyte serum (ATS) 121
Anti-TNF, *see* Tumor necrosis factor α
(TNFα), antibodies
Anti-TNP antibodies 1189
Anti-topoisomerase I antibodies (Scl170)
131–132
Antitoxin therapy, history 2367
Anti-tRNA synthetases 132
Antitumor therapy, *see* Chemotherapy;
Tumor immunotherapy; *under*
Tumor(s)
Antivenoms
arachnids 2472
snake 2472–2473
Antiviral drugs, adenovirus infections 25
Ants, venom 2471, 2472
AP-1 transcription factor
binding to IL-4 gene 1451
cytokine synthesis 700
glucocorticoid action 999

AP-1 transcription factor (continued)
  IL-1 signal transduction 1433
  IL-5 gene 1457
  T cell anergy 109
APACHE scores 2162
Apatite stones 2040, 2041
Aphthous ulceration, food inducing 949
Aphthovirus 1955(Table)
  receptors 1956(Table)
Aplastic anemia
  anti-lymphocyte serum (ALS) treatment
    121, 123
  stem cell transplantation 1066, 1066(Fig)
APO-1, see Fas (CD95)
Apolipoprotein A1 85
Apopain (CPP32) 1028
Apoptosis 220–227, 730, 874
  annexin I role 115
  autoreactive T cells 224-3-225
  B cells, see B cell(s)
  cell death cysteine protease activation
    1028
  chromosomal translocations preventing
    559
  control by IL-2 1438
  cytotoxic lymphocyte killing mechanism
    224
  defects 1983
    diseases 227, 276
  definition 220–221, 2252
  dendritic cells 747
  in disease 227
  Fas/FasL role, see Fas/FasL
    interaction/pathway
  fibronectin role 911–912
  free calcium in T cells causing 2325
  genes, in murine lupus 2252–2253
  granule-mediated 1026, 1028, 1029(Fig)
    see also Granzymes; Perforin
  HSV-encoded genes 1088
  IFNγ regulatory role 1424–1425
  immune privilege maintenance 225–226,
    2012
  in immune system 223–227
  induction
    flaviviruses 929
    HIV 2485
    radiation 2051
    viruses 2485
  inhibition 223
    Chilo iridescent virus (CIV) 1504
    diseases due to 227, 276
    IL-9 1474
  in vitro immune response studies 1234–
    1235, 1240
  lymphocyte lifespan regulation 1582
  macrophage 1643
  mechanisms 222–223, 224(Fig), 1028
    Fas/FasL, see Fas/FasL
      interaction/pathway
    granzyme/perforin, see Granzymes;
      Perforin
    protease activation 223, 1028,
      1029(Fig)
  morphologic features 221–222, 221(Fig)
  negative regulators 2357, 2357(Table)
    Bcl-2, see Bcl-2 protein
  NK cell killing mechanism 225
  phagocytosis of cells 186, 222
  phenotype 223
  positive regulators 2357(Table)
  prevention
    chromosomal translocations 559
    in germinal center 994
    IL-3 receptor action 1448
  recognition/removal of cells after 222
  rescue, bcl-2 role, see Bcl-2 protein
  resistance, tolerance breakdown 227, 276
  signals 2366
  signal transduction 875, 875–876,
    877(Fig)
  SLE 2260

Apoptosis (continued)
  stages 221(Fig)
  T cells, see T cell(s), apoptosis
  thymic nurse cells (TNCs) 2235
  thymocytes 224
  triggers 221
  tumor antigens 2429–2430
Apoptotic bodies 222
apoSAA 85
Apotransferrin, transferrin receptor (TfR)
  complex 2391
Appendix 1249, 1775
  B cells 1775
Aprotinin 1520
Aquagenic urticaria 684
Aqueous humor, NK inhibitory action
  1656
Arabian horses, SCID 1273
Arachidonic acid (AA) 117, 228–232
  formation/liberation from membrane
    2024, 2024(Fig)
  lymphocyte uptake 2025
  mediators, allergic rhinitis 2123
  metabolism 228, 1671, 2024
    after platelet activation 580, 1974
  prostaglandin synthesis 2024
  release by mast cells 1668, 1671
  as second messengers 231–232
  as signal transduction mediator 885
  synthesis inhibition, glucocorticoids 111
    see also Leukotriene(s)
Arachnids, venom 2472
Arachnoid villi 1599
ARAMs, see ITAMs (immunoreceptor
  tyrosine-based activation motifs)
Arboviruses 390, 926
Arenaviruses 232–235
  characteristics and antigens 232–233
  host immune response 233–234
  vaccines 235
    see also Lymphocytic choriomeningitis
      virus (LCMV)
ARFs (ADP Ribosylation Factors)
  852(Table)
Argentine hemorrhagic fever 235
Arginase, macrophage 1725
Arginine 235–237
  immune function and 235–236
  mechanism of action 236–237
  supplements 235
Argon ion lasers, in immunocytochemistry
  1266
Argonne Laboratory colony, beagle dogs
  2309
Arteriviruses 2350(Table)
Arthritis
  adjuvant, see Adjuvant arthritis (AA)
  animal models 2106(Table)
    bystander suppression 1895–1896
    IgG glycosylation 1004
    treatment by oral tolerance induction
      1897
    see also Adjuvant arthritis (AA);
      Collagen-induced arthritis (CIA)
  autoimmune, determinant spreading 755
  chronic relapsing, animal model 1521
  collagen-induced, see Collagen-induced
    arthritis (CIA)
  enteropathic 2120
  in hyper-IgM syndrome 1167
  immunity to hsp65/hsp60 34, 1797
  inflammatory, kallikrein system role
    1521
  Lyme 380–381, 381
  Mycoplasma and Ureaplasma infections
    1800–1801
  psoriatic 2120
  rabbits 2046
  reactive, see Reactive arthritis
  rheumatoid, see Rheumatoid arthritis
    (RA)
  streptococcal cell wall-induced 2231

Arthritis (continued)
  T cell-dependent, TGFβ effect 2397
  T cells responsive to hsp65 in 34
  transient in animals, passive transfer
    2107
Arthrogryposis multiplex congenita 801
Arthus reaction 237–240, 1177, 1223–
  1224
  complement role 237–238
  diseases/conditions with 237(Table)
  generalized 2168
    see also Serum sickness
  inflammatory mediators 239, 239(Table)
  mechanisms, recent advances 239–240
  neutrophils role 238
  pathological changes 238(Fig)
  platelet depletion 239
  reversed passive 237
  selectins role 238
  stages 237
Asbestos, granuloma 1024
Ascariasis 241–243
  clinical features 241
  immune response 242
  treatment 241
  vaccines 242–243
Ascaris lumbricoides 241
  allergen (ABA-1) 241, 242(Fig)
  antigens 241
  excretory/secretory (ES) products 241
  immune evasion strategies 242
  Toxocara canis cross-reaction 2381
Ascaris suum 241
Ascorbic acid, see Vitamin C
Asialoglycoprotein receptor (ASGP-R) 562,
  564
  on phagocytes 1886
Asialo-orosomucoid-containing complexes
  183
Aspartic proteinase, extracellular matrix
  degradation 865
Aspergillus fumigatus
  complement activation 959
  neutrophil action 959
Aspergillus niger, glucose oxidase 814
Aspirin 117
  false food allergy 952(Table)
  hypersensitivity 120
  irreversible binding to COX 118
  mechanism of action 118
Asplenia, congenital 1286
Associated microfibril protein (AMP) 906
Association constant (Kₐ), concentration
  dependence 167
Association constant (Kₐ) 148, 166
Association studies
  disease and markers 2064
    see also HLA, disease association
Astemizole 679–680
Asthma 243–247
  allergic 1365
    allergens 69
    immunotherapy 1354
  clinical presentation 245
  differential diagnosis 245
  epidemiology 243–244
  food-mediated 948
  genetics 243
  occupational 246
  pathogenesis 244–245
  pathology 244
  in pregnancy 246
  seasonal variation 245
  steroid-resistant 1000
  TNFα levels 2439
  treatment 245–246
    nonpharmacologic 245
    pharmacologic 245–246, 246(Table)
  triggers 245
Astrocytes
  cytokines produced 1830, 1832(Fig)

Astrocytes (*continued*)
  progressive multifocal
    leukoencephalopathy (PML) 1990
  TNFα formation 1831
Astronauts 1030–1033
  see also Gravity, effects
A.SW mice, mercury effect 1688
Ataxia telangiectasia (AT) 247–251,
    248(Fig), 559, 1282
  cancer susceptibility 248–249
  chromosomal instability 249
    translocations 249, 559
  gene 249, 250(Fig)
    function 247
    mutations 249, 250(Fig), 559
    screening for mutations 249
  hyper-IgM syndrome association 1166
  immunodeficiency 249, 1282
  neuropathology 247
  radiosensitivity association 247, 247–
    248, 248(Fig), 2053
  related syndromes 249–250
  T cell defects 249
  therapy 250
  tumor development 1244
Atherosclerosis
  macrophage role 1388–1389
  MCP-1 role 1750
  rabbits 2046
  see also Coronary heart disease
Athymic mice, *see* Nude (athymic) mice
Atm gene 2053
Atopic allergy 251–255
  see also Atopy
Atopic dermatitis (atopic eczema) 252,
    254, 787–788, 949–950
  chronic 787
  etiopathogenesis 788, 949
  food inducing 949
  genes associated 788
  model 788
Atopy 65, 787, 1170
  allergens 251
  clinical features 254
  clinical tests 254, 1172–1174
  definition 25
  factors influencing 251–252
  food 254
  genetic influences 252, 1171
  IgE levels 1171
  IgE role 1202, 1207
  IL-13 role 1490
  inheritance 1171
  late-phase response 253, 253(Fig), 254
  mediators 253
  physiological effects 254
  T$_H$2 cells 788, 1171
  treatment 255
  type I hypersensitivity 252–253, 252(Fig)
  see also Allergens; Allergic reactions;
    Allergy; Hypersensitivity, type I
ATPase, in contact hypersensitivity 638
ATP hydrolysis, stress protein binding to
    proteins 2230
Attenuated organisms 255–259
  advantages/disadvantages 258–259
  bacteria and viruses 256(Table)
  genetic stability 257
  history 255–257
  killed vaccines *vs* 258–259
  molecular basis 258
  reversion to virulence 257, 258
  see also Vaccines, live
Attenuation 255–259, 259, 2457
  BCG 256
  definition 255
  history 256
  molecular basis 258
  viruses 2457
  see also Attenuated organisms; Vaccines,
    live
ATTR 85

Autoantibodies 125, 137, 260–265, 266
  acetylcholine receptor, *see* Acetylcholine
    receptor (AChR), antibodies
  in Addison's disease 41–42
    see also Addison's disease
  in amebiasis 77
  anticytokine 704–705, 706
  anti-idiotype, *see under* Anti-idiotype
    antibodies
  autoimmune disease pathogenesis 276–
    276, 288–289
  cell surface structures 277
  cold agglutinins, *see* Cold agglutinins
  cutaneous lupus erythematosus 2186
  dermatomyositis 2118
  detection 260–261, 262(Table)
    complement fixation 617
    indirect immunofluorescence 142, 260
    indirect immunoperoxidase 260
    pernicious anemia 102
  endocrine organs 263
  gastric 102–103
    see also Gastric parietal cells
  in hyper-IgM syndrome 1167
  IDDM animal models 1393
  idiopathic inflammatory myopathy 2118
  idiotype 277
  IgM 1216
  immunoconglutinins as 1257
  isotypes, detection 260
  low-affinity 2363
  lupus mice 2252
  as markers of disease 260
  mitochondrial antigens 264
  muscle antigens 263–264
  natural 266, 287, 1807, 1808
    experimental autoimmune thyroiditis
      2311
    see also Autoimmunity, natural
  neutrophil cytoplasmic antigens
    (ANCAs), *see* Antineutrophil
    cytoplasmic autoantibodies (ANCAs)
  non-organ-specific 261
  normal 260
    see also Autoantibodies, natural
  nuclear antigens, *see* Antinuclear
    antibodies (ANAs)
  organ-specific 261, 288
  in pernicious anemia 102–103,
    103(Table), 263
  persistent, type III hypersensitivity 1176–
    1177
  phospholipid antigens 265
  polymyositis 2003, 2118
  primary biliary cirrhosis (PBC) 2002–
    2003, 2003, 2003(Table)
  receptor editing defect 770
  rheumatoid factor, *see* Rheumatoid
    factor (RF)
  Sjögren's syndrome (SS) 2004, 2182,
    2184
  skin antigens 263
  SLE, *see under* Systemic lupus
    erythematosus (SLE)
  soluble cell products 277
  somatic mutations causing 294
  systemic sclerosis (scleroderma) 2117,
    2117(Table)
  thyroid-specific, *see* Thyroid
    autoantibodies
  tissue-specific 277, 288
  types 262(Table)
  vitiligo 2502
  Wegener's granulomatosis 2120
  see also Autoantigens; *individual*
    autoantibodies
Autoantigens 266–269, 290
  autoimmune disease in neonates 1676
  B cell reactivity 266
  classification 267, 268(Table)
  clearance 184–185
  disease associations 268(Table)

Autoantigens (*continued*)
  epitopes (autoepitopes) 266
    disease-specific 269
    enzyme active site 269
    mapping 267–268
  expression induced by UV 2187,
    2187(Fig)
  HLA associations 267
  as immunogens 267
  injection in experimental autoimmune
    disease 270
  intracellular organelles 267, 269
  modification, autoimmune disease
    pathogenesis 279
  neural products 267
  pathological relevance 267
  'sequestered', privileged sites 2013, 2359,
    2363
  sites, detection 260
  in sperm 1373–1374, 1373(Table)
  structure and sequencing 267
  T cell reactivity 266, 267, 269
  TCRγδ recognition 2272
  see also Self antigens; *specific*
    autoantigens
Autoepitopes 266
  see also under Autoantigens
Autoimmune arthritis, determinant
    spreading 755
Autoimmune bullous dermatoses 2188–
    2189
  see also Pemphigoid; Pemphigus
Autoimmune disease 287–292
  Addison's disease association 42
  age relationship 61, 279
  antinuclear antibody frequencies
    128(Table)
  apoptosis defects 227, 1983
  B1 cells elevated 473
  cardiac, *see* Cardiac disease, autoimmune
  in common variable immunodeficiency
    600
  criteria 275
  definition 266
  diagnosis 291
  in dogs 414
  effector mechanisms 276–278, 290
    autoantibodies 276–276
    B cells 290
    nonspecific 278
    T cells 277–278, 290
  endocrine influences 278–279
  environmental influences 279, 289
  etiology 289–291
  exercise and 848
  experimental models (induced) 270–274,
    288, 293
    anti-idiotype models 273
    bystander suppression 1895–1896
    chemically-induced models 273
    history 270
    immune depletion models 271–272,
      272(Table)
    immunization models 270–272,
      271(Table)
    infection models 272–273
    transgenic models 273–274
    treatment by oral tolerance 1896–1897,
      1897(Table)
  eye, *see* Eye
  gene therapy 978
  genetic linkages 289
  genetic predisposition 278, 289
  heterogeneity 275
  HLA associations 278, 289, 294, 1693
    mechanism 1694
  HLA class II presentation of autoantigens
    1708–1709
  HLA class III association 1120
  IFNγ role 1425, 1428
  in IgA deficiency 1198
  IgM role 1216

Autoimmune disease (*continued*)
IL-2 deficient animals 1437–1438
immune complex formation 1147
immunotherapy, *see* Immunotherapy, of autoimmune disease
induction 289–290
maternal antibodies causing 1674–1676
 see also Maternal antibodies
materno-fetal model 1674
membrane attack complex role 627
modulating factors 278–279
mycobacteria associations 1797
neuroendocrine influences 278–279
neurological, *see* Neurological autoimmune diseases
neuromuscular junction, *see* Neuromuscular junction
nonorgan-specific, maternal antibodies causing 1676
organ-specific
 experimental induction 272(Table)
 spontaneous models 281–283
pathogenesis 275–280, 289–291, 292–293
 apoptosis block causing 227, 1983
 autoantibodies 288–289, 294
 autotolerance breakdown 275–276, 293–295, 2366–2367
 bystander effect role 398
 environmental influences 279, 289
 germline genetic influences 278, 289
 HLA associations, *see above*
 lymphotoxin role 1640
 mechanisms controlling 293–295
 somatic genetic influences 289, 294
 somatic mutation dysregulation 2193
 superantigens role 2242
 toxic agents causing 1365, 1367, 1367(Table)
 see also Tolerance, breakdown
pernicious anemia association 104
polyclonal hypergammaglobulinemia in 1162, 1163(Table)
polyendocrine, *see* Polyendocrine autoimmunity
polyvalent immune serum globulins (ISG) 1347
prevention 293
 B7 mAbs 306
prostaglandins in 2026–2027
regulation 290–291
retroviruses causing 2097
sex hormones effect 2175–2176
sexual dimorphism 2175
Sjögren's syndrome association 2182–2183
skin, *see under* Skin
spontaneous models 270, 278, 280–287, 288
 inbreeding effect 280
 organ-specific 281–283
 scleroderma 283–285
 SLE 285–286
 systemic disease 283–286
 see also Obese strain of chickens
stress proteins as target antigens 2231
T$_H$1 role 1695
thyroid autoimmunity association 2313
TNFα levels/role 2438
treatment 291, 295, 1358
 CD40-CD40L interaction interruption 486–487
 cyclosporine 688–689, 689, 689(Table), 1358
 monoclonal antibodies 1747
 oral tolerance induction 1897–1898, 1897(Table)
 see also Immunotherapy, of autoimmune disease
type I thymic epithelium abnormalities 2234
type II hypersensitivity 1175–1176

Autoimmune disease (*continued*)
types (list) 288(Table)
virus-induced 2483
Witebsky's criteria 1847
see also Autoantibodies; Autoimmunity; *specific diseases*
Autoimmune gastritis, *see* Gastritis
Autoimmune hemolytic anemia (AIHA) 91–93, 94–98
in cats 894
in common variable immunodeficiency 600
drug-induced 95, 99–101
 cell destruction mechanisms 99
 drug-dependent 99–100
 drug-independent 100
 idiosyncrasy 100
 IgG antibodies 100
 α-methyldopa 95, 100, 1739
 serology 100, 100(Table)
 types 95
experimental models 91–93
 antigen specificity of autoantibodies 91–92
 band 3 reactive antibodies 91, 92
 CD4$^+$ T cells role 92–93
 hybridoma pathogenesis study 91
 IgG autoantibodies 91, 92, 93
 IgM autoantibodies 91–92
 ontogenesis 92
 T cell specificity/characterization 92–93
 transgenic mice 92
in idiopathic thrombocytopenic purpura 1975–1976
IgG-induced (cold) 94
IgG-induced (warm) 94–95
 antigen clearance 185
 glucocorticoid therapy 95–96
 hemolysis mechanism 94–95
 Rh autoantibodies 2102–2103
 splenectomy 96–97
IgM-induced, *see* Cold hemagglutinin disease
maternal antibodies causing 1674
in pregnancy 98
SCID mouse model 1129(Table)
therapy 95–98, 96–97
 glucocorticoids 95–96
 immunosuppressive agents 97
 miscellaneous 97–98
 supportive transfusions 98
type II hypersensitivity 1174–1175
warm antibody-induced, *see* IgG-induced *above*
Autoimmune hepatitis, *see* Chronic active hepatitis (CAH)
Autoimmune lymphoproliferative syndrome (ALPS) 878
Autoimmune myocarditis, SCID mouse model 1129(Table)
Autoimmune nephritis, murine model 650
Autoimmune polyendocrinopathy syndrome
 type 1 39, 40(Table)
 autoantibodies 42
 type 2 39, 40(Table)
Autoimmune polyendocrinopathy–candidiasis–ectodermal dystrophy 1984–1985
Autoimmune polyglandular syndromes (APS) 1984
 type I 1984–1985, 1985(Table)
 type II 1985–1986, 1985(Table)
 animal models 1986
 HLA association 1985
Autoimmune renal disease, mercury causing 1688
Autoimmune thrombocytopenic purpura, *see* Idiopathic (autoimmune) thrombocytopenic purpura (ITP)
Autoimmune thyroid disease, *see* Thyroid autoimmunity

Autoimmunity 287–288, 292–296
adrenal, *see* Addison's disease; Adrenal autoimmunity
age-related increase, *see* Autoimmune disease
as antimetatype response 1679
avoidance by privileged sites 2013
as cause of disease 288–289
consequences 292–293
definition 292
development, *see* Autoimmune disease, pathogenesis
feline 894
history 292
immunodominance, dynamic model 1291
immunosuppression goal 1349
interventions 291, 295
mechanisms controlling 293–295
 see also Tolerance, breakdown
natural 287, 292
 purposes 287
 see also Autoantibodies, natural
pathogenesis, *see under* Autoimmune disease
regulation 290–291
spontaneous, coinhibition lack 1983
Y-chromosome accelerator 2253
Autonomic nervous system 2223, 2223(Fig)
hormones 224
nasal blood flow control 2125
pathways to immune system 2224
see also Central nervous system; Nervous system; Neurotransmitters
Autophagocytosis, in *Legionella pneumophila* infection 1543
Autoradiography 296–300
applications 299
control observations 298
development 298
efficiency 296
emulsions 297
 application to samples 297
exposure 297–298
interpretation 298–299
method 296
Northern blotting 1865
radioisotopes 296–297, 297(Table)
 dose/administration 297
resolution 296
Southern blotting 2194, 2197
Autoreactivity, controlled
tolerance concept 2293
see also Autoimmunity; Tolerance
Autosomal dominant disorders 987–988
Autosomal recessive disorders 988
Autotolerance, *see* Tolerance
Auxiliary cholera enterotoxin (ACE) 2372, 2477
Avian immune system 300–304
antibodies 300–301, 302
B cells 301
 development 301, 395–396
 bursa of Fabricius 393–396
 see also Bursa of Fabricius
cells of immune system 301–302
complement 302
gene conversion 303, 396
genes 302–303, 3896
immune responses 300–301
immunoglobulins
 genes 302–303, 3896
lymphoid organs 301
mammalian system differences 300, 396
MHC (B locus) 300, 302
 antigens 303
 genes 303
β$_2$-microglobulin 302, 303
NK cells 302
pathology 303–304
T cells
 development 302

Avian immune system (*continued*)
  T cells (*continued*)
    surface components 302
    TCRs 302, 303
    tolerance 300–301
    vaccines 304
    virus infections 303–304
    see also Birds; Chickens
Avian leukemia viruses 1564
Avian leukosis virus (ALV) 303, 1563, 2097
Avian myeloblastosis virus 1564
Avidin 143, 1260–1261
Avidin–biotin system
  enzyme-labeling of antibodies 814, 815
    ELISA 818
  immunocytochemistry 1260–1261
  Western blotting 2506
Avidity 43, 148–149, 219
  see also under Antibodies
Avipoxvirus 1995, 1995(Table)
Axolotl
  immune system 79–83
  immunoglobulins as B cell receptors 81
  lymphocyte antigen-specific receptors 80–81
  lymphocytes 80
  lymphoid organs 79–80
  major histocompatibility system 81
Axons, in acute motor axonal neuropathy (AMAN) 1837–1838
Azathioprine
  immunodeficiency due to 1285
  immunosuppressive actions 1351
Azimexon, as immunopotentiating agent 1347
Azurocidin (CAP-37) 1723

B

B-1 cells, *see under* B cell(s)
B1 receptors 1518, 1521
B2 receptors 1518, 1521
  antagonist 1521
B3, on T cells 298(Fig), 299
B7 304–308, 452(Table)
  low expression on tumor cells 977
  plasmid DNA, transfer into melanoma 977
  T cell activation 304, 305–306
B7-1 (CD80) 73, 304–308, 452(Table), 652
  absence, tumor immunological escape 2444
  binding to CD28 and CTLA4 305, 307
    as counter-receptor 305, 2148
  CD28 interaction 482, 652, 2146
    blockade 548, 2262
  as CD28 ligand 482
  cross-talk with CD40/CD40L 306, 350, 1228
  deficiency, effect 306
  downregulation 305, 2262
    by UV exposure 1943
  expression 305, 652
    tumor immunotherapy 1364
  function 305–307, 652
  HIV transmission prevention 307
  immune response block 306
  monoclonal antibodies 306, 2262
  structure 304–305
  T cell activation 304, 305–306, 350, 2146–2147, 2262, 2328
  transfection into tumor cells 307, 2444–2445
  upregulation 305
B7-2 (CD86) 304–308, 452(Table), 652
  absence, tumor immunological escape 2444

B7-2 (CD86) (*continued*)
  B cell elimination 652
  binding to CD28 and CTLA4 305, 307, 2146, 2148
    as counter-receptor 305
    interactions 652
  as CD28 ligand 482
  cross-talk with CD40/CD40L 306, 350
  deficiency, effect 306
  downregulation 305, 2262
    by UV exposure 1943
  expression 305, 652
  function 305–307, 652
  HIV transmission prevention 307
  immune response block 306
  monoclonal antibodies 306
  structure 304–305
  T cell activation 304, 305–306, 350, 2328
  transfection into tumor cells 307, 2444–2445
  upregulation 305
B10.D2 mouse strain 635
B16F10 melanoma cell line 1364
B17, UCD 200 chicken strain 285
B19, *see* Parvovirus B19
B29 gene 1194
B144 gene 1047
B220 (CD45α) 493
Babesia, characteristics 308, 309–310, 309(Fig)
Babesia divergens 308, 309
Babesia gibsoni 308
Babesia microti 308, 309, 309(Fig)
  life cycle 309(Fig)
Babesiosis 308–310
  causative organisms 308–309
  clinical features 308, 310
  immune response 309–310
  splenectomy effect 310
  transmission 308
Baboons, xenotransplantation donor 2508
Bacillaceae 311
Bacillary dysentery 967, 2178, 2372
Bacille Calmette–Guérin, *see* BCG
Bacilli, aerobic spore-forming (ASB) 311
Bacillus 311–315
  acquired immunity 314
  antibiotic production 311
  characteristics 311
  as contaminants 311
  distribution 311
  importance and applications 311
  insecticides 311
  passive immunity 314
  species and diseases associated 312
  spore resistance 311
  vaccines 314
  virulence factors 313
    B. anthracis 312
  see also Bacillus anthracis; *Bacillus cereus*
Bacillus anthracis 311, 312
  cap⁺/toxc⁻ strains 314
  capsule 312, 314
  host immune response 314
  PA (protective antigen) 312, 314
    immune response 314
    monoclonal antibodies 314
  pathogenesis 312–313
  toxins 2368, 2374
    EF (edema factor) 312, 2374
    LF (lethal factor) 312, 2374–2375
    susceptibility to 312
  vaccine development 314
  virulence factors 312
  see also Anthrax
Bacillus cereus 311, 312
  toxins 313
Bacillus megaterium, lysozyme action 1723
Bacillus stearothermophilus 311
Bacillus subtilis, lysozyme action 1723

Bacillus subtilis var. *globigii* 311
Bacillus thuringiensis 311
Bacteremia, definition 2162(Table)
Bacteria
  adhesins, Forssman antigen as receptor 954
  agglutination 58–59
  antigen presentation, by CD1 460
  as antigens 206
  attachment to teeth 1888
  attenuated vaccines 256(Table)
  bacteriophage infection 2015
  binding to fibronectin 1937
  capsular polysaccharides 422–423
  capsules 322
    complement resistance 316
    immune evasion mechanism 38, 1936
    structure and antigens 322
    as vaccines 322
  cell envelope 320
    components associated 322–323
  cell walls, *see* Bacterial cell walls
  classification 320–321
  in CNS, immune response 1846
  cross-reacting antigens with Forssman antigen 954
  cytoplasmic membrane 320, 321
  defective clearing, urinary tract infections 2454
  defense against opsonization 1936, 1936(Fig)
  extracellular polysaccharides 423
  flora
    gastrointestinal, *see* Gastrointestinal tract
    pouch of marsupials 1665
    skin 750
  gastrointestinal tract infections 967–968
  gram-negative, *see* Gram-negative bacteria
  gram-positive, bacteriocins 2015
  host immunity to, *see* Bacteria, immunity to
  hsp60 as 'common antigen' 2231
  hydrophobicity 1885
  immune adherence 1219
  immunity to bacteriocins 2014–2015
  immunity to phage, *see* Bacteriophage immunity protein
    to colicins 2014, 2015
    to phage 2016, 2016(Fig)
  infections, monoclonal antibody therapy 1747
  invasion, lectins role 428
  iron requirement 1724
  lectins 1537
  lysogenic 2016
  mutations 2013
  opsonization 1885
  restriction–modification system 2013–2014
  rheumatoid arthritis etiology 2114
  rough (R) mutants 807
  S-form (lipopolysaccharide) 807
  skin infections 750
  transfection, recombinant vaccine development 2460
  urinary tract infections 2065–2066, 2452
  vaccines 2457–2458, 2458(Table)
Bacteria, immunity to 315–320
  antibody role 317
  cell-mediated immunity 318
  complement activation 316, 609
  cytotoxic T cells 318
  granuloma formation 319
  immunopathology mechanisms 319
  interferon γ 318
  lymphokines release 318
  NK cells 318
  nonspecific 315–316
    bacterial structure recognition 315–316
    cytokines 316

Bacteria, immunity to (*continued*)
 nonspecific (*continued*)
  recognition mechanisms 315–316
  response mechanism selection 316
 phagocytic cells
  antimicrobial mechanisms 317–318
  avoidance 318–319
  interactions 317
  killing mechanisms 317
 T$_H$1 and T$_H$2 balance 316
Bacterial cell walls 320–323
 adjuvant properties 37–38
 components associated 322–323
 gram-negative 320, 321–322, 321(Fig)
 gram-positive 320, 321(Fig), 322
 opsonization evasion 1936–1937
 outer membrane proteins (OMPs) 321–322
 peptidoglycan 321
 receptors 315
 structure 320
 see also Bacteria, capsules; *specific bacterial species*
Bacterial immunoglobulin-binding proteins 323–327
 bacterial species 324, 325(Table)
 immunoglobulin types 325(Table), 326
 Staphylococcus aureus 323
 type(s) 323, 324(Table)
 type I IgG-binding protein, *see* Protein A
 type II IgG-binding protein 326
 type III IgG-binding protein, *see* Protein G
 types IV/V/VI IgG-binding proteins 326
Bactericidal/permeability increasing proteins (BPI) 1722, 1857, 1938
 autoantibodies 1722
 lipopolysaccharide binding 1722
 structure 1722
Bacterins, *Pasteurella multocida* infection 1929
Bacteriocins 2013
 bacterial immunity to 2014–2015
 definition 2014
 gram-positive bacteria 2015
 see also Colicins
Bacteriophage 2015
 antibody display, *see* Phage display of antibodies
 bacterial immunity to 2015–2017
 DNA integration into host 2015
 ghosts 2015
 infection of bacteria 2015
 superinfecting 2015–2016
 temperate 2015
  immunity to 2016
  repressor 2016
 virulent 2015
  immunity to 2015–2016, 2016(Fig)
Bacteriophage lambda 2016
Bacteriophage P1, *see* P1 bacteriophage
Bacteriophage T4, *see* T4 bacteriophage
Bacteriuria 2065
Bacteroides 327–329
 abscess formation 328–329
  murine model 328
  prevention 328
 T cell response 328
 vaccine 328
 virulence 327–328
Bacteroides fragilis 327
 capsule 327, 328
 virulence 327–328
Bacteroides thetaiotaomicron 327
Bacteroides vulgatus 327
Baghdad boil 1546
BALB/c mice 1764–1765
 autoimmune gastritis 104
 B cells 1819
 cell lines for mAb preparation 1742
 immunology 1765

BALB/c mice (*continued*)
 infectious agents susceptibility/resistance 1764
 Legionella pneumophila infection 1544
  acquired immunity 1545
 mitogenic effect of mercury 1687
 origin/characteristics 1764
 SCID 1125
 stress and immune regulation 339
 susceptibility to *Coccidioides immitis* 589
 TCR selection 1731–1732
 TCR V$_\gamma$ genes 2269
 T$_H$1 response to *Leishmania* 1548
 T$_H$2 response to *Leishmania* 1062
 thymectomy 104
BALT, *see* Bronchus-associated lymphoid tissue (BALT)
Bare lymphocyte syndrome 329–332, 1277
 type I 329, 329–330
  clinical and immune response 330
  genetic lesions 329–330
  immunodeficiency 329
 type II 329
  CD4⁺ cell reduction 330
  complementation groups 330–331
  genetic defects 330–331
 type III 329, 331–332
  genetic defects 331–332
 'Bare' promoters 331
Basal cell carcinoma, MHC downregulation 1361
Basement membrane 1005
 collagen type IV interaction 1006–1007
 high endothelial cells (HEC) 1096–1097
 lymphatic capillaries 1599
Basigin (CD147) 456(Table)
Basophil(s) 332–334, 1388
 activation, in asthma 244
 chemokines 536(Table)
 cutaneous hypersensitivity 333
 degranulation 253, 333, 737
  morphology 333
  'piecemeal' 2165
  stimuli 1669
 desensitization 334
 exocytosis 2165
 granules 333
  histamine 1101
 IgE receptors 254, 332
  desensitization 334
 mast cell differences 332–333
 mast cell similarity 1667
 mediators released 333, 334
  eosinophil chemotactic factors 819
  inhibition 334
 morphology 333, 333(Fig)
 precursors 332
 releasability 333–334
 role 332
 stimulation, C5a action 90
 surface phenotype 1803
BAT1 gene 1114, 1118(Table), 1119
BAT1 protein mice 1047
Bayou virus 392
Bay sore 1547
BB-DP rat 1273
BB rat 1273, 1390, 2057, 2309
 autoimmune polyglandular syndrome type II model 1986
 characteristics 1391(Table)
 genetics 1391–1392
 insulitis 1393, 1402
 islet pathology 1393
 T cells 1394, 1402
BB/W rats, autoimmune gastritis 104
B cell(s) 363–367, 789, 1144, 1226, 1227
 abnormalities, primary biliary cirrhosis (PBC) 2003
 absence, in Bruton's agammaglobulinemia 387
 activation 349–352, 350(Fig), 363–364, 366, 1581, 1621, 2020

B cell(s) (*continued*)
 activation (*continued*)
  B cell receptor role 349–350
  B cell receptor signaling 350–352
  capping affecting 420, 421
  CD40 ligation 485, 653–654, 1228, 2150
  clustering role 420
  cytokine receptors 2150–2151
  downregulation of IFNγ receptor 1428
  intestinal 1377
  persistent in Chagas' disease 433
  polyclonal, see below
  second signals 2149–2151
  sIg signaling 1298
  suboptimal sIg signal 1298
  suppression by natural antibodies 1808
  T cell help 350, 826
  T-independent antigens 826
  TNF and TNFR members 2150
  see also B cell(s), proliferation; B cell(s), receptor (BCR); B cell(s), stimulation; CD40-CD40L interaction; Helper T lymphocytes
 ADCC 169
 adhesion molecules
  CD22 479–480
  in germinal centers 992
 affinity maturation, *see* Affinity maturation
 age-related changes 61
 allelic exclusion, *see* Allelic exclusion
 allotype restriction 62
 in amphibians 80, 81–82, 82
 anergic, *see* Anergy
 antibody binding site, *see* Antibody combining sites
 antigen presentation to T cells 349, 352–355, 1059, 1298, 1685, 1728
  B1 cells role 473
  cognate interactions, importance 437
  determinant spreading mechanism 756
  hapten carrier systems 353, 397, 437, 1059
  historical aspects 352–352
  in vivo 352–354
  sIg role 1298
  see also B cell(s), membrane Ig (mIg); *under* T cell(s)
 as antigen-presenting cells (APCs) 175–176, 352–352
  μMT knockout mice 353–354
 antigen processing 53, 349, 354–355
  peptide loading of class II 354
 antigen receptor, *see* B cell(s), membrane Ig (mIg); B cell(s), receptors
 antigen recognition 178, 1290
  antigen-specific, numbers 178
 antigen-stimulated, expansion by Fas 878
 antigen stimulation 359
 antigen uptake 1626
 apoptosis 225, 364, 366
  CD5 role 474
  chromosomal translocations preventing 559
  Fas/FasL role 878
  negative regulator 654
  prevention in germinal center 994
  protection from 2149
  radiation effect 2052
  rescue and lifespan regulation 1582
  resistance in *lpr* and *gld* mice 2252
  role in B cell development 225
 appendix 1775
 autoantigen-reactive Ig receptor 156
 autoantigens 266
 autoepitopes 266–267
  see also Autoantigens
 autoimmune disease pathogenesis 290
 autoreactivity, *see* B cell(s), self-reactive
 B1-a cells (CD5⁺) 292
  nude (athymic) mice 1867

B cell(s) (*continued*)
  B1 (CD5+) cells 15, 156, 217, 355, 362, 365, 473–474
    as antigen presenting cells 473
    apoptosis 2253
    CD5 expression 1819
    characteristics 362
    development 362
    elevated in autoimmunity 473
    enriched in motheaten mice 1269
    expression and molecule number 473
    function 474
    lifespan 1581
    (Mac-1), nude (athymic) mice 1867
    mantle zone 993
    natural antibodies from 473, 1807
    polyreactive IgM production 1215–1216
    see also CD5
  B2 cells 355, 1581
    development 1819
    function 474
  B7-1/B7-2 action 350
  bystander
    elimination by Fas/FasL 878
    surface antigens 398
    see also Bystander effects
  bystander responses 397
  calcitriol effect 2495–2496
  CD5 as lineage marker 473
  CD5+ cells, *see* B cell(s), B1 (CD5+) cells
  CD5- cells, *see* B cell(s), B2 cells
  CD19 155, 364
  CD40 364, 2150
    receptor 2366
  CD43+ cells 356, 364
  CD45α (B220) isoform expression 493
  CD45 expression 363
  CD45R expression 155, 1818
  in Chagas' disease 524
  circulating 363, 1580, 1580(Fig)
  circulation
    anergic cells 107
    normal 107, 1580–1581, 1580(Fig)
  clonal anergy, *see* Anergy
  clonal deletion, *see* Clonal deletion
  clonal expansion 878, 1678, 1684
    see also Affinity maturation; B cell(s), proliferation
  clonal selection, *see* B cell(s), repertoire; Clonal selection
  coinhibitor system 1983
  combining sites, *see* Antibody combining sites
  complement receptor complex 364(Table)
    CR1 629
    CR2 631
  costimulation, CD40 1983, 2150
  costimulatory signals for 215
  cytokines released 1832(Fig)
    CD40 ligation action 485
  decreased, in myeloma 1164
  defect, common variable immunodeficiency 601
  deficiency diseases 366
    see also Immunodeficiency
  depletion techniques 178–179
    for non-specific cells 179
  development 155–156, 158, 364–366, 376, 571–572, 1280(Fig), 1818, 2334, 2357–2358
    abnormal in CBA/N strain 1270
    apoptosis role 225
    arrested in SCID mice 1268
    avian 301
    in bone marrow 1247
    bursa of Fabricius 395–396
    in cats 892–893
    IL-1 role 1433
    markers 155, 364
    migration to germinal centers 994
    in neonate 1818–1819, 1820(Table)

B cell(s) (*continued*)
  development (*continued*)
    ovine 1903
    phenotypic changes during 1875–1876
    stages 155–156
    targeted gene deletion 1877
    ungulates 2449
    see also B cell(s), differentiation; B cell(s), growth; B cell(s), maturation
  differentiation 155–156, 355–359, 364–366, 1464(Fig), 1875, 1875(Fig)
    antibody secretion during 145–146
    block in Bruton's agammaglobulinemia 387, 387–388
    Btk role 388
    CD40 role 654
    checkpoints 355, 572
    clonotype elimination during 361, 572
    early stages 356–358
    extrafollicular pathway 358
    failure 356, 358, 359
    germinal center pathway 358–359, 572
    IL-7 role 1463, 1464(Fig), 1465
    IL-10 action 1476–1477
    inhibition by TH1 cells 2365
    J chain expression 1517
    microenvironment 1876
    peripheral lymphoid tissues 358–359
    phenotypic changes during 1875–1876
    to plasma cells 14
    response to TD antigens 358
    sites 355, 1247
    stages 355, 356(Table)
    stromal cells role 1876
    see also Immunoglobulin gene(s), V genes; Immunoglobulin gene rearrangements; Pre-B cells; Pro-B cells
  discovery 501, 1058, 1625
  distribution 363
  diversity 149, 359, 365, 765
    avian 396
    hybridoma application 1151
    junctional 360
    polyreactive IgM role 1216
    somatic mutation role 2192
    VH/DH/JH genes 360
    see also B cell(s), repertoire; Immunoglobulin gene rearrangements
  DNA, Southern blotting 2197
  early 356–358, 364
    malignancies 366
  EBV infection 828, 829
  enrichment techniques 178–181, 1235–1238
    historical aspects 179
    'negative selection' methods 179
    positive 'pre-enrichment' 179–180, 180(Table)
    pre-enrichment 179
  epitopes 437, 825, 826
    to allergens 68
    discontinuous 1188, 1292
  evolution 1948
  exercise effect 845
  feline 892–893
  in fish 922–923
  functions 215, 501, 2019
    abnormal in CBA/N strain 1270
    in neonate 1818–1819, 1820(Table)
  fusion, quadroma formation 139
  gene rearrangements, *see* Immunoglobulin gene rearrangements
  in germinal centers 539, 992, 993, 1145, 1581, 1604, 1726
    B cell differentiation 358–359, 1604
    clonal deletion 572
    memory cell development, *see* B cell(s), memory
    motility 539
    negative selection 2358
    see also Centrocytes; Germinal centers

B cell(s) (*continued*)
  gravity/space flights effect 1032
  growth 2020
    IL-4 regulation of 1452, 1491, 2150
    IL-15 stimulating 1494
    inhibition by natural antibodies 1808
    see also B cell(s), development
  high affinity antibody selection 52–53, 153, 157, 214
    see also B cell(s), memory; Somatic hypermutation
  homing receptors 1778, 1784
  hybridomas, *see* Hybridoma, B cell
  hyperreactivity, SLE-like animal models 285
  IgA1 expression 1303
  IL-1 effects 1433
  IL-2R expression 1437
  IL-2 role 1437
  IL-4 effect 1452, 1491, 2150
  IL-7 role 1463, 1464(Fig)
  IL-9 action 1473
  IL-10 effects 1476–1477
  IL-13 effects 1490, 1491(Table)
  IL-15 effect 1494
  immature 356–357, 364
    CD22 expression 479
    phenotype 1876
  immune response *in vitro* 1233
  immunodominant determinants 1291–1292
  increased in autoimmune gastritis 103
  intracellular features 363
  isolation techniques 178–181
    FACS 933
    histology 181
    transgenic mice 181
    see also Fluorescence-activated cell sorting (FACS)
  lamina propria 1782
  leukotriene B4 (LTB4) actions 229
  lifespan 1581
  loss, motheaten mice 1269
  low-affinity, tolerance escape 295
  Ly1 cells, *see* B cell(s), B1 (CD5+) cells
  in lymph nodes 1605
    lymphoid follicles 1580, 1604, 1605, 1728
    see also Germinal centers
  marker of rheumatic fever 432
  maturation
    CD95 (Fas) as regulator 655
    IL-6 role 1458
    prevention mechanisms 2354(Fig)
    see also B cell(s), development
  mature 156
    absence 366
    clonal deletion 572
    malignancies 366
  medullary 1605
  membrane Ig (mIg) 14, 158, 353, 363, 825, 1298–1301, 2019
    amino acids 1212, 1299
    anergic B cells 107
    antibodies and B cell proliferation 2020
    BCR structure, *see* B cell(s), receptor
    capping 415, 421
    CD22 interaction 480
    clonal selection 575
    clustering 420
    cross-linking 216, 1200–1201, 1299
    deposition 158
    developmental regulation 1301
    development in pigs 1991
    expression development 1301
    in fish 922–923
    functions 1298, 1318
    Igα/Igβ role 1194
    IgD, *see* Immunoglobulin D (IgD)
    IgM 145, 156, 1298–1299, 1876
      loss in anergy 107, 2364
      monomeric 1215

B cell(s) (continued)
  membrane Ig (mIg) (continued)
    IgM (continued)
      structure 1200, 1298–1299
    IgM and IgD 156, 363, 1200, 1323,
      1685, 1876
    memory B cells 1685
    molecule number 417
    natural antibodies 1808
    signaling role 1298
    structure 1200, 1298–1299, 1299(Fig)
    T-independent antigen effect 216
    see also B cell(s), receptor (BCR)
  membrane microdomains 417–418
  memory 52, 539, 1144, 1684, 1684–
    1685, 2192
    as antigen-presenting cells 14
    B7-1/B7-2 expression 305
    clonal selection 575
    defect in hyper-IgM syndrome 486,
      1168
    development 14, 157, 358–359, 366,
      1581
    formation in germinal center 993–994,
      995, 1145, 1604, 1605–1606, 1685,
      1728
    induction and CD40-CD40L role 350
    infectious agents 2459, 2460
    lifespan 1581
    surface phenotype 1685
    T cell cooperation 1685
  MHC class I expression 1108–1109
  MHC class II expression 2020
    IL-10 action 1476–1477
  MHC restriction 157
  migration/locomotion 539, 1249, 1580
    see also Lymphocyte trafficking
  mitogens
    lipopolysaccharide 807
    pokeweed mitogen 1978, 1979
  mucosal 1782–1783
  in multiple sclerosis 1840
  naive (virgin) 1684
  natural antibodies as receptors 1808
  neuroendocrine interactions 2225(Fig),
    2226(Fig)
  nude (athymic) mice 1867–1868
  numbers 154, 363
  ontogeny, see B cell(s), development
  origin of name 363
  ovine 1903
  peripheral pool 1580–1581
  in Peyer's patches 1776, 1777, 1781
  phage display library construction 1932,
    1932(Fig)
  phenotype 1875(Fig)
  plasma cell formation 1581
  polyclonal activation 359, 1678
    activators 215
    autoantibody induction 106
    bystander effect mechanism 398
    complement fixation test 618
    HIV infection 11
    IL-6 dysregulation 1460
    lipopolysaccharide 1982
    mutual antagonism 1982
    significance 398
    tolerance breakdown 276
    Trypanosoma cruzi 522–524
    see also Polyclonal activators
  polyclonal clones 149
  polyreactive IgM 1215–1216
  population dynamics 1580–1581,
    1580(Fig)
  porcine 1992–1993
  precursors 376
    culture and IL-7 role 1462
    see also Pre-B cells
  precursors growth stimulated by IL-3
    1443
  primed, see B cell(s), memory

B cell(s) (continued)
  production, monolayer culture system
    1901
  production rate 155, 1580
  proliferation 156, 1145, 2019–2021
    activation 2020
    assays 2023
    bystander effect 397
    CD40 signaling 485, 2020
    germinal centers 993, 1581
    IL-4 and IL-10 2020
    IL-7 role 1464
    leukotriene B$_4$ action 229
    lipopolysaccharide 2020–2021
    'postmembrane' chemical stimuli 2020
    protein A role 325
    signal transduction 2020
    suppression in multiple myeloma 1284
    see also B cell(s), activation
  quantitating, immune adherence 1219
  receptor (BCR) 349, 359, 363,
    364(Table), 1298–1299, 1875
    activation via 349–350, 350(Fig)
    amphibian 81
    antigen recognition subunit 349
    capping and CD5 role 474
    CD45 regulation of 493
    developmental regulation 1301
    diversity discovery 1626
    function 571
    Igα and Igβ chains 349, 363, 1299
    ITAM homolog 1299
    negative regulation 351–352, 351(Fig),
      654
    precursor 1194
    sIg, see B cell(s), membrane Ig (mIg)
    structure 1200, 1298–1299, 1299(Fig)
    transgenic mice 572
    see also B cell(s), surface
      immunoglobulin
  receptor (BCR) signaling 1194, 1194–
    1195, 1299–1301, 1300(Fig)
    CD40 pathway 64
    CD45 role 350
    defect in xid mutation 1270
    development 1301
    H2 class II molecules role 1044
    Igα/Igβ coupled to protein tyrosine
      kinases 1194, 1299
    inhibition by protein tyrosine
      phosphatase 1c 2253
    mechanisms 1299–1301, 1300(Fig)
    modulators 364(Table)
    PI3K pathway 1301b
    PI hydrolysis pathway 1299–1300
    ras/MAPK pathway 1300–1301
  recirculation 1580, 1580(Fig)
  repeating epitopes on T-independent
    antigens 216
  repertoire (clonotype) 359–362, 365,
    1580
    B cell subpopulations 361–362
    bursa of Fabricius role 395(Fig)
    environmental influences 360–361
    molecular basis 360, 365
    number of specificities 360
    ovine 1903
    primary 364–365
    primary/secondary response comparison
      361
    restricted in neonates 1819
    secondary 361–362
    selection 156
    see also Immunoglobulin gene
      rearrangements
  response
    decreased in copper deficiency 657
    to IL-12 1485
    to IL-13 1491
    inhibition by immune complexes 351
    to stress proteins 2230–2231
    to T-dependent antigens 214, 358, 826

B cell(s) (continued)
  response (continued)
    to T-independent antigens 214, 358
    see also Antibodies; B cell(s),
      stimulation; Humoral immune
      response
  resting
    locomotion 539
    tolerance induction 2360
  rosette markers 2130(Table)
  in SCID 1277–1278
  secondary, repertoire 361–362
  in secondary immune response 53–54,
    153, 157
    see also B cell(s), memory; Somatic
      hypermutation
  self-reactive 106, 107, 156, 266, 266–
    267, 290, 292
    B cell differentiation 357–358, 365
    germinal center formation prevention
      2366
    Ig gene rearrangements 2358
    mutations causing 157
    in peripheral tissues 2246
    persistence 106
    receptor editing to prevent 770
    removal in germinal center 994
    sites 290
    see also Autoimmunity; Receptor
      editing; Tolerance
  signaling, see B cell(s), receptor (BCR)
    signaling
  SLE 2259, 2259(Fig)
  somatic mutation, see Somatic
    hypermutation
  specificity 149
    see also Antibody specificity
  in spleen 2207, 2208
  stimulation
    antigen on follicular dendritic cells 993
    Goodpasture's syndrome 1009
    IL-6 role 504
    T cell-dependent 156–157
    T cell-independent 157–158
    see also B cell(s), activation; B cell(s),
      response
  surface area 417
  surface features/markers 363–364
    bystander effect mechanism 398
    IL-13 modulating expression 1490
    rabbits 2048, 2049(Table)
    T cell interactions 365(Table)
    see also B cell(s), membrane Ig
  surface immunoglobulin, see B cell(s),
    membrane Ig (mIg)
  synthesis rate 155, 1580
  T cell cooperation 1059
    discovery 1625–1626
    IL-2 role 1437
    limiting dilution analysis 1585–1586
    memory development 1685
    MHC restriction 1710–1711
    see also Helper T lymphocytes
  T cell differences 2341
  T cell interactions
    CD22 and CD45 role 480
    CD40-CD40L role, see CD40-CD40L
    failure in anergy 107
    helper cell activation 107, 156–158,
      214, 349
    surface markers 365(Table)
    see also B cell(s), antigen presentation;
      B cell(s), memory; Helper T
      lymphocytes
  T cell separation 1235
    lectin use 1541
  T cell tolerance induction 2360
  T-dependent antigens 156–157, 214,
    358, 826
  TGFβ effects 2396
  thyroglobulin binding 2311

B cell(s) (*continued*)
  T-independent antigens 157–158, 214, 358
  tolerance 295
    IgD role 1201
    induction 361, 365
    transgenic models 106–107
    see also Anergy; Clonal deletion; Tolerance
  tonsils 1775
  trans-stimulation, *see* B cell(s), bystander effect
  turnover 1580
  two L chains expressed 156
  vasoactive intestinal peptide (VIP) effect 1827
  virus infection of 2484–2485
B cell-activating factor, *see* Interleukin-1 (IL-1)
B cell leukemia, *see* Leukemia
B cell lines
  lymphoblastoid 1109
  promiscuous adhesion, LFA-1 activation 1610
  spontaneous point mutations 2193
B cell lymphoma 1634–1635
  after stem cell transplantation 1069
  in AIDS 8
  CD5 473
  chromosomal translocations 558
  differentiation antigens (Igs) expressed 2426
  diffuse large cell 1635, 1636
  IgM secretion block 145–146
  mucosa-associated (B cell MALT) 1635
  see also Lymphoma
B cell neoplasms 366
  CD40 role 485
  chromosomal translocations 555, 555(Table)
  cryoglobulinemia 665, 667
  IgM role 1216
  see also B cell lymphoma; Leukemia
B cell stimulatory factor 1, *see* Interleukin-4 (IL-4)
B cell stimulatory factor 2 (BSF-2)
  functions 1459(Fig)
  see also Interleukin-6 (IL-6)
BCG 335–336, 1343
  as adjuvant 38
  administration 335
  adverse effects 336
  antigenic properties 335
  attenuation method 256, 335
  bladder cancer immunotherapy 336, 1346, 1361
  efficacy 335
    environmental mycobacteria affecting 1793
  immunotherapy 336
  in *Leishmania* vaccine 1550
  lipid content 335–336
  in NOD mice and in diabetes 1346
  non-specific resistance to infections 335
  recommendations for 335
  tuberculosis prevention 2084
  vaccination 1343
bcl-2 gene
  B cell non-Hodgkin's lymphomas 1634, 1635
  knockout mice 1582
  overproduction 1635
  translocation 1634, 1635
Bcl-2 protein
  expression
    in germinal center 994
    induced by IL-2 1438
  homolog
    African swine fever (ASF) virus gene 56
    EBV gene product (BHRF1) 2487
  long-term B cell survival 225
  lymphocyte lifespan regulation 1582

Bcl-2 protein (*continued*)
  negative regulator of apoptosis 876
  negative selection of thymocytes 2357
  in tumorigenesis 559
  upregulation, IgE synthesis 1205
Bcl-XL 654, 876
B complex (avian MHC loci) 300, 303
BCR-ABL chromosomal translocations 556, 1558
Bee venom 680, 2471, 2472
Behavior
  immunity modulating 340
  regulation of immunity 336–340
    Pavlovian conditioning 337–338
    pheromone studies 339
    stressor-associated immune regulation 338–340
Behçet's disease
  lymphocytotoxic antibodies 124
  ocular involvement 867
Beige mouse 527
  gene 528
  mutation 1271
Bence Jones protein (BJP) 147, 341–342, 1164, 1636
  characterization 341
  definition 341
  diagnostic significance 341
  excretion levels in multiple myeloma 1636
  [G]k[g] and [G]l[g] types 341
  in heavy chain disease 1053
  pathogenetic implications 341
  renal disease 341
  serum 341
  urine 341
  see also Immunoglobulin, light (L) chains
Bence Jones proteinuria, in multiple myeloma 1164, 1636
Benign hypergammaglobulinemia purpura of Waldenstrom (BHPW) 1163
Benzoate, false food allergy 952(Table)
Berlin breakage syndrome 249–250
Bernoulli mixture model 2212
Beryllium dust 2134
β barrel 777, 1329
  J chain folds 1516
Beta-blockers, autoimmune disease pathogenesis 279
β cells, *see* Pancreatic β cells
β-elimination, catalytic antibodies reaction 438, 439(Fig)
β_2-microglobulin, *see* β_2-Microglobulin
β sheets 515, 517
  Ig fold structure 775–776, 1209, 1319
  in non-Ig molecules 777
β strands, Ig fold structure 1209, 1319, 1329
Betaglycan 2393
Bethanecol 1722
Bf gene 1046
B-F region 300, 302
bg/bg mice 1271–1272
bg mutation 421
Bg/Nu/Xid immunodeficient mice 546
Bgp35, *see* CD20
Bgp95, *see* CD19
Bgp135, *see* CD22
B-G region 300, 302
BIAcore 2248–2249
Bicarbonate, exchange, in red cell membranes 840
Biglycan 906
Biliary cirrhosis, *see* Primary biliary cirrhosis (PBC)
Biliary epithelial cells, MHC class II expression 2003
Bilins 945
'Binding assays' 1252
  see also Immunoassays
Binding sites
  definition 50

Binding sites (*continued*)
  see also Affinity labeling
Bioaffinity sensors, antibody–antigen interaction energy measurement 167
Bioassays
  cytokines, *see under* Cytokine assays
  design 696
  histamine 1103
  IL-1 1429, 1432
  IL-3 1444
BioBreeding rat, *see* BB rat
Biogenic amines 1668
  in Arthus reaction 239
  mast cell release 1668
  see also Histamine; Serotonin
Biological response modifiers (BRM) 1346
  thymic hormones and peptides 2302–2303
Biomaterial-associated infections, *Staphylococcus* 2210, 2211
Bioreactors, tissue culture 1571–1574
  cell types grown 1574(Table)
  characteristics 1573(Table)
  hollow fiber 1572–1573, 1573(Fig)
  rotary system (NASA) 1573–1574, 1574(Fig)
Biosensors 2247
  surface plasmon resonance (SRP)-based 2248–2249
Biotin 143, 1261, 2490
  antibody labeling 815
    ELISA 818
  deficiency 2490–2491
  immunoelectron microscopy 793
  labeling with 944
  synthesis defects 1286
  see also Avidin–biotin system
Biotinylated reagents 143
Biozzi mice 342–346, 1267
  interline difference 342
  see also Selective breeding
BiP 192
  antigen presentation 2231–2232
  heavy chain interaction 146
Birbeck granules 638, 745, 1528, 1528(Fig), 1529, 2190
  function 1530–1531
Birds
  immune system, *see* Avian immune system
  Pasteurella multocida infections 1927, 1928
  poxviruses 1995
  see also Chickens
Birdshot retinochoroidopathy 867
Birth control vaccines, *see* Contraception, immunological
Bispecific antibodies 138–140
  against T cell receptor (TCR) 138
  applications, antitumor therapy 140, 1363
  genetic engineering method 139(Fig), 140
  heteroconjugates 138–139, 139(Fig)
  infectious disease treatment 140
  lysis mediated by 139
  preparation 138
  quadroma 139–140, 139(Fig)
BK virus 1988
  evasive strategies 1990
  host immune response 1990
  infection 1990
  see also Polyomavirus
Black Creek Canal virus 392
'Black death', *see* Plague, bubonic
Bladder
  cancer, BCG therapy 336, 1346, 1361
  host defense mechanisms 2066
  infections 2065
BLAST-1, *see* CD48
Blastomyces dermatitidis 959
Bleeding, mucosal, idiopathic thrombocytopenic purpura 1180

Blepharitis 873
B-like cells, reptiles 2078, 2078(Fig)
Blindness
    onchocerciasis 1872
    postmeasles 872
    trachoma 872–873
B locus (chickens MHC) 300
Blood
    components for transfusions 2399,
        2400(Table)
        mediators in 2402–2403
        quality 2403
        see also Blood transfusion(s)
    lymph as ultrafiltrate 1597
    processing for transfusions 2399
Blood cells
    development, bone marrow stroma role
        2237
    evolutionary origins/comparisons 1948,
        1949
    invertebrates 1499
    membranes, fluidity, free radicals effect
        134
    see also Erythrocyte(s); Leukocyte(s)
Blood flukes, see Schistosoma
Blood group antigens 2401(Table)
    ABO, see ABO blood group
    alloantigenic diversity 70–71, 71(Table)
    deficiency 837
    fetal expression 799, 1577
    I and i, see I and i antigens
    Kell, see Kell antigen
    P antigen 1923, 2453
    on red cell membrane 837
    terminology and listing 840(Table)
    transfection of cDNA 73
    in tumors 2429
Blood groups 2401(Table)
    ABO, see ABO blood group
    as antigens 203
    Bombay 3, 1568
    Duffy, see Duffy blood group
    feline 894
    genes 2400–2401, 2401(Table)
    Gerbich, see Gerbich blood group
    Kell, see Kell (K) blood group
    minor 70
    MNS 71
    P antigen 1923
        urinary tract infections 2453
    recombinant, for transfusions 2403
    recurrent pyelonephritis linked 2453
    Rh, see Rh (Rhesus) blood groups
    serology, see ABO blood group; under
        Agglutination
    transfusions 2400–2401
    typing, see Blood typing
Blood pressure, regulation, bradykinin role
    1518
Blood products 1966–1967
    CJD transmission risk 1968
    virus inactivation procedures 1968
    virus transmission risk 1967, 1968
    see also Blood, components; Blood
        transfusion(s); Plasma
Blood substitutes 2403
Blood supply, nasal 2124–2125
Blood transfusion(s)
    ABO-incompatible 2400
    allogeneic 2399
    in autoimmune hemolytic anemia (AIHA)
        98
    autologous 2399–2400
    before Guillain–Barré syndrome 1836
    blood components 2399, 2400(Table)
        mediators in 2402–2403
        quality 2403
        recombinant 2403
    blood group antigens 2400–2401,
        2401(Table)
    blood substitutes for 2403

Blood transfusion(s) (continued)
    Creutzfeldt–Jakob disease transmission
        risk 1968
    cross-matching 347, 2401
        agglutination 58
        Coombs' test 116
        see also Blood typing
    in DiGeorge syndrome 763
    directed 2402
    fate of transfused leukocytes 2402
    genotyping and recombinant technology
        2403
    HIV infection transmission 6
        screening 2400
    immunohematology 2400–2401,
        2401(Table)
    immunomodulation 2403
    immunomodulatory effects 2401–2402
        factor affecting 2401, 2402(Table)
    immunosuppression associated 2401
        mechanism 811
    incompatible 4, 347, 2400
        ABO 2400
        HLA mismatches 2402
    intraperitoneal (fetal) 1072
    mononuclear cell microchimerism 2402
    obstacles 2399
    pregraft 811
    screening for infectious agents 2400,
        2403
        markers 2400(Table)
    whole blood 2400(Table), 2401
        immunomodulatory effect 2401
Blood transfusion reactions 346–349
    ABO hemolytic reactions 4
    cytokine-induced febrile reactions 348
    delayed-type hemolytic reactions 347
    febrile reactions 347, 348
    granulocyte alloantibodies 348
    GVHD 2402, 2403(Table)
    hemolytic 4, 347
        signs/symptoms 347
        without detectable antibodies 347
    IgE antibodies against nonhuman
        antigens 348
    plasma protein antibodies 348
    platelet alloantibodies 347–349
    post-transfusion purpura 347–348
    red cell alloantibodies 347
    transfusion-related acute lung injury
        (TRALI) 348
    type II hypersensitivity 1174–1176
Blood typing 2401
    agglutination 58
    lectin use 1536, 1541
    monoclonal antibody use 1746–1747
    see also Blood transfusion(s), cross-
        matching
Blood vessels, histamine effect 1102–1103
Blood–brain barrier (BBB) 1844
    dysfunction in bacterial infections 1846
    ultrastructure 1844(Fig)
Blood–ocular barrier 867–868
Blood–retinal barrier 868
Blood–thymus barrier 1726, 2233
Bloom's syndrome 1282
Blotting techniques 142
    sensitivity increase 143
    see also Northern blotting; Southern
        blotting; Western blotting
B lymphoblastoid cell line (B-LCL), HLA-E
    gene expression 1109
B lymphocytes, see B cell(s)
bm mutants 371–373, 1735
    frequency and sources 372
    functional consequences 372–373
    gene conversion 372
    historical background 371–372
    known mutations mapped 372(Table)
    mutation rates 372
BN 52021 (PAF antagonist) 1971, 1973
BN rats

BN rats (continued)
    autoimmune renal disease 1688
    mercury effect 1689
    mitogenic effect of mercury 1687
Body fluids
    immune complex detection 1221–1222
    see also Blood; Cerebrospinal fluid (CSF);
        Lymph; Urine
Bombay blood group 3, 1568
Bone
    defects in multiple myeloma 1163–1164,
        1636
    resorption
        IL-1β gene variation 1892
        regulation, IL-1 role 1434
Bone marrow 374–377
    B cell differentiation 1247
    cell cryopreservation 669
        evaluation 670
    dendritic cell origin 742
    disorders, anti-lymphocyte serum for 121
    dysfunction, motheaten mice 1269
    long-term culture 2236
    lymphocyte migration 1617
    microenvironment 376, 2236
    monocyte development 1755
    recovery, romurtide inducing 1790
    in SCID mice 1269
    stroma
        blood cell development 2237
        cytokine production 2237
    stromal cells 376, 2236–2237, 2338
        estrogen receptor expression 2176
        IL-3 production 1444
    target tissue for parvovirus B19 1922,
        1923
    T cell removal, method 511
Bone marrow hematopoiesis 374–377
    hematopoietic growth factors 375
    lymphopoiesis 376
    microenvironment 376, 2236
    myelopoiesis 375–376, 1755
    see also Myelopoiesis
    stem cell origin 374–375
    time course 374
    see also Hematopoiesis
Bone marrow transplantation 544–549
    allotype application 76
    anti-CD11a therapy 1609
    autologous (ABMT) 1363
    CD34 cell culture 1575
    complications 1575
    cord blood 548
    cryopreservation and 669
    enhancement of engraftment 546, 547
        megadose transplants 545–546, 548
    future directions 548–549
    'gene therapy' and 548
    GM-CSF use 1022
    GVHD 545–546, 1016–1017, 1363
        prevention 1883
        see also Graft-versus-host disease
            (GVHD)
    hemorrhagic cystitis in recipients 1990
    historical aspects 544
    in HIV infection 12
    host-versus-graft reaction 545, 545–546
    immunodeficiency in 1284
    immunosuppression 547
    indications 544, 548
    megadose approach 545–546, 548
    OKT3 (anti-CD3) therapy 2261
    opportunistic infections 1883
    preparations used 2400(Table)
    purging by monoclonal antibodies 1363,
        2261
    radioprotection effect 544
    registries and donor programmes 2322
    SCID 545, 2174
    SCID mice 546
    T-cell depletion, effects 545
    tissue typing 2318, 2319, 2322

Bone marrow transplantation (*continued*)
  whole-body irradiation before 2052
  see also Graft-versus-host disease
    (GVHD)
Bonferroni's correction 1698
Boophilus microplus (cattle tick) 2458
Border disease virus of sheep (BD) 2350,
  2351
Bordetella 377–379
  see also Bordetella pertussis
Bordetella pertussis 377–379
  adenylate cyclase-hemolysin 2377
  antigens 377–378
  BvgAS system 378
  characteristics 377–378
  evasive strategies 378
  filamentous hemagglutinin (FHA) 377
  fimbriae 378
  host immune response 378
  lipopolysaccharide 378
  outbreaks after vaccine cessation 2463,
    2464(Fig)
  pertactin (PRN) 377
  T_H1 and T_H2 balance 316
  toxins 377–378, 2373–2374, 2373(Fig)
    adenylate cyclase (ACT) 377, 378
    dermonecrotic (DNT) 377, 378
    pertussis (PT) 377, 378, 2373(Fig),
      2374
    tracheal cytotoxin (TCT) 377, 377–378
  vaccines 378–379, 2374, 2458
    acellular 379
    adverse effects 379, 2463
    trivalent 2458
    whole-cell 378, 2463
  virulence factors 378
  see also Pertussis
Borna disease, TGFβ effect 2397
Borrelia 379–382, 2127
  antigens 380
  borreliacidal antibodies 382
  cultivation 381
  evasion strategies 380
  flagella 381
  infections, *see* Borreliosis; Lyme disease
  Osp A and escape mutants 382
  outer cytoplasmic membrane 380
  outer surface proteins (Osp) 380, 382
  slime layer 380
  subspecies 380
  vaccines 382
  variable major proteins (VMP) 380
Borrelia burgdorferi 379
  antigens 380
  culture 381
  immunoglobulin-binding protein 324
  outer cytoplasmic membrane 380
  'patching' ('capping') 380
  see also Lyme disease
Borrelia hermsii 380
  antigenic variation 199
Borreliosis 379
  animal models 381–382
  relapsing fever 380
  see also Borrelia
Botulinum toxin, *see under Clostridium
  botulinum*
Botulism 577
  see also Clostridium botulinum
Bovine coronavirus (BCV) 660, 660(Table)
Bovine enterovirus, epitope location
  1957(Table)
Bovine leukemia virus (BLV) 1565
  genome structure 2094
  leukemia pathogenesis 1565
  R3 and G4 genes 1565
Bovine papillomaviruses (BPV), vaccine
  development 1908
Bovine parainfluenza virus (BPiV), evasive
  strategy 1915
Bovine serum albumin (BSA)

Bovine serum albumin (BSA) (*continued*)
  ABBOSS mimicking islet protein 1400–
    1401
  dual dose tolerance 2360
  serum sickness due to 2168
Bovine spongiform encephalopathy (BSE)
  2409
  infection route 2410
  species barrier crossed 2409, 2410
Bovine viral diarrhea virus (BVDV) 1396–
  1397, 2350, 2351
Bovine viruses, from fetal calf serum 897
Bradykinin (BK) 1518
  in allergic rhinitis 2124
  B2 and B1 receptors 1518, 1521
  biological effects 1518–1519
  blood pressure regulation 1518
  in hereditary angioedema 1520
  inactivation 1520
  release, high molecular weight kininogen
    role 1520
  see also Kallikrein-kinin system
Brain
  IL-1 receptors 2226
  inflammation, TGFβ effects 2395, 2396
  lymphocyte migration 1617
  MHC class I negative 1703
Breast cancer
  in ataxia telangiectasia 248
  growth factor receptors expressed 2429
  IL-11 trials 1481
  immunocytochemistry 1266
  interferon α combined therapy 1416
  mucin underglycosylation 2425
  paraneoplastic cerebellar degeneration
    1842
  stiff man syndrome 1842
Breast milk
  cells transferred 1673
  Ig transfer
    IgG and IgM transfer 1672
    in marsupials 1664
    sIgA 1672
  immunomodulators in 1673
  lactoferrin 1672–1673
  lysozyme 1673
  protection of infant from infections 1672
  T cells 1673
Breath pentane 135
Brevibacterium spp. 661
Brk mutation 216
Bromamines 1724
Bromocriptine 250
5-Bromodeoxyuridine 510
  lymphocyte transformation assay 1623,
    2023
  measurement of cell lifespan 1579–1580
Bronchial hyperresponsiveness (BHR) 243
  TNFα role 2439
Bronchial mucosa, damage, in chronic
  allergic disease 254
Bronchiolitis, obliterative 2413
Bronchitis 2081
Bronchoconstriction, histamine causing
  1103
Bronchodilators, anaphylaxis treatment
  685
Bronchoprovocation 245
Bronchus-associated lymphoid tissue
  (BALT) 190, 1774, 2155
  homing receptors 1778
  in pigs 1994
Brother–sister matings 1369
Brown Norway rats 273
Brucella 383–386
  antigens 383
  characteristics 383
  evasive strategies 385
  host immune response 384–385
  host range 383(Table)
  infection, *see* Brucellosis
  intracellular in macrophage 384

Brucella (*continued*)
  lipopolysaccharide 383, 385
  vaccines 385–386
Brucella abortus 384(Fig), 385
  immunoglobulin-binding proteins 324
  strain 19 385
  vaccine 385
Brucella canis 384(Fig)
Brucella melitensis 384(Fig)
  strain Rev 1 385
Brucella suis 384(Fig)
Brucellosis 383
  immunopathology and granulomata 385
  serodiagnosis 384, 385
  serology 385
  see also Brucella
Brugia malayi 913
Brugia timori 913
Bruton's agammaglobulinemia 366, 386–
  389, 1276, 1279
  B cell differentiation block 387, 387–388
  Btk gene 387, 388
  clinical characteristics 387, 387(Table)
  differential diagnosis 389
  disorders identical 389
  genetics 388–389
  historical background 386–387
  laboratory characteristics 387–388
  therapy 387, 389
Bruton's tyrosine kinase (Btk) 387, 388
  defect 1270
  gene 388
    mutations 387, 388, 389, 1279
  mast cell degranulation 1670
BSAP (sα-BP; NF-sμ-BP), in targeting Ig
  class switching 1305
Bst-1 (CD157) 456(Table)
Btk, *see* Bruton's tyrosine kinase (Btk)
Bubonic plague, *see* Plague, bubonic
Budd–Chiari syndrome 2119
Buffalo, *Pasteurella multocida* infections
  1927, 1928
Buffalo (BUF) rat, *see* BUF rats
Buffalo pox 1998
BUF rats 280, 2309, 2310
  Ig V gene repertoire 2310
Bulk flow model 144
Bulla
  intraepidermal formation 2188
  subepidermal formation 2188
Bullous dermatoses, autoimmune 2188–2189
  see also Pemphigoid; Pemphigus
Bullous disease, linear IgA deposition 1199
Bullous pemphigoid (BP) 263
Bunyamwera virus 390
Bunyaviridae 390–393
  characteristics 390–392
  evasion strategies 392
  genera 390, 391(Table)
  host immune response 392
  proteins 390
  structure 390(Fig)
  transmission 390
  vaccines 392–393
Bunyavirus 390, 391(Table)
  immune response to 392
  see also Bunyaviridae
Burkitt's lymphoma 831, 1360, 1635
  antigen presentation impairment 832
  chromosome translocation 558, 831
  EBV etiological role 1635
  malaria and 831, 1245
Burkitt's lymphoma-associated antigen
  (BLA), *see* CD77
Burnet, M. 1338
Burnet's clonal selection theory, *see* Clonal
  selection theory
Burns, immunodeficiency due to 1286
Bursa of Fabricius 301, 393–396, 572
  central function 395–396
  development 393
  epithelial cells 393

Bursa of Fabricius (*continued*)
  historical background 393
  location 394(Fig)
  mammalian equivalent 396
  peripheral function 396
  stem cells 395
  structure 393–394
Bursectomy 395
  effects 395
  methods 395
Burst forming units-erythroid (BFU-E) 375
Burst-promoting activity, *see* Interleukin-3
    (IL-3)
Butterfly rash 2255, 2256(Fig)
BW5147 thymoma 1152
BXSB mice 285, 2251
  MHC genes and lupus susceptibility
    2252
  origin and characteristics 2251,
    2251(Table)
Bystander effects 396–398
  B cells 397
  cell suppression, *see* Bystander
    suppression
  cytotoxic T cells 397
  definition 397
  drug-induced immune hemolytic anemia
    95
  experimental evidence 397
  in vivo significance 398
  lysis in SLE 2258
  mechanisms 397–398
  regulation, TGFβ function 2397
  T cells 397
Bystander suppression 1357–1358, 1895–
    1896, 1895(Table)
  applications 1896
  autoimmune disease models 1895–1896
  in humans 1896

C

C1 604, 605–606
  activation 606, 1316
  control 610
  structure 605
C1 complex
  composition 1316
  crossed immunoelectrophoresis 1293
C1 esterase, activation by IgM 1215–1215
C1 esterase inhibitor
  administration 684
  deficiency
    acquired angioedema 684
    hereditary angioedema 684
  metabolism, lymphoproliferative
    disorders 684
C1 inhibitor (C1-inh) 1520
  autoantibodies 611
  C1 control 610
  crossed immunoelectrophoresis 1293
  deficiency 611, 613, 615(Table), 1520
  mutants 611
  rocket immunoelectrophoresis 1294,
    1294(Fig)
C1q 604, 605
  activators 609, 1316
  assembly 605–606, 606(Fig)
  autoantibodies 611
  crossed immunoelectrophoresis 1293
  deficiency 612, 614(Table)
  IgG binding 1211, 1316, 1316(Fig)
    glycosylation effect 1002
  IgM binding 1215
  immune complex interaction 1223
  receptors (C1q-R) 611, 630(Table), 632–
    633
    cDNA 632
    types 632

C1q (*continued*)
  structure 605, 1316
C1q-binding assay, immune complex
    detection 1221
C1r 604, 605
  crossed immunoelectrophoresis 1293
  deficiency 614(Table)
  serine protease proenzyme 606
  structure 606, 606(Fig)
C1s 604, 605
  activated 606
  C4 cleavage 606–607
  crossed immunoelectrophoresis 1293
  deficiency 614(Table)
  serine protease proenzyme 606
  structure 606, 606(Fig)
C2 607–608
  C4b complex 608
  as class III MHC 622
  cleavage 608
  control 610
  deficiency 612, 614(Table), 616, 622
    hereditary angioedema 684
  gene 116(Table), 607, 622, 1115
    mice 1046
  vWF-A domain 607
C2a 608
  control 610
C2b 608
CIITA transcription factor 331
C3 608
  activation
    immune adherence 1219
    rate 603
  antigen clearance, cold agglutinin disease
    184–185
  cleavage 602, 604, 608
    by cobra venom factor 587
    enzymes 603
  Cobra venom factor (CVF) similarity, *see*
    Cobra venom factor (CVF)
  cold agglutinin disease 184–185, 593
  Crohn's disease 1378
  deficiency 614(Table), 616
    in dogs 414
  feedback cycle 602–603, 603(Fig)
  immunoconglutinins reacting with 1257
  reactive thiolesters 611
  spontaneous hydrolysis 603–604
  synthesis 608
C3a 608
  actions 87
  as anaphylatoxin 86
  arginine action 236
  bioactivity 87, 89
  C3a$_{desarg}$ 87, 89
  chemotactic activity 89
  formation 86–87
    Arthus reaction 237–238
  as marker of complement activation 87
  mast cell degranulation 253
  mediator release from mast cells 89
  receptor (C3a-R) 88, 90, 630(Table),
    633–634
    cloning 88
  release, bacteria causing 316
  source of eosinophil chemotactic factors
    819
  structure 87
  superagonists 88
  see also Anaphylatoxin(s)
C3b 608
  abnormal reactions 611
  acceptor binding reaction 608
  binding to CR1 629
  C5 binding 624
  cleavage 603
    by CD46 495
    factors decreasing 603
  cobra venom factor similarity 603
  feedback cycle 603
  formation 602, 604, 1886

C3b (*continued*)
  formation (*continued*)
    mechanisms increasing 603
    on HSV 1088
  iC3b 603, 604, 631
    immune complex interaction 1223
    as opsonin 1886
    receptor, *see* Complement receptors,
      CR3
  phagocyte recognition 1937
  receptors 611
    IgG-induced immune hemolytic anemia
      94
C3b,Bb 587, 602
  stabilization 603
C3bi/C3b receptor, *see* CR1
C3 convertase 87, 604, 1886
  for alternative pathway (C3b,Bb) 602
  autoantibodies (nephritic factors) 603,
    611, 1257
  for classical pathway (C4b,2b) 602, 608
  cobra venom factor (CVF)-dependent
    587
  control 610
  decay 610
  inhibition, by decay-accelerating factor
    (DAF) 735
  stabilization 603
C3d (CD21; CR2), *see* CR2 (CD21)
C3dg 629, 1223
  immune complex interaction 1223
C3f 603
C3H/HeJ Bir mice 1383
C3H/HeJ mice 1271
C3H mice 1765–1766
  immunology 1765–1766
  infectious agents susceptibility/resistance
    1765
  origin/characteristics 1765
  SCID mice 1128
C4
  activation 607(Fig)
  binding protein, *see* C4bp
  Chido determinants 607
  as class III MHC 622
  cleavage 606–607
  cold agglutinin disease 593
  Crohn's disease 1378
  deficiency 612, 614(Table), 616, 622
    disease associations 622
    hereditary angioedema 684
    partial 1120
    total 1120
  fast (C4F) and slow (C4S) 607
  gene 116(Table), 607, 622, 1115
    deletions 622
    mice 1046
  immunoconglutinins reacting with 1257
  isotypes (C4A and C4B) 116(Table),
    607, 622, 1115
  roles 622
  null alleles 607, 622
  reactive thiolesters 611, 622
  Rodgers blood group 607
  structure 607
  thiolesters 607
C4a 607
  as anaphylatoxin 86
  formation 86–87
  as marker of complement activation 87
  receptors (C4a-R) 88, 88(Fig), 633–634
  structure 87
C4b 116(Table), 607, 1115
  abnormal reactions 611
  binding to complement activator 607,
    607(Fig)
  C2 complex 608
  cleavage by CD46 495
  nascent 607, 611
  receptors 611
C4b2a 602, 608
C4b2a3b complex 608

C4bp (C4b-binding protein) 583
control of complement activation 610
gene 620
C5
binding to C3b 624
cleavage 604, 624
by cobra venom factor 587
deficiency 612, 614(Table), 616
T cell tolerance 2355
C5a 624
actions 87
outside immune system 90
ADCC modulation 170
as anaphylatoxin 86, 89–90
antibodies, Arthus reaction reduced 239
arginine action 236
bioactivity 87, 89–90
C5a$_{desarg}$ 87, 89, 90
as chemotactic factor 89, 542
cytokine expression stimulated 90
formation 86–87
Arthus reaction 237–238
glycosylation 87
interleukin expression by monocytes 90
mast cell binding 1669
mast cell degranulation 253
mediator synthesis promoted by 90
neutrophil response to 90
receptor (C5a-R) 88–89, 90, 630(Table), 633
structural model 633
two-binding model 89, 89(Fig)
release, bacteria causing 316
source of eosinophil chemotactic factors 819
structure 87
see also Anaphylatoxin(s)
C5b 624
C6 binding 624–625
C7 binding 625
C8 binding 626
C9 binding 626
formation 624
membrane attack complex formation 624
C5 convertase 87, 608
control 610
inhibition, by decay-accelerating factor (DAF) 735
C6
binding to C5b 624–625
deficiency 612, 614(Table)
gene 621–622
C7
binding to C5b 625
deficiency 612, 614(Table)
gene 621–622
C8
binding to C5b 626
CD59 binding 497, 499
deficiency 612, 614(Table)
C8 binding protein (C8bp), deficiency 613
C9
CD59 binding 497, 499
deficiency 612, 614(Table)
gene 621–622
C57BL/6J mice 1766–1767
immunology 1766–1767
infectious agents susceptibility/resistance 1766
origin/characteristics 1766
C57BL/6 mice 636
mercury effect 1688
mixed lymphocyte reaction (MLR) 1735
T$_H$1 response to Leishmania 1062
C57BL/10 mice 636, 1767
origin/characteristics 1767
C57BL/10ScN mice 1271
C57BLKS/J (C57BL/KsJ) mice 1767–1768
origin/characteristics 1767
Ca^{2+}/calmodulin-dependent protein kinases 2029
ca2 antibodies 1358

CA19-9 antigen (sialyl Le^a) 2432
antibodies, uses 2434
Cachectin, see Tumor necrosis factor α (TNFα)
Cachexia, cancer 1561
Cadherins 17, 28(Table), 29, 518, 1382
adhesion mediated by 419
E-cadherin, see E-cadherin
N-cadherin 1382
dominant negative mutants 1382
negative (NCAD) 1382
three-dimensional structure 518
Caenorhabditis elegans 222, 1028
Calbindins 2495
Calcineurin
activation 2325
negative selection of thymocytes 2356
target 2325
Calcitonin gene-related peptide 1827
Calcitriol 2494
administration 2496
antiproliferative actions 2495
cell-regulating properties 2495
effect on cytokines 2495
effect on lymphocytes 2495–2496
effect on macrophage/monocytes 2495
functions 2494
immunological role 2495–2497
in vitro/in vivo effects 2494(Table)
in vitro 2495–2496
in vivo 2496
mediated by receptors 2494–2495
receptor 2494–2495, 2495
synthesis, by macrophage 2495
therapy 2496–2497
cancer 2496
Calcium
anergy signal 2366
binding by lipocortins 111, 112
calcineurin activation 2325
cellular ionized, lymphocyte transformation test 1624
complement activation (classical pathway) 605
in cytotoxic T cell action 726, 732, 733
dependency, Yersinia 2513
fluxes, in red cell membranes 840
increase
cytolysis 733
inhibition in Lambert–Eaton syndrome 1835
mast cell degranulation 1670
T cell signal transduction 2324–2325
integrin requirement 1406
intracellular, methyl mercury effect 1688
leukotriene B$_4$ (LTB$_4$) as 232
metabolism, calcitriol effect 2494, 2496
mobilization, in chemoattractant-stimulated leukocytes 1761
in phagocytosis 1857
release
lymphocyte activation 1681
membrane attack complex function 627
role in cell-mediated lysis 506, 733
role in T cells 2325
in T cell activation 2324–2325
T cell apoptosis 2325
Calcium channels
cytoskeleton interaction 1680–1681
voltage-gated, antibodies 1835, 1849–1850
Calcium-dependent protein kinases 2029
Calcium ionophores
A23187 253
degranulation 737
LTB$_4$ as 232
Calcium phosphate technique 982
Calgranulins A and B, see Calprotectin
Caliciviruses 399–402
antigens 400–401
characteristics 399–401
specific viruses 400

Caliciviruses (continued)
evasive strategies 400, 401
host immune response 400, 401
infections, clinical features 400
open reading frames 399
vaccines 401–402
viruses included 399(Table)
California encephalitis 391
CALLA (CD10) 446(Table), 800–801
cDNA clones 800–801
cells expressing/distribution 800
myeloid cells 1803
function 801, 1806
in leukemia 800
acute lymphoblastic 1555, 1557
Calmodulin 2029
nitric oxide production induction 1859
Calmodulin-dependent protein kinases 2029
Calnexin 192
functions 2232
Calorie restriction, delay in age-related disease 884
Calpain, protein kinase C as target 1942
Calprotectin 1720
bacterial growth inhibition 1720
structure 1720
Calreticulin 192, 1038
functions 2232
Calycins 67–68, 68(Fig)
Camelpox 1998
cAMP, see Cyclic AMP (cAMP)
CAMPATH-1 antigen (CD52) 402–406, 450(Table)
antigen structure 404
GPI anchor 404
genes 405
monoclonal antibodies 121, 404
therapeutic uses 404(Fig), 405–406, 405(Fig)
sequences 404(Fig)
shedding 405
structure 403(Fig)
tissue distribution 404–405
CAMPATH-1G 404
applications 405
CAMPATH-1H 404, 1144
applications 405
autoimmune disease therapy 1358
CAMPATH-1M 404
applications 405
cAMP response element (CRE), H2 class II gene 1042
cAMP response element-binding protein (CREB) 1115
Campylobacter 407–408
antigens 407
characteristics 407
diarrhea due to 968
evasive strategies 408
flagellin 407, 408
host immune response 407–408
infection prevention by breast milk Igs 1672
major outer membrane protein (MOMP) 407, 408
passive immunization 408
serological detection 408
serotyping 407
species 407
vaccines 408
Campylobacter coli 407
Campylobacter fetus subsp. fetus 407
evasive strategies 408
Campylobacter jejuni 407
Guillain–Barré syndrome after infection 1837, 1838
Campylobacter lari 407
Canarypox virus, as adjuvant 38
Cancer
α$_5$β$_1$ expression loss 913
birth control vaccine role 641

Cancer (*continued*)
cachexia 1561
calcitriol treatment 2496
CD44 expression 490
cell surface protein shedding 719
chemotherapy, *see* Chemotherapy
cobra venom factor (CVF) application 588
fibronectin and 913
growth, histamine role 1104
hCG vaccine application 646
HLA association 1693
immune reaction, gene therapy role 974, 976(Table), 977–978
increased galectins and role 1538
membrane attack complex inhibitors action 628
metastases, *see* Metastases
susceptibility, in ataxia telangiectasia 248–249
therapy, *see* Chemotherapy; Immunotherapy, of tumors
TNFα levels 2439
transferrin receptor (TfR) expression 2390
transferrin saturation and iron overload 1507
transplantation preceding 2414–2415
vaccines, *see* Tumor immunotherapy, vaccines
see also Carcinogenesis; Malignant disease; Metastases; Tumor(s)
Candida 409–411
adhesion and virulence factors 410
antigens 409
characteristics 409
evasive strategies 410
host immune response 409, 409–410
phagocytosis 409–410
species 409
vaccines 411
see also Candidiasis
Candida albicans 957, 958
complement activation 959
infections
false food allergy 952
see also Candidiasis
lysozyme action 1723
mannan, antitumor effects 430
neutrophil action 959
oral infections 1891
Candida utilis, mannan, antitumor effects 430
Candidiasis
in AIDS 409, 410
antibodies 960
autoimmune polyendocrinopathy–candidiasis–ectodermal dystrophy 1984–1985
chronic mucocutaneous 410, 1282
lymphocyte transformation test 1624
transfer factor therapy 2388
cutaneous 410
deep 409, 410
diagnostic tests 409
disseminated 409
in immunosuppressed 409, 410
superficial 409, 410
vaccines 411
see also Candida
Canine cyclic hematopoiesis (gray collie syndrome) 413
Canine distemper virus, vaccines 1916
Canine immune system 411–414
cell-mediated immunity 413
evaluation of responsiveness 414
humoral immunity 412–413
maternal immunity 412
natural resistance 412
ontogeny 411–412
pathologic changes 413–414
see also Dogs

Canonical structures 152, 153, 174
catalytic antibodies 439–440
CAP-37 (azurocidin) 1723
Capillaries
lymph formation and 1597
splenic 2207
see also Lymphatic capillaries
Capillary leak syndrome 1022, 1348, 1630
Capping 414–421
abnormalities 421
Borrelia burgdorferi membrane 380
clustered receptors removal 420
clustering of ligands and 416
cocapping 416
colocalization of components and 415–416
consequences 420
definition 415
inhibition of cell activation 420
leukocyte polarization sign 415, 416–417
microtubules and microfilaments 415
mutations 421
as scavenging mechanism 420
Caprine arthritis encephalitis virus (CAEV) 2096
Capripoxvirus 1995, 1995(Table)
genome 1996
vaccination 1998
Capsids 21
Capsular polysaccharides 422–423
Capsules, bacterial, *see* Bacteria, capsules
Carbohydrate(s) 422
antimicrobial effects 428
binding proteins, *see* Lectins
binding to selectins 2158
cold agglutinins against 594–595
complex, colitis due to 1384
diversity 422
immune stimulation 427–31
antitumor effects 429–430
mechanisms 428
types and structures 428(Table)
lectin interactions 1537, 1538(Fig)
lectin specificity 1537
mucins 28
stereoisomeric forms 422
see also Carbohydrate antigens; Polysaccharides
Carbohydrate antigens 422–427
antibodies, inability to generate and GVHD 1017
antibody binding site 150, 427
antibody interaction 427
conformation in solution 426
I and i antigens 594
immune response to 426–427
Schistosoma 2141
sperm 1373
Streptococcus 2218
TCR γδ specificity 2275(Table)
tumor 2432
mAb recognition 2429
vaccine development 426–427
see also Carbohydrate(s); Glycosylation
Carbohydrate-recognition domain (CRD), lectins 1537
Carboxyfluorescein, in tissue typing 2319
Carboxypeptidase N, deficiency 615(Table), 616
Carcinoembryonic antigen (CEA) 799, 800, 1361, 2426, 2432
antibodies, uses 2434
immunocytochemistry application 1266
mAb recognizing 2428
structure and levels 800
in tumors 800
Carcinogenesis
chemical, selective breeding application 345–346
mercury 1686
ultraviolet light role 1943

Carcinogenesis (*continued*)
viral, *see* Oncoviruses; Viral carcinogenesis
see also Cancer; Tumor(s)
Cardiac disease, autoimmune 431–436
cardiomyopathies 433–434
Chagas' disease 432–433
mechanisms, cross-reactivity of microbial proteins 431–432, 434, 435
microbe-induced 431–434
postpericardiotomy syndrome 434
rheumatic fever 431–432
significance 434–435
Cardiac infections 2081–2084
characteristics of organisms 2082–2083
evasive strategies of organisms 2083
immune responses 2083
see also Endocarditis, infective
Cardiac muscle, autoantibodies 263–264
Cardiac myxoma, IL-6 action 1460
Cardiac proteins, cross-reactions (streptococci) 431–434, 435, 1737, 2219
Cardiac transplantation 2413
cyclosporine role 688
historical background 2412
indications and results 2413
survival, CD40L antibodies role 487
tissue typing 2322
TNFα levels 2439
Cardiolipin antibodies 265, 1676
Cardiolipin F 2417
Cardiomyopathy
autoimmune 433–434, 435
Chagas' disease 433, 522, 525
Cardiopulmonary bypass, kallikrein–kinin system role 1520
Cardiovascular disease
multifactorial inheritance 988
see also Coronary heart disease
Cardiovirus 1955(Table)
disease 1956
receptors 1956(Table)
β-Carotene 134
Carrageenan, colitis due to 1384
Carrier ampholytes 1511
commercial sources 1511
Carrier effect 436–437
Carriers 38, 436–438, 1050
birth control vaccines 642, 644
hCG vaccine 646
definition 1337
hapten-carrier system 353, 397, 437
helper T cell determinants 437
historical aspects 436–437, 1337
T and B cell interaction 437
see also Hapten–carrier system
Caseation 1024
Casein kinase 2030
Casein kinase II 1117(Table), 1119
disease association 1120
Caspase 876, 1028, 1029
in apoptosis 223
genes 876
inhibitors 876
see also ICE/CED-3 family; ICE (interleukin 1β-converting enzyme)
Caspase-3 225, 876
Caspase-6 (Mch2) 876, 1028
Caspase-7 225, 876
TNF receptor signaling 2347
Caspase-8 225, 876
Castleman's disease
IL-6 role 1460
polyclonal hypergammaglobulinemia 1162
Castor beans, allergic hazard 2122
Castration, physiological 1852
Cat(s)
allergens 2122
allergy, immunotherapy/vaccine 69
bites 2216

Cat(s) (*continued*)
  febrile response 904
  immune system, *see* Feline immune
    system
  passive transfer of immunoglobulins 893,
    895
  septic shock susceptibility 892, 894
  T cell rosettes 2129
  Toxoplasma gondii immunization 2384
Catabolin, *see* Interleukin-1 (IL-1)
Catalase 38
  highly virulent *Nocardia* 1863
Catalytic antibodies 438–444
  antibody 43C9 443(Fig)
  combining site structure 439–441
  dissociation constant 440
  enzyme comparisons 442–443, 443(Fig)
  kinetics 441–443
  monoclonal 1748
  nature of 441–443
  reaction energy 443
  reaction types 438–439
  screening for catalysis 444
  transition state analogs 438
Cataract-prone subline (CTS) mice 1391,
  1392
Catarrhini 2005
  MHC 2009(Table)
CATCH 22 762
Catenin–cadherin complexes 1382
Cathelin-associated peptides 1724
Cathepsin G
  distribution 1722
  function 1722–1723
  gene 1722
  in neutrophil granules 1722–1723
  reduced in Chédiak–Higashi syndrome
    1722
Cathepsin proteases, *Fasciola hepatica*
  secreting 883
Cationic cyclization, catalytic antibodies
  440(Fig)
Cationic proteins 317
Cattle
  immune system, *see* Ungulate immune
    system
  Pasteurella multocida infections 1927,
    1928
  trypanosomiasis, *see* Trypanosomiasis,
    African
Caveolae 419
CB17, SCID mice 1128
CB-171lcr strain 1268
CBA/J mice 1768
  immunology 1768
  infectious agents susceptibility/resistance
    1768
  origin/characteristic 1768
CBA/N mice 1270
  response to haptenated liposomes 1590
Cbl mutants 2326
CCP1 733
CCR5
  HIV coreceptor 10, 1134
  mutation, AIDS resistance 712
CD antigens 73, 444–457, 508, 1803
  as alloantigens 73
  avian T cells 302
  characteristics 446(Table)-457(Table)
  disease associations 73
  enzymatic activity 73
  functions 73
  historical aspects 444–445
  human 446(Table)-457(Table)
  as ion channels 73
  list 446(Table)-457
  as markers for cell types 73
  molecular weights 446(Table)-457(Table)
  monoclonal antibodies 445, 446(Table)-
    457(Table)
    panels 445
    uses 1746

CD antigens (*continued*)
  new, determination 445
  origin of name 445
  ovine 1903, 1904(Table)
  porcine 1993
  primates (nonhuman) 2005–2008,
    2006(Table)-2008(Table)
  rabbits 2048, 2049(Table)
  as receptors 73
  synonyms 446(Table)-457(Table)
  terminology 445
  as viral receptors 73
  workshops and conferences 445
  *see also specific CD antigens (table page
    446-457)*
CD1 72, 446(Table), 458–463
  αβ T cells, in bacterial infections 318
  amino acid sequence 461
  antigen presentation 459–460, 462
    antigen types 460–461
    inhibition 460
    nonpeptide antigens 458, 460
    peptide loading 459–460
  antigen processing 459–460
  antigen restriction 460–462
  β₂-microglobulin association 458, 460
  CD1a 446(Table)
    expression on Langerhans cells 1530,
      1530(Fig), 2190
  CD1b 446(Table)
    expression in leprosy 462
  CD1c 446(Table)
  CD8⁺ T cell restriction 460, 462
  cells expressing 458
    T_H1 and T_H2 462
  discovery 458
  genes 458–459, 458(Fig), 1035
    intron–exon organization 458(Fig)
    ovine 1903
  group 1 and 2 molecules 459(Table)
  H2-M3 similarity 462
  MHC class I comparison 46(Table), 461
    structural similarity 458
  MHC class II comparison 46(Table), 461
  mouse 461
  recycling pathway 460
  role 462
  structure 458–459, 459(Fig), 459(Table)
  TCRγδ recognition 2272
  T_H1 differentiation 462
  thymocyte population 2336
  in tuberculin-like reactions 740
CDw antigens 445
CD1-restricted antigens 460–462
CD2 28, 31, 446(Table), 463–465, 2146
  B cell receptor signaling 351
  CD2R epitope, *see* CD2R
  CD45 interaction 464
  CD48 binding 463
  CD58 binding 463
  cell-mediated lysis role 506
  cells expressing 464, 4623
    T cells 1613
  gene 463, 1613
  LFA-3 interaction, *see* LFA-3
  as ligand for CD58 2328
  ligands 500, 4623–464
  phytohemagglutinin binding 1952
  polar clustering on APCs 1614
  role 464
  signaling role 464
  structure 517, 517(Fig), 2328, 4623
  T cell activation 464, 502, 2146, 2328
  T cell adhesion 464
  T cell rosette 2129
  tyrosine kinases interacting 464
CD2R 446(Table), 464
  loss in T cell anergy 464
CD3 73, 446(Table), 465–468
  cDNA 465
  δ chain 465, 466
  defects 1277

CD3 (*continued*)
  ε chain 465
    contrasuppressor cells 649
    defect 1277, 2173
    deficiency 2173
  expression 2341
    acute leukemia 1555
    acute lymphoblastic leukemia (ALL)
      1555
    exercise effect 845
  function 463, 467
  γ chain 465, 466
    defects 1277, 2173
    deficiency in SCID 2173
  genes 465, 466
  in leukocyte adhesion to endothelium
    758
  monoclonal antibodies 467
    see also OKT3 (anti-CD3)
  mouse 466
  structure 463–466, 465
  synthesis 1877
  TCR association, *see under* T cell
    receptor (TCR)
  TCR signaling 467
  TCR structure/assembly 463–466
    see also T cell receptor (TCR)
  CD3⁻ endometrial granulated lymphocytes
    (eGL) 899–900
CD4 446(Table), 468–472, 2342
  antibodies, therapeutic, *see* Anti-CD4
    antibodies
  CDR3 cyclized peptide 2263
  cells expressing 468–469
    see also CD4⁺ T cells
  as coreceptor for T cells 469, 471
  domains 1321
    D1 domain and HIV interaction 470
    extracellular 468, 470, 517
    Ig-type 777(Fig)
  functions 471
  genes 468
    human/murine comparisons 468(Table)
    mutations (tailless) 471
  as HIV receptor, *see under* HIV
  human/murine comparisons 468(Table)
  interactions 469–471
    interspecies 470
  loss from cell surface, HIV action 471
  MHC class II interactions 461, 469–470
  mRNA 468–469
  p56^lck interactions 470
  peptides preventing binding 2263
  shutoff in CD8⁺ T cell development 478
  signal transduction 469, 471
  soluble, HIV infection treatment strategy
    12
  structure 468, 517, 517(Fig)
    crystal structure 469(Fig)
  synthetic peptides mimicking 2263
  in T cell activation 471, 2328
    see also T cell activation
  T cell receptor interactions 470
  thymocyte differentiation 471
CD4⁺ T cells 468, 468–469, 1059
  activation, *see* Helper T lymphocytes; T
    cell activation
  adjuvants stimulating 2456
  antibodies 1352, 1358
    see also Anti-CD4 antibodies
  antigen presentation to, *see under* Helper
    T lymphocytes
  autoantibodies 122, 124
  autoimmune hemolytic anemia in NZB
    mice 92
  B3 distribution 298(Fig), 299
  in brucellosis 384
  CD8⁺ T cell ratio
    common variable immunodeficiency
      601
    exercise effect 845
    sex hormones affecting 2176

CD4+ T cells (continued)
Chlamydia infections 551
in contact hypersensitivity 638, 740
contrasuppressor 649
costimulatory protein binding,
    autoradiography 298, 299(Fig)
cryptosporidiosis 677
cysticercosis 692
cytokines released, see under Helper T
    lymphocytes
cytolytic/cytotoxic 504, 507, 725, 726,
    727, 727(Fig), 1059
    cytolysis mechanism 727
    in graft rejection 1013
decline in HIV infection 10, 227, 1135,
    1138, 1229
    inappropriate apoptosis 879, 1138
decreased
    bare lymphocyte syndrome type II 330
    BB rat 1394
    chemotherapy causing 1285
    common variable immunodeficiency
        (CVID) 1280
    gravity/space flights effect 1031
    peripheral blood in sarcoidosis 2136
    primary biliary cirrhosis 2003
    protein-energy malnutrition 1869
    zinc deficiency 2515
diabetes mellitus 1402
experimental autoimmune
    encephalomyelitis 754, 858, 859, 860
FACS studies 932, 936–939
FasL expression 875
function 1703
functional defect in HIV infection 10
fungal infections 960
Goodpasture's syndrome pathogenesis
    1009
graft rejection 1012–1013, 1013
GVHD 1016
HHV-6 replication/tropism 1089
Histoplasma capsulatum infections 1107
HIV infection of 2484
    transmission from Langerhans cells
        1531
    see also HIV
to hsp60 2231
HSV infection 1087
IFNγ production, enhanced by LTB4 229
IL-2 role 1437
IL-2 synthesis 1436
immunotherapeutics 2263
increased in autoimmune gastritis 103
in infections 2459
influenza virus infections 1386, 1387
inhibition
    by LTB4 229
    by monoclonal antibodies 2263
in lamina propria 1779
Langerhans cells interactions 638
lifespan 1581
Listeria monocytogenes infection 1593
lymphopenia, see CD4+ T cells, decreased
lysis 10
malaria 1661
as marker of HIV infection progression 9
memory 1684, 1685
MHC class II interactions 194–198, 502
    see also MHC class II
mixed lymphocyte reaction (MLR) 1734–
    1735
in NOD mouse 1394
numbers, in contact hypersensitivity 639
oral tolerance induction 1894–1895
ovine 1903, 1905
pancreatic β cell destruction 1394–1396,
    1395(Fig)
parasitic infections 1918–1919
peptides preventing binding 2263
in periodontitis 1891
in Peyer's patches 1777

CD4+ T cells (continued)
platelet-activating factor (PAF) effect
    1972
sarcoidosis 2135, 2136
Sjögren's syndrome 2184
skin immune response 2191
thymic epithelium-selected regulatory
    2295, 2296
in thymus 2304, 2305
Toxoplasma gondii infection 2383
virus infections 2482
see also Helper T lymphocytes
CD4+CD8+ cells, see Thymocytes, double
    positive (DP)
CD5 (Ly-1) 15, 217, 446(Table), 472,
    472–474
antibodies 1358
B cells, see B cell(s)
CD72 as ligand 473
cellular distribution 472–473
in chronic lymphocytic leukemia 1558,
    1633
ligands 473
monoclonal antibodies, therapeutic 474
Pap D homology 472
red cell autoantibodies in transgenic mice
    92
role on T cells 473
structure 472
as target for therapy 474
see also B cell(s), B1 cells
CD6 446(Table)
ligand (CD166) 457(Table)
CD7 446(Table)
in acute lymphoblastic leukemia 1555
antibodies 1358
in inflammatory bowel disease 1377
CD8 446(Table), 475–478, 2342
α chain 476, 477
analysis, gene-targeting techniques 478
β chain 446(Table), 476, 477
biochemistry 476–477
expression, by large granular
    lymphocytes 1533
genes 476, 477(Fig)
genetics 476–477
human/murine homology 476–477
Ig-type domains 777, 777(Fig)
knockout mice 233
ligands 476
MHC class I recognition 475–476
    see also MHC class I
p56lck association 477, 478
structure 475, 517
in T cell activation 477, 2328
T cell selection 477–478
transgene 478
see also CD8+ T cells; Cytotoxic T
    lymphocytes (CTL)
CD8+ T cells
αβ 318
activation 177
    superantigens 2242
antigen presentation to 177, 191–194
    bm mutants 372–373
    see also MHC class I
in brucellosis 384
CD1-restricted 460, 462
CD4+ ratio, see under CD4+ T cells
CD38 molecules on 941
Chagas' disease 525
Chlamydia infections 551
coccidiosis 592
contrasuppressor 649
cryptosporidiosis 677
cutaneous lupus erythematosus 2187
cytokines released 700, 1060
cytolytic activity 504, 1841
    in HIV infection 10, 11
    see also Cytotoxic T lymphocytes
        (CTL)
decreased

CD8+ T cells (continued)
decreased (continued)
    BB rat 1394
    gravity/space flights effect 1031
    primary biliary cirrhosis (PBC) 2003
defects in Chédiak-Higashi syndrome 528
development 2337
diabetes mellitus (IDDM) 1402
differentiation, B7/CD28 role 306
equivalent in amphibians 80
estrogen receptor expression 2176
exercise effect 845
FACS studies 932, 936–939
FasL expression 875
functions 1841
fungal infections 960
γδ 318
graft rejection 1012, 1013
GVHD 1016
H2 class I protein binding 1037
helper 1059
    graft rejection 1012
Histoplasma capsulatum infections 1107
HIV infection of 938, 2486
HSV infections 1087
IFNγ synthesis inhibition by IL-10 1476
IL-2 role 1437
IL-2 synthesis 1436
IL-10 production 1476
increased in autoimmune gastritis 103
influenza virus infections 1386
leishmaniasis 1549
lifespan 1581
Listeria monocytogenes infection 1593
malaria 1660, 1662
marker of HIV infection progression 9
memory 1684
mixed lymphocyte reaction (MLR) 1734–
    1735, 1736
    primary response 1735
multiple sclerosis 1841
mycobacterial hsp70 recognition 2231
NOD mouse 1394, 1402
number changes, in HIV infection 11
ovine 1903, 1905
pancreatic β cell destruction 1394–1396,
    1395(Fig)
parasitic infections 1919
in periodontitis 1891
platelet-activating factor (PAF) effect
    1972
in skin 2190
suppressor function
    loss in multiple sclerosis 1841
    see also Suppressor T lymphocytes (Ts)
TGFβ effects 2396
in thymus 2304, 2305
tolerance 2355
Toxoplasma gondii infection 2383
tuberculosis model 1795
to viruses 191
see also Cytotoxic T lymphocytes (CTL);
    Suppressor T lymphocytes (Ts)
CD9 446(Table)
CD10, see CALLA
CD11, in NK cell adhesion to plastic 1629
CD11a, see LFA-1, α chain
CD11a/CD18, see LFA-1
CD11b 446(Table), 1607
    active/inactive conformations 1612
    functions 1610
CD11b/CD18 complex, see CR3
    (CD11b/CD18 complex; Mac-1)
CD11c 446(Table)
CD11c/CD18
    expression, myeloid cells 1805
    leukocyte adhesion to endothelium 758
CDw12 446(Table)
CD13 446(Table)
    expression
        acute myeloid leukemia 1555
        myeloid cells 1803

CD13 (continued)
  function 1805–1806
CD14 186–187, 215, 447(Table)
  antigen clearance 186–187
  characteristics 186–187
  expression
    macrophage 1646(Table)
    myeloid cells 1803
  function 715
  lipopolysaccharide receptor 215
  macrophage activation 187
  monocyte adhesion 1754
  'pattern-recognition molecule' 185, 215
CD15, see Lewis^x (Le^x) antigen
CD15s, see Sialyl Lewis^x (CD15S) antigen
CD16, see FcγRIII
CDw17 447(Table)
CD18, see Integrins, β$_2$; LFA-1, β chain
CD18/CD11b complex, see CR3
    (CD11b/CD18 complex; Mac-1)
CD19 155, 364, 447(Table)
  B cell receptor signaling 351
  CD21 interaction 656
  clonal deletion of B cells 572
  loss from myeloma cells 1163
  Shiga toxin homology 2180
CD20 447(Table)
  in acute lymphoblastic leukemia (ALL)
    1555
CD21, see CR2 (CD21)
CD22 447(Table), 479–481, 1537, 1540
  B cell adhesion molecule 479–480
    regulation 480
    sialic acid role 479
  B cell receptor signaling 351–352, 480–
    481
  CD22Rg 479, 480
  CD45 interaction 480
  cDNA cloning 479
  cells expressing 479, 480
  in chronic lymphoid leukemia (CLL)
    1558
  epitopes with differing functions 481
  extracellular domains 479, 480
  isoforms (CD22α and CD22β) 479
  as ligand for CD45 493
  ligands of 480
  monoclonal antibodies 480–481
  as sialic acid-binding lectin 479–480
  signal transduction role 351–352, 480–
    481
  tyrosine phosphorylation 480
CD23, see FcεRII receptors (CD23)
CD24 447(Table), 2149
  receptor 2149
CD25, see Interleukin-2 (IL-2) receptor, α
    chain
CD25$^+$ thymocytes 2336
CD26 447(Table)
  expression, T cells 1683
CD27 447(Table)
CD28 305, 447(Table), 482–483, 483(Fig),
    2146–2147
  absence, tumor immunological escape
    2444
  antibodies to 482, 1353, 2147
  B7-1/B7-2 binding 305, 482, 502, 652,
    2146
    blockade 548, 2262
  B7-1/B7-2 as counter-receptors 305
  cell-mediated lysis role 506
  cells expressing 482, 652
    T cells 307, 353, 482, 502
  cross-talk with CD40/CD40L 306
  CTLA4-Ig and 482–483
  downregulation by Trypanosoma cruzi
    523
  functions 482, 653
  HIV transmission prevention 307
  immunoglobulin binding 482–483
  intracellular domain 2328
  ligands, see B7-1/B7-2 binding (above)

CD28 (continued)
  signal transduction 482, 2147, 2147(Fig),
    2330
    IL-12 synergy 1486
  structure 482, 2146
  T cell activation 652–653, 1983, 2328,
    2330, 2366
    costimulators 1983, 2146–2147
  as T cell receptor 482, 652–653
  T$_H$1/T$_H$2 memory cell proliferation 2332
CD29 447(Table)
  expression, T cells 1683
  see also Integrin, β$_1$ chain
CD30 447(Table), 2148
  ligand (CD153) 456(Table)
CD31, see PECAM-1 (CD31)
CD32, see FcγRII
CD33 448(Table), 479
  expression
    acute myeloid leukemia 1555
    myeloid cells 1803
  extracellular domains 479
CD34 448(Table)
  cell culture 1575
  dendritic cell culture 745
  expression
    acute lymphoblastic leukemia (ALL)
      1555
    acute myeloid leukemia 1555
    primitive myeloid cells 1803
  L-selectin binding 2159
  thymocyte population 2336
CD35, see CR1 (C3bi/C3b receptor)
CD36 448(Table)
  in antigen clearance 185–186
  expression after ultraviolet radiation
    1531
  phagocytosis of apoptotic cells 222
CD37 448(Table)
CD38 359, 448(Table)
  B cell receptor signaling 351
  thymocyte population 2336
CD39 448(Table)
CD40 215, 350, 364, 448(Table), 484–
    487, 1248, 2150
  antibodies to 1353
  apoptosis prevention in germinal center
    994
  B cell anergy reversal 107, 108
  B cell differentiation 654
  B cell proliferation 2020, 2150
  CD40Ig 2151
  costimulation of B cells 1983
  cross-talk with B7/CD28 306, 350, 1228
  expression 653
  function in vitro 485–486
    B cells 485, 653, 1228, 2150
    dendritic cells 485–486
    endothelial cells 486
    fibroblasts/epithelial cells 486
    monocytes 485–486
  functions in vivo 486–487
  gene 484
  Ig class switching 1215, 1303
  IL-9 cooperation 1474
  immune response regulation 1228
  ligand, see CD40L
  ligation, see CD40-CD40L interactions
  signal transduction 484–485, 654, 2150,
    2150(Fig)
  structure and expression 484, 2150
  T–B cell interaction 215, 358, 485, 653–
    654, 1228
CD40-CD40L interactions 2150
  B cell activation 215, 350, 485, 653–
    654, 1061, 1228, 2150
  consequences 1168(Fig)
  hyper IgM syndrome, see Hyper-IgM
    syndrome
  IL-12 production and 1484
  interruption
    autoimmunity treatment 486–487

CD40-CD40L interactions (continued)
  interruption (continued)
    transplantation tolerance induction 487
  in vitro functions 485–486
  in vivo functions 486–487
  in lysis of anergic B cells 572
  T-B cell interactions 215, 350, 358, 485,
    503, 653–654, 1061
CD40L 195, 350, 456(Table), 484–487,
    2148
  abnormal expression, common variable
    immunodeficiency 601
  antibodies, therapeutic role 487
  cells expressing 484, 653
    persistent in multiple sclerosis 487
  cross-talk with B7/CD28 306
  defects, hyper-IgM syndrome 389, 486,
    1166, 1166–1167, 1167, 2150
  deficiency
    neonates 1820
    oral infections 1891
  expression 484
    inhibited in T cell anergy 109
    intrathymic precursors 2236
    T cells 2148
  functions/actions 653, 1168(Fig)
  gene 1167
  Ig class switching 1205, 1303
  isolation/discovery 484
  knockout mice 486
  as master regulator of immune system
    2328
  mutations 147, 366, 389, 486
    see also CD40L, defects; Hyper-IgM
      syndrome
  signal transduction defect 1167
  structure 484
  T cell activation 2328
  T–B cell interaction 215, 350, 358, 485,
    653–654
    see also CD40-CD40L interactions
  upregulation 157
CD41 448(Table)
CD42a 448(Table)
CD42b 448(Table)
CD42c 448(Table)
CD42d 448(Table)
CD43 364, 448(Table), 2146
  absence 1281
  cells expressing 356
  defective expression 73
  expression 356
    pro-B cells 1876
  ICAM-1 as receptor 804
  T cell proliferation 2146
CD44 28(Table), 29, 449(Table), 488–491,
    1683
  ankyrin complex 1680
  antibodies 29
  cancer metastases 490
  CD44V3-10 488
  CD44V8-10 (epithelial; CD44E) 488
  cell adhesion role 488, 490
  cells expressing 488
    macrophage 1646(Table)
    triple negative thymocytes 2336
  function 488–490
  genes 488, 489(Fig), 1680
    alternative splicing 1680
  glycosylation 1680
  isoforms 488, 1680
  ligands 489
    hyaluronic acid 488–489, 1680
  loss, T cell development 2336
  monoclonal antibodies 490
  mRNA 488
  pathological aspects 490
  rheumatoid arthritis 2114
  standard (CD44s; CD44H) 488, 1680
    ankyrin binding 1680
    domains 1680
  structure 488, 489(Fig)

CD44 (continued)
  variant (CD44v) 488, 490
CD44H (CD44s), see CD44, standard
    (CD44s; CD44H)
CD44R 449(Table)
CD45 363, 449(Table), 491–494
  amino acid sequence 1680
  B cell receptor signaling via 350
  CD2 interaction 464
  CD22 as ligand 480
  CD45α isoform 493, 494
  in cell-cell adhesion 493
  cytoplasmic domain 491
  cytoskeleton interaction 1680
    lymphocyte activation 1680
  epidermal growth factor relationship
    494
  expression 493
    myeloid cells 1805
  extracellular domain 491, 494
  fodrin-binding domain 1680
  functions 493–494
  gene and exons 491, 492(Fig)
  isoforms 491, 492(Table)
    expression patterns 491–493
    structure and size 492(Fig)
  ligands 493
  monoclonal antibodies 491–492, 493
  phosphatase activity 2324
  polymorphism 1680
  structure 491
  T cell apoptosis role 493
  T cell signaling 494, 2324
  transgenic mice 494
CD45-associated protein (CD45AP) 494
  WW domain 494
CD45R 155, 491
CD45RA 449(Table), 491, 493
  T cell expression 1683
CD45RB 449(Table), 1383
  T cell expression 1683
CD45RC 449(Table)
CD45RO 449(Table), 491
  T cell expression 1683
  see also under T cell(s)
CD46 (membrane cofactor protein)
    449(Table), 495–497
  Arthus reaction reduced 239
  functions 495
  gene 496(Fig), 620
  HIV resistance to complement 496
  homologous proteins in other species
    496
  IL-12 production modulation 1485
  isoforms 495, 496
    CYT-1 495
  as measles virus receptor 495, 496
  in reproductive biology 497
  structure 495
    model 496(Fig)
  tissue distribution 496
  transplant rejection prevention 497
CD47 449(Table)
CD48 28, 449(Table), 1613
  CD2 binding 463
CD49 28, 449(Table)
CD49a 449(Table)
CD49b 449(Table)
CD49c 449(Table)
CD49d 449(Table)
CD49e 449(Table)
CD49f 449(Table)
CD50, see ICAM-3
CD51 450(Table)
CDw52 121
CD52, see CAMPATH-1 antigen (CD52)
CD53 450(Table)
CD54, see ICAM-1
CD55, see Decay-accelerating factor
    (DAF)
CD56 450(Table)
  on myeloma cells 1163

CD57 450(Table)
CD58, see LFA-3
CD59 (p18; MIRL) 450(Table), 497–500
  alternative names 497
  binding to C8 and C9 497, 499
  cDNA 498
  cells/tissues expressing 498(Table)
  complement lysis, inhibition 497, 498–
    500
  deficiency 615(Table)
    paroxysmal nocturnal hemoglobinuria
      499–500
  function 497
  gene and exons 498
    mutation 499–500
  GPI anchor 497, 498
  ligand 500
  as Ly-6 homolog 498
  membrane attack complex (MAC)
    regulation 497, 498–500
    formation inhibition 626, 628
  microbial counterparts 500
  structure 498
  T cell activation 500
  transgenics 500
  xenotransplantation 500
CDw60 450(Table)
CD61 450(Table)
CD62E, see E-selectin
CD62L, see L-selectin
CD62P, see P-selectin
CD63 450(Table)
CD64, see FcγRIa
CD65 451(Table)
CD65s 451(Table)
CD66a 451(Table)
CD66b 451(Table), 1803
CD66c 451(Table)
CD66d 451(Table)
CD66e 451(Table)
CD66f 451(Table)
CD67 451(Table)
CD68 451(Table)
CD69 451(Table)
CD70 451(Table)
CD71, see Transferrin receptor (TfR)
CD72 452(Table)
  ligand for CD5 473
CD73 452(Table)
CD74, see Invariant chain (Ii)
CDw75 452(Table)
CDw76 452(Table)
CD77 452(Table)
  Shiga toxin binding 2180
CDw78 452(Table)
CD79, expression, acute leukemia 1555
CD79a, see Igα (CD79a)
CD79b, see Igβ (CD79b)
CD80, see B7-1 (CD80)
CD81 (TAPA-1) 452(Table)
  B cell receptor signaling 351
CD82 452(Table)
CD83 452(Table)
CD84 452(Table)
CD85 452(Table)
CD86, see B7-2 (CD86)
CD87 452(Table)
CD88 452(Table)
CD89, see FcαRI
CDw90 2291
CD90, see Thy-1
CD91 452(Table)
CDw92 452(Table)
CD93 453(Table)
CD94 453(Table)
CD95, see Fas antigen (CD95)
CD96 453(Table)
CD97 453(Table)
CD98 453(Table)
CD99 453(Table)
CD99R 453(Table)
CD100 453(Table)

CD101 453(Table)
CD102, see ICAM-2
CD103 453(Table)
CD104 (integrin β4) 453(Table), 1404
CD105 453(Table)
CD106, see VCAM-1
CD107a 453(Table)
CD107b 453(Table)
CDw108 453(Table)
CD109 453(Table)
CD114 (G-CSF receptor) 453(Table), 1019
CD115 (CSF-1 receptor), see under
    Macrophage colony-stimulating factor
    (M-CSF; CSF-1)
CD116 454(Table)
  see also Granulocyte-macrophage colony-
    stimulating factor (GM-CSF), receptor
CD117 454(Table)
CDw119 454(Table)
  see also Interferon γ (IFNγ), receptor
CD120a, see under TNF receptors
CD120b, see under TNF receptors
CD121a 454(Table)
CDw121b 454(Table)
CDw122, see Interleukin-2 (IL-2) receptor,
    β chain
CDw123 454(Table)
  see also Interleukin-3 (IL-3) receptor
CD124, see Interleukin-4 (IL-4) receptor
CDw125, see Interleukin-5 (IL-5), receptor,
    α chain
CD126, see Interleukin-6 (IL-6), receptor
CD127, see Interleukin-7 (IL-7), receptor
CDw127, see Interleukin-8 (IL-8), receptor
CD130, see gp130
CDw131 455(Table)
CD132, see Common γ chain (γc)
CD134 (OX40) 455(Table), 1358, 2148
CD135 455(Table)
CDw136 455(Table)
CDw137 455(Table)
CD138 455(Table)
CD139 455(Table)
CD140a 455(Table)
CD140b 455(Table)
CD141 (thrombomodulin) 455(Table), 579
CD142, see Tissue factor (TF)
CD143 456(Table)
CD144 456(Table)
CDw145 456(Table)
CD146 456(Table)
CD147 456(Table)
CD148 456(Table)
CDw149 456(Table)
CDw150 456(Table)
CD151 456(Table)
CD152, see CTLA4 (CD152)
CD153 456(Table)
CD154, see CD40L
CD155 (poliovirus receptor) 456(Table),
    1954
CD156 456(Table)
CD157 456(Table)
CD158a 456(Table)
CD158b 457(Table)
CD161 457(Table)
CD162, see PSGL-1
CD163 457(Table)
CD164 457(Table)
CD165 457(Table)
CD166 457(Table)
Cdc24, T cell signaling 2327
Cecal enlargement, in germ-free animals
    990
Cecropins 1500
CED-3, apoptosis mechanism and 222,
    1028
CED-3/ICE protease, see ICE/CED-3
    family
CELIA, see Competitive enzyme-linked
    immunoassay (CELIA)
Celiac disease 1636

Celiac disease (*continued*)
  HLA association 1694
  HLA-DQ trans-complementation 1694
Cell activation, diapedesis effect 760
Cell adhesion, *see* Adhesion, cell
Cell adhesion molecules, *see* Adhesion
  molecules
Cell culture
  antigen-presenting cells (APCs) 194
  B cell precursors 1462
  CD34, bone marrow transplants 1575
  dendritic cells 745, 1575
  endothelial cells 760
  fetal calf serum use 896, 897
  historical aspects 896
  for immunotherapy 1574–1575
  LAK cells 1574
  lectin toxicity 1538
  leukocytes, *see* Leukocyte culture
  macrophage 540
  microgravity 1032
  murine lymphocytes 1623
  serum-free techniques 897
  supplements
    biological 897
    fetal calf serum 896, 897
    see also Fetal calf serum
  tumor-infiltrating lymphocytes (TILs)
    1574–1575
  see also Leukocyte culture; Organ culture
Cell cycle 2019, 2019(Fig)
  analysis, lymphocyte transformation test
    1624
  constitutive 'on', chromosomal
    translocations causing 558
  control 558, 2018–2019
    see also Cyclins
  gene expression correlation, FACS study
    939(Fig)
  key concepts/terms 2020(Table)
  lymphocyte homeostasis 2017–2018,
    2017(Fig)
  lymphocyte proliferation 2018–2019,
    2018(Table), 2019(Fig)
  membrane attack complex function 627
Cell death 730, 733
  genes, in adenoviruses 25
  necrotic 220, 730
  programmed, *see* Apoptosis
  see also Cell-mediated lysis
Cell death cysteine proteases 1028
  activation by granzyme B cleavage 1028
  CPP32 1028
  inhibitors 1028
Cell differentiation, diapedesis effect 760
Cell fusion
  B cell hybridoma development 1148
  monoclonal antibody preparation 1742
  see also Hybridoma
Cell growth, fibronectin role 911–912
Cell lineage, antigens restricted to and
  diversity 211
Cell lines
  cell surface antigen characterization 209
  rabbit 2048, 2048(Table)
  see also B cell lines; *specific cell lines*
Cell-mediated immunity 501–504, 825,
  1226–1228, 2459
  adenovirus infection 23
  African swine fever (ASF) virus 55
  age-related changes 135
  amebiasis 78
  animal models of IDDM 1393–1396
  to arenaviruses 233–234
  autoimmunity in Addison's disease 42
  avian 301
  bacteria 318
  Bordetella pertussis 378
  Candida infections 409, 410
  canine 413
  Chlamydia infections 551
  Clonorchis infections 1880

Cell-mediated immunity (*continued*)
  CMV infection 722–723
  defects/deficiency
    dwarfism in 1279
    elderly 1870
    neonates 1820
    opportunistic infections 1883
    protein-energy malnutrition (PEM)
      1869
    purine nucleoside phosphorylase
      deficiency 748–749
  depression, gravity/space flights effect
    1031–1032
  downregulation
    in onchocerciasis 1873
    by TGFβ 2395–2396
  Echinococcus 784
  Epstein-Barr virus (EBV) infection 830
  evolution, vertebrate 1948
  feline 894
  in fish 924–925
  flavivirus infections 929–930
  fungal infections 958, 960–961
  to gastric antigens 103
  Helicobacter pylori infection 1057
  hepatitis B virus (HBV) 1076–1077
  hepatitis C virus (HCV) 1080–1081
  histamine regulation of 1104–1105
  Histoplasma capsulatum infections 1106–
    1107
  historical aspects 501
  hookworm disease 1124
  HPV infections 751, 1908
  HSV infections 1087
  humoral immunity synergism 501
  inflammatory bowel disease 1377,
    1377(Fig)
  influenza viruses 1386
  invertebrates 1499–1500, 1948
  in vitro 501, 503–504
  in vivo 502–503
  iron deficiency effect 1506
  Legionella pneumophila infection 1544,
    1545
  Listeria monocytogenes infection 1593
  in marsupials 1665, 1666
  MHC role 1705–1706
  models 503–504
  Opisthorchis infections 1880
  paramyxovirus infections 1915
  Pasteurella multocida infections 1928
  picornaviruses 1956, 1958–1959
  polyomavirus infection 1990
  radioresistance 2052
  reovirus infection 2070
  restoration, levamisole action 1347
  Salmonella infections 2132
  schistosomiasis 2140
  secondary (acquired) 14
  Shigella infections 2180
  skin infections 753
  suppressor capacity, age-related changes
    60
  T cell role 2342
  theilerosis 2289
  Toxocara canis infection 2381
  transfer 2385
  tularemia 956
  tumors 2441, 2442
  vitamin A 2489
  xenografts 2510
    rejection 2510
  see also T cell(s)
Cell-mediated lympholysis, in reptiles 2079
Cell-mediated lysis 504–507
  assays 730–731
  cell surface structures in 505
  cytotoxic T cells 726–729
    see also CD8⁺ T cells; Cytotoxic T
      lymphocytes (CTL)
  degranulation role 737
  effector cells 505

Cell-mediated lysis (*continued*)
  effector cells (*continued*)
    see also CD8⁺ T cells; Cytotoxic T
      lymphocytes (CTL); Natural killer
      (NK) cells
  historical aspects 504–505
  'internal disintegration' model 506
  mechanisms 506–507, 730, 733–734
    cytotoxic factors 510
    events in CTL 728
    Fas pathway 504, 506–507, 727, 734
    granzyme/perforin pathway 1028,
      1029(Fig)
    membrane damage (perforin/exocytosis)
      504, 506, 726–727, 728, 733
    see also Fas/FasL interaction/pathway;
      Granzyme(s); Perforin
  by membrane attack complex 626–627
    see also Membrane-attack complex
      (MAC)
  properties 505–506
  quantification 505
  'single hit' 504
  stages 505–506
  see also Microbicidal mechanisms
Cell membranes, *see* Membranes
Cell proliferation
  increase, histamine effect 1104
  transferrin receptor (TfR) role 2390,
    2391
Cell separation techniques 507–512
  based on functional properties 509–510
    adhesive/phagocytic 509–510
    selective cell stimulation/growth 510
    selective depletion 510
  based on physical properties 508–509
  historical aspects 507–508
  immunoselection, *see* Immunoselection
    techniques
  lymphoid cells 508
  'negative' and 'positive' 508
  rosetting 510
  summary of methods 509(Table)
Cell surface antigens 207–214
  allogeneic diversity 208
  cell lineage concepts 209, 211
  characterization and test systems 209–
    211, 210(Table)
  clonogenetic diversity 208
  differentiation 209, 211–214
    diversity generation 209
  diseases due to abnormalities 213
  epigenetic diversity 209
  glycosylation causing diversity 210
  immunogenetic classification 208–209,
    208(Table)
  immunoprecipitation, *see*
    Immunoprecipitation
  internalization 211, 213(Fig)
  modularity concept 214
  secreted antigen differences 211
  spatial restriction/localization 210,
    212(Fig)
  tumors 211, 213, 2428–2429
    see also Tumor antigens
  xenogeneic diversity 208
  see also Adhesion molecules
Cell surface dynamics 414–421
  see also Capping; Clustering; Membrane,
    microdomains
Cell surface receptors
  immunoglobulin superfamily 517–518
  ligand complexes, structures 519–520
  protein domains 515
  superfamilies 515
  three-dimensional structure 515–520,
    516(Table)
  see also Receptors; *specific receptor
    superfamilies*
Cellulitis 752, 2218
Cell wall arthritis, features and
  comparisons 2106(Table)

Cell walls, bacterial, see Bacterial cell walls
CENP-A and CENP-B antigens 125, 131
   antibodies 131
Central nervous system
   anatomical features 1844, 1844(Fig)
   autoimmune diseases 1839–1843
   bacterial infections 1846
   circulating inflammatory cells 1845
   cytokines produced, see under Nervous
      system
   endothelial cells 1844, 1844(Fig)
   food allergy 950
   fungal infections 1846
   histamine effect 1104
   immune capabilities of cells 1844–1845
   immune response in 1845–1846
      see also under Nervous system
   immunomodulatory role 336
   immunosuppressive role of TGFβ 2396
   inflammatory disease, TGFβ role 2395,
      2396
   lymphocyte function regulation 1845
   MHC antigen absent 1844–1845
   parasitic infections 1846
   SLE 2255–2256
   T cells 1845
   transmissible spongiform
      encephalopathies 2410
   virus infections 1845–1846
   see also Autonomic nervous system;
      Nervous system
Centroblasts
   CD antigen expression 993(Fig)
   dark zone of germinal center 992,
      993(Fig)
   fate 994–995
   germinal center development 994
Centrocytes
   CD antigen expression 993(Fig)
   fate 995
   light zone of germinal center 992,
      993(Fig)
   see also B cell(s), in germinal centers
Centromere antigens 125, 131
   antibodies 131
Cephalic neural crest cells, in DiGeorge
      syndrome 761, 762
Cephalothin, immune hemolytic anemia
      due to 95
Ceramide 2029
Ceramide-dependent protein kinase 2029
Ceramide trihexoside, see CD77
Cercarial dermatitis 2139
Cerebral malaria, see Malaria, cerebral
Cerebrospinal fluid (CSF) 1599, 1844
   composition 1844
   oligoclonal bands in multiple sclerosis
      1787
Cereolysin 313
Ceruloplasmin 657
   in copper deficiency 658, 658(Table)
Cervical cancer 1362
   HLA association 1908
   HPV 1907, 1908, 2074
      E7 antigen expression 2426, 2442
      vaccine trials 1908
Cervical intraepithelial neoplasia (CIN)
      1908
Cervical mucus, sperm migration inhibited
      by IgA 1374
Cervicitis, Chlamydia trachomatis causing
      2072
Cestodes
   cystic (larval) stages 690
      see also Cysticercosis
   see also Taenia
Cetirizine 683, 2124
c-fms gene (CD115), see CSF-1);
   Macrophage colony-stimulating factor
      (M-CSF)
c-fos gene, in mast cell degranulation 1670
Chagas' disease 432–433, 434, 521–526

Chagas' disease (continued)
   autoantibodies 525
   autoimmune disease mechanisms 433,
      434–435, 525
   cardiomyopathy 433, 522, 525
   clinical features 522
   cytokines released 523, 524
      role 526(Table)
   denervation 525
   immune response 522–525
      immunodepression 523–524
      protective 524–525
   immunopathology 525
   parasite persistence 433
   pathogenesis 525
   susceptibility 522
   T cells 433, 435, 525
   TNFα role 2439
   vaccines 526
   see also Trypanosoma cruzi
Chancre 753
   syphilitic 2073, 2416
   trypanosomiasis 2422–2423
Chaperones, molecular 2230
   antigen presentation via class I MHC
      192
   H2 class II molecules assembly 1043
   hsp90 2231
   invariant chain association 1496
   PapD 778
   see also Heat shock proteins (hsp)
CHAPS 513
Charcot-Leyden crystals 244, 822
CHARGE association 762
Chédiak-Higashi syndrome 526–528, 543,
      1281–1282
   'accelerated phase' mutation 528
   cathepsin G and elastase reduced 1722
   in cats 895
   CD8+ T cells 528
   clinical features 527
   giant vesicles 526, 527
   large granular lymphocytes hypofunction
      1534
   lysosome defect 527, 527(Fig)
   management 528
   mouse model 421, 1271
      beige mouse 527
   neutrophil defects 527, 1857
   NK cell defects 527–528, 1281
   related disorders 527
   tumor development 1245
   vitamin C effect 2492
Chelators, oxygen-dependent phagocytic
      killing 1717
Chemicals
   animal models of inflammatory bowel
      disease 1383–1384
   experimental autoimmune disease
      induction 273
   in foodstuffs, allergy 950–951
   immunopotentiating 1347
   immunosuppression due to 1367
   tumor antigens induced 1360
Chemiluminescence 143
   in Northern blotting 1865
   in Western blotting 2506
Chemoattractants, see Chemotactic factors
Chemography 298
Chemokines 529–533, 536, 720, 1466,
      1759–1760, 2061–2062
   α (C-X-C) subfamily 529, 530,
      530(Table), 536(Table), 1466,
      1467(Fig), 1759, 2061
      biological actions 531, 532(Table)
      affinity for proteoglycans 907
      amino acid sequences 1467(Fig)
   β (C-C) subfamily 529, 530(Table),
      536(Table), 1466, 1467(Fig), 1759,
      2061
      biological actions 531, 532(Table)
      MCP-1 1748

Chemokines (continued)
   β (C-C) subfamily (continued)
      monocytes response 540
      receptors 2062
   biological activities 531, 532(Table)
   cDNA 529
   characteristics 529–530, 530(Table)
   definition 529
   dimer formation 530
   as eosinophil chemotactic factors 820
   expression 530
   γ (C) subfamily 530(Table), 1759–1760
   genes 1466
   induction, by IL-1 1435
   integrin upregulation on leukocytes 2060
   leukocyte adhesion to endothelium 758
   pathological disease states 531–532
   production, inhibition by IL-13 1490
   receptors 53(Table), 531, 536(Table),
      710, 1760, 2062, 2062(Fig)
      CCCR1-8 540
      CXCR4, HIV coreceptor 10, 532, 712,
         1134
      downregulation by B7-1/B7-2 305–306
      G protein-coupled 2062
      HIV coreceptor 10, 532, 712, 1134,
         2094
      occupancy 2062
      signaling 711, 2062
      see also HIV, receptors
   role, inflammatory bowel disease 1379–
      1380
   sarcoidosis 2137
   secretion, IFNγ action 1424
   for specific cell types 536(Table)
   structure 1466
   synthesis 530
   see also Interleukin-8 (IL-8); Monocyte
      chemoattractant protein 1 (MCP-1)
Chemokinesis 534
   importance in vivo 536–537
Chemokinetic migration 1759
Chemotactic cell agonists 86
Chemotactic factors (chemoattractants)
      1935, 2031–2032, 2061
   definition 534, 536, 542
   fibronectin as 913
   leukocyte migration 30
   leukocytes 1759–1760, 1759(Table),
      2031–2032, 2061
   neutrophils 1935
   receptors 542–543, 1760, 2031
      affinity states 1761
   serotonin effect on secretion 2167
   signaling pathway 2031–2032
   see also Chemokines; Chemotaxis
Chemotactic gradients
   leukocyte perception 535–536
   spatial detection 535
   stochastic model 535–536
   temporal detection 535
Chemotaxis 533–537, 1759, 1935, 2061–
      2062
   assay methods 537
   B cells 539
   C3a 89
   C-reactive protein (CRP) inhibiting 664
   definition 533, 534
   IL-8 role 1466, 1468
   impairment, in iron deficiency 1506
   importance in vivo 536–537
   invertebrates 1501
   lymphocytes 538–539
   macrophage/monocytes, see Macrophage;
      Monocyte(s)
   morphological events 1760
   negative 534
   neutrophils, see Neutrophil(s)
   NK cells 539
   stochastic model 535–536
   T cells 538–539

Chemotaxis (*continued*)
see also Locomotion; Motility of immune cells
Chemotaxogenic substances 819
Chemotherapy (cancer)
GM-CSF with 1022
immunodeficiency due to 1285
leukemia 1559
romurtide use after 1790
thrombocytopenia, reduction by IL-11 1481
see also Cytotoxic drugs
Chicken cholera
vaccination development 1336
vaccine 256
Chickenpox, see Varicella (chickenpox)
Chickens
antibody diversity 156
bursa of Fabricius 393–394
coccidiosis 591–593
immune system 300–304
see also Avian immune system
light chain loci 1309(Fig)
obese strain, see Obese strain of chickens
strains and genetic variability 300
TCR 2272
UCD 200 model, see University of California at Davis (UCD) 200 strain
Chiclero's ulcer 1547
Chido antigens/determinants 607, 837
Chief cells, reduced in autoimmune gastritis 103
Children
adenovirus vaccines 24
AIDS 7
hepatitis B virus infection 1077
HIV infection progression and 8
idiopathic thrombocytopenic purpura 1180, 1180–1181
immunotherapy of allergic disease 1355
iron deficiency 1506
SLE 2257
Chilo iridescent virus (CIV) 1502, 1503, 1504
Chimeras 981
'split' 545
Chimeric antibodies
autoimmune disease therapy 1358
tumor immunotherapy 1748
Chimeric mice, N-cadherin function 1382
Chimeric virus vectors
adverse reactions 2464, 2464(Table)
vaccines 2460, 2461
Chimerism, definition 544
Chimerism, hematopoietic 544–549, 809, 810
cord blood 548
'gene therapy' 548
GVHD or host-versus-graft 545–546
historical aspects 544
human/mouse 546–547
methods 546–547
mixed lymphoid and transplants 547–548
peripheral blood stem cells 546–547
principle 809–810
in utero transplantation of stem cells 549
see also Bone marrow transplantation
Chimpanzees, HIV infection 1136
Chi-square test 1698, 2213
Chlamydia 549–552
antigens 549–550
characteristics 549–550
elementary body 550
evasive strategies 551
host immune response 550–551, 2072
mucosal 2072
infections 550
models 551
persistent/latent 551
intracellular growth 550, 551
lipopolysaccharide 2378(Fig)

Chlamydia (*continued*)
major outer membrane protein (MOMP) 550, 552, 2072
reticulate body 550
species 549
vaccines 552, 2072
Chlamydia pecorum 550
Chlamydia pneumoniae 550
infections 550
Chlamydia psittaci 550, 552
Chlamydia trachomatis
biovars 549, 551
genital tract infection 2072, 2074(Fig)
host immune response 2072
immunobiology 2074(Fig)
trachoma 872–873
Chloramines 1716, 1856
Chlordiazepoxide, immune hemolytic anemia due to 100
Chloride
exchange, in red cell membranes 840
oxygen-dependent phagocytic killing 1715–1716
Chloroquine 460
Cholera 968, 2476
clinical features 2477
historical aspects 2476
immunity 2478
pandemics 2476
pathogenesis 2477
see also Vibrio cholerae
Cholera toxin (CT) 38, 2368, 2372, 2477
A subunit 2477
B subunit 2477
carrier in hCG and LHRH vaccines 642, 644
oral tolerance enhanced 1896
vaccines 2478
gene mutagenesis 258
genes (ctxA and ctxB) 2477
keyhole limpet hemocyanin with, T_H1/T_H2 response 1896
liposome attachment 1591
mechanism of action 968, 2368, 2372, 2373(Fig), 2477
oral tolerance decreased 1896
subunits 2477
Cholesterol, cardiovascular disease risk 988
Cholinergic blockers, in asthma 246(Table)
Cholinergic neuronal differentiation factor, see Leukemia inhibitory factor (LIF)
Chondroitin sulfate (CS) 333, 862, 863(Table), 906
in mast cells 1668
Chorionic gonadotropins
human, see Human chorionic gonadotropin (hCG)
immunization against 1853
Chromatofocusing 1513–1514, 2037
Chromatography, protein 2036–2037
affinity, see Affinity chromatography
hydrophobic interaction 2037
immunoaffinity 51–52
ion exchange 2037
order of procedure 2038, 2038(Fig)
recovery and capacity 2036
resolution and speed 2036
reverse phase 2038
see also Gel filtration
Chromium-release assay 730–731, 730(Fig), 732
LAK activity assay 1628
NK cell measurement 1815
Chromogens, in ELISA 818
Chromosomal translocations 552–560
acute leukemia 1556–1557
B cell neoplasms 555, 555(Table)
non-Hodgkin's lymphomas 1634, 1635
Burkitt's lymphoma 831
DiGeorge syndrome 761
error-prone recombination 552–553

Chromosomal translocations (*continued*)
error-prone recombination (*continued*)
recombinase role 554, 556, 559
hematological malignancies 554–559
immune genes 553–554, 556(Fig)
DNA repair deficiency 559
in 'normal' cells 559–560
pathogenic mechanisms, see below
immune and non-immune genes 556(Fig)
non-immune loci 556, 556(Fig)
nonrandom 554(Table)
pathogenic mechanisms, immune genes 556–559
aberrant signal transduction 558
cell cycle 'on' switch 558
death-defying 558–559
as 'switch' for tumors 557
transcription factor deregulation 557–558, 557(Fig)
T cell neoplasms 555, 555(Table)
TCR 2268
transcription factors 557–558
see also Genetic recombination
Chromosome
abnormalities, error-prone recombination causing 553–554
losses, in heterohybridomas 1150
Chronic active hepatitis (CAH) 561–565
autoantibodies 263, 562, 563, 564
autoimmune 561
features 562
pathogenesis 564
clinical features 561
cryptogenic 561
features 564
drug-associated 561
features 563
experimental models 564
features 561–562
HBV-associated (CAH-B) 561
features 563
HCV-associated (CAH-C) 561
features 563
heterogeneity 561
histology 561, 562(Fig)
historical aspects 561
immunocytotoxic pathway 564
liver-specific autoantigen 564
lupoid 561
pathogenesis 564
SLE similarity 561
'toxic-metabolic' 561
features 563–564
Chronic granulomatous disease (CGD) 565–567, 1715, 1857
autosomal recessive 566, 1715
clinical features 566
diagnosis 566
flavocytochrome b_{558} absent 1715
fungal infections 959
gene therapy 979(Table)
molecular pathology 565–566
phagocytic cell NADPH oxidase absent 565, 752, 959
skin infections 752
therapy 566
IFNγ 1425
variant 565, 566
X-linked 566, 1715
Chronic inflammatory demyelinating polyneuropathy 1838
Churg–Strauss vasculitis 2120
Chylomicron 1601
Chymotrypsin-like cationic proteins (CLCP) 1938
Ciclosporin, see Cyclosporine (CsA)
Cigarette smoking
harmful products in smoke 135
neutrophil activation in lungs 136
thyroid autoimmune disease association 2314
vitamin C requirement 135

CIITA transcription factor 331
Ciliary body cells 870
Ciprofloxacin 1882
Circulatory system 1600(Fig)
  infections, see Endocarditis, infective
Cirrhosis
  cryptogenic 263
  macronodular 561, 562(Fig)
  primary biliary, see Primary biliary
    cirrhosis (PBC)
Cisternal space 849, 850(Fig)
c-Jun, in mast cell degranulation 1670
c-kit 454(Table)
  ligand, see Stem cell factor (SCF)
c-kit receptor 714
  mast cells 1667
CLA, see Cutaneous lymphocyte antigen
  (CLA)
Clades, HIV 1135
Claisen rearrangement 438, 438(Fig)
Class switching, see Immunoglobulin class
  switching
Clathrin 852(Table)
Clathrin-coated pits 211
CLCP (chymotrypsin-like cationic proteins)
  1938
Clindamycin, phagocytosis increased by
  1887
CLIP (class II-associated invariant-chain
  peptides) 196, 354, 1497, 2232
  H2 class II molecules 1043–1044
  peptide release 1497
CLMF (cytotoxic lymphocyte maturation
  factor), see Interleukin-12 (IL-12)
Clodronate, liposome-encapsulated 1591,
  1592(Fig)
Clonal activators, polyclonal activators
  interactions 1980–1982
Clonal anergy, see Anergy
Clonal deletion 106, 293, 569–573, 809,
  1228, 2362, 2363
  B cells 156, 361, 571–572, 2364
    after primary activation 572
    before germinal center formation 572
    chronic stimulation and 572
    membrane bound antigen 107
  definition 569
  'deletion by neglect' 569, 570(Fig)
  by immunosuppressive agents 1350
  mechanism 420
  oral tolerance induction 1894, 1894(Fig)
  T cells 569–571, 570(Fig), 1230, 1734,
    2363–2364
    evidence 2339
    Fas pathway 570–571
    hematopoietic cells inducing 2338
    mature cells 570–571
    'strength' of antigen interaction
      570(Fig)
    in thymus 569–570
  tolerance induction mechanism 106,
    2361
  to ocular antigens 868
  see also Tolerance
Clonal downsizing 654–655, 877, 878(Fig)
  Fas/FasL role 877, 878(Fig)
Clonal expansion 2330
  B cells, see Affinity maturation; B cell(s)
  T cells, see T cell(s)
Clonal selection 178, 360, 569, 573–576
  B cells 52–53, 62, 1684–1685
    Ig receptor 575
    mechanism 1685
    memory B cells 575
  environmental influences 360
  historical perspectives 573–574, 1337–
    1338
  lymphoid cell unipotentiality 574–575
  somatic mutation concept and 53
  theory, see Clonal selection theory
  tolerance 105, 575
  see also Clonal deletion; Tolerance

Clonal selection (continued)
  see also B cell(s), differentiation; B cell(s),
    diversity; B cell(s), repertoire
Clonal selection theory 52–53, 62, 105,
  178, 573–574, 1144, 2330
  evidence supporting 574–575
  idiotype network theory and 1191
  origin/development 1338
  quotations from original theory 574
Clonal suppression 809
Clonogenetic diversity 208
Clonorchiasis 1879–1881
Clonorchis sinensis 1879–1881
  antigens 1879
  evasive strategies 1880
  excretory–secretory (ES) products 1879
  host immune response 1879–1880
  vaccines 1880
Clostridium 576–578
  antigens 576–577
  characteristics 576–577
  evasive strategies 578
  host immune responses 578
  toxins 269, 576–578, 577(Table), 2368
    mechanisms of action 577–578, 2375–
      2376
  vaccines 578
Clostridium bifermentans, toxin 2376
Clostridium botulinum 576
  C2 toxin 2370, 2375–2376
    mode of action 2376(Fig)
  toxin 576, 577(Table)
    site of action 2375(Fig)
    structure/nomenclature 2374, 2374(Fig)
Clostridium difficile
  antibodies to 578
  immunoglobulin-binding protein 324
  infection 578
  toxins 576, 577, 577(Table), 2368
  toxin A 2368
Clostridium novii, toxins 577, 577(Table)
Clostridium perfringens 576
  α toxin 2368, 2376
  toxin 576–577, 577(Table), 2376
Clostridium sordellii, toxins 576, 577,
  577(Table)
Clostridium tetani, toxin 577(Table), 2374
Clotting factors 582–585, 1965
  in acute phase response 18(Table)
  concentrates/products 1966–1967
    virus transmission risks 1967, 1968
  see also individual factors
Clotting system 578–586
  clotting factors 582–585
  coagulation cascade 580–585
  extrinsic pathway 582
  fibrinolysis and modulation of 585
  fibronectin role 912
  intrinsic pathway 582
  kallikrein–kinin system 1519
  local vasoconstriction 579
  platelet components and function 579–
    580
  sequence of events 580–585, 581(Fig)
  see also Fibrinogen; Kallikrein–kinin
    system
Cluster of differentiation antigens, see CD
  antigens
Clustering 414–421
  for cell activation 420
  definition 415
  function 420
c-maf gene, expression, induced by IL-4
  1451, 1453
c-myc gene 2487
  chromosomal translocations involving
    558
  deregulation in Burkitt's lymphoma 831
  see also myc gene
CNTF-R 715
Coagulase, Staphylococcus aureus 2208–
  2209

Coagulation
  contact system 1519
    regulation 1520
  sequence of events 581(Fig)
  Staphylococcus aureus factors 2208–
    2209
  see also Clotting system
Coagulation factors, see Clotting factors
Coagulation proteins, in acute phase
  response 18(Table)
Coatomer 852(Table)
Cobra venom factor (CVF) 183, 586–589
  antibody conjugates 588
  applications 586, 588
  C3 similarity 586, 603
    functional 587
    structural 587–588, 587(Fig)
  cloning 586
  complement interactions 587, 603
  decomplementing activity 586, 587
  as experimental tool 588
  purification methods 586–587
  structure 586–587, 587(Fig)
Cobra venom factor (CVF)-dependent C3
  convertase 603
Coccidial antigens 589
  avian vaccines 304
Coccidioides 589–591
Coccidioides immitis 589, 958
  antigens 589
  host immune response 589–590
  spherules 589
  vaccines 590, 961
  see also Coccidioidomycosis
Coccidioidomycosis 589
  features 589
  hypersensitivity 590
  immune response 589–590
  immunosuppression 590
  skin test 590
  vaccines 590, 961
  see also Coccidioides immitis
Coccidiosis 591–593
  immune response 592
  vaccines 593
  see also Eimeria
Cockroach allergens 68
Cockroaches, toxin resistance 1501
Codocytes (target cells) 834
Coelenterates, venom 2473
Coelomates, immune response 1499
Coelomocytes 1947
Cofilin 464
Cohn cold alcohol fractionation 1967
Coinhibition 1983
  B cells 1983
  lack in autoimmunity 1983
  T cells 1983
Coisogenic strains 635, 1370
Cold agglutinins 593–596
  ABO antigens 4, 594, 595
  biological importance of target antigens
    595
  carbohydrate combining specificities 594–
    595
  cross-reactive idiotypes 594
  IgM 1216
  to I and i antigens 593, 594–595
  see also I and i antigens
  in Mycoplasma pneumoniae infections
    1801
  pathogenesis 595
  raised levels 593
  restricted clonality 594
  titer 94, 593
Cold hemagglutinin disease 94
  antigen clearance 184–185
  chronic 593, 594
  clearance of IgM-coated erythrocytes 97
  hemolysis mechanism 94
  IgG-mediated 94
  primary (idiopathic) 94

Cold hemagglutinin disease (*continued*)
  secondary 94
  therapy 96
    blood transfusions 98
    immunosuppressive agents 97
    plasmapheresis 97
  see also Autoimmune hemolytic anemia
    (AIHA)
Cold tolerance, induction method 683
Cold urticaria, *see* Urticaria, cold
Coley's toxin 1359, 2435
  see also Tumor necrosis factor α (TNFα)
Colicin E3 RNAase 2015
Colicin E9 DNAase 2015
Colicin M 2015
Colicins 2014
  channel-forming 2014, 2014(Fig)
  enzymatic activity 2014–2015
  immunity proteins to 2014
  pore-forming 2014
Coliforms 842
Colinogeny 2014
Colitis
  acetic acid-induced 1384
  carrageenan causing 1384
  Clostridium difficile 578
  dextran sulfate causing 1384
  formalin 1384
  hemorrhagic 842, 844, 967
  immune complex 1384
  indomethacin-induced 1384
  peptido-glycan-polysaccharide polymers
    causing 1384
  spontaneous in animal models 1383
  trinitrobenzene sulfonic acid-induced
    1383–1384
  ulcerative, *see* Ulcerative colitis
Collagen 861–862
  α chain 905
  altered metabolism, UCD 200 chicken
    model 284
  antibodies, in rheumatoid arthritis 2113
  arthritis model, *see* Collagen-induced
    arthritis (CIA)
  defense function 2491
  in extracellular matrix 861, 861–862
    fibroblasts regulating 907
  fibers 906
  fibril 906
  fibril-associated 905, 906
  fibrillar 861, 905, 906
  fibronectin binding 910
  Gly-X-Y repeats 905–906
  network-forming 905
  platelet activation 579
  remodeling by fibroblasts 906
  structure 861, 863(Fig), 905
    three-dimensional 861
  synthesis 905–906
    by fibroblasts 905–904, 905–906, 907
    granulomas 1023
  tissue distribution 861
  type(s) 862(Table), 905
  type I 905
    adjuvant arthritis treatment 1897
    structure 905
  type II
    arthritis model treatment 1897
    autoantigen in rheumatoid arthritis
      2109–2110
    experimental arthritis, *see* Collagen-
      induced arthritis (CIA)
    rheumatoid arthritis treatment 1898
  type IV 1005–1007
    α3(IV)NC1 1008, 1008(Fig), 1009
    antibodies to 1008, 1009
    basement membrane interaction 1006–
      1007
    noncollagenous sequences 1005–1006
    structure 1005–1006, 1007(Fig)
    see also Goodpasture antigen

Collagen (*continued*)
  type XI, *Proteus* IRRET sequence
    mimicry 1740(Fig), 1741
Collagenase
  Clostridium perfringens toxin 577
  neutrophils 1857, 1858
Collagen-induced arthritis (CIA) 2106–
    2108, 2106(Table)
  H-2Aβ chain restriction 2107
  IFNγ role 1425
  IgG glycosylation 1004
  immune response 2106–2107
  immunogenetic regulation 2107–2108
  immunomodulation 2108
  passive transfer 2107
  pathogenesis 2106–2107
  source of type II collagen 2108
  susceptibility 2107
  TCR-V_β involvement 2107
  TGFβ effect 2396
  therapeutic protocols 2108, 2108(Table)
  TNFα role 2438
  type II collagen 2106
Collectin family 187
Collectins 1537
  as opsonins 1887
  structure 1536(Fig)
Colloidal gold conjugates 143
Colloid osmotic pressure (oncotic pressure)
    1597, 1964
Colon, normal flora 1780
Colon carcinoma
  Forssman antigen role 954
  glycoprotein antigens 2428
  immunocytochemistry 1266
  increase, exercise effect 848
  vitamin E effect 2500
Colony-forming assays 374–375
Colony-forming units-dendritic (CFU-DC)
    745
Colony-forming units-erythroid (CFU-E)
    375
Colony-forming units-spleen (CFU-S) 374
Colony-forming units stimulating activity,
    see Interleukin-3 (IL-3)
Colony-stimulating factors (CSF) 375,
    596–599, 720, 1018
  ADCC modulation 170
  assays 596
  clinical use 598–599
  CSF-1, *see* Macrophage colony-
    stimulating factor (M-CSF)
  eosinophil CSF 598
  at fetomaternal interface 900
  IL-1 synergism 1434
  IL-3 as 596
  megakaryocyte CSF 598
  multi-CSF 596
    actions 597(Table)
  nomenclature 596–597
  physiological roles 597(Table), 598
  properties 596
  retrovirus expressing 1564
  sources 597
  structure 598
  synergistic activity 598
  synthesis, endothelial cells 802
  target cells 597(Table)
  see also Granulocyte colony-stimulating
    factor (G-CSF); Granulocyte-
    macrophage colony-stimulating factor
    (GM-CSF); Hematopoietic growth
    factor(s)
Colorectal cancer, *see* Colon carcinoma
Colostrum
  canine, immunity from 412
  Ig transfer in cats 893
  passive transfer of antibody in ungulates
    2451
  sIgA transfer 1672
  in ungulates 2450, 2450–2451
Combinatorial libraries, antibodies 985

Combinatorial techniques, antibody
    microspot arrays 1256
Combining sites, *see* Antibody combining
    sites
Common acute lymphoblastic leukemia
    antigen (CALLA), *see* CALLA
Common β chain 455(Table)
Common γ (γc) chain 455(Table), 1440,
    2171
  constitutive expression 1440
  cytokine receptors sharing 2171(Fig)
  gene mutation in X-linked SCID 1440,
    1441, 1464, 1489, 2170, 2171
  IL-4 receptor 1454
  IL-15 receptor 1494
  mice deficient in 2171
  missense mutations 2171
  see also under Interleukin-2 (IL-2)
    receptor (IL-2R)
'Common mucosal immune system' 1779–
    1780, 1783, 2455
Common variable immunodeficiency (CVI)
    386, 599–602, 1280
  autoimmune diseases in 600
  clinical features 599–600, 600(Table)
  differential diagnosis 389
  HLA class III association 1120
  immunogenetics 600
  immunologic features 600–601
  lymphoproliferative disorders in 600
  prevalence 599
  recurrent infections 599
  spontaneous recovery 1285
  treatment 601
Community-acquired infections
  opportunistic infections 1881–1882
  pneumonia 2082(Table)
Compartments for peptide loading (CPLs)
    354
Competitive enzyme-linked immunoassay
    (CELIA) 1254
  affinity measurement 45–46
Complement 495, 604
  activation, *see* Complement activation
    (*below*)
  in acute phase response 18(Table)
  assays based on 142
  assessment, cobra venom factor (CVF) as
    tool 588
  avian 302
  bacterial interactions 316
  bacterial resistance to 316
  cobra venom factor (CVF) interactions
    587, 588
  control, by decay-accelerating factor
    (DAF) 735
  crossed immunoelectrophoresis
    application 1293–1294, 1293(Fig)
  cytotoxicity
    detection 142
    tumor antigens 2442
  decreased
    protein-energy malnutrition 1869
    SLE 2258
  deficiencies, *see* Complement deficiencies
    (*below*)
  depletion method 510–511
    applications 511
  disease associations, mechanisms 623
  DNA sequence analysis 619
  erythrocyte antibody complement
    rosetting 2130
  factor XIIf action 1520
  feline 894
  fetal 5
  fixation, *see* Complement fixation (CF)
    test (*below*)
  fungal infections 959
  gene clusters 619–622
    C4 622
    membrane attack complex 621–622
    MHC class III 622

Complement (continued)
  gene clusters (continued)
    regulators of complement activation 620–621
  genes 116(Table), 621(Table), 1115
    see also individual complement components
  genetics 619–623
  guinea pig 1034–1035, 1034(Table)
  IgG-induced immune hemolytic anemia 95
  IgM-induced immune hemolytic anemia 94
  immune complex binding to receptors 183
  immune complex interaction, drugs affecting 1225
  immunopathology investigation 1340
  inactivation, by ant venom 2472
  increased consumption, primary biliary cirrhosis 2003
  kallikrein action 1520
  lectin pathway 87
  Legionella pneumophila resistance 1544
  lifespan 1583
  lysis mediated by
    drug-dependent immune hemolytic anemia 99
    effector mechanisms 1175(Fig)
    experimental autoimmune thyroiditis 2312
    inhibition by CD59 497, 498–500
    pore structure 1930(Fig)
  membrane attack complex, see Membrane attack complex (MAC)
  mice 1046
  opsonins 1885, 1886, 1936
  opsonization 1885, 1885(Fig)
  origin/evolution 1950
  polymorphism 619, 620(Table)
  porcine 1992
  poxvirus encoded homolog 1997(Table)
  recognition of bacteria 315
  regulatory proteins
    decreased, in morphea 2189
    expressed by trophoblast 899
  role 604
    in amebiasis 78
    in Arthus reaction 237–238
    in tissue typing method 2319
  virus infections 2481
  vitamin C effect 2492
Complement activation 605(Fig), 1227
  alternative pathway 602–604, 604, 1515
    bacterial infections 316
    C3b feedback cycle 603
    classical pathway vs 605
    components 602–603, 613(Fig)
    control 610–611
    cycle 602–603
    function 613(Fig)
    by IgA 1198, 1316
    protected surface phenomenon 603
    tickover model 603
  babesiosis 310
  cascade, anaphylatoxin formation 87
  Chlamydia 550
  classical pathway 602, 604–612, 1146, 1315, 1515
    activators 609–610, 609(Table)
    alternative pathway vs 605
    C1 605–606
    C2 607–608
    C3 608
    C4 606–607
    components 604–605, 605–608, 613(Fig)
    control mechanisms 610–611
    functions 613(Fig), 623
    pathologic alterations 611
    properties of components 610(Table)
    receptors, see Complement receptors

Complement activation (continued)
  classical pathway (continued)
    see also individual components
  Clonorchis infections 1880
  by cobra venom factor 587
  cutaneous lupus erythematosus 2187
  drug-induced immune thrombocytopenia 1975
  ex vivo 87
  factor B 602
  factors H and I 603
  fungal infections 959
  historical aspects 602
  idiopathic thrombocytopenic purpura 1181
  by immune complexes 1146
  by immunoglobulins 1315–1316
    IgG 1211, 1315–1316
    IgM 1214–1215, 1316
  inflammatory bowel disease 1378
  lectin pathway 605, 606–607
  mannose-binding lectin (MBL) 605
  Opisthorchis infections 1880
  by polysaccharides 216
  properdin pathway 602
    see also Complement activation, alternative pathway
  regulators (RCA) 495, 629
    CR1 629
    genes 620–621
  Streptococcus pneumoniae 2219
  Toxocara canis 2381
  type II hypersensitivity 1174
  type III hypersensitivity 1176
  xenograft 2509
Complementarity determining regions (CDRs) 151–152, 159, 171, 764, 825, 1140, 1329
  AGY sites and somatic mutation hotspots 2192
  canonical structures 152, 153, 174, 439–440
  CDRH1 and CDRL1, somatic hypermutation 1327
  CDRH2, germline diversity 1327
  CDRH3 1327
  contacting surfaces 152
  diversity 1327
  grafting, see Humanized antibodies
  loop structures 152–153
  structures 1331–1332
    three-dimensional 152, 171, 517, 1330
  TCRγδ 2271
  V_H and V_L 171
  see also Antibody combining sites; Antibody specificity
Complement control protein (CCP) 606
Complement control protein repeats (CCPRs) 495
Complement deficiencies 611, 612–616, 620(Table)
  animal experimentation 616
  connective tissue diseases 612–613, 616
  disease association mechanisms 623
  features 614–615(Table)
  HLA association 1693
  immune complex diseases 612–613, 616
  immune complexes 1224
  immune response 616
  incidence 612
  inheritance 614–615(Table), 988
  recurrent/persistent infections 612
  without symptoms 612
Complement fixation (CF) test 142, 617–619
  'anticomplementary' sera 618
  applications 617, 617–618
  B cell enrichment 179
  false positives 618
  immune complexes 1222–1223
  interpretation 617–618
  isotype function 1515

Complement fixation (CF) test (continued)
  principle 617, 618(Fig)
  reproducibility 617
  SLE 2258
Complement-fixing antibodies, in coccidioidomycosis 590
Complement-inhibiting proteins
  Entamoeba histolytica 500
  Schistosoma mansoni 500
Complement receptors 629–634
  C1q-R, see C1q-R
  C3a-R, see C3a, receptor (C3a-R)
  C4a-R, see C4a, receptors (C4a-R)
  C5a-R, see C5a, receptor (C5a-R)
  CR1, see CR1 (C3bi/C3b receptor; CD35)
  CR2, see CR2 (CD21)
  CR3, see CR3 (CD11b/CD18 complex; Mac-1)
  CR4 630(Table), 632, 1937
  CR5 630(Table), 632
  distribution 629–633
  factor H (fH-R) 633
  on macrophage 175
  on monocytes 1752
  on phagocytes 1886, 1937
  structure and specificity 629–633
  type 1, see CR1
  types 629
Complement-related proteins, invertebrates 1501
Concanamycin A 460
Concanavalin A 1536
  applications 1540(Table)
  lymphocyte transformation test 1622
  mitogenic activity 1537–1538
  response, gravity/space flights effect 1032
  T cell response, reptiles 2078–2079
c-onc gene 1563
Concomitant immunity 785, 1245
  lymphatic filariasis 915
  schistosomiasis 2140
Conditioning, Pavlovian 337–338
Congenic mice 634–637, 1370, 1730
  applications 635
  backcrossing 635–636
  background strains 635, 636
  examples of strains 637(Table)
  genetics of donor strains 636
  historical aspects 634–635
  molecular biology techniques 635
  production methods 635–636, 636(Fig)
  symbols and nomenclature 636
Congenic strains 1370, 1730
  recombinant 1370
  see also Congenic mice
Congenital adrenal hyperplasia (CAH) 1120, 1694
Congenital agammaglobulinemia, see Bruton's agammaglobulinemia
Congenital heart block
  anti-Ro/SS-A antibodies 132
  complete 1676
Congenital heart disease, in DiGeorge syndrome 761
Conglutinins 1257
  immune complex detection 1221
  see also Immunoconglutinins
Conjunctivitis
  acute 872
  acute hemorrhagic 871
  allergic, immunotherapy 1354
  HSV-1 infection 872
Connective tissue diseases
  complement deficiencies 612–613, 616
  see also other specific diseases; Rheumatoid arthritis (RA); Systemic lupus erythematosus (SLE); Systemic sclerosis
Connective tissue proteins, cleavage, by granzyme A 1029

Consensus sequences, recombination of
   immune genes 553
Conserved lymphoid element 0 (CLE0)
   1457
Contact allergy, *see* Contact
   hypersensitivity
Contact guidance 534
Contact hypersensitivity 637–640, 740,
   1177–1178, 1178(Table)
   adhesion molecule expression 639–640,
      1178
   adoptive transfer, contrasuppression
      effect 650
   antigen potency 638
   antigen-presenting cells 638, 740, 1178
   CD4+ T cells 638, 740
   clinical aspects 639
   cytokines released 639, 1178
   dose–response relationships 639, 640
   expression 639–640
      dose–response 640
   functional significance 637–638
   genetic factors 638
   high responder characteristics 638
   immunobiology 638
   induction 638–639, 1177
      phases 1177
   keratinocytes and macrophage 1178
   Langerhans cells 638, 1178, 2191
   lymphatic drainage (intact) 638
   mast cells and serotonin role 2166
   quantification 640
   skin immune response 2191
   UV-induced changes 1944
Contacting surfaces 152
Contact sensing (thigmotropism) 410
Contiguous gene syndrome 761
Contraception, immunological 640–648,
   1852–1853
   FSH vaccine 642(Table), 647
   hCG vaccine, *see* Human chorionic
      gonadotropin (hCG)
   LHRH vaccine 641–642, 646–647
      see also Luteinizing hormone releasing
         hormone (LHRH)
   principle 641
   vaccines
      applications 641
      carriers 642, 644, 646
      clinical trials 640, 642(Table), 644–647
      current status 644–647
      experimental stage 643(Table)
      under development 641–644
   see also Human chorionic gonadotropin
      (hCG)
Contrasuppression 648–651
   cell characteristics 649
   concept 648
   contact hypersensitivity 650
   experimental studies 649–650
   historical background 648–649
   human contrasuppressor cells 650
   I-J marker 649
   problems 650–651
   T cell receptors 649
   T cells 648, 648–649
      CD4+ and CD8+ cells 649
   tolerance blocked 649–650
   tumor immunity 650
Contrasuppressor factors 650
Coombs' antibodies 57
Coombs' and Gell's classification 1169,
   1170(Table)
Coombs' test 115–116, 136, 1967
   applications 116
   autoimmune hemolytic anemia 116
      experimental model 91
      glucocorticoid therapy 96
   background 115
   blood transfusion cross-matching 116,
      2401
   cold agglutinins 593

Coombs' test (*continued*)
   direct 116
   hemolytic disease of newborn (HDN)
      1071
   indirect 116
   in SLE 2256
Cooperation, cellular 651–656
   B cell costimulation 653–654
      see also B cell(s), activation
   cell fate influenced by 653–6565
   downregulation of immune response
      654–655
   germinal center development 651–656
   lymphocyte activation 652–653
   T cell activation 652–653
      see also T cell activation
   see also specific CD antigens
COPI/COPII coats 852(Table)
Copper 657–658
   animal studies/models 657–658
   enzymes containing 657, 658(Table)
   human studies 657
   insufficiency 657, 1870
      animal models 657
      pathogenic mechanisms 658
   neonatal deficiency 657
Coproantibodies, in amebiasis 77
Cord blood
   ABO antibodies absent 5
   hemoglobin 1072
   stem cells
      cryopreservation 669
      transfer 548
   transplantation, GHVD after 1017
Cornea
   grafts 2413–2414
   HSV-1 infection 872
   as immune privileged site 2414
   scars 873
   ulceration 872, 873
Coronary heart disease
   C-reactive protein (CRP) as marker 664
   see also Atherosclerosis
Coronaviridae 658
Coronavirus 658–661
   antigenic relationships 659
   diseases 659–660, 660(Table)
      epidemiology 660
      prevention 660–661
      veterinary 659–660
   enteric 659–660, 661
   genome 659
   host immune response 660
   mRNA 659
   protein S 659, 660
   replication 659
   structure 659, 659(Fig)
   vaccines 660–661
Corpus luteum 641
Correlation coefficient, Pearson's 2213
Cortactin 802
Corticostatin 1722
Corticosteroid-binding globulin, obese
   strain of chickens 282
Corticosteroids
   in autoimmune disease 291
   effect on IL-1 synthesis 1431
   eosinophil chemotaxis reduction 821
   in idiopathic thrombocytopenic purpura
      1182
   IL-1 expression inhibition 1431, 1435
   immunosuppressive effects 1351, 2224
   multiple sclerosis 1788
   opportunistic infections associated 1883
   physiological effects 1351, 2224(Table)
   see also Glucocorticoids
Corticosterone 996
   structure 997(Fig)
Corticotropin (ACTH) 2224
   antibody production inhibition 1828,
      1829(Fig)
   glucocorticoids secretion 997, 1828(Fig)

Corticotropin (ACTH) (*continued*)
   increased secretion 39
   multiple sclerosis 1788
   receptors
      on mononuclear cells 1828
      on T cells 1828
   release
      IL-1 1434
      by mononuclear cells 1828
Corticotropin-releasing hormone (CRH)
   2224
   glucocorticoids secretion 997
   IL-1 inhibition 1435
   IL-1 stimulating 340, 1434
   macrophage synthesis of IL-1 2225
Cortisol 996
   levels, diurnal changes 997
   permissive/suppressive actions 996, 997,
      998(Fig)
   release, exercise-induced 847
   structure 997(Fig)
Cortisone 996
   structure 997(Fig)
Corynebacterium 661–662
Corynebacterium diphtheriae 662
   toxin, *see* Diphtheria toxin
Corynebacterium jeikeium 662
Corynebacterium minutissimum 661–662
Corynebacterium ovis 662
Corynebacterium pseudotuberculosis 662
Corynebacterium urealyticum 662
Coryneform bacteria 661–663
   genera 661
Coryza 2081
COS cells 185
   CD22 expression 479
Costimulation 1983
   B cells 1983, 2150
      T-dependent antigens 215
      T-independent antigens 215
      see also CD40
   by polyclonal activators 1980
   T cells, *see* T cell(s)
Co-trimoxazole 1882
   chronic granulomatous disease 566
Cottontail rabbit papillomavirus model
   773
Cotton top tamarins 1383
Counterimmunoelectrophoresis 141, 1296–
   1296
Cowpox virus
   sequence homology with IL-1 receptor
      1432
   vaccination 1335
      history 255–256, 1997
Cowpox virus-derived serpins 223, 1028
Cows' milk
   allergy 948, 950
      selective IgA deficiency 1281
   diabetes mellitus association 1400
COX, *see* Cyclo-oxygenase (COX)
Coxiella burnetii 2126, 2127
   vaccine 2458
Cox regression 2213
Coxsackievirus
   epitope location 1957(Table)
   P2C protein 1400
Coxsackievirus B, experimental
   autoimmune disease 272
Coxsackievirus B3 432
   myocarditis 433
   myosin cross-reactivity 434
Coxsackievirus B4 432
   diabetes mellitus induction 1400
   animal models 1396–1397
CPP32 1028
Cps-1 gene 1047
CR1 (C3bi/C3 receptor; CD35) 183,
   448(Table), 629, 629–631,
   630(Table), 1223
   activation by fibronectin 1887
   C3b binding 629

CR1 (C3bi/C3b receptor; CD35)
   (*continued*)
  complement activation regulation 610,
    629
  deficiency 615(Table), 617
  expression 629
    erythrocytes 183, 184
    monocytes 1752
    myeloid cells 1805
    neutrophils 1856
    red cell membrane 840
    sites/cells 183
  functions 629
  gene 620, 630
  in immune adherence 1219
  murine 630
  in opsonization 1886
  rosetting technique 2130
CR2 (CD21) 216, 447(Table), 630(Table),
   631
  antigen recognition 631
  CD19 interaction 656
  expression 631
  gene 620, 631
  in IgE synthesis 1205
  receptor for EBV 828
  reversed signaling 718
  rosetting technique 2130
  signaling via 631
CR3 (CD11b/CD18 complex; Mac-1) 16,
   630(Table), 631–632, 1875, 1937
  activation by fibronectin 1887
  deficiency 615(Table)
  expression 632, 1407
    macrophage 1646(Table)
    monocytes 1752
    myeloid cells 1805
    neutrophils 1856
  function 631–632, 1407
  gene 632
  granule-derived 632
  ICAM-1 as ligand 804, 1412
  I domain 631
  lectin site 631
  in opsonization 1886
  rosetting technique 2130
  storage 632
  structure 519, 631–632
    three-dimensional 519
CR4 630(Table), 632, 1937
CR5 630(Table), 632
C-reactive protein (CRP) 18, 663–665
  actions/functions 664
  binding to *S. pneumoniae* 1886–1887
  clearance/catabolism 19, 664
  clinical uses/significance 663–664
  coronary heart disease marker 664
  disease activity correlation 20, 663
  disorders with minimal levels 19
  gene 663
  homologous proteins 663
  immunoassays 20
  increased levels 19, 663
  in invertebrates 1500
  normal levels 663
  as opsonin 664, 1886–1887
  production, IL-6 regulation 663
  reactivity 664
  structure 19, 663
  turnover rate 664
Cre/loxP system 982–983, 983(Fig)
Creola bodies 244
Cre recombinase transgene 1525(Fig),
   1526(Fig), 1527, 2406, 2406–2407,
   2407(Fig)
CREST syndrome 2117–2118
  anticentromere antibodies 131
Creutzfeldt-Jakob disease (CJD) 1968,
   2409
  transmission in blood products 1968
Crimean–Congo hemorrhagic fever 392
Crithidia luciliae 129, 129(Table)

CRK, T cell signaling 2326
CrmA 223, 876, 1028
Crohn's disease 1375
  complement levels and activation 1378
  exacerbation by NSAIDs 2027
  IgG2 levels 1378
  IgG glycosylation in 1004
  IL-2 increase 1376–1377
  immunosuppressive factor
    downregulating TfR 2391
  immunotherapy 1359
    antibodies to cytokines 1358
  T cell activation 1376–1377
  see also Inflammatory bowel disease
    (IBD)
Cromer blood group 735
Cromoglycates, in asthma 246(Table)
Croquemort 222
Crossed immunoelectrophoresis, *see*
   Immunoelectrophoresis
Cross-fostering 1370
Crossing-over 969, 972
Cross-linking
  antigen fixation in immunocytochemistry
    1261, 1262
  Fc receptors (FcR) 886, 891
  ICAM-1/ICAM-3 1412
  IgE binding to mast cells 1207, 1669,
    2165
  immunoprecipitation of surface molecules
    514
  T cell receptor (TCR) 506
Cross-linking reagents 51
Cross-reactions of antigens
  cardiac proteins and microbes 431–434,
    435, 1737, 2219
  coxsackievirus B3 and myosin 434
  Forssman antigen 954
  inhaled and food allergens 950
  tolerance breakdown 275, 276, 289, 294
  see also Molecular mimicry
Cross-reactive cationic proteins (CLCP)
   1938
Cross-reactive idiotypes (IdX), *see under*
   Idiotype(s)
Cross-reactivity of antibodies, *see*
   Antibodies; *specific antibodies*
Cruzipain 522
Cryoglobulin 665–667
  classification 665–666
  definition 665
  detection 666–667, 667(Fig)
  normal levels 665
  type I 665–666, 665(Fig)
  type II 666
  type II-III type 667
  type III (mixed) 666, 667
Cryoglobulinemia
  in B cell tumors 665, 667
  chronic hepatitis with 666
  clinical features 666, 666(Fig),
    666(Table)
  essential mixed 666
    diagnosis 667
  immunohistology 667
  laboratory investigations 666–667,
    667(Fig)
  type I 665, 666
Cryoprecipitate 1966
  indications 1966
Cryopreservation of immune cells 668–671
  cryoprotectants 668–669
  dimethylsulfoxide (DMSO) 69, 668, 669,
    670
  evaluation of cells 670–671
  freezing process 668–669
  hemopoietic stem cells 669
  historical aspects 668
  lymphocytes 668, 670
  storage 668, 668–669
  techniques 669–670
  thawing process 669

Cryopreservation of immune cells
   (*continued*)
  toxicity of DMSO 669
Cryoprotectants 668–669
  DMSO 69, 668, 669, 670
Cryptococcosis 671–673
  in AIDS 672, 673
  antibodies 960
  clinical features 672
  disseminated 673
  immunotherapy 961
  meningitis 671, 672
Cryptococcus neoformans 671
  capsular polysaccharides 423
  comparison with pathogenic fungi
    672(Table)
  complement activation 959
  distribution 671
  evasive strategies 673
  from bird droppings 671–672
  growth and temperature conditions 672
  host immune response 672–673
    cell-mediated immunity 960
  immunosuppression 673
  infections, *see* Cryptococcosis
  NK cell action 959–960
  pigments 673
  serotypes 671
  vaccine 961
  virulence 672–673, 673(Fig)
Cryptogenic cirrhosis 263
Cryptosporidiosis 674–677
  diagnosis 676
  diarrhea 674, 675, 676, 968
  in hyper-IgM syndrome 1167
  laboratory investigations 676–677
  persistent 676
  prevalence 676
  prevention 677
  transmission 676
  treatment 677
Cryptosporidium 674
  antigens 676
  autoinfection 674
  characteristics 674
  host immune response 677
  in immunodeficient animals 676–677
  infection, *see* Cryptosporidiosis
  intracellular-extracytoplasmic 674
  laboratory cultivation 676–677
  life cycle 674
  natural history 674, 675(Fig)
  species 674
Cryptosporidium parvum 674
CsA, *see* Cyclosporine (CsA)
CSF, *see* Colony-stimulating factors (CSF)
CSF-1, *see* Macrophage colony-stimulating
   factor (M-CSF)
CSF2a, *see* Interleukin-3 (IL-3)
CSF2b, *see* Interleukin-3 (IL-3)
CIITA transcription factor 331
CTL, *see* Cytotoxic T lymphocytes (CTL)
CTLA1 733
CTLA4 (CD152) 305, 306, 456(Table),
   2147–2148
  B7-1 and B7-2 binding 305, 307, 482,
    2148
    counter-receptors 305
  CTLA4-Ig 2151
    autoimmune disease therapy 1359
  downregulation of T cells 653, 1983,
    2148, 2262, 2332, 2366
    T cell apoptosis 2332
  expression 653
  function as negative regulator 653, 2332
    see also downregulation of T cells
    (above)
  gene 653
  immunoglobulin binding 482–483
  mice deficient in 482
  signal transduction 2148
  T cell expression 307, 353, 502

CTS mice, *see* Cataract-prone subline (CTS) mice
C-type lectin fold 518
CUB module 606
Culture
  bacteria, *see specific bacteria*
  bioreactors for, *see* Bioreactors, tissue culture
  bone marrow 2236
  cell, *see* Cell culture; Leukocyte culture
  organ, *see* Organ culture of lymphoid cells
Cumulative distribution function (CDF) 2214
Cumulative distribution plot 2214
  reverse 2214
Cuproenzymes 658(Table)
Curschman spirals 244
Cushing's syndrome 996
Cutaneous anaphylaxis 678–685
  causes 678(Table)
  clinical features 678
  treatment 684–685
  see also Urticaria
Cutaneous basophil hypersensitivity 333, 738–739
Cutaneous lupus erythematosus 2185–2188
  ADCC 2187
  autoantibodies 2186
  complement activation 2187
  histopathology 2186
  Ig deposits at dermo-epidermal junction 2187
  immunopathogenesis 2187
  immunotherapy 2187–2188
  nonspecific 2186
  photosensitivity 2186(Table), 2187
  specific form 2186
    acute/subacute/chronic types 2186, 2186(Table)
Cutaneous lymphocyte antigen (CLA) 29, 2190
  E-selectin binding 2160
  as skin homing receptor 2160
Cutaneous T cell lymphomas 2191
Cu-Zn superoxide dismutase, in copper deficiency 658, 658(Table)
CXCR4, *see under* Chemokines, receptors
Cyanosis 593
Cyclic AMP 2029
  LFA-1 activation inhibition 1610
  toxin mode of action 2368, 2373(Fig)
    Bacillus anthracis toxins 2374
    cholera toxin 2477
Cyclic AMP-dependent protein kinase (PKA) 2028–2029, 2029
  oxygen-dependent phagocytic killing 1713
  see also Protein kinase A
Cyclic AMP response element (CRE), H2 class II gene 1042
Cyclic AMP response element-binding protein (CREB) 1115
  Tax protein interaction and leukemogenesis 1565
Cyclin(s) 2018
  chromosomal translocations 558
  homolog in HHV-8 1091
  interferon β inhibition 1420
Cyclin B 2018
Cyclin D 2019
Cyclin D1 558
Cyclin-dependent kinases (CDKs) 2018
  CDK1 2019
  CDK6 2019
  interferon β action 1420
Cyclin E 2019
Cyclohexylamine-formaldehyde 1261
Cyclo-oxygenase (COX) 117, 228, 2024
  COX-1 118, 2024
    inhibitors 2025

Cyclo-oxygenase (COX) (*continued*)
  COX-1 (*continued*)
    prostaglandin formation in inflammation 2025
  COX-2 118, 2024
    inhibitors 119, 2025
      NSAID action 119
      selective inhibitors 119
  inhibition by NSAIDs 117, 118–119
  irreversible binding by aspirin 118
  mechanism of action 118(Fig)
  metabolites, mast cell activation 1172
  platelet 1974
  reversible binding by NSAIDs 118
Cyclophilin pseudogene 1114(Fig)
Cyclophosphamide
  autoimmune hemolytic anemia (AIHA) 97
  conditioning experiment 337
  conditioning for stem cell transplantation 1063
  immunodeficiency due to 1285
Cyclosporine (CsA) 686–689
  actions 1352
  adverse reactions 689
  in autoimmunity 688–689, 689, 689(Table), 1358
  development/history 1352, 2412
  dosages 689
  drugs used in combination 1352
  eosinophil chemotaxis reduction 821
  GVHD association 1017
  GVHD prevention 1068, 2261
  immunodeficiency due to 1285
  immunosuppressive action 686, 688–689
  mechanism of action 686, 687(Fig)
  nephrotoxicity 689
    reduction by n-3 PUFAs 885
  pharmacokinetic interactions 689
  pharmacology 686–688
  as research tool 686
  structure 686, 686(Fig)
  in transplantation 688, 2414
Cyp21a1 gene 1046
Cyp21a2 gene 1046
CYP450 2D6 antigen, autoantibodies 562, 563
Cysteine proteinase
  cell death, *see* Cell death cysteine proteases
  extracellular matrix degradation 865
Cysticercosis 690–694
  neurocysticercosis 690
  types 690
  see also specific Taenia species
Cysticercus cellulosae 690
Cysticercus epilepsy 690
Cystic fibrosis 988
  gene therapy 25
  lung transplantation 2413
  Pseudomonas aeruginosa infection 2042, 2044
  prevention 2045
Cystic fibrosis transmembrane conductance regulator (CFTR) 988, 2044
Cystitis 2065, 2066–2067, 2452
  hemorrhagic, BK virus causing 1990
  predisposing factors 2066(Table)
Cytoadhesins
  characteristics 1405(Table)
  functions 1408
Cytochalasins, antagonism of LFA-1 actions 1609, 1612
Cytochemistry, antigen detection 815
Cytochrome *b*
  α and β subunits 1713–1714
  oxygen-dependent phagocytic killing 1713–1714
Cytochrome *c*
  immunodominant determinants 1291
  peptides, TCR V_α recognition 2267
  pigeon, autoreactive T cell clones 2344

Cytochrome *c* oxidase, in copper deficiency 658, 658(Table)
Cytochrome P450
  autoantibodies, Addison's disease 41
  cholesterol side-chain cleavage (SCC) 42
  drug binding and adverse reactions 1052
  side-chain cleavage enzyme, autoantibodies 42, 1985
Cytofluorometry
  cell surface antigen characterization 209
  see also Fluorescence-activated cell sorting (FACS)
Cytokine(s) 694, 719–722
  abnormalities in rheumatoid arthritis, *see under* Rheumatoid arthritis (RA)
  ADCC modulation 170
  as adjuvants 38
  antibodies
    allergic disease immunotherapy 1356
    autoimmune disease therapy 1358–1359
  Arthus reaction 239
  bacterial infections 316
  balance, agonists/antagonists 704
  in blood components for transfusion 2402–2403
  bystander effect mechanism 398
  cell cycle control 2019
  cells as producers and targets 713
  cellular distribution 700
  changes in copper deficiency 657–658
  chemotactic, *see* Chemokines
  contact hypersensitivity 639
  control of acute phase proteins 18
  cross-talk at fetomaternal interface 900
  cytotoxic mechanism 504
  decreased, protein-energy malnutrition 1869
  delayed-type hypersensitivity 740
  detection, *see* Cytokine assays
  directional secretion by T cells 702
  in EAE 859
  in eczema 786
  effect of polyunsaturated fatty acids on 884
  endothelial cell activation 30, 805–806
  excessive release, septic shock 319, 2163, 2163(Table)
  exercise effect 846
  experimental autoimmune thyroiditis 2311
  expression
    C5a action 90
    Listeria monocytogenes infection 1594
    TGFβ regulating 2396
    see also Cytokine(s), synthesis; Cytokine genes
  febrile blood transfusion reactions induced by 348
  feline 893
  in fetal calf serum 897(Table)
  in fish 924–925
  flavivirus infections 931
  functional assays 698
  functions/actions 699, 702, 720–721
    on endothelial cells 805–806
    on macrophage 1644, 1645(Fig), 1645(Table)
  fungal infections 961
  genes, *see* Cytokine genes
  in gene therapy 980
  gene transfer and antitumor effect 977
  germinal center generation 994
  glucocorticoids secretion stimulation 998
  graft rejection 1014
  gravity/space flights effect 1032
  GVHD 1016
  half-life 720
  '4-helix-bundle' 1443
  high endothelial venules (HEV) development 1100
  Histoplasma capsulatum infections 1107

Cytokine(s) (*continued*)
HLA class I expression modulation 1109
HLA class II expression induced by 1112
humanized antibodies to 1142(Table)
in IDDM 1402
  animal models 1396
IFNγ production regulation 1423
Ig switch recombination 1305
for immune response *in vitro* 1233, 1236(Table)
  primary response 1239
  secondary response 1240
immunomodulatory, rheumatoid arthritis 2113–2114
immunotherapy
  allergic disease 1356
  autoimmune disease 1358–1359, 1359
  tumors 977, 1362
induction
  Legionella pneumophila infection 1544
  by LTB$_4$ 231
  by muramyl dipeptide derivatives 1792
  see also Cytokine(s), production/release
interspecies cross-reactivity 696
invertebrates 1501
iron deficiency effect 1507
leukocyte adhesion to endothelium 758
lifespan 1583
LTB$_4$ inducing 231
Lyme disease 381–382
mRNA degradation 701
neuroendocrine regulation of immunity 1830–1831, 1831(Table)
nitric oxide formation induction 1859
NK cell response 1812–1813
nomenclature 719–720
NSAID action 2026–2027
oral tolerance induction 1894
overlapping bioactivities 696, 698
Peyer's patches 1777
in pigs 1993
pleiotropic 720
polyclonal activation induction 1980
production/release
  asthma 244
  by astrocytes 1830
  bacterial infections 316
  bone marrow stroma 2237
  Chagas' disease 523, 524, 526(Table)
  by CTL 728–729
  defect in SLE 2258–2259
  by dendritic cells 746–747
  ELISA *vs* ELISPOT assays 798
  by endothelial cells 806
  by eosinophils 823
  by fibroblasts 905, 908, 908(Table)
  glucocorticoid inhibition of 1000
  immune system 1832(Fig)
  inflammatory bowel disease 1378–1380
  inhibition in T cell anergy 109
  inhibitors, *see* Cytokine inhibitors
  by large granular lymphocytes 1534
  lymphocyte transformation test 1624
  by mast cells 1172, 1669
  measurement 1179
  by microglial cells 1830
  multiple sclerosis 1787
  murine lupus 2252
  by myeloma cells 1163
  nervous system 1832(Fig)
  by NK cells 1809, 1813, 1814
  platelet-activating factor (PAF) effect 1972
  process 701–702
  sex hormone effect 2176–2177
  shigellosis 2180
  by skin cells 750
  by T cells, *see* T cell(s)
  thymic epithelium 2236
  transfer factors 2386–2387
  virus infections 2482
  see also Cytokine(s), synthesis

Cytokine(s) (*continued*)
pro-inflammatory 2113, 2114
properties 721(Table)
pyrogenic 902
rabbit 2047
receptors, *see* Cytokine receptors
recombinant
  immunopathology mediated by 1342
  resistance to *Listeria monocytogenes* 1594, 1595
  stem cell transplantation 1064, 1064(Table)
  therapeutic use 1353, 1362
  tumor immunotherapy 1362
regulation 721–722
  GVHD prevention 2262–2263
  of IFNγ production 1423
  of macrophage priming 1644
  of monocyte synthesis 1751
sarcoidosis 2136–2137
schistosomiasis 2141
secretion process 701–702
septic shock pathophysiology 319, 2163, 2163(Table)
sex hormones controlling 2176–2177
signal transduction 2032
soluble ligands 703
structure 720
synthesis 720
  cell lineage-specific 699–700
  coordinate/differential 700
  enhanced by NSAIDs 2026–2027
  inducibility 700
  inhibition by PGE$_2$ 2026
  pathways 700
  T cell–macrophage interactions 2026, 2026(Fig)
  see also Cytokine(s), production/release
in T cell development 1248
TGFβ role/effect 2393–2394, 2394(Fig)
T$_H$1 and T$_H$2 cells, *see* Helper T lymphocytes
therapeutic
  diabetes prevention in animal models 1397
  uses 1346, 1346(Table)
thymic epithelium effect 2236
thymic peptides effects 2303
tolerance breakdown mechanism 276
tolerance modulation 2361
transferrin receptor expression 2391
units and specific activity 696
urinary tract infection pathogenesis 2452–2453
UV-induced changes 1944
vitamin A deficiency 2489
vitamin E effect 2500
see also individual cytokines
Cytokine assays 694–699
bioassays 696–699
  design 696
  inhibitors of 696, 699
  properties 696, 698
  specificity 698
  target cells 696
comparison of methods 695(Table)
ELISPOT 796
FACS 941
functional 698
immunoassays 694–696
  advantages/disadvantages 696
  ELISA 694–695, 695(Fig)
  IRMA 695, 695(Fig)
  standard preparations 696
in organ culture 698
proliferative 698
radio-receptor binding assays 697(Table), 699
specific cytokines 697(Table)-698(Table)
Cytokine genes
ovine 1903
regulation 699–702, 703

Cytokine genes (*continued*)
regulation (*continued*)
  cell lineage-specific synthesis 699–700
  enhancer/promoters 701
  inducibility 700
  mRNA degradation 701, 703
  RNA processing/transport 701
  signal transduction 700–701, 703
  transcriptional activation 701, 703
  translation and secretion 701–702, 703
  transfer and antitumor effect 977
Cytokine inhibitors 696, 702–707, 721–722
autoantibodies 704–705, 706
biological activities 706
gp130 706
IL-1 704–705
IL-4 705
IL-12 706
levels 703–704
lymphotoxin 705
mechanisms 703(Fig), 704, 704(Table), 722
nonreceptor proteins 706
therapeutic implications 706–707
TNF 705
Cytokine receptors 708–712, 720
cell-bound 712–713
characteristics 708
chemokine, *see* Chemokines
class I
  AIC2A 1446
  structure 708–709, 709(Table)
  see also Hematopoietic growth factor receptor (HGFR) family
class II (interferon receptor family) 709, 709(Table)
complexity 708
in disease 711–712
distribution 708
extracellular domains 713
immunoglobulin, *see* Immunoglobulin gene superfamily (IgSF)
on macrophage 1646(Table)
modulated by IFNγ 1424
poxvirus encoded homologs 1997(Table)
second signals
  for B cell activation 2150–2151
  for T cell activation 2149
sharing common γ (γc) chain 2171(Fig)
signaling 710–711, 711(Fig)
soluble (SRs) 703, 712–719
  alternative splicing 714
  amino acid sequence 714
  antibodies as 714
  as 'buffers' 715
  cleavage 714–715
  diagnostic implications 718–719
  formation mechanisms 714–715
  functions 713, 713(Fig), 715, 718
  in vitro effects 713(Fig), 715, 718
  in vivo functions 715
  ligand function assistance 715
  modes of action 713–714, 713(Fig)
  novel ligand activity 718
  reversed signaling inhibition 715
  signaling inhibitors 715
  structural forms 713, 713(Fig), 714–715
  substitution for cell-surface receptors 715
  therapeutic implications 718
  types 714, 716(Table)-717(Table)
structure 520, 708–710
TGFβ 710
TNF receptor family, *see* Tumor necrosis factor receptor family
on tumor cells 711
upregulation 720
Cytokine receptor superfamily 708–712
colony-stimulating factors 598, 708, 709(Table)

Cytokine-secreting cell (CSCs), detection 796
 ELISPOT assay 798
'Cytokine soup', for *in vitro* studies 1236(Table), 1239
Cytokine synthesis inhibiting factor (CSIF) 1475
 see also Interleukin-10 (IL-10)
Cytolysin, SH-activated 2377
Cytolysis, *see* Cell-mediated lysis
Cytolytic T cells, *see* Cytotoxic T lymphocytes (CTL)
Cytomegalovirus (CMV) 722–724
 adoptive transfer of immunity 723, 729
 antigens 722
 binding to β2-microglobulin 1286
 characteristics 722
 evasive strategies 723
 gB vaccine 723
 genome 722
 HLA expression decreased 723
 host immune responses 722–723
  cell-mediated 722–723
  humoral 723
 immunodeficiency due to 1286
 immunopathology 723
 immunosuppression 723
 infection of granulocytes 2486
 NK cell infection 2485–2486
Cytomegalovirus (CMV) infection
 after stem cell transplantation 1067, 1069
 bone marrow transplant recipients 1883
 Guillain–Barré syndrome after 1836
Cytopenia, drug-induced 100
 see also Autoimmune hemolytic anemia (AIHA), drug-induced
Cytoplasmic membrane
 bacterial 320, 321
 cells, *see* Membranes
Cytoskeleton 1679
 hydrostatic pressure effect 1155
 in mast cell degranulation 1670–1671
 see also Membrane-associated cytoskeleton
Cytostatic agents, as immunosuppressive agents 1351
Cytotactin (tenascin C) 1046, 1115
Cytotonic toxins 2369, 2369–2372
Cytotoxic differentiation factor (CDF) 726
Cytotoxic drugs
 immunodeficiency due to 1285
 as immunosuppressive agents 1351
 see also Chemotherapy (cancer)
Cytotoxic factor, *see* Lymphotoxin
Cytotoxicity
 assays 730–731, 1628
  chromium-release assay 730–731, 730(Fig), 732
  dye exclusion test 730, 730(Fig)
 by cytotoxic T cells, *see* Cytotoxic T lymphocytes (CTL)
 functions 732
 historical aspects 732
 by large granular lymphocyte 1533–1534
 lymphotoxin role 1639
 mechanisms 732–734
 melanocyte damage in vitiligo 2502
 molecular studies 733–734
 by NK cells, *see* Lymphokine-activated killer (LAK) cells; Natural killer (NK) cells
 non-MHC restricted, *see* Lymphokine-activated killer (LAK) cells; Natural killer (NK) cells
 passive resistance of trophoblast 898–899
 phenomenological studies 732–733
Cytotoxic lymphocyte maturation factor (CLMF), *see* Interleukin-12 (IL-12)
Cytotoxic T lymphocytes (CTL) 318, 725–730, 789, 1227, 2342
 activation 726

Cytotoxic T lymphocytes (CTL) (*continued*)
 activation (*continued*)
  costimulatory signals 726
  fibronectin inducing 912
  see also Cytotoxic T lymphocytes (CTL), induction
 Addison's disease 42
 adhesion to target cells, LFA-1 function 1610
 adoptive transfer, EBV infection 833
 African swine fever 55
 antigen presentation 726, 727(Fig), 1236(Fig)
 antigens stimulating 726
 autoimmune disease pathogenesis 290
 bacterial infections 318
 bystander effects 397
  no cytolysis 729, 7298
 CD4+ cells 725, 727, 727(Fig)
  cytolysis mechanism 734
  TH1 727
 CD8+ cells 475
 cell lines 726
 cell-lysis mechanisms 225, 504, 506, 726–729, 733–734, 876
  apoptosis role 225
  calcium-dependent 726–727, 732, 733, 1026
  calcium-independent 727
  conjugate formation/adherence 728
  Fas/FasL 727, 728(Fig), 734
  lethal hit delivery 728
  perforin/granzyme 726–727, 728(Fig), 733
  quantification 727–728
  recognition step 732
  TNFα mechanism 727
  see also Fas/FasL interactions; Granzymes; Perforin
 cell-mediated lysis 505, 730
  blocked by LFA-3 1613
  lymphotoxin role 1639, 1641
  mitogenic lectin role 1538
  polarization 733
  target cell lysis 728
 cell surface molecules 725
 cloning 1363
 CMV infection 722–723
 cytokines released 728–729
 cytolysis, *see* cell-mediated lysis (above)
 differentiation 789
  CD8 role 478
 differentiation antigen recognition 2425
 discovery 725, 1625
 EBV infection 829–830
 enhancement
  by IL-15 1494
  by LTB4 230
 enrichment, hybridoma generation 1153
 experimental autoimmune thyroiditis 2312
 Fas ligand expression 507
 flavivirus infections 930
 generation
  DNA vaccines 771
  T cell help 1061
 graft rejection 1012, 1013
 granules 728, 733, 1026, 1929
  contents 1026, 1027(Table)
  granzymes 1026
  see also Granzymes
 growth 726
 hepatitis B virus (HBV) infection 1076, 1078
 hepatitis C virus (HCV) 1081
 historical background 725, 1625
 HIV infection 10, 11, 1135
 HSV infections 1087
 H-Y antigen 1158, 1159
 immune response *in vitro* 1233
 induction 726, 727(Fig)

Cytotoxic T lymphocytes (CTL) (*continued*)
 induction (*continued*)
  antigen-ISCOM complexes 1509
  arginine effect 236
  by liposome-associated antigens 1590
  see also Cytotoxic T lymphocytes (CTL), activation
 ineffective in neonates 1820
 in infections 2459
 influenza virus infection 1386
 influenza virus vaccine 728
 in vivo function 729
 justification for existence 732
 killing mechanisms, *see* cell-lysis mechanisms (above)
 large granular lymphocytes 1534
 Listeria monocytogenes infection 1593
 lymphocytic choriomeningitis virus (LCMV) 232, 233
 memory 726
 MHC restriction 1711
  class I 725, 726
  class II 725, 726
  see also MHC class I
 mutation-bearing cells, lysis 732
 ovine 1905
 parasitic infections 1918
 platelet-activating factor (PAF) effect 1972
 precursors 726
  conditioning trials 338
  deletion by veto cells 2474
  limiting dilution analysis 1584–1585
 radioresistance 733
 recognition, adhesion molecules role 29
 reovirus infection 2070
 resistance/sensitivity to cytotoxicity 733
 response to MHC-restricted minor histocompatibility antigens 1730
 to retroviruses 2096
 TCR of 477
  bispecific antibodies 139, 140
 transfer factors 2387
 tumor antigens 2425, 2441
  recognition 2424
 tumor cell rejection role 732
 tumors 2444, 2445
 vaccine development 729
 virus recognition 2481–2482
 see also CD8+ T cells; Large granular lymphocytes (LGL)
Cytotoxic toxins 2369, 2369–2372
Cytotoxin, *see* Tumor necrosis factor α (TNFα)
Cytotrophoblasts
 extravillous 898, 899
 HLA-G expression 1109, 1110

D

D1 antibody 150, 151, 161, 1188
 HEL complex, structures 173, 173(Fig)
984D4 monoclonal antibody 2245
D8/17 antibodies 432, 435
Dacryocytes 834
Danazol 683, 684
 autoimmune hemolytic anemia 98
 idiopathic thrombocytopenic purpura 1976
Danger theory/model 295, 2367
Dapsone 683
Darwin, C. 1336
Data analysis, statistics 2213–2214
Daudi cells, β2-microglobulin and MHC class I expression 370
DB3 antibodies, cross-reactivity 2202, 2204(Fig)
DBA/1 mice 1768–1769

DBA/1 mice (continued)
  immunology 1768
  infectious agents susceptibility 1768
  origin/characteristics 1768
DBA/2 mice 1769
  immunology 1769
  infectious agents susceptibility/resistance
    1769
  origin/characteristics 1769
  resistance to Coccidioides immitis 589
DEAD-box protein family 1119
Death domains 570, 654, 734, 875, 1641
  FAS-associated (FAD) 711
  lymphotoxin signaling and 1641
  TNF receptor-associated (TRADD) 711,
    1641, 2347, 2348(Fig)
  TNF receptor (CD120a) 2346, 2347,
    2348(Fig)
Death-signaling molecular reaper 734
Decarboxylation, catalytic antibodies
  reaction 438, 439(Fig)
Decay-accelerating factor (DAF; CD55)
  450(Table), 735–736
  anti-inflammatory agent 239
  C3/C5 convertase inhibition 735
  cloning 735
  control of complement activation 610,
    628, 735
  deficiency 615(Table), 735
    paroxysmal nocturnal hemoglobinuria
      499, 735
  gene 620, 735
  glycolipid anchor 735
  murine 735–736
  receptor for viruses 735
  soluble 735
  structure 735
  in xenograft 2509
Decomplementation 616
  by cobra venom factor (CVF) 586, 587
Decongestants, allergic rhinitis 2125
Decorin 906
Decoy receptor 713
Deer, immune system, see Ungulate
  immune system
Defensins 317, 1719, 1720–1722, 1781,
  1938–1939
  α- 1720, 1721
    HD-5 and HD-6 1721
  β- 1720
  genes 1720
  human HNP types 1720–1721
  mechanism of action 1721
  phagocytosis enhancement 1887
  rabbit (NP-3a) 1722
  spectrum of activity 1939
  storage in azurophil granules 1720
  structure and sequences 1720, 1721(Fig)
  synthesis 1720
Degranulation 736–738
  definition 736
  eosinophils 244, 822, 823–824,
    823(Table)
  exocytosis 737, 851
  mast cells, see Mast cell(s)
  mechanisms 737–738
  neutrophils, see Neutrophil(s)
  quantitation 736
  role 737
  signal transduction 737
Dehydration, epitope–paratope interstitial
  spaces 165
Delayed cold urticaria 683
Delayed graft rejection 2509–2510
Delayed-onset hypersensitivity 738
  see also Delayed-type hypersensitivity
    (DTH)
Delayed pressure urticaria 682–683
Delayed-type hemolytic reactions 347
Delayed-type hypersensitivity (DTH) 501,
  738–742, 789, 1177–1179
  allergic contact dermatitis 787

Delayed-type hypersensitivity (DTH)
  (continued)
  anergy 109
  antigen persistence 739, 741
  antigen presentation 739, 740
  antigens inducing 681, 739
  basophils 738–739
  brucellosis 385
  Candida infections 410
  in cats 894
  cell types involved 739, 740–741
  chronic (granulomatous) 741
  classification 738
  clinical manifestations 741
  contact, see Contact hypersensitivity
  cytokines in 740
  decline, age-related 135
  decreased
    antioxidant deficiency 134
    gravity/space flights effect 1031
    oral tolerance 1894
    protein-energy malnutrition (PEM)
      1869
  definitions 738
  development phase 739
  discovery 1177
  diseases associated 741
  effector phase 739, 739–740, 1177
    antigen/lymphocyte interactions 740,
      2165
  egg granuloma in schistosomiasis 2139–
    2140
  enhancement
    arginine effect 236
    by multivitamins 135
    by vitamin E 135
  events 2165–2166
  flare-up reactions 741
  focal reactions 741
    see also Granuloma
  Fusobacterium necrophorum 963
  generalized 741
  graft rejection 1013–1014
  HSV infection 1087
  immunopathology mechanism 1341–
    1342
  impairment, in histoplasmosis 1107
  in infections 2459
  Jones–Mote hypersensitivity (transient)
    738
  kinetics 738
  Langerhans cells role 739
  to latex rubber 681
  leprosy antigens, UV role 1945
  local reactions 741
  macrophage migration inhibitory factor
    (MIF) activity 1655
  in marsupials 1666
  measurement 1179
  memory 1682
  passive transfer 739
    by transfer factor 1345
  permanent type 738
  poxvirus infections 1996
  radioresistance 2052
  reovirus infection 2070
  Salmonella 2132
  schistosomiasis 2140
  sensitization phase 739, 1177
  serotonin role 2165–2166
  T$_H$1 cells 502–503, 739
  transfer factors 1345, 2386
    specificity 2386(Table)
  transient type 738
  Treponema 2417
  tuberculin reaction, see Tuberculin
    reaction
  types 1177
  UV-induced changes 1944
  virus infections 2482
  vitamin C effect 2492
  see also Contact hypersensitivity

DELFIA 143
Delhi sore 1546–1547
Dematin, in red cell membrane 835,
  838(Table)
Demethylation, induction, Ig switch
  recombination 1304
Demyelinating neuropathy 1838
Demyelination 860
  acute inflammatory demyelinating
    polyneuropathy (AIDP) 1836
  antimyelin-associated glycoprotein
    (MAG) antibodies 1838
  EAE 856, 859
  multiple sclerosis 1786, 1839
  see also Myelin
Dendritic cell family 1529(Table)
Dendritic cells 188, 742–748, 1757
  of afferent lymph 746
  as antigen-presenting cells 175, 746
    CD40 function 486
    respiratory tract 191
  antigen processing 746
  apoptosis 747
  bone marrow origin 742
  CD40 function and expression 485–486
  culture 1575
  cytokines produced 746–747
  depletion, in HIV infection 11
  dermal 2191
  development 175, 745–746, 2336
  differentiation 742
  distribution 742, 1529(Table), 1757
  epidermal, see Langerhans cells
  follicular, see Follicular dendritic cells
    (FDCs)
  from epithelia 746
  function 1226
  germinal centers 747
  graft rejection 1012
  half-life 745, 747
  homing 747
  immature 742
  interstitial 745
  in lamina propria 745, 746
  lifespan 1583
  in liver 745, 746
  lymphoid 746–747
    secondary lymphoid tissues 746–747
    thymus 747, 2235
  macrophage similarity 1757
  maturation 175, 745–746
  mature 742
  MHC class II expression 175, 644(Table)
  migration 746, 747
    peripheral blood 746
  mixed lymphocyte reaction (MLR) 1736
  in mononuclear phagocyte system (MPS)
    1756–1757
  nonlymphoid 745
  origin 175
  ovine 1903–1904
  Peyer's patches 1777, 1781
  phenotype 743(Table)-744(Table)
    ovine 1903
  progenitors 175, 742, 745, 1757
    culture 745
    in vivo 742, 745
  recruitment 742, 745, 746
  of skin, see Langerhans cells
  subsets 747
  in thymus 747, 2235
  veiled, see Veiled cells
  virus infection of 2486
  see also Langerhans cells
Denervation, Chagas' disease 525
Dengue fever 926, 926–927
  emergence/evolution 928
  immune response 930
  vaccination 931
Dengue hemorrhagic fever/shock syndrome
  (DHF/DSS) 926–927
  immunopathogenesis 929–930, 929(Fig)

Dengue virus 926, 927(Table)
Density gradient centrifugation 508–509, 2447
  media 2447
Dental amalgam 1686
Dental caries 1888–1889
  causative organisms 1888
  germ-free animals use 991
Dental plaque 1888, 1889
  subgingival 1888
Dental research, germ-free animals use 991
Deoxyadenosine, accumulation 1278
Deoxycytidine 749
Deoxycytidine kinase 749
1-[2-deoxy 2-fluoro-β-D-arabinofuranosyl]-5 iodouracil (FIAU) 1524, 1525
Deoxyguanosine 748–750
  metabolism 749
    T cell ontogeny 749
  toxicity 749–750
    reversal 749
Depigmentation 2501
Dermabacter hominis 662
Dermal dendrocytes 745
Dermatan sulfate (DS) 862, 863(Table), 906
Dermatitis
  atopic, *see* Atopic dermatitis (atopic eczema)
  flea-bite, in cats 894
  see also Eczema
Dermatitis herpetiformis 1199
Dermatological infections, *see* Skin infections
Dermatomyositis 2118
Dermatophagoides 2125
Dermatophagoides farinae 66
Dermatophagoides pteronyssinus 66
  see also House dust mite
Dermis 2190
  cell types 2190
Dermo-epidermal junction (DEJ), Ig deposits 2186, 2187
Dermographism 682
  simple 682
  symptomatic 682, 682(Fig)
Der p I allergen, oral administration 1897
Desensitization 1353, 1354
  atopy allergic disease 255
  basophils 334
  drug allergy 782
  food allergy 953
  see also Immunotherapy, of allergic disease
Desferrioxamine, tumor growth inhibition 1506
Detergents 513
  tissue permeabilization in immunocytochemistry 1262
Determinant selection model 1230–1271
Determinant spreading 754–757, 1291
  autoimmune arthritis 755
  cryptic epitopes 754
  definitions 754
  in EAE 754–755
  in IDDM 755, 755–756
  implications for immunotherapy 756
  intermolecular 755
  intramolecular 754, 755, 1228
  mechanisms 755
  reciprocal T and B cell 755
  SLE model 755
  T cell tolerance breaking 755
Detoxification, germ-free animal studies 991
Deuterostomes 1946
Dexamethasone
  apoptosis induction and IL-9 effect 1474
  structure 997(Fig)
DEX antigen 273
Dextra N 279 150
Dextran

Dextran (*continued*)
  antibody interaction 150
  as anticancer agent 429
  as antigen 203
α1-3 Dextran 1877
Dextran sulfate, colitis due to 1384
'Diabetes' (*db*) mutants 1273
Diabetes-like syndrome, reovirus causing 2069
Diabetes mellitus, insulin-dependent (IDDM) 1399–1404
  AGE products 1046
    lysozyme binding 1723
    role 1115, 1120
  animal models 1390–1398
    autoantibodies 1393
    cell-mediated immunity 1393–1396
    environmental factors 1396–1397
    free radicals role 1396
    genetics 1391–1393
    humoral immunity 1393
    immunopathology 1393–1396
    islet pathology 1393
    LCMV infection 1895–1896
    macrophage 1393–1394, 1394–1396
    murine 1273
      see also NOD mouse
    pathogenesis 1393–1396
    prevention 1394, 1397, 1403
    retroviruses causing 2097
    SCID mouse 1129(Table)
    sex hormones effect 2175–2176
    spontaneous 282–283
    T cells 1394–1396
    TNFα 1396, 2438
    see also BB rat; NOD mouse
  autoantibodies 1391(Table), 1401, 1401(Table)
    animal models 1393
    frequencies 1401(Table)
    GAD 1401, 1842
    insulin receptor 1986
  autoantigens 1399, 1401, 1895
  autoimmunity, development 1395(Fig)
  BCG trials 1346
  cell-mediated immunity 1401–1402
    animal models 1393–1396
  characteristics 1391(Table)
  cytokines role 1402
    animal models 1396
  determinant spreading 755, 755–756
  in dogs and DLA-B4 association 414
  environmental factors 1401–1402
    animal models 1396–1397
  ethnic groups and 1399, 1695, 1696
  etiology 283, 294, 1390(Fig), 1675
    autoimmune 283, 294
  exposure *in utero* protective 1674, 1675
  gender and 289
  genetic intervals 1399–1400, 1400(Table)
  genetic loci 283, 1399–1400, 1400(Table), 1731
  genetic predisposition 289, 1391(Table), 1399–1400, 1399(Table)
  genetics 1391(Table), 1399–1400, 1399(Table), 1400(Table), 1731
  HLA association 278, 1399–1400, 1690, 1694, 1696
    concordance rates 1699
    HLA-DQB1 1699–1700
    linkage disequilibrium 1696
    MHC gene combinations 1699
    polygenic nature 1699
  insulin resistance 1986
  maternally induced tolerance 1674
  MHC class II association in animals 1391
  natural history 1400(Fig)
  pancreas transplantation 2413
  pathogenesis
    lymphotoxin role 1639

Diabetes mellitus, insulin-dependent (IDDM) (*continued*)
  pathogenesis (*continued*)
    macrophage/T cell synergy 1394–1396, 1395(Fig)
    prevention 1403
    risk of inheritance from diabetic father 1674, 1675
    risk reduced in breast fed infants 1673
    spontaneous in animal models 282–283
      see also BB rat; NOD mouse
    T$_H$1 cells role 1695
    TNFα role 2438
    transient neonatal 1675
    treatment 1402–1403
      oral insulin 1898
    type II hypersensitivity 1176
    vaccine development 1403
Diabetes-prone biobreeding (DP-BB) rat 282, 283, 1391
  see also BB rat
Diacylglycerol (DAG) 580, 1299
  chemoattractant-stimulated leukocytes 1761
  cytokine synthesis 700
  membrane attack complex function 627
  oxygen-dependent phagocytic killing 1713
  phorbol ester substitute 1940
  structure 1941(Fig)
  T cell activation 2325
Diagnostic tests
  antibody detection, *see* Antibody detection methods
  candidiasis 409
  hCG 1746
  HIV 2507
  immune adherence (I-A) as 1219
  luteinizing hormone (LH) 1746
  monoclonal antibody uses 1746–1747
  see also specific infections
Dialysis, *see* Equilibrium dialysis; Hemodialysis
Diamine oxidase 1101, 1102(Fig)
Diamino-benzidine 1263
Diapedesis 757–760, 1619, 2060
  blood vessel types 760
  cell activation/differentiation 760
  definition 757
  experimental models 760
  as final event in transmigration 757, 758–759, 1097, 1098(Fig), 1619
  inflammatory conditions 759
  inflammatory mediators 759
  integrin involvement 759, 2060
  lymphocytes 1097
  mechanism 758–759
  monocytes 1754, 1935
  neutrophils 1854
  noninflammatory conditions 759
  see also Leukocyte(s); Lymphocyte trafficking; Transmigration of leukocytes
Diarrhea 967
  adenovirus causing 21
  bacterial infections causing 967–968
  Bruton's agammaglobulinemia 387
  Campylobacter causing 407, 968
  cholera 2477
  cryptosporidiosis 674, 675, 676, 968
  Escherichia coli causing, *see under Escherichia coli*
  parasites causing 968
  Shigella causing 2178
  viral infections causing 968
  watery 967
  see also Gastroenteritis
Diazoketones, in affinity labeling 51
Dictyocaulus 242
  vaccines 1921
Didelphis 1664, 1664(Table)
Diels–Alder reaction 439, 439(Fig)

Diet
  diabetes mellitus association 1400
    animal models 1397
  experimental autoimmune thyroiditis
    induction 2311
  fatty acids, see Fatty acids (dietary)
  food allergy treatment 952
  oligoallergenic 951
  SLE management 2260
  see also Food; Nutrition
Dietary recall 134
Diethylcarbamazine, onchocerciasis 873
Differentiation antigens 1362
  leukocyte 73
  porcine 1993
  recognized by monoclonal antibodies
    2427–2428, 2428(Table)
  tumors 2425–2426, 2426(Table), 2442
Differentiation-inducing factor (DIF), see
    Leukemia inhibitory factor (LIF);
    Tumor necrosis factor α (TNFα)
Differentiation inhibitory activity, see
    Leukemia inhibitory factor (LIF)
Differentiation-retarding factor, see
    Leukemia inhibitory factor (LIF)
Differentiation-stimulating factor, see
    Leukemia inhibitory factor (LIF)
Diffuse infiltrative lymphocytosis (DILS)
    2183
Diffusion in gels, see Immunodiffusion
DiGeorge sequence (DGS) 761, 762
  features 762, 762(Fig)
  mouse 762
DiGeorge syndrome 761–764, 1277
  chromosomal deletions 761, 762, 763
  chromosomal translocation 761
  clinical features 762
  diagnosis 763
  genotype 761, 761(Fig)
  immunologic findings 762–763
  phenotype 762
  treatment 763
Digoxigenin (DIG) 1261
Digoxin, antibody binding site 2203(Fig)
1α,25-Dihydroxyvitamin D₃ 2494
  see also Calcitriol
Dimethylsulfoxide (DMSO) 1864
  cryopreservation 69, 668, 669, 670
  toxicity 669
Dinitrochlorobenzene (DNCB)
  allergic contact dermatitis 787
  Langerhans cells not activated 638
  oral tolerance 1893
Dinitrofluorobenzene 149
2,4-Dinitrophenol (DNP) 436, 2199
Dinitrophenyl haptens, in affinity labeling
    51
Dinitrophenyl proteins, as antigen 2094
Dioxetane phosphate esters 143
Dioxins, immunosuppression due to 1367
Dipeptidylpeptidase IV, see CD26
Diphtheria 662
  antitoxin 1345
  toxin, see Diphtheria toxin
  toxoid 2458
    carrier in hCG and LHRH vaccines
      642, 644
Diphtheria, tetanus and pertussis (DTP)
    vaccine 378, 2458
  adverse reactions 2463
Diphtheria toxin 2368, 2370
  genetically engineered 2370
  IL-2 receptor fusion protein 2370
  mode of action 2370, 2370(Fig)
    DTA fragment entry 2371(Fig)
    protein synthesis inhibition 2372(Fig)
  monoclonal antibodies linked 2261–
    2262, 2262(Fig)
  post-translational modification 2370(Fig)
Dipole-induced dipole (dispersion)
    interactions 163

Dipole-induced dipole (induction)
    interactions 163
Dipole–dipole (orientation) interactions
    163
'Dipstick' techniques 142
Direct antiglobulin test (DAT) 100
Direct immunofluorescence, pemphigus and
    pemphigoid 2188
Discocyte 834, 834(Fig)
Discriminant analysis 2213
Disease susceptibility motif (DSM) 267,
    289
Disease–marker associations 2064–2065
  see also HLA, disease association
Disinfection, immunoadsorbents 1252
Dismutation, superoxide anion 1715
Disrupted alleles 1527
Disseminated intravascular coagulation
    (DIC)
  filoviral hemorrhagic fever 918
  therapy
    cryoprecipitate 1966
    fresh frozen plasma (FFP) 1966
Dissociation constant, see Equilibrium
    dissociation constant (K_D)
Distemper 1909
Dithiothreitol, LFA-1 activation 1611
Ditiocarb 1347
Diversity (D) segments, see
    Immunoglobulin
Diversity generation, antibodies 105–106,
    150, 171, 764–770, 765, 985, 1327–
    1328, 1678
  B cell repertoire development 360, 764–
    770, 1626
  see also B cell(s)
  CDRs 1327–1328
  chickens 156
  combinatorial, see Diversity generation,
    antibodies, germline
  fish 156
  germline 765–766, 767, 1325, 1326,
    1327, 1327–1328
    heavy/light chain association 770
  historical aspects 1626
  junctional 360, 1325, 1326, 1327
  mechanisms 153
  N-segment and P-nucleotide additions
    767–769
  see also Immunoglobulin gene
    rearrangements
  origin/evolution 1950
  potential range 1325
  rabbits 2047
  recombination role 973
  somatic hypermutation, see Somatic
    hypermutation
  VDJ combinatorial, see also
    Immunoglobulin gene rearrangements
  VDJ recombination, see Immunoglobulin
    gene rearrangements
  see also Immunoglobulin gene
    rearrangements
Diversity generation, TCR, see under T cell
    receptor (TCR)
DLA-B4, diabetes mellitus association 414
DLA system 413
DM (class II product)
  CLIP peptide release 1497, 2232
  see also HLA-DM
DNA
  amplification 981
  antibodies, see Anti-DNA antibodies
  as antigen 204
  breaks, detection, ataxia telangiectasia
    gene 247
  complementary (cDNA), libraries 984
  conserved protein, DNA vaccines 772
  damage
    cell-mediated lysis 506
    UV-induced 1944–1945
  disintegration 733

DNA (continued)
  disintegration (continued)
    assay 731
    in cell death 1028
  'diversity segments' 1950
  electrophoresis 2195
  see also Southern blotting
  fragmentation
    assay 731
    induction by lymphotoxin 1639
  heteroduplex
    asymmetric 971
    formation and correction 970–971
  hybridization 982
  see also Hybridization; in situ
    hybridization
  immunization 2460, 2461
  in lymphocytes, FACS study 941
  methods of introduction into cells 982
  microbial, immunogenicity 217
  microinjection 2405, 2405(Fig)
  nonreciprocal transfer, see Gene
    conversion
  as photoreceptor 1945
  polymorphisms, monitoring of inbred
    strains 1371
  rearrangements, see Immunoglobulin
    gene rearrangements
  reciprocal transfer (crossing-over) 969
  recombination, see Genetic
    recombination
  repair, see DNA repair
  replication, regulation by annexin II 115
  sequencing 981
    tissue typing method 2319
    for Southern blotting 2194
  synthesis
    decreased, iron deficiency 1506
    immunoglobulin class switching 1303
    mercury inhibiting 1687
  tissue typing method, see Tissue typing
  vectors for transfer 974
DNAase colicins 2015
DNA-binding proteins
  analysis 983, 984
  sites on H2 class II genes 1042–1043
DNA gene, in HLA class II region 1112
DnaK 2230
DNA polymerase, in polymerase chain
    reaction 1987
DNA polymerase I, Klenow fragment 2196
DNA probes 1253
  Mycoplasma infections 1802
  Northern blotting 1865
  Southern blotting 2196
DNA protein kinase (DNA-PK) 768, 1028
  deficiency in SCID mice 1125, 1269
DNA repair
  aging and 59
  defects 1282
  deficiency, chromosomal translocations
    affecting 559
  double-strand break 971–972, 971(Fig)
  gene conversion role 970
DNA vaccines 771–774, 2454, 2460, 2461
  adjuvant activity 773
  administration 2454
  antigen presentation 773
  applications 771
  cottontail rabbit papillomavirus model
    773
  CTL generation 771
  development 771
  DNA for conserved protein 772
  DNA-encoding proteins 772
  efficacy 771
  flaviviruses 931
  herpes simplex virus 1088
  hookworms 1125
  HSV-2 DNA 773
  immune response 771
  influenza virus 772

DNA vaccines (*continued*)
intradermal 773
intramuscular 773
in vivo injection of DNA 771
Leishmania 1550
Mycobacterium tuberculosis 773
NPmut immunization 772
nucleoprotein (NP) 772, 773
safety 773–774
T$_H$1 responses 773
see also individual infections
DNCB, *see* Dinitrochlorobenzene (DNCB)
DOB gene 1112
Dog leukocyte antigens (DLA) 413
Dogs
anaphylaxis 413
bites 2216
Echinococcus infections 783, 784
immediate hypersensitivity 413
immune system, *see* Canine immune system
model of Addison's disease 42
placenta/colostral transfer of immunity 412
thyroiditis model 2309
X-linked SCID 1273
Dolichos biflorus 1541
Domains, immunoglobulin-type 775–778
homo-/hetero-dimers 776, 777
in immunoglobulins 775–777
in non-Ig molecules 777–778
structural diversity 776(Fig)
topology 775
Dominant alleles 987
Dominant negative mutants 1275
Dominant white spotting (W) mice 1272
Donor-specific immunosuppression, *see* Immunosuppression, donor-specific
D-Dopachrome tautomerase (DDT), MIF relationship 1657
Dopamine-β-mono-oxygenase, in copper deficiency 658, 658(Table)
Dorsal root ganglion neuronitis 1838
Dot blots/blotting 142, 2507
HLA typing 1693
Double copy retroviral vectors 2087
Double diffusion technique 141
Double immunodiffusion, *see* Immunodiffusion, double
Down's syndrome, amyloid β protein 85–86
'Downstream promotion' of expression 1563
Doxepin 682, 683
DP-BB rats, *see* Diabetes-prone biobreeding (DP-BB) rat
DR-BB rats 1396
Drepanocytes 834
Drosophila
immune response regulation 1501
Notch 1115
suicide gene reaper 875
Drug allergy 778–782
in AIDS and HIV infection 11
classification 780, 781(Table)
clinical manifestations 780–781
desensitization 782
diagnosis 781
factors influencing 780
hypersensitivity reaction types 780
management 781–782
mechanism 779–780
Drug-induced immune hemolytic anemia, *see* Autoimmune hemolytic anemia (AIHA)
Drug-induced immune thrombocytopenia 1974, 1975
Drug-induced lupus 611, 2257
Drug-induced serum sickness 2169
Drugs
adverse reactions, immunogenic drugs 1052

Drugs (*continued*)
as antigens 779–780
autoimmune disease pathogenesis 279, 289, 293
cutaneous anaphylaxis 681
food allergy treatment 952
haptenation 779, 779(Fig), 780, 1052
hypersensitivity, *see* Drug allergy
immune complex–complement interactions 1225
immunodeficiency due to 1285
liposome-encapsulated 1588, 1589
resistance, in quadroma formation 139
urticaria due to 679
DSP (dithiobis succinimydyl propionate) 514
Duchenne muscular dystrophy 421
Duffy-binding ligands, *Plasmodium* antigens 1660
Duffy blood group 837
IL-8 binding 1467
Duncan's syndrome, *see* X-linked lymphoproliferative syndrome (XLPS)
Dust mites, *see* House dust mites
Duvenhage virus 2099
Dwarfism 1279
Dye exclusion, leukocyte viability assessment 2474–2475
Dysentery
amebic 77
bacillary 967, 2372
Shigella causing 2178
Dystorphia myotonica 1287

E

E2 elimination, catalytic antibodies reaction 438, 439(Fig)
E2F transcription factor 662
interferon β binding 1420
Ea-1 antigen 1232
EAEC, *see* Escherichia coli, enteroaggregative
East Coast fever, vaccines 1921
Ebola virus 916–920
structure 918(Fig)
see also Filoviruses
E-cadherin 28(Table), 29, 1382
prethymic precursor migration 2236
see also Cadherins
Eccytosis 849
Ecdysteroid 2239
receptors, *Strongyloides stercoralis* 2239
Echinococcosis, alveolar 784
Echinococcus 783–786
antigens 783–784
recombinant DNA analysis method 784
characteristics 783
concomitant immunity 785
coproantigens 784
definitive hosts 783, 785
immunodiagnosis 784
evasive strategies 785
immunodiagnosis 784–785
immunology 783–784
intermediate hosts 783, 785
immunodiagnosis 785
oncospheres 783, 785
transmission 783
vaccination 785
Echinococcus granulosus 783, 784
immunodiagnosis 784–785
Echinococcus multilocularis 783
Echinocytic cells 834, 834(Fig)
Echinoderms
alloaggression 1499
complement-related proteins 1501
Echoviruses, receptor 735
'Economic correction' 60, 61

Ectodermal dystrophy 1984–1985
Ectothermic organisms 2076
Ectromelia 1030
infection 1996
Eczema 786–788
allergic contact, *see* Allergic contact dermatitis
atopic, *see* Atopic dermatitis (atopic eczema)
classification 786(Table)
factors associated 786
food-mediated 948
histopathology 786
see also Dermatitis
Eczema vaccinatum 1998
Edema
formation 15, 17
inflammatory mediators involved 16(Table)
in inflammation 15, 17, 2025
ED-LCA, secretion 2167
EF2 (elongation factor 2) 662, 1420
Effector lymphocyte, *see* Lymphocyte
EHEC, *see* Escherichia coli, enterohemorrhagic
Ehrlich, P. 1337, 1535, 2198, 2362
Ehrlichia canis 2127
Eicosanoids 884, 2024
overproduction 885
production, fatty acids effects 884–885
see also Leukotriene(s); Prostaglandin(s)
EIEC, *see* Escherichia coli, enteroinvasive
Eimeria 591
antigens 591–592
characteristics 591–592
evasive strategies 592–593
host immune response 592
infections, *see* Coccidiosis
life cycle 591–592, 592(Fig)
vaccines 593
EJ antibody 2118
ELAM-1, *see* E-selectin
Elasmobranchs, Ig evolution 1307
Elastase
bactericidal activity of PMNs 1939
effect on *Acinetobacter* 1723
gene 1723
Pseudomonas aeruginosa toxin 2369
reduced in Chédiak–Higashi syndrome 1722
Elastin 862
deposits 862
microfibrils 906
production, by fibroblasts 906
Elderly
free radical damage 135
immune response 1870–1871
nutritional deficiencies 1871
vitamin B$_6$ deficiency 2490
vitamin E effect 2500
vitamin supplementation effect 135
see also Age-related changes
Electrofocusing–immunoelectrophoresis 1296
Electrofusion, hybridoma generation 1153
Electroimmunoassay (rocket immunoelectrophoresis) 1294–1295, 1294(Fig), 1295, 1295(Fig)
fused 1296
Electroimmunofocusing 1296
Electroimmunoprecipitation 1292, 1296
see also Immunoelectrophoresis
Electrolytes, plasma 1965, 1965(Table)
Electronic imagers 2197
Electron microscopy 790–795
applications 791
historical background 790
principles 790–791
scanning 790
application 792(Fig)
principle 791
transmission 790

Electron microscopy (*continued*)
transmission (*continued*)
principles 790–791
see also Immunoelectron microscopy
Electrophoresis
agarose, *see* Agarose gel electrophoresis
cryoglobulin detection 667
isoelectric focusing, *see* Isoelectric
focusing (IEF)
polyacrylamide gel 2143, 2504
see also SDS-polyacrylamide gel
electrophoresis (SDS–PAGE)
protein size/charge determination 2035
serum proteins 964, 964(Fig), 1293
hypergammaglobulinemia detection
1161, 1162(Fig), 1163
titration curve analysis 2035, 2035(Fig)
two-dimensional, in PEG isoelectric
focusing 1513
Western blotting 2504
see also Immunoelectrophoresis
Electrophoresis–immunofixation 1294
Electrophoretic mobility shift assay
(EMSA) 1304–1305
IL-5 gene 1457
Electroporation 982
Electrostatic forces 163
Electrostatic interactions 164, 2200
antibody–antigen binding 2200,
2202(Fig)
ELISA 142, 796, 816–819
affinity of humanized antibodies 1143
affinity measurement 45
allergen exposure measurement 69
antibody quantitation 817
anti-DNA antibodies 129, 129–130,
129(Table)
antigen quantitation 816–817
antinucleosome antibodies 130
anti-snRNP antibodies 131
applications 796
biotin-labeled antibodies 818
brucellosis diagnosis 385
catalytic antibody screening 444
competitive assays 816–817
affinity measurement 45–46
cytokine assay 694–695, 695(Fig), 696
development 816
Echinococcus detection 784
enzyme conjugates 818
evaluation of factors influencing 818–819
haptens, measurement 45
Helicobacter pylori detection 1057
hepatitis C virus (HCV) detection 1080
IL-1 detection 1432
immunopathology investigation 1340
method 694–695
noncompetitive assay 817
nonspecific adsorption problem 817, 818
principle 796, 816–817
'sandwich' assay 817
IL-12 1487
schistosomiasis diagnosis 2142
sensitivity 818
solid phase 817–818
covalent binding 817
types 817
TGFβ detection 2394
ELISASPOT assays, *see* ELISPOT assay
ELISPOT assay 796–698, 1961(Table),
1962
antigen-specific Ig-secreting cell detection
797
applications 797–798
cytokine-secreting cell detection 798
development 796
principles 796, 797(Fig)
solid phase 797
Elk1 transcription factor 2327
Elliptocytosis 837
Elongation factor 2 (EF2) 662, 1420
Embden–Meyerhof pathway, red cells 837

Embedding, tissue 1262
Embryogenesis
β₂-microglobulin expression 368
organ culture use in studies 1899
TNFα functions 2437
Embryology
ABO blood group 4
amphibian thymus 80
bone marrow hematopoiesis 374
bursa of Fabricius 393
canine 411–412
lymphoid organs 396
see also Ontogeny of immune response
Embryonic antigens 798–801, 1361
ABO blood group 4, 799
see also Alphafetoprotein (AFP); CALLA;
Carcinoembryonic antigen (CEA);
Fetal antigens
Embryonic stem cell growth factor
(ESCGF), *see* Leukemia inhibitory
factor (LIF)
Embryonic stem (ES) cells 1525
DNA introduction 2406
gene disruption in 981
genetically modified 1525–1526,
1525(Fig), 1566
Emetic principle 313
Emetine, T cell hybridoma selection 1153–
1154
Emiocytosis 849
EMIT (enzyme-multiplied
immunotechnique) 815, 816
Emotional disturbances, impact on immune
system 1831–1832
Emphysema, neutrophils 1858
Emulsions, as adjuvants 37
Encapsulation
invertebrates 1499–1500
iridoviruses 1504
Encephalitis
Japanese, *see* Japanese encephalitis (JE)
postvaccinal 1998
Rasmussen's 1843
reovirus-induced 2070
tickborne, *see* Tickborne encephalitis
(TBE)
toxoplasmosis 2384
Encephalomyelitis
experimental autoimmune, *see*
Experimental autoimmune
encephalomyelitis (EAE)
Hu-specific antibodies 1842
paraneoplastic 1842
postinfectious 1830
postmeasles 272
postrabies vaccination 1830
proteolipoprotein-induced experimental
487
Encephalomyocarditis (EMC) virus,
diabetes induction 1396
Encephalopathy
Bordetella pertussis vaccine causing 2463
bovine spongiform, *see* Bovine
spongiform encephalopathy (BSE)
HIV, *see* HIV encephalopathy
postvaccinal 1998, 2463
transmissible spongiform, *see*
Transmissible spongiform
encephalopathies (TSEs)
see also Progressive multifocal
leukoencephalopathy (PML)
Endocarditis, infective 567–568
causative organisms 567, 2082(Table)
culture-negative 568
diagnosis 567
immune response 567–568
staphylococcal 567, 568
streptococcal 567
subacute 567
Endocarditis, Libman–Sachs 2255
Endocrine system

Endocrine system (*continued*)
autoimmune disease pathogenesis 278–
279
feedback system 1851, 1852(Fig)
Endocytosis 849
exocytosis coupling 851, 853, 855(Fig)
receptor-mediated, macrophage 1644
transferrin receptor recycling 2390–2391,
2391(Fig)
Endogenous pyrogen (EP), *see* Interleukin-
1 (IL-1); Tumor necrosis factor α
(TNFα)
Endoglin (CD105) 453(Table)
Endometrial granulated lymphocytes (eGL)
899–900
Endometrium
adaptations, fetal protection 899
leukemia inhibitory factor (LIF)
expression 1561
maternal, MHC antigen expression 899
Endomysial membranes, autoantibodies
264
Endonucleases, Holliday junctions
resolution 971
Endoperoxides 2024
Endoplasmic reticulum (ER) 849
antibody retention 144
antibody secretion 144, 158
antigen (protein) transport to 192
degradation of newly synthesized
proteins 147
Legionella pneumophila association 1543
MHC class I, peptide antigen interaction
192–193
MHC class II molecules 196, 354
H2 assembly 1043–1044, 1043(Fig)
protein secretion 144
protein translocation 144, 354, 849, 851
hsp70 role 2230
rough 849
H2 class I synthesis 1037–1038,
1039(Fig)
β-Endorphin 1829, 2225
synthesis 2225
Endorphins 1829
release, exercise-induced 847
Endosomes
lysosomal granule fusion 737
recycling, transferrin receptor (TfR)
marker 2390
Endosome–lysosome complexes 853
Endothelial cells 802–806
activated, E-selectin expression 803
activation 30
hyperacute xenograft rejection 2509
type II, acute xenograft rejection 2510
adhesion molecules 803–805
three-dimensional structure 518–519
see also Addressins; ICAM-1; PECAM-
1; Selectins; VCAM-1
after diapedesis of leukocytes 759
as APCs in sheep 1905
apoptosis, UCD 200 chicken strain 285
CD5 expression 473
CD40 function 486
cell-to-cell junctions 758, 802–803
CNS 1844
opening/triggering 802–803
cerebrovascular 1844, 1844(Fig), 1845
clefts 802, 803
colony-stimulating factors synthesis 802
contact hypersensitivity 1178
cytokines effect on 805–806
cytokines produced by 806
delayed type hypersensitivity 741
estrogen receptor expression 2176
'flat' 1093, 1094
G-CSF actions 805–806, 1019
graft rejection 1012
in high endothelial venules (HEV) 1093
see also High endothelial venules
(HEV)

Endothelial cells (*continued*)
high (HEC), *see* High endothelial cells (HEC)
IL-13 effects 1490–1491
in inflammation 17, 805
leukocyte adhesion, *see* Leukocyte(s), adhesion
leukocyte extravasation, *see* High endothelial venules (HEV); *transmigration of leukocytes (below)*
leukocyte rolling, *see* Leukocyte(s), rolling
M-CSF from 1651
monocyte interactions 1237(Fig), 1754
monolayer culture 760
neutrophil adherence 1854–1855
neutrophil migration 802–803
permeability 802
prostacyclin (PGI₂) 2024
retraction 759
due to neutrophils 17
role in filoviral hemorrhagic fever 918, 919(Fig)
sheep 1905
in spleen 2207
T cell interactions 1237(Fig)
in thrombosis 805
tight junctions, in CNS 1844
TNFα effect 2439–2440
transmigration of leukocytes 757–759, 802–803, 803(Fig), 1249, 1619–1620
see also Diapedesis; High endothelial venules (HEV); Transmigration of leukocytes
vasoconstriction 579
vasodilators secreted 579, 805
Endothelial-derived relaxing factor (EDRF) 579
Endothelin 579
Endothelium 802–806
cytokines and 805–806
integrity 759
pigs 2509
platelet adhesion 1973–1974
see also Endothelial cells
Endotoxic shock 424
see also Septic shock
Endotoxin 806–809, 2377–2379
origin of term 806–807
see also Lipopolysaccharide (LPS)
Energetics, antibody–antigen interactions 166, 2199–2200, 2203
Energy
antibody–antigen bonds 165, 2199–2200, 2203
catalytic antibody reactions 443
fat-derived intake 884
free, van der Waals interactions 163
Gibbs free energy 2200
metabolism in red cell membranes 837
Enhancement, immunological 809–812, 2486
active 810, 810–811
blood transfusions 811
factors favouring 810–811
sensitization risk 810, 811
hyperacute rejection and 812
'induction' phase 810
'maintenance' phase 810
passive 810, 811–812
Fc region role 812
mechanisms 811–812
potency 812
specificity of antibodies 812
prevention, vitamin E 2500
principles 809–810
Enhanceosome 1419
Enkephalinase (CD10) 1806
Enkephalins 1829
Enrichment techniques
B cells, *see under* B cell(s)
T cells 181–182, 1235–1238

Enrichment techniques (*continued*)
T cells (*continued*)
hybridoma generation 1153
Entamoeba dispar 77, 78
Entamoeba histolytica 77
antigens 77
characteristics 77
complement-inhibiting proteins 500
cysts 77
infections 968
SREHP 77, 79
see also Amebiasis
Enteritis, *Campylobacter* 407–408
Enterobacteriaceae 842, 2039, 2512
lipopolysaccharide 807
Enterococcus faecalis, endocarditis 567
Enterocytes
antigen uptake 190
class II MHC expression 190
M cell attachment 189
Enteropathic arthritis, clinical features 2120
Enteropathy
food-sensitive 948
gluten-sensitive, *see* Celiac disease
Enterotoxins
accessory cholera (ACE) 2372, 2477
Bacillus cereus 313
Escherichia coli 843, 968
Staphylococcal B (SEB) 538, 2209
Staphylococcus 2209
S. aureus, see Staphylococcus aureus
Streptococcus 2218
superantigen, *see Staphylococcus aureus*
TCR γδ specificity 2275(Table)
Enteroviral meningoencephalitis 599
Enterovirus 871, 1955(Table)
receptors 1954, 1956(Table)
Enteroviruses
eye infections 871, 872
infections, diabetes mellitus association 1400
nonpathogenic, effect on pathogenic strains 259
receptor for 1954, 1956(Table)
Enthalpy 166
Entropy 166
Environmental antigens, type III hypersensitivity 1176
Environmental factors/influences
Addison's disease etiology 43
animal models of IDDM 1396–1397
atopy 252
autoimmune disease pathogenesis 279
B cell repertoire 360–361
cardiovascular disease 988
in multifactorial conditions 988
thyroid autoimmunity induction 2314
experimental 2311
Environmental pressure, evolution 1950–1951
Enzyme(s)
copper requirement 657, 658(Table)
cytoplasmic 127
granule-associated, *see* Granzymes
as labels 813–814, 814, 1262–1263
characteristics 813–814
in ELISA 818
enzymes, used 814
see also Enzyme labeling
as markers 1258–1267
see also Enzyme labeling
in mast cells 1668
nuclear 126
in red cell membranes 837
synthesis by macrophage 1388
as tracers 813
Enzyme immunoassays (EIA) 813
antigen quantitation 815–816
enzyme inhibitors in 815
heterogeneous 815
see also ELISA

Enzyme immunoassays (EIA) (*continued*)
historical aspects 816
homogeneous 815, 816
Enzyme immunocytochemistry, antigen localization 815
Enzyme labeling 813–816, 1263
antibodies 814–815
applications 813
coupling procedures 814
methods 814–815
sandwich immunoelectrophoresis technique 1296
sensitivity and Ig type 814
antibody detection 813
antigens 813
detection 813, 815, 1263
localization 815
quantitation 815–816
in ELISA 818
enzymes used, *see under* Enzyme(s)
in immunoassays 1253, 1255
immunocytochemistry 1258–1267
principles 813
Enzyme-linked immunoassay, competitive, *see* Competitive enzyme-linked immunoassay (CELIA)
Enzyme-linked immunosorbent assay (ELISA), *see* ELISA
Enzyme-multiplied immunotechnique (EMIT) 815, 816
Eosin dye test, in tissue typing method 2319
Eosinophil(s) 822–825, 1388
accumulation 819
activation 822–823
T_H2 cell role 1918
autoimmune bullous dermatoses 2188
biological activities 822, 823(Table)
chemokines 536(Table)
chemotactic factor, *see* Eosinophil chemotactic factors
chemotaxis 819
in vivo 820–821
modulation 821
degranulation 822, 823–824, 823(Table)
in asthma 244
development/hematopoiesis 823
growth factors affecting 823, 824, 824(Table)
discovery 819
in disease 823–824
Echinococcus infections 784
exocytosis, C3a action 89
fascioliasis 881
FcγR function 889–890
functions 822, 823, 823(Table)
regulation 824, 824(Table)
granules 822, 1724
contents 822–823
degranulation, *see above*
see also Major basic protein (MBP)
growth factor effects 823, 824, 824(Table)
IL-5 receptors 1457
leukotrienes produced 823
microbicidal mechanisms 1724–1725
migration and extravasation 821, 823
nonchemokine attractants 537(Table)
numbers 822
onchocerciasis 1873
parasitic infections 1173
phagocytosis 823
production 1456
IL-5 role 1456
receptors for cytokines 823
recruitment, IL-4 role 1452
respiratory burst 823, 823(Table)
role in lung damage 1456
schistosomiasis 2140–2142
skin infections 752–753
structure and biochemistry 822–823
surface phenotype 822, 1803

Eosinophil(s) (continued)
toxic oxygen metabolites from 823(Table)
Eosinophil activating factor 824(Table)
Eosinophil cationic protein (ECP) 822, 1724
Eosinophil chemotactic factors 819–824, 820(Table), 824
chemical nature 819–820
function 819–820
inactivation 821
in vivo action 820–821
in mast cells 1668
sources 819–820
Eosinophil cytotoxicity-enhancing factor 824(Table)
Eosinophil-derived neurotoxin (EDN) 822
Eosinophil hematopoietins 823, 824, 824(Table)
Eosinophilia 819, 822
allergic rhinitis 2123
fascioliasis 881
hookworm disease 1124
IL-4-mediated 1452
IL-5-induced 820–821
parasitic infections 1173
space flights causing 1030, 1031
transgenic mice overexpressing IL-5 1456
tropical pulmonary 914
Eosinophilic granular cells (EGCs), in fish 924
Eosinophilic granulomata, Toxocara canis 2381
Eosinophil peroxidase (EPO) 822, 1716
Eotaxin, eosinophil chemotaxis 820
Ep-CAM 2428
EPEC, see Escherichia coli, enteropathogenic
Epibody 1187
Epidemic keratoconjunctivitis 872
Epidemiological risk estimate 1698
Epidermal growth factor (EGF) 907
CD45 relationship 494
module in C1r and C1s 606
in tumors 2429
Epidermal growth factor (EGF) repeat 865
Epidermal growth factor receptor (EGFR) 710
δEGFR 2429
internalization by adenovirus 22
in tumors 2429
Epidermis 2190
cell types 2190
Epidermodysplasia verruciformis 751
Epidermolysis bullosa
acquired 2188
congenital 2516
Epigenetic diversity 209
Epilepsy
anti-phospholipid antibodies 1843
Cysticercus 690
Epinephrine (adrenaline) 2224
anaphylaxis treatment 684–685, 685
emergency self-treatment kits 685
exercise-induced 847
inhalations 685
Epipolarization microscopy 1264
Epithelial cells
CD40 function 486
EBV infection 828, 829
in lymphoid organs 1249
Epithelioid cells 1756
granuloma 1023, 1024
Epithelium
follicle-associated (FAE) 1776
Peyer's patches 1776
TCR γδ cells 2272
Epithelium membrane antigen (EMA), immunocytochemistry application 1266
Epitopes 150, 202, 219, 825–827, 1228, 2465

Epitopes (continued)
artificial, of proteins 1050
of autoantigens (autoepitopes), see under Autoantigens
B cell, see under B cell(s)
'conformation' recognition, by antibodies 150
continuous (sequential) 202, 826, 1290
cross-reactive 2202
cryptic 1228, 1290
response to 754
tolerance breakdown 294
definition 201, 266, 825, 1290
discontinuous 150, 202, 826, 1188, 1290, 1292
disease-associated, experimental autoimmune thyroiditis 2310
dominant 1228, 1290
functional (energetic), cross-reactivity and 2203–2205
haptens as 1050
idiotypes as, see Idiotype(s)
immunodominant 1290, 1290–1292
see also Immunodominance
immunopotent 202
immunosilent 202
mapping, surface plasmon resonance (SPR) 2250
number (valency) 2465
see also Valency
polysaccharides 427
repeating, on T-independent antigens 216
sequential 202, 826, 1290
single in monovalent antigens 2466
single or multiple overlapping 2202
spreading, see Determinant spreading
subdominant 1290
T cell, see under T cell(s)
as vaccines 437
Epitope–paratope bonds 164–165, 165
ep mice 1272
Epstein–Barr virus (EBV) 828–833
adoptive transfer of CTLs 833
antigens 828, 1360, 2487
early and late 828
attachment to CD21 (CR2) 631
B cell infection 828, 829
B cell transformation 2487
mAb preparation 1745, 1745(Fig)
BHRF1 homology with Bcl-2 2487
BZLF-1 protein 828
carriers 828, 832
characteristics 828
diseases 831–832
Burkitt's lymphoma 1635
lymphomas 831–832, 2487
nasopharyngeal carcinoma 832
tumors 1360
see also Burkitt's lymphoma; Infectious mononucleosis
evasive strategies 832
gp340 830, 833
Guillain–Barré syndrome after 1836
HHV-8 relationship 1090
Hodgkin's disease etiology 1634
host immune responses 828–832
EBV-associated disease 831–832
persistent infection, see below
in hu-SCID mice 1274
immunodeficiency-associated lymphomas 1635–1636
immunodeficiency due to 1286
latency 828–829, 832
LMP1 2487
LMP2 832
lymphocyte proliferation due to 2021
lymphocytes in SCID mice 1128
lytic cycle 828, 830
membrane antigen (MA) 828
antibodies 830, 831
nuclear antigens (EBNA) 828, 829(Table), 832, 2487

Epstein–Barr virus (EBV) (continued)
nuclear antigens (EBNA) (continued)
antibodies 830
EBNA3A 829, 833
EBNA5 2487
evasive strategies 832
nucleocapsid (VCA) 828
antibodies 830
persistent infections 828–831, 830(Fig)
immune response 828–831
sites and mechanism 829
primary infection 830, 830(Fig)
primate models 2005
proteins 828, 829(Table)
reactivation, stress association 2222
receptor 828
rheumatoid arthritis etiology 2114
Sjögren's syndrome (SS) etiology 2183
transmission 828
in transplant recipients 1884
treatment of infections 833
vaccine 833
Epstein–Barr virus (EBV)-cell lines
IL-2 synthesis 1436
IL-12 1484
Equilibration time, definition 1597, 1599
Equilibrium binding, surface plasmon resonance (SRP) measurement 2249
Equilibrium dialysis
affinity of hapten-specific antibody 1051
affinity measurement 45
Equilibrium dissociation constant (K_D), catalytic antibodies 440
Equilibrium dissociation constant (K_D) 44, 148, 166
Equine arteritis virus 2350
Equine infectious anemia virus (EIAV) 2096
antigenic variation 200
erbA gene 1564
erbB gene 1564
overexpression 1563
Ergotype 2285
ERK, see Extracellular signal-regulated kinases (ERK)
Error-in-variables model 2213
Erysipelas 752, 2218
Erythema nodosum leprosum (ENL) 1797
Erythroblastosis fetalis, see Hemolytic disease of newborn (HDN)
Erythroblasts, fetal, isolation 801
Erythrocyte(s) 833–841
adhesion test 1219
agglutination, see Agglutination; Coombs' test; Hemagglutination
aging and destruction 840–841
alloantibodies 347
anion channel protein 91, 840
antigen adherence to 1219
antigens, see ABO blood groups; Blood groups; Rh (Rhesus) blood groups
autoantibodies
experimental models 91–93
human, see Autoimmune hemolytic anemia (AIHA)
autoantigen clearance 184–185
CR1 expression 183, 184, 840
CR1 function 629
'dense' 840
development/maturation 833–834
glycolipids 3, 834–835
IgG-coated, sequestration in spleen 96
I and i antigens 594
autoantibodies to 94
immune adherence 1219
immune complex interaction 1223
lifespan 840
lysis
extravascular 100
membrane attack complex 626
neonatal 901
plaque-forming cell assays 1960

Erythrocyte(s) *(continued)*
  membrane 834–840
    antigens 835, 837
    band 3 protein 835, 837, 840
    biochemistry 834–835
    blood group antigens 837
    defects, Rh deficiency syndrome 2105
    energy metabolism 837
    enzymes 837
    ion pumps/channels 837, 840
    lipids 834–835, 835(Table)
    microdomains 418
    proteins 835
    receptors 840
    Rh polypeptides 837
    skeleton 835
  natural antibodies 1806
  osmotic fragility 841
  phagocytosis, spleen 2207
  radiolabeled, antigen clearance studies
      185
  rosetting techniques, *see* Rosetting
      techniques
  splenic sequestration, in babesiosis 310
  structure and shape 833–834, 836(Fig)
    disorders 834
    surface remodeling 834
  tannic acid-treated, agglutination 57
  tissue typing 2318
  transfusions 2400(Table)
  transport 1965
Erythrocyte-antibody-complement (EAC)
    assay 669
  complex 1219
  rosette inhibition test 1221–1222
Erythrogenic toxins 2218
Erythroid burst-forming unit (BFU-E),
    development, GM-CSF role 1021
Erythroid burst-promoting activity, IL-9
    1473
Erythroid progenitor cells, phenotype 1803
Erythrolysis
  neonatal 901
  see also Erythrocyte(s)
Erythropoiesis, suppression, parvovirus
    B19 infection 1925
Erythropoietin 375
  feedback system 2017
  function in myelopoiesis 375
  preparations, quality control 1513(Fig)
  receptor, structure 520
ESCGF (embryonic stem cell growth
    factor), *see* Leukemia inhibitory factor
    (LIF)
Escherichia coli 842–845
  adherence 2452
  adhesins 844, 2066
  antigens 842
    K, H and O types 842
  attaching and effacing lesions 843, 844
  bactericidal/permeability increasing
      proteins (BPI) action 1722
  characteristics 842
  cloning 981–983
  colicin action 2014
  colonization factor antigens (CFA) 842,
      845
  diarrhea due to 842–844, 845, 967, 968
    pathogenesis 843
  enteroaggregative (EAEC) 842,
      843(Table), 844
    adhesins 844
  enterohemorrhagic (EHEC) 842,
      843(Table), 844
  enteroinvasive (EIEC) 842, 843(Table),
      844, 967
  enteropathogenic (EPEC) 842, 843–844,
      843(Table)
    adherence factor (EAF) 843
    diarrhea due to 843–844, 968
  enterotoxigenic (ETEC) 269, 842–843,
      843(Table)

Escherichia coli (continued)
  enterotoxigenic (ETEC) *(continued)*
    diarrhea 843, 845, 967
    enterotoxins 269
    LT genes 2373
    LT toxin 38, 843, 968, 2369, 2370
    LT toxin mode of action 2373–2374,
        2373(Fig)
    ST toxin 38, 843, 968, 2369, 2370
    fimbriae 842, 844, 1536(Fig), 2452
    GVVPQ fimbriae 844
    lectin structure 1536(Fig)
    urinary tract infections 2452, 2453
  β-galactosidase 814
  heat-labile toxin, *see LT toxin* above
  hemolysin 2377
  host immune response 844–845
  hsp60 and hsp70 2229
  lipopolysaccharide (endotoxin) 2452
    in systemic inflammatory response
        syndrome 1520
  mannose-binding protein (MBP)
      interaction 187
  microbicidal mechanisms 1938
  mismatch repair downregulation 973
  normal gastrointestinal flora 842, 844
  pili 842, 844, 2452
    'longus' 843
  receptors 1538
  recombination 972
    mutations associated 972
  serotypes and classification 842
  thyroid autoimmune disease 2314
  toxins 38, 842, 843
    Shiga-like 844
  TSH binding 2314
  urethral infection 2075
  urinary tract infections 2065, 2452
  uropathogenic 2452
    adherence 2452
    colonization 2452
    predisposing factors 2453
  vaccines 845
  virotypes 842–844
  virulence factors 842, 844, 2452
Escherichia coli K100, capsular antigens
    423
Escherichia coli O157:H7 842, 844
E-selectin (CD62E; ELAM-1) 16,
    27(Table), 28, 450(Table), 2160–2161
  expression 2160
    endothelial cells 803–804, 2160
    regulation 803–804
  function 1539, 2160
  knockout mice 32, 1566, 1566(Table)
  leukocyte rolling 2160
  Lewis^x (Le^x) and sialyl-Le^x as ligands
      1578–1579
  ligands 27(Table), 28, 450(Table), 2160–
      2169
  monoclonal antibodies 804
  neutrophil binding defect, LAD II
      syndrome 1568
  neutrophil migration 1935, 2160
  in pigs 1993
  rheumatoid arthritis 2114
  structure 1536(Fig), 2160
  X-ray 518–519
ESL-1 29
Estradiol, TNFα release increased 2437
Estrogen 2176
  IFNγ production 2177
  receptors 2176
ETEC, *see Escherichia coli*, enterotoxigenic
Ethidium bromide, in tissue typing method
    2319
Ethylenediamine tetraacetic acid (EDTA)
    1717
Euglobulins 964
European brown hare syndrome virus
    (EBHSV) 400
  antigens 400–401

Europium^{3+} 143
Evolution
  amphibians 79
  antibody diversity 1950
  B cells 1948
  blood cells 1948, 1949
  cell-mediated immunity 1948
  complement 1950
  elasmobranchs Ig 1307
  environmental pressure and 1950–1951
  extracellular matrix (ECM) 861
  HIV 1134–1135
  hookworms 1122
  humoral immune response 1948
  Igs, *see* Immunoglobulin
  immunoglobulin gene superfamily (IgSF)
      1322
  innate immunity 1388, 1948
  interferons 1414
  lectins 1950
  β₂-microglobulin 367–368, 1950
  natural selection 1701–1702
  pathogens 255, 259
  primates (nonhuman) 2010(Fig)
  privileged sites 2013
  recognition molecules 1948, 1949–1950
  T cell receptor (TCR) 2278–2282
  T cells 1948
  see also Phylogeny of immune response
Exanthem subitum 1089
Excretory/secretory (ES) products
  Ascaris lumbricoides 241
  Clonorchis sinensis 1879
  hookworms 1122
  Opisthorchis viverrini 1879
  Toxocara canis 2380
Exercise 845–848
  animal models of tumor growth 848
  ataxia telangiectasia (AT) 250
  autoimmune disease and 848
  benefits 845
  cholinergic urticaria after 683
  colon cancer and 848
  cytokines and 846
  immune cell interactions 846–847
  immunity and 847–848
  infections and 847
  lymphocyte functions 846, 846–847
  lymphocyte subpopulations 845–846
  neuroendocrine interactions 846–847
  'open window' hypothesis 847
Exfoliatin 2209
Exocrine tissues
  Ig-producing cells 2155
  pIg transport 2155
  secretory component expression 2155
Exocytosis 849–856, 1026, 2165
  cell-lysis mechanism 726, 1028
  cytomorphological infrastructure 849–
      851
  definition 849
  in degranulation 737, 851
  endocytosis coupling 851, 853, 855(Fig)
  historical background 849
  membrane flow and conservation 853,
      856
  membrane fusion proteins/components
      852(Table)
  m-exocytosis to cell membrane 849,
      850(Fig), 851, 853
    targeting/capture of vesicles 854(Fig)
  role 853, 856
  sequential (compound) 851
  s-exocytosis to extracellular space 849,
      850(Fig), 851
    regulated/constitutive 851
    sites/occurrences 851
    targeting/capture of vesicles 851,
        854(Fig)
  vesicle translocation 849, 851, 853
Experimental allergic encephalomyelitis
    (EAE), *see* Experimental autoimmune
    encephalitis (EAE)

Experimental allergic neuritis (EAN) 860, 1836–1837
Experimental animals, see Animal models
Experimental autoimmune anterior uveitis (EAAU) 868(Table)
Experimental autoimmune encephalomyelitis (EAE) 271, 856–860, 1357
  autoimmune T cells 1694
  bystander suppression 1895
  CD4+ T cells as effectors 858, 859, 860
  chronic relapsing (CREAE) 858
  clinical aspects 858
  cytokines 859
  determinant spreading 754–755, 755–756, 756
  donor-specific immunosuppression 810
  encephalitogenic antigens 857–858, 858(Table)
    myelin basic protein (MBP) 857–858
    myelin oligodendrocyte glycoprotein (MOG) 858
    proteolipid protein (PLP) 857–858, 1895
    sequences 857, 857(Fig)
  genetics 859
  historical aspects 856
  immunopathology 858–859
  induction 857–858
    mice 858
  inflammatory lesions 858–859
  inhibition and recovery 860
  lymphotoxin 1640
  MHC association 859, 859(Table)
  mucosal tolerance, TGFβ role 2392
  as multiple sclerosis model 1786, 1841
  pathogenesis 859
  as postrabies vaccination encephalomyelitis model 1830
  prevention, calcitriol 2496
  recovery, TGFβ role 2397
  regulation 859–860
  relapsing form 271
  resistance, T cell vaccination 2284
  suppressor T cells 859, 1841
  TCR genes 2310
  TCR repertoire 859, 859(Table)
  TGFβ effect 1894, 2396, 2397
    nitric oxide formation inhibition 2396
  T$_H$1 cells 1695
  therapy 860
    by oral tolerance 1896
Experimental autoimmune myasthenia gravis (EAMG) 1835, 1849
  TGFβ role 2392–2393
  tolerance induction 2397
  treatment by AChR 1897
Experimental autoimmune neuritis (EAN) 860, 1836–1837
Experimental autoimmune uveoretinitis (EAU) 868–871
  adjuvant use 868
  adoptive transfer 869
  antigens 870
  genetics and MHC association 869
  histopathology 868, 870(Fig)
  immunotherapy 869
  induction 868
  interphotoreceptor retinoid-binding protein (IRBP) 870
  molecular mimicry role 869
  T$_H$2 role in regulation 869
Experimental models, see Animal models
Extracellular matrix (ECM) 861–866
  cell receptors 866
  collagens 861, 861–862, 907
  components 861
    synthesized by fibroblasts 903(Fig), 905, 907
  degradation 865
  diversity 861
  elastin 862

Extracellular matrix (ECM) (continued)
  evolution 861
  fibrous proteins 861–862
  glycoproteins 864–865
  mesenchymal origin 861
  protein A binding 2210
  proteins, in thymopoiesis 2236
  proteoglycans 862–864
  resorption 865
  turnover 865–866
  ultraviolet irradiation affecting 907
  see also Collagen; Glycoprotein(s); Proteoglycans
Extracellular matrix receptor III (ECMRIII), see CD44
Extracellular signal-regulated kinases (ERK)
  activation 2327
  ERK-1 2327
  ERK-1,2 MAP kinases, IL-3 receptor signal transduction 1443
  ERK-2 2327
    Elk1 regulation 2327
    regulation 2327
  ERK-2 MAP kinase, IL-2 receptor signal transduction 1441
  TCR signaling 2327–2328
  TNF receptor signaling 2347
Extracellular space, exocytosis 851
Extraocular muscle hypertrophy 2316
Extravasation of leukocytes, see Leukocyte(s)
Extrinsic alveolitis 1176
Eye
  antigens, see Ocular antigens
  autoimmune diseases 867–871
    animal models 867, 868(Table)
    preventive mechanisms 870
    see also Experimental autoimmune uveoretinitis (EAU)
  dry, Sjögren's syndrome (SS) 2181
  as immunologically privileged site 867
  as mediator of immune privilege 1656
  ontogeny 868
Eye infections 871–874
  bacteria 873
  host defense mechanisms 871
  leptospirosis 1553
  long-term 872–874
  onchocerciasis 1873
  short-term 871–872
  strategies 871
  viral 871–872, 872–873

F

F1 hybrids 1370
F(ab')$_2$
  distribution in tumors 2433
  structure 2432, 2432(Fig)
Fab fragment 775, 1329
  functions 1315
  IgG, glycosylation 1002, 1003–1004
  libraries 1745
  structure 2432, 2432(Fig)
Fab' fragment, structure 2432, 2432(Fig)
Fab–hapten complexes, structures 171
FACIT (fibril associated collagens with interrupted triple helices) 861
FACS, see Fluorescence-activated cell sorting (FACS)
Facteur thymique serique, see Thymulin
Factor B
  C3b complex with 602
  as class III MHC 622
  cleavage into Ba and Bb 587
  gene 116(Table), 622, 1115
Factor D 602
Factor H 603

Factor H (continued)
  cobra venom factor (CVF) resistance 587
  deficiency 615(Table)
  gene 620
  receptor (fH-R) 633
Factor I (complement) 603
  cleavage 629
  cobra venom factor (CVF) resistance 587
  deficiency 615(Table)
Factor Va 583
Factor VIII
  activation 582
  in cryoprecipitate 1966
  fibronectin binding 910
  inhibitors 1967
  preparation, immunoaffinity chromatography 52
Factor VIIIa 583
Factor IX 583, 585
Factor X, function 583, 585
Factor Xa 582, 583
Factor XI 582
  deficiency 583
Factor XII 582, 1519
  activation 1519, 1519–1520
  deficiency 583
Factor XIIa 1519, 1520
  inhibitor 1520
Factor XIIf 1519, 1520
  inhibitor 1520
Factor XIII, in cryoprecipitate 1966
Factor XIIIa 582
FADD, see Fas-associated death domain (FADD)
FAK (focal adhesion kinase), mast cell degranulation 1670
FALL-39 1724
Fallopian tubes, gonococcal infection 2073(Fig)
Familial amyloid polyneuropathy 85
Familial hypercholesterolemia 987–988
  LDL-apheresis 1252
Familial reticuloendotheliosis (Omenn's syndrome) 1279
FAN, TNF receptor signaling 2348
Fanconi syndrome 341
Farr assay 129, 129(Table), 130, 141, 1052
  hapten–antibody binding 1052
Fas-associated death domain (FADD) 225, 711, 875, 876, 1028
  TNF receptor signaling 2347
Fas (CD95) 453(Table), 654–655, 874–880, 875
  agonists 876
  antagonists 876
  apoptosis, see Fas/FasL interaction/pathway
  in cell-mediated lysis 507
    see also Fas/FasL interaction/pathway
  clonal deletion pathway 570–571, 655, 876, 878
  costimulatory function 655–656, 878
  deficiency 878
    hyper-IgM syndrome 1168
  downregulation of immune response 654–655, 877, 878(Fig)
  expansion of antigen-stimulated B cells 878
  expression 571, 655, 875(Table), 876
  functions 875, 875(Table)
    duration of immune response 877
    immune regulation 877
    see also Fas/FasL interaction/pathway
  ligand, see Fas ligand (FasL)
  mutation, see lpr mutation
  overexpression 879
  receptor trimerization 876
  regulator of T cell/B cell maturation 655
  T cell downregulation 655
  T cell proliferation 878
  see also Fas/FasL interaction/pathway

Fasciitis 2218
Fasciola hepatica 800
  antigens 800–881
    somatic 881
    tegumental 881
    vaccines 883
  cercariae and cysts 880
  characteristics 800–881
  evasive strategies 883
  host immune response 881–882, 883
  life cycle 880, 882(Fig)
  morphology 881(Fig)
  vaccines 883
Fascioliasis 880–883
  acute/chronic phases 881
  immune response 881–882, 883
  primary infection 881
  resistance 881
  see also *Fasciola hepatica*
Fas/FasL interaction/pathway
  activation-induced cell death 2332
  apoptosis 224, 225, 874–875, 877(Fig)
    autoreactive B cells 2366
    B cells 878
    dysregulation and pathology 878–879
    effector phase 876
    Fas role 223, 225, 226, 654–655
    graft rejection 879, 1012
    mechanisms 875–876, 877(Fig)
    T cells 876–877, 878, 879, 1012
  cell-mediated lysis 506–507, 655, 734
    anergic B cells 572, 878
    cytotoxic T cells 727, 728(Fig), 876
    Fas action 507
  clonal deletion 570–571, 655, 876, 878
  defects, murine lupus 2252–2253, 2260
  deficiency 878
  Hashimoto's thyroiditis 879
  hepatitis 879
  HIV infection 879
  immune escape by tumor cells 879
  immune function and regulation 876–878
  in immune privilege 879, 2012
  influenza virus infections 1386
  mechanisms 875–876, 877(Fig)
    receptor trimerization 876
  virus-induced apoptosis 2485
  see also Fas (CD95); Fas ligand (FasL)
Fas ligand (FasL) 364, 507, 655, 874–880,
    875
  autocrine death, role 571
  cell lysis mechanism 504
  clonal deletion pathway 570–571, 655,
    876–877
  expression 571, 875(Table), 876
    immune privileged sites 879
    T cells 875
    tumors 879
  functions 655, 875(Table)
  lpr mutation 875
  overexpression 879
Fat
  dietary, tumorigenesis 885
  energy intake by 884
  total intake 884
  see also Fatty acids (dietary); Lipid
Fatal familial insomnia (FFI) 2409
Fatty acid binding promoter (Fabpi) 1382
Fatty acids (dietary) 884–886
  eicosanoid production 884–885
  energy intake by 884
  free fatty acid metabolism 788
  membrane composition changes 885–886
  monounsaturated 884
  recommendations for intake 884
  sources 884
  unsaturated bonds 134
  see also Polyunsaturated fatty acids
    (PUFAs)
FcαR 891, 1318
  expression, cytokines influencing 891
  function 1318

FcαR (*continued*)
  on phagocytes 1886
  structure 891
FcαRI 452(Table)
  on monocytes 1752
FcεR 890–891, 1171, 1203–1204, 1317–
    1318
  antibodies preventing binding,
    immunotherapy 1356
  characteristics 1204(Table)
  distribution 890
  domains 890–891
  expression 890
    IL-4 stimulating 1452
  functional properties 891
  genes encoding 890–891
  modulation 891
  numbers per cell 890
  properties 890
  types 890
FcεRI (high-affinity) 251, 254, 886, 890,
    1171, 1203, 1317–1318
  affinity 1203
  aggregation, mast cell activation 1669,
    1670
  cells expressing 1171, 1317
  characteristics 1204(Table)
  cross-linking, cytokines released 891
  cytoplasmic domain 1669
  expression 1207
  extracellular domain 1669
  functional properties 891, 1318
  gene 252
  ITAM motif 1669–1670
  on mast cells 1669, 1783
  modulation 891
  phosphorylation of subunits 1670
  species-specificity 1669
  structure 887(Fig), 1203, 1669
FcεRII (low-affinity; CD23) 252, 254,
    447(Table), 890, 891, 1171, 1204
  cells expressing 891, 1171, 1318
    phagocytes 1886
  characteristics 1204(Table)
  clonal deletion of activated B cells 572
  expression, PAF effect 1972
  FcεRIIB, on monocytes 1752
  function 891, 1171, 1318
  IgE synthesis control 1205–1207
  isoforms 890, 1171
    alternative splicing of genes 891
  lectin domain 1204
  modulation/upregulation 891
  soluble 890, 891
    function 718
  structure 887(Fig), 1204
FcγR 168, 886–888, 1317
  allelic variants 889
  B cells 888
  cells expressing 886, 888, 1174
  deficiency, Arthus reaction reduced 239
  distribution 888
  eosinophils 889–890
  expression 886, 888
    IFNγ role 1424
    modulation 889
    numbers per cell 889
  functional properties 889–890
  functions 886, 1317
  γ chain in phagocytosis and ADCC 889
  genes encoding 88–889
  glycosylation 1002, 1003
  high-affinity, see FcγRI
  HL-60 cells 890
  on HSV 1088
  IgG-induced immune hemolytic anemia
    94–95, 96, 98
  in infectious disease 890
  large granular lymphocytes 888, 890
  ligand-binding domains 170
  low-affinity, see FcγRII
  medium-affinity, see FcγRIII

FcγR (*continued*)
  mononuclear phagocytes 889
  myeloid cells 1805
  neutrophils 889, 1856
  NK cells 888, 890
  phagocytes 1885
  in phagocytosis 1937
  properties 888, 888(Table)
  structures 887(Fig)
  THP-1 cells 890
  U937 cells 890
FcγRI (high-affinity; CD64) 168,
    450(Table), 888, 1317, 1937
  cells expressing 889
  FcγRIa 886
    properties 888, 888(Table)
  FcγRIb2 888, 888(Table)
  FcγRIc 888, 888(Table)
  functional properties 889–890, 1317
  IgG binding site 1317
  monocytes 1752
  structure 887(Fig), 1211, 1317
FcγRII (low-affinity; CD32) 168,
    448(Table)
  in Arthus reaction 240
  expression 1317
  FcγRIIB1 351
  FcγRIIB, B cell coinhibition 1983
  FcγRIIc, on NK cells 1811
  functional properties 889–890, 1317
  isoforms 888, 1317
    expression 889
  ITAMs and ITIMs (motifs) 888
  mast cells 1669
  monocytes 1752
  phagocytes 1885, 1937
  properties 888
  structure 887(Fig), 1211
FcγRIII (medium-affinity; CD16) 168,
    447(Table), 886, 1752
  FcγRIIIa 447(Table), 886, 1752
  FcγRIIIb 447(Table), 1752
    isoforms, expression 889
  functional properties 889–890
  GPI-linked form (FcγRIIIB) 1752
  isoforms 888
  mast cells 1669
  monocytes 1752
  NK cell activation 1810
  in placental transfer of IgG 1672
  properties 888
  structure 887(Fig), 1211
  on syncytiotrophoblast 1672
  transmembrane form (FcγRIIIA) 1752
FcμR 1811
  on NK cells 1811
Fc receptors (FcR) 775, 886–892, 1329
  antigen–antibody complexes 886
  bacteria 1318
  bacterial proteins binding 323
  biological responses initiated 886, 891–
    892
  cells expressing 168, 886, 1317
  cross-linking 886
  cytokines effect on 892
  enhancing antibodies 812
  in erythrocyte antibody rosetting 2129
  Fc-Fc interactions 1318
  functions 891–892, 1317
  fusion proteins, autoimmune disease
    therapy 1359
  for IgA, see FcαR
  for IgD 886
  for IgE, see FcεR
  for IgG, see FcγR
  for IgM 886, 1811
  immune complex interaction 1224
  inhibitory, polyclonal inhibitors 1980,
    1982(Table)
  ITAMs 2032
  macrophage 175, 1646(Table)
  β2-microglobulin binding 371

Fc receptors (FcR) (continued)
  natural killer (NK) cells 505
  neonatal, see FcRn
  polyclonal inhibitor action via 1980
  poly Ig receptor (pIgR) 886
  protein A interactions 325
  structures 887(Fig)
  subfragments, polyclonal antibodies 1318
FcRn 72, 1318
  structure 520
Febrile reactions, nonhemolytic 1967
Feline calicivirus (FCV) 399, 400
  antigens 400
  evasive strategies 400, 401
  F9 vaccine 401
  host immune response 401
  persistence 401
  vaccine 401–402
Feline endogenous virus RD114 2090
Feline histocompatibility (FLA) system 894
  class I genes 894
  class II genes 894
Feline immune system 892–895
  autoimmunity 894
  blood groups 894
  cell-mediated immunity 894
  complement 894
  cytokines 893
  gammopathies 895
  hemolytic disease 894
  hypersensitivity 894
  immunodeficiencies 895
  immunoglobulins 893, 893(Table)
  lymphocytes 892–893
  lymphoid tissues 892
  major histocompatibility complex 894
  mitogenic response 893
  see also Cat(s)
Feline immunodeficiency virus (FIV) 401,
    895
Feline infectious peritonitis virus (FIPV)
    660, 660(Table)
Feline leukemia virus (FeLV) 893, 894,
    2097
Feline panleukopenia 895
Females, antibodies to sperm membrane
    antigens 1374
Fenton reaction 1717
Fenton's reagent 1717
Fermentation, historical aspects 1335–1336
Fernandez reaction 1025
Fertility-control vaccines 2458–2459
  see also Human chorionic gonadotropin
    (hCG)
Fetal antigens 798–801, 801
  see also Alphafetoprotein (AFP)
Fetal bovine serum, see Fetal calf serum
Fetal calf serum 896–898
  applications 897
  biohazards 897
  contamination 896, 897
  factors for cell culture from 897(Table)
  future prospects 897
  historical background 896
  leukocyte culture 1569
  production process 896–897
    preparation 896
    quality assurance 896–897, 896(Table)
  rationale for use 896
  substitutes 897
Fetal hemoglobin, see Hemoglobin, fetal
α-Fetoprotein, see Alphafetoprotein (AFP)
Fetus
  ABO blood groups 4, 5
  antibody synthesis 1673
  B cell development 1818–1819,
    1820(Table)
  blood group antigens expression 799
  complement 5
  hyperthyroidism 1675, 2315
  IgM synthesis 1818–1819
  immune system development, see

Fetus (continued)
  immune system development, see
    Neonatal immune response; Ontogeny
    of immune response (continued)
    Neonatal immune response; Ontogeny
    of immune response
  maternal antibody transfer, see
    Immunoglobulin, placental transfer;
    Maternal antibodies
  MHC expression absent 898–899
  parvovirus B19 infections 1925
  proteins 799
    see also Alphafetoprotein (AFP);
      Carcinoembryonic antigen (CEA)
  recurrent loss 1676
  red cell transfer across placenta 1070
  see also Neonates; Trophoblast
Fetus as allograft 898–901, 1375, 1853
  active maternal immunoregulatory
    responses 899–900, 1110
  CD3⁻ endometrial granulated
    lymphocytes (eGL) 899–900
  complement regulatory proteins
    expression 899
  cytokine cross-talk 900
  endometrial adaptations 899
  historical aspects 898
  HLA-G expression 899, 1110
  MHC antigens not expressed 898–899
  NK cell accumulation 1814
  passive resistance to cytotoxicity 898–
    899
  protection from maternal IgG 900–901
  recurrent spontaneous abortion and 900
  rodent models 900
  'trapping' of maternal antibodies by
    placenta 900–901
Fever 901–905, 2026
  age-related responses 904
  beneficial effects 904
  in cats 904
  endogenous pyrogens 902–903
    see also Pyrogens
  endotoxin inducing 902
  function 904
  generation 117
  host defense activation 2026
  induction mechanisms 903–904, 903(Fig)
    prostaglandin-independent pathway
      903–904
    prostaglandins 903, 2025–2026
    sites of mediator action 903
  rapid-onset 903
  slow-wave sleep duration increased 904
FIAU 1524, 1525
Fibrillin 862, 906
  defective 862
Fibrin
  adhesive action 1966
  deposits in delayed-type hypersensitivity
    740
  fibronectin binding 910, 912
'Fibrin glue' 1966
Fibrinogen 580, 582
  in cryoprecipitate 1966
  ICAM-1 interaction 804
  as ligand for ICAM-1 804
Fibrinolysis 585
  inhibitors 584(Table)
Fibrinopeptides 582
'Fibrin sealant' 1966
Fibroblast(s) 905–909, 1757
  adhesive proteins from 907
  CD40 function 486
  chemotaxis 908
  collagen production 905
  collagen remodeling 906
  cytokine production 905, 908,
    908(Table)
  diseases associated 905
  elastin production 906

Fibroblast(s) (continued)
  extracellular matrix production 903(Fig),
    905
    regulation 907
  function 905
  glycosaminoglycans 906–907
  growth factors for 907
  hyperplasia, rheumatoid arthritis 2116
  metalloproteinases production 906
  MHC antigen expression 905
  multipotential, see Mesenchymal cells
  proteoglycans 906–907
  structural proteins 905–906
  in thymus 2235–2236
  tissue repair and 908
Fibroblast activation protein α (FAPα)
    2429
Fibroblast growth factors (FGFs) 906, 907
  effect on endothelial cells 805–806
  types and functions 907
'Fibroblast interferon', see Interferon β
    (IFNβ)
Fibromodulin 906
Fibronectin 579, 864, 909–913
  apoptosis and 911–912
  bacteria binding 1937
  cancer and 913
  cell growth and 911–912
  cells producing 907, 910
  as chemotactic factor 913
  CR1 and CR3 activation 1887
  CS-1 domain 1407
  developmental defects and 911
  distribution 910
  domain structure 864, 865(Fig), 909,
    910(Fig)
  expression 910
  fibrin binding 910, 912
  gene encoding 909, 910(Fig)
  hemostasis 912
  Ig-type domains 778
  immune responses and 912
  inflammation 912
  integrin binding sites 909, 910, 911(Fig)
  integrin interactions 909, 910, 911
  isoforms 907
  ligands 910
  mesenchymal cell adherence 864
  mutations 911
  phagocytosis 912
    enhancement 1887, 1937
  production, by fibroblasts 907
  RGD sequence 909, 910, 911(Fig), 1887
  sarcoidosis 2136
  signaling 911, 912(Fig)
  Staphylococcus binding 2209, 2209–
    2210
  structure and assembly 909, 910(Fig)
    synergy region 909
  three-dimensional structure 517(Fig),
    518
  synthesis, leukemia inhibitory factor
    (LIF) role 1561
  VLA-5 binding 1407
  wound healing and fibrosis 913
Fibrosis 1023
  diseases 907
  fibronectin action 913
Fibrotic disorders 905
Ficoll-Hypaque 509, 1621
Field-effect transistors (FETs) 1255
Field inversion gel electrophoresis (FIGE)
    2195
Fifth disease 1924
Filamin 1612
Filarial nematodes 1873
  see also Onchocerca volvulus
Filariasis, lymphatic 913–915
  animal models 914, 915
  asymptomatic microfilaremia 914
  clinical features 914

Filariasis, lymphatic (*continued*)
  downregulation of immune response
      914–915
  'endemic normal' group 914, 915
  immunological features 914–915
  pathology, determinants 915
  protective immunity 915
  vaccines 915
Filobasidiella neoformans 671–672
Filoviruses 916–920
  antigens 916–918
  characteristics 916–918, 917(Fig)
  glycoprotein 918, 919
  hemorrhagic fevers 916, 916(Table),
      918–919
    clinical features 918
    pathogenesis 918–919
    pathophysiology 918–919, 919(Fig)
  host immune response 919
  L-proteins 916–917
  passive immunization 919
  transmission 917
  vaccines 919–920
Fimbriae 322–323
  Bordetella pertussis 378
  Escherichia coli, see Escherichia coli
  lectins 1536(Fig), 1537
  Proteus mirabilis 2040, 2041
  Salmonella 2131
'First-dose syndrome' 122
Fish
  allergy 950
  diseases 925
  farming, vaccination of fish 925
  immune system, *see also* Fish immune
      system
  methyl mercury 1686
Fisher's exact test 2213
Fish immune system 920–926
  antibody diversity 156
  antigen presentation 923
  functional anatomy 920–922, 921(Fig)
  IgM 1212
    polyreactive 1216
  immune response 924–925
    antibodies 924
    cell-mediated 924–925
  kidney 922
  leukocytes 923–924
    granulocytes 923–924
    mast cells 924
    monocytes/macrophage 923
    natural cytotoxic cells 924
  lymphocyte subpopulations 922, 922–
      923
  lymphoid tissues 920, 921(Fig)
  melanomacrophage 922
  memory 925
  spleen 922
  temperature dependency 924
  tolerance 925
  vaccination 925–926
Fish oils
  intake and effects 885
  supplements 885
Fixation, in immunocytochemistry, *see*
      Immunocytochemistry (ICC)
FK506 (tacrolimus) 1068, 1352, 1358
  actions 1352
  development/history 2412
  GVHD prevention 2261
  transplantation 2414
Flagella, bacterial 323
  see also specific bacteria species
Flagellin 381
  Campylobacter 407, 408
  Helicobacter pylori 1057
  Listeria monocytogenes 1593
Flavin adenine dinucleotide (FAD), oxygen-
      dependent phagocytic killing 1714
Flaviviridae 1079
  genome 2351

Flaviviruses 926–932
  animal models 929
  antigenic groups 926–927, 927(Table)
  characteristics 926–929
  E protein 926, 928
    structure and domains 928–929,
      928(Fig)
  genome
    sequences 927–928
    structure 927(Fig)
  host immune responses 929–931
    antibodies 929
    cell-mediated 929–930
    importance 929
    memory 931
  host susceptibility factors 928
  infections 926
    see also Dengue fever; Yellow fever
      (YF)
  NS1 protein 929
  persistence 929
  phylogenetic tree 928
  vaccines 931
    DNA 931
  virulence 928
Flavocytochrome b_{558} 565, 1714
  absence 1715
FLICE 225, 876, 1028
  TNF receptor signaling 2347
'Flippase' 834
Flocculation 1999
  reaction 2000(Fig), 2001
  time 2001
Flora, normal, *see* Microflora (normal)
Flow cytometry 142, 932–943
  B cell enrichment 179
  four-color/dual-laser 947
  gene expression detection 982
  history 932–933
  laser-based 944, 945, 946–947
  leukocyte viability assessment 2475
  phage antibody selection method 1933
  two-color/single-laser 944, 946–947,
      946(Fig)
  see also Fluorescence-activated cell
      sorting (FACS)
Floxed alleles 1527
flt-3 ligand 745
Flufenamic acid, immune hemolytic anemia
      due to 100
Fluorescein 142, 943
  labeling with 944
Fluorescein isothiocyanate 260
Fluorescence
  affinity measurement 45
  immunocytochemistry analysis 1266
  see also Immunofluorescence
Fluorescence-activated cell sorting (FACS)
      142, 180–181, 508, 512
  advantages 933
  AIDS prognosis 941
  B cell isolation 180–181, 933
  channels 181
  cytokine assays 941
  disadvantages 180
  DNA content in lymphocytes 941
  fluorescent dyes for 934, 935(Fig)
  forward scatter measurement 935–936
  functional characterization by 933
  gene expression, cell cycle correlation
      939(Fig)
  glutathione measurement 941
  history 932–933
  immunopathogenesis of disease 938
  intracellular gene expression analysis
      938(Fig)
  live *vs* dead cells 940
  lymphocyte subpopulations 933–934
  method 512
  molecular/functional studies 939–942
  monoclonal antibody reagents 934, 1745

Fluorescence-activated cell sorting (FACS)
      (*continued*)
  multiparameter 934–936, 934(Fig),
      936(Fig), 937(Fig)
    power of 936–939
  nephelometry use 1824
  physiological state of cells 940
  purity difficulties 180–181
  reporter gene studies 939
  samples 933
  single-cell based assays 933
  T cells
    isolation 182
    subsets 932, 936–939
Fluorescence microscopy 945–946
Fluorescence polarization method 1051–
      1052
Fluorescence quenching, affinity of hapten-
      specific antibody 1051
Fluorescent dyes
  FACS studies 934, 935(Fig)
  lymphocyte migration studies 1618
Fluorescent labels 1253
Fluorochrome labeling 943–947
  biotin 944
  control reagents 944
  dual/triple color analysis 944
  fluorescein 944
  phycobiliproteins 945
  phycocyanins 945
  precautions 944
  reagents 943, 944(Table), 1253
  rhodamine 944
Fluorochromes 790, 934, 943, 944(Table)
  FACS studies 934, 935(Fig)
  leukocyte viability assessment 2475
Fluoroimmunoassay 1253
Flushing, histamine effect 1102
FLY packaging cell lines 2090
fMLP (formyl-met-leu-phe) 86
  C3a receptor homology 88
  C5a bioactivity 90
  C5a receptor homology 89
  as chemotactic factor 542
Foamy viruses 2085, 2093(Table)
  bel genes 2095
  vectors 2090
Focal adhesion kinase (FAK), mast cell
      degranulation 1670
Fodrin 223, 1680
  CD45 domain binding 1680
Folate, deficiency 2490
Follicle-stimulating hormone (FSH) 641
  immunization against 1853
  vaccines
    clinical trials 642(Table)
    current status 647
Follicular dendritic cells (FDCs) 539, 742,
      992
  antigen on and B cell stimulation 993,
      1726, 1728, 1777
  'beaded' 1728
  cellular cooperation 651
  clonal deletion of activated B cells 572
  in germinal centers 1685
  in HIV infection 11
  as HIV reservoir 1138, 1729
  lifespan 1583
  in lymph node 1604, 1605, 1726
  microenvironment 1728
  in Peyer's patches 1777
  retrovirus trapping 1728
  role 993
  'spongework' formation 1728
Folliculitis 752
Food
  adverse reactions, classification 947–948
  anaphylaxis due to 950
  antigens, tolerance 1785
  contact urticaria 681
  elimination, allergy diagnosis 951
  histamine-releasing agents in 949

Food (*continued*)
  IgG against, transfer in breast milk 1673
  nonspecific histamine release 949, 950
Food additives 950–951
  contact urticaria 681
  urticaria due to 679
Food allergens 67(Table), 949, 950–951
  chemicals 950–951
  contact urticaria 681
  cross-reactions with inhaled allergens 950
  disorders associated 948–950
  infants 948, 951
Food allergy 947–953
  age of onset 948
  allergic rhinitis 948
  allergic vasculitis 949
  aphthous ulceration 949
  asthma associated 948
  atopic eczema 949
  in cats 894
  clinical features 948
  CNS reactions 950
  cross-reactions with inhaled allergens 950
  diagnosis 951, 951(Table)
  eczema 948, 949
  elimination-reintroduction of foods 951
  false (pseudoallergy) 947, 948, 951–952,
    952(Table)
  gastrointestinal tract reactions 948–950
  IgE antibodies 69
    tests 951
  investigations 951(Table)
  mechanisms 951
  migraine 950
  quick-onset 948
  respiratory tract reactions 948–949
  secretory otitis media 949
  skin reactions 949
  slow-onset 948
  soya milk 948, 953
  treatment 952–953
    hyposensitization 952–953
    rush–desensitization 953
  urticaria 949
Food anaphylaxis 950
Food colorings, false food allergy
  952(Table)
Food hypersensitivity, *see* Food allergy
Food poisoning
  Bacillus cereus 312
  Escherichia coli 842
  Salmonella 2131
  Staphylococcus 2209
Foot-and-mouth disease virus (FMDV)
  epitope location 1957(Table)
  pigs 56
  receptor 1955
  vaccine 1959
'Forbidden clone' theory 293
  see also Clonal deletion
Foreign body granuloma 1024
Forensic science, allotype application 76
Forest yaws 1547
Formaldehyde, tissue fixation 1261
Formalin
  colitis 1384
  tissue fixation 1261
Formyl-met-leu-phe, *see* fMLP
Formyl peptides 315
  chemotactic factor 542
Forssman antigen 204, 953–955, 1092
  antibodies 953, 1092
  cellular distribution 954, 955(Fig)
  cross-reacting antigens 954
  detection and isolation 954
  as developmental/differentiation antigen
    954
  disease associations 954
  glycosphingolipid 953, 954
  as receptor for bacterial adhesins 954
  shock 953, 955
  species distribution 954, 954(Table)

Forssman antigen (*continued*)
  structure 953, 953–954
Fos proteins, T cell receptor signaling 2327
Fowl typhoid 2131
Foxes, *Echinococcus* infection 784
Fragmentin-2, *see* Granzyme B
Francisella tularensis 956–957
  antigens 956
  biovars 956
  capsule 956, 956–957
  characteristics 956
  culture 956
  evasive strategies 956–957
  host immune responses 956
  vaccines 957
Free fatty acid, metabolism, atopic eczema
  788
Free radicals 133
  animal models of IDDM 1396
  blocking, diabetes prevention 1397
  effects 134
  formation 2500
  immune cell function and 134
    clinical examples 134–126
  increased, by PUFA intake 884
  vitamin E protection 2500
  see also Reactive oxygen species; *specific
    free radicals*
Freeze-drying of tissue 1262
Freezing
  immune cells 668–669
  tissue permeabilization for
    immunocytochemistry 1262
  see also Cryopreservation of immune
    cells
Fresh frozen plasma (FFP) 1964
  indications/uses 1966
  storage 1966
Freund's adjuvant
  complete (FCA) 33, 37, 220, 1981, 2456
    arthritis and IFNγ role 1425
    BCG 335
    composition 37
    experimental autoimmune uveoretinitis
      (EAU) 868
  incomplete 37, 220
Friedlander's bacillus, *see Klebsiella
  pneumoniae*
Friend erythroleukemia 1564
Friend murine leukemia virus 165
Frog virus 3 (FV3) 1503(Table), 1504
β2-1 Fructosan 1878
β2-6 Fructosan 1877
Fucose
  blood group A 1737
  metabolism defect 1568
Fucosylation 594
Fucosyltransferase 2, 1098
Fujinami sarcoma virus 1115
Fu locus 635
Fungal glycans, immunomodulators from
  1345
Fungal infections 957–962
  CNS 1846
  cytokines 961
  etiological agents 958(Table)
  host defenses 958
  immunotherapy 961
  non-specific immunity 958–960
    complement 959
    monocytes/macrophage 959
    neutrophils 959
    NK cells 959–960
  specific immunity 960–961
    activated macrophage 961
    antibodies 960
    cell-mediated 960–961
  vaccination 961
Fungi 957
  allergens 67(Table)
    hypersensitivity 960
  of medical importance 958

Fusion, *see* Cell fusion
Fusion promotion, paramyxoviruses 1911
Fusion proteins, autoimmune disease
  therapy 1359
Fusobacterium 962–963
  infections 962, 962–963
    predisposing factors 962
  species 962
  synergistic infections 962, 963
  virulence 962
Fusobacterium necrophorum 963
  delayed hypersensitivity 963
  immunization 963
Fusobacterium nucleatum
  antigens 963
  immunosuppression by 962
  infections 963
Fx, Tβ4 similarity 2301

G

G1 protein 1117(Table), 1119
G5a gene 1117(Table), 1119
G7a gene 1047
G7a protein 1117(Table), 1119
G9a gene 1047
G9a protein 1116(Table), 1118
G9 gene 1116(Table), 1118–1119
G11a protein 1115, 1116(Table), 1118
G11 gene 116(Table), 1115, 1118
G13 protein 1046, 1115, 1116(Table)
G17 gene 1115, 1116(Table)
G250 antigen 2428
Gα₁₂
  functions 1383
  knockout, inflammatory bowel disease
    model 1383
GABA
  agonists 1842
  formation 1842
GAF transcription factor 1415
GAL5 protein 984
Galactan, monoclonal antibodies to 427
β1-6 Galactan 1877
Galactose, IgG glycosylation 1002
  disease association 1004
Galactose (α1,3) galactose, xenoantigen
  2415
β-Galactosidase
  B cell 2499
  in ELISA 818
  gene, FACS studies 938(Fig), 939(Fig)
Galactosyltransferase 2
Galanin 1827
Galectin-1, as ligand for CD45 493
Galectin-3 430, 1204
Galectins 1537
  functions 1538–1539
  increased, in cancer 1538
Galleria mellonella 1503
GALT, *see* Gut-associated lymphoid tissue
  (GALT)
Gametes, formation, gene conversion role
  970
Gamma-aminobutyric acid, *see* GABA
Gamma camera 2434
Gammaglobulin 964–966
  autoimmune hemolytic anemia 97–98
  Bruton's agammaglobulinemia therapy
    387, 389, 966
  Cohn–Oncley alcohol fractionation 964,
    965(Fig)
  disease prevention 966
  fraction II 964, 965(Fig)
  high-dose 387
  historical aspects 964–965
  human (HGG)
    experimental tolerance induction 2359–
      2360

Gammaglobulin (*continued*)
  human (HGG) (*continued*)
    tolerance induction, cytokine effect
      2361
  human (HGG), deaggregated
    dose in tolerance induction 2360
    tolerance induction 2359–2360, 2360,
      2363
  intramuscular 966, 2469
    immunodeficiency therapy 966
  intravenous infusion, *see* Intravenous
    immunoglobulin
  lyophilized powder 965
  preparations 965–966
  safety 966
  terminology 964
Gammopathy
  feline 895
  human *see* Hypergammaglobulinemia
Gangliosides
  GD$_{1b}$, antibodies 1839
  GM1, *see* GM1 ganglioside
  GM3, antibodies 124
  GQb1 1838
  synthesis 2429
  tumor antigens recognized by mAbs
    2428–2429
Gangrene, in cryoglobulinemia 666,
  666(Fig)
GAP, *see* GTPase-activating protein (GAP)
Gas gangrene 269, 578, 2368
Gastric acid secretion
  histamine effect 1103–1104
  'permission hypothesis' 1103–1104
  'transmission hypothesis' 1103–1104
Gastric antigens
  autoantibodies 102–103
  autoantigens 102
  cell-mediated immunity to 103
Gastric atrophy 103
Gastric autoantibodies 102–103
Gastric cancer, *Helicobacter pylori*-
  associated 1058
Gastric mucin oligoglycan 425
Gastric parietal cells
  absence in pernicious anemia 101
  autoantibodies (GPCA) 102, 262–263
    detection 102, 262(Table), 263
    experimental models 104
    prevalence 104
  autoantigen 102, 263
  reduced in autoimmune gastritis 103
  regeneration 104
Gastric ulcers, NSAIDs causing 120
Gastrin
  gastric acid secretion control 1103
  high levels
    autoimmune gastritis 102, 103
    pernicious anemia 102, 103
Gastritis 103–104
  autoimmune 101, 102, 103–104
    animal models 104
    see also Pernicious anemia
  autoimmune polyglandular syndrome
    type II 1985
  chronic, increased secretory component
    expression 2156–2157
  Helicobacter pylori-associated 1057
  pernicious anemia type 103
  type A 103–104
  type B 103
Gastroenteritis
  adenovirus 21
  Salmonella 2131
  see also Diarrhea; Gastrointestinal tract
    infections
Gastrointestinal disease, in chronic
  granulomatous disease 566
Gastrointestinal tract
  allergic reaction to foods 948–950
  antigen uptake 189–190
  colonization resistance 1882

Gastrointestinal tract (*continued*)
  colonization resistance (*continued*)
    germ-free animal studies 991
  host defense 967, 1780–1781
  host defense mechanisms 967
  lymphatic system 1601
  lymphoid tissue
    in pigs 1993–1994
    see also Gut-associated lymphoid tissue
      (GALT)
  microchemical environment, germ-free
    animal studies 991
  nonimmunological host defense 1780–
    1781
  normal flora 967
    absent in germ-free animals 990
    Escherichia coli 842, 844
    Fusobacterium necrophorum 963
    germ-free animal studies 991
    gravity/space flights effect 1031
  smooth muscle, histamine effect 1103
Gastrointestinal tract infections 967–969
  bacterial 967–968
  in common variable immunodeficiency
    599–600
  parasitic 968–969
  vaccine development 969
  viral 968
  see also Diarrhea; Gastroenteritis
γc chain, *see* Common γ chain (γc); *under*
  Interleukin-2 (IL-2) receptor
GcMAF 2498
  clinical significance 2499
  formation 2498, 2498(Fig)
  see also Gc protein
Gc protein (vitamin D$_3$-binding protein)
  2497, 2499
  clinical significance 2499
  glycosidase pathways 2498, 2498(Fig)
  metabolism 2498, 2498(Fig)
G-CSF, *see* Granulocyte colony-stimulating
  factor (G-CSF)
GD$_{1b}$ ganglioside, antibodies 1839
Gelatinase, neutrophils 1857, 1858
Gel electrophoresis
  see Immunoelectrophoresis
  DNA fragments 2194, 2195
Gel filtration
  columns 2037
  protein separation 2037
Gene
  alternative splicing, *see* Alternative
    splicing
  distances comparison with physical
    distances 1587
  duplication, MHC evolution 1701, 1950
  expression, cell cycle correlation 939(Fig)
  linkage disequilibrium, *see* Linkage
    disequilibrium
  mapping, linkage disequilibrium use
    1587
  one gene–one polypeptide concept 987
  phenotypic expression 987–988
  pleotropic 988
  rearrangements, *see* Gene rearrangements
    (*below*)
  sequencing, historical development 1626
  structure, analysis 981–983
  therapy, *see* Gene therapy (*below*)
  transfer
    methods 982
    vectors 974
Gene conversion 969–973
  avian B cells 303, 396
  bm mutants 372
  cell differentiation role 970
  crossing-over relationship 969
  degree of sequence similarity 972–973
  DNA repair 970
    double-strand break, model 971–972,
      971(Fig)
  ectopic recombination 972

Gene conversion (*continued*)
  fidelity 972
  mechanisms 970, 971–972
  meiotic recombination model 970–971,
    970(Fig)
  mismatch repair downregulation 973
  in pigs 1993
  recombination and mutations 973
  role in meiosis 970
  TCR repertoire generation 2281
Gene disruption
  animal models of inflammation 1382–
    1383
  B and T cell development 1877
  conditional 1525(Fig), 1526(Fig), 1527
  homologous recombination method
    1524–1525, 1524(Fig)
  knockout, *see* Knockout mice
  tissue-specific 1526(Fig), 1527
  see also Transgenic mice
Gene expression libraries 1745
'Gene gun' 771, 2454, 2461
Generalized estimating equations (GEE)
  2212
Gene rearrangements 552
  immunoglobulin, *see* Immunoglobulin
    gene rearrangements
  T cell receptor (TCR), *see* T cell receptor
    (TCR)
  vesicular stomatitis virus 258
  see also Genetic recombination
Gene targeting 982
  B cell differentiation 355–356,
    357(Table)
  CD8 analysis 478
  T cell differentiation 2335
Gene therapy 974–981
  adenosine deaminase (ADA) deficiency
    978, 979(Table), 2174
  animal models 978–979
  antitumor response stimulation 974,
    976(Table), 977–978, 1364
    cytokine genes 977
    effector cell costimulatory molecules
      977–978
    tumor antigens 974, 1364
  autoimmune disease 978
  clinical trials 975(Fig), 976(Table)-
    977(Table)
  diseases 975(Fig)
  future prospects 980
  graft-versus-host disease management
    978
  graft-versus-leukemia effect 978
  immune deficiencies 978, 979(Table)
  immune disorders 978, 979(Table)
  immune reactivity against
    vectors/transgenes 979–980
  liposome application 1589–1590
  long-term expression of gene 980
  methods 975(Fig)
  principles 975(Fig)
  rabbit model 2046
  SCID 2174
  transduction efficiency 980
  tumor immunotherapy, *see* antitumor
    response stimulation (*above*)
  vectors 24–25, 974, 975(Fig)
    adenoviruses 24–25
    retroviral 2084
    see also Vectors
Genetic analysis
  definitions/concepts 986
  molecular 981–986
    gene expression 982–983
    gene regulation 983–984
    gene structure 981–983
    history 981
    large-scale protein production 984–985
    specificity 985
    structure–function 982
  phenotypic level 986–989

Genetic analysis (*continued*)
  phenotypic level (*continued*)
    multifactorial inheritance 988–989
    protein structure 987
    single gene expression 987–988
Genetic counselling, in ataxia telangiectasia (AT) 250
Genetic disorders
  age of onset 59
  autosomal dominant 987–988
  autosomal recessive 988
  genotype/phenotype relationship 988
  monogenic 987–988
  multifactorial inheritance 988–989
Genetic engineering
  antibody combining sites 174
  bispecific antibodies 139(Fig), 140
  see also Gene disruption; Knockout mice; Transgenic animals
Genetic knockout, *see* Knockout mice
Genetic rearrangements, *see* Gene rearrangements; Immunoglobulin gene rearrangements
Genetic reassortment, influenza virus 258
Genetic recombination
  cell surface antigen diversity 208
  consensus sequence 553, 767
  crossing-over 969
  diversity generation role 973
  ectopic 972
  error-prone 552–553
    chromosomal aberrations due to 553–554
  gene conversion, *see* Gene conversion
  homologous
    barrier 972
    gene disruption by 1524–1525, 1524(Fig)
    genetic/physical distance comparison 1587
  Ig class switching, *see* Immunoglobulin class switching
  Ig genes, *see* Immunoglobulin gene rearrangements
  immune genes 552, 553–554
  interlocus 554, 556
  intralocus 553–554
  linkage disequilibrium 1586
  meiotic, model 970–971, 970(Fig)
  signal sequences, VDJ recombination 767, 768
  T cell receptor (TCR) genes 2265, 2280
  VDJ, process 767
  VDJ recombinase 553, 554, 556, 559
    see also Immunoglobulin gene rearrangements
  see also Chromosomal translocations
Genital infections, *see* Reproductive tract infections
Genital warts 2074–2075
Genome
  human 1587
    mapping project 981, 1762
    'proofreading', by CTL 732
    short tandem repeats (STRs) 1988
Genotype 986
  see also Genetic analysis
Geometric mean (GM) 2211–2212
Geotrichum candidum, infections, false food allergy 952
Gerbich blood group 835, 837
  antigen deficiency 837
Gerbils, amebiasis model 78
Germ-free animals 990–992
  applications 990–991
  characteristics 990
  historical aspects 990
  preparation 990
Germinal center reaction 1726
Germinal centers 992–995, 1604
  affinity maturation, *see* Affinity maturation

Germinal centers (*continued*)
  antiapoptotic signals 994
  apoptosis in 993–994, 1604
  B cells, *see* B cell(s), in germinal centers
  Bruton's agammaglobulinemia 387
  cellular composition 992–993
  centroblasts 992, 993(Fig)
  centrocytes 992, 993(Fig)
  cytokines effect 994
  dark zone 992, 1604
  dendritic cells (GCDCs) 651, 747, 1604
    see also Follicular dendritic cells (FDCs)
  development 994, 1726, 1728
  fate 994–995
  formation 358–359, 363, 366, 539, 992, 1605–1606
    cytokines role 994
    follicular dendritic cell role 993
  function 993–994
  Ig class switch site 993
  lacking, in hyper-IgM syndrome 1167
  light zone 992, 1604
  macrophage in, *see* Tingible body macrophage (TBM)
  malignancies 993
  memory B cell formation, *see* B cell(s), memory
  microenvironment 1726–1728, 1727(Fig), 1728
    affinity maturation 1728
    AIDS pathogenesis 1728–1729
  organization 992–993
  Peyer's patches 1776, 1781
  'progressively transformed' 995
  radiosensitivity 2051
  'regressively transformed' 995
  sites 1728
  somatic hypermutation site 769, 993, 1728, 2192
    see also Somatic hypermutation
  spleen 2206
  structural organization 1604, 1605(Fig)
  T cells 993, 1604, 2355
  thymic 1834
  zones 1604, 1605(Fig)
  see also Lymphoid follicles
Gerstmann–Strōussler syndrome (GSS) 2409
Giant cells
  granulomas 1023
  sarcoidosis 2136
Giant pronormoblasts 1923
Giardia lamblia
  in common variable immunodeficiency 599
  diarrhea due to 968
Gibbon ape leukemia virus (GaLV) 2090
Gibbs free energy 2200
Giemsa staining 833
GIL (galactose/N-acetyl-D-galactosamine inhibitable lectin) 78, 79
Gingival crevice (GC) 1888, 1889
Gingival crevicular fluid (GCF) 1889, 1890
Gingival inflammation, gravity/space flights effect 1031
Gingival tissue, polymorphonuclear cells role 1889
Gingivitis 1888, 1889
Glanzmann's thrombasthenia 31, 1409
gld gene 286
  mutation 2251
    apoptosis association 2252
    clonal deletion of T cells 570, 655
gld mice
  gld/gld mice 877, 878
  T cell accumulation 2252
Glial cells, MHC expression 1845
Glioblastoma, adherent LAK cells and A-NK cells 1629
Globoside, as parvovirus B19 receptor 1923

Globulins 964
Glomerulonephritis
  autoimmune, mercury causing 1688
  immune complexes 1225
    chronic serum sickness as model 2169
  mesangial proliferative (MPGN), IL-6 role 1460
  post-streptococcal 1176, 2218
  Streptococcus pyogenes 2218
Glucan(s)
  as anticancer agents 429
  antimicrobial effects 428
  intravenous 429
  macrophage stimulation 428
Glucan-binding proteins 1498
Glucocorticoid regulatory elements, in IL-1 genes 1429–1430
Glucocorticoids 996–1001, 2224
  abnormal response, obese strain of chickens 282
  ADCC inhibition 170
  altered secretion, UCD 200 chicken strain 285
  anti-inflammatory effects 111, 112, 997, 1000–1001
  atopy allergic disease 255
  autoimmune hemolytic anemia therapy 95–96
    dosage and tapering 96
    mechanism of action 95–96
    side-effects 96
  binding to hormone response elements 999
  binding to type I steroid receptors 999
  control of acute phase proteins 18
  cytokine secretion inhibition 1000
  deficiency 996, 1000
  discovery 996
  feedback regulation 998, 998(Fig)
  functions 996
  historical background 996–998
  hypophysectomy effect 1827
  idiopathic thrombocytopenic purpura treatment 1976
  in IL-1 feedback regulation 1434
  immunosuppressive effects 998(Fig), 1000–1001, 2224
  inflammatory mediators regulation 1000, 1000(Table)
  leukocyte distribution changes 1000
  mechanism of action 111, 999
    annexin similarity, *see* Annexins (lipocortins)
  monocyte decrease 1751
  neutrophil increases due to 1000
  permissive actions 996, 997, 998(Fig)
  physiology 996–998
  platelet production increase 1976
  production, ACTH stimulating 1828(Fig)
  receptors 998–1000
    cytokine-induced reduction 1000
    gene expression modulation 999
    mechanism of action 999, 999(Fig)
  secretion
    cytokines stimulating 998
    regulation 997–998
  stress relationship 996, 997, 998
  Strongyloides stercoralis infection regulation 2239
  T cell proliferation inhibition, MIF counteraction 1656
  therapeutic uses 996, 996–997
  thymocytes, negative selection 2357
  thymocyte sensitivity 2305
  types 996
  in UCD 200 chicken strain 285
  see also Corticosteroids
Glucose, metabolism, red cells 837
Glucose oxidase 814, 1263
Glutamic acid decarboxylase (GAD)
  autoantibodies
    animal models of IDDM 755, 1393
    GAD$_{65}$ 1401

Glutamic acid decarboxylase (GAD) (*continued*)
  autoantibodies (*continued*)
    human diabetes 1401, 1842
    stiff man syndrome 1842
  in IDDM model 755
  nasal administration, NOD mice treatment 1897
Glutamine, in exercise–immune cell interactions 847
Glutamine hypothesis 847
Glutaraldehyde
  enzyme-labeling of antibodies 814
  tissue fixation 1261
Glutathione
  FACS measurement 941
  microbial sensitivity to oxygen-dependent killing 1718
Glutathione peroxidase 133
Glutathione-S-transferase (GST)
  Fasciola hepatica 883
  MIF relationship 1657
  purification by SDS-PAGE 2144, 2144(Fig)
GlyCAM-1 28(Table), 29, 2159
Glycerol, in cryopreservation 668
Glycoconjugates, detection, lectin use 1540
Glycoforms 1001
Glycolipids 422
  red blood cells 3, 425
  structure 425
  tumor antigens recognized by mAbs 2428–2429
Glycophorin A 835, 839(Table)
Glycophorin B 835, 839(Table)
Glycophorin C 835, 837, 839(Table)
Glycophorin D 837, 839(Table)
Glycophorin E 837, 839(Table)
Glycophorins, in red cell membrane 835, 839(Table)
Glycophosphaditylinositol (GPI), *see* GPI anchor (GPI proteins)
Glycoprotein 1b (GP1b) 1974
  autoantibodies 1974
  receptors 1974
Glycoprotein 85 (gp85), *see* CD44
Glycoprotein(s) 422, 864–865
  acute phase proteins 19
  'adhesive' 864
  α-HS 1887
  alloantigens 73
  antibodies 154
  clearance, C-type lectins role 1539
  collagens 861
  detection, immobilized lectins 1540
  domains 864, 865
  extracellular matrix (ECM) 864–865
  glycoforms 1001
  HSV vaccines 1088
  matrix 864–865
  microfibril-associated (MAGP) 906
  myelin-associated (MAG), antibodies 1838
  myelin oligodendrocyte (MOG) 858
  oncodevelopmental antigens 425
  phagocytic (Pgp-1), *see* CD44
  phytohemagglutinin (PHA) binding 1952
  platelet, *see* Platelet(s)
  renal cell carcinoma 2428
  RGD sequences 864, 865
  Rh antigen complexes 2104–2105
  structure 424–425
  trafficking, C-type lectins role 1539
  tumor antigens 2428
    recognized by mAbs 2428
  varicella-zoster virus (VZV) 2468, 2469
  viruses 425–426
  ZP1, ZP2 and ZP3 1374
  see also entries beginning gp
β_2-Glycoprotein (β_2-GPI) 265
Glycoprotein IIb/IIIa (gpIIb/IIIa) integrin 579, 580, 1408, 1409, 1974

Glycosaminoglycan (GAG)
  chains 862, 863(Table)
  functions 864
  production, by fibroblasts 906–907
  Staphylococcus binding 2210
  structure 906
Glycosidases, macrophage-activating factor formation 2498, 2498(Fig), 2499
Glycosphingolipid, Forssman antigen 953, 954
Glycosylation 1001–1004
  analytical isoelectric focusing 1512
  antibody secretion and 144, 146–147
  cell specific 1001
  cell surface antigens diversity 210, 1001
  glycoforms 1001
  IgE 1202
  IgG 1002–1004
    agalactosyl 1002, 1004
    age-related variations 1002
    disease etiopathology 1004
    functional consequences 1002–1004
    N-/O-linked oligosaccharides 1002
    sites 1002
    solubility 1003–1004
    structural aspects 1002
  N-glycosylation 1001, 1002
  O-glycosylation 1001, 1002
  sites 1001
  structural/functional consequences 1001–1002, 1002–1004
  see also Carbohydrate antigens
Glycosylation-inhibiting factor (GIF) 1218, 1655, 2246
  see also I-J; Macrophage migration inhibitory factor (MIF)
Glycosylphosphatidylinositol 735
  IL-2 signal transduction pathway 1441
  see also GPI anchor
Glycosyltransferase 1–2, 422
  cloning 595
Glycotype 1001
Glyoxal 1864
GM1 ganglioside 425
  antibodies 1837, 1838, 1839
GM3 ganglioside, autoantibodies 124
GM-CSF, *see* Granulocyte-macrophage colony-stimulating factor (GM-CSF)
Gm haplotypes 1588
GMP-140, *see* P-selectin (CD62P)
Gnotobiotic animals 990
  see also Germ-free animals
Goats, immune system, *see* Ungulate immune system
Goitre 2313
  see also Hyperthyroidism; Thyroid autoimmunity
Gold
  colloidal, immunocytochemistry 1263–1264
  immunodeficiency due to 1285
Golgi apparatus 849
  MHC class I–peptide complex transport 193
  protein secretion 144
  protein translocation 849, 851
  transmembrane secretory component (pIgR) 2154
Gonadotrophin releasing hormone (GnRH) 641
  immunization 1853
  vaccines 641
Gonococcal infection 2072
  immune response 1817
  immunobiology 2073(Fig)
  uncomplicated (UGI) 1816, 1817
  see also Neisseria gonorrhoeae
Gonococcus, *see Neisseria gonorrhoeae*
Goodpasture antigen 1005, 1005–1008
  alternative splicing 1010
  autoantibody interaction 1008–1009
  epitope 1005–1008, 1008(Fig)

Goodpasture antigen (*continued*)
  localization 1006(Fig)
  structure 1005–1008, 1006(Fig)
  see also Collagen, type IV
Goodpasture's syndrome 1005–1011, 1175, 1341
  autoantibodies 1005, 1008–1009
  diagnosis 1005
  experimental 1008–1009
  natural antibodies in 1009
  organs affected 1005(Fig)
  pathogenesis 1009–1010, 1009(Fig)
Gottron's sign 2118
gp1b, *see* Glycoprotein 1b (GP1b)
gp39, *see* CD40L
gp41, *see* CD48
gp45, *see* CD38
gp75 2425
gp80 (CD39) 448(Table)
gp85, *see* CD44
GP90^{Hermes}, *see* CD44
gp95, *see* CD43
gp110 (CD68) 451(Table)
gp120, *see* CD26
gp130 (CD130) 454(Table), 706, 715
  IL-6 receptor 1461, 1462
  in IL-11 receptor 1478
    signal transduction 1479
  transgenic mice 1562
gp, *see specific gp antigens under CD antigen table* 446(Table)-457(Table)
GPI anchor (GPI proteins)
  alloantigens as 73
  antigens with 405
  biosynthesis 406
  CAMPATH-1 antigen (CD52) 404
  CD59 497, 498
  deficiency 406, 835
  promiscuity 418
  proteins in red cell membrane 835
  soluble cytokine receptors 714
  in T cells 419
  Thy-1 linked 2291
gpIIa, *see* CD29
GPIIb (CD41) 448(Table)
gpIIb/IIIa integrin 579, 580, 1408, 1409, 1974
gpIIIb, *see* CD36
GPLA complex 1034, 1034(Table)
GPR15 1134
G proteins 1760–1761
  activation, IL-8 1467
  C5a receptor 88–89
  chemoattractant-stimulated leukocytes 1760–1761, 2062
  chemokine receptors 2062
  cytokine receptor signaling 711
  heterodimers and α chain knockout 1383
  microbicidal killing mechanism 1714, 1937–1938
  see also GTP-binding proteins
Gr-1 antigen 1875
Graft
  privileged sites, antigen escape 2012
  see also Transplantation
Graft rejection 1011–1015
  acute 1011
    xenografts 2509–2510
  afferent phase 1011–1012
    antigens 1011–1012
    cells involved 1012
    privileged sites 1012
  cell-mediated, xenograft 2510
  chronic 1011, 1014, 1017
    xenografts 2510
  cytokines involved 1014
  delayed xenograft 2509–2510
  dendritic cells in 175
  efferent phase 1012–1014
    antibodies 1013
    cytotoxic T cells 729, 1013

Graft rejection (*continued*)
  efferent phase (*continued*)
    delayed-type hypersensitivity 1013–1014
    LAK cells 1014
    NK cells 1014
    nonspecific reactions 1013
    specificity 1013
    target cells 1014
    T cell help 1012–1013
  experimental studies 1011–1012
    prevention by oral antigen 1897
  hyperacute 82, 1013
    membrane attack complex role 628
    xenografts 2509, 2510
  immunosuppression
    goal 1349–1350, 1350(Fig)
    role 1349, 2414
  mechanisms 503
  MHC antigens 1011
  MHC role 1705
    H2 class I molecules 1039
    HLA class I role 1110
  minor histocompatibility antigens 1011
  monoclonal antibody application 1747
  prevention 2414
    calcitriol 2496
    CD46 role 497
    CTLA4-Ig and anti-B7-1 and B7-2 mAbs 306
    cyclosporine 688, 2414
    FasL expression 879, 1012
    see also Immunosuppressive agents/therapy; Transplantation therapy, TGFβ 2397
  tolerance induction 1014
  xenotransplantation 2509
Graft-versus-host disease (GVHD) 544, 1015–1016, 2264, 2402
  acute 1015, 1016, 1067–1068
  autologous 1017
  causes 1016
  chronic 1015, 1016, 1068
    AIDS similarity 1137
  clinical features 1015, 1016
  cord blood transplantation 1017
  cytokines involved 1016
  effector cells 1016
  endotoxin role 1015
  gene therapy in 978
  histocompatibility differences 1016
    MHC 1016, 1017
    non-MHC 1016
  host-versus-graft relationship 545–546
  immunosuppression in 1016, 1017, 1068
  intestinal enteropathy association 1860
  mechanism 545
  minor transplantation (histocompatibility) antigens 1732
  mixed lymphoid chimerism and 547–548
  model 1015–1016
  prevention 544–545, 1068, 1068(Table), 1363, 1883, 2264
    antibody-directed approaches 2261–2262
    CAMPATH-1M antibodies 405
    CD4-CD63 cyclized peptide 2263
    CD40L antibodies role 487
    cyclosporine 688, 1068, 2261
    megadose hematopoietic transplants 545–546
    pharmacological agents 2264
    targeting of agents 2264–2264
    T cell costimulation blockade 2262
    T cell depletion 545, 1068, 1363
    T$_H$2 cytokines 2262
  risk factors 1068(Table)
  in SCID 2170
  stem cell transplant, see Stem cell transplantation
  T cell subpopulation causing 546
  TNFα levels increased 2439

Graft-versus-host disease (GVHD) (*continued*)
  transfusion-associated 2402
    frequency 2402, 2403(Table)
Graft-versus-host reaction 1015–1018
  anti-lymphocyte serum (ALS) 121
  clinical manifestation, see Graft-versus-host disease (GVHD)
Graft-versus-leukemia (GVL) 545, 1017
  management, gene therapy 978
Gram-negative bacteria
  cell walls 320, 321–322, 321(Fig)
  colicins 2014–2015
  endotoxins 2377–2379
  lipopolysaccharide, see Lipopolysaccharide (LPS)
  opportunistic 2377
Gram-positive bacteria
  bacteriocins 2015
  cell walls 320, 321(Fig), 322
Granulation tissue
  fibroblasts in 908
  formation 908
Granule-associated enzymes, see Granzyme(s)
Granules 736
  contents 737
  discharge, see Degranulation
  endosome fusion 737
  staining 726
  see also Basophil(s); Eosinophil(s); Mast cell(s); Neutrophil(s)
Granulocyte(s) 1388, 1854
  alloantibodies, blood transfusion reactions 348
  in fish 923–924
  function, inflammatory bowel disease 1378
  GM-CSF action 1021
  IL-2 action/response 1437
  invertebrates 1500
  Lewis^x (Le^x) and sialyl-Le^x expression 1578
  neutrophil, see Neutrophil(s)
  porcine 1992
  recovery, after stem cell transplantation 1067
  virus infection of 2486
  see also Basophil(s); Eosinophil(s); Neutrophil(s)
Granulocyte chemotactic peptide (GCP), see Interleukin-8 (IL-8)
Granulocyte colony-stimulating factor (G-CSF) 375, 596, 1018–1020
  actions/functions 597(Table), 1019
  ADCC modulation 170, 1019
  assay 697(Table)
  effect on endothelial cells 805–806, 1019
  FcγRI expression increased 889
  gene 1018
  neutrophil production/survival 1019
    time-course of release 1020
  preclinical/clinical studies 1019–1020
  receptor (CD114) 453(Table), 1019
  secretion, regulation 1018
  sources 598, 1018
  stem cell increase 1019
  structure and X-ray crystallography 1018
  synergy with GM-CSF and M-CSF 1019
  target cells 1019
    hematopoietic 1019
Granulocyte-macrophage colony-stimulating factor (GM-CSF) 596, 1020–1023
  actions/functions 504, 597(Table), 598
  assays 697(Table), 1020–1021
  binding to IL-3 receptor 1446
  biological effects
    in vitro 1021–1022
    in vivo 1022
  effect on endothelial cells 805–806
  eosinophil function regulation 823, 824

Granulocyte-macrophage colony-stimulating factor (GM-CSF) (*continued*)
  erythroid burst-forming unit development 1021
  G-CSF synergy 1019
  gene 1021
    IL-3 gene similarity 1443
    regulation 1021
  granulocyte/macrophage function enhancement 1021
  hyper-IgM syndrome therapy 1168
  IL-3 synergy 1444
  IL-9 synergy 1473
  immunotherapy in fungal infections 961
  Langerhans cell growth 1530
  molecular biology 1021
  myelopoiesis 375
  overexpression 1022
  phagocytosis enhancement 1021
  in pulmonary homeostasis 1022
  receptors 376, 454(Table), 598, 1021
    eosinophils 823
  recombinant 1022
  rheumatoid arthritis 2114
  signal transduction 1021–1022
  sources 598, 1020
  structure 598, 1021
  synthesis, IL-12 effect 1486
  therapeutic uses 1022
Granulocyte-monocyte progenitor cell 1755, 1755(Table)
Granulocytosis, gravity/space flights effect 1031
Granuloma 1023–1026, 1342
  brucellosis 385
  cell types 1023
  chronic granulomatous disease 566
  classification 1024(Table)
  eosinophilic, *Toxocara canis* 2381
  epithelioid 1023, 1024, 2135(Fig)
  foreign body 1024
  formation 741, 1023, 1179–1179, 1342
    cytokines controlling 2136
    events in sarcoidosis 2135(Fig)
    Histoplasma capsulatum infections 1106
    macrophage role 1646
  historical aspects 1023
  hypersensitivity 1023, 1024, 1178–1179
  immunological 1023
  leishmaniasis 1023, 1025
  leprosy 753–754, 1023, 1024–1025
  mycobacterial diseases causing 1024–1025
  necrotizing T cell 319
  nonimmunological 1023
  retina 2379
  sarcoidosis 2135–2136, 2135(Fig), 2137
  schistosomiasis 1024, 1920, 2139–2140, 2139(Fig)
  silicosis 1023, 1024
  tuberculosis 1024, 1025
Granulomatosis, Wegener's, see Wegener's granulomatosis
Granulomatous disease
  chronic, see Chronic granulomatous disease (CGD)
  immune-mediated, sarcoidosis 2136
  T$_H$1 response 2137
Granulomatous hypersensitivity 1023, 1024, 1178–1179
Granulomatous reactions 738, 741
  see also Granuloma
Granzyme(s) 225, 728, 1026–1030, 1027(Table)
  apoptosis induction 1026–1027, 1029(Fig)
  cell death protease activation 1028, 1029(Fig)
  mechanism 1027–1028
  simple diffusion model 1027

Granzyme(s) (*continued*)
  'Asp-ase' specificity 1027, 1028
  'charge relay triad' 1026
  cytolysis by cytotoxic T cell 726–727
  functions 1026, 1028–1030
  historical aspects 1026
  knockout mice 1026
  number 1026
  specificity 1026–1027
  structure 1026
  synergistic action with perforin 1026,
    1027–1028, 1930
  synthesis 1027
Granzyme A 734, 1026
  actions 1028
  functions 1029–1030
  gene disruption 1029–1030
Granzyme B 225, 734, 1026
  apoptosis induction 1026, 1027–1028
  cell death protease activation 1028
  functions 1028–1029, 1930
Graphical methods, statistical analysis
    2213–2214
Graves' disease 1675, 2313, 2315
  autoantibody assays 2315
  clinical presentations 2315
  etiology 2313–2314
  HLA association 2313
  recurrence 2314
  thyroid growth inducing/inhibiting
    antibodies 2315
  TSH receptor autoantibodies 261–262,
    2315
  TSH receptor blocking antibodies
    (TSHRBAb) 2315
  type V hypersensitivity 1179
Graves' ophthalmopathy 2315–2316
Gravity, effects 1030–1033
  B cells 1032
  cell culture studies 1032
  cell-mediated immunity 1031–1032
  cytokines 1032
  granulocytes 1030, 1031
  humoral immunity 1032
  macrophage/monocytes 1031
  T cells 1031–1032
Gray collie syndrome 413
GRB-2 (growth factor receptor protein 2)
  IL-2 receptor signal transduction 1440
  IL-4 signal transduction 1455
  p21^{ras} regulation 2326
  structure 2326
'Greek key barrel' 775
Green fluorescent protein (GFP) 939
GRE sequences, annexins 113
Growth, intrauterine retardation 1800
Growth factor 720
  expression in tumors 2429
  for fibroblasts 907
  leukocyte culture 1569, 1570
  overexpression, viral carcinogenesis 1564
  poxvirus encoded homologs 1997(Table)
  receptors 2030
    expression regulated by B7-1/B7-2 305
    in tumors, mAbs recognizing 2429
    rheumatoid arthritis 2114, 2116
    signal transduction 2032
  T cell proliferation 503
Growth factor receptor protein 2, *see*
  GRB-2
Growth hormone
  deficiency 1279–1280
  functional (energetic) epitopes and cross-
    reactivity 2204
  immune response modulation 1829, 2224
  increase, exercise-induced 847
  increased release, arginine mechanism of
    action 236
  receptor
    Ig-type domains 777(Fig)
    structure 519(Fig), 520
  soluble receptors, function 715

grp78, *see* BiP
grp90 2231
grp95 2232
GTP, T cell signaling 2326
GTPase, toxin mode of action 2373(Fig)
GTPase-activating protein (GAP) 1300–
    1301
  mast cell degranulation 1670
  T cell signaling 2326
GTP-binding proteins
  clostridial toxin effect 578
  oxygen-dependent phagocytic killing
    1714, 1937–1938
  see also G proteins
Guanine nucleotide binding-proteins, *see* G
  proteins
Guillain–Barré syndrome 1836–1838
  acute inflammatory demyelinating
    polyneuropathy (AIDP) 1836–1837
  animal model 1836
  clinical features 1838
  Forssman antigen role 954
  in Hodgkin's disease 1836
  infections preceding 1837, 1838
    Campylobacter 407, 408
    Mycoplasma pneumoniae 1800
  influenza vaccine causing 2463
  model 860
  molecular mimicry in 1836
  subtypes 1836–1838
Guinea pig
  complement proteins (Cp) 1034–1035,
    1034(Table)
  experimental autoimmune
    encephalomyelitis (EAE) 271
  Forssman shock 953, 955
  GPLA complex 1034, 1034(Table)
  histamine sensitivity 1103
  inbred strains 1033–1035
    MHC class I molecules 1034
    MHC class II molecules 1033–1034
    S-antigens 1034
  macrophage/T cell interactions 1709–
    1710
  β_2-microglobulin 368
  skin grafts 1033
  skin tests 1365–1366
  strain 2 animals 1033–1035
  strain 13 animals 1033–1035
Guinea pig hypersensitivity assays 1366
Gusperimus 1352
Gut-associated lymphoid tissue (GALT)
    190, 1774, 1775–1776, 1893, 2155
  antigen degradation 1893
  functional anatomy 1775–1777, 1893
  histology 1894(Fig)
  mucosal administration of vaccines 2455
  oral tolerance and, *see* Oral tolerance
  organization 1775, 1893
  rabbit 2047
  reptiles 2078
  vaccination route 1893
  see also Appendix; Mucosa-associated
    lymphoid tissue (MALT); Peyer's
    patches
GVHD, *see* Graft-versus-host disease
  (GVHD)
GYPA gene 71
GYPB gene 71

H

H$^+$,K$^+$-adenosine triphosphatase (H$^+$,K$^+$-
  ATPase), gastric autoantigen 102, 263
H$_1$ antihistamines
  anaphylaxis treatment 685
  second-generation, eosinophil chemotaxis
    reduction 821
  urticaria 679

H$_1$ antihistamines (*continued*)
  urticaria (*continued*)
    chronic idiopathic 682
H$_1$ histamine receptors 1101
H$_1$-receptor antagonists, *see* H$_1$
  antihistamines
H$_2$ antihistamines
  chronic idiopathic urticaria 682
  gastric acid secretion inhibition 1104
  tumor destruction 1104
  urticaria 680
H$_2$ histamine receptors 1101
H2A, β chain, collagen-induced arthritis
    2107
H2A–H2B/DNA 130
H2^b
  haplotype 371
  murine lupus susceptibility 2252
  mutations 372
H2 class I molecules 1035–1040
  CD1 genes 1035, 1036
  class Ia gene (classical) 1035, 1230
  class Ib (nonclassical) 1035, 1039
  functions 1035, 1037
    as Ir genes 1230–1231
  genes 1036
    K/D/L genes 1036
    mapping 1036
    polymorphism 1036
    Qa genes 1036
    structure 1036
  historical aspects 1035–1036
  invariant light chain 1037
  I$^{-/-}$ mice, graft rejection study 1011–1012
  K/D/L proteins 1035
    anchor residues 1039
  mating preferences 1040
  peptide binding specificity 1039
  Qa region 1036
  structure 1036, 1037(Fig)
  synthesis/assembly 1037–1038,
    1038(Fig), 1039(Fig)
  TL region 1036
  in transplantation 1039
H2 class II molecules 1040–1045
  animal models of diseases 1044
  antigen presentation role 1040, 1044
  antigens 1041
  assembly/transport 1043–1044
  cell types expressing 1042
  discovery 1040–1041
  functions 1040, 1044
  genes 1041
    expression 1042–1043
    promoter 1042, 1042(Fig)
    regulation of expression 1042
    structure and polymorphism 1041–
      1042, 1041(Fig)
    see also I-A loci/region; I-E region;
      Immune response (Ir) genes
  genetic organization 1041, 1041(Fig)
  I-A and I-E antigens 1041
    see also Ia antigens
  II$^{-/-}$ mice, inflammatory bowel disease
    model 1383
  invariant chain (Ii) 1043
    degradation 1043
    see also Invariant chain (Ii)
  knockout mice 1040, 1044
  mixed lymphocyte reaction (MLR) 1735
  peptide interactions 1042
  peptide loading 1043–1044
  recombination hot spot 1041
  signaling pathway for B cells 1044
  structure 1042
H2 class III molecules 1045–1047
  disease susceptibility 1047
  genes 1045, 1045–1046
  organization 1045, 1045(Fig)
  HLA differences 1045
H2 complex 636, 1730
  allogeneic diversity and 208

H2 complex (*continued*)
analysis, using *bm* mutants 373
antigen diversity and 209
class I, *see* H2 class I molecules
class II molecules, *see* H2 class II
molecules
discovery 1230
genes 635
H-Y graft rejection 1158
polymorphism 372, 1704
see also H2 class I molecules; H2 class
II molecules
history 1035–1036, 1230
IDDM loci in NOD mice 1392–1396,
1392(Table)
I-region 1041, 1230–1231
see also Immune response (Ir) genes
mutations, *bm* mutants 371–372
H2-D, *bm* mutants 372(Table)
H2-D^b 1731
H2-K, *bm* mutants 372(Table)
H2-M3 72
antigen presentation by 72, 462
CD1 similarity 462
H2-T antigens 72
H₃ histamine receptors 1101
HA-1 (minor histocompatibility antigen)
1731
HA-5 (minor histocompatibility antigen)
1731
Haber–Weiss reaction 1717, 1938
Haemonchus contortus 1125
vaccines 1921
Haemophilus influenzae 1048–1050
antigens 1048
characteristics 1048
host immune response 1048–1049
htrB gene 1049
infection prevention by breast milk Igs
1672
lipooligosaccharides (LOS) 1048, 1049
meningitis 1048
nonencapsulated/nontypeable (NTHI)
1048
colonization 1048
immune response to 1049
infections 1048, 1049
vaccine 1049
otitis media 1048
outer membrane proteins (OMPs) 1048
polyribosyl-ribitol phosphate (PRP) 1048
antibodies 1048
vaccine 1049
respiratory tract colonization 1048
serotype b (Hib), *see Haemophilus
influenzae* type b (Hib)
vaccines 1049
antibody level after, allotype effect 76
Haemophilus influenzae type b (Hib) 1048
capsule 423
evasive strategies 2083
as hapten 1050
host immune response 2083
immunogenicity 1050
vaccine 1049, 2083–2084, 2458
adverse reaction 2464
failure in infants 1285
Haemophilus somnus 326
Hairless nu/nu mice, *see* Nude (athymic)
mice
Hairy-cell leukemia (HCL) 1558,
1558(Table), 1633
interferon α therapy 1416
'Hairy' leukoplakia 832, 833
Halogenated aromatic hydrocarbons,
immunosuppression due to 1367
HAMA (human antimouse antibody) 1140,
2432
Hanganutziu–Deicher (H-D) system 1092
Hanging drop method, culture 1900(Fig),
1901
Hanker–Yates reagent 1263

Hantaan virus 391–392
Hantavirus 391–392, 391(Table)
immune response to 392
rodents relationships 392(Table)
vaccines 392–393
Hantavirus pulmonary syndrome 392
Haploinsufficiency, of genes 761
Haplotypes 75–76
Gm 75–76, 75(Table)
Hapten 219, 1050–1052, 2094, 2466
in affinity labeling 50–51
allergens as 66
allergic contact dermatitis 787
antibodies and myeloma proteins against
50–51
antibody binding
affinity measurement 1051–1052
monitoring 1051–1052
as antigenic determinant 1050
artificial epitope of proteins, generation
1050
borderline immunogenicity 1050
carrier coupling, *see* Hapten–carrier
systems
definition 202–10–203, 1050, 1337
drug-induced immune hemolytic anemia
95
drugs as 779, 779(Fig), 780, 1052
free, inhibition of binding to antibodies
1051
historical aspects 1050, 1337, 2199
IgM reactions 1215
liposomes as carriers 1590
macromolecule 1050
measurement, ELISA 817
peptides as 1051
uses in immunology 1050
Haptenation, drugs 779, 779(Fig), 780,
1052
Hapten–carrier system 436–438, 1050
antigen presentation to T cells 353, 397,
437
conjugates, B cell–T cell cooperation
1059
immunogenicity 1050
monitoring of hapten binding 1051–1052
preparation 1051
structures participating in coupling
1051(Table)
Haptotactic action, IL-8 1468
Haptotactic response 1759
Haptotaxis 535
Harder's gland 301
*Hartmannella vermiformis, Legionella
pneumophila* ingestion 1542
Hashimoto's thyroiditis 2313, 2316
animal model 104
see also Obese strain of chickens
autoantibodies 293
Fas/FasL pathway role 879
in neonates 1675
type II hypersensitivity 1176
Hassall's corpuscles 2235, 2305
enlargement, protein-energy malnutrition
(PEM) 1869
in pigs 1991
HAT selection, *see* Hypoxanthine,
aminopterin, thymidine (HAT)
selection
Haurowitz, F. 1337
Haverhill fever 2216
Hawaii virus (HV) 400
Hayfever, *see* Allergic rhinitis
H box 1042
hCAP-18 1724
H-D antigen 1092
H-D system (Hanganutziu–Deicher) 1092
Heart
autoantibodies reactive 435
see also Cardiac disease, autoimmune
histamine effect 1103
infections, *see* Cardiac infections

Heart block, complete, in neonates 1676
Heart disease, autoimmune, *see* Cardiac
disease, autoimmune
Heart transplantation, *see* Cardiac
transplantation
Heart valve, infections 2082
Heart–lung transplantation 2413
cyclosporine role 688
Heat shock 2228
Heat shock proteins (hsp) 319, 2228
autoimmunity and 319
groups 2228–2230, 2229(Table)
hsp10 2229(Table)
hsp60 34, 2229(Table)
adjuvant arthritis 2231
as bacterial 'common antigen' 2231
CD4+ T cells 2231
functions 2230
Histoplasma capsulatum 1106, 1107
homolog in *Helicobacter pylori* 1057
mycobacterial infections 2231
structure 2230
hsp65
adjuvant arthritis 34–35
arthritis models association 1797
cross-reactivity 34
in mycobacteria 1794, 1797
in NZB mice 93
specificity of immunity 34
HSP70-1 and HSP70-2 genes
1117(Table), 1119
hsp70 2229(Table)
antibodies blocking MHC class II
restriction 2231
antigen presentation 2231–2232
disease association 1120, 2231
functions 1119
gene expression 1117(Table), 1119
mice 1047
normal functions 2230, 2231
sequence homologies 2229
structure 2230
HSP70 gene, as primordial MHC gene
1701
hsp90 2229(Table)
antigen presentation 2231
functions 2230
release, glucocorticoid binding 999
hsp110 2229(Table)
mycobacteria (Bhsp65) 755
rat (Rhsp65) 755
rheumatoid arthritis etiology 2114–2115
small hsps 2229(Table)
see also Molecular mimicry; Stress
proteins
Heat stable antigen (HSA; CD24) 2149
receptor 2149
Heavy chain, *see* Immunoglobulin heavy
(H) chains
Heavy chain binding protein, *see* BiP
Heavy chain (HC) diseases 1053–1056
α-HCD 1053
cellular/nucleic acid data 1054–1056
CH1 domain lacking 1056
clinical features 1053
diagnosis 1053
γ-HCD 1053
HC subclass restriction 1053
μ-HCD 1053
structural changes to HCD proteins
1053–1054, 1054(Table), 1055(Fig)
HECA 452 antibodies 1094, 2160
Helicase 1118
Helicobacter pylori 968, 1056–1058
antigens 1056–1057
characteristics 1056–1057
colonization 1057, 1058
detection 1057
evasive strategies 1058
genome 1056
hemagglutinins 1057
host immune response 1057–1078

Helicobacter pylori (*continued*)
  immunohistology and T cells 1057
  infection prevention by breast milk Igs
    1672
  lipopolysaccharide 322
  MALT lymphomas 1635
  monoclonal antibodies 1056
  recurrent infections 1057
  urease 1056–1057
  VacA and CagA proteins 1057
  vaccines 1058
Helmet cells (keratocytes) 834
Helminth worms 1916–1917
  gastrointestinal infections 967, 968
  host immune response
    strategies 1917
    T cells 1919
  immune adherence 1219
  see also Parasites
Helper T lymphocytes 789, 1058–1062,
    2342
  activation 177, 502
    failure in B cell anergy 107
  age-related changes 60
  antigen presentation 157, 177, 1059,
    1236(Fig)
    see also T cell(s), antigen presentation
  antigen-presenting cell (APC) interactions
    195
  antigen recognition 53, 467, 502
  antinuclear autoantibodies induction 132
  apoptosis 876–877, 878, 879
  autoimmune hemolytic anemia in NZB
    mice 92
  autoreactive
    Chagas' disease 433
    mercury inducing 1687
  B7-2 as costimulator 306
  B cell stimulation 156–157, 350, 826
    CD40-CD40L interaction 350, 1061
    mechanisms 1061
  in cats 893
  CD4 expression 1059
  CD8⁺ cells, cytokines 2331
  characteristics 1059, 1895(Table)
  clonal expansion 2330–2331, 2331(Fig)
  cytokines released 700, 1060, 1227,
    2330, 2342
    inhibition by suppressor T cells 2245
  cytotoxic T cell generation 1061
  defect, in common variable
    immunodeficiency 601
  development 2337
  differentiation 502
    cytokines required 2330
  discovery 1058
  in dogs 413
  enrichment, hybridoma generation 1153
  in graft rejection 1012–1013
  in hepatitis B 1077
  historical aspects 1058, 2264
  I-J expression 1218
  immune response *in vitro* 1233
  impairment in urodeles 82
  mercuric chloride effect 1687
  MHC restriction 1059, 2264
    see also MHC class II
  in neonates 1820
  radioresistance 2052
  reptiles 2080
  response to tumor antigens 2441
  in rheumatic fever 432
  subsets
    characteristics 1895(Table)
    discovery 1626
    in vivo 1061–1062
    responses 1060–1061, 1062
    see also T$_H$0 cells; T$_H$1 cells; T$_H$2 cells
  suppressor T cell action 2245
  TGFβ effects 2396
  T$_H$0, *see* T$_H$0 cells
  T$_H$1, *see* T$_H$1 cells

Helper T lymphocytes (*continued*)
  T$_H$2, *see* T$_H$2 cells
  T$_H$3, *see* T$_H$3 cells
Hemacytometer 2475
Hemadsorption (HAD), by African swine
    fever (ASF) virus 54
Hemagglutination 57, 58
  assays 141
  erythrocytes 58
  factors influencing 57
  I-A 1219, 1220(Fig)
  inhibition (HAI) 57
    adenovirus antibody detection 23
    Staphylococcus 2210
  see also Agglutination, red blood cells
Hemagglutinin
  antibodies 1385
  antigenic drift and 200
  filamentous, *Bordetella pertussis* 377
  Helicobacter pylori 1057
  influenza viruses 1384, 1385
  paramyxovirus attachment 1911
Hematologic malignancy
  chromosomal translocations 554–559
  opportunistic infections 1882–1883
  stem cell transplantation 1063(Fig),
    1064–1065, 1064(Table), 1065(Fig)
  see also Leukemia; Lymphoma; Myeloma
Hematopoiesis
  IL-3 role 1442, 1442–1443, 1444
  IL-3 synergy 1459
  IL-6 role 1459
  mononuclear phagocytes origin 1755
  porcine 1991
  regulation
    IL-1 role 1434
    NK cell role 1814
  reptiles 2076
  stem cell origin 374–375
  stimulation
    by GM-CSF 1022
    by romurtide 1792
  see also Bone marrow hematopoiesis;
    Stem cell(s)
Hematopoietic cells
  as APCs 2338
  avian 302
  G-CSF actions 1019
  identification, rosetting techniques 2129
  leukemia inhibitory factor (LIF) function
    1561
  proliferation, IL-3 role 1442–1443
  stem cells, *see* Stem cell(s)
  T cell clonal deletion induction 2338
  transferrin receptor (TfR) expression
    2390, 2390(Table)
Hematopoietic chimerism, *see* Chimerism,
    hematopoietic
Hematopoietic growth factor(s) 375
  late-acting 375
  receptors 375–376
  synergistic 375
  see also Colony-stimulating factors
    (CSF); Interleukin-3 (IL-3)
Hematopoietic growth factor receptor
    (HGFR) family 708–709, 709(Table)
  as cytokine receptors 708
  extracellular/cytoplasmic domains 708
  oligomerization 708–709
  promiscuous use of subunits 708–709
  structure 708–709
Hematopoietic stem cells, *see* Stem cell(s)
Hematopoietic syndrome 2050
Hematopoietic system, colony-stimulating
    factors role 598
'Hematopoietin family' 721
Hematopoietin receptor superfamily 721
  IL-2 in 1436
  IL-2 receptor β chain 1440
  IL-9 receptor 1472
Hemochromatosis 1507
  hereditary 1693

Hemocyanin markers, immunoelectron
    microscopy 792
Hemocytes 1947
Hemodialysis, amyloidosis association 84,
    85
Hemoglobin
  abnormal 988
  β-chain, mutation in sickle cell anemia
    988
  cord 1072
  embryonic 374
  fetal 374, 798
    antibodies to 801
  modified solutions as blood substitute
    2403
  switching 374
Hemolymph 1500
Hemolysin
  Bordetella pertussis 2377
  El Tor (*Vibrio cholerae*) 2477–2478
  Escherichia coli 2377
  Proteus mirabilis 2040, 2041
  Staphylococcus 269, 2209, 2377
Hemolysin I (cereolysin), *Bacillus cereus*
    toxin 313
Hemolysin II (HBL), *Bacillus cereus* toxin
    313
Hemolysis
  extravascular 100
  see also Erythrocyte(s), lysis
Hemolytic anemia
  autoimmune, *see* Autoimmune hemolytic
    anemia (AIHA)
  hereditary 835
  in Rh (Rhesus) disease 1071
Hemolytic disease, feline 894
Hemolytic disease of newborn (HDN) 4–5,
    1070–1073, 1674, 2102
  ABO incompatibility 1070–1071, 1072,
    1674
  blocking (incomplete) antibodies 1071
  Coombs' test 116, 1071
  in monkeys 1072
  prophylaxis 1072, 2102
  serology 1071
  severity and factors affecting 5
  severity prediction 1072
  treatment 1071, 1072, 1967, 2102
  see also Rh (Rhesus) disease
Hemolytic drop procedure 1962
Hemolytic plaque-forming cell, *see* Plaque-
    forming cells (PFC)
Hemolytic uremic syndrome (HUS) 844
  Shigella causing 2178, 2180
  therapy, fresh frozen plasma (FFP) 1966
Hemophilus influenzae, *see* *Haemophilus
    influenzae*
Hemorrhagic colitis 842, 844, 967
Hemorrhagic factor, *see* Tumor necrosis
    factor α (TNFα)
Hemorrhagic fever
  filoviral, *see under* Filoviruses
  flaviviruses causing 926
Hemorrhagic fever with renal syndrome
    (HFRS) 391, 918
Hemostasis 1973–1974
  fibronectin role 912
  see also Clotting system
Hen egg lysozyme (HEL)
  antibodies, electrostatic fields 2202(Fig)
  as antigen 205
  antigen processing 197(Fig)
  double transgenic mice, IgD role 1201
  immune complexes with, structures 172,
    2201(Fig)
  immunodominant peptide presented by I-
    A^k 1231, 1291
  transgenic B cells 106
  transgenic mice, tolerance mechanism
    2364, 2366
Hepadnaviridae 1975
Heparan sulfate (HS) 862, 863(Table), 906

Heparan sulfate (HS) (continued)
 anti-DNA antibodies interaction 130
Heparin
 fibronectin binding 910
 immune complex removal 2169
 in mast cells 1668
 platelet factor 4 complexes 1975
 porcine 1975
 thrombocytopenia due to 1975
Hepatic failure, see Liver, failure
Hepatic fibrosis, see Liver, fibrosis
Hepatitis
 chronic, cryoglobulinemia with 666
 chronic active, see Chronic active
   hepatitis (CAH)
 chronic persistent 561
 Fas/FasL pathway role 879
 lupoid 561
 non-ABCDE 1083
 viral, see specific hepatitis viruses (below)
Hepatitis A 1073
 clinical features 1074
 epidemiological patterns 1074
 incubation period 1073, 1074
 laboratory diagnosis 1074
 management 1074
 prevalence 1074
 prevention 1074
 in travelers 1074
Hepatitis A virus (HAV) 1073–1075
 characteristics 1073
 classification 1073
 epitope location 1957(Table)
 evasive strategies 1959
 human immunoglobulin (HNIG) 966,
   1074
 vaccines 1074, 1959
 see also Picornaviruses
Hepatitis B
 acute 1076–1077, 1077(Fig)
 chronic
  immune complexes 2483
  thymic humoral factor (THF) effect
    2303
 interferon α therapy 1416
 persistent infection 1077–1078, 1975
  chronic active hepatitis, see Chronic
    active hepatitis (CAH)
  mechanisms 1077
  natural history 1077–1078, 1077(Fig)
Hepatitis B virus (HBV) 1075–1079
 blood product screening 2400
 common 'a' determinant 1078, 1079
 core antigen (HBcAg) 563, 1076, 1975
 'e' antigen (HBeAg) 563, 1077, 1975
  -negative viremia phase 1077(Fig),
    1078
  -positive viremia phase 1077
 envelope 1975
 escape mutant 1078
 genome 1075, 1076(Fig)
  integration in host genome 1076
 host immune response
  antibodies 1076
  cell-mediated 1076–1077, 1078
 immunization, stress effect 2222
 immunobiology 1076–1078
 latent infection phase 1077(Fig), 1078
 polypeptides 1975
 replication 1078
 seroconversion phase 1078
 surface antigen (HBsAg) 563, 1076,
   1975
  aa124-137 in vaccine 1078
  antibodies 1078
  genetic variation 1078–1079
  immune complexes, clearance 184
 vaccines 1078
  HBsAg in 1078, 2457
 variants 1079
 X protein 1076
Hepatitis C

Hepatitis C (continued)
 autoimmunity in 1079
 immune complexes in 1225
 persistent infection
  chronic active hepatitis, see Chronic
    active hepatitis (CAH)
  cryoglobulinemia 667
  therapy 1079
   interferon α 1416
Hepatitis C virus (HCV) 1079–1081
 antibodies (anti-HCV) 1080
 antigens 1079–1080
 blood product screening 2400
 carriers 1079
 characteristics 1079–1080
 detection 1080
 E2 protein, hypervariable 1080, 1081
 evasive strategies 1081
 genome 1079, 1080(Fig)
 genotypes 1080
 host immune response 1080–1081
 NS gene products 1080
 quasispecies 1081
 replication, extrahepatic 1081
 transmission 1079
  by gammaglobulin preparations 966
 vaccines 1081
Hepatitis E virus (HEV) 400, 1082–1083
 characteristics 400
 epitopes, localization 1082
 genome 1082
 host immune response 1083
 infection
  clinical features 1082–1083
  pathology 1083
  prophylaxis 1083
  seroprevalence 1082
  transmission and sources 1082
 vaccine 1083
 viremia and virus excretion 1082
Hepatitis F viruses (HFV) 1083
Hepatitis G virus (HGV) 1083–1084
Hepatocellular carcinoma (HCC) 1075,
   1076
 chronic active hepatitis (CAH) 561, 563
 see also Liver cancer
Hepatocytes
 IL-6 receptor 1461
 intralobular necrosis, in hepatitis E 1083
Hepatocyte-stimulating factor (HSF)
 acute phase response 1459
 functions 1459(Fig)
 see also Interleukin-6 (IL-6)
Hepatocyte-stimulating factor 3 (HSF-3),
  see Leukemia inhibitory factor (LIF)
Hepatoma, see Hepatocellular carcinoma
  (HCC)
Hepatosplenomegaly, in brucellosis 385
Hepatovirus 1955(Table)
 receptors 1956(Table)
Hereditary amyloid polyneuropathy 84
Hereditary angioedema 611, 613, 684
 C1 esterase inhibitor deficiency 684
 features 684
 kallikrein–kinin system role 1520
 oral infections 1891
 rocket immunoelectrophoresis 1294
Hereditary hemochromatosis, non-HLA
  loci mutations 1694
Hermes antigen, see CD44
'Herpes esthiomenos' 2186, 2255
Herpes simplex virus (HSV) 1084–1088
 after stem cell transplantation 1067
 antibodies, natural IgG 1808
 antigens 1086–1087, 1087
 characteristics 1084–1085
 delayed-type hypersensitivity 1087
 evasive strategies 1085, 1087–1088
 Fc and C3b receptor on 1088
 gene expression 1085
 genes for apoptosis 1088
 genome 1085, 2075

Herpes simplex virus (HSV) (continued)
 guinea pig vaginal model 1087
 host immune response 1085–1087,
   1086(Fig), 2075
  antibodies 1087
  cell-mediated 1087
  immune effectors and sites 1086(Table)
 HSV-1 1084
  eye infection 872
  genital tract infection 2075
  see also Herpes simplex virus type 1
    (HSV-1) ophthalmia (HSVO)
 HSV-2 1084
  DNA vaccines 773, 1088
  genital tract infection 2075
 immunopathology 1087
 infection 1086(Fig), 2075
  acute 1085, 1086(Fig)
  clinical aspects 1085
  latent 1085
  management 1088
  recurrence 2075
  treatment, transfer factors 2388
 infection process 1085
 latency-associated transcripts (LATs)
   1085
 lytic cycle 1085
 macrophage infection 2486
 NK cell response 1086
 reactivation 1085, 1882
  transplant recipients 1884
  UV role 1945
 receptors 1085
 thymidine kinase gene (HSV-tk) 25, 978
  knockout mice development 1524
 transmission 1085
 vaccines 1088, 2075
  glycoprotein 1088
  for mucosal immune system 1088
Herpes simplex virus type 1 (HSV-1)
  ophthalmia (HSVO) 872
 experimental 872
 features 872
 susceptibility 872
 vaccines and immunization 872
Herpesvirus-6, see Human herpesvirus type
  6 (HHV-6)
Herpesviruses 2468
 CMV 722
 EBV 828
 immunodeficiency 1286
Herpesvirus saimiri (HVS), sequence
  homology to CD59 500
Herpes zoster (shingles) 2468, 2469
Heteroconjugates 138–139, 139(Fig)
'Heterogeneity test' 1698
Heterogeneous nuclear ribonucleoproteins
  (hnRNPs) 126
Heterologous reaction 1092
Heterophile antibodies 1092–1093
 definition 1092
 Forssman system, see Forssman antigen
 Hanganutziu–Deicher (H-D) system 1092
 Paul–Bunnell (P-B) system 1092
Heterophile antigens, see Antigen,
  heterophile
Heterophile reaction 1092
Heterotransplantation 2508
 see also Xenotransplantation
Heterozygous, definition 986
HEV, see Hepatitis E virus (HEV); High
  endothelial venules (HEV)
HEVin protein 1096
Hexose monophosphate pathway, red cells
  837
HHV-8, see Human herpesvirus type 8
  (HHV-8)
High-density lipoprotein (HDL)
 effect on TNFα production 2439
 serum amyloid A (SAA) association 85
High endothelial cells (HEC) 1093–1094
 arrangements 1095–1096

High endothelial cells (HEC) (continued)
  basement membrane surrounding 1096–
    1097
  height 1094
  histochemistry/biochemistry 1094
  lymphocyte migration across 1096
  markers 1094
  number, antigen stimulation effect 1095
  'spot welds' 1096
High endothelial venules (HEV) 1093–
    1101
  absence in sheep 1905
  addressins (adhesion molecules), see
    Addressins
  anatomical aspects 1093–1094
  chemoattractants released 1762
  contractility, T cell regulation of 1099
  definition 1093, 1093–1094
  development 1098–1099
    cytokines role 1100
    defects 1100
    extranodal 1099–1100, 1099(Fig)
    nodal 1098–1099(Fig)
    origin 1093, 1099
  distribution 1094–1095
  endothelial cells, see High endothelial
    cells (HEC)
  extranodal 1093, 1099–1100
  intermediate lymph formation 1601
  lymphocyte extravasation 1095–1098,
    1098(Fig), 1762
    adhesion cascade 1097–1098, 2060
    adhesion molecules role 1097–1098,
      2060
    adhesion phase 1093, 1097–1098,
      1099
    chemoattractants 1098
    knockout mice 1098
    LFA-1 role 1097–1098
    L-selectin/$\alpha_4\beta_7$ integrin roles 1097–
      1098
    lymphocyte morphology change 1096
    migration route 1095
    migration stage 538, 1097, 1617
    nonrandom migration 1097
    overview 1098(Fig)
    recognition stage 1097
    rolling phase 1097
    structural aspects 1094, 1095–1097
    T cell migration 30
    see also Lymphocytes; Transmigration
      of leukocytes
  markers 1093, 1094, 1097
  monoclonal antibodies 1094
  nodal 1093–1094, 1095(Fig), 1604
  Peyer's patches 1099, 1776
  sites/location 1093, 1094–1095,
    1095(Fig), 1604
  structural aspects 1094, 1095–1097
High molecular weight kininogen
    (HMWK) 582, 1519
  actions 1519
  active cofactor (HKa) 1520
  bradykinin release 1520
  cleavage 1519
  deficiency 1519
  gene 1519
  kallikrein action on 1520
  procoagulant properties 1519
High-pressure liquid chromatography
    (HPLC)
  affinity chromatography with 48
  heteroconjugate formation 138
Hippocampus, lesions 2224
HIRA gene 761
Histaminase 1101, 1102(Fig)
Histamine 1101–1105
  allergic reactions 1101–1102
  anaphylaxis 1102
  bioassay 1103
  carcinogenesis role 1104
  cardiovascular system 1102–1103

Histamine (continued)
  cardiovascular system (continued)
    blood vessels 1102–1103
    heart 1103
  cell proliferation increase 1104
  chemistry 1101, 1102(Fig)
  distribution 1101
  effect on CNS 1104
  effect on immune system cells 1104–
    1105
  false food allergy 952(Table)
  gastric acid secretion 1103–1104
  metabolism/catabolism 1101, 1102(Fig)
  nonvascular smooth muscle response
    1103
  pharmacologic effects 254, 1101–1105
    classification by severity 1102,
      1103(Table)
  receptors 1101
    antagonism 1101
    genes 1101
    second messengers for 1101
  red spot response 1103
  release 737, 1101, 1104
    allergic rhinitis 2123, 2124
    by basophils 333–334
    by foods 949, 950
    by mast cells 1101, 1104, 1668, 2123
  structure 1101, 1102(Fig)
  synthesis 1668
  'triple response' 1102
Histamine-N-methyltransferase 1101
Histamine-producing cell-stimulating
    activity, see Interleukin-3 (IL-3)
Histamine-releasing factor 681
Histaminergic neurons 1101, 1104
Histatins 1889
Histidine 1101, 1102(Fig)
  false food allergy 952(Table)
Histidine decarboxylase, inhibitors 1104
Histiocytes 1757
  in skin infections 753–754
Histiocytic cell system 1756
Histiocytic reticulum cells, see Histiocytes
Histiocytosis X, Langerhans cells in 1529
Histocompatibility antigens
  ABO antigens 4
  major, see MHC
  mice, see H2 complex
  minor, see Minor transplantation
    (histocompatibility) antigens
Histocompatibility Workshops 2319, 2322
Histones
  antibodies 131
  anti-DNA antibodies interaction 130
  in nucleosome 125–126
Histoplasma capsulatum 958, 1105–1108
  antigens 1106
  characteristics 1105–1106
  Downs strain 1105
  evasive strategies 1107
  gene expression 1105
  granuloma formation 1106
  heat shock protein 60 (hsp60) 1106,
    1107
  host immune response 1106, 1106–1107
  infection, see Histoplasmosis
  infection route 1105, 1106
  macrophage infection 1106–1107
  NK cell action 959–960
  phase transition 1105
  vaccines 1107
  see also Histoplasmosis
Histoplasmin 1106
Histoplasmosis 1106
  clinical features 1106
  disseminated 1106, 1107
  in hyper-IgM syndrome 1167
  see also Histoplasma capsulatum
Historical aspects 1334–1339
  see also Immunology; individual subjects
HIV-1 6, 1131

HIV-1 (continued)
  genome organization 1132(Fig)
  receptors 2094
  type B virus 6
  type E virus 6
  see also HIV; HIV infection
HIV-2 6, 1131
  genome organization 1132(Fig)
  receptors 2094
HIV 1130–1139, 2096
  allostimulation due to 1137
  antigenic variation 1134–1135
  antigens, immunization with 12, 1136
  attachment process 10, 1133
  blood product screening 2400
  CD4$^+$ T cell infection 2484
    see also CD4$^+$ T cells
  CD8$^+$ T cell infection 2486
  cell death (direct/indirect) 1138
  clades (genetic subtypes) 1135
  classification 1131
  complement resistance, CD46 role 496
  diagnosis/assays
    agglutination 141
    Western blotting 2507
  drug resistance 12
  envelope 1134
  env gene 1132
  evasive strategies 1134, 1135, 1136
  evolution 1134–1135
  feline immunodeficiency virus similarities
    895
  follicular dendritic cell-entrapped 1729
  gag gene 1131–1132
  Gag-Pol polyprotein 1132
  Gag protein, vaccine 1136
  genes
    regulatory/accessory 1132–1133
    structural 1131–1132
  genetic heterogeneity 200
  genome 1131, 2095
    structure/functional organization 1131,
      1132(Fig)
  gp41 1132
    CD4 interaction 471
  gp120 10, 425–426, 1132, 1134
    CD4 interaction 470–471, 1134
    V3 loop 1135, 1136
    vaccine 1136
  groups O and M 1135
  half-life 1138
  in ISCOM complexes 1508
  lifecycle 1133
  load quantification by PCR 9
  long terminal repeats (LTR) 1131, 1133
  lymphocyte proliferation due to 2021
  in macrophage 10, 11
  mutations and recombination 1134
  nef gene 1133
    defect 9
  nef product, CD4 interaction 471
  neutralization epitopes 1136
  neutralization resistance 1136
  origin 1131
  p24 antigenemia 9
  pol gene 1132
  protein synthesis control 1132
  provirus 1131, 1132
    DNA 1131, 1133
  receptors 1133, 1133–1134
    'Bonzo' and 'Bob' coreceptors 1134
    CC-CKR3 and CC-CKR5 532, 712
    CCR5 and CXCR4 10, 532, 712, 1134
    CD4 10, 470–471, 1133–1134
    chemokine receptors 712, 2094
    coreceptors 2094
    see also Chemokines, receptors
  replication 10, 1133, 1729
    genes involved 1133
  reservoir in FDC cells 1138
  reverse transcriptase 1131
    errors 1134

HIV (*continued*)
  rev gene 1132–1133
  seronegative after exposure 1135
  structure 1131, 1131(Fig)
  tat gene 1132, 2095
  tax gene 2095
  T cell apoptosis
    LFA-3–CD2 interaction/role 1614
    pathway 2485
  transmission 6
    by gammaglobulin preparations 966
    heterosexual 6
    prevention, B7/CD28 307
    vertical, *see below*
  tropism 1134
  T tropic strains 1134
  turnover 1137–1138
  vaccine development/problems 1135–
    1137
    'cocktail' of antigens 1136
    safety/efficacy testing 1136
    specificity 1137
    strategies 1136
    subunit 1136
  vaccines 12–13
    gp120 12–13, 1136
  vertical transmission 6, 2488
    reduced by zidovudine 12
  vif and vpu genes 1133
  viremia 1728–1729
  vpr gene and vpx gene 1133
  see also HIV-1
HIV encephalopathy 7
  neuropathogenesis 11
HIV enteropathy 8
HIV infection
  animal models 1268, 1274, 2005
  attachment/infection process 10, 1133
  case number and spread 6
  CD4+ cell decline, *see under* CD4+ T cells
  CD4+ function impairment 10
  CD8+ cell changes 938
  chronic GVHD similarity 1137
  chronic symptomless 7
  CNS 1845
  diffuse infiltrative lymphocytosis (DILS)
    2183
  distribution 6
  FcγR role 890
  fungal infections in 960
  GM-CSF therapy 1022
  HIV load quantification by PCR 9
  immune activation in 1137
  immune defects in 10–11
  immune response 12, 1135
    antibodies 9, 1135
    T$_H$1 role 1135, 1138
  immunity 6
    HLA association 6
    role 9
  immunodeficiency 1285
  immunopathogenesis, *see under* AIDS
  initiation 1133
  Langerhans cells role 1531
  leishmaniasis and 1920–1921
    reactivation 1550
  Mycoplasma as cofactor 1801
  natural history 8–9
  nonprogression 8, 9, 1135
  parasitic infections 1920–1921
  pathogenesis 1137
  pneumococcal pneumonia 2219
  polyneuritis 1836
  primate models 2005
  progression 7
    age affecting 8
    FACS assessment 934
    HIV strains 9
    HLA association 8
    immune activation 1137
    infections affecting 8
    malnutrition affecting 9

HIV infection (*continued*)
  progression (*continued*)
    predictive markers 9–10
    pregnancy and 8–9
    risk 8
    T$_H$2 response 1138
    T-tropic strains 307
  protection from 1135
  rabbit model 2046
  seroconversion and antibodies 7
  sexual 6
  Sjögren's syndrome (SS) association 2183
  skin diseases, pathogenesis 1531
  spectrum 7–8
  spread 1136
  symptoms 7
  TGFβ in 2398
  therapy, *see under* AIDS
  TNFα levels 2439
  transient, in infants 7
  transmission, *see* HIV, transmission
  tuberculosis 1794
  vaccines, *see under* HIV
  in vitamin A deficiency 2488
  vitamin E effect 2501
  see also AIDS
HIV seroconversion illness 7
H+,K+-ATPase, gastric autoantigen 102,
  263
HL-60 cells, FcγR functions 890
HLA 1108–1111, 1111–1113, 1114–1121
  expression
    level, regulation 1696
    platelets 1974
  gene region 1690
    loci 1691–1692
    genetic map 1691(Fig)
  Gm haplotype interaction 76
  HIV infection
    immunity 6
    progression risk 8
  linkage disequilibrium 1586–1587, 1587–
    1588
  matching for transplantation, *see* Tissue
    typing
  maternal, binding by nontrophoblastic
    cells 900–901
  microchimerism after transplantation
    2402
  nomenclature 1692
  null expression 329
    see also Bare lymphocyte syndrome
  pernicious anemia association 105
  polymorphism 1692, 1704
  in primates (nonhuman) 2008
  purification 1540
  specificities/alleles, listing 2319,
    2320(Table)–2321(Table)
  transfusion-associated GVHD (TA-
    GVHD) 2402
  WHO nomenclature 2319
  see also MHC
HLA, disease association 988, 1232, 1587,
    1690–1700, 1690(Table), 2322
  absolute risk 1698
  autoimmune disease, *see* Autoimmune
    disease
  autoimmune polyglandular syndrome
    type II 1985
  cancer 1693
    cervical cancer 1908
  class II-associated 1690(Table), 1788
    see also HLA class II
  class III 1119–1120
  complement deficiency 1693
  environmental factors 1699
  epidemiological risk estimate 1698
  HLA/pathogen genotype interactions
    1699
    amino acid residues role 1699
    issues associated 1699
  Lambert–Eaton syndrome 1835, 1850

HLA, disease association (*continued*)
  linkage analysis 1697
  linkage disequilibrium 1586–1587, 1587–
    1588, 1696–1697, 2064
  mechanisms 267, 1693–1696
    linkage disequilibrium 1693
    molecular mimicry 1695–1696
    peptide binding 1694
    regulation 1696
    T cell repertoire 1695
    T$_H$1/T$_H$2 subsets 1695
  MHC gene combinations 1699
  multiple genes (polygenic nature) 1699,
    2065
  multiple sclerosis 1694, 1788
  myasthenia gravis 1834, 1848
  nonrandom association, *see* Linkage
    disequilibrium
  null hypothesis of no linkage 1697
  odds ratio 1697–1698
  pemphigus vulgaris 1694, 1696
  population attributable risk 1698
  population genetics 1696–1697
  predisposition to disease 1698–1699
  relative risk 1698, 2064
  rheumatoid arthritis, *see* Rheumatoid
    arthritis (RA)
  risk estimates 1697, 1698, 1698(Table),
    1899(Table), 2064–2065
  sarcoidosis 2134
  Sjögren's syndrome (SS) 2182, 2183
  SLE 2257
  statistics 1698
  thyroid autoimmunity 2313
  tissue typing application 2322
  toxoplasmosis 2384
  see also HLA types; *individual diseases*
HLA-A2
  melanoma 2425
  β$_2$-microglobulin structural similarity 368
  as most successful HLA allele 2322
  ovarian tumors 2425
  structure 1110
HLA-B12, vitamin B$_{12}$ malabsorption 105
HLA-B27
  ankylosing spondylitis, *see* Ankylosing
    spondylitis
  autoimmune disease and 278
  gram-negative bacteria interaction 2121
  HIV infection progression risk 8
  Klebsiella pneumoniae mimicry 1522,
    1696, 1738(Fig), 1739
    see also Ankylosing spondylitis
  reactive arthritis due to *Yersinia* 2513
  sequence/structure 1738(Fig), 2121
  spondyloarthropathy association 2121
  transgenic rats 1383
  Yersinia molecular mimicry 2513
HLA-B35, HIV infection progression risk 8
HLA-C 1691
  as declining gene 1110
  functions 1110
HLA class I 1108–1111, 1691
  α1 and α2 chains 1692
  allelic diversity 1691(Table)
    sequences 1692
  expression, platelets 1974
  gene expression patterns 1108–1109
    cytokines modulating 1109
  genes 1108
    allele numbers 1109
    functions 1109–1110
    HLA-E/-F/-G 1108
    numbers 1108
    polymorphism 1109–1110
  in graft rejection 1110
  heavy chains 1108
    domains 1109
  invariant subunit 1108
  peptide binding, disease association 1694
  polymorphism 1692
  pseudogenes 1108

HLA class I (*continued*)
  structure 1691
  see also HLA-A; HLA-B; HLA-C; HLA-
    E; HLA-F; HLA-G; MHC class I
HLA class II 1111–1113, 1691
  α and β chains 1112, 1691
  αβ heterodimers 1111
  allelic diversity 1112, 1691(Table)
    sequences 1692
  in autoimmune diseases 1112
  β chain polymorphism 1692
  cloning 1111
  discovery 1111
  expression on antigen presenting cells
    1112
  functions 1111, 1112–1113
  gene mapping 1111, 1111(Fig)
  genes, nonfunctional 1111
  isotypic diversity 1112, 1112–1113
  peptide binding, disease association 1694
  polymorphism 1111, 1692, 1704
  signalling via 1113
  structure and diversity 1111–1112
  superantigens binding 1113
  see also HLA-D; MHC class II
HLA class III 1114–1121
  disease associations 1119–1120
  genes 1114
    map 1114(Fig)
  proteins encoded 1114–1119,
    1116(Table)-1118(Table)
  see also MHC class III
HLA-D 1111, 1691
  polymorphism 1692
  structure 1691
  subregions 1691
HLA-DM 196, 331, 1497
  deletions 459–460
HLA-DMA 72, 459
HLA-DMB 72, 459
HLA-DP 1111, 1691
  genes 1111
  recombination between HLA-DQ 1587
HLA-DQ 1111, 1691–1692
  diabetes mellitus association 1399
  genes 1111
  HLA-DRB1 peptide presentation
    2109(Fig)
  recombination between HLA-DP 1587
  trans-complementation 1694
HLA-DQ8
  rheumatoid arthritis model 2108–2109
  transgenic mice 2108–2109
HLA-DQA1, Sjögren's syndrome (SS) 2183
HLA-DQA1*0501, Graves' disease 2313
HLA-DQB, evolution 1701
HLA-DQB1, IDDM association 1699–
    1700
HLA-DQP, evolution 1701
HLA-DR 1111, 1691–1692
  β chains 1399, 1692
  diabetes mellitus association 1399
  Dw series 1112
  genes 1111
  HLA-B distance from 1587
  polymorphism 1112
  typing 1691
HLA-DR3
  diabetes mellitus 278
  Graves' disease 2313
  Sjögren's syndrome (SS) 2183
HLA-DR4
  diabetes mellitus 278
  rheumatoid arthritis 294, 1741
  sequences 1740(Fig), 1741
HLA-DR5
  HIV infection progression risk 8
  Sjögren's syndrome (SS) 2183
HLA-DRB1 1692
  linked loci 1696, 1697
  malaria resistance 1696

HLA-DRB1 (*continued*)
  peptide presentation by HLA-DQ
    2109(Fig)
  rheumatoid arthritis 2108, 2109
  sequences 1740(Fig), 1741
HLA-DRB3 1692
HLA-DRB4 1692
HLA-Dw2, intrinsic factor antibodies 105
HLA-E
  function 1110
  gene expression 1109
  genes 1108, 1109
HLA-F
  function 1110
  gene expression 1109
  genes 1108, 1109
HLA-G 72, 1108
  function 899, 1110
  gene expression 1109
    by extravillous cytotrophoblast 899,
      1109, 1110
    sites 1109, 1110
  genes 1108, 1109
    in extraembryonic tissues 1109, 1110
  interferon-stimulated response element
    (ISRE) absent 899
HLA typing 1691, 1692–1693
  allele-specific amplification 1693
  amplification refractory mutation system
    (ARMS) 1693
  DNA-based techniques 1693
  'dot blot' 1693
  PCR-based methods 1691, 1693
  PCR role 1987–1988
  'reverse blot' method 1693
  sequence-specific priming 1693
  serologic/cellular methods 1692–1693
  SSO method 1693
  see also Tissue typing
H locus 635
  see also H2 system
Hodgkin's disease 1633–1634
  in AIDS 1884
  EBV association 1634
  Guillain–Barré syndrome in 1836
  pathogenesis, IL-9 role 1474
  polyclonal hypergammaglobulinemia in
    1162
  Rye classification 1634
  secondary immunodeficiency in 1284
  spread 1634
  tuberculosis 1883
  vitamin B₆ deficiency 2490
  whole-body irradiation 2052
'Hole in the repertoire' model 1230, 1231,
    1232, 1695, 1705
Holliday junctions 971, 971–972
Holotransferrin 2391
Homeothermic animals 904
Homing cell adhesion molecule (HCAM),
    see CD44
Homing receptors 1097, 1618, 1778,
    1784, 2060
  B cell 1778, 1784
  bronchus-associated lymphoid tissue
    (BALT) 1778
  nasal-associated lymphoid tissue (NALT)
    1778
  peripheral, L-selectin 1097
  skin, cutaneous lymphocyte antigen
    (CLA) 2160
  T cell 1778, 1784, 2330
  see also Integrins; Selectins
Homocytotropic antibodies 64
Homologous restriction factor (HRF) 626
Homologous restriction factor 20
    (HRF20), *see* CD59
Homopolysaccharide, monoclonal
    antibodies 427
Homosexual men
  HHV-8 transmission 1091
  HIV infection and AIDS 6

Homozygous, definition 986
Honeybee, venom 2471
Hookworm 1121–1125
  antigens 1122
  arrested development 1122
  characteristics 1121–1123
  cryptic epitopes 1125
  cuticle 1123
  enzymes secreted 1122, 1124
  evasive strategies 1124–1125
  evolution 1122
  excretory–secretory (ES) antigens 1122
  IgA digestion 1123, 1124
  infection route 1121–1122
  life cycle 1121–1122
  species 1121, 1122(Table)
Hookworm disease
  animal experiments 1123–1124
  causative agents 1121, 1122(Table)
  eosinophilia 1124
  epidemiology 1123
  immune response 1123–1124
    antibodies 1124
    cell-mediated 1124
  vaccines 1125, 1921
    DNA 1125
  volunteer infections 1123
  worm burdens 1123, 1124
Hormonal therapy, in autoimmune
    hemolytic anemia 98
Hormone response elements (HREs) 999
  glucocorticoid binding 999
Hormones 224
  autoimmune disease pathogenesis 279
  immunization against 1851, 1852–1853
  sex 641(Fig)
  transport in plasma 1965
  see also Steroid hormones
'Horror autotoxicus' 292
Horseradish peroxidase (HRP) 142, 260,
    814, 1262
  in ELISA 818
Horse red blood cells (HRBCs) 179
  bystander effects 397
Horseshoe crabs 1500
Hospital-acquired infections, *see*
    Nosocomial infections
Host defense
  against infections
    eye infections 871
    fungal infections 958
    lung infections 1543–1545
    respiratory tract infections 2083
    urinary tract infections 2066, 2453
  bladder 2066
  fever role 904, 2026
  gastrointestinal tract 967, 1780–1781
  membrane attack complex (MAC) 627
  mucosal 1780–1781
    IgA 1784
  oral cavity 1888
  skin 188, 2190
  urinary tract 2066, 2453
  vitamin C role 2491
  zinc role 2516
Host-versus-graft (HVG) reaction 545–546
House dust mites 2125
  allergens 66, 2125
    sequences and functions 66–68
  IgE upregulation 68
  tertiary structure 68
House-keeping proteins, annexins as 113
HOX-11 557–558
HRF20, *see* CD59
HRX protein 1118
α2-HS glycoprotein 1887
hsp, *see* Heat shock proteins (hsp)
H substance 1737
  see also ABO blood group
HTLV-1 infection, *see* Human T
    lymphotropic virus type I (HTLV-I)

Human antimouse antibody (HAMA) 1140, 2432
Human β-defensin (hBD-1) 1720
Human caliciviruses (HuCV) 399, 400
  host immune response 401
Human chorionic gonadotropin (hCG) 641
  antibodies 641, 1375
  diagnostic tests 1746
  Talwar heterospecies dimer 1853
  vaccines 642, 2458–2459
    βhCG CTP 645, 645(Table)
    βhCG-TT 645, 645(Table)
    carrier 646
    characteristics 645(Table)
    clinical trials 642(Table)
    current status 644–646
    heterospecies dimer (HSD) 644, 645, 645(Table)
    live recombinant 646
    optimization of HSD 645–646
    use in lung cancer 646
Human Genome Mapping Project 981, 1762
Human growth hormone (hGH), see Growth hormone
Human herpesvirus type 6 (HHV-6) 1089–1090
  antigens 1089
  cell tropism 1089
  characteristics 1089
  diseases association 1089
  evasive strategies 1090
  genome 1089
  host immune responses 1089
  infection, clinical features 1089
  latent infections 1089
  malignant disease association 1089
  as opportunist pathogen 1089
  prevalence 1089
  vaccine development 1090
  variants A and B 1089
Human herpesvirus type 8 (HHV-8) 1090–1091
  detection 1090
  diseases associated 1090
  genome 1091
  Kaposi's sarcoma due to 8, 1091
  lymphocyte proliferation due to 2021
  prevalence 1091
  relationship to herpesviruses 1090
  transmission 1091
Human immunodeficiency viruses, see HIV; HIV-1; HIV-2
Human interleukin for DA cells (HILDA), see Leukemia inhibitory factor (LIF)
Humanized antibodies 1139–1144, 1344
  affinity measurement 1143
  aim 1140
  applications 1139–1140
  autoimmune disease therapy 1358
  CDR grafting 1139, 1140–1141
    methods 1141–1143, 1141(Fig)
    principles 1140–1141
  clinical/preclinical studies 1142(Table), 1143–1144
  monoclonal antibody preparation 1742, 1745
  NEWM antibody 1140(Fig)
  principles/background 1140
  products available 1143
    properties 1143(Table)
  structure 1140
  tumor immunotherapy 1363
  veneering/resurfacing method 1143
Human leukocyte antigen, see HLA
Human Leukocyte Differentiation Antigens 1803
  see also CD antigens; Myeloid antigens
Human metallothionein (hMT) promoter 1306
Human papillomaviruses (HPV) 1907–1909

Human papillomaviruses (HPV) (continued)
  antigens 1360
  E6 and E7 proteins 1907, 1908, 2426, 2442
  evasive strategies 1908
  genital warts 2074–2075
  genome 1907, 1907(Fig)
  host immune response 1908
  immortalization 2074
  infections
    genital tract 2074–2075
    interferon α therapy 1416
    skin 750–751
  proteins 1907, 1907(Table)
  structure 1907, 2074
  subtypes 1907
  tumors 1360, 2074, 2426
    progression 1362
    see also Cervical cancer
  vaccines 1908
    tumor regression 1908
Human parainfluenza virus (HPIV), host immune response 1915
Human parvovirus B19, see Parvovirus B19
Human prolactin receptor (hPRLR) 520
Human rhinoviruses (HRV)
  receptor for 1954, 1956(Table)
  see also Rhinoviruses
Human SCID mice, see hu-SCID mice
Human T lymphotropic virus type I (HTLV-I) 1564–1565, 1633, 2097
  genome 2095
  infection, cytokine receptor expression 711
  leukemia pathogenesis 1564–1565, 2487
  lymphocyte proliferation due to 2021
  neurological disease due to 2097
  rabbit model 2046
  tax gene 1564–1565
    mechanism of action 1565
  Tax protein 1565, 2097, 2487
  tax transgenic mouse 2183
  transformation mechanism 1564–1565
  transformed human T cell line, IL-15 expression 1492
  see also Adult T cell leukemia/lymphoma (ATLL)
Human T lymphotropic virus type II (HTLV-II) 2096
Human umbilical vein endothelial cells (HUVEC)
  A-NK cell adhesion 1813
  lymphocyte migration studies 1618
  VCAM-1 induced by IL-13 1490
Human urokinase plasminogen activator receptor (HUPAR), gene structure 498
Humoral immune response 825, 956, 1144–1147, 1226–1228
  aberrant 1146–1147
  adenovirus infections 23
  African swine fever (ASF) virus 55
  African trypanosomiasis 2422
  amebiasis 77–78
  autoimmunity, see Autoimmunity
  bacterial infections 317
  brucellosis 384
  bunyaviridae 392
  Campylobacter 407–408
  Candida infections 409, 410
  canine 412–413
  cell-mediated immunity synergism 501
  Chlamydia infections 551
  CMV infection 723
  Coccidioides immitis 590
  complement activation by 1146
  decreased, in protein-energy malnutrition 1869
  down-regulation, by TGFβ 2395–2396
  EBV infection 830
  Echinococcus infections 784

Humoral immune response (continued)
  enhancement, by conditioning 338
  evolution, vertebrate 1948
  in fish 924
  flavivirus infections 929
  function 1146
  fungal infections 960
  gravity/space flights effect 1032
  histamine regulation of 1104–1105
  human papillomaviruses (HPV) 1908
  IDDM animal models 1393
  influenza virus infections 1385, 1386
  invertebrates 1499–1500, 1948
  iron deficiency effect 1506
  Legionella pneumophila 1544, 1545
  Leptospira 1553
  manipulation 1147
  see also Immunization
  in marsupials
    adults 1666
    pouch young 1665
  maturation 1145–1146
  see also Affinity maturation
  MHC role 1705–1706
  in neonate 1819
  onchocerciasis 1873
  oral cavity 1890
  parasitic infections 1918
  parvovirus B19 infection 1923–1924
  phage display technology mimicking 1931
  picornaviruses 1956
  poxvirus infections 1996
  primary response 14, 218, 1684
  rabies 2100
  radiosensitivity 2051–2052
  reptiles 2080
  secondary response 13, 14, 53, 218, 1684
    radioresistance 2052
  self-directed 1146–1147
  Shigella infections 2179–2180
  suppressor capacity, age-related changes 60
  T-dependent response 1145
  theilerosis 2289
  T-independent response 1145
  Toxoplasma gondii 2382
  viruses 2480, 2481
  vitamin A 2489
  see also Antibodies; B cell(s); Immunoglobulin
hu-SCID mice 1125–1130, 1274
  applications 1126, 1127–1130, 1127(Fig)
    limitations 1126–1127
  development 1126–1127
    lymphoid cell source 1126, 1128
    transplantation routes 1126
  EBV infection 1274
  hu-PBL-SCID mice 1126, 1128
  leaky mice 1128
  lymphocyte decline 1126
  memory T cells 1126, 1127
  modeling of immune-mediated disease 1127–1130
    improvements 1128, 1130
  see also SCID mice
Hu-specific antibodies 1838, 1842
HUT-78 cell line, transferrin receptor (TfR) role 2391
HUT-102 cell line, IL-15 expression 1492
HUTCH-1, see CD44
Hyaluronan (HA) 862, 863, 906
Hyaluronic receptor, see CD44
Hyaluronic acid 863(Table)
  as ligand for CD44 488–489, 1680
  Streptococcus capsule 2217
Hyaluronidase, hookworms secreting 1122–1123
H-Y antigen 72, 1158–1161, 1730, 1731
  antibodies 1158
  epitopes 1160

H-Y antigen (*continued*)
  genes 1159, 1160
  human epitope 1160
  in vitro response 1158–1159
  in vivo response 1158
  MHC/non-MHC restricted response
    1159
  sex determination role 1159–1160
  skin graft rejection 1014, 1158
  T cell responses 1159
Hybridization
  conditions 2196–2197
  DNA 982
  historical background 2194
  in situ, see In situ hybridization
  Southern blotting 2196–2197
Hybridoma 171, 1742
  cell surface antigen characterization 209
  discovery 445, 1148
  hybrid, quadroma formation 139
  in vitro studies 1233
  Mott 147
  nude mice use 1868
Hybridoma, B cell 1148–1151, 1742
  applications 1151
  cell fusion 1148, 1743
    frequency 1148
    partners 1150, 1743
    selective markers 1148–1150, 1743
  heterohybridomas 1150–1151
  historical background 445, 1148
  immunization procedures 1150
  interspecies 1150–1151
  nonfused cell removal 1148–1150
  origin of term 1148
  production 1148–1150, 1149(Fig)
  rabbit cell lines 1151
  see also Monoclonal antibodies
Hybridoma, T cell 1152–1154
  advantages 1152
  applications 1152
  cell lines used 1154
  cloning from 1154
  differences from antigen-specific T cells
    1154
  generation 1152–1154
    cell fusion methods 1153
    hybrid cell selection 1152, 1153–1154
    screening 1154
    T cell enrichment 1153
    T lymphoma line choice 1152,
      1152(Table)
  problems 1154
Hybridoma antibodies 149
  autoimmune hemolytic anemia (AIHA) in
    NZB mice 91
  see also Monoclonal antibodies
Hybridoma/plasmacytoma growth factor
    (HPGF)
  functions 1459(Fig)
  see also Interleukin-6 (IL-6)
Hydatid cysts 783
  immunodiagnosis 785
Hydatid infections, immunodiagnosis 785
Hydralazine, autoimmune disease
    pathogenesis 279
Hydrogen bonding/bonds 159, 163, 164,
    172, 2200
  direct 164
Hydrogen peroxide 317, 1716
  formation 1715, 1938
    monocytes 1751
    neutrophils 1856
  microbial sensitivity 1718
  reaction with peroxidase 1715–1716
  resistance by *Histoplasma capsulatum*
    1107
  toxicity and compounds formed 1715
Hydrophilic acid–base interactions 164
Hydrophobic acid–base interactions 164
Hydrophobic compounds, as adjuvants 37

Hydrophobic effect, antibody–antigen
    binding 2200
Hydrophobic interaction chromatography
    2037
Hydrophobicity
  bacteria 1885
  of protein 2034
    determination 2035–2036
Hydrops 1071, 1071(Fig)
Hydrostatic pressure 1155–1157
  antigen presentation changes 1155
  blood 1597
  cell surface changes 1155, 1156(Fig),
    1157
  compressible compartments 1155–1156
  definition 1155
  effect on cytoskeletal network 1155
  effect on membrane lipid 1155, 1157
  immune function 1157
  immunogenicity augmented by 1157
  in vitro systems 1156
  membrane protein changes 1155
  protein assemblies released by 1155
  protein synthesis induced 1155,
    1156(Table)
Hydroxamic acid inhibitors 715
Hydroxyethyl starch (HES) 668, 669
17α-Hydroxylase, autoantibodies 42
21-Hydroxylase
  autoantibodies 1986
    Addison's disease 41
  gene 1115
Hydroxyl radicals
  formation 1717, 1857
  oxygen-dependent phagocytic killing
    1717, 1857
Hydroxylysine 906
Hydroxyproline 906
11β-Hydroxysteroid dehydrogenase 999
5-Hydroxytryptamine, *see* Serotonin
Hyperacute rejection, *see* Graft rejection,
    hyperacute
Hyperalgesia 2025
  reduction, by thymulin 2301
Hyperattenuation 258
Hyperbaric oxygenation, immune function
    1157
Hypercalcemia 2496
Hypercalciuria 2496
Hypereosinophilia syndrome, idiopathic
    824
Hypergammaglobulinemia 1161–1166
  lupus mice 2252
  monoclonal 1161, 1163–1166
    'benign' 1164
    diseases causing 1164–1166,
      1164(Table)
    pathophysiology 1163–1164
    prognostic factor 1164
    recognition/diagnosis 1163
    T cells and B cells 1164
  polyclonal 1161, 1161–1163
    diseases causing 1162–1163,
      1163(Table)
    pathophysiology 1161–1162
    recognition/diagnosis 1161, 1162(Fig),
      1163
Hyper-IgD syndrome 1162
Hyper-IgE syndrome 1161–1162
  Candida infections 410
Hyper-IgG syndrome 1162
Hyper-IgM syndrome 147, 350, 358, 484,
    486, 1161, 1166–1169, 1215
  autoantibodies 1167
  CD40L defects 486, 1166, 1166–1167,
    1167, 2150
    mutations 389
  clinical characteristics 1166–1167
  defective CD40-CD40L interaction 653–
    654, 712, 1168, 1168(Fig)
  diagnosis 1166–1167
  differential diagnosis 389

Hyper-IgM syndrome (*continued*)
  immune defects in 654, 1166–1167
  immunodeficiency 147, 366, 1166, 1280
  infections in 1166, 1168
  molecular pathology 1167, 1303
  pathogenesis 1167–1168
  T cells 1166, 1167(Fig)
  therapy 1168
  X-linked 2192–2193
  X-linked immunodeficiency with 1280
Hyperimmune globulin therapy 1344,
    1967
Hyperimmune mice, mAb production
    1743, 1745
Hyperkinetic syndrome 950
Hypermutation, somatic, *see* Somatic
    mutation
Hypersensitivity 1169–1179
  aspirin 120
  classification 1169, 1170(Table)
  in coccidioidomycosis 590
  contact, *see* Contact hypersensitivity
  cutaneous basophil 333, 738–739
  'delayed-onset' 738
    see also Delayed-type hypersensitivity
      (DTH)
  drugs 1052
    see also Drug allergy
  feline 894
  to fungal allergens 960
  granuloma 1023, 1024, 1178–1179
  Jones–Mote (transient) 738
  NSAIDs 120
  schistosomiasis 2139
  shock, acute, *see* Anaphylaxis
  toxic agents causing 1365, 1367(Table)
    testing 1365–1366
  type I (immediate) 252(Fig), 678, 1147,
    1170–1174
    antigen presentation 1171
    atopy 252–253
    clinical effects 254
    discovery 1170
    in dogs 413
    to drugs 780
    food allergy 254, 947
    IgE role 1170–1171, 1207
    immunopathology mechanism 1341
    inductor/effector mechanisms 1172(Fig)
    mast cell activation 1172
    mast cell degranulation 1172
    role 1181–1172
    tests 1172–1174
    see also Allergic reactions; Atopy;
      Cutaneous anaphylaxis;
      Immunoglobulin E (IgE)
  type II (antibody-dependent cytotoxic)
    1174–1176
    to drugs 780
    effector mechanisms 1174, 1175(Fig)
    immunopathology mechanism 1341
    transfusion reactions 1174–1176
    see also Hemolytic disease of newborn
      (HDN)
  type III (immune-complex mediated)
    1176–1177
    experimental models 1177
    immune complex deposition 1176
    immunopathology mechanism 1341
    serum sickness, *see* Serum sickness
  type IV (cell-mediated), *see* Delayed-type
    hypersensitivity (DTH)
  type V 1169, 1179
Hyperthyroidism 1675, 2313
  feline 894
  fetal and neonatal 1675, 2315
  Graves' disease 2315
  Graves' ophthalmopathy 2316
  induction mechanism 2315
Hypervariable regions, *see*
    Complementarity determining regions
    (CDRs)

Hypoalbuminemia 1965
Hypobromous acid 1724
Hypochlorhydria, in autoimmune gastritis 102
Hypochlorous acid 1716
  formation 1715–1716, 1751, 1938
  neutrophils 1856
Hypogammaglobulinemia 1276
  acquired 386
  in chronic lymphocytic leukemia 1283
  common variable (CVH; CVID) 1280
    see also Common variable immunodeficiency (CVI)
  congenital anemia associated with parvovirus B19 1925
  Mycoplasma infections 1799
  opportunistic infections 1883
  Streptococcus pneumoniae pneumonia 2219
  thymoma 1281
  transient of infancy 1281
  see also Immunodeficiency, primary; Immunodeficiency, secondary
Hypoglycemia, autoantibodies to insulin receptor causing 1986
Hypoglycemic agents, oral 1403
Hypoparathyroidism, in DiGeorge syndrome 761
Hypophysectomy 1827
Hyposensitization
  food allergy treatment 952–953
  see also Desensitization
Hypotension, sepsis-induced 2162(Table)
Hypothalamo–pituitary–adrenal (HPA) axis 1826
  atrophy 998
  glucocorticoids secretion 997–998
  mediators 1827–1830
  stress and immune regulation 339
Hypothalamus 224
  lesions 2224
  perturbations affecting immune system 2224
  temperature regulation 903
Hypothiocyanous acid 1716
Hypothyroidism, neonatal 2316
  transient 1675
Hypoxanthine, aminopterin, thymidine (HAT) selection
  B cell hybridomas 1148–1150, 1743
  metabolism 1149(Fig)
  rationale 1148–1149
  T cell hybridomas 1153
  toxic analogs used 1149(Table), 1153
Hypozincemia 2516

I

IA-2B tyrosine phosphatase
  autoantibodies in animal models of IDDM 1393
  autoantibodies in human diabetes 1401
Ia-4 locus 1217
I-A, see Immune adherence (I-A)
Ia antigens 1230, 1704
  in EAE 1694
  genes 1230
  hybrid molecules 1230
  I-A^b 1231
  I-A and I-E 1230
  I-A^k 1231
  immune response control 1230–1231
  novel, in NOD mouse 1392
  structure 1230
Ia-bearing molecules, guinea pig inbred strains 1033
I-A^b 1231
I-A hemagglutination assay 1219, 1220(Fig)

I-A^k 1231
I-A loci/region 1041, 1041(Fig), 1217, 1218
  molecules, see Ia antigens
I-A molecules, see Ia antigens
i antigen, see I and i antigens
Ibuprofen, TNFα production increased 2027
ICA-512 antibodies 1401
ICAM, expression 1608
ICAM-1 27(Table), 28, 450(Table), 1407, 1409–1412
  antibodies, therapeutic role 1609
  antigen recognition by T cells and 502, 1411
  as CD43 receptor 804
  characteristics 1410(Table)
  in contact hypersensitivity 638, 639
  cross-linking 1412
  diapedesis of leukocytes 759, 1411
  downregulation, TGFβ role 2397
  expression 804, 1410–1411, 1608
    endothelial cells 804
    IFNγ effect 805
    IFNγ-induced increase 805, 1424
    regulation 1410–1411
    VIP effect 1827(Fig)
  fibrinogen interaction 804
  functions 1409–1410
  glycosylation 1608
  knockout mice 1411, 1566, 1566(Table)
  leukocyte adhesion to endothelium 758, 804, 1411, 2060
  as ligand for CD11a/CD18 (LFA-1) 804
    see also LFA-1
  ligands 1410(Table)
    fibrinogen 804
  mice deficient in 1411
  microbes binding 1609
  as receptor
    for parasites 1411
    for picornaviruses 1954
    for viruses/Plasmodium 804, 1411, 1609
  signal transduction role 1412
  structure 519, 1608, 1608(Fig)
    domain deletion 1412
    function relationship 1412
    Ig domains 1412
ICAM-2 27(Table), 28, 453(Table), 1407, 1409–1412
  binding to LFA-1 1608
  characteristics 1410(Table)
  constitutive expression 1411
  expression 1608
    regulation 1410–1411
  ligands 1410(Table)
  recirculation of LFA-1 lymphocytes 1411
  role in leukocyte adhesion 1411
  structure 1608, 1608(Fig)
    function relationship 1412
ICAM-3 27(Table), 28, 449(Table), 1407, 1409–1412
  binding to LFA-1 1608
  characteristics 1410(Table)
  constitutive expression 1411
  cross-linking 1412
  expression 1410–1411, 1608
    regulation 1410–1411
  glycosylation 1608
  ligands 1410(Table)
  rheumatoid arthritis 2114
  role in leukocyte adhesion 1411
  signal transduction role 1412
  structure 1608, 1608(Fig)
    function relationship 1412
Iccosomes 1728, 1777
ICE/CED-3 family 225
  TNF receptor signaling 2347
  see also Caspase
ICE (interleukin 1β-converting enzyme) 705, 1430

ICE (interleukin 1β-converting enzyme) (continued)
  activation by granzyme B 1028
  apoptosis mechanism 221, 222, 223, 876, 1028
  negative selection of thymocytes 2357
  perforin-mediated lysis 1930–1931
  related proteases, in apoptosis 223
  TNF receptor signaling 2347
  upregulation by LPS and IFNγ 1430
  see also Caspase
Idd loci, NOD mice 1392–1396, 1392(Table)
IDDM, see Diabetes mellitus, insulin-dependent (IDDM)
Idiopathic (autoimmune) thrombocytopenic purpura (ITP) 1347, 1975–1976
  chronic 1975, 1975–1976
  diseases associated 1975
  IgG and IgM antibodies 1975
  maternal antibodies causing 1674
  treatment 1976
  vincristine 1976
Idiopathic thrombocytopenic purpura (ITP) 1180–1182, 1974
  acute 1180–1181
    clinical aspects 1180
    pathogenesis 1180
    therapy 1180–1181, 1347, 1967
    autoantibodies 1181, 1181(Table)
  chronic 1181–1182
    clinical findings 1181
    laboratory findings 1181
    pathogenesis 1181–1182
    therapy 1182, 1967
  in common variable immunodeficiency 600
Idiotopes 151, 1183, 1190
  regulatory 1192
Idiotype(s) 204, 1182–1186, 1679
  Ab1 clones 1186, 1190
    Ab2 clones relationship 1190, 1191
  Ab2 clones 1186, 1187, 1190
    Ab1 clones relationship 1190, 1191
    Ab2β 1187, 1189
    classification/types 1187, 1187(Fig)
    criteria defining 1187–1188
    see also Anti-idiotype antibodies
  Ab3 1192
  antibodies, see Anti-idiotype antibodies
  antigen-inhibitable 1183
  autoantibodies 277
  autoimmunogenicity 1190
  B cell recognition 1184, 1190
  classification 1183–1184
  conventional 1184
  cross-reactive (IdX) 1183, 1184, 1190
    cold agglutinins 594
    IdX linked to allotype 1183
    ontogeny of immune response 1877
    subgroups 1183
  definition 1182–1183, 1184, 1186
  dominant 1184, 1190
  expression, order during ontogeny 1877
  framework associated 1183, 1187
  historical aspects 1182–1182
  immunochemical requirements for expression 1183
  internal image 1186–1189, 1192
    functions 1186
    memory stimulation 1186, 1191
    mimicry 1187, 1188–1189, 1192
    practical applications 1189
    structural basis of mimicry 1188–1189
    T cell recognition 1188
  interspecies 1183
  interstrain 1183
  light and heavy chains 1183
  as markers of variable region genes 1184
  maternal 1192–1193
  minor 1184
  in pandemics explanation 1193

Idiotype(s) (*continued*)
  polymorphism 1184–1185
  regulatory 1184, 1192, 1193
  shared by immunoglobulins 1184
  silent 1184
  site-directed mutagenesis 1185
  structural correlates 1185
  as target of regulatory processes 1191
  T cell receptor (TCR) 1185
  T cell recognition 1185, 1190
  vaccine development 1189
  X-ray crystallography 1185
Idiotype network 1186, 1190–1193, 1678–
    1679
  background to theory 1190–1191
  cascade activation 1192
  clonal homeostasis 1191
  degeneracy 1192
  natural antibodies 1807, 1808
  ontogenetic/phylogenetic significance
    1192–1193
  postulates 1191–1192
  regulatory 1193
  short-lived lymphocytes 1191
Idiotype–anti-idiotype interactions 204,
    1190–1193
  see also Idiotype network
Idiotypic antibodies, *see* Anti-idiotype
    antibodies
I-E molecules 1230
I-E region 1218, 1704
  autoreactive T cells 2344
  defect in NOD mouse 283
  mercury actions influenced by 1688
IgA, *see* Immunoglobulin A (IgA)
IgA nephropathy 1198
Igα (CD79a) 452(Table), 1194–1195
  in B cell receptors 349, 363, 1299
    protein tyrosine kinase association
      1194, 1299
  expression 1195
  gene 1194
Igβ (CD79b) 452(Table), 1194–1195
  in B cell receptors 349, 363, 1299
    protein tyrosine kinase association
      1194, 1299
  expression 1195
  gene 1194
IgD, *see* Immunoglobulin D (IgD)
IgE, *see* Immunoglobulin E (IgE)
IgE-binding factor (IgE-BF), *see* FcεRII
IgE binding protein (εBP; galectin 3) 1171,
    1204
Ig fold, *see under* Immunoglobulin
IgG, *see* Immunoglobulin G (IgG)
IgM, *see* Immunoglobulin M (IgM)
IgN 1308
IgNARC 1309
IgSF, *see* Immunoglobulin gene superfamily
IgW 1309, 1313
IgX, *see* Immunoglobulin X (IgX)
IgY, *see* Immunoglobulin Y (IgY)
I and i antigens 594
  autoantibodies, *see* Cold agglutinins
  carbohydrate structure 594–595
  fetal expression 799
  oligosaccharides sequences 594(Fig), 595
  structure 1577, 1577(Fig)
I-J 649, 1217–1218
  biochemical characteristics 1218
  cellular source 1217–1218
  function 1217
  gene mapping 1218
  on helper T cells 1218
  on macrophage 1218
  molecular biology 1218
  monoclonal antibodies 1217
  structure 1218
  on suppressor T cells 1217, 1218
I-J region 2244
Ikaros gene 1877
IkBα, glucocorticoid action 999

IkB kinase 711
IkBL protein 1118(Table), 1119
  mice 1047
IL-1, *see* Interleukin-1 (IL-1)
IL-T protein 1492
  see also Interleukin-15 (IL-15)
Imexon, as immunopotentiating agent
    1347
Immediate hypersensitivity, *see*
    Hypersensitivity, type I (immediate)
Immune adherence (I-A) 182–183, 629,
    1146, 1219–1220
  appearance 1219(Fig), 1220(Fig)
  applications 1219
  as diagnostic test 1219
  hemagglutination test 1219, 1220(Fig)
  receptors 629
Immune-associated antigens, *see* Ia
    antigens
Immune complex disease 1222(Table),
    1225
  after infections 1176
  in complement deficiencies 612–613, 616
  experimental 1226–1224
  immunopathology and
    immunopathogenesis 1341
  mice 1224
  in rabbits 1223, 1224
Immune complexes 182, 1176, 1220–1225
  African trypanosomiasis 2423
  AIDS 2096
  analysis, rate zonal ultracentrifugation
    2448
  antigen binding site structures 171–173
  antigen clearance by 182–185, 1222
  Arthus reaction 237, 237–238, 1223
  B cell response inhibition 351, 351(Fig)
  binding to receptors 182–183, 1223
  'blocking factors' in tumor escape 2445
  circulating 1223
    SLE 2258
  clearance
    CR1 function 629
    plasmapheresis effect 1970
  coccidioidomycosis 590
  complement activation 1146, 1223
  in complement deficiency 623, 1224
  complement fixation (CF) test 617
  complement interaction 1222–1223
    Clq interaction 1221
    drugs affecting 1225
  cutaneous lupus erythematosus 2187
  definition 1220
  deposition
    complement deficiency 623
    experimental autoimmune thyroiditis
      2312
    factors influencing 1176
    SLE 2258
  detection
    nephelometry 1822
    screening tests 1221–1222
    ultracentrifugation 2447–2448
    see also Immunodiffusion
  detection in fluids/tissues 1221–1222
    Raji test 1221
    solid-phase 1221
  diseases due to 1176–1177
    see also Immune complex disease
  erythrocyte interaction 1223
  Fc receptor interaction 1224
  formation 1226–1224
    in Arthus reaction 237, 237–238
    in autoimmune disease 1147
    control 1224, 1224(Fig)
    immunopathology mechanism 1341
    mercury role 1688
    in normal individuals 2258
    single radial immunodiffusion 1287
  functions 1222
  IgG-containing, FcγRI activation 1224
  IL-10 production 1224

Immune complexes (*continued*)
  increased formation 1224
  isolation 1221(Fig)
  light scattering by 1822–1823
  preparative techniques 1222
  processing
    in vivo studies in animals 183–184,
      1222–1223
    in vivo studies in humans 814
  models 184
  proteins fixed to 1220
  screening tests 1221–1222
  SLE 184, 1225, 2258
  three-dimensional structure 1220, 2199,
    2201(Fig)
    see also Antibody–antigen interactions
  transient formation 1222
  ultracentrifugation studies 2447
  in virus infections 2483
  X-ray crystallography 2199
  Yersinia 2513
Immune complex/formalin colitis 1384
Immune complex-mediated
    hypersensitivity, *see* Hypersensitivity,
    type III
Immune depletion models, autoimmune
    disease 271–272, 272(Table)
Immune enhancement, *see* Enhancement,
    immunological
Immune enhancer, vitamin A 2489
Immune escape, *see under* Immune
    surveillance
Immune evasion, *see specific micro-
    organisms*
Immune exclusion, IgA function 1198
Immune genes, *see* Immunoglobulin, genes;
    T cell receptor (TCR), genes
Immune priming, by maternal antibodies
    1673–1674
Immune privilege 2012, 2395
  antigens, immune response 2012–2013
  dendritic cells 745
  Fas/FasL role 879, 2012
  maintenance 2013
    apoptosis role 225–226
  MIF as mediator 1656
  sites 225, 2012–2013
    allografts in 1012, 2012
    anterior chamber of eye 870, 2013
    cornea 2414
    evolutionary adaptation 2013
    eye 867
    features 2012, 2013
    location 2012
    molecules expressed 2012
  TGFβ role 2395
Immune regulation, *see* Immune response,
    regulation
Immune response 1144, 1226–1229
  acquired, *see* Acquired immune response
  activation *vs* tolerance 1228
  adaptive 1226–1227
  age-related changes 60
    see also Age-related changes
  to allergens 68–69
  alterations by UV light 1943–1944
  blocked by CTLA4 and B7 306
  development, *see* Neonatal immune
    response; Ontogeny of immune
    response
  downregulation
    by FasL/Fas interaction 654–655
    in lymphatic filariasis 914–915
    see also Immunosuppression
  duration, Fas role 877
  in fish 924–925
  homeostasis 1191
  hyper *vs* hyporesponsiveness 1228–1229
  innate *vs* adaptive 1226
    see also Innate (natural) immunity
  in vitro, *see* Immune response *in vitro*
  maternal 70

Immune response (*continued*)
maternal (*continued*)
see also Maternal antibodies
maturation, see Maturation of immune
response
modifiers, see Immunomodulation;
Immunopotentiation; Immunotherapy
nutritional regulation 1870–1871
ontogeny, see Ontogeny of immune
response
phylogeny, see Evolution; Phylogeny of
immune response
primary 1684
B cell lineages produced 1685
T cell 1682
see also Humoral immune response
in prokaryotes, see Prokaryotes,
immunity in
radiosensitivity, see Radiosensitivity
regulation
adhesion molecules role 29–30
CD40L as master regulator 2328
cells involved 2245
by Ir genes, see Immune response (Ir)
genes
TCR γδ role 2277
T_H1/T_H2 interaction 2245
see also Immunoregulation
secondary 13, 53, 153, 1684
in amphibians 82
see also Acquired immune response;
Humoral immune response
statistical analysis 2213
stimulation, see Immunopotentiation;
Immunotherapy
suppression, see Immunosuppression
T_H1 vs T_H2 1227
tissue typing application 2322
to viruses, see Viruses
see also B cell(s); Cell-mediated
immunity; Humoral immune response;
T cell(s)
Immune response in vitro 1233–1243
accessory cells for 1233, 1234(Table)
apoptosis 1234, 1240
interactions 1237(Fig)
preparation 1237(Fig), 1238(Fig)
antigen presentation 1236(Fig), 1239–
1240, 1239(Fig), 1241
applications 1233
enrichment of cells 1235–1238, 1238
initiation of primary response 1239–1240
antigen choice/use 1240
antigen processing/presentation 1239–
1240, 1239(Fig)
cytokines 1239
initiation of secondary response 1239–
1241
antigen choice/use 1241
antigen processing/presentation 1241
cytokines 1241
memory cell development 1240
practical aspects 1234–1235
cell death problem 1234–1235, 1240
deviations from in vivo 1234
lymphocyte concentrations 1238, 1240
source of cells 1234, 1237(Fig)
primary response 1238–1240
requirements 1233, 1234(Table),
1235(Fig)
antigenic 1233
cellular 1233, 1234(Table)
cytokines 1233, 1236(Table)
secondary response 1239–1241,
1241(Fig)
applications 1241–1242
in vaccine efficacy 1233
Immune response (Ir) genes 206, 1041,
1044, 1158, 1229–1232, 1703, 1710
definition 1229
determinant selection model 1230–1271
experiments 195

Immune response (Ir) genes (*continued*)
historical background 1229–1230
'hole in the repertoire' model 1230,
1231, 1232
human genes 1232
Ir-1A locus 1230
Ir-1 locus 1230
Ir-2 locus 1232
Ir-3/Ir-4/Ir-5 loci 1232
malaria resistance and 1232
MHC-linked 1230–1231
Ia antigens (class II) 1230–1231
mechanisms 1231
MHC class I 1231
MHC class II 1230–1231
T cells not stimulated 1231
non-MHC 1159, 1231–1232
T cell response to H-Y and 1159
see also H2 class II molecules; Ia
antigens
Immune serum globulins (ISG) 1344, 1347
polyvalent 1347
mechanism of action 1347–1348
see also Carbohydrate(s)
Immune stimulation, by carbohydrates 428
see also Carbohydrate(s)
Immune surveillance 1243–1247, 1349
escape
mechanisms 1243
by MHC downregulation 1360, 1361
tumors, see Tumor immunological
escape
experimental/clinical evidence
opposing theory 1244(Table)
supporting theory 1244–1245,
1244(Table)
historical background 1243
in immunodeficiency
primary 1244, 1245–1246
secondary (acquired) 1245, 1246
MHC role 1705
spontaneous regression of tumors 1245,
1246
TGFβ 2393–2394
theory 1243
tumor-infiltrating cells 1245, 1246
tumors 1243, 1284, 1359
EBV/Burkitt's lymphoma model 1360
escape/defects, see Tumor
immunological escape
immunotherapy 1245
MHC role 1705
Immune system
aging 59–61
amphibian, see Amphibian immune
system
anatomy 1247–1250
see also Lymphoid organs
avian, see Avian immune system
canine, see Canine immune system
diversity
generation 105–106
see also Diversity generation
feline, see Feline immune system
hydrostatic pressure effect 1157
nervous system interactions, see Nervous
system
polyclonal activation and inhibition 1983
selective breeding effect 345
ungulate, see Ungulate immune system
see also Immune response
Immune thrombocytopenic purpura (ITP),
see Idiopathic thrombocytopenic
purpura (ITP)
Immunity, passive transfer, see Passive
immunity
Immunization
active 1147
against hormones 1851, 1852–1853
dendritic cell culture for 1575
experimental autoimmune disease models
270–272, 271(Table)
intranasal 1779

Immunization (*continued*)
mucosal surfaces, IgA induction 1199
passive, see Passive immunization
pre-/postimmunization antibody levels,
statistics 2214
routes 219
Western blotting application 2507
see also Vaccination; Vaccines
Immunoadhesins 1428
soluble cytokine receptors 718
Immunoadhesion method 511
Immunoadsorbents 817, 1250–1252
affinity chromatography 48
agarose–antibody coupling 1250–1251
application/elution of sample 1251
clinical applications 1252
definition 1250
disinfection 1252
inactivation 1252
in LDL-apheresis 1252
monoclonal antibodies 1251–1252,
1251(Table)
preparation, comparison of methods
1250(Table)
protein A 1252
solid supports 1250
Immunoaffinity chromatography 51–52
Immunoaffinity columns 511
Immunoassays 1252–1257, 2053
antibody microspot arrays 1256
cell agglutination in 1253
competitive/noncompetitive 1254
cytokines 694–696
direct/indirect measurements 1254
direct observation 1253
disadvantages 1254
enzyme, see Enzyme immunoassays (EIA)
enzyme labels 1253, 1255
Farr type, see Farr assay
hapten–antibody binding 1051–1052
high sensitive 'microspot' 1256
liposome-based 1591
microparticle-enhanced nephelometric
1824
multianalyte 1256
new technologies 1255–1256
nonisotopic labels 1253, 1255
plaque-forming cell (PFC) assay
comparison 1962
principles 1254
radioisotopic 1253
sandwich/two-site assays 1254–1255
sensitivity 1254
single domain antibodies in 1256
specificity 1253
terminology for labels 1253
two-site dual antibody 1255
see also ELISA; Immunoradiometric
assay (IRMA)
Immunoblasts 739
in central lymph 1601
formation 1602
plasma cell formation 1601
Immunoblotting 142
antigen detection 815
see also Western blotting
Immunocompetence, assessment using
mitogenic lectins 1541
Immunocompromised patients
adenovirus infections 23
Legionnaire's disease 1544
nocardiosis 1862
TCR γδ role 2277
vaccine adverse reaction risk 2464
see also Immunodepression;
Immunosuppression
Immunoconglutinins 1257–1258
increased in intravascular infections 1257
minimal change nephritic syndrome 1257
nephritic factors 1257
Immunocytochemistry (ICC) 1258–1267
antibodies 1260–1261

Immunocytochemistry (ICC) (*continued*)
  antibodies (*continued*)
    labeling 1258
    monoclonal 1260
    nonspecificity 1260
    preparation and testing 1260
    purification 1260
    size 1260
    strength (avidity) 1260
  antigens 1261–1262
    retrieval procedures 1261
  bridge indirect methods 1259, 1259(Fig)
  controls 1265
    antiserum specificity 1265
    method 1265
  definition 1258
  direct method 1258, 1259(Fig)
  double staining methods 1259(Fig), 1260
  embedding techniques 1262
  enzyme 1259, 1262–1263
    antigen localization 815
  false-positives 1265
  fixation of antigens/tissue 1261
    combination 1261–1262
    cross-linking 1261, 1262
    precipitating fixatives 1261
  freeze-drying of tissue 1262
  history 1258
  immunopathology investigation 1340
  indicator molecules 1262–1265,
    1263(Table)
    enzymes 1263
    glucose oxidase 1263
    gold 1263–1264
    metallomarkers 1263
    peroxidase 1263, 1264(Fig)
  indirect method 1258–1259, 1259(Fig)
  in situ hybridization techniques 1266–
    1267
  interpretation 1266
  methods 1258–1260, 1259(Fig)
  optical systems 1266
  permeabilization of tissues 1262
  postembedding techniques 1262
  quantitation 1266
  radio-immunocytochemistry 1266
  requirements 1258
  tissue sectioning 1262
  uses/applications 1266
  see also Immunohistochemistry
Immunocytotoxic pathway, liver disease
  564
Immunodeficiency 1228–1229
  acquired, *see* Immunodeficiency,
    secondary (*below*)
  animal models, *see below*
  congenital, parvovirus B19 infection
    1924
  in dogs 414
  feline 895
  immune surveillance theory 1244–1245
    alternative explanation 1245–1246
  investigation, lymphocyte transformation
    test 1624
  lymphomas associated 1635–1636
  management
    gene therapy 978
    immunoglobulin replacement therapy
    966
  opportunistic infections 1883
  oral health and infections 1891
  persistent parvovirus B19 infection
    1924–1925
  polyclonal hypergammaglobulinemia in
    1163
  radiosensitivity association 2053
  retroviruses causing 2096
    see also AIDS; HIV infection
  T cell, *see* T cell(s), deficiency
  urinary tract infections 2454
Immunodeficiency, animal models 1267–
  1276

Immunodeficiency, animal models
  (*continued*)
  acquired immunodeficiency 1268
  applications 1274
  defects in other organs with 1270–1273
  human immunodeficiency disease models
    1273–1274, 1274(Table)
  importance 1267
  maintenance/use 1273–1274
  mice 1267–1273
  non-murine models 1273
  novel immunodeficiencies 1274–1276
    see also Knockout mice; Transgenic
    mice
  primary immunodeficiency 1268–1270,
    1273–1274, 1274(Table)
    motheaten mice 1269–1270
    SCID, *see* SCID mice
  responsiveness to lipopolysaccharide
    1270
  X-linked immunodeficiency 1270–1271
  see also specific murine strains/mutants
Immunodeficiency, primary 1276–1282
  animal models 1268–1270, 1273–1274,
    1274(Table)
    see also Motheaten mice; SCID mice
  antibody deficiencies 1279–1281
    see also Agammaglobulinemia;
    Hypogammaglobulinemia
  ataxia telangiectasia (AT) 249, 1282
    see also Ataxia telangiectasia (AT)
  bare lymphocyte syndrome 329, 331,
    1277
    see also Bare lymphocyte syndrome
  common variable, *see* Common variable
    immunodeficiency (CVI)
  gene therapy 978, 979(Table)
  historical aspects 1276–1277
  hyper-IgM syndrome, *see* Hyper-IgM
    syndrome
  immune surveillance theory and 1244,
    1245–1246
  inheritance 988
  partial, disorders 1281–1282
    see also Wiskott–Aldrich syndrome
    (WAS)
  in purine nucleoside phosphorylase
    deficiency, *see* Purine nucleoside
    phosphorylase deficiency
  SCID, *see* Severe combined
    immunodeficiency (SCID)
  selective immunoglobulin deficiencies
    1281
  selective T cell deficiencies 1277
  terminology 1277
  tumor development 1244
  type 2 T-independent antigens 217
  X-linked, *see* X-linked immunodeficiency
Immunodeficiency, secondary 1283–1287
  in aging 1285
  AIDS and HIV infection 7, 1285
    see also AIDS; HIV infection
  in bone marrow transplantation 1284
  causes 1283(Table)
  classification 1283, 1283(Table)
  drug-induced 1285
  gene therapy 978, 979(Table)
  immune surveillance theory and 1245,
    1246
    evidence 1245
  increased loss/catabolism of Igs 1286–
    1287
  malignancy and 1283–1284
  metabolic disorders 1286
  nutritional 1284
  in prematurity 1284–1285
  splenectomy 1286
  terminology 1283
  thymectomy 1286
  trauma/surgery/burns causing 1286
  viral-induced 1285–1286
  see also Immunosuppression

Immunodepression
  parasitic infections 1919–1920
  by *Trypanosoma cruzi* 523–524
  see also Immunosuppression
Immunodiagnosis, drug allergy 781
Immunodiffusion 1287–1289, 2000(Fig)
  definition 1287
  development 1287
  double 1287, 2001
    method 2000
  historical aspects 1287–1288
  Ouchterlony's technique 2001(Fig), 2002
  Oudin's technique 1287, 2001–2002
  reversed (RSRI) 1287
  simple 2001
  single radial 1287, 2002
    accuracy/sensitivity 1289
    applications 1287
    McSwiney's scale 1289, 1289(Fig)
    measurement method 1289, 1289(Fig)
    mechanisms 1287–1289
    methodology 1289
    reliability 1287
Immunodominance 1228, 1290–1292,
    1297, 2203
  in autoimmunity, dynamic model 1291
  B cell determinants 1291–1292, 2203
  hen egg lysozyme (HEL) peptides 1231,
    1291
  mechanisms 1291
  T cell determinants 1290–1291
    characteristics 1291
Immunoelectron microscopy
  definition 790
  direct/indirect labeling 793, 794(Fig)
  future prospects 795
  hepatitis E virus (HEV) 1082
  immunolabeling methods 793, 795
  immunoreagents 792–793
  markers 791–792
  principles 790–791
  unlabeled antibody bridge method 793
Immunoelectro-osmophoresis 1296–1296
Immunoelectrophoresis 1292–1297, 2002
  affinity electrophoretic method 1296
  amplification methods 1296
  Bence Jones proteins (BJP) 341
  cathodal/anodal intermediate gels 1295
  counter immunoelectrophoresis 1296–
    1296
  crossed immunoelectrophoresis 1293–
    1294
    applications 1293
    C1 complex 1293, 1293(Fig)
  definition 1292
  'double decker' 1295, 1295(Fig)
  electrofocusing technique 1296
  electrophoresis–immunofixation 1294
  historical aspects 1292–1293
  immunoelectro-osmophoresis 1296–1296
  intermediate gel techniques 1295
  modifications 1295
  radioimmunoelectrophoresis 1296
  rocket (electroimmunoassay) 1294–1295,
    1294(Fig)
    'double decker' 1295, 1295(Fig)
    fused 1296
  sandwich technique 1296
  tandem crossed 1296
  in Western blotting 2504
Immunoenhancement, *see* Enhancement,
  immunological
Immunofluorescence 142
  enzyme-labeled antibodies 813
  immunopathology investigation 1340
  Treponema pallidum detection 2417
  see also entries beginning Fluorescence
Immunofluorescent technique, indirect
  (IFT) 125
  anti-DNA antibodies 129
  antinuclear antibodies (ANA) 127–128
  autoantibody detection 260

Immunofluorometric assay 1253
Immunogen 1297
  definition 201, 218, 1290, 1297
  see also Adjuvant(s)
Immunogenicity 266
  carbohydrate antigens 426
  definition 201, 1050, 1290, 1297
Immunoglobulin
  allelism 74
  allotypes, see Allotypes
  as antigen 204
    see also Anti-antibodies (AAs); Anti-
      idiotype antibodies
  antigen-binding sites, see
    Complementarity determining regions
    (CDRs)
  assembly, hsp70 role 2230
  avian 302
  bacterial proteins binding, see Bacterial
    immunoglobulin-binding proteins
  as B cell receptors 1875
    see also B cell(s), membrane Ig (mIg)
  catabolism 1318
  C domains 776
    structure 775
    three-dimensional structure 517
    see also Immunoglobulin, constant
      regions
  cell surface 1298–1301
    function 1298
    see also B cell(s), membrane Ig (mIg); B
      cell(s), receptor (BCR);
      Immunoglobulin D (IgD);
      Immunoglobulin M (IgM)
  classes 1145(Table)
    evolution 1307–1308, 1310(Table)-
      1313(Table)
    functions 1145(Table)
  complementarity-determining regions, see
    Complementarity determining regions
    (CDRs)
  concentrates, see Gammaglobulin
  constant regions 1329
    genes 1323, 1323(Table), 1514–1515
    haplotypes 75–76
  deficiency 1281
    in Bruton's agammaglobulinemia 387
    see also Agammaglobulinemia;
      Hypogammaglobulinemia;
      Immunodeficiency, primary
  deposition, dermo-epidermal junction
    2186, 2187
  detection, see under Antibodies
  D_H gene clusters 766
  discovery 775, 965
  diversity, see Diversity
  diversity (D) segments
    genes 1323(Table)
    VDJ recombination, see
      Immunoglobulin gene rearrangements
  D_μ 1195
  domain pairing 1330
  evolution 1307–1315, 1949
    classes of Igs 1307–1308, 1310(Table)-
      1313(Table)
    classes in vertebrates 1307–1308,
      1313(Table)
    distribution of Ig classes 1313(Table)
    heavy chains 1308, 1310(Table)-
      1313(Table)
    historical studies 1307
    Ig gene rearrangements 1308–1309
    light chains 1308, 1308(Fig),
      1309(Fig), 1314(Table)
    multiplicity 1309, 1313
    phylogenetic tree 1308(Fig)
    variable region diversity 1313
  feline 893, 893(Table)
  fold 775–777, 1210, 1319, 1329, 1329–
    1331
    basic structure 775–776
    domain association 776–777

Immunoglobulin (continued)
  fold (continued)
    'signature' 776
    TCRγδ protein relationship 2271
    three-dimensional structure 1322(Fig)
    topology 775
  fragments 2432–2433, 2432(Fig)
  framework regions (FRs) 1329
  functions 1145(Table), 1315–1319
    complement activation 1315–1316
    Fc receptor binding 1317–1318
    miscellaneous 1318–1319
    virus neutralization 1318
    see also Complement activation
  as gammaglobulins 964
  gene rearrangements, see
    Immunoglobulin gene rearrangements
  genes, see Immunoglobulin gene(s)
  heavy chains, see Immunoglobulin heavy
    (H) chains
  hinge region 1330
    distal hinge 1332
    functions 1514–1515
    proximal hinge 1332
    structure 1332–1334
  historical aspects 775, 965
  hypermutation, see Somatic
    hypermutation
  intravenous, see Intravenous
    immunoglobulin
  invertebrates 1500
  isotypes 1514–1515
    IFNγ role 1424
    switching, see Immunoglobulin class
      switching
    see also Isotype
  J chain, see J chain
  J (joining) segments 765
    genes 1323(Table), 1326, 1329
    VDJ recombination, see
      Immunoglobulin gene rearrangements
  levels
    allotype association 76
    in sheep 1903
  lifespan 1581, 1583
  light chains, see Immunoglobulin light
    (L) chains
  linkage of two Igs, heteroconjugates
    138–139, 139(Fig)
  β_2-microglobulin similarity 368
  microheterogeneity, isoelectric focusing
    1512–1513
  mRNA 158
  origin 1313
    see also Immunoglobulin, evolution
  passive transfer, in cats 893, 895
  in pigs 1992–1993, 1992(Table)
  placental transfer 1672
    absent in ruminants 2450
    see also Immunoglobulin G (IgG);
      Maternal antibodies
  in plasma 1965
  poly-Ig receptor (pIgR), see Secretory
    component (SC)
  polymeric
    affinity for free secretory component
      2154
    transport through secretory epithelia
      2155
    see also Immunoglobulin A (IgA);
      Immunoglobulin M (IgM)
  polymeric receptor (pIgR), see Secretory
    component (SC)
  pseudogenes 1515
  rabbit 2047
  receptor, polymeric, see Secretory
    component (SC)
  repertoire
    in nude mice 1868
    see also B cell(s), repertoire
  reptiles 2080
  secretion, see Antibody secretion

Immunoglobulin (continued)
  secretory 148
  structure 149(Fig), 764, 764(Fig), 775,
    1144–1145, 1145(Fig), 1329–1334,
    2432–2433
    β sheets 775–776
    three-dimensional 775–777, 1330(Fig)
  synthesis, see Antibody synthesis
  TCR similarities 2282
  therapeutic 1347, 1967
    in HIV infection 12
    see also Intravenous immunoglobulin
  topology 775
  transfer, failure in young marsupials
    1664
  tumors secreting 1636–1637
    see also Multiple myeloma;
      Waldenström's macroglobulinemia
  valency 163
  variable regions 1329
    evolution of diversity 1313
    genes, see Immunoglobulin gene(s), V
      genes
    hypervariable, see Complementarity
      determining regions (CDRs)
    phage display library construction
      1932–1933, 1932(Fig)
    pseudogenes 1309
    somatic mutation, see Somatic
      hypermutation
  V domains 764
    β-barrel structure 171
    CDR regions, see Complementarity
      determining regions (CDRs)
    framework regions (FR) 764
    homodimers 776
    structure 517, 764, 775–776
  V genes, see Immunoglobulin gene(s), V
    genes
Immunoglobulin α, see Igα
Immunoglobulin A (IgA) 1196–1199,
    1329, 1515
  A2m antibodies 348
  ABO antibodies 5
  antibodies, blood transfusion reactions
    348
  antiphospholipid antibodies 2119
  bacterial binding protein 326
  to bacterial vaccines 1779
  Candida infections 410
  catabolism 1196
  in cats 893
  cholera 2478
  class switching to, see Immunoglobulin
    class switching
  in colostrum, ungulates 2450
  complement activation 1198, 1316
  cysticercosis 691
  deficiency 1198
    ataxia telangiectasia (AT) 249
    common variable immunodeficiency
      (CVID) 1280
    HLA class III association 1120
    respiratory infections 2083
    selective, see below
  degradation, by Proteus mirabilis
    protease 2041
  delivery to gut by bile, in ungulates 2450
  deposition 1198–1199
  digestion by hookworms 1123, 1124
  dimeric 1197, 1197(Fig), 1515, 1784
    in ungulates 2450
  distribution 1196
  dogs 413
  Echinococcus infections 784, 785
  enteromammaric link 1672
  Fc receptors, see FcαR
  functions 891, 1197–1198
    protective 1146
  heavy chain (α) 1197, 1197(Fig)
  Helicobacter pylori colonization 1057
  hepatic uptake 1785

Immunoglobulin A (IgA) (*continued*)
hepatitis E 1083
hinge region 1197
IgA1 1197, 1784, 1889
  degradation by protease 1889
  expression 1303
  Neisseria protease cleaving 1817
IgA2 1197, 1784, 1889
  allotypic forms 1197
immune complex clearance 1198
in immune exclusion 1198
in immunization 1199
immunopathology associated 1198–1199
induction 1199
inflammatory bowel disease 1378
influenza viruses 1385
intracellular transport 1726, 1784–1785
isotypes 1197
J chains 1197, 1517, 1784
  role 1517, 1784
  in ungulates 2450
  see also J chain
Klebsiella pneumoniae 1522
lifespan 1583
local response, in oral tolerance 1785
in mammary tissue 1196
marker of HIV infection progression 9
mucosal host defense 1784
nasopharyngeal carcinoma 832
natural antibodies 1807
nephropathy 1198
opsonization 1886
in oral cavity 1890
ovine 1903
parasitic infections 1918
pathogen elimination 1198
pemphigus 2188
in pigs 1994
plasma cells secreting 1782
polymeric (pIgA) 1197, 1198, 1784,
  2152, 2467
  affinity for free secretory component
    2154
  transport through secretory epithelia
    2155
polymerization, J chain role 1517, 1784
production/synthesis 1196
  in gut 1602, 1782, 1784
  IL-6 role 1458
  mucosal tissue 1196, 1784
  quantity 1196
  rate 1784
  regulation 1196
  sites 1196
  TGFβ role 1894, 1895
receptor (pIgR) 1196
  see also Secretory component (SC)
reduced 600, 601
salivary 1889
  decreased with endurance exercise 846
in secretions 1196
secretory component
  cleavage 1785
  sIgA formation 1198, 1726, 1784,
    2152, 2153(Fig)
  see also Secretory component (SC)
secretory (sIgA) 148, 1515, 1726,
  1784(Fig), 1889
  antibody combining sites 148
  bacterial infections 317
  in breast milk 1672
  Campylobacter infections 408
  Clonorchis infections 1880
  decreased in protein-energy
    malnutrition 1869
  Escherichia coli infections 845
  formation 1198, 1726, 1784, 2153(Fig)
  function 1198
  Opisthorchis infections 1880
  production 1778
  Shigella vaccines 2180
  structure 1197

Immunoglobulin A (IgA) (*continued*)
selective deficiency 1281, 1285
  in dogs 413
serum 1778, 1784(Fig)
Shigella infections 2179
to sperm membrane antigens 1374
structure 1196–1197
trichuriasis 2419
ungulates 2449, 2449(Table), 2450
Immunoglobulin β, *see* Igβ
Immunoglobulin class switching 157, 358,
  1145, 1227, 1302–1306, 1323
amphibians 81, 82
CD40 ligation and IL-10 role 485, 1303
coexpression of IgM with IgG/IgA/IgE
  1303
CR2 role 631
cytokines influencing 1205, 1304
defect in hyper-IgM syndrome 1166,
  1168, 1303
  see also Hyper-IgM syndrome
direction and T$_H$2 role 1205
DNA synthesis after 1303
failure 366
frequencies 1303
from IgM 1215
in germinal centers 993
to IgA 1781, 1782
  Peyer's patches 1776, 1777, 1781,
    1782
to IgE 1205
  IL-4 role 1452
induction 1303–1304, 1305(Fig)
  antigens triggering 1303
  CD40-CD40L role 1303
isotypes and 1515
maturation of immune response 1678
mechanism 1167(Fig), 1205, 1302–1303,
  1305(Fig)
mitotic switch recombination 1303
molecular basis 1302–1303
recombinase 1305–1306
  activation 1305(Fig)
recombination
  cis and *trans* 1303
  events 1302–1303, 1305(Fig)
  pathway 553, 1305(Fig)
  secondary/tertiary 1303
sites 1302
switch (S) regions 1302
  intra-S recombination 1303
  sequences 1302
  targeting to 1304–1305
  transcription 1304
targeting to S regions 1304–1305
  cytokines role 1305
T cell-independent antigens 1678
T$_H$1 2151
Immunoglobulin D (IgD) 1199–1202,
  1329, 1515
association with [G]L[g] chains 1200
bacterial binding protein 326
on B cell surface 363, 1200, 1215, 1876
  anergic cells 107
  IgM coexpression 156, 363, 1200,
    1323, 1685, 1876
  see also Immunoglobulin D (IgD),
    membrane
in B cell tolerance 1201
function 1201
gene 1200
heavy chain (δ) 1199
  gene 1200
hinge region 1515
J chains in cells producing 1517
membrane 1200–1201
  function 1201
  heterodimers 1200
  internalized 1200
  see also above
myeloma 341, 1200
production, in HIV infection 11

Immunoglobulin D (IgD) (*continued*)
serum levels 1200
structure 1199
T cell interaction 1201
Immunoglobulin E (IgE) 1170, 1202–1208,
  1329, 1515
in ADCC 169
against nonhuman antigens, blood
  transfusion reactions 348
to allergens 65, 68–69, 252, 1171
allergic rhinitis 2123
anaphylaxis 1207
  cutaneous 678, 1207
antigen presentation role 1171, 1207
ascariasis 242, 243
asthma 244
atopic eczema 788
atopy/allergy 251, 1171, 1202, 1207
binding to mast cells 253, 1669, 2165
  cross-linking 1207, 1669, 2165
  mast cell mediator release 2165
binding protein (galectin-3) 430, 1204
in cats 893
characteristics 1170–1171, 1203(Table)
class switching to 252, 1205
  cytokines control 1205
  heavy chain genes 1205
Clonorchis infections 1880
discovery 25
dogs 413
drug allergy, desensitization 782
expression, second signal 252–253
Fc receptors, *see* FcεR
food allergy 947
to foods, tests 951
functions 1171, 1207
  beneficial 1173–1174, 1207
genetic influences 252
glycosylation 1202
heavy chains (ε) 1202
  gene 1204–1205, 1205
helminth infections 1919
high affinity Fcε receptors, *see* FcεRI
hinge region absent 1202, 1515
hookworm disease 1124
immunologic contact urticaria 680–681
increased
  allergy 1171
  parasitic infections 1173–1174
  see also Atopy; Hypersensitivity, type I;
    Immunoglobulin E (IgE), atopy/allergy
insect venom reaction 2471
lifespan 1583
low affinity Fcε receptors, *see* FcεRII
mast cell degranulation 2467
onchocerciasis 1873
Opisthorchis infections 1880
opsonization 1886
parasite killing 254
parasitic infections 1173–1174, 1207,
  1919
receptors 1171, 1203–1204
  cells with 254–255, 332
  see also Basophil(s); FcεR; Mast cell(s)
regulation 1171
schistosomiasis 2141
secretion, IL-4 role 1452
to seminal plasma 1373
serum concentrations 251, 1202
skin infections 752–753
structure 203(Fig), 251, 1202–1203,
  1203(Fig)
synthesis 252, 1204–1207, 1206(Fig)
  control 1171, 1204–1207
  CR2 role 631, 1205
  downregulation 1205
  FcεRII role 1205–1207
  IL-4 role 1061, 1171, 1205, 1490
  induced by IL-13 1490
  inhibition by IL-8 1468
  T$_H$2 cells role 1171, 1205
  upregulation 1205

Immunoglobulin E (IgE) (continued)
synthesis (continued)
X-linked SCID 1489–1490
tests, drug allergy diagnosis 781
tuberculosis 1795
ungulates 2449–2450, 2449(Table)
upregulation, by house dust mite allergen 68
valency 2467
Immunoglobulin gene(s) 62, 765, 1323–1328, 1329
amphibian 81
avian 302–303
chromosomal translocations, see Chromosomal translocations
constant regions 1323, 1323(Table), 1514–1515
D_H 766
D_μ 1195
germline $V_{[G]L[g]}$ and $J_{[G]L[g]}$ segments 1326–1327
germline $V_{H/D/JH}$ segments 1326
germline V_k and J_k segments 1326
J segments 1323(Table), 1326, 1329
location 1323
organization 1323, 1324(Fig)
rearrangements, see Immunoglobulin gene rearrangements
somatic hypermutation, see Somatic hypermutation
V genes 62, 765, 1323(Table), 1324–1325
as acceptors in humanized antibodies 1141, 1142
assembly 62–64, 155
families 766
germ-line 1326, 1326–1327, 1878
heavy chain disease 1054(Table)
idiotype 1184, 1192
as markers 1184
mouse 766
ontogeny 1878
ordered expression during ontogeny 1877–1878
rearrangements, see Immunoglobulin gene rearrangements
repertoire in thyroiditis experimental model 2310
segments 766(Table)
tolerance breakdown 275
$V_{[G]\lambda[g]}J_{[G]\lambda[g]}$, nonfunctional complex 63
$V_H D_J H$ complex 64, 153, 766(Fig), 767, 1326
V_H region, origin/evolution 1950
Immunoglobulin gene rearrangements 62–64, 153, 155, 363
12/23 rule 1324
amphibians 81, 82
avian comparison 396
avian species 303
B1 cells 362
B cell repertoire 360
see also B cell(s), repertoire
chromosomal translocations due to 554–559
class switch, see Immunoglobulin class switching
deletional joining 1325
dynamic process 63–64
early B cell differentiation 356, 364, 1876
evolution 1308–1309
extra nucleotides 553, 557, 559, 767–769
mechanisms 767–769
heavy chains 62, 63–64, 155–156, 356, 360, 767, 1324–1325
acute leukemia 1556
avian species 303
Igα and Igβ 1194–1195
reading frame bias 1194–1195
hybrids 559

Immunoglobulin gene rearrangements (continued)
hypermutation pathway, see Immunoglobulin, hypermutation
invert joining 1325
light chain genes 62–63, 64, 156, 356, 767, 1876
avian 303
$V_{[G]L[g]}$ and $J_{[G]L[g]}$ 1326–1327
V_k and J_k segments 1326
mechanisms 1324–1325, 1325(Fig), 7645–770
in neonates 1819
N-segment additions 767–769
P-nucleotide additions 767–769
recombination errors 557–558
recombination pathway 553
Southern blotting 2197
stages 553(Fig), 1325(Fig)
stochastic model 63
translocations and, see Chromosomal translocations
VDJ recombinase 553, 554, 556, 559
IL-7 signal role 1464
VDJ recombination 62–64, 153, 155–156, 360, 553, 554, 766–767, 766(Fig), 767, 1324–1325, 1325(Fig)
biases 767
defective in SCID mice 1269
deletional 767, 769(Fig)
domains 764(Fig)
double-strand breaks 767
evolution 1308–1309
Igα an Igβ signals 1194–1195
inversional 767, 769(Fig)
nonproductive 767
nonrandom 1878
pathway 553
process 767
signal sequences 767, 768
V_H rearrangements 63–64, 767
V_L rearrangements 64, 767
Immunoglobulin gene superfamily (IgSF) 27(Table), 28, 710, 777, 1210, 1319–1323
adhesion molecules on monocytes 1753, 1753(Table)
alloantigens 73
CD3 465
CD22 480
cell surface receptors 517–518
cellular cooperation 652
criteria for inclusion 1319
disulfide bonds 517
diversification 1322
domains 777–778
patterns 1322
domains lacking disulfide bonds 1321
evolution 1322
functions 1322
Ig fold 517, 1322(Fig)
members 1320(Table)-1321(Table)
β2-microglobulin 368
mosaic proteins 1319
proteolysis resistance 1322
sequence comparison of members 1319, 1322
structural domains 710
three-dimensional structure 517, 517(Fig)
Immunoglobulin G (IgG) 1208–1211, 1329
ABO antibodies 4–5
detection, see Coombs' test
affinities for monocyte Fc receptors 1003
agalactosyl 1002
in tuberculosis 1797
aggregation into IgG complexes, glycosylation role 1004
to allergens 68–69
allotypes 75(Table)
amebiasis 77
antigen binding 1210

Immunoglobulin G (IgG) (continued)
antigen-binding sites, structure 1331–1332
autoantibodies, SLE 2259
avidity 1209
bacterial proteins binding 323–327, 1211
see also Bacterial immunoglobulin-binding proteins
binding to cell receptors 1211
biological properties 1209(Table), 1210–1211
blocking antibody, to insect venom 2472
in breast milk 1672
to CAMPATH-1 antigen (CD52) 404
Campylobacter 408
carbohydrate in 103–1004, 1002, 1210
in cats 893
classes, C1q binding 1316
Clonorchis infection 1880
C1q interaction 1211, 1316, 1316(Fig)
binding site 1316
glycosylation effect 1002
complement activation 1211, 1315–1316
'cytophilic', in sheep 1904
deposits in adrenal cortex 40
dogs 413
domains 1208, 1209
constant 1210
variable 1210
in erythrocyte antibody rosetting 2129
evolution 1308
excretion 1210
Fab fragment 1209
functions 1210
glycosylation 103–1004, 1002
Fc fragment 1209
ADCC triggered by 168
functions 1210
glycosylation 1002, 1003–1004
half-life 1210
IgM binding, see Rheumatoid factor (RF)
receptors, see FcγR
flexibility 1316(Fig)
fragments 2432–2433, 2432(Fig)
functions 1208, 1210–1211, 1315–1316
glycosylation, see under Glycosylation
to GMI ganglioside 1837
haplotypes 75–76
HLA interaction 76
race-associated 75, 76(Table)
to haptenated liposomes/liposome-associated antigens 1590
heat-aggregated, immune complexes 184
heavy chains (γ) 1208, 1209
noncovalent interactions 1209
Helicobacter pylori colonization 1057
in hepatitis E 1083
hinge region 1208–1209, 1330
binding site for FcγRI 1317
deletion 1333
structure 1332–1334
hypervariable region 1210
idiopathic thrombocytopenic purpura (ITP) 1975
Ig fold 1210
IgG1
deficiency 1281
placental transfer 2315
secretion, IL-4 role 1424
TSH receptor autoantibodies 2315
ulcerative colitis 1378
IgG2
absence in premature infants 1285
ataxia telangiectasia (AT) 249
Crohn's disease 1378
deficiency 249, 1281
in AIDS 7
secretion, IFNγ role 1424
IgG2a, production, IL-12 effect 1485
IgG3
deficiency 1281

Immunoglobulin G (IgG) (*continued*)
  IgG3 (*continued*)
    hinge region 1515
    nephritic factors 1257
    primary biliary cirrhosis (PBC) 2003
    ulcerative colitis 1378
  IgG4
    deficiency 1281
    hinge region 1515
    Strongyloides stercoralis 2238
    synthesis induced by IL-13 1490
    tuberculosis 1795
  induction, IL-9 action 1473
  infectious mononucleosis 831
  to influenza viruses 1385
  intravenous 1347
    see also Intravenous immunoglobulin
  intravenous polyvalent concentrate 1976
  to ISCOM–antigen complexes 1509
  isotypes
    distribution 1515
    feline 893
  leptospirosis 1553
  lifespan 1583
  light chains 1208
    in cats 893
  lymphatic filariasis 914
  in marsupial neonates 1664
  maternal
    FcRn binding 72
    fetal protection from 900–901
    transfer, *see placental transfer (below)*
    see also Maternal antibodies
  natural antibodies 1807
  in neonates 1672
  noncomplement fixing, passive
    enhancement 812
  oligoglycan on 425
  Opisthorchis infections 1880
  opsonization 1885, 1885(Fig)
  in oral cavity 1890
  ovine 1903
  parvovirus B19 infection 1923–1924
  physical/chemical properties 1209(Table)
  placental transfer 900, 1147, 1210, 1672
    IgG1 2315
    see also Maternal antibodies; *under*
    Immunoglobulin
  plasmapheresis effect 1970
  protease resistance 1209
  'protective receptor' binding 1318
  protein A binding 1211
  red cell autoantibodies
    experimental models 91, 92, 93
    human 91, 94–95
    IgG classes 93
    see also Autoimmune hemolytic anemia
    (AIHA)
  reduced, in common variable
    immunodeficiency 600
  rheumatoid factors (RFs) 137
  salivary, *Helicobacter pylori* detection
    1057
  secondary (acquired) immune response
    14
  secretion, ulcerative colitis 1378
  to sperm membrane antigens 1374
  structure 149(Fig), 1208, 1208–1210,
    1329, 2432–2433, 2432(Fig)
  subclasses 1210
    antiphospholipid antibodies 2119
    complement activation 1211
    deficiencies 1281, 1515
    maturation 1515
    properties 1209(Table)
    to T-dependent antigens 1515
    to T-independent antigens 1515
  synthetic rate 1970
  therapy, in parvovirus B19 infection
    1924
  in type II hypersensitivity 1174
  ungulates 2449, 2449(Table)

Immunoglobulin G (IgG) (*continued*)
  valency 2467
  vitamin C action 2492
Immunoglobulin G (IgG)/Y 302
  see also Immunoglobulin Y (IgY)
Immunoglobulin heavy (H) chains 155,
  765, 1145, 1329
  in antibody-combining site 51
  assembly 62, 155
  binding protein, *see* BiP
  C_H2 region 1514
  class switching, *see* Immunoglobulin class
    switching
  constant domain (C_H1) 146
  degradation 147
  fusion protein with IFNγ receptor 1428
  genes 765, 1054(Table), 1323, 1326,
    1514
    constant region 1514
    loci 62
    murine 1302
    rearrangements, *see* Immunoglobulin
    gene rearrangements
    variable, ontogeny 1878
    see also under specific immunoglobulin
    types
  Gm haplotypes 1588
  interaction with BiP 146
  isotypes 1514–1515
  light (L) chain association 146, 770
  membrane and secretory forms 145
  β_2-microglobulin binding 368, 371
  ontogeny 1878
  rearrangements, *see also* Immunoglobulin
    gene rearrangements
  sequences, comparison in vertebrates
    1308, 1310(Table)-1313(Table)
  VDJ recombination, *see* Immunoglobulin
    gene rearrangements
Immunoglobulin light (L) chains 155,
  1145, 1329
  amyloid AL 85
  in antibody-combining site 51
  assembly 62, 146
  B cells expressing two 156
  in cold agglutinins 594
  evolution 1308, 1308(Fig), 1309(Fig),
    1314(Table)
  genes 1323, 1326
    loci 62–63
    rearrangements, *see* Immunoglobulin
    gene rearrangements
    V_k, ontogeny 1878
  [G]k[g] 1323, 1329
    deficiency 1281
    genes 1326
  [G]L[g] 1323, 1326–1327, 1329
  heavy chain association 146, 770
  monoclonal free, *see* Bence Jones
    proteins (BJP)
  nonsecreted, in heavy chain disease 1053
  phylogenetic tree 1308(Fig)
  rabbits 2047
  secretion of free L chains 147
  somatic mutation localization 767,
    769(Fig)
  synthesis, in heavy chain disease 1056
Immunoglobulin M (IgM) 1212–1217,
  1329
  ABO antibodies 4
  African trypanosomiasis 2422
  amebiasis 77
  antibody combining sites 149
  in antibody response 1215
  antiphospholipid antibodies 2119
  autoimmune hemolytic disease, *see* Cold
    hemagglutinin disease
  autoimmunity and 1216
  in axolotl 81, 82
  bacterial binding protein 324, 326
  on B cell surface, *see* B cell(s)
  in breast milk 1672

Immunoglobulin M (IgM) (*continued*)
  to *Brucella* 384
  to *Campylobacter* 407–408
  carbohydrate content 1213
  in cats 893
  class switching 1215
    see also Immunoglobulin class
    switching
  Clq binding 1215, 1316
  to *Coccidioides immitis* 590
  coexpression with IgD, *see under* B
    cell(s)
  coexpression with IgG/IgA/IgE 1303
  cold agglutinins 594
  complement activation 1214–1215, 1316
  cryoglobulins 666
  deficiency 1281
  dogs 412–413
  domains 1212
  elevated and immunodeficiency with 366
    see also Hyper-IgM syndrome
  in erythrocyte antibody rosetting 2129
  evolution 1307, 1309
  in fish 924, 1212
  to haptenated liposomes 1590
  heavy chains (μ) 1212
    formation 64
    site-directed mutation 1517
  Helicobacter pylori colonization 1057
  hepatitis E 1083
  HHV-6 infection 1089
  hinge region absent 1212, 1515
  idiopathic thrombocytopenic purpura
    (ITP) 1975
  immunoconglutinins 1257
  induction, IL-9 action 1473
  infective endocarditis 567, 568
  to ISCOM–antigen complexes 1509
  isotype distribution 1515
  J chains 146, 1212, 1213, 1517
    role 1517
    see also J chain
  leptospirosis 1553
  lifespan 1583
  in marsupial neonates 1664
  membrane, structure 1200, 1298–1299,
    1299(Fig)
  monoclonal 1165
  monomeric 1212
    on B cells 1215
    structure 1212
  natural antibodies 1215–1216, 1807
    antigens 1215
  neoplasia and 1216
  nonpolymeric, secretion block 146
  opsonization 1885
  paraprotein 1636
  parvovirus B19 infection 1923
  pentameric (pIgM) 1212, 1213, 1227,
    1515, 2152, 2467
    affinity for free secretory component
    2154
    hapten reactions 1215
    synthesis 2153(Fig)
    see also Immunoglobulin M (IgM),
    polymeric
  picornavirus infection 1956
  plasma/serum levels 1212
    women/men 2176
  polymeric 1212
    functions 1216
    secretion 146
    secretory component in 2152,
    2153(Fig)
    see also Immunoglobulin M (IgM),
    pentameric (pIgM)
  polymerization 146, 1212–1213
    in absence of J chain 1213
    J chain role 1517
  polyreactive 1215–1216
    in fish 1216
  red cell autoantibodies

Immunoglobulin M (IgM) (continued)
  red cell autoantibodies (continued)
    experimental models 91–92
    human, see Cold hemagglutinin disease
  reduced, in iron overload 1507
  rheumatoid factors (RFs) 137, 1216,
    1318
    see also Rheumatoid factor (RF)
  secretion 145
    blocked in B cell lymphomas 145–146
    developmental control 146
    J chain role 146
  secretory 2155
    formation 2153(Fig)
  selective deficiency 1281
  Shigella infections 2179
  structure 1212–1214, 1213(Fig),
    1214(Fig)
    EM 1213–1214, 1214(Table)
  synthesis
    in amphibians 80
    fetus/newborn 1818–1819
  synthetic rate 1970
  T-independent response 1145
  transport, J chain role 1517
  to Trypanosoma lewisi 1216
  in type II hypersensitivity 1174
  valency 1214–1215, 2467
  vitamin C action 2492
  in Xenopus 81, 82
Immunoglobulin-secreting cells (ISCs)
  detection 796
    ELISPOT 797
    specificities 797
Immunoglobulin X (IgX) 1308
  Xenopus 81
Immunoglobulin Y (IgY) 302, 1308
  axolotl 81, 82
  reptiles 2080
  Xenopus 81, 82
Immunogold, in immunocytochemistry
  1263–1265
Immunogold techniques 143
Immunohistochemistry 142–143, 2503
  cell surface antigen characterization 209
  fetal antigens 801
  tissue 143
  see also Immunocytochemistry (ICC)
Immunolabeling methods 793, 795
Immunoliposomes 1588–1589
  long-circulating 1589
  single chain Fv fragments in 1934
Immunological contraception, see
  Contraception, immunological
Immunological diversity generation 105–
  106
  see also Diversity generation
Immunological enhancement, see
  Enhancement, immunological
Immunological escalation, experimental
  autoimmune thyroiditis 2311
Immunological 'homunculus' 2286
Immunologically privileged sites, see
  Immune privilege
Immunological memory, see Memory,
  immunological
Immunological tolerance, see Tolerance
Immunology, history 1334–1339
  first paradigm (etiology/immunization)
    1335–1337
  modern (cellular/molecular) 1338
  preparadigmatic 1334–1335
  protoimmunology 1334–1335
  second paradigm (clonal selection) 1337–
    1338
  see also specific aspects
Immunomagnetic beads 511
Immunomodulation
  CNS role 336
  Pavlovian conditioning 337–338
  stressor-associated 338

Immunomodulation (continued)
  see also Immunopotentiation;
    Immunotherapy
Immunomodulators
  of biological origin 1345–1346,
    1345(Table)
  pyrogenic 903
Immunonephelometry, see Nephelometry
Immunopathology 1339–1342
  antibody analysis 1340
  bacterial infections 319
  as breach of tolerance 1339–1340
  complement component analysis 1340
  definition 1339
  developments 1342
  as dysregulation at molecular level 1342
  failure to induce immune response and
    1342
  hypersensitivity reactions 1341
  IDDM animal models 1393–1396
  immunological mechanisms 1340–1342
  immunophysiology and 1339–1340
  investigative techniques 1340
  mechanisms 1341–1342
  parasitic infections 1919–1920
  T cell 1342
  virus 2483
  see also Hypersensitivity; specific
    diseases/infections
Immunoperoxidase 260, 1263
Immunopharmacology 1352
Immunophysiology 1339, 1339–1340
Immunopotency 202
Immunopotentiating agents 1342
  of biological origin 1345–1346,
    1345(Table)
  synthetic chemicals 1347
  thymosin and thymic hormones 1346
    cytokines 1346
  see also Muramyl dipeptide (MDP)
Immunopotentiation 1342–1348
  classification 1343, 1343(Table)
  definition 1342, 1349
  historical aspects 1343
  nonspecific mechanisms 1345–1348
    active nonspecific 1345–1347
    adoptive nonspecific 1348
    passive nonspecific 1347–1348
    see also Immunopotentiating agents;
      Intravenous immunoglobulin
  specific mechanisms 1343–1345
    active specific 1343–1344
    adoptive specific 1344–1345
    passive specific 1344
    see also Hyperimmune globulin;
      Vaccination
Immunopotent peptides 1297
Immunoprecipitation 141, 1999
  see also Precipitin (precipitation) reaction
Immunoprecipitation of cell surface
  molecules 513–515
  cross-linking 514
  large-scale 514
  method 513
  MHC purification 514–515
  principle 513
  rationale/purpose 513
  sequential 513–514
  solubilization of membrane molecules
    513
Immunoproliferative small intestinal
  lymphoma (IPSID) 1053
Immunoradiometric assay (IRMA) 1253
  cytokines 695, 695(Fig), 696
  method 695(Fig)
Immunoregulation
  active maternal 899–900
  contrasuppression, see Contrasuppression
  see also Immune response, regulation
Immunoregulators, thymic hormones and
  peptides 2302–2303

Immunorestorative therapy, see
  Immunopotentiation; Immunotherapy
Immunoscintigraphy
  applications 2434
  tumor imaging 2433–2434, 2433(Table)
Immunoselection techniques 508, 510–512
  FACS, see Fluorescence-activated cell
    sorting (FACS)
  immunoadhesion 511
  immunomagnetic beads 511
  immunotoxicity 510–511
  magnetic cell sorting 511–512
Immuno-stimulating complex, see ISCOM
Immunostimulation
  in HIV infection 12
  see also Immunopotentiation;
    Immunotherapy
Immunosuppression 1349–1353
  α-fetoprotein (AFP) role 800
  blood transfusion association 2401
  bystander cells 1357–1358
  causes/induced by
    chemicals 1367
    cytomegalovirus (CMV) 723
    exercise 847
    filoviruses 919
    Fusobacterium nucleatum 962
    glucocorticoids 998(Fig), 1000–1001,
      1351, 2224
    Histoplasma capsulatum 1107
    hookworms 1124
    hyperbaric conditions 1157
    live Leishmania vaccine 1550
    Opisthorchis viverrini 1880
    paramyxoviruses 1915
    Taenia 693
    toxic agents, see below
    trauma/surgery 1286
    UV 1945
  definition 1349
  donor-specific 809
    in transplantation 810
    see also Enhancement, immunological
  infections in
    candidiasis 409, 410
    coccidioidomycosis 590
    Cryptococcus neoformans 673
    opportunistic 1883
    Pneumocystis carinii 1977
  mediated by activated macrophage 1648
  nonselective, in autoimmune disease
    therapy 1357, 1358
  oral tolerance mechanism 1894–1895,
    1894(Fig)
  plasmapheresis effect 1970
  selective
    autoimmune disease therapy 1357
    goal 1349–1350, 1350(Fig)
  tolerance induction, see Tolerance
  toxic agents causing 1367–1368,
    1367(Table)
  testing methods 1367
  see also Immunodeficiency, secondary;
    Immunodepression
Immunosuppressive agents/therapy
  anti-lymphocyte serum (ALS) 121, 1351
  autoimmune disease 291, 295
  autoimmune hemolytic anemia (AIHA)
    97
  CAMPATH-1 antibodies 405
  cutaneous lupus erythematosus 2187–
    2188
  cyclosporine (CsA) 686, 688–689
  development 1351–1352
  diabetes prevention/onset delay 1403
    animal models 1397
  goals 1349–1350, 1350(Fig)
  graft-versus-host disease (GVHD) 1016,
    1017
  ideal 1350
  IL-2 as 1438
  immunopharmacology 1352

Immunosuppressive agents/therapy
  (*continued*)
  indications 1349
  infections associated, *see under*
    Immunosuppression
  in vitro actions 1350
  modern trends 1352–1353
  monoclonal antibodies 2414
  requirements 1350
  therapeutic index 1350
  in transplantation 2412, 2414
    drugs 2414
    history 2412
    monoclonal antibodies 2414
    role 1349
    see also Graft rejection;
      Transplantation
  tumor association, immune surveillance
    theory 1245, 1246
  tumor development 1245
  xenograft survival prolongation 2510
  see also Corticosteroids; Cyclosporin;
    FK506
Immunosuppressive factors, ocular fluids
  870
Immunotherapy 2459
  of allergic disease 69, 255, 1353–1356
    allergens 69, 1354
    antigen identification 1354
    antigen-nonspecific approaches 1355–
      1356
    antigen-specific methods 1355,
      1355(Table)
    children 1355
    contraindications 1354
    current practices 1354–1355
    doses 1354
    efficacy 1354
    fatalities 1354–1355
    future developments 1355
    history 1353–1354
    inhalant allergens 1354
    insect venom 1354
    mechanism of action 1355
    standardization of allergens 1355
    T_H2 response change to T_H1 1355
    ultrapure allergens in 1355
  allotype matching in 76
  in asthma 246(Table)
  of autoimmune disease 291, 1356–1359
    antibody-dependent 1358–1359
    definitions 1356
    nonselective immunosuppression 1357,
      1358
    selective immunosuppression 1357
    types 1357
    see also Immunosuppression;
      Immunosuppressive agents/therapy
  cobra venom factor (CVF) 588
  culture of cells for 1574–1575
  determinant spreading implications 756
  experimental autoimmune uveoretinitis
    (EAU) 869
  fungal infections 961
  HIV infection 12
  insect venom 2472
  Pseudomonas aeruginosa infections
    2044–2045, 2044(Table)
  rheumatoid arthritis 2112
  targeting, *see* Targeting of immunological
    agents
  of tumors, *see* Tumor immunotherapy
Immunotoxicity, cell separation technique
  510–511
Immunotoxicology 1365–1369
  autoimmunity 1367
    agents causing 1367(Table)
  definition 1365
  direct/indirect effects of agents 1366(Fig)
  germ-free animal studies 991
  hypersensitivity 1365–1367
    agents causing 1367(Table)

Immunotoxicology (*continued*)
  immunosuppression 1367–1368
    agents causing 1367(Table)
  local immunity 1368–1369
  pulmonary immunotoxicants 1368
  testing methods 1365, 1365–1366, 1367
Immunotoxins 2261
  single-chain Fv (scFV) fusion 2261–2262,
    2262(Fig)
  tumor therapy 2434
Impetigo 752
  bullous 752
Implantation 641
Inab, decay-accelerating factor (DAF)
  deficiency 735
Inbred strains 1369–1372
  coisogenic 1370
  congenic 1370
    see also Congenic mice
  definition 1369–1370
  derivatives 1370
  fitness 1372
  genetic monitoring 1371
  homozygosity 1369, 1371
  identifiability 1372
  individuality 1372
  international distribution 1372
  isogenicity 1371
  isogenic strains 1369
  long-term stability 1371
  maintenance 1370–1371
  mice, *see* Mice, inbred strains
  nomenclature 1370
  phenotypic uniformity 1371
  properties 1371–1372
  rat, *see* Rat, inbred strains
  research uses 1372
  sensitivity 1372
  transgenic 1370
    see also Transgenic mice
Inclusion body myositis 2118
Indirect immunofluorescence (IIF), *see*
    Immunofluorescent technique, indirect
    (IFT)
Indirect immunoperoxidase (IIP),
    autoantibody detection 260
Indoleamine 2,3-dioxygenase, macrophage
  1725
Indomethacin
  actions 119
  colitis due to 1384
  immune hemolytic anemia due to 100
  ineffective in inflammatory bowel disease
    1380
  $TNF\alpha$ production increased 2027
Induced fit hypothesis 2201–2203
Induration phenomenon 740
Infants
  food allergy 948, 953
    allergens 948, 951
  infection prevention by breast milk Igs
    1672
  low birthweight, *see* Low birthweight
    infants
  transient HIV infection 7
Infections
  agglutination as protective mechanism
    58–59
  antibody preventing 2459
  eradication 2457
    factors favouring 2461(Table)
  etiology, historical aspects 1336
  experimental autoimmune thyroiditis
    induction 2311
  $Fc\gamma R$ role 890
  gravity/space flights effect 1031, 1032
  HIV infection progression and 8
  immune complex diseases after 1176
  immune response 2459
    see also Antibody-dependent cellular
      cytotoxicity (ADCC); Cytotoxic T
      lymphocytes (CTL)

Infections (*continued*)
  immunological memory development
    2459
  in infants, breast milk role in prevention
    1672
  limitation, antibody role 2459
  opportunistic, *see* Opportunistic
    infections
  persistent, in complement deficiencies
    612
  polyclonal hypergammaglobulinemia in
    1162, 1163(Table)
  prostaglandins role 2025–2026
  recovery, antibodies/T cells role 2459
  recurrent
    common variable immunodeficiency
      599
    complement deficiencies 612
  sepsis interrelationship 2163(Fig)
  stress association 2222
  stress proteins as target antigens 2230–
    2231
  susceptibility
    after radiation 2052
    after transplantation 2414
    in iron deficiency 1506
  systemic inflammatory response
    syndrome (SIRS) interrelationship
    2163(Fig)
  $TNF\alpha$ function 2438–2439
  treatment
    bispecific antibodies 140
    see also Antibiotics
  in vitamin A deficiency 2488
  see also individual infections/organs
Infectious bronchitis virus (IBV) 660,
  660(Table)
Infectious bursal disease (IBD) virus 303
Infectious diseases, *see* Infections
Infectious mononucleosis 831
  immune response 831
  Paul–Bunnell antibodies 1092
Infective endocarditis, *see* Endocarditis,
    infective
Infertility 497, 1373–1375
  antibodies to sperm membrane antigens
    1374
  autoimmune reactions causing 1373
  definition 1373
  immunity to semen 1373–1374
  immunity to trophoblast 1375
  immunity to zona pellucida 1374–1375
  'unexplained' 1373
Inflammation/inflammatory reactions 501
  acute 15–17
    complement role 1146
  adverse effects 16
  anaphylatoxins action 87
  antigen/lymphocyte interaction 740
  antigen-presenting cell/T cell interactions
    177
  in asthma 244
  cause 16
  cell adhesion mechanisms 2059–2061
    see also specific cell types
  cells involved 16–17, 1857–1858
    see also Neutrophil(s)
  chronic 2059
  diapedesis of leukocytes 759
  downregulation, by IL-1ra 1435
  fibronectin action 912
  glucocorticoid anti-inflammatory action
    111, 112, 997, 1000–1001
  IgE role 1207
  IL-1 effect on endothelial cells 805
  IL-13 and IL-4 roles 1491
  inhibition
    by annexins 113
    by glucocorticoids 111, 112
    by NSAIDs 117–118
  initiation, by macrophage 1643
  intestinal 1376

Inflammation/inflammatory reactions
    (*continued*)
  intestinal (*continued*)
    chemicals inducing 1383–1384
    see also Inflammatory bowel disease
      (IBD)
  kinetics 738
  late-phase in allergic disease 253,
    253(Fig)
  leukocyte recruitment 529, 529(Fig),
    2059
  lymphotoxin role 1638
  mediators, *see* Inflammatory mediators
  memory T cell influx 1683
  monocyte extravasation 1754
  mononuclear phagocytes in 1755–1756
  neutrophils 1857–1858
  proinflammatory effects
    chemokines 531
    NSAIDs 119–120
  prostaglandins role 117, 119, 2025
    see also Prostaglandin(s)
  resolution, apoptosis role 226–227
  selective breeding application 345
  tissue injury mechanisms 1175(Fig)
  type III hypersensitivity 1176
  vascular leakage 17
  see also Inflammatory diseases
Inflammatory bowel disease (IBD) 1375–
    1381
  activating events 1376(Fig)
  animal models 1381–1385, 1382(Table)
    chemical-induced inflammation 1383–
      1384
    gene disruption-induced 1382–1383
    spontaneous colitis 1383
  autoantibodies, bactericidal/permeability
    increasing proteins (BPI) 1722
  cell-mediated immunity 1377, 1377(Fig)
  chemokines role 1379–1380
  complement activation 1378
  cytokine production 1378–1380
  epithelial barrier importance 1382
  exacerbation by NSAIDs 2027
  granulocyte function 1378
  immunoglobulin synthesis 1378
  inflammatory events 1380(Fig)
  leukotriene synthesis 1381
  lymphocyte activation 1376–1377
    intestinal 1377
    peripheral blood lymphocytes 1376–
      1377
  macrophage function 1378
  mechanisms of tissue injury 1378,
    1379(Fig)
  NSAID not effective 1380
  phagocytosis 1380(Fig)
  prostaglandin production 1380
  therapy, soluble TNF receptors 2349
  see also Crohn's disease; Ulcerative
    colitis
Inflammatory diseases
  IL-1 therapy 1435
  IL-11 therapy 1481
Inflammatory exudate, cells in, terminology
    1758
Inflammatory mediators 15, 16(Table), 17
  actions 16(Table)
  Arthus reaction 239, 239(Table)
  diapedesis of leukocytes 759
  IL-1 role 1433
  inflammatory bowel disease 1378
  LCMV infection 233
  leukemia inhibitory factor (LIF) 1561
  nasal allergy 2123–2124
  neutrophils 1858
  regulation, glucocorticoid action 1000,
    1000(Table)
  released by mast cells in atopy 1172,
    1173(Fig)
  synthesis, by membrane attack complex
    627

Inflammatory mediators (*continued*)
  see also Inflammation
Influenza A virus 1385
  antigenic drift 200, 1385, 1386
  antigenic shift 200, 1386
  antigenic variation 199, 200
Influenza B virus 1385
Influenza C virus 1385
Influenza viruses 1385–1387
  antigenic drift 200, 1385, 1386
  antigenic shift 200, 1386
  attenuation 258
  avian 1385
  cell-mediated immunity 1386
  DNA vaccines 772
  escape mutants 1386
  genetic reassortment 258
  hemagglutinin 1385
    antibodies 1384
    function 1538
    hsp70 role 2230
    transgenic mice 1397
  humoral immunity 1385–1386
  in ISCOMs 1509
  lectins role 1538, 1539(Table)
  macrophage activation 1386
  macrophage infection 2486
  neuraminidase 1385, 1385–1386
    antibodies 1385–1386
    antibody combining sites 150
    N9, cross-reactive epitopes 2202
  NK cell infection 2485–2486
  NK cell response 1386
  subtypes 1385
  T cells 1386
    specificity and memory 1386–1387
  vaccines 1385, 2083
    inactivated virus 1387
    side-effects 2463
Inguinal lymph nodes, enlargement in HIV
    infection 7
Inhaled allergens, *see* Allergens
Inheritance of genetic diseases, *see* Genetic
    disorders
Inhibition assays 1254
Innate (natural) immunity 1387–1389,
    1388(Fig)
  adaptive immunity *vs* 1226
  definition 1387
  enzyme synthesis 1388
  evolution 1388, 1948
  granular leukocytes 1388
  history 1387–1388
  IL-12 role 1484, 1486, 1487
  interferon production 1389
  invertebrates 1948
  lipid synthesis 1388–1389
  NK cells, *see* Natural killer (NK) cells
  nomenclature 1387–1388
  nongranular leukocytes 1388
  phagocytosis, *see* Phagocytosis
  vitamin A 2488–2489
Innocent bystander reaction, *see* Bystander
    effects
Inosine pranobex (isoprinosine), in HIV
    infection 12
Inositol 1,4,5-triphosphate (IP$_3$) 1299
  cytokine synthesis 700
  IL-8 signaling 1467
  receptor, ankyrin binding 1681
  signal transduction in HIV infection 10
  in T cell activation 2325
Insect(s) 2471
  antibacterial peptides 1500
  Ig gene superfamily 1322
  vectors, vaccines against 2458
Insect bites and stings 254
  allergic reactions 680
  localized and systemic reactions 680
  prevention 680
  see also Insect venom
Insect defensins 1500

Insecticides, *Bacillus* species 311
Insect venom 2470, 2471–2472
  allergens 67(Table), 2471(Table)
  allergic reactions 69, 2471
  IgE-mediated reactions 2471
  immunotherapy 1354, 2472
  sting challenge 2471–2472
  see also Insect bites and stings
Insect viruses 1502
In situ hybridization 982
  techniques, immunocytochemistry 1266–
    1267
  TGFβ detection 2394
Instructive-type theory, antibody formation
    1337
Insulin
  antibodies 273, 294
  as antigen 779
  as autoantigen in IDDM 1401
  diabetes prevention/onset delay 1403
    animal models 1397
  effect on immune system 2224
  gene 1400
  MIF colocalization in β cells 1656
  oral, NOD mice treatment 1897
  oral tolerance 1403
  receptor
    internalization by adenovirus protein
      22
    on red cell membrane 840
  replacement in diabetes 1402
  resistance, syndromes 1986
Insulin-dependent diabetes mellitus
    (IDDM), *see* Diabetes mellitus,
    insulin-dependent (IDDM)
Insulin growth factor 1 (IGF-1),
    sarcoidosis 2136
Insulin receptor substrate (IRS)
  IL-9 signal transduction 1473
  IRS-2, IL-4 signal transduction 1452,
    1454–1455
Insulitis 1402
  BB rat 1393
int-3 gene 1045, 1115
Integrin associated protein (CD47)
    449(Table)
Integrins 26–28, 866, 1404–1409, 1885,
    1936
  α$_4$
    functions 1407–1408
    knockout mice 1408
  α$_4$β7 1408
    lymphocyte adhesion to HEVs 1097–
      1098
    as mucosal homing receptor 1097,
      1778, 1784
  α$_5$β$_1$
    expression loss in cancer 913
    fibronectin binding 910, 912
  αβ heterodimers 1404
  activation, for leukocyte recruitment 30
  α$_D$β$_2$ 1407
  α$_E$β7 1408
  α$_E$ 453(Table)
  α$_M$β$_2$, *see* CR3 (CD11b/CD18 complex;
    Mac-1)
  α subunits 26, 28, 1404
    I domains 1404, 1407
  α$_v$ (CD51) 450(Table)
  β$_1$ (CD29) 447(Table), 2061(Fig)
  β$_2$ (CD18) 447(Table), 2061(Fig)
    defects 543
    functions 31, 1407
    ICAM binding 1409
    leukocyte adhesion deficiency 1409
    monocyte diapedesis 1754
    mutation in dogs/cattle 1566
    see also LFA-1
  β$_3$ (CD61) 450(Table), 2061(Fig)
    functions 1408
  β$_4$ (CD104) 453(Table), 1404
  β$_7$ 2061(Fig)

Integrins (*continued*)
β subunits 26, 28, 1404
cells expressing 27(Table), 1404
characteristics 1405(Table)
counter-receptors 28
definition 1607
in diapedesis 759
fibronectin interactions 909, 910, 911,
1407
functions 1404, 1407–1408
adhesion cascade 1408, 1408(Fig),
2060, 2061(Fig)
knockout mice 1408–1409
leukocyte 1607, 2060, 2061(Fig)
characteristics 1405(Table)
leukocyte adhesion to endothelium 419,
758, 1249, 1408, 1408(Fig), 2059
leukocyte transmigration, *see*
Transmigration of leukocytes
ligands 26, 866, 1406–1407
specificity 26, 28
lymphocyte expression, VIP effect 1827
metal ion-binding sites 1406–1407
mice deficient in 32, 1408–1409
MIDAS motifs 1406(Fig), 1407
on monocytes 1753, 1753(Table)
non-leukocyte (disintegrins) 1609
phagocytosis stimuli 1713
in pigs 1993
receptor for picornaviruses 1955
RGD recognition 1407
signal transduction 31
structure 26, 28, 1404–1406
domains 1406(Fig)
model 910, 912(Fig)
types, names and ligands 27(Table)
see also LFA-1; VLA (very late antigen)
Integrin superfamily 1404
Intercellular adhesion molecules, *see*
ICAM-1; ICAM-2; ICAM-3
Interdigitating cells (IDCs) 177, 188,
189(Fig), 190, 651, 747
contact allergy 2191
lymph nodes 1604, 2191
phenotype 747
Interdigitating reticulum cells 1757
Interferon 720
action on nervous and immune systems
1831(Table)
classification 1413, 1420–1421
discovery 1413
in early pregnancy 1413
as endogenous pyrogen 902
evolution 1414
feline 893
functions 1413
iron deficiency effect 1507
immune, *see* Interferon γ (IFNγ)
induction in rabies 2100
MHC expression modulation
HLA class I 1109
tumors 1361
poxvirus encoded homologs 1997(Table)
production
by macrophage 1389
vitamin C enhancing 2492
receptors 1413, 1414
trophoblast 1414
tumor immunotherapy 1362
type I 1413
see also Interferon α (IFNα); Interferon
β (IFNβ)
type II 1413
see also Interferon γ (IFNγ)
Interferon α/β family 1413–1414
Interferon α (IFNα) 902, 1413–1417,
1420–1421
antiproliferative actions 1416
antiviral actions 1416
cells producing 2481
classification 1413
discovery 1413

Interferon α (IFNα) (*continued*)
EBV infection 833
evolution 1414
functions 1413, 2481
genes 1413
in birds 1413
mapping 1413
regulation of expression 1414
genes induced by 1414, 1415–1416
leukemia therapy 1559
MHC class I expression enhanced 1704
NK activation 2481
pseudogenes 1413
receptor 709, 1413, 1414
side-effects 1416
signal transduction pathway 1414–1415
therapeutic uses 1416–1417
combined therapy 1416
doses and duration 1416
tumor immunotherapy 1362
virus-inducible element (VRE) 1414
Interferon β (IFNβ) 902, 1417–1421, 1421
administration 1421
antiviral activity 1419
biological 'justification' for 1421
cell growth inhibition 1420
cells producing 2481
endogenous induction 1420
functions 1419–1420, 2481
in vitro 1417
gene 1413
mapping 1417
PRDII 1418–1419
PRDIV element 1419
regulation of expression 1414, 1418–
1419
regulatory domain (PRDI) 1418
structure 1417–1418
genes induced by 1414, 1415–1416
glycosylation 1417
HMG I(Y) for assembly of
enhanceosome 1419
induction/production 1418–1419
levels of mRNA 1418
MHC class I expression enhanced 1704
multiple sclerosis 1840
murine, sequence 1418
NK activation 2481
oral tolerance enhanced 1896
reason for subdivision into 1420–1421
receptor 1419
sequence homologies 1419
structure 1419
signal transduction pathway 1419–1420
therapeutic 1421
Interferon γ (IFNγ) 720, 902, 1421–1426
absence
effects 1425
in NOD mice 1396
ADCC modulation 170
as adjuvant 38
administration, multiple sclerosis after
1840
animal models of IDDM 1396
antigen presentation enhancement 1424
apoptosis regulation 1424–1425
in autoimmune disease 1425, 1428
bacterial infections 318
bacteriostatic effect on *Legionella
pneumophila* 1544
bare lymphocyte syndrome 331
brucellosis 384
cells producing 1422
Chagas' disease 524, 525(Table)
characteristics 1422(Table)
Chlamydia infections 551
CNS inflammation 2395
coccidioidomycosis 589
cryptococcosis 672
cryptosporidiosis 677
cytokine receptor modulation 1424
dengue 930

Interferon γ (IFNγ) (*continued*)
discovery 1421
in disease 1425
dual role in diseases 1425
effect on endothelial cells 805
effect on nervous and immune systems
1831, 1831(Table)
exercise effect 846
expression, upregulation by TNFα 2113
extranodal development of HEVs 1100
FcγRI expression increased 889
functions 1423, 2114
gene 1271, 1422
cloning 1421
mapping 1422
murine 1422
genes induced by 1423
genes inhibited by 1423
germinal center generation prevention
994
glycosylated and nonglycosylated 1422
Histoplasma capsulatum infections 1107
ICAM-1 expression stimulated by 805,
1424
immunoregulatory functions 1423–1425
cells activated by 1423–1424
Ig isotypes 1424
increased
Sjögren's syndrome 2184
SLE 2259
induction 1422–1423
antigen-ISCOM complexes 1509
LCMV infection 233
Legionella pneumophila replication
inhibition 1543
leishmaniasis 1548
Listeria monocytogenes infection 1594
lymphatic filariasis 914
lymphotoxin synergy 1639
macrophage activation 1423–1424,
1643–1644, 1645, 1648
amebiasis 78
mechanism of action 1423
MHC antigen expression by macrophage
503
MHC class I expression enhanced 1704
MHC class II expression induced 1424
β2-microglobulin expression induced 368
murine cutaneous leishmaniasis 1920
nomenclature 1421
oral tolerance decreased 1896
overexpression 1425
receptor (*ifngr*) 454(Table), 709, 1421,
1423, 1426–1429
distribution 1428
downregulation in B cell activation
1428
fusion protein with Ig heavy chain
1428
genes 1427
ifngr-1 (IFNγR1; α chain) 1426–1427
ifngr-2 (IFNγR2; b chain) 1426–1427
inappropriate activation 1428
knockout mice 1428
signal transduction pathway 1423,
1427–1428, 2151
structure 520, 1427, 1427(Fig), 2151
subunits and properties 1426(Table)
upregulation in T cell activation 1428
reduction, mercuric chloride causing
1689
release
in contact hypersensitivity 640
experimental autoimmune
encephalomyelitis 859
by LAK cells 1628
by T cells 1060
rheumatoid arthritis 2113–2114
sarcoidosis 2136
sensitization to lipopolysaccharide 808
signal transduction pathway 1423, 1427–
1428, 2151

Interferon γ (IFNγ) (*continued*)
  structure 1422
  synthesis/production 1422–1423
    by African swine fever (ASF) virus 55
    cytokines regulating 1423
    enhanced by LTB₄ 229
    estrogen-enhanced 2177
    IL-12 effect 1486, 1813–1814
    IL-12 regulation of 1422
    increase, by B7-1/B7-2 306
    inhibition by calcitriol 2496
    LFA-3 stimulated T cells 1614
    macrophage 1395
    by NK cells induced by IL-12 1813–1814
    Toxoplasma gondii infection 2382–2383
  TfR expression regulation 1543, 2391
  in T$_H$1 response 1424
  therapeutic 1425
    chronic granulomatous disease 1425
    fungal infections 961
  TNFα cooperative action 1424
  TNFα production by macrophage 1548
  transgenic expression, animal models of IDDM 1396
  transgenic mice 1425
  tryptophan deprivation 318
  in tuberculosis model 1795
  upregulation of IL-1β converting enzyme (ICE) 1430
  viral infections 2481
Interferon γ (IFNγ)-activated sites (sequences) (GAS) 1423, 1427
Interferon γ (IFNγ) response region (GRR), IL-10 signal transduction 1477
Interferon [G]w[g] 1413
  proteins 1413
Interferon-inducible genes (ISG) 1414–1415, 1415
Interferon receptor family 709, 709(Table)
Interferon regulatory factor 1 (IRF1) 1414, 1418, 1420, 2051
  interferon γ actions 1423
Interferon regulatory factor 2 (IRF2) 1414, 1418
Interferon-stimulated gene factor 3 (ISGF3) 1414–1415
Interferon-stimulated response element (ISRE) 1414, 1420
  absent from HLA-G 899
Interferon τ (IFNτ; trophoblast IFN) 1414
  antiviral actions 1416
Interleukin(s)
  as adjuvants 38
  in dogs 413
  immune response to allergens 69
  nomenclature 719
  origin of term 1060
  release age-related changes 60
  T cell secretion, in allergy 69
Interleukin-1 (IL-1) 719, 1429–1435
  ACTH release stimulation 1434
  action on nervous and immune systems 1830, 1831(Table)
  amino acid sequence 1430
  antibodies 1435
  antitumor effects 1434
  in Arthus reaction 239
  Bacillus anthracis toxin action 2375
  B cell development 1433
  binding to IL-1 receptors 1429, 1432
    affinity 1432
    sphingomyelinase activation 1433
  bioassay 697(Table), 1429, 1432
  biological effects 1433–1434
    in vitro 1434(Table)
    in vivo 1433(Table)
    minimum size for 1430
  blocking 1435
    gene therapy 978

Interleukin-1 (IL-1) (*continued*)
  blocking (*continued*)
    see also Interleukin-1 (IL-1) receptor antagonist (IL-1ra)
  bone resorption regulation 1434
  cellular sources 1430–1432
  Chagas' disease, role in 526(Table)
  corticotropin-releasing hormone release 340, 1434
  CSF synergy 1434
  cytokines induced by 1433
  cytoplasmic 1430
  decreased, in iron deficiency 1507
  detection methods 1432
    see also Interleukin-1 (IL-1), bioassays
  in dogs 413
  effect on endothelial cells 805
  effect on peripheral nerves 2226
  as endogenous pyrogen 902, 1434
  feedback regulation, by glucocorticoids 1434
  feline 893
  functions 2113
  genes 1429–1430, 1431(Fig)
    deletion 1435
    regulatory sequences 1429
  hematopoiesis regulation 1434
  IL-1α 705, 1429
    autoantibodies 704–705
    biological activities 902
    gene 1429
    inflammatory actions 1378
    overexpression 1434
    size and structure 1430
  IL-1β 1429
    animal models of IDDM 1396
    binding to poxviruses 705
    biological activities 902
    endotoxemia 1431
    fragment 1430
    gene 1429
    gene variation, bone resorption 1892
    inflammatory actions 1378
    mice deficient 1435
    production inhibition by IL-13 1490
    secretion, inflammatory bowel disease 1379
    size and structure 1430
  IL-1β converting enzyme (ICE), *see* ICE
  IL-2 receptor expression induced 1433
  immunological effects 1433–1434
  increase, inflammatory bowel disease 1378–1379, 1379
  inflammatory effects 1429, 1433–1434
  inhibitors 704–705, 1435
  knockout mice 1435
  leukocyte recruitment 1433–1434
  MHC class II expression induced 1433
  mice deficient 1434, 1435
  neural effects 1830, 1831(Table), 2226
  NK cell increase 1434
  periodontal disease 1891
  pituitary gland production 1830
  precursors 1430
    cleavage 1430
  prostaglandin synthesis 117–118, 904
    hormones inhibiting 904
  recombinant 1429
  release, stimulation by glucans 429
  rheumatoid arthritis 2113
  secreted forms 1430
  signal transduction 1432, 1432–1433, 2032
  structure 1430
  in synovial fluid 1435
  synthesis 1430, 1430–1431, 2113
    astrocytes/microglial cells 1830
    cytokines stimulating 1431
    endothelial cells 806
    induction 1431–1432
    inhibition by PGE₂ 2026
    macrophage 1431, 2225–2226

Interleukin-1 (IL-1) (*continued*)
  synthesis (*continued*)
    platelet-activating factor (PAF) effect 1972
    T cell proliferation 1433
    therapeutic effects 1434–1435
      in inflammatory diseases 1435
    in thrombosis and inflammation 805
    thymocyte maturation 1433
    tolerance modulation 2361
    tumor metastases development 1434
Interleukin-1 converting enzyme (ICE), *see* ICE
Interleukin-1 (IL-1) receptor 454(Table), 1432
  accessory protein 1432
  brain 2226
  cells expressing 1432
  decoy, *see* type II (*below*)
  expression regulation 1432
  extracellular domain 1432
  IL-1 binding, *see under* Interleukin-1 (IL-1)
  internalization 1432–1433
  signal transduction 1432, 1432–1433
  structure 520
  T cell second signal 2149
  type I 704, 1432
    knockout mice 1433
  type II (decoy) 704, 713, 1432
    acquisition by viruses 1435
    virus sequence homology 1432
Interleukin-1 (IL-1) receptor antagonist (IL-1ra) 704, 720, 1429
  cells producing 1431
  cytokines enhancing synthesis 705
  expression 704
  functions/actions 721, 1435
  gene 1429
  immunotherapy 1359
  intracellular form (icIL-1Ra) 705
  precursor 1430
  regulation 1431
  rheumatoid arthritis 978
  secretion 706
  synthesis 705, 1431
    by macrophage 1431
  therapeutic role 706, 1435
Interleukin-2 (IL-2) 1436–1438
  action on nervous and immune systems 1831(Table)
  adoptive nonspecific immunopotentiation 1348
  AIDS 1438
  in amphibians 80
  apoptosis control by 1438
  assay 697(Table)
  B cell response 1437
  Bcl-2 expression induced 1438
  biological actions 1437, 1437(Fig)
  CD3⁺ T cell activation 1628
  Chagas' disease, role in 526(Table)
  clinical aspects 1438
  cloned, adoptive specific immunopotentiation 1345
  cryptococcosis 672
  decreased
    gravity/space flights effect 1032
    in iron deficiency 1507
    in neonates 1820
  deficiency 1441
    autoimmunity in animals 1437–1438
  as endogenous pyrogen 902
  feline 893
  functions 1060, 1437, 1437(Fig)
  gene 1436
    transcription inhibition by IL-10 1476
    transcription regulation 1436
  germinal center generation prevention 994
  glycosylation 1436
  granulocytes response 1437

Interleukin-2 (IL-2) (*continued*)
  as immunosuppressive agent 1438
  increased
    Crohn's disease 1376–1377
    mercuric chloride effect 1687
  induction
    antigen-ISCOM complexes 1509
    by tax gene of HTLV-1 1565
  knockout mice 1438, 1494
    inflammatory bowel disease model
      1382
  LAK cell immunotherapy 1630
  large granular lymphocyte growth 1534
  lymphocyte proliferation, negative
    control 1437–1438
  molecular characterization 1436
  monocyte response 1437
  NK cell proliferation 1810
  NK cell response 1437
  platelet-activating factor (PAF) effect
    1972
  rheumatoid arthritis 2114
  role in activation-induced cell death
    (AICD) 1438
  role in T cells 1437
  signaling 2149
  structure 1436, 1436(Fig)
  synthesis 1436
    arginine effect 236
    detect in SLE 2258
    IL-12 effect 1486
    increase by B7-1/B7-2 306
    inhibition by anti-LFA-1 1609
    inhibition in T cell anergy 109, 1436
    Pro-Tα and thymosin Tα1 effect 2301
    suppression in tumors 1284
    by T cells 1060, 1436, 2330
  targets 1437
  in T-B cell cooperation 1061, 1437
  T cell chemotaxis 538
  T cell growth 503
  as T cell growth factor 1060, 1436
  T$_H$1 cells producing 2332
  therapeutic 1438
  tumor immunotherapy 1362, 1438
  UCD 200 chicken strain 285
Interleukin-2 (IL-2) receptor (IL-2R) 1439–
    1442, 2149
  α chain (CD25; Tac antigen) 155,
    447(Table), 720, 1440
    antibodies 1352, 1358, 1440
    CD28-induced expression of 482
    expression by activated CTL 726
    expression in contact hypersensitivity
      639
    expression on thymocytes 2336
    gene expression control 1440
    LTB$_4$ inducing 231
    production, by NK cells 1810
    role 1440
    structure 1440
    sushi domain 1440
  β chain 454(Table), 1439, 1440
    downregulation by IL-4 1453
    expression 1440
    IL-6 receptor homology 1461
  decrease, by IL-1ra 1435
  downregulation by *Trypanosoma cruzi*
    523
  expression 1437, 1439, 1439–1440,
    1439(Fig), 2149
    B cells 1437
    induced by IL-1 1433
    monocytes 1437
    NK cells 1437
  fusion protein with diphtheria toxin
    2370
  γc chain 1439, 1440
    constitutive expression 1440
    domains 1440
    gene in X-SCID 1440, 1441
    homology with α chain 1440

Interleukin-2 (IL-2) receptor (IL-2R)
    (*continued*)
  γc chain (*continued*)
    in IL-7 receptor 1463
    mice deficient 1441
    mutation in X-linked SCID 1440,
      1441, 1464, 1489, 2170, 2171
    see also Common γ (γc) chain
  gene disruption 1441
  gravity/space flights effect 1032
  high-affinity 1439, 1439(Fig)
  intermediate affinity 1439
  knockout mice 1494
  low-affinity (IL-2α) 1439
  marker of HIV infection progression 9
  mitogenic component, JAK3 role 1441
  monoclonal antibodies, in transplantation
    2414
  Pro-Tα and thymosin Tα1 effect 2301
  signal transduction 1440–1441
    JAK1/JAK3 and STAT5 1441, 2171–
      2172, 2172(Fig)
    JAK3 binding site 2172(Fig)
    other systems 1441
    Ras/MAP kinase pathway 1441
  structure 1439–1440, 1439(Fig),
    2172(Fig)
    subunit composition 1439
  tax gene of HTLV-1 mechanism 1565
  T cell second signal 2149
Interleukin-2 (IL-2) receptor inducing
  factor (IL-2RIF), *see* Interleukin-12
  (IL-12)
Interleukin-3 (IL-3) 1442–1445
  age-related changes 60
  alternative names 1442
  antagonists 1444
  antibodies 1444
  assay 697(Table), 1444
  binding to IL-3Rα 1443
  bioassays 1444
  Chagas' disease, role in 526(Table)
  clinical significance 1444–1445
  as colony-stimulating factor 596, 1442–
    1443
  discovery/historical aspects 1442
  eosinophil function regulation 823, 824
  functions 504
  genes 1443
  genes induced by 1443
  glycosylation 1443
  GM-CSF synergistic actions 1444
  half-life 1444
  as hematopoietic factor 1442, 1442–
    1443, 1444, 1459
  IL-6 synergistic action 1459
  leishmaniasis 1445
  levels required 1444
  mast cell differentiation 1668
  mast cell production 1442, 1443, 1444
  myelopoiesis 375, 1442–1443
  physiology 1444
  production 1444
    bone marrow stromal cells 1444
  sources 1444
  structure 1443
    Ala-Pro motif 1443
  in tumorigenesis 1445
  variant 1445
Interleukin-3 (IL-3) receptor 454(Table),
    598, 1443–1444, 1446–1451
  AIC2A protein (murine β subunit) 1446,
    1450(Fig)
  AIC2B 1446, 1450(Fig)
  apoptosis prevention 1448
  β common (β$_c$) chain 1443, 1447
    amino acid sequence 1450(Fig)
    structure 1450(Fig)
  cDNA 1446
  dimerization of β subunit 1447
  DUK-1 (human α subunit) 1446
  eosinophils 823

Interleukin-3 (IL-3) receptor (*continued*)
  GM-CSF competition 1446
  high-affinity 1443, 1446
  IL-3 binding 1443
  KH97 (human β subunit) 1446
  low affinity (IL-3Rα) 1443, 1446
  numbers per cell 1446
  signal transduction 1443–1444, 1447–
    1448
    JAK2 kinase pathway 1443–1444,
      1447–1448, 1449(Fig)
    proliferative response 1448
    receptor subdomains 1448
    STAT5 role 1443–1444, 1447
    subunit requirements 1447
  structure 1446–1447, 1447(Fig),
    1450(Fig)
    human 1446–1447, 1447(Fig)
    murine 1446, 1447(Fig)
  SUT-1 (α subunit) 1446
  WSXWS motif 1446, 1448(Fig)
Interleukin-4 (IL-4) 1451–1453
  age-related changes 60
  allergic rhinitis 2123
  assay 697(Table)
  B cell anergy reversal 107, 108
  B cell growth regulation 1452
  B cell proliferation 2020, 2150
  as B cell stimulatory factor 1061, 1452
  Chagas' disease, role in 526(Table)
  c-*maf* expression induction 1451, 1453
  downregulation, in BALB/c mice in
    leishmaniasis 1548
  downregulation of IL-2R β chain 1453
  effect on endothelial cells 806
  eosinophil recruitment 1452
  functions 706, 1451(Table), 1452, 1453
  genes 1451
    transcriptional regulation 1451
  germinal center generation 994
  in GVHD 1016
  high-affinity binding sites 1453
  Ig class switching 1205
    to IgE 1452, 1490
  IgE synthesis 1061, 1171, 1452, 1490
  IgG1 secretion 1424
  IL-1ra synthesis enhanced 705
  IL-13 actions similarity 1490
  IL-13 functional properties comparison
    1491, 1491(Table)
  immunotherapy
    allergic disease 1356
    autoimmune disease 1359
    fungal infections 961
  inhibitors 705
  leukemia therapy 1559
  lymphatic filariasis 914
  MHC class II expression 1452
  mice deficient 1452
  molecular mechanisms of action 1452–
    1453
  mRNA appearance 1491
  nitric oxide synthesis prevention 1549
  oral tolerance induction 1894, 1895
  production 1451
    T$_H$2 cells 1060, 1451, 2332
  recombinant 1356, 1451
  rheumatoid arthritis 2114
  signal transduction, *see under*
    Interleukin-4 (IL-4) receptor
  soluble, immunotherapy 961
  storage, in mast cells 253
  T cell growth 503
  T cell/thymocyte differentiation 1452
  T$_H$1 and T$_H$2 memory cell proliferation
    2332
  T$_H$2 cell differentiation 1451, 1452,
    1452–1453
  T$_H$2 cells producing 1060, 1451, 2332
  transgenic mice overexpressing 1452
  UV-induced changes 1944

Interleukin-4 (IL-4) receptor 454(Table), 1453–1455
  α chain 1451
    IL-13Rα dimerization 1490
    in IL-13R complex 1489
  alternative splicing in 1454
  cloning 1454
  complexes, models 1454(Fig)
  expression 1451
  γc chain 1451, 1454
    see also Common γ (γc) chain
  gene, structure 1454(Fig)
  high-affinity (IL-4Rα) 1454
  IL-13R as second receptor 1489
  signal transduction 1452–1453, 1454–1455, 1491
    insulin receptor substrate (IRS-2) 1452, 1454–1455
    JAK1/JAK3 and STAT6 pathway 1452, 1454, 1455
  soluble, function 715
  structure 1453–1454, 1489(Fig)
  type I 1454
  type II 1454
  WSXWS motif 1454
Interleukin-5 (IL-5) 1456–1458
  antibodies 1456
  assay 697(Table)
  cDNA 1456
  as colony-stimulating factor 598
  eosinophil chemotaxis 820–821
  eosinophil function regulation 823, 824
  eosinophil production control 1456
  gene 1457
    conserved lymphoid element 0 (CLE0) 1457
    disruption 1456
    regulation and repressor 1457
  glycosylation 1456
  lymphatic filariasis 914
  mice deficient 1456
  overexpression 1456
  receptor 1456, 1457
    α chain 454(Table), 1457
    β chain 1456, 1457
    eosinophils 823
    high-affinity 1457
    JAK2 kinase activation 823
  signal transduction 823
  structure 1456
  transgenic mice 1456
Interleukin-6 (IL-6) 1458–1461
  in acute phase response 1459
  antibodies 1458
    autoimmune disease therapy 1359
  assay 697(Table)
  autoimmune disease 1460, 1460(Table)
  B cell maturation 1458
  B cell stimulation 504
  cDNA 1458
  Chagas' disease, role in 526(Table)
  characteristics 1458(Table)
  coccidioidomycosis 589
  C-reactive protein (CRP) synthesis control 663
  in disease 1460, 1460(Table)
  feline 893
  functions/actions 720, 1458, 1458–1460, 1459(Fig)
    acute phase response 1459
    hematopoiesis 1459
    immune response 1458–1459, 1830, 1831(Table)
    nervous system 1460, 1830, 1831(Table)
  gene 1458
  germinal center generation 994
  IgA synthesis enhanced 1458
  increase
    exercise effect 846
    inflammatory bowel disease 1379
  inflammatory actions 1378, 1459

Interleukin-6 (IL-6) (continued)
  knockout mice 18, 1460
  monoclonal hypergammaglobulinemia pathogenesis 1163
  myeloma growth 1163, 1460
  myelopoiesis 375
  in neoplasia 1460, 1460(Table)
  periodontal disease 1891
  pituitary gland production 1830
  in polyclonal hypergammaglobulinemia 1162–1163
  production
    dysregulation, polyclonal B cell activation 1460
    endothelial cells 806
    LTB₄ inducing 231
  receptor 454(Table), 721, 1461–1462
    ambivalence 706
    antibodies, autoimmune disease therapy 1359
    cDNA 1461
    expression by cells/cell lines 1461
    gp130 protein 1461, 1462
    mouse 1461
    number per cell 1461
    soluble, see below
    structure/sequence 1461
  recombinant 1458, 1459
  rheumatoid arthritis 2114
  soluble receptors 1462
    function 715
    in vivo functions 718
  structure 1458
  T cell differentiation 1458
  T cell help for B cells 1061
  T_H2 cells in Peyer's patches 1777
  transgenic mice 1460
  urinary tract infection pathogenesis 2453
Interleukin-6 (IL-6) family, leukemia inhibitory factor (LIF) 1560
Interleukin-7 (IL-7) 1462–1466
  assay 697(Table)
  B cell differentiation 1463
  in B lymphopoiesis 1465
  cDNA 1462–1463
  functions 1462, 1463–1465
  γc-deficient mice and effect 2171
  human/mouse homology 1463
  identification/discovery 1462
  null mutant mice 1463, 1464(Fig), 1465
  production, thymic epithelium 2236
  receptor 454(Table), 1441
    γc chain 1463
    γc gene mutation 1464, 2171
    IL-7Rα 1462, 1463, 1465
    IL-7Rα null mutant 1463, 1464(Fig), 1465
    structure 1463
    tissue expression 1463
  signal transduction pathway 1464, 1465(Fig)
    role in VDJ recombination 1464
  structure 1462–1463
  T cell differentiation 1463
  tissue expression 1463
Interleukin-8 (IL-8) 1466–1471
  alternative names 1466
  amino acid sequences 1466, 1467(Fig)
  antagonists 1470
  antibodies 1470
  assay 697(Table)
  biochemical properties 1466
  biological activities
    experimental animals 1468–1470
    in vitro 1468, 1469(Fig)
  bronchoalveolar fluid 1470
  chemotaxis by 1466, 1468
    neutrophils 1469, 1470
  clinical significance 1470
  dimerization 1466
  elevated
    diseases associated 1470(Table)

Interleukin-8 (IL-8) (continued)
  elevated (continued)
    inflammatory bowel disease 1380
  genes 1466
    expression 1467
    targeted disruption 1470
  G protein activation 1467
  haptotactic action 1468
  Helicobacter pylori infection 1057
  mutant 1466
  production 1467
  receptor 454(Table), 1467–1467
    amino acid sequences 1468(Fig)
    cDNA 1467
    expression 1467, 1468(Table)
    type A and type B 1467, 1468(Fig)
    type II, chemokines binding 530
  signaling pathway 1467–1468, 1469(Fig)
  therapeutic applications 1470
  transgenic mice 1470
  urinary levels 1470
  urinary tract infection pathogenesis 2453
  see also Chemokines
Interleukin-9 (IL-9) 1471–1475
  antiapoptotic effect 1474
  biological activities 1473–1474, 1473(Table)
    neuronal cells 1474
  CD40 cooperative effect 1474
  cDNA 1471, 1474
    human/mouse homology 1471
  characteristics 1472(Table)
  effect on B cells 1473
  erythroid burst-promoting activity 1473
  gene 1471
  gene expression regulation 1471
  GM-CSF synergy 1473
  leukemia development 1474
  lymphoma pathogenesis 1474
  mast cell-enhancing activity 1473
  molecular biology 1471–1472
  receptor
    characteristics 1472(Table)
    molecular biology 1471–1472
    mouse 1472
    WSEWE motif 1472
  signal transduction 1472–1473, 1472(Fig)
  as T cell growth factor 1473
  transgenic mice 1474
Interleukin-10 (IL-10) 1475–1478
  ADCC modulation 170
  antibodies, fungal infections 961
  assay 697(Table)
  B7 downregulation 2262
  B cell differentiation induction 1476–1477
  B cell proliferation 2020
  B cell secretion of, CD40 ligation action 485
  biological actions 706, 1476–1477
  cDNA 1475
  cellular sources 1476
  Chagas' disease, role in 526(Table)
  effect on macrophage/monocytes 1476
  effect on NK cells 1476
  functions 706, 1476–1477
  gene expression regulation 1476
  gene structure 1475–1476
  germinal center generation 994
  GVHD prevention 2262
  IFNγ synthesis inhibition 1476
  IL-12 production modulation 1484
  immunotherapy, autoimmune disease 1359
  increase, SLE 2259
  knockout mice, inflammatory bowel disease model 1382
  lymphatic filariasis 914
  macrophage deactivation 1648
  MHC class II downregulation on T cells 1476

Interleukin-10 (IL-10) (*continued*)
  MHC class II expression on B cells 1476–1477
  mouse and human cDNAs 1475
  mRNA 2263
  oral tolerance induction 1894
  physical properties 1475
  production
    immune complex-induced 1224
    T$_H$2 cells 1476
  receptor 1477
    gene 1477
    mouse and human 1477
  signal transduction 1477
  in T cell anergy 110, 2263
  T$_H$1 cytokine synthesis inhibition 1476
  Toxoplasma gondii infection 2383
  UV-induced changes 1944
Interleukin-11 (IL-11) 1478–1483
  assay 697(Table)
  biological activities 1480–1481
    in experimental models 1482(Table)
    in vitro 1480(Table)
    in vivo (normal animals) 1481(Table)
  cancer trials 1481
  cDNA 1478
    human/mouse homology 1478
  characteristics 1479(Table)
  clinical significance 1481
  functions 1478
  gene 1478
  gene expression control 1478
  gp130 signal 1478, 1479
  hematopoietic effects 1482(Table)
  receptor 1478–1479
    characteristics 1479(Table)
    IL-11Rα genes 1479
  signal transduction 1479–1480, 1479(Fig)
    kinases 1479–1480
    phosphatases 1480
    transcription factors 1480
  therapeutic applications 1481
    administration 599
    autoimmune disease 1359
    inflammatory disorders 1481
Interleukin-12 (IL-12) 187, 1483–1488
  adjuvant actions 1487
  in AIDS 1487
  alternative names 1483
  antibodies 1484, 1487
  assays 1487–1488
  autoimmune disease pathogenesis 278, 1487
  in autoimmunity 1487
  brucellosis 384
  CD28 signaling 1486
  cells producing 1484
  cells responsive to 1485–1487
    regulation 1487
  Chagas' disease, role in 526(Table)
  characteristics 1485(Table)
  competitive inhibition by murine IL-12(p40)$_2$ 1484
  cryptosporidiosis 677
  delayed-type hypersensitivity 739
  discovery 1483
  downregulation, by measles virus 1915
  host resistance to *Legionella pneumophila* 1544
  IFNγ production
    by NK cells 1486, 1813–1814
    regulation 1422
  IL-15 synergy 1494
  immune modulation by 1487
  immunotherapy in fungal infections 961
  impaired production, CD40L absence 486
  inhibitors 706
  in innate resistance 1484, 1486, 1487
  in NOD mice 1396
  oral tolerance decreased 1896

Interleukin-12 (IL-12) (*continued*)
  p35 1484, 1488
  p40 chain 1484
    antibodies 1488
    characteristics 1485(Table)
    excess 1484
    murine, IL-12 inhibition 1484
    production 1484, 1484–1485
      regulation 1484
      stimuli/modulators 1484–1485, 1486(Fig), 1486(Table)
  receptor
    characteristics 1485(Table)
    expression 1487
    IL-12Rβ$_2$ 1487
    structure 1484
  recombinant, oral administration 1892
  secretion process 702
  signal transduction 1484
  structure 1484
  tumor immunity induction 1487
  UV-induced changes 1944
  in viral infections 1487
Interleukin-13 (IL-13) 1489–1492
  assay 697(Table)
  atopic diseases 1490
  B cell phenotype change 1490
  biological actions 1490, 1491(Table)
  characteristics 1489
  chemokine production inhibition 1490
  cytokine production inhibition 1490
  effect on B cells 1490, 1491(Table)
  effect on endothelial cells 806, 1490–1491
  effect on monocytes 1490–1491
  effect on T cells 1491, 1491(Table)
  functions 1489
  gene 1489
  IL-4 actions similarity (not synergistic) 1490
  IL-4 functional properties comparison 1491, 1491(Table)
  in inflammatory response 1491
  isoforms and alternative splicing 1489
  mRNA appearance 1491
  production 1491(Table)
    T cells 1491
  receptor 1489
    α chain 1454, 1489
    α chain expression 1490
    expression 1489, 1491
    structure 1489(Fig)
  signal transduction 1491
Interleukin-15 (IL-15) 1492–1495
  biological effects 1494
  cells expressing 1492–1493
  characteristics 1493(Table)
  discovery 1492
  functions 1492
  IL-12 synergy 1494
  knockout mice 1494
  mRNA expression 1492–1493
  physiological roles 1494
  receptor 1492, 1493–1494
    α chain 1493, 1494
      characteristics 1493(Table)
    β and/or Gc chain absence 1494
    β and Gc chains 1494
    IL-15 binding affinities 1493(Table)
  rheumatoid arthritis pathogenesis 1494
  signaling pathway 1494
  T cell chemotaxis 538
Interleukin-16 (IL-16) 2167
  serotonin-induced secretion 2167
  T cell chemotaxis 538
Internalin 1594
Internal ribosome entry sites (IRES), retroviral vectors 2086–2087
Interphase 2018
Interphotoreceptor retinoid-binding protein (IRBP) 870
  uveitis treatment 1897

Intestinal antigens, absorption 190
Intestinal enteropathy, GVHD association 1860
Intestinal flora, *see under* Gastrointestinal tract
Intestinal lymphangiectasia 1287
Intestinal lymphocytes, inflammatory bowel disease 1377
Intimin 843
Intracellular tyrosine-based activation motifs (ITAMs), *see* ITAM motifs
Intraepithelial lymphocytes (IELs) 189, 1249, 1778, 1779, 1781, 1782
  γδTCR 1779, 1782
  integrins 1778, 1784
  in MALT 1249
  proliferation 1779, 1782
  role 1779
Intramolecular spreading, *see* Determinant spreading, intramolecular
Intravenous immunoglobulin 965, 1347, 1964
  DiGeorge syndrome 763
  idiopathic thrombocytopenic purpura 1180
  immunodeficiency therapy 966
  indications 1967
  mechanism of action 1347–1348
  preparation methods 965–966, 1967
  Pseudomonas aeruginosa infections 2045
Invariant chain (Ii) 196, 354, 452(Table), 1043, 1495–1498
  absence 1496
  in antigen presentation 459, 1496, 1497, 2232
  antigen processing in B cells 354
  CLIP region, *see* CLIP region
  coexpression with MHC class II molecules 1496
  cysteine-rich thyroglobulin-like domain 1497
  degradation 196, 1043
  expression 1496
  function 1496–1497, 2232
  functional domains 1497
  functional redundancy 1497
  gene 1495, 1497
    exons 1497
  gene expression regulation 1496
  isoforms 1497
  isolation 1495
  knockout mice 1497
  in MHC class II transport 1496
  p31 and p41 isoforms 1497
  structure 1495–1496, 1496(Fig)
  synthesis 331
Invasin, *Yersinia* 2514
Invertebrate immune system 1498–1502
  alloaggregation 1499
  blood cells 1499
  cell adhesion molecules 1500
  cell surface markers 1499
  cellular immune response 1499–1500, 1948
  chemotaxis 1501
  complement-related proteins 1501
  C-reactive protein 1500
  cytokines 1501
  defense responses 1498
  effector molecules 1498, 1500–1501
  encapsulation 1499–1500
  erythrocyte lysis 1501
  glucan-binding proteins 1498
  humoral immune response 1499–1500, 1948
  immunoglobulins 1500
  lectins 1500, 1538
  lymphocyte-like cells 1499
  macrophage-like cells 1499
  memory in alloaggression 1499
  phagocytosis 1499, 1500
  phylogeny 1947–1948

Invertebrate immune system (*continued*)
  plasma clotting 1500
  prophenoloxidase activating system 1500
  recognition molecules 1500
  regulation of responses 1501
  scavenging cells 1499
  serine proteases 1500, 1501
Invertebrates
  circulatory systems 1947
  viruses 1502
[131]Iodide 2054, 2433
Iodine, thyroid autoimmunity induction
    2314
  experimental 2311
[125]Iodine 2054
Ion channels
  anion, in erythrocytes (band 3) 91, 840
  calcium, *see* Calcium channels
  CD antigens as 73
  defensins forming 1721
  erythrocyte membrane 837, 840
  potassium 1850
Ion exchange chromatography (IEX) 2037
Ionizing radiation 2050
  see also Radiation
Ion pumps, in red cell membranes 837,
    840
'I' region genes 1041
Ir genes, *see* Immune response (Ir) genes
Iridoviridae 1502, 1504
  classification and characteristics
    1503(Table)
Iridovirus 1502–1505
  assembly 1504
  characteristics 1502–1504, 1503(Table)
  DNA 1503
    two-step replication 1504
  host immune response 1504
  host range 1503
  iridescence 1502
  phagocytosis 1503, 1504
  proteins 1503
  replication 1503–1504
  structure 1502–1503
Iritis, in leprosy 873
Iron 1505–1507
  chelators, oxygen-dependent phagocytic
    killing 1717
  deficiency, *see* Iron deficiency
  depletion, lactoferrin mechanism of
    action 1724
  excess, *see* Iron, overload
  fortification 1506
  overload, effect on immunity
    1505(Table), 1507
  redistribution during infections 1505–
    1506
  requirement 1505, 2390
    bacterial 1724
    Legionella pneumophila 1543
    Yersinia 2514
  sources, in phagocytes 1717
  status, effect on immune response 1505–
    1506, 1505(Table)
  TfR expression regulation 2391
  uptake, transferrin receptor role 2391
Iron-binding protein (IRP), TfR binding
    2391
Iron deficiency 1284, 1505, 1870
  anemia 1505
  cytokine production and 1507
  effect on immune response 1505–1506,
    1505(Table), 1870
    cell-mediated immunity 1506
    humoral 1506
  maternal 1506
  susceptibility to infection 1506
Irradiation, *see* Radiation; Ultraviolet light
IRS, *see* Insulin receptor substrate (IRS)
Ir-Tg 2310
Isaac's syndrome (acquired neuromyotonia)
    1850

ISCOM (immuno-stimulating complex)
    1507–1510
  adjuvant actions 1507–1508
  electron microscopy 1508–1509
  HIV 1508
  immunogenicity of antigens 1509
  influenza virus 1509
  mycobacterial hsp60 2231
  preparation of antigen complexes 1508–
    1509, 1508(Fig)
  protective immunity induced 1509,
    1509(Table)
  rationale for 1508
  vaccines 1508
    storage 1509
Iscoprep 703™ 1508
Islet cell antibodies 262(Table), 263, 1675
  cytoplasmic
    animal models of IDDM 1393
    diabetes mellitus (human) 1401
  surface, animal models of IDDM 1393
Islet cell antigens 1399, 1401
Islets, *see* Pancreatic islets
Isoantibodies 1674
Isoelectric focusing (IEF) 987, 1510–1514
  agarose 1512
  anticonvection devices 1512
  artifactual results 1514
  cathodic drift 1512
  columns 1511–1512
    advantages 1512
    methodology 1511
  pH gradients 1511
  polyacrylamide gel 1512, 1513(Fig)
    two-dimensional electrophoresis 1513
  poly amino carboxylic acids 1511
  principles 1510–1511
  protein size/charge determination 2035
  quality control 1514
  as steady-state procedure 1511
  uses 1512–1514
    Ig microheterogeneity 1512–1513
    protein microheterogeneity 1512
    quality control of products 1513
Isoelectric point (pI) 1510, 1511
Isoelectric precipitation, proteins 2036
Isoerythrolysis, neonatal, in cats 894
Isogenic strains 1369, 1371
Isoprinosine 2259
  as immunopotentiating agent 1347
Isotype 1514–1516
  complement activation 1515
  distribution 1515
  heavy chain 1514
  Ig class switching 1515
  L chain 1514
  see also specific immunoglobulins; under
    Immunoglobulin
ITAMs (immunoreceptor tyrosine-based
    activation motifs) 888, 1194, 1299
  CD22 and sIg interaction 480
  in FcεRI 1669–1670
    mast cell degranulation mechanism
    1670
  Fc receptors 2032
  phosphorylation 1670
  polyclonal inhibitor action via 1980
  sequence 2324, 2324(Fig)
  T cell signal transduction 2324
  TCR 2324
ITIMs (immunoreceptor tyrosine-based
    inhibitor motifs) 888
ITK, signal transduction in T cell
    activation 2324
Ivermectin 1874
  onchocerciasis 874
IXN/A5 cell line 1463

J

J539 myeloma protein 150
Jack bean lectin 1535
JAK tyrosine kinases 701
  cytokine signal transduction 2032
  GM-CSF signal transduction 1021–1022
  IFNα/β signal transduction 1414
  IFNγ signal transduction 1423, 1427
  IL-10 signal transduction 1477
  IL-11 signal transduction 1479
  leukemia inhibitory factor (LIF) signaling
    1560–1561
JAK1 tyrosine kinase
  IFNγ signaling pathway 1423, 1427
  IL-2 signal transduction 1440–1441
  IL-4 signal transduction 1452, 1454,
    1455
  IL-9 signal transduction 1472
JAK2 tyrosine kinase
  IFNγ signaling pathway 1423, 1427
  IL-3 signal transduction 1443–1444,
    1447–1448, 1449(Fig)
  IL-5 pathway and eosinophil
    development 823
  IL-11 signal transduction 1480
JAK3 tyrosine kinase 109
  deficiency in SCID 1278, 2171–2172
  γc-mediated signaling 1441
  IL-2 signal transduction 1441, 2171–
    2172, 2172(Fig)
  IL-4 signal transduction 1452, 1454,
    1455, 1491
  IL-7 signal transduction 1464
  IL-9 signal transduction 1472
  mice deficient in 2172
  mutation, disease 1441, 1464
  negative selection of thymocytes 2356
  in X-linked SCID 2171
Janus tyrosine kinase family 710, 2031,
    2171
  see also JAK tyrosine kinases
Japanese encephalitis (JE) 926
  vaccination 931
Japanese encephalitis (JE) virus 926
Jarisch–Herxheimer reaction 381
J chain 146, 1212, 1516–1518, 1784
  affinity for secretory component 2155
  antigenic determinants 1516
  B cell differentiation 1517
  cellular origin 1517
  characteristics 1516
  deficiency 1517
  evolution 1516
  expression 2155
  fold into β barrel 1516
  free form 1517
  functions 1517, 1784, 2155
  gene 1517
  IgD-producing cells 1517
  IgG-producing cells 1517
  mRNA in invertebrates 1516
  polymeric IgA, *see* Immunoglobulin A
    (IgA)
  polymeric IgM, *see* Immunoglobulin M
    (IgM)
  regulation 2155–2156
  structure 1516–1517
  synthesis 158
  in T cells 1517
  vertebrate species 1516
JC virus 1988
  evasive strategies 1990
  host immune response 1990
  infection 1989–1990, 1989(Fig)
    see also Progressive multifocal
    leukoencephalopathy (PML)
  pathology 1989(Fig)
    see also Polyomavirus
Jejunal tumors 1636
JE (murine MCP-1) 1748, 1749

Jenner, E. 256, 1997, 2456
Jerne, N. 1338
Jerne plaque assay 1506
JNK, *see* JUN N-terminal kinase (JNK)
Jo-1 antibody 2118
Job's syndrome (hyper-IgE syndrome) 1161–1162
Joining chain, *see* J chain
Joining (J) segments, *see under* Immunoglobulin
Joints, antigen, hsp65 mimicry 34
Jones–Mote hypersensitivity (transient) 738
J segments, *see under* Immunoglobulin
Junin virus 233, 234, 235
JUN N-terminal kinase (JNK)
  activation by CD40 ligation 484
  JNK-1
    T cell activation 2325
    T cell receptor signaling 2328
  JNK-2
    T cell activation 2325
    T cell receptor signaling 2328
  T cell anergy 109
  TNF receptor signaling 2347
Juvenile rheumatoid arthritis, oral collagen administration 1898

K

Kala-azar (visceral leishmaniasis) 1547
Kallidin 1520
Kallikrein 585, 603, 1518
  complement activation 1520
  formation 1519
  functions/actions 1520
  increase, cardiopulmonary bypass 1520
  inhibition/inhibitors 1520
  overexpression, transgenic mice 1518
Kallikrein–kinin system 1518–1521
  activation and amplification 1519–1520
  in cardiopulmonary bypass 1520
  coagulation system 1519
  components 1519(Table)
  in disease 1520–1521
  experimental models 1520
  regulation 1520
Kallistatin 1518
Kaposi's sarcoma 7, 8, 1090, 1091, 1884
  antigens 1360
  endemic 1090
  HHV-8 as causative agent 1091
  induction 1360
  interferon α therapy 1416
Kaposi's sarcoma-associated human herpesvirus (KSHV), *see* Human herpesvirus 8 (HHV-8)
Kartagener's syndrome, in dogs 413
Katayama fever 2139
Kawasaki's disease 2242
  therapy 1347
Kell antigen
  blood transfusions 2400
  hemolytic disease of newborn (HDN) 1071
Kell (K) blood group 837
Keratan sulfate (KS) 862, 906
Keratinization 750
Keratinocyte(s) 2190
  antigen uptake 188–189
  class II MHC expression 188
  contact hypersensitivity 1178
  delayed type hypersensitivity 740
  IL-15 production 1493
  response to calcitriol 2495
  UV-induced changes 1944
  in vitiligo 2502
Keratinocyte growth factor (KGF; FGF-7) 907
Keratitis, onchocercal 1873

Keratocytes (helmet cells) 834
Keto-deoxy-octulosonic acid (KDO) 424
Ketotifen 683
Keyhole limpet hemocyanin (KLH)
  B cells as APCs 354
  cholera toxin with, T_H1/T_H2 response 1896
  conditioning experiments 338
  oral tolerance 1893
  response, inulin effect 428
Keystone virus 391
Ki-1 antigen (CD30) 447(Table), 2148
Ki-24 antigen (CD70) 451(Table)
KIAA0052 protein 1118
Kidney
  in fish 922
  infections, *see* Pyelonephritis
  mercury toxicity 1689
  SLE 2256
  transplantation, *see* Renal transplantation
  see also entries beginning Renal
Kilham rat virus 1396
Killer cell inhibitory receptors (KIRs), on NK cells 1809, 1811–1812
Killer (K) cells 505
  in dogs 413
  see also Antibody-dependent cellular cytotoxicity (ADCC); Cytotoxic T lymphocytes (CTL); Natural killer (NK) cells
Killing mechanisms, *see* Microbicidal mechanisms; *under* Cytotoxic T lymphocytes (CTL)
Kinase inhibitors, LFA-1 activation 1611
Kininogen
  high molecular weight, *see* High molecular weight kininogen (HMWK)
  low molecular weight (LK) 1519
Kininogenases 254
Kinin system, *see* Kallikrein–kinin system
Kiwi fruit, allergy 950
Klebsiella, species 1522
Klebsiella pneumoniae 1522
  ankylosing spondylitis association 1522
  antibodies 1522, 1740–1741
  capsule 1522, 1522–1523, 1523, 1523(Fig)
  characteristics 1522
  endotoxin 1523
  evasive strategies 1522–1523
  extracellular toxic complex (ETC) 1523
  growth in culture 1522
  histopathology 1522
  host immune response 1522
  infection 1523
    animal models 1522
    predisposing factors 1522
    route 1739–1740
  inflammation and chronic disease 1741
  K antigens 1522
  molecular mimicry
    ankylosing spondylitis 1522, 1696, 1737–1741
    anterior uveitis 869
    proteins and sequences involved 1738(Fig), 1739
    see also Ankylosing spondylitis
  nitrogenase 1739, 1739(Fig), 1741
  O antigens 1522
  plasmid 1522
  pulA (pullanase) 1739, 1739(Fig)
  pulD secretion protein (DRDE) 1739, 1739(Fig)
  vaccine development 1523
  virulence factors 1522–1523, 1523
Kleihauer technique 1072
Klinokinesis 534
Klotz equation 44
Knockout animals 2404
  techniques 1524–1528
  see also Transgenic animals
Knockout mice 982, 1268, 1275–1276, 1524–1528

Knockout mice (*continued*)
  $α_4β7$ integrin 1098
  adhesion molecules, effect on leukocyte recruitment 2060, 2062(Table)
  advantages 1275–1276
  applications 1526–1527
  ataxia telangiectasia 249
  bcl-2 1582
  CD5 474
  CD8 233
  CD18 1566
  CD40L 486
  CD120a (TNFR) 2346
  compensation for defect 1276
  disadvantages 1276
  floxed and disrupted alleles 1527
  $Gα_{12}$ 1383
  G-CSF 1019
  generation 982, 983(Fig), 1524–1527
    conditional gene disruption, *see below*
    by homologous recombination 1524–1525, 1524(Fig)
    by modified embryonic stem cells 1525–1526, 1525(Fig)
    selection markers 1524
  genes deleted 1275(Table)
  GM-CSF gene 375
  granzymes 1026
  H2 class II molecules 1040, 1044
  ICAM-1 1566, 1566(Table)
  IFNγ receptor 1428
  IL-1 1435
  IL-1 receptors 1433
  IL-2 1438, 1494
    inflammatory bowel disease model 1382
  IL-2Rα 1494
  IL-6 18, 1460
  IL-10, inflammatory bowel disease model 1382
  IL-15 1494
  inducible nitric oxide synthase (iNOS) 1860
  integrins 1098, 1408–1409
  invariant chain (Ii) 1497
  J chain 146
  5-lipoxygenase (5-LOX) 232
  L-selectin 1098, 1566, 1619
  μMT 353–354
  NOD and heavy chain 1402
  perforin 233
  second generation (conditional gene disruption) 1525(Fig), 1526(Fig), 1527
    Cre recombinase 1525(Fig), 1526(Fig), 1527
    tissue-specific 1526(Fig), 1527
  selectins 1566, 1566(Table)
  selection markers 1524
  selection method 1275
  TNF receptor (CD120a) 2346
Knockout techniques 1524–1528
Koch, R. 1336–1337
Koch phenomenon 319, 1795
Kol IgG1 1333
Kolmogorov–Smirnov test 2214
Korean hemorrhagic fever 391
Kruskal–Wallis test 2212
Ku antigens 126, 768, 2053
  antibodies 126, 131
Kupffer cells 1591, 1755
  motility loss 540
  virus infection of 2486
Kveim reaction 1024, 2135
Kveim–Siltzbach test 2135
Kwashiorkor 1869

L

L1 protein, *see* Calprotectin

L3T4, *see* CD4
L5 antigen, *see* Lewis^x (Le^x) antigen
La (SS-B) antigen 127, 2184
  antibodies 132, 1676, 2183, 2184
    SLE 2257
  structure and distribution 2184
Labeled anti-immunoglobulin reagents 142
Labeling
  affinity, *see* Affinity labeling
  antibodies, *see* Antibodies, labeling
  DNA probes for Southern blotting 2196
    end-labeling 2196
  DNA/RNA, Northern blotting 1865
  enzyme, *see* Enzyme labeling
  for Western blotting 2506
  see also Biotin; Fluorochrome labeling;
    Radiolabeling
Labor, delayed, NSAIDs causing 120
LACK 1548, 1550
La Crosse virus 391
β-Lactam antibiotics
  adverse reactions 1052
  haptenation 779, 1052
Lactate dehydrogenase (LDH), C4
    isoenzyme on sperm 1373–1374
Lactate dehydrogenase (LDH) virus 2350
  macrophage infection 2486
'Lactoferricin' 1724
Lactoferrin 1672–1673, 1717, 1723–1724
  bacteriostatic effects 1724, 1939
  forms 1724
  mechanism of action 1724, 1857, 1939
  neutrophils 1857
  in saliva 1889
Lactonization, catalytic antibody reaction
    441(Fig)
Lactoperoxidase (LPO) 1716, 1780
Lactosylceramide (CDw17) 447(Table)
Lactrodectism 2472
lacZ gene, FACS measurement 939
Lagomorpha (order) 2046
Lagomorphs
  immune complex processing 183
  see also Rabbit; Rabbit immune system
Lagos bat virus 2099
LAK cells, *see* Lymphokine-activated killer
    (LAK) cells
LAM-1, *see* L-selectin
Lambda bacteriophage 2016
Lambert–Eaton myasthenic syndrome
    1835–1836, 1847, 1849–1850
  clinical features 1849
  HLA association 1835, 1850
  pathogenesis 1835, 1849–1850
  small cell lung cancer 1835, 1842, 1849–
    1850
Lamellipodium 533, 1760
Lamina propria 189, 1601, 1782
  B cells 1782
  dendritic cells 745, 746
  high endothelial venules (HEV) 1099
  as mucosal effector site 1778
  in pigs 1994
  plasma cells 1778
  T cells 1778–1779, 1782
Laminins 864–865
  production, by fibroblasts 907
Landsteiner, K. 1337, 1535
Langerhans, P. 1528
Langerhans cells 175, 745, 1226, 1528–
    1532, 1757
  abnormal, UV radiation causing 1531
  activation 638
  adhesion molecules expressed 638, 1529–
    1530, 1529(Table)
  allergic contact dermatitis 787, 1530
  allergic rhinitis 2124
  antigen capture/uptake 188, 1207
  antigen presentation, in skin 2190
  antigen-presenting cells 750, 1530–1531,
    1531(Fig)
  antigen processing 188, 638, 1530

Langerhans cells (*continued*)
  atopic allergy 252
  Birbeck granules 1528, 1528(Fig), 1529,
    2190
    function 1530–1531
  bypass, tolerance induction 2191
  CD1a expression 1530, 1530(Fig), 2190
  CD4+ T cell interactions 638
  cell surface markers 1528, 1529–1530,
    1529(Table)
  circulation, skin 2190
  contact hypersensitivity 638, 740, 1178,
    1530, 2191
  cytokine profile 1530
  delayed-type hypersensitivity 739, 1530
  depletion
    in motheaten mice 1269
    UV light effect 1531
  distribution 745
  functions 1530–1531
  historical aspects 1528–1529,
    1529(Table)
  HIV infection 1531
  HPV infections 1908
  maturation 2191
    see also Interdigitating cells
  'mature' 1530
  MHC antigens 1710
  MHC class II expression 1530, 2190
  migration 188, 189(Fig), 1530
  in mononuclear phagocyte system (MPS)
    1756–1757
  nasal mucosa in allergic rhinitis 2124
  origin 1528
  precursors 745, 1530
  receptors downregulated by 746
  skin 2190
  structure 1528(Fig)
  UV-induced changes 2191
  UV-irradiated 1943
    T_H1 activation failure 1943
  as veiled cells 1604
    see also Veiled cells
  virus infection of 2486
  see also Dendritic cells
Langerin plot 166
Lantibiotics 2015
Large granular lymphocytes (LGL) 1532–
    1535, 1628
  CD8 expression 1533
  cytokines released 1534
  cytolysis by 505, 1533–1534
  defects 1534
  development 1534(Fig)
  FcγR 888
    function 890
  functions 1533–1534
  granules 1532
  growth regulation 1534
  hypofunction in Chédiak–Higashi
    syndrome 1534
  leukemia 1534
  lymphocytosis 1633
  morphology 1532–1533, 1533(Fig)
  NK cell differences 1533
  phenotypic markers 1533
  response to IL-2 1534
    see also Cytotoxic T lymphocytes (CTL);
    Natural killer (NK) cells; T cell
    receptor (TCR), γδ
Laser
  high sensitive 'microspot' immunoassays
    1256
  leukocyte viability assessment 2475
Laser-based flow cytometry 944, 945
  dual-laser/four-color 947
  single-laser/two-color 946–947, 946(Fig)
Lassa virus 233, 234, 235
Latency-associated peptide (β-LAP), in
    TGFβ 2393
Latency-associated transcripts (LATs) 1085

Latent infection membrane proteins, *see*
    entries beginning LMP
Latent TGFβ-binding protein (LTBP) 2393
Late-phase response
  atopy 253, 253(Fig), 254
  food allergy 948
  inflammation 253, 253(Fig)
Latex 681
  as allergen 67(Table)
  allergy 67(Table), 681, 2122
  particles 141
Latex agglutination, autoantibody
    detection 260
Law of Mass Action 44, 165–166
Lazy leukocyte syndrome 543
LB2 monoclonal antibodies (to ICAM-1)
    804
Lbw genes 2254
Lck 470
  gene 558
  see also p56^lck
LDL-apheresis 1252
Leach phenotype 837
LECAM-1, *see* L-selectin
LE cell(s) 128, 561
LE cell phenomenon 128, 130
LE cell test 128
Lecithinase, *see* Phospholipase C
'Lectin fold' superfamily 663
Lectin pathway, complement activation
    605, 606–607
Lectins 427, 1535–1541
  animal, structure 1537
  antibody differences 1535
  applications 1540–1541
  bacterial 1537, 1539(Table)
    inhibitors 1538
  bacterial invasion via 428, 1537
  biological activities 1537–1538
  blood group-specific 1536, 1541
  blood typing 1536, 1541
  carbohydrate interactions, bonds/sites
    1537, 1538(Fig)
  carbohydrate-recognition domain (CRD)
    1537, 1538(Fig)
  carbohydrate specificity 1537
  cell–cell recognition 1539(Table)
  C-type 217, 1537
    adhesive interactions 1539
    functions 1539(Table)
    on NK cells 1540
    see also Mannose-binding lectin (MBL);
    Selectins
  definition 1535
  endocytic 1539
  erythrocyte agglutination 58, 1541
  evolution 1950
  functions 1535, 1538–1540
  glycoprotein clearance/trafficking 1539
  hemagglutination 58, 1541
  historical aspects 1535–1536
  immobilized, glycoprotein detection 1540
  inhibition of action 1535
  in invertebrates 1500, 1538
  legume 1536
    carbohydrate interactions 1537
    structure 1536, 1536(Fig)
  as ligand in triad recognition systems
    1579
  on macrophage 428
  as mitogens 1537–1538, 1541
  oligosaccharide binding 1535, 1537
  P-type 1537
  as recognition determinants 1535,
    1539(Table)
  structures 1536–1537, 1536(Fig)
    subunits 1536
  S-type, *see* Galectins
  toxicity in culture 1538
  tumor cell killing 1538
  viral 1538
  see also Sialoadhesins

Legionella 1542–1546
Legionella pneumophila 1542–1546
  acquired immunity 1545
  A/J mouse model 1544–1545, 1545
  BALB/c mice 1544, 1545
  endoplasmic reticulum association 1543
  host immune response 1543–1545
    cellular 1544, 1545
    humoral 1544, 1545
    IFNγ and cytokines 1544
  ingestion by amebae 1542
  intracellular replication 1542
  iron availability affecting 1543
  lipopolysaccharide 424
  macrophage infection process 1542–
    1543, 1543(Fig)
  multiplication 1543
    inhibition by IFNγ 1543
    intracellular 1542
  mutants 1542
  opsonization, clearance 1545
  passive transfer of antibody 1545
  phagocytosis evasion 1542–1543
  primary lung infections, host defense
    1543–1545
  protease 2369, 2376
Legionnaires' disease 1542, 1543–1545
  immunocompromised patients 1544
  see also Legionella pneumophila
Legume lectins, *see* Lectins, legume
Leishmania
  amastigotes 1548, 1549
  antigens 1546–1548
  characteristics 1546–1548
  evasive strategies 1549–1550, 1917
  host immune response, *see under*
    Leishmaniasis
  intracellular parasite 1546, 1547
  killing by nitric oxide 1548–1549,
    1549(Fig), 1860
  life cycle 1548, 1548(Fig)
  lipophosphoglycan (LPG) 1548
    immune evasive 1549
  promastigotes 1548
  promastigote surface protease (PSP;
    gp63) 1548
  transmission cycle 1547–1548, 1547(Fig)
  vaccines 1343, 1550
    killed preparation with BCG 1550
    live parasite 1550
    route and delivery system 1550
Leishmania homolog of receptor for
  activated C kinase (LACK) 1548,
  1550
Leishmaniasis 1546–1551
  AIDS/HIV infection and 1550, 1920–
    1921
  animal reservoirs 1547
  clinical features 1547
  cutaneous (CL) 1546
    murine, immune response 1920
  diagnosis 1547
  diffuse cutaneous (DCL) 1547
  granuloma 1023, 1025
  IL-3 action 1445
  immune response 1548–1549
    age-related changes 60
    T cells 1919
    T$_H$1 cells 1548–1549
  incidence 1546
  mucocutaneous (MCL) 1547
    TNFα role 2439
  Old World and New World 1546
  reactivation in HIV infection 1550
  T$_H$1 cytokines 1227, 1548–1549
  treatment 1547
  vaccination, *see under Leishmania*
  visceral (VL) 1547
    as zoonosis 1547
Leishmanin 1547
Lek^a 1974
Lens

Lens (*continued*)
  antibodies 867
  MIF expression 1656
Lens-induced uveitis 867
Lentinan
  antimicrobial effects 428
  as antitumor agents 429–430
  immune stimulation by 428
Lentiviruses 2092, 2093(Table)
  antigenic variation 199, 200–201
  diseases 2096
  proteins 2090
  vectors 2090
Leporipoxvirus 1995(Table)
Lepra reaction 873
Lepromin reaction 1024
Leprosy 753, 1796–1797
  CD1b expression 462
  eye disease 873
  granuloma 753–754, 1023, 1024–1025
  lepromatous 753, 1025, 1025(Table),
    1796–1797
    absence of immune response 1796
    macrophage 1796
    T$_H$2 1797
  model 1868
  Ridley–Jopling scale 1025, 1025(Table)
  spectrum 1796
  susceptibility 1794
  tuberculoid 753, 1025, 1025(Table),
    1796
    failure of intact immune response 1796
  vaccination 1343
  see also Mycobacterium leprae
Leptospira 1551–1554
  in animals 1552
  antigens 1551–1552
  characteristics 1551–1552
  cultivation 1551
  host immune response 1553
  pathogenicity 1552–1553
  species 1551
  transmission 1552
  vaccines 1553
Leptospira biflexa 1551
Leptospira interrogans 1551, 1552
  geno-species 1551
Leptospirosis 1551–1552, 1552
  in animals 1552
  chronic 1552–1553
  clinical features 1552
  immunity 1553
  incubation phase 1552
LESTR/SDF-1 receptor 712
'Lethargic' (*lh*) mutation 1272
Leu8 antigen, *see* L-selectin
Leu13, B cell receptor signaling 351
Leu23 (CD69) 451(Table)
Leukapheresis, stem cell collection 1063
Leukemia 1554–1559, 1562
  acute 1554, 1554–1558
    chromosomal translocations 1556–
      1557
    classification 1554–1557, 1555(Table)
    FAB types 1554
    immunophenotype 1554–1556
    minimal residual disease detection
      1557–1558
    morphology and cytochemistry 1554
    prognostic indicators 1557
    TCR gene rearrangements 1556
    treatment 1559
  acute lymphoblastic (ALL) 1554, 1632–
    1633
    B-ALL 366, 800, 1555, 1556, 1557
    CALLA (CD10) antigen 800, 1555
    chromosomal translocations 554
    'common' 1555
    immunophenotypes 1555, 1555(Table)
    'null' 1555
    pre-B ALL 1632
    prognostic indicator 1557

Leukemia (*continued*)
  acute lymphoblastic (ALL) (*continued*)
    T-ALL 1555, 1556, 1557
  acute myeloid (AML) 1554
    chromosomal translocations 554, 1557
    immunophenotypes 1555, 1555(Table)
    stem cell transplant outcome 1064(Fig),
      1065, 1065(Fig)
  'acute undifferentiated' 1556
  anti-lymphocyte serum (ALS) use 122
  in ataxia telangiectasia 248
  CALLA (CD10) expression 800, 1555
  chronic 1554, 1558–1559
    treatment 1559
  chronic lymphocytic (CLL) 1558–1559,
    1633
    B cell 1558, 1633
    CD antigens expressed 1558
    γ-heavy chain disease in 1053
    IgM role 1216
    immunophenotypes 1558, 1558(Table)
    opportunistic infections 1883
    secondary immunodeficiency 1283–
      1284
    stem cell transplant outcome 1065
    T cell 1633
    variants 1633
  chronic myelogenous (CML) 1558
    blast crisis 1558
    chromosomal translocations 554
    stem cell transplant outcome 1065,
      1065(Fig), 1068
  differentiation antigens 2427–2428,
    2428(Table)
  graft-versus 545, 1017
    management 978
  GVHD prevention 545
  hairy cell (HCL) 1558, 1558(Table),
    1633
  large granular lymphocyte 1534
  lymphoma spillovers 1633
  'mixed'/'biphenotypic' 1555–1556
  myeloid, G-CSF role 1020
  pathogenesis
    bovine leukemia virus system 1565
    chromosomal translocations 554
    chromosomal translocations of immune
      genes 557
    HTLV-1 system 1564–1565
    IL-9 role 1474
    multistep 1563
    viral, *see* Leukemia viruses; Viral
      carcinogenesis
  persistent parvovirus B19 infection 1924
  polyclonal hypergammaglobulinemia in
    1162
  prolymphocytic (PLL) 1558,
    1558(Table), 1633
    CAMPATH-1H therapy 404(Fig)
  secondary cold hemagglutinin disease 94
  Sézary 1633
  T cell
    in ataxia telangiectasia 248
    CALLA expression 800
    chromosomal translocations 558, 559
    T cell prolymphocytic (T-PLL) 1559,
      1633
    in ataxia telangiectasia 248, 249
  treatment advances 1559
  varicella-zoster virus vaccine 2470
Leukemia inhibitory factor (LIF) 375,
  824(Table), 1560–1562
  acute phase response induction 1561
  in cancer and metastases 1561
  expression in endometrium 1561
  functions 1561
  gene expression 1560
  hematopoietic stem cell expansion 1561
  neurotransmitter expression 1561
  role in nervous system 1561
  signal transduction 1560–1561
  structure 1560, 1560(Table)

Leukemia inhibitory factor (LIF)
  (*continued*)
  synonyms 1560(Table)
  transgenic mice 1562
Leukemia viruses 1562–1565
  acute transforming 1563
  avian 1564
  helper 1563, 1564
  human leukemia 1564–1565
  nonacutely transforming 1563
  oncogenesis mechanism, *see* Viral
    carcinogenesis
  see also Oncoviruses; Retroviruses
'Leukins' 1719
Leukocidin, *Staphylococcus* 2209
Leukocyte(s)
  activation 2063
  in acute inflammation 15
  adhesion to endothelial cells 758, 802,
    1097, 1619, 2060(Fig)
    adhesion molecules role 1619, 2059–
      2060
    cascade and LFA-1/Mac-1 role 1408,
      1408(Fig), 1409
    defects 1567(Fig)
      see also Leukocyte adhesion defect
        (LAD)
    ICAMs role 1411
    mechanisms 2059–2061
    selectins role 1540, 2059
    see also High endothelial venules
      (HEV)
  adhesion molecules, three-dimensional
    structure 518–519
  chemoattractants 1759–1760,
    1759(Table)
    see also Chemokines; Chemotactic
      factors
  chemotaxis 2061–2062
    by macrophage products 541
    see also Chemotaxis
  culture, *see* Leukocyte culture
  diapedesis, *see* Diapedesis
  differentiation antigens, alloantigens 73
  distribution, glucocorticoid-induced
    changes 1000
  extravasation 757, 802–803, 803(Fig),
    1618
    endothelial cells role 802–803,
      803(Fig), 1097–1098, 1098(Fig)
    monocytes 1754
    see also High endothelial venules
      (HEV); Lymphocyte, extravasation;
      Lymphocyte trafficking;
      Transmigration
  fish 923–924
  granular, *see* Granulocyte(s)
  killed by *Entamoeba histolytica*
    trophozoites 78
  locomotion
    definitions relating to 534–535
    morphological events 533–534
  migration, *see* Leukocyte(s),
    extravasation; Lymphocyte trafficking;
    Transmigration of leukocytes
  nongranular 1388
    see also Lymphocyte; Monocyte(s)
  perception of chemotactic gradients 535–
    536
  polarization 1760
    capping 415, 416–417
  porcine 1992
    ontogeny 1991
  recirculation, adhesion molecules role
    29–30
  recruitment 2059
    adhesion molecules role 29–30
    apoptosis after 2063
    clearance of stimulus 2063
    deficiency 2063
    IL-1 role 1433–1434
    IL-1/TNFα role 805

Leukocyte(s) (*continued*)
  recruitment (*continued*)
    in inflammation 529, 529(Fig)
    see also Leukocyte(s), adhesion;
      Leukocyte(s), rolling
  rolling 30, 757, 803, 1097, 1098(Fig),
    1408(Fig), 1618, 2059–2060
    adhesion molecules 2059–2060
    arrest 758
    cessation and LFA-1 role 1610
    defect in LAD 2 syndrome 1568
    E-selectin 2160
    P-selectin 2159
    selectin functions 2160(Fig)
    see also Neutrophil(s), rolling
    ruffling of plasma membrane 1760
  trafficking 529(Fig)
    see also Leukocyte(s), extravasation;
      Lymphocyte trafficking;
      Transmigration of leukocytes
  transfused, fate 2402
  transmigration, *see* Transmigration of
    leukocytes
  vertebrates 1948
  viability assessment 2319, 2474–2475
    flow cytometry 2475
    hemacytometer 2475
    laser use 2475
    percentage calculation 2475
    trypan blue exclusion 2474–2475
Leukocyte adhesion deficiency (LAD) 421,
    543, 759, 1409, 1566–1569, 1754,
    1855
  adhesion cascade defects 1567(Fig),
    1568(Table)
  animal models 1566
  knockout mice 1566, 1566(Table)
  LAD 1 syndrome 31–32, 1566–1567,
    1568(Table), 1609
    clinical features 1567
    pathogenesis 1567, 1567(Fig)
  LAD 2 syndrome 32, 1568, 1568(Table)
'Leukocyte cascade' 1207
Leukocyte common antigen (LCA), *see*
  CD45
Leukocyte culture 1569–1576
  applications 1574–1575
    CD34 cells for bone marrow
      transplants 1575
    dendritic cells for immunization 1575
    for immunotherapy 1574–1575
  bioreactors 1571–1574
    see also Bioreactors
  cell types grown 1574(Table)
  growth factors 1569, 1570
  historical aspects 1569
  large-scale 1569, 1571
  media 1569, 1569–1570
    serum-free 1570, 1570(Table)
  tissue culture vessels 1570–1571
    culture bags 1570–1571, 1571(Fig)
    flasks and bags comparison
      1572(Table)
    polystyrene flasks 1569, 1571
Leukocytic endogenous mediators, *see*
  Interleukin-1 (IL-1)
Leukocytosis, exercise-induced 846–847
Leukoencephalitis, acute necrotizing
  hemorrhagic 1841
Leukoencephalopathy, progressive
  multifocal, *see* Progressive multifocal
    leukoencephalopathy (PML)
Leukopenia, in SLE 2256
Leukosialin, *see* CD43
Leukotriene(s) 228–232
  synthesis/production
    by eosinophils 823
    increase by NSAIDs 120
    inflammatory bowel disease 1381
    by mast cells 1172
Leukotriene B$_4$ (LTB$_4$) 228
  allergic rhinitis 2123

Leukotriene B$_4$ (LTB$_4$) (*continued*)
  Arthus reaction 239
  C5a-induced synthesis 90
  cellular sources 228–229
  as chemotactic factor 542
  as endogenous calcium ionophore 232
  eosinophilotactic activity 819
  functions/actions 228, 229–231
    B cells 229
    cytokine production 231
    cytotoxic T cells 230
    monocytes/macrophage 230–231
    NK cells 230
    PMNs 231
    T cells 229
  inflammatory bowel disease 1381
  proinflammatory agent 229
  receptors 228
  as second messengers 231–232
  synthesis and factors controlling 228–
    229, 228(Table)
Leukotriene C$_4$ (LTC$_4$)
  C5a-induced synthesis 90
  eosinophils producing 823, 824
  release from mast cells 1668
Leukotriene CysLT$_1$-receptor antagonists,
  eosinophil chemotaxis 821
Leukotriene D$_4$ (LTD$_4$), eosinophils
  producing 823, 824
Levamisole, as immunopotentiating agent
  1347
Levans, antitumor activity 430
Lewis^a (Le^a) 1577, 1577(Fig), 1578–1579
Lewis rat, encephalitogenic antigens 857–
  858
Lewis^x (Le^x) antigen (CD15) 447(Table),
  595, 1576–1579
  discovery 1576
  expression
    granulocytes/monocytes 1578
    myeloid cells 1803
  L5 antigen as 1578
  as ligand for selectins 1578–1579
  murine stage-specific embryonic antigen 1
    as 1576–1577
  structure 1576–1577, 1577(Fig)
  as tumor-associated antigen 1578
Lewis^y (Le^y) 1577, 1577(Fig), 2429
LEW sublines 2058
LEX A protein 984
Le^y antigen 1577, 1577(Fig), 2429
LFA-1 29, 446(Table), 1607–1612, 2146
  α chain (CD11a) 446(Table), 1607
    A domain 1607
    antibodies 1609
    expression 1607
    I domain 1607, 1609–1610, 1610
    MIDAS motif 1607, 1610
    polymorphisms 1608
    structure 1607
  activation 1610
    by anti-LFA-1 1609, 1610
    constitutive 1610
    experimental 1610–1611
    inhibition by cAMP 1610
    mechanism 1611–1623(Fig)
    regulation 1607
  antibodies
    activation of LFA-1 1609, 1610
    effects 1609–1610
    effects on T cells 1609
    functionally neutral 1609
    therapeutic applications/trials 1609
  β chain (CD18) 632, 1607
    antibodies 1609
    cytoplasmic domain 1607, 1610
    deficiency, *see* Leukocyte adhesion
      deficiency (LAD), LAD-1
    expression 1607
    knockout mice 1566
    leukocyte adhesion deficiency 1409,
      1567

LFA-1 (*continued*)
  β chain (CD18) (*continued*)
    mutations in cattle 1566
    NK cell adhesion to plastic 1629
    polymorphisms 1608
    structure 1607–1608
    see also CR3 (CD11b/CD18 complex; Mac-1)
  cell–cell adhesion 1609
    B cell 1610
    CTLs adherence to target 1610
  contact hypersensitivity 638
  counter-receptor 29
  expression 1407, 1607
    by lymphocytes, circulation and ICAM-2 role 1411
  functions 1407, 1607, 1609
    antagonism by cytochalasins 1609, 1612
    regulation 1610–1612
  ICAM-1 binding 804, 1411, 1412, 1607, 1608, 2146
    binding site 1610
    low affinity 1611–1612
  ICAMs binding 1608–1609
  immune response role 1609
  'inside-out signaling' 1607, 1611
  leukocyte adhesion to HEVs 758, 1097–1098
  ligands 1608–1609, 2146
    ICAMs 804, 1608–1609, 2146
    microbial 1609
  magnesium requirement 1609, 1610, 1611
  molecular basis of function 1609–1610
  'outside-in signaling' 1607
  polymorphisms 1608
  rapid activation/inactivation 1610
  structure 1607–1608, 1608(Fig), 2146
  T cell activation 502, 2146
  T cell rolling cessation 1610
LFA-3 (CD58) 28, 29, 450(Table), 1612–1615, 2146
  antibody-blocking studies 1613
  CD2 interactions 463, 1613, 2146, 2328
    binding regions 1613
    costimulatory signal for T cells 1614, 2146
    T cell anergy/apoptosis 1614
  cell stimulatory signals 1614
  discovery 1613
  distribution 1613
  expression 1612
    antigen-presenting cells 1613
    erythrocytes 1612
    monocytes 1614
    T cells 1683
  gene 1613
  lipid-linked form 1612, 1613
  number of molecules per cell 1613
  T cell activation 502, 1614, 2146
  transmembrane form 1612, 1613
L-forms of bacteria 321
Libman–Sachs endocarditis 2255
Lichen planus, mercury causing 1689
Lifespan of immune cells/molecules 59, 1579–1583
  B cells 1581
    B1 cells 1581
  complement 1583
  cytokines 1583
  dendritic cells 1583
  erythrocytes 840
  follicular dendritic cells 1583
  Immunoglobulin 1581, 1583
  macrophage 1583, 1643
  mast cells 1668
  measurement 1579–1580
  memory B cells 1581
  memory T cells 1683, 2331
  monocytes 1583, 1751
  neutrophils 1854, 1855(Fig)

Lifespan of immune cells/molecules (*continued*)
  plasma cells 1581
  T cells 1581–1582, 2018, 2294, 2295, 2331
    activated 1581–1581
    CD4+ cells 1581
    CD45RO cells 1581, 1582
    naive (CD45RA) 1581, 1582
Lifshitz–van der Waals (LW) interactions 163
Ligase I, defect 1282
Light chain, *see* Immunoglobulin light (L) chains
Light scattering
  detection 1823
  by immune complexes 1822–1823
Lilac rings 2189
Lima bean lectin 1536
Limiting dilution analysis 1387, 1584–1586
  applications 1585–1586
  definition 1584
  formulae 1584
  method 1584–1585, 1585(Fig)
  plaque-forming cell assays with 1962–1963
  precursor frequency calculation 1584
  single-hit curves 1585, 1585(Fig)
  statistical methods 1585
LIMP (CD63) 450(Table)
Limulin 1950
Linkage analysis, HLA–disease association 1697
Linkage disequilibrium 1586–1588, 2064
  calculation 1586–1587
  definition 1586
  genetic/physical distance comparison 1587
  Gm haplotypes 1588
  HLA complex 1586–1587, 1587–1588
  HLA–disease association 1693, 1696–1697
  T cell receptor (TCR) 1588
  use for gene mapping 1587
Linoleic acid
  abnormal, atopic eczema 788
  age-related disease increase 884
  in cell membranes 885
Lipid
  antigens 203, 204
  'auxiliary' 204
  synthesis 1388–1389
  see also Fat; Fatty acids (dietary)
Lipid A 322, 807
  action 2378
  complement activation 1950
  endotoxic activity 807
  functions/biological activities 808(Table)
  monoclonal antibodies 1747
  orientation 423–424
  structure 423, 807, 2378(Fig)
Lipid bilayer 834, 853
Lipid kinase PI3K, *see* PI3K pathway
Lipoarabinomannan (LAM) 319, 1795
  antigen presentation by CD1 460–461
Lipocortins, *see* Annexins (lipocortins)
Lipoglycans, antigen presentation by CD1 460–461
Lipomodulin 111
  see also Annexin I
Lipo-oligosaccharide (LOS) 322
  Neisseria gonorrhoeae 2072
Lipopolysaccharide (LPS; endotoxin) 321, 322, 423–424, 806–809, 2377–2379
  as adjuvant 37
  as antigen 203
  bactericidal/permeability increasing proteins binding 1722
  B cell proliferation 2020–2021
  biological properties 807, 808(Table), 2378

Lipopolysaccharide (LPS; endotoxin) (*continued*)
  biological properties (*continued*)
    beneficial 807
  Bordetella pertussis 378
  Brucella 383, 385
  CD14 interaction 186
  chemistry/composition 322, 423–424, 807
    core oligosaccharide 423, 807
    lipid A, *see* Lipid A
    O-polysaccharide 423–424, 807
    orientation of components 423–424
  Chlamydia 550
  CNS inflammation, mechanism 2395
  complement resistance mechanism 316
  'deep rough' mutants 550, 807
  drug allergy affected by 780
  effects 322
  endogenous pyrogens secreted in response 902–903
  Escherichia coli 2452
  fever induction 902
  in GVHD 1015
  heterogeneity 807
  historical aspects 806–807
  immunomodulators from 1345
  isolation 807
  lethal amounts 808
  mechanisms of action 808
  mitogenic activity 807
  monoclonal antibodies 1747
  Neisseria gonorrhoeae 1817
  neutralization 2379
  oral tolerance enhanced 1896
  Pasteurella multocida 1927, 1928
  as polyclonal activator 1981–1982
    mutual antagonism 1982
  probes 1500
  receptor, CD14 215
  response to 1435
    IL-1 action 1435
  responsiveness, murine models/mutations 1270
  rough (R) mutants 807
  Salmonella 424, 2131, 2378(Fig)
  signal transduction 2032–2033
  S (smooth)-form 807
  structure 2378(Fig)
  susceptibility 808
  tolerance and sensitization 808
  toxicity, reduced by liposome association 1591
  as type 1 T-independent antigen 215
  upregulation of IL-1β converting enzyme (ICE) 1430
  Vibrio cholerae 2478
  Yersinia 2513
Lipopolysaccharide (LPS)-binding protein (LBP) 186, 215, 809
  bactericidal/permeability increasing proteins action homology 1722
Lipoprotein lipase inhibitor, *see* Leukemia inhibitory factor (LIF)
Liposomes 204, 1588–1592
  adjuvant role 37, 1590
    lipopolysaccharide/protein A enhancement 1591
  as antigen carriers 1590–1591
    CTL induction 1590
    entrapped/exposed epitopes 1590
    haptens and IgM response 1590
    IgG response 1590
  applications 1588, 1588–1590
    cancer immunotherapy 1591
    gene therapy 1589–1590
    targeting of drugs 1588, 1589
  biodegradable 1588, 1590
  cationic 1589
  cholera toxin in 1591
  clodronate in, macrophage depletion 1591, 1592(Fig)

Liposomes (continued)
  composition 1588, 1589(Fig)
  drugs encapsulated 1588, 1589, 1592
  fate 1591
  haptenated 1590
  immunoassays based on 1591
  immunoliposomes 1588–1589, 1589
  ingestion by macrophage 1590, 1591
  in vivo distribution 1588
  long circulating 1589
  macrophage function modulation 1591–1592
  macrophage 'suicide approach' 1590, 1591–1592
  phagocytosis modulation 1589
  pH-sensitive 1589
  pH-sensitive cationic 1589–1590
  preparation 1588
Lipoteichoic acid 322
5-Lipoxygenase (5-LOX) 228, 1381
  expression 229(Table)
  inflammatory bowel disease 1381
  knockout mice 232
  products 1381
5-Lipoxygenase (5-LOX)-activating protein (FLAP) 228, 229(Table)
Listeria 1592–1596
  killing, nitric oxide action 1860
Listeria ivanovii 1592
Listeria monocytogenes 1592
  actA protein 1595
  antigens 1593
  characteristics 1592–1593
  cytokine expression 1594
  evasive strategies 1594–1595, 1595(Fig)
  hemolysins 319
  host immune response 1593–1594, 1594(Fig)
    neutrophils 1593
    T cells 1593, 1704
  host resistance, recombinant cytokines 1594, 1595
  innate resistance to 1593
  internalin 1594
  intracellular replication 1593, 1594, 1595(Fig)
    in hepatocytes 1593
  phagocytosis 1593
  prfA gene 1594
  protein p60 1594
  receptor 29
  recombinant, as vaccine vector 1595
  vaccines 1595
  virulence factors 1593
Listeriolysin 2377
Listeriosis 1592
  innate resistance 1593
  murine 1593
  see also Listeria monocytogenes
Liver
  dendritic cells 745, 746
  failure
    fulminant, hepatitis E 1082
    immunodeficiency in 1286
  in fascioliasis 880, 881
  fetal, hematopoiesis 374
  fibrosis
    fascioliasis 881
    schistosomiasis 2140, 2141
  mononuclear phagocytes origin 1755
  piecemeal necrosis 561, 562(Fig)
Liver cancer
  primary, elevated α-fetoprotein 799–800
  TNFα levels 2439
  see also Hepatocellular carcinoma (HCC)
Liver disease, immunocytotoxic pathway 564
Liver flukes 1879
  see also Clonorchis sinensis; Fasciola hepatica; Opisthorchis viverrini
Liver and kidney microsome (LKM antigen) 562

Liver oils 2489
Liver-specific autoantigen, chronic active hepatitis (CAH) 564
Liver transplantation 2412–2413
  cyclosporine role 688
  historical background 2412
  indications and results 2412–2413
  tissue typing 2322
Lizards
  mixed lymphocyte reaction 2079(Table)
  skin graft rejection 2079(Table)
  thymus development 2077(Fig)
LKM antigen, in chronic active hepatitis 562
LMP1 484–485, 2487
LMP2 192, 1703
  loci, evolution 1702
LMP7 192, 1703
  diabetes mellitus association 1399
  evolution 1702
Ln (Lu)-related-p80 glycoprotein, see CD44
Local lymph node assay (LLNA) 1366
Lock and key paradigm 2202
Locomotion
  capacity 534–535
  definitions relating to 534–535
  directional 534
  leukocytes, see Leukocyte(s)
  random 534
  responses to physical/chemical cues 534
  see also Chemotaxis; specific cell types
Locus control regions (LCRs), in transgenic animals 2406
Löffler syndrome 241
Logistic regression 2213
Long-acting thyroid stimulator (LATS) 2313
Long terminal repeats (LTR)
  HIV 1131, 1133
  retroviruses 2086, 2092–2083
Lotus tetragonolobus 1541
Low birthweight infants
  immunodeficiency 1284–1285
  nutritional regulation of immune response 1870
Low-density lipoproteins (LDL) 987
  apheresis 1252
  effect on TNFα production 2439
  receptors, mutations 987–988
Low molecular weight kininogen (LK) 1519
5-LOX-activating protein (FLAP) 228, 229(Table)
Loxoscelism 2472
loxP 982–983, 983(Fig)
  sites 1525(Fig), 1526(Fig), 1527, 2406
lpr^cg (lpr complementing gene) mutation 2251
  apoptosis association 2252
lpr mice 876, 877
  histologic/serologic manifestations 2251
  MHC class II genes deletion 2252
  MHC genes and lupus susceptibility 2252
  T cell accumulation 2252
lpr mutation 875, 878, 2251
  apoptosis association 2252
  clonal deletion of T cells 65, 570
LPS, see Lipopolysaccharide (LPS)
lps^d allele 1271
lps locus, mutation 1271
LPXTG, gram-positive cell walls 322
Lrdm1 and Lrdm2 2253
L-selectin (CD62L) 16, 27(Table), 28, 450(Table), 2158–2159
  antibodies 1540
  CD34 binding 2159
  expression 2158–2159
    monocytes 1753
    T cells 2330
  functions 2159

L-selectin (CD62L) (continued)
  gene 2159
  knockout mice 1566, 1566(Table), 1619
  ligands 2159
    Lewis^x (Le^x) and sialyl-Le^x 1578–1579
  loss (shedding) from cell surface 30, 2159
  lymphocyte rolling/adhesion to HEVs 1097–1098, 1539
  lymphocyte trafficking 2159
  monocyte rolling/adhesion 1754
  neutrophil chemotaxis/migration 1935, 2159
  as peripheral homing receptor 1097
  plasma, diseases with 2159
LSTc carbohydrate 2245
Lugdunensis 2210
Luminol 143
Lung
  antigen clearance 191
  damage, eosinophil role 1456
  fluid exchange 1599
  local effects of immunotoxicants 1368
  neutrophil infiltration 16
  NK cells 1368
  in pigs 1994
  T cells in sarcoidosis 2136
  transplantation 2413
    cyclosporine role 688
Lung cancer
  hCG vaccine application 646
  small cell, see Small cell lung cancer
Lungworms 242
  vaccines 1921
Lupoid hepatitis 561
Lupus anticoagulant 1676, 2119, 2257
  function and induction 2119
  see also Antiphospholipid antibodies (aPL)
Lupus erythematosus
  concept 2186
  cutaneous, see Cutaneous lupus erythematosus
  drug-induced 611, 2257
  mice, see Murine lupus
  neonatal 1676, 2186
  spectrum 2186
  systemic, see Systemic lupus erythematosus (SLE)
Lupus erythematosus (LE) cells, see LE cell(s)
Lupus nephritis 2256
Lupus pernio 2134
Luria–Delbrück experiment 1338
Luteinizing hormone (LH) 641
  diagnostic tests 1746
  immunization against 1853
Luteinizing hormone releasing hormone (LHRH) 641
  antibodies 641–642
    clinical trials 642(Table)
    consequences 641
  release, in copper deficiency 658
  vaccine 641–642
    current status 646–647
    New Delhi vaccine 646–647
    Population Council vaccine 647
LVAP-2 28(Table), 29
Ly-1 antigen, see CD5
Ly-2,3 antigen 472, 475
Ly-6 antigen
  CD59 as human homolog 498
  upregulation, by mercury 1689
Ly-24 antigen, see CD44
Ly-49 family 1811
Ly antigens 475
LYL-1 557
Lyme arthritis 380–381, 381
Lyme disease 379
  animal models 381–382
  clinical features 380, 381
  diagnosis 381
  pathogenesis 381

Lyme disease (*continued*)
  vaccine 382
  see also Borrelia burgdorferi
Lymph 1596
  afferent, ovine 1903–1904
  antigen transport 1602
  central 1599, 1601–1602
  composition 1597–1599
  formation 1597–1599, 1598(Fig)
  hepatic 1599
  intermediate 1599, 1601
  intestinal 1601
  milky 1601
  movement and propulsion 1599
  peripheral 1599, 1601
Lymphadenitis, caseous 662
Lymphadenopathy
  persistent generalized 7
  SLE 2256
  theilerosis 2288
Lymphatic capillaries 1597
  basement membrane 1599
Lymphatic drainage, dendritic cell
  migration 746
Lymphatic pulse 1599
Lymphatic sinuses 1604
Lymphatic system 1596–1603
  experimental methodology 1596–1597
  function 1596
  in gut 1601
  see also Lymph; Lymphoid organs
Lymphatic vessels 1596, 1600(Fig)
  afferent/efferent 1603, 1604
  pulsation 1599
Lymph ducts, cannulation 1597
Lymph nodes 1596, 1603–1606
  afferent vessels 1603, 1604
  antigen transport 1602, 1605, 1726–
    1728
  APC and T cell interactions 177, 1605
  B cells in 1605
    see also Germinal centers
  B-dependent area, *see* Lymph nodes,
    cortex
  blood supply 1604
  cannulation 1902
  capsule 1603
  cortex 1603–1604, 1605, 1606(Fig)
  efferent vessel 1603, 1604
  functional anatomy 1605–1606,
    1606(Fig)
  functions 1603
  germinal centers, *see* Germinal centers
  high endothelial venules (HEV) 1093–
    1095, 1095(Fig), 1604
    see also High endothelial venules
    (HEV)
  inguinal, enlargement 7
  innervation 2224
  interdigitating cells 2191
  interfollicular cortical tissue 1604
  inverted, in pigs 1991
  irradiation, SLE 2260
  lymphocytes, 'recruitment' 1602
  lymphocyte trafficking 1602, 1606, 1617
    in pigs 1602
    see also Lymphocyte trafficking
  macrophage role 1605
  medulla 1604, 1605
    high endothelial venules 1094–1095
  mesenteric 1601
  microenvironment 1726–1728
  organization 1249, 1603
  ovine 1905
  paracortex 1604, 1605
    high endothelial venules 1094
  postcapillary venules, *see* Postcapillary
    venules
  primary follicles 1603–1604
  reticular cells 1596, 1603
  reticulum 1603
  secondary follicles 1604

Lymph nodes (*continued*)
  sites/distribution 1603, 1604(Fig)
  'spongework' formation 1728
  structure 1603–1605, 1605(Fig),
    1606(Fig)
  subcapsular sinus 1726, 1727(Fig)
  T cell stimulation 1682
  T-dependent zone, *see* Lymph nodes,
    paracortex
  in ungulates 2450
  see also Lymphoid follicles
Lymphoblastoid cell lines (LCLs), EBV
  infection 828
Lymphoblasts
  migratory routes 1617
  proliferation, platelet-activating factor
    (PAF) effect 1972
Lymphocystis disease virus (LCDV-1)
  1503(Table), 1504
Lymphocyte 1144, 1388, 1625–1627,
  2017
  activated
    radioresistance 2050, 2052
    therapeutic use 1344–1345
  activation 2018, 2145
    autonomous 1979
    bystander effect mechanism 398
    calcium release 1681
    CD45 interaction with cytoskeleton
      1680
    inflammatory bowel disease 1376–1377
    intestinal 1377
    lymphocyte transformation test studies
      1624
    mercury inhibiting 1688
    second signals 2145–2151
    see also B cell(s); T cell(s)
  adhesion
    to endothelial cells, *see under*
      Leukocyte(s)
    LFA-1 dependent 1609
  amphibian 80
  antibodies 124
    see also anti-lymphocyte serum (ALS)
  antigen specificity 789
  arachidonic acid uptake 2025
  assays, after cryopreservation 669
  autonomous activation 1979
  canine, development 411
  CD3⁺ CD8⁺ I-J⁺ 2310
  cell cycle 2018–2019, 2018(Table),
    2019(Fig)
  cell division 2018
  cell types 2342
  chemoattractants, serotonin effect 2167
  chemotaxis 538–539
  circulating pool 1616, 1618
  coinhibition 1983
  costimulation 1983
  cryopreservation 668, 670
  definition 2341
  depression, African trypanosomiasis 2422
  differentiation, adhesion molecules role
    30
  discovery 1625
  dysfunction after stem cell
    transplantation 1067
  effector 789–790
    see also B cell(s); *specific T cell types*
  endometrial granulated (eGL) 899–900
  eosinophil chemotactic factors released
    820
  exercise effect 845–846
  expansion and adoptive transfer 1348
  extravasation 1601
    addressins role, *see* Addressins
    granzyme role 1028–1029
    high endothelial venules 1093, 1095–
      1098
    in sheep 1903
    see also High endothelial venules

Lymphocyte (*continued*)
  extravasation (*continued*)
    see also High endothelial venules
      (HEV); Leukocyte(s), extravasation;
      Transmigration of leukocytes
      (*continued*)
      (HEV); Leukocyte(s), extravasation;
      Transmigration of leukocytes
  feline 892–893
  fish 922, 922–923
  fluorescence-activated cell sorting (FACS)
    933–934
  functions
    discovery 1625
    exercise effect 846, 846–847
  fusion, quadroma formation 139
  glucocorticoid effect 1000
  heterogeneity 1625
  historical aspects 1625–1627
  HLA class I expression 1108–1109
  homeostasis 2017, 2017–2018, 2017(Fig)
  homing 1783–1784, 1783(Fig)
    discovery 1626
    mucosal lymphoid tissues 1777–1778,
      1783–1784
    radiation-induced loss 2051
  homing receptors, *see* Homing receptors;
    Integrins; Selectins
  hu-SCID mice establishment 1126, 1128
  inactivation, after polyclonal activation
    1980
  interphase survival 2018
  isolation methods 2318–2319
  labeling 1618
  large, *see* Immunoblasts; Large granular
    lymphocytes (LGL)
  lifespan
    in humans 1581, 1616
    mice 1581, 1582
    regulation 1582
  marginal pool 1618, 1619(Table)
  mass 2017
  migration, *see* Lymphocyte trafficking
  mitogenic response, in cats 893
  mitosis 2018
  murine
    culture method 1623
    preparation 1622
  networks, T cell vaccination 2285–2286
  numbers 1247
  ontogeny, porcine 1991
  organ culture, *see* Organ culture of
    lymphoid cells
  origin/phylogeny 1247, 1949
  overproduction, IL-2 deficiency 1438
  peripheral blood
    bone marrow transplantation and 546–
      547
    preparation 1621
  peripheral mature and resident (PMR)
    2295
  platelet-activating factor (PAF) effect
    1971–1972
  polyclonal activation, *see* B cell(s);
    Polyclonal activation; T cell(s)
  polyclonal inhibition 1980
  preparation 1621
  proliferation 2017–2023
    antigen-induced 2018
    assays 2023
    cell cycle 2018–2019, 2018(Table),
      2019(Fig)
    experimental approaches 2022–2023
    experimental systems/reagents
      2021(Table)
    inhibition by PAF 1971
    key concepts 2018(Table)
    molecular mimicry causing 2021–2022
    multiple stimuli 2023
    regulating mechanisms 2017–2018(Fig)
    viruses causing 2021–2022,
      2022(Table)

Lymphocyte (*continued*)
proliferation (*continued*)
vitamin B₆ supplements 2490
vitamin C action 2492
radiation effects 2050
radiolabeling 2054
recirculation 538, 1616–1620, 1726–
1728, 1761–1762
mucosal immune system 1783–1784,
1783(Fig)
sheep 1905
see also Lymphocyte trafficking
recognition, adhesion molecules role 29
recruitment
acquired immunity to *Legionella
pneumophila* 1545
see also Leukocyte(s), recruitment
reptiles 2078, 2078(Fig)
resting state 2019
virus infection 2484–2485
rolling, *see* High endothelial venules
(HEV); Leukocyte(s)
selective depletion method 510
separation techniques 508
serotonin regulatory role 2167
short-lived, idiotype network 1191
small, *see* B cell(s); T cell(s)
small recirculating 538
in spleen 1616–1617
tethering 1618
trafficking, *see* Lymphocyte trafficking
triggering (adhesion to endothelial cells)
1619
unipotentiality 574–575
unprimed, radiosensitivity 2050
see also B cell(s); T cell(s)
Lymphocyte-activating factor (LAF), *see*
Interleukin-1 (IL-1)
Lymphocyte chemoattractant factor (LCF),
see Interleukin-16 (IL-16)
Lymphocyte function-association antigen 1,
see LFA-1
Lymphocyte function-association antigen 3,
see LFA-3
Lymphocyte-like cells, invertebrates 1499
Lymphocyte trafficking 529(Fig), 538,
1093, 1095–1098, 1606, 1616, 1616–
1620, 1761–1762
entry into lymphoid organs 1618–1619,
1619(Table)
evolutionary aspects 1620
gravity/space flights effect 1032
in vitro study techniques 1618
in vivo study techniques 1618
L-selectin role 2159
in lymph nodes 1602, 1726–1728
lymphoblasts 1617
memory lymphocytes 1618, 1684
morphology change during 1096
nonrandom 1097, 1249
numbers per day 1616, 1616(Fig)
pig lymphocytes 1620
radiation-induced changes 2051
regulation 1095, 1616, 1618–1620,
1619(Table)
routes 1095, 1616–1617, 1616(Fig)
selectins role 1539, 1619
sheep 1620, 1903–1904, 1905
steps 1617(Fig), 1618
systemic *vs* mucosal immunity 1249
techniques (study) 1618
transit and exit phases 1619–1620
see also Transmigration of leukocytes
see also High endothelial venules (HEV);
Leukocyte(s), extravasation;
Lymphocyte, recirculation; T cell(s),
migration; Transmigration of
leukocytes
Lymphocyte transformation test 1179,
1621–1624
assays 1623–1624
clinical applications 1624

Lymphocyte transformation test
(*continued*)
dose-response studies 1622
historical background 1621
murine lymphocyte culture 1623
nonisotopic assays 1623
principle 1621
procedure 1621–1624
murine lymphocytes 1622
peripheral blood lymphocytes 1621–
1622
positive/negative selection 1622,
1622(Table)
whole blood 1623
quantitation 1623
serum factors inhibiting 1624
transfer factors 2387, 2387(Fig)
Lymphocytic choriomeningitis virus
(LCMV) 232–235
cytotoxic T cell response 232, 233
diabetes model 1397, 1895–1896
host immune response 233–234
immune evasion 234–235
immunopathology 2483
infection, TGFβ effect 2397
murine model infections 235(Fig)
transgenic models of experimental
autoimmunity 274
transmission 233
vaccines 235
Lymphocytopenia, in Crohn's disease 1376
Lymphocytotoxic antibodies 124
Lymphocytotoxic drugs, as
immunosuppressive agents 1351
Lymphogranulovenereum (LGV) 2072
Lymphoid cells, *see* Lymphocyte
Lymphoid follicles
antigen processing 1728
antigen-retaining reticulum 1728
B cells in 1580, 1604, 1605, 1726, 1728
germinal centers, *see* Germinal centers
mantle zone 993, 993(Fig)
microenvironment 1726–1728
primary 992, 1603–1604
secondary 992, 1604
'spongework' 1728
Lymphoid nodules, *see* Lymphoid follicles
Lymphoid organs 1247–1250, 1247(Fig),
1596
amphibian 80
avian 301
central 1247–1248
see also Bone marrow; Thymus
development, lymphotoxin role 1638
lymphocyte migration, *see* Lymphocyte
trafficking
in marsupials 1665–1666
neural innervation 1824, 2224
neurotransmitters in 1824
peripheral 1248–1249, 1603
B-dependent/T-dependent zones 1248
organization 1248–1249
see also Lymph nodes
reptilian 2076–2078
see also Lymphoid tissues
Lymphoid tissues
atrophy, protein-energy malnutrition
(PEM) 1869
central 1247, 1247–1248
diffuse 1726
feline 892
fish 920, 921(Fig)
microenvironment 1726
radiosensitivity 2051
secondary
dendritic cells 746–747
see also Mucosa-associated lymphoid
tissue (MALT)
see also Lymphoid organs
Lymphokine-activated killer (LAK) cells
505, 789, 1348, 1534, 1627–1631
activity measurement 1628

Lymphokine-activated killer (LAK) cells
(*continued*)
activity measurement (*continued*)
quality control of assays 1628
adherence to plastic 1628, 1629
adoptive transfer 1629–1630
age-related changes 60
culture 1574
cytokines released 1628
cytotoxic T cells 1627
decrease, cryopreservation effect 669
definition 1627
in glioblastoma 1629
graft rejection 1014
immunotherapy 1348, 1362, 1629–1630
animal models 1629–1630
IL-2 with 1630
tumors 1362, 1438, 1630
lysis of African swine fever-infected
macrophage 55
morphology 1628
NK cell relationship 1627, 1628, 1812
origin 1627
separation techniques 509–510
surface markers 1627–1628
tumors resistant to 1348
Lymphokines 719
experimental autoimmune thyroiditis
expression 2311–2312
production, in fish 924–925
released in bacterial infections 318
see also Cytokines
Lymphoma 1631–1637
adult T cell, *see* Adult T cell
leukemia/lymphoma
in AIDS, *see* AIDS
anaplastic large cell 1474, 1636
angiocentric 1636
angioimmunoblastic 1636
apoptosis inhibition by IL-9 1474
B cell, *see* B cell Lymphoma
B lymphoblastic 1634
B lymphocytic 1634
Burkitt's, *see* Burkitt's lymphoma
chromosomal translocations 558, 560
classification 1634(Table)
in common variable immunodeficiency
600
cutaneous T cell 2191
definition 1631
differentiation antigens 2427–2428,
2428(Table)
diffuse large B cell 1635, 1636
diversity 1632
enteropathy-associated T cell 1636
follicle-center (follicular) 558, 560,
1634–1635
Hodgkin's disease, *see* Hodgkin's disease
Ig-secreting 1636–1637
see also Multiple myeloma;
Waldenström's macroglobulinemia
immunodeficiency-associated 1635–1636
immunosuppressed patients, EBV
infection 831–832
large cell anaplastic 1474, 1636
lineages 1631
lymphoid leukemia, *see* Leukemia, acute
lymphoblastic (ALL); Leukemia,
chronic lymphocytic (CLL)
MALT
B cell 1635
Helicobacter pylori-associated 1058
T cell 1636
mantle cell 558, 1634
mucosa-associated B cell (B cell MALT)
1635
nomenclature/classification 1632,
1632(Table)
non-Hodgkin's 1634–1636
in AIDS 1884
chromosomal translocations 1634,
1635

Lymphoma (*continued*)
  non-Hodgkin's (*continued*)
    classification 1632
    Helicobacter pylori-associated 1058
    immune surveillance theory and 1245, 1246
    immunosuppressive therapy association 1245
    opportunistic infections 1883
    polyclonal hypergammaglobulinemia in 1162
    secondary cold hemagglutinin disease 94
    T cell 1636
    T cell line for hybridoma 1152, 1152(Table)
  pathogenesis
    chromosomal translocations of immune genes 557
    IL-9 role 1474
  peripheral T cell 1636
  persistent parvovirus B19 infection 1924
  REAL classification 1632
  secondary immunodeficiency in 1284
  in Sjögren's syndrome (SS) 2182
  spillovers 1633
  T lymphoblastic 1636
Lymphomagenesis, *see* Lymphoma, pathogenesis
Lymphopenia
  BB rat 1394
  bone marrow transplantation 1284
  CAMPATH-1 antibodies causing 405
  in cats 895
  space flights causing 1030
Lymphopoiesis 374, 376
  control 2017–2018
  rabbit 2047
  see also Lymphocyte, proliferation
Lymphoproliferative disorders
  anti-lymphocyte serum (ALS) 123
  C1 esterase inhibitor metabolism 684
  in common variable immunodeficiency 600
Lymphotactin 530, 1759–1760
  actions 1759–1760
Lymphotoxin 510, 1637–1641
  actions 1637
  autoimmune disease pathogenesis 1640
  biological roles 1638–1640
  cells producing 1637
  in CTL killing 1639, 1641
  DNA fragmentation induction 1639
  experimental allergic encephalomyelitis 1640
  genes 1118(Table), 1119, 1637, 1640, 1640(Fig)
    expression regulation 1640
    mice 1047
  heterotrimer (LTα₁β₂) 1637
  HIV replication 1637
  IDDM pathogenesis 1639
  in inflammation 1638
  inhibitors 705
  interferon γ synergy 1639
  LTα 1637, 2346, 2436
    binding to LTβ 2346
    deficient mice 1638, 1639(Fig)
    expression 1638
    gene 1118(Table), 1119, 1640, 2436
    mediator for killing by CTLs 1639, 1641
    production in autoimmune disease 1640
    receptor 1638, 1640
    secretion 2346
    signaling 1640
    transport 1640
  LTβ 1637–1638, 2346
    functions 2347
    gene 1117(Table), 1119, 1640
    LTα binding 2346

Lymphotoxin (*continued*)
  LTβ (*continued*)
    mice deficient 2347
    promoter 1640
    receptor 1638, 1640, 2346
    signaling 1640
  lymphoid organ development 1638
  mRNA 1638, 1640
  signaling mechanism 1640–1641
  soluble form 1637
  TNFα relationship 1638, 1638(Fig)
Lyn tyrosine kinase 363
  activation, in mast cell degranulation 1670
  Lyn-deficient mice 1194
lyp gene 1392
Lysis 504
  cell-mediated, *see* Cell-mediated lysis
Lysosomal-associated membrane protein (LAMP) 453(Table)
'Lysosomal cationic proteins' 1719, 1720
  see also Defensins
Lysosomes
  in Chédiak-Higashi syndrome 527, 527(Fig)
  fusion, *Trypanosoma cruzi* invasion 522
  phagosome fusion, *see under* Phagosomes
  primary and secondary 851
Lysosomotropic alkalinizing agents 192
Lysozyme 1723
  antibody combining sites 150, 2203(Fig)
  in breast milk 1673
  cross-reactive epitopes 2202
  deficiency 1723
  gene 1723
  insects 1500
  macrophage 1725
  neutrophils 1719, 1723, 1857
  organisms resistant to 1723
Lyssavirus 2099
  antigen variation 2098
  see also Rabies virus
Lyst gene 421, 1271
  deficiency 421
Lyt-2 475
  expression on CTL 725
Lytic units 1628, 1815

M

M1 cell line, IL-6 receptor 1461–1462
M13 phage, antibody display 1931
Mac-1, *see* CR3 (CD11b/CD18 complex; Mac-1)
MAC, *see* Membrane attack complex (MAC)
Macaques, SIV infection 1136
MACH 1/FLICE 225, 876, 1028
  TNF receptor signaling 2347
Machupo virus 233, 234
MAC inhibitory factor, *see* CD59
McLeod antigens 837
Macrocortin 111
γ Macroglobulin, *see* Immunoglobulin M (IgM)
α₂-Macroglobulin 706, 1520
Macroglobulinemia 1632, 1636
  Waldenström's, *see* Waldenström's macroglobulinemia
Macroparasites 1917
Macrophage
  accumulation 1758
    in GM-CSF overexpression 1022
  activated 1758
    experimental autoimmune thyroiditis 2312
    fungal infections 961
    HSV infection 1087
    protective/injurious actions 1645–1648

Macrophage (*continued*)
  activated (*continued*)
    surface receptors 1644, 1656(Table)
  activation 1642–1649, 1752, 1758
    amebiasis 78
    cascade 2497
    CD14 187
    defects 2499
    definition 1642, 1758
    by glucans 429
    IFNγ role 1423–1424, 1643–1644, 1645, 1648
    immunosuppression mediated by 1648
    intracellular pathogen action 1648
    by lipopolysaccharide 808
    MAF role, *see* Macrophage-activating factor (MAF)
    malaria 1661
    markers 1645–1648
    by muramyl dipeptide derivatives 1792
    prostaglandin effect 2026
    role 1642
    Toxoplasma gondii infections 2382, 2383(Fig)
    two-stage induction 1643–1644, 1644(Fig)
  activator, from *Mycoplasma* 1799
  acute motor axonal neuropathy (AMAN) 1838
  ADCC 169
  African swine fever (ASF) virus in 55, 55–56, 55(Fig)
  alveolar, *see* Alveolar macrophage
  'angry' 1642
  animal models of IDDM 1393–1394
  antigen presentation by 175
    noradrenergic activity effect 1826, 1826(Fig)
  as antigen-presenting cell 175
  antimicrobial peptide synthesis 1725
  apoptosis 1643
  arginine–nitric oxide pathway 236
  Arthus reaction 239
  atherosclerosis onset 1388–1389
  babesiosis 310
  in bone marrow 2236
  bronchoalveolar, in fungal infections 959
  Brucella in 384
  calcitriol effect on 2495
  calcitriol receptor expression on 2495
  calcitriol synthesis by 2495
  Chagas' disease 524
  Chédiak-Higashi syndrome 527(Fig)
  chemoattractant binding 1761
  chemokines 536(Table)
  chemotaxis 540–541, 1761
    chemotactic response 540–541
    clinical abnormalities 541
  Chlamydia infections 550
  coiling phagocytosis 1542, 1543(Fig)
  complement and Fc receptors 175, 1646(Table)
  contact hypersensitivity 1178
  culture, motility loss 540
  cytokine actions on 1644, 1645(Fig), 1645(Table)
    T$_H$1 and T$_H$2 cytokines 1645(Table)
  cytokine receptors 1646(Table)
  cytokines produced 1832(Fig)
    inhibition by IL-10 1476
    leukocyte attraction 541
    see also Macrophage, secretory products
  deactivation, by IL-10 1648
  defects in C3H/HeJ mice 1271
  degranulation 737
  in delayed-type hypersensitivity 739
  dendritic cell similarities 1757
  depletion
    diabetes prevention in animal models 1397

Macrophage (*continued*)
depletion (*continued*)
selective, by clodronate 1591, 1592(Fig)
destruction by *Streptobacillus* 2216
development/differentiation 1642, 1758
M-CSF requirement for 1651–1652, 1653(Table)
dietary fat effect on 885
in dogs 413
Echinococcus infections 784
elicited (evoked) 1643, 1758
enzymes produced 1388, 1725
estrogen receptor expression 2176
evasion by *Streptococcus pneumoniae* 2219
exudate, definition 1758
exudate-resident, definition 1758
exudative 1751, 1755, 1756
monocyte differentiation into 1751
fate 1755
Fc receptors
Fcγ in IgG-induced immune hemolytic anemia 94–95, 96, 98
idiopathic thrombocytopenic purpura 1975, 1976
in filoviral hemorrhagic fever 918, 919(Fig)
fish 923
functions 1591, 1642–1643
impairment in HIV infection 11
induction of antibody/CTL responses 1590
inflammatory bowel disease 1378
protective 1645–1648
suppression by liposome-encapsulated drugs 1592
fungal infections 959, 960(Table)
GM-CSF action 1021
granuloma formation 1023, 1646
gravity/space flights effect 1031
heterogeneity 540, 1642–1643, 1643(Fig)
HIV infection of 10, 11
apoptosis of bystander T cells 879
human/murine differences 1107
I-J expression 1218
IL-1 synthesis 1430–1431, 2225–2226
neural effects 2226
IL-10 effect 1476, 1648
IL-12 production 1484
IL-15 expression 1492–1493
immune enhancement by viruses 2486
immunologically primed 1643
regulation by cytokines 1644
increase in inflammation 1755–1756
induced 1758
inflammation initiation 1643
inflammatory stimulus effect 1756
influenza virus infections 1386
interferon (IFNγ) effects, *see* Macrophage, activation
interferon (IFNγ) production 1389, 1395
intracellular pathogens 1648
Brucella 384
Chlamydia 550
Histoplasma capsulatum 1106–1107
HIV, *see above*
Leishmania 1547
Listeria monocytogenes 1593, 1594
paramyxovirus 1915
Salmonella 2131–2132
uptake mechanism 1648(Fig)
viruses 2486
in vitro effects in amebiasis models 78
killing, *Toxoplasma gondii* 2382
killing mechanisms 317, 1725
antimicrobial products 1725
parasites 1918
lectins on 428
Legionella pneumophila infection 1542
infection process 1542–1543, 1543(Fig)
Leishmania invasion 1547

Macrophage (*continued*)
lepromatous leprosy 1796
lifespan 1583, 1643
lipid synthesis 1388–1389
liposome-encapsulated molecules 1589
liposome ingestion 1590
liposome-mediated 'suicide approach' 1590, 1591–1592
Listeria monocytogenes replication in 1593, 1594
LTB$_4$ actions 230–231
in lymph nodes 1604, 1605
antigen transfer role 1605
lysosomes, acid phosphatase 1388
MHC class II expression 175, 503
serotonin role 2166
MHC class II-negative, in thymus 2235
migration/locomotion 540
chemokines inducing 531
inhibition 1655
monocyte differentiation into 1642, 1751, 1755
multiple sclerosis 1840
myasthenia gravis 1835
neuroendocrine interactions 2226(Fig)
neutrophil removal after inflammation 226
nitric oxide formation 524, 959, 1424, 1718, 1751, 1859, 1862
Nocardia killing 1862
NOD mouse 1402
nonchemokine attractants 537(Table)
obese strain of chickens 281–282
ontogeny, in pigs 1991–1992
in oral immunity 1891
pancreatic β cell destruction mechanism 1394–1396, 1395(Fig)
in pancreatic islets 1394
paramyxovirus infection of 1915
in parasitic infections 1918
peroxidase loss 1716, 1752
in Peyer's patches 1776, 1777, 1781
phagocytosis 1388, 1648(Fig), 1935
calcitriol effect 2495
coiling 1542, 1543(Fig)
enhancement by substance P 1827
LTB$_4$ action 230
process 1751–1752, 1751(Fig)
serotonin modulation 2166
platelet-activating factor (PAF) effect 1972
porcine 1992
proliferation 1758
prostaglandin formation 2024–2025
protective actions 1645–1648
protein kinases 2031–2033
pulmonary, *see* Kupffer cells
pulmonary intravascular, *see* Pulmonary intravascular macrophage
radioresistance 2050
reactive oxygen species release 524
recruitment 1643
recycling of antimicrobial peptides 1725
resident ('normal') 1642–1643, 1643(Fig), 1758
resistance to infections 1648
respiratory burst 1716
response to tumor antigens 2441
Salmonella growth in 2131–2132
sarcoidosis 2135, 2136
scavenger receptors 185
as scavengers 185, 191
in SCID mice 1268–1269
secretory products from 175, 1643, 1647(Table)
see also Macrophage, cytokines produced
secretory response, protective/injurious effects 1645–1648
serotonin effect 2166
sheep erythrocyte receptor 1537
signaling pathways 1645–1648

Macrophage (*continued*)
skin infections 753
specialization 1758
in spleen 1591, 2207
stimulated 1758
stimulation, by carbohydrates 428
surface molecules 175, 1643
MHC, *see above*
surface receptors 1644–1645, 1656(Table)
cytokine 1646(Table)
effects mediated by 1644
estrogens 2176
as target for lipopolysaccharide 808
T cell interactions
cytokine synthesis 2026, 2026(Fig)
MHC restriction 1709–1710
terminology 1756, 1756(Table)
tingible body (TBM) 993, 994, 1728
tissue, types 1583
tissue damaging effects 1645–1648
TNFα effect on 1646
trichuriasis 2419
in tumors 1245
response to antigens 2441
ubiquicidin 1742
virus infection of 2486
see also Monocyte(s)
Macrophage-activating factor (MAF)
GcMAF 2498, 2498(Fig)
clinical significance 2499
Gc protein (vitamin D-binding protein) as precursor 2497, 2497–2498
defects 2499
enzymatic conversion 2498, 2498(Fig)
synthesis 2496(Fig), 2497–2498
Macrophage cationic peptide-1 (MCP-1) 1887
Macrophage cationic peptide-2 (MCP-2) 1887
Macrophage chemotactic factor (MCF), no response in marsupials 1666
Macrophage colony-stimulating factor (M-CSF) 596, 1650–1654
ADCC modulation 170
cell surface form 1650
CSF-1 596
actions 597(Table)
source 598
from endothelial cells 1651
function 1650
G-CSF synergy 1019
gene, null mutation 1651
genomic organization 1651, 1652(Fig)
half-life and clearance 1651
humoral regulation 1650(Fig)
interferon β induction 1420
local effects, regulation 1650(Fig), 1651
local expression 1652–1653
in neoplasia 1654
op/op mouse 1651, 1651(Table)
receptor (CSF-1R; CD115) 454(Table), 1322, 1650, 1651
expression 1653(Fig)
regulation of target cells 1653(Fig)
requirement for macrophage development 1651–1652, 1653(Table)
signal transduction 1651
structure 1651, 1652(Fig)
synthesis 1650, 1651, 1652(Fig)
Macrophage cytotoxic factor (MCF), *see* Tumor necrosis factor α (TNFα)
Macrophage cytotoxin (MCT), *see* Tumor necrosis factor α (TNFα)
Macrophage inflammatory protein 1 (MIP-1) 902–903
MIP-1α 538
MIP-1αβ chemokine 1760
Macrophage-like cells
invertebrates 1499
in skin 2191

Macrophage migration inhibitory factor
(MIF) 1655–1658, 2387
acute respiratory distress syndrome
(ARDS) 1656
colocalization with insulin 1656
discovery 1655
D-dopachrome tautomerase (DDT)
relationship 1657
DTH-related activity 1655
as enzyme 1657
expression 1656
functions 1657
gene 1656–1657
glutathione *S*-transferase relationship
1657
in lens 1656
as lymphokine activity 1655
as mediator of immune privilege 1656
melanin synthesis 1657
monoclonal antibodies 1655
mouse 1655
as pituitary hormone 1656
role outside immune system 1656
Macrophage-proactivating factor 2497
Macrophage-stimulating protein receptor
(MSPR; CDw136) 455(Table)
'Macrophage system' 1756
Macrosialin (CD68) 451(Table)
MAdCAM-1 27(Table), 28, 29, 1099,
1249, 1778
antibodies 1097
in lymphocyte migration 1619, 2159
Madurella grisea, mannan, antitumor
effects 430
MAG (sialoadhesin), 1540
MAGE (melanoma antigen) 208, 1245,
1361, 1363, 2425(Table), 2442
genes 2424, 2424(Table)
in melanomas 1245
see also Melanoma, malignant
'Magic bullets' 1578, 2440
Magnesium
complement activation 605
integrin requirement 1406
LFA-1-dependent adhesion 1610, 1611
Magnetic beads
lymphocyte isolation 2318–2319
tumor imaging 2434
Magnetic cell sorting 511–512
Magnetic resonance imaging, multiple
sclerosis 1788
Major basic protein (MBP) 1724
effect on mast cells 1669
eosinophil granules 822
see also Eosinophil(s)
Major breakpoint region (MBR) 558–559
Major histocompatibility complex (MHC),
see MHC
Malabsorption, in common variable
immunodeficiency 599–600
Malaria 1658–1663
Burkitt's lymphoma 831, 1245
cerebral 1445, 1662, 1846
TNFα in 1662, 2439
hsp90 2231
immune response 1660–1662, 1920
antibodies 1660, 1662
B cells 1662
CD4+ T cells 1661
CD8+ T cells 1660, 1662, 1920
experimental models 1660
γδ T cells 1662
pathological consequences 1662
T$_H$1 and T$_H$2 cells 1661
macrophage activation 1661
nephrotic syndrome 1662
Plasmodium killing 1661
prevalence 1917
resistance
HLA association 1696
HLA-B*5301 allele 1232
TNFα production and roles 1920, 2439

Malaria (*continued*)
transmission 1660
tropical splenomegaly 1662
vaccination 1658
vaccines 1662–1663, 1921
development 2460
Spf66 1663, 1921
types and targets 1663(Table)
see also Plasmodium
Malassezia furfur 751
Maleimide, in enzyme-labeling of
antibodies 814
Males, antibodies to sperm membrane
antigens 1374
Male-specific transplantation antigen, *see*
H-Y antigen
Malignant disease
apoptosis block 227
epithelial 1882
opportunistic infections 1882–1883
secondary immunodeficiency in 1283–
1284
see also Cancer; Tumor(s)
Malnutrition 1869–1871
HIV infection progression and 9
mucosal surface defects 189
protein-energy, *see* Protein-energy
malnutrition (PEM)
MALT, *see* Mucosa-associated lymphoid
tissue (MALT)
MALT lymphoma, *see under* Mucosa-
associated lymphoid tissue (MALT)
Mamu-AG gene 2010
Mamu-G gene 2010
Mancini technique 1287, 2002
Mannan
antimicrobial effects 428
antitumor effects 429, 430
Mannan-binding protein (MBP), *see*
Mannose-binding lectin (MBL)
Mannose-binding lectin (MBL) 186(Fig),
187, 608
activators 609, 610
complement activation 605
deficiency syndrome 1539
functions 1539
as opsonin 1887
structure 519, 1538(Fig)
Mannose-binding protein (MBP), *see*
Mannose-binding lectin (MBL)
Mannose-6-phosphate receptors 1539
Mannose receptors 187
on macrophage 1646(Table)
Mann–Whitney–Wilcoxon test 2212
M antigen 1070
Mantle zone 993, 993(Fig)
MAPK, *see* MAP kinase
MAPK-activated protein kinases (MAPK-
APK) 2030
MAP kinase (MAPK) 31, 711, 2030
as dual specificity kinase 2327
IL-2 signal transduction 1440
IL-3 signal transduction 1443–1444,
1448
IL-8 signal transduction 1468
IL-11 signal transduction 1479
lipopolysaccharide-stimulated cells 2033
mast cell degranulation 1670
as proline-directed protein kinases 2030
T cell activation 2325
T cell receptor signaling 2327(Fig), 2328
TNF receptor signaling 2347
see also MAPK pathway; p38 MAPK;
Ras/MAP kinase pathway
MAP kinase kinase (MEK; MKK), 2030,
2327
MAP kinase kinase kinase (NIK) 2030,
2348
MAPK kinase (MAPKK) 2030, 2327
MAPKK kinase (MAPKKK) 2030, 2348
MAPK pathway
cascade 2029–2030

MAPK pathway (*continued*)
cascade (*continued*)
multiple forms 2030
cytokine signal transduction 2032
layers of protein kinase activity 2030
leukemia inhibitory factor (LIF) signaling
1561
see also MAP kinase (MAPK)
MAPK phosphatase, in IL-11 signal
transduction 1480
MAR1 lymphoid tumor, *Xenopus* 82
Marburg virus 916–920
structure 918(Fig)
see also Filoviruses
MARCKS, in IL-3 receptor signal
transduction 1448
MARCO, *see* SR-A (MARCO)
Marek's disease of fowl 303, 1632
Marek's virus 1836
Marfan syndrome 862
Marine animals, venom 2473
Marsupial immune system 1663–1667
adults 1665–1666
cellular immunity 1666
humoral response 1666
lymphoid organs 1665–1666
male 'die back' 1666
mycobacterial infections 1666
pouch young 1664–1665
bacterial flora 1665
cellular immunity 1665
development 1664, 1664(Table)
humoral immunity 1665
Ig transfer by milk 1664
immune incompetence at birth 1664
immunity development 1665
maternal antibody 1664–1665
thymic maturation 1665
MASP (MBP-associated serine protease),
187
MASP-1 605, 608
MASP-2 605, 608
Mast cell(s) 1667–1671
activation 1172, 1669, 1669–1670
asthma 244
mechanism 1669–1671
see also Mast cell(s), degranulation
allergic rhinitis 2123
atypical (MMCs) 1668
autoimmune bullous dermatoses 2188
basophil differences 332–333
basophil similarity 1667
in brain, histamine effect 1104
C5a binding 1669
characteristics 1667–1668
chemotactic factors released 253, 1668
chymase/carboxypeptidase-containing
1668
circulation 1667
c-kit receptor 1667
connective tissue type (CTMCs) 1668
contact sensitivity 2166
degranulation 253, 333, 851, 1147,
1172, 1207
antigen valency role 2467
bee venom causing 680
chronic idiopathic urticaria 682
cutaneous anaphylaxis 678
cysticercosis 691
defensins causing 1721
IgE 2467
'piecemeal' 2165
signal transduction pathways 1670–
1671
stimuli 1669, 2165
ultrastructure 2165
degranulation mechanism 1172, 1669–
1671, 2165
Btk and FAK role 1670
calcium increase 1670
cytoskeletal reorganization 1670–1671
Lyn activation and Syk role 1670

Mast cell(s) (*continued*)
  degranulation mechanism (*continued*)
    phosphorylated ITAM role 1670
    protein kinase C role 1670
    Ras pathway 1670
  delayed type hypersensitivity 740
  desensitization, in drug allergy 782
  development/differentiation
    IL-3 effect 1668
    murine models 1272
  distribution 1667
  eosinophil chemotactic factors released 819
  exocytosis 2165
  FcεRI 254, 1669, 1783
    aggregation 1669, 1670
    cross-linking 1669
    subunits/domains, binding 1669–1670
  in fish 924
  granules 726, 1668
    composition 1668
  growth-enhancing activity, of IL-9 1473
  heterogeneity 1667–1668
  histamine release 1101, 1104, 1668, 2123
  human types 1668
  IgE binding 253, 1669, 2165
    bridging/cross-linking mechanism 1207, 1669, 2165
  IgE receptors, *see* FcεRI (*above*)
  IL-4 production 1451
  IL-4 storage 253
  lifespan 1668
  LTC₄ released 1668
  mediators released 678(Table), 1172, 1207, 1668–1669, 1780, 2165
    biogenic amines 1668
    C3a action 89
    chemotactic factors 253, 1668
    cytokines 1669
    effects 254
    functions 1173(Fig)
    histamine, *see* histamine release (*above*)
    lipid mediators 1668, 1668–1669, 1671
    neutral proteases 1668
    release mechanisms, *see* Mast cell(s), degranulation
    serotonin 2164
  mucosal type (MMCs) 1668, 1783, 2124
  nasal 2124
  origin 1667
  PGD₂ released 1668
  production, IL-3 role 1442, 1443, 1444
  response to secretagogues 1668
  rodent types 1668
  in SCID mice 1268–1269
  staining 1668
  stem cell factor effect 1667
  surface receptors 1667
  transdifferentiation 1668
  tryptase-containing 1668
  ultrastructure 1667–1668, 1667(Fig)
Mast cell growth factor, *see* Interleukin-3 (IL-3)
Mast cell tryptase, detection 781
Mastocytosis 2025
  blocked by IL-3 antagonists 1444
Maternal antibodies 13, 1671–1677
  to ABO antigens 4, 5, 1674
  diseases caused by 1671, 1674–1676
    autoimmune disease 1674–1675
    autoimmune hemolytic anemia 1674
    autoimmune thrombocytopenic purpura 1674
    diabetes mellitus 1675
    lupus syndrome 1676
    myasthenia gravis 1675–1676
    thyroid diseases 1674–1675
    see also Hemolytic disease of newborn (HDN)

Maternal antibodies (*continued*)
  effect of maternal immunity on child 1672–1674
    passive protection of Igs 1672–1673
    priming effect 1673–1674
  enhancing effects 1673
  IgG against food antigens, transfer 1673
  interventions by 1676–1677
  in utero transfer 1671, 1672
    see also Immunoglobulin, placental transfer
  maternal immunological memory 1671
  in pigs 1991
  placental transfer, *see* Immunoglobulin, placental transfer; Immunoglobulin G (IgG)
  tolerance induction 1673–1674
  transfer, in ungulates 2450–2451, 2451(Table)
  transfer in breast milk 1672
  'trapping' in placenta 900–901
Maternal autoimmune disease, effect on offspring 1674
Maternal immune response 70
  HLA-G role 1110
  see also Pregnancy
Maternal infection, parvovirus B19 1925
Maternal–fetal interface, *see* Fetus, as allograft
Mating preferences
  MHC role 1705
  mice 1040
Matrix metalloproteinases (MMPs) 865–866, 866(Table)
  inhibitors 865–866
  regulation 865
Maturation of immune response 1677–1679
  affinity of antibodies, *see* Affinity maturation
  Ig class switching, *see* Immunoglobulin class switching
  memory development 1678
  somatic hypermutation, *see* Somatic hypermutation
  T cells 1678
  see also Memory, immunological
MAXX strains, mercury effect 1689
Mazotti reaction 873, 874
mb-1 gene 1194
MBP, *see* Mannose-binding lectin (MBL)
MBP-associated serine protease (MASP), *see* MASP; MASP-1; MASP-2
M cells 189–190
  antigen transport 189–190
  antigen uptake/sampling 189–190, 1776
  Peyer's patches 1776, 1781
  pinocytosis 1781
  reovirus infection route 2068, 2070
  Shigella infection 2179
  tonsils 1775
  ultrastructure 189, 190(Fig)
Mch2 (caspase-6) 876, 1028
MCP-1, *see* Macrophage cationic protein 1 (MCP-1); Monocyte chemoattractant protein 1 (MCP-1)
mcr region ('minor cluster region') 559
M-CSF, *see* Macrophage colony-stimulating factor (M-CSF)
mDRE1 repressor, IL-5 gene 1457
ME491 450(Table)
Measles 1909
  eradication aim 2457
  immunity, memory role 1682
  in vitamin A deficiency 2488
  vitamin A supplementation 2489
Measles, mumps and rubella (MMR) vaccine 2457
Measles virus
  evasive strategies 1915
  eye infections 872
  NK cell infection 2485–2486

Measles virus (*continued*)
  persistent infection 1915, 2485
  vaccines 1916
  see also Paramyxoviruses
MECA 79 antibodies 1094, 1097
MECA 325 antibodies 1094, 1099
MECA 367 antibodies 1094
Mechnikoff 1387
Mefenamic acid, immune hemolytic anemia due to 95, 100
Megakaryocyte
  maturation, IL-6 role 1459
  phenotype 1803
Megakaryocyte growth and differentiation factor, *see* Thrombopoietin (TPO)
Megapoietin, *see* Thrombopoietin (TPO)
Meiosis, gene conversion role 970
Meiotic recombination, model 970–971, 970(Fig)
Mel-14 antigen, *see* L-selectin
Melanin 2501
  synthesis 1657
Melanization, invertebrates 1500
Melanocyte(s)
  antigen 2502
  autoantibodies 2502
  cytotoxic damage 2502
  damage 2501
  destruction 2502–2503
  in vitiligo 2502
Melanocyte differentiation antigens 2425, 2426(Table)
Melanocyte-specific antibodies 2502
α-Melanocyte-stimulating hormone, UV-induced changes 1944
β-Melanocyte-stimulating hormone, IL-1 inhibition 1435
Melanoma, malignant
  antigens, *see* MAGE (melanoma antigen)
  antitumor effects of glucans 429
  cobra venom factor action against 588
  cytotoxic T cell response 2425
  differentiation antigens 2425, 2426(Table)
  HLA-A2⁺ 2425
  immunotherapy 2425, 2442
    A-NK cell 1630(Fig)
    BCG 336
    IL-2 1362, 1438
    IL-2 and interferon α therapy 1362
    LAK cell and IL-2 1630
    LAK therapy 1348, 1630
    thymic hormones and peptides 2301
    thymosin Tα1 2301
    TNFα 2439
  peptide immunization 1344
  phage antibody selection method 1933
  plasmid DNA encoding B7 transferred 977
  proliferation, IL-8 action 1468
Melanomacrophage 922
  centers 922
Melanoma-derived lipoprotein lipase inhibitor, *see* Leukemia inhibitory factor (LIF)
Melanosomes 922
  giant, in Chédiak-Higashi syndrome 527
Mellitin 253
MEM-133 (CDw149) 456(Table)
Membrane
  adhesion and recognition domains 419–420
  blebbing 221–222, 223
  bypass activation 2022-9-2023
  capping and clustering, *see* Capping; Clustering
  colocalization of components 415–416
  component freedom and fluidity 417
  compression by hydrostatic pressure 1155
  dynamic structure 210
  exocytosis mechanisms, *see* Exocytosis

Membrane (*continued*)
  fatty acids effects 885–886
  flow 853
    functions 849
  lipid bilayer 834, 853
  lipid composition 885–886
  lipids, hydrostatic pressure effect 1155, 1157
  microdomains 416, 417–418
    caveolae 419
    clonal deletion and 420
    submembranous protein networks 418–419
    topography 419
    see also Capping
  microvilli 419
    retraction 420
  molecular boundaries and proximity 418
  n-3:n-6 PUFAs ratio 885
  phospholipids, arachidonic acid liberation 2024, 2024(Fig)
  promiscuity of components 418
  protein changes, due to hydrostatic pressure 1155
  proximity of components 418
  receptor recycling 855(Fig)
  recycling 849
  red cell, *see* Erythrocyte(s)
  ruffling 1760
  solubilization of molecules 513
  structure 207
  surface antigen localization 210, 212(Fig)
  targeting and docking proteins 851, 852(Table)
  toxin action, *see* Toxins
Membrane-associated cytoskeleton 1679–1681
  calcium channel interaction 1680–1681
  CD44 interaction 1680
  CD45 interaction, lymphocyte activation 1680
Membrane attack complex (MAC) 624–628
  assembly 624–626
  components 624, 624(Table)
    properties 624(Table)
  control 626
  cutaneous lupus erythematosus 2187
  deficiency 623
  gene 621–622
  host defense role 627
  inhibition by CD59 498–500
  inhibitors 624(Table), 626
    biological importance 628
  lysis mechanism 626–627
  pathological significance 626–628
  physiological significance 626–628
  regulation by CD59 497
  signal transduction pathways 627
  structure 624–626
Membrane attack complex (MAC) inhibitory factor (MACIF), *see* CD59
Membrane cofactor protein (MCP), *see* CD46 (membrane cofactor protein)
Membrane inhibitor of reactive lysis (MIRL), *see* CD59
'Membrane stressing' 418
Memory, immunological 14–15, 1681–1686
  adverse effects 1682
  B cell 1684–1685
    see also B cell(s), memory
  cells 1226
    development for *in vitro* studies 1240
    function of idiotype internal image 1186, 1191
    trafficking 1618
    see also T cell(s); *under* B cell(s)
  development 1678
  in fish 925
  implications 1685–1686
  infections generating 2459, 2460

Memory, immunological (*continued*)
  longevity 1682
  multifactorial nature 1682
  ovine 1903, 1905
  synergy/cooperation of cells 1685
  T cell 1682–1684
    see also T cell(s)
  transfer by maternal antibodies 1671
  vaccination aim 1682
me (motheaten) mouse strain, *see* Motheaten mice
Mendelian traits 987
Meningitis 1846
  cryptococcal 671, 672
  Haemophilus influenzae 1048
  meningococcal 1816
  see also Neisseria meningitidis
Meningococcal septicemia, rash 319
Meningoencephalitis, enteroviral 599
Menkes' syndrome 657
β₂-Mercaptoethanol 1239
Mercuric chloride
  autoimmune disease pathogenesis 289
  effects on immune system 1687
  polyclonal activator 1686
Mercury 1686–1689
  allergic contact dermatitis 1689
  autoimmune renal disease 1688
  carcinogenic effect 1686
  effects on immune system 1687–1688
    antibodies 1687–1688
    mitogenic 1687
    T cells 1687
  exposure, sources/causes 1686–1687
  genetic influence on effects 1688–1689
  immune complex formation 1688
  levels (human) 1687
  oral lichen planus 1689
  therapeutic/other uses 1686
  toxicity on kidney 1686, 1689
  see also Mercuric chloride; Methyl mercury
Mesangial cells, IL-6 as growth factor 1460
Mesangial proliferative glomerulonephritis (MPGN), IL-6 role 1460
Meselson and Radding model of recombination 970–971, 970(Fig)
Mesenchymal cells 905
  adherence to fibronectin 864
Mesenteric lymph nodes 1601
Mesocestoides corti 696
Mesoerythritol 385
Metabisulfite, false food allergy 952(Table)
Metacyclogenesis 1548
Metal ion-dependent adhesion site (MIDAS) motif, *see* MIDAS motif
Metalloenzymes, zinc in 2515
Metallomarkers, in immunocytochemistry 1263–1264
Metalloproteinases
  hookworms secreting 1123
  inhibitor, effect on TNFα 2437
  production, by fibroblasts 906
  see also Matrix metalloproteinases (MMPs)
Metalloproteins, integrins as 1406
Metallothionein, zinc binding 2516
Metals, deficiency 1284
Met-ase, NK expression 1029
Metastases
  A-NK cell immunotherapy 1630
  carbohydrate structure involvement 1579
  CD44 expression 490
  development, IL-1 role 1434
  leukemia inhibitory factor (LIF) role 1561
  prevention
    by NK cells 1814
    by romurtide 1792

Metastases (*continued*)
  reappearance after latent period 1245, 1246
  reduction
    thymic humoral factor (THFγ2) 2301
    thymostimulin and thymosin Tα1 2301
  spontaneous regression 1245, 1246
  see also Cancer; Malignant disease; Tumor(s)
Metatype 1679
Metazoa, alloaggregation 1499
Metchnikoff, E. 1498, 1719, 1756, 2059
Methicillin-resistant coagulase-negative staphylococci (MRSE) 2210
Methicillin-resistant *Staphylococcus aureus* (MRSA) 2210
Methotrexate, in autoimmune disease 1358
Methylcholanthrene
  experimental autoimmune thyroiditis induction 2311
  tumor induction 429
α-Methyldopa
  adverse reaction 1052
  autoimmune hemolytic anemia 95, 100, 1739
  experimental autoimmune disease induction 273
  hypersensitivity 1052
Methyl inosine monophosphate (MIMP) 1347
Methyl mercury
  effect on immune system 1688
  exposure 1686
Methylprednisolone, in transplantation 2414
4-Methylumbelliferyl-β-[SC]D[sc]-galactoside 818
Methylxanthines, in asthma 246(Table)
MGC-24 (CD164) 457(Table)
MHC
  absent from CNS 1844–1845
  allelic sequence diversity 1692
  alloantigens 71–72
  amphibian 81
  ancestral 1949
  antagonists 1708–1709
  antigen loading 1626
  antigen presentation
    via class I antigens 191–194, 826
    via class II antigens 194–198
    see also MHC class I; MHC class II
  antigens, TCR γδ specificity 2273(Table)
  avian 300, 302
    genes 303
  B17, UCD 200 chicken strain 285
  blockers 1357
  CD1 genes 458
  chickens (B locus) 300
  class I-like molecules, encoded outside MHC 72
  class I-related, MIC 72
  disease associations 1690–1700
    see also HLA, disease association
  disease susceptibility motif (DSM) 267, 289
  dogs 413
  donor, antibodies in passive enhancement 811
  downregulation
    immune surveillance escape 1360, 1361
    by tumors 1360, 1361
  drug allergy affected by 780
  evolution 1700–1702, 1948, 1949–1950
    allelic lineages and motifs 1702
    gene deletion 1701
    gene duplication 1701, 1950
    long allele persistence time 1702
    positive/negative selection 1701–1702
    in primates 2010
    primordial gene 1701
  expression 1703
    fibroblasts 905

MHC (*continued*)
  expression (*continued*)
    interferons affecting 1704
    lymphocyte transformation test 1624
  feline 894
  functions 1703–1706
    graft rejection 1705
    immune surveillance 1705
    mating preferences 1705
    physiological 1705
    T cell targeting and effector function 1703–1704
    TCR repertoire selection 1704–1705
    tolerance 1704–1705
  genes 72
    T cell response to H-Y 1159
  genetic map 1691(Fig)
  graft rejection 1011
  graft-versus-host disease (GVHD) and 1016
  guinea pig (GPLA complex) 1034, 1034(Table)
  Ig integration, evolution 1949–1950
  isolation 514–515
  β₂-microglobulin origin 1950
  mouse, *see* H2 complex
  nonclassical antigens
    class Ib 72
    class II antigens 72
    TCRγδ recognition 2272
  ovine 1903
  peptide-binding, *see* MHC class I; MHC class II
  peptide-binding regions 2282
    evolution 1701–1702, 1702
  peptide complexes
    isolation 514
    structural aspects 2282–2283
    tolerance induction 1357
  polymorphism 72, 1692, 1704
  porcine 1992
  primates (nonhuman) 2005, 2008–2010
  purification 514–515
  rats 2055
  reptiles 2079
  restriction 157, 175, 177, 194, 202, 215, 349, 353, 826, 1159, 1625, 1705, 1709–1712
    bm mutants 372–373
    CD4⁺ cells, *see under* MHC class II
    CD8⁺ cells, *see under* MHC class I
    CTL target cells 1711
    cytotoxic T cells 725
    definition 1230, 2264, 2341
    development in thymus 1711–1712
    helper T cells 1059
    historical aspects 1625
    macrophage/T cell interactions 1709–1710
    to minor histocompatibility antigens 1730–1731
    T-B cell interactions 1710–1711
    see also MHC class I; MHC class II
  self-MHC, tolerance 1704–1705
  as 'self-surveillance complex' 1705–1706
  T cell activation 2323–2324
  in T cell epitopes 825, 826–827
  trophoblast not expressing 898
  tumor antigens 1361
  in zebrafish 1702
  see also HLA
MHC class I 1690, 1703
  antagonists 1708–1709
  antigen presentation 191–194, 459, 826, 1227, 1231, 1236(Fig)
    antigen-ISCOM complexes 1509
    assembly of peptide-MHC complex 192–193, 2282, 2283
    catabolism of protein antigen 192
    CD1 role 459
    cellular events 192–193, 459
    differences with class II 191

MHC class I (*continued*)
  antigen presentation (*continued*)
    hsp90 role 2232
    peptide binding, *see* MHC class I, peptide binding
    peptide coupling in ER 191, 192
    peptide transport to ER 192
    proteins internalized in vesicles 193
    stages 192–193
    tumor antigens 1361
    ubiquitin role 2232
    viruses inhibiting 193
  antigens 71(Table), 206
    α₁/α₂ domains and β sheets 193
    amphibians 81
    function 71–72
    upregulated in graft rejection 1011
  binding to influenza viruses 1386–1387
  BiP association 2231–2232
  CD1 comparison 46(Table), 461
    structural similarity 458
  CD8⁺ cell interaction 175, 177, 191–194, 475–476, 502, 725, 725–726, 726, 1703–1704, 2307, 2338–2339
    bm mutants 372–373
    discovery 1625
    mechanism 475–476, 477
    site 192–193
    see also Cytotoxic T lymphocytes (CTL); MHC, restriction; MHC class I, antigen presentation
  class Ib, role 1704
  disease association, *see* HLA, disease association
  downregulation by HPV 1908
  expression 1108–1109, 1703
    absent in brain 1703
    cell types 1108–1109
    failure on tumors 1705
    macrophage 503
    microglial cells 1833(Fig)
    reduced in bare lymphocyte syndrome 329, 329–330
  function, T cell targeting 1704
  genes 1108
    autoimmune thyroiditis induction in animals 2310
    class Ia, amphibians 81
    intron–exon organisation 458(Fig)
    rhesus monkey homologs 2008–2010
    see also HLA class I
  guinea pig inbred strains 1034
  Ig-type domains 777(Fig)
  as immune response genes 1231
  induced in bare lymphocyte syndrome 330, 331
  loss, immunological escape of tumors 2444
  β₂-microglobulin association 367, 370–371
  mixed lymphocyte reaction (MLR) 1733–1734
  mouse
    H2-M3 462
    see also H2 class I molecules
  non-classical, ovine 1903
  ovine 1903
  peptide binding 193–194, 459, 826–827, 1230, 1231, 1703
    allele-specific 1708
    anchors 1708, 1709
    disease association 1694
    inhibitory residues 1708
    peptide-binding motifs 1707(Table), 1708
    prediction and rules for 1708
    sequence-dependent 1707–1708
    sequence-independent 1707
  peptide-binding site
    cleft 1707
    structure 1706–1707, 2282–2283
  porcine 1992

MHC class I (*continued*)
  positive selection of T cells 2306–2307, 2338
  primates (nonhuman) 2008, 2009(Table)
  rabbits 2047
  stabilization by β₂-microglobulin 370
  structure 459(Fig), 827, 2282
    β₂-microglobulin similarity 368
    three-dimensional 1230
  veto cell specificity 2474
  see also H2 class I molecules; HLA class I
MHC class II 1690, 1703
  α2 domain, CD4 interaction 470
  αβ dimers 1706
    assembly 1496
  antagonists 1708–1709
  antigen presentation 194–198, 354, 1059, 1112, 1236(Fig), 1291
    antigen binding site 197–198, 827
    atopic allergy 252
    block in EAE therapy 860
    CD1 role 459–460
    cellular events 459–460, 1955
    CLIP 460
    compartments for peptide loading 354
    differences with class I 191
    historical aspects 194–195
    hsp70 antibodies blocking 2231
    immunodominant epitopes 1291
    influenza viruses 1387
    invariant chain role 1496, 1497
    peptide binding, *see below*
    peptide loading 196–197, 354, 459–460
    peptide loading prevention by *Leishmania* 1549
    processing 196
    self/nonself peptides 198
    T cell contact with APCs 195
  antigen processing 195–197, 1059, 1112
  antigens 71(Table), 206
    amphibians 81
    function 71–72
    upregulated in graft rejection 1011
  β2 domain, CD4 interaction 469
  CD1 comparison 46(Table), 461
  CD4⁺ cell interaction 175, 194–198, 469–470, 471, 502, 1059, 1704, 2264, 2307, 2338–2339
    bm mutants 373
    discovery 1625
    mechanisms and domains 469–470
    see also MHC, restriction
  CD8⁺ cell interaction 725, 726
  deficiency 1277, 1279
    in SCID 1277, 2173–2174
  as dimers on APC 2283
  disease associations 1690(Table)
    see also HLA, disease association
  downregulation, by IL-10 1476
  in endoplasmic reticulum 196
  experimental autoimmune encephalomyelitis association 859, 859(Table)
  expression 177, 330, 1703
    aberrant, autoimmunity pathogenesis 294
    absent in bare lymphocyte syndrome type II 330
    on activated T cells 1113
    Addison's disease 41, 43
    B cells 1476–1477, 2020
    biliary epithelial cells 2003
    cells expressing 177
    CIITA and RFX5 role 331
    cytokines inducing 1112
    dendritic cells 175
    enterocytes 190
    IFNγ inducing 1424
    IL-1 inducing 1433
    IL-4 stimulating 1452

MHC class II (*continued*)
  expression (*continued*)
    IL-10 inducing 1476–1477
    induced on neurons 1831
    induction in tolerance breakdown 2367
    in inflammation 177
    keratinocytes 188
    Langerhans cells 1530, 2190
    macrophage 175, 503, 2166
    microglial cells 1833(Fig)
    obese strain of chickens 282
    PGE_2 inhibiting 2027
    pre-B cells 1876
    reduced in invariant chain knockout
      mice 1497
    Sjögren's syndrome 2184
  function, T cell targeting 1704
  genes
    deletion in *lpr* mice 2252
    intron–exon organisation 458(Fig)
    primates (nonhuman) 2010–2011
    thyroiditis experimental models 2310,
      2311
  guinea pig inbred strains 1033–1034
  half-life 196
  Ia antigens 1230
  immature, transport and invariant chain
    role 1496
  as immune response genes 1230–1231
  invariant-chain peptides associated, *see*
    CLIP
  invariant chains, *see* Invariant chain (Ii)
  in maternal endometrium and placenta
    899
  mice deficient, superantigen activation of
    T cells 2241
  mixed lymphocyte reaction (MLR) 1733–
    1734
  molecular chaperones 2232
  not detected in nude mice 1867
  ovine 1903
  peptide binding 197–198, 459, 827,
    1231
    allele-specific 1708
    disease association 1694
    inhibitory residues 1708
    peptide-binding motifs 1707(Table),
      1708
    prediction and rules for 1708
    sequence-dependent 1707–1708
    sequence-independent 1707
  peptide-binding site
    cleft 1707
    structure 1113, 1706–1707, 1707(Fig),
      2241, 2283
  peptide complexes, tolerance induction
    1357
  polymorphism 1706
  porcine 1992
  positive selection of T cells 2306–2307,
    2338
  primates (nonhuman) 2008, 2009(Table)
  primitive myeloid cells 1803
  rabbits 2047–2048
  in rat 1391
  signalling role 1113
  structure 459(Fig), 827
    three-dimensional 1230
  superantigen binding 2241
    T cell activation 2242
  synthesis, invariant chain role 1496
  see also H2 class II; HLA class II
MHC class II compartment (MIIC), *see*
  MIIC compartment
MHC class III
  C2 622
  C4 622
  evolution 1702
  factor B 622
  genes 206
    C2 607
  H2 class III differences 1045

Mi-2 antigen, antibodies 2118
MICA gene 1114, 1118(Table), 1119
MICB gene 1114, 1118(Table), 1119
Mice
  adhesion molecule expression deficiency
    32
  age-related changes of suppressor
    capacity 60
  antiserum preparation 219
  athymic, *see* Nude (athymic) mice
  backcrossing 1275, 1730
  C_H genes 1302
  coat color mutations 1271
  complement 1046
  congenic, *see* Congenic mice
  dominant negative mutants 1275
  embryonic stem cells, DNA introduction
    2406
  genes deleted, *see* Knockout mice
  high-/low-responder, transfer factors
    2387
  human/mouse chimeras 546–547
  immunodeficiency models 1267–1273
    see also Immunodeficiency, animal
      models
  immunoglobulin allotypes 75(Table)
  inbred strains 634–635, 1369b-1370,
    1762–1770
    as genetic tools 1762–1763
    origins 1771–1774
    veto cell discovery 2474
    see also Congenic mice; Inbred strains;
      specific strains
  inbreeding, nude mice strains 1866
  knockout, *see* Knockout mice
  LCMV infection 233–235, 235(Fig),
    2483
  lupus, *see* Murine lupus
  lymphocytes, preparation 1622
  mating preferences 1040
  MHC, *see* H2 complex
  NOD, *see* NOD mouse
  odors 1040
  osteopetrotic (op) 1651, 1651(Table)
  phylogeny 1772(Fig)
  rabies resistance 2100
  recombinant strains, I-J region 1217
  reovirus infections 2069
  SCID, *see* SCID mice
  species 1771–1774
    Asian 1772
    European 1772
    laboratory and wild 1773
    Mus musculus 1771–1772
  STAT1 deficient 1415, 1415(Fig)
  transgenic, *see* Transgenic mice
  wild
    in laboratory 1772–1773
    relationship with laboratory species
      1773
  see also entries beginning Mouse; specific
    strains/mutants
MIC gene family 72
  proteins 1118(Table), 1119
Michaelis–Menten rate, catalytic antibody
  reactions 441–443
Microbicidal mechanisms 317, 1713–1718,
  1937–1939
  bacteria 317
  oxygen-dependent 317, 1713–1718,
    1751, 1856–1857, 1937–1938
    biochemistry 1713–1718, 1714(Fig),
      1856–1857, 1937–1938
    chronic granulomatous disease 1715
    cytochrome *b* 1713–1714
    hydrogen peroxide 1715, 1856, 1938
    hydroxyl radicals 1717, 1857
    hypochlorous acid 1715–1716, 1856,
      1938
    importance of peroxidase 1716–1717
    iron chelators 1717
    long diffusion distances 1717, 1718

Microbicidal mechanisms (*continued*)
  oxygen-dependent (*continued*)
    microbial protection from 1718
    in myeloperoxidase deficiency 1717
    myeloperoxidase reactions/complexes
      1715–1716, 1716(Fig), 1856, 1938
    NADPH oxidase activation 1713–1714,
      1856
    neutrophils 1856–1857
    nitric oxide action 1860
    nitric oxide formation 1718
    $O^{[G]t[g]}_2$ 1717
    organisms killed 1716
    regulation 1714
    scavenging of agents 1858
    short-diffusion distances 1717, 1718
    signal transduction 1713
    singlet oxygen 1717, 1857
    superoxide anion formation 1715,
      1856, 1938
    see also Nitric oxide; Respiratory burst
  oxygen-independent 317, 1719–1725,
    1751–1752, 1938–1939
    bactericidal/permeability increasing
      proteins (BPI) 1722, 1938
    calprotectin 1720
    cathelin-associated peptides 1724
    CLCP (cationic proteins) 1938
    defensins 1720–1722, 1938–1939
    eosinophils 1724–1725
    lactoferrin 1723–1724, 1939
    lysozyme 1723
    monocytes/macrophage 1725
    neutrophils 1719–1724
    serine proteases and congeners 1722–
      1723
    type II phospholipase A_2 1722
    see also individual enzymes/peptides
  physical/chemical stimuli 1713
  see also Cell-mediated lysis; Phagocytosis
Microbiology, germ-free animals use 991
Microchimerism 547
  leukocytes 2402
  mononuclear cells 2402, 2403
  organ recipients 2402
Microconversion, *see* Gene conversion
Microcytotoxicity assay, HLA typing 1692
Microdomains, membrane, *see* Membrane
  microdomains
Microenvironment 1725–1729
  AIDS pathogenesis 1728–1729
  B cell differentiation 1876
  bone marrow 376, 2236
  definition 1725
  germinal centers, *see* Germinal centers
  lymphoid follicles 1726–1728
  thymus, *see* Thymus
Microfibril-associated glycoprotein
  (MAGP) 906
Microfilaments, capping 415
Microfilaremia 914
Microfilariae 914, 1872
  in cornea 873
  inflammatory response against 1873–
    1874
  skin 1874
Microfilarial infections, skin 752
Microflora (normal)
  gravity/space flights effect 1031
  protection against pathogenic organisms
    259
  skin 750
  see also Gastrointestinal tract
Microfold cells, *see* M cells
Microglial cells
  cytokines produced 1830, 1832(Fig)
  MHC expression 1833(Fig)
  nitric oxide production 2396
  TGFβ expression 2395, 2396
  TNFα formation 1831
β2-Microglobulin 85, 367–371
  alleles 368

β₂-Microglobulin (*continued*)
  avian 302, 303
  biochemical characteristics 367–368
  CD1 association 458, 460
  CMV binding 1286
  elevated, in myeloma 1164
  evolution 367–368, 1950
  experimental graft rejection study 1012
  expression 368, 370
    cytokines affecting 368
    time course 368
  function 370–371
  gene 367, 368
    evolution 1701
  immunoglobulin heavy chain binding 368, 371
  immunoglobulin similarity 368
  MHC class I, structural similarity 368
  MHC class I association 367, 370–371, 1108
    H2 class I 1037
  mutants deficient in 370
  origin 1950
  polymorphism 368
  in reptiles 2079–2080
  requirement by mycobacteria 1795
  sequence identity 367
  structure 101(Fig), 102(Fig), 368
Microhemagglutination tests, *Treponema pallidum* detection 2417
Micro lymphocyte cytotoxicity test 2318, 2319
Micromagnetic beads, in tumor imaging 2434
Microparasites 1916
Microparticle-enhanced nephelometric immunoassay 1824
Microphages 1756
Microplate agglutination techniques 58, 142, 143
Microrecombination, *see* Gene conversion
Microsatellites 1988
  markers, monitoring of inbred strains 1371
Microscopy
  electron, *see* Electron microscopy
  fluorescence 945–946
Microsomal antigens, thyroid epithelial cells 261
Microsporidians, in AIDS 1921
Microspot immunoassays 1256
Microtubules 419
  capping 415
Microvilli 419
  retraction 420
MIDAS motif 519
  LFA-1 α chain (CD11a) 1607, 1610
MIF, *see* Macrophage migration inhibitory factor (MIF)
MIF/DDT family 1657
Migraine
  anti-phospholipid antibodies 1843
  food-induced 950
Migration of cells, *see* Motility of immune cells; Transmigration of leukocytes
MIIC compartment 460
  H2 class II molecules 1044
Milk
  allergic rhinitis 2122
  contamination, *Streptobacillus moniliformis* 2216
  Ig transfer in ungulates 2450, 2451
  see also Breast milk
Miller Fisher syndrome 1838
Mimicry, *see* Molecular mimicry
mi/mi mutation 1272
mi mutations 1273
Mineralocorticoids 996
  discovery 996
  receptors 999
Minimal change nephritic syndrome 1257

Minisatellite loci, monitoring of inbred strains 1371
'Minor cluster region' (mcr) 559
Minor histocompatibility antigens, *see* Minor transplantation (histocompatibility) antigens
Minor lymphocyte-stimulating (Mls) antigens 72, 2095
  mixed lymphocyte reaction (MLR) 1734
  Mls-1ᵃ 1232
  T cell anergy induction 110
Minor transplantation (histocompatibility) antigens 72, 1729–1732
  alleles 1730
  alloantigens 72, 1731
  discovery 1729–1730
  evolutionary selection 1732
  graft rejection 1011, 1732
  GVHD 1732
  H-Y, *see* H-Y antigen
  MHC-restricted responses to 1730–1731
  molecular identification methods 1731
  Mta 1704
  non-MHC genes and autoimmunity 1731
  pathological/physiological role 1732
  strength, measurement 1730
  T cell repertoire selection 1731–1732
MIP-1, *see* Macrophage inflammatory protein 1 (MIP-1)
Miscarriage, recurrent, vaccination against 1344
Mitochondrial autoantibodies 264
Mitochondrial autoantigens 2004
  primary biliary cirrhosis 2003, 2003(Table), 2004
Mitochondrial dehydrogenases, annexins binding 113
Mitogen 510, 1621
  action in amphibians 80
  lectins as 1537–1538
  mercury as 1687
Mitogen-activated protein kinase, *see* MAP kinase; MAPK pathway
Mitogenic agents, *see* Mitogen
Mitosis, lymphocytes 2018
Mixed antiglobulin reaction (MAR), antibodies to sperm membrane antigens 1374
Mixed connective tissue disease (MCTD) 2118
  anti-snRNP antibodies 131
Mixed leukocyte reaction (MLR)
  amphibians 80
  reptiles 2079
  see also Mixed lymphocyte reaction (MLR)
Mixed lymphocyte culture (MLC), secondary 1730
Mixed lymphocyte reaction (MLR) 72, 505, 1040, 1623, 1733–1736
  antigen presenting cells for 1736
  bidirectional 1733
  biological significance 1736
  CD4⁺ and CD8⁺ cells 1734–1735
  in copper deficiency 657
  dendritic cells role 1736
  H2 class II molecules discovery 1040–1041
  historical background 1733
  HLA typing 1692
  magnitude of response and quality 1733
  MHC alloantigens 1733–1734
  Mls determinants 1734
  non-MHC antigens 1734
  ontogeny 1734
  precursor frequency of T cells 1734
  rodents 1733
  syngeneic (autologous) 1735
  target antigens 1733–1734
  technical features 1733
  unidirectional 1733
Mixture models, statistical analysis 2212

Mizoribine 1352
MLL gene
  abnormalities 1557
  chromosomal translocations 556
Mls-1ᵃ 1232
mls (minor lymphocyte stimulating) protein, *see* Minor lymphocyte-stimulating (Mls) antigens
MMR vaccine 2457
MNS blood group system 70–71
MO-1, babesiosis 309
Mo5 (CD157) 456(Table)
Mø, *see* Macrophage
Mokola viruses 2099
Molecular chaperones, *see* Chaperones, molecular
Molecular genetics
  specificity in immunology 985
  see also Genetic analysis; Genetic engineering
Molecular mimicry 267, 269, 1695, 1736–1742
  Addison's disease etiology 43
  ankylosing spondylitis, *see* Ankylosing spondylitis
  anterior uveitis 869
  autoantigens 267
  autoimmune disease pathogenesis 275, 276, 289, 294, 319
  definition 1736, 1739, 1742
  experimental autoimmune disease induction 273
  experimental autoimmune uveoretinitis (EAU) 869
  Guillain–Barré syndrome 1836
  hsp65 in arthritis 34, 1797
  idiotype internal image 1187, 1188–1189, 1192
  Klebsiella pneumoniae and HLA-B27 1522, 1737–1741
    see also Ankylosing spondylitis; *Klebsiella pneumoniae*
  lymphocyte proliferation due to 2021–2022
  mechanism of HLA–disease association 1695–1696
  multiple sclerosis etiology 1788
  multistep hypothesis 2115–2116, 2115(Fig)
  Proteus and HLA sequences 1740(Fig), 1741–1742
  rheumatic fever and streptococcal antigen 1737
  rheumatoid arthritis, *see* Rheumatoid arthritis (RA)
  sarcoidosis etiology 2134
  Streptococcus 1737, 2219
  stress proteins as target autoantigens 2231
  Taenia solium infections 692–693
  taxol 151
  thyroid autoimmune disease 2314
  tolerance breakdown 276, 289
  viruses associated 2483
  Yersinia and reactive arthritis 2513
  Yersinia and thyroglobulin 2311
  see also Cross-reactions of antigens
Mollicutes, *see* Mycoplasma; Ureaplasma
Molluscipoxvirus 1995(Table)
Molluscs, alloaggression 1499
Moloney leukemia virus (MoLV) 1563
Moloney murine leukemia virus (Mo-MuLV) 2086
Monoblasts 1755
Monoclonal antibodies (mAbs) 1742–1748, 2466
  affinity (Kₐ) 44, 45, 45(Fig), 1745–1746
  allotype assays 76
  allotype matching 76, 1746–1747
  anti-lymphocyte 122
  applications, cell separation technique 508

Monoclonal antibodies (mAbs) (*continued*)
B7-1 (CD80) and B7-2 (CD86) 306
B cell characteristics 1742
bone marrow purging 1363
catalytic 1748
CD antigens 445, 1746
cell surface antigen characterization 209
class, determination 141
cross-reactions 1746
cryoglobulins 665
984D4 2245
definition/concept 1742
diagnostic applications 1746–1747
immunological research 1746
tumor diagnosis 1362, 2430
discovery/history 1626
epitope recognition, hybridoma
application 1151
in FACS studies 934, 1746
to fish lymphocytes 923
to galactan 427
humanized, *see* Humanized antibodies
immunoadsorbents from 1251–1252,
1251(Table)
immunocytochemistry 1260
immunoelectron microscopy 792–793
immunosuppression 1352–1353
in transplantation 2414
isoelectric focusing 1512–1513,
1513(Fig)
linkage, heteroconjugates 138–139,
139(Fig)
lymphocyte isolation 2319
murine, isoelectric focusing 1512–1513,
1513(Fig)
natural antibodies 1807, 1808
from phage display technology 1934
in nephelometry 1824
overspecific 1746
polyspecific 1746
preparation methods 149, 1148,
1150(Fig), 1742–1745, 1744(Fig)
alternative recombination methods
1745
cells to be fused 1742
fusion process 1742
human mAbs 1742–1745, 1745(Fig)
selection and cloning 1742
selectivity markers 1742
see also Hybridoma, B cell
primates (nonhuman) 2005, 2006(Table)-
2008(Table)
properties 1745–1746
rabbit cell markers 2048, 2049(Table)
reshaping 1139
rodent, limitations to use 1139, 1140
in schistosomiasis 2142
selective cytolysis of cells 510
in Sjögren's syndrome (SS) 2182
specificity 149, 1745–1746
structures 171–172
T cell receptor (TCR) 1357
T cells 2334
therapeutic applications 1345, 1747–
1748
autoimmune disease 291, 1747
bacterial infections 1747
GVHD 2261–2262
transplant rejection 1747
tumor immunotherapy 1362–1363,
1747–1748, 2430
Toxocara canis ES antigen 2381
tumor antigens, *see* Tumor antigens
tumor imaging 2431
valency and 2466
in Western blotting 2505, 2506
Monoclonal gammopathy, *see*
Hypergammaglobulinemia,
monoclonal
Monoclonal gammopathy of undetermined
significance (MGUS) 1164
Monocyte(s) 1387, 1388, 1750–1754

Monocyte(s) (*continued*)
ADCC 169
adhesion molecules 1753–1754,
1753(Table)
transendothelial emigration 1754
antitumor activity, CD40 stimulating 486
calcitriol effect on 2495
CD40 function and expression 485–486
CD45 isoform expression 493
chemoattractant binding 1761
chemokines 536(Table), 540
chemotaxis 540–541, 2061–2062
vasoactive intestinal peptide 1785
circulation/marginating pool 1755
coccidioidomycosis 590
complement receptors (CR1 and CR3)
1752
cytokines, synthesis inhibition by IL-10
1476
decreased, glucocorticoids causing 1751
diapedesis 1754, 1935
differentiation into macrophage 1642,
1751, 1755
endothelial cell interactions 1237(Fig),
1754
extracellular stimulation 2031–2033
Fc receptors 1752
calcitriol effect 2495
fish 923
formation 1642, 1750–1751
cytokines regulating 1751
functions 1751–1752
fungal infections 959
granule-associated peptides/enzymes 1752
gravity/space flights effect 1031
half-life 1751
heteroconjugates binding via Fc receptors
138
IL-2 action/response 1437
IL-6 receptor 1461
IL-10 production 1476
IL-13 effects 1490–1491
immune response *in vitro* 1233
in inflammation 1755–1756
interleukin synthesis, C5a action 90
kinetics 1750-2-1751
Lewis^x (Le^x) and sialyl-Le^x expression
1578
LFA-3 expression 1614
lifespan 1583
locomotion 540
LTB$_4$ actions 230–231
LTB$_4$ synthesis 228
membrane characteristics 1752–1754
microbicidal mechanisms 1725, 1751–
1752
oxygen-dependent 1751
oxygen-independent 1751–1752
migration and extravasation 1754, 1761,
1935
inhibition by NSAIDs 119
rolling and adhesion phases 1754,
1935, 2059–2060
nonchemokine attractants 537(Table)
numbers in blood 1751
ontogeny 1750, 1755(Table)
origin 1750-2-1751, 1755
peroxidase 1715–1716
see also Myeloperoxidase
phagocytosis 1935
process 1751–1752, 1751(Fig)
zipper mechanism 1751, 1751(Fig)
platelet-activating factor (PAF) effect
1972
porcine 1992
proliferation 1755
IL-10 role 1477
protein kinases 2031–2033
pseudopods 1751
removal, methods 509–510
rosette markers 2130(Table)
secretory products 1752

Monocyte(s) (*continued*)
size heterogeneity 1750
structure 1750
surface molecules 1643, 1752–1754
vertebrates 1948
virus infection of 2486
Monocyte chemoattractant protein 1
(MCP-1) 908, 1748–1750
amino acid sequence 1748
atherosclerosis 1750
biological effects 1749(Table)
chemotactic actions 1749
disease associations 1749(Table)
genes 1748
inducers and suppressors 1749(Table)
inflammatory bowel disease 1380
JE (murine analog) 1748
tumors producing 1749
mRNA 1749
receptor 1748
sources 1748(Table)
tumor growth role 1750
Monocyte-derived neutrophil chemotactic
factor (MDNCF), *see* Interleukin-8
(IL-8)
Monogenic disorders 987–988
Monogenic trait 986
Monokines 719
Mononegavirales 1909
Mononuclear cell(s)
ACTH receptors 1828
definition 1755
FcγR role 889
IL-1 synthesis 1430–1431
Legionella pneumophila infection 1542
microchimerism 2402, 2403
neuropeptide hormones (ACTH) secreted
1828
origin 1755
separation techniques 509–510
UCD 200 chicken model 284
see also Macrophage; Monocyte(s)
Mononuclear cell factor, *see* Interleukin-1
(IL-1)
Mononuclear phagocytes
definition 1755
see also Mononuclear cell(s)
Mononuclear phagocyte system (MPS)
1755–1759
candidate cells 1756–1757, 1757(Fig)
cell classification 1756
cells not belonging 1757
concept 1756
heterogeneity of cells 1758
immune complex processing 183
terminology 1757–1758
historical aspects 1756, 1756(Table)
see also Macrophage; Monocyte(s)
Monophyletic origin 1946
Monosaccharides, lectin specificity 1537
Monosodium glutamate, false food allergy
952(Table)
MOPC 315 (myeloma protein) 51
Morbilliviruses 1910(Table)
Morphea 2189
MORT1 876
TNF receptor signaling 2347
Mosaic proteins 1319
Motheaten mice (*me*) 1269–1270, 2253
features 1269, 2253
molecular basis of mutation 1270
protein tyrosine phosphatase 1c (PTP1C)
absence 2253
viable motheaten (me^v) 1269, 2253
Motility of immune cells 1759–1762
biochemical changes 1760–1761
chemokinetic migration 1759
chemotactic migration, *see* Chemotaxis
haptotactic response 1759
leukocyte chemoattractants 1759–1760
leukocytes 1759–1762
migratory properties of cells 1761–1762

Motility of immune cells (continued)
  morphological events 1760
  random migration 1759
  see also Chemotaxis; Lymphocyte
    trafficking; Neutrophil(s);
    Transmigration of leukocytes
Mott cells 147
Mott hybridomas 147
Mouse, see Mice
Mouse embryonic stem cells
  DNA introduction 2406
  see also Embryonic stem (ES) cells
Mouse Genome Database (MGD) 1762
Mouse hepatitis virus (MHV) 660,
  660(Table), 1273
Mouse inbred strains, see Inbred strains;
  Mice, inbred strains
Mouse leukemia virus (MLV), see Murine
  leukemia virus (MLV)
Mouse mammary tumor virus (MMTV)
  1045, 2097
  B cell infection and virus replication
    2485
  genes 1734
  genome structure 2095
  lymphocyte proliferation due to 2021
  MMTV-7 1232
  superantigens 2240–2241, 2242
Mouth
  dry, Sjögren's syndrome (SS) 2181
  see also Oral cavity
M protein 38, 316, 1164, 2217–2218,
  2219
  cross-reaction with cardiac proteins 431
  Streptococcus pyogenes, clindamicin-
    increased phagocytosis 1887
  vaccines 2219–2220
MRL mice 285, 2251
  origin and characteristics 2251,
    2251(Table)
  pathology 2251
MRL/Mp-lpr/lpr mice 285
mRNA
  assay/analysis 982
  transcription 986
  see also specific genes
MRP8/MRP14, see Calprotectin
MS2 (CD156) 456(Table)
Mta antigen 1704
mTOR 1441
Mu bacteriophage 2016
MUC1 gene product 2428
Muc18/S-endo 456(Table)
Mucins 28–29, 28(Table), 1780
  polymorphic epithelial (PEM) 2428
  production by normal cells 2432
  salivary 1888–1889
  tumor antigens 2432
  in tumors 2425
  underglycosylation 2425
Mucociliary clearance 378
  evasion by Bordetella pertussis 378
  fungal infection prevention 958
Mucocutaneous candidiasis, see
  Candidiasis
Mucormycosis 958
Mucosa-associated lymphoid tissue
  (MALT) 1247, 1248–1249, 1774–
  1780, 1781–1782, 2155
  in animals, see Bronchus-associated
    lymphoid tissue (BALT); Gut-
    associated lymphoid tissue (GALT);
    Nasal-associated lymphoid tissue
    (NALT)
  in humans, see Gut-associated lymphoid
    tissue (GALT); Nasal-associated
    lymphoid tissue (NALT)
  immunoregulation 2155–2156
  intraepithelial lymphocytes in, see
    Intraepithelial lymphocytes (IELs)
  lymphoma
    B cell 1635

Mucosa-associated lymphoid tissue
  (MALT) (continued)
  lymphoma (continued)
    Helicobacter pylori-associated 1058
    T cell 1636
  organization 1249, 1774–1775
  role in IgA responses 1776, 1776(Fig)
  terminology 1774
  see also Mucosal immune system
Mucosal addressin, see Addressins,
  mucosal
Mucosal addressin cell adhesion molecule,
  see MAdCAM-1
Mucosal administration, vaccines 2455
Mucosal bleeding, idiopathic
  thrombocytopenic purpura 1180
Mucosal immune system 188, 1774, 1780–
  1786
  animal models 1785
  B cells 1782–1783
  common system, see 'Common mucosal
    immune system'
  definition 1780
  effector sites 1774–1775, 1778–1779,
    1779
  genital mucosa 2075
  IgA role 1784
    see also Immunoglobulin A (IgA)
  intraepithelial lymphocytes, see
    Intraepithelial lymphocytes (IELs)
  lymphocyte homing 1777–1778, 1783–
    1784
  lymphocyte recirculation 1783–1784,
    1783(Fig)
  mast cells 1783
  mucosal T cells 1782
  neuroimmune interactions 1785
  nonimmunological host defense 1780–
    1781
  nonorganized (diffusely distributed) cells
    1782
    see also Lamina propria
  oral tolerance 1785
  organization 1774–1775, 1781–1783
  organized mucosal lymphoid tissue 1781
    see also Peyer's patches
  regulation 2155–2157
    of secretory immunity 2155–2157
  reovirus infections 2070
  vitamin A role 2488–2489
    see also Mucosa-associated lymphoid
      tissue (MALT)
Mucosal surfaces
  antigen uptake 189, 252
  defects 189
  disruption, allergy/atopy in 252
Mucosal tolerance 1896
  see also Oral tolerance
Mucous membranes, host defense 188
Multicolony-stimulating factor, see
  Interleukin-3 (IL-3)
Multifactorial traits 986
Multifocal motor neuropathy with
  conduction block 1839
Multinucleated giant cells 1756
  types 1756
Multiple antigenic peptides (MAPs) 38
Multiple myeloma 366, 1163, 1632, 1636
  amyloidosis association 84, 85
  CD19 loss 1163
  CD56 expression 1163
  IL-6 as growth factor 1163, 1460
  J chains in 1517
  secondary immunodeficiency in 1284
  smoldering (SMM) 1164
  see also Myeloma
Multiple organ dysfunction syndrome
  2161, 2162(Table)
Multiple sclerosis (MS) 1786–1789, 1830–
  1841, 1839–1841
  animal models 754, 1841
    SCID mouse 1129(Table)

Multiple sclerosis (MS) (continued)
  animal models (continued)
    see also Experimental autoimmune
      encephalomyelitis (EAE)
  autoantigens 1786, 1840, 1895
    myelin antigens 1787(Table)
    myelin basic protein 1694, 1787,
      1787(Table)
  as autoimmune disease 1840
  B cells 1840
  chronic progressive 1786, 1841
  chronic relapsing 1786
  clinical evaluation 1788
  clinical features 1786, 1839–1840
  diagnosis 1788
  etiology 1788
    environmental factors and viruses
      1788, 1840
    genetic factors 1788, 1840
  HLA class II association 1788
  mechanism 1694
  IFNγ administration causing 1840
  interferon β effect 1840
  lesions 1786–1787
  lymphotoxin role 1841
  macrophage 1840
  magnetic resonance imaging 1788
  oligoclonal bands in CSF 1787
  pituitary hormones and prolactin action
    1841
  relapsing–remitting 1786
  stress preceding 1840
  sympathetic innervation defect 1841
  T cell receptors 1786–1787, 1787, 1788
  T cell response 1787
    adhesion molecules/integrins 1787
    against myelin basic protein 858, 1787
    CD8+ suppressor cell loss 1841
    T$_H$1 and IFNγ formation 1841
  T cells expressing CD40L 487
  T cell vaccination 2286
  TGFβ elevation 2397
  TGFβ role in inhibiting nitric oxide
    formation 2396
  T$_H$3 (TGFβ-secreting T cells) 1895
  therapeutic interventions 1788–1789,
    1841
    CAMPATH-1 antibody therapy 405–
      406
    oral tolerance induction trials 1897–
      1898
    T cell vaccination 1788–1789
  TNFα pathogenic role 1840–1841
Multipotential lymphoid progenitors 2336
Multivalency 2465
Mumps 1909
Mumps virus
  vaccines 1916
  see also Paramyxoviruses
Murabutide 37
  structure 1791(Fig)
Muramyl dipeptide (MDP) 321, 1789–
  1793
  analog 37
  clinical toxicology 1792
  derivatives/compounds 37, 1789
    B30-MDP 1790–1791, 1791(Fig)
    development 1790
    lipophilic 1790–1792
    MDP-Lys, see Romurtide
    MDP-Thr 1792
    MTP-PE 1791, 1791(Fig), 1792
    as multicytokine inducers 1792
    murabutide 1791, 1791(Fig)
    structures 1791(Fig)
    see also Romurtide
  discovery 1789
  in Freund's adjuvant 2456
  future applications 1792
  immunoadjuvant activity 37, 1789,
    1790(Fig)
  immunopharmacology 1789–1790, 1790

Muramyl dipeptide (MDP) (*continued*)
  receptor 1792
  structure 1789(Fig)
  toxicology 1789–1790
Muramyl tripeptide 37
  as adjuvant for HSV vaccine 1088
Murine acquired immunodeficiency
    syndrome (MAIDS) 2183
  vitamin E supplementation 2501
Murine leukemia virus (MLV) 208, 2097
  genome 2093
Murine lupus 2251–2255, 2255
  apoptosis genes 2252–2253
  autoantibodies 2252
    anti-DNA antibodies 2258
  cellular abnormalities 2252
  cytokine changes 2252
  genetics 2254
  histologic/serologic manifestations 2251–2252
  low-affinity antibodies 2258
  MHC genes 2252
  mice strains 2251, 2251(Table)
  NZB mice 2251, 2252
  susceptibility loci 2253–2254, 2254(Table)
    MHC genes 2252
  Y-chromosome accelerator of
    autoimmunity 2253
  see also gld mice; lpr mice
Mus castaneous 2253
Muscle
  autoantibodies 263–264
  autoantigens 263–264
  lymphocyte migration 1617
  tumors, MHC downregulation 1361
Mus musculus 1771–1772, 1772
  central populations 1771, 1771(Fig)
  origins 1771–1772, 1771(Fig)
  peripheral species 1771
Mus spretus 1772
Mutagenesis, idiotype structures 1185
Mutations 986
  adaptive 973
  detection 987
  historical aspects 1338
  neutral 986, 987
  point 986
  recombinational mechanism 972, 973
  somatic, see Somatic hypermutations
  tumor antigens resulting from 2426, 2427(Table)
mXBP protein 1043
Mx proteins 1416, 1420
My9, see CD33
My10, see CD34
Myasthenia gravis 1147, 1175–1176, 1834–1836, 1847, 1847–1849
  acetylcholine receptor antibodies 264, 1834, 1847–1848
    detection/titer 1835, 1848
    heterogeneity 1848
  acute crisis 1835
  clinical features 1847
  experimental autoimmune, see
    Experimental autoimmune myasthenia
    gravis (EAMG)
  HLA-B8-DR3 association 1834, 1848
  immunotherapy 1835
  macrophage 1835
  maternal antibodies causing 1675–1676
    idiotype effect 1193
  neonatal 1847
  pathogenesis 1835
    antibody-mediated mechanisms 1848
    thymus role 1848
  prevalence 1847
  SCID mouse model 1129(Table)
  T cells 1848, 1848–1849
  TGFβ in 2398
  therapy 1849
myb gene 1564

myc gene 1564
  Burkitt's lymphoma 1635
  overexpression 1563
  see also c-myc gene
Mycobacteria 1793–1797
  acid-fastness 323
  antigens 1794
    TCR γδ specificity 2273(Table)
  autoimmunity association 1797
  environmental
    cross-reactions 1794
    as normal flora 1793
    relevance/importance 1793, 1797
  experimental autoimmune disease
    induction 272
  hsp, TCRγδ recognition 2272
  hsp60, autoimmune response 2231
  hsp65 755, 1794, 1797
  immunomodulators from 1345
  pathogenic 1793
  sarcoidosis etiology 2134
  species 1793
  stress proteins 2231
  T_H1 pattern response 1793, 1794–1795, 1795, 1796
  see also Mycobacterium leprae;
    Mycobacterium tuberculosis
Mycobacterial disease
  diagnosis 1794
  granulomas in 1024–1025
  host factors and susceptibility 1794
  marsupials 1666
  see also Leprosy; Tuberculosis
*Mycobacterium
    avium/intracellulare/scrofulaceum*
    (MAIS) 1794
Mycobacterium leprae 1793
  avoidance of antimicrobial mechanisms
    319
  inoculation into nude mice 1868
  skin lesions 753
  see also Leprosy
Mycobacterium tuberculosis 1793
  adjuvant action 1981
  adjuvant arthritis 33
  antigens 2231
  BCG history 335
  delayed-type hypersensitivity (DTH)
    1177
  DNA vaccines 773
  epitope recognized by clone A2b 34
  heat shock proteins 2231
    hsp70, T cell recognition 2231
  immunity to 1794–1795
    humans 1795
    mouse 1794–1795
    T_H1 pattern 1794–1795
    T_H1 and T_H2 balance 316
  lipoarabinomannan 1795
  macrophage killing 319
  tissue response 1341
  see also Tuberculosis
Mycolic acid 336, 460, 460(Fig)
Mycophenolate mofetil (RS61443) 1068, 1352
  in transplantation 2414
Mycoplasma 1798–1802
  characteristics 1798
  genome 1798
  history 1798
  host–pathogen interactions 1798–1799
    adhesion 1798–1799
  infections, see Mycoplasma infections
  in vitro effects on immune system 1799
  macrophage activator 1799
  phagocytosis survival 1799
  phase variation 1799
  virulence factors 1799
Mycoplasma arthritidis 1799, 1800
  mitogenic activity 2242
Mycoplasma fermentans 1798(Fig), 1801
Mycoplasma genitalium 1798

Mycoplasma genitalium (*continued*)
  urethritis 1800
Mycoplasma hominis 1800
  urethritis 1800
Mycoplasma hyorhinis 1798(Fig)
Mycoplasma infections 1799–1801
  animal models 1799
  arthritis 1800–1801
  diagnosis 1801, 1801–1802
  HIV infection and 1801
  in hypogammaglobulinemia 1799
  respiratory tract 1800
  treatment 1802
    antibiotic susceptibilities 1801(Table), 1802
  urogenital 1800
Mycoplasma mycoides subspecies *mycoides*
    1799
Mycoplasma penetrans 1798, 1801
Mycoplasma pneumoniae 1798, 1798(Fig)
  adhesins 1799
  cultivation/isolation 1801
  infections
    cold agglutinins 593, 595
    diagnosis 1801
    neurological 1800
    pneumonia 1800
  secondary cold hemagglutinin disease 94
Mycosis fungoides 1633
Myelin
  autoantigens 1787(Table)
  destruction
    acute inflammatory demyelinating
      polyneuropathy (AIDP) 1836
    multiple sclerosis 1786, 1839
    TNFα role 1840–1841
    see also Demyelination
  P_0 and P_2 antigens 1836–1837
Myelin-associated glycoprotein (MAG),
    antibodies 1838
Myelin basic protein (MBP)
  administration, bystander suppression
    1895–1896
  autoantibodies
    multiple sclerosis 1694, 1786
    postinfectious encephalomyelitis 1830
  as autoantigen in multiple sclerosis 1694
    T cell vaccination 2286
  as dominant neuroantigen 2285
  EAE 754, 755, 857–858, 1694, 1896–1897
    treatment 1896–1897
  peptide-induced tolerance 1357
  sequence 857, 857(Fig)
  T cell vaccination 2284, 2285, 2286
  TCR αβ recognition 2267
  tolerance induction 1357, 2397
  viruses homology 1696
Myelin oligodendrocyte glycoprotein
    (MOG) 858
Myelin sheaths, complement and IgM
    deposits 1838
Myeloblasts 1854
Myelodysplastic syndromes, stem cell
    transplantation complication 1067
Myeloid antigens 1803–1806
  characteristics 1804(Table)
  differentiation-associated expression
    1803, 1805(Fig)
  functional aspects 1805–1806
  identification/purification 1803
Myeloid cells 1854
  antigens expressed 1803, 1804(Table), 1805
  primitive, CD antigen expression 1803
  protein kinases, see Protein kinase(s)
  see also Granulocyte(s); Neutrophil(s)
Myeloid progenitor cells, radiation effects
    2050
Myeloma
  Bence Jones protein 341
  extraosseous sites, see Plasmacytoma

Myeloma (*continued*)
  IgD 341
  immunoglobulin secretion defects 147
  monoclonal antibody preparation 1742
  multiple, *see* Multiple myeloma
  proteins 150
  sclerosing (POEMS syndrome) 1839,
    1986
  solitary 1636–1637
Myelopathy, necrotizing 1841
Myeloperoxidase (MPO) 1715–1716
  activity changes, mercury causing 1689
  decreased, in iron deficiency 1506
  deficiency/absence 317, 1716–1717
  expression, acute myeloid leukemia 1555
  neutrophils 1715–1716, 1719, 1856
  reactions/complexes formed 1715–1716,
    1716(Fig), 1938
  requirements 1716
Myelopoiesis 375–376
  bone marrow microenvironment 376
  hematopoietic growth factors 375
Myocarditis, autoimmune 263
Myoclonus 1843
Myocytes, antigen expression, DNA
    vaccines 773
Myofibroblasts 908
Myoid cells 2235
  in myasthenia gravis 1848
  role 2235
Myopathy, idiopathic inflammatory 2118
Myosin light chain kinase 2029
Myxedema, primary (atrophic thyroiditis)
    2313

N

Na⁺,K⁺-ATPase 102
  in red cell membranes 837
NAD, in antibody detection methods 143
NADPH oxidase (phagocytes) 1713
  absence 565
    chronic granulomatous disease 565,
      752, 959
  active enzyme formation 1856
  composition 565
  cytochrome b interaction 1713
  deficiency 565, 752, 959
  in neutrophils 1856
  proteins comprising 1856
  regulatory components 1714
  superoxide formation 1751, 1856
Nagana 2420
Nairobi sheep disease 392
Nairovirus 391(Table), 392
NALT (nose-associated lymphoid tissue),
    see Nasal-associated lymphoid tissue
    (NALT)
NASA 1031
Nasal allergy, mediators 2123–2124
Nasal-associated lymphoid tissue (NALT)
    189, 190, 1774, 1775(Fig)
  functional anatomy 1775–1777
  homing receptors 1778
  see also Mucosa-associated lymphoid
    tissue (MALT)
Nasal blood vessels 2124–2125
  blood flow 2125
Nasal mucosa
  clinical appearance 2122
  mast cells 2124
  response to allergens 2123–2124
Nasal obstruction 2122, 2122(Table)
  treatment 2124, 2125
Nasal polyps 2121, 2123
Nasal tolerance 1896
Nasopharyngeal carcinoma 832
Natural antibodies 153, 573, 1215, 1806–
    1809

Natural antibodies (*continued*)
  ABO antibodies 4
  anti-antibodies (AAs) 136–137
  antierythrocyte 1806
  antigen-induced 1806
  antigens stimulating 1807
  anti-idiotypic-like network 1807, 1808
  anti-lymphocyte serum 124
  autoantibodies 1807, 1808
  to bacteria and viruses 1806, 1808
  biological functions 1807–1808,
    1807(Table)
  broad specificity 1806
  characteristics 1807
  complement depletion method 511
  definition/concept 1806–1807
  germ-line encoded 1808
  historical aspects 1806
  IgM 1215–1216, 1807
  monoclonal 1807, 1808, 1934
  monospecific 1807
  occurrence 1807
  opsonization role 1808
  pathological states 1808
  pig α-Gal endothelial determinant 2509
  polyreactive 1807
    monoclonal 1807–1808
  properties 1807–1808
Natural cytotoxic cells (NCCs), in fish 924
Natural killer cell stimulatory factor
    (NKSF), *see* Interleukin-12 (IL-12)
Natural killer (NK) cell/large granular
    lymphocyte (LGL) syndrome 1163
Natural killer (NK) cells 789, 1389, 1809–
    1816, 2342
  activated 1629, 1809, 1813
  activation 1629, 2481
    arginine effect 236
    CD25 formation 1810
    FcγRIII 1810
    IFNγ role 1424
    IL-2 role 1810
    signaling pathway 1811
    by viruses 2481
  activity
    abnormal 1814
    depressed, *see decreased activity
      (below)*
    enhancement by IL-15 1494
    measurement 1815
    thymulin effect 2302
  ADCC 168–169, 505
    see also Antibody-dependent cellular
      cytotoxicity (ADCC)
  adherent, *see* Natural killer (NK) cells,
    A-NK cells
  adhesion molecules 1809, 1810(Table),
    1811
  age-related changes 60–61, 61
  agranular 1533
  A-NK cells 1628, 1629, 1812–1813,
    1813
    in cancers 1629
    CD11 and CD18 in 1629
    generation method 1629, 1630
    immunotherapy with 1629–1630
    melanoma immunotherapy 1630(Fig)
    podosomes 1813
    receptors expressed 1813
    regulation 1814
  antitumor activity, enhanced by serotonin
    2166
  avian 302
  bacterial infections 318
  biological importance 1813–1814,
    1813(Table)
  in cats 893
  Chagas' disease 524
  chemokines/cytokines regulating 1813,
    1814
  Chlamydia infections 550–551
  cryptococcosis 672

Natural killer (NK) cells (*continued*)
  C-type lectins on 1540
  cytokine receptors on 1810(Table)
  cytokines, NK response to 1812–1813
  cytokines produced 1809, 1813, 1814
    IL-15 role 1494
  cytolysis 505, 730, 1812
    inhibition 1811, 1811(Fig)
    mechanism 506, 1812(Fig)
    signals inducing 1811(Fig)
  cytotoxicity 168, 1533
    decreased in iron overload 1507
    enhanced by LTB₄ 230
    enhanced by serotonin 2166
    mechanisms 2486
    murine model 1272
  decreased activity
    in iron deficiency 1506
    by stress 2221, 2222
  decreased levels 1814–1815, 1814–1819
    cryopreservation effect 669
    gravity/space flights effect 1031
    tumor development 1244
  defects in Chédiak-Higashi syndrome
    527–528
  development/maturation 1813, 2336
  discovery 1809
  in disease 1814–1815
  in dogs 413
  elevated levels 1815
    induced by IL-1 1434
  exercise effect 845, 846
  experimental autoimmune thyroiditis
    2312
  FcγR 888, 890
  Fc receptors 505, 1810, 1811
  fibronectin action 912
  functional characteristics 1812–1813
  functional definition 1809
  functions 1226, 1809, 1812(Table),
    1813–1814
    assessment 1815
    exercise effect 846
    impaired in beige mutation 1271–1272
    impaired in HIV infection 11
    regulation 1813, 1814
  fungal infections 959–960
  graft rejection 1014
    xenografts 2510
  granules, granzymes 1026
  growth, IL-15 stimulating 1494
  hematopoiesis regulation 1814
  HLA-G role in protection of fetus from
    899
  hormone receptors 1814
  in HPV infections 1908
  in HSV infections 1086
  IFNγ synthesis
    induced by IL-12 1813–1814
    inhibition by IL-10 1476
    Toxoplasma gondii infection 2383
  IL-2 action/response 1437
  IL-2 receptor expression 1437
  IL-3 production 1444
  IL-12, response to 1485, 1486
  immunoregulatory role 1814
  influenza virus infections 1386
  intercellular communication 1813
  killing, of viruses 2481
  killing mechanisms 225, 1812
    nonsecretory (apoptosis) 225, 1812
    secretory (necrosis) 1812
    see also Natural killer (NK) cells,
      cytolysis
  LAK cell relationship 1628
  large granular lymphocytes difference
    1533
  Legionella pneumophila lysis 1544
  leishmaniasis 1549
  loss, motheaten mice 1269
  LTB₄ actions 230
  in lung 1368

Natural killer (NK) cells (*continued*)
  at maternal–fetal interface 1814
  mature, phenotype 1810
  MHC class I recognition 1809
    binding by K cell inhibitory receptors
      1811
  motility 539, 1814
  neuroendocrine system interactions 1814
  in nude (athymic) mice 1866
  numbers 1809
    measurement 1815
  ontogeny, porcine 1991
  opioid receptor agonists effect 1829
  parasitic infections 1918, 1919
  phenotype characteristics 1809–1812,
    1810(Table)
  plastic-adherent (A-NK), *see* Natural
    killer (NK) cells, A-NK cells
  platelet-activating factor (PAF) effect
    1972
  porcine 1993
  precursors 1814
  proliferation 1813
  receptors 1533
  recirculation 1812
  in SCID mice 1128, 1268
  SLE 2259
  in spleen 2207
  subsets 1809–1810
  surface receptors 1809, 1810(Table)
    killer cell inhibitory (KIRs) 1809,
      1811–1812, 1812(Table)
    NK activating (NKARs) 1809, 1810–
      1811
  therapy 1815
  tissue-associated 1809
  Toxoplasma gondii infections 1920
  transferrin receptor as target 2392
  tumor antigens, response to 2441
  in viral infections 1813–1814
  virus infection of 2485–2486
  virus recognition 2480–2481
  see also Large granular lymphocytes
    (LGL)
Natural selection theory 573
  antibody formation 1338
  MHC evolution 1701–1702
NC41–neuraminidase complex 159
N-cadherin 1382
  dominant negative mutants 1382
nck, in IL-4 signal transduction 1455
Necator americanus 1121, 1123
Necrobacillosis 963
  synergistic infections 963
Necrosin, *see* Tumor necrosis factor α
  (TNFα)
Necrosis 220, 730, 1342
  lysis of cells 222
  in tuberculosis 1795–1796
Necrotaxis 537
Necrotizing myelopathy 1841
'Negative acute phase proteins' 18, 85
Negative selection
  germinal center B cells 2358
  MHC evolution 1701–1702
  T cells, *see* Thymic selection
  see also Tolerance
Neisseria 1816–1818
  antigens 1816(Table)
  characteristics 1816
  evasive strategies 1817
  host immune response 1817
  pilin 1817
  vaccines 1817–1818
Neisseria gonorrhoeae 1816–1818, 2072
  antigens 1816(Table)
  cathepsin G action against 1723
  infection, *see* Gonococcal infection
  killing by membrane attack complex 627
  lipo-oligosaccharide (LOS) 2072
  lipopolysaccharide 1817
  peptidoglycan 2072

Neisseria gonorrhoeae (*continued*)
  phase/antigenic variation 1817, 2072
  proteins (I/II/III) 2072
  serovars 1816–1817
  toxins 269
  virulence factors 2072
  see also Gonococcal infection
Neisseria meningitidis 1816–1818
  antigens 1816(Table)
  killing by membrane attack complex 627
  meningitis 1816
  meningococcal septicemia 319
  outer membrane proteins (OMPs) 1818
  phase/antigenic variation 1817
  serogroups 1817
  vaccines 1817–1818
    polysaccharide 1817–1818
    serogroup B strains 1818
Nematodes 241
  filarial 1873
  infections 1121–1125
  lymphatic filariasis 913–915
  Toxocara canis cross-reactions 2381
  see also Ascariasis; Hookworm;
    Onchocerca volvulus; *Toxocara canis*;
    Trichuris trichiura
NEM-Sensitive Fusion ATPase proteins
  (NSFs) 852(Table)
Neoglycoprotein 425
Neomycin phosphotransferase, retroviral
  vector marker 2087
Neonatal Fc receptor (FcRn), *see* FcRn
Neonatal immune response 1818–1821,
  1870
  B cell development/function 1818–1819,
    1820(Table)
  cytokines produced by T cells 1820
  IgM synthesis 1818–1819
  preterm infants 1870
  restricted antibody repertoire 1819
  T cell development/function 1819–1820,
    1821(Table), 2294
    cytotoxic T cells 1820
    helper T cells 1820
  tolerance induction 1820
  see also Ontogeny of immune response
Neonates
  hemolytic disease, *see* Hemolytic disease
    of newborn (HDN)
  hepatitis B virus infection 1077
  hyperthyroidism 1675, 2315
  hypothyroidism 2316
    transient 1675
  IgG levels 1672
  immune system, *see also* Neonatal
    immune system
  infection resistance 1672
  lupus syndrome 1676, 2186
  myasthenia gravis 1675–1676, 1847
  neutropenia 1674
  passive transfer of antibodies, ungulates
    2450–2451
  thrombocytopenia 1674, 1976
  tolerance induction 2363
  transient diabetes mellitus 1675
  Ureaplasma urealyticum carriage 1800
  see also Fetus
Neoplasia, *see* Cancer; Malignant disease;
  Tumor(s)
Neopterin, marker of HIV infection
  progression 9
Neoral[R] 688
Nephelometry 1822–1824
  advantages/disadvantages 1824
  applications 1824
  definition 1822
  laser 1824
  light scattering by immune complexes
    1822–1823
    detection mechanism 1824
  microparticle-enhanced immunoassay
    1824

Nephelometry (*continued*)
  monoclonal antibodies 1824
  rate 1824
  sensitive 1824
  turbidimetry differences 1822
Nephritic factors 603, 611, 1257
Nephritis, tubulointerstitial, BK virus
  causing 1990
Nephrotic syndrome
  increased loss/catabolism of Igs 1286–
    1287
  in malaria 1662
Nephrotoxicity, cyclosporine (CsA) 689
Nerve growth factor receptor (NGFR)
  709–710
  structures 519–520, 519(Fig)
Nerves, trauma, leukemia inhibitory factor
  (LIF) action 1561
Nerve–muscle junction, *see* Neuromuscular
  junction
Nervous system
  autoimmune diseases, *see* Neurological
    autoimmune diseases
  cytokine production 1830–1831,
    1831(Table), 1832(Fig)
  cytokines 1845, 2225
  disease
    in AIDS 7
    retroviruses causing 2097
  homeostatic balance with immune system
    1833, 1833(Fig)
  immune system interactions 1824(Fig),
    1825(Fig), 2222–2224
    bidirectional 2223, 2226
    immune pathways to nervous system
      2225–2226, 2226(Fig)
    neuroendocrine pathways to immune
      system 2224–2225, 2225(Fig)
    overview 2227(Fig)
  infections 1844–1847
  neural/immune/psychosocial domain
    coherence 2227(Fig)
  neuromediators, *see* Neuromediators
  see also Autonomic nervous system;
    Central nervous system;
    Neuroendocrine regulation of
    immunity; Neuroendocrine system
Neu-1 locus 1118–1119, 1120
Neural tube defects, elevated α-fetoprotein
  799
Neuraminidase
  antibodies 1385–1386
  antigenic shift and 200
  influenza viruses, *see* Influenza viruses
  Vibrio cholerae 2478
Neuroblastoma, MHC class I
  downregulation 1361
Neurocysticercosis 690
Neuroendocrine regulation of immunity
  1824–1834, 2224–2225
  cytokines role 1830–1831, 1831(Table)
  homeostatic balance 1833, 1833(Fig)
  hormones 224–2225
  HPA axis mediators 1827–1830, 2224
  immune system pathways to nervous
    system 2225–2226, 2226(Fig)
  mucosal immune system 1785
  neuromediators effects 1830(Table),
    2225
  pathways to immune system 2224–2225,
    2225(Fig)
  see also Nervous system
Neuroendocrine system 2223, 2223(Fig)
  effects of stress 339
  interactions with NK cells 1814
Neurofibromin 1301
Neuroglian, Ig-type domains 777(Fig), 778
Neurological autoimmune diseases 1834–
  1843
  CNS 1839–1843
  see also Multiple sclerosis
  nerve–muscle junction 1834–1836

Neurological autoimmune diseases
(*continued*)
nerve–muscle junction (*continued*)
see also Myasthenia gravis
peripheral nerves 1836–1839
see also Guillain–Barré syndrome
Neurological disease/infections, *see under*
Nervous system
Neuromediators 1824–1827, 2224–2225
effects on immune system 1830(Table),
2225
synthesis by immune cells 2225
see also Neurotransmitters
Neuromuscular junction
acetylcholine action 1834
autoimmune disease 1834–1836, 1847–
1851
acquired neuromyotonia 1850
see also Lambert–Eaton myasthenic
syndrome; Myasthenia gravis
Neuromyotonia, acquired (Isaacs'
syndrome) 1850
Neuronal cells
IL-6 action 1460
IL-9 action 1474
Neuronitis, dorsal root ganglion 1838
Neurons, cytokines produced 1832(Fig)
Neuropathy
acute motor axonal (AMAN) 1837–1838
acute sensori-motor axonal (ASMAN)
1838
multifocal motor 1839
sclerosing myeloma (POEMS syndrome)
1839, 1986
see also Polyneuropathy
Neuropeptides 1826–1827, 2225
release by mononuclear cells 1828
Neuropeptide Y 1827
Neurothelin (CD147) 456(Table)
Neurotoxins, arachnids 2472
Neurotransmitters 1785, 1824, 1826,
2224–2225
leukemia inhibitory factor (LIF) action
1561
in lymphoid organs 1824
see also Acetylcholine (ACh)
Neutralization of biological reactions by
antibodies 1851–1854
experimental manipulation 1852–1853
hormones neutralized 1851, 1852(Table)
rationale 1851–1852
see also Contraception, immunological
Neutral proteases, mast cell release 1668
Neutral red dye 1388
Neutropenia
bone marrow transplantation 1575
CD34 cell preparations for 1575
common variable immunodeficiency 600
drug-induced 100
fever 1882
hematologic malignancy 1882
hyper-IgM syndrome 1167
in neonate 1674
opportunistic infections 1882
Pseudomonas aeruginosa infection 2042
respiratory infections 2083
Neutrophil(s) 1388, 1719, 1854–1858
accumulation, IL-8 transgenic mice 1470
activation 16, 1856(Fig)
by chemotactic factors 543
IFNγ role 1424
in lungs of smokers 136
acute inflammation 16–17, 1858
adherence to endothelial cells 541, 1854–
1855, 1935
adhesion molecules 1935–1936, 2059–
2060
stimuli 1855
autocytotoxicity prevention by defensins
1720
autoimmune bullous dermatoses 2188

Neutrophil(s) (*continued*)
azurophil (primary) granules 1715, 1719,
1857
bactericidal/permeability increasing
proteins 1722, 1857, 1938
cathepsin G 1722–1723
contents 1857, 1857(Table), 1938
defensins storage 1720
development 1854
lysozyme 1723
serine proteases 1722–1723
calprotectin 1720
Candida growth in 410
Candida phagocytosis 409–410
chemoattractant-stimulated 1760
chemokines 536(Table)
chemotactic factors 541, 542,
542(Table), 1855, 1935
binding 1761
receptors 542–543, 1760
signaling pathway 2031–2032
chemotaxis 16, 541–543, 1760, 1855,
1935, 2061–2062
Entamoeba histolytica 78
events 1935–1936, 1936(Fig)
IL-8 role 1466, 1469, 1470
see also Neutrophil(s),
migration/locomotion
circulation 1854
collagenase 1857, 1858
complement receptors 1856
CR1 expression 183
defects
Chédiak-Higashi syndrome 527, 1857
chronic granulomatous disease 565,
566, 1857
degranulation 737, 1719–1720, 1856,
1857
chemoattractant-stimulated 1760
priming agents 1857
diapedesis 1854
in dogs 413
endothelial retraction 17, 1854
E-selectin binding, defect in LAD II
syndrome 1568
FcγR function 889
Fc receptors 1856
flexibility 1854
fungal infections 959
gelatinase 1857, 1858
giant granules 1857
GM-CSF action 1021
granules 16–17, 17
azurophil, *see azurophil (primary)
(above)*
deficiency 543, 1857
secretory, *see below*
halogenated molecules released 134
IL-12 production 1484
increased
by G-CSF 1019, 1020
glucocorticoid-induced 1000
infiltration 17, 541
mechanisms 16
in noninflammatory disease 1858
in noninflammatory reactions 1857–1858
in LAD II syndrome 1568
lifespan 1854, 1855(Fig)
Listeria monocytogenes infection 1593
marginated pool 1854
maturation 1854, 1854(Fig)
microbicidal killing 1855–1857
Coccidioides immitis resistance 590
nonoxidative mechanisms 1719–1724
oxygen-dependent 1719, 1856–1857
oxygen-independent 1719–1724
significance 1857
see also Microbicidal mechanisms
migration/locomotion 16, 17, 541–542,
1761, 1854–1855
chemokines inducing 531
clinical defects 543

Neutrophil(s) (*continued*)
migration/locomotion (*continued*)
endothelial cells 802–803
E-selectin role 1935, 2160
failure in LAD I syndrome 1567
in inflammation 541
inhibition by NSAIDs 119
morphology 534(Fig)
polarity 543
signaling 543
morphology 1854
myeloperoxidase 1715–1716, 1719, 1856
NADPH oxidase 1856
absent in chronic granulomatous
disease 565, 566
nitroblue tetrazolium test 566
nonchemokine attractants 537(Table)
nucleus 1854
numbers 1854
oxidative burst 134, 1857
peroxidase 1715–1716
phagocytic vacuoles 1720
phagocytosis 1388, 1855–1857
mechanism 1856
'plugging' in lung 16
precursor cells 1854
recruitment 16
removal, apoptosis 226
response to C5a 90
role, Arthus reaction 238
rolling 16, 1855, 1935, 2059–2060,
2159
rupture 1856
secretory (nonazurophil) granules 1719
contents 1857(Table)
deficiency 1857
development 1854
lactoferrin 1723–1724, 1857
lysozyme 1719, 1723, 1857
type II phospholipase A₂ 1722
secretory vesicles 1857
SLE 2259
specific granules, development 1854
spreading 1855
surface phenotype 1803
survival, increased by G-CSF 1019
tissue injury mediated by 16–17, 1858
urinary tract infection pathogenesis 2453
vitamin C action 2492
Neutrophil-activating factor (NAF), *see*
Interleukin-8 (IL-8)
Neutrophil-activating peptide 1 (NAP-1),
see Interleukin-8 (IL-8)
Neutrophilia
increased IL-8 1470
space flights causing 1030, 1031
Neutrophil immobilizing factor (NIF), *see*
Calprotectin
Neutrophil inhibitory factor (NIF) 1123
Newborn infants, *see* Neonates
Newcastle disease virus (NDV) 1912
vaccines 1916
NEWM human antibody 1140(Fig)
New Zealand Black (NZB) mice 285, 2251
autoimmune hemolytic anemia (AIHA)
91–93
in conditioning experiment 337
genetics 286–286
immune complex disease 1224
MHC genes and lupus susceptibility
2252
NZB/NZW mouse
autoimmunity 1177, 2175
F1 hybrids, suppressor T cell discovery
2243
microsatellite markers, lupus 2253
sex hormones affecting 2175
origin and characteristics 2251,
2251(Table)
pathology 2251
red cell autoantigens 91
response to hsp65 93

New Zealand Black (NZB) mice
(*continued*)
T cells 92–93
thymectomy effect on red cell antibodies 92
xid mutation 92
see also Autoimmune hemolytic anemia (AIHA)
New Zealand white (NZW) mice 2251
origin and characteristics 2251, 2251(Table)
pathology 2251
NF-AT transcription factor
binding to IL-4 gene 1451
binding to IL-5 gene 1457
defects 1279
NFATp, calcineurin action 2325
NF-AT transcription factor family 700
NFkB transcription factor
cytokine synthesis 700, 701
glucocorticoid action 999
HIV replication 1133
in HTLV-1 leukemogenesis 1565
IL-1 signal transduction 1433
IL-8 binding site 1467
macrophage gene expression 1645
relB subunit 746
TNF receptor signaling 2347–2348
NF-Y protein 1042–1043
Niacin 2490
Nickel, allergic contact dermatitis 787
NIF (neutrophil inhibitory factor) 1123
NIH test 2318
Nijmegen-breakage syndrome 249, 1282
NIK, TNF receptor signaling 2348
Nil-2a, T cell anergy 109
Nippostrongylus brasiliensis, eosinophilia due to, anti-IL-5 effect 1456
Nisin 2015
Nitric oxide (NO) 317, 1859–1861
arginine action 236
in Arthus reaction 239
feedback regulation 1859
Legionella pneumophila growth inhibition 1544
Leishmania killing 1548–1549, 1549(Fig), 1860, 1920
Listeria killing 1860
measurement 1860
microbicidal activity 1860
microorganisms evading 1860
pancreatic β cell destruction 1396
parasitic infections 1918, 1919, 1920
pathology caused 1860–1861
phagocytic killing mechanism 317
parasites 1918
production 1859(Fig)
arginine requirement 236
Chagas' disease 524–525
cytokines stimulating 1859
by glial cells 2396
HSV infection 1087
human 1862
induction 1859
in leishmaniasis 1548
L-NMMA inhibiting 1860
by macrophage, *see under* Macrophage
prevention by IL-4 1549
regulation 1859–1860
septic shock 2163
tissue damage 1860–1861
toxic shock induction 1860
Nitric oxide synthase 317
endothelial eNOS 1859
inducible (iNOS) 1859
gene in NOD mouse 1392
interferon γ action 1423
knockout mice 1860
in leishmaniasis 1549
isoforms 1859
neuronal cNOS 1859

Nitric oxide synthase (*continued*)
synthesis, *Legionella pneumophila* infection 1544
T_H1, inducing 1859, 1860(Fig)
T_H2 inhibiting 1859, 1860(Fig)
Nitroblue tetrazolium test (NBT) 566, 1263
Nitrocellulose membrane 142, 2194, 2195
ELISPOT assay 797
Western blotting 2505
NK1 expression, in nude mice 1867
NK cells, *see* Natural killer (NK) cells
NK cytotoxic factor (NKCF) 510
L-NMMA, nitric oxide production inhibition 1860
Nocardia 1861–1864
antigens 1861–1862
characteristics 1861–1862
evasive strategies 1863
glycolipid trehalose-dimycolate (cord factor) 1863
highly virulent 1863
host immune response 1862–1863
macrophage killing 1862
species 1861
vaccines 1863
virulence, categories 1863
Nocardia asteroides complex 1861, 1861(Fig)
T cells in 1862–1863
virulent strains 1862
Nocardia brasiliensis 1862
Nocardiosis 1862
clinical features 1862
diagnosis 1862
experimental 1862
in immunocompromised 1862
T cells 1862–1863
NOD mouse 283, 1390
anti-B7-1/anti-B7-2 mAbs actions 306
autoimmune polyglandular syndrome type II model 1986
BCG exposure 1346
characteristics 1391(Table)
determinant spreading 755, 755–756, 756
diabetes prevention 1394, 1397, 1403
genetics 283, 1392–1396
IDDM loci (Idd) 1392–1396, 1392(Table)
heavy chain knockout mice 1402
islet pathology 1393
macrophage 1393, 1402
sex hormones affecting 2175
T cells 1394, 1402
thyroiditis 2309
treatment, oral insulin 1897
see also Diabetes mellitus, insulin-dependent (IDDM)
Non-Hodgkin's lymphoma, *see* Lymphoma, non-Hodgkin's
Nonobese diabetic (NOD) mouse, *see* NOD mouse
Nonparametric methods of statistical analysis 2212
Nonrandom association, *see* Linkage disequilibrium
Nonsteroidal anti-inflammatory drugs (NSAIDs) 117–121
adverse effects 120, 2025
anti-inflammatory effects 117–118, 118–119, 120(Fig)
autoimmune disease exacerbation 2027
avoidance, in chronic idiopathic urticaria 682
classes 117(Table)
cyclo-oxygenase interaction 118–119
cytokine production enhanced 2026–2027
edema formation inhibition 2025
effects on prostaglandins 1380, 2024

Nonsteroidal anti-inflammatory drugs (NSAIDs) (*continued*)
ineffective in inflammatory bowel disease 1380
mechanisms of action 119, 2025
proinflammatory effects 119–120, 120(Fig)
prostaglandin synthesis inhibition 117–118, 118–119, 120(Fig), 903, 1380, 2024, 2025
tissue injury 119
Noradrenaline, *see* Norepinephrine
Noradrenergic innervation
effect on antigen presentation by macrophage 1826, 1826(Fig)
spleen 1825(Fig)
Norepinephrine (noradrenaline) 2224, 2225
exercise-induced release 846, 847
Norfloxacin 1882
Normal flora, *see* Microflora (normal)
Northern blotting 1864–1865
procedure 1864–1865
hybridization with probe 1865
RNA separation by gel electrophoresis 1864–1865
RNA transfer to membrane 1865
Norwalk virus (NV) 400
infections 968
reinfection 401
Norwegian scabies 753
Nosocomial infections
opportunistic 1882
Proteus mirabilis 2039
Pseudomonas aeruginosa 2042, 2044
NOTCH3 gene 1115, 1116(Table)
Novobiocin, resistance 2210
NP-3a (corticostatin) 1722
Npy gene 1392
Nuclear antigens 125–126
Nuclear envelope 849
Nuclear enzymes 126
Nuclear factor IV, *see* Ku antigen
Nuclear factor kappa B, *see* NFkB transcription factor
Nucleic acid
as antigens 204
see also DNA; RNA
Nucleolar organizer region (NOR) 303
Nucleoli, antigens 125
Nucleoprotein (NP), DNA vaccines 772, 773
Nucleoside metabolism 749, 749(Fig)
Nucleosomes 125
antibodies 130–131, 133
anti-DNA antibodies interaction with histones 130
antigens 125–126
Nucleus
antibodies, *see* Anti-DNA antibodies
antigens 125
micromanipulation, B cell isolation 181
Nude (athymic) mice 1274, 1866–1868
applications 1868
graft growth 1868
T cell differentiation 1868
tumor development 1868
Bacteroides abscess formation 328
B cells 1867–1868
breeding/maintenance 1866
breeding systems 1866
discovery 1866
immunological characteristics 1866–1868
inbreeding 1866
leprosy model 1868
NK cells 1866
phagocytes 1866
strains available 1866
streaker mutation 1866
T cells 1866–1867
differentiation 1867
T independent antigen response 1868

nude gene mutants 1273
nu gene 1866
Null hypothesis of no linkage 1697, 2064
nu/nu-xid mice 1270
nur77 570
Nutrients, transport in plasma 1965
Nutrition 1869–1871
  deficiencies 1870
    elderly 1871
    immunodeficiency in 1284
  elderly 1870–1871
  fat-derived energy intake 884
  fatty acids, *see* Fatty acids (dietary)
  germ-free animal studies 991
  low-birth weight infants 1870
  practical applications 1871
  regulation of immune function 1870–1871
  see also Diet; Protein-energy malnutrition (PEM)
NYVAC virus 2464

O

OA3 (CD47) 449(Table)
'O' antigens 322
'Obese' (*ob*) mutants 1273
Obese strain of chickens 104, 281–282, 281(Fig), 300, 2309
  adoptive transfer experiments 281, 282
  autoantibodies 281
  autoimmune disease pathogenesis 279
  autoimmune polyglandular syndrome type II model 1986
  autoreactive T cells 277
  genetics 282
  glucocorticoid response 282
  hypothyroidism 281
  immune hyperreactivity 281
  MHC class II genes/expression 282, 2310
  thyroiditis, retroviruses causing 2097
Occupational hazards, allergic 2122
Ocular antigens
  antibodies 868
  tolerance 867–868
    induction 867–868, 879
Ocular autoimmunity, *see* Eye, autoimmune disease
Ocular fluids, immunosuppressive factors 870
Ocular larva migrans 2379
Odds ratio 1698
Ogive (cumulative distribution plot) 2214
OK-432, diabetes prevention in animal models 1397
OKM-5 antigen, *see* CD36
OKT3 (anti-CD3) 122, 467
  in autoimmune disease 1358
  in bone marrow transplant recipients 2261
  mechanism of action and uses 123
  side-effects 2261
  therapeutic uses 1352
  in transplantation 2414
2'5'-Oligoadenylate synthetase, interferon-induced 1416, 1419, 1423
Oligodendrocytes, JC virus infection 1989
Oligosaccharides
  as antigenic determinants 150
  'complex', in IgM 1213
  I and i antigens 594(Fig), 595
  lectins binding 1535, 1537
  as ligand in triad recognition systems 1579
  polypeptide glycosylation 1001
  see also Glycosylation
  structure, conserved population 1001
Olive oil 885
Omenn's syndrome 1279

Onchocerca, species 1872
Onchocerca volvulus 873, 1872
  antigens 1873, 1874
  characteristics 1872–1873
  evasive strategies 1874
  host immune response 1873–1874
    cell-mediated 1873
    IgG and IgE 1873
    T$_H$1 response 1873
  lifecycle 1872, 1872(Fig)
  skin infections 752
  transmission 1872
  vaccines 1874
Onchocerciasis (river blindness) 873, 1872–1875
  animal models 1874
  generalized 1873
  immunoregulation 1873
  localized (sowda) 1873
  ocular pathology 1873
  prevalence 1872
Onchocercomata 1872, 1874
Oncodevelopmental antigens 207, 213
  glycoproteins and glycolipids 425
Oncofetal antigens 800
Oncogenes 1361, 2487
  see also individual genes
Oncogenic viruses, *see* Oncoviruses
Oncology
  germ-free animals use 990–991
  see also Cancer; Tumor(s)
Oncotic pressure 1597, 1964
Oncoviruses 1562–1563, 2092, 2093(Table), 2096–2097, 2487
  antigens 2426
  carcinogenesis mechanism 1563–1564, 2097
  see also Viral carcinogenesis
  'downstream promotion' of expression 1563
  helper viruses 2097
  leukemia pathogenesis 1562–1563
  'proviral enhancement' 1563
  'regional activation' 1563
  replication-defective 1563, 2097
  transformation by 1562–1563
  see also Retroviruses; Viral carcinogenesis
Ontogeny of immune response 1875–1879
  ABO blood group 4
  amphibians 82
  canine immune system 411–412
  Ig gene rearrangements 1876
    see also Immunoglobulin gene rearrangements
  lymphocyte differentiation 1875(Fig)
  molecular changes 1876–1877
  ordered expression of V gene families 1877–1878
  phenotypic changes 1875–1876
  porcine 1991–1992
  TCR development 1876–1877
    see also T cell receptor (TCR)
  see also Embryology; Neonatal immune response; *specific cell types*
Oocyte, birth control vaccine 642, 643(Table)–644(Table)
Ophthalmia, HSV-1, *see* Herpes simplex virus type 1 (HSV-1) ophthalmia (HSVO)
Ophthalmopathy, Graves' 2315–2316
Opiates 2225
  allergic reaction 778
Opioid
  ADCC modulation 170
  invertebrate immune response 1501
Opioid receptors agonists 1829
Opisthorchiasis 1879–1881
Opisthorchis viverrini 1879–1881
  antigens 1879
  evasive strategies 1880
  excretory–secretory (ES) products 1879

Opisthorchis viverrini (continued)
  host immune response 1879–1880
  immunosuppression due to 1880
  monoclonal antibodies 1879
  vaccines 1880
op/op mouse 1651, 1651(Table)
Opportunistic infections 1881–1884
  in AIDS/HIV infection 7, 8, 1884
    treatment 11
    see also AIDS
  community-acquired 1881–1882
  in corticosteroid therapy 1883
  gram-negative bacteria 2377
  in hematologic malignancy 1882–1883
  in immunodeficiency 1881(Table), 1883
    SCID 2170
  in malignant disease 1882–1883
  management 1882
  nosocomial (hospital-acquired) 1882
  oral 1891
  organisms 1881
  pattern 1881(Table), 1882
  pneumococcal pneumonia 2219
  prevention, prothymosin α (Pro-Tα) and thymosin Tα1 2301
  in protein-energy malnutrition (PEM) 1869
  respiratory tract 2083
  Staphylococcus 2210
  in transplant recipients 1883–1884
Opportunistic tumors, AIDS and HIV infection 7, 8
Opposum, immune system 1664
Opsoclonus–myoclonus 1843
Opsonins 1227, 1885, 1936, 2032
  acute phase proteins 1886–1887
  collectins 1887
  complement components 1885, 1886, 1936
  C-reactive protein (CRP) 664
  discovery 1885
  FcγR and complement synergy 1886
  immunoglobulins 1885–1886, 1936
    IgA 1886
    IgE 1886
    IgG 1885
    IgM 1885
  in monocyte phagocytosis 1751
  signaling pathways 2032
Opsonization 629, 1146, 1222, 1885–1888, 1936–1937, 1936(Fig)
  antimicrobial drug effect 1887
  bacterial defense against 1936, 1936(Fig)
  Klebsiella pneumoniae 1522
  mechanism 1175(Fig), 1936–1937
  picornaviruses 1956
  role of natural antibodies 1808
  Streptococcus pneumoniae 2219
  in type II hypersensitivity 1174, 1175(Fig)
  viruses 2481
Oral cavity 1888–1893
  anatomy 1888
  flora 1888
  host defenses 1888
  humoral immunity 1890
  polymorphonuclear cells 1889–1890
  T cells 1890–1891
  vaccine administration, *see* Vaccines, oral
Oral disease
  immune-mediated 1891–1892
  infections in immunodeficiency diseases 1891
  passive immunization 1892
  vaccines 1892
Oral health, immunodeficiency diseases 1891
Oral immunology 1888–1893
  see also entries beginning Dental; Oral cavity
Oral poliovirus vaccine (OPV), *see* Poliovirus vaccine

Oral tolerance 1785, 1893–1899, 2365
   autoimmune disease treatment 1357,
      1897(Table)
      animal models 1896–1897,
         1897(Table)
      human 1897–1898, 1897(Table)
   definition 1893
   GALT 1893
   high antigen doses 1894, 1894(Fig)
   historical aspects 1893
   insulin 1403
   low antigen doses 1894, 1894(Fig)
   mechanisms 1893, 1894–1895
      bystander suppression 1895–1896,
         1895(Table)
      cellular suppression 1894–1895,
         1894(Fig)
      clonal anergy/deletion 1894, 1894(Fig)
      IgA production 1894, 1895
      TGFβ role 1894–1895
      T$_H$2 cells 1894–1895
   modulation 1896
      cytokines enhancing 1896, 1896(Table)
      cytokines/factors decreasing 1896,
         1896(Table)
Orch-1 1120
Organ culture of lymphoid cells 1899–
      1902
   applications 1899, 1900–1901
   B cell production 1901
   cell purification techniques 1900
   historical aspects 1899
   in vivo transplantation use 1901
   methods 1899–1900
      hanging drop 1900(Fig), 1901
      plasma clot method 1899, 1900(Fig)
      raft culture 1900, 1900(Fig)
      transmembrane system 1900, 1900(Fig)
   monolayer 1901
   role of thymic microenvironment 1900–
      1901
   T cell differentiation studies 1901
   thymic epithelium 1900–1901
   thymic fragment 1901
   tissue slices 1901
   Whitlock–Witte system 1901, 2236
Organ transplantation, see Transplantation
Organum vasculosum laminae terminalis
      (OVLT) 903
Oriental sore 1546
Ornithine decarboxylase, inhibition 1434
Oropouche virus 391
Orotic aciduria 1286
Orthokinesis 534
Orthomyxoviruses 1385–1387
   see also Influenza viruses
Orthopoxvirus 1995, 1995(Table)
Orthoreovirus 2067
OS chickens, see Obese strain of chickens
Osteoclast, formation 1755
Osteoclast-activating factor, see
      Interleukin-1 (IL-1); Leukemia
      inhibitory factor (LIF)
Osteopetrosis 2499
Osteoporosis 2177
Otitis media
   C1 components 1294
   Haemophilus influenzae 1048
   secretory, food-mediated 949
Ouchterlony's technique 141, 2001(Fig),
      2002
   comparative plate 2001(Fig), 2002
Ouchterlony–Elek plate technique 1287,
      1288
Oudin's tube single diffusion technique
      1287, 2001–2002
Outer membrane proteins (OMPs) 321–
      322
   antigenic variation 322
Ovalbumin, bystander suppression in vitro
      1896
Ovarian cancer

Ovarian cancer (continued)
   HLA-A2$^+$ 2425
   M-CSF (CSF-1) levels 165
   paraneoplastic cerebellar degeneration
      1842
Ovary, autoantibodies 262(Table), 263
Ovine immune system 1902–1906
   absence of HEVs 1905
   afferent lymph 1903–1904
   antigen-presenting cells 1905
   B cells 1903
   CD antigens 1903, 1904(Table)
   cytokine genes 1903
   dendritic cells 1903–1904
   efferent lymph 1905
   lymph node 1905
   memory cells 1903, 1905
   MHC 1903
   T cells 1903, 1905
   T$_H$1 and T$_H$2 1903
Ovulation 1853
   blocking 641
   TNFα inducing 2437
OX40 (CD134) 455(Table), 1358, 2148
Oxidation, periodate-dependent, catalytic
      antibody reaction 441(Fig)
Oxidative burst, see Respiratory burst
Oxidative stress 133
Oxygen
   hyperbaric, effect on immune function
      1157
   phagocytic killing mechanisms, see
      Microbicidal mechanisms
   reactive species, see also Reactive oxygen
      species
   singlet
      formation 1717, 1857
      vitamin E action 2500
Oxyperoxidase 1715–1716
Oxytocin 1853
Ozone, depletion 1943

P

P1A gene 2424, 2424(Table)
P1 bacteriophage 2016
   Cre recombinase 1525(Fig), 1526(Fig),
      1527
   vectors for transgenes 2406
P2 protein, antibodies 860
p15E, tumor immunological escape 2445
p21, in interferon α action 1416
p21^{rac} 565
p21^{ras} 2325–2326
   activation, PKC role 2327
   adapter molecules in TCR coupling to
      2326
   B cell receptor signaling mechanism 1300
   cytokine synthesis pathway 700
   regulators 2326
   T cell signaling 2326, 2327
p21^{ras}-GTP complexes 2326
p21^{ras}/MAP kinase pathway, T cell anergy
      109
p21^{src} 1713
p24 (CD9) 446(Table)
p36, TCR signaling 2326
p38 kinase
   IL-3 receptor signal transduction 1443
   T cell receptor signaling 2328
   TNF receptor signaling 2347
   see also Stress-activated protein kinase
      (SAPK)
p47^{phox} 1275, 1713
   gene therapy 979(Table)
p52^{shc}, in IL-3 receptor signal transduction
      1448
p53
   mutation

p53 (continued)
   mutation (continued)
      bovine leukemia virus 1565
      in Burkitt's lymphoma 1635
      upregulation by radiation 2051
p55 (IL-2α) 720
   receptor, see Tumor necrosis factor
      receptor (TNFR), CD120a
   see also Interleukin-2 (IL-2) receptor (IL-
      2R), α chain
p56^{fyn}, signal transduction in T cell
      activation 2324
p56^{lck} 10
   antigen recognition by TCR on CD4$^+$ cell
      467
   CD4 interactions 470
   CD8 association 477, 478
   signal transduction in T cell activation
      2324
   transgenic mice lacking 477
p60 receptor, see Tumor necrosis factor
      receptor (TNFR), CD120a
p60^{src}, in IL-11 signal transduction 1480
p62^{yes}, in IL-11 signal transduction 1480
p67^{phox} 1713
p70^{S6K} kinase 711
p75 receptor, see Tumor necrosis factor
      receptor (TNFR), CD120b
p80 receptor, see Tumor necrosis factor
      receptor (TNFR), CD120b
p150,95, expression and function 1407
p185^{HER2} 2429
P450c21A gene 1115, 1116(Table)
P450c21B gene 1115, 1116(Table)
   deficiency 1120
PA317 cell line 2088–2089
PADGEM, see P-selectin (CD62P)
PAF, see Platelet-activating factor (PAF)
Pain
   prostaglandins role 117
   relief, NSAIDs role 117
'Pale ear' (ep) mice 1272
Pallidin, in red cell membrane 835,
      838(Table)
'Pallid' (pa) mice 1272
pa mice 1272
Pancreas transplantation 1402, 2413
   cyclosporine role 688
   problems 2413
   results 2413
   tissue typing 2322
Pancreatic β cells
   autoantigens 1391
   destruction mechanism 1394–1396,
      1395(Fig)
      cytokines role 1396
      free radicals 1396
      TNFα role 2438
   loss, in IDDM animal models 1393
   tolerogenic 2367
Pancreatic islets
   autoantibodies, see Islet cell antibodies
   autoantigens, see Islet cell antigens (ICA)
   ICA-69 protein mimicked by BSA protein
      (ABBOSS) 1400–1401
   pathology in IDDM animal models 1393
   transgenic models, experimental
      autoimmunity 274
   transplantation 1402, 2413
   see also Diabetes mellitus, insulin-
      dependent (IDDM)
Pandemics, absence of idiotype expansion
      1193
Pandysautonomia, acute 1838
Paneth cells 1781
   defensins in 1721
   type II phospholipase A$_2$ 1722
'Panning' 179
Pannus 135
Panspecific hematopoietin, see Interleukin-3
      (IL-3)
P antigen, see under Blood groups

Panton–Valentine factors, *Staphylococcus* 2209
Pantothenic acid 2490
  deficiency 2490
PapD
  CD5 (Ly-1) homology 472
  Ig-type domains 778
Papillomavirus 1907–1909
  bovine (BPV) 1908
  human, *see* Human papillomaviruses (HPV)
  rabbit 1907
Papovaviridae 1989
Pappenhiemer pore theory 1597
Parabenzoquinone (PBQ) 1261
Paracetamol (acetaminophen), prostaglandin synthesis inhibition 118
Paracoccidioides brasiliensis, NK cell action 959–960
Paradigms, in science 1334
Paraffin embedding 1262
Paraformaldehyde, tissue fixation 1261
Paramagnetic beads, B cell enrichment 179
Paramyosin (antigen B) 690, 693
  protection against lymphatic filariasis 915
Paramyxovirinae 1909, 1910(Table)
Paramyxoviruses 1909–1916
  assembly 1914
  attachment proteins 1909–1910, 1911, 1911(Fig), 1915
  characteristics 1909–1911
  classification 1909, 1910(Table)
  effect on host cells 1914–1915
  evasive strategies 1915–1916
  experimental autoimmune thyroiditis induction 2311
  fusion proteins 1909, 1912, 1912(Fig)
    domains 1912
    role 1913
  genome 1911, 1911(Fig)
    mutations 1915
  host immune response 1915
  H protein 1915
  infection initiation 1911, 1913
  infections caused by 1909, 1910(Table)
  infectious cycle 1913–1914, 1914(Fig)
  L proteins 1913
  M proteins 1910, 1912, 1914
  nucleocapsid proteins 1913
  persistent infections 1915
  P proteins/P gene-encoded proteins 1913
  proteins 1909–1911, 1911–1913
  receptors 1913
  replication 1913
  RNAase resistance 1913
  RNA synthesis 1913
  SH (small hydrophobic) proteins 1913
  syncytia formation 1909, 1914
  vaccines 1915, 1916
  virion structure 1909–1911, 1910(Fig)
Paraneoplastic cerebellar degeneration (PCD) 1842
Paraneoplastic encephalomyelitis 1842
Paraneoplastic syndromes, autoimmune-mediated 1850
Parapoxvirus 1995–1996, 1995(Table)
  vaccination 1998
Paraproteins 1636
Parasites 1916
  antigens 1918
    cross-reacting with Forssman antigen 954
  in CNS 1846
  load 1917
  microparasites and macroparasites 1916–1917
  see also Helminth worms; *individual parasites/infections*; Protozoa
Parasites, immunity to 1916–1922
  antigen-presenting cells 1918
  cytokines produced 1919

Parasites, immunity to (*continued*)
  cytotoxic T cells 1918
  evidence for immunity 1917
  humoral immunity 1918
  immune responses 1917–1918
    strategies 1917
  immunopathology 1919–1920
  macrophage 1918
  nitric oxide role 1918, 1919
  NK cells 1918, 1919
  phagocytosis 1918
  specific infections 1920
  T cells, CD8+ cells 1919
  T cell subsets 1918, 1918–1919
  vaccine development 1921
Parasitic infections 1917
  chronic 1917
  gastrointestinal tract 968–969
  HIV and 1920–1921
  IgE role 1173–1174
  skin 750
  vaccination 1921
  see also individual infections
Parasitism 1916
Parathyroid autoantibodies 262(Table), 263
Paratopes 43, 202, 2465
  definition 43, 202, 266
  valency 2465
  see also Antibody combining sites
Parechovirus 1955(Table)
  receptors 1956(Table)
Parietal cells, gastric, *see* Gastric parietal cells
Parotitis, chronic lymphocytic, in AIDS 7
Paroxysmal nocturnal hemoglobinuria (PNH) 73, 406
  CD59 deficiency 499–500
  complement deficiency 613, 616
  decay accelerating factor absence 499, 735
  GPI-linked proteins absent 835
PARP (poly-ADP ribose polymerase) 876, 1028
Parry's disease, *see* Graves' disease
Parvovirus 1922–1927
  antibodies in pigs 1991
  classification 1922
  feline infections 895
  infections 1922
Parvovirus B19 1922–1927
  acute infection 1924
    clinical features 1924
  in AIDS 1924, 1924–1925, 1926
  biology 1922–1923
  cytopathology 1923
  detection 1923
  discovery 1922
  diseases caused by 1924(Table)
  DNA 1923
  genome organization 1922
  IgG therapy 1924
  immune response 1923–1924
  in immunocompetent host 1924, 1924(Table)
  in immunocompromised host 1924–1926, 1924(Table)
  infection, complement fixation test problem 618
  intrauterine infections 1925
  maternal infection 1925
  natural infection 1923–1924
  persistent disease in immunodeficiency 1924–1925
    anemia 1925
    antibody production patterns 1924
    treatment 1925–1926
  proteins 1922–1923, 1923
  receptors 1923
  replication 1923
  syndrome of congenital anemia 1925
  target tissue 1922, 1923

Parvovirus B19 (*continued*)
  transmission 1924
  vaccine development 1926
  viremia 1923, 1925
  VP1 and VP2 1923
Passive immunity 218
  cryptosporidiosis 677
  maternal transfer of IgG, *see* Immunoglobulin, placental transfer; Immunoglobulin G (IgG)
  in ungulates 2450–2451
Passive immunization 218, 1147
  dogs 412
  hepatitis A virus 1074
  oral disease 1892
  see also Intravenous immunoglobulin
Passive specific immunopotentiation 1345
Passive transfer, delayed-type hypersensitivity (DTH) 739
Pasteur, L. 256, 1335–1336, 2457
Pasteurella multocida 1927–1929
  aggressins 1928
  antigens 1927–1928, 1928
  capsule antigens 1927, 1928
  characteristics 1927–1928
  depolymerization of capsules 1927, 1927(Table)
  diseases associated 1928(Table)
  evasive strategies 1928
  host immune responses 1928
  hosts 1927
  identification by mucopolysaccharidase use 1927, 1927(Table)
  lipopolysaccharide 1927
    antibodies 1928
  natural acquired immunity 1928
  serogroups 1927
  serotypes 1927
  shared/cross-reactive epitopes 1928
  toxins 1928
  vaccines 1929
    development 256
  virulence 1928
Pasteurization 385–386
Patch tests, allergen-specific T cells 69
Paternity testing, allotype application 76
'Pathogenic zymodeme' 77
Pathogens, evolution 255, 259
'Pattern-recognition molecules' 185, 215
Pattern-recognition receptor 186–187
Pauling, L. 2199
Paul–Bunnell antibodies 831, 1092
Paul–Bunnell antigen 1092
Pavlovian conditioning 337–338
P blood group 1923
  recurrent pyelonephritis 2453
Pbx2 gene 1046
PBX2 protein 1046, 1115
PC12 cell line, IL-6 action 1460
P cell stimulating factor, *see* Interleukin-3 (IL-3)
PCR, *see* Polymerase chain reaction (PCR)
PD genes 1992
Peak expiratory flow rate (PEFR) 246
Peanut agglutinin 1540
  applications 1540(Table)
Peanut allergy 950
Peanut lectin 1536
Pearson's correlation coefficient 2213
PECAM-1 (CD31) 28, 30, 448(Table), 804–805
  in diapedesis 759
  on endothelial cells 804–805
  function 805
  on monocytes 1754
Pectin, antitumor activity 430
Pelvic inflammatory disease (PID) 1816, 1817
  Neisseria gonorrhoeae causing 2072
Pemphigoid 2188
  autoantibody detection 2188
  clinical/pathological features 2188

Pemphigoid (*continued*)
  immunotherapy 2189
  pathogenesis 2188–2189
Pemphigus 2188
  autoantibody detection 2188
  clinical/pathological features 2188
  IgA 2188
  immunotherapy 2189
  paraneoplastic 2188
  pathogenesis 2188–2189
  types 2188
Pemphigus vulgaris 263, 2188
  HLA association 1694
PEM (polymorphic epithelial mucin) 2428
Penetrin 522
Penicillamine, immunodeficiency due to
    1285
Penicillin
  drug-induced immune hemolytic anemia
    95, 100
  mechanism of action 321
Penillici, in spleen 2207
Pentane 135
Pentons 21, 22
Pentoxifylline 2439
  TNFα synthesis reduction 2439
Pentraxin family 663
  in invertebrates 1500
  see also C-reactive protein (CRP)
Pep5 2015
Peptide elution, minor transplantation
    antigens 1731
Peptide-induced tolerance 1357
Peptides
  'altered ligands' 1357
  as haptens 1051
  immunization, in tumors 1344
  as immunogens 2199
  MHC complexes, tolerance induction
    1357
  random peptide libraries 985
  synthesis, catalytic antibody reaction
    441(Fig)
  T cell receptor (TCR) 1357
Peptide transporter (TAP), *see* TAP
    (Transporter Associated with antigen
    Processing)
Peptidoglycan 321, 423
  bacterial cell walls 321
  Neisseria gonorrhoeae 2072
  Streptococcus 2218
Peptido-glycan-polysaccharide polymers,
    colitis due to 1384
Peptido-leukotrienes, increase, NSAIDs
    causing 120
Peptidyl dipeptidase A (CD143) 456(Table)
Peptidylglycine α-amidating mono-
    oxygenase, in copper deficiency 658,
    658(Table)
Peptococcus magnus 326
PERB (Perth MHC β-block) 1114
Percoll 509
Perfluorocarbon emulsions, as blood
    substitute 2403
Perforin 225, 733, 1026, 1929–1931
  apoptosis induction 1026–1027,
    1029(Fig)
    mechanism 1027–1028
  cell lysis mechanism 504, 506, 726–727,
    1029(Fig), 1929, 1930–1931
    cell death protease activation 1028
    cytotoxic T cells 278(Fig), 726–727
  deficient mice 729
  historical aspects 1026
  knockout mice 233, 729
  molecular properties 1929–1930
  molecular weight 1930
  monomer polymerization 1930
  pores formed, structure 1930(Fig)
  structural organization 1930(Fig)
  synergistic action with granzymes 1026,
    1930

Perforin (*continued*)
  synergistic action with granzymes
      (*continued*)
    granzyme B 1027–1028, 1930
Perhydroxyl radical 1715
Pericarditis 2083
Perinuclear antineutrophil cytoplasmic
    autoantibodies (P-ANCA) 264, 2120
Perinuclear factors, antibodies, in
    rheumatoid arthritis 2113
Periodontal disease 1889, 1890
  germ-free animals use 991
  IL-1/IL-6 and PGE₂ 1891
  prevention 1890
  vaccines/management 1892
  see also Periodontitis
Periodontitis 1889
  chronic 1891
  immune-mediated 1891
  localized juvenile (LJP) 1890
  prepubertal 1890
  T cells 1891
  treatment 1892
Peripheral addressins, *see* Addressins,
    peripheral
Peripheral blood lymphocytes, *see*
    Lymphocyte
Peripheral blood progenitor cells
  mobilization, GM-CSF use 1022
  see also Stem cell(s)
Peripheral nerve
  IL-1 stimulating 2226
  P_0 and P_2 antigens 1836–1837
Peripheral nerve disease 860
  autoimmune 1836–1838
Peripheral nervous system, HSV infection
    1085
Pernicious anemia 101–105
  autoantibodies 102–103, 103(Table), 263
  autoimmune diseases associated 104
  autoimmune polyglandular syndrome
    type II 1985
  clinical features 101–102
  hematologic features 101–102
  inheritance 104–105
  refractory 101
  treatment 101, 105
  see also Gastritis, autoimmune
Peroxidase
  eosinophils 1716
  in immunocytochemistry 1263, 1264(Fig)
  macrophage 1716, 1752
  oxygen-dependent phagocytic killing
    1715–1716
  probe labeling in Northern blotting 1865
  see also Horseradish peroxidase (HRP);
    Myeloperoxidase (MPO)
Peroxidase–antiperoxidase (PAP) technique
    815
Peroxynitrite 134
Peroxynitrite anion 1860
Pertactin (PRN) 377
Pertussigen 377, 378, 2373(Fig), 2374
  mode of action 2373(Fig)
Pertussis
  case number 377
  diagnosis 377
  immune response 378
  notifications in England/Wales 2464(Fig)
  toxin, *see Bordetella pertussis*, toxins;
    Pertussigen
  vaccines, *see under Bordetella pertussis*
  see also Bordetella pertussis
Pesticides, chromosomal translocations 559
Pestiviruses 2350(Table)
  congenital infection 2352
  genome 2351
  tolerance 2351
Petri dishes, cell adherence 511
Peyer's patches 190(Fig), 396, 1249, 1601,
    1774, 1775–1777, 1781, 2155
  antigen delivery to APCs 1776

Peyer's patches (*continued*)
  antigen-presenting cells (APCs) 1777,
    1781
  antigen uptake/sampling mechanism
    1776, 1781
  avian 1776
  B cells 1776, 1777, 1781
  CTL response in reovirus infections 2070
  cytokines 1777
  dendritic cells 1777
  disassociated cells 1777
  discovery 1775–1776
  follicle-associated epithelium 1776
  follicles (B cell zone) 1776, 1781
  follicular dendritic cells 1777
  germinal centers 1776, 1781
  HEVs 1099, 1776
  IgA synthesis 1776, 1777, 1781, 1782
  location 1781
  lymphocyte migration 1617
  macrophage 1776, 1777, 1781
  M cells 1776, 1781
  microenvironment 1726
  numbers 1781
  ontogeny, in ungulates 2450
  in pigs 1991, 1994
  regions 1776
  single ileal, ungulates 2449
  T cells 1777
  T cell zone 1776
  types in animals 1617
  see also Gut-associated lymphoid tissue
    (GALT)
Pgp-1 1683
  see also CD44
pH
  gradients, isoelectric focusing (IEF) 1511
  plasma 1965
Phacoanaphylaxis 867
Phage display of antibodies 1358, 1931–
    1934
  antibody fragments expressed 1931
  cloned V gene segments (semisynthetic
    library) 1932–1933
  library construction 1931(Fig), 1932,
    1932(Fig), 2433
  multivalent antibody fragments 1933–
    1934
  naive ('nonimmunized') libraries 1932–
    1933
  'natural' monoclonal antibodies 1934
  phage selection strategies 1933,
    1933(Fig)
  principle 1931–1932
  single chain Fv fragments 1931, 1934
  in tumor imaging 2433
  vector systems 1931
Phage expression system, screening for
    catalytic antibodies 444
Phagemid vector 1931, 1932(Fig)
Phagocytes 14, 1387, 1935
  activation 317
    by fibronectin 912
  ADCC 169
  adhesion mechanisms 2059–2061
  asialoglycoprotein receptor 1886
  bacterial interactions 317
  bacteria uptake 317
  complement receptors 1886
    CR1 and CR3 in opsonization 1886
  discovery 1719, 1885
  FcαR 1886
  FcεRII 1886
  FcγR 1885
  FcγRII 1885
  invertebrates 1500
  iron sources 1717
  killing mechanisms 317, 1713–1718,
    1751–1752, 1856–1857
  see also Microbicidal mechanisms
  Listeria monocytogenes infections 1593
  migration, *see* Monocyte(s), migration;

Phagocytes (*continued*)
  migration, *see* Monocyte(s), migration;
    Neutrophil(s), migration;
    Transmigration of leukocytes
    (*continued*)
    Neutrophil(s), migration;
    Transmigration of leukocytes
  mononuclear, *see* Macrophage;
    Monocyte(s)
  NADPH oxidase, *see* NADPH oxidase
    (phagocytes)
  in nude (athymic) mice 1866
  oxidase (phox) 1713
    see also NADPH oxidase
  phylogeny 1949
  types 1387
    see also Macrophage; Monocyte(s);
    Neutrophil(s)
Phagocytic glycoprotein 1 (Pgp-1), *see*
  CD44
'Phagocytin' 1719
Phagocytosis 1388, 1713, 1935–1940
  apoptotic cells 185–186, 222
  attachment process 1937
  bacterial evasion 1936–1937
  C3b role 604
  calcium changes 1857
  cell separation techniques based on 509–
    510
  chemical stimuli 1713
  Coccidioides immitis 590
  'coiling' 1542, 1543(Fig)
  complement role 1146
  damaged cells 185–186
  decreased
    iron overload 1507
    protein-energy malnutrition 1869
    vitamin A deficiency 2489
  digestion 1939
  enhancement
    clindamycin 1887
    defensins 1887
    fibronectin 912, 1887, 1937
    tuftsin 1887
    vitronectin 1887
  by eosinophils 823
  evasion by *Legionella pneumophila*
    1542–1543
  FcγR role 889, 1937
  Fc receptor γ chain 889
  GM-CSF action 1021
  historical background 1719
  inflammatory bowel disease 1380(Fig)
  integrins involved 1713
  invertebrates 1499, 1500
  iridovirus 1503, 1504
  killing mechanisms, *see* Microbicidal
    mechanisms
  Legionella pneumophila resistance 1544
  liposome-encapsulated molecules 1589
  by macrophage/monocytes 1648(Fig),
    1751–1752, 1751(Fig)
  mannose receptors 187
  mechanism 1856
  neutrophils 1855–1857
  opsonization role 1146, 1175(Fig), 1856,
    1936–1937
    see also Opsonization
  in oral cavity 1889
  parasitic infections 1918
  physical stimuli 1713
  platelets 1181
  porcine 1992
  process 1935(Fig), 1937
  pseudopodia 1937
  receptor-mediated ingestion 1937
  respiratory tract infections and 2083
  rickettsiae 2127
  in spleen 2207
  stimulating factors 1886–1887
  thorium dioxide, s-exocytosis 851
  uptake without opsonization 1937

Phagolysosomes 1388, 1937
  Histoplasma capsulatum infections 1107
Phagosomes 1388, 1751, 1856, 1937
  granule fusion 737
  lysosome fusion 1751, 1937
    avoidance by *Legionella pneumophila*
      1543
    Nocardia inhibiting 1863
    prevention by *Chlamydia* 551
  pH 1715
  ribosomes, *Legionella pneumophila*
    infection 1543
Pharyngitis, streptococcal 2218, 2219
Phase variation
  Mycoplasma 1799
  Neisseria 1817
  Neisseria gonorrhoeae 2072
Pheblovirus 392
pHEN1 1931, 1932(Fig)
Phenomenon of multiple proportions 2000
Phenotype 986, 987
  see also Genetic analysis
Phenylethylamine, false food allergy
  952(Table)
Phenytoin, immunodeficiency due to 1285
Pheochromocytoma cell line PC12, IL-6
  action 1460
Pheromone studies, stress and immune
  regulation 339
Philadelphia chromosome 554, 1556–1557,
  1558
Phlebotomus fever 392
Phlebovirus 391(Table)
Phorbol, structure 1941(Fig)
Phorbol esters 1940–1942
  LFA-1 activation 1610–1611
  mechanism of action 2327
  origin 1940
  protein kinase C activation 2325
  receptors, *see also* Protein kinase C
  signal transduction pathways 1940
  structures 1941(Fig)
Phosphatases
  IL-11 signal transduction 1480
  signal transduction in T cell activation
    2324
Phosphatidylcholine, in liposomes
  1589(Fig)
Phosphatidylethanolamine, in liposomes
  1589
Phosphatidylinositol hydrolysis (PI
  hydrolysis), signaling by B cell
  receptor 1299–1300
Phosphatidylinositol-3-kinase pathway
  B cell signaling 1301
  IL-2 receptor signal transduction 1441
  IL-3 receptor signal transduction 1447–
    1448
  IL-7 receptor signal transduction 1464
  IL-11 receptor signal transduction 1480
Phosphatidylinositol-4 phosphate kinase
  (PIP-K), IL-8 receptor signal
  transduction 1467
Phosphatidylserine, exported by apoptotic
  cells 222
Phosphocholine, C-reactive protein (CRP)
  binding 664
Phosphodiesterase, abnormal, atopic
  eczema 788
Phosphokinase C (PKC), activation
  IL-3 signal transduction 1448
  membrane attack complex function 627
Phospholipase A₂ (PLA₂) 111, 1722
  activation
    IL-1 signal transduction 1433
    in type II hypersensitivity 1174
  contaminant of cobra venom factor 586–
    587
  inhibition by annexins 111
  inhibitory proteins 111, 112
  platelet activation effect 580
  type II (secretory) 1722

Phospholipase C (lecithinase)
  activation 1940
    chemoattractant-stimulated leukocytes
      1760–1761
    events after 2324
    T cell activation 2325
  β (PLCβ), activation 1761
  β₂ (PLCβ2), IL-8 signaling 1467
  Bacillus cereus toxin 313
  Clostridium perfringens toxin 577, 2368,
    2376
  phosphorylation, in mast cell
    degranulation 1670
  platelet activation effect 580
  signal transduction 1940
Phospholipid
  annexins binding 113
  antibodies 1676, 1843
  arachidonic acid liberation 2024,
    2024(Fig)
  hydrolysis 2029
  in liposomes 1588, 1589(Fig)
Phospholipid antigens, autoantibodies 265
Phospholipid-dependent protein kinases
  2029
  ceramide-dependent 2029
  protein kinase C, *see* Protein kinase C
    (PKC)
Phosphorylase kinase 2029
Phosphorylation 2028
  mast cell degranulation 1670
  protein kinases mediating, *see* Protein
    kinase(s)
  role in stimulus–response coupling 2028
Photoaffinity labeling 50
  labels 51
Photocarcinogenesis 1943
Photoimmunology 1942–1946
  definition 1942
  environmental concerns and 1943
  humans 1945–1946
  see also Ultraviolet light
Photoimmunosuppression 1945
Photons, effect on immune system 1942–
  1946
Photoreceptors, *see under* Retina
Photosensitivity, cutaneous lupus
  erythematosus 2186(Table), 2187
Phycobiliproteins 945
Phycocyanins 945
Phycoerythrin 945
Phylogeny, animals 1946–1947, 1947(Fig)
Phylogeny of immune response 1946–1952
  blood cells origins/comparisons 1948,
    1949
  evolutionary/environmental pressures
    1950–1951, 1951(Table)
  invertebrate 1947–1948
  recognition molecules 1949–1950
    invertebrates 1948
  steps 1951(Table)
  vertebrate 1948
  see also Evolution
Phytates 2516
Phytohemagglutinin (PHA) 1536, 1952–
  1953
  applications 1540(Table), 1953
  binding to CD2 1952
  binding to glycoproteins 1952
    in CD3 complex 1952
  glycoprotein mixture 1952
  lymphocyte transformation test 1621,
    1622
  mitogenic activity 1537–1538, 1952,
    1953
  response in amphibians 80
  structure 1536
  subunits (E and L) 1952
  T cell activation 1952–1953
    accessory cells role 1953
  T cell proliferation 1952, 1953
  tetrameric proteins 1952

Phytolacca americana 1978
PI3K pathway, *see* Phosphatidylinositol-3-
  kinase pathway
Pian bois 1547
Picornaviridae 1073
Picornaviruses 1953–1960
  antigens 1954, 1957(Table)-1958(Table)
    vaccine development 1959
  characteristics 1953–1955
  disablement 1956
  epitopes 1954, 1957(Table)-1958(Table)
  evasive strategies 1959
  eye infections 871
  genera 1954, 1955(Table)
  genome 1954, 1954(Fig)
  host immune response 1956–1959
    cell-mediated 1956, 1958–1959
  infection process/route 1954, 1955
  persistent infections 1959
  polypeptides 1953–1954
  polyprotein 1954
  receptors 1954, 1956(Table)
  serotypes 1954
  T cell damage prevention 1959
  TCR repertoire restriction 1958–1959,
    1959
  vaccines 1954, 1959
  see also Poliovirus
  viremia 1955
  see also Hepatitis A virus (HAV);
    Poliovirus
PIG-A gene, mutation 499
Pigs
  African swine fever (ASF), *see* African
    swine fever (ASF)
  antigen clearance by immune complex
    formation 184
  endothelium 2509
  genetically modified 2511
  immune system, *see* Porcine immune
    system
  lymphocyte trafficking in lymph node
    1602
  transgenic 2511
  xenotransplantation 2508
Pili 322–323
Pilin, *Neisseria* 1817
Pinocytosis 849
Pinta 2415, 2417–2418
Pip (Pu interaction partner) 1414
Pit cells 1532
Pituitary gland 224
  absence 1827
  autoantibodies 262(Table), 263
Pituitary hormones
  MIF as 1656
  in multiple sclerosis 1841
PL-7 antibody 2118
PL-12 antibody 2118
Placebo effect, plasmapheresis 1970
Placenta
  antibodies crossing 4, 13
  endotheliochorial 412
  epitheliochorial, in pigs 1991
  fetal red cell transfer 1070
  hemochorial 412
  HLA-G expression 1109, 1110
  IgG transfer, *see under* Immunoglobulin
    G (IgG)
  MHC antigen expression 899
  'trapping' of maternal antibodies 900–
    901
    escape 901
  types in animals 2451(Table)
  vertebrate types 2451(Table)
Plague, bubonic 2512, 2513
  history 1335
  vaccine 2514
  see also Yersinia pestis
PL^{Ai} 1974
Plants
  contact urticaria 681

Plants (*continued*)
  toxins 2261
Plaque, dental, *see* Dental plaque
Plaque-forming cell (PFC) 145,
  1961(Table)
Plaque-forming cell (PFC) assays 796,
  1960–1964, 1961(Table)
  applications 1962–1963
  blocking procedures 1960–1961
  direct 1960, 1961(Table)
  indirect 1960, 1961(Table)
  limiting dilution-type protocols 1962–
    1963, 1963(Fig)
  methodological variations 1961–1962
  micro assays 1961
  principle 1960
  procedures 1960–1961
  'reverse' hemolytic 1961(Table), 1962
  sensitivity 1962
  size of hemolytic zones 1961
  solid-phase 1961–1962
  terminology and definitions 1961(Table)
Plasma 1964–1969
  clinical uses 1964, 1966–1967
    risk estimates 1968
    risks associated 1966, 1967–1968
    see also specific blood products
  composition 1964–1965, 1965(Table)
  cryoprecipitate from 1966
  definition 1964
  donated source 1968
  electrolytes 1965, 1965(Table)
  exchange, SLE 2260
  fresh frozen (FFP), *see* Fresh frozen
    plasma (FFP)
  function 1965
  oncotic pressure 1964
  pasteurization 1968
  pH 1965
  pooled 1964
  removal from blood, *see* Plasmapheresis
  transfusion 1966, 2399, 2400(Table)
    complications 1968
    screening for infectious agents 2400
    see also Fresh frozen plasma (FFP)
  virus inactivation procedures 1968
  virus transmission 1967, 1968
  viscosity, rise in macroglobulinemia 1636
  see also Serum
Plasmablasts, generation in germinal center
  994] 995
Plasma cells 1144, 1248
  antibody secretion, *see* Antibody
    secretion
  in central lymph 1601
  formation 14, 1581
  Ig synthesis in oral cavity 1890
  Immunoglobulin secretion defects, *see*
    Mott cells
  increased in hypergammaglobulinemia
    1161
  in lamina propria 1778
  lifespan 1581
  precursors, *see* Plasmablasts
  radioresistance 2051
  tumor
    Bence Jones protein 341
    see also Multiple myeloma
Plasma clot method, organ culture 1899,
  1900(Fig)
Plasmacytoma 1637
  cytokine receptor expression 711
  feline 895
  mAb preparation 1742
  monoclonal 1148
  mutant, in hybridoma selection 1149
Plasmalemma 853
  docking sites for proteins 851
  turnover 853
  see also Membrane
Plasma membrane, *see* Membrane
Plasmapheresis 1348, 1968, 1969–1971

Plasmapheresis (*continued*)
  acute inflammatory demyelinating
    polyneuropathy 1837
  advantages 1970
  autoimmune hemolytic anemia 97
  definition 1968, 1969
  hemolytic disease of newborn 1072
  historical background 1969
  immunosuppressive effect 1970
  indications 1968, 1970
  methods 1969
  myasthenia gravis 1835
  pathophysiological basis 1969–1970
  placebo effect 1970
  therapeutic effects 1970
  Waldenström's macroglobulinemia 1970
  xenograft survival prolongation 2510
Plasma proteins 964, 1964–1965
  acute phase, *see* Acute phase proteins
  antibodies, blood transfusion reactions
    348
  decreased, in acute phase response 18,
    18(Table)
  electrophoresis 964, 964(Fig)
  see also Electrophoresis
  gravity/space flights effect 1031
  Igs 1965
  increased, in acute phase response 18,
    18(Table)
  plasmapheresis effect 1970
Plasmids
  DNA vaccines 771
  gene disruption 1524–1525, 1524(Fig)
Plasmin 585, 603
  generation 1520
Plasminogen 1520
  plasmin generation 1520
Plasminogen activator inhibitor (PAI) 585,
  1520
Plasmodium
  acquired immunodeficiency in animal
    models 1268
  antigens 1659–1660, 1659(Table)
  asexual stage 1659, 1660, 1661(Fig)
  characteristics 1658–1660
  circumsporozoite protein (CSP) 1659,
    1662
  erythrocyte-binding protein (EBPs) 1659–
    1660
  erythrocyte membrane protein 1 (EMP-1)
    1659–1660
  evasive strategies 1662
  exo-erythrocytic (EE) stage 1659
  extracellular forms 1659, 1660
  host immune response, *see under* Malaria
  intraerythrocytic forms 1659, 1660–1661
  killing by macrophage 1661
  lifecycle 1659
  merozoites, immune response to 1660–
    1661
  merozoite surface protein (MSP-1) 1659,
    1662
  species 1658
  thrombospondin-related anonymous
    protein (TRAP) 1659
  vaccines, *see under* Malaria
Plasmodium falciparum 1658
  HLA-B*5301 allele as Ir gene 1232
  ICAM-1 as receptor 804, 1411, 1609
  see also Malaria; *Plasmodium*
Plastic, NK cell adherence 1628, 1629
  see also Natural killer (NK) cells, A-NK
    cells
Plastic embedding techniques 1262
Platelet(s) 1973–1976
  activation 579–580, 1974
    consequences 579–580, 1974
    factors inhibiting 580
  adhesion 579, 1974
    fibronectin action 912
    signal transduction after 1974
  Trypanosoma brucei 182–183

Platelet(s) (*continued*)
  aggregation 118, 580, 1974
  α granules 579
    fibronectin 912
    products 580
  alloantibodies 347–349
  antigenicity 1974
  autoantibodies 1974, 1975, 1976
    idiopathic thrombocytopenic purpura 1181, 1181(Table)
  components 579–580
  defective production 1974–1975
  dense granules 579
    defect in Chédiak-Higashi syndrome 527
    products 580
  depletion
    Arthus reaction 239
    in ITP 1180, 1181, 1975
    see also Thrombocytopenia
  destruction, in ITP 1181, 1974
  drugs binding to 1975
  excess destruction 1975
  functions 579–580, 1973–1974
  glycoproteins 447(Table), 448(Table)
  GP1b 1974
  GPIIa, *see* CD29
  GPIIb/IIIa integrin 579, 580, 1408, 1409, 1974
  HLA antigen expression 1974
  ICAM-2 expression 1411
  immune adherence 1219
  membrane proteins 579
  phenotype 1803
  plug formation 579
  production, glucocorticoids increasing 1976
  proteins secreted 579
  recovery, after stem cell transplantation 1067
  storage, spleen 2207
  structure 1973–1974
  transfusions 2400(Table)
    idiopathic thrombocytopenic purpura 1976
    incompatible 1974
  see also Thrombocytopenia
Platelet-activating factor (PAF) 579, 1971–1973
  allergic rhinitis 2123
  analogs 1972
  antagonists 1971
    BN 52021 1971, 1973
  in Arthus reaction 239
  C5a-induced synthesis 90
  cells producing 1971
  cytokine production 1972
  effect on lymphocytes 1971–1972
    T cell subsets 1972
  effect on macrophage/monocytes 1972
  effect on NK cells 1972
  eosinophilotactic activity 819, 821
  functions 824, 1971
  glucocorticoid inhibition of 111
  graft rejection 1973
  IL-2-stimulated lymphoblast proliferation 1972
  inhibitor (acetylhydrolase) 1971
  late-phase allergic response 254
  receptor 1971
    structure 1971(Fig)
  release by mast cells 1172, 1668–1669
  in septicemic shock 319
Platelet-activating factor (PAF) acetylhydrolase 1971
Platelet-derived growth factor (PDGF) 907
  receptor 455(Table), 710
Platelet-endothelial tetraspan antigen (PETA)-3 456(Table)
Platelet factor 4 1974, 1975
Platelet-specific antibodies, transfusion reaction 347

Platelet storage pool deficiency 527
Platyrrhini 2005
  MHC 2009(Table)
Pleiotropy, cytokine 720
Pluripotent stem cells 155
  characteristics 544
  discovery 544
  see also Stem cell(s)
Pneumococcal vaccines 426, 2083, 2220
  subunit 2458
Pneumococcus, *see Streptococcus pneumoniae*
Pneumoconiosis, occupational 1368
Pneumocystis carinii 1977–1978
  antigens 1977
  classification 1977
  evasive strategies 1977
  host immune response 1977
  infection 1977
    after stem cell transplantation 1067
    immunodeficient mice 1273
    see also Pneumocystis carinii pneumonia
  major surface glycoprotein (MSG) 1977
  trophozoite and cyst 1977
  vaccines 1977
Pneumocystis carinii pneumonia 1883, 1977
  in AIDS 8
  in hyper-IgM syndrome 1166
  prevention 1882
Pneumocystosis 1977
  see also Pneumocystis carinii
Pneumolysin 2377
  Streptococcus pneumoniae 2219
Pneumonia 2081
  atypical, *Mycoplasma pneumoniae* 1800
  causes 2082, 2082(Table)
  community-acquired 2082(Table)
  diagnosis 2082
  influenza 1386
  lobar, *Klebsiella pneumoniae* 1523
  pneumococcal (*Streptococcus pneumoniae*) 2219
  Pneumocystis carinii, see Pneumocystis carinii pneumonia
  Pseudomonas aeruginosa 2369
  TNFα-mediated 2439–2440
Pneumonitis, lymphocytic interstitial, in AIDS 7
Pneumovirinae 1909, 1910(Table)
Pneumoviruses
  attachment proteins 1911
  see also Paramyxoviruses
Podosomes 1813
POEMS syndrome 1839, 1986
Poikilothermia, viral hemorrhagic septicemia protection 2100
Poikilotherms 2076
Pokeweed mitogen (PWM) 1978–1979
  applications 1540(Table)
  biological activity 1979
  characterization 1978–1979
  CVID investigation 601
  fractions 1978
  mitogenic activity 1537–1538, 1978, 1979
  preparation/isolation 1978
  structure 1978–1979
Polar capping, *see* Capping
Polar forces, *see* Hydrogen bonding/bonds
Poliomyelitis, eradication aim 2457
Poliovirus
  epitope location 1957(Table)
  neurovirulence, attenuation 256
  receptor for 456(Table), 1954
  replicative capacity reduction 258
Poliovirus vaccine 1959
  attenuated (Sabin), *see below*
  inactivated (IPV; Salk) 259, 1959
  oral (OPV; Sabin) 1959
    attenuating mutations 258

Poliovirus vaccine (*continued*)
  oral (OPV; Sabin) (*continued*)
    development 256–257, 257(Fig)
    inactivated (IPV) comparison 259
    intestinal immunity induction 259
    reversion to virulence 257, 258
Pollen
  cross-reactions with ingested allergens 950
  seasonal allergic rhinitis 2123
Pollutants, vitamin E protection 2500
Polyacrylamide 2143
  concentration in SDS-PAGE 2043
  formation 2143
Polyacrylamide gel
  assay, anti-DNA antibodies 129, 129(Table)
  isoelectric focusing 1512, 1513(Fig)
Polyacrylamide gel electrophoresis (PAGE) 2143, 2504
  protein size/charge determination 2035
  SDS, *see* SDS-polyacrylamide gel electrophoresis (SDS–PAGE)
  Western blotting 2504
Poly-ADP ribose polymerase (PARP) 876, 1028
Polyagglutination, differential diagnosis 1541
Polyamines, precursor, arginine requirement 236
Poly amino carboxylic acids 1511
Polyarteritis nodosa, plasmapheresis 1970
Polyarthritis, parvovirus B19 infection 1924
Polybuffer™ 2037
Polychlorinated biphenyls (PCBs), immunosuppression due to 1367
Polyclonal activation 1979, 1980
  B cells, *see* B cell(s), polyclonal activation
  costimulation and coinhibition 1983
  by endogenous agents 1982
  excess and septic shock in 1982
  lymphocyte proliferation 2022
  receptors 1982
  T cells, *see* T cell(s), polyclonal activation
  see also B cell(s); Polyclonal activators
Polyclonal activators 1979–1984
  classes 1980, 1981(Table)
  clonal activator interactions 1980–1982
    antagonism 1982
    synergism 1980–1982
  costimulation 1980, 1983
  definition 1979–1980
  endogenous agents 1982
  excess, septic shock in 1982
  inhibition due to 1980
  lipopolysaccharide 1981–1982
  lymphocyte inactivation/death after 1980
  superantigens 1982
Polyclonal antisera 1742
  immunoelectron microscopy 792
  tumor imaging 2431
  see also Antibodies, polyclonal; Antiserum
Polyclonal gammopathy, *see* Hypergammaglobulinemia, polyclonal
Polyclonal inhibitors 1980, 1982(Table)
  coinhibition and 1983
  mechanism of action 1980
Polyendocrine autoimmunity 1984–1986
  miscellaneous syndromes 1986
  see also Autoimmune polyglandular syndromes (APS)
Polyethylene glycol (PEG)
  cell fusion method for hybridoma generation 1153
  immune complex detection 1221
  protein separation 2036
Polygenic traits 986, 988–989
Poly Ig receptor (pIgR), *see* Secretory component (SC)

Polylysine, causing degranulation 851
Polymerase chain reaction (PCR) 981,
    1747, 1987–1988
  applications 1987–1988
  B cell isolation 180
  complement analysis 619
  Cryptosporidium 676
  development 1987
  Echinococcus detection 784
  HLA typing 1691, 1693, 1987–1988
  Lyme disease diagnosis 381
  minimal residual disease detection in
    leukemia 1558
  Mycoplasma diagnosis 1801, 1802
  principles 1987, 1987(Fig)
  procedure 1987
  profile of reaction 1987(Fig)
  reverse transcription (RT-PCR) 982
    hepatitis C virus (HCV) 1080
    hepatitis E virus (HEV) 1082
  short tandem repeats (STRs) 1988
  Southern blotting comparison 2198
  tissue typing method 2319
  tumor detection after stem cell
    transplants 1069
Polymeric Ig receptor, *see* Secretory
    component (SC)
Polymorphic epithelial mucin (PEM) 2428
Polymorphism 619, 986
  complement 619, 620(Table)
Polymorphonuclear cells (PMNs)
  activation 1935
  chemotactic factors, signaling pathway
    2031–2032
  Chlamydia infections 550
  conditioned response 337
  deficiencies 1889, 1890
  extracellular stimulation 2031–2033
  LTB₄ actions 231
  LTB₄ synthesis 228
  in oral cavity 1889–1890
    inflammation promotion 1891
    migration into gingival crevice 1889,
      1891
  phagocytic cells 1935
    see also Phagocytes; Phagocytosis
  protein kinases 2031
  radiosensitivity 2050
  skin infections 751–752
  turnover rate 1935
  vertebrates 1948
  see also Granulocyte(s); Neutrophil(s)
Polymyositis 2118
  autoantibodies 2003, 2118
Polyneuropathy
  acute inflammatory demyelinating, *see*
    Acute inflammatory demyelinating
    polyneuropathy (AIDP)
  chronic inflammatory demyelinating
    1838
Polyomavirus 1988–1990
  antigens 1988–1990
  capsid 1989
  characteristics 1988–1990
  evasive strategies 1990
  genome 1989
  host immune response 1990
  replication 1989
  vaccines 1990
  see also BK virus; JC virus
Polypeptides, synthetic, antigenic 205
Polyphyletic origin 1946
Polysaccharides 422
  α(1-4) linkages 423
  antibodies elicited by 427
  antigens 203, 203–204
  β(1-3) linkages 422
  capsular of bacteria, *see under* Bacteria
  complement activation 216
  conformation in solution 426
  conjugate vaccines 217

Polysaccharides (*continued*)
  idiotype expression during ontogeny
    1877
  molecular weight distribution 422
  naturally occurring 422
  structure 422–426
  sugar residues 422
  tertiary (globular) structure 426
  T-independent antigens 216
  as type 2 T-independent antigens 216–
    217
Polyunsaturated fatty acids (PUFAs) 884
  age-related disease increase 884
  eicosanoid production 884–885
  high intake levels, effects 885
  immune system interactions 885
  n-3 884
    effect on eicosanoid synthesis 885
  n-6 884
    effect on eicosanoid synthesis 885
  see also Fatty acids (dietary)
Polyvinyl difluoride membrane, Western
    blotting 2505
Polyvinylpyrrolidone (PVP) 668
Popliteal lymph node assay (PLNA) 1367
Population attributable risk 1698
Porcine immune system 1991–1994
  ADCC 1993
  adhesion molecules 1993
  African swine fever (ASF) virus, response
    55
  B cells 1992–1993
  complement components 1992
  cytokines 1993
  differentiation antigens 1993
  epitheliochorial placenta 1991
  fetal and perinatal ontogeny 1991–1992
  granulocytes 1992
  gut lymphoid tissue 1993–1994
  immunoglobulins 1992–1993,
    1992(Table)
  inverted lymph nodes 1991
  lungs 1994
  lymphocytes 1991
  MHC 1992
  monocytes/macrophage 1992
  NK cells 1993
  peripheral leukocytes 1992
  Peyer's patches 1991
  T cells 1993
    phenotypic profiles 1993
  see also Ungulate immune system
Pore-forming protein 1929
Pores
  complement-formed 1930(Fig)
  lymphocyte-generated 1929
    see also Cell-mediated lysis; Perforin
  perforin-formed 1930(Fig)
  toxins inducing 2377
Porins 321
PorMch4 1028
Porphyromonas gingivalis 1889, 1890
  immunomodulation of infection 1892
  SCID mice resistant 1890–1891
Positive selection
  B cells, *see* B cell(s), repertoire; Clonal
    selection
  MHC evolution 1701–1702
  T cells, *see* Thymic selection
Postcapillary venules 1094, 1601
  lymphocyte entry via 1618
  neutrophil infiltration 16
  permeability, prostaglandins increasing
    2026
  see also High endothelial venules (HEV)
Posterior uveitic disease 867
Post-infectious encephalomyelitis 1830
Post-measles encephalomyelitis 272
Post-partum thyroid dysfunction (PPTD)
    2317
Post-pericardiotomy syndrome 434

Post-rabies vaccination encephalomyelitis
    1830
Post-streptococcal glomerulonephritis
    1176, 2218
Post-transfusion purpura 347–348
Post-translational modification,
    glycosylation, *see* Glycosylation
Post-vaccinal encephalitis 1998
Post-vaccinal encephalopathy 1998
Potassium, transport, in red cell
    membranes 837
Potassium channels, voltage-gated,
    antibodies 1850
Poultry, *see* Avian immune system;
    Chickens
Poxviruses 1995–1998
  as adjuvant 38
  of birds 1995
  evasive strategies 1996–1997
  genera and classification 1995,
    1995(Table)
  genome 1996
  host cell factor homologs encoded 1997,
    1997(Table)
  host immune response 1703, 1996
  IL-1β binding 705, 1997
  immune interactions 1996–1997
  recombinants 1998
  replication 1997
  TNF viroceptors 2349
  vaccines 1997–1998
    complications 1998
    discovery 1997
    veterinary 1998
    see also Cowpox; Smallpox
  as vector 1998
  virokines 1997
  see also Smallpox
PP2A, in IL-11 signal transduction 1480
pp90ʳˢᵏ, in IL-11 signal transduction 1480
pp125ᶠᴬᴷ 31, 32
  in mast cell degranulation 1670
PPD, *see* Purified protein derivative (PPD)
P-proteins, ribosomal 127
PRAD1 558
Praziquantel, schistosomiasis 2142
PRDI regulatory domains, interferon β
    1418
Pre-B cell receptor 155, 364(Table)
  formation 64, 356
Pre-B cells 64, 356, 364, 376
  antigen expression 1818
  apoptosis 1424
  CD22 expression 479
  in fetus 1818
  large cycling 1876
  MHC class II expression 1876
  phenotype 1876
  small resting 1876
  surface Ig 1301
  see also B cell(s), differentiation
Pre-B I cells, *see* Pro-B cells
Pre-B II cells
  large 155
  small 155–156
Precipitin (precipitation) reaction 141,
    1287, 1318, 1999–2002, 2466
  acceleration 141
  affinity measurement 45
  antigen/antibody excess 1822, 1822(Fig),
    2466–2467
  autoantibody detection 260
  characteristics 1822, 1822(Fig), 2466–
    2467
  equivalence 2466
  in fluids 1999–2001
    characteristics 1999–2000, 2000
  in gels 2001–2002
    immunoelectrophoresis 2002
    Ouchterlony's technique 2001(Fig),
      2002
  see also Immunodiffusion

Precipitin (precipitation) reaction (*continued*)
nephelometry based on 1822
phenomenon of multiple proportions 2000
precipitation curve 1999(Fig), 2000
procedures 1999
sensitivity 141
stages 1999–2000
zone of complete inhibition 2000
zone of equivalence 2000
see also Immunoprecipitation of cell surface molecules
Prednisolone
SLE 2260
structure 997(Fig)
Prednisone, autoimmune hemolytic anemia therapy 95–96
Pregnancy
active maternal immunoregulatory responses 899–900
α-fetoprotein in 799
'alloimmune', failure 1344
asthma 246
autoimmune hemolytic anemia 98
fetus as allograft, *see* Fetus as allograft
HIV infection progression and 8
immunization in, effects 1673
interferons in 1413
parvovirus B19 infections 1925
regulation, antibodies against hormones 1853
SLE 2257
varicella-zoster immune globulin 2469
see also entries beginning Maternal; Maternal antibodies
Prekallikrein 1519
activation 582
cleavage to kallikrein 1519
gene 1519
Prematurity 1870
immunodeficiency 1284–1285
Preservation of cells, *see* Cryopreservation of immune cells
Pressure, hydrostatic, *see* Hydrostatic pressure
Pre-Tα
TCRβ chain linked and selection 2339
TCR development 2337
Pre-TCR 2339
Preterm infants 1870
immunodeficiency 1284–1285
Pretibial myxedema 2315
Prezone (prozone) phenomenon 57–58, 385
Prick testing 254, 680, 1172
Primary biliary cirrhosis (PBC) 2002–2004
autoantibodies 263, 264, 2002–2003, 2003, 2003(Table)
autoantigen (PDC-E2) 267
B cell abnormalities 2003
characteristics 2002
clinical features 2003
diagnostic assay 2004
as ductal disease 2004
etiology 2004
mitochondrial autoantigens 2003, 2003(Table), 2004
SCID mouse model 1129(Table)
T cell abnormalities 2003, 2004
treatment 2003
Primary sclerosing cholangitis, autoantibodies 1722
Primates (nonhuman)
classification 2005
evolutionary tree 2010(Fig)
as models 2004, 2005
New World 2005, 2010
Old World 2005
xenotransplantation donor 2508
Primates (nonhuman) immune system 2004–2011

Primates (nonhuman) immune system (*continued*)
antigen clearance by immune complex formation 183
CD antigens 2005–2008, 2006(Table)-2008(Table)
lymphocyte markers similarity to humans 2005–2008, 2006(Table)-2008(Table)
MHC 2005, 2008–2010, 2009(Table)
class I genes 2008–2010
class II genes 2010–2011
evolution 2010
monoclonal antibodies 2005
TCR genes 2011
Prion protein (PrP) 2409
PrP^{Sc} 2409, 2410
Prions 2409
Pristane arthritis, features and comparisons 2106(Table)
Privileged sites, *see* Immune privilege
Pro-B cells (pre-BI cells) 64, 364, 1876
receptor structure 1194
reduced in IL-7 receptor mutations 1463
Procainamide, autoimmune disease pathogenesis 279, 293
Procollagen 905
biosynthesis 905–906
Procyclin 2420
Progenitor cells 374
Progesterone 2176
TNFα release increased 2437
Programmed cell death, *see* Apoptosis
Progressive multifocal leukoencephalopathy (PML) 1989, 1989(Fig)
in AIDS 1989
clinical features 1989
immune response 1990
pathogenetic events 1989–1990
see also JC virus
Pro-IL-1 1430
Prokaryotes, immunity in 2013–2017
to bacteriocins 2014–2015
see also Colicins
to bacteriophage 2015–2017
see also Bacteriophage
see also Bacteria
Prolactin
immune response modulation 1829–1830, 2225
increased release, arginine mechanism of action 236
in multiple sclerosis 1841
role 1853
Proliferating cell nuclear antigen (PCNA) 126
antibodies 131
Proliferation of lymphocytes, *see* B cell(s), proliferation; Lymphocyte, proliferation; T cell(s), proliferation
Proline, hydroxylation 2491
Proline-directed protein kinases 2030
Prolymphocytic leukemia, *see* Leukemia, prolymphocytic (PLL)
Promiscuity, membrane components 418
'Promiscuous epitopes' 69
Promonocytes 1755
Promoter, analysis 983
Pro-opiomelanocortin (POMC) 1828, 2225
ProPak-A cell line 2090
Properdin 602, 603
deficiency 615(Table)
Prophenoloxidase activating system, invertebrates 1500
Propidium iodide, in tissue typing method 2319
Propionibacterium 662
Propionibacterium acnes 662
Propionibacterium propionicus 662
Proportional hazards (Cox) regression 2213
Prostacyclin (PGI$_2$) 118, 2024
functions/actions 2025

Prostacyclin (PGI$_2$) (*continued*)
secretion by endothelial cells 579, 806
vasodilatation 805
Prostaglandin(s) 2024–2027
actions 117, 120, 2025–2027
in Arthus reaction 239
biosynthetic pathways 2024–2025, 2024(Fig)
see also Arachidonic acid (AA)
chronic autoimmune disease 2026–2027
fever generation 117, 903, 2025–2026
fever induction independent of 903–904
in infections 2025–2026
inflammatory role 117, 2025
macrophage activation decreased 2026
NSAID effect, *see* Nonsteroidal anti-inflammatory drugs (NSAIDs)
pain due to 117, 2025
sleep pattern in African trypanosomiasis 2423
synthesis 117–118
hormones inhibiting 904
inflammatory bowel disease 1380, 2027
inhibition by NSAIDs, *see* Nonsteroidal anti-inflammatory drugs (NSAIDs)
macrophage 2024–2025
sites 903
vitamin E effect 2500
T cell and macrophage inhibition by 2026–2027, 2026(Fig)
vasodilator 2025
local release 2026
Prostaglandin D$_2$ (PGD$_2$), released from mast cells 1668
Prostaglandin E$_2$ (PGE$_2$)
cytokine synthesis inhibition 2026
fever induction mechanism 903
formation in fever 2025
functions/actions 2025
in inflammation 2025
MHC class II expression inhibition 2027
in nasal mucosa 2125
in periodontal disease 1891
rheumatoid factor production increase 2027
UV-induced changes 1944
Prostaglandin G$_2$ (PGG$_2$) 2024
Prostaglandin H$_2$ (PGH$_2$) 580, 2024
Pro-Tα, *see* Prothymosin α (Pro-Tα)
Protamine sulfate, protein separation 2036
Proteases
CED-3/ICE, *see* Caspase; ICE/CED-3 family
hookworms secreting 1122–1123, 1124
ICE-related, in apoptosis 223
inhibitors 12
see also Proteinase inhibitors
Proteasome 192
enzymes 192
expression, induced by IFNγ 1424
rheumatoid arthritis 2113
Protected surface phenomenon, complement 603
Protectin, *see* CD59
Protein 4, in red cell membrane 835, 838(Table)
Protein(s)
abnormalities, *see* Mutations
amino acid substitutions 987
antigens, *see* Antigen
artificial epitopes, generation 1050
assays 2034
binding to SDS 2143
biospecificity 2034
determination 2035–2036
characterization 2035–2036
dietary, diabetes mellitus induction 1397
epitopes 150
folding, stabilization by hsps 2230
fractionation, SDS-PAGE 2143, 2144
fusion 984

Protein(s) (*continued*)
  haptenation 780, 1051
  hydrophobicity 2034
    determination 2035–2036
  inappropriate expression in tumors 1361
  large-scale production 984–985
  microheterogeneity, isoelectric focusing
    1512
  polymorphism, monitoring of inbred
    strains 1371
  post-translational modification 144
  secretion 144, 849–851
    antibodies as model system 144–145
    constitutive or regulated 144–145
    'positive sorting' 144
  sequencing, Western blotting 2506
  size and charge 2034, 2035
  sorting, transmembrane secretory
    component (pIgR) 2154
  stability 2034–2035
  structure 2034
    phenotypic variation 987
    three-dimensional 2199
  synthesis
    induced by hydrostatic pressure 1155,
      1156(Table)
    inhibition by diphtheria toxin
      2372(Fig)
    quality control steps 145
  translocation
    endoplasmic reticulum 144, 354, 849,
      851
    hsp70 role 2230
    m-exocytosis 853
    s-exocytosis 851
  transport 849–851
    directed/undirected 851
    exocytosis pathways 849–851
  unfolded, ubiquitin as molecular tag
    2230
Protein A 217, 323, 325, 1318–1319,
    2209–2210
  affinity and bivalence 325
  in affinity chromatography 49
  in antibody detection methods 143
  applications 325, 326
  Fc region interaction 325
  IgG binding 1211
  immunocytochemistry system 1260
  immunosorbent columns 1252
  opsonization evasion by bacteria 1937
  sepharose beads 513
  as superantigen 325
  wheal and flare reaction 325
Protein A-coated columns, blocking
    antibodies removal 1348
Proteinase 3, antibodies 2120
Proteinase inhibitors 12, 18(Table), 1858
  invertebrates 1501
'Protein binding' assays 1252
Protein blotting, *see* Western blotting
Protein calorie malnutrition, *see* Protein-
    energy malnutrition (PEM)
Protein chromatography, *see*
    Chromatography
Protein C inhibitor 1520
Protein-energy malnutrition (PEM) 1869
  antibody responses decreased 1869
  delayed hypersensitivity reduced 1869
  immunodeficiency in 1284
  phagocytosis decreased 1869
  zinc deficiency 2516
Protein G 323, 326
  in affinity chromatography 49
  in antibody detection methods 143
  applications 326
  IgG complexes 326
Protein kinase(s) 2028–2033
  cascades 2028
  categories 2028–2031
  control 2033
  cyclic-AMP dependent (PKAs) 2029

Protein kinase(s) (*continued*)
  definition 2028
  interferon-induced 1416, 1419, 1423
  in myeloid cells 2031–2033
    chemotactic factor action 2031–2032
    cytokines/growth factor actions 2032–
      2033
    extracellular stimulation 2031–2033
    LPS action 2032–2033
    opsonin action 2032
  role 2028, 2033
  sensitivity to extracellular stimuli 2028
  serine/threonine-directed, *see*
    Serine/threonine-directed protein
    kinases
  stimulus–response coupling 2028
  subcellular localization 2033
  tyrosine-directed, *see* Tyrosine-directed
    protein kinases (PTKs)
Protein kinase A 2029
  Goodpasture antigen phosphorylation
    1010
  oxygen-dependent phagocytic killing
    1713, 1938
Protein kinase C (PKC) 2029
  activation, IL-1 signal transduction 1433
  activity 2029
  B cell receptor signaling mechanism
    1299–1300
  CD40 signaling and B cell activation
    2150
  cell-mediated lysis mechanism 506
  chemoattractant-stimulated leukocytes
    1761
  cofactor requirements 2029
  cytokine synthesis pathway 700
  isozyme PKC[G]z[g] 1301
  isozymes (subspecies) 1941–1942, 2325
    structure 1942(Fig)
  mast cell degranulation 1670
  memory T cell activation 1684
  as phorbol ester receptor 1940–1941
  phorbol esters activating 2325
  PKC[G]t[g] 2325
  role 1942
    in p21^{ras} activation 2327
  signal transduction pathways 1940
  structure 1941–1942, 1942(Fig)
  subgroups/isoforms 2029
  as target for calpain 1942
  in T cell activation 2325–2326
Protein-losing enteropathy, increased
    loss/catabolism of Igs 1287
Protein Reviews on the Web (PROW)
    database 445, 457
Protein S 583
Protein separation techniques 2034–2039
  affinity chromatography 48, 2038
  assays during 2034
  differential solubility 2036
  preliminary considerations/decisions
    2034–2035
  preliminary separation 2036
  protein biospecificity/hydrophobicity
    2035–2036
  protein size/charge determination 2035
  protein stability 2034–2035
  selection of extraction method 2036
  source/material for 2034
  specific techniques 2036–2038
  see also Chromatography
Protein superfamilies 515
Protein tyrosine kinases, *see* Tyrosine-
    directed protein kinases (PTKs)
Protein-tyrosine phosphatase (PTPase),
    CD45 491
Protein tyrosine phosphatase 1c (PTP1C)
  absence in motheaten mice 2253
  B cell signaling inhibition 2253
Protein X, autoantigen in primary biliary
    cirrhosis (PBC) 2003, 2003(Table)
Proteoglycans 862–864

Proteoglycans (*continued*)
  arthritis due to, features/comparisons
    2106(Table)
  chemokines/cytokines with affinity for
    907
  classification 863–864
  glycosaminoglycan (GAG) chains 862–
    863, 863(Table), 864
  heterogeneity 862
  interactions and hydration 864
  large aggregating 864
  in mast cells 1668
  production, by fibroblasts 906–907
  small matrix 863–864
  structure 862–863
Proteoglycan–polysaccharide, chronic
    relapsing arthritis model 1521
Proteolipid protein (PLP) 754, 755, 857–
    858, 858
  sequence 857(Fig)
Proteolipoprotein-induced experimental
    encephalomyelitis 487
Proteus 2039–2042
  infections 2039–2040
  molecular mimicry, rheumatoid arthritis
    HLA 1740(Fig), 1741
  morphology 2039(Fig)
  rabbit antibodies to 137–138
  swarming 2039(Fig)
Proteus mirabilis 2039
  characteristics 2039
  fimbriae 2040, 2041
  flagella 2041
  hemolysin 2040, 2041
  host immune response 2040
  IgA-degrading protease 2041
  outer membrane protein (OM) 2040
  pathogenesis model 2041
  rheumatoid arthritis 2040
  swarming 2041
  urease 2039, 2040
  urinary tract infections 2039–2040,
    2040(Fig)
  virulence factors 2040–2041, 2041(Fig)
Prothrombin, activation 582
Pro-thymocytes 2300
Prothymosin α (Pro-Tα) 2301
  IL-2 receptors and IL-2 synthesis 2301
  opportunistic infection prevention 2301
Protoimmunology 1334–1335
Protoplasts 321
Protostomes 1946
Protozoa 1916
  antigenic variation 199
  as antigens 206
  evasive strategies 1917
  host immune response strategies 1917
  immune adherence 1219
  immunity 969
  see also Parasites; *specific infections*
Provirus 2487
Proxicromil 2166
Proximity, membrane components 418
Prozone (prezone) phenomenon 57–58
  brucellosis diagnosis 385
P-selectin (CD62P) 16, 27(Table), 28,
    450(Table), 804, 2159–2160
  adult respiratory distress syndrome
    (ARDS) 2159
  antibodies 1540
  diapedesis of leukocytes 759
  in endothelial cells 804
  expression regulation 30, 804
  function 1539
  in inflammation 541
  knockout mice 1566, 1566(Table)
  leukocyte rolling 2159
  Lewis^x (Le^x) and sialyl-Le^x as ligands
    1578–1579
  ligands 2160
  mice deficient in 32, 1566, 1566(Table)
  mobilization 2159

P-selectin (CD62P) (*continued*)
  neutrophil migration 1935
  PSGL-1 as ligand 2160
  storage, Weibel–Palade bodies 2159
  structure 2159
P-selectin glycoprotein ligand 1 (PSGL-1)
  29, 804, 2160
Pseudoallergy 253
  food 253, 947, 948, 951–952
Pseudogenes, gene conversion 972
  mamu-G gene 2010
Pseudoglobulins 964
Pseudolymphoma 2182
Pseudomonas
  exotoxin A 2370
  exotoxin S 2370
Pseudomonas aeruginosa 2042–2045
  antibiotic resistance 2042
  antigens 2043(Table), 2044
  elastase toxin 2369
  host immune response, antibodies
    2043(Table)
  immunogenicity 2043(Table), 2044–2045
  immunotherapy 2044–2045, 2044(Table)
  infection process 2042–2044
  infections
    in cystic fibrosis 2042, 2044
    nosocomial 2042, 2044
    pneumonia 2369
    predisposing factors 2042
    rapidly progressing 2044
  outer membrane proteins 2044
  passive immunization 2045
  toxin 2372(Fig)
  vaccines 2044(Table)
  virulence factors 2042–2043
Pseudomonas pyocyanea 57
Pseudoplaques 1962
Pseudopods
  monocytes 1751, 1937
  neutrophils 1857, 1937
PSGL-1 29, 457(Table), 804, 2160
Psoriasis
  in AIDS 8
  calcitriol treatment 2496
  guttate 2219
  live *Leishmania* vaccine and 1550
Psoriatic arthritis 2120
Psychoneuroimmunology 1824, 1831–1832
Psychosocial processes, neural/immune
  system interactions 2227(Fig)
Pulmonary homeostasis, GM-CSF role
  1022
Pulmonary hypersensitivity, ascariasis 241
Pulmonary immunotoxicants 1368
Pulmonary intravascular macrophage
  alveolar macrophage differences 1994
  in cats 892
  in pigs 1994
Pulmonary surfactant proteins, SP-A and
  SP-D 1887
Pulmonary surfactants, GM-CSF role 1022
Pulmonary thromboembolism 2119
Pulse field gel electrophoresis (PFGE) 2195
Purified protein derivative (PPD) 335, 1794
  T cell locomotion and 538
Purine nucleoside 748
Purine nucleoside phosphorylase (PNP)
  deficiency 748–749, 1278, 2172–2173
    immunodeficiency 748–749
  gene 749
  substrates 749
Purkinje cells
  antibodies against proteins in 1842
  deficiency 247
Purpura
  in cryoglobulinemia 666
  idiopathic thrombocytopenic, *see*
    Idiopathic thrombocytopenic purpura
    (ITP)
  post-transfusion 347–348
  thrombocytopenic, in HIV infection 7

Pus, formation 1856
Pyelonephritis 2065
  acute 2066, 2452–2453
    pathogenesis 2452–2453
  chronic 2066
  predisposing factors 2066(Table)
  recurrent, blood group types 2453
  xantho-granulomatous 2066
Pyonephrosis 2066
Pyrexia, *see* Fever
Pyridoxal phosphate (PLP) 2490
Pyrogens
  endogenous 902–903, 2025
    cytokines 902
  endotoxins 807
  see also Fever
Pyroninophilic cells 739
Pyronin Y 2023
Pyruvate dehydrogenase complex,
  autoantigen in primary biliary
  cirrhosis 2003, 2003(Table), 2004

Q

Qa-1 molecules 72
Qa-2 molecules 72
Q fever 2126
  vaccine 2458
Quadromas 139–140, 139(Fig)
Quantitative genetics 342
Quantitative trait loci (QTLs) 1370
Quasispecies 200, 256, 1081
Quil A 37
Quillaja saponins 1507, 1508
Quinidine 1974, 1975
  drug-induced immune hemolytic anemia
    95
Quinine 1974, 1975
Quokka, immune system 1664
QUPC52 myeloma protein 150

R

R1 mouse cell line 370
RA-33 126
  antibodies 131
RA-associated nuclear antigen 2113, 2114
  antibodies 2113
Rabbit
  antiserum preparation 219
  arthritis 2046
  atherosclerosis 2046
  as disease models 2046
  experimental autoimmune myasthenia
    gravis 1849
  gene therapy model 2046
Rabbit hemorrhagic disease virus (RHDV)
  400
  antigens 400–401
  recombinant virus-like particles 402
  vaccine 401, 402
Rabbit immune system 2046–2049
  cell lines 2048, 2048(Table)
  cytokines 2047
  GALT 2047
  immunoglobulins 2047
  lymphoid cell markers 2048, 2049(Table)
  lymphopoiesis 2047
  MHC 2047–2048
  polymeric Ig receptor 2154
  TCR 2048
Rabbit pox 1998
Rabies 2098
  dumb (paralytic) 2100
  furious 2100
  high/low dose paradoxical phenomenon
    2100

Rabies (*continued*)
  immune response 2100
  interferon induction 2100
  nonspecific immunity 2100
  resistance, genetic control 2100
  vaccination 2100
    early death phenomenon 2100
    encephalomyelitis after 1830
  vaccines 2100–2101
    conventional 2100–2101
    development 256
    for domestic animals 2101
    EAE induction 856–857
    for humans 2100
    recombinant 2101
    side-effects 856
    for wild animals 2101
  see also Rabies virus
Rabies-related viruses 2099
Rabies virus
  animal reservoirs 2099–2100, 2101
  characteristics 2098
  epidemiology 2099–2100
  evasive strategies 2100
  genome 2098
  G protein and immunity to 2099
  proteins 2098
  structure 2099(Fig)
  transmission 2100
  see also Rabies
Rab proteins 852(Table)
rac
  in mast cell degranulation 1671
  in oxygen-dependent phagocytic killing
    1714
Races
  Gm haplotypes 75, 76(Table)
  IDDM, *see* Diabetes mellitus, insulin-
    dependent (IDDM), ethnic groups
Radiation 2050–2053
  doses 2050
  immunodeficiency and 2053
  immunotherapeutic applications 2052–
    2053
  infection susceptibility after 2052
  lymphocyte migration changes 2051
  resistance, *see* Radioresistance
  sensitivity of cells, *see* Radiosensitivity
  see also Ultraviolet light
Radioallergosorbent test (RAST) 254, 1173
  insect bites/sting reactions 680
Radiocontrast media, reaction prevention
  782
Radioimmunoassay (RIA) 141, 816, 1253
  affinity measurement 45
  anti-DNA antibodies 129
  autoantibody detection 260–261
  high affinity antibodies use 2466
  IL-1 detection 1432
Radio-immunocytochemistry (RICH) 1266
Radioimmunoelectrophoresis 1296
Radioimmunoguided surgery 2434
Radioisotopes 2054
  autoradiography 296–297, 297(Table)
  half-life 297
  in immunoassays 1253
  see also Radionuclides
Radiolabeling 2053–2055
  biosynthetically labeled 2054, 2054(Fig)
  DNA/RNA probes, Northern blotting
    1865
  living cells 2054
  soluble molecules 2054
Radionuclides 2433(Table)
  antibody conjugates in tumor therapy
    2434
  tumor imaging 2433–2434, 2433(Table)
  see also Radioisotopes
Radioprotection 544
Radio-receptor binding assays, cytokines
  697(Table), 699
Radioresistance 2051(Table)

Radioresistance (*continued*)
 activated lymphocytes 2050, 2052
 cell-mediated immunity 2052
 helper T cells 2052
 macrophage and PMN 2050
 plasma cells 2051
 secondary immune response 2052
Radiosensitivity 2050, 2051(Table)
 ataxia telangiectasia 247, 247–248,
  248(Fig)
 cell types 2051(Table)
 immune response 2051–2052
  cellular 2052
  humoral immunity 2051–2052
 immunodeficiency and 2053
 lymphocytes 2050
 lymphoid tissues 2051
 macrophage 2050
 PMNs 2050
Raf-1 kinase
 IL-3 receptor signal transduction 1448
 T cell receptor signaling 2327
Raf pathway, in mast cell degranulation
  1670
Raft culture methods 1900, 1900(Fig)
RAG genes
 defects 1279
  SCID 2172
 deletion 1877
 mice deficient in 1128
 TCR gene rearrangement 2337
RAG-1 gene 62, 155, 356, 363, 1876
 activation 1876
 deficiency in SCID 2172
 evolution 1313
 function in VDJ recombination 768
 RAG-deficient mice 1128
RAG-2 gene 62, 155, 356, 363, 1876
 activation 1876
 deficiency in SCID 2172
 function in VDJ recombination 768
 RAG-deficient mice 1128
RAGE 1115, 1116(Table)
 diabetic complications and 1120
 gene 1046, 2424, 2424(Table)
 see also Advanced glycation end-products
  (AGE)
Raji cell test 1221
Ranitidine 680
RANTES
 eosinophil chemotaxis 820
 in SCID mice 1128
 T cell locomotor response 538
Rapamycin (sirolimus) 1352, 1441, 2261
 in transplantation 2414
Rapid plasma reagin (RPR) test 2073
Ra-reactive factor (RaRF) 608, 609
 see also Mannose-binding lectin (MBL)
Ras/MAP kinase pathway 911
 block, T cell anergy induction 110
 IL-2 receptor signal transduction 1441
 see also MAP kinase (MAPK); Ras
  pathway/protein
Rasmussen's encephalitis 1843
Ras pathway/protein 1670
 activation 2326
 B cell receptor signaling 1300–1301
 constitutive mutant 2326
 dominant negative mutant 2326
 mast cell degranulation 1670
 mutants 2327
 see also see Ras/MAP kinase pathway
 T cell signaling 2326, 2327
 see also p21^{ras}
Ras-Raf-1-MAPK cascade, IL-3 receptor
  signal transduction 1448
RAST, *see* Radioallergosorbent test (RAST)
Rat
 adjuvant arthritis 33
 immunoglobulin allotypes 75(Table)
 inbred strains 2055–2058
  biochemical markers 2057–2058

Rat (*continued*)
 inbred strains (*continued*)
  genealogic tree 2055
  genetic characteristics 2056(Table)-
   2057(Table)
  immunoglobulin allotypes 2057
  immunological features 2057,
   2057(Table)
  MHC (RT system) 2055, 2056(Table)-
   2057(Table), 2057
  origin and breeders 2055
  strain nomenclature 2055
  surface antigens 2055, 2056(Table)-
   2057(Table), 2057
  synonyms for strains 2056(Table)-
   2057(Table)
  see also Inbred strains
 MHC class II region 1391
 spontaneous hypertensive 1518, 2058
Rate zonal centrifugation 2447, 2448
Rat insulin promoter (RIP) 1638,
  1639(Fig)
Rattus norvegicus 2055
RAW264 cells 313
Raynaud's phenomenon 132, 666, 2182
RBL-2H3 mast cells, in mast cell
  degranulation 1670
Rb protein 911
RD114 virus 2090
RD gene, mice 1046
Reactive arthritis
 clinical features 2120
 Mycoplasma/Ureaplasma infections 1801
 Shigella causing 2180
 Yersinia 2513
Reactive oxygen species 133
 adverse effects 134
 deficiency in amebiasis model 78
 formation 1715–1717, 1938
  by neutrophils 1856–1857
  scavengers 1718, 1718(Fig)
 inhibition of proteinase inhibitors 1858
 macrophage action 1646
 parasite killing mechanism 1918
 release in Chagas' disease 524–525
 role in ADCC 169
 see also Microbicidal mechanisms,
  oxygen-dependent; Respiratory burst
Reagin, definition 25
'reaginic' antibodies 64
REAL classification, lymphomas 1632
'Recall' response 1683
RecA protein 970, 972
'Recent thymic emigrants' (RTEs) 2295–
  2298
Receptor editing 156, 360, 770, 2353,
  2358
Receptor interference 471
Receptors
 seven transmembrane-spanning domains
  2031
 three-dimensional structure 515–520,
  516(Table)
 see also specific receptors
Recessive alleles 987
Recognition molecules
 evolution/phylogeny 1948, 1949–1950
 see also Immunoglobulin; Lectins; MHC
Recombinant DNA technology
 historical development 1626
 see also Genetic engineering
Recombinase activating gene, *see* RAG
  genes
Recombination, *see* Genetic recombination
Recombination signal sequences 767, 768
Recruitment 2059–2063
 activation after 2063
 adhesion molecules involved 2059–2060
 cell adhesion mechanisms 2059–2061
 chemotaxis 2061–2062
 dendritic cells 742, 745, 746
 eosinophils 1452

Recruitment (*continued*)
 leukocytes, *see* Leukocyte(s)
 macrophage 1643
 migration inhibition 2062–2063
 neutrophils 16
 resolution/clearance of stimulus 2063
 self-perpetuating 2063
Rectal administration, vaccines 2455
Red blood cells, *see* Erythrocyte(s)
Red-cell adhesion test 1219
Red kidney bean, phytohemagglutinin, *see*
  Phytohemagglutinin (PHA)
Red kidney bean lectin 1536
 see also Phytohemagglutinin (PHA)
Reed–Sternberg cell 1633
Regression (statistical) 2212
 logistic 2213
 percentile 2212
 proportional hazards (Cox) 2213
Regulators of complement activation
  (RCA), *see under* Complement
  activation
Reiter's syndrome 867, 1690
 in AIDS 8
Relapsing fever 380
Relative incidence ratio 2064
Relative risk 1698, 2064–2065
 formulae 2064
Rel family, transcription factors 1119
Renal carbuncle 2066
Renal cell carcinoma
 glycoprotein antigens 2428
 IL-2 immunotherapy 1362, 1438
 IL-2 and interferon α therapy 1362
 IL-2 and LAK cell immunotherapy 1630
 LAK therapy 1348
Renal disease
 Bence Jones proteins (BJP) 341
 membrane attack complex role 627
Renal failure, immunodeficiency in 1286
Renal infections 2065–2067
 leptospirosis 1552–1553
 parenchymal 2066
 see also Pyelonephritis; Urinary tract
  infections (UTI)
Renal injury, NSAIDs causing 120
Renal papillary necrosis 2066
Renal stones, struvite and apatite 2040,
  2041
Renal transplantation 2412
 cyclosporine role 688
 historical background 2411–2412
 immunosuppression 2414
 rejection, TNFα levels 2439
 survival, early immunosuppressive agents
  1351
 tissue typing 2318, 2322
Renocortin 111
Reoviridae 2067
Reovirus 3/D 2067, 2068, 2069, 2070
Reovirus 2067–2071
 animal models 2068–2069
 antigens 2067–2068
 avian infections 2071
 capsid proteins 2067
 characteristics 2067–2068
 encephalitis due to 2070
 genome 2067, 2068(Fig)
  segmentation 2067–2068
 host immune responses 2069–2070
  mucosal 2070
 infection route and spread 2068–2069
 intermediate subviral particles (ISVPs)
  2068
 monoclonal antibodies 2069–2070
 pathology 2069
 reassortant virions 2067–2068
 strains 2067(Table)
 structure 2068(Fig)
 uses in viral spread/pathogenesis studies
  2069, 2069(Table)
 vaccines 2070–2071

Repeated measures analyses 2212
Repertoire-selection technology 985
Reproductive physiology
  fertility-control vaccines 2458–2459
  neutralization of hormones 1851–1852
  see also Contraception, immunological;
    Human chorionic gonadotropin
    (hCG); Mucosal immune system
Reproductive tract infections 2071–2076
  causative organisms 2071
  Chlamydia trachomatis 2072, 2074(Fig)
  genital mucosa immunity 2075
  HPV, *see* Human papillomaviruses
    (HPV)
  HSV-1 and HSV-2 2075
  mycoplasmas and ureaplasmas 1800
  Neisseria gonorrhoeae 2072, 2073(Fig)
  other pathogens 2075
  Treponema pallidum, see Syphilis
  see also individual infections/pathogens;
    Mucosal immune system
Reptiles 2076
  ABH antigens 4
Reptilian immune system 2076–2081
  antibody production 2080
  GALT 2078
  IgY 2080
  lymphoid cells 2078, 2078(Fig)
  lymphoid organs 2076–2078
  mechanism of changes 2080
  MHC 2079
  mixed leukocyte reaction (MLR) 2079
  seasonal changes 1079, 2080
    mechanism 2080
  spleen 2077–2078
  T cell functions 2078–2080
    seasonal changes 2079
  T helper cells 2080
  thymus development 2076–2077,
    2077(Fig)
Reserpine 2166
Respiratory burst 134, 1713, 1937
  biochemistry 1713–1717, 1937–1938
  defect, chronic granulomatous disease
    1715
  eosinophils 823, 823(Table)
  failure
    immunosuppression mechanism 1648
    intracellular pathogens 1648
  hydrogen peroxide toxicity/products
    1715
  impairment
    chronic granulomatous disease 565,
      566
    iron deficiency 1506
  macrophage 1716
  minimization by *Legionella pneumophila*
    1542–1543
  monocytes 1751
  myeloperoxidase deficiency 1717
  products 1715
  see also Microbicidal mechanisms,
    oxygen-dependent
Respiratory syncytial virus (RSV)
  host immune response 1915
  respiratory infections 2463
  vaccines 1916, 2463
    side-effects 2463
  see also Paramyxoviruses
Respiratory tract
  allergic reaction to foods 948–949
  antigen uptake 190–191
  disease, coronavirus causing 659–660
  influenza virus infection 1386
  sensitizers 1365–1366
  upper, in pigs 1994
Respiratory tract infections 2081–2084
  adenovirus 21, 24
  characteristics of organisms 2081–2083
  evasive strategies of organisms 2083
  host defenses 2083
  immune responses 2083

Respiratory tract infections (*continued*)
  lower tract 2081
  upper tract 2081
  vaccines 2083–2084
Restrictin (tenascin R) 1046
Restriction enzymes, in Southern blotting
  2194–2195
Restriction fragment length polymorphism
  (RFLP) 2197
  HLA-DR 1112
  HLA typing 1693
Reth motif 465
Reticular cells 1596, 1603, 1757
Reticular dysgenesis 1279
Reticular fibroblasts
  in bone marrow 2236
  in thymus 2235
Reticuloendothelial system 194, 806, 1756
  criticisms 1756
  erythrocyte trapping 841
  SLE 2259
  see also Mononuclear phagocyte system
    (MPS)
Reticuloendothelial viruses (Rev) 2090
Reticulo-histiocyte system 1756
Reticulum cells 1757
Retina
  granuloma 2379
  photoreceptor-derived proteins
    869(Table)
  photoreceptors 1945
    destruction 868
  scars 873
Retinal glial cells (Müller cells) 870
Retinal soluble antigen (S-Ag) 867
  antibodies 867
Retinoblastoma 2380
Retinoblastoma protein 1420
Retinochoroidopathy, birdshot 867
Retinoic acid 2488
Retinoic acid receptors (RAR) 2488
  α gene (RARA), acute myeloid leukemia
    1557
Retinoids, TGFβ activation 2393
Retinoid-X receptors (RXR) 2488
Retinol-binding protein (RBP) 2488
Retroviral vectors 974, 2084–2092
  bicistronic constructs 2087
  definition 2084
  designs 2086, 2091
  double copy 2087
  in gene therapy 2084
  internal promoters 2086–2087
  internal ribosome entry sites (IRES)
    2086–2087
  lyophilization effect 2091
  multigene 2086
  packaging cell line 2086, 2088–2090,
    2089(Table)
    aim 2088
    evolution 2088(Fig), 2089
    foamy viruses 2090
    lentiviruses 2090
    'split' 2089
    type C retroviruses 2089–2090
  preparation method 2086
  'producer' cells 2086
  'pseudotyped' 2088, 2090
    VSV-G 2091
  replication competent (RCR) 2088, 2091
    assays 2091
  reverse orientation 2087
  safety 2091
  self-inactivating (SIN) 2087
  single-gene 2086
  splicing vectors 2087
  suicide vectors 2087
  temperature and centrifugation effects
    2091
  titer manipulation 2091
  tricistronic constructs 2087
  types 2086(Fig)

Retroviral vectors (*continued*)
  with/without selectable markers 2087–
    2088
Retroviruses 10, 2085–2086, 2092–2097
  acutely transforming 1563
  amphototropic 2089, 2089–2090
  antigens 2095–2096
  assembly 2093–2094
  A-type 2092
  B-type 2092
  classification 2085, 2092, 2093(Table)
  control proteins 2095
  cross-species transmission 2511
  C-type 2085, 2092
    packaging cells 2089–2090
  cytotoxic T cell response 2096
  defective, quadroma formation 139
  D-type 2092
  ecotropic 2089, 2089–2090
  'empty' virions vector preparation 2086
  envelope 2085, 2094
    immunoelectron microscopy 791,
      792(Fig)
  env gene 2085–2086, 2093, 2094
  env protein, host range determination
    2089
  gag gene 2085–2086, 2093
  gag protein 2095
    retroviral (vector) packaging cell line
      2086, 2088
  genes, RNA processing 2095
  genome 2085–2086, 2091, 2091(Fig),
    2092
    cis-acting element 2086
    common features 2092–2095
    C-type virus 2085, 2093, 2094(Fig),
      2095
    MMTV group 2095
    structure and function 2092–2095
    trans-acting elements 2085–2086, 2095
  host range 2089–2090
  immunodeficiency, animal models 1268
  infection process, membrane fusion 2085,
    2094–2095
  internal promoters 2086–2087
  internal ribosome entry sites (IRES)
    2086–2087
  leukemia pathogenesis 1562–1563
  life cycle 2085, 2093–2094
  long terminal repeats (LTRs) 2086,
    2092–2093
    HIV 1131, 1133
  lymphocyte proliferation due to 2021
  Nef protein 2095
  nonacutely transforming 1563
  pathogenesis/involvement in disease
    2095–2097
    autoimmune disease 2097
    immunodeficiency/wasting diseases
      2096
    neoplasia 2097
    neurological disease 2097
    rheumatoid arthritis 2114
    Sjögren's syndrome (SS) 2183
  pol gene 2085–2086, 2093
  pol protein, retroviral (vector) packaging
    cell line 2086, 2088
  provirus 2085
  receptors 2085, 2089, 2094
    amphotropic 2089–2090
    ecotropic 2089–2090
  replication competent (RCR) 2088, 2091
  reverse transcription 2085, 2092–2093
  rev gene 2095
  rex gene 2095
  ribosomal frameshifting 2093
  structural protein genes 2093
  superantigens 1137, 1232, 2242
  SU (surface) proteins 2094
  TM (transmembrane) protein 2094
  transactivating genes (*tat/tax*) 2095
  transformation of lymphoid cells 2487

Retroviruses (*continued*)
   transmission, horizontal and vertical
      2092
   trapping by follicular dendritic cells
      (FDCs) 1728
   types 2093(Table)
   ultrastructure 2092
   vectors, *see* Retroviral vectors
   Vif/Vpu/Vpx/Vpr proteins 2095
   xenotropic 2089
   see also HIV; HIV-1; HIV-2; Human T
      lymphotropic virus type I (HTLV-I);
      Oncoviruses; Viral carcinogenesis
Reverse blot method, HLA typing 1693
Reverse cumulative distribution (RCD) plot
   2214
Reversed single radial immunodiffusion
   (RSRI) 1287
Reverse orientation vectors 2087
Reverse phase chromatography (RPC)
   2038
Reverse transcriptase 1131, 2085, 2092
   inhibitors 11–12
      non-nucleoside 12
      see also Zidovudine (AZT)
Reverse transcription, retroviruses 2085,
   2092–2093
Reverse transcription polymerase chain
   reaction (RT-PCR), *see under*
   Polymerase chain reaction (PCR)
Rev response elements (RRE), HIV 1132–
   1133
Rfp-Y region 303
RFX5 gene, mutation 2174
RFX5 transcription factor 331
RGD sequence 910
   fibronectin and integrin interaction 909,
      910, 911(Fig)
   fibronectin and vitronectin 1887
   glycoproteins 864, 865
   integrin recognition 1407
Rhabdoviridae 2098–2101
   characteristics 2098–2099
   classification and hosts 2098
   see also Lyssaviruses
Rhabdoviruses 2098–2101
Rhadinovirus 1090
Rh antigens, *see* Rh (Rhesus) blood groups
Rh (Rhesus) blood groups 1070
   antigens 1071, 1174, 2102–2105
      alloantigens 70–71
      amino acid changes 2104(Table)
      clinical importance 2102
      expression 2103
      glycoprotein complexes 2104–2105
      historical aspects 2102
      α-methyldopa-induced hemolytic
         anemia 95
      names 2102, 2103(Table)
      nonglycosylated 2104–2105
      on red cell membrane 837, 1071
   autoantibodies in 'warm' autoimmune
      hemolytic anemia 98, 2102–2103
   in blood transfusions 2400
   D antigen (Rh1) 2102
   deficiency syndrome 2105
   discovery 115, 2102
   D^u 1071
   gene conversion 2104, 2104(Table)
   genes 2103
      expression 2103, 2105
   immunoglobulin 2102
   incompatibility, maternally induced
      tolerance 1673
   nomenclature 1071, 2102, 2103(Table)
   null phenotype 837
   partial D state 2103–2104, 2104(Table)
   RHD gene 2103
   Rh$_{mod}$ phenotype 2105
   Rh-negative 2102
   Rh$_{null}$ phenotype 2105
   Rh-positive 2102

Rh (Rhesus) disease 1070, 1174, 1674,
   2102
   antibody detection, temperature 1070
   blocking (incomplete) antibodies 1071
   clinical features 1071
   historical aspects 1070
   naturally occurring protective
      mechanisms 1070–1071
   prevention 1070, 1147, 2102
RHCE gene 2103
RHD gene 2103
Rhesus deficiency syndrome 2105
Rhesus monkeys
   MHC class I genes 2008–2010
   see also Primates (nonhuman)
Rheumatic chorea 431
Rheumatic fever 431–432, 434, 1737
   acute 2219
   autoimmune mechanisms 431–432, 434
   B cell markers 432
   blood group A antigen similar to
      streptococcal antigen 1737
   chorea 1737
   Streptococcus pyogenes causing 1737
   susceptibility 432
   T helper cells in 432, 435
Rheumatic heart disease 431–432
Rheumatoid arthritis (RA) 2111–2116
   adhesion molecules 2114
   animal models 2106–2110
      adjuvant arthritis, *see* Adjuvant
         arthritis (AA)
      comparison with human RA
         2106(Table)
      HLA-transgenic mice 2108–2110
      SCID mouse model 1129(Table)
      see also Collagen-induced arthritis
         (CIA)
   antioxidants effects 135
   autoantibodies 2113
      various 2113
      see also Rheumatoid factor
   autoantigens 2113
      type II collagen 2109–2110
   clinical features 2111
   cytokine abnormalities 2113–2114
      immunomodulatory 2113–2114
      pro-/anti-inflammatory balance 2114
      proinflammatory 2113
   diagnostic criteria 2111, 2111(Table)
   etiopathogenesis 2106
      antigen-independent mechanisms 2116
      infectious agents 2114–2115
      model 2114–2116
      shared epitope and, *see below*
      see also Rheumatoid arthritis (RA),
         pathogenesis
   fish oil supplements 885
   gene therapy 978, 979(Table)
   genetics 2112–2113
   growth factors 2114, 2116
   HLA associations 1694, 1741, 2108–
      2110, 2112, 2112(Table)
      molecular mimicry theory 2116
      QKRAA sequence 2112, 2115, 2116
   HLA-DQ8 2108–2109
   HLA-DR4 294, 1741, 2112
   HLA-DRB1 2108, 2109, 2112(Table)
   hsp60 and hsp70 role 2231
   IgG glycosylation decreased 1004
   IgM rheumatoid factors 1216, 2113
      see also Rheumatoid factor (RF)
   IL-1 role 1434, 2113
   IL-2 role 2114
   IL-4 role 2114
   IL-6 role 1460, 2114
   immune complexes in 1225
   immunological abnormalities
      2111(Table), 2113–2114
   immunotherapy 1359, 2112
      see also therapy (below)
   incidence 2111

Rheumatoid arthritis (RA) (*continued*)
   juvenile 1285
      oral collagen administration 1898
   molecular mimicry 1741–1742, 2115–
      2116, 2115(Fig), 2231
      EQRRAA susceptibility sequence and
         Proteus 1740(Fig), 1741
      hsp65 34, 2115
      QKRAA sequence 2116
   NSAIDs action 2027, 2112
   pannus 135
   pathogenesis
      destructive process 2116
      IL-15 1494
      see also etiopathogenesis (above)
   pathology, rheumatoid factor role 137
   polyclonal hypergammaglobulinemia in
      1162
   proteasomes 2113
   Proteus mirabilis, immune response to
      2040
   reactive oxygen species effects 134
   shared epitope 2108, 2112, 2112(Fig),
      2114
      binding hypothesis 2115
      molecular mimicry, *see above*
      role 2115–2116
   T cell receptors 221–2113
   TGFβ 2114
   T$_H$1 pattern 2114
   T$_H$1/T$_H$2 imbalance 276, 2114
   therapy 1359, 2112
      antibodies to cytokines 1358
      anti-TNFα 1344, 2112, 2438
      collagen type II administration 1898
      IFNγ 1425
      soluble TNF receptors 2349
      TNFα levels/role 2438
   transporter genes 2113
   vitamin E supplementation 135
   'Rheumatoid arthritis cassette' 2116
Rheumatoid arthritis nuclear antigens
   (RANA) 2113, 2114
Rheumatoid factor (RF) 137, 265, 1318,
   2113
   affinity 2113
   as autoantibodies 137, 265
   B cells 2116
   detection 265
   formation 137
   heterogeneity 137
   IgG 137
   IgM 137, 1216
   immune complex detection 1221
   as natural antibodies 1808
   in normal individuals 2113
   pathological role 137
   production, PGE$_2$ increasing 2027
   in rheumatoid arthritis 1216, 2113
   Sjögren's syndrome (SS) 2182
   specificity 137
   transgenic mice B cells 2361
Rheumatological disorders 2117–2121
   etiopathogenesis 2117
   MHC genes and 2117
   see also Rheumatoid arthritis (RA);
      Systemic sclerosis
Rhinderpest virus, vaccines 1916
Rhinitis
   allergic, *see* Allergic rhinitis
   classification 2121, 2122(Table)
   diagnosis 2122(Table)
   infectious 2121, 2122(Table)
   noninfectious 2121, 2122(Table)
      see also Allergic rhinitis
   seasonal, *see* Allergic rhinitis
   treatment 2125
   vasomotor 2121
Rhinoviruses 1955(Table)
   antiviral drug development 1959
   binding to ICAM-1 1609
   ICAM-1 as receptor 804

Rhinoviruses (*continued*)
  receptors 1954, 1956(Table)
  structure 1959
  vitamin C action 2492
Rho
  mast cell degranulation 1671
  oxygen-dependent phagocytic killing
    1714
RhoA, IL-8 signaling 1467
Rhodamine 142
  labeling with 944
Rhodococcus 662
Rhodopsin superfamily 86
  chemokine receptors 531
  chemokines 536
Rh system, *see* Rh (Rhesus) blood groups
RIA, *see* Radioimmunoassay (RIA)
Ri antigen, antibodies 1843
Riboflavin 2490
  deficiency 2490–2491
Riboflavin carrier protein, birth control
    vaccine 643(Table)
Ribonucleoprotein
  heterogeneous nuclear (hnRNPs) 126
  small cytoplasmic (scRNP) 127, 127(Fig)
  small nuclear (snRNP) 126
Ribosomal frameshifting, retroviral vectors
    2093
Ribosomal RNP (rRNP) 127
Ribozyme, gene therapy 979(Table)
Ricin, applications 1540(Table)
Rickets 2496
Rickettsia 2126, 2126–2128, 2127
  antigens 2126–2127
  characteristics 2126–2127
  diseases due to 2126
  evasive strategies 2127
  host immune response 2127
  persistent infections 2127
  recrudescent disease 2127
  transmission 2126, 2127
  vaccines 2127–2128
Rickettsiaceae 2126
Rickettsia prowazekii 2127
Rickettsia typhi 2127
Rida (Icelandic scrapie) 2409
Ridley–Jopling scale 1025, 1025(Table)
Rift Valley Fever virus 392
  immune response to 392
  vaccine 392
RING finger Zn-finger motif 1313
RIP, TNF receptor signaling 2347
Risk, relative 2064–2065
Risk estimates
  definition 1698, 1698(Table)
  HLA–disease association 1697, 1698,
    1699(Table), 2064
River blindness, *see* Onchocerciasis
RK-13 cell line 2048
RLA-A 2048
RLA-D 2048
Rls (regulator of sex limitation) gene 1046
RNA
  as antigen 204
  messenger, *see* mRNA
  processing/transport, cytokine expression
    701
  separation, in Northern blotting 1864
  small nuclear (snRNA) 126
  synthesis
    mercury inhibiting 1687
    paramyxoviruses 1913
RNAase colicins 2015
RNA-dependent protein kinase (PKR)
    2030
RNA probes, in Northern blotting 1865
RNA synthetase, autoantibodies 2003
Ro52 antigen 127
Ro60 antigen 127
Ro (SS-A) antigen 127, 2184
  antibodies 132, 1676
    Sjögren's syndrome (SS) 2183, 2184

Ro (SS-A) antigen (*continued*)
  antibodies (*continued*)
    SLE 2184, 2257
    maternal antibodies 132
Rochalimaeae quintana 2126, 2127
Rocket immunoelectrophoresis, *see*
    Immunoelectrophoresis, rocket
Rodgers blood group 607, 837
Rolling of leukocytes, *see* Leukocyte(s);
    Neutrophil(s)
Romurtide 1790–1792
  bone marrow recovery 1790
  cancer metastasis prevention 1792
  future applications 1792
  as multicytokine inducer 1792
  side effects/toxicology 1792
  structure 1791(Fig)
  therapeutic applications 1790
Roseola infantum 1089
Rosette, definition 2128
Rosetting 179
Rosetting techniques 510, 1235, 2128–
    2130
  applications 2128
  B cell identification 2129
  erythrocyte antibody complement (EAC)
    rosette 2130
  erythrocyte antibody (EA) rosette 2129–
    2130
  erythrocyte (E) rosette 2129
  hematopoietic cell identification 2129
  markers on T/B cells and monocytes
    2130(Table)
  neuraminidase treatment 2129
  T cell populations 2129–2130
  T cell surface markers 2129
  T helper cell identification 2129
Rossmann fold 519
Rotoviruses, infections 968
Rough (R) mutants, lipopolysaccharide
    807
Roundworm infection, *see* Ascariasis
Rous-associated virus type 1 (RAV-1) 1563
Rous sarcoma virus 1564, 2097
RPR (rapid plasma reagin) test 2073
RT1B locus 1391
RT1D locus 1391
RT6 marker 1273, 1394, 1688
RT-PCR, *see under* Polymerase chain
    reaction (PCR)
RT system 2055, 2056(Table)-2057(Table),
    2057
RTX toxins 2377
RU 486, structure 997(Fig)
Rubella 2351
  congenital infection 2352
    animal model 2352
    diabetes mellitus association 1400
    teratogenesis mechanism 2352
  vaccination 2351
Rubella virus, immunodeficiency induced
    by 1285
Rubivirus 2350(Table)
Rubulaviruses 1910(Table)
  attachment proteins 1911
Ruminants
  Ig transfer 2450
  see also Ungulate immune system
'Runting syndrome' 2069
Ryanodine receptor, ankyrin association
    1681
Rye classification 1634

S

Sabin, A. 256–257, 257(Fig)
Saccharomyces cerevisiae, glucans,
    antitumor effect 429
Salicylic acid 119

Saliva 1888–1889
  components 1888–1889
  mucins 1888–1889
Salivary glands
  diffuse infiltrative lymphocytosis (DILS)
    2183
  in Sjögren's syndrome (SS) 2182
Salmonella 2131–2133
  antigens 2131
  attenuated 38
    as delivery system for recombinant
      antigens 2133
    uses 2132–2133
  carriers 2131
  characteristics 2131
  'cryptic' plasmid 2132, 2133
  enterobacterial common antigen (ECA)
    2131
  evasive strategies 2131–2132
  growth in macrophage 2131–2132
  host immune response 2132
  infection route 2131
  lethal/sublethal infections 2132
  lipopolysaccharide 424, 2131
    structure 2378(Fig)
  ompR 2132
  recombinant 2133
    HSV vaccine 1088
  rough mutants 2131
  species 2131
  vaccines 2132–2133
    Aro mutants 2133
    galE mutants 2132–2133
    live 2132, 2132–2133
    seroconversion rates 2133
    Vi antigen, antibodies 2132
Salmonella tranaroa 1877
Salmonella typhi 2131
  evasive strategies 2131
  mutants 2132–2133, 2133
  vaccines 2458
Salmonella typhimurium 2131
  Aro mutants 2133
  bactericidal/permeability increasing
    protein action 1722
  sialidase 1118–1119
Salpingitis
  Chlamydia trachomatis causing 2072
  Neisseria gonorrhoeae causing 2072
Salt fractionation, proteins 2036
Salt links, antibody–antigen interactions
    159
Sanarelli–Shwartzman reaction 1841
Sandimmune[R] 688
Sandwich techniques 143
  immunoassays 1254–1255
  immunoelectrophoresis 1296
  monoclonal antibody use 1746
San Miguel sea lion virus 399, 400
S-antigen, uveitis treatment 1897, 1898
Sapecins 1500, 1501
Saponin 37
  Quillaja 1507, 1508
  tissue permeabilization in
    immunocytochemistry 1262
Sarcoidosis 2133–2137
  calcitriol synthesis 2495
  chemokines 2137
  cytokines 2136–2137
    interactions 2137
  epidemiology 2134
  etiology 2134, 2134–2135
    mycobacterial DNA 2134
  genetics 2134
  granuloma formation 2135–2136,
    2135(Fig), 2137
  historical perspective 2134
  HLA association 2134
  IFNγ expression 2136
  immunological features 2135(Table)
  Kveim reaction 1024, 2135
  Kveim–Siltzbach test 2135

Sarcoidosis (continued)
  macrophage 2135, 2136
  molecular mimicry 2134
  mononuclear phagocytes 2136–2137
  pathogenesis, hypothesis 2137
  pathology 2135–2136
  remissions 2133–2134
  T cells 2136
    CD4+ cells 2135, 2136
    lung 2136
    T_H1 response 2134, 2137
  TCR gene expression 2136
  treatment 2134, 2137
Sarcoma, transferrin receptor (TfR)
    expression 2390
Sarcoptes scabiei 753
SAR proteins 852(Table)
Sca-1 antigen 1875
Scabies 753
Scanning electron microscopy, *see* Electron
    microscopy
Scarlet fever 2218
Scatchard analysis 166
  equation 44
Scavenger receptors 185–186
  in phagocytosis 1937
  subclasses 185
  type A (SR-A) on macrophage 1644,
    1646(Table)
Scavenging
  capping for 420
  reactive oxygen compounds 1858
Schaumann bodies 2136
Schistosoma
  antigen mimicry hypothesis 2142
  antigens 2139
    carbohydrate 2141
    loss in immune evasion 2142
  characteristics 2138–2139
  eggs 2139
    antigens 2140
    granuloma, *see under* Schistosomiasis
    immunopathology due to 2139–2140
    output suppression 2141
    response in mice 2140
    T_H2 response 2141
  evasive strategies 2141–2142
  life cycle 2138–2139, 2138(Fig)
  lifespan 2138
  molluscan hosts 2138
  species 2137
Schistosoma bovis 2142
  vaccines 1921
Schistosoma haematobium 2137
  immunity 2140–2142
Schistosoma intercalatum 2137
Schistosoma japonicum 2137
Schistosoma mansoni 2137
  ADCC induced by IgE 169
  complement-inhibiting proteins 500
  IgE role 1207
  recombinant vaccine development 2142
Schistosoma mekongi 2137
Schistosomiasis 2137–2143
  ADCC 1920, 2141, 2141(Fig)
  age-dependent resistance to reinfection
    2140
  concomitant immunity 2140
  cytokines 2141
  egg-induce immunopathology 2139–2140
  eosinophils 2140–2142
  eradication 2139
  granuloma 1024, 2139–2140, 2139(Fig)
    formation 1920
    TNFα role 2141
  hepatic fibrosis 2140, 2141
  immune response 1920, 2139–2141
    antigens 2141
    IgE 2141
    target 2140
    T cell 2140
  immunity (anti-infection) 2140–2141

Schistosomiasis (continued)
  immunodiagnosis 2142
  monoclonal antibodies 2142
  morbidity 2139
  murine models 2140
  prevalence 1917
  small hsps 2231
  T_H1/T_H2 response 2141
  TNFα, egg granulomas 2141
  vaccination 2142
  vaccines, recombinant 2142
Schwartzman reaction, *see* Shwartzman
    reaction
SCID, *see* Severe combined
    immunodeficiency (SCID)
SCID mice 1125, 1268–1269, 2174
  applications/role 1274
  as autoimmune disease models 1128–
    1130, 1129(Table)
  as B cell deficiency model 1274
  CB17 and C3H 1128
  CD45RB expression 1383
  differences with human SCID 1269
  EBV-positive lymphocytes 1128
  human (hu-SCID), *see* hu-SCID mice
  human mAb preparation 1745
  leaky mice 1128, 1273
  lymphoid organs 1269
  macrophages 1268–1269
  mast cells 1268
  mutation 1125, 1269
    DNA-pk deficiency 1125, 1269
  NK cells 1128, 1268
  offspring 1273
  reovirus infection 2069
  resistance to *Porphyromonas gingivalis*
    1890–1891
  T and B cell development arrested 1268
  transplantation 546
SCL, chromosomal translocations 556, 558
Scl170 antibodies (anti-topoisomerase I
    antibodies) 131–132
Scleroderma, *see* Systemic sclerosis
    (scleroderma)
Scleroderma–polymyositis overlap
    syndrome, anti-Ku antibodies 131
Sclerosing myeloma, neuropathy (POEMS
    syndrome) 1839, 1986
Scorpion, venom 2472
Scorpionfish, venom 2473
Scrapie 2409
  immune system 2410
  spread 2409(Fig)
Scrapie agent 2409
scurfy (*sf*) mutation 1270–1271
SDF-1 chemokine 1760
SDS (sodium dodecyl sulfate) 2143
  protein binding 2143
  sieving properties 2143
SDS-polyacrylamide gel electrophoresis
    (SDS–PAGE) 2035, 2143–2144
  acrylamide gradient 2043
  application 2143, 2144
  Laemlli system 2144
  protein binding 2143
SDS–protein complexes 2143
Second messengers 2028
  arachidonic acid (AA) 231–232
  of glucocorticoids 111
    see also Annexins (lipocortins)
  histamine receptors 1101
  leukotrienes 231–232
  types 2028
  see also Calcium; Cyclic AMP (cAMP)
Second signals 2145–2151
  B cells 2149–2151
  T cells 2145–2149
  see also B cell(s), activation; T cell(s),
    costimulation; T cell activation
Secretagogues 2164, 2165
Secretase 2159
Secretion 849

Secretors and nonsecretors 4
Secretory component (SC) 148, 886, 1196,
    1726, 1778, 2152–2158
  cytokines regulating 2156
  expression 2155
    regulation 2155–2156
  free 2152, 2154
    pIg affinity 2154
  function 2152–2154
  gene locus (PIGR) 2152
  historical aspects 2152
  increased expression in disease 2156–
    2157
  I region 2154
  J chain affinity 2155
  molecular biology 2152–2154
  polymeric Ig binding
    binding sites 2154–2155
    IgA formation 1784
    J chain role 1517, 2155
    pentameric IgM 2153(Fig)
    sIgA 1198, 1726, 1784, 2152,
      2153(Fig)
  structure 2152–2154, 2153(Fig)
  synthesis 2154
  transmembrane (pIgR) 2152, 2153(Fig),
    2154
    domains 2152–2154
    intracellular sorting 2154
    intracellular transport 2154
    mRNA 2154
    pIg interactions 2154–2155
    rabbit 2154
    as sacrificial receptor 2154
  transport of pIg through secretory
    epithelia 2155
  in ungulates 2450
Secretory immunity 2155–2157
  see also Immunoglobulin A (IgA);
    Mucosal immune system; Secretory
    component (SC)
Secretory immunoglobulins 148
  see also Immunoglobulin A (IgA)
Secretory piece, *see* Secretory component
    (SC)
Sedimentation equilibrium studies 2446
Sedimentation separation 508
Sedimentation velocity studies 2446, 2447
SEK kinase 2328
Selectins 16, 27(Table), 28, 803–804,
    1537, 2158–2161
  carbohydrate binding 2158
  knockout mice 1566, 1566(Table)
  leukocyte adhesion to endothelial cells
    1540
  leukocyte rolling 757, 803, 2160(Fig)
  leukocyte trafficking role 1539, 2159
  ligands 2158, 2158(Fig)
    Lewis^x (Le^x) and sialyl-Le^x 1578–1579
  neutrophil and monocyte migration
    1761, 1935
  role, Arthus reaction 238
  signal transduction 31
  structure 2158, 2158(Fig)
  see also E-selectin; L-selectin; P-selectin
Selective breeding 342–346
  bidirectional 342–346
  chemical carcinogenesis 345–346
  immune system changes 345
  inflammatory reaction 345
Selenium 133
  deficiency 1284
Self antigens 106, 203
  agonist, negative selection of T cells
    2308
  antagonist, positive selection 2307
  class II MHC binding 198
  immune response, *see* Autoantibodies;
    Autoimmunity
  membrane-bound 107
  nonreactivity mechanisms 809
    clonal suppression 809

Self antigens (*continued*)
  nonreactivity mechanisms (*continued*)
    see also Anergy ; Clonal deletion
    nonresponse, immunophysiology and 1339
    positive selection of T cells 2306–2308, 2307(Fig)
    in privileged sites 295
    T cell clonal anergy induction 2332–2333
    tolerance, *see* Tolerance
    see also Autoantigens
Self antigens/non-self antigen discrimination 266, 1893
  danger theory 295, 2367
  idiotype network theory and 1191
  tolerance, *see* Tolerance
Self-inactivating (SIN) vectors 2087
'Self-surveillance' 1704
'Self-surveillance complex', MHC as 1705–1706
Self-tolerance, *see* Tolerance
Semen, immunity to 1373–1374
Semliki Forest virus 390
Sendai virus, evasive strategy 1915
Sensitization (to antigen), risk in immunological active enhancement 810, 811
Sensory ganglia, HSV infection 1085
Sephacel DEAE media 2037
Sephadex™ 2037
Sepharose™ 513, 1540, 2037
Sepharose CL-4B 514, 2037
Sepharose Fast Flow 2038
Sepharose protein A 513
Sepsis 2161
  definition 2162, 2162(Table)
  incidence and prognosis 2161
  severe, definition 2161, 2162, 2162(Table)
  systemic inflammatory response syndrome (SIRS)/infection interrelationships 2163(Fig)
  TNFα role 2438–2439
  treatment
    pentoxifylline 2439
    TNFα synthesis reduction 2439
Sepsis syndrome, *see* Septic shock
Septic shock 319, 1980, 2161–2164
  in anthrax 313
  central mediators as 'black knights' 2161, 2163
  definition 2161, 2162, 2162(Table)
  epidemiology 2162
  excess polyclonal activation 1982
  nitric oxide 2163
  pathogenesis 187
  pathophysiology 2161, 2162–2164
    mediators 2163(Table)
    stages 2163
  prognosis 2161, 2162
  susceptibility, cats 892, 894
  systemic inflammatory response syndrome (SIRS) interrelationship 2163(Fig)
  therapy, soluble TNF receptors 2349
  TNF 2163
Sequence-specific oligonucleotide probe (SSOP), HLA typing 1693, 2319
Sequence-specific primer (SSP)
  HLA typing 1693
  tissue typing method 2319
Serine kinase mTOR 1441
Serine protease 582, 604, 1858
  complement activation 603
  granzymes, *see* Granzyme(s)
  inhibitors 1858
    poxvirus encoded homologs 1997(Table)
    see also Serpins
  invertebrates 1500, 1501
  neutrophil granules 1722–1723

Serine protease (*continued*)
  proenzyme 606, 607
Serine/threonine-directed protein kinases 2028–2030
  Ca²⁺/calmodulin-dependent 2029
  cyclic nucleotide-dependent 2028–2029
  MAPK signaling pathway 2029–2030
  other groups 2030
  phospholipid-dependent 2029
  see also MAPK pathway
Serology
  definition 218
  HLA typing methods 1692
  immunopathology investigation 1340
  monitoring of inbred strains 1371
Serotonin 2164–2168
  cells releasing 2164
  in contact sensitivity 2166
  DTH and 2165–2166
  effect on macrophage 2166
  formation 1668
  lymphocyte chemoattractant factor secretion 2167
  lymphocyte regulation 2167
  NK cell activity enhancement 2166
  phagocytosis modulation 2166
  release mechanism 2164–2165
  structure 2164(Fig)
  T cell regulation 2167
Serpentine receptor superfamily 542
  chemokine receptors 531, 2031
Serpins
  cowpox virus-derived 223, 1028
  poxvirus encoded homologs 1997(Table)
  see also Serine protease, inhibitors
Sertoli cells, FasL expression 879
Serum 1964
  therapeutic uses 1967
  see also Plasma
Serum amyloid A (SAA) protein 85
  clearance/catabolism 19
  disease activity correlation 20
  disorders with minimal levels 19
  increased levels 19
  structure and genes 19
Serum amyloid P (SAP) component 19, 85, 663
Serum mannan-binding proteins (S-MBP), as CD45 ligand 493
Serum protein electrophoresis, *see* Electrophoresis
Serum sickness 1177, 1223, 1345, 2168–2170
  antibodies 1092
  anti-lymphocyte serum (ALS) 122
  causes 2169
  clinical features 2169
  cytokines involved 2169
  drug-induced 2169
  experimental models 2168, 2168–2169
    acute 2168–2169
    chronic 2169
    time course 2168, 2169(Fig)
  histopathology 2168–2169, 2169
  humans 2169
  snake antivenom 2473
  treatment 2169
Setonix 1664, 1664(Table)
Seven transmembrane-spanning domain receptors 531, 542, 2031
Severe combined immunodeficiency (SCID) 1276, 1277–1279, 2170–2175
  ADA deficiency, *see* Adenosine deaminase (ADA)
  Arabian horses 1273
  autosomal recessive (AU-SCID) 2170
    JAK3 defect 2171
    mutations causing 2170
  B cells 1277–1278
  bone marrow transplantation 545, 2174
  Bruton's agammaglobulinemia *vs* 389
  CD3γ and CD3ε deficiency 2173

Severe combined immunodeficiency (SCID) (*continued*)
  cellular immune defects 1279
  classification 2170, 2170(Fig)
  clinical features 1277, 2170–2171
  in dogs 414
  gene therapy 978, 979(Table), 2174
  GVHD in 2170
  investigation, lymphocyte transformation test 1624
  JAK3 kinase deficiency 1278, 2171–2172
  MHC class II deficiency 1277, 1279, 2173–2174
  mice, *see* SCID mice
  NF-AT transcription factor defects 1279
  Omenn's syndrome 1279
  opportunistic infections 2170
    management 2174
  oral infections 1891
  prevalence of types 2170, 2170(Fig)
  purine nucleoside phosphorylase (PNP) deficiency 1278, 2172–2173
  radiosensitivity association 2053
  RAG defects 1279, 2172
  reticular dysgenesis 1279
  stem cell transplantation 1066
  T cells 1277, 2174
  treatment 2174
    gene therapy 978, 979(Table), 2174
  X-linked 1276, 1278, 2170, 2171
    B cell numbers 2171
    cytokine receptors role 712
    in dogs 1273
    γc gene in 1440, 1441, 1464, 1489
    IgE production 1489–1490
    IL-13 receptor complex 1489–1490
    mutations 2170, 2171
    ZAP-70 defects 1279, 2173
Sex, experimental autoimmune thyroiditis link 2310
Sex determination, role of H-Y antigen 1159–1160
Sex hormones 641(Fig), 2175–2178
  autoimmune disease 2175–2176
  control of acute phase proteins 18
  cytokines controlled 2176–2177
  immune cells affected 2177(Fig)
  immune interactions 2176, 2224
  immune organs affected 2177(Fig)
  summary of effects 2177(Table)
  targets of action 2176
Sex-specific antigen, H-Y 72
Sézary syndrome 1633
  thymic hormones and peptides immunotherapy 2301
SH-activated cytolysins 2376–2377
Sharks
  Ig evolution 1307, 1309
  IgW 1309, 1313
  light chain loci 1309(Fig)
SHC (shc)
  IL-2 receptor signal transduction 1440
  IL-4 signal transduction 1455
  mast cell degranulation 1670
  TCR signaling 2326
SHC–GRB-2–SOS complexes, TCR signaling 2326
Shear forces, transmigration of leukocytes 757, 758(Fig)
'Sheddases' 715, 2159
Sheep
  cannulation of lymph nodes 1902
  Echinococcus infections 783, 784
  fasciliasis resistance absence 881, 883
  immune system, *see* Ovine immune system; Ungulate immune system
  lymphocyte recirculation 1620
  vaccination against fascioliasis 883
  wasting disease 2096
Sheep erythrocyte
  bystander effects 397
  rosetting techniques 2129

Sheep erythrocyte (*continued*)
  TIITS protein 2129
Sheep erythrocyte receptor of macrophage 1537
Shiga-like toxins (SLTs) 844, 2370
  mode of action 2372(Fig)
Shiga toxin 2179–2180, 2369, 2370, 2372
  B subunits 2372
  CD antigens homology 2180
  hemolytic–uremic syndrome 2180
  mode of action 2372, 2372(Fig)
Shigella 2178–2181
  antigens 2179
  attenuated strain 38
  characteristics 2178–2179
  cytokine production due to 2180
  diseases associated 2178
  dysentery 967
  hemolytic–uremic syndrome 2178, 2180
  host immune response 2179–2180
    TCR repertoire 2180
  immunization 2179
  infection prevention by breast milk Igs 1672
  infection route, M cells 2179
  postinfectious reactive arthritis after 2180
  reinfection 2179
  species 2179
  vaccines 2179, 2180–2181
    killed 2181
    live attenuated 2180
  virulence 2179
Shigella boydii 2179
Shigella dysenteriae 2179, 2179–2180
  dysentery 967, 2178, 2370
Shigella flexneri 2179
  live attenuated vaccine 2180
Shigella sonnei 2179
Shigellosis 2179
  cytokine production 2180
Shingles, *see* Herpes zoster
Shock
  anaphylactic, *see* Anaphylaxis
  endotoxic 424
    see also Septic shock
  filoviral hemorrhagic fever 916, 918
  Forssman 953, 955
  increased eicosanoids in 885
  septic, *see* Septic shock
  toxic 1980
    excess polyclonal activation 1982
    nitric oxide role 1860
Short consensus repeats (SCRs) 495, 620, 629
  decay-accelerating factor (DAF) 735
Short tandem repeats (STRs) 1988
SHP-1
  absent in motheaten mice 1270
  B cell coinhibition 1983
  B cell receptor signaling 351
  NK lysis inhibition 1811
SHP-2, IL-2 receptor signal transduction 1440
Shprintzen/DiGeorge locus 763
Shprintzen syndrome 762
SHR strain 2058
Shwartzman reaction 319
  generalized 2218, 2378
Sialic acid 426, 1537
  CD22 recognition 479
  Trypanosoma cruzi invasion mechanism 521
Sialic acid-binding lectin, CD22 479–480
Sialidases 1118–1119
  deficiency 1120
Sialoadhesins 1537, 1539(Table)
  cell–cell interactions 1540
  on macrophage 1646(Table)
Sialoglycoproteins, alloantigens 73
Sialomucin, tumor immunological escape 2445

Sialophorin (CD43), *see* CD43
Sialyl Lewis[a] 803, 2432
Sialyl Lewis[x] (CD15S) antigen 28–29, 447(Table), 803, 1576–1579, 1578
  blood vessels expressing 1098
  defective synthesis, LAD II syndrome 1568
  expression on granulocytes/monocytes 1578
  lectin specificity 1537
  in leukocyte rolling 757
  as ligand for selectins 1578–1579
  saccharide, *see* Addressin, peripheral
  structure 1577(Fig)
  as tumor-associated antigen 1578
α2,6-Sialyltransferase, CD22 regulation 480
Sickle-cell anemia 988, 1286
  parvovirus B19 infection 1924
Side-chain theory 1337
Signaling, *see* Signal transduction
Signaling lymphocyte activation antigen (SLAM) 456(Table)
Signal (leader) sequence, immunoglobulin 144, 145(Fig)
Signal recognition particle (SRP) 144
  antibodies 2118
  receptor 144
'Signal three' 2367
Signal transduction
  aberrant, chromosomal translocations causing 558
  acetylcholine at neuromuscular junction 1834
  adhesion molecules role 31
  apoptosis 875, 875–876, 877(Fig)
    see also Fas/FasL interactions
  basic concepts 2028
  B cell activation pathway 349–350, 350(Fig)
  B cell proliferation 2020
  B cell receptor 1194, 1194–1195, 1299–1301
    modulation 350–352
  CD2 role 464
  CD3 role 467
  CD4 role 469
  CD5 role 473
  CD22 role 351–352, 480–481
  CD28 482, 2147, 2147(Fig)
  CD40 250, 484–485, 654, 2150(Fig)
    see also CD40; CD40-CD40L interactions
  CD45-mediated 1680
  chemokine receptors 711
  chemotactic factors 2031–2032
  CTLA-4 2148
  by cytokine receptors 710–711, 711(Fig), 2032
  cytokine synthesis 700–701, 703
  defect in hyper-IgM syndrome 1167
  degranulation 737
  fibronectin interaction with integrins 911
  fibronectin pathway 911, 912(Fig)
  GM-CSF 1021–1022
  growth factors 2032
  ICAMs role 1411–1412
  Igα and Igβ mediating 1194–1195
  IL-1 receptors 1432, 1432–1433, 2032
  IL-2 receptors 1440–1441, 2149, 2172(Fig)
  IL-3 receptors, *see* Interleukin-3 (IL-3) receptor
  IL-4 receptors, *see under* Interleukin-4 (IL-4) receptor
  IL-5 receptors 823
  IL-6 receptors 1461–1462
  IL-7 receptors 1464, 1465(Fig)
  IL-8 receptors 1467–1468, 1469(Fig)
  IL-9 receptors 1472–1473, 1472(Fig)
  IL-10 receptors 1477
  IL-11 receptors, *see* Interleukin-11 (IL-11)

Signal transduction (*continued*)
  IL-12 receptors 1484
  IL-13 receptors 1491
  IL-15 receptors 1494
  inhibition, soluble cytokine receptors 715
  interferon α/β 1414–1415, 1419–1420
  interferon γ 1423, 1427–1428, 2151
  kinases 31, 2028
    see also Protein kinase(s); *specific protein kinases*
  leukemia inhibitory factor (LIF) 1560–1561
  lipopolysaccharide 2032–2033
  lymphocyte activation, *see* B cell(s); T cell(s)
  macrophage 1645–1648
  mast cell degranulation 1670–1671
  M-CSF (CSF-1) 1651
  membrane-associated cytoskeletal protein role 1680–1681
  membrane attack complex role 627
  MHC class II molecules role 1113
  opsonins 2032
  oxygen-dependent phagocytic killing 1713
  phorbol esters 1940
  phospholipase C 1940
  platelet adhesion generating 1974
  protein kinase role 2028
  receptors role 2028
  reversed 715, 718
    inhibition by soluble cytokine receptors 715
  second messengers 2028
  selectins role 28
  T cell activation, *see* T cell activation
  T cell receptor 467
    TCR/CD3 complex 73
  T cells 687(Fig)
  TNF receptors 2347–2348, 2348(Fig)
  vitamin D-binding protein 2497–2498
    see also Second messengers; *specific kinases*
Signal transduction and activation of transcription, *see* STAT
SIL, chromosomal translocations 556
Silicone implants 1367
Silicosis, granulomas 1023, 1024
Silver, in autoradiography 296, 298
Simian acquired immunodeficiency syndrome (SAIDS) 2096–2097
Simian immunodeficiency virus (SIV) 2005, 2175
  coreceptors 1134
Simian lentiviruses 2096
Simian parvovirus (SPV) 1926
Simian retroviruses 2096–2097
Simian virus-40 (SV40) 2442
  adenovirus hybrid 24
  in adenovirus vaccines 21, 24
  tumors 1360
Simple-sequence length polymorphisms (SSLP) 2253
Sinc gene 2409
Singer–Nicolson model 415, 416–417
Single-chain Fv fragments (scFv)
  binding affinities 2433
  immunotoxin fusion 2261–2262, 2262(Fig)
  in tumor imaging 2433, 2434
Single photon emission computerized tomography (SPECT) 2434
Singlet oxygen, *see* Oxygen
Sin Nombre virus 392
Sipunculid worms 1499
SIRC rabbit cell line 2048
Sirolimus, *see* Rapamycin
Sixth disease 1089
SJL/J mice 1400
  experimental autoimmune encephalomyelitis 1787
SJL mice 1769–1770

SJL mice (continued)
  immunology 1770
  infectious agents susceptibility/resistance 1769–1770
  mercury effect 1688
  origin/characteristics 1769
Sjögren's syndrome (SS) 2181–2185
  animal models 2183
  autoantibodies 2004, 2182, 2184
  autoimmune diseases associated 2182–2183
  CD4+ T cells 2184
  clinical features 2182
  diagnostic criteria 2182
  epidemiology 2182–2183
  etiology, viral 2183–2184
  extraglandular disease 2183
  historical aspects 2181–2182
  HLA association 2182, 2183
  HLA class II expression 2184
  HLTV-1 tax gene association 2183
  IFNγ levels 2184
  IgM role 1216
  immune response 2184
  immunogenetics 2182–2183
  increased secretory component expression 2156–2157
  lymphoma in 2182
  monoclonal Igs 2182
  polyclonal hypergammaglobulinemia in 1162, 2184
  primary 2182, 2184
  rheumatoid factors 2182
  salivary flow decrease and infections 1891
  secondary 2182
  SLE association 2182
  treatment 2184
SK-HEP-1 cell line 1463
Skin 2190–2192
  allergic reactions to foods 949
  antigen-presenting cells 175
  antigen uptake 188–189
  autoantibodies 263
  autoantigens 263
  autoimmune disease 2185–2189
    bullous dermatoses 2188–2189
    types 2185(Table)
    see also Cutaneous lupus erythematosus; Pemphigoid; Pemphigus
  barrier 750, 787
  CLA as homing receptor 2160
  contact allergy 2191
    see also Contact hypersensitivity
  cytokines synthesized 750
  host defense system 188, 750, 787, 2190
  immune response 2190–2191
    mechanisms 2191
  immune system 2190
  Langerhans cells 2190
    see also Langerhans cells
  local effects of immunotoxicants 1368–1369
  lymphocyte migration 1617
  normal flora 750
  organotypic culture 787
  proinflammatory organ 786
  targets of UV radiation 1944–1945
  'tolerance' induction 787
Skin-associated lymphoid tissue (SALT) 2191
Skin cancer
  immune surveillance theory and 1246
  squamous cell, MHC downregulation 1361
  UV-induced 1942, 1943, 1945
Skin diseases, in HIV infection 1531
Skin grafts 2414
  monitoring of inbred strains 1371
  rejection
    H-Y antigen role 1014, 1158
    model 1013

Skin grafts (continued)
  rejection (continued)
    suppression by active enhancement 810
Skin infections 750–754
  bacterial 750
  causative organisms 751(Table)
  eosinophils response 752–753
  histiocytic response 753–754
  IgE-mediated response 752–753
  lymphocytic response 753
  minimal/moderate immune response 750–751
  parasitic 750
  PMN response 751–752
Skin-prick tests 254, 680, 1172
SKY strain 2058
Sleep
  pattern in African trypanosomiasis 2423
  slow-wave, increased by fever 904
Sleeping sickness, see Trypanosomiasis, African
Slow viruses, in transmissible spongiform encephalopathies 2409
SLP-76, signal transduction in T cell activation 2324
Slp (sex-limited protein) gene 1046
Sm (antigen), antibodies 131, 2182
Small cell cancer of lung 1835, 1842, 1849–1850
  origin 1850
Small cytoplasmic RNP (scRNP) 127, 127(Fig)
Small-for-gestational age (SGA) infants 1870
Small nuclear RNA (snRNA) 126
Small nuclear RNP (snRNP) 126
Smallpox
  eradication 1998, 2457
  history 255–256, 1335
  vaccination
    adverse reactions 2464(Table)
    complications 1998
    history 255–256, 1335
  vaccine 2457
  variolation 1681
Small round structured viruses (SRSV) 400, 401
SMCY gene 72, 1160
Smoking, see Cigarette smoking
Smoldering multiple myeloma (SMM) 1164
Smooth muscle
  autoantibodies 263
  histamine effect 1103
Snakes
  antivenom, serum sickness 2169
  mixed lymphocyte reaction 2079(Table)
  skin graft rejection 2079(Table)
  thymus development 2077(Fig)
Snake venom 2472–2473
  crotalid 2472, 2473
  management 2472–2473
  types 2472
SNAPs (Soluble NSF Attachment Proteins) 852(Table)
Snaptophysins 852(Table)
SNAREs 852(Table)
Sneezing 2122, 2122(Table)
Snowshoe hare virus 391
Sodium, transport, in red cell membranes 837
Sodium bisulfite, false food allergy 952(Table)
Sodium cromoglycate, food allergy treatment 952
Sodium dodecyl sulfate, see SDS
Sodium pump, in red cell membranes 837
Soft agar selection, T cell hybridomas 1154
Solar urticaria 684
Solitary lymphoid nodules (SLN) 1775, 1781

Solvent/detergent (S/D) treatment, viruses 1968
Somatic evolution, antibodies 53–54
Somatic hypermutation 769–770, 1145, 1325–1326, 1325–1327, 2192–2193
  5' boundary 770
  amphibians immunoglobulin genes 81, 82
  antinuclear antibodies (ANAs) 133
  autoimmunity pathogenesis 294, 2193
  B cells 2193
  B cell repertoire development 358, 360, 366, 2192
    see also Affinity maturation
  B cells 53–54, 153, 157, 214, 358
    amphibians 81, 82
  CDRH1 and CDRL1 regions 1327
  cellular cooperation 651
  characteristics of process 770
  clonal selection mechanism 1685
  clonogenetic diversity of cell surface antigens 208
  definition 2192
  dysregulation, autoimmunity development 2193
  evolutionary considerations 1950–1951
  germinal centers 769, 993, 994, 1728, 2192
  high affinity antibodies 53–54, 153, 157, 226, 769–770
  hotspots 770, 2192
    AGY sites 2192
  Ig flanking sequences regulating 2193
  [G]k[g] enhancer 2193
  as maturation of immune response 1678
  molecular basis/mechanism 2193
  mutations localized to light chain 767, 769(Fig)
  productive/nonproductive 770
  rare, for TCR 2267
  rates 2192
  recombination pathway for Ig genes 553
  substitution mutations 2193
  timing and sites 2192
  vertebrates 1950–1951
  V regions 2192
Somatic recombination, see Genetic recombination; Immunoglobulin gene rearrangements
Somatostatin 1785
SOS factor 1300
  mast cell degranulation 1670
  p21ras regulation 2326
Southern blotting 1864, 2194–2198
  apparatus 2195, 2195(Fig)
  applications 2194, 2197
  autoradiography 2194, 2197
  buffer 2195
  definition 2194
  DNA for analysis 2194
  DNA electrophoresis 2195
  electrophoretic blotting 2196
  gel preparation 2195
  historical background 2194
  hybridization and stringency 2196–2197
  membrane choice 2195
  PCR comparison 2198
  principle 2194
  probe detection 2197
  probes 2195
    labeling 2196
    repetitive DNA sequences 2196
  procedure 2195–2196
  restriction enzyme digestion 2194–2195
  reuse of blots 2197
  vacuum blotting 2196
Sowda (localized onchocerciasis) 1873
Soya milk, allergy 948, 953
Soybean agglutinin (SBA) 1536
  applications 1540(Table)
Sp1 1133
SP-A 1887
Space flights

Space flights (*continued*)
  effects 1030–1033
  see also Gravity, effects
SPARC 1096
SP-D 1887
Specificity
  antibodies, *see* Antibody specificity
  antigenic 201, 1297
  transfer factors 2385–2386, 2386(Table)
Spectrin, in red cell membrane 835,
    838(Table)
Spectrin family 418
Spergualin 1352
Sperm
  antibodies 1853
  antigens
    birth control vaccine 643(Table)
    vaccines 642
  autoantigens 1373–1374, 1373(Table)
  CAMPATH-1 antigen (CD52) 405
  IgA-covered 1374
  immune response prevention 1373
  LDH-C₄-specific isoenzyme 1853
  maturation, markers 1853
  membrane antigens, antibodies 1374
  motile, antibodies 1374
  sequestration of antigens 1373
Sperm-coating antigens 1373–1374,
    1373(Table)
Spherocytes 834
Spherocytosis, hereditary, parvovirus B19
    infection 1924
Spheroplasts 321
Sphingomyelinase 2377
  activation by IL-1 binding to IL-1
    receptors 1433
  neutral 2029
sph mutation 421
Spi-1 products/gene 1564
Spiders, venom 2472
Spina bifida 681
Spinal muscular atrophy 227
Spirochetes
  Borrelia 380
  features 380
  Treponema, see Treponema
Spleen 1248, 2205–2208
  amphibian, embryology 80
  anatomy/structure 2206–2207, 2206(Fig)
  antigen clearance in warm hemolytic
    anemia 185
  APCs and T cell interactions 177, 2207
  arterial capillaries 2207
  B cells in 1580, 2207
  capsule 2206
  cellular cords 2207
  central arteries 2206
  congenital absence 1286
  dendritic cells 747
  erythrocyte phagocytosis 2207
  fish 922
  functional anatomy 2207–2208
  functions 2205
  germinal centers 2206
  infarction 1286
  lymphatics 2206, 2207
  lymphocyte migration 1616–1617
  macrophage 1591, 2207
  marginal zone 2206, 2207
  NK cells 2207
  noradrenergic innervation 1825(Fig)
  organization 1249
  periarteriolar lymphoid sheaths (PALS)
    2205, 2206, 2207(Fig), 2365
  radiosensitivity 2051
  red pulp 2206, 2206–2207
  reptiles 2077–2078
  sequestration of erythrocytes
    babesiosis 310
    IgG-coated 96
  T cell zone 2207

Spleen (*continued*)
  transmissible spongiform
    encephalopathies 2410
  veins 2206
  white pulp 2206
Spleen focus-forming virus (SFFV) 1564
Spleen necrosis virus (SNV) 2090
Splenectomy
  autoimmune hemolytic anemia 96–97
  babesiosis 310
  idiopathic thrombocytopenic purpura
    1182, 1976
  immunodeficiency due to 1286
  side-effects 97
Splenic artery 2205, 2206
Splenic sinuses 2206
Splenocytes, proliferation, DNA vaccines
    772–773
Splicing retroviral vectors 2087
Spondyloarthropathy 2120–2121
  HLA-B27 association 2121
Spongiosis 786
Spontaneously hypertensive rats 1518
  blood pressure reduction by kallikrein
    1518
SPOTELISA 796
Spotted fever group, rickettsiae 2126
S protein, in microbicidal killing
    mechanism 1938
Squamous cell skin carcinoma, MHC
    downregulation 1361
SR-A (MARCO) 185
Src tyrosine kinases 710, 2031, 2324
  activation by CD45 491
  IL-3 receptor signal transduction 1447
  IL-11 signal transduction 1480
  signaling 710
    in T cell activation 2324
SS-A, *see* Ro/SS-A
SS-B, *see* La/SS-B
SSO method, HLA typing 1693
Stage-specific embryonic antigen 1 (SSEA-
    1) 595
  as Lewisˣ (Leˣ) antigen 1576–1577
Stanozolol 683, 684
Staphylococcal enterotoxin B (SEB) 538,
    2209
Staphylococcal scalded skin syndrome
    (SSSS) 269, 2209
Staphylococcus 2208–2211
  antigens 2208–2209
  β-hemolysin 269, 2209, 2377
  characteristics 2208–2209
  coagulase 2208–2209
  colonization enhancement 2210
  δ-hemolysin 269
  disease spectrum 2208(Table),
    2209(Table), 2210
  enterotoxins 2209
  exfoliatin 269
  extracellular enzymes 2209
  fibronectin binding 2209, 2209–2210
  glycosaminoglycan binding 2210
  hemagglutination 2210
  hemolysins 2209, 2376
  host immune response 2210–2211
  infections
    biomaterial-associated 2210, 2211
    eye 873
    opportunistic 2210
  leukocidin 2209
  Panton–Valentine factors 2209
  protein A, *see* Protein A
  species 2208, 2208(Table)
  species differentiation 2210
  toxic shock syndrome (TSS) 2209
  toxic shock syndrome toxin (TSST-1)
    2209, 2211
  toxins 269
    enterotoxins 2209
    pore-forming 2377
  vaccines 2211

Staphylococcus (*continued*)
  vitronectin binding 2210
Staphylococcus aureus 2208, 2210
  antibiotic sensitivity 2210
  disease spectrum 2209(Table), 2210
  endocarditis 567
  enterotoxins 2240
    biochemical studies 2241
    MHC class II binding site 2241
    structure 2240
    as superantigens 2240, 2240(Table)
  epidermolytic toxin (exfoliatin) 2209
  eye infection 873
  immunoglobulin-binding proteins 323
  impetigo 752
  infections in chronic granulomatous
    disease 566
  methicillin-resistant (MRSA) 2210
  microbicidal mechanisms 1938
  plasma coagulation 2208–2209
  polysaccharides 423
  protein A 323, 2209
  vaccine 2211
Staphylococcus epidermidis 2210
  diseases 2210
  eye infection 873
Staphylococcus hemolyticus, diseases 2210
Staphylococcus lugdunensis 2210
Staphylococcus saprophyticus 2210
  urinary tract infection 2210
Staphylococcus zooepidermicus 326
Staphylokinase 2209
STAT 701, 711, 2171
  CD5 and B1 cells role 474
  cytokine signal transduction 2032
  GM-CSF signal transduction 1022
  IL-11 signal transduction 1480
  STF-IL4 in targeting Ig class switching
    1305, 1452
STAT1
  gene disruption 1415
  IL-7 signal transduction 1464
  IL-10 signal transduction 1477
  IL-11 signal transduction 1480
  interferon α/β signal transduction 1414,
    1420
  interferon γ signal transduction 1423,
    1427
  mice deficient in 1415, 1415(Fig)
STAT2, interferon α/β signal transduction
    1414
STAT3
  IL-10 signal transduction 1477
  IL-11 signal transduction 1480
  leukemia inhibitory factor (LIF) signal
    transduction 1561
  transgenic mice 1562
STAT5
  IL-2 receptor signal transduction 1440
  IL-3 receptor signal transduction 1444,
    1447–1448, 1449(Fig)
  IL-7 signal transduction 1464
STAT6
  IL-4 receptor signal transduction 1452,
    1454, 1455, 1491
  IL-13 signal transduction 1491
Statistics 2211–2215
  analysis of concentrations/titers 2211–
    2212
  analysis of proportions responding 2213
  assay comparison studies 2213
  graphical methods 2213–2214
  HLA–disease association risk estimates
    1698
  see also specific statistical methods
Status thymolymphaticus 2051
Steel locus factor (SLF) 598, 1272
  receptor 454(Table), 598
Steel mouse 375
Stem cell(s) 374–375, 2017
  B cell development 364
  bursal 395

Stem cell(s) (continued)
commitment 374
concentration technique 669
cord blood 548
cryopreservation 669
development, vitamin D effect 2495
differentiation 374–375
harvesting 2399
increased by G-CSF 1019
isolation technique 1069
mobilization, by IL-3 1444
mononuclear phagocytes origin 1755
multipotential 374
noncycling 374
in SCID mice 1269
self-renewal, age-related changes 59, 61
source 1063
thymus 2306, 2336
transfusions 2403
in utero transplantation 549
see also Stem cell transplantation
vertebrates 1948
see also Cord blood; Embryonic stem
(ES) cells
Stem cell factor (SCF) 375, 376, 598, 1757
mast cell development 1667
soluble receptor 454(Table), 714
'Stem cell niche' 376
Stem cell therapy 2399, 2403
Stem cell transplantation 1062–1070, 2403
autologous 1063
complications 1067–1069
conditioning regimes 1063–1064,
1064(Table)
toxicities 1067, 1067(Table)
donors 1063
ex vivo progenitor cell expansion 1069
failure 1068–1069
future prospects 1069
GM-CSF use 1022
GVHD 1017, 1067–1068
acute 1067–1068
chronic 1068
prevention 1068, 1068(Table)
risk factors 1063, 1066, 1068(Table)
hematologic/immune recovery 1067
HLA-matched 1063, 1063(Fig)
HLA-mismatched 1062, 1067
indications 1062, 1063(Table)
infections after 1067, 1069
in malignancy 1062–1063
hematologic 1063(Fig), 1064–1065,
1064(Table), 1065(Fig)
recurrence/relapse 1068, 1069
solid tumors 1065–1066
tumor detection by PCR 1069
for nonmalignant disorders 1066,
1066(Fig)
recombinant cytokines use 1064,
1064(Table)
results 1064–1067
source of stem cells 1063
stem cell isolation 1069
Steroid hormones 996
in asthma 246(Table)
poxvirus encoded homologs 1997(Table)
receptors 999
mechanism of action 999, 999(Fig)
see also Glucocorticoids; Hormones; Sex
hormones
Sterol, target for SH-activated cytolysins
2377
Stiff man syndrome 1842–1843
Stimulus–response phenomena 1677
protein kinase role 2028
see also Signal transduction
Stomach, adenocarcinoma, Forssman
antigen role 954
Stomatocytic cells 834, 834(Fig)
Stomatocytosis 837
Stonefish, venom 2473

Storage of immune cells, cryopreserved
668, 668–669
Streptavidin 143, 815
immunoelectron microscopy 793
Streptavidin–biotin system
enzyme-labeling of antibodies 814, 815
see also Biotin
Streptobacillary fever 2216
Streptobacillus 2215–2217
antigens 2215
characteristics 2215
culture 2215
Streptobacillus moniliformis 2215
antigens 2215
distribution 2216
evasive strategies 2216
host immune response 2216
infections 2216
animal 2216
vaccines 2216
Streptococcal cell wall-induced arthritis
2231
Streptococcal toxic shock syndrome 2218
Streptococcus 2217–2220
antigen, mimicry in rheumatic fever 1737
β-hemolytic 2218
capsule 2217
vaccines 2220
carbohydrate antigens 2218
cell wall structure 2218
cross-reaction with cardiac proteins 431–
432, 431–434, 435, 1737, 2219
diseases caused by 2217(Table)
enterotoxins 2218
enzymes 2218
evasive strategies 2218, 2219
group A
antigen, natural antibodies 1808
diseases caused by 2218–2219
serotypes 2217
see also Streptococcus pyogenes
host immune response 2218
Lancefield groups 2218
molecular mimicry 1737, 2219
M protein, see M protein
pyrogenic exotoxins 2218
superantigen 2219
toxins 269, 2218
T proteins 2217–2218
vaccines 2219–2220
viridans group, endocarditis 567
virulence 2217
Streptococcus mutans 1888, 1889
endocarditis 567
oral infections 1888, 1889
immunomodulation 1892
Streptococcus oralis, endocarditis 567
Streptococcus pneumoniae
antigens 203
capsular polysaccharides 422–423
immune response to 426
colonization and infection process 2219
C-reactive protein binding 664, 1886–
1887
disease caused by 2217(Table)
evasive strategies 2083
host immune response 2083, 2219
in immunodeficiency 2219
pneumolysin 2219, 2377
pneumonia 2219
polysaccharide 203, 664
vaccines 426, 2083, 2220
Streptococcus pyogenes
adherence, CD46 role 495, 496
diseases caused by 2217(Table)
glomerulonephritis 1176, 2218
M protein, clindamicin-increased
phagocytosis 1887
rheumatic fever 1737
toxin 2377
Streptococcus sanguis 1723
Streptococcus sobrinus, endocarditis 567

Streptolysin O 2377
Streptomycin, bacterial resistance 2013
Streptozotocin-induced diabetes mellitus
273, 1397
Stress 2220–2228
animal studies 2221–2222
autoimmune disease pathogenesis 279
cholinergic urticaria after 683
contextual importance rather than event
2222
definition 338, 2220
experimental autoimmune thyroiditis
induction 2311
glucocorticoids relationship 996, 997,
998
immune regulation 338–340
immunity and 1831–1832, 2222
difficulties in assessing 2222
as individual assessment 2220, 2221
infection association 2222
multiple sclerosis after 1840
nervous system influence on immune
system, see Nervous system
neuroendocrine effects 339, 2222–2224,
2224–2225
NK activity depression 1814, 2221, 2222
perception of 2220, 2222
physical, immune regulation 339
psychosocial 338–339, 2227(Fig)
study methods 2220–2221, 2221(Table)
thymic atrophy 2305
thyroid autoimmunity induction 2314
Stress-activated protein kinase 2, see p38
kinase
Stress-activated protein kinase (SAPK) 484
see also Jun N-terminal kinase (JNK)
Stress hormones, increase, exercise causing
846
Stressors
acute/chronic 2220
applied 2221(Table), 2222
naturalistic 2221(Table), 2222
physical (animal studies) 2221, 2222
'standard' 2220
Stress proteins 2228–2232
accumulation 2229
in antigen presentation 2231–2232
B cell responses 2230–2231
binding to denatured proteins 2230
function 2230
normal 2230
thermotolerance 2230
groups 2228–2230, 2229(Table)
as target antigens 2230–2231
autoimmune disease 2231
infections 2230–2231
T cell/B cell recognition 2230
T cell responses 2231
transcription induction 2228
see also Heat shock proteins (hsp);
Ubiquitin
Stress response 2228
STRL33 1134
Stroke, anti-phospholipid antibodies 1843
Stromal antigens, in tumors 2429
Stromal cell-derived factor 1 (SDF-1) 538
Stromal cells 376, 2233–2237
B cell differentiation 1876
bone marrow 2236–2237, 2338
cell types 2236
mesenchymal origin 2236
cytokines, T cell tolerance induction
2357
definition 2233, 2237
epithelial 2338
T cell development 2235, 2338
thymus, see Thymic stromal cells
Strongyloides
life cycle 2238
species 2238
Strongyloides stercoralis 2238
antigens 2238

Strongyloides stercoralis (continued)
autoinfection 2238
cellular immune response 2238–2239
ecdysteroids 2239
humoral immune response 2238
hyperinfection 1921, 2238, 2239
infection in AIDS 1921, 2239
life cycle 2238
regulatory mechanisms 2239
Strongyloidiasis 2238–2239
Struvite stones 2040, 2041
Subacute sclerosing panencephalitis (SSPE) 1915
Subendothelial cells (SECs), platelet action 579
Subendothelium, platelet adhesion 1973–1974
Substance P 1827
in nasal mucosa 2125
Substrains, mice 1370
Suicide vectors 2087
Suipoxvirus 1995(Table)
Sulfasalazine, immunodeficiency due to 1285
Sulfated sephadex 603
Sulfo-Le^x, structure 1577(Fig)
Sulfonamides, adverse reactions 1052
Sulfur dioxide, false food allergy 952(Table)
Sun exposure
cutaneous lupus erythematosus 2185–2186
see also Ultraviolet light
Superantigen 217, 1319, 2239–2243
alloantigens 72
autoimmune response development 2242
bacterial 2240(Table), 2242
see also Staphylococcus aureus, enterotoxins
diabetes mellitus association 1400
in disease 1624, 2242–2243
family 2240(Table)
immunotherapy of cancer 2242–2243
MHC class II binding 2241, 2242
mouse mammary tumor virus (MMTV) 2240–2241, 2242
Mycoplasma arthritidis 1799, 2242
as polyclonal activators 1982
as polyclonal inhibitors 1980
protein A 325
retroviral 1137, 1232, 2242
Staphylococcus aureus enterotoxins, *see Staphylococcus aureus*
Streptococcus 2219
T cell activation 2242
absence of MHC class II 2241
MHC class II binding 2241, 2242
T cell anergy induction 110
T cell tolerance 2359, 2361
TCR interaction 2241–2242
binding site 2242
TCR αβ recognition 2267
TCR-Vβ recognition 2240(Table)
tolerance breakdown 276, 2242
tumor-specific 2243
Yersinia 2514
Superantigen-dependent cell-mediated cytotoxicity (SDCC) 2242
Superoxide anion 317
dismutation reactions 1715, 1856
formation
monocytes 1751
neutrophils 1856
hydrogen peroxide formation 1715, 1856
oxygen-dependent phagocytic killing 1715, 1856, 1938
Superoxide dismutase (SOD) 38, 133, 1715
Cu-Zn, in copper deficiency 658, 658(Table)
highly virulent *Nocardia* 1863
'Supersensitivity' reactions 64

Suppression, soluble mediators 2244
Suppressor T lymphocytes (Ts) 648, 789, 2243–2247
action at T helper cell level 2245
antigen-specific 2244, 2245, 2246(Fig)
in cats 893
cell lines 2245
contrasuppressor cells interfering 648
defective
Addison's disease 43
SLE 2258
in dogs 413
elevated in myeloma 1164
evidence for existence 2244
experimental autoimmune encephalomyelitis (EAE) 859, 1841
functions 2245
historical background 2243–2244
hybridomas 2245, 2246
I-J region 1217, 1218, 2244
induction
by LTB$_4$ 229
by UVB 1943
inhibition
by deoxyguanosine 749
by mercury 1687
loss in multiple sclerosis 1841
molecular basis of specificity 2246
molecular biology 2244–2246
in neonates 1820
nonspecific 2246(Fig)
phenotype 2244–2245
proliferation, annexins regulating 114
TCR complex 2245, 2246
tolerance maintenance 2246
tolerance mechanism 2365
T suppressor factors (TSF), *see* T suppressor factors (TSF)
Suramin, onchocerciasis 873
Surface plasmon resonance (SPR) 1255–1256, 2247–2250
advantages 2250
affinity of hapten-specific antibody 1051, 2250
antibody–antigen measurement 2249(Fig)
applications 2250
BIAcore 2248–2249
biosensors based on 2248–2249
definition 2248
detection system 2248
limitations 2250
principles 2248, 2249(Fig)
detection 2248–2249
Surfactants
gene transcription inhibited by TNFα 2439
GM-CSF role 1022
SP-A and SP-D 1887
Surgery
germ-free animals use 990
immunodeficiency due to 1286
SV40, *see* Simian virus-40 (SV40)
SWC (swine-specific) molecules 1993
Swimmer's itch 2139
Swine vesicular disease virus (SVDV), epitope location 1957(Table)
Swiss type agammaglobulinemia 1277
SWR/J mice 1770
immunology 1770
origin/characteristics 1770
Syk tyrosine kinase 363, 1194, 1195, 2031
mast cell degranulation 1670
signaling in T cell activation 2324
Syk-deficient mice 1194
Sympathectomy, chemical, autoimmune disease 279
Sympathetic nervous system
in multiple sclerosis 1841
nasal blood flow control 2125
Sympathetic ophthalmia (SO) 867
Synaptotagmins 852(Table)

Syncytia, formation, paramyxoviruses 1909, 1914
Syncytiotrophoblast 898
FcγRIII 1672
MHC expression absent 898
Syndecan-1 (CD138) 455(Table)
Syndrome, definition 2162
Synexin 114
Synovia, lymphocyte migration 1617
Synovial fluids, IL-1 in 1435
Syntaxins 852(Table)
Syntex adjuvant formulation (SAF) 37
Syphilis 2072–2074, 2415, 2416–2417
in AIDS 2417
chancre 2073
clinical features 2416
congenital 2416
endemic 2415, 2417
immune response 2073, 2417
immunity acquisition 2417
infection phases 2416
primary 753, 2073, 2416
rabbit model 2046
secondary 2073, 2416
serodiagnosis 2417
tertiary 1024, 2073, 2416
treatment 2417
see also Treponema pallidum
Syrian hamster, allografts in cheek pouch 1012
Systemic inflammatory response syndrome (SIRS) 16
kallikrein–kinin system role 1520
sepsis/infection interrelationships 2163(Fig)
Systemic lupus erythematosus (SLE) 2255–2260
annexin autoantibodies 114
anti-DNA antibodies 128–129, 2257, 2258
cross-reactions 2258
pathogenic role 130
antinuclear antibodies (ANA) 128, 2257
anti-Ro/La antibodies 2184, 2257
apoptosis 2260
autoantibodies 2003–2004, 2257
B cells 2259, 2259(Fig)
in children 2257
chronic active hepatitis (CAH) similarity 561
clinical features 2255–2256, 2256(Table)
complement fixation 2258
cytokine production 2258–2259
drug-induced 611, 2257
etiology 2257
experimental models 2251–2255
anti-B7-1/B7-2 mAbs action 306
determinant spreading 755
SCID mouse 1129(Table)
sex hormone effect 2175
spontaneous 285–286
see also Murine lupus
genetic factors 2257
hematological abnormalities 2256–2257
historical aspects 2255
HLA associations 2257
IFNγ elevation 2259
IgA deficiency in 1285
IL-10 increase 2259
immune complexes 184, 1225, 2258
immunopathogenesis 130, 184
immunopathology 2258–2260
investigations 2256–2257
natural history 2257
neutrophil defects 2259
NK cell changes 2259
outcome 2257
polyclonal hypergammaglobulinemia in 1162
in pregnancy 2257
serological abnormalities 2257
Sjögren's syndrome (SS) association 2182

Systemic lupus erythematosus (SLE) (*continued*)
T cells 2258, 2259(Fig)
treatment 2260
Systemic sclerosis (scleroderma) 2117–2118
animal models 283–284
UCD 200 strain 283–285
autoantibodies 2117, 2117(Table)
antinuclear antibodies (ANA) 127
anti-topoisomerase I antibodies (Scl170) 132
clinical/pathological features 2117
HLA class III association 1120
localized, *see* Morphea
related disorders 2117
T cell abnormalities 2117

T

T3, *see* CD3
T4 bacteriophage 2015–2016
immunity gene/protein 2016
T19 marker 1903
Ta1, *see* CD26
TAC, *see* Interleukin-2 (IL-2) receptor, α chain (CD25)
Tacaribe virus 234, 235
Tachyphylaxis 2166
Tacrolimus, *see* FK506
T-activin 1346
Taenia
antigens 690
characteristics 690
evasive strategies 692–693
host immune response 691–692
immunosuppression by 693
vaccines 693–694
Taenia crassiceps 693
Taenia hydatigena 690
Taenia multiceps 690
Taenia ovis 690
GST-45B/X antigen 694
vaccines 693, 693(Table), 1921
Taenia pisiformis 690, 691, 693
Taenia saginata 690
Taenia solium 690
antigen B 690, 693
cysticerca, in CNS 1846
evasive strategies 692–693
host immune response 691–692, 692(Fig)
life cycle 691(Fig)
secretory products 693
Taeniastatin 693
Taenia taeniaeformis 690, 691, 693
TAG-72 antigen 2428
Tahyna virus 392
Talc, granuloma 1024
Talin 419
TAME (*N*-α tosyl-L-arginine methyl ester) esterase 2123
Tamoxifen, interferon α combined therapy 1416
TAN-1 gene 558
TANK (I-TRAF), TNF receptor signaling 2348
TAP (Transporter Associated with antigen Processing) 192, 1703
CD1 antigen presentation independent of 460
gene, defects 1277
H2 class I molecules synthesis 1038
proteins 852(Table)
downregulation in Burkitt's lymphoma 832
TAP1 and TAP2, *see below*
TAP-1 transporter proteins 192, 460
downregulation by HPV 1908
expression, induced by IFNγ 1424
H2 class I molecules synthesis 1038

TAP-2 transporter proteins 192, 460
expression, induced by IFNγ 1424
H2 class I molecules synthesis 1038
mutation in bare lymphocyte syndrome type I 329–330
rheumatoid arthritis 2113
Tapasin 192–193
Tapeworms
cystic (larval) stages 690
see also Cysticercosis; *Taenia* species
Echinococcus spp., *see Echinococcus*
Targeting of immunological agents 2261–2264
antibody-directed approaches 2261–2262
CD4 immunotherapeutics 2263
cytokine regulation 2262–2263
pharmacological agents 2261
T cell costimulation blockade 2262
in tumors 2442
see also Immunotherapy
TATA box
IL-1 gene 1429
IL-5 gene 1457
tax gene
HIV 2095
HTLV-1 1564–1565
Taxol, mimicry by anti-idiotypic antibody 151
Tax proteins 1565
Tax transactivator 1565
T-BAM, *see* CD40L
T box 1042
TCDD, immunosuppression due to 1367
T cell(s) 1226, 1227, 2341–2343
A2b clone 34
αβ
in pigs 1993
see also under T cell receptor (TCR)
abnormalities, primary biliary cirrhosis (PBC) 2003, 2004
ACTH receptors 1828
activated 2341
CD2 expression 464
cytokines released 700
Fas ligation and apoptosis 878
lifespan 1581–1581
in lymph node 1606
in T cell vaccines 2284
see also Lymphokine-activated killer (LAK) cells
activation, *see* T cell activation
activation-induced cell death 2332
ADCC 169
adhesion, CD2 role 464
in allergen response 69
amphibian 80, 82
anergy, *see* Anergy
antibodies 121
diabetes prevention in animal models 1397
antiergotypic 2285
antigen overdose, unresponsiveness 2245
antigen presentation 14, 157, 177, 349, 352–355, 1227, 1291, 2330
by B cells, *see* B cell(s)
bm mutants 373
CD1 role 460
by Langerhans cells 2190
LFA-3–CD2 interaction/role 502, 1614
MHC restriction, *see* MHC; MHC class I; MHC class II
via MHC class I 191–194
via MHC class II 194–198
see also Helper T lymphocytes; *under* B cell(s)
antigen-presenting cells (APCs) interaction 175, 175(Table), 177, 1709
mechanism 654, 654(Fig)
antigen receptor, *see* T cell receptor (TCR)

T cell(s) (*continued*)
antigen recognition 202, 501–502, 1290, 2334
CD2, LFA-3 and ICAM-1 role 502
fate after 2297(Fig)
immunodominant epitopes 1290–1291
sequential determinants 1290
structural aspects 2282–2284
X-ray crystallography 2282
see also MHC; T cell receptor (TCR)
antigen-specific
clonal expansion 14–15
isolation 182
antimouse 1127
antinuclear autoantibodies induction 132
apoptosis 225, 1682, 2148, 2332
autoreactive cells 224-3-225
B7/CTLA4 interaction 307, 2148, 2332
calcium level effect 2325
defects in murine lupus 2252
Fas/FasL 876–877, 878
free calcium role 2325
galectin 1 interaction with CD45 493
helper cells 876–877, 878, 879
in HIV infection 879
LFA-3–CD2 interaction/role 1614
positive/negative regulators 2357, 2357(Table)
at positive selection stage 2307–2308
resistance and tolerance breakdown 276
autoepitopes 266, 267
autoimmune disease pathogenesis 277–278, 278
autoreactive 198, 266, 267, 269, 277–278, 290, 292, 2343–2344
activation 1228
apoptosis 224-3-225, 876–877
deletion 502, 1230
from antigen-stimulated precursors 2344
Goodpasture's syndrome 1009–1010
I-E specific 2344
multiple sclerosis 1694
'normal' 2344
origin 2343–2344
in peripheral tissues 2246
persistence 2343
regulation by suppressor T cells 2246
rheumatic fever 432
significance and role 2344
avian 302
B3 distribution 298(Fig), 299
in *Bacteroides* infections 328
B cell activation by, *see* Helper T lymphocytes
in B cell anergy 107
B cell cognate interactions, *see under* B cell(s)
B cell differences 2341
B cell separation 1235
lectin use 1541
beneficial effects of fever 904
in breast milk 1673
bystander 217, 397
in HIV infection, apoptosis 879
calcitriol effect 2495–2496
CAMPATH-1 antigen (CD52) 405
in cats 893
CD1-restricted, autoreactive 462
CD1 role 462
CD2 expression 464
CD3+
intraepithelial lymphocytes 1782
in lamina propria 1778–1779
see also T cell receptor (TCR)
CD3+ CD56+ 1627–1628
CD4⁻CD8⁻, *see under* Thymocytes
CD4⁻CD8⁻ CD1-restricted αβ 318
CD5 (Ly-1) role 473, 474
CD8+ and CD8⁻ subsets 475

T cell(s) (*continued*)
CD25 expression, contact hypersensitivity 639
CD26 expression 1683
CD28 expression 307, 353, 482, 2146–2147, 2147
CD29 expression 1683
CD45 expression 492, 493
CD45RA (CD45R) expression, *see* T cell(s), naive
CD45RB expression 1683
CD45RO expression 1683
IL-10 production 1476
lifespan of cells 1581, 1582
CD58 expression 1683
Chagas' disease 524
chemokines 536(Table), 538
chemotaxis 538–539
clonal anergy, *see* Anergy
clonal deletion, *see* Clonal deletion
clonal expansion 14–15, 2330–2334
effector cells 2330–2332
memory cells 2331–2332
naive T cells 2330
negative regulation 2332
prevention 2332–2333
primary/secondary immune response 2331(Fig)
see also T cell(s), proliferation
clonal populations 503
cloning 1152
in CNS 1845
regulation 1845
coccidioidomycosis 589
complement receptor CR1 629
in contact allergy 2191
contrasuppressor cells 648, 648–649
characteristics 649
costimulatory signals for, *see* T cell activation
CTLA4 expression 307, 353, 2147–2148
cytokines released 503, 699, 699–700, 1060, 1832(Fig), 2330
autoreactive T cells 2344
B cell surface marker interactions 365(Table)
bystander effect mechanism 398
in CNS 1845
directional secretion 702
macrophage interactions 2026, 2026(Fig)
in neonates 1820
T cell proliferation and 503
see also Helper T lymphocytes; T$_H$1 cells; T$_H$2 cells
cytotoxic, *see* Cytotoxic T lymphocytes (CTL)
cytotoxicity against APCs 2242
death by neglect 2307–2308, 2307(Fig), 2354
decreased/depleted
after stem cell transplantation 1067
gravity/space flights effect 1031
GVHD prevention 545, 1068, 1363
iron deficiency 1506
lectin use 1541
motheaten mice 1269
thymectomy effect 2305
defect 601
deficiency 1277
eosinophil development reduced 823
experimental autoimmune disease induction 272
oral infections 1891
definition 2341–2343
determinant spreading mechanism 756
development 569–570, 1247–1248, 1866, 2305, 2334, 2342
amphibians 81–82
arrested in SCID mice 1268
calcitriol effect 2496
CD4 expression shut off 478

T cell(s) (*continued*)
development (*continued*)
cytokines role 1248
in neonate 1819–1820, 1821(Table), 2294
targeted gene deletion 1877
thymic nurse cell role 2235
time course 2305, 2309(Fig), 2336
tolerance induction 2354–2355
see also maturation (*below*); T cell differentiation
development stages 2335(Table), 2336–2338
differentiation, *see* T cell differentiation
in DiGeorge syndrome 762–763
discovery 501, 1058, 1625, 2290–2291
in dogs 413
double negative, *see under* Thymocytes
double positive, *see under* Thymocytes
downregulation
CD95 (Fas) role 655
by CD152 (CTLA4) 653, 1983, 2148
education 2295–2298, 2297(Fig)
effector cells, expansion 2330–2332
effector functions 2331(Fig)
MHC function 1703–1704
endothelial cell interactions 1237(Fig)
enrichment techniques 181–182, 1235–1238
hybridoma generation 1153
epitopes 437, 825–826, 826–827
allergens 69
immunodominant 1290–1291
peptide sequences 827
ERK-1 and ERK-2 expression 2327
evolution 1948
experimental autoimmune thyroiditis 2311
extrathymic production sites 2308–2309
fates after antigen recognition 2297(Fig)
in fish 922–923
fluorescence-activated cell sorting (FACS) 933–934
functions 501, 2342
in neonate 1819–1820, 1821(Table)
in reptiles 2078–2080
thymic hormone effect 2302
γδ, *see* T cell receptor γδ (TCRγδ)
germinal centers 993, 1604
negative selection 2355
GPI proteins 419
growth
IL-15 stimulating 1494
TCR occupancy and 467
helper, *see* Helper T lymphocytes
high endothelial venules (HEV) contractility 1099
HLA class I expression 1108–1109
homing receptors 1778, 1784, 2330
see also Homing receptors
in HSV infections 1087
hybridomas, *see* Hybridoma, T cell
in hyper-IgM syndrome 1166, 1167(Fig)
ICAM-1 expression 1410
IDDM 1401–1402
animal models 1394
pathogenesis 283
idiotype recognition 1185, 1190
internal image 1188
IgA synthesis regulation 1196
IgD interaction 1201
IL-1 receptors 1432
signal transduction 1433
IL-2 production 2330
IL-2 role 1437
IL-2R role 2149
IL-2 signaling 2149
IL-3 synthesis 1444
IL-7 expression 1463
IL-13 effects 1491, 1491(Table)
immature 502
immune response *in vitro* 1233

T cell(s) (*continued*)
immunity to hsp65, adjuvant arthritis 34
immunodominant epitopes 1290–1291
inactivation, veto cells 2473–2474
increased in autoimmune gastritis 103
inflammatory effects, in allergy 69
in intermediate lymph 1601
isolation techniques 181–182
J chain mRNA 1517
killer, *see* Cytotoxic T lymphocytes (CTL)
lamina propria 1778–1779, 1782
leukotriene B$_4$ (LTB$_4$) actions 229
lifespan 1581–1582, 2018, 2294, 2295, 2331
lymphotoxin production 1637
lysis of anergic B cells 572
macrophage interactions
cytokine synthesis 2026, 2026(Fig)
MHC restriction 1709–1710
in malaria 1920
maturation
affinity/avidity model 2355
CD95 (Fas) as regulator 655
IL-4 role 1452
prevention mechanisms 2354(Fig)
site 1247–1248
mature
CD45R expression 493
CD45RO expression 1683
clonal deletion 570–571
IL-7 signaling role 1465
in thymic medulla 2304
time course of production 2305
membrane microdomains 417–418
memory 14–15, 1581–1581, 1682–1683, 1682–1684
actions 1683
activation 1684
CD4$^+$ cells 1684
CD8$^+$ cells 1684
CD45RO expression 1683
contact hypersensitivity 639
costimulation for proliferation 2332
expansion 2331–2332
formation 1683
hu-SCID mice 1126, 1127
increased in murine lupus 2252
infectious agents 2459, 2460
in inflammatory response 1683
influenza 1386–1387
interphase survival 2018
lifespan 1581, 1683, 2331
migration 1684
migratory routes 1618
numbers 2022
ovine 1903
reduced in neonates 1820
response to LFA-1 and ICAM-1 1407
surface molecules expression 1683
T$_H$1 and T$_H$2 2332
tolerance maintenance 2294
VLA-4 expression 1408
migration/locomotion 538–539
in contact hypersensitivity 639
from skin in sheep 1904
IL-15 role 1494
memory cells 1618, 1684
in sheep 1903–1904
thymic medullary epithelium role 2235
see also Lymphocyte trafficking
mitogens 1952, 1953
phytohemagglutinin (PHA) 1536, 1952, 1953
pokeweed mitogen 1978, 1979
protein A 325
in reptiles 2078–2080
mitotic trigger, Thy-1 role 2291
monoclonal antibodies to 2334
mucosal 1782
myasthenia gravis 1848, 1848–1849

T cell(s) (*continued*)
  naive (CD45RA) 1682, 1683, 2297, 2330
    clonal expansion 2330
    lifespan 1581, 1582
    sensitization in lymph nodes 1682
  negative selection 1248, 2235, 2245, 2268
    see also Thymic selection
  neuroendocrine interactions 2225(Fig), 2226(Fig)
  NK1+, CD1 role 462
  nocardiosis 1862–1863
  NOD mouse 1394
  nonchemokine attractants 537(Table)
  nude (athymic) mice 1866–1867
  ontogeny, *see* T cell(s), development; T cell differentiation
  in oral cavity 1890–1891
  output from thymus 2308
  ovine 1903, 1905
  pan-T cell marker, CD5 474
  peripheral mature and resident (PMR) 2295, 2297
  perivascularly located 2190
  Peyer's patches 1777, 1781
  Pgp-1 bright cell (memory) 1683
  Pgp-1 dull cells (naive) 1683
  phenotype 1875(Fig), 2341–2342
  in pigs 1993
  polyclonal activation 538
    by antibodies to TCR 2022
    membrane bypass activation 2022-9-2023
    superantigens 1982
    see also Polyclonal activators
  pool size 2309
  population kinetics 1581–1582
  positive selection 2268
    thymic nurse cell role 2235
    see also Thymic selection
  precursors 2336
    see also T cell(s), development; Thymocytes
  primary response 1682, 2331(Fig)
  production, isoprinosine action 1347
  proliferation 2021
    adhesion molecules role 2145–2146
    assays 2023
    dendritic cell role 746
    endorphin action 1829
    Fas role 878
    growth factors 503
    IL-1ra inhibition of 1435
    IL-1 role 1433
    IL-7 role 1464
    IL-9 role 1473
    inhibition by anti-LFA-1 1609
    inhibition by IL-10 1476
    MIF counteraction of glucocorticoid action 1656
    mixed lymphocyte reaction (MLR) 1736
    phytohemagglutinin 1952, 1953
    requirements 2021
    suppression by prolactin 1829–1830
    TGFβ suppressing 2395, 2396
    see also T cell(s), clonal expansion
  proliferation phase 2323
  'promiscuous' epitopes 69
  'recall' response 1683
  'recent thymic emigrants' (RTEs) 2295–2298
  regulatory
    autoimmune thyroiditis induction in animals 2310
    diversification 2298, 2298(Fig)
    formation 2297(Fig)
    thymic epithelium-dependent selection 2236, 2294–2295, 2296(Fig)
    tolerance maintenance 2299
  repertoire

T cell(s) (*continued*)
  repertoire (*continued*)
    foreign antigen and foreign MHC 1712
    HLA association with disease 1695
    hole in 1230, 1231, 1232, 1695, 1705
    nonrandom expression 2338
    selection, *see* Thymic selection
    see also under T cell receptor (TCR)
  response
    decreased in copper deficiency 657
    to H-Y 1159
    to IL-12 1485, 1486
    inhibition by targeting of agents 2264–2264
    to stress proteins 2231
    see also Cell-mediated immunity
  resting 2295
    CD2 expression 464
    HLA-E expression 1109
    ICAM-3 expression 1411
  restriction, *see under* MHC
  rosette markers 2130(Table)
  rosetting techniques, *see* Rosetting techniques
  in SCID 1277
  secondary immune response 2331(Fig)
  selection, *see* Thymic selection
  self, *see* T cell(s), autoreactive
  self *vs* nonself 2338
    H2 class II molecule role 1044
    see also Thymic selection
  serotonin regulatory role 2167
  signaling pathways, *see under* T cell activation
  single-positive (SP) 2304, 2337
  in skin 2190
  SLE 2258, 2259(Fig)
  in spleen 2207
  stimulation, by carbohydrates 428
  subsets, CD antigens 475
  suppression, mechanism of immune enhancement 810
  suppressor, *see* Suppressor T lymphocytes (Ts)
  surface antigens 2334
    avian 302
    FACS studies 934
    rabbits 2048, 2049(Table)
    TCDD-induced changes 1368
  targeting, MHC function 1703–1704
  T$_c$1 and T$_c$2 cells 2331
  TfR expression 2390
  TGFβ formation 2392
  therapeutic depletion, CD5 474
  tolerance, *see* Tolerance
  trans-stimulation, *see* T cell(s), bystander
  tumor antigen recognition 2424–2427, 2424(Table)
  in tumors 1245
  turnover 1581
  tyrosine phosphoproteins 2326
  UCD 200 chicken model 284, 285
  vasoactive intestinal peptide (VIP) effect 1827
  virus infection of 2484–2485
  virus recognition 2481–2482
  vitamin C effect 2492
  zinc deficiency 2515
T cell activation 467, 825, 827, 1642, 2323–2329
  abnormal
    common variable immunodeficiency 601
    tolerance breakdown 275–276
  adhesion molecules 2145–2146
  in asthma 244
  B7 receptors 2146–2148
    see also CD28 (below)
  B7 role 304, 305–306, 502, 652, 2262, 2328
  CD2 role 464, 502, 2328
    signal 1614, 2146

T cell activation (*continued*)
  CD3 role 73
  CD4 role 471, 1060, 2328
  CD5 as negative regulator 473
  CD5 positive role 473
  CD8 role 477, 2328
  CD28 as costimulator 482, 502, 652–653, 1983, 2146–2147, 2262, 2328, 2330, 2366
  CD30 role 2148
  CD40L role 2148, 2328
  CD43 role 2146
  CD59 role 500
  cellular cooperation 652–653
  chemotactic response 538–539
  costimulation 109, 195, 215, 2262
    absence 2332
    absence in tumor immunological escape 2444–2445
    blockade 2262
    LFA-3–CD2 interactions 502, 1614, 2146, 2328
    positive 2366
    signaling 352
  costimulatory molecules/signals 215, 2145–2149, 2323, 2328, 2330, 2334, 2356
    B3 298(Fig), 299
    CD2 2328
    CD4/CD8 2328
    CD28, *see above*
    CD154 (CD40L) 2328
    ICAMs and LFA-1 binding 1411, 2146
    IL-12 1486
    mixed lymphocyte reaction (MLR) 1736
  cyclosporine (CsA) inhibition 686
  cytokine receptor role 2149
  downregulation 2262
    by CD152 (CTLA4) 653, 2148, 2262, 2366
  fibronectin inducing 912
  genes expressed during 2323
  hapten–carrier system 437
  heat stable antigen receptor 2149
  IFNγ receptor upregulation 1428
  impairment in neonates 1820
  inflammatory bowel disease 1376–1377
  intestinal 1377
  LFA-1 2146
  LFA-3 1614, 2146
  maintenance, CD45 role 2324
  membrane molecules cooperating 652–653
  by mitogens 1621
  one signal and anergy induction 1436, 2328
  partial/full 2329
  phorbol esters action 2326–2327
  phytohemagglutinin 1952–1953
  polyclonal, *see* T cell(s), polyclonal activation
  primary/secondary immune response 2331(Fig)
  proliferation failure after 2332
  second signals 2145–2149
  signal transduction 2324–2328, 2325(Fig)
    agonistic/antagonistic 2328–2329
    anergic 2328
    calcium pathway 2324–2325
    inhibition in anergy 2332
    ITAMs role 2324
    kinetic model 2329
    MAP/ERK pathways 2327–2328, 2327(Fig)
    p21^{ras} coupling to adapter molecules in TCR 2326
    pathways 687(Fig), 2333(Fig)
    phosphatases roles 2324
    phospholipase C activation 2324
    PKC pathway 2325–2326

T cell activation (*continued*)
  signal transduction (*continued*)
    PKC role in p21^{ras} activation 2327
    protein tyrosine kinase activation 2324
    Ras pathways 2326, 2327
  as spectrum of activity 2328–2329
  by superantigens, *see* Superantigen
  surface Ig (sIg) function 1298
  TCR binding to antigen/MHC 2323–2324
  TGFβ suppressing 2396
  time course/phases 2323
  TNF and TNFR members 2148
  transferrin receptor (TfR) role 2391–2392
  two-signal 175, 195, 304, 352, 502, 652, 1228, 1436, 2145, 2145(Fig), 2323, 2362
    tolerance induction 2366
T cell-dependent antigens 202, 205, 214–218, 349, 1677
  autoantigens 294
  B cell differentiation 358
  B cell stimulation 156–157, 358, 826
  humoral immune response 1145
  IgG1 and IgG3 response 1515
  in lymph nodes 1605, 1606
T cell-derived lymphocyte chemoattractant factor (LCF) 820
T cell differentiation 502, 1278(Fig), 1464(Fig), 1682, 1712, 1875, 1875F, 1875(Fig), 2331(Fig), 2334–2341, 2343
  adhesion molecules role 30
  cytokines required 2330
  deoxyguanosine metabolism 749
  developmental stages 2336–2338
  early phase 2336–2337
    β selection 2339
    TCR β gene rearrangements 2337
    see also Thymocytes
  final stage 2337–2338
    see also Thymic selection
  gene targeting 2335
  IL-6 role 1458
  IL-7 role 1463, 1464(Fig)
  IL-12 action 1486
  later phase 2337–2338
    TCR gene rearrangement completion 2337
  lineage commitments 2339–2340
  memory cell formation 1683
  nude mice use 1868
  organ culture studies 1901
  pathway 1278(Fig), 1875
  phenotypic changes 1876
  prethymic and thymic phases 1876
  'recent thymic emigrants' (RTEs) 2297
  selection, *see* Thymic selection
  stages in mouse/human 2335(Table)
  study methods 1736
  surface markers 2305, 2309(Fig), 2335(Table), 2336
  T$_H$1 cells 2330
  in thymus 2306–2309
  time course 2305, 2309(Fig), 2323
  tolerance development 2294
  transferrin receptor (TfR) role 2391–2392
  see also T cell(s), development;
    Thymocytes; Tolerance
T cell growth factor (TCGF), *see*
    Interleukin-2 (IL-2); Interleukin-9 (IL-9)
T cell-independent (TI) antigens 15, 156, 202, 205, 214–218, 349, 1677
  B cell differentiation 358
  B cell stimulation 157–158, 826
  haptenated liposomes 1590
  humoral immune response 1145
  IgG2 response 1515
  in lymph node 1605

T cell-independent (TI) antigens (*continued*)
  ontogeny of response 1878
  polysaccharides 426
  response in nude (athymic) mice 1868
  type 1 antigens 157, 215, 1590
    CD14 role 215
    see also Lipopolysaccharide
  type 2 antigens 157, 216–217, 1590
    adjuvant effect 217
    effects on B cell receptor 216
    effects on nonantigen receptors 216–217
    immunodeficiencies 217
T cell leukemias, *see* Leukemia
T cell lymphoma, *see* Lymphoma
T cell neoplasms
  chromosomal translocations 555, 555(Table)
  see also Leukemia; Lymphoma
T cell receptor αβ (TCRαβ) 1876–1877, 2264–2268, 2334, 2341
  α chain 2265
    structure–function 2267
    in T suppressor factors (TSF) 2246
  α chain genes 2266–2267, 2266(Fig)
    recombination signals 2266
  antigen recognition 2282–2283
  antigens recognised 2267
  β chain 2265
    pre-Tα linked 2339
    pre-TCR complex formation 2337
    selection 2339
    structure 518, 2265
    structure–function 2267
  β chain genes 2265–2266, 2266(Fig), 2279(Fig), 2282
    allelic exclusion 64
    amphibians 80–81
    ancestral 2280–2281
    recombination signals 2266
  β chain genes rearrangement
    selection processes 2339
    time course 2306, 2336
  CD5 expression 472–473
  CDR1 and CDR2 regions 2265, 2282
  CDR3 2265, 2282–2283
  core 465, 502
  D$_β$ gene segments 2266
  divergence from γδ lineage 2340
  diversity 2267, 2278, 2282
  evolution 2280
  expression, time course 2306
  genes 2282
    rearrangements 2334
    see also under T cell receptor (TCR)
  genes cloned 2334
  genomic organization 2265–2267, 2266(Fig), 2279(Fig)
  historical aspects 2264
  interaction with ligands 2267
  J$_α$ gene segments 2266
    evolution 2281
  J$_β$ gene segments 2266
  MHC–peptide complex 2282–2283
    low affinity binding 2283
    structure 2282–2283
  mice deficient 2277
  in nude mice 1867
  ontogeny 2275
  ovine 1905
  precursors 2337
  random generation in thymus 2268
  repertoire, generation 2278–2280
  sarcoidosis 2136
  specificity 2267
  structure 2264–2265, 2266(Fig), 2335(Fig)
  TCRαβ^{hi} 2306, 2354
  TCRαβ^{lo} 2306
  thymic medulla 2304
  thymic selection 2268, 2304

T cell receptor αβ (TCRαβ) (*continued*)
  thymic selection (*continued*)
    positive selection 2268, 2272, 2307
  tolerance induction 2354
  tonsils 1775
  V$_α$ gene segments 2266, 2278
    cytochrome *c* peptide recognition 2267
  V$_β$ gene segments 2265, 2265–2266
    elimination 1695
    evolution 2281
    superantigen interaction 2240(Table), 2241–2242
  V–C interaction 2283
  X-ray crystallography 2265
T cell receptor γδ (TCRγδ) 2334, 2341, 2342
  antigen recognition process 2282–2283
  antigen specificity 2272, 2273(Table)-2275(Table)
  antigens recognized 2273(Table)-2275(Table)
  APC interaction 2277
  autoreactivity and selection 2272
  in bacterial infections 318
  in breast milk 1673
  CD1 recognition 2272
  cDNA 2272
  in cell-mediated lysis 506
  chickens 2272
  complementarity-determining regions 2271, 2282–2283
    CDR1 and CDR2 regions 2271
    CDR3 region 2271, 2283
  cytolysis by 505
  δ chain 2268, 2339
    constant regions 2268
  δ chain genes 2266, 2266(Fig), 2269
    human 2269, 2270(Fig)
    murine 2269, 2270(Fig)
    nomenclature 2269
    sizes of gene families 2269
    structure and exons 2269–2271
  D$_δ$ gene segments 2269
  development 1877, 2272, 2275
  divergence from αβ lineage 2340
  'divergence trees' 2271
  double negative 2272
  epithelial 2272, 2283
  evolution 2280
  expression 2340
  fetal 2340
  functions 2275, 2277
  γ chain 2268, 2339
    constant regions 2268, 2270
  γ chain genes 2269
    human 2269, 2270(Fig), 2270(Table)
    murine 2269, 2269(Table), 2270(Fig), 2280
    nomenclature 2269(Table), 2270(Table)
    rearrangements 2339–2340
    structure and exons 2269–2271
  γδ chains 502, 1876–1877, 2268–2278
  gene rearrangements 2334
    'heptamer–nonamer' motifs 2268, 2269
    see also under T cell receptor (TCR)
  genes cloned 2334
  gene structure 2269–2271
  Helicobacter pylori infection 1057
  HSV infection 1087
  IL-4 production 1451
  in immunocompromised 2277
  immunoregulatory role 2277
  intraepithelial cells 1779, 2272
  J$_δ$ gene segments 2269
  J$_γ$ gene segments 2269
    'glycine-X-glycine' motif lacking 2270
  large granular lymphocytes 1534
  leishmaniasis 1549
  Listeria monocytogenes infection 1593
  lymphoid 2272
  malaria 1662
  maturation 2272

T cell receptor γδ (TCRγδ) (continued)
to mycobacterial hsps 2231
in nude mice 1867
ovine 1903
in pigs 1993
as precursors for αβ cells 2340
protein structure 2271
repertoire 2271, 2275
generation 2278–2280
sarcoidosis 2136
target cells 2276(Table)-2277(Table)
in thymus 2305
Toxoplasma gondii infection 2383–2384
in tuberculosis model 1795
UCD 200 chicken model 284
in ungulates 2449
upregulation of CD4+ T cells 1779
V_δ gene segments 2269
V_γ gene segments 2269
human, nomenclature 2270(Table)
murine, nomenclature 2269(Table)
see also Large granular lymphocytes
(LGL)
T cell receptor (TCR) 1227, 1703, 1875,
2323, 2330, 2334
abnormal, tolerance breakdown 275
absent in T cell mutants, Thy-1 role
2291
activation, *see* T cell activation
adapter molecules coupling to p21^ras
2326
affinity/avidity, tolerance induction 2355,
2356(Fig)
amphibian 80–81
ancestral gene families 2280
antibodies 138
monoclonal 503, 1357
polyclonal activation due to 2022
antigen recognition by 467, 501–502,
2282–2284
function 2264
structural aspects 2283
antigen specificity 2272, 2273(Table)-
2275(Table)
'arthrigenic' peptide affinity 2113
autoimmune thyroiditis induction in
animals 2310
avian 302, 303
CD3 complex 73, 465–466, 2173(Fig),
2265, 2323, 2334
amino acids interacting 2265
CD2 signaling via 464, 2328
cell-mediated lysis 506
negative selection of thymocytes 2357
phytohemagglutinin (PHA) 1952
structure 2335(Fig)
time course for development 2337
CD4 association 470
on CD4+ cells, antigen recognition 467
CD5 role 473
CD45 regulation of 493
chromosomal translocations 2268
aberrant signal transduction 558
DNA repair deficiency 559
collagen-induced arthritis 2107
combining sites 202
constant domains 2265
contrasuppressor cells 649
cross-linking, cell-mediated lysis
mechanism 506
of cytotoxic T lymphocytes (CTL)
bispecific antibodies 139, 140
TCR/CD8 complex 477
see also MHC class I
density, reduced in nude mice 1867
development 2336–2337
discovery 2264
diversity 1682, 2267
discovery 1626
generation 2278–2280
germline 2267, 2278
junction 2267, 2278

T cell receptor (TCR) (continued)
diversity (continued)
N-region 2267, 2278
nucleotide addition 2280
see also T cell receptor (TCR),
repertoire
evolution 2278–2282
extracellular chains 2265
gene disruption, inflammatory bowel
disease model 1383
gene rearrangements 502, 553, 569,
1876–1877, 2278, 2334
acute leukemia 1556
α gene 2266
β gene, *see under* T cell receptor αβ
(TCRαβ)
clonal deletion and 569–570
completion phase 2337
fetal 2275
γδ 2334
germline 2336–2337
γ genes 2339–2340
'heptamer–nonamer' motifs 2268, 2269
looping/excision model 2266
in neonate 1819–1820
ordered 1877, 2337
patterns 2266
preferential usage of V segments 2337
RAG gene expression 2337
thymocyte development phase 2336
time course 1877, 2336
genes
amphibians 80
avian species 303
EAE 2310
primates (nonhuman) 2011
rabbits 2048
Southern blotting 2197
heterogeneity, in multiple sclerosis 1787,
1788
historical background 725, 2264
hypervariable regions 2280, 2282
idiotypes 1185
IL-12 synergistic action 1486
invariant subunits 465
assembly 465–466
ε chain 465, 466
functions 467
[G]z[g] 465, 466, 2324, 2326
[G]z[g] and CD5 interaction 473
structural data 466(Table)
structure 465–466
ITAMs 2324
signal transduction role 2324
joining region, anti-idiotypic response to
vaccination 2285
lamina propria T cells 1782
ligand dissociation, partial/full T cell
activation 2329
ligation
T cell proliferation 2145
see also T cell activation
linkage disequilibrium 1588
in malignancies 2268
membrane microdomains 417–418
MHC recognition 195, 2282–2284
structural aspects 2282–2284
model 467(Fig)
monoclonal antibodies 503, 1357
in multiple sclerosis 1786–1787, 1787,
1788
NOD mice 1394
peptides, tolerance induction 1357
persistent signaling, Fas upregulation
2332
precursor 2339
pre-TCR complex formation 2337
protein tyrosine kinases associated 2324
pseudogenes 2281
rabbits 2048
repertoire 985
EAE 859, 859(Table)

T cell receptor (TCR) (continued)
repertoire (continued)
estimates 2267(Table)
extent 2308
Fas/FasL role 876
H2 class II molecule role 1044
hole, *see* Hole in the repertoire model
negative selection of self 1704–1705
in nude mice 1867
picornavirus infections 1958–1959,
1959
selection involving minor H antigens
1731–1732
Shigella infection 2180
see also T cell(s), repertoire; T cell
receptor (TCR), diversity
repertoire generation 2278–2280
ancestral DNA conservation 2280–
2281
gene conversion 2281
mutation 2281
in species 2280–2281
rheumatoid arthritis 221–2113
animal model 2107
sarcoidosis 2136
selection 1731
signal transduction 467, 700, 2324,
2324–2328
CD4 role 471
for cell-mediated lysis 505
see also under T cell activation
somatic mutations 2192
rare 2267
somatic recombination 2265, 2280
specificity 202, 2267
stimulation
adhesion molecules role 30
anergy induction 502
structure 193–194, 518, 2264–2265
T cell anergy induction 109
T cell epitope interaction 825, 826–827
T cell vaccination 2284–2285
TCR1 2282
see also T cell receptor γδ (TCRγδ)
TCR2 2282
see also T cell receptor αβ (TCRαβ)
thymic selection, *see* Thymic selection
Ti 2323
transgenic mice 110, 1581, 1731, 2335,
2338, 2354, 2361
transmembrane portions 2265, 2283
transmembrane signaling complex 2145
vertebrates, conserved sequences 2269
V regions, in T cell vaccination 2284–
2285
V (variable) domains 2265
T cell stimulatory factor (TSF), *see*
Interleukin-12 (IL-12)
T cell vaccination 2284–2286
clinical applications 2286
definition 2284
disease models 2284
in EAE 2284, 2285–2286
ergotypic 2285
hsp65 in adjuvant arthritis 34
lymphocyte networks 2285–2286
mechanism 2285
multiple sclerosis 1788–1789, 2286
myelin basic protein T cells 2284, 2285,
2286
naked V region DNA 2285
TCR 2284–2285
TCR-independent 2285
T_H1 to T_H2 switch 2285
T cell vaccines 2286
TCR, *see* T cell receptor (TCR)
[3H]TdR 510
99mTechnetium 2433
Teeth
bacteria attachment 1888
decay, *see* Dental caries
Teichoic acid 322, 423

TEL–AML1 rearrangements 1557
Temperature, body
  increased, *see* Fever
  regulation 903
    prostaglandins 117–118
Temperature
  cryopreservation 668
  fish, immune response and 924
  reptilian immune system changes 2080
  retroviral vector titers 2091
  thermodynamics of antibody–antigen
    interactions 166–167
Template theory, antibody formation
  1337, 1338
Tenascin, in tumors 2429
Tenascin C (cytotactin) 1046, 1115
Tenascin R (restrictin) 1046
Tenascin X 1046, 1115
Terfenadine 679, 2125
Terminal deoxynucleotidyl transferase
  (TdT) 155, 363, 1876
  age-related decrease in cells synthesizing
    59
  B1 cell repertoire restriction 362
  expression, thymosins increasing 2301
  limited in neonates 1819
  VDJ recombination 768
Testis-determining gene (SRY) 1159
Tetanus 577
  antitoxin 1345
Tetanus toxin
  site of action 2375(Fig)
  structure/nomenclature 2374, 2374(Fig)
Tetanus toxoid
  carrier in hCG and LHRH vaccines 642,
    644
  immune complexes, clearance 184
Tethering, lymphocytes 1618
Tetracycline, transgene expression control
  2406
Tetrazolium salts 2023
Texas Red 944, 945
TFAFs, TNF receptor signaling 2347
TGFβ, *see* Transforming growth factor β
  (TGFβ)
T$_H$0 cells 1060, 1170
  IL-13 synthesis 1491
  see also Helper T lymphocytes
T$_H$1 cells 1060–1061, 1169–1170, 1227,
    1895(Table), 2244, 2262
  African trypanosomiasis 2422
  anergy 2332
  apoptosis 1424–1425
  autoimmune disease pathogenesis 277–
    278, 1695
  autoimmune hemolytic anemia in NZB
    mice 93
  B cell differentiation inhibition 2365
  cytokines 503, 706, 1060, 1170, 1227,
    1436, 1695, 1918, 2330
    effect on macrophage 1645(Table)
    graft rejection 1014
    synthesis inhibition by IL-10 1476
  cytotoxic 727
  delayed hypersensitivity 502–503, 739
  differentiation
    CD1 role 462
    IL-12 role 1486
    in EAE 1695
  experimental autoimmune uveoretinitis
    (EAU) 869
  functions 1170, 1918
  in fungal infections 960
  granulomatous inflammation 2137
  HIV infection 1135, 1138
  IFNγ secretion 1424, 1841
  Ig class switching 2151
  IL-2 synthesis 1436
  IL-12 production 1484
  IL-12 role 1487
  immunity to *Legionella pneumophila*
    1545

T$_H$1 cells (*continued*)
  induction of nitric oxide synthase 1859,
    1860(Fig)
  inhibition in oral tolerance enhancement
    1896
  leishmaniasis 1227, 1548–1549
    murine cutaneous 1920
    resistance 1548
  leprosy 1796
  Listeria monocytogenes infection 1594
  macrophage activation 1642
  malaria 1661, 1920
  memory cells, proliferation 2332
  multiple sclerosis pathogenesis 1841
  onchocerciasis immunity 1873
  ovine 1903
  response
    antigen-ISCOM complexes 1509
    IL-12 role 1487
    to *Leishmania* in C57BL/6 mice 1062
    to mycobacteria 1793
  rheumatoid arthritis 2114
  sarcoidosis 2134, 2137
  shift to T$_H$2, UV-induced 1944
  spontaneous model of IDDM 283
  switch to T$_H$2
    EAE 860
    T cell vaccination 2285
  systemic sclerosis (scleroderma) 2117
  T$_H$2 cross-regulation 1918–1919, 2262
  T$_H$2 interaction 2245
  TNFα formation 1841
  in tuberculosis 1795
  in tuberculosis model 1794–1795
  UV-induced response change 1943, 1944
  vs T$_H$2 importance 1227
  see also Helper T lymphocytes
T$_H$1/T$_H$2 balance
  allergic rhinitis treatment 2125
  bacteria affecting 316
  CD1 role 462
  in IDDM 1402
  impairment, tolerance breakdown 276
  rheumatoid arthritis 2114
  schistosomiasis 2141
  vitamin E effect 2501
T$_H$2 cells 1060–1061, 1169–1170, 1227,
    1895(Table), 2244, 2262
  actions 1918
  anergic cells differences 110
  anergy 2332
  ascariasis 242
  asthma 244
  atopic eczema 788
  autoimmunity protective role 1695
  in CNS 1845
  cytokines 503, 706, 788, 1060, 1170,
    1227, 1436, 1695, 1918, 2330
    effect on macrophage 1645(Table)
  differentiation, IL-4 role 1451, 1452,
    1452–1453
  functions 1170
  GVHD prevention 2262
  helminth infections 1919
  HIV infection progression 1138
  IgE production 1171, 2151
  IL-4 production 1451
  IL-4 role in development 1548
  IL-10 synthesis 1476
  IL-13 synthesis 1491
  inhibition of nitric oxide synthase 1859,
    1860(Fig)
  leishmaniasis susceptibility 1538, 1548,
    1549(Fig)
  lepromatous leprosy 1797
  loss of IL-12 reactivity 1487
  malaria 1920
    chronic 1661
  memory cell, proliferation 2332
  onchocerciasis infection 1873
  in oral cavity 1890–1891
  oral tolerance induction 1896

T$_H$2 cells (*continued*)
  ovine 1903
  in Peyer's patches 1777
  response
    change to T$_H$1 by immunotherapy
      1355
    inhaled allergens 66
    to *Leishmania* in BALB/c mice 1062
  schistosomiasis 1920
  Toxocara canis infection 2381
  Trichuris muris infections 2419
  in tuberculosis 1795
  tumor escape mechanism 2445
  UV-induced shift of T$_H$1 to 1944
  see also Helper T lymphocytes
T$_H$3 cells 1895(Table)
  multiple sclerosis 1895, 1897–1898
  oral tolerance induction 1895
  TGFβ secretion 1895
  see also Helper T lymphocytes
β-Thalassemia
  iron overload effect 1507
  stem cell transplantation 1066, 1066(Fig)
Thalidomide, in tuberculosis 1795
Theileria 2286
  antigens 2288–2289, 2288(Table)
  carriers 2289
  characteristics 2287–2289
  control 2286
  detection 2289
  distribution 2286, 2287(Fig)
  evasive strategies 2289
  host immune response 2289
  polymorphic immunodominant molecule
    (PIM) 2288
  species 2286, 2287(Table)
  sporozoites 2287–2288, 2289
  transmission 2286
  vaccines 2289–2290
    live 2289–2290
    subunit 2290
Theileria annulata 2287
  antigens 2288(Table)
  SPAG1 2289
  vaccine 2289–2290
Theileria mutans 2288(Table)
Theileria parva 2287
  antigens 2288, 2288(Table)
  genes 2289
  life cycle 2287(Fig)
  vaccine
    live 2290
    subunit 2290
Theilerosis 2286–2290
  clinical features 2288
  drug therapy 2289
  vaccines 1921
Theiler's murine encephalomyelitis virus
  1957(Table)
Thermodynamics, antibody–antigen
  reactions 2199–2200
Thermoregulation 903
Thermotolerance, stress protein function
  2230
Theta antigen, *see* Thy-1
Thiamin 2490
  deficiency 2490–2491
Thigmotropism 410
Thiocyanate 1716
Thiopurines, in autoimmune hemolytic
  anemia (AIHA) 97
Third population cells, *see* Large granular
  lymphocytes (LGL)
Thoracic duct 1601
Thorium dioxide 851
THP-1 cells, FcγR functions 890
Thrombin 582, 1974
  inhibition 583
  platelet activation 579
  receptor, cleavage by granzyme A 1028
  role 582
Thrombocytopenia 1974, 1974–1975

Thrombocytopenia (continued)
autoimmune, in cats 894
drug-induced immune 100, 1974, 1975
heparin causing 1975
idiopathic, see Idiopathic (autoimmune)
thrombocytopenic purpura (ITP)
neonatal 901, 1674, 1976
platelet transfusion reactions 348
reduction by IL-11 1481
in SLE 2256
see also Platelet(s)
Thrombocytopenic purpura
in HIV infection 7
immune (ITP), see Idiopathic
(autoimmune) thrombocytopenic
purpura (ITP)
thrombotic 1966
Thromboembolism, in antiphospholipid
syndrome 2119, 2120
β-Thromboglobulin 1974
Thrombomodulin 455(Table), 579
Thrombopoietin (TPO) 375
applications 598
feedback system 2017
Thrombosis
antiphospholipid syndrome 2119, 2120
IL-1 role 805
Thrombospondin-binding ligand, apoptotic
cells 222
Thrombotic microangiopathy 2180
Thrombotic thrombocytopenic purpura,
fresh frozen plasma therapy 1966
Thromboxane 118
synthesis, aspirin effect 118
Thromboxane A$_2$ 579
biosynthesis 2024
function 1974
production by platelets 1974
Thrush, oral 1891
Thy-1 209, 211, 452(Table), 1875, 2290–
2292
alloantigenic variants (Thy-1.1 and Thy-
1.2) 2290
antibodies 2291–2292
biochemical analysis 2291
discovery 2290
expression 2291, 2342
functions 2291
GPI link 2291
in humans (CDw90) 2291
localization 2291
species with 2291
synthesis 2291
T cell detection/selection 2291
T cell mitosis triggering 2291
thymocyte adhesion to thymic epithelium
2292
Thy-1 inducing factor, see Interleukin-3
(IL-3)
Thymectomy
BALB/c mice 104
effects 2305
in amphibians 81
experimental autoimmune disease
induction 271
immunodeficiency due to 1286
in myasthenia gravis 1835, 1849
neonatal, NOD mice 1394, 1397
Thymic aplasia 1277
Thymic atrophy 1278, 2305, 2308, 2309
in dogs 414
Thymic cells 2233–2235
apoptosis, CD45 and galectin 1 role 493
ontogeny, porcine 1991
see also Thymic epithelium; Thymic
stromal cells; Thymocytes
Thymic cysts, reptilian 2077
Thymic epithelioma, see Thymoma
Thymic epithelium 1900–1901, 2233–
2235, 2234(Fig)
cell types and characteristics 2233–2235
cortical cells (TECs) 2234–2235, 2300

Thymic epithelium (continued)
cytokines produced 2236
medullary 2235, 2236
organ culture-purified, use 1901
origin 2235
positive selection 2304
regulation of T cell tolerance 2292–2299
see also under Tolerance
structure 2304–2305
subcapsular/subtrabecular/perivascular
2233–2234
thymocyte adhesion, Thy-1 role 2292
tolerance transfer 2293–2294
type I (lining) cells 2233–2234
type 2 and 3 cells 2234
Thymic fragment organ culture 1901
Thymic hormones and peptides 1346,
2300–2304, 2300(Table)
applications 1346
cancer immunotherapy 2301
clinical research 2301
functions and interactions 2302,
2302(Fig)
as immunoregulators 2302–2303
in vitro effects 2302–2303
in vivo effects 2301
receptors 2302
serum levels 2302
thymic humoral factor 2300(Table),
2301
thymopoietin 2300(Table), 2301
thymosins 2300(Table), 2301
thymulin 2300, 2300–2301
zinc binding 2515
see also each individual hormone/peptide
Thymic humoral factor (THF)
2300(Table), 2301
effect in chronic hepatitis B 2303
THFγ2 2301
metastases reduction 2301
Thymic hyperplasia 2235
Thymic hypoplasia 762
in cats 895
DiGeorge syndrome 761
Thymic nurse cells (TNCs) 2234–2235
apoptosis 2235
MHC expression 2235
site of positive T cell selection 2235
Thymic rudiment 1867
organ culture 1901
Thymic selection 2247, 2268, 2309–2309,
2337
autoreactive T cell development 2344
events 2338–2339
negative 1248, 2235, 2245, 2268,
2307(Fig), 2308, 2339, 2359
clonal deletion 2363–2364
definition 2337
failure by tissue-specific antigens 2308
germinal center CD4$^+$ T cells 2355
glucocorticoid action 2357
mechanism 2308, 2339
mode of antigen presentation 2355
quantitative aspects 2308
role 2339, 2343
sites 2308, 2355
TCR high-affinity/avidity 2355,
2356(Fig)
TCR low-affinity 2355
thymocytes and signals for 2356–2357
time course 2337, 2339
see also Tolerance
positive 2307(Fig), 2309–2308, 2338,
2343, 2359
definition 2337
developmental stage 2354
mechanisms 2306–2308, 2338–2339
signaling mechanism 2307
TCR low-affinity/avidity 2355,
2356(Fig)
stromal cells role 2338
TCRαβ 2268

Thymic selection (continued)
TCR β gene rearrangement stage 2339
TCR repertoire 2278–2280
thymus role 2247
'Thymic selection' model 1712
Thymic stromal cells 2233–2236
epithelial 2233–2235
see also Thymic epithelium
heterogeneity 2233, 2235
influence on thymopoiesis 2236
nonepithelial 2235–2236
TCRγδ maturation 2272
Thymic stromal-derived lymphopoietin
(TSLP) 1464
Thymidine incorporation
lymphocyte proliferation assay 1623,
2023
measurement of lifespan of cells 1579–
1580
Thymocytes 2305, 2341
accumulation of deoxyGTP 749
adhesion to thymic epithelial cells 2292
apoptosis 224
canine 411
CD3 expression 466
CD4 expression development 2337
CD8 expression development 2337
CD25$^+$ 2336
CD45 expression 492
deletion 2354
depletion, motheaten mice 1269
development 2300
in neonate 1819
differentiation 2306
CD4 role 471
fibronectin inducing 912
double negative (CD4$^-$/CD8$^-$) 1876, 1877
CD1-restriction 462
cytolysis by 505
ovine 1903
double positive (DP; CD4$^+$/CD8$^+$) 502,
1876, 1877, 2305, 2337
apoptosis 224, 2307–2308
blast cells 2306
CD8 selection 478
clonal deletion 569
death 2338
death by neglect 2307–2308,
2307(Fig), 2354
functions 2337
location/site 2304
numbers 2307
positive selection 2306–2308,
2307(Fig), 2354
resistance to deletion 2354
see also Thymic selection
early development phase 2336–2337
surface markers 2336
TCR gene rearrangements 2336
glucocorticoid sensitivity 2305
immature single positive stage (ISP) 2337
later development phase 2337–2338
maturation
IL-1 role 1433
IL-4 role 1452
migration 2236
adhesion molecules 2236
mixed lymphocyte reaction (MLR) 1734
negative selection, signals 2356–2357
obese strain of chickens 282
proliferation 1248
IL-9 role 1473
radiosensitivity 2051
semimature single-positive 2354–2355
separation, lectin use 1540
single positive 2337
surface markers 2305
TfR expression 2390, 2392
in thymic cortex 2234
triple negative (TN; CD3$^-$CD4$^-$CD8$^-$)
2336, 2337
CD44 expression 2336

Thymocytes (*continued*)
triple negative (TN; CD3⁻CD4⁻CD8⁻) (*continued*)
homing/precursor activity 2337
see also T cell(s)
Thymoma (thymic epithelioma) 1281, 1834, 1835, 1848
acquired neuromyotonia in 1850
cross-reactive protein with AChR 1848
Thymomimetic drugs 1347
Thymomodulin 1346
Thymopentin (TP5) 1346, 2303
antibody avidity 2301
functions 2301
Thymopoiesis, thymic stroma role 2236
Thymopoietin 2300(Table), 2301
functions 2301
mRNA 2301
Thymosin 1346, 2300(Table), 2301
cDNA 2301
Tα1 1346, 2301
combination therapy in cancer 2301
IL-2R and IL-2 synthesis 2303
opportunistic infection prevention 2301
sequence homologies 2301
Tβ4 2301
Fx identical 2301
hormone secretion 2301
Thymosin fraction 5 (TF5) 1346, 2301
functions 2301
Thymostimulin (TP1) 2301
Thymulin 2300, 2300–2301
antibody avidity 2301
in cancer 2301
functions 2300–2301, 2301
hyperalgesia reduction 2301
as immunomodulator 2302
synthesis and release 2300
zinc coupled to 2300
Thymus 2304–2309
abnormalities, in myasthenia gravis 1834
absence in mice, *see* Nude (athymic) mice
age-related changes 60
amphibian, embryology 80
atrophy, *see* Thymic atrophy
avian 301, 394(Fig)
calf, thymic hormones from 2300, 2301
canine, development 411
clonal deletion of T cells 569–570
cortex 2233, 2234–2235, 2304
negative selection site 2308
dendritic cells 747
epithelium, *see* Thymic epithelium
fish 920–921
germinal centers 1834
historical background 2304
involution
marsupials 1665–1666
motheaten mice 1269
reptilian 2077
lambs 2450
lymphocyte migration 1617
maturation, in marsupials 1665
medulla 2233, 2235, 2304
negative selection site 2308
T cell development 2306
MHC restriction development 1711–1712
microenvironment 1726, 2300
role and organ culture for 1900–1901
myasthenia gravis 1848
nonepithelium 2235–2236
ontogeny 2305
reptiles 2076–2077, 2077(Fig)
radiosensitivity 2051
reptiles 2076–2077
role 1866
sex hormones affecting 2176
stem cells 2306, 2336
structural organization 2304–2305
structure 2232(Fig), 2233
T cell development 2334

Thymus (*continued*)
T cell development (*continued*)
maturation 1247–1248
mouse and humans 2336
time course 2336
see also T cell(s), development; T cell differentiation
T cell outputs 2308
T cell selection, *see* Thymic selection
TCRαβ random generation 2268
trabeculae 2233
transplantation, fetal 763
ungulates 2450
Thymus-derived lymphocytes, *see* T cell(s)
Thym-uvocal 1346
Thyostimulin 1346
Thyroglobulin
allotypes, experimental autoimmune thyroiditis 2310
autoantibodies 261, 2316
detection 261
normal 261
obese strain of chickens 281
B cells binding 2311
oral, autoimmune thyroiditis suppression 1897
T cells response 2311
transport, thyroid microsome (TMA) role 2316
Yersinia molecular mimicry 2311
Thyroid acropachy 2315
Thyroid autoantibodies 261–262, 292–293
autoimmune thyroiditis 2316
detection 260
epithelial cells 261, 2316
Graves' disease 2315
pernicious anemia 103(Table)
thyroglobulin, *see* Thyroglobulin
thyroid growth stimulation/inhibition 2315
thyroid microsome (TMA) 261, 2316
thyroid peroxidase 261, 293, 2316, 2317
TSH receptor 261–262, 1179, 1675, 2315
TSH receptor blocking antibodies 2315, 2316
Thyroid autoantigens 261–262
Thyroid autoimmunity 292, 2313–2317
Addison's disease 1986, 2313
autoantibodies, *see* Thyroid autoantibodies
autoimmune diseases associated 2313
chronic, etiology 2313–2314
chronic idiopathic urticaria in 681
environmental factors inducing 2314
etiology 2313–2314
genetic factors 2313
HLA associations 2313
immunization against 2317
infectious agents associated 2314
maternal antibodies causing 1674–1675, 2315
molecular mimicry 2314
smoking association 2314
stress inducing 2314
see also Graves' disease; Thyroiditis
Thyroid autoimmunity, experimental models 2309–2312, 2313
activated macrophage 2312
B cells 2311
cytokines 2311
cytotoxic T cells 2312
environmental factors inducing 2311
experimentally-induced thyroiditis 2309
expression 2311–2312
genetic factors affecting organ susceptibility 2310
genetic factors influencing immune response 2310
immunological escalation 2311
induction 2310–2311
lymphokines 2311–2312

Thyroid autoimmunity, experimental models (*continued*)
NK cells 2312
prevention, calcitriol 2496
progression 2311
SCID mouse model 1129(Table)
spontaneous thyroiditis 2309
T cells 2311
TNF 2312
Thyroid disease, autoimmune, *see* Thyroid autoimmunity
Thyroid dysfunction, postpartum 2317
Thyroid epithelial cells, autoantibodies 261, 2316
Thyroid function
inhibition by TSH receptor blocking antibodies 2315
stimulation by TSH receptor autoantibodies 2315
Thyroid gland
failure 2316
growth inducing/inhibiting antibodies 2315
obese strain of chickens 282
Thyroiditis 2316
atrophic (primary myxedema) 2313, 2316
autoantibody assays 2316
autoimmune, experimental 271
chronic autoimmune 2316
autoantibodies 261
experimental, *see* Thyroid autoimmunity, experimental models
goitrous, *see* Hashimoto's thyroiditis
Hashimoto's, *see* Hashimoto's thyroiditis
spontaneous autoimmune 281
see also Obese strain of chickens
Thyroid microsome (TMA)
autoantibodies 261, 2316
TPO as autoantigenic determinant 2316
Thyroid peroxidase (TPO) 2316
autoantibodies 261, 293, 2316, 2317
autoantigenic determinant of thyroid microsome (TMA) 2316
cloning 2314
Thyroid stimulating hormone (TSH), bacteria binding 2314
Thyroid stimulating hormone (TSH) receptor
autoantibodies 261–262, 1179, 1675, 2315
blocking antibodies (TSHRBAb) 2315
atrophic thyroiditis 2316
cloning 2315
structure 2315
Thyroid susceptibility gene 282
Thyrotropin (TSH), *see* Thyroid stimulating hormone (TSH)
Thyroxine 2224
Tickborne encephalitis (TBE) 926
vaccination 931
Tickborne encephalitis (TBE) virus 926
Tight junctions
antigen uptake by mucosal cells 189
see also Endothelial cells
Tight-skin (TSK) mouse 283–284
Time-resolved fluorescence techniques 143, 1255
Tinea versicolor 751
Tingible bodies 993
Tingible body macrophage (TBM) 993, 994, 1728
Tipula iridescent virus (TIV) 1502, 1503
Tissue
injury, inflammation after 16
repair, fibroblasts role 908
slices 1901
swelling, in inflammation 17
Tissue culture
bioreactors, *see* Bioreactors
vessels for leukocyte culture, *see* Leukocyte culture

Tissue factor (TF) 455(Table), 579, 582
  function 583
  production, C-reactive protein (CRP)
    stimulating 664
  structure 520
Tissue factor (TF) pathway inhibitor
    (TFPI) 583
Tissue inhibitors of metalloproteinases
    (TIMPs) 865–866
Tissue-plasminogen activator (t-PA) 585
Tissue typing 2318–2323
  anthropological studies 2322
  bone marrow transplants 2319, 2322
    minor mismatches 2318, 2319
  dead leukocytes 2318, 2319
  definition 2318
  disease association application 2322
  DNA-based methods 2318, 2319
    anthropological studies 2322
    bone marrow 2322
    limitations 2318
  eosin dye test 2319
  fluorescence test 2319
  historical aspects 2318
  HLA antigens 2318, 2319
    bone marrow transplants 2319, 2322
    transplantation 2412
  immune response research 2322
  methods 2318–2319
    mineral oil importance 2319
    serological 2318–2319
  microlymphocyte cytotoxicity test 2318,
    2319
  NIH test 2318
  principles 2318
  red blood cells 2318
  renal transplants 2318, 2319, 2322
  see also HLA typing
T-like cells, reptiles 2078, 2078(Fig)
TLX antigen 899
T lymphocytosis 1633
TM anchor (TM proteins) 419
  promiscuity 418
TNFα, see Tumor necrosis factor α
    (TNFα)
TNFαR, see Tumor necrosis factor α
    (TNFα) receptor
TNFB*1 allele 2436
TNFB*2 allele 2436
TNFR, see Tumor necrosis factor receptor
    (TNFR)
TNF receptor-associated death domain
    (TRADD) 711
TNF receptor-associated protein, see TRAP
Tnx gene 1046
α-Tocopherol, see Vitamin E
δ-Tocopherol 2500
Tocotrienol 2500
Togaviridae 2350
  budding of viruses 2351
  characteristics 2350
  classification 2350, 2350(Table)
  enhancement of replication 2351
  envelope proteins (E1 and E2) 2351
  genome 2350–2351
  immunity to 2351
  tolerance 2351–2352
  transmission 2350
  viremia control 2350
Togaviruses 2350–2352
Tolerance 109, 203, 290–291, 293, 1146,
    1228
  absolute absence 287
  anergy, see Anergy
  antigen-specific 2243
  avian species and chickens 300–301
  B cell
    anergy 2361
    antigen presentation mode 2360
    deletion 2364
    developmental stage 2363
    induction 106–107, 293, 361, 365

Tolerance (continued)
  B cell (continued)
    induction models 106
    induction sites 2365
    mechanisms 2353, 2353(Fig), 2364
    T cell comparison 2362
    tolerance susceptible window 2365
    transgenic models 106–107
  B cell–T cell cooperation 107
  blocked by contrasuppressor cells 649–
    650
  breakdown 275–276, 290–291, 293–295,
    1349, 2366–2367
    aberrant MHC class II expression 294
    abnormal T cell activation 275–276
    abnormal TCR repertoire 275
    albumin 2308
    anti-idiotypes 291, 293, 294
    in autoimmunity 2366–2367
    B cell anergy loss 2308
    cross-reactions 275, 276, 289, 294
    cryptic epitope presented 294
    cytokines role 276
    defective differentiation 275
    determinant spreading 755
    HLA association 294
    immunopathology as 1339–1340
    low-affinity cells 2308
    lymphocyte resistance to apoptosis 276
    molecular mimicry 275, 276, 289, 294
    multifactorial nature 294–295, 295(Fig)
    peripheral loss 275–276, 290
    polyclonal activation 276
    'signal three' 2367
    somatic mutations of antibodies 294
    superantigens 276, 2242
    T$_H$1 and T$_H$2 imbalance 276
    thyroid autoimmune disease 2314
    see also Autoimmune disease;
      Autoimmunity
  central 2352–2358, 2364(Fig)
    B cell 2357–2358
    definition 2352
    mechanism 275, 290
    T cell 2354–2357
  clonal selection hypothesis and 575
    see also Clonal selection hypothesis
  concepts 2292–2293
    Burnet/Lederberg theory 2292
    controlled autoreactivity 2293
    Jerne's network hypothesis 2292–2293
  controlled levels 287
  'critical period' 2295–2296
  cytokine modulation 2361
  definition 106, 1357, 1893, 2352, 2359,
    2362
  deletion 2361
  as developmental problem 2293–2294
    antigen persistence 2293
    shift to immunity 2294
  'dominant' 290–291
  'education' phenomenon 2295–2298,
    2297(Fig), 2299
  experimental models 2359–2361, 2363
    antigen dose 2360–2361
    antigen presentation 2360
    cytokine modulation 2361
    deaggregated human gamma globulin
      2359–2360
    deletion vs anergy 2361
    mature animals 2359–2360
  factors affecting 2363
  in fish 925
  gatekeeping 2366
  history 2362
  induction 361
    anti-CD4 1358
    in autoimmune disease therapy 1357
    B cells, see above
    bypass of Langerhans cells 2191
    bystander suppression 1357
    diabetes prevention in models 1397

Tolerance (continued)
  induction (continued)
    dual dose 2360
    by maternal antibodies 1673–1674
    mature animals 2359–2360
    mechanisms 1228, 2352–2353
    myelin basic protein 2397
    neonatal animals 2359
    neonates 1820, 2363
    ocular antigens 867–868, 879
    peptide–MHC complexes 1357
    sites 2365
    superantigens 2359, 2361
    T cells 293, 294, 2306, 2308, 2354–
      2357
    TGFβ function 2397
    transplanted organs 1352
    xenograft survival 2511
    see also Immunosuppression, donor-
      specific; Immunosuppressive
      agents/therapy
  'infectious' 2243, 2294
  inhalation 1357
  as learning process 2293
  maintenance 2294
    regulatory T cells 2299
    suppressor T cells 2246
  maternally-induced, rhesus-negative
    women 1673
  mechanisms 2359, 2363–2365, 2364(Fig)
    anergy 2363
    deletion 2363
    suppression 2363
    see also Anergy ; Clonal deletion
  nasal and aerosol mucosal 1896
  need for 105–106
  oral, see Oral tolerance
  peptide-induced 1357
  perinatal period 2299
  peripheral 2362–2367, 2364(Fig)
    mechanisms 2363–2365, 2364(Fig)
    sites 2365–2366
    properties 2362–2363
  self-MHC 1704–1705
  to sequestered antigens 2359, 2363
  signals 2366
  'split' 2355
  suppression, T cells 2365
  T cell 293, 2314, 2354–2357, 2363–
    2364
    altered peptide ligands (APL) 2355
    anergy 2365
    antigen concentration/dose 2355, 2360
    antigen presentation mode 2355, 2360
    APC role 2355
    B cell comparison 2362
    B cell role 2360
    breakdown 275, 290
    breaking, determinant spreading 755
    to C5 2355
    cell-interaction molecules 2355–2356
    developmental stage 2354–2355, 2363
    duration 2362
    glucocorticoid action 2357
    induction 293, 294, 2306, 2308, 2354–
      2357
    mechanisms 2353, 2353(Fig)
    peripheral mature and resident (PMR)
      2295, 2297
    peripheral regulation 2295–2298
    recent thymic emigrants (RTEs) 2295,
      2297
    regulation by thymic epithelium 2292–
      2299
    regulatory cells 2297, 2297(Fig), 2299
    signals for negative selection 2356–
      2357
    stromal cytokines 2357
    TCR affinity/avidity 2355
    transgenic mice 2354
  thymic epithelium role 2293–2294
    regulatory mechanisms 2295

Tolerance (*continued*)
  thymic epithelium role (*continued*)
    regulatory T cell selection 2236, 2294–
      2295, 2296(Fig)
    see also Thymic epithelium
  tissue-specific 2299
    thymic-dependent 2294
  transfer 2243, 2293–2294, 2362
  transgenic mice 2361, 2364
  transplantation, thymic epithelium-
    dependent 2295
  window of tolerization 2293, 2294, 2299
  see also Anergy; Anergy ; Clonal
    deletion; Thymic selection, negative
Tolerogen 203
Tolerogenesis, 'dominant' 290–291
Tolerogens, definition 1297
Tolpocladium inflatum 686
Toluene diisocyanate (TDI) 1365
Tonsilar papillae, in pigs 1991
Tonsillitis, streptococcal 2218
Tonsils 1249
  antigen presentation 1775
  antigen-presenting cells (APCs) 1775
  B cells 1775
  lymphocyte migration 1617
  nasopharyngeal (adenoids) 1775
  palatine 1775, 1775(Fig)
Topoisomerase I 126
  antibodies 131–1332
Tospovirus 390, 391(Table)
Total body irradiation (TBI)
  conditioning for stem cell transplantation
    1063
  historical background 2411
Total lymphoid irradiation (TLI) 2052
Total parenteral nutrition (TPN), albumin
  use 1967
Toxicology, *see* Immunotoxicology
Toxic shock syndrome
  Staphylococcus 2209
  streptococcal 2218
Toxic shock syndrome toxin 1 (TSST-1)
  antibodies 2211
  Staphylococcus 2209, 2242
  streptococcal 2218
Toxins 2367–2379
  ADP-ribosyl transferases 2369
  antitoxin therapy 2367, 2457
  Bacillus anthracis, *see Bacillus anthracis*
  binary 2369, 2374–2376
  botulinum C2 2370, 2375–2376,
    2376(Fig)
  cholera, *see* Cholera toxin (CT)
  Clostridium, *see Clostridium*; *specific*
    Clostridium species
  Clostridium botulinum, *see* Botulinum
    toxin
  deregulating cells 2369
  diabetes mellitus induction 1397
  diphtheria, *see* Diphtheria toxin
  endotoxins, *see also* Lipopolysaccharide
    (LPS)
  enterotoxins, *see* Enterotoxins
  Escherichia coli, *see under Escherichia*
    coli
  gene mutations 2369
  gram-negative bacteria (endotoxins)
    2377–2379
    see also Lipopolysaccharide (LPS)
  historical background 2367–2369
  iota group 2375
  Legionella pneumophila protease 2369,
    2376
  listeriolysin 2377
  mechanisms of action
    binary 2369, 2374–2376
    cytotonic 2369, 2372–2374
    cytotoxic 2369, 2370–2372
    membrane actions 2369
    membrane-damaging 2376–2377
    noncellular/extracellular elements 2369

Toxins (*continued*)
  monoclonal antibodies linked 2261–2262
  Neisseria gonorrhoeae 269
  phospholipases 2376
  pore-forming 2377
  Pseudomonas aeruginosa 2372(Fig)
    elastase 2369
  Pseudomonas exotoxin A 2370
  Pseudomonas exotoxin S 2370
  RTX toxins 2377
  SH-activated cytolysins 2377
  Shiga, *see* Shiga toxin
  staphylococcal, *see Staphylococcus*
  Streptococcus 269, 2218
  Streptococcus pneumoniae 2377
  Streptococcus pyogenes 2377
  transfer across membranes 2369–2375
  vero 2370
  see also specific toxins
Toxocara canis 2379–2382
  ABO blood group cross-reactions 2380
  antigens 2380–2381
    shedding 2381
  characteristics 2379–2381
  evasive strategies 2381
  excretory/secretory (ES) antigens 2380
    monoclonal antibodies 2381
  granuloma 2379, 2381
  host immune response 2381
  infection process 2379
  larvae 2379, 2380(Fig)
  life cycle 2379, 2380(Fig)
  nematodes cross-reacting 2381
  ocular larva migrans 2379
  vaccines 2381
  visceral larva migrans 2379
Toxocariasis 2379–2382
  clinical features 2379
  immunodiagnosis 2381
  prevalence 2381
  syndromes 2379
Toxoplasma gondii 2382–2384
  antigens 2382
  characteristics 2382
  in CNS 1846
  evasive strategies 1917, 2384
  genes 2382
  host immune response 1920, 2382–2384
    antibodies 2382
    macrophage 2382–2383, 2383(Fig)
    IFNγ role 2382–2383
  life cycle 2382
  macrophage killing of 2382
  tachyzoites 2382, 2384
  TGFβ and IL-10 role 2383
  vaccines 1921, 2384
Toxoplasmosis 2382–2384
  diagnosis, microplate agglutination 58
  encephalitis 2384
  HLA association 2384
  transmission 2382
Trabeculae, lymph node 1604
Trace elements, deficiency 1284
Trachoma 551, 552, 872–873
  features 873
  immune response 873
TRADD 711, 1641
  TNF receptor signaling 2347
TRAF proteins 1641, 2148
  signal transduction by CD40 484–485,
    2148, 2150
  signal transduction by lymphotoxin 1641
  TRAF-3 653, 2150
Tranexamic acid 684
Transactivating responsive region (TAR),
  HIV 1132
Transactivation, by viral gene products
  1564–1565
Transcobalamin II, deficiency 1284
Trans-complementation, HLA-DQ 1694
Transcription 986
  activation of cytokine genes 701, 703

Transcription (*continued*)
  control, acute phase proteins 18
  immunoglobulin mRNA 158
  lymphocytes, cyclosporine (CsA) action
    686
  reverse 2092–2093
Transcription factors
  access to DNA 701
  AP-1, *see* AP-1 transcription factor
  binding to TNFα gene 2436
  CIITA 331
  cytokine gene regulation 701
  deregulated by chromosomal
    translocations 557–558
  features and classes 557
  glucocorticoid action 999
  HIV replication 1133
  IL-1 signal transduction 1433
  inhibitors 704
    IkB 1119
  NF-AT, *see* NF-AT transcription factor
  NFkB, *see* NFkB transcription factor
  Rel family 1119
  RFX5 331
  in signal transduction, *see* STAT
Transcytosis 851
Transfection
  B7 gene 307
  recombinant vaccine development 2460
  retroviral vectors 2086
Transfer factors 1345, 2385–2389
  affinity purification 2385
  antigen interactions 2386
  clinical studies 2388
  cytokine production 2386–2387
  cytotoxic T cell activity 2387
  discovery 2385
  DTH 2386
  future research prospects 2388
  genetic studies 2387, 2388(Fig)
  immunological activities 2385–2387
  lymphocyte transformation responses
    2387, 2387(Fig)
  nature/characteristics 2385
  specificity 2385–2386, 2386(Table)
Transferrin 1939
Transferrin receptor (TfR) 451(Table),
  2389–2392
  apotransferrin complex 2391
  discovery 2389
  downregulated by IFNγ 1543
  endocytosis 2390–2391, 2391(Fig)
  expression 2392
    regulation 2390–2391
    tumors 2390
  functions 2391–2393
    cell proliferation 2390, 2391
    T cell activation/differentiation 2391–
      2392
  iron-responsive element (IRE) 2391
  monoclonal antibodies 2389
  ontogeny 2390
  recycling 2390–2391
  structure 2389–2390, 2389(Fig)
  target for antitumor therapy 2390
  tissue expression 2390, 2390(Table)
Transformation, malignant 1562–1563
  transactivation by viral gene product
    1564–1565
  see also Viral carcinogenesis
Transforming growth factor α (TGFα)
  receptor, in tumors 2429
  in tumors 2429
Transforming growth factor β (TGFβ)
  2392–2399
  activation 2393
  anti-inflammatory effects 2392, 2398
  assays 697(Table), 2394–2395
  autoimmune diseases
    experimental 859, 2396, 2397
    human 2397–2398
  autoinduction of transcription 2396

Transforming growth factor β (TGFβ)
(continued)
  bifunctional properties 2395–2396,
    2395(Fig)
  binding proteins 2393
  CNS effects 1831(Table), 2396
  deficient mice 1894
  detection 2394–2395
  downregulation of LTB$_4$ synthesis 228
  effect on endothelial cells 805–806
  effects on T cells 2395–2396
  functions 2392
  genes 2393
  in graft rejection 2397
  half-life 2393, 2394
  in HIV infection and AIDS 2398
  Ig production inhibited 2396
  IL-1β decrease due to 1431
  IL-12 production modulation 1484
  immune privilege role 2395
  immune response 1831(Table), 2395–
    2396, 2395(Fig)
    inhibition 2395–2396, 2395(Fig)
    promotion 2395(Fig), 2396
  in immune surveillance 2393–2394, 2445
  as immunomodulator 2392, 2395(Fig)
  immunosuppressive role in CNS 2396
  infectious diseases
    experimental 2397
    human 2397–2398
  isoforms 2393
  latent TGFβ-binding protein 2393
  local effects 2397, 2398(Fig)
  molecular structure 2393
  mRNA 2394, 2397
  multiple sclerosis 2397
  myasthenia gravis 2398
  nitric oxide production inhibition 2396
  oral tolerance induction 1894–1895,
    2397
  physicochemical properties 2393(Table)
  post-transcriptional regulation 2393,
    2394–2395
  production
    in osteoporosis 2177
    T cells 2392
    T$_H$3 role 1895
    thymic epithelium 2236
  receptors 710, 2393
    signal transduction 2393
    TGFβRI and TGFβRII 2393
  rheumatoid arthritis 2114
  role in Chagas' disease 526(Table)
  role in cytokine network 2393–2394,
    2394(Fig)
  secretion process 702
  TGFβ1, extracellular matrix regulation
    907
  therapeutic, wound healing 2397
  tolerance induction 1894–1895, 2397
  Toxoplasma gondii infection 2383
  Trypanosoma cruzi invasion 522
  tumor immunological escape 2445
  upregulation for bystander regulation
    2397
Transforming growth factor β (TGFβ)
  superfamily 2393
  proteins included 2393
Transfusion-associated GVHD (TA-
  GVHD) 2402
  frequency 2402, 2403(Table)
Transfusion medicine 2399
Transfusion-related lung injury (TRALI)
  348
  plasma-containing products causing 1967
Transfusions 2399–2404
  blood/blood components, see Blood
    transfusion(s)
  blood substitutes 2403
  see also Blood transfusion(s)
Transgene 974, 975(Fig)
  expression 2406

Transgene (continued)
  expression (continued)
    at ectopic sites 2406
      modulation 2406–2407
    immune reactivity against 979–980
    inducible activation 2407
    inducible control 2406
    inducible inactivation 2406–2407
    integration 2405
    'integration position effects' 2406
    'minigenes' 2406
    optimal design 2406
    'position effect variegation' 2406
    in retroviral vectors 2086
    temporal control 2406
    tetracycline role 2406
    tissue-specific activation 2406, 2407(Fig)
Transgenic animals 2404–2408
  applications 2404, 2407–2408
  definition 2404
  experimental autoimmune disease 273–
    274
  generation 982
  GM-CSF 1022
  historical aspects 2404
  inbred strains 1370
  MHC genes, experimental autoimmunity
    274
  optimal transgene design 2406
  production techniques 1370, 2405–2406,
    2405(Fig)
    DNA introduction methods 2405–2406
    DNA microinjection 2405, 2405(Fig)
  see also Transgene
Transgenic mice 1275, 1276
  acute phase response 19
  applications 1275
  B cell, for rheumatoid factors 2361
  B cell differentiation 355–356,
    357(Table)
  B cell isolation 181
  B cell receptor 572
  B cell tolerance 106–107
  BDC2/NOD 1394
  CD8 lacking p56^{lck} 477
  CD45 494
  DNA fragments used 2406
  double, HEL and anti-HEL 1201
  gp130 1562
  historical aspects 1626, 2404
  HLA, rheumatoid arthritis model 2108–
    2110
  HLA-DQ8, rheumatoid arthritis model
    2108–2110
  IFNγ 1425
  IgM for H2-K^k 2364
  IgM for hen egg lysozyme, tolerance
    2364, 2366
  IL-4 1452
  IL-5 1456
  IL-6 1460
  IL-8 1470
  IL-9 1474
  influenza hemagglutinin 1397
  kallikrein overexpression 1518
  LCMV immune response 233
  leukemia inhibitory factor (LIF) 1562
  monoclonal antibody preparation 1745,
    1745(Fig)
  production techniques 2405–2406,
    2405(Fig)
  red cell autoantibodies 92
  STAT3 1562
  T cell anergy 110
  T cell receptor (TCR) 110, 1581, 1731,
    2335, 2338, 2354, 2361
  TCRβ/NOD 1394
  truncated Int3 gene 1045
  vector systems 2406
  see also Gene disruption
Transgenic pigs
  CD59 gene 500

Transgenic pigs (continued)
  xenotransplantation 2511
Transgenic rats, HLA-B27 1383
Transient aplastic crisis 1924
Transient hypogammaglobulinemia of
  infancy 1281
Transition state 438
Translation, immunoglobulin mRNA 158
Transmigration of leukocytes 531(Fig),
  757, 1097–1098, 1098(Fig), 1619,
  2059, 2060, 2062
  adhesion molecules role 30, 1097–1098,
    1098(Fig), 1408, 1408(Fig), 2059–
    2060, 2060
    ICAM-2 1411
  diapedesis as final event, see Diapedesis
  inflammatory bowel disease 1378
  inhibition 2059, 2062–2063
  lymphocytes, see also High endothelial
    venules (HEV)
  monocytes 1754
  shear forces 757, 758(Fig)
  species differences 1620
  surface contact 535
  see also High endothelial venules (HEV);
    individual cell types
Transmissible spongiform encephalopathies
  (TSEs) 2409–2411
  diseases 2409
  host genes controlling infection 2409–
    2410
  incubation period 2409, 2410
  infection route 2410
  pathogen 2409
  pharmacological control strategies 2410
  spread of infection 2410
  see also Creutzfeldt–Jakob disease
Transmission electron microscopy, see
  Electron microscopy
Transplantation 2411–2415
  bone marrow, see Bone marrow
    transplantation
  cancer after 2414–2415
  complications 2414–2415
  cyclosporine role 688, 2414
  donors 2412
    live donors 2412
  donor-specific cytotoxic antibodies 2412
  donor-specific immunosuppression 810
  experimental models, rejection prevention
    by oral antigens 1897
  FasL expression, rejection prevention 879
  H2 class I molecules 1039
  hematopoietic stem cells, see Stem cell
    transplantation
  historical background 1011, 2411–2412
  HLA matching 2412
    see also HLA typing; Tissue typing
  immunosuppression, see
    Immunosuppressive agents/therapy
  in vivo, organ culture-purified thymic
    epithelium 1901
  microchimerism after 2402
  mixed lymphoid chimerism and 547–548
  nude mice use 1868
  opportunistic infections after 1884, 2414
  organ preservation 2412
  passenger leukocytes, depletion 1012
  rejection, see Graft rejection
  tissue typing 2319, 2322, 2412
    see also Tissue typing
  tolerance induction 1352
    CD40-CD40L interaction interrupted
      487
  whole-body irradiation before 2052
  xenografts, see Xenotransplantation
  see also specific organs/tissues
Transplantation antigens
  male-specific, see H-Y antigen
  minor, see Minor transplantation
    (histocompatibility) antigens

Transplantation antigens (*continued*)
  tumor-specific, *see* Tumor-specific
    transplantation antigens (TSTA)
Transporter, *see* TAP (Transporter
  Associated with antigen Processing)
Transporter genes, rheumatoid arthritis
  2113
Transport proteins, in acute phase
  response 18(Table)
Trans-sialidase, *Trypanosoma cruzi*
  invasion 521
Trans-stimulation of lymphocytes, *see*
  Bystander effect
Transthyretin (TTR) 2488
  variants 85
TRAP 711
TRAP-1, *see* CD40 ligand (CD40L)
Trauma
  immunodeficiency due to 1286
  increased eicosanoids in 885
Travelers
  diarrhea 842
  hepatitis A 1074
Trematodes 880
  see also Fasciola hepatica
Trench fever 2126
Treponema 2415–2418
  antigens 2416
  characteristics 2416
  delayed-type hypersensitivity 2417
  diseases 2415
    nonvenereal 2416(Table)
    venereal, *see* Syphilis
  species 2415
Treponema carateum 2416(Table)
Treponema pallidum 380, 2072–2074
  antibodies 2417
  characteristics 2416
  detection 2417
  evasive strategies 2417
  host immune response 2073, 2417
  membrane-associated lipoproteins 2416
  morphology 2072–2073
  Nichols strain 2416
  outer membrane 2416, 2417
  skin infections 753
  vaccine/immunization 2417
  see also Syphilis
Treponema pallidum immobilization test
  (TPI) 2417
Treponema pertenue 2416, 2416(Table)
Treponematoses
  nonvenereal 2416(Table), 2417–2418
  venereal, *see* Syphilis
Triad recognition system
  (receptors/ligands/carriers) 1579
Trichinella spiralis, IL-3 action 1444
Trichuriasis 2418–2419
  epidemiology 2418, 2419
  macrophage 2419
  transmission 2418
Trichuris muris
  chronic infections 2419
  host immune response 2419
  T_H2 response 2419
Trichuris trichiura 2418
  antigens 2418
  characteristics 2418
  evasive strategies 2419
  host immune response 2418–2419
  vaccines 2419
Trinitrobenzene sulfonic acid-induced
  colitis 1383–1384
Triton X-100 513
Trophoblast 898
  antigens 1853
  complement regulatory proteins
    expression 899
  cytotoxicity resistance 898–899
  immune response to antigens 1375
  immunity to 1375
  interferon (IFNτ) 1414

Trophoblast (*continued*)
  MHC expression absent 898
  NK cell role 1814
  see also Fetus
Tropical diseases
  TNFα role 2439
  see also Leishmaniasis; Malaria;
    Trypanosomiasis; *other specific
    diseases*
Tropical pulmonary eosinophilia 914
Tropical spastic paraparesis 2097
Tropical splenomegaly 1662
Tropomodulin, in red cell membrane 835,
  839(Table)
Tropomyosin, in red cell membrane 835,
  839(Table)
Trypan blue exclusion, leukocyte viability
  assessment 2474–2475
Trypanosoma, species 2420
Trypanosoma brucei
  platelet adherence 182–183
  see also Trypanosomes
Trypanosoma brucei brucei 2420
Trypanosoma brucei gambiense 2420
Trypanosoma brucei rhodesiense 2420
Trypanosoma congolense 2420
Trypanosoma cruzi 432
  acquired immunodeficiency in animal
    models 1268
  antigenic variation 525–526
  antigens 521–522
  characteristics 521–522, 521(Fig)
  cross-reactions 525
    with neuronal antigens 433
  evasive strategies 525–526, 1917, 1919
  host immune response, *see under* Chagas'
    disease
  invasion of host cells 521–522, 524(Fig)
    lysosome fusion 522, 524(Fig)
  life cycle 521, 523(Fig)
  morphology 522, 524(Fig)
  natural antibodies 1808
  outcome of infection by 522
  protective immunity by ISCOM-antigen
    complexes 1509
  see also Chagas' disease
Trypanosoma lewisi, IgM 1216
Trypanosoma vivax 2420
Trypanosomes
  antigenic variation 199–200, 525–526,
    2420, 2421–2422, 2421(Fig)
    vaccine design difficulties 2421–2422
  antigens 2420–2421
  characteristics 2420–2421
  evasive strategies 2420
  genes, differential expression 199–200
  host immune response, *see under*
    Trypanosomiasis, African
  minichromosomes 2421
  procyclin 2420
  serodemes 2421, 2422
  vaccine, difficulties 2421–2422
  variable antigen type (VAT) 2421
    bloodstream (B-VAT) 2423
    metacyclic (M-VAT) 2421, 2422,
      2422–2423
    repertoire 2421
    switching 2421
  variant surface glycoprotein (VSG) 199,
    2420
    gene expression 2421
    genes 199
    metacyclic (M-VSG) 2422
Trypanosomiasis, African 1917, 2420–
  2423
  cattle 2420, 2422
  causative organisms 2420
  chemoprophylaxis and control 2420
  hsp90 2231
  immune complex formation 2423
  immune depression 2422
  immune response 2421, 2422–2423

Trypanosomiasis, African (*continued*)
  immune response (*continued*)
    T_H1 2422
  lymphoid proliferative phase 2423
  neurological features 2423
  pathology 2422–2423
  prostaglandins and sleep pattern 2423
  remission 2421
  TNFα role 2439
  transmission 2420
  trypanotolerant cattle 2422
  see also Trypanosomes
Trypanosomiasis, American, *see* Chagas'
  disease
Trypanotolerance 2422
Tryptase 254, 334
  in mast cells 1668
Tryptophan
  in antigen-binding site 159
  deprivation of bacteria 318
T suppressor factors (TSF) 2245
  structure 2246
t-test 2212
Tuberculin 1794, 1795
Tuberculin reaction 738, 741, 1178, 1794
  mechanisms 740
Tuberculin shock 741
Tuberculosis 1794–1796
  agalactosyl IgG 1797
  antibodies 1794, 1795
  disseminated, vitamin D deficiency 2496
  granuloma 1024, 1025
  in HIV infection 1794
  in Hodgkin's disease 1883
  IgG glycosylation in 1004
  immunity to 1794–1795
    T_H1 pattern 1795
  immunopathology 1341, 1795–1796
    mechanism 1795–1796
  immunotherapy 1796
  lipoarabinomannan role 1795
  prevention, BCG vaccine 2084
  susceptibility 1794
  thalidomide treatment 1795
  TNFα role 1795, 1796
  see also Mycobacterium tuberculosis
Tubulointerstitial nephritis, BK virus
  causing 1990
Tuftsin 1887
Tularemia 956–957
  mortality 956
  see also Francisella tularensis
Tumor(s)
  adhesion molecules expression
    modulation 32
  age-related decrease in factors affecting
    60
  antiproliferative effect, desferrioxamine
    1506
  B7-1/B7-2 transfection 2444–2445
  carbohydrates as immune stimulants
    429–430
  chromosomal translocations causing, *see*
    Chromosomal translocations
  cytokine receptors 711
  development
    dietary fat role 885
    in nude mice 1868
    see also Carcinogenesis; Viral
      carcinogenesis
  germ-free animals use 990–991
  growth
    control by MCP-1 1750
    exercise effect in models 848
    histamine role 1104
    NK cells limiting 1814
    stress accelerating 2221
  Ig-secreting 1636–1637
    see also Multiple myeloma;
      Waldenström's macroglobulinemia
  IL-1 inhibition of 1434
  IL-3 role 1445

Tumor(s) (*continued*)
IL-6 role 1460, 1460(Table)
immune response, *see* Tumor immunity/immune response
immune surveillance, *see* Immune surveillance
immunogenicity 1229
  enhancement 974, 1364
  increased by hydrostatic pressure 1157
immunotherapy, transferrin receptor (TfR) as target 2390
M-CSF (CSF-1) and CSF-1 receptor 1654
metastases, *see* Metastases
MHC class I expression absence 1705
MHC downregulation 1360, 1361
nonimmunogenic 1229
opportunistic, in AIDS/HIV infection 7, 8
paraneoplastic cerebellar degeneration 1842
polyclonal hypergammaglobulinemia in 1162–1163, 1163(Table)
in primary immunodeficiency 1244
progression, antigen presentation failure 1362
proliferation inhibition by granzyme B 1029
regression, HPV vaccines 1908
resistance, immunocompromised animals role 1274
resistance to LAK cells 1348
response to calcitriol 2495
retroviruses causing 2097
  see also Human T lymphotropic virus type I (HTLV-I); Oncoviruses
serotonin-enhanced cytotoxicity 2166
spontaneous regression 1245, 1246
stem cell transplantation, *see* Stem cell transplantation
tumor antigen expression 2425, 2425(Table)
vaccination, *see under* Tumor immunotherapy
see also Cancer; Malignant disease; *specific tumors*
Tumor antigens 974, 1359, 1360–1362, 2424–2431, 2431–2432, 2441
antibodies to 1362
α-associated antigens 2431–2432
  humanized antibodies to 1142(Table)
  Lewis^x (Le^x) and sialyl-Le^x 1578
carbohydrate 2429, 2432
chemically-induced 1360
clinical aspects 2426–2427
differentiation antigens (TADA) 1362, 2425–2426, 2442
  loss 2444
embryonic 1361
expression, tumor types 2425, 2425(Table)
genes 2424(Table)
in gene therapy 1364
identification 2424
immune response to 2441–2442
immunization 2441
immunogenicity increase 974, 1364
immunotherapy target 2425, 2440–2441
inappropriate expression of proteins 1361
MHC antigens 1361–1362
modulation, tumor immunological escape 2444
normal cells expressing 2424–2425
presentation defect after UV light 1531
recognized by monoclonal antibodies 2427–2430, 2432
  carbohydrate 2429
  cell surface antigens 2428–2429
  clinical aspects 2430
  diagnostic/therapeutic use 2430
  differentiation antigens 2427–2428, 2428(Table)
  endothelial expression 2429–2430

Tumor antigens (*continued*)
  recognized by monoclonal antibodies (*continued*)
    glycolipids 2428–2429
    glycoproteins 2428
    growth factor receptors 2429
    stromal antigens 2429
  resulting from mutations 2426, 2427(Table)
  screening 2430
  shared antigens 2424–2425, 2424(Table)
  -specific antigens 207, 2431, 2440–2441, 2443–2444
    loss 2444
    proliferation-related 213
    transformation-related 213
    types 211, 213
  T cell recognition 2424–2427, 2424(Table)
  transplantation antigens (TSTA), *see* Tumor-specific transplantation antigens (TSTA)
  in tumor vaccines 2427
  types 2442
  vaccination trials 1343–1344
  viral antigens 2426
  virally-induced 1360
  see also Alphafetoprotein (AFP); Carcinoembryonic antigen (CEA); Cell surface antigens
Tumor cells
  cytokine gene transfer 977
  development, process 1244(Fig)
  killing
    cobra venom factor 588
    mitogenic lectin role 1538
  low expression of B7 977
  rejection, cytotoxicity role 732
  transfection 2441
Tumor imaging 2431–2435
  antibody structure 2432–2433
  applications 2434
  Fab fragments 2432–2433, 2432(Fig)
  micromagnetic beads 2434
  monoclonal antibodies 2431
  phage display library construction 2433
  polyclonal antisera 2431
  radionuclide technology 2433–2434
    radionuclides 2433(Table)
  single-chain Fv 2433
Tumor immunity/immune response 2440–2443
  antibodies 2441–2442
  concomitant tumor immunity 2445
  contrasuppressor cells role 650
  cytotoxic T cells 2444, 2445
  human neoplasms 2442–2443
  impaired, in iron deficiency 1506
  induction by IL-12 1487
  T cells 2441
  T$_H$1 and T$_H$2 cells 2441, 2445
  to tumor antigens 2441–2442
  see also Tumor immunotherapy
Tumor immunological escape 1284, 1360, 1364, 2443–2446
  antigenic modulation 2444
  'blocking factors' 2445
  costimulation absent 2444–2445
  Fas/FasL role 879
  loss of MHC class I antigens 2444
  loss of tumor-specific antigens 2444
  p15E and suppressive factors 2445
  'sneaking through' mechanism 2445
  'suppressor' cells 2445
  TGFβ-induced suppression 2445
  T$_H$2 in 2445
  see also Immune surveillance
Tumor immunology
  diagnostic relevance 1362
  history 1243, 2440–2441
Tumor immunotherapy 1245, 1345, 1359–1364, 1362

Tumor immunotherapy (*continued*)
  adoptive transfer of lymphocytes 2441, 2442
  antibody-radionuclide conjugates 2434
  antigens, *see* Tumor antigens
  anti-idiotype antibodies 1189
  bispecific antibodies 140, 1363
  gene therapy 1364
  IL-2 1362, 1438
  IL-11 1481
  immune response modifiers 1362
  immunomodulators 1345–1346
  Lewis^x (Le^x) and sialyl-Le^x 1578
  liposome application 1591
  monoclonal antibody application 1362–1363, 1747–1748
    chimeric Abs 1748
    reasons for lack of success 1747
  superantigen role 2242–2243
  targeting 2442
  thymic hormones and peptides 2301
  tumor antigen targets 2425, 2440–2441
  vaccines 1363, 1363(Table), 2441
    active enhancement 810
    antigens in 2427
    development 2442
    strategies 2442
    trials 1343–1344
Tumor-infiltrating lymphocytes (TILs) 1534
  culture 1574–1575
  expansion 1345, 1362
  tumor immunotherapy 1362, 1438
  immune surveillance theory 1245
    alternative explanation 1246
Tumor necrosis factor α convertase (TACE) 705, 715, 1638
Tumor necrosis factor α (TNFα) 2345, 2346, 2435–2440
  action on nervous and immune systems 1831(Table)
  ADCC modulation 170
  adenovirus protein inhibiting 22
  airway hyperresponsiveness 2439
   amebiasis 78
  antibodies
    autoimmune disease therapy 1358, 2438
    rheumatoid arthritis therapy 1344, 2112, 2438
  antitumor activity of mannans 430
  in Arthus reaction 239
  asthma 2439
  in autoimmune disease 2438
    therapy 1358, 2112, 2438
  babesiosis 310
  biochemistry 2436–2437
  biological actions/effects 2113, 2436(Table)
  blocking, by soluble receptors 718
  in cancer 2439
  caseation due to 1024
  cell-bound 2346, 2347, 2437
  cell-mediated lysis 510
  cells expressing 2436(Table)
  cerebral malaria 1662, 2439
  Chagas' disease, role 526(Table), 2439
  characteristics 2346
  coccidioidomycosis 590
  cytolysis mechanism in CTL 727
  diabetes mellitus 2438
    animal models 1396, 2438
  discovery 2435
  effect on endothelial cells 805, 2439
  effect on macrophage 1646
  egg granuloma formation in schistosomiasis 2141
  elevated levels 2437–2438, 2439
    inflammatory bowel disease 1379
  embryonic development 2437
  as endogenous pyrogen 902
  eosinophil regulation 824(Table)

Tumor necrosis factor α (TNFα)
(*continued*)
exercise effect 846
experimental autoimmune thyroiditis
2312
extranodal development of high
endothelial venules 1100
at fetomaternal interface 900
filoviral hemorrhagic fever 918
functions 504, 2113
gene 1117(Table), 1119, 2436, 2437(Fig)
polymorphisms 2436
promoter 2436
sequence 2438(Fig)
transcription factors binding 2436
in GVHD 1016, 2439
in HIV infection and AIDS 2439
HLA class I expression modulation 1109
IFNγ cooperative action 1424
IFNγ production regulation 1423
upregulation 2113
immunoregulation, TNF receptor
CD120b role 2347
inducers 2435(Table)
LFA-3 role 1614
in infectious diseases 2438–2439
inflammatory actions 1378
inhibitors 705, 2349
LCMV infection 233
Legionella pneumophila infection 1544
lethal shock due to 808
Listeria monocytogenes infection 1594
lymphotoxin relationship 1638
macrophage activation, *Toxoplasma*
infections 2383
metalloproteinase inhibitor action 2437
β$_2$-microglobulin expression induced 368
multiple sclerosis pathogenesis 1840–
1841
murine, biochemistry 2437
myelin destruction 1840
ovulation induction 2437
paracrine effects, TNF receptor CD120b
role 2347
receptor 720
release
CD14 role 187
estradiol/progesterone effect 2437
by LAK cells 1628
rheumatoid arthritis 2113, 2438
in SCID mice 1269
sepsis/septicemic shock 319, 2163, 2438–
2439
Shwartzman reaction 319
signal transduction pathway 2032
soluble 2346
structure 2437
suppressors 2435(Table)
synonyms 2435, 2435(Table)
synovial fluid 2437–2438
synthesis 2345
astrocytes and microglial cells 1831
high-density/low-density lipoproteins
effect 2439
IL-12 effect 1486
increased by NSAIDs 2027
leishmaniasis 1548
LTB$_4$ inducing 231
malaria 1920
synthesis inhibition
by IL-13 1490
inhibitors 705, 2349
by PGE$_2$ 2026
by thymic hormones 2302
TNF1 and TNF2 2436
Tnf cluster, mice 1047
TNF receptor binding 2346
Toxoplasma gondii infections 1920
transcription 2436
transmembrane/membrane-bound 2346,
2347, 2437
transplantation 2439

Tumor necrosis factor α (TNFα)
(*continued*)
tropical diseases 2439
tuberculosis 1794, 1795, 1796
UV-induced changes 1944
viral infections 2481
viroceptors 2349
see also Leukemia inhibitory factor (LIF)
Tumor necrosis factor α (TNFα) receptor
1638, 1640
p55, recombinant 706
soluble (sTNFR) 2438, 2439
function 715
TNFRI and TNFRII 1638
see also Tumor necrosis factor receptor
(TNFR)
Tumor necrosis factor β, *see* Lymphotoxin,
LTα
Tumor necrosis factor (TNF) family 2148
CD40L 484, 653, 2148
cell fate influenced by 653–655
cellular cooperation 652
FasL 570, 875
genetic map 1640(Fig)
role in clonal deletion 570–571
signaling mechanism 1640–1641
T cell activation second signals 2148–
2149
Tumor necrosis factor receptor (TNFR)
2345–2349
binding properties 2346
CD120a (type I) 454(Table), 1638, 2346
functions 2346
knockout mice 2346
CD120b (type II) 454(Table), 713, 1638,
2346, 2347
binding to cell-bound TNFα 2346,
2347
expression 2347
death domains 2346, 2347, 2348(Fig)
expression 2346
functions 2346–2347
in vivo 718
fusion proteins, autoimmune disease
therapy 1359
ligand interactions 2345(Fig), 2346
location 2346
signaling mechanisms 2347–2348,
2348(Fig)
adapter proteins 2347
soluble, therapeutic use 2348–2349
structure 2346
viroceptors relationship 2349
see also Tumor necrosis factor α (TNFα)
receptor
Tumor necrosis factor receptor (TNFR)
associated factor, *see* TRAF
Tumor necrosis factor receptor (TNFR)
family 709–710, 709(Table), 720
activation mechanism 711
CD40 484, 653
cell fate influenced by 653–655
cellular cooperation 652
Fas 570, 875
lymphotoxin 1638
signal transduction 484, 1641
structures 519–520, 519(Fig), 720
T cell activation second signals 2148–
2149
see also Lymphotoxin; Tumor necrosis
factor α (TNFα)
Tumor necrosis factor receptor-related
protein 1638
Tumor-specific antigens, *see under* Tumor
antigens
Tumor-specific transplantation antigens
(TSTA) 1360, 2440–2441, 2443–2444
loss 2444
Tumor suppressor genes 1361
inactivation 1565
see also p53
Tumor vaccines, *see under* Tumor
immunotherapy

tum⁻ antigens 208
Tunicamycin, *Trypanosoma cruzi* invasion
prevention 521
Turbidimetry, nephelometry differences
1822
Turtles, thymus development 2077(Fig)
Typhoid fever 2131, 2132
vaccines 2132, 2133
Typhus 2126
Tyramine, false food allergy 952(Table)
Tyrosinase peptides, differentiation
antigens 2425
Tyrosine, antigen-binding site 159
Tyrosine-directed protein kinases (PTKs)
31, 2028, 2030–2031
activation 710
CD40 ligation 484
in B cell activation 349
CD2 interaction 464
Igα/Igβ coupling of B cell receptor to
1194
in IL-2 receptor signal transduction 1440
in IL-3 receptor signal transduction
1447–1448
JAK, *see* JAK tyrosine kinases
in mast cell degranulation 1670
nonreceptor-linked 2030–2031
classes 2031
see also Janus tyrosine kinase family;
Src tyrosine kinases; Syk tyrosine
kinase
p72^{syk} 356
phosphorylation 710
see Tyrosine phosphorylation
receptor-linked 2030
activation 2030
invertebrates 1500
receptors containing 710
SH2 domains 710
signaling mechanism 710, 710–711,
711(Fig), 1299–1301
src family 710
in T cell activation 2324
TCR-associated 2324
see also JAK tyrosine kinases; Protein
kinase(s); Signal transduction; *other
specific kinases*
Tyrosine kinase, *see* Tyrosine-directed
protein kinases (PTKs)
Tyrosine phosphatase CD45, *see* CD45
Tyrosine phosphatase IA2 autoantibodies
1401
animal models of IDDM 1393
Tyrosine phosphatase SHP-1, *see* SHP-1
Tyrosine phosphoproteins, T cell 2326
Tyrosine phosphorylation 700, 710
B cell activation 349
CD22 480
see also Tyrosine-directed protein kinases
(PTKs)

U

U1-RNP, antibodies 131
U2-RNP, antibodies 131
U937 cells, FcγR functions 890
Ubiquicidin, macrophage 1742
Ubiquitin 192, 2229(Table)
abnormal protein degradation 2230
antigen presentation 2232
functions 2230
UCD strain, *see* University of California at
Davis (UCD) 200 strain
Ulcerative colitis 1375
exacerbation by NSAIDs 2027
IgG secretion 1378
see also Inflammatory bowel disease
(IBD)
Ulex europaeus 1541
Ultracentrifugation 2446–2448

Ultracentrifugation (*continued*)
  applications 2447–2448
  density gradient 2447
  historical aspects 2446–2447
  immune complexes 2447–2448
  isopyknic 2447, 2448
  rate zonal 2447, 2448
  see also Centrifugation
Ultracentrifuges 2447
  developments 2448
Ultrafiltration, lymph formation 1597
Ultrasonic standing wave, agglutination
    testing 58
Ultraviolet light 1942
  abnormal Langerhans cells 1531
  autoantigen expression 2187, 2187(Fig)
  autoimmune disease pathogenesis 289
  B7 and B7 downregulation 1943
  carcinogenesis 1943
  CD36⁺ cells after 1531
  delayed/contact hypersensitivity changes
    1944
  DNA damage 1944–1945
  extracellular matrix composition 907
  immune response alterations 1943–1944,
    1945
    cytokines 1944
    mechanisms 1943–1944
    T$_H$1 activation change 1943
    T$_H$1 shift to T$_H$2 1944
  immunosuppression due to 1945
  Langerhans cell changes 1943, 2191
  Langerhans cell depletion 1531
  molecular targets in skin 1944–1945
  photoreceptors 1945
  selective cell depletion method 510
  skin cancers induced 1942, 1943, 1945
  tumor antigen presentation defect 1531
  UVA 1942
  UVB 1942, 1943
    cutaneous lupus erythematosus 2187
    suppressor T cell induction 1943
  UVC 1942
Umbilical cord blood, *see* Cord blood
Undernutrition 1869
Undifferentiated connective tissue disease
    (UCTD) 2118
Ungulate immune system 2449–2451
  cellular components 2449
  IgA delivery to gut by bile 2450
  immunoglobulins 2449, 2449–2450,
    2449(Table)
    transfer in milk 2450
  lymphoid tissue 2449
  ontogeny 2450
  passive transfer of immunity 2450–2451,
    2451(Table)
  T cells 2449
  see also Porcine immune system
University of California at Davis (UCD)
    200 strain 283–285
  autoantibodies 284–285
  collagen metabolism changes 284
  endothelial cell apoptosis 285
  mononuclear and T cell infiltrates 284
  pathogenesis 285
  phenotypic changes 284
Unresponsiveness, *see* Tolerance
Ureaplasma 1798–1802
Ureaplasma infections 1799–1801
  arthritis 1800–1801
  urogenital 1800
Ureaplasma urealyticum
  phase variation 1799
  prevalence 1800
  urogenital infection 1800
  virulence factor 1799
Urease, *Proteus mirabilis* 2039, 2040
Urethral infections, *Escherichia coli* 2075
Urethral syndrome, acute 2066
Urethritis 2067
  Chlamydia trachomatis causing 2072

Urethritis (*continued*)
  Mycoplasma genitalium causing 1800
  Mycoplasma hominis causing 1800
  non-specific 2067
Uridine monophosphate synthase deficiency
    1286
Urinary tract, defense mechanisms 2453
Urinary tract infections (UTI) 2065, 2452–
    2454
  acute inflammatory response 2453
  adenovirus 21
  ascending 2065, 2452
  bacterial 2452
  colonization process 2452
  defective clearing of bacteria 2454
  epidemiology 2065, 2452
  Escherichia coli 2065–2066, 2452,
    2452–2453
    see also Escherichia coli, uropathogenic
  etiology/pathogenesis 2065–2066
  frequency 2452
  host defense mechanisms 2066, 2453
  host resistance 2453–2454
  IL-8 and IL-6 actions 2453
  in immunodeficiency states 2454
  neutrophil influx 2453
  pathogenesis 2452–2453, 2453(Fig)
  predisposing factors 2066(Table)
  Proteus mirabilis 2039–2040, 2040(Fig)
  Staphylococcus saprophyticus 2210
  see also Cystitis
Urine 2065
  defense mechanism 2453
  neutrophils 2453
U-RNAs 126
Urocanic acid 1945
  as photoreceptors 1945
Urochordates 1947
Urodeles, *see* Axolotl
Uroepithelial cell, adhesin 2041
Urokinase plasminogen activator receptor
    (uPAR) 28(Table), 29, 31
Uromodulin 706
Uropod 533
Urosepsis 2453
Ursodeoxycholic acid (UDCA) 2003
Urticaria 678–684
  acute 678, 678(Fig), 679(Table)
  aquagenic 684
  C1 component, crossed
    immunoelectrophoresis 1293,
    1293(Fig)
  causes 679, 679(Table)
  cholinergic 683
  chronic 678, 678–679, 679(Table)
  chronic idiopathic 681–682
  classification 678, 679(Table)
  clinical features 678, 678(Fig), 679(Fig)
  cold 683
    delayed 683
    familial 683
    idiopathic 683
    primary acquired 683
    secondary 683
  contact 680–681
    causes 681
    food-related 681
    immunologic 680–681
    latex causing 681
    nonimmunologic 681
  delayed pressure 682–683
  foods inducing 949
  insect bites and stings 680
  management 679
  physical 682–684
  prevalence 678
  solar 684
Urticarial vasculitis 679, 682
U-snRNPs 126, 127(Table)
  antibodies 131
Uta 1547
Uty gene 1160

Uveitic diseases 867
  autoimmune 867
Uveitis
  anterior, molecular mimicry 869
  histopathology 868, 870(Fig)
  lens-induced 867
  T cells role 869
  treatment, S-antigen administration 1897,
    1898

V

Vaccination 15, 1147, 1343–1344
  as active specific immunopotentiation
    1343–1344
  adjuvants, *see* Adjuvants
  administration routes 219, 2454–2456
    DNA vaccines 2454
    mucosal 2455, 2455(Table)
    nasal 1779
    ocular 2455
    oral 2455
    parenteral 2454–2455
    rectal 2455
    vaginal 2455
  against recurrent miscarriage 1344
  aim 1682
  antigen formulation 2455
  benefits 1627
  discovery 14, 1997, 2284
  historical aspects 1335, 1336, 2456–
    2457, 2462, 2462–2463
  immunopotentiation 2455–2456
  livestock 2462
  origin of term 1336
  vehicle 2455
  see also Immunization
Vaccines 2456–2462
  adjuvants, *see* Adjuvants
  adverse reactions 2462–2465, 2483
    childhood vaccines 2464
    chimeric virus vectors 2464,
      2464(Table)
    groups at risk 2464–2465
    Haemophilus influenzae type b (Hib)
      2464
    influenza vaccine 2463
    pertussis 2463
    RSV candidate vaccines 2463
    smallpox 2464(Table)
  against insect vectors 2458
  antigen preparations 206
  anti-idiotype preparations 2460
  attenuated organisms 255–259
  avian viral infections 304
  bacterial 2457–2458, 2458(Table)
    subunit 2458
  Biken 931
  birth control, *see* Contraception,
    immunological
  cancer, *see* Tumor immunotherapy,
    vaccines
  candidate 2463
  chimeric vectors 2460, 2461
    adverse reactions 2464, 2464(Table)
  chronic diseases 2459
  clinical trials, stages 2463
  cold storage/transport 37
  conjugate 426
  CTL generation 771
  current/under trial 2457–2458
  development
    factors favouring 2461(Table)
    factors preventing 2461(Table)
    gastrointestinal tract infections 969
    new approaches 2460
  disease eradication, factors favouring
    2461(Table)
  DNA, *see* DNA vaccines

Vaccines (*continued*)
  DNA (genetic) immunization 2460, 2461
  efficacy 2459
    in vitro studies 1233
  fertility-control 2458–2459
    see also Human chorionic
      gonadotropin (hCG)
  future prospects 2461, 2462(Table)
  genetically engineered, bacterial 258
  historical aspects 255–256, 2456–2457
  idiotype mimicry use 1189
  immune response 2459
  immunological requirements/expectations
    2459–2460
  ISCOM 1508
    storage 1509
  killed 255
  live 255
    history 255–257
    rational design 258
    reversion to virulence 257, 258
  live *vs* killed 258–259
  mucosal, reovirus infection 2070
  'negative' in autoimmune disease 291
  new, diseases targeted for 2461,
    2462(Table)
  oral 1892
    common mucosal immune system 1779
    GALT 1893
  origin of name 256
  parasitic infections 1921, 2460
  peptide-based preparations 2460
  plants as future sources 2460, 2461
  polysaccharide, failure in infants 1285
  poxviruses as vectors 1998
  preparation, aluminium compounds as
    adjuvants 37
  Q fever 2458
  recombinant 2460, 2464
    fish vaccination 925
    Taenia 693, 693(Table)
  recombinant *Listeria monocytogenes* as
    vector 1595
  romurtide application 1792
  safety 2459
  synthetic, immunodominant B cell
    epitopes 1292
  synthetic peptides 437
  toxicity testing 2462
  tumor 2427
  viral 2457, 2457(Table), 2479
    attenuation process 2457
    disease eradication 2457
    inactivated 2457, 2457(Table)
    live attenuated 2457, 2457(Table)
    subunits 2457, 2457(Table)
  see also specific vaccines
Vaccinia, progressive 1998
Vaccinia virus 1997
  as adjuvant 38
  diseases controlled 1998
  origins 1997
  recombinant, DNA transfer 982
  sequence homology with IL-1 receptor
    1432
  vaccination 1996
    complications 1998
    as vaccine vector 2461
    adverse reactions 2464, 2464(Table)
  see also Poxviruses
Vaccinology 2457
Vaginal administration, vaccines 2455
Vaginosis, bacterial 1800
Valency 2465–2467
  antibodies 2465, 2467
  antigens 163, 216, 2465, 2466–2467
  definition 2465
  immunoglobulins 163
Valium 250
VAMPS (Vesicle-Associated Membrane
    Proteins) 852(Table)

van der Waals forces 159, 163, 163–164,
    172, 2200
  types and phenomena contributing to
    163
van der Waals–London interaction 163
VAP-1 28(Table), 29
Variability plot 151, 151(Fig)
Variance, analysis (ANOVA) 2212
Varicella (chickenpox) 2468
  antibodies 2468
    bone marrow transplant recipients 1884
  'breakthrough' after vaccine 2470
  clinical features 2468
  immune response 2468–2469
  pathogenesis 2469(Fig)
Varicella-zoster virus (VZV) 2468–2470
  antibodies 2469
    natural IgG 1808
  characteristics 2468
  diseases due to 2468
  genome 2468, 2468(Fig)
  glycoproteins 2468, 2469
  Guillain–Barré syndrome after 1836
  host immune response 2468–2469
    after reactivation 2469
  IE62 regulatory protein 2469
  immune globulin (VZIG) 2469
  persistent infection 2485
  reactivation 2469, 2485
    after stem cell transplantation 1067
  transfer factor therapy 2388
  vaccines 2469–2470
    'breakthrough chickenpox' 2470
    Oka strain 2469–2470
Variolation 255, 258, 1681, 2456, 2462
Vascular addressins, *see* Addressins
Vascular endothelial cell cadherin (VE-
    Cadherin; CD144) 456(Table)
Vascular endothelial growth factor
    receptor (VEGFR), in tumors 2429
Vascular leakage, in inflammation 17
Vascular permeability, increased
  Arthus reaction 237, 238
  inflammation 17
  by prostaglandins 2025, 2026
  serum sickness 2169
Vasculitis 1341
  ANCA antibodies 2120
  in lupus erythematosus 2187
  urticarial 679, 682
Vasoactive amines
  histamine, *see* Histamine
  release, type III hypersensitivity 1176
Vasoactive intestinal peptide (VIP) 1785,
    1826–1827
  effect on immune system 1826–1827,
    1827(Fig)
  integrin expression 1827
  monocyte chemotaxis 1785
  in nasal mucosa 2125
  secretion 1826
Vasoconstriction, local 579
Vasodilatation
  contact hypersensitivity 639
  histamine effect 1102
Vasopressin, glucocorticoids secretion 997
Vav 2327
  IL-3 receptor signal transduction 1448
  mast cell degranulation 1670
  T cell signaling 2324, 2327
vav gene 1301
VCAM-1 (CD106) 27(Table), 28,
    453(Table), 804
  binding to VLA-4 804
  contact hypersensitivity 639
  diapedesis of leukocytes 759, 2060
  on endothelial cells 804
  eosinophil migration 821
  gene 804
  induction, by IL-13 1490
  receptor for picornaviruses 1955
  rheumatoid arthritis 2114

VCAM-1 (CD106) (*continued*)
  structure 519
VDJ recombination, *see under*
    Immunoglobulin gene rearrangements
Vectors
  adenoviruses as 24–25
  bacteriophage as 2406
  chimeric for vaccines, *see under* Vaccines
  for DNA transfer 974
  gene therapy 24–25, 974, 975(Fig)
  immune reactivity against 979–980
  phage display of antibodies 1931
  phagemid 1931, 1932(Fig)
  recombinant allergen production 68
  retroviral, *see* Retroviral vectors
  transgenic mice production 2406
  for vaccines, *see* Vaccines
Veiled cells 188, 189(Fig), 746, 1601(Fig)
  in lymph nodes 1604
  in peripheral lymph 1599
  see also Dendritic cells; Langerhans cells
Velocardiofacial (VCF) syndrome 762
Velocity sedimentation 508
Veneered antibodies 1143
Venereal Disease Research Laboratory
    (VDRL) 2073, 2417
Venezuelan equine encephalitis virus 2351
Venom 2470–2474
  allergens 67(Table)
  amphibians 2472–2473
  arachnids 2472
  historical background 2470–2471
  insect, *see* Insect venom
  marine animals 2473
  reptiles 2472–2473
  see also Snake venom
Veno-occlusive disease 1067
Verruca vulgaris 751
Versican 864
Vertebrates
  blood cell origins 1948
  Ig evolution, *see* Immunoglobulin,
    evolution
  immunity, phylogeny 1948
  MHC evolution 1700–1702
  poikilothermic 904
Very late activation proteins, *see* VLA
Very low-density lipoproteins, HCV
    association 1081
Vesicles
  coat proteins 852(Table)
  exocytosis 849, 851, 853, 854(Fig)
  giant, in Chédiak-Higashi syndrome 526,
    527
  translocation 849, 851, 853
Vesicular exanthema of swine virus 399,
    400
Vesicular stomatitis virus (VSV) 1037(Fig),
    2098
  B cell infection and activation 2485
  genetic rearrangements 258
  glycoprotein, pseudotyped vectors 2091
Vesiculovirus 893, 2098
Veto cells 2473–2474
  evidence for 2474
  functions/actions 2474
v-*fms* gene 1564, 1654
Viability of leukocytes, *see* Leukocyte(s),
    viability
Vibrio cholerae 2476–2479
  adherence and colonization 2478
  antigens 2476–2477
  characteristics 2476–2477
  environmental O1 strain 2479
  flagellum 2476, 2476(Fig), 2478
  host immune response 2478
  infection prevention by breast milk Igs
    1672
  lipopolysaccharide 2478
  morphology 2476(Fig)
  neuraminidase 2478
  non-O1 (non-cholera vibrios) 2476

Vibrio cholerae (*continued*)
  O1 serotypes 2476
    classical biotype 2476–2477
    El Tor biotype 2476–2477, 2478, 2479
    Inaba and Ogawa serotypes 2477
  O139 (Bengal) serotype 2476, 2477, 2478
  O serogroups 2476, 2477
  protective antigens 2478
  toxin-coregulated pilus (TCP) 2477
  toxins 2477–2478
    ACE (accessory cholera enterotoxin) 2372, 2477
    cholera toxin (CT), *see* Cholera toxin (CT)
    El Tor hemolysin 2477–2478
    ZOT (zonula occludens) 2372–2373, 2477
  vaccines 2478–2479
    attenuated strains 2478–2479
    chimeric 2479
    CVD103Hg^R 2479
    subunit 2478
  virulence factors 968
  see also Cholera
Vicia graminea 1541
Vicia villosa lectin 649, 650
Vincent's angina 963
Vincristine 1976
Viral carcinogenesis 1563, 2487
  evidence against immune surveillance theory 295
  leukemia pathogenesis 1564–1565
  mechanisms 1563–1564, 2487
    growth factor overexpression 1564
    HTLV-1 tax gene 1565
    overexpression of v-*onc* gene 1563
    proto-oncogene capture in retrovirus 1563–1564
    viral protein and c-*onc* cooperation 1564
    viral protein as mitogen 1564
    v-*onc* gene combinations 1564
  multistep mechanism 2074
  transactivation by viral gene product 1564–1565
  see also Human papillomaviruses (HPV); Human T lymphotropic virus type I (HTLV-I); Oncoviruses
Viral hemorrhagic septicemia, protection 2100
Viral infections
  CNS, immune response 1845–1846
  C-reactive protein (CRP) levels 663
  delayed-type hypersensitivity 2482
  diagnosis, agglutination 58
  evolutionary pressures 1951
  eye 871–872
  gastrointestinal tract 968
  in utero 2483
  isoprinosine action 1347
  latency 1845
  latent 2482
  lytic 2482
  NK cells role 1813–1814
  persistent 2482, 2482–2483, 2485
  tumor antigens induced by 1360
  see also individual infections; Viruses
Viral vectors, *see* Viruses, vectors
Virchow cells 1023
Virchow–Robin spaces 1844, 1844(Fig)
  inflammation within 1845(Fig)
Virino 2409
Viroceptors 714
  in vivo functions 718
Virokines 1997
Virotyping 842
  Escherichia coli 842–844
Virulence 2457
Viruses 2479
  agglutination by antibody 2481
  antigenic variation 2482

Viruses (*continued*)
  antigen presentation inhibition 193
  as antigens 206, 2480
  antigens
    bispecific antibodies 139, 140
    as tumor antigens 2426
  apoptosis induction 2485
  attenuated vaccines 256(Table)
  autoimmune disease association 2483
    experimental 272
  carcinogenesis, *see* Viral carcinogenesis
  complement-mediated lysis 1318
  cytokine release induced 2482
  enveloped 2480
  evasive strategies 2482–2483, 2483(Table)
  genome integration into host 2485
  glycoproteins 425–426
  IDDM-induction 1400
    animal models 1396–1399
  IFNα and IFNβ role 2481
  immune response 2480–2482
    ADCC 2481, 2486
    CD4$^+$ T cells 2482
    complement 2481
    CTLs 2481–2482
    humoral 2480, 2481
    phases 2480(Table)
    viral molecules modulating 2483(Table)
  immunity to 2479–2484
    nonspecific 2480–2481
  immunocompetent cell infection 2483
  immunopathology 2483
  inactivation, in blood products 1968
  infection of immune cells 2484–2487
    dendritic cells 2486
    granulocytes 2486
    Langerhans cells 2486
    macrophage 2486
    monocytes 2486
    NK cells 2485–2486
    nonpermissive/permissive state 2485
    resting lymphocytes 2484–2485
    T and B cells 2484–2485
  infection process 2480, 2484
  interferon activities, *see specific* Interferons
  lymphocyte proliferation due to 2021–2022, 2022(Table)
  multiple sclerosis etiology 1788
  neutralization, by IgG 1318
  non-neutralizing antibodies 2482, 2483
  opsonization 2481
  passage in cell culture 256
  pathogenicity, cytokine receptors role 712
  proteins 2480
  replication 2480, 2485
  rheumatoid arthritis etiology 2114
  role in obese strain of chickens 282
  secondary immunodeficiency due to 1285–1286
  structure 2480
  transformation by 2487
  transmission in blood products 1967, 1968
  tropism 2484
  vaccines, *see under* Vaccines
  vectors 2084
    for gene transfer 974
    retroviruses, *see* Retroviral vectors
    see also Vectors
  see also Oncoviruses; Viral carcinogenesis; Viral infections
Virus-inducible element (VRE) 1414
Visceral larva migrans 2379
Visna virus, antigenic variation 200
Vitali criteria 2182
'Vitalism' 1336
Vitamin A 2488–2489
  acquired immunity 2489
  deficiency 872, 1870, 2488

Vitamin A (*continued*)
  deficiency (*continued*)
    antibody response impaired 2489
    cytokines 2489
    infections associated 2488
    infections predisposing to 2488
    mucosal surface defects 189
    phagocytosis defect 2489
  as immune enhancer 2489
  innate immunity and 2488–2489
  metabolism 2488
  sources 2488
  supplementation 1284, 2489
  transport 2488
Vitamin B$_6$ 2490–2491
  deficiency 1870, 2490
Vitamin B$_{12}$ 2490
  binding to intrinsic factor 102
    inhibition 101
  deficiency 101, 1284, 2490
  malabsorption 102, 105
Vitamin B group 2490, 2490–2491, 2491
Vitamin C 134, 2491–2494
  action via maintenance of vitamin E 2493
  antibody synthesis 2492
  antimicrobial/antiviral effects 2492
  as antioxidant 134, 2491, 2493
  complement levels 2492
  concentrations (plasma/leukocyte) 2491, 2492
  deficiency 134
  delayed-type hypersensitivity 2492
  effect on rhinovirus (colds) 2492
  lymphocyte proliferation 2492
  mechanism of action 2493
  neutrophil function 2492
  nonspecific immune functions 2491–2492
  requirement, smokers 135
  specific immune functions 2492
Vitamin D 2494–2499
  analogs 2496
  deficiency 2496
  receptors 2494
  see also Calcitriol
Vitamin D-binding protein
  conversion to MAF 2498, 2498(Fig)
  D$_3$-binding protein (DBP; Gc protein), *see* Gc protein
  as macrophage-activating factor precursor 2497
  role 2497–2499
  signal transduction 2497–2498
  see also GcMAF; Gc protein
Vitamin E 134, 2500–2501
  as antioxidant 134, 2500, 2501
  ataxia telangiectasia (AT) 250
  cytokine production regulation 2500
  delayed-type hypersensitivity enhancement 135
  effect on immune response 2500
  in HIV infection 2501
  immunoenhancement prevention 2500
  scavenging action 2493
  sources 2500
  supplementation 2500, 2500–2501
    elderly 135
    rheumatoid arthritis 135
    smokers 136
  vitamin C action via 2493
Vitiligo 2425, 2501–2503
  animal model 2502
  autoantibodies 2502
  autocytotoxic hypothesis 2502
  autoimmune features 2502–2503
  autoimmune hypothesis 2502
  characteristics 2501–2502
  neural hypothesis 2502
  pathological mechanisms 2502
  types 2502
Vitronectin
  phagocytosis enhancement 1887

Vitronectin (*continued*)
 receptor (CD51) 450(Table)
 RGD sequence 1887
 Staphylococcus binding 2210
VLA (very late antigen) 26, 1407–1408
 characteristics 1405(Table)
VLA-1, α chain 449(Table)
VLA-2 1407
 α chain 449(Table)
VLA-3, α chain 449(Table)
VLA-4 449(Table), 1407, 2146
 in Arthus reaction 238
 eosinophil migration 821, 823
 expression and function 1407–1408
 monocyte adhesion 1754
 T cell activation 2146
 VCAM-1 binding 804
VLA-5 449(Table), 1407, 1408
VLA-6 449(Table), 1408
Vogt–Koyanagi–Harada syndrome, ocular
 involvement 867
Voltage-gated calcium channels (VGCC),
 antibodies 1835, 1849–1850
Voltage-gated potassium channels (VGKC),
 antibodies 1850
Volume expanders, synthetic 1965
von Basedow's disease, *see* Graves' disease
v-*onc* gene 1563
 overexpression 1563
von Willebrand factor (vWF) 579, 1973–
 1974
 C2 homology 607
 in cryoprecipitate 1966
 multimers 1973
 role 579
 vWF-A domain 607

W

W3129 myeloma protein 150
WA-1, babesiosis due to 309
Waaler–Rose test 265
WAG sublines 2058
Waldenström's macroglobulinemia 366,
 1165, 1216, 1636
 Bence Jones protein 341
 therapy, plasmapheresis 1970
Waldeyer's ring 190, 1601, 1774
Warm antibody-induced hemolytic anemia,
 see Autoimmune hemolytic anemia
Warts 751, 2074
 causative virus 1907
Wasp, venom 2471
WASP gene 1270–1271
 mutations 217
WASP protein 978, 1270–1271, 1281
 see also Wiskott-Aldrich syndrome
 (WAS)
'Wasted mice', radiosensitivity association
 2053
'Wasted' (*wst*) mutation 1272
Wasting disease, sheep 2096
Water contamination
 Cryptosporidium 676
 hepatitis E transmission 1082
 Legionella pneumophila 1542
 Leptospira transmission 1552
WD40 repeats, beige mouse gene 528
Weakness, diseases with 1837
 Lambert–Eaton syndrome 1849
 myasthenia gravis 1847
Wegener's granulomatosis 2120
 autoantibodies 2120
 CAMPATH-1 antibody therapy 405(Fig)
 clinical features 2120
 radiosensitivity association 2053
WEHI-3B cells 1442, 1445
Weibel–Palade bodies 804, 2158
 P-selectin storage 2159

Weil–Felix agglutination test 2126
Western blotting 142, 2503–2507
 affinity purification of antibodies 2506
 antigenicity of blotted proteins 2506
 autoantibody detection 261
 components used 2505(Table)
  antibodies 2505, 2506
  membranes 2505
 development 2503
 immunization 2507
 ligand blotting 2506
 nocardiosis diagnosis 1862
 pathogen fingerprinting 2506
 procedural steps 2503–2506, 2504(Fig)
  antibody incubation 2505
  blocking of residual binding 2505
  detection of bound antibody 2505–
   2506
  electrophoretic separation 2504
  transfer to membrane 2504–2505,
   2504(Fig)
  visualization of total protein pattern
   2505
 protein antigens characterization 2504
 protein sequencing 2506
 quantification 2506
 special techniques 2506–2507
Wheal 254
Wheal and flare reaction 678
 drug allergy 782
 foods inducing 949
 IgE role 1202
 localized in contact urticaria 680–681
 prick testing 680
 protein A 325
Wheezing 245
WHHL rabbit 2046
White blood cells, *see* Leukocyte(s)
White Leghorn chickens 281(Fig), 300
Whitlock–Witte culture system 1901, 2236
 IL-7 identification 1462
Whole-body irradiation 2052
 bone marrow transplantation 2052
Whooping cough, *see* Pertussis
Wiseana iridescent virus (WIV) 1502,
 1503(Fig), 1504(Fig)
Wiskott-Aldrich syndrome (WAS) 73, 217,
 1281
 management, gene therapy 978,
  979(Table)
 tumor development 1244
Wiskott–Aldrich syndrome protein
 (WASP), *see* WASP protein
Wistar rat 2055
Witebsky's criteria, autoimmune disease
 1847
W locus 1272
World Health Organization (WHO)
 allotype nomenclature 74
 BCG recommendations 335
 disease eradication by vaccines 2457
 Expanded Program for Immunization
  (EPI) 2458
 schistosomiasis vaccine 2142
 vaccine development 1921
Wound healing
 fibroblasts role 908
 fibronectin action 913
 TGFβ function 2397
 zinc role 2516
wst mutation 1272
Wuchereria bancrofti 913
 antigen 914

X

X2 box 1043
XA gene 1115, 1116(Table)
X box 1042

XB (TN-X) gene 1115, 1116(Table)
X chromosome, homologs for Smcy and
 Uty 1160
Xenoantigens 2415
Xenogeneic antibody
 preparation 1345
 therapy 1345
Xenogeneic diversity 208
Xenopus laevis 79
 B cells 81–82
 immunoglobulin genes 81
 lymphocyte antigen-specific receptors 80–
  81
 lymphocytes 80
 lymphoid organ development 80
 major histocompatibility system 81
 MAR1 lymphoid tumor 82
 metamorphosis 82
 ontogeny of immune response 82
 T cells 81–82
 TCR β chain genes 80–81
 tumors 82–83
Xenopus lymphoid cell lines 83
Xenotransplantation 500, 2415, 2508–
 2512
 'bridge' 2508
 CD59 gene 500
 cell-mediated response 2510
 clinical history 2508
 cobra venom factor (CVF) application
  588
 complement activation 2509
 concordant 2508, 2509
 definition 2508
 discordant 2508
 disease transmission 2511
 donor species 2508–2509
 endothelial damage 2509
 humoral response 2509
 immunologic barriers 2509
 infection transmission 2415
 limitations 2511
 physiologic incompatibilities 2511
 prolonged survival of grafts 2510–2311
  accommodation 2510
  donor animal modifications 2511
  immune suppression 2510
  tolerance induction 2511
 rejection 2509–2510
  acute vascular (delayed) 2509–2510
  cell-mediated 2510
  chronic 2510
  hyperacute 2509, 2510
 transgenic technology 2407
 xenozoonoses 2511
Xenozoonoses 2511
Xeroderma pigmentosum (XP) 1282
xid locus 1270
 mutation 366, 388, 1270
xid mice 216
X-linked agammaglobulinemia (XLA) 216,
 1279–1280
 see also Bruton's agammaglobulinemia
X-linked hyper-IgM syndrome, *see* Hyper-
 IgM syndrome
X-linked immunodeficiency 366
 with hyper-IgM 147, 366, 1166, 1280
 murine models 1270–1271
X-linked lymphoproliferative syndrome
 (XLPS; Duncan's syndrome) 832,
 1280–1281
 tumor development 1244–1245
X-linked SCID, *see under* Severe combined
 immunodeficiency (SCID)
XLR (X-linked lymphocyte-regulated)
 locus 1270
X-ray crystallography
 alloantigens 74
 antibody combining sites 152
 idiotype structures 1185

Y

Yaa gene 2253
YA gene 116(Table), 1115
YAMA-1 (CPP32) 1028
Yatapoxvirus 1995(Table)
Yaws 2415, 2417–2418
YB gene 116(Table), 1115
Y box 1042
Y chromosome, genes 1159
Y-chromosome accelerator of
    autoimmunity 2253
Yeast
    double hybrid system 984
    mating-type switches 970
Yeast artificial chromosomes (YACs),
    vectors for transgenes 2406
Yellow fever (YF) 926, 928
    vaccination 931
    vaccine development 256, 931
Yellow fever (YF) virus 926
Yersinia 2512–2525
    adhesin 2514
    calcium dependency 2513
    diarrhea due to 968
    diseases 2512
    evasive strategies 2513–2514
    host immune response 2513
    immune complexes 2513
    intracellular 2513
    invasin 2514
    lipopolysaccharide 2513
    molecular mimicry 2513
        thyroglobulin 2311

Yersinia (*continued*)
    outer membrane proteins (YOPs) 2514
    reactive arthritis due to 2513
    species 2512
    superantigens 2514
    vaccines 2514
    virulence 2513
    virulence plasmid 2513, 2514
Yersinia enterocolitica 2512, 2513
    thyroid autoimmune disease 2314
    TSH binding 2314
Yersinia pestis 2512
    iron requirement 2514
    low calcium response (calcium
        dependency) 2513
    virulence plasmid 2513, 2514
Yersinia pseudotuberculosis 2512, 2513
Yersiniosis 2512
    clinical features 2513
    vaccine 2514
Yolk sac
    mononuclear phagocytes origin 1755
    reptiles 2076
Yo-specific antibodies 1842
Y-RNAs 127

Z

ZAP-70 467, 1275, 2173
    defects 1279
    deficiency, in SCID 2173
    functions 2173

ZAP-70 (*continued*)
    signaling in T cell activation 2324
Zebrafish, MHC evolution/organization
    1702
Zeta-associated protein 70, *see* ZAP-70
Zidovudine (AZT) 11–12
    interferon α combined therapy 1416
Zie IgG2 1333
Zinc 2515–2516
    absorption 2516
    binding to thymic hormones 2515
    deficiency 1284, 1870, 2515–2516
        effect on immunity 2515–2516
        in malnutrition 2516
        reversibility 2516
    distribution, acute phase reaction effect
        2516
    functions 2515
    intake 2516
    in metalloenzymes 2515
    supplementation 2516
    thymulin coupled to 2300
    thymulin levels in cancer and 2301
Zona pellucida, immunity to 1374–1375
Zonula occludens toxin (ZOT), *see under*
    Vibrio cholerae
Zoster
    bone marrow transplant recipients 1884
    transplant recipients 1884
ZOT toxin 2372–2373
    see also Vibrio cholerae
ZP1, ZP2 and ZP3 glycoproteins 1374
Zwitterions 1510
    isoelectric point 1510, 1511
Zymogen granules 851